Algebra 2
Common Core

Randall I. Charles
Basia Hall
Dan Kennedy
Allan E. Bellman
Sadie Chavis Bragg
William G. Handlin
Stuart J. Murphy
Grant Wiggins

PEARSON

Boston, Massachusetts • Chandler, Arizona • Glenview, Illinois • Upper Saddle River, New Jersey

Acknowledgments appear on page T1052, which constitutes an extension of this copyright page.

ISBN-13: 978-0-13-318609-3
ISBN-10:   0-13-318609-1

2 3 4 5 6 7 8 9 10   V057   15 14 13 12 11

PEARSON

Algebra 2 *Teacher's Edition Contents*

Teacher Handbook

Series *Authors*

Randall I. Charles, Ph.D., is Professor Emeritus in the Department of Mathematics and Computer Science at San Jose State University, San Jose, California. He began his career as a high school mathematics teacher, and he was a mathematics supervisor for five years. Dr. Charles has been a member of several NCTM committees and is the former Vice President of the National Council of Supervisors of Mathematics. Much of his writing and research has been in the area of problem solving. He has authored more than 75 mathematics textbooks for kindergarten through college.

Dan Kennedy, Ph.D., is a classroom teacher and the Lupton Distinguished Professor of Mathematics at the Baylor School in Chattanooga, Tennessee. A frequent speaker at professional meetings on the subject of mathematics education reform, Dr. Kennedy has conducted more than 50 workshops and institutes for high school teachers. He is coauthor of textbooks in calculus and precalculus, and from 1990 to 1994 he chaired the College Board's AP Calculus Development Committee. He is a 1992 Tandy Technology Scholar and a 1995 Presidential Award winner.

Basia Hall currently serves as Manager of Instructional Programs for the Houston Independent School District. With 33 years of teaching experience, Ms. Hall has served as a department chair, instructional supervisor, school improvement facilitator, and professional development trainer. She has developed curricula for Algebra 1, Geometry, and Algebra 2 and co-developed the Texas state mathematics standards. A 1992 Presidential Awardee, Ms. Hall is past president of the Texas Association of Supervisors of Mathematics and is a state representative for the National Council of Supervisors of Mathematics (NCSM).

Consulting *Authors*

Stuart J. Murphy is a visual learning author and consultant. He is a champion of helping students develop learning skills so they become more successful students. He is the author of MathStart, a series of children's books that presents mathematical concepts in the context of stories. A graduate of the Rhode Island School of Design, he has worked extensively in educational publishing and has been on the authorship teams of a number of elementary and high school mathematics programs. He is a frequent presenter at meetings of the National Council of Teachers of Mathematics, the International Reading Association, and other professional organizations.

Grant Wiggins, Ed.D., is the President of Authentic Education in Hopewell, New Jersey. He earned his Ed.D. from Harvard University and his B.A. from St. John's College in Annapolis. Dr. Wiggins consults with schools, districts, and state education departments on a variety of reform matters; organizes conferences and workshops; and develops print materials and Web resources on curricular change. He is perhaps best known for being the coauthor, with Jay McTighe, of *Understanding by Design* and *The Understanding by Design Handbook*[1], the award-winning and highly successful materials on curriculum published by ASCD. His work has been supported by the Pew Charitable Trusts, the Geraldine R. Dodge Foundation, and the National Science Foundation.

[1] ASCD, publisher of the "Understanding by Design Handbook" co-authored by Grant Wiggins and registered owner of the trademark "Understanding by Design", has not authorized or sponsored this work and is in no way affiliated with Pearson or its products.

Program *Authors*
Algebra 1 and Algebra 2

Allan E. Bellman, Ph.D., is a Lecturer/Supervisor in the School of Education at the University of California, Davis. Before coming to Davis, he was a mathematics teacher for 31 years in Montgomery County, Maryland. He has been an instructor for both the Woodrow Wilson National Fellowship Foundation and the T^3 program. He has been involved in the development of many products from Texas Instruments. Dr. Bellman has a particular expertise in the use of technology in education and speaks frequently on this topic. He was a 1992 Tandy Technology Scholar and has twice been listed in Who's Who Among America's Teachers.

Sadie Chavis Bragg, Ed.D., is Senior Vice President of Academic Affairs at the Borough of Manhattan Community College of the City University of New York. A former professor of mathematics, she is a past president of the American Mathematical Association of Two-Year Colleges (AMATYC), co-director of the AMATYC project to revise the standards for introductory college mathematics before calculus, and an active member of the Benjamin Banneker Association. Dr. Bragg has coauthored more than 50 mathematics textbooks for kindergarten through college.

William G. Handlin, Sr., is a classroom teacher and Department Chairman of Technology Applications at Spring Woods High School in Houston, Texas. Awarded Life Membership in the Texas Congress of Parents and Teachers for his contributions to the well-being of children, Mr. Handlin is also a frequent workshop and seminar leader in professional meetings throughout the world.

Geometry

Laurie E. Bass is a classroom teacher at the 9–12 division of the Ethical Culture Fieldston School in Riverdale, New York. A classroom teacher for more than 30 years, Ms. Bass has a wide base of teaching experience, ranging from Grade 6 through Advanced Placement Calculus. She was the recipient of a 2000 Honorable Mention for the Radio Shack National Teacher Awards. She has been a contributing writer for a number of publications, including software-based activities for the Algebra 1 classroom. Among her areas of special interest are cooperative learning for high school students and geometry exploration on the computer. Ms. Bass is a frequent presenter at local, regional, and national conferences.

Art Johnson, Ed.D., is a professor of mathematics education at Boston University. He is a mathematics educator with 32 years of public school teaching experience, a frequent speaker and workshop leader, and the recipient of a number of awards: the Tandy Prize for Teaching Excellence, the Presidential Award for Excellence in Mathematics Teaching, and New Hampshire Teacher of the Year. He was also profiled by the Disney Corporation in the American Teacher of the Year Program. Dr. Johnson has contributed 18 articles to NCTM journals and has authored over 50 books on various aspects of mathematics.

Common Core State Standards
for Mathematics High School

The following shows the High School Standards for Mathematical Content that are taught in *Pearson Algebra 2 Common Core Edition* ©2012. Included are all of the standards that make up Achieve's Pathway for High School Algebra 2. Standards that are not part of Achieve's Pathway are indicated with an asterisk (*) on the standard code. Standards that begin with (+) indicate additional mathematics that students should learn in order to take advanced courses.

Number and Quantity		Where to Find
The Complex Number System		**N.CN**
Perform arithmetic operations with complex numbers		
N.CN.1	Know there is a complex number i such that $i^2 = -1$, and every complex number has the form $a + bi$ with a and b real.	4-8
N.CN.2	Use the relation $i^2 = -1$ and the commutative, associative, and distributive properties to add, subtract, and multiply complex numbers.	4-8
Use complex numbers in polynomial identities and equations		
N.CN.7	Solve quadratic equations with real coefficients that have complex solutions.	4-8, 5-5, 5-6
N.CN.8	(+) Extend polynomial identities to the complex numbers.	4-8, 5-5, 5-6
N.CN.9	(+) Know the Fundamental Theorem of Algebra; show that it is true for quadratic polynomials.	5-6
Vector and Matrix Quantities		**N.VM**
Represent and model with vector quantities		
N.VM.1*	(+) Recognize vector quantities as having both magnitude and direction. Represent vector quantities by directed line segments, and use appropriate symbols for vectors and their magnitudes (e.g., v, $\|v\|$, $\|v\|$, v).	12-6
N.VM.2*	(+) Find the components of a vector by subtracting the coordinates of an initial point from the coordinates of a terminal point.	12-6
N.VM.3*	(+) Solve problems involving velocity and other quantities that can be represented by vectors.	12-6
Perform operations on vectors		
N.VM.4	(+) Add and subtract vectors.	12-6
N.VM.4.a*	Add vectors end-to-end, component-wise, and by the parallelogram rule. Understand that the magnitude of a sum of two vectors is typically not the sum of the magnitudes.	12-6
N.VM.4.b*	Given two vectors in magnitude and direction form, determine the magnitude and direction of their sum.	12-6
N.VM.4.c*	Understand vector subtraction $v - w$ as $v + (-w)$, where $-w$ is the additive inverse of w, with the same magnitude as w and pointing in the opposite direction. Represent vector subtraction graphically by connecting the tips in the appropriate order, and perform vector subtraction component-wise.	12-6
N.VM.5	(+) Multiply a vector by a scalar.	12-6
N.VM.5.a*	Represent scalar multiplication graphically by scaling vectors and possibly reversing their direction; perform scalar multiplication component-wise, e.g., as $c(vx, vy) = (cvx, cvy)$.	12-6

Number and Quantity		Where to Find
N.VM.5.b*	Compute the magnitude of a scalar multiple $c\mathbf{v}$ using $\|c\mathbf{v}\| = |c|\,\mathbf{v}$. Compute the direction of $c\mathbf{v}$ knowing that when $|c|\,\mathbf{v} \neq 0$, the direction of $c\mathbf{v}$ is either along $\mathbf{v}$ (for $c > 0$) or against $\mathbf{v}$ (for $c < 0$). Perform operations on matrices and use matrices in applications.	12-6
N.VM.6*	(+) Use matrices to represent and manipulate data, e.g., to represent payoffs or incidence relationships in a network.	12-2, CB 12-2, 12-5
N.VM.7*	(+) Multiply matrices by scalars to produce new matrices, e.g., as when all of the payoffs in a game are doubled.	12-2, 12-5
N.VM.8*	(+) Add, subtract, and multiply matrices of appropriate dimensions.	12-1, CB 12-1, 12-2, 12-4, 12-5
N.VM.9*	(+) Understand that, unlike multiplication of numbers, matrix multiplication for square matrices is not a commutative operation, but still satisfies the associative and distributive properties.	12-2
N.VM.10*	(+) Understand that the zero and identity matrices play a role in matrix addition and multiplication similar to the role of 0 and 1 in the real numbers. The determinant of a square matrix is nonzero if and only if the matrix has a multiplicative inverse.	12-1, 12-3
N.VM.11*	(+) Multiply a vector (regarded as a matrix with one column) by a matrix of suitable dimensions to produce another vector. Work with matrices as transformations of vectors.	12-6
N.VM.12*	(+) Work with 2×2 matrices as a transformations of the plane, and interpret the absolute value of the determinant in terms of area.	12-3, 12-6

Algebra		Where to Find
Seeing Structure in Expressions		**A.SSE**
Interpret the structure of expressions		
A.SSE.1	Interpret expressions that represent a quantity in terms of its context.	5-2, 8-4
A.SSE.1.a	Interpret parts of an expression, such as terms, factors, and coefficients.	4-5, 5-1, 8-4
A.SSE.1.b	Interpret complicated expressions by viewing one or more of their parts as a single entity.	1-6, 7-1, 7-2, 7-3, 8-4
A.SSE.2	Use the structure of an expression to identify ways to rewrite it.	4-4, 5-3, 6-1, 6-2, 6-3, 8-4
Write expressions in equivalent forms to solve problems		
A.SSE.4	Derive the formula for the sum of a finite geometric series (when the common ratio is not 1), and use the formula to solve problems.	CB 9-5, 9-5
Arithmetic with Polynomials and Rational Expressions		**A.APR**
Perform arithmetic operations on polynomials		
A.APR.1	Understand that polynomials form a system analogous to the integers, namely, they are closed under the operations of addition, subtraction, and multiplication; add, subtract, and multiply polynomials.	5-4
Understand the relationship between zeros and factors of polynomials		
A.APR.2	Know and apply the Remainder Theorem: For a polynomial $p(x)$ and a number a, the remainder on division by $x - a$ is $p(a)$, so $p(a) = 0$ if and only if $(x - a)$ is a factor of $p(x)$.	5-4
A.APR.3	Identify zeros of polynomials when suitable factorizations are available, and use the zeros to construct a rough graph of the function defined by the polynomial.	4-5, 5-2, 5-6, CB 5-7
Use polynomial identities to solve problems		
A.APR.4	Prove polynomial identities and use them to describe numerical relationships.	CB 5-5
A.APR.5	(+) Know and apply the Binomial Theorem for the expansion of $(x + y)^n$ in powers of x and y for a positive integer n, where x and y are any numbers, with coefficients determined for example by Pascal's Triangle.	5-7
Rewrite rational expressions		
A.APR.6	Rewrite simple rational expressions in different forms; write $\frac{a(x)}{b(x)}$ in the form $q(x) + \frac{r(x)}{b(x)}$, where $a(x)$, $b(x)$, $q(x)$, and $r(x)$ are polynomials with the degree of $r(x)$ less than the degree of $b(x)$, using inspection, long division, or, for the more complicated examples, a computer algebra system.	5-4, 8-6

Algebra	Where to Find

A.APR.7	(+) Understand that rational expressions form a system analogous to the rational numbers, closed under addition, subtraction, multiplication, and division by a nonzero rational expression; add, subtract, multiply, and divide rational expressions.	8-5, 8-6

Creating Equations	A.CED

Create equations that describe numbers or relationships

A.CED.1	Create equations and inequalities in one variable and use them to solve problems. *Include equations arising from linear and quadratic functions, and simple rational and exponential functions.*	1-4, 1-5, 1-6, 4-1, 4-5, CB 8-1, 8-6
A.CED.2	Create equations in two or more variables to represent relationships between quantities; graph equations on coordinate axes with labels and scales.	2-2, 2-3, 2-4, 2-5, 2-8, 3-1, 3-2, 4-2, CB 4-5, 7-1, 7-2, 8-1, 8-2, 8-3
A.CED.3	Represent constraints by equations or inequalities, and by systems of equations and/or inequalities, and interpret solutions as viable or non-viable options in a modeling context.	3-1, 3-2, 3-3, 3-4, CB 3-4, 4-9, CB 7-6
A.CED.4	Rearrange formulas to highlight a quantity of interest, using the same reasoning as in solving equations.	1-4, 6-5, 8-1

Reasoning with Equations and Inequalities	A.REI

Understand solving equations as a process of reasoning and explain the reasoning

A.REI.2	Solve simple rational and radical equations in one variable, and give examples showing how extraneous solutions may arise.	6-5, 8-6

Solve systems of equation

A.REI.5*	Prove that, given a system of two equations in two variables, replacing one equation by the sum of that equation and a multiple of the other produces a system with the same solutions.	3-2
A.REI.6*	Solve systems of linear equations exactly and approximately (e.g., with graphs), focusing on pairs of linear equations in two variables.	3-1, 3-2, 3-3
A.REI.7*	Solve a simple system consisting of a linear equation and a quadratic equation in two variables algebraically and graphically.	4-9
A.REI.8*	(+) Represent a system of linear equations as a single matrix equation in a vector variable.	3-6

Represent and solve equations and inequalities graphically

A.REI.11	Explain why the x-coordinates of the points where the graphs of the equations $y = f(x)$ and $y = g(x)$ intersect are the solutions of the equation $f(x) = g(x)$; find the solutions approximately, e.g., using technology to graph the functions, make tables of values, or find successive approximations. Include cases where $f(x)$ and/or $g(x)$ are linear, polynomial, rational, absolute value, exponential, and logarithmic functions.	3-1, 5-3, 7-5, CB 7-6, 8-6
A.REI.12*	Graph the solutions to a linear inequality in two variables as a half-plane (excluding the boundary in the case of a strict inequality), and graph the solution set to a system of linear inequalities in two variables as the intersection of the corresponding half-planes.	3-3

Functions	Where to Find

Interpreting Functions	F.IF

Understand the concept of a function and use function notation

F.IF.1*	Understand that a function from one set (called the domain) to another set (called the range) assigns to each element of the domain exactly one element of the range. If f is a function and x is an element of its domain, then $f(x)$ denotes the output of f corresponding to the input x. The graph of f is the graph of the equation $y = f(x)$.	2-2
F.IF.3*	Recognize that sequences are functions, sometimes defined recursively, whose domain is a subset of the integers.	9-2, 9-3

Interpret functions that arise in applications in terms of the context

F.IF.4	For a function that models a relationship between two quantities, interpret key features of graphs and tables in terms of the quantities, and sketch graphs showing key features given a verbal description of the relationship.	2-3, 2-5, 4-1, 4-2, 4-3, 5-1, 5-8, CB 7-3, 13-1, 13-4, 13-5

Functions		Where to Find
F.IF.5	Relate the domain of a function to its graph and, where applicable, to the quantitative relationship it describes.	4-3, 5-8
F.IF.6	Calculate and interpret the average rate of change of a function (presented symbolically or as a table) over a specified interval. Estimate the rate of change from a graph.	2-5, 4-1, 4-2, CB 4-3, 5-8
Analyze functions using different representations		
F.IF.7	Graph functions expressed symbolically, and show key features of the graph, by hand in simple cases and using technology for more complicated cases.	2-3, 2-4, CB 2-4, 2-6, 2-7, 4-1, 4-2, 5-1, 5-2, 5-8, 6-8, 7-2, CB 8-2, 8-3
F.IF.7.b	Graph square root, cube root, and piecewise-defined functions, including step functions and absolute value functions.	CB 2-4, 2-7, 2-8, 6-8
F.IF.7.c	Graph polynomial functions, identifying zeros when suitable factorizations are available, and showing end behavior.	5-1, 5-2, 5-9
F.IF.7.d*	Graph rational functions, identifying zeros and asymptotes when suitable factorizations are available, and showing end behavior.	CB 8-2
F.IF.7.e*	Graph exponential and logarithmic functions, showing intercepts and end behavior, and trigonometric functions, showing period, midline, and amplitude.	7-1, 7-2, 7-3, CB 7-5, 13-4, 13-5, 13-6, 13-7, 13-8
F.IF.8	Write a function defined by an expression in different but equivalent forms to reveal and explain different properties of the function.	2-4, 4-2, 5-9, 6-8, 7-2, 7-3, CB 7-5
F.IF.9	Compare properties of two functions each represented in a different way (algebraically, graphically, numerically in tables, or by verbal descriptions).	2-4, 4-2, 5-9, 7-3
Building Functions		**F.BF**
Build a function that models a relationship between two quantities		
F.BF.1	Write a function that describes a relationship between two quantities.	2-2, 2-5, 4-2, 5-2, 6-6, 7-2, 8-2, 8-3
F.BF.1.b	Combine standard function types using arithmetic operations.	6-6, 7-2, 8-3
Build new functions from existing functions		
F.BF.3	Identify the effect on the graph of replacing $f(x)$ by $f(x) + k$, $k\,f(x)$, $f(kx)$, and $f(x + k)$ for specific values of k (both positive and negative); find the value of k given the graphs. Experiment with cases and illustrate an explanation of the effects on the graph using technology.	2-6, 2-7, 4-1, 5-9, 8-2
F.BF.4.a	Solve an equation of the form $f(x) = c$ for a simple function f that has an inverse and write an expression for the inverse.	6-7, 7-3
F.BF.4.c*	(+) Read values of an inverse function from a graph or a table, given that the function has an inverse.	6-7
Linear and Exponential Models		**F.LE**
Construct and compare linear and exponential models and solve problems		
F.LE.4	For exponential models, express as a logarithm the solution to $ab^{ct} = d$ where a, c, and d are numbers and the base b is 2, 10, or e; evaluate the logarithm using technology.	7-5, 7-6
Trigonometric Functions		**F.TF**
Extend the domain of trigonometric functions using the unit circle		
F.TF.1	Understand radian measure of an angle as the length of the arc on the unit circle subtended by the angle.	13-3
F.TF.2	Explain how the unit circle in the coordinate plane enables the extension of trigonometric functions to all real numbers, interpreted as radian measures of angles traversed counterclockwise around the unit circle.	13-4, 13-5, 13-6
Model periodic phenomena with trigonometric functions		
F.TF.5	Choose trigonometric functions to model periodic phenomena with specified amplitude, frequency, and midline.	13-4, 13-5, 13-6, 13-7

Functions		Where to Find
F.TF.6*	Understand that restricting a trigonometric function to a domain on which it is always increasing or decreasing allows its inverse to be constructed.	14-2
F.TF.7*	Use inverse functions to solve trigonometric equations that arise in modeling contexts; evaluate the solutions using technology, and interpret them in terms of the context.	14-2
Prove and apply trigonometric identities		
F.TF.8	Prove the Pythagorean identity $\sin^2(\theta) + \cos^2(\theta) = 1$ and use it to calculate trigonometric ratios.	14-1
F.TF.9*	Prove the addition and subtraction formulas for sine, cosine, and tangent and use them to solve problems.	14-6, 14-7

Geometry		Where to Find
Congruence		**G.CO**
Experiment with transformations in the plane		
G.CO.2*	Represent transformations in the plane using, e.g., transparencies and geometry software; describe transformations as functions that take points in the plane as inputs and give other points as outputs. Compare transformations that preserve distance and angle to those that do not (e.g., translation versus horizontal stretch).	12-5
G.CO.5*	Given a geometric figure and a rotation, reflection, or translation, draw the transformed figure using, e.g., graph paper, tracing paper, or geometry software. Specify a sequence of transformations that will carry a given figure onto another.	12-5
Similarity, Right Triangles, and Trigonometry		**G.SRT**
Define trigonometric ratios and solve problems involving right triangles		
G.SRT.6*	Represent transformations in the plane using, e.g., transparencies and geometry software; describe transformations as functions that take points in the plane as inputs and give other points as outputs. Compare transformations that preserve distance and angle to those that do not (e.g., translation versus horizontal stretch).	14-3
G.SRT.8*	Given a geometric figure and a rotation, reflection, or translation, draw the transformed figure using, e.g., graph paper, tracing paper, or geometry software. Specify a sequence of transformations that will carry a given figure onto another.	14-3
Apply trigonometry to general triangles		
G.SRT.9*	Represent transformations in the plane using, e.g., transparencies and geometry software; describe transformations as functions that take points in the plane as inputs and give other points as outputs. Compare transformations that preserve distance and angle to those that do not (e.g., translation versus horizontal stretch).	14-4
G.SRT.10*	Given a geometric figure and a rotation, reflection, or translation, draw the transformed figure using, e.g., graph paper, tracing paper, or geometry software. Specify a sequence of transformations that will carry a given figure onto another.	14-4, 14-5
G.SRT.11*	Understand and apply the Law of Sines and the Law of Cosines to find unknown measurements in right and non-right triangles (e.g., surveying problems, resultant forces).	14-4, CB 14-4, 14-5
Expressing Geometric Properties with Equations		**G.GPE**
Translate between the geometric description and the equation for a conic sections		
G.GPE.1*	Derive the equation of a circle of given center and radius using the Pythagorean Theorem; complete the square to find the center and radius of a circle given by an equation.	10-3, 10-6
G.GPE.2*	Derive the equation of a parabola given a focus and directrix.	10-2, 10-6
G.GPE.3*	Derive the equations of ellipses and hyperbolas given foci and directrices.	10-4, 10-5

Statistics and Probability	Where to Find

Interpreting Categorical and Quantitative Data — S.ID

Summarize, represent, and interpret data on two categorical and quantitative variables

S.ID.2*	Use statistics appropriate to the shape of the data distribution to compare center (median, mean) and spread (interquartile range, standard deviation) of two or more different data sets.	11-10
S.ID.4	Use the mean and standard deviation of a data set to fit it to a normal distribution and to estimate population percentages. Recognize that there are data sets for which such a procedure is not appropriate. Use calculators, spreadsheets, and tables to estimate areas under the normal curve.	11-7, 11-10

Making Inferences and Justifying Conclusions — S.IC

Understand and evaluate random processes underlying statistical experiments

S.IC.1	Understand statistics as a process for making inferences to be made about population parameters based on a random sample from that population.	11-8
S.IC.2	Decide if a specified model is consistent with results from a given data-generating process, e.g., using simulation.	CB 11-3

Make inferences and justify conclusions from sample surveys, experiments, and observational studies

S.IC.3	Recognize the purposes of and differences among sample surveys, experiments, and observational studies; explain how randomization relates to each.	11-8
S.IC.4	Use data from a sample survey to estimate a population mean or proportion; develop a margin of error through the use of simulation models for random sampling.	11-8, CB 11-10a
S.IC.5	Use data from a randomized experiment to compare two treatments; use simulations to decide if differences between parameters are significant.	CB 11-10b
S.IC.6	Evaluate reports based on data.	11-6, 11-7, 11-8

Conditional Probability and the Rules of Probability — S.CP

Understand independence and conditional probability and use them to interpret data

S.CP.2*	Understand that two events A and B are independent if the probability of A and B occurring together is the product of their probabilities, and use this characterization to determine if they are independent.	11-3
S.CP.3*	Understand the conditional probability of A given B as $\frac{P(A \text{ and } B)}{P(B)}$, and interpret independence of A and B as saying that the conditional probability of A given B is the same as the probability of B.	11-4
S.CP.4*	Construct and interpret two-way frequency tables of data when two categories are associated with each object being classified. Use the two-way table as a sample space to decide if events are independent and to approximate conditional probabilities.	11-4
S.CP.5*	Recognize and explain the concepts of conditional probability and independence in everyday language and everyday situations.	11-3, 11-4

Use the rules of probability to compute probabilities of compound events in a uniform probability model

S.CP.6*	Find the conditional probability of A given B as the fraction of B's outcomes that also belong to A, and interpret the answer in terms of the model.	11-4
S.CP.7*	Apply the Addition Rule, $P(A \text{ or } B) = (P(A) + P(B) - P(A \text{ and } B))$, and interpret the answer in terms of the model.	11-3
S.CP.8*	Apply the general Multiplication Rule in a uniform probability model, $P(A \text{ and } B) = (P(A)P(B|A) = P(B)P(A|B)$, and interpret the answer in terms of the model.	11-4
S.CP.9*	Use permutations and combinations to compute probabilities of compound events and solve problems.	11-1

Using Probability to Make Decisions — S.MD

Use probability to evaluate outcomes of decisions

S.MD.6	(+) Use probabilities to make fair decisions (e.g., drawing by lots, using a random number generator).	11-5
S.MD.7	(+) Analyze decisions and strategies using probability concepts (e.g., product testing, medical testing, pulling a hockey goalie at the end of a game).	11-5

Algebra 2 *Leveled Pacing Chart*

This Leveled Pacing Chart is provided as a guide to help you customize your course and to provide for differentiated instruction. The suggested number of days for each chapter is based on a traditional 45-minute class period and on a 90-minute block period. The total of 160 days of instruction leaves time for assessments, projects, assemblies, or other special days.

KEY
✓ = Algebra 2 Content
○ = Reviews the previous year
❑ = Content for Enrichment

		Common Core State Standards	Basic	Core	Advanced
Chapter 1 Expressions, Equations, and Inequalities			**Traditional 6 Block 3**		
1-1	Patterns and Expressions	Reviews A.SSE.3	✓	○	
1-2	Properties of Real Numbers	Reviews N.RN.3	✓	○	
1-3	Algebraic Expressions	Reviews A.SSE.1.a	✓	○	
1-4	Solving Equations	A.CED.1, A.CED.4	✓	✓	✓
1-5	Solving Inequalities	A.CED.1	✓	✓	✓
1-6	Absolute Value Equations and Inequalities	A.SSE.1.b, A.CED.1	✓	✓	✓
Chapter 2 Functions, Equations, and Graphs			**Traditional 10 Block 5**		
2-1	Relations and Functions	Reviews F.IF.1, F.IF.2	✓	○	
2-2	Direct Variation	A.CED.2, F.IF.1, F.BF.1	✓	✓	✓
2-3	Linear Functions and Slope-Intercept Form	A.CED.2, F.IF.4, F.IF.7	✓	✓	✓
2-4	More About Linear Equations	A.CED.2, F.IF.7, F.IF.8, F.IF.9	✓	✓	✓
Concept Byte: Piecewise Functions		F.IF.7, F.IF.7.b	✓	✓	✓
2-5	Using Linear Models	A.CED.2, F.IF.4, F.IF.6, F.BF.1	✓	✓	✓
2-6	Families of Functions	F.IF.7, F.BF.3	✓	✓	✓
2-7	Absolute Value Functions and Graphs	F.IF.7, F.IF.7.b, F.BF.3	✓	✓	✓
2-8	Two-Variable Inequalities	A.CED.2, F.IF.7.b	✓	✓	✓
Chapter 3 Linear Systems			**Traditional 8 Block 4**		
3-1	Solving Systems Using Tables and Graphs	A.CED.2, A.CED.3, A.REI.6, A.REI.11	✓	✓	✓
3-2	Solving Systems Algebraically	A.CED.2, A.CED.3, A.REI.5, A.REI.6	✓	✓	✓
3-3	Systems of Inequalities	A.CED.3, A.REI.6, A.REI.12	✓	✓	✓
3-4	Linear Programming	A.CED.3	✓	✓	✓
Concept Byte: Linear Programming		A.CED.3	✓	✓	✓
Concept Byte: Graphs in Three Dimensions		Extends A.REI.6		❑	❑
3-5	Systems With Three Variables	Extends A.REI.6		❑	❑
3-6	Solving Systems Using Matrices	A.REI.8	✓	✓	✓
Chapter 4 Quadratic Functions and Equations			**Traditional 16 Block 8**		
4-1	Quadratic Functions and Transformations	A.CED.1, F.IF.4, F.IF.6, F.IF.7, F.BF.3	✓	✓	✓

	Common Core State Standards	Basic	Core	Advanced
Chapter 4 Quadratic Functions and Equations			**Traditional 16 Block 8**	
4-2 Standard Form of a Quadratic Function	A.CED.2, F.IF.4, F.IF.6, F.IF.7, F.IF.8, F.IF.9, F.BF.1	✓	✓	✓
4-3 Modeling With Quadratic Functions	F.IF.4, F.IF.5	✓	✓	✓
Concept Byte: Identifying Quadratic Data	F.IF.6	✓	✓	✓
4-4 Factoring Quadratic Expressions	A.SSE.2	✓	✓	✓
Algebra Review: Square Roots and Radicals	Reviews N.RN.2	✓	○	
4-5 Quadratic Equations	A.SSE.1.a, A.APR.3, A.CED.1	✓	✓	✓
Concept Byte: Writing Equations From Roots	A.CED.2	✓	✓	✓
4-6 Completing the Square	Reviews A.REI.4.b	✓	○	
4-7 The Quadratic Formula	Reviews A.REI.4.b	✓	○	
4-8 Complex Numbers	N.CN.1, N.CN.2, N.CN.7, N.CN.8	✓	✓	✓
Concept Byte: Quadratic Inequalities	Prepares for A.CED.3	✓	✓	✓
4-9 Quadratic Systems	A.CED.3, A.REI.7	✓	✓	✓
Concept Byte: Powers of Complex Numbers	Extends N.CN.2		❏	❏
Chapter 5 Polynomials and Polynomial Functions			**Traditional 14 Block 7**	
5-1 Polynomial Functions	A.SSE.1.a, F.IF.4, F.IF.7, F.IF.7.c	✓	✓	✓
5-2 Polynomials, Linear Factors, and Zeros	A.SSE.1, A.APR.3, F.IF.7, F.IF.7.c, F.BF.1	✓	✓	✓
5-3 Solving Polynomial Equations	A.SSE.2, A.REI.11	✓	✓	✓
5-4 Dividing Polynomials	A.APR.1, A.APR.2, A.APR.6	✓	✓	✓
5-5 Theorems About Roots of Polynomial Equations	N.CN.7, N.CN.8	✓	✓	✓
Concept Byte: Solving Polynomial Inequalities	A.APR.4	✓	✓	✓
5-6 The Fundamental Theorem of Algebra	N.CN.7, N.CN.8, N.CN.9, A.APR.3	✓	✓	✓
Concept Byte: Graphing Polynomials Using Zeros	A.APR.3	✓	✓	✓
5-7 The Binomial Theorem	A.APR.5	✓	✓	✓
5-8 Polynomial Models in the Real World	F.IF.4, F.IF.5, F.IF.6, F.IF.7	✓	✓	✓
5-9 Transforming Polynomial Functions	F.IF.7.c, F.IF.8, F.IF.9, F.BF.3	✓	✓	✓
Chapter 6 Radical Functions and Rational Exponents			**Traditional 14 Block 7**	
Algebra Review: Properties of Exponents	Reviews N.RN.1	✓	○	
6-1 Roots and Radical Expressions	A.SSE.2	✓	✓	✓
6-2 Multiplying and Dividing Radical Expressions	A.SSE.2	✓	✓	✓
6-3 Binomial Radical Expressions	A.SSE.2	✓	✓	✓
6-4 Rational Exponents	Reviews N.RN.1 and N.RN.2	✓	○	
6-5 Solving Square Root and Other Radical Equations	A.CED.4, A.REI.2	✓	✓	✓
6-6 Function Operations	F.BF.1, F.BF.1.b	✓	✓	✓
6-7 Inverse Relations and Functions	F.BF.4.a, F.BF.4.c	✓	✓	✓
Concept Byte: Graphing Inverses	Extends F.BF.4.a		❏	❏
6-8 Graphing Radical Functions	F.IF.7, F.IF.7.b, F.IF.8	✓	✓	✓
Chapter 7 Exponential and Logarithmic Functions			**Traditional 10 Block 5**	
7-1 Exploring Exponential Models	A.SSE.1.b, A.CED.2, F.IF.7.e	✓	✓	✓
7-2 Properties of Exponential Functions	A.SSE.1.b, A.CED.2, F.IF.7, F.IF.7.e, F.IF.8, F.BF.1, F.BF.1.b	✓	✓	✓

	Common Core State Standards	Basic	Core	Advanced
Chapter 7 Exponential and Logarithmic Functions			**Traditional 10 Block 5**	
7-3 Logarithmic Functions as Inverses	A.SSE.1.b, F.IF.7.e, F.IF.8, F.IF.9, F.BF.4.a	✓	✓	✓
Concept Byte: Fitting Curves to Data	F.IF.4	✓	✓	✓
7-4 Properties of Logarithms	Prepares for F.LE.4	✓	✓	✓
7-5 Exponential and Logarithmic Equations	A.REI.11, F.LE.4	✓	✓	✓
Concept Byte: Using Logarithms for Exponential Models	F.IF.7.e, F.IF.8	✓	✓	✓
7-6 Natural Logarithms	F.LE.4	✓	✓	✓
Concept Byte: Exponential and Logarithmic Inequalities	A.CED.3, A.REI.11	✓	✓	✓
Chapter 8 Rational Functions			**Traditional 14 Block 7**	
8-1 Inverse Variation	A.CED.2, A.CED.4	✓	✓	✓
Concept Byte: Graphing Rational Functions	A.CED.1, F.IF.7, F.IF.7.d	✓	✓	✓
8-2 The Reciprocal Function Family	A.CED.2, F.BF.1, F.BF.3	✓	✓	✓
8-3 Rational Functions and Their Graphs	A.CED.2, F.IF.7, F.BF.1, F.BF.1.b	✓	✓	✓
Concept Byte: Oblique Asymptotes	Extends F.IF.7.d	✓		
8-4 Rational Expressions	A.SSE.1, A.SSE.1.a, A.SSE.1.b, A.SSE.2	✓	✓	✓
8-5 Adding and Subtracting Rational Expressions	A.APR.7	✓	✓	✓
8-6 Solving Rational Equations	A.APR.6, A.APR.7, A.CED.1, A.REI.2, A.REI.11	✓	✓	✓
Concept Byte: Systems With Rational Equations	Extends A.REI.11		❏	❏
Concept Byte: Rational Inequalities	Extends A.REI.11		❏	❏
Chapter 9 Sequences and Series			**Traditional 8 Block 4**	
9-1 Mathematical Patterns	Prepares for A.SSE.4	✓	○	
9-2 Arithmetic Sequences	F.IF.3	✓	○	
Concept Byte: The Fibonacci Sequence	F.IF.3	✓	○	
9-3 Geometric Sequences	Prepares for A.SSE.4	✓	○	
9-4 Arithmetic Series	Extends F.IF.3		❏	❏
Concept Byte: Geometry and Infinite Series	A.SSE.4	✓	✓	✓
9-5 Geometric Series	A.SSE.4	✓	✓	✓
Chapter 10 Quadratic Relations and Conic Sections			**Traditional 12 Block 6**	
10-1 Exploring Conic Sections	Prepares for G.GPE.1, G.GPE.2, G.GPE.3	✓	✓	✓
Concept Byte: Graphing Conic Sections	Prepares for G.GPE.1, G.GPE.2, G.GPE.3	✓	✓	✓
10-2 Parabolas	G.GPE.2	✓	✓	✓
10-3 Circles	G.GPE.1	✓	✓	✓
10-4 Ellipses	G.GPE.3	✓	✓	✓
10-5 Hyperbolas	G.GPE.3	✓	✓	✓
10-6 Translating Conic Sections	G.GPE.1, G.GPE.2	✓	✓	✓
Concept Byte: Solving Quadratic Systems	Extends A.REI.7, A.REI.11		❏	❏
Chapter 11 Probability and Statistics			**Traditional 10 Block 5**	
11-1 Permutations and Combinations	S.CP.9	✓	○	
11-2 Probability	Prepares for S.IC.2	✓	○	
11-3 Probability of Multiple Events	S.CP.2, S.CP.5, S.CP.7	✓	○	
Concept Byte: Probability Distributions	S.IC.2	✓	✓	✓

	Common Core State Standards	Basic	Core	Advanced
Chapter 11 Probability and Statistics		**Traditional 10**	**Block 5**	
11-4 Conditional Probability	S.CP.3, S.CP.4, S.CP.5, S.CP.6, S.CP.8	✓	✓	✓
11-5 Probability Models	S.MD.6, S.MD.7	✓	✓	✓
11-6 Analyzing Data	S.IC.6	✓	✓	✓
11-7 Standard Deviation	S.ID.4, S.IC.6	✓	✓	✓
11-8 Samples and Surveys	S.IC.1, S.IC.3, S.IC.4, S.IC.6	✓	✓	✓
11-9 Binomial Distributions	Extends S.CP.9	❏	❏	❏
11-10 Normal Distributions	S.ID.2, S.ID.4	✓	✓	✓
Concept Byte: Margin of Error	S.IC.4	✓	✓	✓
Concept Byte: Drawing Conclusions from Samples	S.IC.5	✓	✓	✓
Chapter 12 Matrices		**Traditional 12**	**Block 6**	
12-1 Adding and Subtracting Matrices	N.VM.8, N.VM.10		❏	❏
Concept Byte: Working With Matrices	N.VM.8		❏	❏
12-2 Matrix Multiplication	N.VM.6, N.VM.7, N.VM.8, N.VM.9		❏	❏
Concept Byte: Networks	N.VM.6		❏	❏
12-3 Determinants and Inverses	N.VM.10, N.VM.12			❏
12-4 Inverse Matrices and Systems	N.VM.8			❏
12-5 Geometric Transformations	N.VM.6, N.VM.7, N.VM.8, G.CO.2, G.CO.5			❏
12-6 Vectors	N.VM.1, N.VM.2, N.VM.3, N.VM.4, N.VM.4.a, N.VM.4.b, N.VM.4.c, N.VM.5, N.VM.5.a, N.VM.5.b, N.VM.11, N.VM.12			❏
Chapter 13 Periodic Functions and Trigonometry		**Traditional 14**	**Block 7**	
13-1 Exploring Periodic Data	F.IF.4, Prepares for F.TF.5	✓	✓	✓
Geometry Review: Special Right Triangles	Reviews G.SRT.6	✓	○	
13-2 Angles and the Unit Circle	Prepares for F.TF.2	✓	○	
Concept Byte: Measuring Radians	Prepares for F.TF.1	✓	○	
13-3 Radian Measure	F.TF.1	✓	✓	✓
13-4 The Sine Function	F.IF.4, F.IF.7.e, F.TF.2, F.TF.5	✓	✓	✓
Concept Byte: Graphing Trigonometric Functions	Prepares for F.TF.5	✓	○	
13-5 The Cosine Function	F.IF.4, F.IF.7.e, F.TF.2, F.TF.5	✓	✓	✓
13-6 The Tangent Function	F.IF.7.e, F.TF.2, F.TF.5	✓	✓	✓
13-7 Translating Sine and Cosine Functions	F.IF.7.e, F.TF.5	✓	✓	✓
13-8 Reciprocal Trigonometric Functions	F.IF.7.e	✓	✓	✓
Chapter 14 Trigonometric Identities and Equations		**Traditional 12**	**Block 6**	
14-1 Trigonometric Identities	F.TF.8	✓	✓	✓
14-2 Solving Trigonometric Equations Using Inverses	F.TF.6, F.TF.7		❏	❏
14-3 Right Triangles and Trigonometric Ratios	G.SRT.6, G.SRT.8		❏	❏
14-4 Area and the Law of Sines	G.SRT.9, G.SRT.10, G.SRT.11		❏	❏
Concept Byte: The Ambiguous Case	G.SRT.11			❏
14-5 The Law of Cosines	G.SRT.10, G.SRT.11			❏
14-6 Angle Identities	F.TF.9			❏
14-7 Double-Angle and Half-Angle Identities	F.TF.9			❏

1 Expressions, Equations, and Inequalities

Chapters 1 & 2

Algebra

Seeing Structure in Expressions
Interpret the structure of expressions

Creating Equations
Create equations that describe numbers or relationships

Functions

Interpreting Functions
Interpret functions that arise in applications in terms of the context
Analyze functions using different representations

Building Functions
Build a function that models a relationship between two quantities

Functions, Equations, and Graphs

Visual See It!

Reasoning Try It!

Practice Do It!

3

Linear Systems

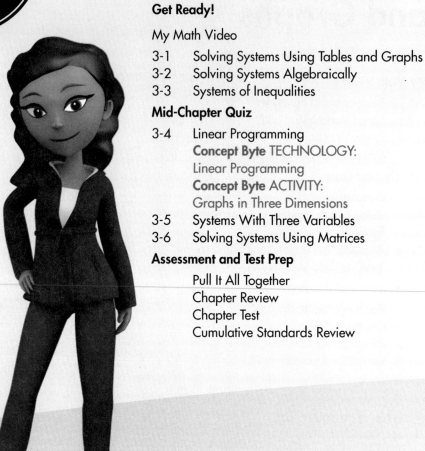

Chapters 3 & 4

Number and Quantity

The Complex Number System
Perform arithmetic operations with complex numbers
Use complex numbers in polynomial identities and equations

Functions

Interpreting Functions
Interpret functions that arise in applications in terms of the context
Analyze functions using different representations

Building Functions
Build new functions from existing functions

Algebra

Seeing Structure in Expressions
Interpret the structure of expressions

Arithmetic with Polynomials and Rational Expressions
Understand the relationship between zeros and factors of polynomials

Creating Equations
Create equations that describe numbers or relationships

Reasoning with Equations and Inequalities
Solve systems of equations
Represent and solve equations and inequalities graphically

Quadratic Functions and Equations

Visual See It!

Reasoning Try It!

Practice Do It!

5

Polynomials and Polynomial Functions

Chapters 5 & 6

Number and Quantity
The Complex Number System
Use complex numbers in polynomial identities and equations

Functions
Interpreting Functions
Interpret functions that arise in applications in terms of the context
Analyze functions using different representations

Building Functions
Build a function that models a relationship between two quantities
Build new functions from existing functions

Algebra
Seeing Structure in Expressions
Interpret the structure of expressions

Creating Equations
Create equations that describe numbers or relationships

Arithmetic with Polynomials and Rational Expressions
Understand the relationship between zeros and factors of polynomials
Use polynomial identities to solve problems

Radical Functions and Rational Exponents

Visual See It!

Reasoning Try It!

Practice Do It!

COMMON CORE

Exponential and Logarithmic Functions

Chapters 7 & 8

Algebra

Seeing Structure in Expressions
  Interpret the structure of expressions
Creating Equations
  Create equations that describe numbers or relationships
Arithmetic with Polynomials and Rational Expressions
  Rewrite rational expressions
Reasoning with Equations and Inequalities
  Represent and solve equations and inequalities graphically

Functions

Interpreting Functions
  Analyze functions using different representations
Building Functions
  Build a function that models a relationship between two quantities
  Build new functions from existing functions
Linear and Exponential Models
  Construct and compare linear and exponential models and solve problems

Rational Functions

Visual **See It!**

Reasoning **Try It!**

Practice **Do It!**

9

Sequences and Series

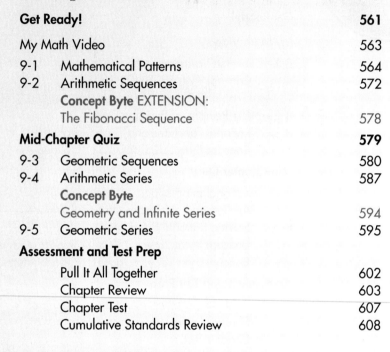

Chapters 9 & 10

Algebra
Seeing Structure in Expressions
   Write expressions in equivalent forms to solve problems
Functions
Interpreting Functions
   Understand the concept of a function and use function notation
   Analyze functions using different representations

Geometry
Expressing Geometric Properties with Equations
   Translate between the geometric description and the equation
   for a conic section

Quadratic Relations and Conic Sections

Visual See It!

Reasoning Try It!

Practice Do It!

11

Probability and Statistics

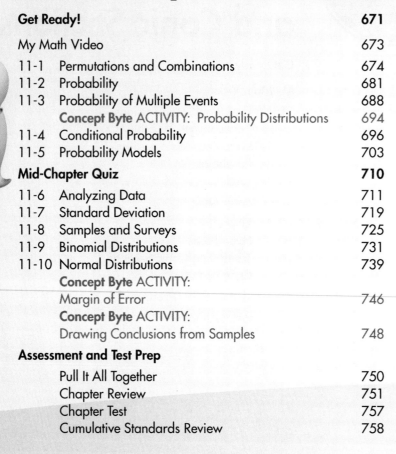

Chapters 11 & 12

Number and Quantity
Vector and Matrix Quantities
- Represent and model with vector quantities
- Perform operations on vectors
- Perform operations on matrices and use matrices in applications

Statistics and Probability
Interpreting Categorical and Quantitative Data
- Summarize, represent, and interpret data on a single count or measurement variable

Making Inferences and Justifying Conclusions
- Understand and evaluate random processes underlying statistical experiments
- Make inferences and justify conclusions from sample surveys, experiments, and observational studies

Conditional Probability and the Rules of Probability
- Understand independence and conditional probability and use them to interpret data
- Use the rules of probability to compute probabilities of compound events in a uniform probability model

Use Probability to Make Decisions
- Use probability to evaluate outcomes of decisions

12 Matrices

Visual See It!

Reasoning Try It!

Practice Do It!

13

Periodic Functions and Trigonometry

Chapters 13 & 14

Functions
Interpreting Functions
Interpret functions that arise in applications in terms of the context
Analyze functions using different representations
Trigonometric Functions
Extend the domain of trigonometric functions using the unit circle
Model periodic phenomena with trigonometric functions
Prove and apply trigonometric identities

Geometry
Similarity, Right Triangles, and Trigonometry
Define trigonometric ratios and solve problems involving right triangles
Apply trigonometry to general triangles

Trigonometric Identities and Equations

Visual See It!

Reasoning Try It!

Practice Do It!

Training on
your schedule!

Visit **myPearsonTraining.com** any time to get the training you need from our comprehensive library of complimentary tutorials and resources.

Got Questions? Watch an animated step-by-step tutorial to learn how to use your technology or walk through your textbook teaching resources.

Need an answer fast? Visit our Frequently Asked Questions section for quick answers. We're always there when you need us!

Get Ready!

 Lesson 2-2 ◈ **Using Direct Variation**

For each direct variation, find the constant of variation. Then find the value of y when $x = -3$.

1. $y = 4$ when $x = 3$ **2.** $y = 1$ when $x = -1.5$

3. $y = -5$ when $x = \frac{3}{2}$ **4.** $y = -16$ when $x = 7$

Lesson 4-4 ◈ **Factoring Quadratic Expressions**

Factor each expression.

5. $x^2 + x - 6$ **6.** $4x^2 + 17x + 15$

7. $9x^2 - 25$ **8.** $x^2 - 12x + 36$

9. $3x^2 + 10x + 8$ **10.** $x^2 - 5x + 6$

Lesson 4-5 ◈ **Solving Quadratic Equations**

Solve each equation.

11. $x^2 + 7x - 8 = 0$ **12.** $\frac{1}{4}x^2 + \frac{7}{2}x = -12$

13. $3x^2 = 18x - 24$ **14.** $9x^2 + 6x = 0$

15. $4x^2 + 16 = 34x$ **16.** $x^2 - 13x - 30 = 0$

 **Looking Ahead Vocabulary**

17. If you need to drive 30 miles, you have many options. For instance, you can drive 15 miles per hour for 2 hours, 30 miles per hour for 1 hour, or 60 miles per hour for half an hour. Notice that when you double your speed, it takes half as much time to get to your destination. Mathematicians describe this kind of relationship as an *inverse variation*. Why do you suppose they use the word *inverse* to describe it?

18. Suppose you are hiking on a trail and find that the bridge over the river has been washed out, making a gap or *discontinuity* in the trail. Graphs can have gaps too. Sketch what you think a graph with a discontinuity might look like.

Get Ready!

Assign this diagnostic assessment to determine if students have the prerequisite skills for Chapter 8.

Lesson	Skill
2-2	Use Direct Variation
4-4	Factor Quadratic Equations
4-5	Solve Quadratic Equations

To remediate students, select from these resources (available for every lesson).
• Online Problems (PowerAlgebra.com)
• Reteaching (All-in-One Teaching Resources)
• Practice (All-in-One Teaching Resources)

Why Students Need These Skills

USING DIRECT VARIATION
Understanding direct variation is essential to identifying and understanding inverse variation.

FACTORING QUADRATIC EXPRESSIONS
Students will need to be able to factor quadratic expressions in order to determine the domain and the range of rational functions.

SOLVING QUADRATIC EQUATIONS
Students will need to solve quadratic equations in order to solve rational equations.

Looking Ahead Vocabulary

INVERSE VARIATION Ask students what other meanings they know for the word *inverse*, both in daily life and in math.

DISCONTINUITY Suggest students graph the path a washed-out bridge takes to see what the discontinuity might look like.

Answers

Get Ready!

1. $\frac{4}{3}$; -4

2. $-\frac{2}{3}$; 2

3. $-\frac{10}{3}$; 10

4. $-\frac{16}{7}$; $\frac{48}{7}$

5. $(x + 3)(x - 2)$

6. $(4x + 5)(x + 3)$

7. $(3x - 5)(3x + 5)$

8. $(x - 6)^2$

9. $(3x + 4)(x + 2)$

10. $(x - 3)(x - 2)$

11. $1, -8$

12. $-6, -8$

13. $4, 2$

14. $0, -\frac{2}{3}$

15. $8, \frac{1}{2}$

16. $15, -2$

17. Answers may vary. Sample: Inverse is used when one quantity increases as the other quantity decreases.

18. Answers may vary. Sample:

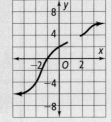

Chapter 8 Overview

BIG idea Proportionality
ESSENTIAL QUESTION Are two quantities inversely proportional if an increase in one corresponds to a decrease in the other?
- Students will identify and describe inverse and direct variation functions.

BIG idea Function
ESSENTIAL QUESTION What kinds of asymptotes are possible for a rational function?
- Students will graph asymptotes of rational functions.
- Students will identify whether a rational function has an asymptote.
- Students will differentiate between vertical, horizontal, and oblique asymptotes.

BIG idea Equivalence
ESSENTIAL QUESTION Are a rational expression and its simplified form equivalent?
- Students will define the domains of simplified rational expressions to make them equivalent to the originals.

Content Standards

Following are the standards covered in this chapter. Modeling standards are indicated by a star symbol (★).

CONCEPTUAL CATEGORY Algebra

Domain Seeing Structure in Expressions A.SSE
Cluster Interpret the structure of expressions. (Standards A.SSE.1.a★, A.SSE.1.b★, A.SSE.2)
LESSON 8-4

Domain Creating Equations A.CED
Cluster Create equations that describe numbers or relationships. (Standards A.CED.1, A.CED.2★)
LESSONS 8-1, 8-2, 8-6

Domain Arithmetic with Polynomials and Rational Expressions A.APR
Cluster Understand the relationship between zeros and factors of polynomials. (Standard A.APR.3)
LESSON 8-3
Cluster Use polynomial identities to solve problems. (Standards A.APR.6, A.APR.7)
LESSONS 8-5, 8-6

Domain Reasoning with Equations and Inequalities A.REI
Cluster Understand solving equations as a process of reasoning and explain the reasoning. (Standard A.REI.2)
LESSON 8-6
Cluster Represent and solve equations and inequalities graphically. (Standard A.REI.11★)
LESSON 8-6

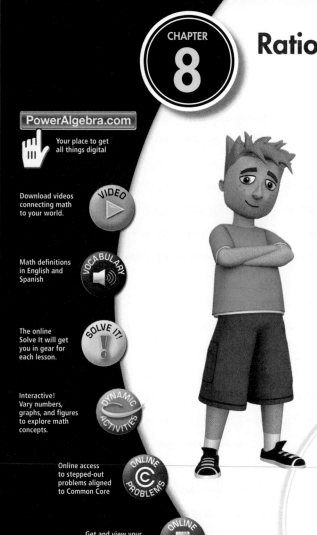

Rational Functions

PowerAlgebra.com

Your place to get all things digital

Download videos connecting math to your world.

Math definitions in English and Spanish

The online Solve It will get you in gear for each lesson.

Interactive! Vary numbers, graphs, and figures to explore math concepts.

Online access to stepped-out problems aligned to Common Core

Get and view your assignments online.

Extra practice and review online

DOMAINS
- Arithmetic with Polynomials and Rational Expressions
- Building Functions
- Creating Equations

Rational functions help explain how surface tension allows some animals to tread across a pond's surface.

How can you graph rational functions and solve rational equations? You will learn how in this chapter.

Vocabulary

English/Spanish Vocabulary Audio Online:

English	Spanish
combined variation, *p. 501*	variación combinada
complex fraction, *p. 536*	fracción compleja
continuous graph, *p. 516*	gráfica continua
discontinuous graph, *p. 516*	gráfica discontinua
inverse variation, *p. 498*	variación inversa
joint variation, *p. 501*	variación conjunta
point of discontinuity, *p. 516*	punto de discontinuidad
rational equation, *p. 542*	ecuación racional
rational expression, *p. 527*	expresión racional
rational function, *p. 515*	función racional
reciprocal function, *p. 507*	función recíproca

PowerAlgebra.com

Chapter 8 Overview

Use these online assets to engage your students. These include support for the Solve It and step-by-step solutions for Problems.

Show the student-produced video demonstrating relevant and engaging applications of the new concepts in the chapter.

Find online definitions for new terms in English and Spanish.

Start each lesson with an attention-getting Problem. View the Problem online with helpful hints.

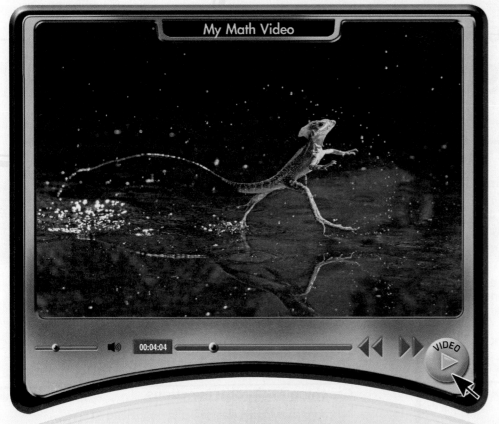

My Math Video

My Math Video

Use this photo to introduce the concept of inverse variation.

Q What do you see in the photo? **[a lizard walking on its hind legs across some water]**

Q The lizard has webbed feet. How might these help it cross the water? **[The webs can catch air bubbles underneath their feet, displacing water and so helping the lizard float.]**

Q Do you think the lizard could keep walking on the water indefinitely? Why or why not? **[No; samples: the lizard will eventually get tired; the lizard has to maintain a very fast pace in order to stay above the water and will eventually slow too much.]**

EXTENSION

Suggest students research the use of snowshoes. Have them find out how the snowshoe distributes the pressure a person exerts on a surface of snow, allowing a person to walk on top of snow. Have them determine how the size of the snowshoe affects the pressure on the snow.

BIG ideas

1 Proportionality
Essential Question Are two quantities inversely proportional if an increase in one corresponds to a decrease in the other?

2 Function
Essential Question What kinds of asymptotes are possible for a rational function?

3 Equivalence
Essential Question Are a rational expression and its simplified form equivalent?

Chapter Preview

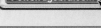

Chapter 8 Rational Functions 497

Content Standards (cont')

CONCEPTUAL CATEGORY Functions

Domain Building Functions F.BF

Cluster Build a function that models a relationship between two quantities. (Standard F.BF.1.b★)
LESSON 8-3

Cluster Build new functions from existing functions. (Standard F.BF.3)
LESSON 8-2

 Increase students' depth of knowledge with interactive online activities.

 Show Problems from each lesson solved step by step. Instant replay allows students to go at their own pace when studying online.

 Assign homework to individual students or to an entire class.

 Prepare students for the Mid-Chapter Quiz and Chapter Test with online practice and review.

RATIONAL FUNCTIONS
Math Background © PROFESSIONAL DEVELOPMENT

Understanding by Design principles were central to the development of the Big Ideas and the Essential Understandings. These will help your students build a structure on which to make connections to prior learning.

Proportionality

BIG idea Two quantities are *proportional* if they have the same ratio in each instance where they are measured together. Two quantities are *inversely proportional* if they have the same product in each instance where they are measured together.

ESSENTIAL UNDERSTANDINGS

8-1   In a direct variation, two positive quantities either increase together or decrease together. In an inverse variation, as one quantity increases the other decreases.

8-2   Transformations of the parent reciprocal function include stretches, compressions (or shrinks), reflections, and horizontal and vertical translations.

Function

BIG idea A function is a relationship between variables in which each value of the input variable is associated with a unique value of the output variable. Functions can be represented in a variety of ways, such as graphs, tables, equations, or words. Each representation is particularly useful in certain situations. Some important families of functions are developed through transformations of the simplest form of the function.

ESSENTIAL UNDERSTANDINGS

8-2   See above.

8-3   A rational function is a ratio of polynomial functions. If a rational function is in simplified form and the polynomial in the denominator is not constant, the graph of the rational function features asymptotic behavior. It looks quite different from the graphs of either of its polynomial components.

Equivalence

BIG idea A single quantity may be represented by many different expressions. The facts about a quantity may be expressed by many different equations (or inequalities).

ESSENTIAL UNDERSTANDINGS

8-4   You can use much of what you know about multiplying and dividing fractions to multiply and divide rational expressions.

8-5   To operate with rational expressions, you can use much of what you know about operating with fractions. To add or subtract rational expressions, you first find a common denominator—preferably the least common multiple (LCM) of the denominators.

8-6   To solve an equation containing rational expressions, first multiply each side by the least common denominator of the rational expressions. Doing this, however, can introduce extraneous solutions.

Inverse Variation and Graphing

Inverse variation occurs when one quantity increases as another decreases proportionally. It can be represented in the forms:

$$xy = k, \qquad y = \frac{k}{x}, \qquad x = \frac{k}{y}$$

where $k \neq 0$ and k is the constant of variation.

Combined variation occurs when one quantity varies with respect to two or more quantities. **Joint variation** occurs when one quantity varies directly with two or more quantities. The following equations represent combined variations.

$$z = kxy \qquad z = \frac{kxy}{w} \qquad z = \frac{kx}{wy}$$

Graphing Reciprocal Functions

Functions that model inverse variations belong to a family whose parent is the reciprocal function $f(x) = \frac{1}{x}$. The branches of the parent function $y = \frac{1}{x}$ are in Quadrants I and III.

Stretches and compressions of the parent function remain in the same quadrants. **Reflections** are in Quadrants II and IV.

For $y = \frac{a}{x}$, where $x \neq 0$:
- stretch: ($|a| > 1$)
- shrink: ($0 < |a| < 1$)
- reflection in the *x*-axis: ($a < 0$)

Reciprocal functions can also be **translated** horizontally or vertically.

$y = \frac{a}{x - h} + k,\ x \neq h$; translated vertically by k and horizontally by h.

Sketch the Graphs

Example: Compare the graph of $g(x) = \frac{5}{x - 2} + 3$ with $f(x) = \frac{1}{x}$.

Solution: The graph of $g(x)$ has been stretched by a factor of 5 and shifted 3 units vertically and 2 units horizontally.

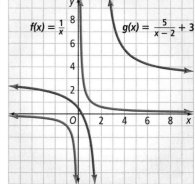

© Mathematical Practices

Model with mathematics. Make sense of problems and persevere in solving them. Rational functions are introduced as models of real-world behavior through inverse variation and averaging problems before algebraic manipulations are studied and practiced.

Graphs of Rational Functions

The graph of a rational function is **continuous** if it has no jumps, breaks, or holes.

- $\frac{x}{x^2 + 3}$ is continuous because there is no real value of x that makes the denominator 0.

Rational functions are **discontinuous** at the points where the function is undefined. A **removable discontinuity** occurs when the function can be redefined. A **non-removable discontinuity** occurs when there is no way to redefine the function at the point to make it continuous.

- $\frac{(x - 5)(x + 1)}{(x + 1)}$ has removable discontinuity at $x = -1$.
- $\frac{(x - 5)}{(x + 1)}$ has a non-removable discontinuity at $x = -1$.

Asymptotes

An asymptote is a line that the graph approaches as x or y increases in absolute value. A **vertical asymptote** occurs at $x = a$ if this is a non-removable discontinuity. The graph of a rational function can have any number of vertical asymptotes.

The graph of a rational function can have no more than one **horizontal asymptote**. If the degree of the numerator is m and the degree of the denominator is n, then:

- if $m < n$, the graph has a horizontal asymptote, $y = 0$.
- if $m > n$, the graph has no horizontal asymptote.
- if $m = n$, the graph has a horizontal asymptote, $y = \frac{a}{b}$, where a is the numerator's leading coefficient and b is the denominator's leading coefficient.

Graphing

The graph of a rational function will never touch a vertical asymptote. The graph may touch a horizontal asymptote for other than large absolute values of x.

Example: Graph $y = \frac{-3x + 5}{x - 4}$.

Vertical asymptote: $x = 4$

Horizontal asymptote: $y = \frac{-3}{1} = -3$

x-intercept: $(2, 0)$

y-intercept: $\left(0, -\frac{3}{2}\right)$

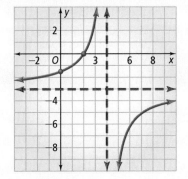

ⒸMathematical Practices

Reason abstractly and quantitatively. Look for and make use of structure. Function transformations are revisited with families of reciprocal functions, which are analyzed algebraically, graphically, and numerically with tables.

Solving Rational Equations

Rational Expressions

A rational expression is the quotient of two polynomials. It is in simplest form when its numerator and denominator have no common divisors. Rational expressions may contain restrictions to prevent the denominator of the original expression from being zero.

Operations With Rational Expressions

Example: Find the product of $\frac{5}{x + 3} \cdot \frac{x^2 + 7x + 12}{x + 2}$. State any restrictions.

Solution: Factor and simplify.

$$\frac{5}{(x + 3)} \cdot \frac{(x + 3)(x + 4)}{(x + 2)} = \frac{5(x + 4)}{(x + 2)}.$$

The domain of the original expression does not include -3 and -2. Therefore, -3 and -2 are restricted values.

Use the **Least Common Denominator (LCD)** when needed to add or subtract.

Example: What is $\frac{5}{2x + 6} + \frac{x - 1}{2}$? State any restrictions.

Solution: Factor and find LCD.

$\frac{5}{2(x + 3)} + \frac{x - 1}{2}$ and LCD is $2(x + 3)$

$$\frac{5}{2(x + 3)} + \frac{x - 1}{2}\left(\frac{x + 3}{x + 3}\right) = \frac{5 + (x - 1)(x + 3)}{2(x + 3)}$$
$$= \frac{x^2 + 2x + 2}{2(x + 3)}$$

The restricted value is -3.

Solving Rational Expressions

A rational equation contains at least one rational expression. Multiply the equation by the LCD to clear the denominators and solve. Check all solutions to determine if solutions are extraneous.

Example: Solve $\frac{3}{x^2 + 4x} + \frac{1}{x + 4} = \frac{1}{x^2 + 4x}$.

Solution: The LCD is $x^2 + 4x$.

$(x^2 + 4x)\left[\frac{3}{x^2 + 4x} + \frac{1}{x + 4}\right] = (x^2 + 4x)\frac{1}{x^2 + 4x}$

$3 + x = 1$, so $x = -2$.

A check of this solution shows that the solution is correct.

ⒸMathematical Practices

Attend to precision. Look for and express regularity in repeated reasoning. Construct viable arguments and critique the reasoning of others. The appearance of extraneous roots in solving rational equations is analyzed, and students learn the importance of verifying answers.

RATIONAL FUNCTIONS
Pacing and Assignment Guide

		TRADITIONAL			BLOCK
Lesson	**Teaching Day(s)**	**Basic**	**Average**	**Advanced**	**Block**
8-1	1	Problems 1–5 Exs. 6–24, 28–38 even, 44–60	Problems 1–5 Exs. 7–21 odd, 22–40, 44–60	Problems 1–5 Exs. 7–21 odd, 22–60	**Day 1** Problems 1–5 Exs. 7–21 odd, 22–40, 44–60
8-2	1	Problems 1–3 Exs. 8–25, 49–67	Problems 1–5 Exs. 9–29 odd, 30–43, 49–67	Problems 1–5 Exs. 9–29 odd, 30–67	Problems 1–5 Exs. 9–29 odd, 30–43, 49–67
	2	Problems 4–5 Exs. 26–32, 42, 43			
8-3	1	Problems 1–3 Exs. 13–28, 50–76	Problems 1–3 Exs. 13–27 odd, 50–76	Problems 1–3 Exs. 13–27 odd, 50–76	**Day 2** Problems 1–5 Exs. 13–35 odd, 36–47, 50–76
	2	Problems 4–5 Exs. 29–42	Problems 4–5 Exs. 29–35 odd, 36–47	Problems 4–5 Exs. 29–35 odd, 36–49	
8-4	1	Problems 1–2 Exs. 8–19, 50–67	Problems 1–2 Exs. 9–19 odd, 50–67	Problems 1–4 Exs. 9–25 odd, 27–67	**Day 3** Problems 1–4 Exs. 9–25 odd, 27–44, 50–67
	2	Problems 3–4 Exs. 20–27, 31–33, 37	Problems 3–4 Exs. 21–25 odd, 27–44		
8-5	1	Problems 1–3 Exs. 7–21, 48–65	Problems 1–3 Exs. 7–21 odd, 48–65	Problems 1–3 Exs. 7–21 odd, 48–65	**Day 4** Problems 1–5 Exs. 7–29 odd, 31–45, 48–65
	2	Problems 4–5 Exs. 22–33, 37, 38, 40, 45	Problems 4–5 Exs. 23–29 odd, 31–45	Problems 4–5 Exs. 23–29 odd, 31–47	
8-6	1	Problems 1–2 Exs. 8–20, 30, 32	Problems 1–2 Exs. 9–19 odd, 30–35, 47–53	Problems 1–2 Exs. 9–19 odd, 30–35, 47–53	**Day 5** Problems 1–3 Exs. 9–29 odd, 30–53, 57–75
	2	Problem 3 Exs. 21–29, 36–38, 42, 57–75	Problem 3 Exs. 21–29 odd, 36–46, 57–75	Problem 3 Exs. 21–29 odd, 36–46, 54–75	
Review	1	Chapter 8 Review	Chapter 8 Review	Chapter 8 Review	**Day 6** Chapter 8 Review Chapter 8 Test
Assess	1	Chapter 8 Test	Chapter 8 Test	Chapter 8 Test	
Total		**13 Days**	**12 Days**	**11 Days**	**6 Days**

Note: Pacing does not include Concept Bytes and other feature pages.

Resources

	For the Chapter	8-1	8-2	8-3	8-4	8-5	8-6
Planning							
Teacher Center Online Planner & Grade Book	I	I	I	I	I	I	I
Interactive Learning & Guided Instruction							
My Math Video	I						
Solve It!		I M	I M	I M	I M	I M	I M
Student Companion		P M	P M	P M	P M	P M	
Vocabulary Support		I P M	I P M	I P M	I P M	I P M	I P M
Got It? Support		I P	I P	I P	I P	I P	I P
Dynamic Activity		I	I	I			
Online Problems		I	I	I	I	I	I
Additional Problems		M	M	M	M	M	M
English Language Learner Support (TR)		E P M	E P M	E P M	E P M	E P M	E P M
Activities, Games, and Puzzles		E M	E M	E M	E M	E M	E M
Teaching With TI Technology With CD-ROM			✓ P	✓ P			✓ P
TI-Nspire™ Support CD-ROM		✓	✓	✓	✓	✓	✓
Lesson Check & Practice							
Student Companion		P M	P M	P M	P M	P M	P M
Lesson Check Support		I P	I P	I P	I P	I P	I P
Practice and Problem Solving Workbook		P	P	P	P	P	P
Think About a Plan (TR)		E P M	E P M	E P M	E P M	E P M	E P M
Practice Form G (TR)		E P M	E P M	E P M	E P M	E P M	E P M
Standardized Test Prep (TR)		P M	P M	P M	P M	P M	P M
Practice *Form K* (TR)		E P M	E P M	E P M	E P M	E P M	E P M
Extra Practice	E M						
Find the Errors!	M						
Enrichment (TR)		E P M	E P M	E P M	E P M	E P M	E P M
Answers and Solutions CD-ROM	✓	✓	✓	✓	✓	✓	✓
Assess & Remediate							
ExamView CD-ROM	✓	✓	✓	✓	✓	✓	✓
Lesson Quiz		I M	I M	I M	I M	I M	I M
Quizzes and Tests *Form G* (TR)	E P M			E P M			E P M
Quizzes and Tests *Form K* (TR)	E P M			E P M			E P M
Reteaching (TR)		E P M	E P M	E P M	E P M	E P M	E P M
Performance Tasks (TR)	P M						
Cumulative Review (TR)	P M						
Progress Monitoring Assessments	I P M						

(TR) Available in All-In-One Teaching Resources

1 Interactive Learning

Solve It!

PURPOSE To use an inverse variation equation to solve an area problem

PROCESS Students may
- express cubic measurement as $\ell \times w \times h$ with the height being $\frac{1}{4}$ ft. Thus 1 bag covers $8 \times 1 \times \frac{1}{4}$ ft. The area covered by one bag is 8 ft^2, thus 20 bags cover 160 ft^2.
- express cubic feet as height $\times$ area. In this case, 2 ft^3 = 0.25 ft $\times$ area, or $(2)(4)$ ft^2 = area covered by one bag.

FACILITATE
Q What dimensions would give 2 ft^3? Give all dimensions in feet. **[2 × 1 × 1]**

Q What is 3 in. measured in ft? $\left[\frac{1}{4}\text{ ft}\right]$

ANSWER See Solve It in Answers on next page.
CONNECT THE MATH In the Solve It, students used an inverse variation equation to solve an area problem. In the lesson, they will define, identify, and model inverse and combined variations.

2 Guided Instruction

Problem 1   SYNTHESIZING

Q What is the constant of variation in 1A? **[30]**

Q Why does a quick look at the table and graph just *suggest* an inverse relationship? **[Not all tables where an increase in x correlates to a decrease in y actually show an inverse relationship. You have to make sure that the product of x and y is constant.]**

BIG idea Proportionality

ESSENTIAL UNDERSTANDINGS
- If a product is constant, a decrease in the value of one factor must accompany an increase in the value of the other factor.
- In a direct variation, two positive quantities either increase together or decrease together. In an inverse variation, as one quantity increases the other decreases.
- Quantities x and y are inversely proportional only if increasing x by the factor k ($k \neq 0$) means shrinking y by the factor $\frac{1}{k}$.

Math Background
Direct and inverse variations show a relationship between two quantities.
For direct variation,
- $y = kx$ for nonzero constant k.
- the absolute values of both quantities increase together.
- the graph is a line.

- the quotient of the y-values and the corresponding x-values is constant.

For inverse variation,
- $y = \frac{k}{x}$ for nonzero constant k.
- the absolute value of one quantity increases as the absolute value of the other quantity decreases.
- the product of the y-values and the corresponding x-values is constant.

In a combined variation, one quantity varies with respect to two or more other quantities.
- z varies jointly with x and y: $z = kxy$.
- z varies jointly with x and y and inversely with w: $z = \frac{kxy}{w}$.
- z varies jointly with x and inversely with the product wy: $z = \frac{kx}{wy}$.

Mathematical Practices
Attend to precision. Students will define and make explicit use of the terms "direct variation" and "indirect variation."

Content Standards
A.CED.2 Create equations in two or more variables to represent relationships between quantities; graph equations on coordinate axes with labels and scales.
Also A.CED.4

8-1 Inverse Variation

Objectives To recognize and use inverse variation
To use joint and other variations

Getting Ready!

You have 20 bags of mulch. You plan to spread the mulch from all the bags to make a rectangular layer that is 3-in. thick. How many square feet can you cover? If ℓ and w represent the length and width of the rectangle in feet, what equation relates ℓ and w? Justify your reasoning.

Solve a simpler problem first. How many square feet will one bag cover?

Lesson Vocabulary
- inverse variation
- combined variation
- joint variation

Among all rectangles with a given area, the longer the length of one side, the shorter the length of an adjacent side.

Essential Understanding If a product is constant, where the constant is positive, a decrease in the value of one factor must accompany an increase in the value of the other factor.

As an equation, direct variation has the form $y = kx$, where $k \neq 0$. **Inverse variation** can have the form $xy = k$, $y = \frac{k}{x}$, or $x = \frac{k}{y}$, where $k \neq 0$. When two quantities vary inversely, as one quantity increases, the other decreases proportionally. For both inverse and direct variation, k is the constant of variation.

Problem 1 Identifying Direct and Inverse Variations

Is the relationship between the variables a *direct variation*, an *inverse variation*, or *neither*? Write function models for the direct and inverse variations.

Think
How can you tell if the quantities vary directly or inversely?
If the product of corresponding x- and y-values is constant, they vary inversely. If the ratio of corresponding x- and y-values is constant, they vary directly.

A

x	y
2	15
4	7.5
10	3
15	2

As x increases, y decreases. This might be an inverse relationship. A plot confirms that an inverse relationship is possible. Test to see whether xy is constant.

$2 \cdot 15 = 30$ $4 \cdot 7.5 = 30$
$10 \cdot 3 = 30$ $15 \cdot 2 = 30$

The product of each pair is 30, so $xy = 30$ and y varies inversely with x. The constant of variation is 30 and the function model is $y = \frac{30}{x}$.

PowerAlgebra.com

1 Interactive Learning

Solve It!
Step out how to solve the Problem with helpful hints and an online question. Other questions are listed above in Interactive Learning.

Dynamic Activity This activity allows students to compare and contrast the graphs of direct and inverse variations. They will see that the graph of a direct variation is a straight line, whereas the graph of the inverse variation is a curve.

B

x	y
2	10
4	8
10	3
15	1.5

A plot of the points suggests that an inverse relationship is possible. Test to see whether the products of x and y are constant.

$2 \cdot 10 = 20, 4 \cdot 8 = 32, 10 \cdot 3 = 30,$ and
$15 \cdot 1.5 = 22.5$

Since the products are not constant, the relationship is not an inverse variation.

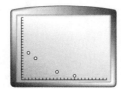

Got It? 1. Is the relationship between the variables a *direct variation*, an *inverse variation*, or *neither*? Write function models for the direct and inverse variations.

Dynamic Activity
Direct and Inverse Variation

a.

x	y
0.2	8
0.5	20
1.0	40
1.5	60

b.

x	y
0.2	40
0.5	16
1.0	8.0
2.0	4.0

c.

x	y
0.5	40
1.2	12
2	10
2.5	6

Problem 2 Determining an Inverse Variation

Suppose x and y vary inversely, and $x = 4$ when $y = 12$.

A What function models the inverse variation?

$y = \frac{k}{x}$ Write the general function form for inverse variation.

$12 = \frac{k}{4}$ Substitute for x and y.

$k = 48$ Solve for k.

The function is $y = \frac{48}{x}$.

Plan

Is it reasonable to connect the points of this function with a smooth curve?
Yes, $\frac{48}{x}$ is defined for every real number except $x = 0$.

B What does the graph of this function look like?

Make a table of values. Sketch a graph.

x	y
3	16
4	12
6	8
8	6
12	4
16	3

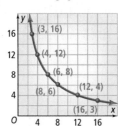

C What is y when $x = 10$?

$y = \frac{48}{x}$ Write the function.

$y = \frac{48}{10}$ Evaluate y for $x = 10$.

$y = 4.8$, when $x = 10$.

Got It?   ERROR PREVENTION

Q How do you write the inverse function model? [$y = \frac{k}{x}$ or $k = xy$.]

Q Why is a graph a good way to start to identify the type of variation in a table, but not enough by itself? [**A graph shows the rough relationship but does not prove the presence of direct or inverse variations.**]

Problem 2   SYNTHESIZING

It is helpful to write the general form of the inverse variation as a first step when completing a modeling problem.

Q What are the three steps for determining an inverse variation model? [**Write the general form for inverse variation. Substitute values for x and y into the general equation. Solve for the constant of variation.**]

Q What values should you use to determine the table for the graph? [**Any values can be used for x except $x = 0$. It is easiest to use x-values that divide evenly into 48.**]

Q Graph $y = \frac{48}{x}$ on a graphing calculator. Why do you see two curves? [**The curve in Quadrant I contains pairs of positive x- and y-values. The curve in Quadrant III contains pairs of negative x- and y-values.**]

---

2 Guided Instruction

Each Problem is worked out and supported online.

Problem 1
Identifying Direct and Inverse Variations

Problem 2
Determining an Inverse Variation

Problem 3
Modeling an Inverse Variation
Animated

Problem 4
Using Combined Variation
Animated

Problem 5
Applying Combined Variation
Animated

Support in Algebra 2 Companion
• Vocabulary
• Key Concepts
• Got It?

Answers

Solve It!
160 ft^2; $\ell w = 160$

Got It?
1. **a.** direct; $y = 40x$
   b. inverse; $y = \frac{8}{x}$
   c. neither

Got It?

Q Why will the orientation of the graph of the function in the Got It be different from the one in Problem 2B? **[because k will be less than 0]**

Q What do you need to complete 2b? **[Answers may vary. Sample: the function rule]**

Q How would the graph appear different in the Got It than in Problem 2? **[In Problem 2 the branches of the graph will be in Quadrants I and III. In the Got It the branches will be in Quadrants II and IV.]**

Problem 3

Q Which of the functions, $nt = 255$ and $t = \frac{255}{n}$, is written in function form? Explain. **[$t = \frac{255}{n}$; in function form, one variable must be isolated on one side of the equation.]**

Q Does it matter which equation you use to answer 3B? Explain. **[No; they will both give the same answer. The only difference is that $d = \frac{255}{n}$ is written in function form.]**

Q Would you have used a different model if list L3 contained 256, 255, 252, and 258? Explain. **[Not necessarily; all of these are approximately 255, and their average is 255.25.]**

Got It?

Q Which variable determines the domain for the equation that models this situation? **[n, the number of students needed]**

Q What are the two different interpretations of the situation where $n = 3.5$? **[It would take 4 students to clear the debris in the assigned amount of time, or it would take 3 students working full time and one working half time to clear the debris.]**

Think

Can you still use inverse variation to model the data if $12 \times 21 = 252$?
Often, you cannot describe real life data exactly with a function rule. But 252 is close enough to 255 for inverse variation to still be a good model.

 Got It? 2. Suppose x and y vary inversely, and $x = 8$ when $y = -7$.
   a. What is the function that models the inverse variation?
   b. What does the graph of this function look like?
   c. What is y when $x = 2$?

ⓒ **Problem 3** Modeling an Inverse Variation

Your math class has decided to pick up litter each weekend in a local park. Each week there is approximately the same amount of litter. The table shows the number of students who worked each of the first four weeks of the project and the time needed for the pickup.

Park Cleanup Project

Number of students (n)	3	5	12	17
Time in minutes (t)	85	51	21	15

Ⓐ **What function models the data?**

Step 1 Investigate the data. The more students who help, the less time the cleanup takes. An inverse variation seems appropriate. If this is an inverse variation, then $nt = k$. From the table, nt (or **L1 · L2**) is almost always 255.

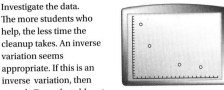

Step 2 Determine the model. $nt = 255$

Ⓑ **How many students should there be to complete the project in at most 30 minutes each week?**

$nt = 255$ Use the model from part A.

$n(30) = 255$ Substitute for t.

$n = \frac{255}{30} = 8.5$ Solve for n.

There should be at least 9 students to do the job in at most 30 minutes.

 Got It? 3. After a major storm, your math class volunteers to remove debris from yards. The table shows the time t in minutes that it takes a group of n students to remove the debris from an average-sized yard.

Number of students (n)	1	3	5	14
Time in minutes (t)	225	75	45	16

   a. What function models the time needed to clear the debris from an average-sized yard relative to the number of students who do the work?
   b. How many students should there be to clear debris from an average-sized yard in at most 25 minutes?

Additional Problems

1. Is the relationship between the variables a *direct variation*, an *inverse variation*, or *neither*?

a.

x	y
1	52
2	34
5	4
6	2

b.

x	y
0.2	0.80
0.4	0.40
0.5	0.32
1.0	0.16

ANSWERS

a. neither   **b.** inverse

2. Suppose x and y vary inversely, and $x = 2$ when $y = 8$.

a. What is the function of the inverse variation?

b. What is the graph of this function?

c. What is y when $x = 4$?

ANSWERS

a. $y = \frac{16}{x}$

b.

c. 4

3. Your employer decides to hire extra help to deliver newspapers during the holidays. The table shows the number of employees who delivered papers each week and the time needed for delivery.

Number of employees	2	4	10	20
Time in minutes	100	50	20	10

a. What function models this problem?

b. How many employees should there be to deliver newspapers in at most 40 minutes each week?

ANSWERS

a. $y = \frac{200}{x}$ **b.** at least 5

4. Multiple Choice The volume of a cone varies jointly with its height and the square of its base radius. A cone has a base radius of 4 ft, height 6 ft, and volume 100.48 ft³. What is the volume of a cone with a height of 3 ft and a base radius of 3 ft?

A. 14.13 ft³   **C.** 33.56 ft³
B. 28.27 ft³   **D.** 50.25 ft³

ANSWER B

5. The volume of gas varies directly with its temperature and inversely with pressure. Volume is 100 m³ when the temperature is 150 K and the pressure is 15 lb/cm². What is the volume when the temperature is 250 K and the pressure is 20 lb/cm²?

ANSWER 125 m³

You have seen many variation formulas in geometry. Some, like the formula for the perimeter of a square, are simple direct variations. Others, like the volume of a cone, relate three or more variables.

When one quantity varies with respect to two or more quantities, you have a **combined variation**. When one quantity varies directly with two or more quantities, you have **joint variation**. The volume of a cone varies jointly with the area of the base and the height of the cone, $V = kBh$.

Key Concept Combined Variations

Combined Variation	Equation Form
z varies jointly with x and y.	$z = kxy$
z varies jointly with x and y and inversely with w.	$z = \dfrac{kxy}{w}$
z varies directly with x and inversely with the product wy.	$z = \dfrac{kx}{wy}$

Ⓒ Problem 4 Using Combined Variation

Multiple Choice The number of bags of grass seed n needed to reseed a yard varies directly with the area a to be seeded and inversely with the weight w of a bag of seed. If it takes two 3-lb bags to seed an area of 3600 ft², how many 3-lb bags will seed 9000 ft²?

Ⓐ 3 bags Ⓑ 4 bags Ⓒ 5 bags Ⓓ 6 bags

$n = \dfrac{ka}{w}$ n varies directly with a and inversely with w.

$2 = \dfrac{3600k}{3}$ Substitute for n, a, and w.

$\dfrac{(2)(3)}{3600} = k$ Solve for k.

$k = \dfrac{6}{3600} = \dfrac{1}{600}$ Simplify.

The combined variation equation is $n = \dfrac{a}{600w}$.

$n = \dfrac{a}{600w}$ Use the combined variation equation.

$= \dfrac{9000}{600 \cdot 3}$ Substitute for a and w.

$= 5$

You need five 3-lb bags to seed 9000 ft². The correct choice is C.

✓ **Got It? 4.** The number of bags of mulch you need to cover a planting area varies jointly with the area to be mulched a in square feet and the depth of the mulch d in feet. If you need 10 bags to mulch 120 ft² to a depth of 3 in., how many bags do you need to mulch 200 ft² to a depth of 4 in.?

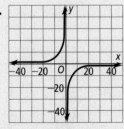

Plan

How can you write the model?
Write the constant of variation and direct variation variable in the numerator. Write the inverse variation variable in the denominator.

Q Solve each equation for k. How can the formulas be expressed in terms of direct and inverse variations? [$\frac{z}{xy} = k$: **z varies directly with the product xy**; $\frac{zw}{xy} = k$: **z varies directly with the product xy and inversely with w**; $\frac{zwy}{x} = k$: **z varies directly with x and inversely with the product wy.**]

Problem 4
There are three variables in this situation. The number of bags depends on the weight of a bag of seed and the area to be reseeded.

Q What is another form of the equation you can use? [$\frac{nw}{a} = k$]

Q If two three-pound bags will reseed 3600 ft², how much area can be reseeded by one pound of grass seed? [**600 ft²**]

Q How many pounds of seed would be needed to reseed 9000 ft²? [**15 lb**]

Got It?   EXTENSION

Q What variation does "joint" imply? [**direct variation**]

Q What are two forms of the function rule? [$n = kad, k = \frac{n}{ad}$]

Q What are you trying to find? [**the number of bags needed to mulch 200 ft² to a depth of 4 in.**]

Answers

Got It? (continued)

2. a. $y = -\dfrac{56}{x}$

b.

c. -28

3. a. $t = \dfrac{225}{n}$

b. 9 students

4. 23 bags

Problem 5

Joules are the SI units of energy. One joule equals $1 \text{ kg} \cdot \frac{m^2}{sec^2}$. The units for the gravitational constant g are m/sec^2.

> **Q** What sentence helps you write the formula? **[the first sentence]**
>
> **Q** What part of the first sentence shows you that this is a combined variation problem? **[PE varies directly with 2 quantities.]**

Got It?

ERROR PREVENTION

> **Q** Do you have to develop a formula to solve problem 5a? Explain. **[No, use the formula in Problem 5.]**
>
> **Q** What information are you given for 5a? **[m = 41 kg, h = 10 m]**

Problem 5 Applying Combined Variation **STEM**

Physics Gravitational potential energy *PE* is a measure of energy. *PE* varies directly with an object's mass *m* and its height *h* in meters above the ground. Physicists use *g* to represent the constant of variation, which is gravity.

The skateboarder in the photo has a mass of 58 kg and a potential energy of 2273.6 joules. What is the gravitational potential energy of a 65-kg skateboarder on the halfpipe shown?

HEIGHT 4 M

Know	Need	Plan
• The mass of each skateboarder • The height of each skateboarder • The potential energy of the first skateboarder	The potential energy of the second skateboarder	• Write the variation for potential energy. • Use the known information to find *g*. • Then find the potential energy of the second skateboarder.

Step 1 Write the formula for potential energy. Potential energy varies directly with mass and height. $PE = gmh$

Step 2 Use the given data to find *g*.

$PE = gmh$ Potential energy formula

$\frac{PE}{mh} = g$ Solve for *g*.

$\frac{2273.6}{(58)(4)} = g$ Substitute.

$9.8 = g$ Simplify.

Step 3 Use the formula to find the potential energy of the second skateboarder.

$PE = 9.8mh$ Potential energy formula

$= 9.8(65)(4)$ Evaluate for $m = 65$ and $h = 4$.

$= 2548$ Simplify.

The second skateboarder has 2548 joules of potential energy.

Got It? 5. a. How much potential energy would a 41-kg diver have standing on a 10-m diving platform?

b. Reasoning An 80-kg diver stands on a 6-m diving platform. At what height should a 40-kg diver stand to have equal potential energy? Do you need to find the potential energy of either diver to solve this? Explain.

Answers

Got It? (continued)

5. a. 4018 joules

b. 12 m; no, you need not calculate *P* to find the height. Substitute the mass and height of the first diver and the mass of the second diver in $P = mgh$ and set the two quantities equal to calculate the height of the second diver. Solve the equation for *h*

Lesson Check

1. inv.; $y = \frac{6}{x}$

2. direct; $y = 5x$

3. In direct variation, two positive quantities either increase together or decrease together. In an inverse variation, as one quantity increases, the other quantity decreases and vice versa.

4. *p* varies directly with *q*, *r*, and *t* and inversely with *s*.

5. *d* varies directly with the cube root of *r* and inversely with the square of *t*.

Practice and Problem-Solving Exercises

6. direct; $y = 5x$ **7.** neither

8. neither   **9.** inverse; $y = \frac{0.3}{x}$

10. $y = \frac{11}{x}$; 1.1;

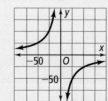

11. $y = -\frac{1300}{x}$; -130;

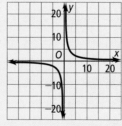

12. $y = \frac{1}{x}$; $\frac{1}{10}$;

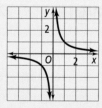

13. $y = \frac{5}{x}$; $\frac{1}{2}$;

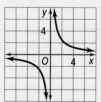

14. $y = \frac{3.6}{x}$; 0.36;

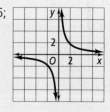

Lesson Check

Do you know HOW?

Is the relationship between the variables in each table a *direct variation*, an *inverse variation*, or *neither*? Write equations to model the direct and inverse variations.

1.

x	y
1	6
3	2
12	0.5
15	0.4

2.

u	v
−3	−15
5	25
6	30
16	80

Do you UNDERSTAND?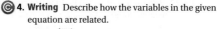

3. Compare and Contrast Describe the difference between direct variation and inverse variation.

4. Writing Describe how the variables in the given equation are related.
$$p = \frac{kqrt}{s}$$

5. Error Analysis A student described the relationship between the variables in the equation below as d varies directly with r and inversely with t. Correct the error in relating the variables.
$$d = \frac{k\sqrt[3]{r}}{t^2}$$

Practice and Problem-Solving Exercises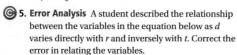

 Practice

Is the relationship between the values in each table a *direct variation*, an *inverse variation*, or *neither*? Write equations to model the direct and inverse variations.

See Problem 1.

6.

x	y
3	15
8	40
10	50
22	110

7.

x	y
3	14
5	8.4
7	6
10.5	4

8.

x	y
0.5	1
2.1	4.2
3.5	7
11	22

9.

x	y
0.1	3
3	0.1
6	0.05
24	0.0125

Suppose that *x* and *y* vary inversely. Write a function that models each inverse variation. Graph the function and find *y* when *x* = 10.

See Problem 2.

10. $x = 1$ when $y = 11$

11. $x = -13$ when $y = 100$

12. $x = 1$ when $y = 1$

13. $x = 1$ when $y = 5$

14. $x = 1.2$ when $y = 3$

15. $x = 2.5$ when $y = 100$

16. $x = 20$ when $y = -4$

17. $x = 5$ when $y = -\frac{1}{3}$

18. $x = -\frac{4}{15}$ when $y = -105$

19. Fundraising In a bake sale, you recorded the number of muffins sold and the amount of sales in a table as shown.

a. What is a function that relates the sales and the number of muffins?

b. How many muffins would you have to sell to make at least $250.00 in sales?

See Problem 3.

Number of muffins (m)	Sales (s)
5	$12.50
8	$20.00
13	$32.50
20	$50.00

15. $y = \frac{250}{x}$; 25;
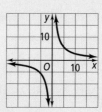

16. $y = -\frac{80}{x}$; −8;
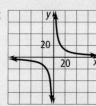

17. $y = -\frac{5}{3x}$; $-\frac{1}{6}$;
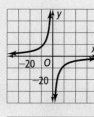

18. $y = \frac{28}{x}$; 2.8;
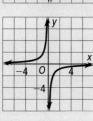

19. a. $s = 2.5m$

b. 100 muffins

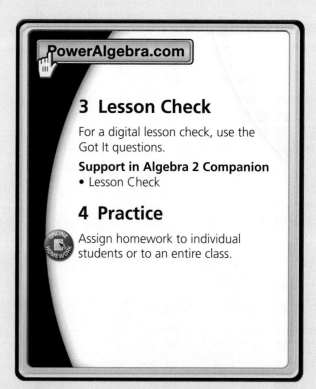

3 Lesson Check

Do you know HOW?

• For Exercises 1 and 2, students can plot the points to see whether a direct or inverse variation is reasonable. Then, they can determine whether there is a constant of variation and use it to write the equation.

Do you UNDERSTAND? ERROR INTERVENTION

• Instruct students to break down the equations in Exercises 4 and 5 into products and quotients. Then refer students to the Combined Variations Take Note box.

Close

Q How can you tell whether two sets of data show direct variation or inverse variation? **[Answers may vary. Sample: If the quotient of the *y*-values and corresponding *x*-values is constant, the data show direct variation. If the product of the *y*-values and corresponding *x*-values is constant, the data show inverse variation.]**

PowerAlgebra.com

3 Lesson Check

For a digital lesson check, use the Got It questions.

Support in Algebra 2 Companion
• Lesson Check

4 Practice

Assign homework to individual students or to an entire class.

4 Practice

ASSIGNMENT GUIDE
Basic: 6–24 all, 28–38 even
Average: 7–21 odd, 22–40
Advanced: 7–21 odd, 22–43
Standardized Test Prep: 44–48
Mixed Review: 49–60

Ⓒ **Mathematical Practices** are supported by exercises with red headings. Here are the Practices supported in this lesson:

MP 1: Make Sense of Problems Ex. 22
MP 2: Reason Quantitatively Ex. 43
MP 3: Communicate Ex. 4, 41
MP 3: Construct Arguments Ex. 42
MP 3: Compare Arguments Ex. 3
MP 3: Critique the Reasoning of Others Ex. 5

Applications exercises have blue headings. Exercises 23 and 25 support MP 4: Model.

STEM exercises focus on science or engineering applications.

EXERCISE 24: Use the Think About a Plan worksheet in the **Practice and Problem Solving Workbook** (also available in the Teaching Resources in print and online) to further support students' development in becoming independent learners.

HOMEWORK QUICK CHECK
To check students' understanding of key skills and concepts, go over Exercises 7, 11, 22, 23, and 24.

---

20. Painting The number of buckets of paint n needed to paint a fence varies directly with the total area a of the fence and inversely with the amount of paint p in a bucket. It takes three 1-gallon buckets of paint to paint 72 square feet of fence. How many 1-gallon buckets will be needed to paint 90 square feet of fence? ◀ See Problem 4.

STEM 21. Potential Energy On Earth with a gravitational acceleration g, the potential energy stored in an object varies directly with its mass m and its vertical height h. ◀ See Problem 5.
   a. What is an equation that models the potential energy of a 2-kg skateboard that is sliding down a ramp?
   b. The acceleration due to gravity is $g = -9.8 \text{ m/s}^2$. What is the height of the ramp if the skateboard has a potential energy of $-39.2 \text{ kg m}^2/\text{s}^2$?

Ⓒ **22. Think About a Plan** The table shows data about how the life span s of a mammal relates to its heart rate r. The data could be modeled by an equation of the form $rs = k$. Estimate the life span of a cat with a heart rate of 126 beats/min.
   • How can you estimate a constant of the inverse variation?
   • What expression would you use to find the life span?

Heart Rate and Life Span

Mammal	Heart rate (beats/min)	Life span (min)
Mouse	634	1,576,800
Rabbit	158	6,307,200
Lion	76	13,140,000

Source: *The Handy Science Answer Book*

STEM 23. Physics The force F of gravity on a rocket varies directly with its mass m and inversely with the square of its distance d from Earth. Write a model for this combined variation. Write an equation to find the mass of the rocket in terms of F and d.

Ⓑ **Apply**

24. The spreadsheet shows data that could be modeled by an equation of the form $PV = k$. Estimate P when $V = 62$.

	A	B
1	P	V
2	140.00	100
3	147.30	95
4	155.60	90
5	164.70	85
6	175.00	80
7	186.70	75

STEM 25. Chemistry The formula for the Ideal Gas Law is $PV = nRT$, where P is the pressure in kilopascals (kPA), V is the volume in liters (L), T is the temperature in Kelvin (K), n is the number of moles of gas, and $R = 8.314$ is the universal gas constant.
   a. Write an equation to find the volume in terms of P, n, R, and T.
   b. What volume is needed to store 5 moles of helium gas at 350 K under the pressure 190 kPA?
   c. A 10 L cylinder is filled with hydrogen gas to a pressure of 5,000 kPA. The temperature of gas is 300 K. How many moles of hydrogen gas are in the cylinder?

Write the function that models each variation. Find z when $x = 4$ and $y = 9$.

26. z varies directly with x and inversely with y. When $x = 6$ and $y = 2$, $z = 15$.

27. z varies jointly with x and y. When $x = 2$ and $y = 3$, $z = 60$.

28. z varies inversely with the product of x and y. When $x = 2$ and $y = 4$, $z = 0.5$.

Each pair of values is from a direct variation. Find the missing value.

29. $(2, 5), (4, y)$ **30.** $(4, 6), (x, 3)$ **31.** $(3, 7), (8, y)$ **32.** $(x, 12), (4, 1.5)$

Each ordered pair is from an inverse variation. Find the constant of variation.

33. $(6, 3)$ **34.** $(0.9, 4)$ **35.** $\left(\frac{3}{8}, \frac{2}{3}\right)$ **36.** $(\sqrt{2}, \sqrt{18})$

Answers

Practice and Problem-Solving Exercises (continued)

20. ≈4 buckets

21. a. $PE = 2gh$
   b. 2 m

22. about 7,900,000 min, or 15 yrs

23. $F = \frac{km}{d^2}$; $m = \frac{Fd^2}{k}$

24. 226

25. a. $V = \frac{nRT}{P}$
   b. ≈76.58 L
   c. ≈20 moles

26. $z = \frac{5x}{y}$; $\frac{20}{9}$

27. $z = 10xy$; 360   **28.** $z = \frac{4}{xy}$; $\frac{1}{9}$

29. 10   **30.** 2

31. $18\frac{2}{3}$ **32.** 32

33. 18   **34.** 3.6

35. $\frac{1}{4}$ **36.** 6

Each pair of values is from an inverse variation. Find the missing value.

37. $(2, 5), (4, y)$ **38.** $(4, 6), (x, 3)$ **39.** $(3, 7), (8, y)$ **40.** $(x, 12), (4, 1.5)$

C Challenge

41. Writing Explain why 0 cannot be in the domain of an inverse variation.

© 42. Reasoning Suppose that (x_1, y_1) and (x_2, y_2) are values from an inverse variation. Show that $\frac{x_1}{x_2} = \frac{y_2}{y_1}$.

© 43. Open-Ended The height h of a cylinder varies directly with its volume V and inversely with the square of its radius r. Find at least four ways to change the volume and radius of a cylinder so that its height is quadrupled.

Standardized Test Prep

SAT/ACT

44. Which equation represents inverse variation between x and y?

Ⓐ $x = \frac{y}{z}$ Ⓑ $x = -\frac{15z}{y}$ Ⓒ $z = -\frac{15y}{x}$ Ⓓ $xz = 5y$

45. How can you rewrite the expression $(8 - 5i)^2$ in the form $a + bi$?

Ⓕ $39 + 80i$ Ⓖ $39 - 80i$ Ⓗ $89 + 80i$ Ⓘ $89 - 80i$

46. The height of a ball thrown straight up from the ground with a velocity of 96 ft/s is given by the quadratic function $h(t) = -16t^2 + 96t$. What is the maximum height the ball reaches?

Ⓐ 6 ft   Ⓑ 128 ft   Ⓒ 144 ft   Ⓓ 160 ft

47. Which expression is NOT equivalent to $\sqrt[6]{81x^4y^8}$?

Ⓕ $(3xy^2)^{\frac{2}{3}}$ Ⓖ $(3x)^{\frac{2}{3}}y^{\frac{4}{3}}$ Ⓗ $(3x^2y^2)^{\frac{1}{3}}$ Ⓘ $\sqrt[3]{9x^2y^4}$

Short Response

48. What is the inverse of $y = 4x^2 + 5$? Is the inverse a function?

Mixed Review

Solve each equation. Check your answers.   ◀ See Lesson 7-6.

49. $\ln 4 + \ln x = 5$ **50.** $\ln x - \ln 3 = 4$ **51.** $2\ln x + 3\ln 4 = 4$

Multiply and simplify.   ◀ See Lesson 6-2.

52. $-5\sqrt{6x} \cdot 3\sqrt{6x^3}$ **53.** $3\sqrt[3]{2x^2} \cdot 7\sqrt[3]{32x^4}$ **54.** $\sqrt{5x^3} \cdot \sqrt{40xy^7}$

Get Ready! To prepare for Lesson 8-2, do Exercises 55–60.

Graph each equation. Then describe the transformation of the parent function $f(x) = |x|$.   ◀ See Lesson 2-7.

55. $y = |x| + 2$ **56.** $y = |x + 2|$ **57.** $y = |x| - 3$

58. $y = |x - 3|$ **59.** $y = |x + 4| - 5$ **60.** $y = |x - 10| + 7$

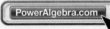

---

37. 2.5   **38.** 8

39. 2.625   **40.** 0.5

41. Div. by zero is undefined.

42. $x_1y_1 = k$ and $x_2y_2 = k$, def. of inv. variation; $x_1y_1 = x_2y_2$, transitivity; $\frac{x_1}{x_2} = \frac{y_2}{y_1}$, divide each side by x_2y_1.

43. Answers may vary. Sample: Quadruple the volume and leave the radius constant, halve the radius and leave the volume constant, multiply the volume by 16 and double the radius, and multiply the volume and radius by $\frac{1}{4}$.

Standardized Test Prep

44. B   **45.** G

46. C   **47.** H

48. [2] $x = 4y^2 + 5$

$x - 5 = 4y^2$

$\frac{x - 5}{4} = y^2$

$\frac{\pm\sqrt{x - 5}}{2} = f^{-1}(x), x \geq 5$

No, the inv. is not a function.

[1] appropriate methods, with one computational error OR correct inv., without work shown OR inv. incorrectly called a function

---

Mixed Review

49. $\frac{e^5}{4} \approx 37.1$ **50.** $3e^4 \approx 163.79$

51. $\frac{e^2}{8} \approx 0.92$ **52.** $-90x^2$

53. $84x^2$ **54.** $10x^2y^3\sqrt{2y}$

55. $y = |x|$ translated 2 units up;

56. $y = |x|$ translated 2 units to the left;

57. $y = |x|$ translated 3 units down;

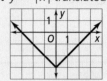

58. $y = |x|$ translated 3 units to the rt.;

59. $y = |x|$ translated 4 units to the left and 5 units down;

60. $y = |x|$ translated 10 units to the rt. and 7 units up;

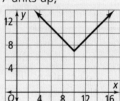

Lesson Resources

Differentiated Remediation

Additional Instructional Support

Algebra 2 Companion

Students can use the **Algebra 2 Companion** worktext (4 pages) as you teach the lesson. Use the Companion to support

- New Vocabulary
- Key Concepts
- Got It for each Problem
- Lesson Check

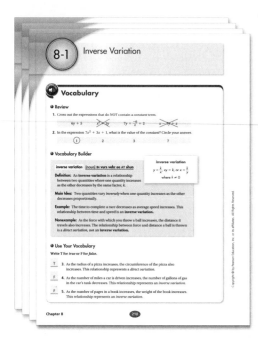

ELL Support

Focus on Language Write the equation forms on the board for all of the variations. The activity steps are as follows:

1. Choose an equation form, and state the rule. (Example: *x* and *y* vary inversely.)
2. Substitute values for *x* and *y* and compute *k*.
3. Write the function rule with the *k* value.
4. Choose values for all variables except one, and determine its missing value.
5. Repeat.

Ask for one volunteer to complete step 1. This volunteer is responsible for choosing another student for step 2. The process is repeated until all students have participated and all formulas have been used.

5 Assess & Remediate

Lesson Quiz

x	y
2	9
3	6
4	4.5
5	3.6

1. Is the relationship between the variables a *direct variation*, an *inverse variation*, or *neither*? If the relation is a variation, write the function rule.

2. Suppose *x* and *y* vary inversely, and *x* = 5 when *y* = 10.
   a. What is the function of the inverse variation?
   b. What is the graph of this function?
   c. What is *y* when *x* = 2?

3. **Do you UNDERSTAND?** The electrical resistance *r* of a wire varies directly with its length ℓ and inversely with the square of its diameter *d*. If 100 m of wire with diameter 3 mm has a resistance of 8 ohms, what is the resistance of 150 m of wire with a diameter of 4 mm?

ANSWERS TO LESSON QUIZ

1. Inverse variation; $y = \dfrac{18}{x}$

2. a. $y = \dfrac{50}{x}$
   b.
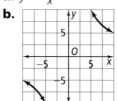
   c. 25

3. 6.75 ohms

PRESCRIPTION FOR REMEDIATION

Use the student work on the Lesson Quiz to prescribe a differentiated review assignment:

Points	Differentiated Remediation
0–1	Intervention
2	On-level
3	Extension

5 Assess & Remediate

Assign the Lesson Quiz. Appropriate intervention, practice, or enrichment is automatically generated based on student performance.

Intervention

- **Reteaching** (2 pages) Provides reteaching and practice exercises for the key lesson concepts. Use with struggling students or absent students.

- **English Language Learner Support** Helps students develop and reinforce mathematical vocabulary and key concepts.

All-in-One Resources/Online
Reteaching

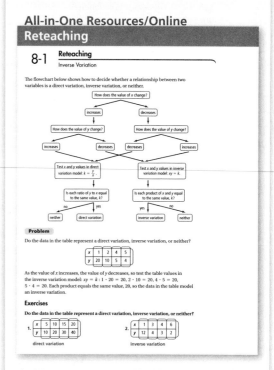

All-in-One Resources/Online
English Language Learner Support

Differentiated Remediation *continued*

On-Level

- **Practice (2 pages)** Provides extra practice for each lesson. For simpler practice exercises, use the Form K Practice pages found in the All-in-One Teaching Resources and online.

- **Think About a Plan** Helps students develop specific problem-solving skills and strategies by providing scaffolded guiding questions.

- **Standardized Test Prep** Focuses on all major exercises, all major question types, and helps students prepare for the high-stakes assessments.

Extension

- **Enrichment** Provides students with interesting problems and activities that extend the concepts of the lesson.

- **Activities, Games, and Puzzles** Worksheets that can be used for concepts development, enrichment, and for fun!

Practice and Problem Solving Wkbk/All-in-One Resources/Online
Practice page 1

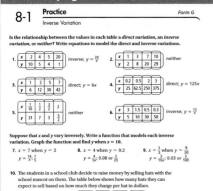

8-1 **Practice** *Form G*
Inverse Variation

Practice and Problem Solving Wkbk/All-in-One Resources/Online
Practice page 2

8-1 **Practice** (continued) *Form G*
Inverse Variation

All-in-One Resources/Online
Enrichment

8-1 **Enrichment**
Inverse Variation

Each situation below can be modeled by a direct variation, inverse variation, joint variation, or combined variation equation. Decide which model to use and explain why.

1. The circumference C of a circle is about 3.14 times the diameter d.
Direct variation; answers may vary. Sample: This relationship can be modeled by the equation $C = 3.14d$, where 3.14 is the constant of variation.

2. The number of cavities that develop in a patient's teeth depends on the total number of minutes spent brushing.
Inverse variation; answers may vary. Sample: As the number of minutes spent brushing increases, the number of cavities should decrease. This suggests an inverse variation.

3. The time it takes to build a bridge depends on the number of workers.
Inverse variation; answers may vary. Sample: As the number of workers increases, the time it takes to build a bridge should decrease. This suggests an inverse variation.

4. The number of minutes it will take to solve a problem set depends on the number of problems and the number of people working on the problem set.
Combined variation; answers may vary. Sample: The time to solve a problem set increases as the number of problems increases, but decreases as the number of people working on the set increases. This suggests a combined variation.

5. The current I in an electrical circuit decreases as the resistance R increases.
Inverse variation; answers may vary. Sample: As one variable increases, the other decreases. This suggests an inverse variation.

6. Charles's Gas Law states the volume V of an enclosed gas at a constant pressure will increase as the absolute temperature T increases.
Direct variation; answers may vary. Sample: As one variable increases, so does the other. This suggests a direct variation.

7. Boyle's Law states that the volume V of an enclosed gas at a constant temperature is related to the pressure P. The pressure of 3.45 L of neon gas is 0.926 atmosphere (atm). At the same temperature, the pressure of 2.2 L of neon gas is 1.452 atm.
Inverse variation; answers may vary. Sample: As the pressure increases, the volume decreases. This suggests an inverse variation.

Practice and Problem Solving Wkbk/All-in-One Resources/Online
Think About a Plan

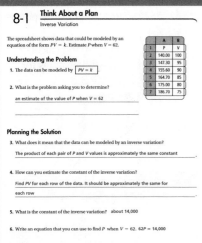

8-1 **Think About a Plan**
Inverse Variation

Practice and Problem Solving Wkbk/All-in-One Resources/Online
Standardized Test Prep

8-1 **Standardized Test Prep**
Inverse Variation

Multiple Choice

For Exercises 1–5, choose the correct letter.

1. Which equation represents inverse variation between x and y? B
Ⓐ $4y = kx$ Ⓑ $xy = 4k$ Ⓒ $y = 4kx$ Ⓓ $4k = \frac{x}{y}$

2. The ordered pair (3.5, 1.2) is from an inverse variation. What is the constant of variation? H
Ⓕ 2.3   Ⓖ 2.9   Ⓗ 4.2   Ⓘ 4.7

3. Suppose x and y vary inversely, and $x = 4$ when $y = 9$. Which function models the inverse variation? A
Ⓐ $y = \frac{36}{x}$ Ⓑ $x = \frac{y}{36}$ Ⓒ $y = \frac{x}{36}$ Ⓓ $\frac{x}{y} = 36$

4. Suppose x and y vary inversely, and $x = -3$ when $y = \frac{1}{3}$. What is the value of y when $x = 9$? H
Ⓕ -9 Ⓖ -1 Ⓗ $-\frac{1}{9}$ Ⓘ $\frac{1}{9}$

5. In which function does t vary jointly with q and r and inversely with s? D
Ⓐ $t = \frac{kq}{rs}$ Ⓑ $t = \frac{ks}{qr}$ Ⓒ $t = \frac{s}{kqr}$ Ⓓ $t = \frac{kqr}{s}$

Short Response

6. A student suggests that the graph at the right represents the inverse variation $y = \frac{3}{x}$. Is the student correct? Explain.
No; for each point on the graph $xy = 6$, not 3.
[2] correct answer with explanation
[1] correct answer, without explanation
[0] no answer given

Online Teacher Resource Center
Activities, Games, and Puzzles

8-1 **Puzzle: Constant of Variation**
Inverse Variation

Answer the following questions about inverse and combined variation.

Each ordered pair is from an inverse variation. Find the constant of variation.

1. (2, 1) 2   2. (−1, 5) −5   3. (0.4, 0.5) 0.2
4. (−5.2, −0.25) 1.3   5. $\left(2, -\frac{1}{3}\right)$ $-\frac{2}{3}$ 6. $\left(\frac{1}{2}, \frac{7}{5}\right)$ 0.7

Suppose that x and y vary inversely. Find the constant of variation.

7. $x = 6$ when $y = \frac{1}{2}$ 3   8. $x = -3$ when $y = 2$ −6   9. $x = 0.5$ when $y = -2.2$ −1.1
10. $x = 0.2$ when $y = 2$ 0.4   11. $x = \frac{2}{3}$ when $y = \frac{2}{3}$ $\frac{4}{9}$ 12. $x = \frac{9}{10}$ when $y = -\frac{5}{3}$ $-\frac{3}{2}$

Each pair of values is from an inverse variation. Find the missing value.

13. (2, 6), (−4, y) −3   14. (9, −2), (x, −3) 6   15. (7, 0.2), (5, y) 0.28   16. $\left(\frac{4}{5}, \frac{2}{3}\right)$, $\left(x, \frac{5}{9}\right)$ 1.6

For the following, find z when $x = 2$ and $y = 10$.

17. z varies jointly with x and y when $x = -8$ and $z = -3$, $z = 6.5$. 5
18. z varies directly with x and inversely with y. When $x = 4$ and $y = 20$, $z = -1$. −1
19. z varies directly with the square of y and inversely with x. When $x = 0.6$ and $y = 0.3$, $z = 0.09$. 30

The numerical solutions correspond to letters according to the table below.

−6	−6.28	−5	−3.1	−1.1	−1	$-\frac{2}{3}$	0.2	0.28	0.4	$\frac{4}{9}$
A	B	C	D	E	F	G	H	I	J	K	L	M

0.7	1.3	1.4	1.5	1.6	2	3	4	5	6	10	30	50
N	O	P	Q	R	S	T	U	V	W	X	Y	Z

The numbers below the spaces correspond to the exercise numbers. Write the letter corresponding to the exercise solution in each space. The resulting quotation is by mathematician and philosopher Bertrand Russell.

T H E   D E G R E E   O F   O N E ' S
7 12 9   13 9 5 16 9 9   4   9 1 9 · 5

E M O T I O N S   V A R I E S
9 11 4 7 3 4 6 1   17 8 16 3 9 1

I N V E R S E L Y   W I T H
3 1 17 9 16 1 9 12 9   14 3 7 1

O N E ' S   K N O W L E D G E   O F
4 6 9 · 1   15 6 4 9 12 9 13 5 9   4 18

T H E   F A C T S
7 12 9   18 8 2 7 1

Guided Instruction

PURPOSE To graph rational functions

PROCESS Students will
- use the dot-and-connected mode on a graphing calculator to graph rational functions.
- describe the behavior of the graph.

DISCUSS This Concept Byte introduces graphs of rational functions, a topic examined in detail in Lesson 8-3. Draw five columns on the board with the titles *function*, *sketch*, *increases*, *decreases*, and *approaches*. Ask students to copy and complete the columns as they work through the Example.

Example

> **Q** At what value is the graph undefined? **[3]**
>
> **Q** What happens to the *y*-values as *x* approaches 3 from the right? **[They increase.]**
>
> **Q** What happens to the *y*-values as *x* approaches 3 from the left? **[They decrease.]**
>
> **Q** Where is the graph increasing? **[nowhere]**
>
> **Q** Where is the graph decreasing? **[throughout its domain]**
>
> **Q** What is the domain of this function? **[all real numbers except x = 3]**

Exercises

> **Q** How does the calculator table show where the function is undefined? **[Error]**
>
> **Q** For Exercise 5, at how many values is the function undefined? **[two]**
>
> **Q** For Exercise 5, how many parts make up the graph? **[3]**

 Mathematical Practices This Concept Byte supports students in becoming proficient in using appropriate tools, Mathematical Practice 5.

Concept Byte
For Use With Lesson 8-2
TECHNOLOGY

Graphing Rational Functions

Content Standard
F.IF.7.d Graph rational functions, identifying zeros and asymptotes when suitable factorizations are available, and showing end behavior.

You can use your graphing calculator to graph *rational functions* and other members of the reciprocal function family. It is sometimes preferable to use the **DOT** plotting mode rather than **CONNECTED** plotting mode. The **CONNECTED** mode can join branches of a graph that should be separated. Try both modes to get the best graph.

MATHEMATICAL PRACTICES

Example

Graph $y = \dfrac{4}{x-3} - 1.5$.

Step 1 Press the (mode) key. Scroll down to highlight the word **DOT**. Then press (enter).

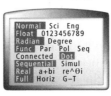

Step 2 Enter the function. Use parentheses to enter the denominator accurately.

Step 3 Graph the function.

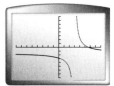

Exercises

1. a. Graph the parent reciprocal function $y = \frac{1}{x}$.
  b. Examine both negative and positive values of *x*. Describe what happens to the *y*-values as *x* approaches zero.
  c. What happens to the *y*-values as *x* increases? As *x* decreases?

 2. a. Change the mode on your calculator to **CONNECTED**. Graph the function from the example.
  b. Press (trace) and trace the function. What happens between $x \approx 2.8$ and $x \approx 3.2$?
  c. Reasoning How does your graph differ from the graph in the example? Explain the differences.

Use a graphing calculator to graph each function. Then sketch the graph.

3. $y = \dfrac{7}{x}$

4. $y = \dfrac{3}{x+4} - 2$

5. $y = \dfrac{x+2}{(x+1)(x+3)}$

6. $y = \dfrac{4x+1}{x-3}$

7. $y = \dfrac{2}{x-2}$

8. $y = \dfrac{1}{x+2} + 3$

9. $y = \dfrac{2x}{x+3}$

10. $y = \dfrac{x^2}{x^2-5}$

11. $y = \dfrac{20}{x^2+5}$

Answers

Concept Byte

1. a.

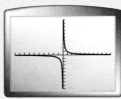

b. If *x* is negative and approaches 0, the *y*-values approach $-\infty$. If *x* is positive and approaches 0, the *y*-values approach $+\infty$.

c. If *x* is positive, as *x* increases, the *y*-values approach 0. If *x* is negative, as *x* decreases, the *y*-values approach 0.

2. a.

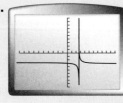

b. Answers may vary. Sample: The *y*-values change from very large negative values to very large positive values.

c. In connected mode, the calculator will try to connect the values for $x \approx 2.8$ and $x \approx 3.2$.

3.

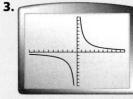

4.

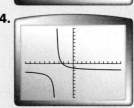

5–11. See back of book.

The Reciprocal Function Family

© **Content Standards**
F.BF.3 Identify the effect on the graph of replacing f(x) by f(x) + k, kf(x), f(kx), and f(x + k) for specific values of k . . .
A.CED.2 Create equations in two or more variables to represent relationships between quantities . . .
Also A.APR.1

Objectives To graph reciprocal functions
To graph translations of reciprocal functions

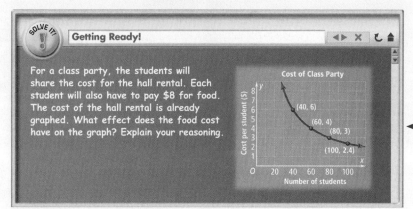

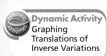
Dynamic Activity
Graphing Translations of Inverse Variations

Lesson Vocabulary
• reciprocal function
• branch

Functions that model inverse variation have the form $f(x) = \frac{a}{x}$, where $x \neq 0$. They belong to a family whose parent is the **reciprocal function** $f(x) = \frac{1}{x}$, where $x \neq 0$.

Essential Understanding Transformations of the parent reciprocal function include stretches, compressions (or shrinks), reflections, and horizontal and vertical translations.

Key Concept General Form of the Reciprocal Function Family

The general form of a member of the reciprocal function family is $y = \frac{a}{x-h} + k$, where $x \neq h$.

The inverse variation functions, $y = \frac{a}{x}$, are stretches, shrinks, and reflections of the parent reciprocal function, depending on the value of a.

The graph of the parent reciprocal function $y = \frac{1}{x}$ is shown at the right.

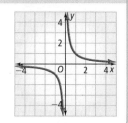

1 Interactive Learning

Solve It!
PURPOSE To apply a translation of a reciprocal function graphically and algebraically
PROCESS Students may
• sketch points of a new graph with the new y-values plotted eight units higher than the original.
• write an algebraic function for the graph and add eight as a constant value.

FACILITATE

Q What is the value of the product of the x-coordinate and y-coordinate? What is its real world meaning? **[240; the total cost of renting the hall before the food fee is added]**

Q What equation expresses the cost per student as a function of the number of students if the cost is C and the number of students is x? **[$f(x) = \frac{C}{x}$]**

Q How can you modify the function to include the additional eight dollars each class member must pay? What effect does this have on the graph? **[Add eight to the function; $f(x) = \frac{C}{x} + 8$; it translates the graph up 8 units.]**

ANSWER See Solve It in Answers on next page.
CONNECT THE MATH The Solve It is solved by translating a reciprocal function. In the lesson students will graph transformations of reciprocal functions.

2 Guided Instruction

Take Note

Q What happens to the graph as x gets close to 0? **[The absolute values of the y-values increase very quickly.]**

Preparing to Teach

BIG ideas Function
Proportionality
ESSENTIAL UNDERSTANDINGS
• Transformations of the parent reciprocal function include stretches, compressions (or shrinks), reflections, and horizontal and vertical translations.
• A rational function may have zero or one horizontal or oblique asymptote and zero or more vertical asymptotes.
• Quantities x and y are inversely proportional only if increasing x by the factor k ($k \neq 0$) means shrinking y by the factor $\frac{1}{k}$.

Math Background
The function $y = \frac{1}{x}$ is the parent function of all reciprocal functions, including the inverse variation function, $y = \frac{a}{x}$, and the functions expressing transformations of the parent function, given in general form as $y = \frac{a}{x-h} + k$. Transformations work the same way with rational functions as they did with linear, absolute value, quadratic, and exponential functions.
• a indicates a stretch when $|a| > 1$ and a shrink when $0 < |a| < 1$, each by a factor of a.
• If a is negative, the transformation involves a reflection in the x-axis.
• h indicates a horizontal translation.
• k indicates a vertical translation.
• $x = h$ is a vertical asymptote.
• $y = k$ is a horizontal asymptote.

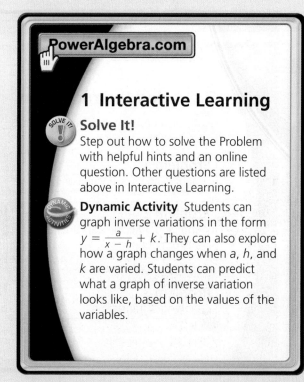

1 Interactive Learning

Solve It!
Step out how to solve the Problem with helpful hints and an online question. Other questions are listed above in Interactive Learning.

Dynamic Activity Students can graph inverse variations in the form $y = \frac{a}{x-h} + k$. They can also explore how a graph changes when a, h, and k are varied. Students can predict what a graph of inverse variation looks like, based on the values of the variables.

Problem 1

Q Why is it important to include a fractional value for x? **[The function may change very significantly close to where it is undefined, in this case where x is fractional.]**

Q Why is it necessary to include so many values in the table? **[While it may only take two points to determine a line, you need to look at many points when you are graphing curves by plotting points.]**

Q Why are the points $(\frac{1}{2}, 16)$ and $(-\frac{1}{2}, -16)$ not connected? **[They are not connected because the function is not defined at zero. Also, the function is going in different vertical directions on either side of zero.]**

Q In what way do the asymptotes help you graph a reciprocal function? **[The asymptotes provide boundaries for the branches of the graph to approach when you sketch the graph. This helps provide the curve's shape.]**

EXTENSION

Q How would you describe the symmetry of the graph? **[The graph is symmetric about the lines $y = -x$ and $y = x$, and about the origin.]**

Got It?

Q How can you tell the function has two asymptotes? **[There is a variable in the denominator, and the numerator is never zero.]**

Ⓒ **Problem 1** Graphing an Inverse Variation Function

What is the graph of $y = \frac{8}{x}, x \neq 0$? Identify the x- and y-intercepts and the asymptotes of the graph. Also, state the domain and range of the function.

Think

What values should you choose for x?
Choose values of x that divide nicely into 8. Make a table of points that are easy to graph.

Step 1 Make a table of values that includes positive and negative values of x.

x	y	x	y
-16	$-\frac{1}{2}$	$\frac{1}{2}$	16
-8	-1	1	8
-4	-2	2	4
-2	-4	4	2
-1	-8	8	1
$-\frac{1}{2}$	-16	16	$\frac{1}{2}$

Step 2 Graph the points.

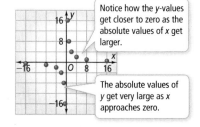

Notice how the y-values get closer to zero as the absolute values of x get larger.

The absolute values of y get very large as x approaches zero.

Step 3 Connect the points with a smooth curve. x cannot be zero, so there is no y-intercept.
The numerator is never zero, so y is never 0.
There is no x-intercept.

The x-axis is a horizontal asymptote.
The y-axis is a vertical asymptote.
Knowing the asymptotes provides you with the basic shape of the graph.
The domain is the set of all real numbers except $x = 0$.
The range is the set of all real numbers except $y = 0$.

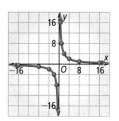

Ⓒ ✓ **Got It?** **1. a.** What is the graph of $y = \frac{12}{x}$? Identify the x- and y-intercepts and the asymptotes of the graph. Also, state the domain and range of the function.

b. Reasoning Would the function $y = \frac{6}{x}$ have the same domain and range as $y = \frac{8}{x}$ or $y = \frac{12}{x}$? Explain.

Each part of the graph of a reciprocal function is a **branch**. The branches of the parent function $y = \frac{1}{x}$ are in Quadrants I and III. Stretches and compressions of the parent function remain in the same quadrants. Reflections are in Quadrants II and IV.

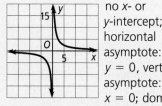

2 Guided Instruction

Ⓒ Each Problem is worked out and supported online.

Problem 1
Graphing an Inverse Variation Function

Problem 2
Identifying a Reciprocal Function Transformation
Animated

Problem 3
Graphing a Translation

Alternative Problem 3
Graphing a Translation

Problem 4
Writing the Equation of a Transformation
Animated

Problem 5
Using a Reciprocal Function
Animated

Support in Algebra 2 Companion
• Vocabulary
• Key Concepts
• Got It?

Answers

Solve It!
It will raise the graph 8 units up. The cost with food is $8 more.

Got It?

1. a.

no x- or y-intercept; horizontal asymptote: $y = 0$, vert. asymptote: $x = 0$; domain: all real numbers except $x = 0$, range: all real numbers except $y = 0$

b. Yes; they have similar graphs.

2. a. $y = \frac{1}{2x}$ is a shrink of the graph of $y = \frac{1}{x}$ by a factor of $\frac{1}{2}$.

b. $y = \frac{2}{x}$ is a stretch of the graph of $y = \frac{1}{x}$ by a factor of 2.

c. $y = -\frac{1}{2x}$ is a reflection across the x-axis and a shrink of the graph of $y = \frac{1}{x}$ by a factor of $\frac{1}{2}$.

© Problem 2 Identifying Reciprocal Function Transformations

For each given value of *a*, how do the graphs of $y = \frac{1}{x}$ and $y = \frac{a}{x}$ compare? What is the effect of *a* on the graph?

A *a* = 6

The graph (in red) of $y = \frac{6}{x}$ is a stretch of the graph of $y = \frac{1}{x}$ (in black) by the factor 6.

B *a* = 0.25

The graph (in blue) of $y = \frac{0.25}{x}$ is a shrink of the graph of $y = \frac{1}{x}$ (in black) by the factor $\frac{1}{4}$.

C *a* = −6

The graph of $y = \frac{-6}{x}$ is the stretch by the factor 6 in part A followed by a reflection across the *x*-axis.

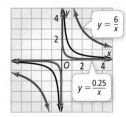

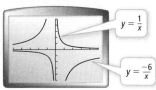

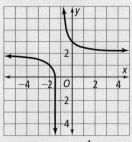

Think

How does the negative sign affect the graph?
The *y*-values have signs that are opposite those in part A. The graph in A reflects across the *x*-axis.

✓ **Got It?** 2. For each given value of *a*, how do the graphs of $y = \frac{1}{x}$ and $y = \frac{a}{x}$ compare? What is the effect of *a* on the graph?

a. $a = \frac{1}{2}$ **b.** $a = 2$ **c.** $a = -\frac{1}{2}$

You can translate any reciprocal function horizontally or vertically just as you can other functions.

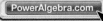

Key Concept   The Reciprocal Function Family

Parent function	$y = \frac{1}{x}, x \neq 0$
Stretch ($|a| > 1$) Shrink ($0 < |a| < 1$) Reflection ($a < 0$) across *x*-axis	$y = \frac{a}{x}, x \neq 0$
Translation (horizontal by *h*; vertical by *k*) with vertical asymptote $x = h$ horizontal asymptote $y = k$	$y = \frac{1}{x - h} + k; x \neq h$
Combined	$y = \frac{a}{x - h} + k; x \neq h$

Problem 2

Q How can you mathematically show that $y = \frac{6}{x}$ is a stretch of $y = \frac{1}{x}$ by a factor of 6? **[Sample: Express the *y*-values as a ratio: $\frac{6}{x} \div \frac{1}{x} = 6$.]**

EXTENSION

Q By what factor is 2A a stretch of 2B? How do you know? **[24; express the *y*-values as a ratio: $\frac{6}{x} \div \frac{0.25}{x} = 24$.]**

Q How does the effect of *a* on the reciprocal function compare to previous functions you have studied? **[Sample: *a* has the same effect on the graph of the quadratic ($y = ax^2$) and absolute value ($y = a|x|$) functions.]**

Got It?

Q How can you tell whether the transformation will be a shrink or a stretch? **[Sample: When $|a|$ is between 0 and 1, the transformation will be a shrink. When $|a|$ is greater than 1, the transformation will be a stretch.]**

Take Note   ERROR PREVENTION

If students translate the graph of a reciprocal function vertically before they reflect it in the *x*-axis, they will likely end up with the wrong graph. Point out the difference between $-a(\frac{1}{x}) + k$ and $-a(\frac{1}{x} + k)$. Ask which form corresponds to a reflection followed by a translation and which corresponds to a translation followed by a reflection.

Additional Problems

1. What is the graph of $y = \frac{128}{x}, x \neq 0$? Identify the *x*- and *y*-intercepts and the asymptotes of the graph. Also, state the domain and the range of the function.

ANSWER

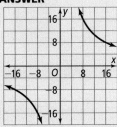

no *x*- or *y*-intercepts; asymptotes: $x = 0$ and $y = 0$; domain: all real numbers except $x = 0$; range: all real numbers except $y = 0$

2. How does the graph of $y = \frac{-1.5}{x}$ compare to the graph of $y = \frac{1}{x}$?

ANSWER The graph is reflected across the *x*-axis and stretched by a factor of 1.5.

3. What is the graph of $y = \frac{1}{x - 2} + 3$? Identify the domain and range.

ANSWER

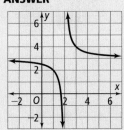

domain: all real numbers except $x = 2$; range: all real numbers except $y = 3$

4. This graph of a function is a translation of the graph of $y = \frac{1}{x}$. What is an equation for the function?

ANSWER $y = \frac{1}{x + 1} + 2$

5. A mystery society is renting a Victorian mansion for a murder mystery party. The owner is charging the group, which has 75 members, $650 for the weekend rental but does not want more than 30 people in the house. All of the members attending the party will split the cost of the rental equally except that the member playing the dead body does not have to pay. Model the cost per member *C* as a function of the number of members attending *n*. How many members have to attend for the cost to be less than $25 per person?

ANSWER $C = \frac{650}{n - 1}$; between 28 and 30, inclusive

Problem 3

Q In Step 1, why does $h = -1$ instead of 1?
[Sample: Rewrite $x + 1$ as $x - (-1)$, since the expression is $x - h$.]

Q Algebraically, why is -1 not included in the domain? [-1 leads to division by zero.]

Q Algebraically, why can y never equal -2?
[For y to equal -2, the expression $\frac{1}{x+1}$ would have to equal zero. A rational expression only equals zero if the numerator equals zero. The numerator is never zero, so y can never equal -2.]

Got It?

Q How are the domain and range related to the asymptotes? [The x-value of the vertical asymptote is excluded from the domain, and the y-value of the horizontal asymptote is excluded from the range.]

Problem 4   EXTENSION

Q Where does the value for a come from? [from the original function, which is a transformation of the parent function]

Q How do you find a from the graph if you do not have the pre-translated function? [Use the asymptotes to write the function in $y = \frac{a}{x-h} + k$ form, substitute a point in the graph for (x, y), and then solve for a.]

Got It?

Q What are the domain and range of the function?
[The domain is all real numbers except $x = 1$; the range is all real numbers except $y = -4$.]

When you graph a translated reciprocal function, a good first step is to draw the asymptotes.

Problem 3   Graphing a Translation

Think
How do you find the asymptotes?
The asymptotes of $y = \frac{1}{x}$ (the axes) translate 1 unit to the left and 2 units down.

What is the graph of $y = \frac{1}{x+1} - 2$? Identify the domain and range.

Step 1   Draw the asymptotes (red).

For, $y = \frac{1}{x+1} - 2$, $h = -1$ and $k = -2$.

The vertical asymptote is $x = -1$.

The horizontal asymptote is $y = -2$.

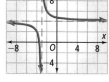

Step 2   Translate the graph of $y = \frac{1}{x}$.

The graph of $y = \frac{1}{x}$ contains the points $(1, 1)$ and $(-1, -1)$. Translate these points 1 unit to the left and 2 units down to $(0, -1)$ and $(-2, -3)$, respectively. Draw the branches through these points (blue).

The domain is the set of all real numbers except $x = -1$. The range is the set of all real numbers except $y = -2$.

✓ **Got It?**   **3.** What is the graph of $y = \frac{1}{x-4} + 6$? Identify the domain and range.

If you know the asymptotes of the graph of a reciprocal function and the value of a, you can write the equation of the function.

Problem 4   Writing the Equation of a Transformation

Multiple Choice This graph of a function is a translation of the graph of $y = \frac{2}{x}$. What is an equation for the function?

   Ⓐ $y = \frac{2}{x+3} + 4$ Ⓒ $y = \frac{2}{x-3} + 4$

   Ⓑ $y = \frac{2}{x+3} - 4$ Ⓓ $y = \frac{2}{x-3} - 4$

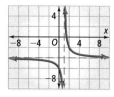

Plan
How can you get started?
Identify the asymptotes of the graph.

The asymptotes are $x = -3$ and $y = 4$. Thus $h = -3$ and $k = 4$.

$y = \frac{a}{x-h} + k$ Use the general form.

$y = \frac{2}{x-(-3)} + 4$ Substitute for a, h, and k.

$y = \frac{2}{x+3} + 4$ Simplify.

The correct choice is A.

✓ **Got It?**   **4.** This graph of a function is a translation of the graph of $y = \frac{2}{x}$. What is an equation for the function?

Answers

Got It? (continued)

3.

domain: all real numbers except $x = 4$, range: all real numbers except $y = 6$

4. $y = \frac{2}{x-1} - 4$

© **Problem 5** Using a Reciprocal Function

Clubs The rowing club is renting a 57-passenger bus for a day trip. The cost of the bus is $750. Five passengers will be chaperones. If the students who attend share the bus cost equally, what function models the cost per student C with respect to the number of students n who attend? What is the domain of the function? How many students must ride the bus to make the cost per student no more than $20?

Know	Need	Plan
• The bus holds 57 passengers. • The bus costs $750. • Five riders are chaperones who pay nothing for the bus.	• A function for the cost per student • The number of students needed so that the cost does not exceed $20 per student	• Write a reciprocal function for the situation. • Graph the function and solve an inequality using the $20 limit.

To share the cost equally, divide 750 by the number of students, n, who attend.

The function that models the cost per student is $C = \frac{750}{n}$.

The bus has a capacity of 57 passengers and there will be 5 chaperones. The maximum number of students is $57 - 5 = 52$.

The domain is the integers from 1 to 52.

Think

Is the domain $x \leq 52$?
No; the domain is the possible numbers of students, so only positive integers make sense.

Use a graphing calculator to solve the inequality $\frac{750}{n} \leq 20$. Let **Y1** $= \frac{750}{x}$ and **Y2** $= 20$.

Change the window dimensions to get a closer look at the graph. Use the **intersect** feature.

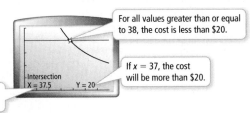

For all values greater than or equal to 38, the cost is less than $20.

If $x = 37$, the cost will be more than $20.

Intersection X = 37.5   Y = 20

The number of people must be a whole number.

At least 38 students must ride the bus.

✓ **Got It?** **5.** The junior class is renting a laser tag facility with a capacity of 325 people. The cost for the facility is $1200. The party must have 13 adult chaperones.
  a. If every student who attends shares the facility cost equally, what function models the cost per student C with respect to the number of students n who attend? What is the domain of the function? How many students must attend to make the cost per student no more than $7.50?
  b. The class wants to promote the event by giving away 30 spots to students in a drawing. How does the model change? Now how many paying students must attend so the cost for each is no more than $7.50?

Problem 5

Q How would you describe the range of the function? **[Sample: The range consists of all possible money values between and including the least amount a student would have to pay ($750 ÷ 52), about $14.42, and the most a student would have to pay, $750.]**

Q What is a function that models the cost per student with respect to the number of people on the bus? **[$c = \frac{750}{n - 5}$]**

Q Why can you ignore the other branch of the graph of the function altogether? **[No x-values from the other branch of the graph are included in the domain.]**

Q What is a good window in which to view the relevant portion of the graph to answer the final question? Explain. **[x-values from 0 to 52 and y-values from 0 to 25; the domain is a good set of values for x, and a portion of the range that includes the $20 limit is a good set of values for y; in addition, include zero in both the domain and range in order to see the x- and y-axes on the graph.]**

Got It?

Q What inequality will you write to model the situation in 5a? **[$\frac{1200}{n} \leq 7.5$]**

Q How will your inequality change for 5b? **[$\frac{1200}{n - 30} \leq 7.5$]**

5. a. $C = \frac{1200}{n}$; domain: whole numbers from 1 to 312; 160 students

b. $C = \frac{1200}{n - 30}$; domain: whole numbers from 1 to 282; 160 students

3 Lesson Check

Do you know HOW?
- For Exercise 1, students struggling with graphing may need to make a table of values and plot points to check their graphs.
- For Exercises 2 and 3, if students are having difficulty describing the transformations, have them graph both the given function and the parent function on the same set of axes.
- For Exercise 4, if students are having difficulty identifying the asymptotes from the equation, have them rewrite the equation as $y = \frac{5}{x - (-2)} - 7$.

Do you UNDERSTAND?
- For Exercise 5, if students cannot identify the transformation, ask, "Is dividing by two the same as multiplying by $\frac{1}{2}$?"
- For Exercise 7, if students are unsure whether the function $y = \frac{a}{x}$ is a stretch or a compression, suggest they compare $y = \frac{a}{x}$ to a quadratic function with the same value for a and determine the effect by comparison. Then experiment with various values for a on a graphing calculator.

Close

> **Q** How are functions of the form $y = \frac{a}{x - h} + k$ related to the parent function $y = \frac{1}{x}$? **[The functions are stretched or compressed by a factor of a, reflected in the x-axis if the value of a is negative, translated h units horizontally, and translated k units vertically.]**

 Lesson Check

Do you know HOW?
1. Graph the equation $y = \frac{3}{x}$.

 Describe the transformation from the graph of $y = \frac{1}{x}$ to the graph of the given function.

2. $y = \frac{1}{x} + 5$ **3.** $y = \frac{-4}{x}$

4. What are the asymptotes of the graph of $y = \frac{5}{x + 2} - 7$?

Do you UNDERSTAND? MATHEMATICAL PRACTICES
5. Vocabulary What transformation changes the graph of $y = \frac{1}{x}$ into the graph of $y = \frac{1}{2x}$?

6. Open Ended Write an equation of a stretch and a reflection of the graph $y = \frac{1}{x}$ across the x-axis.

7. Writing Explain how you can tell if a function $y = \frac{a}{x}$ is a stretch or compression of the parent function $y = \frac{1}{x}$.

 Practice and Problem-Solving Exercises MATHEMATICAL PRACTICES

A Practice   Graph each function. Identify the x- and y-intercepts and the asymptotes of the graph. Also, state the domain and the range of the function.   **See Problem 1.**

8. $y = \frac{2}{x}$ **9.** $y = \frac{15}{x}$ **10.** $y = \frac{-3}{x}$ **11.** $y = -\frac{10}{x}$ **12.** $y = \frac{10}{x}$

Graphing Calculator Graph the equations $y = \frac{1}{x}$ and $y = \frac{a}{x}$ using the given value of a. Then identify the effect of a on the graph.   **See Problem 2.**

13. $a = 2$ **14.** $a = -4$ **15.** $a = 0.5$ **16.** $a = 12$ **17.** $a = 0.75$

Sketch the asymptotes and the graph of each function. Identify the domain and range.   **See Problem 3.**

18. $y = \frac{1}{x} - 3$ **19.** $y = \frac{-2}{x} - 3$ **20.** $y = \frac{1}{x - 2} + 5$ **21.** $y = \frac{1}{x - 3} + 4$

22. $y = \frac{2}{x + 6} - 1$ **23.** $y = \frac{10}{x + 1} - 8$ **24.** $y = \frac{1}{x} - 2$ **25.** $y = \frac{-8}{x + 5} - 6$

Write an equation for the translation of $y = \frac{2}{x}$ that has the given asymptotes.   **See Problem 4.**

26. $x = 0$ and $y = 4$ **27.** $x = -2$ and $y = 3$ **28.** $x = 4$ and $y = -8$

STEM 29. Construction The weight P in pounds that a beam can safely carry is inversely proportional to the distance D in feet between the supports of the beam. For a certain type of wooden beam, $P = \frac{9200}{D}$. What distance between supports is needed to carry 1200 lb?   **See Problem 5.**

B Apply   **30. Think About a Plan** A high school decided to spend $750 on student academic achievement awards. At least 5 awards will be given, they should be equal in value, and each award should not be less than $50. Write and sketch a function that models the relationship between the number a of awards and the cost c of each award. What are the domain and range of the function?
- Which equation describes the relationship between a and c?
- What information can you use to determine the domain and range?

Answers

Lesson Check
1.

2. $y = \frac{1}{x}$ translated 5 units up

3. $y = \frac{1}{x}$ reflected across the x-axis and stretched by a factor of 4

4. horizontal asymptote: $y = -7$, vert. asymptote: $x = -2$

5. shrink of the graph of $y = \frac{1}{x}$ by a factor of $\frac{1}{2}$

6. Answers may vary. Sample: $y = -\frac{2}{x}$

7. for $y = \frac{a}{x}$: stretch if $|a| > 1$ and compression if $0 < |a| < 1$

Practice and Problem-Solving Exercises

8.

no x- or y-intercept; horizontal asymptote: $y = 0$, vert. asymptote: $x = 0$; domain: all real numbers except $x = 0$, range: all real numbers except $y = 0$

9.

no x- or y-intercept; horizontal asymptote: $y = 0$, vert. asymptote: $x = 0$; domain: all real numbers except $x = 0$, range: all real numbers except $y = 0$

10–30. See back of book.

31. Open-Ended Write an equation for a horizontal translation of $y = \frac{2}{x}$. Then write an equation for a vertical translation of $y = \frac{2}{x}$. Identify the horizontal and vertical asymptotes of the graph of each function.

Sketch the graph of each function.

32. $xy = 3$ **33.** $xy + 5 = 0$ **34.** $3xy = 1$ **35.** $5xy = 2$ **36.** $10xy = -4$

37. Writing Explain how knowing the asymptotes of a translation of $y = \frac{1}{x}$ can help you graph the function. Include an example.

38. Multiple Choice The formula $p = \frac{69.1}{a + 2.3}$ models the relationship between atmospheric pressure p in inches of mercury and altitude a in miles.

Use the data shown with the photo. At which location does the model predict the pressure to be about 23.93 in. of mercury? (*Hint:* 1 mi = 5280 ft.)

Sahara Desert average alt. 1500 ft

Kalahari Desert average alt. 3100 ft

Mt. Kilimanjaro alt. 19,340 ft

Vinson Massif alt. 16,680 ft

- Ⓐ Sahara Desert
- Ⓑ Kalahari Desert
- Ⓒ Mt. Kilimanjaro
- Ⓓ Vinson Massif

 Graphing Calculator Graph each pair of functions. Find the approximate point(s) of intersection.

39. $y = \frac{6}{x - 2}, y = 6$ **40.** $y = -\frac{1}{x - 3} - 6, y = 6.2$ **41.** $y = \frac{3}{x + 1}, y = -4$

42. Reasoning How will the domain and the range of the parent function $y = \frac{1}{x}$ change after the translation of its graph by 3 units up and by 5 units to the left?

43. a. Gasoline Mileage Suppose you drive an average of 10,000 miles each year. Your gasoline mileage (mi/gal) varies inversely with the number of gallons of gasoline you use each year. Write and graph a model for your average mileage m in terms of the gallons of gasoline used.

  b. After you begin driving on the highway more often, you use 50 gal less per year. Write and graph a new model to include this information.

  c. Calculate your old and new mileage assuming that you originally used 400 gal of gasoline per year.

Challenge **Reasoning** Compare each pair of graphs and find any points of intersection.

44. $y = \frac{1}{x}$ and $y = \left|\frac{1}{x}\right|$ **45.** $y = \frac{1}{x}$ and $y = \frac{1}{x^2}$ **46.** $y = \left|\frac{1}{x}\right|$ and $y = \frac{1}{x^2}$

47. Find two reciprocal functions such that the minimum distance from the origin to the graph of each function is $4\sqrt{2}$.

48. Write each equation in the form $y = \frac{k}{x - b} + c$, and sketch the graph.

  a. $y = \frac{2}{3x - 6}$ **b.** $y = \frac{1}{2 - 4x}$ **c.** $y = \frac{3 - x}{x + 2}$ **d.** $xy - y = 1$

ASSIGNMENT GUIDE

Basic: 8–29 all, 30–32, 42, 43

Average: 9–29 odd, 30–43

Advanced: 9–29 odd, 30–48

Standardized Test Prep: 49–53

Mixed Review: 54–67

Mathematical Practices are supported by exercises with red headings. Here are the Practices supported in this lesson:

MP 1: Make Sense of Problems Ex. 30
MP 2: Reason Abstractly Ex. 6, 31, 44–46
MP 3: Communicate Ex. 7, 32
MP 3: Construct Arguments Ex. 42
MP 5: Use Appropriate Tools Ex. 39–41

Applications exercises have blue headings. Exercises 29 and 43 support MP 4: Model.

EXERCISE 43: Use the Think About a Plan worksheet in the **Practice and Problem Solving Workbook** (also available in the Teaching Resources in print and online) to further support students' development in becoming independent learners.

HOMEWORK QUICK CHECK

To check students' understanding of key skills and concepts, go over Exercises 9, 27, 30, 42, and 43.

---

31. Check students' work.

32.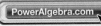

33.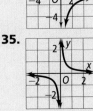

34.

35.

36.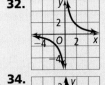

37. Answers may vary. Sample: The graph of the translation looks similar to the graph of $y = \frac{1}{x}$, so knowing the asymptotes helps to position the translation; check students' work.

38. B

39. 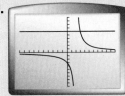 ; (3, 6)

40. 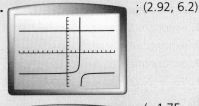 ; (2.92, 6.2)

41. 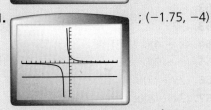 ; (−1.75, −4)

42. translated function is $y = \frac{1}{x + 5} + 3$; domain: all real numbers except $x = -5$, range: all real numbers except $y = 3$

43. a. $m = \dfrac{10,000}{g}$

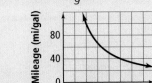

Mileage (mi/gal)
Gasoline Used (gal)

b. $m = \dfrac{10,000}{g - 50}$

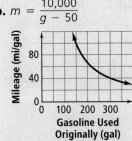

Mileage (mi/gal)
Gasoline Used Originally (gal)

c. 25 mi/gal; 28.57 mi/gal

44. The branches of $y = \frac{1}{x}$ are in Quadrants I and III. The branches of $y = \left|\frac{1}{x}\right|$ are in Quadrants I and II. The graphs intersect at all points on $y = \frac{1}{x}$ in Quadrant I.

45–48. See next page.

Answers

Practice and Problem-Solving Exercises (continued)

45. The branches of $y = \frac{1}{x^2}$ are in Quadrants I and II. The branches of $y = \frac{1}{x}$ are in Quadrants I and III. The graphs intersect at $(1, 1)$. The graph of $y = \frac{1}{x^2}$ is closer to the x-axis for $x > 1$, and the graph of $y = \frac{1}{x}$ is closer to the y-axis for $0 < x < 1$.

46. The branches of both graphs are in Quadrants I and II. The graphs intersect at $(1, 1)$ and $(-1, 1)$. The graph of $y = \frac{1}{x^2}$ is closer to the x-axis for $x > 1$ and $x < -1$.
The graph of $y = \left|\frac{1}{x}\right|$ is closer to the y-axis for $-1 < x < 0$ and $0 < x < 1$.

47. $y = \frac{16}{x}$, $y = -\frac{16}{x}$

48. a. $y = \frac{0.66\overline{6}}{x - 2}$;

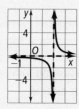

b. $y = -\frac{0.25}{x - 0.5}$;

c. $y = \frac{5}{x + 2} - 1$

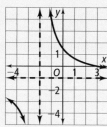

d. $y = \frac{1}{x - 1}$

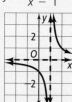

Standardized Test Prep

49. A
50. F
51. A
52. F
53. [2] $81 = 27b^{-1}$

$$81 = \frac{27}{b}$$

$$b = \frac{27}{81}$$

$$b = \frac{1}{3}$$

[1] correct answer, without work shown

SAT/ACT

49. What is an equation for the translation of $y = \frac{2}{x}$ that has asymptotes at $x = 3$ and $y = -5$?

Ⓐ $y = \frac{2}{x - 3} - 5$　　Ⓑ $y = \frac{2}{x + 3} + 5$　　Ⓒ $y = \frac{2}{x + 5} - 3$　　Ⓓ $y = \frac{2}{x - 5} + 3$

50. The graph at the right shows which inequality?

Ⓕ $y < -2.5x + 5$　　　　　Ⓗ $-2.5x + y < 5$

Ⓖ $2.5x + y \geq 5$　　　　　Ⓘ $5x + y \leq 5$

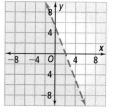

51. If p and q vary inversely, and $p = 10$ when $q = -4$, what is q when $p = -2$?

Ⓐ 20　　　　Ⓑ $\frac{4}{5}$　　　　Ⓒ $-\frac{4}{5}$　　　　Ⓓ -20

52. Which equation represents the inverse of the graph at the right?

Ⓕ $y = \log_3 x$　　　　　　Ⓗ $y = \log_x 3$

Ⓖ $x = \log_3 y$　　　　　　Ⓘ $x = \log_y 3$

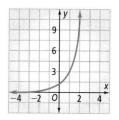

Short Response

53. What is b if the graph of $y = 27b^x$ includes the point $(-1, 81)$?

Mixed Review

Suppose that x and y vary inversely. Write a function that models each inverse variation and find y when $x = -5$.
　　　　　　　　　　　　　　　　　　　　　　　　　　See Lesson 8-1.

54. $x = 2$ when $y = 12$　　　**55.** $x = 25$ when $y = 2$　　　**56.** $x = 12$ when $y = 4$

Without graphing, determine whether the function represents exponential growth or exponential decay. Then find the y-intercept.
　　　　　　　　　　　　　　　　　　　　　　　　　　See Lesson 7-1.

57. $y = 3(4)^x$　　　**58.** $y = 0.1(2)^x$　　　**59.** $y = 5(0.8)^x$　　　**60.** $y = 3\left(\frac{1}{2}\right)^x$

Multiply.
　　　　　　　　　　　　　　　　　　　　　　　　　　See Lesson 6-3.

61. $(5\sqrt{3} - 2)^2$　　　　**62.** $(4 + 2\sqrt{3})(6 - 3\sqrt{3})$　　　**63.** $(\sqrt{3} + \sqrt{5})(\sqrt{3} - \sqrt{5})$

Get Ready!　To prepare for Lesson 8-3, do Exercises 64–67.

Factor each expression.
　　　　　　　　　　　　　　　　　　　　　　　　　　See Lesson 4-4.

64. $x^2 - 6x + 8$　　　**65.** $x^2 + 6x - 27$　　　**66.** $2x^2 + x - 28$　　　**67.** $2x^2 - 19x + 24$

Mixed Review

54. $y = \frac{24}{x}$; $-\frac{24}{5}$

55. $y = \frac{50}{x}$; -10

56. $y = \frac{48}{x}$; $-\frac{48}{5}$

57. exponential growth; 3

58. exponential growth; 0.1

59. exponential decay; 5

60. exponential decay; 3

61. $79 - 20\sqrt{3}$

62. 6

63. -2

64. $(x - 4)(x - 2)$

65. $(x + 9)(x - 3)$

66. $(2x - 7)(x + 4)$

67. $(2x - 3)(x - 8)$

Additional Instructional Support

Algebra 2 Companion

Students can use the **Algebra 2 Companion** worktext (4 pages) as you teach the lesson. Use the Companion to support

- New Vocabulary
- Key Concepts
- Got It for each Problem
- Lesson Check

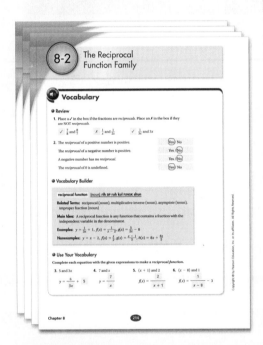

ELL Support

Assess Understanding To check that students understand the roles of *a*, *h*, and *k* in the general form of the reciprocal function, have them graph $y = \frac{3}{x}$, $y = \frac{-3}{x}$, $y = \frac{1}{x} + 3$, and $y = \frac{1}{x - 3}$ using a graphing calculator. Have students copy each graph and explain in words each transformation. Check the students' explanations for correctness. Then have the students work in pairs and explain to each other aloud their transformations, using the algebraic terms listed in the Essential Understanding on page 507. If students did not use those terms in their written explanations, help them rewrite their explanations of the transformations using the algebraic terms.

5 Assess & Remediate

Lesson Quiz

1. What transformation changes the graph of $y = \frac{1}{x}$ into the graph of $y = \frac{-2}{x}$?

2. What is the graph of $y = \frac{1}{x + 3} + 1$? Identify the domain and range, the *x*- and *y*-intercepts, and the asymptotes of the graph.

3. **Do you UNDERSTAND?** A local theater will hold an after-prom movie. The theater seats 300 people, and the total cost is $400. If ten parents go as chaperones, model the cost per student *C* as a function of the number of attendees *n*. How many students must attend the movie for the cost to be no more than $3.25 per student? Assume the chaperones do not pay.

ANSWERS TO LESSON QUIZ

1. The graph is reflected in the *x*-axis and stretched by a factor of 2.

2.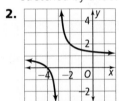

   domain: all real numbers except $x = -3$;
   range: all real numbers except $y = 1$;
   x-intercept: $(-4, 0)$; *y*-intercept: $(0, \frac{4}{3})$;
   vertical asymptote: $x = -3$, horizontal asymptote: $y = 1$

3. $C = \frac{400}{n - 10}$; at least 124 students

PRESCRIPTION FOR REMEDIATION

Use the student work on the Lesson Quiz to prescribe a differentiated review assignment:

Points	Differentiated Remediation
0–1	Intervention
2	On-level
3	Extension

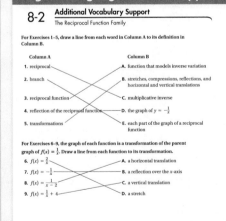

PowerAlgebra.com

5 Assess & Remediate

Assign the Lesson Quiz. Appropriate intervention, practice, or enrichment is automatically generated based on student performance.

Differentiated Remediation

Intervention

- **Reteaching** (2 pages) Provides reteaching and practice exercises for the key lesson concepts. Use with struggling students or absent students.

- **English Language Learner Support** Helps students develop and reinforce mathematical vocabulary and key concepts.

All-in-One Resources/Online
Reteaching

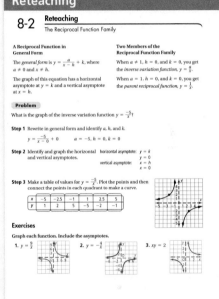

All-in-One Resources/Online
English Language Learner Support

Differentiated Remediation *continued*

On-Level

- **Practice** (2 pages) Provides extra practice for each lesson. For simpler practice exercises, use the Form K Practice pages found in the All-in-One Teaching Resources and online.

- **Think About a Plan** Helps students develop specific problem-solving skills and strategies by providing scaffolded guiding questions.

- **Standardized Test Prep** Focuses on all major exercises, all major question types, and helps students prepare for the high-stakes assessments.

Extension

- **Enrichment** Provides students with interesting problems and activities that extend the concepts of the lesson.

- **Activities, Games, and Puzzles** Worksheets that can be used for concepts development, enrichment, and for fun!

Practice and Problem Solving Wkbk/All-in-One Resources/Online
Practice page 1

8-2 Practice — Form G
The Reciprocal Function Family

Graph each function. Identify the x- and y-intercepts and the asymptotes of the graph. Also, state the domain and the range of the function.

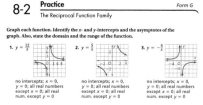

1. $y = \frac{12}{x}$
no intercepts; $x = 0$, $y = 0$; all real numbers except $x = 0$; all real num. except $y = 0$

2. $y = \frac{5}{x}$
no intercepts; $x = 0$, $y = 0$; all real numbers except $x = 0$; all real num. except $y = 0$

3. $y = -\frac{4}{x}$
no intercepts; $x = 0$, $y = 0$; all real numbers except $x = 0$; all real num. except $y = 0$

Use a graphing calculator to graph the equations $y = \frac{1}{x}$ and $y = \frac{a}{x}$ using the given value of a. Then identify the effect of a on the graph.

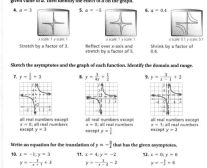

4. $a = 3$
Stretch by a factor of 3.

5. $a = -5$
Reflect over x-axis and stretch by a factor of 5.

6. $a = 0.4$
Shrink by a factor of 0.4.

Sketch the asymptotes and the graph of each function. Identify the domain and range.

7. $y = \frac{1}{x} + 3$
all real numbers except $x = 0$; all real numbers except $y = 3$

8. $y = \frac{3}{4x} + \frac{1}{2}$
all real numbers except $x = 0$; all real numbers except $y = \frac{1}{2}$

9. $y = \frac{1}{x-1} + 2$
all real numbers except $x = 1$; all real numbers except $y = 2$

Write an equation for the translation of $y = -\frac{3}{x}$ that has the given asymptotes.

10. $x = -1$; $y = 3$
$y = \frac{3}{x+1} + 3$

11. $x = 4$; $y = -2$
$y = \frac{3}{x-4} - 2$

12. $x = 0$; $y = 6$
$y = -\frac{3}{x} + 6$

Practice and Problem Solving Wkbk/All-in-One Resources/Online
Practice page 2

8-2 Practice (continued) — Form G
The Reciprocal Function Family

13. The length of a pipe in a panpipe ℓ (in feet) is inversely proportional to its pitch p (in hertz). The inverse variation is modeled by the equation $p = \frac{495}{\ell}$. Find the length required to produce a pitch of 220 Hz. 2.25 ft

Write each equation in the form $y = \frac{k}{x}$.

14. $y = \frac{4}{5x}$ 15. $y = -\frac{7}{2x}$ $y = \frac{-3.5}{x}$ 16. $xy = -0.03$ $y = \frac{-0.03}{x}$

Sketch the graph of each function.

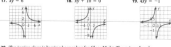

17. $xy = 6$ 18. $xy + 10 = 0$ 19. $4xy = -1$

20. The junior class is buying keepsakes for Class Night. The price of each keepsake p is inversely proportional to the number of keepsakes s bought. The keepsake company also offers 10 free keepsakes in addition to the class's order. The equation $p = \frac{1800}{s + 10}$ models this inverse variation.
a. If the class buys 240 keepsakes, what is the price for each one? $7.20
b. If the class pays $5.55 for each keepsake, how many can they get, including the free keepsakes? 324
c. If the class buys 400 keepsakes, what is the price for each one? $4.39
d. If the class buys 50 keepsakes, what is the price for each one? $30

Graph each pair of functions. Find the approximate point(s) of intersection.

21. $y = \frac{3}{x} - 4$; $y = 2$ (5.5, 2)

22. $y = \frac{2}{x} - 5$; $y = -1.5$ (−6.3, −1.5)

All-in-One Resources/Online
Enrichment

8-2 Enrichment
The Reciprocal Function Family

Understanding Horizontal Asymptotes

The line $y = \frac{3}{4}$ is a horizontal asymptote for the graph of the function $y = \frac{3x + 5}{4x - 8}$. By using long division, you can rewrite this function in the form quotient + remainder divided by the divisor: $y = \frac{3}{4} + \frac{11}{4x - 8}$.

Examine what happens to the remainder divided by the divisor and the value of y as the value of x gets larger. Fill in the following table to four decimal places.

	x	$\frac{11}{4x-8}$	$y = \frac{3}{4} + \frac{11}{4x-8}$
1.	3	2.7500	3.5000
2.	10	0.3438	1.0938
3.	100	0.0281	0.7781

Note that as x gets larger, both the remainder and the value of y get smaller. Although the value of y is always greater than $\frac{3}{4}$, it gets closer to $\frac{3}{4}$ as x gets larger. As x gets infinitely large, y approaches $\frac{3}{4}$ from above. Write this as: As $x \to +\infty$, $y \to \frac{3}{4}$ from above.

Examine what happens as x gets smaller. Fill in the following table to four decimal places.

	x	$\frac{11}{4x-8}$	$y = \frac{3}{4} + \frac{11}{4x-8}$
4.	−3	−0.5500	0.2000
5.	−10	−0.2292	0.5208
6.	−100	−0.0270	0.7230

Here the value of y is always less than $\frac{3}{4}$, but it gets closer to $\frac{3}{4}$ as x gets smaller (more negative). Write this as: As $x \to -\infty$, $y \to \frac{3}{4}$ from below.
In both cases, y approaches $\frac{3}{4}$, so the horizontal asymptote is $y = \frac{3}{4}$.

Practice and Problem Solving Wkbk/All-in-One Resources/Online
Think About a Plan

8-2 Think About a Plan
The Reciprocal Function Family

a. **Gasoline Mileage** Suppose you drive an average of 10,000 miles each year. Your gasoline mileage (mi/gal) varies inversely with the number of gallons of gasoline you use each year. Write and graph a model for your average mileage m in terms of the gallons g of gasoline used.
b. After you begin driving on the highway more often, you use 50 gal less per year. Write and graph a new model to include this information.
c. Calculate your old and new mileage assuming that you originally used 400 gal of gasoline per year.

1. Write a formula for gasoline mileage in words.

The mileage is equal to the number of miles divided by the number of gallons

2. Write and graph an equation to model your average mileage m in terms of the gallons g of gasoline used.
$m = \frac{10,000}{g}$

3. Write and graph an equation to model your average mileage m in terms of the gallons g of gasoline used if you use 50 gal less per year.
$m = \frac{10,000}{g - 50}$

4. How can you find your old and your new mileage from your equations?
Evaluate each equation at $g = 400$

5. What is your old mileage? 25 mi/gal

6. What is your new mileage? about 28.6 mi/gal

Practice and Problem Solving Wkbk/All-in-One Resources/Online
Standardized Test Prep

8-2 Standardized Test Prep
The Reciprocal Function Family

Multiple Choice

For Exercises 1–3, choose the correct letter.

1. What is an equation for the translation of $y = -\frac{4.5}{x}$ that has asymptotes at $x = 3$ and $y = -5$? A
Ⓐ $y = -\frac{4.5}{x-3} - 5$
Ⓒ $y = -\frac{4.5}{x-5} + 3$
Ⓑ $y = -\frac{4.5}{x+3} - 5$
Ⓓ $y = -\frac{4.5}{x+5} + 3$

2. What is the equation of the vertical asymptote of $y = \frac{2}{x} - 5$? I
Ⓕ $x = -5$ Ⓖ $x = 0$ Ⓗ $x = 2$ Ⓘ $x = 5$

3. Which is the graph of $y = \frac{1}{x+1} - 2$? D

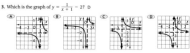

Extended Response

4. A race pilot's average rate of speed over a 720-mi course is inversely proportional to the time in minutes t the pilot takes to fly a complete race course. The pilot's final score s is the average speed minus any penalty points p earned.
a. Write a function to model the pilot's score for a given t and p. (*Hint: $d = rt$*)
b. Graph the function for a pilot who has 2 penalty points.
c. What is the maximum time a pilot with 2 penalty points can take to finish the course and still earn a score of at least 3?

[4] $s = \frac{720}{t} - p$;

144 min

[3] correct answer with most of work shown and appropriate strategies used OR incorrect answer with all work shown and appropriate strategies used
[2] correct answer with little work shown OR incorrect answer but work shown reflects some understanding of problem
[1] answer is incomplete or incorrect and no work is shown
[0] no answer given

Online Teacher Resource Center
Activities, Games, and Puzzles

8-2 Activity: Family First
The Reciprocal Function Family

Complete this activity on your own.

A Function Fable

Given: $g(x) = \frac{1}{x}$, $s(x) = \frac{1}{x-2}$, $d(x) = \frac{1}{x-3}$, $m(x) = \frac{1}{x-3} + 6$, $p(x) = \frac{1}{x+2} + 3$, and $f(x) = \frac{-1}{x+2} - 3$.

Grandma function $g(x)$ had two children. Her son Steve $s(x)$ was left-handed and her daughter Diana $d(x)$ was right-handed. Diana had one very tall child Michel $m(x)$, who towered above her. Steve had two children as well. Pat $p(x)$ and Jo $f(x)$ were twins, but opposites of one another.

Graph the functions $g(x)$, $s(x)$, and $p(x)$ on the grids below.

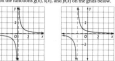

Activity

Make a reciprocal function family with at least 3 "generations" and 6 individual functions. Explain the transformations that yield each member. Have at least one member in the third generation be a driving, graduate-athlete given:
- A horizontal translation corresponds to being a driver.
- A vertical translation corresponds to being an athlete.
- A reflection corresponds to being a high-school graduate.

Note: In the fable above, Jo was the only driving, graduate-athlete.

Then sketch a graph of one function from each generation (including the driving, graduate-athlete), showing all asymptotes.

Check student's work.
Optional Extension: Have students come up with their own creative story about a family, as in the fable. It should also have details based in mathematics.

8-3 Rational Functions and Their Graphs

© Content Standards
A.APR.3 Identify zeros of polynomials when suitable factorizations are available, and use the zeros to construct a rough graph of the function . . .
F.BF.1.b. Combine standard function types using arithmetic operations.

Objectives To identify properties of rational functions
To graph rational functions

SOLVE IT!

Getting Ready! ◄► ✕ ↻ ⬆

Last season, you made 40% of your basketball shots. The Game 1 shot chart shows that you did not start this season so well. Starting with Game 2, how many consecutive shots must you make to raise this season's percentage to 40%? If you never miss another shot this season, how high can you raise your percentage? Explain your reasoning.

GAME 1

● Made
○ Missed

Solve a simpler problem to better understand the situation. Suppose you make baskets in your next two attempts. What will your percentage be?

© MATHEMATICAL PRACTICES

You use a ratio of polynomial functions to form a *rational function*, like $y = \frac{x+3}{x+16}$.

Essential Understanding If a function has a polynomial in its denominator, its graph has a gap at each zero of the polynomial. The gap could be a one-point hole in the graph, or it could be the location of a vertical asymptote for the graph.

A **rational function** is a function that you can write in the form $f(x) = \frac{P(x)}{Q(x)}$ where $P(x)$ and $Q(x)$ are polynomial functions. The domain of $f(x)$ is all real numbers except those values for which $Q(x) = 0$.

Here are graphs of three rational functions:

$y = \frac{x^2}{x^2+1}$

$y = \frac{(x+3)(x+2)}{(x+2)}$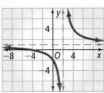

$y = \frac{x+4}{x-2}$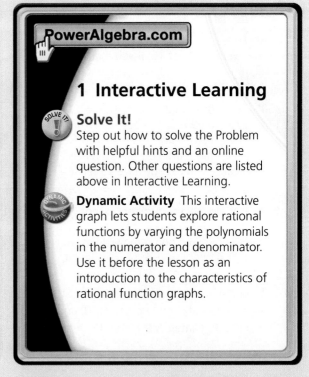

Dynamic Activity
Rational Functions

Lesson Vocabulary
• rational function
• continuous graph
• discontinuous graph
• point of discontinuity
• removable discontinuity
• non-removable discontinuity

---

1 Interactive Learning

Solve It!
PURPOSE To model a real-world situation using a rational function
PROCESS Students may
• guess and check to find the answer using integer values for x.
• input the rational function into a graphing calculator, and use the Table function to find the least integer x-value that returns y ≥ 0.4.
• solve $0.4 = \frac{x+3}{x+16}$.

FACILITATE
Q What is your percentage if you make your next shot? your next two? **[0.24, 0.28]**
Q What function gives your percentage if you make your next x shots? **[$\frac{3+x}{16+x}$]**
Q Can you reach 100%? 99%? Explain your answers. **[No; yes; since you already missed some shots you can never reach 100%. You will reach 99% if you make your next 1284 shots without a miss.]**

ANSWER See Solve It in Answers on next page.
CONNECT THE MATH In the Solve It students write two linear functions—one for shots made and one for shots attempted—and form a rational function as the quotient of the two linear functions to find the answer. In the lesson, students analyze and graph rational functions and use them to solve concentration problems.

8-3 Preparing to Teach

BIG ideas Equivalence
Function

ESSENTIAL UNDERSTANDINGS
• A rational function is a ratio of polynomial functions.
• If a function has a polynomial in its denominator, its graph has a gap at each zero of the polynomial. The gap could be a one-point hole in the graph, or it could be the location of a vertical asymptote for the graph.
• A rational function may have no asymptotes, one horizontal or oblique asymptote, and any number of vertical asymptotes.
• A reasonable graph for a rational function can be sketched by finding all intercepts and asymptotes. Sometimes a few extra points should be plotted to get a good sense of the shape of the graph.

Math Background
A rational function is a ratio of polynomial functions $\frac{P(x)}{Q(x)}$. The domain is all real numbers except x-values where $Q(x) = 0$. Near these x-values, the graph may increase or decrease without bound. The zeros of $Q(x)$ can signify discontinuities, holes, and vertical asymptotes. The zeros of $P(x)$ signify x-intercepts.

To graph the function, plot intercepts and asymptotes, then plot a few points between and beyond each intercept and vertical asymptote. Finally sketch a smooth curve to complete the graph.

© Mathematical Practices
Make sense of problems and persevere in solving them. Students will explain correspondences between a rational function and its graph.

PowerAlgebra.com

1 Interactive Learning

Solve It!
Step out how to solve the Problem with helpful hints and an online question. Other questions are listed above in Interactive Learning.

Dynamic Activity This interactive graph lets students explore rational functions by varying the polynomials in the numerator and denominator. Use it before the lesson as an introduction to the characteristics of rational function graphs.

Lesson 8-3 515

2 Guided Instruction

Q Which of the functions you have studied were continuous for all values of *x*? **[linear, quadratic, absolute value, polynomial, exponential]**

Take Note

Q Input $y = ((x + 3)(x + 2))/(x + 2)$ into your graphing calculator. Set $\Delta\text{Tbl} = 0.1$. What happens to *y* as *x* approaches -2 from lesser *x*-values? as *x* approaches -2 from greater *x*-values? **[As *x* approaches -2 from the left, *y* increases at a constant rate towards 1. As *x* approaches -2 from the right, *y* decreases at a constant rate towards 1.]**

Q Input $y = (x + 4)/(x - 2)$ into your graphing calculator. What happens to *y* as *x* approaches 2 from lesser *x*-values? greater *x*-values? **[As *x* approaches 2 from the left, *y* decreases at an increasing rate towards $-\infty$. As *x* approaches 2 from the right, *y* increases at an increasing rate towards $+\infty$.]**

Problem 1

Q Why do you find the *x*-intercept by setting only the numerator equal to zero? **[When the numerator of the function is 0, $y = 0$. The *x*-intercept is defined as the *x*-value at $y = 0$.]**

Q Why do you find the *y*-intercept by evaluating the function at $f(0)$? **[The *y*-intercept is defined as the *y*-value at $x = 0$.]**

Q How many discontinuities would you expect to find and why? **[You would expect two because the denominator is a factorable quadratic.]**

For the first rational function, $y = \frac{x^2}{x^2 + 1}$, there is no value of *x* that makes the denominator 0. The graph is a **continuous graph** because it has no jumps, breaks, or holes. You can draw the graph and your pencil never leaves the paper.

For the second rational function, $y = \frac{(x + 3)(x + 2)}{x + 2}$, *x* cannot be -2. For $y = \frac{x + 4}{x - 2}$, *x* cannot be 2. The second and third graphs are **discontinuous graphs**.

Key Concept Point of Discontinuity

If *a* is a real number for which the denominator of a rational function $f(x)$ is zero, then *a* is not in the domain of $f(x)$. The graph of $f(x)$ is not continuous at $x = a$ and the function has a **point of discontinuity** at $x = a$.

The graph of $y = \frac{(x + 3)(x + 2)}{x + 2}$ has a **removable discontinuity** at $x = -2$. The hole in the graph is called a removable discontinuity because you could make the function continuous by redefining it at $x = -2$ so that $f(-2) = 1$.

The graph of $y = \frac{x + 4}{x - 2}$ has a **non-removable discontinuity** at $x = 2$. There is no way to redefine the function at 2 to make the function continuous.

When you are looking for discontinuities, it is helpful to factor the numerator and denominator as a first step. The factors of the denominator will reveal the points of discontinuity. The discontinuity caused by $(x - a)^n$ in the denominator is removable if the numerator also has $(x - a)^n$ as a factor.

Problem 1 Finding Points of Discontinuity

What are the domain and points of discontinuity of each rational function? Are the points of discontinuity removable or non-removable? What are the *x*- and *y*-intercepts?

A $y = \dfrac{x + 3}{x^2 - 4x + 3}$

Factor the numerator and denominator to check for common factors.

$$y = \frac{x + 3}{x^2 - 4x + 3} = \frac{x + 3}{(x - 3)(x - 1)}$$

The function is undefined where $x - 3 = 0$ and where $x - 1 = 0$, at $x = 3$ and $x = 1$. The domain of the function is the set of all real numbers except $x = 1$ and $x = 3$.

There are non-removable points of discontinuity at $x = 1$ and $x = 3$.

The *x*-intercept occurs where the numerator equals 0, at $x = -3$.

To find the *y*-intercept, let $x = 0$ and simplify.

$$y = \frac{0 + 3}{(0 - 3)(0 - 1)} = \frac{3}{(-3)(-1)} = \frac{3}{3} = 1$$

Think

Are the discontinuities removable?
There are no common factors in the numerator and denominator. Any discontinuity is non-removable.

Answers

Solve It!

6; You have made 3 of 16. If you make *x* consecutive shots, $x \geq 0$, your percentage will be $\frac{3 + x}{16 + x} \cdot 100$, from 18.75% ($x = 0$), to 50% ($x = 10$; 13 of 26), to 90% ($x = 114$; 117 of 130), to 99% ($x = 1284$; 1287 of 1300), to any percentage less than 100 for *x* great enough. But you cannot reach 100% because you already have 13 misses.

Got It?

1. a. domain: all real numbers except $x = 4$ and $x = -4$; pts. of discontinuity: non-removable at $x = 4$ and $x = -4$; no *x*-intercept, *y*-intercept: $\left(0, -\frac{1}{16}\right)$

b. domain: all real numbers; no pts. of discontinuity; *x*-intercepts: (1, 0) and (−1, 0), *y*-intercept: $\left(0, -\frac{1}{3}\right)$

PowerAlgebra.com

2 Guided Instruction

Each Problem is worked out and supported online.

Problem 1
Finding Points of Discontinuity
Animated

Problem 2
Finding Vertical Asymptotes
Animated

Problem 3
Finding Horizontal Asymptotes

Problem 4
Graphing Rational Functions
Animated

Problem 5
Using a Rational Function

Support in Algebra 2 Companion
• Vocabulary
• Key Concepts
• Got It?

Think

When is the denominator zero?
x^2 is at least 0, so $x^2 + 1$ is always greater than 0.

B $y = \frac{x - 5}{x^2 + 1}$

You cannot factor the numerator or the denominator. Also, there are no values of x that make the denominator 0. The domain of the function is all real numbers, and there are no discontinuities.

The x-intercept occurs where the numerator equals 0, at $x = 5$.

To find the y-intercept, let $x = 0$ and simplify: $y = \frac{0 - 5}{0^2 + 1} = \frac{-5}{1} = -5$

C $y = \frac{x^2 - 3x - 4}{x - 4}$

Factor the numerator and denominator: $y = \frac{x^2 - 3x - 4}{x - 4} = \frac{(x - 4)(x + 1)}{(x - 4)}$

The function is undefined where $x - 4 = 0$, at $x = 4$. The domain of the function is the set of all real numbers except $x = 4$.

Because $y = x + 1$, except at $x = 4$, there is a removable discontinuity at $x = 4$.

At $x = 4, y = x + 1 = 4 + 1 = 5$, so you can redefine the function to remove the discontinuity.

$$y = \begin{cases} \frac{x^2 - 3x - 4}{x - 4}, & \text{if } x \neq 4 \\ 5, & \text{if } x = 4 \end{cases}$$

Graph contains a hole at $x = 4$.

The x-intercept occurs where the numerator equals 0, at $x = -1$.

To find the y-intercept, let $x = 0$ and simplify.

$$y = \frac{0^2 - 3 \cdot 0 - 4}{0 - 4} = \frac{0 - 0 - 4}{-4} = \frac{-4}{-4} = 1$$

Got It? **1.** What are the domain and points of discontinuity of the rational function? Are the points of discontinuity *removable* or *non-removable*? What are the x- and y-intercepts of the rational function?

 a. $y = \frac{1}{x^2 - 16}$ **b.** $y = \frac{x^2 - 1}{x^2 + 3}$ **c.** $y = \frac{x + 1}{x^2 + 3x + 2}$

In Chapter 7, you learned that an asymptote is a line that a graph approaches as x or y increases in absolute value. If a rational function has a non-removable discontinuity at $x = a$, the graph of the rational function will have a vertical asymptote at $x = a$.

take note

Key Concept **Vertical Asymptotes of Rational Functions**

The graph of the rational function $f(x) = \frac{P(x)}{Q(x)}$ has a vertical asymptote at each real zero of $Q(x)$ if $P(x)$ and $Q(x)$ have no common zeros. If $P(x)$ and $Q(x)$ have $(x - a)^m$ and $(x - a)^n$ as factors, respectively and $m < n$, then $f(x)$ also has a vertical asymptote at $x = a$.

Q In 1B, is the graph symmetrical across the y-axis? How do you know? **[No; the only x-intercept is at $x = 5$, so the graph cannot be symmetrical across the y-axis.]**

ERROR PREVENTION

Q In 1C, why does the function not have an x-intercept at $(4, 0)$? **[The function has a removable discontinuity at $x = 4$. Because the $(x - 4)$ factor in the numerator can be factored out, the point $(4, 0)$ does not count as an x-intercept.]**

Got It?

Q In 1a, what is the x-intercept? **[The function has no x-intercept because the numerator cannot be zero.]**

Q In 1b, why are there two x-intercepts? **[The numerator, $x^2 - 1$, can be factored as $(x + 1)(x - 1)$. Neither factor is also present in the denominator.]**

Q In 1b, why are there no discontinuities? **[because there are no real solutions to $x^2 + 3 = 0$]**

Q In 1c, how would you redefine $f(-1)$? Why? **[$f(-1) = 1$; $x = -1$ is a removable discontinuity. Factoring the equation gives $f(x) = \frac{1}{x + 2}$. $f(-1) = \frac{1}{-1 + 2} = 1$.]**

Take Note

Q What is an example of a rational function that fits the first sentence? **[Sample: $\frac{x + 3}{x - 4}$.]**

Q What is an example of a rational function that fits the second sentence? **[Sample: $\frac{(x - 4)^2}{(x - 4)^3}$.]**

Additional Problems

1. What are the domain and points of discontinuity of $y = \frac{x^2 + 4x + 4}{x + 2}$? Are the points of discontinuity removable or non-removable? What are the x- and y-intercepts?

ANSWER domain: all real numbers except $x = -2$; removable discontinuity: $x = -2$; y-intercept: 2; no x-intercept

2. What are the vertical asymptotes for the graph of $y = \frac{x - 3}{(x^2 - 3x + 2)(x^2 - 7x + 12)}$?

ANSWER $x = 1, 2, 4$

3. What is the horizontal asymptote for the graph of $y = \frac{x^2 + 1}{-3x + 6}$?

ANSWER The graph has no horizontal asymptote.

4. What is the graph of the rational function $y = \frac{x^2 + 1}{-3x + 6}$?

ANSWER

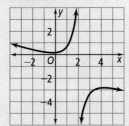

5. Whole milk contains 3.7% fat. You want to add 2%-fat milk to 5 fl oz of whole milk to make 3%-fat milk. The function $y = \frac{(5)(0.037) + x(0.02)}{5 + x}$ gives the percentage of fat in a new concentration after you add x fluid ounces of the 2% milk. How many fluid ounces of 2% milk must you add?

ANSWER 3.5 fl oz

Answers

Got It? (continued)

1c. domain: all real numbers except $x = -2$ and $x = -1$; pts. of discontinuity: non-removable at $x = -2$, removable at $x = -1$; no x-intercept, y-intercept: $\left(0, \frac{1}{2}\right)$

Problem 2

Q What is the maximum number of vertical asymptotes in a function with a denominator of degree n? Why? **[n; a polynomial of degree n has at most n real roots.]**

Q When does a function with a denominator of degree n have fewer than n vertical asymptotes? **[when the numerator has an identical factor; when the denominator has multiple identical factors; when the denominator has complex roots]**

Got It?

Q In 2c, is there a vertical asymptote? How could you redefine the function to remove the discontinuity? **[No; define $f(-1) = -2$.]**

Take Note

Q Why does a function with a denominator of greater degree than the numerator have a horizontal asymptote at $y = 0$? **[As $|x|$ increases, the absolute value of the denominator grows much faster than the absolute value of the numerator, so their quotient gets closer to 0.]**

Problem 3

Q In 3B, do you have to factor the denominator to find the horizontal asymptote? Explain. **[No. The horizontal asymptote is dependent only on the degrees of the numerator and denominator.]**

Got It?

Q In 3a, why does the graph approach $y = -2$ for large $|x|$? **[As $|x|$ increases, the constant coefficients +6 and −5 have less influence on the shape of the graph. The graph comes to resemble $y = \frac{-2x}{x} = -2$.]**

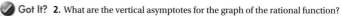

Plan

How can you locate a vertical asymptote?
Find factors $x - a$ of the denominator that have no matching factor in the numerator. $x = a$ is a vertical asymptote.

© Problem 2 Finding Vertical Asymptotes

What are the vertical asymptotes for the graph of $y = \frac{(x + 1)}{(x - 2)(x - 3)}$**?**

Since 2 and 3 are zeros of the denominator and neither is a zero of the numerator, the lines $x = 2$ and $x = 3$ are vertical asymptotes.

Got It? 2. What are the vertical asymptotes for the graph of the rational function?

  a. $y = \frac{x - 2}{(x - 1)(x + 3)}$ **b.** $y = \frac{x - 2}{(x - 2)(x + 3)}$ **c.** $y = \frac{x^2 - 1}{x + 1}$

While the graph of a rational function can have any number of vertical asymptotes, it can have no more than one horizontal asymptote.

 Key Concept Horizontal Asymptote of a Rational Function

To find the horizontal asymptote of the graph of a rational function, compare the degree of the numerator m to the degree of the denominator n.

If $m < n$, the graph has horizontal asymptote $y = 0$ (the x-axis).

If $m > n$, the graph has no horizontal asymptote.

If $m = n$, the graph has horizontal asymptote $y = \frac{a}{b}$ where a is the coefficient of the term of greatest degree in the numerator and b is the coefficient of the term of greatest degree in the denominator.

Plan

How can you find the horizontal asymptote when the numerator and denominator have equal degree?
Find the quotient, q, of the leading coefficients of the numerator and denominator. $y = q$ is the horizontal asymptote.

© Problem 3 Finding Horizontal Asymptotes

What is the horizontal asymptote for the rational function?

Ⓐ $y = \frac{2x}{x - 3}$

The degree of the numerator and denominator are the same.

The horizontal asymptote is $y = \frac{2}{1}$ or $y = 2$.

Ⓑ $y = \frac{x - 2}{x^2 - 2x - 3}$

The degree of the numerator is less than the degree of the denominator. The horizontal asymptote is $y = 0$.

Ⓒ $y = \frac{x^2}{2x - 5}$

The degree of the numerator is greater than the degree of the denominator. There is no horizontal asymptote.

Got It? 3. What is the horizontal asymptote for the rational function?

  a. $y = \frac{-2x + 6}{x - 5}$ **b.** $y = \frac{x - 1}{x^2 + 4x + 4}$ **c.** $y = \frac{x^2 + 2x - 3}{x - 2}$

Answers

Got It? (continued)

  2. a. $x = 1$ and $x = -3$

    b. $x = -3$

    c. no vert. asymptotes

  3. a. $y = -2$

    b. $y = 0$

    c. no horizontal asymptote

Essential Understanding You can get a reasonable graph for a rational function by finding all intercepts and asymptotes. Sometimes you will also have to plot a few extra points to get a good sense of the shape of the graph.

© **Problem 4** Graphing a Rational Function

What is the graph of the rational function $y = \dfrac{x^2 + x - 12}{x^2 - 4}$?

Plan

How can you graph this function?
Find the horizontal and vertical asymptotes and the x- and y-intercepts. Look for holes and find additional points to help get a better sense of the graph.

Think

Write

The degrees of the numerator and denominator are equal.

$$y = \frac{x^2 + x - 12}{x^2 - 4}$$

horizontal asymptote: $y = \frac{1}{1} = 1$

Factor the numerator and the denominator. They have no common factor. The graph has no holes. It has two vertical asymptotes at the zeros of the denominator.

$$y = \frac{(x + 4)(x - 3)}{(x + 2)(x - 2)}$$

vertical asymptotes: $x = -2$, $x = 2$

Find the x- and y-intercepts. The x-intercepts occur where $y = 0$. The y-intercepts occur where $x = 0$.

When the numerator equals zero, $y = 0$.
x-intercepts: $(-4, 0)$ and $(3, 0)$

$$y = \frac{(0 + 4)(0 - 3)}{(0 + 2)(0 - 2)} = 3$$

y-intercept: $(0, 3)$

Find a few more points on the graph.

More points on the graph:
$(-3, -\frac{6}{5})$, $(-1, 4)$, $(1, \frac{10}{3})$ and $(4, \frac{2}{3})$

Graph the asymptotes. Then plot the intercepts and additional points. Use the points to sketch the graph.

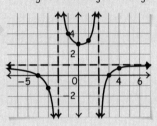

✓ **Got It?** 4. What is the graph of the rational function $y = \dfrac{x + 3}{x^2 - 6x + 5}$?

Problem 4

Q How do you know that the graph goes toward $-\infty$ as x approaches -2 from the left? **[The points $(-4, 0)$ and $(-3, -\frac{6}{5})$ show that the graph is decreasing. There is no other x-intercept between -3 and -2, so the graph continues decreasing, approaching the asymptote at $x = -2$.]**

Q The graph goes toward $+\infty$ as x approaches -2 from the right. How do the x-intercepts tell you that the graph also goes toward $+\infty$ as x approaches $+2$? **[Because there is no x-intercept from -2 to $+2$, the graph cannot cross the x-axis over that range. The graph must curve back up toward $+\infty$.]**

EXTENSION

Q Can you change a single number in the numerator of the function so that the graph goes toward $-\infty$ as x approaches $+2$ from the left? How does this work? **[Yes. Sample: Changing the factor $(x - 3)$ to $(x - 1)$ moves the x-intercept from $(3, 0)$ to $(1, 0)$. Now the graph crosses the x-axis and decreases towards $-\infty$.]**

Got It? ERROR PREVENTION
Students may not realize that a graph can cross its horizontal asymptote. A graph will never cross a vertical asymptote.

Q What is the horizontal asymptote of this graph? What is the x-intercept? What can you say about the behavior of the graph before and after the x-intercept? **[The horizontal asymptote is $y = 0$. The x-intercept is $(-3, 0)$. The graph has a turning point at $(-3, 0)$ so the function changes sign.]**

4.

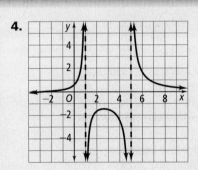

Problem 5

Q Your textbook shows how to solve this problem by using a graphing calculator. This problem can also be solved algebraically. How would you do that? Describe the steps. **[You want to solve for $y = 0.009$, so you can set the given formula equal to 0.009: $0.009 = \frac{(100)(0.02) + x(0.005)}{100 + x}$. Multiply both sides by $(100 + x)$ and simplify: $0.9 + 0.009x = 2 + 0.005x$. Isolate the x-terms: $0.004x = 1.1$. Divide both sides by 0.004: $x = 275$.]**

Q How many mL of 0.9% solution do you end up with? **[375 mL (100 mL of 2% solution and 275 mL of 0.5% solution)]**

Q Where is the vertical asymptote of the graph of this function? Do you have to think about the behavior of the graph at that point? Why or why not? **[The function has a vertical asymptote at $x = -100$. In this problem, x represents an amount of solution added. Adding a negative amount does not make sense for this problem, so the vertical asymptote does not matter.]**

Got It?

Q What are three different ways to solve this problem? **[Answers may vary. Samples: Graph the formula with $y = 0.4$; use a table on a graphing calculator; solve an equation.]**

Q What is the domain of the function that makes sense for this problem? **[$x \geq 0$]**

Q What is the range of this function for the domain you just defined? **[$0.1 < y \leq 1$]**

Problem 5 Using a Rational Function STEM GRIDDED RESPONSE

Chemistry You work in a pharmacy that mixes different concentrations of saline solutions for its customers. The pharmacy has a supply of two concentrations, 0.5% and 2%. The function $y = \frac{(100)(0.02) + x(0.005)}{100 + x}$ gives the concentration of the saline solution after adding x milliliters of the 0.5% solution to 100 milliliters of the 2% solution. How many milliliters of the 0.5% solution must you add for the combined solution to have a concentration of 0.9%?

Plan

How can you use a calculator to solve the problem?
Graph
$y = \frac{(100)(0.02) + x(0.005)}{100 + x}$
and $y = 0.009$ in the calculator and find the point of intersection.

Step 1 Use a graphing calculator to graph **Y1** $= \frac{(100)(0.02) + x(0.005)}{100 + x}$ and **Y2** $= 0.009$.

  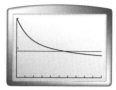

Step 2 Find the point of intersection of the two functions.

Graphic Solution

Intersection X=275 Y=.009

Table Solution

X=275

You should add 275 mL of the 0.5% solution to get a 0.9% solution. Write 275 in the grid.

Check $y = \frac{(100)(0.02) + x(0.005)}{100 + x}$

$y \stackrel{?}{=} \frac{(100)(0.02) + (275)(0.005)}{100 + 275}$ Substitute 275 for x.

$y \stackrel{?}{=} \frac{2 + 1.375}{375}$

$y = 0.009$ ✔

Got It? 5. a. You want to mix a 10% orange juice drink with 100% pure orange juice to make a 40% orange juice drink. The function $y = \frac{(2)(1.0) + x(0.1)}{2 + x}$ gives the concentration y of orange juice in the drink after you add x gallons of the 10% drink to 2 gallons of pure juice. How much of the 10% drink must you add to get a drink that is 40% juice?

b. Reasoning If you wanted a drink that is 80% orange juice, would you need to add half as much as your answer in part (a)? Explain.

520 Chapter 8 Rational Functions

Answers

Got It? (continued)

5. a. 4 gal

b. No, because the graph changes when $y_1 = 0.8$ and intersects the graph of $y_2 = \frac{2 + (0.1)x}{2 + x}$ at $x \approx 0.6$. So, to have 80% orange juice, about 0.6 gal should be added.

Lesson Check

1. at $x = -5$ and $x = -4$

2. at $x = 9$ and $x = -2$

3. at $x = -1$

4. at $x = \frac{1}{3}$ and $x = 2$

5. $x = -5$

6. $x = -2$ and $x = -3$

7. $x = 1$

8. $x = 1$ and $x = -3$

9.

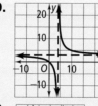

10.

11. The function at $x = 1$ and $x = -3$; is undefined.

12. degree 2; function is discontinuous at 2 values of x

Practice and Problem-Solving Exercises

13. domain: all real numbers except $x = 0$ and $x = 2$; pts. of discontinuity: non-removable at $x = 0$ and $x = 2$; no x- or y-intercept

14. domain: all real numbers; no pts. of discontinuity; x-intercepts: $(0, 0)$ and $(-2, 0)$, y-intercept: $(0, 0)$

15. domain: all real numbers except $x = \pm 1$; pts. of discontinuity: non-removable at $x = -1$, removable at $x = 1$; no x-intercept, y-intercept: $(0, 3)$

16. domain: all real numbers except $x = 2$ and $x = 3$; pts. of discontinuity: non-removable at $x = 3$, removable at $x = 2$; no x-intercept, y-intercept: $(0, 1)$

17. vert. asymptote at $x = -2$

18. hole at $x = -5$

19. vert. asymptotes at $x = -\frac{3}{2}$ and $x = 1$

20. vertical asymptote at $x = -1$, hole at $x = 2$

21. hole at $x = -2$

22. none

520 Chapter 8

Lesson Check

Do you know HOW?

Find any points of discontinuity for each rational function.

1. $y = \dfrac{x + 5}{x^2 + 9x + 20}$ **2.** $y = \dfrac{x^2 + 2x}{x^2 - 7x - 18}$

3. $y = \dfrac{x - 1}{(x + 1)^2}$ **4.** $y = \dfrac{x^2 - x - 2}{3x^2 - 7x + 2}$

Find the vertical asymptotes of the graph of each rational function.

5. $y = \dfrac{x - 3}{x + 5}$ **6.** $y = \dfrac{x - 3}{x^2 + 5x + 6}$

7. $y = \dfrac{2x + 2}{x^2 - 1}$ **8.** $y = \dfrac{x^2 + 2x + 3}{x^2 + 2x - 3}$

Sketch the graph of each rational function.

9. $y = \dfrac{3x}{x - 4}$ **10.** $y = \dfrac{x + 3}{(x - 1)(x - 6)}$

Do you UNDERSTAND?

For Exercises 11 and 12, use the following table. The table shows data for a rational function.

11. What do the **Y1** values for **X = −3** and **X = 1** tell you about the rational function?

12. Reasoning Assume that there are no more **ERROR** values in the **Y1** column. What is the lowest possible degree of the denominator? Explain how you know.

Practice and Problem-Solving Exercises MATHEMATICAL PRACTICES

A Practice   Find the domain, points of discontinuity, and *x*- and *y*- intercepts of each rational function. Determine whether the discontinuities are removable or non-removable.   See Problem 1.

13. $y = \dfrac{2x^2 + 5}{x^2 - 2x}$ **14.** $y = \dfrac{x^2 + 2x}{x^2 + 2}$ **15.** $y = \dfrac{3x - 3}{x^2 - 1}$ **16.** $y = \dfrac{6 - 3x}{x^2 - 5x + 6}$

Find the vertical asymptotes and holes for the graph of each rational function.   See Problem 2.

17. $y = \dfrac{3}{x + 2}$ **18.** $y = \dfrac{x + 5}{x + 5}$ **19.** $y = \dfrac{x + 3}{(2x + 3)(x - 1)}$

20. $y = \dfrac{(x + 3)(x - 2)}{(x - 2)(x + 1)}$ **21.** $y = \dfrac{x^2 - 4}{x + 2}$ **22.** $y = \dfrac{x + 5}{x^2 + 9}$

Find the horizontal asymptote of the graph of each rational function.   See Problem 3.

23. $y = \dfrac{5}{x + 6}$ **24.** $y = \dfrac{x + 2}{2x^2 - 4}$ **25.** $y = \dfrac{x + 1}{x + 5}$

26. $y = \dfrac{x^2 + 2}{2x^2 - 1}$ **27.** $y = \dfrac{5x^3 + 2x}{2x^5 - 4x^3}$ **28.** $y = \dfrac{3x - 4}{4x + 1}$

Sketch the graph of each rational function.   See Problem 4.

29. $y = \dfrac{x^2 - 4}{3x - 6}$ **30.** $y = \dfrac{4x}{x^3 - 4x}$ **31.** $y = \dfrac{x + 4}{x - 4}$

32. $y = \dfrac{x(x + 1)}{x + 1}$ **33.** $y = \dfrac{x + 6}{(x - 2)(x + 3)}$ **34.** $y = \dfrac{3x}{(x + 2)^2}$

STEM 35. Pharmacology How many milliliters of the 0.5% solution must be added to the 2% solution to get a 0.65% solution? Use the rational function given in Problem 5.   See Problem 5.

23. $y = 0$ **24.** $y = 0$ **25.** $y = 1$ **32.**
26. $y = \dfrac{1}{2}$ **27.** $y = 0$ **28.** $y = \dfrac{3}{4}$

29.

30.

31.

33.

34.

35. 900 mL

---

3 Lesson Check

Do you know HOW?

- In Exercises 1–8, the first step should be to factor the numerator and denominator, when possible.
- In Exercises 1 and 2, make sure students understand the question: find all discontinuities and not just vertical asymptotes.
- In Exercises 2, 4 and 7, make sure students factor the numerator.
- In Exercise 8, the discriminant shows that the numerator does not have any real roots. Thus there are no *x*-intercepts and no common factor in the denominator and numerator. Thus there is no need to factor the numerator.

Do you UNDERSTAND?

- In Exercise 11, students have no way of knowing from the **Y1** values on the calculator whether the error is caused by a removable discontinuity or an asymptote.

Close

Q What causes discontinuities in a graph? What is the first step in finding them? **[A denominator that can equal 0; factor the denominator, and set each factor to zero.]**

Q How does the graph of a function behave as it approaches removable and non-removable discontinuities? **[A function tends toward a single specific value near a removable discontinuity. A function tends towards ±∞ near a nonremovable discontinuity.]**

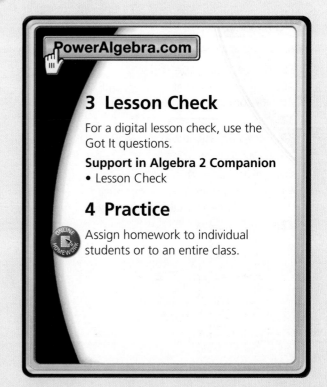

PowerAlgebra.com

3 Lesson Check

For a digital lesson check, use the Got It questions.

Support in Algebra 2 Companion
- Lesson Check

4 Practice

Assign homework to individual students or to an entire class.

4 Practice

ASSIGNMENT GUIDE

Basic: 13–35 all, 36–42

Average: 13–35 odd, 36–47

Advanced: 13–35 odd, 36–49

Standardized Test Prep: 50–54

Mixed Review: 55–76

Mathematical Practices are supported by exercises with red headings. Here are the Practices supported in this lesson:

MP 1: Make Sense of Problems Ex. 30

MP 3: Communicate Ex. 12, 47

MP 3: Construct Arguments Ex. 12

MP 3: Critique the Reasoning of Others Ex. 41

MP 4: Model with Mathematics Ex. 48

Applications exercises have blue headings. Exercises 35 and 46 support MP 4: Model.

STEM exercises focus on science or engineering applications.

EXERCISE 40: Use the Think About a Plan worksheet in the **Practice and Problem Solving Workbook** (also available in the Teaching Resources in print and online) to further support students' development in becoming independent learners.

HOMEWORK QUICK CHECK

To check students' understanding of key skills and concepts, go over Exercises 13, 29, 39, 40, and 41.

 Apply   Find the vertical and horizontal asymptotes, if any, of the graph of each rational function.

36. 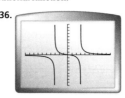   37. 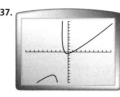   38.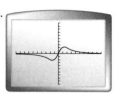

39. Think About a Plan A basketball player has made 21 of her last 30 free throws—a percentage of 70%. How many more consecutive free throws does she need to raise her free throw percentage to 75%?
  • How can you model the player's free throw percentage as a rational function? (*Hint:* Let $x =$ the number of additional free throws needed.)
  • How can a graph help you answer this question?

40. Grades A student earns an 82% on her first test. How many consecutive 100% test scores does she need to bring her average up to 95%? Assume that each test has equal impact on the average grade.

41. Error Analysis A student listed the asymptotes of the function $y = \dfrac{x^2 - 3x + 2}{x^2 + 6x + 5}$ as shown at the right. Explain the student's error. What are the correct asymptotes?

vertical asymptotes:
x = 1, x = 2
horizontal asymptotes:
y = −1, y = −5

Sketch the graph of each rational function.

42. $y = \dfrac{2x + 3}{x - 5}$ **43.** $y = \dfrac{x^2 + 6x + 9}{x + 3}$ **44.** $y = \dfrac{4x^2 - 100}{2x^2 + x - 15}$ **45.** $y = -\dfrac{x}{(x - 1)^2}$

46. Business CDs can be manufactured for $.19 each. The development cost is $210,000. The first 500 discs are samples and will not be sold.
  a. Write a function for the average cost of a disc that is not a sample. Graph the function.
  b. What is the average cost if 5000 discs are produced? If 15,000 discs are produced?
  c. How many discs must be produced to bring the average cost under $10?
  d. What are the vertical and horizontal asymptotes of the graph of the function?

47. Writing Describe the conditions that will produce a rational function with a graph that has no vertical asymptotes.

Challenge   **48. Reasoning** Look for a pattern in the sequence of file folders below.
  a. Write a model for the number of yellow folders $Y(n)$ at each step n.
  b. Write a model for the number of green folders $G(n)$ at each step n.
  c. Write a model for the ratio of $Y(n)$ to $G(n)$. Use it to predict the ratio of yellow folders to green folders in the next figure. Verify your answer.

Answers

Practice and Problem-Solving Exercises (continued)

36. vert. asymptotes at $x = -3$ and $x = 3$, horizontal asymptote at $y = 0$

37. vert. asymptote at $x = -2$

38. horizontal asymptote at $y = 0$

39. 6 free throws

40. 3 test scores

41. correct answer: vert. asymptotes: $x = -5$ and $x = -1$, horizontal asymptote: $y = 1$

42.
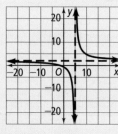

43.
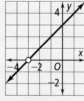

44.

45.

46. a. $y = \dfrac{0.19x + 210,000}{x - 500}$

  b. $46.88; $14.68
  c. at least 21,917 discs
  d. $x = 500$, $y = 0.19$

47. Answers may vary. Sample: There is no value of x for which the denominator equals 0.

48. a. $4(n - 1) + 1$
  b. $4(n - 1)^2$
  c. $\dfrac{Y(n)}{G(n)} = \dfrac{4(n - 1) + 1}{4(n - 1)^2}$
  $= \dfrac{4(4 - 1) + 1}{4(4 - 1)^2} = \dfrac{13}{36}$

49. Write a rational function with the following characteristics.
   a. Vertical asymptotes at $x = 1$ and $x = -3$, horizontal asymptote at $y = 1$, zeros at 3 and 4
   b. Vertical asymptotes at $x = 0$ and $x = 3$, horizontal asymptote at $y = 0$, a zero at -4
   c. Vertical asymptotes at $x = -2$ and $x = 2$, horizontal asymptote at $y = 3$, only one zero at -1.

Standardized Test Prep

SAT/ACT

50. What is the x-coordinate of the hole in the graph of $y = \dfrac{x^2 - 9}{2x^2 - x - 15}$?

51. Suppose z varies directly with x and inversely with y. If z is 1.5 when x is 9 and y is 4, what is z when x is 6 and y is 0.5?

52. What is the y-coordinate of the vertex of the parabola $y = -3(x - 4)^2 + 5$?

53. What is the real solution of $54x^3 - 16 = 0$ written as a fraction?

54. Using the Change of Base Formula, what is the value of $\log_7 15$ rounded to the nearest hundredth?

Mixed Review

Sketch the asymptotes and the graph of each equation. Identify the domain and range.   ● See Lesson 8-2.

55. $y = \dfrac{3}{x} + 4$ **56.** $y = \dfrac{2}{x + 3}$ **57.** $y = \dfrac{-1}{x + 1} + 1$

58. $y = \dfrac{5}{x - 7} - 3$ **59.** $y = \dfrac{4}{x}$ **60.** $y = \dfrac{-2}{x - 1} + 2$

Find the inverse of each function. Determine if the inverse is a function.   ● See Lesson 6-7.

61. $y = 2x - 3$ **62.** $y = 6 - x$ **63.** $y = 2x^2$

64. $y = \dfrac{x^2}{5}$ **65.** $y = \dfrac{1}{x + 2}$ **66.** $y = \sqrt{x - 2} + 1$

Solve each inequality. Graph the solution.   ● See Lesson 1-5.

67. $6a - 17 < 47$ **68.** $2(x + 9) \geq 90$ **69.** $5(x - 11) + 13 \geq 47$

70. $6 + y < 3y - 2$ **71.** $49 > 7x + 28$ **72.** $12 - 2b > 3(b - 3) - 4$

Get Ready!   To prepare for Lesson 8-4, do Exercises 73–76.

Factor each expression.   ● See Lesson 4-4.

73. $2x^2 - 3x + 1$ **74.** $4x^2 - 9$ **75.** $5x^2 + 6x + 1$ **76.** $10x^2 - 10$

58.

domain: all real numbers except $x = 7$, range: all real numbers except $y = -3$

59.
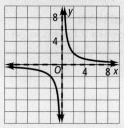
domain: all real numbers except $x = 0$, range: all real numbers except $y = 0$

60.
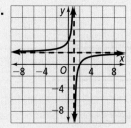
domain: all real numbers except $x = 1$, range: all real numbers except $y = 2$

61. $y = \dfrac{x + 3}{2}$; yes   **62.** $y = 6 - x$; yes

63. $y = \pm\sqrt{\dfrac{x}{2}}$; no   **64.** $y = \pm\sqrt{5x}$; no

65. $y = \dfrac{1}{x} - 2$; yes

66. $y = (x - 1)^2 + 2$; yes

67. $a < 10\dfrac{2}{3}$

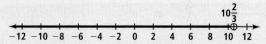

68. $x \geq 36$

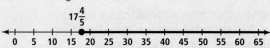

69. $x \geq 17\dfrac{4}{5}$

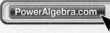

70. $y > 4$

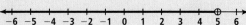

71. $x < 3$

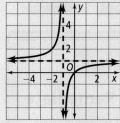

72. $b < 5$

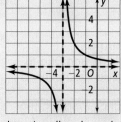

73. $(2x - 1)(x - 1)$
74. $(2x - 3)(2x + 3)$
75. $(5x + 1)(x + 1)$
76. $10(x - 1)(x + 1)$

---

49. Answers may vary. Samples:
   a. $y = \dfrac{x^2 - 7x + 12}{x^2 + 2x - 3}$
   b. $y = \dfrac{x + 4}{x^2 - 3x}$
   c. $y = \dfrac{3(x + 1)^2}{x^2 - 4}$

Standardized Test Prep

50. 3   **51.** 8   **52.** 5
53. $\dfrac{2}{3}$ **54.** 1.39

Mixed Review

55.
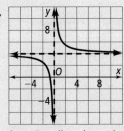
domain: all real numbers except $x = 0$, range: all real numbers except $y = 4$

56.
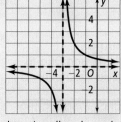
domain: all real numbers except $x = -3$, range: all real numbers except $y = 0$

57.

domain: all real numbers except $x = -1$, range: all real numbers except $y = 1$

8-3 Lesson Resources

Additional Instructional Support

Algebra 2 Companion

Students can use the **Algebra 2 Companion** worktext (4 pages) as you teach the lesson. Use the Companion to support

- New Vocabulary
- Key Concepts
- Got It for each Problem
- Lesson Check

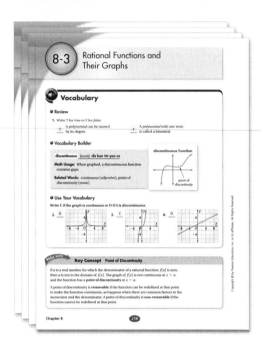

ELL Support

Focus on Language Discuss the meaning of the words *nation* and *national*. Ask how adding *-al* to the end of a word changes the meaning. Ask students for other words, like *person*, that form an adjective by adding *-al*. Explain that a function that is a *ratio* of functions is a *rational* function.

Discuss the meaning of the words *agree* and *disagree*. Ask how adding *dis-* to a word changes its meaning. Ask students for other examples, such as *disorient* or *disregard*. Explain that a *discontinuous* function has a point where it does *not* go on as usual.

5 Assess & Remediate

Lesson Quiz

1. What are the domain and points of discontinuity of $y = \frac{x - 4}{x^2 + 8x - 20}$? What are the x- and y-intercepts?

2. What are the vertical and horizontal asymptotes for the graph of $y = \frac{x^2 + 3x}{x(x^2 + 4)}$?

3. What is the graph of the rational function $y = \frac{x^2}{x^2 + 4x + 3}$?

4. **Do you UNDERSTAND?** You are making iced tea for a friend who prefers it at 80% strength. The function $y = \frac{(6)(1.0) + x(.5)}{6 + x}$ gives the concentration of the tea after adding x fluid ounces of a 50% tea solution to 6 fluid ounces of 100% strength tea. How many fluid ounces of 50% strength tea should you add to 6 fl oz of 100% strength tea?

ANSWERS TO LESSON QUIZ

1. domain: all real numbers except $x = 2$ and $x = -10$; nonremovable discontinuities at $x = 2$ and $x = -10$; x-intercept (4, 0); y-intercept $(0, \frac{1}{5})$

2. no vertical asymptote; horizontal asymptote at $y = 0$

3.

4. 4 fl oz

PRESCRIPTION FOR REMEDIATION

Use the student work on the Lesson Quiz to prescribe a differentiated review assignment:

Points	Differentiated Remediation
0–2	Intervention
3	On-level
4	Extension

PowerAlgebra.com

5 Assess & Remediate

Assign the Lesson Quiz. Appropriate intervention, practice, or enrichment is automatically generated based on student performance.

Differentiated Remediation

Intervention

- **Reteaching** (2 pages) Provides reteaching and practice exercises for the key lesson concepts. Use with struggling students or absent students.

- **English Language Learner Support** Helps students develop and reinforce mathematical vocabulary and key concepts.

All-in-One Resources/Online
Reteaching

8-3 Reteaching
Rational Functions and Their Graphs

All-in-One Resources/Online
English Language Learner Support

8-3 Additional Vocabulary Support
Rational Functions and Their Graphs

Differentiated Remediation *continued*

On-Level

- **Practice** (2 pages) Provides extra practice for each lesson. For simpler practice exercises, use the Form K Practice pages found in the All-in-One Teaching Resources and online.

- **Think About a Plan** Helps students develop specific problem-solving skills and strategies by providing scaffolded guiding questions.

- **Standardized Test Prep** Focuses on all major exercises, all major question types, and helps students prepare for the high-stakes assessments.

Extension

- **Enrichment** Provides students with interesting problems and activities that extend the concepts of the lesson.

- **Activities, Games, and Puzzles** Worksheets that can be used for concepts development, enrichment, and for fun!

Practice and Problem Solving Wkbk/All-in-One Resources/Online
Practice page 1

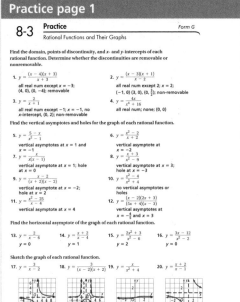

Practice and Problem Solving Wkbk/All-in-One Resources/Online
Practice page 2

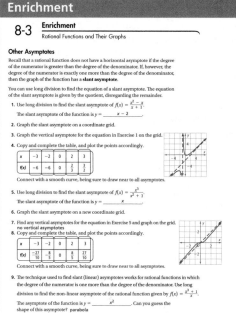

All-in-One Resources/Online
Enrichment

Practice and Problem Solving Wkbk/All-in-One Resources/Online
Think About a Plan

Practice and Problem Solving Wkbk/All-in-One Resources/Online
Standardized Test Prep

Online Teacher Resource Center
Activities, Games, and Puzzles

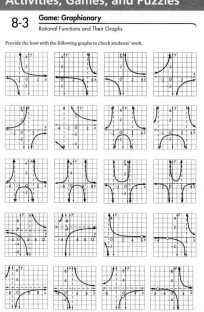

Guided Instruction

PURPOSE To identify and write equations for oblique asymptotes

PROCESS Students will
- graph a rational function and its oblique asymptote using a graphing calculator.
- use a table to verify that the end behavior of a graph and the graph of the asymptote get closer as the value of x increases.
- algebraically find the oblique asymptote of a rational function.

Example 1   VISUAL LEARNERS

> **Q** How do the x- and y-values compare close to zero? **[Sample: The closer x gets to zero, the farther apart the values for y are.]**

> **Q** What algebraic argument can you make that the values in **Y1** and **Y2** will never be equal? **[The expression $\frac{6x^2 + 1}{3x}$ can be written as $2x + \frac{1}{3x}$ and so will never quite equal $2x$.]**

EXTENSION

The numbers students get when subtracting **Y2** values from **Y1** values are the numbers you get when you substitute values from the X column in the expression $\frac{1}{3x}$. Students can verify this algebra by entering the function $y = \frac{1}{3x}$ into **Y3** and checking the table.

ⓒ **Mathematical Practices** This Concept Byte supports students in becoming proficient in using appropriate tools, Mathematical Practice 5.

Concept Byte **Oblique Asymptotes**

For Use With Lesson 8-3

TECHNOLOGY

ⓒ **Content Standard**
Extends F.IF.7.d Graph rational functions, identify zeros and asymptotes when suitable factorizations are available, and showing end behavior.

In Lesson 8-2, you saw that the graphs of some rational functions have horizontal and vertical asymptotes. The graphs of some rational functions can have *oblique asymptotes*. **Oblique asymptotes** are asymptotes that are neither horizontal nor vertical. These asymptotes only occur in rational functions in which the degree of the numerator is one greater than the degree of the denominator.

  MATHEMATICAL PRACTICES

Example 1

Compare the graphs of $y = \frac{6x^2 + 1}{3x}$ and $y = 2x$ using a graphing calculator.

The graph of $y = \frac{6x^2 + 1}{3x}$ gets closer to $y = 2x$ as $|x|$ gets increasingly large.

The graph of $y = 2x$ is an oblique asymptote of $y = \frac{6x^2 + 1}{3x}$.

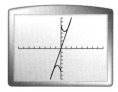

Example 2

Use a spreadsheet to find the differences between $f(x) = \frac{6x^2 + 1}{3x}$ and $g(x) = 2x$ for the values from 1 to 10.

Step 1 Label each column in Row 1.

Step 2 Enter the x-values in column A.

Step 3 Enter the formulas for $f(x)$, $g(x)$, and $f(x) - g(x)$ into cells B2, C2, and D2.

$B2 = (6 \times (A2)^2 + 1))/(3 \times A2)$

$C2 = 2 \times A2$

$D2 = B2 - C2$

	A	B	C	D
1	x	f(x) = (6x^2 + 1)/(3x)	g(x) = 2x	f(x) − g(x)
2	1	2.333	2	0.333
3	2	4.167	4	0.167
4	3	6.111	6	0.111

Step 4 In columns B, C, and D fill the formulas down to find the values of $f(x)$, $g(x)$, and $f(x) - g(x)$ for each corresponding x-value.

As the values of x get larger, the value $6x^2$ becomes much larger than the constant term in the numerator. As a result, the constant term has a smaller effect on the value of the function. So, as x increases, the value of $\frac{6x^2 + 1}{3x}$ gets closer to the value of $\frac{6x^2}{3x} = 2x$, for $x \neq 0$. The spreadsheet confirms this conclusion by showing that the difference between these two values gets closer to zero as x gets larger.

Answers

Concept Byte

1. $y = x$

2. $y = -\frac{2}{3}x$

3. $y = -\frac{1}{4}x$

4. $y = 2x$

5. Step 1 Label each column in row 1.

Step 2 Enter the x-values in column A.

Step 3 Enter the formulas for $f(x)$, $g(x)$, and $f(x) - g(x)$ into cells B2, C2, and D2.

$B2 = (12*A2^2 - 7)/(3*A2)$

$C2 = 4*A2$

$D2 = B2 - C2$

	A	B	C	D
1	x	f(x) = 12x^2 − 7)/(3x)	g(x) = 4x	f(x) − g(x)
2	1	1.66666667	4	−2.33333333
3	2	6.83333333	8	−1.16666667
4	3	11.2222222	12	−0.77777778

Step 4 Fill the formulas down to find the values of $f(x)$, $g(x)$, and $f(x) - g(x)$ for each corresponding x-value. As the values of x get larger, the value $12x^2$ becomes much larger than the constant term in the numerator. As a result, the constant term has a smaller effect on the value of the function. So, as x increases, the value of $\frac{12x^2 - 7}{3x}$ gets closer to the value of $\frac{12x^2}{3x} = 4x$, for $x \neq 0$. The spreadsheet confirms this conclusion by showing that the difference between these two values is getting closer to zero as x gets larger.

Sometimes it is not as easy to find the oblique asymptote. For example, the asymptote of $y = \frac{2x^2 - 3x + 3}{x - 2}$ is not $\frac{2x^2}{x}$ or $2x$. You can use polynomial division to find the oblique asymptote of any rational function.

Example 3

Determine the oblique asymptote of $y = \frac{2x^2 - 3x + 3}{x - 2}$.

Divide the numerator by the denominator.

$$
\begin{array}{r}
2x + 1 \\
x - 2 \overline{)2x^2 - 3x + 3} \\
\underline{2x^2 - 4x} \\
x + 3 \\
\underline{x - 2} \\
5
\end{array}
$$

Ignore the remainder. The asymptote is the quotient, $y = 2x + 1$.

Check

Use a graphing calculator to check your answer.

Exercises

Graphing Calculator For each function determine the oblique asymptote. Check with a graphing calculator.

1. $y = \frac{x^2 - 1}{x}$

2. $y = -\frac{2x^2}{3x + 2}$

3. $y = \frac{4 - x^3}{4x^2 - 1}$

4. $y = \frac{2x^4 + 99{,}999}{x^3}$

5. Technical Writing Write a step-by-step manual for classmates to use so they can use a spreadsheet to explore the differences between $f(x)$ and $g(x)$ as the value of x increases.

$$f(x) = \frac{12x^2 - 7}{3x} \qquad\qquad g(x) = 4x$$

6. Open-Ended Write three rational functions that have an oblique asymptote of $y = 2x$. Graph to check your work.

Describe the asymptotes of the graph of each function.

7. $f(x) = \frac{2x + 1}{x^2 - 1}$

8. $f(x) = \frac{x^2 - 9}{x + 3}$

9. $f(x) = \frac{5x + 11}{4x + 6}$

10. $f(x) = \frac{4x^2 + x - 3}{7x - 1}$

11. $y = \frac{2x^2 - 7x - 5}{2x + 3}$

12. $y = \frac{6x^2 + 14x + 7}{2x + 3}$

← (arrow pointing to Example 3 sidebar)

Example 2

Q How can you find the equation of an oblique asymptote for a rational function where both the numerator and the denominator have only one term that has a variable in it? **[Divide the term of the numerator with the variable by the term of the denominator with the variable to get the equation of the oblique asymptote.]**

Example 3

Q What happens in the graph if there is no remainder when you divide? **[Since you ignore the remainder, the asymptote will be the same.]**

Exercises   ERROR PREVENTION

Q For Exercise 2, does it matter whether you attach the negative sign to the numerator or the denominator? Explain. **[No; either would give a result of a line with a negative slope.]**

For Exercise 4, students may have trouble checking their answers with the calculator if they cannot find the correct viewing window. A window of $[-100, 100] \times [-100, 100]$ works well. You might suggest they try larger numbers in increments of 25 to help them find it themselves.

AUDITORY LEARNERS

For Exercise 5, have students explain the procedure aloud to each other before writing their answer.

6. Answers may vary. Samples:

$y = \frac{4x^2 - 1}{2x + 3}$,

$y = \frac{2x^2 + 5}{x + 1}$, $y = -\frac{6x^2}{5 - 3x}$

7. vertical asymptotes at $x = \pm 1$, horizontal asymptote at $y = 0$

8. none

9. vert. asymptote at $x = -\frac{3}{2}$, horizontal asymptote at $y = \frac{5}{4}$

10. vert. asymptote, at $x = \frac{1}{7}$, oblique asymptote at $y = \frac{4}{7}x + \frac{11}{49}$

11. vertical asymptote at $x = -\frac{3}{2}$, oblique asymptote at $y = x - 5$

12. vertical asymptote at $x = -\frac{3}{2}$, oblique asymptote at $y = 3x + 2.5$

Answers

1. $z = 5xy$ **2.** $z = \dfrac{20x}{y}$ **3.** $z = \dfrac{180}{xy}$

4. neither **5.** direct **6.** inverse

7. $y = \dfrac{221}{x}$ **8.** $y = \dfrac{-48}{x}$ **9.** $y = \dfrac{-13}{x}$

10. The graph of y_2 is a stretch of the graph of y_1 by a factor of $\frac{9}{4}$.

11. The graph of y_2 is the graph of y_1 translated 5 units up.

12. The graph of y_2 is the graph of y_1 translated 4 units down and 2 units to the rt.

13. vert. asymptotes at $x = -5$ and $x = 2$, horizontal asymptote at $y = 0$

14. hole at $x = -2$, vert. asymptote at $x = 3$, horizontal asymptote at $y = 0$

15. vert. asymptote at $x = 1$, horizontal asymptote at $y = 0$

16. vert. asymptote at $x = -2$, horizontal asymptote at $y = 5$

17. 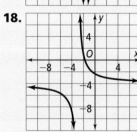 domain: all real numbers except $x = 0$; range: all real numbers except $y = 0$

18. 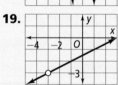 domain: all real numbers except $x = -3$; range: all real numbers except $y = -4$

19. 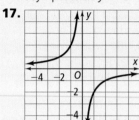 domain: all real numbers except $x = -3$; range: all real numbers except $y = -3$

20. 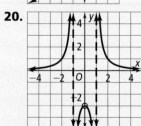 domain: all real numbers except $x = -1$, $x = 0$, and $x = 1$; range: $y < -3$ or $y > 0$

Do you know HOW?

If $z = 30$ when $x = 3$ and $y = 2$, write the function that models the relationship.

1. z varies jointly with x and y.

2. z varies directly with x and inversely with y.

3. z varies inversely with the product of x and y.

Is the relationship between the values in the table a *direct variation*, an *inverse variation*, or *neither*?

4.

x	y
22	104
35	174
48	239
54	269

5.

x	y
2	−4.8
6	−14.4
12	−28.8
19	−45.6

6.

x	y
15	2.4
18	2
20	1.8
45	0.8

Suppose that x and y vary inversely. Write a function that models the inverse variation.

7. $x = 13$ when $y = 17$

8. $x = -12$ when $y = 4$

9. $x = -52$ when $y = \frac{1}{4}$

Explain how the graph of y_2 is related to the graph of y_1.

10. $y_1 = \dfrac{4}{x}$ and $y_2 = \dfrac{9}{x}$

11. $y_1 = \dfrac{1}{x}$ and $y_2 = \dfrac{1}{x} + 5$

12. $y_1 = \dfrac{1}{x - 1} + 2$ and $y_2 = \dfrac{1}{x + 1} - 2$

Find any holes and vertical or horizontal asymptotes for the graph of each rational function.

13. $y = \dfrac{1}{x^2 + 3x - 10}$

14. $y = \dfrac{x + 2}{(x + 2)(x - 3)}$

15. $y = \dfrac{x - 1}{x^2 - 2x + 1}$

16. $y = \dfrac{5x - 2}{x + 2}$

Sketch the graph of each rational function. Then identify the domain and range.

17. $y = \dfrac{-2}{x}$

18. $y = \dfrac{5}{x + 3} - 4$

19. $y = \dfrac{x^2 - 9}{2x + 6}$

20. $y = \dfrac{3x}{x^3 - x}$

21. $y = \dfrac{x + 3}{x - 3}$

22. $y = \dfrac{x^2 - 2x}{x - 2}$

Do you UNDERSTAND?

Ⓒ **Open-Ended** Write a rational function with the given characteristics.

23. a vertical asymptote at $x = 8$ and a horizontal asymptote at $y = 0$

24. a vertical asymptote at $x = -4$ and a horizontal asymptote at $y = 3$

25. a hole at $x = -5$ and a vertical asymptote at $x = 2$

Ⓒ **26. Reasoning** How many inverse variation functions have (2, 3) as a solution?

Ⓒ **27. Reasoning** The graph of an inverse variation function contains the point (a, b). Using a and b, identify 3 other points on the graph.

Ⓒ **28. Reasoning** Graph the equations $y = \dfrac{x^2 + x - 6}{x^2 - 5x + 6}$ and $y = \dfrac{x + 3}{x - 3}$. Are they equivalent? Explain.

21. 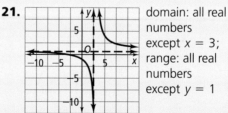 domain: all real numbers except $x = 3$; range: all real numbers except $y = 1$

22. 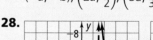 domain: all real numbers except $x = 2$; range: all real numbers except $y = 2$

23. Answers may vary. Sample: $y = \dfrac{1}{x - 8}$

24. Answers may vary. Sample: $y = \dfrac{3x}{x + 4}$

25. Answers may vary. Sample:
$y = \dfrac{(x + 5)}{(x - 2)(x + 5)}$

26. one

27. Answers may vary. Sample answer:
$(-a, -b), \left(2a, \dfrac{b}{2}\right), \left(3a, \dfrac{b}{3}\right)$

28.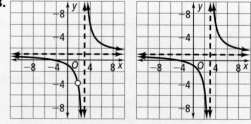

They are not equivalent functions. The first function has a hole at $x = 2$.

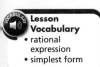

8-4 Rational Expressions

© Content Standards

A.SSE.2 Use the structure of an expression to identify ways to rewrite it.

A.SSE.1.b. Interpret complicated expressions by viewing one or more of their parts as a single entity.

Also A.SSE.1.a

Objectives To simplify rational expressions
To multiply and divide rational expressions

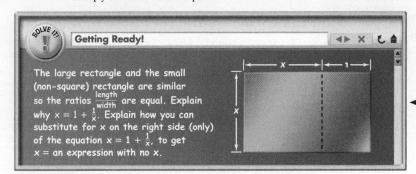

SOLVE IT!

Getting Ready!   ◄► ✕ ↻ ⌂

The large rectangle and the small (non-square) rectangle are similar so the ratios $\frac{length}{width}$ are equal. Explain why $x = 1 + \frac{1}{x}$. Explain how you can substitute for x on the right side (only) of the equation $x = 1 + \frac{1}{x}$, to get $x =$ an expression with no x.

Lesson Vocabulary
• rational expression
• simplest form

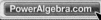

The expression $1 + \frac{1}{x}$ in the Solve It is equivalent to the *rational expression* $\frac{x+1}{x}$. A **rational expression** is the quotient of two polynomials. You will find that, at different times, it is helpful to think of rational expressions as ratios, as fractions, or as quotients.

Essential Understanding You can use much of what you know about multiplying and dividing fractions to multiply and divide rational expressions.

A rational expression is in **simplest form** when its numerator and denominator are polynomials that have no common divisors.

In simplest form	Not in simplest form
$\frac{x+1}{x-1}, \frac{x^2+3x+2}{x+3}$	$\frac{x}{x^2}, \frac{3(x-3)}{x-3}, \frac{x^2-x-6}{x^2+x-2}$

You simplify a rational expression by dividing out the common factors in the numerator and the denominator. Factoring the numerator and denominator will help you find the common divisors.

A rational expression and any simplified form must have the same domain in order to be equivalent.

$$\frac{x^2-x-6}{x^2+x-2} = \frac{(x-3)(x+2)}{(x-1)(x+2)} \text{ and } \frac{x-3}{x-1}, x \neq -2, \text{ are equivalent.}$$

In the example above, you must exclude -2 from the domain of $\frac{x-3}{x-1}$ because -2 is not in the domain of $\frac{x^2-x-6}{x^2+x-2}$. Note that this restriction is not evident from the simplified expression $\frac{x-3}{x-1}$.

1 Interactive Learning

Solve It!

PURPOSE To explore rational expressions through examination of the Golden Rectangle

PROCESS Students may

• write and compare ratios of $\frac{length}{width}$ for the small and large non-square rectangles.

• repeatedly substitute for a variable to establish an infinite expression.

FACILITATE

Q If you define $x + 1$ as the length of the large rectangle, what is the ratio of the length of the large rectangle to the length of the similar smaller rectangle? **[$\frac{x+1}{x}$]**

Q Can you rewrite the ratio $\frac{x+1}{x}$ as $1 + \frac{1}{x}$? If so, how? **[Yes; rewrite the ratio as two ratios with the common denominator x. Then $\frac{x}{x}$ simplifies to 1.]**

Q How many times do you have to substitute for x on the right side of the equation to get "an expression with no x"? Explain. **[An infinite number of times. Each substitution for x replaces the x with x.]**

ANSWER See Solve It in Answers on next page.

CONNECT THE MATH In the Solve It, students write an equation using two rational expressions and then rewrite the expression and simplify it. Students will simplify rational expressions in this lesson.

8-4 Preparing to Teach

BIG ideas Equivalence
Function

ESSENTIAL UNDERSTANDINGS

• Much of what is true about multiplying and dividing fractions can be used to multiply and divide rational expressions.

• A rational expression is in simplest form when its numerator and denominator are polynomials that have no common divisors.

• A rational function may have zero or one horizontal or oblique asymptote and zero or more vertical asymptotes.

• Functions such as $f(x) = \frac{x+a}{x^2-a^2}$ and $g(x) = \frac{1}{x-a}, x \neq \pm a$, are equivalent.

Math Background

Operations with rational expressions are like operations with fractions. However, in order for the simplified rational expression

to be equivalent to the original rational expression, domain restrictions must be defined. To simplify a rational expression:

• factor each polynomial in the numerator and denominator;

• identify the domain restrictions by setting each polynomial in the denominator equal to 0 and solving for x; and

• divide out common factors, identifying excluded values.

Sometimes the domain restrictions are not evident in the simplified expression. For example, $\frac{x^2-1}{x-1}$ has the domain restriction $x \neq 1$. The simplified expression is $x + 1$; the restriction $x \neq 1$ is not evident but must be included for the expressions to be equivalent. The simplified expression is $x + 1, x \neq 1$.

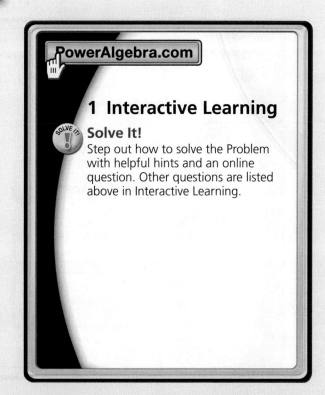

PowerAlgebra.com

1 Interactive Learning

Solve It!

Step out how to solve the Problem with helpful hints and an online question. Other questions are listed above in Interactive Learning.

2 Guided Instruction

Problem 1

> **Q** Why is −5 not excluded from the domain?
> **[because $(x + 5)$ is not a factor of the denominator]**

Got It?

> **Q** The rational expression in 1c factors as $\frac{4(3 - x)}{(x + 3)(x - 3)}$. How can you cancel the factors $(x - 3)$ and $(3 - x)$? **[Factor out −1 from one factor so that the factors are the same.]**

Problem 2

> **Q** Why can you divide out a factor from the numerator of the first rational expression and a factor from the denominator of the second rational expression, and vice versa? **[When you multiply fractions or rational expressions, all the numerators become one numerator and all the denominators become one denominator. This does not happen when the terms are in a sum.]**

Got It?

> **Q** The denominator of the expression of the product has four factors. Why are there not four exclusions from the domain? **[There are repeated factors.]**

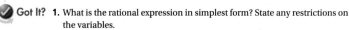 **Problem 1** Simplifying a Rational Expression

What is $\frac{x^2 + 7x + 10}{x^2 - 3x - 10}$ in simplest form? State any restrictions on the variable.

$\frac{x^2 + 7x + 10}{x^2 - 3x - 10} = \frac{(x + 2)(x + 5)}{(x + 2)(x - 5)}$ Factor the numerator and denominator.

$= \frac{(x + 2)(x + 5)}{(x + 2)(x - 5)}$ Divide out common factors.

$= \frac{x + 5}{x - 5}$ Simplify.

Think

Is there more than one restriction?
Yes, before you divided the common factors out, $(x + 2)$ was one of the factors of the denominator so $x \neq -2$.

The simplified form is $\frac{x + 5}{x - 5}$ for $x \neq 5$ and $x \neq -2$. The restriction $x \neq -2$ is not evident from the simplified form, but is needed to prevent the denominator of the original expression from being zero.

Got It? **1.** What is the rational expression in simplest form? State any restrictions on the variables.

   a. $\frac{24x^3y^2}{-6x^2y^3}$ **b.** $\frac{x^2 + 2x - 8}{x^2 - 5x + 6}$ **c.** $\frac{12 - 4x}{x^2 - 9}$

You can use what you know about simplifying rational expressions when you multiply and divide them.

Problem 2 Multiplying Rational Expressions

What is the product $\frac{x^2 + x - 6}{x - 5} \cdot \frac{x^2 - 25}{x^2 + 4x + 3}$ in simplest form? State any restrictions on the variable.

Plan

How is multiplying rational expressions like multiplying fractions?
To multiply rational expressions, you multiply the numerators and multiply the denominators.

$\frac{x^2 + x - 6}{x - 5} \cdot \frac{x^2 - 25}{x^2 + 4x + 3}$

$= \frac{(x + 3)(x - 2)}{x - 5} \cdot \frac{(x + 5)(x - 5)}{(x + 3)(x + 1)}$ Factor all polynomials.

$= \frac{(x + 3)(x - 2)}{x - 5} \cdot \frac{(x + 5)(x - 5)}{(x + 3)(x + 1)}$ Divide out common factors.

$= \frac{(x - 2)(x + 5)}{x + 1}$ Simplify.

The product is $\frac{(x - 2)(x + 5)}{x + 1}$ for $x \neq -3$, $x \neq 5$, and $x \neq -1$. The restrictions $x \neq -3$ and $x \neq 5$ are not evident from the simplified form, but are needed to prevent the denominators in the original product from being zero.

Got It? **2.** What is the product $\frac{2x - 8}{x^2 - 16} \cdot \frac{x^2 + 5x + 4}{x^2 + 8x + 16}$ in simplest form? State any restrictions on the variable.

 PowerAlgebra.com

2 Guided Instruction

(c) Each Problem is worked out and supported online.

Problem 1
Simplifying a Rational Expression

Problem 2
Multiplying Rational Expressions
Animated

Problem 3
Dividing Rational Expressions
Animated

Problem 4
Using Rational Expressions to Solve a Problem
Animated

Support in Algebra 2 Companion
• Vocabulary
• Key Concepts
• Got It?

Answers

Solve It!

Take the ratios of both of the rectangles and set them equal: $\frac{x + 1}{x} = \frac{x}{1}$. Simplify the equation to get $x = 1 + \frac{1}{x}$. Replace x on the right side with $1 + \frac{1}{x}$ to get $x = 1 + \frac{1}{1 + \frac{1}{x}}$. Replace x with $1 + \frac{1}{x}$ again on the right side to get $x = 1 + \frac{1}{1 + \frac{1}{1 + \frac{1}{x}}}$. Continue in this way

to get the continued fraction

$x = 1 + \cfrac{1}{1 + \cfrac{1}{1 + \cfrac{1}{1 + \cfrac{1}{\ddots}}}}.$

To divide rational expressions, you multiply by the reciprocal of the divisor, just as you do when you divide rational numbers.

Ⓒ Problem 3 Dividing Rational Expressions

What is the quotient $\dfrac{2-x}{x^2+2x+1} \div \dfrac{x^2+3x-10}{x^2-1}$ in simplest form? State any restrictions on the variable.

Plan

How do you start?
Think of division as multiplying by the reciprocal.

Think

To divide, you multiply by the reciprocal.

The expressions may have common factors. So, factor the numerators and denominators.

Factor −1 from (2 − x) to get a second (x − 2).

Divide out common factors.

Rewrite the remaining factors.

Identify the restrictions from the denominator of the simplified expression and from any other denominator used.

Write

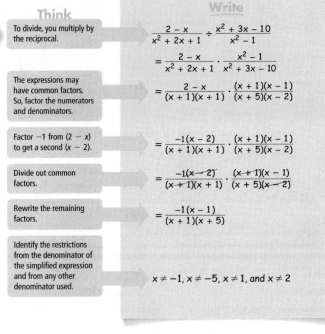

$$\dfrac{2-x}{x^2+2x+1} \div \dfrac{x^2+3x-10}{x^2-1}$$

$$= \dfrac{2-x}{x^2+2x+1} \cdot \dfrac{x^2-1}{x^2+3x-10}$$

$$= \dfrac{2-x}{(x+1)(x+1)} \cdot \dfrac{(x+1)(x-1)}{(x+5)(x-2)}$$

$$= \dfrac{-1(x-2)}{(x+1)(x+1)} \cdot \dfrac{(x+1)(x-1)}{(x+5)(x-2)}$$

$$= \dfrac{-1(x-2)}{(x+1)(x+1)} \cdot \dfrac{(x+1)(x-1)}{(x+5)(x-2)}$$

$$= \dfrac{-1(x-1)}{(x+1)(x+5)}$$

$$x \neq -1, x \neq -5, x \neq 1, \text{ and } x \neq 2$$

Ⓒ ✓ **Got It? 3. a.** What is the quotient $\dfrac{x^2+5x+4}{x^2+x-12} \div \dfrac{x^2-1}{2x^2-6x}$ in simplest form? State any restrictions on the variable.

b. Reasoning Without doing the calculation, what is greatest number of restrictions the quotient $\dfrac{x^2+8x+7}{x^2-x-12} \div \dfrac{x^2+2x-8}{x^2+13x+24}$ could have? Explain.

PowerAlgebra.com   Lesson 8-4   Rational Expressions   529

Problem 3

Q Which polynomials in the original problem may restrict the possible values of the variable? Explain. **[x^2+2x+1, x^2-1, and $x^2+3x-10$ may restrict the possible values of x; any values for x that make one of the expressions 0 will cause division by zero.]**

Q The $x^2+3x-10$ is in the numerator, so why is it involved in the restrictions? **[Because division is the same as multiplying by the reciprocal, this expression becomes a denominator.]**

Got It?

Q Suppose a student accidentally inverts the first rational expression and multiplies. How will the student's answer be different from the correct answer? **[The student's simplified expression will be inverted, and the restrictions on the variable will be incorrect.]**

EXTENSION

Q For 3b, would the number of possible restrictions be the same if the question were a product instead of a quotient? **[No, only restrictions from the original denominators would need to be considered. The maximum number of restrictions would be only four.]**

Additional Problems

1. What is $\dfrac{9x^2+6x}{36x+24}$ in simplest form? State any restrictions on the variable.
ANSWER $\dfrac{x}{4}; x \neq -\dfrac{2}{3}$

2. What is the product $\dfrac{x^2-3x+2}{x+2} \cdot \dfrac{x^2-36}{x^2+5x-6}$ in simplest form? State any restrictions on the variable.
ANSWER $\dfrac{(x-2)(x-6)}{x+2};$ $x \neq 1, x \neq -2, x \neq -6$

3. What is the quotient $\dfrac{6x-3x^2}{36-x^2} \div \dfrac{x^3-x^2-2x}{x^2-5x-6}$ in simplest form? State any restrictions on the variable.
ANSWER $\dfrac{3}{6+x}; x \neq -1,$ $x \neq 0, x \neq 2, x \neq 6, x \neq -6$

4. Which jewelry box uses less material for the bottom and for the lid if the perimeters of the boxes are the same: a jewelry box shaped like a circle or a jewelry box shaped like a regular hexagon?
ANSWER circle

Answers

Got It?

1. a. $-\dfrac{4x}{y}; x \neq 0, y \neq 0$

b. $\dfrac{x+4}{x-3}; x \neq 2 \text{ or } 3$

c. $-\dfrac{4}{x+3}; x \neq \pm 3$

2. $\dfrac{2(x+1)}{(x+4)^2}; x \neq \pm 4$

3. a. $\dfrac{2x}{x-1}; x \neq 1, -1, -4,$ or 3

b. Six restrictions; 2 in each of the original denominators, and two in the reciprocal of the second rational expression.

Lesson 8-4   529

Problem 4

Q Why express the ratio of $\frac{\text{Area}}{\text{Perimeter}}$ in terms of P? [The perimeter is a shared parameter value. Expressing the ratio in terms of P allows you to compare the ratios.]

Q Are there values for P so $\frac{P}{4\pi}$ is not greater than $\frac{P}{16}$? What are they? Are these values important in the context of the problem? [Yes. If $P = 0$, then $\frac{P}{4\pi} = \frac{P}{16}$. If $P < 0$, then $\frac{P}{4\pi} < \frac{P}{16}$. These values are not possible because you cannot have zero or negative fencing.]

Got It?

Q If you use s to represent the length of a side of an equilateral triangle with given perimeter P, can you also use s to represent the length of the side of the square? Explain. [No; the square's perimeter would be greater than the perimeter of the equilateral triangle.]

3 Lesson Check

Do you know HOW?   ERROR INTERVENTION
• If students do not get the correct answers for Exercises 1–4, have them check their factoring by multiplying.

Do you UNDERSTAND?
• If students have trouble with Exercise 5, ask "What are the factors of $x^2 + 1$?"

Close

Q Why is it important to examine the factors of the original problem to determine variable restrictions? [Some restrictions may not be obvious after factors are divided out and multiplication and division have been performed.]

 Problem 4 Using Rational Expressions to Solve a Problem **STEM**

Construction Your community is building a park. It wants to fence in a play space for toddlers. It wants the maximum area for a given amount of fencing. Which shape, a square or a circle, provides a more efficient use of fencing?

One measure of efficiency is the ratio of *area fenced* to *fencing used*, or area to perimeter. Which of the two shapes has the greater ratio?

Square		Circle
Area $= s^2$	Define area and perimeter.	Area $= \pi r^2$
Perimeter $= 4s$		Perimeter $= 2\pi r$
$s = \frac{P}{4}$	Express s and r in terms of a common variable, P.	$r = \frac{P}{2\pi}$
$\frac{\text{Area}}{\text{Perimeter}} = \frac{s^2}{P}$	Write the ratios.	$\frac{\text{Area}}{\text{Perimeter}} = \frac{\pi r^2}{P}$
$= \frac{\left(\frac{P}{4}\right)^2}{P}$	Substitute for s and r.	$= \frac{\pi\left(\frac{P}{2\pi}\right)^2}{P}$
$= \frac{P}{16}$	Simplify.	$= \frac{P}{4\pi}$

Think

How can you compare $\frac{P}{16}$ and $\frac{P}{4\pi}$ without evaluating P?
Since the numerators are the same, the fraction with the smaller denominator is the larger fraction.

Since $\frac{P}{4\pi} > \frac{P}{16}$, a circle provides a more efficient use of fencing.

Check Assume $P = 40$ ft. The area of the circle is $\pi\left(\frac{40}{2\pi}\right)^2 \approx 127$ ft^2. The area of the square is $\left(\frac{40}{4}\right)^2 = 100$ ft^2. The area of the circle is greater.

Got It? 4. Which shape of play space provides for a more efficient use of fencing, a square or an equilateral triangle? (*Hint:* The area of an equilateral triangle in terms of one side is $\frac{1}{2}(s)\left(\frac{\sqrt{3}}{2}s\right)$. The perimeter of an equilateral triangle is $3s$.)

Lesson Check

Do you know HOW?

Simplify each rational expression. State any restrictions on the variables.

1. $\frac{4z - 12}{8z + 24}$

2. $\frac{3x - 3}{x^2 - x}$

Multiply or divide. State any restrictions on the variables.

3. $\frac{x^2 + 3x - 10}{x^2 + 4x - 12} \cdot \frac{3x + 18}{x + 3}$

4. $\frac{x^2 - 7x + 10}{x^2 - 8x + 15} \div \frac{4 - x^2}{x^2 + 3x - 18}$

Do you UNDERSTAND?   MATHEMATICAL PRACTICES

5. Vocabulary Is the equation $y = \frac{x + 1}{x^2 + 1}$ in simplest form? Explain how you can tell.

6. Error Analysis A student claims that $x = 2$ is the only solution of the equation $\frac{x}{x - 2} = \frac{2}{x - 2}$. Is the student correct? Explain.

7. Reasoning The width of the rectangle is $\frac{a + 10}{3a + 24}$. Write an expression for the length of the rectangle in simplest form.

[Rectangle with $\frac{2a + 20}{3a + 15}$ and w on the sides, ℓ on the bottom]

---

3 Lesson Check

For a digital lesson check, use the Got It questions.

Support in Algebra 2 Companion
• Lesson Check

4 Practice

ONLINE HOMEWORK

Assign homework to individual students or to an entire class.

Answers

Got It? (continued)

4. a square

Lesson Check

1. $\frac{z - 3}{2(z + 3)}$; $z \neq -3$

2. $\frac{3}{x}$; $x \neq 0$ or 1

3. $\frac{3(x + 5)}{x + 3}$; $x \neq -3, -6,$ or 2

4. $-\frac{x + 6}{x + 2}$; $x \neq -6, -2, 2, 3,$ or 5

5. Yes; the numerator and denominator are polynomials with no common factor.

6. No; $x = 2$ will make the denominator of $\frac{x}{x - 2}$ equal to 0, so $x = 2$ is not a solution. There is no solution to the eq.

7. Length $= \frac{2(a + 8)}{a + 5}$; $a < -8$ or $a > -5$, $a \neq -10$

Practice and Problem-Solving Exercises MATHEMATICAL PRACTICES

A Practice

Simplify each rational expression. State any restrictions on the variables.

See Problem 1.

8. $-\dfrac{5x^3y}{15xy^3}$

9. $\dfrac{2x}{4x^2 - 2x}$

10. $\dfrac{6c^2 + 9c}{3c}$

11. $\dfrac{49 - z^2}{z + 7}$

12. $\dfrac{x^2 + 8x + 16}{x^2 - 2x - 24}$

13. $\dfrac{12 - x - x^2}{x^2 - 8x + 15}$

Multiply. State any restrictions on the variables.

See Problem 2.

14. $\dfrac{4x^2}{5y} \cdot \dfrac{7y}{12x^4}$

15. $\dfrac{2x^4}{10y^{-2}} \cdot \dfrac{5y^3}{4x^3}$

16. $\dfrac{8y - 4}{10y - 5} \cdot \dfrac{5y - 15}{3y - 9}$

17. $\dfrac{2x + 12}{3x - 9} \cdot \dfrac{6 - 2x}{3x + 8}$

18. $\dfrac{x^2 - 4}{x^2 - 1} \cdot \dfrac{x + 1}{x^2 + 2x}$

19. $\dfrac{x^2 - 5x + 6}{x^2 - 4} \cdot \dfrac{x^2 + 3x + 2}{x^2 - 2x - 3}$

Divide. State any restrictions on the variables.

See Problem 3.

20. $\dfrac{7x}{4y^3} \div \dfrac{21x^3}{8y}$

21. $\dfrac{3x^3}{5y^2} \div \dfrac{6y^{-3}}{5x^{-5}}$

22. $\dfrac{6x + 6y}{y - x} \div \dfrac{18}{5x - 5y}$

23. $\dfrac{3y - 12}{2y + 4} \div \dfrac{6y - 24}{8 + 4y}$

24. $\dfrac{x^2}{x^2 + 2x + 1} \div \dfrac{3x}{x^2 - 1}$

25. $\dfrac{y^2 - 5y + 6}{y^3} \div \dfrac{y^2 + 3y - 10}{4y^2}$

STEM **26. Industrial Design** A storage tank will have a circular base of radius r and a height of r. The tank can be either cylindrical or hemispherical (half a sphere).

See Problem 4.

　　a. Write and simplify an expression for the ratio of the volume of the hemispherical tank to its surface area (including the base). For a sphere, $V = \frac{4}{3}\pi r^3$ and $SA = 4\pi r^2$.

　　b. Write and simplify an expression for the ratio of the volume of the cylindrical tank to its surface area (including the bases).

　　c. Compare the ratios of volume to surface area for the two tanks.

　　d. Compare the volumes of the two tanks.

　　e. Describe how you used these ratios to compare the volumes? Which measurement of the tanks determines the volumes?

B Apply

Simplify each rational expression. State any restrictions on the variables.

27. $\dfrac{x^2 - 5x - 24}{x^2 - 7x - 30}$

28. $\dfrac{2y^2 + 8y - 24}{2y^2 - 8y + 8}$

29. $\dfrac{xy^3 - 9xy}{12xy^2 + 12xy - 144x}$

30. Open-Ended Write three rational expressions that simplify to $\frac{x}{x + 1}$.

---

4 Practice

ASSIGNMENT GUIDE

Basic: 8–26 all, 27, 31–33, 37

Average: 9–25 odd, 27–44

Advanced: 9–25 odd, 27–49

Standardized Test Prep: 50–53

Mixed Review: 54–67

Ⓒ Mathematical Practices are supported by exercises with red headings. Here are the Practices supported in this lesson:

MP 1: Make Sense of Problems Ex. 31

MP 2: Reason Quantitatively Ex. 7, 36

MP 3: Construct Arguments Ex. 30, 45

MP 3: Critique the Reasoning of Others Ex. 6

Applications exercises have blue headings.

Exercises 26 and 37 support MP 4: Model.

EXERCISE 37: Use the Think About a Plan worksheet in the **Practice and Problem Solving Workbook** (also available in the Teaching Resources in print and online) to further support students' development in becoming independent learners.

HOMEWORK QUICK CHECK

To check students' understanding of key skills and concepts, go over Exercises 15, 21, 27, 31, and 37.

Practice and Problem-Solving Exercises

8. $-\dfrac{x^2}{3y^2}$; $x \neq 0$, $y \neq 0$

9. $\dfrac{1}{2x - 1}$; $x \neq 0$ or $\frac{1}{2}$

10. $2c + 3$; $c \neq 0$

11. $7 - z$; $z \neq -7$

12. $\dfrac{x + 4}{x - 6}$; $x \neq 6$ or -4

13. $-\dfrac{x + 4}{x - 5}$; $x \neq 5$ or 3

14. $\dfrac{7}{15x^2}$; $x \neq 0$, $y \neq 0$

15. $\dfrac{xy^5}{4}$; $x \neq 0$, $y \neq 0$

16. $\dfrac{4}{3}$; $y \neq \frac{1}{2}$ or 3

17. $-\dfrac{4(x + 6)}{3(3x + 8)}$; $x \neq 3$ or $-\frac{8}{3}$

18. $\dfrac{x - 2}{x(x - 1)}$; $x \neq 0, 1, -1$, or -2

19. 1; $x \neq -2, -1, 2$, or 3

20. $\dfrac{2}{3x^2y^2}$; $x \neq 0$, $y \neq 0$

21. $\dfrac{y}{2x^2}$; $x \neq 0$, $y \neq 0$

22. $\dfrac{-5(x + y)}{3}$; $x \neq y$

23. 1; $y \neq -2$ or 4

24. $\dfrac{x(x - 1)}{3(x + 1)}$; $x \neq -1, 1$, or 0

25. $\dfrac{4(y - 3)}{y(y + 5)}$; $y \neq 2, -5$, or 0

26. a. $\dfrac{\frac{2}{3}\pi r^3}{2\pi r^2 + \pi r^2} = \dfrac{2r}{9}$

　　b. $\dfrac{\pi r^2(r)}{2\pi r^2 + 2\pi r(r)} = \dfrac{r}{4}$

　　c. The ratio for the cylindrical tank is always larger.

　　d. For a given value of r, the cylindrical tank will have a larger volume.

　　e. You can use the constant part of each ratio. Comparing $\frac{2}{9}$ and $\frac{1}{4}$ tells you that a cylindrical tank will always have a larger volume than a hemispherical tank with the same radius. The radius is the measurement that determines the volume.

27. $\dfrac{x - 8}{x - 10}$; $x \neq -3$ or 10

28. $\dfrac{y + 6}{y - 2}$; $y \neq 2$

29. $\dfrac{y(y + 3)}{12(y + 4)}$; $x \neq 0$, $y \neq -4$ or 3

30. Check students' work.

Lesson 8-4 **531**

Answers

Practice and Problem-Solving Exercises (continued)

31. $R_{cylinder} = \dfrac{V_{cylinder}}{SA_{cylinder}} = \dfrac{rh}{2(r + h)}$;

$R_{cube} = \dfrac{V_{cube}}{SA_{cube}} = \dfrac{s}{6}$; if $r = h = s$, then

$R_{cylinder} = \dfrac{r}{4}$ and $R_{cube} = \dfrac{r}{6}$. $R_{cylinder} > R_{cube}$.

The cylindrical-shaped box is more efficient. If $s = h = 2r$ (diameter), then $R_{cylindrical} = R_{cube}$. The boxes are equally efficient.

32. $\dfrac{4}{x}$; $x \neq 0, -5, 4,$ or 1

33. $\dfrac{18x}{(x + 9)(x + 3)}$; $x \neq -9, -3,$ or 3

34. $\dfrac{x + 1}{x - 4}$; $x \neq -3, \frac{1}{2}, 2,$ or 4

35. $\dfrac{x + 1}{x - 1}$; $x \neq -\frac{1}{2}, \frac{1}{2}, 1,$ or -2

36. a. $\dfrac{6(a + 1)}{a - 3}$

    b. You analyze the denominators of the dimensions of the rectangle, $a + 3$ and $2a - 6$, and the simplified expression for the area.

    c. Because division by zero is undefined, $a \neq 3$ and $a \neq -3$. Since length and area must be positive, $a < -3$ or $a > 3$.

37. They are equally efficient.

38. sometimes

39. never

40. always

41. never

42. $\dfrac{x(x - 1)^3}{x + 4}$; $x \neq -4, 0,$ or 1

43. 2; $x \neq -3$ or 1

44. $\dfrac{18x^5}{y^2}$; $x \neq 0, y \neq 0$

45. a. $2x^n + 1$

    b. 2 is a factor of $2x^n$, so $2x^n$ is even and $2x^n + 1$ is odd.

46. $\dfrac{4x}{3y}$; $x \neq 0$ or $-1, y \neq 0$

47. $\dfrac{-3a^2b^2}{4}$; $a \neq 0, a \neq b, b \neq 0$

48. $\dfrac{15}{4n^2}$; $m \neq 0, m \neq -\frac{2}{3}n, n \neq 0$

49. $\dfrac{(x + 1)(x + 5)}{(x - 3)(x + 4)}$; $x \neq 3, -3, -4, 1,$ or -5

---

31. Think About a Plan A cereal company wants to use the most efficient packaging for their new product. They are considering a cylindrical-shaped box and a cube-shaped box. Compare the ratios of the volume to the surface area of the containers to determine which packaging will be more efficient.
- How can you measure the cereal box's efficiency?
- What formulas will you need to use to solve this problem?

Multiply or divide. State any restrictions on the variables.

32. $\dfrac{6x^3 - 6x^2}{x^4 + 5x^3} \div \dfrac{3x^2 - 15x + 12}{2x^2 + 2x - 40}$

33. $\dfrac{2x^2 - 6x}{x^2 + 18x + 81} \cdot \dfrac{9x + 81}{x^2 - 9}$

34. $\dfrac{x^2 - x - 2}{2x^2 - 5x + 2} \div \dfrac{x^2 - x - 12}{2x^2 + 5x - 3}$

35. $\dfrac{2x^2 + 5x + 2}{4x^2 - 1} \cdot \dfrac{2x^2 + x - 1}{x^2 + x - 2}$

36. a. Reasoning Write a simplified expression for the area of the rectangle at the right.

    b. Which parts of the expression do you analyze to determine the restrictions on a? Explain.

    c. State all restrictions on a.

$\dfrac{4a + 4}{a + 3}$

$\dfrac{3a + 9}{2a - 6}$

STEM 37. Manufacturing A toy company is considering a cube or sphere-shaped container for packaging a new product. The height of the cube would equal the diameter of the sphere. Compare the volume-to-surface area ratios of the containers. Which packaging will be more efficient? For a sphere, $SA = 4\pi r^2$.

Decide whether the given statement is *always*, *sometimes*, or *never* true.

38. Rational expressions contain exponents.

39. Rational expressions contain logarithms.

40. Rational expressions are undefined for values of the variables that make the denominator 0.

41. Restrictions on variables change when a rational expression is simplified.

Simplify. State any restrictions on the variables.

42. $\dfrac{(x^2 - x)^2}{x(x - 1)^{-2}(x^2 + 3x - 4)}$

43. $\dfrac{2x + 6}{(x - 1)^{-1}(x^2 + 2x - 3)}$

44. $\dfrac{54x^3y^{-1}}{3x^{-2}y}$

Challenge 45. a. Reasoning Simplify $\dfrac{(2x^n)^2 - 1}{2x^n - 1}$, where x is an integer and n is a positive integer. (*Hint:* Factor the numerator.)

    b. Use the result from part (a). Which part(s) of the expression can you use to show that the value of the expression is always odd? Explain.

Use the fact that $\dfrac{\frac{a}{b}}{\frac{c}{d}} = \dfrac{a}{b} \div \dfrac{c}{d}$ **to simplify each rational expression. State any restrictions on the variables.**

46. $\dfrac{\frac{8x^2y}{x + 1}}{\frac{6xy^2}{x + 1}}$

47. $\dfrac{\frac{3a^3b^3}{a - b}}{\frac{4ab}{b - a}}$

48. $\dfrac{\frac{9m + 6n}{m^2n^2}}{\frac{12m + 8n}{5m^2}}$

49. $\dfrac{\frac{x^2 - 1}{x^2 - 9}}{\frac{x^2 + 3x - 4}{x^2 + 8x + 15}}$

50. Which function is graphed at the right?

Ⓐ $y = (x + 4)(x - 1)(x + 2)$

Ⓑ $y = (x - 4)(x - 1)(x + 2)$

Ⓒ $y = (x - 4)(x + 1)(x - 2)$

Ⓓ $y = (x + 4)(x + 1)(x - 2)$

51. Which function generates the table of values at the right?

Ⓕ $y = \log_{\frac{1}{2}} x$

Ⓖ $y = -\log_2 x$

Ⓗ $y = \log_2 x$

Ⓘ $y = \left(\frac{1}{2}\right)^x$

x	y
$\frac{1}{2}$	-1
1	0
2	1
4	2

52. Which expression equals $\dfrac{x}{x^2 - 2x - 3} \cdot \dfrac{2x - 6}{x^2 - 4x + 3}$?

Ⓐ $\dfrac{2x - 1}{(x - 1)(x + 3)(x + 1)}$

Ⓑ $\dfrac{2x + 1}{(x - 1)(x + 1)(x - 3)}$

Ⓒ $\dfrac{2x}{(x - 1)(x + 1)(x - 3)}$

Ⓓ $\dfrac{2x}{(x + 3)(x - 1)(x + 1)}$

53. What is the solution of the equation $3^{-x} = \frac{1}{243}$?

Mixed Review

Find the vertical asymptotes and holes for the graph of each rational function. ◀ **See Lesson 8-3.**

54. $y = \dfrac{x - 3}{x - 3}$

55. $y = \dfrac{x - 1}{(3x + 2)(x + 1)}$

56. $y = \dfrac{(x - 4)(x + 5)}{(x + 3)(x - 4)}$

Evaluate each logarithm. ◀ **See Lesson 7-3.**

57. $\log_4 64$

58. $\log_2 \frac{1}{32}$

59. $\log_5 5\sqrt{5}$

60. $\log_{16} 8$

Solve. Check for extraneous solutions. ◀ **See Lesson 6-5.**

61. $\sqrt{x} - 3 = 4$

62. $\sqrt{x + 1} - 5 = 8$

63. $\sqrt{5x - 3} = \sqrt{2x + 3}$

Get Ready! To prepare for Lesson 8-5, do Exercises 64–67.

Add or Subtract. ◀ **See p. 973.**

64. $\frac{5}{19} + \frac{7}{38}$

65. $\frac{2}{15} + \frac{3}{25}$

66. $\frac{7}{24} - \frac{5}{36}$

67. $\frac{11}{12} - \frac{7}{45}$

Standardized Test Prep

50. D

51. H

52. C

53. [2] $-x \log 3 = \log \frac{1}{243}$

$$-x = \frac{\log \frac{1}{243}}{\log 3}$$

$$-x = -5$$

$$x = 5$$

[1] correct answer, without work shown

Mixed Review

54. hole at $x = 3$

55. vert. asymptotes at $x = -\frac{2}{3}$ and $x = -1$

56. hole at $x = 4$, vert. asymptote at $x = -3$

57. 3

58. -5

59. $\frac{3}{2}$

60. $\frac{3}{4}$

61. 49

62. 168

63. 2

64. $\frac{17}{38}$

65. $\frac{19}{75}$

66. $\frac{11}{72}$

67. $\frac{137}{180}$

Additional Instructional Support

Algebra 2 Companion

Students can use the **Algebra 2 Companion** worktext (4 pages) as you teach the lesson. Use the Companion to support
- New Vocabulary
- Key Concepts
- Got It for each Problem
- Lesson Check

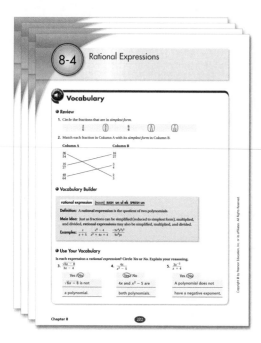

ELL Support

Focus on Communication Have students write out instructions as a list of steps to solve Lesson Check Exercise 3 or 4. Pair students with different problems and have them trade instruction steps. Students should then solve the other exercise following the exact instruction steps. Student pairs should then orally help each other revise their instructions as necessary to be complete and accurate.

5 Assess & Remediate

Lesson Quiz

1. What is $\dfrac{x^2 + x - 12}{x^2 + 2x - 8}$ in simplest form? State any restrictions on the variable.

2. What is the product $\dfrac{x + 3}{x^2 - 9} \cdot \dfrac{x^2 + 2x - 15}{x^2 - 2x + 1}$ in simplest form? State any restrictions on the variable.

3. What is the quotient $\dfrac{16 - x^2}{x^2 + 2x - 3} \div \dfrac{x - 4}{x^2 + 4x + 3}$ in simplest form? State any restrictions on the variable.

4. **Do you UNDERSTAND?** A friend gives you a puppy for your birthday and offers to buy fencing for a dog run. For a given amount of fencing, what shape gives your puppy more area to run: a rectangle whose length is twice the width or a regular hexagon?

ANSWERS TO LESSON QUIZ

1. $\dfrac{x - 3}{x - 2}$; $x \neq -4$, $x \neq 2$

2. $\dfrac{x + 5}{(x - 1)^2}$; $x \neq 3$, $x \neq -3$, $x \neq 1$

3. $-\dfrac{(x + 4)(x + 1)}{x - 1}$, $x \neq 1$, $x \neq -3$, $x \neq 4$ $x \neq -1$

4. regular hexagon

PRESCRIPTION FOR REMEDIATION

Use the student work on the Lesson Quiz to prescribe a differentiated review assignment:

Points	Differentiated Remediation
0–2	Intervention
3	On-level
4	Extension

PowerAlgebra.com

5 Assess & Remediate

Assign the Lesson Quiz. Appropriate intervention, practice, or enrichment is automatically generated based on student performance.

Differentiated Remediation

Intervention

- **Reteaching** (2 pages) Provides reteaching and practice exercises for the key lesson concepts. Use with struggling students or absent students.

- **English Language Learner Support** Helps students develop and reinforce mathematical vocabulary and key concepts.

All-in-One Resources/Online
Reteaching

All-in-One Resources/Online
English Language Learner Support

Differentiated Remediation *continued*

On-Level

- **Practice** (2 pages) Provides extra practice for each lesson. For simpler practice exercises, use the Form K Practice pages found in the All-in-One Teaching Resources and online.

- **Think About a Plan** Helps students develop specific problem-solving skills and strategies by providing scaffolded guiding questions.

- **Standardized Test Prep** Focuses on all major exercises, all major question types, and helps students prepare for the high-stakes assessments.

Extension

- **Enrichment** Provides students with interesting problems and activities that extend the concepts of the lesson.

- **Activities, Games, and Puzzles** Worksheets that can be used for concepts development, enrichment, and for fun!

Practice and Problem Solving Wkbk/ All-in-One Resources/Online
Practice page 1

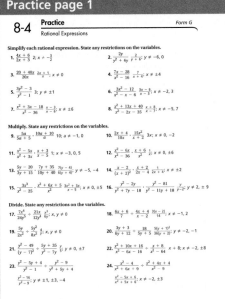

8-4 **Practice** — Form G
Rational Expressions

Simplify each rational expression. State any restrictions on the variables.

Practice and Problem Solving Wkbk/ All-in-One Resources/Online
Practice page 2

8-4 **Practice** *(continued)* — Form G
Rational Expressions

25. A farmer must decide whether to build a cylindrical grain silo or a rectangular grain silo. The cylindrical silo has radius *r*. The rectangular silo has width *r* and length 2*r*. Both silos have the same height *h*.

All-in-One Resources/Online
Enrichment

8-4 **Enrichment**
Rational Expressions

Practice and Problem Solving Wkbk/ All-in-One Resources/Online
Think About a Plan

8-4 **Think About a Plan**
Rational Expressions

Manufacturing A toy company is considering a cube or sphere-shaped container for packaging a new product. The height of the cube would equal the diameter of the sphere. Compare the ratios of the volumes to the surface areas of the containers. Which packaging will be more efficient? For a sphere, $SA = 4\pi r^2$.

Practice and Problem Solving Wkbk/ All-in-One Resources/Online
Standardized Test Prep

8-4 **Standardized Test Prep**
Rational Expressions

Online Teacher Resource Center
Activities, Games, and Puzzles

8-4 **Puzzle: Multiply and Conquer**
Rational Expressions

1 Interactive Learning

Solve It!

PURPOSE To review finding the least common multiple (LCM)

PROCESS Students may
- make a table of minutes with a row for each runner and columns for numbers of laps.
- guess and check using multiples of 2 minutes.
- write each rate as a decimal fraction and find the LCM of the rates.

FACILITATE

Q How long will it take each runner to go 3 laps? **[Sue 4:30, Drew 6:00, Stu 3:36, Marylou 4:00]**

Q Where on the track are Sue, Drew, and Stu after 6 minutes? **[All at the same spot, just on different laps.]**

Q How do you know that the solution will be a multiple of 2 minutes? **[Drew has the slowest rate—one lap every 2 minutes. The solution must be a multiple of his rate.]**

ANSWER See Solve It in Answers on next page.
CONNECT THE MATH To answer the Solve It, students add or subtract fractions by finding the LCM of the denominators. In the lesson they will use the same method to add and subtract rational expressions.

2 Guided Instruction

Problem 1

Q What does *prime factor* mean? **[Prime factor means a factor that cannot be divided evenly by any factors except 1 and itself.]**

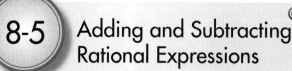
Objective To add and subtract rational expressions

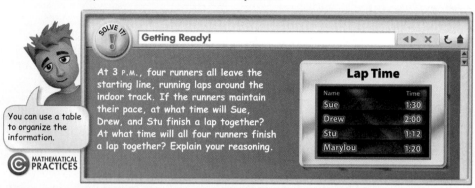

You use common multiples of polynomials to add and subtract rational expressions, just as you use common multiples of numbers to add and subtract fractions.

Essential Understanding To operate with rational expressions, you can use much of what you know about operating with fractions.

To add or subtract rational expressions, you first find a common denominator—preferably the least common multiple (LCM) of the denominators.

To find the LCM of several expressions, factor the expressions (numbers or polynomials) completely. The LCM is the product of the prime factors, each raised to the greatest power that occurs in any of the expressions.

Lesson Vocabulary
• complex fraction

© **Problem 1** Finding the Least Common Multiple

Plan

How do you determine the exponent of each factor for the LCM?
Use the exponent from the expression that has that factor to the greatest power.

What is the LCM of $12x^2y(x^2 + 2x + 1)$ and $18xy^3(x^2 + 5x + 4)$?

Step 1 Find the prime factors of each expression.

$$12x^2y(x^2 + 2x + 1) = 2^2 \cdot 3x^2y(x + 1)^2$$

$$18xy^3(x^2 + 5x + 4) = 2 \cdot 3^2xy^3(x + 1)(x + 4)$$

Step 2 Write the product of the prime factors, each raised to the greatest power that occurs in either expression.

$$2^2 \cdot 3^2x^2y^3(x + 1)^2(x + 4)$$

The LCM is $2^2 \cdot 3^2x^2y^3(x + 1)^2(x + 4)$, or $36x^2y^3(x + 1)^2(x + 4)$.

8-5 Preparing to Teach

BIG ideas Function
Equivalence

ESSENTIAL UNDERSTANDINGS
- Much of what is true about operating with fractions can be used to operate with rational expressions. Rational expressions can be added or subtracted by first finding a common denominator—preferably the least common multiple (LCM) of the denominators.
- The LCM of denominators is the product of their prime factors, each raised to the greatest power that occurs in any of the expressions.

Math Background
Rational expressions can be added and subtracted using the same methods as for adding and subtracting fractions.
- Factor the denominators.
- Find the LCM of the denominators, which will be the LCD (least common denominator).
- Rewrite each expression with the LCD by multiplying by the necessary factors.

- Add or subtract the numerators, combining like terms.
- Factor the numerator.
- Simplify the expression by dividing out any common factors.

A complex fraction is a rational expression that contains fractions in the numerator and/or denominator. To simplify a complex fraction,
- combine the fractions in the numerator and denominator,
- multiply the fraction in the numerator by the reciprocal of the fraction in the denominator, and
- simplify by dividing out any common factors.

In order for the simplified result to be equivalent to the original form, it is necessary to note which values of *x* must be excluded from the domain to allow for the simplification.

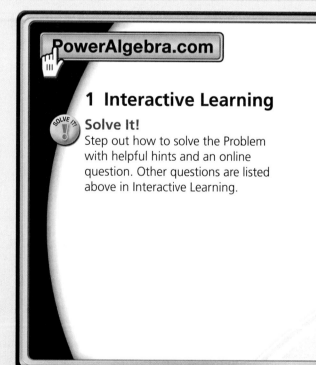

PowerAlgebra.com

1 Interactive Learning

Solve It!
Step out how to solve the Problem with helpful hints and an online question. Other questions are listed above in Interactive Learning.

Got It? **1.** What is the LCM of the expressions?

  a. $2x + 4$ and $x^2 - x - 6$

  b. $x^2 + 3x - 4$, $x^2 + 2x - 8$, and $x^2 - 4x + 4$

The LCM of the denominators of two rational expressions is also the Least Common Denominator (LCD) of the rational expressions. You can use the LCD to add or subtract the expressions.

Recall how you used the LCD to add fractions.

$$\frac{1}{8} + \frac{1}{10} = \frac{1}{2^3} + \frac{1}{2 \cdot 5} = \frac{1}{2^3}\left(\frac{5}{5}\right) + \frac{1}{2 \cdot 5}\left(\frac{2^2}{2^2}\right) = \frac{5}{40} + \frac{4}{40} = \frac{9}{40}$$

 Problem 2 Adding Rational Expressions

Plan

How does the LCD help you simplify this sum?
The LCD is $(x - 1)(x - 2)$. Multiply the first expression by $\frac{x-2}{x-2}$ to get a common denominator.

What is the sum of the two rational expressions in simplest form? State any restrictions on the variable. $\frac{x}{x-1} + \frac{2x-1}{x^2-3x+2}$

$$\frac{x}{x-1} + \frac{2x-1}{x^2-3x+2} = \frac{x}{x-1} + \frac{2x-1}{(x-1)(x-2)} \qquad \text{Factor the denominators.}$$

$$= \frac{x}{x-1} \cdot \frac{x-2}{x-2} + \frac{2x-1}{(x-1)(x-2)} \qquad \text{Rewrite each expression with the LCD.}$$

$$= \frac{x^2-2x}{(x-1)(x-2)} + \frac{2x-1}{(x-1)(x-2)}$$

$$= \frac{x^2-2x+2x-1}{(x-1)(x-2)} \qquad \text{Add the numerators. Combine like terms.}$$

$$= \frac{x^2-1}{(x-1)(x-2)}$$

$$= \frac{(x-1)(x+1)}{(x-1)(x-2)} \qquad \text{Factor the numerator and divide out the common factors.}$$

$$= \frac{x+1}{x-2}, x \neq 1$$

The sum of the expressions is $\frac{x+1}{x-2}$ for $x \neq 1$ and $x \neq 2$.

 Got It? **2.** What is the sum of the two rational expressions in simplest form? State any restrictions on the variable.

  a. $\frac{x+1}{x-1} + \frac{-2}{x^2-x}$

  b. $\frac{x}{x^2-4} + \frac{1}{x+2}$

  c. **Reasoning** Is it possible to add the rational expressions in Problem 2 by finding a common denominator, but not the *least* common denominator? Explain.

Got It?

Q In 1a, what prime factor do the two expressions share? **[x + 2]**

Q Under what circumstance would simply multiplying the expressions result in the LCM? **[When the expressions share no common factors, then the product of the expressions is the LCM.]**

Problem 2

Q Why is the LCM $(x - 1)(x - 2)$ and not $(x - 1)^2(x - 2)$? **[Common factors indicate the greatest number of times they appear in either expression, not both.]**

Q What does the second expression need to be multiplied by in order to add the expressions? Explain. **[Nothing; the denominator of the second expression already contains both factors that make up the LCD of the two expressions.]**

Q Once you add the two numerators, why not multiply the factors of the denominator to get a simpler form? **[Once you simplify the numerator you need to factor the numerator and look for common factors in the numerator and denominator.]**

Got It?

Q After finding the LCD in 2a, the sum is $\frac{x^2 + x - 2}{x(x-1)}$. Is this expression in simplest form? Explain. **[No. $x^2 + x - 2 = (x + 2)(x - 1)$. The $(x - 1)$ factors in the numerator and denominator can be divided out.]**

---

2 Guided Instruction

 Each Problem is worked out and supported online.

Problem 1
Finding the Least Common Multiple

Problem 2
Adding Rational Expressions
Animated

Problem 3
Subtracting Rational Expressions
Animated

Alternative Problem 3
Subtracting Rational Expressions

Problem 4
Simplifying a Complex Fraction
Animated

Problem 5
Using Rational Expressions to Solve a Problem

Support in Algebra 2 Companion
• Vocabulary
• Key Concepts
• Got It?

Answers

Solve It!
3:06 P.M.; 3:12 P.M.; Explanations may vary. Sample: Convert the times to seconds, and test times that are multiples of 120 s to see if they are divisible by the other runners' lap times. After 360 s, or 6 min, Sue, Drew, and Stu will finish a lap together, at 3:06 P.M. Then you can test multiples of 360s for divisibility by 80 s, Marylou's lap time. After 720 s, or 12 min, all four runners finish a lap together, at 3:12 P.M.

Got It?
1. a. $2(x + 2)(x - 3)$
  b. $(x - 1)(x - 2)^2(x + 4)$

2. a. $\frac{x + 2}{x}, x \neq 1$ or 0

  b. $\frac{2(x - 1)}{x^2 - 4}; x \neq \pm 2$

  c. Yes, however the denominator would have to be factored more and there could be additional, incorrect limitations on x.

Problem 3

Q What do you need to watch for when you subtract the $\frac{x^2 + 2x}{2x(x - 2)}$ term? **[that you distribute the negative sign to both terms in the numerator]**

Q How does $\frac{x + 2}{x^2 - 2x} - \frac{x + 2}{2x - 4}$ differ from $-\frac{x + 2}{2x}$? **[The first expression has a discontinuity at $x = 2$, while $-\frac{x + 2}{2x}$ is defined at $x = 2$.]**

Q If two rational expressions are functions, is the sum or difference of the expressions also a function? Explain. **[Yes. The definition of a function states that for each x-value the function will return a single y-value. The sum or difference of two y-values at any x will also be a single value at that x, and thus the sum or difference of the two expressions is a function.]**

Got It?

ERROR PREVENTION

When multiplying expressions to get a common denominator, students should multiply out the numerators but leave the denominator factored.

Q What is the difference between the restrictions on the problems and on the answers? **[No difference; they are the same.]**

Problem 3 Subtracting Rational Expressions

What is the difference of the two rational expressions in simplest form? State any restrictions on the variable. $\frac{x + 2}{x^2 - 2x} - \frac{x + 2}{2x - 4}$

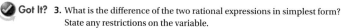

Plan

How is this problem similar to Problem 2? The method is the same except you subtract the rational expressions instead of adding them.

$$\frac{x + 2}{x^2 - 2x} - \frac{x + 2}{2x - 4} = \frac{x + 2}{x(x - 2)} - \frac{x + 2}{2(x - 2)} \qquad \text{Factor the denominators.}$$

The LCD is $2x(x - 2)$.

$$= \frac{x + 2}{x(x - 2)} \cdot \frac{2}{2} - \frac{x + 2}{2(x - 2)} \cdot \frac{x}{x} \qquad \text{Rewrite each expression with the LCD.}$$

$$= \frac{2(x + 2)}{2x(x - 2)} - \frac{x(x + 2)}{2x(x - 2)}$$

$$= \frac{2x + 4}{2x(x - 2)} - \frac{x^2 + 2x}{2x(x - 2)} \qquad \text{Simplify the numerators.}$$

$$= \frac{2x + 4 - (x^2 + 2x)}{2x(x - 2)} \qquad \text{Subtract the numerators.}$$

$$= \frac{-x^2 + 4}{2x(x - 2)} \qquad \text{Combine like terms.}$$

$$= \frac{-(x^2 - 4)}{2x(x - 2)} \qquad \text{Factor } -1 \text{ from the numerator.}$$

$$= \frac{-(x - 2)(x + 2)}{2x(x - 2)} \qquad \text{Factor } x^2 - 4 \text{ and divide out the common factors.}$$

$$= \frac{-(x + 2)}{2x}$$

The difference is $\frac{-(x + 2)}{2x}$ for $x \neq 2$ and $x \neq 0$.

✓ **Got It? 3.** What is the difference of the two rational expressions in simplest form? State any restrictions on the variable.

a. $\frac{x + 3}{x - 2} - \frac{6x - 7}{x^2 - 3x + 2}$ **b.** $\frac{x - 1}{x + 5} - \frac{x + 3}{x^2 + 6x + 5}$

A **complex fraction** is a rational expression that has at least one fraction in its numerator or denominator or both. Here are some examples.

$$\frac{\frac{1}{x} + \frac{1}{y}}{\frac{1}{xy}} \qquad \frac{\frac{x + 3}{2}}{\frac{2}{x - 4}} \qquad \frac{\frac{x + 3}{x^2 - 2x + 1} + \frac{x}{x^2 - 3x + 2}}{\frac{x}{x^2 - 4x + 4} - \frac{2}{x^2 - 4}}$$

Additional Problems

1. What is the LCM of $x^2 + 4x - 12$, and $x^2 - 6x + 8$?

ANSWER
$(x - 2)(x - 4)(x + 6)$

2. What is the sum $\frac{4}{x^2 + 3x} + \frac{x - 2}{x^2 + 6x + 9}$ in simplest form? State any restrictions on the variable.

ANSWER $\frac{x^2 + 2x + 12}{x(x + 3)^2}$; $x \neq 0, x \neq -3$

3. What is the difference $\frac{x + 1}{x^2 + 2x - 8} - \frac{x}{4x - 8}$ in simplest form? State any restrictions on the variable.

ANSWER $\frac{-(x + 2)}{4(x + 4)}$; $x \neq 2$, $x \neq -4$

4. What is a simpler form of $\frac{3x - \frac{1}{y}}{\frac{y^2}{x} + x}$?

ANSWER $\frac{3x^2y - x}{x^2y + y^3}$

5. Your Internet connection has a download speed of 1400 kilobytes per second (kb/s) and an upload speed of 350 kb/s. If you download a picture to your computer and then upload the same picture to your blog, what is the combined rate for the entire process?

ANSWER 560 kb/s

Answers

Got It? (continued)

3. a. $\frac{x - 2}{x - 1}$, $x \neq 1$ or 2

b. $\frac{x^2 - x - 4}{x^2 + 6x + 5}$; $x \neq -5$ or -1

Sometimes you can simplify a complex fraction by multiplying the numerator and the denominator by the LCD of all the rational expressions. You can also simplify them by combining the fractions in the numerator and those in the denominator. Then multiply the new numerator by the reciprocal of the new denominator.

© **Problem 4** **Simplifying a Complex Fraction**

What is a simpler form of the complex fraction?

$$\frac{\frac{1}{x} + \frac{x}{y}}{\frac{1}{y} + 1}$$

Think

What is the LCD of $\frac{1}{x}$, $\frac{x}{y}$, and $\frac{1}{y}$?
The LCD of the rational expressions is xy.

Method 1 Multiply both the numerator and the denominator by the LCD of all the rational expressions and simplify the result.

$$\frac{\frac{1}{x} + \frac{x}{y}}{\frac{1}{y} + 1} = \frac{\left(\frac{1}{x} + \frac{x}{y}\right) \cdot xy}{\left(\frac{1}{y} + 1\right) \cdot xy}$$ Multiply the numerator and the denominator by xy.

$$= \frac{\frac{1}{x} \cdot xy + \frac{x}{y} \cdot xy}{\frac{1}{y} \cdot xy + 1 \cdot xy}$$ Use the Distributive Property.

$$= \frac{y + x^2}{x + xy}$$ Simplify.

Method 2 Combine the expressions in the numerator and those in the denominator. Then multiply the new numerator by the reciprocal of the new denominator.

$$\frac{\frac{1}{x} + \frac{x}{y}}{\frac{1}{y} + 1} = \frac{\frac{1}{x} \cdot \frac{y}{y} + \frac{x}{y} \cdot \frac{x}{x}}{\frac{1}{y} + 1 \cdot \frac{y}{y}}$$ Write equivalent expressions with common denominators.

$$= \frac{\frac{y}{xy} + \frac{x^2}{xy}}{\frac{1}{y} + \frac{y}{y}}$$ Multiply.

$$= \frac{\frac{y + x^2}{xy}}{\frac{1 + y}{y}}$$ Add.

$$= \frac{y + x^2}{xy} \div \frac{1 + y}{y}$$ Divide the numerator fraction by the denominator fraction.

$$= \frac{y + x^2}{xy} \cdot \frac{y}{1 + y}$$ Multiply by the reciprocal.

$$= \frac{y + x^2}{x + xy}$$ Divide out the common factor, y.

Think

How do you divide a fraction by a fraction?
Multiply the numerator by the reciprocal of the denominator.

✔ **Got It?** **4.** What is a simpler form of the complex fraction?

a. $\dfrac{x}{\frac{1}{x} + \frac{1}{y}}$

b. $\dfrac{\frac{x-2}{x} + \frac{2}{x+1}}{\frac{3}{x-1} - \frac{1}{x+1}}$

Problem 4

Q What is a *reciprocal*? **[Sample: A reciprocal r of an expression a is defined so that $ra = 1$. Thus, $r = \frac{1}{a}$. You can find the reciprocal of a rational expression by swapping the numerator and denominator.]**

Q Both methods return the same simplified fraction. How are the methods the same? How are they different? **[Answers may vary. Sample: Both methods multiply all the terms by the LCD of all the rational expressions in the complex fraction. The first method does this all at once. The second method does this in separate steps that may allow for simplifying during the multiplication.]**

Q In the second multiplication step of Method 2, do you have to multiply the numerator of the left expression by y? Explain. **[No, you do not have to multiply by y because it cancels with the y in the denominator of the left expression.]**

Got It?

Have students find the answer to each problem using both Method 1 and Method 2.

Q What types of problems do you think Method 1 is better for? Method 2? **[Answers may vary. Sample: Method 1 is better when the LCM has fewer factors; Method 2 is better for more complicated problems.]**

4. a. $\dfrac{x^2 y}{x + y}$; $x \neq 0, x \neq -y, y \neq 0$

   b. $\dfrac{(x-1)^2}{2x}$; $x \neq -2, -1, 0,$ or 1

Problem 5

ERROR PREVENTION

Students often think that averaging the two rates provides the solution. Help students to focus on the ratio of *total* miles to *total* gallons.

Q An increase from 10 mpg to 11 mpg is what percent increase? from 60 mpg to 80 mpg? **[10%; 33%]**

Q For any distance, *x*, that the SUV and hybrid both drive, what fraction of the total gallons goes to the SUV? to the hybrid? $[\frac{6}{7}; \frac{1}{7}]$

Q Why does Option 1 result in a better combined mpg than Option 2? **[Answers may vary. Sample: The SUV uses so much more gasoline than the hybrid that increasing the efficiency of the hybrid by 33% does not have as great an effect on the combined mpg as increasing the efficiency of the SUV by 10%.]**

EXTENSION

Q What is the combined mpg before any change to the vehicles is made? **[17.1 mpg]**

Got It?

EXTENSION

Q At what mpg of the hybrid would the combined mpg be equal to Option 1 (assuming the SUV remains at 10 mpg)? Write an equation and solve to the nearest whole number. **[133 mpg; $18.6 = \frac{x + x}{\frac{x}{10} + \frac{x}{m}}$, where *m* is the mpg of the hybrid.]**

Q How were you able to solve for two unknowns with only one equation? (the distance, *x*, and the mpg of the hybrid)? **[The distance variable, *x*, cancels out so that a single solution can be found for the mpg of the hybrid.]**

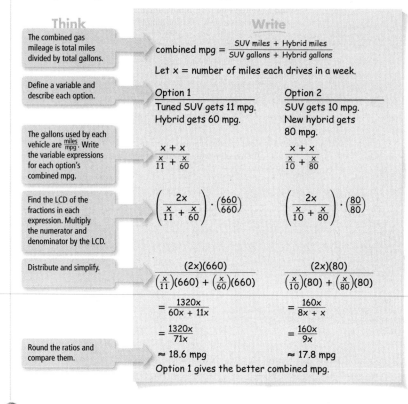

Problem 5 Using Rational Expressions to Solve a Problem

Fuel Economy A woman drives an SUV that gets 10 mi/gal (mpg). Her husband drives a hybrid that gets 60 mpg. Every week, they travel the same number of miles. They want to improve their combined mpg. They have two options on how they can improve it.

Option 1: They can tune the SUV and increase its mileage by 1 mpg and keep the hybrid as it is.

Option 2: They can buy a new hybrid that gets 80 mpg and keep the SUV as it is.

Which option will give them a better combined mpg?

Think

The combined gas mileage is total miles divided by total gallons.

Define a variable and describe each option.

The gallons used by each vehicle are $\frac{miles}{mpg}$. Write the variable expressions for each option's combined mpg.

Find the LCD of the fractions in each expression. Multiply the numerator and denominator by the LCD.

Distribute and simplify.

Round the ratios and compare them.

Write

$$\text{combined mpg} = \frac{\text{SUV miles} + \text{Hybrid miles}}{\text{SUV gallons} + \text{Hybrid gallons}}$$

Let x = number of miles each drives in a week.

Option 1
Tuned SUV gets 11 mpg.
Hybrid gets 60 mpg.

$\frac{x + x}{\frac{x}{11} + \frac{x}{60}}$

$\left(\frac{2x}{\frac{x}{11} + \frac{x}{60}}\right) \cdot \left(\frac{660}{660}\right)$

$\frac{(2x)(660)}{\left(\frac{x}{11}\right)(660) + \left(\frac{x}{60}\right)(660)}$

$= \frac{1320x}{60x + 11x}$

$= \frac{1320x}{71x}$

≈ 18.6 mpg

Option 2
SUV gets 10 mpg.
New hybrid gets 80 mpg.

$\frac{x + x}{\frac{x}{10} + \frac{x}{80}}$

$\left(\frac{2x}{\frac{x}{10} + \frac{x}{80}}\right) \cdot \left(\frac{80}{80}\right)$

$\frac{(2x)(80)}{\left(\frac{x}{10}\right)(80) + \left(\frac{x}{80}\right)(80)}$

$= \frac{160x}{8x + x}$

$= \frac{160x}{9x}$

≈ 17.8 mpg

Option 1 gives the better combined mpg.

Got It? **5.** Suppose Option 3 is to buy a new hybrid that will get double the mileage of the present hybrid. The SUV mileage stays the same. Which of the three options will give the best combined mpg?

Answers

Got It? (continued)

5. Option 1 still gives the better combined mpg since Option 3 gives 18.46 mpg.

Lesson Check

1. $\frac{2a - 10}{3a - 5}$, $a \neq \frac{5}{3}$

2. $\frac{6x - 11}{x^2 - 4}$; $x \neq \pm 2$

3. $\frac{-11m}{3m + 6}$; $m \neq -2$

4. $\frac{-4(2b - 5)}{(b - 4)(b + 4)(b - 2)}$; $b \neq 2$ or ± 4

5. error in dividing by the denominator:

$$\frac{1 + \frac{1}{x}}{\frac{3}{x}} = \frac{\frac{x + 1}{x}}{\frac{3}{x}}$$

$$= \frac{x + 1}{x} \cdot \frac{x}{3}$$

$$= \frac{x + 1}{3}$$

6. Answers may vary. Sample:

$$\frac{x^2 - 1}{x^2 - 6x + 5}, \frac{x^2 + 6x + 5}{x^2 - 25}$$

Practice and Problem-Solving Exercises

7. $9(x + 2)(2x - 1)$

8. $(x - 1)(x + 1)^2$

9. $5(y + 4)(y - 4)$

10. $2(x + 5)(x^2 - 32x - 10)$

11. $\frac{1}{x}$; $x \neq 0$

12. $\frac{2(d - 2)}{2d + 1}$; $d \neq -\frac{1}{2}$

Lesson Check

Do you know HOW?

Simplify each sum or difference. State any restrictions on the variables.

1. $\frac{a+11}{3a-5} + \frac{a-21}{3a-5}$

2. $\frac{1}{x^2-4} + \frac{6}{x+2}$

3. $\frac{m}{3m+6} - \frac{4m}{m+2}$

4. $\frac{b-4}{b^2+2b-8} - \frac{b+2}{b^2-16}$

Do you UNDERSTAND? MATHEMATICAL PRACTICES

5. Error Analysis Describe and correct the error made in simplifying the complex fraction.

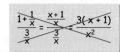

6. Open-Ended Write two rational expressions that simplify to $\frac{x+1}{x-5}$.

Practice and Problem-Solving Exercises MATHEMATICAL PRACTICES

A Practice

Find the least common multiple of each pair of polynomials. ◆ See Problem 1.

7. $9(x+2)(2x-1)$ and $3(x+2)$

8. x^2-1 and x^2+2x+1

9. $5y^2-80$ and $y+4$

10. $x^2-32x-10$ and $2x+10$

Simplify each sum or difference. State any restrictions on the variables. ◆ See Problems 2 and 3.

11. $\frac{1}{2x} + \frac{1}{2x}$

12. $\frac{d-3}{2d+1} + \frac{d-1}{2d+1}$

13. $\frac{-2}{x} - \frac{1}{x}$

14. $\frac{-5y}{2y-1} - \frac{y+3}{2y-1}$

15. $\frac{5y+2}{xy^2} + \frac{2x-4}{4xy}$

16. $\frac{5x}{x^2-9} + \frac{2}{x+4}$

17. $\frac{y}{2y+4} - \frac{3}{y+2}$

18. $\frac{x}{3x+9} - \frac{8}{x^2+3x}$

19. $\frac{-3x}{x^2-9} + \frac{4}{2x-6}$

20. $\frac{5x}{x^2-x-6} + \frac{4}{x^2+4x+4}$

21. $\frac{2x}{x^2-x-2} - \frac{4x}{x^2-3x+2}$

Simplify each complex fraction. ◆ See Problem 4.

22. $\frac{\frac{1}{x}}{\frac{2}{y}}$

23. $\frac{1-\frac{1}{4}}{2-\frac{3}{5}}$

24. $\frac{\frac{2}{x+y}}{3}$

25. $\frac{\frac{1}{3}}{\frac{3}{b}}$

26. $\frac{1}{1+\frac{x}{y}}$

27. $\frac{3}{\frac{2}{x}+y}$

28. $\frac{\frac{2}{x+y}}{\frac{5}{x+y}}$

29. $\frac{\frac{3}{x-4}}{1-\frac{2}{x-4}}$

30. Your car gets 25 mi/gal around town and 30 mi/gal on the highway. ◆ See Problem 5.
  a. If 50% of the miles you drive are on the highway and 50% are around town, what is your overall average miles per gallon?
  b. If 60% of the miles you drive are on the highway and 40% are around town, what is your overall average miles per gallon?

13. $\frac{-3}{x}$; $x \neq 0$

14. $\frac{-3(2y+1)}{2y-1}$; $y \neq \frac{1}{2}$

15. $\frac{xy+8y+4}{2xy^2}$; $x \neq 0, y \neq 0$

16. $\frac{7x^2+20x-18}{(x-3)(x+3)(x+4)}$; $x \neq \pm3$ or -4

17. $\frac{y-6}{2(y+2)}$; $y \neq -2$

18. $\frac{x^2-24}{3x(x+3)}$; $x \neq 0$ or -3

19. $\frac{-x+6}{(x-3)(x+3)}$; $x \neq \pm3$

20. $\frac{5x^2+14x-12}{(x-3)(x+2)^2}$; $x \neq 3$ or -2

21. $\frac{-2x(x+3)}{(x-2)(x-1)(x+1)}$; $x \neq \pm1$ or 2

22. $\frac{y}{2x}$

23. $\frac{15}{28}$

24. $\frac{2}{3(x+y)}$

25. $\frac{b}{9}$

26. $\frac{y}{x+y}$

27. $\frac{3x}{2+xy}$

28. $\frac{2}{5}$

29. $\frac{3}{x-6}$

30. a. about 27.27 mi/gal
   b. about 27.78 mi/gal

3 Lesson Check

Do you know HOW? ERROR INTERVENTION

- If students are unsure how to find restrictions on the variable in Exercises 1–4, have them set the denominator of each rational expression equal to zero. For instance in Exercise 1, solve $3a - 5 = 0$.
- In Exercise 3, be sure that students factor the first denominator before attempting to find the LCD.

Do you UNDERSTAND? ERROR INTERVENTION

- If students have trouble identifying the error in Exercise 5, have them perform the steps in Method 2 of Problem 4 in the lesson.
- The simplest way to answer Exercise 6 is by writing two rational expressions that are multiples of the given expression.

Close

Q Why should you find the *least* common denominator when adding or subtracting rational expressions? **[Answers may vary. Sample: Any common denominator can be used to add or subtract rational expressions, but using the least common denominator means that fewer factors will be multiplied across or canceled out. This makes the calculation simpler.]**

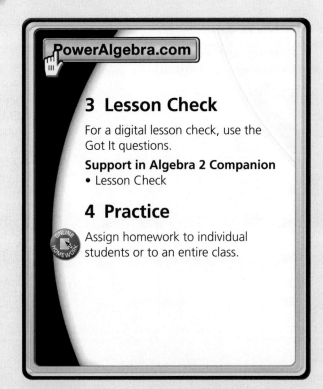

PowerAlgebra.com

3 Lesson Check

For a digital lesson check, use the Got It questions.

Support in Algebra 2 Companion
- Lesson Check

4 Practice

Assign homework to individual students or to an entire class.

4 Practice

ASSIGNMENT GUIDE

Basic: 7–30 all, 31–33, 37, 38, 40, 45

Average: 7–29 odd, 31–45

Advanced: 7–29 odd, 31–47

Standardized Test Prep: 48–52

Mixed Review: 53–65

 **Mathematical Practices** are supported by exercises with red headings. Here are the Practices supported in this lesson:

MP 1: Make Sense of Problems Ex. 37

MP 3: Communicate Ex. 40

MP 3: Construct Arguments Ex. 6, 39

MP 3: Critique the Reasoning of Others Ex. 5

Applications exercises have blue headings. Exercises 38 and 46 support MP 4: Model.

STEM exercises focus on science or engineering applications.

EXERCISE 38: Use the Think About a Plan worksheet in the **Practice and Problem Solving Workbook** (also available in the Teaching Resources in print and online) to further support students' development in becoming independent learners.

HOMEWORK QUICK CHECK

To check students' understanding of key skills and concepts, go over Exercises 11, 23, 37, 38, and 40.

 Apply Add or subtract. Simplify where possible. State any restrictions on the variables.

31. $\frac{3}{4x} - \frac{2}{x^2}$

32. $\frac{3}{x+1} + \frac{x}{x-1}$

33. $\frac{4}{x^2-9} + \frac{7}{x+3}$

34. $\frac{5x}{x^2-x-6} - \frac{4}{x^2+4x+4}$

35. $3x + \frac{x^2+5x}{x^2-2}$

36. $\frac{5y}{y^2-7y} - \frac{4}{2y-14} + \frac{9}{y}$

37. Think About a Plan For the image of the overhead projector to be in focus, the distance d_i from the projector lens to the image, the projector lens focal length f, and the distance d_o from the transparency to the projector lens must satisfy the thin-lens equation $\frac{1}{f} = \frac{1}{d_i} + \frac{1}{d_o}$. What is the focal length of the projector lens if the transparency placed 4 in. from the projector lens is in focus on the screen located 8 ft from the projector lens?
- Can you write the equation for the unknown variable?
- What units would you use for the focal length of the lens?

STEM 38. Optics To read small font, you use a magnifying lens with the focal length 3 in. How far from the magnifying lens should you place the page if you want to hold the lens at 1 foot from your eyes? Use the thin-lens equation from Exercise 37.

39. Reasoning Does the Closure Property of rational numbers extend to rational expressions? Explain and describe any restrictions on rational expressions.

40. Writing Explain how factoring is used when adding or subtracting rational expressions. Include an example in your explanation.

Simplify each complex fraction.

41. $\dfrac{\frac{2}{x} + \frac{3}{y}}{\frac{-5}{x} + \frac{7}{y}}$

42. $\dfrac{1 + \frac{2}{x}}{2 + \frac{3}{2x}}$

43. $\dfrac{\frac{1}{xy} - \frac{1}{y^2}}{\frac{1}{x^2y} - \frac{1}{xy^2}}$

44. $\dfrac{\frac{2}{x+4} + 2}{1 + \frac{3}{x+4}}$

STEM 45. Harmony The harmonic mean of two numbers a and b equals $\dfrac{2}{\frac{1}{a} + \frac{1}{b}}$. As you vary the length of a violin or guitar string, its pitch changes. If a full-length string is 1 unit long, then many lengths that are simple fractions produce pitches that harmonize, or sound pleasing together. The harmonic mean relates two lengths that produce harmonious sounds. Find the harmonic mean for each pair of string lengths.

a. 1 and $\frac{1}{2}$ **b.** $\frac{3}{4}$ and $\frac{1}{2}$ **c.** $\frac{3}{4}$ and $\frac{3}{5}$ **d.** $\frac{1}{2}$ and $\frac{1}{4}$

Challenge **46.** Show that the sum of the reciprocals of three different positive integers is greater than 6 times the reciprocal of their product.

STEM 47. Electricity The resistance of a parallel circuit with 3 bulbs is $\dfrac{1}{\frac{1}{R_1} + \frac{1}{R_2} + \frac{1}{R_3}}$.
a. Find the resistance of a parallel circuit with 3 bulbs that have resistances 5 ohms, 4 ohms, 2.5 ohms.
b. The resistance of a parallel circuit with 3 bulbs is 1.5 ohms. Find the resistances of the bulbs, if two of them have equal resistances, while the resistance of the 3rd is 3 ohms less.

Answers

Practice and Problem-Solving Exercises (continued)

31. $\frac{3x-8}{4x^2}$; $x \neq 0$

32. $\frac{x^2+4x-3}{(x+1)(x-1)}$; $x \neq \pm 1$

33. $\frac{7x-17}{(x-3)(x+3)}$; $x \neq \pm 3$

34. $\frac{5x^2+6x+12}{(x-3)(x+2)^2}$; $x \neq 3$ or -2

35. $\frac{x(3x^2+x-1)}{x^2-2}$; $x \neq \pm\sqrt{2}$

36. $\frac{3(4y-21)}{y(y-7)}$; $y \neq 0$ or 7

37. 3.84 in.

38. 4 in.

39. Yes; when you add, subtract, multiply, or divide rational expressions you get another rational expression. The restriction is that you must divide by a nonzero rational expression.

40. Factoring is used to determine the LCM of the denominators; check students' work.

41. $\frac{3x+2y}{7x-5y}$

42. $\frac{2(x+2)}{4x+3}$

43. x

44. $\frac{2(x+5)}{x+7}$

45. a. $\frac{2}{3}$

b. $\frac{3}{5}$

c. $\frac{2}{3}$

d. $\frac{1}{3}$

46. Let x, y, and z be any distinct pos. integers. Then $\frac{1}{x} + \frac{1}{y} + \frac{1}{z} = \frac{xy + yz + xz}{xyz}$. Also, 6 times the reciprocal of their product is $6\frac{1}{xyz}$.

To show: $\frac{xy + yz + xz}{xyz} > \frac{6}{xyz}$, i.e, $xy + yz + xz > 6$, which is true for any three distinct pos. integers since it is true for the three smallest positive integers, 1, 2, and 3.

47. a. ≈ 1.18 ohms
b. 6 ohms, 6 ohms, 3 ohms

Standardized Test Prep

48. Which expression equals $\frac{5x}{x^2 - 9} - \frac{4x}{x^2 + 5x + 6}$?

Ⓐ $\frac{7x}{(x - 3)(x + 3)(x + 2)}$

Ⓒ $\frac{x^2 + 22x}{(x - 3)(x + 3)(x + 2)}$

Ⓑ $\frac{x^2 - 2x}{(x - 3)(x + 3)(x + 2)}$

Ⓓ $\frac{9x^2 - 2x}{(x - 3)(x + 3)(x + 2)}$

49. Which of the relationships is represented by the graph at the right?

Ⓕ $y = \log_4(x - 1) + 5$

Ⓖ $y = \log_4(x - 1) - 2$

Ⓗ $y = \log_4(x + 2) - 2$

Ⓘ $y = \log_4(x - 1) - 1$

50. What is a simpler form of $\frac{\frac{2}{x} - 5}{\frac{6}{x} - 3}$?

Ⓐ $\frac{2 - 5x}{6 - 3x}$

Ⓑ $\frac{2 + 5x}{6 - 3x}$

Ⓒ $\frac{2x - 5}{6x + 3}$

Ⓓ $\frac{6 + 3x}{2 - 5x}$

51. What word makes the statement "The domain and range of a(n) _____ function is the set of all real numbers" *sometimes* true?

Ⓕ polynomial

Ⓗ exponential

Ⓖ logarithmic

Ⓘ quadratic

52. What is the least common denominator for the rational expressions $\frac{1}{x^2 - 5x - 6}$ and $\frac{1}{x^2 - 12x + 36}$? Show your work.

Mixed Review

Divide. State any restrictions on the variable.

◀ See Lesson 8-4.

53. $\frac{3x^2 - 9x}{x - 2} \div \frac{x^2 - 9}{4x - 8}$

54. $\frac{3x - 6}{12x - 24} \div \frac{x^2 - 5x + 6}{3x^2 - 12}$

55. $\frac{5x + 15}{10x - 10} \div \frac{x^2 + 6x + 9}{3x^2 - 3}$

Write each logarithmic expression as a single logarithm.

◀ See Lesson 7-4.

56. $\log_3 y + 4 \log_3 t$

57. $7 \log p + 2 \log q$

58. $\log_5 x - \frac{1}{5} \log_5 y$

Let $f(x) = x^2 + 1$ and $g(x) = 3x$. Evaluate each expression.

◀ See Lesson 6-6.

59. $(g \circ f)(-3)$

60. $(f \circ g)(-3)$

61. $(g \circ f)\left(\frac{1}{2}\right)$

62. $(f \circ f)(3)$

Get Ready! To prepare for Lesson 8-6, do Exercises 63–65.

Solve each equation. Check your answers.

◀ See Lesson 1-4.

63. $-3(x - 4) = 2(x + 8)$

64. $0.2(x + 8) - 3.4 = 2.4$

65. $\frac{x}{2} + \frac{x}{3} = 15$

Standardized Test Prep

48. C

49. G

50. A

51. F

52. [2] First factor both denominators:
$x^2 - 5x - 6 = (x - 6)(x + 1)$
$x^2 - 12x + 36 = (x - 6)^2$

The LCD would have to include the factors $(x - 6)$, $(x + 1)$ and $(x - 6)^2$, so the LCD is $(x - 6)^2(x + 1)$.

[1] correct LCD, without work shown

Mixed Review

53. $\frac{12x}{x + 3}$; $x \neq 2$ or ± 3

54. $\frac{3(x + 2)}{4(x - 3)}$; $x \neq \pm 2$ or 3

55. $\frac{3(x + 1)}{2(x + 3)}$; $x \neq \pm 1$ or -3

56. $\log_3 yt^4$

57. $\log p^7 q^2$

58. $\log_5 \frac{x}{\sqrt[5]{y}}$

59. 30

60. 82

61. $\frac{15}{4}$

62. 101

63. $-\frac{4}{5}$

64. 21

65. 18

Additional Instructional Support

Algebra 2 Companion

Students can use the **Algebra 2 Companion** worktext (4 pages) as you teach the lesson. Use the Companion to support

- New Vocabulary
- Key Concepts
- Got It for each Problem
- Lesson Check

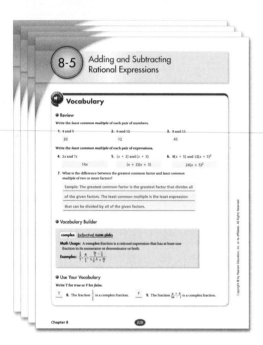

ELL Support

Focus on Language Pick up two common classroom objects, such as a pen and pencil. "What do these objects have *in common*?" Pick another pair of objects and ask the same question. Bring out the idea that two objects have something *in common* because they share something; because there is something both objects have. Have students write two simple quadratic expressions on separate index cards or small pieces of paper. Encourage them to make their quadratics by multiplying factors with ±1, ±2, and ±3. Have them trade one card with a neighbor. "Each of these quadratic expressions is made up of two factors. Examine your expressions. Do they contain any *common* factors? Are there any factors that both expressions have?" Allow students to show their expressions and common factors. Have them write the LCM of the two expressions. Tell them the LCM will have each of its factors in common with at least one of the expressions.

5 Assess & Remediate

Lesson Quiz

1. What is the LCM of $8x - 24$ and $2(x^2 - 6x + 9)$?

2. What is the sum $\frac{x}{x+3} + \frac{7x+6}{x^2+x-6}$ in simplest form? State any restrictions on the variable.

3. What is the difference $\frac{x+2}{x^2+4x-5} - \frac{3}{x^2+6x+5}$ in simplest form? State any restrictions on the variable.

4. What is a simpler form of $\dfrac{\frac{y}{1}}{\frac{1}{xy}+1}$?

5. **Do you UNDERSTAND?** Your friend flew to Miami in a plane that averaged 600 mi/h. She drove back home, averaging 50 mi/h. What is her average speed in miles per hour for the whole trip? Assume the distances by plane and car are equal.

ANSWERS TO LESSON QUIZ

1. $8(x-3)^2$

2. $\frac{x+2}{x-2}$; $x \neq 2$, $x \neq -3$

3. $\frac{x^2+5}{(x-1)(x+1)(x+5)}$; $x \neq 1$, $x \neq -1$, $x \neq -5$

4. $\frac{xy^2}{1+xy}$

5. about 92 mi/h

PRESCRIPTION FOR REMEDIATION
Use the student work on the Lesson Quiz to prescribe a differentiated review assignment:

Points	Differentiated Remediation
0–2	Intervention
3–4	On-level
5	Extension

PowerAlgebra.com

5 Assess & Remediate

Assign the Lesson Quiz. Appropriate intervention, practice, or enrichment is automatically generated based on student performance.

Intervention

- **Reteaching** (2 pages) Provides reteaching and practice exercises for the key lesson concepts. Use with struggling students or absent students.

- **English Language Learner Support** Helps students develop and reinforce mathematical vocabulary and key concepts.

All-in-One Resources/Online
Reteaching

8-5 **Reteaching**
Adding and Subtracting Rational Expressions

All-in-One Resources/Online
English Language Learner Support

8-5 **Additional Vocabulary Support**
Adding and Subtracting Rational Expressions

Differentiated Remediation *continued*

On-Level

- **Practice** (2 pages) Provides extra practice for each lesson. For simpler practice exercises, use the Form K Practice pages found in the All-in-One Teaching Resources and online.

- **Think About a Plan** Helps students develop specific problem-solving skills and strategies by providing scaffolded guiding questions.

- **Standardized Test Prep** Focuses on all major exercises, all major question types, and helps students prepare for the high-stakes assessments.

Extension

- **Enrichment** Provides students with interesting problems and activities that extend the concepts of the lesson.

- **Activities, Games, and Puzzles** Worksheets that can be used for concepts development, enrichment, and for fun!

Practice and Problem Solving Wkbk/All-in-One Resources/Online
Practice page 1

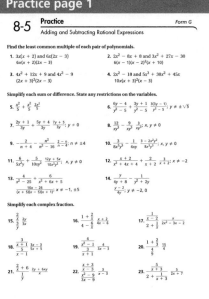

Practice and Problem Solving Wkbk/All-in-One Resources/Online
Practice page 2

All-in-One Resources/Online
Enrichment

Practice and Problem Solving Wkbk/All-in-One Resources/Online
Think About a Plan

Practice and Problem Solving Wkbk/All-in-One Resources/Online
Standardized Test Prep

Online Teacher Resource Center
Activities, Games, and Puzzles

1 Interactive Learning

Solve It!

PURPOSE To use proportions to determine an unknown

PROCESS Students may
- use the Pythagorean Theorem to determine the length of the shortcut.
- use a proportion to find the time on the shorter route.

FACILITATE

Q How can you find the new distance? **[Use the Pythagorean Theorem.]**

Q Is it possible to find the constant rate of walking from the information given? Explain. **[Yes; to find a rate you need the number of minutes it takes to go a certain distance. It takes 25 minutes to walk along 1.7 miles, so the rate is $\frac{1.7\text{ mi}}{25\text{ min}}$, which is about 0.068 mi/min.]**

Q What information is needed to find the amount of time saved by the shortcut? Explain how to find this information. **[Sample: The length of the shortcut and the rate you walk; divide the length of the shortcut by the rate and subtract the result from 25 min.]**

ANSWER See Solve It in Answers on next page.

CONNECT THE MATH Students use proportions to answer the question in the Solve It. In this lesson students use proportions and the LCD to solve rational equations.

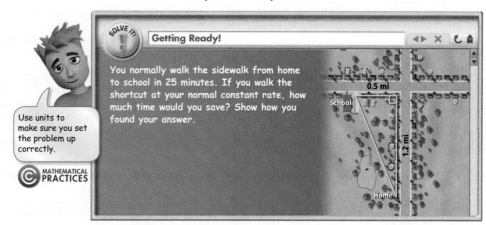

8-6 Solving Rational Equations

© **Content Standards**
A.APR.7 . . . Add, subtract, multiply, and divide rational expressions.
Also A.APR.6, A.CED.1, A.REI.11

Objectives To solve rational equations
To use rational equations to solve problems

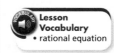

Getting Ready!

You normally walk the sidewalk from home to school in 25 minutes. If you walk the shortcut at your normal constant rate, how much time would you save? Show how you found your answer.

Use units to make sure you set the problem up correctly.

© **MATHEMATICAL PRACTICES**

Lesson Vocabulary
- rational equation

Sometimes you can solve a problem using a proportion—an equation involving two rational expressions set equal to each other.

Essential Understanding To solve an equation containing rational expressions, first multiply each side by the least common denominator of the rational expressions. Doing this, however, can introduce extraneous solutions.

A **rational equation** contains at least one rational expression. You can simplify solving a rational equation if you first clear the equation of denominators. You can do this by multiplying by the LCD of the rational expressions in the equation.

Rational Equation

$$\frac{x}{x+1} + \frac{x}{x-1} = \frac{2}{x^2-1}$$

Not a Rational Equation

$$x + \frac{1}{2} = \frac{2}{3}$$

Any time you multiply each side of an equation by an algebraic expression, it is possible to introduce an extraneous solution. Recall that an extraneous solution is a solution of the derived equation, but not a solution of the original equation. You must check all solutions in the original equation to confirm that they are indeed solutions.

542   Chapter 8   Rational Functions

8-6 Preparing to Teach

BIG idea Equivalence
ESSENTIAL UNDERSTANDING
- Solving an equation containing rational expressions begins by multiplying each side by the least common denominator of the rational expressions. Doing this, however, can introduce extraneous solutions.

Math Background

Rational equations contain at least one variable in the denominator, so they cannot always be solved simply by using inverse operations to isolate the variable.

When solving a rational equation algebraically, one method is to clear all denominators in order to solve.
- Factor the denominators to find the LCD.
- Multiply both sides of the equation by the LCD to clear the denominators.
- Simplify and solve.

Rational equations can also be solved with a graphing calculator.
- Graph each side of the equation as a separate function.
- Identify the intersection. This may be done visually on the graph or by looking at the table of values and finding each x-value that makes the functions equal, or by using the intersect feature in the CALC menu of a graphing calculator.

© **Mathematical Practices**
Reason abstractly and quantitatively.
Students will know and flexibly use the basic operations to solve rational equations. They will also check for extraneous solutions using substitution.

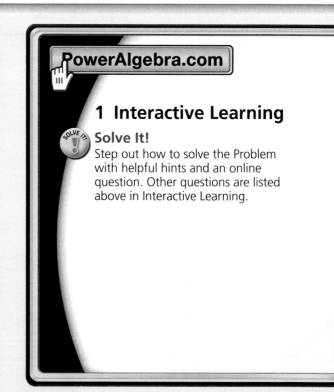

PowerAlgebra.com

1 Interactive Learning

Solve It!
Step out how to solve the Problem with helpful hints and an online question. Other questions are listed above in Interactive Learning.

Problem 1 · Solving a Rational Equation

What are the solutions of the rational equation?

A $\dfrac{x}{x-3} + \dfrac{x}{x+3} = \dfrac{2}{x^2-9}$

Think	**Write**
Factor the denominators to find the LCD.	$\dfrac{x}{x-3} + \dfrac{x}{x+3} = \dfrac{2}{(x-3)(x+3)}$
Multiply each side by the LCD to clear denominators.	$(x-3)(x+3)\left[\dfrac{x}{x-3} + \dfrac{x}{x+3}\right] = (x-3)(x+3)\dfrac{2}{(x-3)(x+3)}$
Now simplify and solve.	$x^2 + 3x + x^2 - 3x = 2$ $2x^2 = 2$ $x^2 = 1$, so $x = \pm 1$
Check whether $x = 1$ or $x = -1$ is extraneous. Use the original equation.	$\dfrac{1}{1-3} + \dfrac{1}{1+3} \stackrel{?}{=} \dfrac{2}{(1)^2-9}$ $\qquad$ $\dfrac{-1}{-1-3} + \dfrac{-1}{-1+3} \stackrel{?}{=} \dfrac{2}{(-1)^2-9}$ $-\dfrac{1}{2} + \dfrac{1}{4} = -\dfrac{1}{4}$ ✔ $\qquad\qquad$ $\dfrac{1}{4} + -\dfrac{1}{2} = -\dfrac{1}{4}$ ✔
Write the solutions.	The solutions are $x = 1$ and $x = -1$.

B $\dfrac{x-1}{x^2+3x+2} + \dfrac{2x}{x+2} = \dfrac{x-1}{x+1}$

Use a computer algebra system (CAS) to solve this rational equation.

Step 1 On the Home screen, choose **New Document**. Then select **Add Calculator**.

Step 2 Choose **Menu, Algebra, Solve.**

Step 3 Enter the equation, followed by a comma and x. Then press enter to solve.

The calculator shows a warning because there may be extraneous solutions. The original equation restricts x so that $x \neq -2$ and $x \neq -1$. There is no solution.

 Got It? 1. What are the solutions of the rational equation?

a. $\dfrac{x-1}{x+2} = \dfrac{x^2+2x-3}{x+2}$ $\qquad\qquad$ **b.** $\dfrac{x}{x+1} + \dfrac{3}{x+4} = \dfrac{x+3}{x+4}$

---

2 Guided Instruction

Problem 1

Q What are the restrictions on the variable in 1A? 1B? Explain. **[The denominators cannot be 0. For 1A, x cannot be 3 or −3. For 1B, x cannot be −1 or −2.]**

Q How is solving a rational equation similar to adding rational expressions? How is it different? **[Both require the use of the LCD. When solving an equation, you use the LCD to remove denominators. When you add rational expressions, you use the LCD to get a common denominator.]**

Q How can you use the methods for adding rational expressions to solve 1A? **[Multiply each fraction on the left by a ratio equal to 1, simplify, and combine terms:**

$\dfrac{x}{x-3} \cdot \left(\dfrac{x+3}{x+3}\right) + \dfrac{x}{x+3} \cdot \left(\dfrac{x-3}{x-3}\right) = \dfrac{2}{x^2-9}$

$\dfrac{x^2+3x}{x^2-9} + \dfrac{x^2-3x}{x^2-9} = \dfrac{2}{x^2-9}$

$\dfrac{2x^2}{x^2-9} = \dfrac{2}{x^2-9}$

Cross-multiply, or equate the numerators, and solve.]

Got It?
SYNTHESIZING

Q What methods can you use to solve 1b? Explain. **[Multiply each side by the LCD of $(x+1)(x+4)$. Or, subtract $\dfrac{3}{x+4}$ from both sides, forming a proportion after combining terms. Solve the equation by cross-multiplying.]**

---

2 Guided Instruction

 Each Problem is worked out and supported online.

Problem 1
Solving a Rational Equation
Animated

Problem 2
Using Rational Equations
Animated

Problem 3
Using a Graphing Calculator to Solve a Rational Equation
Animated

Support in Algebra 2 Companion
• Vocabulary
• Key Concepts
• Got It?

Answers

Solve It!
Your speed along the normal route is $\dfrac{0.5+1.2}{25} = 0.068$ mi/min, so the time it takes to walk the shortcut is $\dfrac{\sqrt{(0.5)+(1.2)^2}}{0.068} \approx 19$ min. The time saved is about $25 - 19 = 6$ min.

Got It?
1. a. 1
$\quad$ **b.** 0

Problem 2 ERROR PREVENTION

Remind students that when adding rational expressions, it is necessary to multiply each ratio by a form of 1 so as not to change the expression.

Because this problem involves an equation, multiplying both sides of the equation by the same number will not change the equation as long as extraneous roots are excluded.

Q Could this equation be solved using a proportion? Explain. **[Yes; multiply each fraction by the correct ratio to get denominators of $(480 + x)(480 - x)$. Then add the fractions to get one ratio and cross-multiply to solve the proportion.]**

Q What is a reasonable domain for this equation? Explain. **[$0 < x < 480$. Wind speed must be positive, and the rate must also be positive, so the speed cannot be greater than 480. If the speed were 480, the denominator of the rational equation would be zero, so it must be less than 480.]**

Got It?

Q To find the wind speed, do you need to know whether the trip has a headwind or tailwind? Explain. **[No. You know the distance in both directions is 4 mi. The rate you ride will be either $10 + x$ or $10 - x$, depending on headwind or tailwind. Because the numerator will be 4 for each ratio, you do not need to know whether the trip to the store had a headwind or tailwind.]**

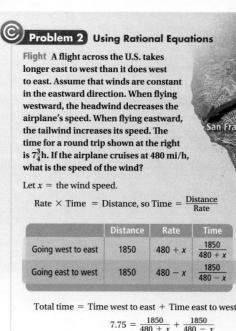

Problem 2 Using Rational Equations

Flight A flight across the U.S. takes longer east to west than it does west to east. Assume that winds are constant in the eastward direction. When flying westward, the headwind decreases the airplane's speed. When flying eastward, the tailwind increases its speed. The time for a round trip shown at the right is $7\frac{3}{4}$ h. If the airplane cruises at 480 mi/h, what is the speed of the wind?

Let x = the wind speed.

$$\text{Rate} \times \text{Time} = \text{Distance, so Time} = \frac{\text{Distance}}{\text{Rate}}$$

	Distance	Rate	Time
Going west to east	1850	$480 + x$	$\frac{1850}{480 + x}$
Going east to west	1850	$480 - x$	$\frac{1850}{480 - x}$

Total time = Time west to east + Time east to west

$$7.75 = \frac{1850}{480 + x} + \frac{1850}{480 - x}$$

> Multiply both sides by the LCD, $(480 + x)(480 - x)$.

$$(480 + x)(480 - x)\,7.75 = (480 + x)(480 - x)\frac{1850}{480 + x} + (480 + x)(480 - x)\frac{1850}{480 - x}$$

$$7.75(480 + x)(480 - x) = 1850(480 - x) + 1850(480 + x)$$

$$1{,}785{,}600 - 7.75x^2 = 888{,}000 - 1850x + 888{,}000 + 1850x$$

$$-7.75x^2 = -9600$$

$$x^2 = \frac{-9600}{-7.75}$$

$$x \approx \pm 35$$

Wind speed is positive, so $x \approx 35$. The west-to-east wind speed is about 35 mi/h.

Think

If you substitute 35 for x will the equation check exactly?
No; since 35 is an approximation it is likely that the values will be nearly equal, but probably not equal.

Check $7.75 = \frac{1850}{480 + x} + \frac{1850}{480 - x}$

$$7.75 \stackrel{?}{=} \frac{1850}{480 + 35} + \frac{1850}{480 - 35}$$

$$7.75 \approx 3.6 + 4.2 \checkmark$$

Got It? 2. a. You ride your bike to a store, 4 mi away, to pick up things for dinner. When there is no wind, you ride at 10 mi/h. Today your trip to the store and back took 1 hour. What was the speed of the wind today?

b. Reasoning Explain why there is no difference between the travel time to and from the store when there is no wind.

Additional Problems

1. What are the solutions of the rational equation?

a. $\frac{4}{x + 2} = \frac{5}{2x + 3}$

b. $\frac{1}{x^2 - 5x} + \frac{x - 7}{x} = \frac{4}{x^2 - 5x}$

ANSWERS

a. $-\frac{2}{3}$

b. 8 and 4

2. A carpenter can build a desk in 6 h. Another carpenter can build the same desk in 8 h. How long will it take the carpenters working together to build one desk?

ANSWER about 3.43 h

3. What are the solutions of the rational equation?

$\frac{5}{x + 1} + \frac{x}{x - 1} = 5$

ANSWER 0 and 1.5

Answers

Got It? (continued)

2. a. ≈ 4.47 mi/h

b. The direction of wind affects the speed (rate) of the bike. Since the speed is inversely related to time, change in speed will lead to change in time. Since there is no wind, the speed of the bike will remain the same to and from the store, hence the time to and from the store will remain the same.

You can also use a graphing calculator to solve a rational equation.

 Problem 3 Using a Graphing Calculator to Solve a Rational Equation

What are the solutions of the rational equation? Use a graphing calculator to solve.

$$\frac{2}{x+2} + \frac{x}{x-2} = 1$$

Plan

How do the graphs of the two sides of the equation help you solve the equation?
The x-values of the points of intersection are the solutions to the equation.

Enter one side of the equation as Y_1. Enter the other side as Y_2.

There appears to be only one intersection point, at $x = 0$.

$Y_1 = Y_2$ when $x = 0$.

```
Plot1  Plot2  Plot3
\Y1 ≣ (2/(X+2))+(X/(X−2))
\Y2 ≣ 1
\Y3 =
\Y4 =
\Y5 =
\Y6 =
\Y7 =
```

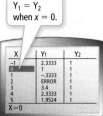

X	Y1	Y2
−1	2.3333	1
0	1	1
1	−.3333	1
2	ERROR	1
3	3.4	1
4	2.3333	1
5	1.9524	1
X=0		

The solution is $x = 0$.

Check $\frac{2}{x+2} + \frac{x}{x-2} = 1$

$\frac{2}{0+2} + \frac{0}{0-2} \overset{?}{=} 1$

$1 + 0 = 1$ ✔

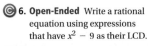 **Got It?** 3. What are the solutions of the rational equation $\frac{x+2}{1-2x} = 5$? Use a graphing calculator to solve.

✓ **Lesson Check**

Do you know HOW?

Solve each equation. Check each solution.

1. $\frac{4}{x-2} = \frac{x-1}{x-2}$

2. $\frac{2a+1}{6} + \frac{a}{2} = \frac{a-1}{3}$

3. $\frac{2}{n} + \frac{n+2}{n+1} = \frac{-2}{n^2+n}$

4. **Flight** If the speed of an airplane is 350 mi/h with a tail wind of 40 mi/h, what is the speed of the plane in still air?

Do you UNDERSTAND?  MATHEMATICAL PRACTICES

5. **Error Analysis** Describe and correct the error made in solving the equation.

$\frac{5}{x} + \frac{9}{7} = \frac{28}{x}$

~~$\frac{14}{x+7} = \frac{28}{x}$~~

~~$14x = 28(x+7)$~~

~~$14x = 28x + 196$~~

~~$-196 = 14x$~~

~~$-14 = x$~~

6. **Open-Ended** Write a rational equation using expressions that have $x^2 - 9$ as their LCD.

7. **Reasoning** Describe two methods you can use to check whether a solution is extraneous.

Problem 3

Q How can the graph be used to determine the restrictions on the variable? **[The vertical asymptotes are at $x = 2$ and -2, so x cannot be 2 or -2.]**

Got It?   EXTENSION

Q Which method would you choose to solve this equation without using a graph or table? Explain. **[sample: multiplying both sides by the LCD]**

3 Lesson Check

Do you know HOW?   ERROR INTERVENTION

• For Exercises 1–3, if students are not sure how to start, remind them to eliminate the denominators by multiplying by the LCD.

Do you UNDERSTAND?

• If students have trouble correcting the error in Exercise 5, remind them that several methods can be used to find a solution. Ask students to identify the method the student was trying to use and what the steps are for that method. Then have them follow the student's problem to see if they can find the error.

Close

Q Which methods can be used to solve a rational equation? **[Multiply through by the LCD, rearrange the equation into a proportion and use cross products, use a table or graph to find a solution, or add the rational expression on each side of the equal sign and then use cross products.]**

---

3. $0.\overline{27}$

Lesson Check

1. 5

2. −1

3. −2

4. 310 mi/h

5. The LCD was not found; the correct answer is

$\frac{35 + 9x}{7x} = \frac{28(7)}{7x}, x \neq 0$

$9x = 161$

$x = \frac{161}{9} = 17.\overline{8}.$

6. Answers may vary.

Sample: $\frac{2}{x-3} + \frac{1}{x+3} = \frac{5x}{x^2-9}$

7. Answers may vary. Sample: (1) Substitute the solution into the original eq. (2) Check to see if the solution is in the domain of the graph of the original eq.

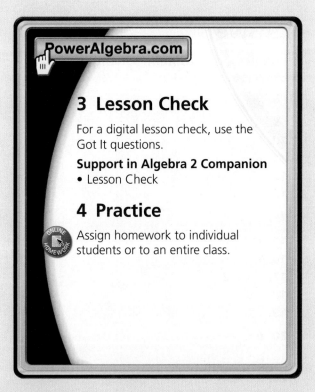

PowerAlgebra.com

3 Lesson Check

For a digital lesson check, use the Got It questions.

Support in Algebra 2 Companion
• Lesson Check

4 Practice

Assign homework to individual students or to an entire class.

4 Practice

ASSIGNMENT GUIDE
Basic: 8–29 all, 30, 32, 36–38, 42

Average: 9–29 odd, 30–53

Advanced: 9–29 odd, 30–56

Standardized Test Prep: 57–60

Mixed Review: 61–75

Mathematical Practices are supported by exercises with red headings. Here are the Practices supported in this lesson:

MP 1: Make Sense of Problems Ex. 36
MP 3: Communicate Ex. 7
MP 3: Construct Arguments Ex. 6, 55
MP 3: Critique the Reasoning of Others Ex. 5, 40
MP 5: Use Appropriate Tools Ex. 21–29

Applications exercises have blue headings.

Exercises 41 and 42 support MP 4: Model.

EXERCISE 37: Use the Think About a Plan worksheet in the **Practice and Problem Solving Workbook** (also available in the Teaching Resources in print and online) to further support students' development in becoming independent learners.

HOMEWORK QUICK CHECK
To check students' understanding of key skills and concepts, go over Exercises 9, 25, 36, 37, and 42.

 Practice and Problem-Solving Exercises MATHEMATICAL PRACTICES

 Practice **Solve each equation. Check each solution.** See Problem 1.

8. $\frac{1}{4} - x = \frac{x}{8}$

9. $\frac{y}{5} + \frac{y}{2} = 7$

10. $\frac{2x}{3} - \frac{1}{2} = \frac{2x+5}{6}$

11. $\frac{3x-2}{12} - \frac{1}{6} = \frac{1}{6}$

12. $\frac{1}{x} + \frac{x}{2} = \frac{x+4}{2x}$

13. $\frac{11}{3x} - \frac{1}{3} = \frac{-4}{x^2}$

14. $\frac{3}{2x} - \frac{5}{3x} = 2$

15. $\frac{5x}{4} - \frac{3}{x} = \frac{1}{4}$

16. $\frac{2}{y} + \frac{1}{2} = \frac{5}{2y}$

17. $x + \frac{6}{x} = -5$

18. $\frac{1}{4x} - \frac{3}{4} = \frac{7}{x}$

19. $\frac{5}{2x} - \frac{2}{3} = \frac{1}{x} + \frac{5}{6}$

20. Transportation The speed s of an airplane is given by $s = \frac{d}{t}$, where d represents See Problem 2.
the distance and t is the time.
 a. A plane flies 700 miles from New York to Chicago at a speed of 360 mi/h. Find the time for the trip.
 b. On the return trip from Chicago to New York, a tail wind helps the plane move faster. The total flying time for the round trip is 3.5 h. Find the speed x of the tail wind.

Graphing Calculator Solve each equation. Check each solution. See Problem 3.

21. $\frac{3}{x} = 5$

22. $\frac{1}{3x} = -2$

23. $\frac{2}{x-1} = 4$

24. $\frac{4}{x+3} = 5$

25. $\frac{5x-2}{x-4} = -3$

26. $\frac{3x-1}{x+2} = 7$

27. $\frac{2}{x} = \frac{x}{2}$

28. $\frac{2}{x+3} = \frac{x-3}{2}$

29. $\frac{2}{x-1} + \frac{3}{x+1} = 4$

 Apply **Solve each equation for the given variable.**

30. $m = \frac{2E}{V^2}; E$

31. $\frac{c}{E} - \frac{1}{mc} = 0; E$

32. $\frac{m}{F} = \frac{1}{a}; F$

33. $\frac{1}{c} - \frac{c}{a^2 - b^2} = 0; c$

34. $\frac{\ell}{T^2} = \frac{g}{4\pi^2}; T$

35. $\frac{q}{m} = \frac{2V}{B^2r^2}; B$

36. Think About a Plan You and a classmate have volunteered to contact every member of your class by phone to inform them of an upcoming event. You can complete the calls in six days if you work alone. Your classmate can complete them in four days. How long will it take to complete the calls working together?
 • If N is the total number of calls, what expression represents the number of calls that you can make per day? What expression represents the number of calls your friend can make per day?
 • What is the expression for the number of days needed to make N calls if you are working together?

37. Storage One pump can fill a tank with oil in 4 hours. A second pump can fill the same tank in 3 hours. If both pumps are used at the same time, how long will they take to fill the tank?

Answers

Practice and Problem-Solving Exercises

8. $\frac{2}{9}$

9. 10

10. 4

11. 2

12. −1, 2

13. −1, 12

14. $-\frac{1}{12}$

15. ≈−1.45, ≈1.65

16. 1

17. −3, −2

18. −9

19. 1

20. a. $\frac{35}{18}$ h

 b. 90 mi/h

21. 0.6

22. $-0.1\overline{6}$

23. 1.5

24. −2.2

25. 1.75

26. −3.75

27. ±2

28. ≈±3.6

29. ≈1.69, ≈−0.44

30. $E = \frac{mV^2}{2}$

31. $E = mc^2$

32. $F = ma$

33. $c = \pm\sqrt{a^2 - b^2}$

34. $T = \pm 2\pi\sqrt{\frac{\ell}{g}}$

35. $B = \pm\sqrt{\frac{2Vm}{r^2q}}$

36. 2.4 days

37. $1\frac{5}{7}$ h

38. Teamwork You can stuff envelopes twice as fast as your friend. Together, you can stuff 6750 envelopes in 4.5 hours. How long would it take each of you working alone to complete the job?

39. Grades On the first four tests of the term your average is 84%. You think you can score 96% on each of the remaining tests. How many consecutive test scores of 96% would you need to bring your average up to 90% for the term?

 40. Error Analysis Describe and correct the error made in solving the equation.

$$x - \frac{2}{x-2} = \frac{x+1}{x+2}$$
$$x - 2(x+2) = (x+1)(x-2)$$
$$x - 2x - 4 = x^2 - x - 2$$
$$0 = x^2 + 2$$
$$-2 = x^2$$

There is no square root of a negative number, so the equation has no solution.

41. Fuel Economy Suppose you drive an average of 15,000 miles per year, and your car gets 24 miles per gallon. Suppose gasoline costs $3.60 a gallon.
  a. How much money do you spend each year on gasoline?
  b. You plan to trade in your car for one that gets x more miles per gallon. Write an expression to represent the new yearly cost of gasoline.
  c. Write an expression to represent your total savings on gasoline per year.
  d. Suppose you can save $600 a year with the new car. How many miles per gallon does the new car get?

STEM 42. Woodworking A tapered cylinder is made by decreasing the radius of a rod continuously as you move from one end to the other. The rate at which it tapers is the taper per foot. You can calculate the taper per foot using the formula $T = \frac{24(R - r)}{L}$. The lengths R, r, and L are measured in inches.

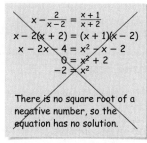

  a. Solve this equation for L.
  b. What is L for $T = 0.75, 0.85,$ and 0.95, if $R = 4$ in.; $r = 3$ in.?

Solve each equation. Check each solution.

43. $\frac{15}{x} + \frac{9x - 7}{x + 2} = 9$

44. $\frac{2}{x + 2} - \frac{1}{x} = \frac{-4}{x(x + 2)}$

45. $\frac{1}{b + 1} + \frac{1}{b - 1} = \frac{2}{b^2 - 1}$

46. $c - \frac{c}{3} + \frac{c}{5} = 26$

47. $\frac{1}{x - 5} = \frac{x}{x^2 - 25}$

48. $\frac{k}{k + 1} + \frac{k}{k - 2} = 2$

49. $\frac{5}{x^2 - 7x + 12} - \frac{2}{3 - x} = \frac{5}{x - 4}$

50. $\frac{10}{2y + 8} - \frac{7y + 8}{y^2 - 16} = \frac{-8}{2y - 8}$

51. $\frac{7x + 3}{x^2 - 8x + 15} + \frac{3x}{x - 5} = \frac{1}{3 - x}$

52. $\frac{2}{x + 3} - \frac{3}{4 - x} = \frac{2x - 2}{x^2 - x - 12}$

 53. Writing Write and solve a problem that can be modeled by a rational equation.

---

38. you: 6.75 h; your friend: 13.5 h

39. 4 test scores

40. The first term, x, was not multiplied by the LCD $(x - 2)(x + 2)$. The solution should be:

$$x - \frac{2}{x - 2} = \frac{x + 1}{x + 2}$$
$$\frac{x(x - 2)(x + 2) - 2(x + 2)}{(x - 2)(x + 2)}$$
$$= \frac{(x + 1)(x - 2)}{(x - 2)(x + 2)}$$
$$x^3 - 4x - 2x - 4 = x^2 - x - 2,$$
$$\text{LCD} = (x - 2)(x + 2)$$
$$x^3 - x^2 - 5x - 2 = 0$$
$$x \approx -1.47283, -0.462598, 2.93543$$

41. a. $2250

  b. $\frac{15{,}000}{24 + x}(3.60)$

  c. $2250 - \frac{15{,}000}{24 + x}(3.60)$

  d. ≈ 32.7 mpg

42. a. $L = \frac{24(R - r)}{T}$

  b. 32 in.; ≈ 28.24 in.; ≈ 25.26 in.

43. 3

44. no solution

45. no solution

46. 30

47. no solution

48. -4

49. no solution

50. 6

51. $1, -\frac{2}{3}$

52. -1

53. Check students' work.

Answers

Practice and Problem-Solving Exercises (continued)

54. 5 attendants

55. a–c. Check students' work.

56. in the yr 2037

Standardized Test Prep

57. D

58. I

59. B

60. [4] Write and solve the system of eqs.:
Let n = no. of nonfiction books, Let
f = no. of fiction books,
$$\begin{cases} f + n = 48 \\ 15f + 20n = 900 \end{cases}$$
solution: $n = 36$.

   [3] appropriate methods, but with one computational error

   [2] incorrect system solved correctly OR correct system solved incorrectly

   [1] correct answer, without work shown

Mixed Review

61. $\dfrac{-y - 13}{4(y + 1)}$

62. $\dfrac{5xy - 12}{2y(y + 2)}$

63. $\dfrac{x^2 + 3}{2(x - 1)(x + 3)}$

64. $x = -3$

65. $x = -1$

66. $x = -0.875$

67. $y = \dfrac{5 - x}{2}$; yes

68. $y = \pm\sqrt{x - 1}$; no

69. $y = \sqrt[3]{x + 4}$; yes

70. add 2; 9, 11, 13

71. subtract 2; −10, −12, −14

72. multiply by 5; 625, 3125, 15625

73. subtract 5; 30, 25, 20

74. multiply by 2; 128, 256, 512

75. subtract 4; −19, −23, −27

 Challenge **54. Sports** An automatic pitching machine can pitch all its baseballs in $1\frac{1}{4}$ hours. One attendant can retrieve all the baseballs pitched by one machine in $3\frac{1}{2}$ hours. At least how many attendants working at the same rate should be hired so that the baseballs from 10 machines are all retrieved in less than 8 hours?

55. Open-Ended Write a rational equation that has the following.
  a. one solution   **b.** two solutions   **c.** no real solution

STEM **56. Industry** The average hourly wage $H(x)$ of workers in an industry is modeled by the function $H(x) = \dfrac{16.24x}{0.062x + 39.42}$, where x represents the number of years since 1970. In what year does the model predict that wages will be $25/h?

Standardized Test Prep

SAT/ACT

57. What is the solution of $x + \frac{1}{x} = -2$?
  Ⓐ 1, −1   Ⓑ 0 only   Ⓒ $-\frac{1}{2}$ only   Ⓓ −1 only

58. Which of the following is equivalent to $\dfrac{6\sqrt{24}}{2\sqrt{3}}$?
  Ⓕ $2\sqrt{2}$ Ⓖ $3\sqrt{2}$ Ⓗ $5\sqrt{2}$ Ⓘ $6\sqrt{2}$

59. An investment of $750 will be worth $1500 after 12 years of continuous compounding at a fixed interest rate. What is that interest rate?
  Ⓐ 2.00%   Ⓑ 5.78%   Ⓒ 6.93%   Ⓓ 200%

Extended Response

60. A librarian orders 48 fiction and nonfiction books for the school library. A fiction book costs $15 and a nonfiction book costs $20. The total cost of the order was $900. How many nonfiction books did the librarian order? Show your work.

Mixed Review

Simplify each difference.   See Lesson 8-5.

61. $\dfrac{3y + 1}{4y + 4} - \dfrac{2y + 7}{2y + 2}$ **62.** $\dfrac{5x}{2y + 4} - \dfrac{6}{y^2 + 2y}$ **63.** $\dfrac{x + 1}{2x - 2} - \dfrac{2x}{x^2 + 2x - 3}$

Solve each equation.   See Lesson 7-5.

64. $\log_{10} 0.001 = x$ **65.** $\log_3 27 = 3x + 6$ **66.** $\log_{0.5}(x + 1) = 3$

Find the inverse of each function. Is the inverse a function?   See Lesson 6-7.

67. $y = 5 - 2x$ **68.** $y = x^2 + 1$ **69.** $y = x^3 - 4$

Get Ready!   **To prepare for Lesson 9-1, do Exercises 70–75.**

Identify the pattern and find the next three terms.   See Lesson 1-1.

70. 1, 3, 5, 7, . . .   **71.** −2, −4, −6, −8, . . .   **72.** 0.2, 1, 5, 25, 125, . . .

73. 50, 45, 40, 35, . . .   **74.** 16, 32, 64, . . .   **75.** −3, −7, −11, −15, . . .

Additional Instructional Support

Algebra 2 Companion

Students can use the **Algebra 2 Companion** worktext (4 pages) as you teach the lesson. Use the Companion to support

- New Vocabulary
- Key Concepts
- Got It for each Problem
- Lesson Check

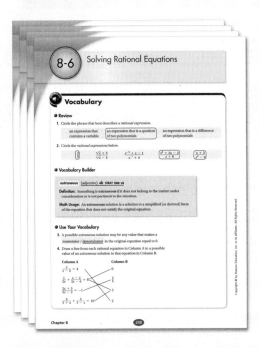

ELL Support

Use Role Playing Have students act out the distance problem from Problem 2 to help them understand the meaning of the terms used. Use a map or two points in the classroom to indicate San Francisco and Chicago. Instruct students to make a sign indicating both locations as well as the distance between them. Next, have students use a picture or make a paper airplane and write the speed or rate on the airplane. Use the words "speed" and "rate" interchangeably, so students are aware that speed is a type of rate. Use a fan or students holding paper fans at either location to represent a headwind and tailwind. Point out that if the airplane is moving towards the fan, the wind is a headwind and the rate of the airplane is slower. Conversely, if the airplane is moving away from the fan, the wind is a tailwind and the rate of the airplane is faster. Have students fill in the table from Problem 2 as they act out each part of the demonstration.

5 Assess & Remediate

Lesson Quiz

1. What are the solutions of the rational equation $\frac{3}{x^2 + 6x + 8} + \frac{x + 1}{x + 2} = \frac{1}{x + 2}$?

2. **Do you UNDERSTAND?** A gardener completes park maintenance in 12 h. Another gardener takes 10 h. How long it will take both gardeners working together to complete the maintenance?

3. What are the solutions of the rational equation $6 = \frac{3a + 6}{a} + \frac{1}{a}$? Use a graphing calculator to solve.

ANSWERS TO LESSON QUIZ

1. -3 and -1
2. about 5.45 h
3. $\frac{7}{3}$

PRESCRIPTION FOR REMEDIATION

Use the student work on the Lesson Quiz to prescribe a differentiated review assignment:

Points	Differentiated Remediation
0–1	Intervention
2	On-level
3	Extension

PowerAlgebra.com

5 Assess & Remediate

Assign the Lesson Quiz. Appropriate intervention, practice, or enrichment is automatically generated based on student performance.

Intervention

- **Reteaching** (2 pages) Provides reteaching and practice exercises for the key lesson concepts. Use with struggling students or absent students.
- **English Language Learner Support** Helps students develop and reinforce mathematical vocabulary and key concepts.

All-in-One Resources/Online
Reteaching

8-6 Reteaching (continued)
Solving Rational Equations

You often can use rational equations to model and solve problems involving rates.

Problem

Quinn can refinish hardwood floors four times as fast as his apprentice, Jack. They are refinishing 100 ft² of flooring. Working together, Quinn and Jack can finish the job in 3 h. How long would it take each of them working alone to refinish the floor?

Let x be Jack's work rate in ft²/h. Quinn's work rate is four times faster, or $4x$.

square feet refinished per hour by Jack and Quinn together	=	square feet of floor they refinish together	÷	hours worked together
ft²/h	=	ft²	÷	h

$x + 4x = \frac{100}{3}$ Their work rates sum to 100 ft² in 3 h.

$3(x) + 3(4x) = 3\left(\frac{100}{3}\right)$ They work for 3 h. Refinished floor area = rate × time.

$15x = 100$ Simplify.

$x \approx 6.67$ Divide each side by 15.

Jack works at the rate of 6.67 ft²/h. Quinn works at the rate of 26.67 ft²/h.

Let j be the number of hours Jack takes to refinish the floor alone, and let q be the number of hours Quinn takes to refinish the floor alone.

$6.67 = \frac{100}{j}$ $26.67 = \frac{100}{q}$

$j(6.67) = j\left(\frac{100}{j}\right)$ $q(26.67) = q\left(\frac{100}{q}\right)$

$6.67j = 100$ $26.67q = 100$

$j \approx 15$ $q \approx 3.75$

Jack would take 15 h and Quinn would take 3.75 h to refinish the floor alone.

Exercises

13. An airplane flies from its home airport to a city and back in 5 h flying time. The plane travels the 720 mi to the city at 295 mi/h with no wind. How strong is the wind on the return flight? Is the wind a headwind or a tailwind? about 14 mi/h; headwind

14. Miguel can complete the decorations for a school dance in 5 days working alone. Nasim can do it alone in 3 days, and Denise can do it alone in 4 days. How long would it take the three students working together to decorate? about 1.3 days

All-in-One Resources/Online
English Language Learner Support

8-6 Additional Vocabulary Support
Solving Rational Equations

Problem

What are the solutions of the rational equation? Justify your steps.

$\frac{x}{x-2} + \frac{1}{x-4} = \frac{2}{x^2 - 6x + 8}$ Write original equation.

$\frac{x}{x-2} + \frac{1}{x-4} = \frac{2}{(x-2)(x-4)}$ Factor the denominators to find the LCD.

$(x-2)(x-4)\left[\frac{x}{x-2} + \frac{1}{x-4}\right]$
$= (x-2)(x-4)\left[\frac{2}{(x-2)(x-4)}\right]$ Multiply each side by the LCD to clear the denominators.

$x(x-4) + 1(x-2) = 2$ Distribute and simplify.

$x^2 - 4x + x - 2 = 2$ Distribute.

$x^2 - 3x - 4 = 0$ Simplify.

$(x-4)(x+1) = 0$ Factor the quadratic.

$x = 4$ or $x = -1$ Solve for x.

$x = 4$ causes division by 0, so $x = 4$ is an extraneous solution. Check for extraneous solutions.

Because $\frac{-1}{-1-2} + \frac{1}{-1-4} = \frac{2}{(-1)^2 - 6(-1) + 8}$, the solution is $x = -1$.

Exercise

What are the solutions of the rational equation? Justify the steps.

$\frac{5}{x} + \frac{4}{x+3} = \frac{8}{x^2 + 3x}$ Write the original equation

$\frac{5}{x} + \frac{4}{x+3} = \frac{8}{x(x+3)}$ Factor the denominator to find the LCD

$x(x+3)\left[\frac{5}{x} + \frac{4}{(x+3)}\right] = x(x+3)\left[\frac{8}{x(x+3)}\right]$ Multiply each side by the LCD

$9x + 15 = 8$ Distribute and simplify

$x = -\frac{7}{9}$ Solve

Differentiated Remediation *continued*

On-Level

- **Practice** (2 pages) Provides extra practice for each lesson. For simpler practice exercises, use the Form K Practice pages found in the All-in-One Teaching Resources and online.

- **Think About a Plan** Helps students develop specific problem-solving skills and strategies by providing scaffolded guiding questions.

- **Standardized Test Prep** Focuses on all major exercises, all major question types, and helps students prepare for the high-stakes assessments.

Extension

- **Enrichment** Provides students with interesting problems and activities that extend the concepts of the lesson.

- **Activities, Games, and Puzzles** Worksheets that can be used for concepts development, enrichment, and for fun!

Practice and Problem Solving Wkbk/All-in-One Resources/Online
Practice page 1

8-6 Practice — Form G
Solving Rational Equations

Solve each equation. Check each solution.

1. $\frac{x}{3} + \frac{x}{2} = 10$ 12
2. $\frac{1}{x} - \frac{6}{9} = 0$ ±3
3. $-\frac{4}{x+1} = \frac{5}{3x+1} - \frac{9}{1}$
4. $\frac{4}{x} = \frac{x}{4}$ ±4
5. $\frac{3x}{4} = \frac{5x+1}{3} - \frac{1}{4}$ −11
6. $\frac{3}{2x} - 3 = 5 - \frac{1}{2x}$ 4
7. $\frac{x-4}{3} = \frac{x-2}{2}$ −2
8. $\frac{2x-1}{x+3} = \frac{5}{3}$ 18
9. $\frac{y}{5} + \frac{2}{6} = \frac{y}{2} - \frac{1}{6}$ 5
10. $\frac{1}{2x} + \frac{5}{x^2} = \frac{1}{x}$ 7
11. $\frac{2}{x+1} + \frac{5}{x-1} = \frac{6}{x^2-9}$ −9

12. An airplane flies from its home airport to a city 510 mi away and back. The total flying time for the round-trip flight is 3.9 h. The plane travels the first half of the trip at 255 mi/h with no wind.
   a. How strong is the wind on the return flight? Round your answer to the nearest tenth. about 13.4 mi/h
   b. Is the wind on the return flight a headwind or a tailwind? tailwind

Use a graphing calculator to solve each equation. Check each solution.

13. $\frac{x-1}{6} = \frac{x}{4} - \frac{1}{4}$ −2
14. $\frac{x-2}{10} = \frac{x-7}{5} - \frac{7}{5}$ 12
15. $\frac{4}{x+3} = \frac{10}{2x-1}$ −17
16. $\frac{3}{x-2} = \frac{4}{x+4}$ 6
17. $\frac{3y}{5} + \frac{1}{2} = \frac{y}{10}$ −1
18. $5 - \frac{4}{x-1} = 6$ −5
19. $\frac{2}{3} + \frac{3x}{6} - 1 = \frac{5}{2}$ 4
20. $\frac{4}{x} = \frac{5}{x-2}$ −3
21. $\frac{1}{x} - \frac{2}{x+3} = 0$ 3

Solve each equation for the given variable.

22. $h = \frac{3A}{b}; b$ $b = \frac{3A}{h}$
23. $\frac{1}{f} = \frac{1}{d_i} + \frac{1}{d_o}; d_o$ $d_o = \frac{fd_i}{d_i - f}$
24. $\frac{h}{t} + 16t = v_o; h$ $h = v_o t - 16t^2$
25. $m = \frac{y_2 - y_1}{x_2 - x_1}; x_1$ $x_1 = x_2 - \frac{y_2 - y_1}{m}$
26. $\frac{xy}{z} + 2x = \frac{y}{z}; x$ $x = \frac{z^2}{y^2 + 2yz}$
27. $\frac{S - 2wh}{2w + 2h} = \ell; S$ $S = 2\ell w + 2wh + 2\ell h$

Practice and Problem Solving Wkbk/All-in-One Resources/Online
Practice page 2

8-6 Practice (continued) — Form G
Solving Rational Equations

28. One delivery driver can complete a route in 6 h. Another driver can complete the same route in 5 h.
   a. Let N be the total number of deliveries on the route. Write expressions to represent the number of deliveries each driver can make in 1 hour. $\frac{N}{6}, \frac{N}{5}$
   b. Write an expression to represent the number of hours needed to make N deliveries if the drivers work together. $\frac{N}{\frac{N}{6} + \frac{N}{5}}$
   c. If the drivers work together, about how many hours will they take to complete the route? Round your answer to the nearest tenth. 2.7 h

29. A fountain has two drainage valves. With the first valve open, the fountain drains completely in 4 h. With only the second valve open, the fountain drains completely in 5.25 h. About how many hours will the fountain take to drain with both valves open? Round your answer to the nearest tenth. 2.3 h

30. A pen factory has two machines making pens. Together, the machines make 1500 pens during an 8-h shift. Machine A makes pens at 2.5 times the rate of Machine B. About how many hours would Machine A need to make 1500 pens by itself? Round your answer to the nearest tenth. 11.2 h

31. **Error Analysis** Describe and correct the error made in solving the equation. The student did not check the solutions in the original equation. The solution $x = -3$ is extraneous.
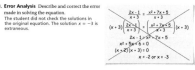
$$(x+3)\left(\frac{2x-1}{x+3}\right) = \left(\frac{x^2+7x+5}{x+3}\right)(x+3)$$
$$2x-1 = x^2+7x+5$$
$$x^2+5x+6 = 0$$
$$(x+2)(x+3) = 0$$
$$x = -2 \text{ or } x = -3$$

32. The formula $V = hH\left(\frac{b_1+b_2}{6}\right)$ gives the volume of a pyramid with a trapezoidal base.
   a. Solve this equation for b_2. $b_2 = \frac{6V}{hH} - b_1$
   b. Find b_2 if $b_1 = 5$ cm, $h = 8$ cm, $H = 9$ cm, and $V = 216$ cm^3. 13 cm

---

All-in-One Resources/Online
Enrichment

8-6 Enrichment
Solving Rational Equations

Gravitational Attraction

Many physical phenomena obey inverse-square laws. That is, the strength of the quantity is inversely proportional to the square of the distance from the source.

Isaac Newton was the first to discover that gravity obeys an inverse-square law. The gravitational force F between objects of masses M and m separated by a distance D is given by $F = \frac{GMm}{D^2}$, where G is a constant.

Suppose that two stars, Alpha Major and Beta Minor, are separated by a distance of 6 light-years. Alpha Major has four times the mass of Beta Minor. Let M represent the mass of Beta Minor. Suppose that an object, represented by point P, of mass m is placed between the two stars at a distance of D light-years from Beta Minor.

1. Write an expression for the gravitational force between this object and Beta Minor. $\frac{GMm}{D^2}$
2. Write an expression for the gravitational force between this object and Alpha Major. $\frac{4GMm}{(6-D)^2}$
3. What is the distance of a neutral position of the object P with mass m from Beta Minor? At neutral position, both Beta Minor and Alpha Major exert equal force on point P. 2 light-yr

A spaceship is stationary between a planet and its moon, experiencing an equal gravitational pull from each. When measurements are taken, it is determined that the craft is 300,000 km from the planet and 100,000 km from the moon.

4. What is the ratio of the mass of the planet to the mass of the moon? 9 : 1
5. What would be the ratio of their masses if the distance of the spaceship from the planet was R times the distance of the spaceship to the moon? R^2 : 1

Once every 277 yr, the two moons of the planet Omega Minus line up in a straight line with the planet. The moons are equal in mass, and the inner moon is equidistant from the outer moon and from the planet. Measurements show that an object two thirds of the distance from the planet to the inner moon, and in the same line as all three, experiences an equal gravitational pull in both directions.

6. What is the ratio of the mass of the planet to the mass of one of its moons? 17 : 4

Practice and Problem Solving Wkbk/All-in-One Resources/Online
Think About a Plan

8-6 Think About a Plan
Solving Rational Equations

Storage One pump can fill a tank with oil in 4 hours. A second pump can fill the same tank in 3 hours. If both pumps are used at the same time, how long will they take to fill the tank?

Understanding the Problem

1. How long does it take the first pump to fill the tank? 4 h
2. How long does it take the second pump to fill the tank? 3 h
3. What is the problem asking you to determine?
   the length of time it takes for both pumps to fill the tank when used at the same time

Planning the Solution

4. If V is the volume of the tank, what expressions represent the portion of the tank that each pump can fill in one hour?
   First pump: $\frac{1}{4}V$ Second pump: $\frac{1}{3}V$

5. What expression represents the part of the tank the two pumps can fill in one hour if they are used at the same time?
   $\frac{1}{4}V + \frac{1}{3}V$

6. Let t be the number of hours. Write an equation to find the time it takes the two pumps to fill one tank.
   $\left(\frac{1}{4}V + \frac{1}{3}V\right)t = V$

Getting an Answer

7. Solve your equation to find how long the pumps will take to fill the tank if both pumps are used at the same time.
   $\left(\frac{1}{4}V + \frac{1}{3}V\right)t = V$
   $\left(\frac{1}{4} + \frac{1}{3}\right)t = 1$
   $\frac{7}{12}t = 1$
   $t = \frac{12}{7} = 1\frac{5}{7}$ hours

Practice and Problem Solving Wkbk/All-in-One Resources/Online
Standardized Test Prep

8-6 Standardized Test Prep
Solving Rational Equations

Gridded Response

For Exercises 1–8, what are the solutions of each rational equation? Enter your answer in the grid provided. If necessary, enter your answer as a fraction.

1. $\frac{3}{x} - x = \frac{6}{x} - x$
2. $\frac{2}{6x+2} = \frac{x}{3x^2+11}$
3. $\frac{3}{2x-4} = \frac{5}{3x+7}$
4. $\frac{2}{x+2} + \frac{5}{x-2} = \frac{6}{x^2-4}$
5. $\frac{7}{x^2-5x} + \frac{2}{x} = \frac{3}{2x-10}$
6. $\frac{1}{1-5x} = \frac{3}{x+9}$
7. $\frac{7}{2} = \frac{7x}{8} - 4$
8. $4 + \frac{2y}{y-5} = \frac{8}{y-5}$

Answers

Online Teacher Resource Center
Activities, Games, and Puzzles

8-6 Game: Rational Learning
Solving Rational Equations

Points	Vocabulary: Question	Answer
10	Rational equation?	An equation containing rational expressions
20	Least common denominator?	The smallest integer that can be evenly divided by all the denominators
30	Cross products?	For the equation $\frac{a}{b} = \frac{c}{d}$, ad and bc
40	Solution of rational equation?	A value that, when substituted for the variable, makes the rational equation true
50	Extraneous solution?	A solution of the derived equation, but not of the original equation

Points	Solution: Question	Answer	Points	Solve: Question	Answer
10	$\frac{4}{x} = \frac{6}{9}$; $x = 6$ and $x = -6$	yes; yes	10	$\frac{2y}{3} + \frac{1}{6} = \frac{7}{2} - \frac{1}{6}$	5
20	$\frac{3}{x-7} = \frac{-3}{x+1}$; $x = 3$ and $x = 4$	yes; no	20	$\frac{x}{x+3} = \frac{4}{x+5}$	−4, 3
30	$\frac{8(x-1)}{x-7} = \frac{4}{x-2}$; $x = 4$	no	30	$x + \frac{10}{x-3} = \frac{x^2+3x}{x-2}$	no solution
40	$\frac{1}{2x-1} = \frac{14}{2x+4}$; $x = 3$	no	40	$\frac{2}{x} + \frac{1}{x+1} = \frac{5}{x^2+x}$	1
50	$1 + \frac{2}{x-4} = \frac{15}{x^2-4x}$; $x = -3$ and $x = 5$	yes; yes	50	$\frac{x+3}{x^2+3x-4} = \frac{x+2}{x^2-16}$	−5

Points	Review: Question	Answer
10	What is the next number in the pattern 1, 4, 7, 10, . . . ?	13
20	What is the next number in the pattern 1, −3, 9, −27, . . . ?	81
30	Solve $5n + 2 = 37$.	7
40	What is the 4n term of the expansion of $(2x + 3y)^5$?	$4320x^2y^3$
50	Solve $-6144 = -3(2^n)$.	11

© **Content Standard**
Extends A.REI.11 Explain why the *x*-coordinates of the points where the graphs of the equations $y = f(x)$ and $y = g(x)$ intersect are the solutions of the equation $f(x) = g(x)$ ...

You can solve systems with rational equations using some of same methods you used with linear systems.

Activity 1

Follow each direction to solve the system $\begin{cases} y = \frac{x}{3x - 1} \\ y = \frac{1}{x + 1} \end{cases}$.

1. Set the expressions for *y* equal to each other.

2. Solve for *x*.

3. Check your answer by substituting in the original system.

Activity 2

Follow each direction to solve the system $\begin{cases} x - 2 = \frac{6}{y} \\ y + 1 = x \end{cases}$.

4. Solve each equation for *y*.

5. Set the resulting expressions equal to each other.

6. Solve for *x*.

7. Check your answer by substituting in the original system.

Exercises

Solve each system.

8. $\begin{cases} \frac{y}{x^2 - 4x + 3} = -2 \\ x - 2y = 3 \end{cases}$

9. $\begin{cases} y = \frac{1}{x} \\ y = \frac{3}{4 - x^2} \end{cases}$

10. $\begin{cases} y = x^2 - 2x - 2 \\ y = \frac{x^2 + x - 6}{x + 3} \end{cases}$

11. $\begin{cases} y = \frac{x + 2}{x^2 + 3x + 2} + 2 \\ y - 3 = x \end{cases}$

© 12. **Reasoning** It is possible for the graph of a system of rational equations to include a point of intersection that is an extraneous solution? Explain.

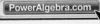

Guided Instruction

PURPOSE To show how methods for solving rational equations can be used to solve systems of rational equations

PROCESS Students will
• solve both equations for one variable and solve to find the intersections.
• set equations equal to each other to find the values of each variable.

DISCUSS Various methods for solving rational equations can be used to solve systems, including
• finding the intersection of the graphs of the equations.
• using algebraic manipulation.

Activity 1

Q Could you solve by eliminating *x*? **[No; adding or subtracting a multiple of the equations would not eliminate the *x*'s in the denominator.]**

Activity 2

Q Why might you choose to solve this system by graphing rather than by substitution? Explain. **[Sample: once you solve for *y*, you can easily enter the equations into the calculator and find the intersection points.]**

© **Mathematical Practices** This Concept Byte supports students in making sense of problems, Mathematical Practice 1.

Answers

Activity 1

1. $\frac{x}{3x - 1} = \frac{1}{x + 1}$

2. $x = 1, y = \frac{1}{2}$

3. no extraneous solutions

Activity 2

4. $y = \frac{6}{x - 2}, y = x - 1$

5. $\frac{6}{x - 2} = x - 1$

6. $x = -1, y = -2; x = 4, y = 3$

7. no extraneous solutions

Exercises

8. $\left(\frac{3}{4}, -\frac{9}{8}\right)$

9. $(1, 1); \left(-4, -\frac{1}{4}\right)$

10. $(0, -2); (3, 1)$

11. $(0, 3)$

12. No; any pts. of intersection in a graph of a system of rational eqs. are solutions to the system.

Guided Instruction

PURPOSE To solve rational inequalities
PROCESS Students will
- solve a rational inequality algebraically.
- solve a rational inequality by graphing.

DISCUSS This Concept Byte introduces three methods to solve a rational inequality. Two of the three methods use a graphing calculator.

Activity 1

Q What part of the graph contains the solution? **[the curve below $y = 3$]**

Q As x increases from 0, what happens to the curve? **[The curve approaches $y = +\infty$.]**

Q As x decreases from 0, what happens to the curve? **[The curve approaches $y = -1$.]**

Q Why is $x = 4$ not part of the solution? **[The graph is undefined at 4.]**

Activity 2

Q What function are you analyzing? **[$y = \frac{x}{4-x}$]**

Q What inequality are you solving? **[$\frac{x}{4-x} < 3$]**

Q What is true of the function when the y-coordinate reads ERROR? **[The function is undefined at that point.]**

Q What is true about all y-values when x is between 3 and 4? **[They are greater than 3.]**

Activity 3

Q Why do you not know the sign of the multiplier? **[It is a variable expression.]**

Ⓒ Mathematical Practices This Concept Byte supports students in becoming proficient in using appropriate tools, Mathematical Practice 5.

Concept Byte
For Use With Lesson 8-6
TECHNOLOGY

Rational Inequalities

Ⓒ Content Standard
Extends A.REI.11 Explain why the x-coordinate the points where the graphs of the equations $y =$ and $y = g(x)$ intersect are the solutions of the eq $f(x) = g(x) \ldots$

Consider the rational inequality $\frac{x}{4-x} < 3$.

Ⓒ MATHEMATICAL PRACTICES

Activity 1

1. Enter $y_1 = \frac{x}{4-x}$ and $y_2 = 3$ in your graphing calculator. Graph the functions using the settings at the right. Use the calculator's **INTERSECT** feature to find where the two functions are equal. Use the graph to find the solution of the inequality $\frac{x}{4-x} < 3$.

WINDOW
Xmin=-6
Xmax=12
Xscl=1
Ymin=-7
Ymax=5
Yscl=1
Xres=1 ▇

Activity 2

Using the functions you entered in Activity 1, set up the table as shown.

2. Scroll to x-values less than 3. Do they make the inequality true?

3. Scroll to x-values greater than 4. Do they make the inequality true?

4. What happens to the inequality when $x = 3$? When $x = 4$?

5. Change ΔTbl to 0.1. Investigate the inequality between $x = 3$ and $x = 4$.

6. Make a conjecture about the solution of the inequality based on your results in Steps 2–5.

Activity 3

Now use algebra to solve the inequality. You can multiply both sides of a rational inequality by the same algebraic expression just as you have done with equations. But you must keep in mind the properties of inequalities. Consider the first step, multiplying each side by $(4 - x)$.

$$\frac{x}{4-x} < 3$$

$$(4-x)\frac{x}{4-x} < (4-x)3$$

Depending on whether the factor $(4 - x)$ is positive or negative, there are two possible solutions to the inequality.

Answers

Activity 1

1.
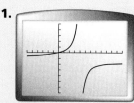

Activity 2

2. yes   3. yes

4. $y_1(3) = 3$; not true; $y_1(4)$ is undefined.

5. The values of y_1 increase from 3 to 39 between $x = 3$ and $x = 3.9$. At $x = 4$, the denominator approaches 0 and y_1 becomes undefined.

6. $x < 3$ or $x > 4$

Activity 3

7. **a.** Mult. Prop. of Inequality
   b. Distr. Prop. of Inequality and Inverse Prop. of Mult.
   c. Add. Prop. of Inequality
   d. Div. Prop. of Inequality

8. $x < 3$

9. **a.** Mult. Prop. of Inequality
   b. Distr. Prop. of Inequality and Inverse Prop. of Mult.
   c. Add. Prop. of Inequality
   d. Div. Prop. of Inequality

10. $x > 4$ 11. $x < 3$ or $x > 4$

Exercises

12. $-1 < x < 1$ or $x > 2$

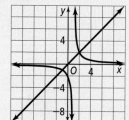

7. First, consider the case where $4 - x > 0$, or $x < 4$. Justify each step.
Hint: The solution must satisfy both $x < 3$ and $x < 4$.

$$\frac{x}{4-x} < 3$$

a. $(4-x)\frac{x}{4-x} < (4-x)3$

b. $\qquad x < 12 - 3x$

c. $\qquad 4x < 12$

d. $\qquad x < 3$

8. Combine this result with the given condition $x < 4$. What is the solution for this case?

9. Now consider the case where $4 - x < 0$, or $x > 4$. Justify each step.
Hint: The solution must satisfy both $x > 3$ and $x > 4$.

$$\frac{x}{4-x} < 3$$

a. $(4-x)\frac{x}{4-x} > (4-x)3$

b. $\qquad x > 12 - 3x$

c. $\qquad 4x > 12$

d. $\qquad x > 3$

10. Combine this result with the given condition $x > 4$. What is the solution for this case?

11. Examine your solutions for Exercises 8 and 10. Now, write the solution of the inequality $\frac{x}{4-x} < 3$.

Exercises

For Exercises 12–17, solve each inequality graphically and algebraically.

12. $\frac{2}{x-1} < x$

13. $x + 1 > \frac{x+5}{x+2}$

14. $\frac{2x}{(x-2)(x+3)} < 1$

15. $\frac{2x+2}{x-1} < x + 1$

16. $\frac{x^2+1}{x} < 2x$

17. $\frac{x-1}{x-2} < \frac{x+3}{x-1}$

18. For Exercises 12–17, check your work by using a table to solve each inequality.

The equation $d = rt$ relates the distance d you travel, the time t it takes to travel that distance, and the rate r at which you travel. So the time it takes to travel a distance d at a rate r is $t = \frac{d}{r}$. If you increase your rate by a to $r + a$, then it takes less time, $t = \frac{d}{r+a}$. In fact, the time you save by going at the faster rate is $T = \frac{d}{r} - \frac{d}{r+a}$.

19. a. You normally take a 500-mi trip, averaging 45 mi/h. You want to increase the rate so that you save at least an hour. Write an inequality that describes the situation.

   b. Solve your inequality from part (a).

Q Could $x < 4$ be the solution? Explain. **[No; the curve is undefined at $x = 4$, and y-values are greater than 3 when x is between 3 and 4.]**

Q Does the result $x < 3$ contradict the given $x < 4$? Explain. **[No; values that are less than 3 are also less than 4.]**

Exercises

Q For Exercise 14, by what expression would you multiply both sides if solving algebraically? **[$(x-2)(x+3)$]**

Q Which exercises result in quadratic equations? **[12–16]**

Q For Exercise 17, what are the undefined values of the curve? **[$x = 1, 2$]**

Q For Exercise 18, how do you determine the table starting value? **[Find any value less than the leftmost undefined value.]**

Q Which Exercises have only one undefined value? **[12, 13, 15, 16]**

Q In Exercise 19, identify d, r, and T. **[500, 45, 1]**

Q In Exercise 19, if you change the equation form to an inequality, as written, what symbol will you use? **[$\geq$]**

Q If you solve 19 by graphing, what two equations would you graph? **[$y = 1$, $y = \frac{500}{45} - \frac{500}{45+a}$]**

Q Why should you use $y = 1$ instead of $y = 60$? **[The left side of the equation expresses a time difference of one hour not 60 minutes.]**

7–12. See page 550.

13. 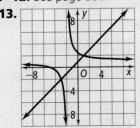 $-3 < x < -2$ or $x > 1$

14. 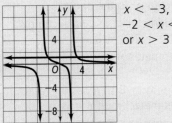 $x < -3$, $-2 < x < 2$, or $x > 3$

15. 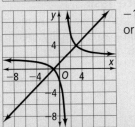 $-1 < x < 1$ or $x > 3$

16. $-1 < x < 0$ or $x > 1$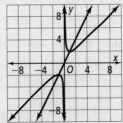

17. $x > \frac{7}{3}$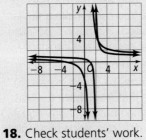

18. Check students' work.

19. a. $\frac{500}{45} - \frac{500}{45+a} \geq 1$

   b. $a \geq 4\frac{41}{91}$

Performance Task

Pull It All Together

Understanding by Design principles indicate the importance of performance tasks that assess understanding.

- Make sense of problems and persevere in solving them.
- Construct viable arguments.

The following questions are designed to

- Help support students as they do the Performance Tasks.
- Help you gauge their progress toward becoming mathematically proficient.

Performance Task 1

Use a function to model and solve a problem.

- What equation represents the perimeter of rectangle *R*? For which variable should you solve?

Performance Task 2

Write a function to model a problem and analyze the function to solve a problem.

- What equation represents the area of rectangle *R*? For which variable should you solve?

Performance Task 3

Analyze the relationship between a function and its parent function.

- What are the linear factors of the numerator and denominator?

Performance Task 4

Write and solve a rational equation to solve a work problem.

- How can you use rational expressions to write the rates for each person working alone and the combined rate of working together?

Pull It All Together ASSESSMENT

To solve these problems, you will pull together concepts and skills related to rational expressions, functions, and equations.

BIG idea Proportionality

Inverse proportionality involves a relationship in which the products of two quantities remain constant as the corresponding values of the quantities change.

Performance Task 1

Rectangle *R* has varying length ℓ and width *w* but a constant perimeter of 4 ft.
- **a.** Express the area *A* as a function of ℓ. What do you know about this function?
- **b.** For what values of ℓ and *w* will the area of *R* be greatest? Give an algebraic argument. Give a geometric argument.

Performance Task 2

Rectangle *R* has varying length ℓ and width *w* but a constant area of 4 ft².
- **a.** Express the perimeter *P* as a function of ℓ. What kind of function is *P*? What is its domain?
- **b.** What are the asymptotes of *P*? Describe the look of the rectangle close to the asymptotes. Explain why you couldn't make a similar description of the rectangle in Performance Task 1.
- **c.** For what values of ℓ and *w* will the perimeter of *R* be least? Give a calculator-based argument. Give a geometric argument.

BIG idea Function

You can represent functions in a variety of ways (such as graphs, tables, equations, or words). Each representation is particularly useful in certain situations.

Performance Task 3

Study the function $f(x) = \dfrac{x^2 + x - 6}{x^2 - 5x + 6}$.
- **a.** Describe the points of discontinuity for the function. Explain your answers.
- **b.** How can you use the equation $x + 3 = x - 3 + 6$ to create an equivalent form of *f* to show how the graph of *f* is related to the graph of $y = \frac{1}{x}$? Describe the relationship.

BIG idea Equivalence

You can use symbols to represent an equation in an unlimited number of ways, where all equations have the same solution.

Performance Task 4

Delia and Kari have the same size bathroom. It takes Delia 3 hours longer to finish tiling her bathroom than Kari. If they work together it takes them 2 hours to lay the tiles per bathroom. How long does it take Kari to lay the tiles in her bathroom by herself? How long does it take Delia to finish her bathroom if she works alone? Show your work.

Assess Performance

Pull It All Together

See p. 49 for a holistic scoring rubric to gauge a student's progress on Understanding the Problem, Planning a Solution, Getting an Answer, and Assessing Autonomy.

SOLUTION OUTLINES

Performance Task 1

- **a.** Represent the perimeter of rectangle *R*. ($2 = \ell + w$) Solve for *w*. ($w = 2 - \ell$) Substitute your result into $A = \ell w$. ($A = 2\ell - \ell^2$; *A* is a polynomial function of degree 2.)
- **b.** Algebraic argument: Factor -1 from $2\ell - \ell^2$ to get $-(\ell^2 - 2\ell)$. Complete the square to get $A = -(\ell + 1)^2 + 1$. The vertex of the parabola represents the maximum area. ($\ell = 1$, $w = 1$) Geometric argument: Graph your result for part (a) and find the maximum value.

Performance Task 2

- **a.** Represent the area of rectangle *R*. ($4 = \ell \cdot w$) Solve for *w*. $\left(w = \dfrac{4}{\ell}\right)$ Substitute into $P = 2\ell + 2w$. ($P = 2\ell + \dfrac{8}{\ell}$; *P* is a rational function. The domain is all real numbers except $x = 0$.)
- **b.** Graph your result from part (a). (The graph of $P = 2\ell + \dfrac{8}{\ell}$ is asymptotic to the *y*-axis and the line $y = 2x$. *R* can be very long and narrow near the asymptotes. You can't make a similar statement about *R* in Task 1, because in Task 1 the perimeter is constant.)
- **c.** Geometric argument:

  First step: From the graph in part (b), you can see that *R* will have the least perimeter when both ℓ and *w* equal 2. To prove this, consider a rectangle with area 4 and dimensions $(2 - x)$ and $(2 + y)$.

  Second step: Represent the area of the new rectangle. ($4 = (2 - x)(2 + y)$ or $-2x + 2y = xy$)

  Third step: Represent the perimeter of the new rectangle. ($P = 2(2 - x) + 2(2 + y)$ or $P = 8 - 2x + 2y$)

  Fourth step: Use your results to compare the perimeter of the new rectangle to the original.

  (Perimeter of original rectangle: $2(2) + 2(2) = 8$;

  Perimeter of new rectangle:
  $8 - 2x + 2y = 8 + xy$;
  $8 + xy > 8$ so *R* has the least perimeter when $\ell = w = 2$.)

Performance Task 3

- **a.** Possible Plan: Factor the numerator and denominator. Simplify. Identify any points of discontinuity.

8 Chapter Review

Connecting BIG ideas and Answering the Essential Questions

1 Proportionality
Quantities x and y are inversely proportional only if growing x by the factor k ($k > 1$) means shrinking y by the factor $\frac{1}{k}$.

Inverse Variation (Lesson 8-1)
Are ℓ and w inversely proportional?
$A = \ell w$
$P = 2\ell + 2w$
- for a constant area—yes
- for a constant perimeter—no

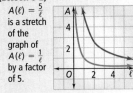

The Reciprocal Function Family (Lesson 8-2)
$A(\ell) = \frac{5}{\ell}$ is a stretch of the graph of $A(\ell) = \frac{1}{\ell}$ by a factor of 5.

2 Function
A rational function may have no asymptotes, one horizontal or oblique asymptote, and any number of vertical asymptotes.

Rational Functions and Their Graphs (Lesson 8-3)
Asymptotes:
For $y = \frac{2x^2}{x^2 - 9}$
horizontal: $y = 2$
vertical: $x = \pm 3$
For $y = \frac{2x^3 + 6x^2}{x^2 + 1}$
oblique: $y = 2x + 6$.
$y = \frac{x^4 + 5}{x^2 + 1}$ has no asymptotes.

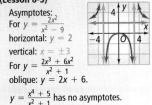

Solving Equations Involving Rational Expressions (Lessons 8-4, 8-5, and 8-6)
$\frac{2x^2}{x^2 - 9} = \frac{x - 6}{x - 3} + \frac{18}{x^2 - 9}$
$\frac{2x^2}{x^2 - 9} = \frac{(x - 6)(x + 3)}{(x - 3)(x + 3)} + \frac{18}{x^2 - 9}$
$2x^2 = x^2 - 3x - 18 + 18$
$x^2 + 3x = 0$
$x(x + 3) = 0$
$x = 0$ ✓   or $x = -3$ ✗

3 Equivalence
$f(x) = \frac{x + a}{x^2 - a^2}$, $x \neq \pm a$, and $g(x) = \frac{1}{x - a}$, $x \neq \pm a$, are equivalent.

Chapter Vocabulary

- branch (p. 508)
- combined variation (p. 501)
- complex fraction (p. 536)
- continuous graph (p. 516)
- discontinuous graph (p. 516)
- inverse variation (p. 498)
- joint variation (p. 501)
- non-removable discontinuity (p. 516)
- oblique asymptote (p. 524)
- point of discontinuity (p. 516)
- rational equation (p. 542)
- rational expression (p. 527)
- rational function (p. 515)
- reciprocal function (p. 507)
- removable discontinuity (p. 516)
- simplest form (p. 527)

Choose the correct term to complete each sentence.

1. When the numerator and denominator of a rational expression are polynomials with no common factors, the rational expression is in   ? .

2. If a quantity varies directly with one quantity and inversely with another, it is a(n)   ? .

3. A(n)   ?   has a fraction in its numerator, denominator, or both.

4. If a is a zero of the polynomial denominator of a rational function, the function has a(n)   ?   at $x = a$.

5. A(n)   ?   of the graph of a rational function is one of the continuous pieces of its graph.

PowerAlgebra.com | Chapter 8   Chapter Review | 553

Essential Questions

BIG idea Proportionality
ESSENTIAL QUESTION Are two quantities inversely proportional if an increase in one corresponds to a decrease in the other?
ANSWER Quantities x and y are inversely proportional only if increasing x by the factor k ($k > 1$) means shrinking y by the factor $\frac{1}{k}$.

BIG idea Function
ESSENTIAL QUESTION What kinds of asymptotes are possible for a rational function?
ANSWER A rational function may have zero or one horizontal or oblique asymptote, and zero or more vertical asymptotes.

BIG idea Equivalence
ESSENTIAL QUESTION Are a rational expression and its simplified form equivalent?
ANSWER $f(x) = \frac{(x + a)}{(x^2 + a^2)}$, $x \neq \pm a$, and $g(x) = \frac{1}{(x - a)}$, $x \neq \pm a$, are equivalent.

$f(x) = \frac{x^2 + x - 6}{x^2 - 5x + 6} = \frac{(x - 2)(x + 3)}{(x - 2)(x - 3)} = \frac{(x + 3)}{(x - 3)}$; There is a nonremovable point of discontinuity at $x = 3$. There is a removable discontinuity at $x = 2$.

b. Dividing each side of the equation by $x - 3$ gives you $\frac{x + 3}{x - 3} = 1 + \frac{6}{x - 3}$. $\frac{x + 3}{x - 3}$ is now in the form $y = \frac{a}{x - h} + k$. So, the graph of $f(x)$ is a transformation of $y = \frac{1}{x}$.

Performance Task 4

Possible Plan: Write expressions for each person's rate working alone. The sum of the two rates working alone equals the rate working together.

If it takes Kari x hours to finish, then her rate is $\frac{1}{x}$. It takes Delia 3 hours longer, so her rate is $\frac{1}{x + 3}$.

It takes Delia and Kari 2 hours to finish a bathroom working together,

so the combined rate is $\frac{1}{2}$. Write an equation and solve for x.

$\frac{1}{x} + \frac{1}{x + 3} = \frac{1}{2}$

Multiplying by $2x(x + 3)$ gives you $2(x + 3) + 2x = x^2 + 3x$, which simplifies to $0 = x^2 - x - 6$. Solving for x, the solutions are $x = 3$ or $x = -2$. Since time cannot be negative, $x = 3$. So, it takes Kari 3 hours working alone and Delia 6 hours working alone.

Answers

Chapter Review

1. simplest form
2. combined variation
3. complex fraction
4. pt. of discontinuity
5. branch

Summative Questions

Use the following prompts as you review this chapter with your students. The prompts are designed to help you assess your students' understanding of the BIG ideas they have studied.

- When one value changes with respect to another, how can you tell whether they show inverse or direct variation?
- When you simplify rational expressions, why must you include any restrictions on the domain of the original expression, even when they are not restrictions on the simplified form?
- How are operations with rational expressions like operations with fractions? How are they different?
- What would be the first step in the solution process of $\frac{x}{x + 2} - \frac{x}{x - 2} = \frac{3}{x^2 - 4}$ if solved algebraically? graphically?

Chapter Review   **553**

Answers

Chapter Review (continued)

6. 12

7. $y = \frac{72}{x}$

8. $y = 6x$

9. $z = \frac{7}{4}xy$; 56

10. $z = \frac{4x}{y}$; 2

11.

no x- or y-intercept; vert. asymptote: $x = 0$, horizontal asymptote: $y = 0$

12.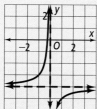

no x- or y-intercept; vert. asymptote: $x = 0$, horizontal asymptote: $y = 0$

13.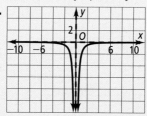

x-intercept: $(-0.25, 0)$, no y-intercept; vert. asymptote: $x = 0$, horizontal asymptote: $y = -4$

14.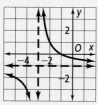

x-intercept: $(-1, 0)$, y-intercept: $\left(0, -\frac{1}{3}\right)$; vert. asymptote: $x = -3$, horizontal asymptote: $y = -1$

15. $y = \frac{4}{x} + 3$

16. $y = \frac{4}{x - 2} + 2$

17. $y = \frac{4}{x + 3} - 4$

18. $y = \frac{4}{x - 4} - 3$

8-1 Inverse Variation

Quick Review

An equation in two variables of the form $y = \frac{k}{x}$ or $xy = k$, where $k \neq 0$, is an **inverse variation** with a **constant of variation** k. **Joint variation** describes when one quantity varies directly with two or more other quantities.

Example

Suppose that x and y vary inversely, and $x = 10$ when $y = 15$. Write a function that models the inverse variation. Find y when $x = 6$.

$y = \frac{k}{x}$

$15 = \frac{k}{10}$, so $k = 150$.

The inverse variation is $y = \frac{150}{x}$.

When $x = 6$, $y = \frac{150}{6} = 25$.

Exercises

6. Suppose that x and y vary inversely, and $x = 30$ when $y = 2$. Find y when $x = 5$.

Write a direct or inverse variation equation for each relation.

7.

x	3	4	8
y	24	18	9

8.

x	5	7	9
y	30	42	54

Write the function that models each relationship. Find z when $x = 4$ and $y = 8$.

9. z varies jointly with x and y. When $x = 2$ and $y = 2$, $z = 7$.

10. z varies directly with x and inversely with y. When $x = 5$ and $y = 2$, $z = 10$.

8-2 The Reciprocal Function Family

Quick Review

The graph of a **reciprocal function** has two parts called **branches**. The graph of $y = \frac{k}{x - b} + c$ is a translation of $y = \frac{k}{x}$ by b units horizontally and c units vertically. It has a vertical asymptote at $x = b$ and a horizontal asymptote at $y = c$.

Example

Graph the equation $y = \frac{3}{x - 2} + 1$. Identify the x- and y-intercepts and the asymptotes of the graph.

$b = 2$, so the vertical asymptote is $x = 2$.

$c = 1$, so the horizontal asymptote is $y = 1$.

Translate $y = \frac{3}{x}$ two units to the right and one unit up.

When $y = 0$, $x = -1$.

The x-intercept is $(-1, 0)$.

When $x = 0$, $y = -\frac{1}{2}$.

The y-intercept is $\left(0, -\frac{1}{2}\right)$.

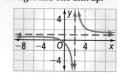

Exercises

Graph each equation. Identify the x- and y-intercepts and the asymptotes of the graph.

11. $y = \frac{1}{x}$

12. $y = \frac{-2}{x^2}$

13. $y = \frac{-1}{x} - 4$

14. $y = \frac{2}{x + 3} - 1$

Write an equation for the translation of $y = \frac{4}{x}$ that has the given asymptotes.

15. $x = 0, y = 3$

16. $x = 2, y = 2$

17. $x = -3, y = -4$

18. $x = 4, y = -3$

8-3 Rational Functions and Their Graphs

Quick Review

The **rational function** $f(x) = \frac{P(x)}{Q(x)}$ has a **point of discontinuity** for each real zero of $Q(x)$.

If $P(x)$ and $Q(x)$ have

- no common factors, then $f(x)$ has a vertical asymptote when $Q(x) = 0$.
- a common real zero a, then there is a hole or a vertical asymptote at $x = a$.
- degree of $P(x) <$ degree of $Q(x)$, then the graph of $f(x)$ has a horizontal asymptote at $y = 0$.
- degree of $P(x) =$ degree of $Q(x)$, then there is a horizontal asymptote at $y = \frac{a}{b}$, where a and b are the coefficients of the terms of greatest degree in $P(x)$ and $Q(x)$, respectively.
- degree of $P(x) >$ degree of $Q(x)$, then there is no horizontal asymptote.

Example

Find any points of discontinuity for the graph of the rational function $y = \frac{2.5}{x + 7}$. Describe any vertical or horizontal asymptotes and any holes.

There is a vertical asymptote at $x = -7$ and a horizontal asymptote at $y = 0$.

Exercises

Find any points of discontinuity for each rational function. Sketch the graph. Describe any vertical or horizontal asymptotes and any holes.

19. $y = \frac{x - 1}{(x + 2)(x - 1)}$

20. $y = \frac{x^3 - 1}{x^2 - 1}$

21. $y = \frac{2x^2 + 3}{x^2 + 2}$

22. The start-up cost of a company is $150,000. It costs \$.17 to manufacture each headset. Graph the function that represents the average cost of a headset. How many must be manufactured to result in a cost of less than $5 per headset?

8-4 Rational Expressions

Quick Review

A **rational expression** is in **simplest form** when its numerator and denominator are polynomials that have no common factors.

Example

Simplify the rational expression. State any restrictions on the variable.

$$\frac{2x^2 + 7x + 3}{x - 4} \cdot \frac{x^2 - 16}{x^2 + 8x + 15}$$

$$= \frac{(2x + 1)(x + 3)}{x - 4} \cdot \frac{(x - 4)(x + 4)}{(x + 3)(x + 5)}$$

$$= \frac{(2x + 1)(x + 4)}{x + 5}, x \neq -5, x \neq -3, \text{ and } x \neq 4$$

Exercises

Simplify each rational expression. State any restrictions on the variable.

23. $\frac{x^2 + 10x + 25}{x^2 + 9x + 20}$

24. $\frac{x^2 - 2x - 24}{x^2 + 7x + 12} \cdot \frac{x^2 - 1}{x - 6}$

25. $\frac{4x^2 - 2x}{x^2 + 5x + 4} \div \frac{2x}{x^2 + 2x + 1}$

26. What is the ratio of the volume of a sphere to its surface area?

19. pts. of discontinuity: $x = -2, 1$;

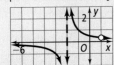

vert. asymptote: $x = -2$, horizontal asymptote: $y = 0$; hole at $x = 1$

20. pts. of discontinuity: $x = 1, -1$

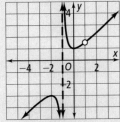

vert. asymptote: $x = -1$; hole at $x = 1$

21. no pts. of discontinuity

horizontal asymptote: $y = 2$

22.

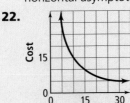

$\approx 31{,}056$ headsets

23. $\frac{x + 5}{x + 4}$; $x \neq -4$ or -5

24. $\frac{(x - 1)(x + 1)}{x + 3}$; $x \neq -4, -3,$ or 6

25. $\frac{(2x - 1)(x + 1)}{x + 4}$; $x \neq -4, -1,$ or 0

26. $\frac{r}{3}$, where r is the radius

Answers

Chapter Review (continued)

27. $\dfrac{3(3x - 4)}{(x - 2)(x + 2)}$; $x \neq \pm 2$

28. $\dfrac{-x^2 + 3x + 2}{x(x + 1)(x - 1)(x + 3)}$; $x \neq \pm 1, 0,$ or -3

29. $\dfrac{2(x - 1)}{3x - 1}$

30. $\dfrac{1}{4(x + y)}$

31. -1

32. no solution

33. $-12, 9$

34. you: 10 mi/h friend: 8 mi/h

8-5 Adding and Subtracting Rational Expressions

Quick Review

To add or subtract rational expressions with different denominators, write each expression with the LCD. A fraction that has a fraction in its numerator or denominator or in both is called a **complex fraction**. Sometimes you can simplify a complex fraction by multiplying the numerator and denominator by the LCD of all the rational expressions.

Example

Simplify the complex fraction. $\dfrac{\frac{1}{x} + 3}{\frac{5}{y} + 4}$

$$\frac{\frac{1}{x} + 3}{\frac{5}{y} + 4} = \frac{\left(\frac{1}{x} + 3\right) \cdot xy}{\left(\frac{5}{x} + 4\right) \cdot xy}$$

$$= \frac{\frac{1}{x} \cdot xy + 3 \cdot xy}{\frac{5}{x} \cdot xy + 4 \cdot xy}$$

$$= \frac{y + 3xy}{5y + 4xy}$$

Exercises

Simplify the sum or difference. State any restrictions on the variable.

27. $\dfrac{3x}{x^2 - 4} + \dfrac{6}{x + 2}$

28. $\dfrac{1}{x^2 - 1} - \dfrac{2}{x^2 + 3x}$

Simplify the complex fraction.

29. $\dfrac{2 - \frac{2}{x}}{3 - \frac{1}{x}}$

30. $\dfrac{\frac{1}{x + y}}{4}$

8-6 Solving Rational Equations

Quick Review

Solving a **rational equation** often requires multiplying each side by an algebraic expression. This may introduce extraneous solutions—solutions that solve the derived equation but not the original equation. Check all possible solutions in the original equation.

Example

Solve the equation. Check your solution.

$$\frac{1}{2x} - \frac{2}{5x} = \frac{1}{2}$$

$$10x\left(\frac{1}{2x} - \frac{2}{5x}\right) = 10x\left(\frac{1}{2}\right)$$

$$5 - 4 = 5x$$

$$x = \frac{1}{5}$$

Check $\dfrac{1}{2\left(\frac{1}{5}\right)} - \dfrac{2}{5\left(\frac{1}{5}\right)} = \dfrac{5}{2} - 2 = \dfrac{1}{2}$ ✔

Exercises

Solve each equation. Check your solutions.

31. $\dfrac{1}{x} = \dfrac{5}{x - 4}$

32. $\dfrac{2}{x + 3} - \dfrac{1}{x} = \dfrac{-6}{x(x + 3)}$

33. $\dfrac{1}{2} + \dfrac{x}{6} = \dfrac{18}{x}$

34. You travel 10 mi on your bicycle in the same amount of time it takes your friend to travel 8 mi on his bicycle. If your friend rides his bike 2 mi/h slower than you ride your bike, find the rate at which each of you is traveling.

Do you know HOW?

Write a function that models each variation.

1. $x = 2$ when $y = -8$, and y varies inversely with x.

2. $x = 0.2$ and $y = 3$ when $z = 2$, and z varies jointly with x and y.

3. $x = \frac{1}{3}$, $y = \frac{1}{5}$, and $r = 3$ when $z = \frac{1}{2}$, and z varies directly with x and inversely with the product of r^2 and y.

Is the relationship between the values in each table a *direct variation*, an *inverse variation*, or *neither*? Write equations to model any direct or inverse variations.

4.

x	y
3	6
5	8
7	10
9	12

5.

x	y
4	32
8	16
16	8
32	4

Write and graph an equation of the translation of $y = \frac{7}{x}$ that has the given asymptotes.

6. $x = 1; y = 2$　　**7.** $x = -3; y = -2$

For each rational function, identify any holes or horizontal or vertical asymptotes of the graph.

8. $y = \frac{x+1}{x-1}$　　　　**9.** $y = \frac{x+3}{x+3}$

10. $y = \frac{x-2}{(x+1)(x-2)}$　　**11.** $y = \frac{2x^2}{x^2-4x}$

12. $y = \frac{1}{x+2} - 3$　　**13.** $y = \frac{x^2+5}{x-5}$

Simplify each complex fraction.

14. $\dfrac{\frac{2}{x}}{1 - \frac{1}{y}}$　　　　**15.** $\dfrac{3 - \frac{3}{x}}{\frac{1}{2} - \frac{1}{x}}$

Simplify each rational expression. State any restrictions on the variable.

16. $\dfrac{x^2 + 7x + 12}{x^2 - 9}$

17. $\dfrac{(x+3)(2x-1)}{x(x+4)} \div \dfrac{(-x-3)(2x+1)}{x}$

18. $\dfrac{x^2 - 1}{x^2 + 2x - 3} - \dfrac{x+1}{x+3}$

19. $\dfrac{x(x+4)}{x-2} + \dfrac{x-1}{x^2-4}$

Solve each equation. Check your solutions.

20. $\frac{x}{2} = \frac{x+1}{4}$　　**21.** $\frac{3}{x-1} = \frac{4}{3x+2}$

22. $\frac{3x}{x+1} = 0$　　　　**23.** $\frac{3}{x+1} = \frac{1}{x^2-1}$

24. $\frac{1}{x} + \frac{1}{3} = \frac{6}{x^2}$　　**25.** $\frac{1}{x} + \frac{x}{x+2} = 1$

26. Your neighbor can seal your driveway in 4 hours. Working together, you and your neighbor can seal it in 2.3 hours. How long would it take you to seal it working alone?

Do you UNDERSTAND?

27. Vocabulary Describe a situation that represents an inverse variation.

28. Compare and Contrast How is simplifying rational expressions similar to simplifying fractions? How is it different?

29. Writing When does a discontinuity result in a vertical asymptote? When does it result in a hole in the graph?

30. Open-Ended Write a function whose graph has a hole, a vertical asymptote, and a horizontal asymptote.

31. Reasoning State any restrictions on the variable in the complex fraction. $\dfrac{\frac{x-3}{x+4}}{\frac{x^2-1}{x}}$

17. $-\dfrac{2x-1}{(x+4)(2x+1)}$; $x \neq -4, -3, -\frac{1}{2}$, or 0

18. 0; $x \neq -3$ or 1

19. $\dfrac{x^3 + 6x^2 + 9x - 1}{x^2 - 4}$; $x \neq \pm 2$

20. 1

21. -2

22. 0

23. $\frac{4}{3}$

24. -6, or 3

25. 2

26. ≈ 5.4 h

27. Check students' work.

28. Answers may vary. Sample: In both situations, you find common factors and cancel them. Also, the denominator cannot be zero. Rational expressions may contain variable expressions, whereas fractions may contain only numbers.

29. A discontinuity is a vert. asymptote when the denominator is zero and the numerator and denominator have no common factors. When the numerator and denominator have a common factor a, then the discontinuity is a hole at $x = a$.

30. Check students' work.

31. $x \neq \pm 1$, 0, or -4

Answers

Chapter Test

1. $y = -\dfrac{16}{x}$

2. $z = \dfrac{10}{3}xy$

3. $z = \dfrac{2.7x}{r^2 y}$

4. neither

5. inv. variation; $y = \dfrac{128}{x}$

6. $y = \dfrac{7}{x-1} + 2$;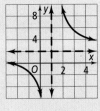

7. $y = \dfrac{7}{x+3} - 2$;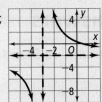

8. vert. asymptote: $x = 1$, horizontal asymptote: $y = 1$

9. hole at $x = -3$

10. hole at $x = 2$; vert. asymptote: $x = -1$, horizontal asymptote: $y = 0$

11. hole at $x = 0$; vert. asymptote: $x = 4$, horizontal asymptote: $y = 2$

12. vert. asymptote: $x = -2$, horizontal asymptote: $y = -3$

13. vert. asymptote: $x = 5$

14. $\dfrac{2y}{x(y-1)}$

15. $\dfrac{6(x-1)}{x-2}$

16. $\dfrac{x+4}{x-3}$; $x \neq -3$, or 3

Item Number	Lesson	© Content Standard
1	8-4	A.SSE.2
2	8-6	A.APR.7
3	7-5	F.LE.4
4	6-6	F.BF.1.b
5	8-5	A.APR.7
6	7-5	F.LE.4
7	6-5	A.REI.2
8	6-3	A.SSE.2
9	6-6	F.BF.1.b
10	4-8	N.CN.2
11	4-1	F.BF.3
12	7-6	F.LE.4
13	8-6	A.CED.1
14	7-5	F.LE.4
15	3-2	A.REI.6
16	5-4	A.APR.6
17	5-2	A.APR.3
18	5-3	A.SSE.2
19	3-6	A.REI.8
20	5-2	A.APR.3
21	6-1	A.SSE.2
22	5-4	A.APR.2
23	1-4	A.CED.4
24	5-1	F.IF.7.c
25	7-1	F.IF.7.e
26	7-5	F.LE.4
27	6-6	F.BF.1.b
28	8-2	F.BF.3
29	6-7	F.BF.4.a
30	4-8	N.CN.7
31	2-7	F.BF.3
32	6-5	A.REI.2

TIPS FOR SUCCESS

Some problems ask you to find the lateral area or the (total) surface area of a three-dimensional figure. Read the sample question at the right. Then follow the tips to answer the question.

What is the approximate lateral area of the cone shown below?

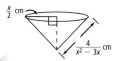

$\frac{x}{2}$ cm

$\frac{4}{x^2 - 3x}$ cm

A $\frac{3}{x + 3}$

C $\frac{3}{x - 3}$

B $\frac{6}{x - 3}$

D $\frac{6}{x + 3}$

TIP 1
Use the formula for the lateral area of a cone: $S = \pi r \ell$.

TIP 2
Use the information from the diagram for the values you need in the formula.

Think It Through

radius: $r = \frac{x}{2}$

slant height: $\ell = \frac{4}{x^2 - 3x}$

$S = \pi r \ell$

$= \pi \left(\frac{x}{2}\right)\left(\frac{4}{x^2 - 3x}\right)$

$= \frac{2\pi}{x - 3}$

Since $\pi \approx 3$, the correct answer is B.

Vocabulary Builder

As you solve test items, you must understand the meanings of mathematical terms. Match each term with its mathematical meaning.

A. joint variation

B. branch

C. point of discontinuity

D. inverse variation

E. reciprocal function

I. a point where the graph of a function breaks into branches

II. each piece of a discontinuous graph

III. a relation represented by an equation of the form $y = \frac{k}{x}$ or $xy = k$, where $k \neq 0$

IV. a function that can be written in the form $f(x) = \frac{a}{x - h} + k$, where $a \neq 0$

V. one variable varies directly with two or more other variables

Multiple Choice

Read each question. Then write the letter of the correct answer on your paper.

1. Which expression equals $\frac{5x}{x^2 - 9} - \frac{4x}{x^2 + 5x + 6}$?

A $\frac{7x}{(x - 3)(x + 3)(x + 2)}$

B $\frac{x^2 - 2x}{(x - 3)(x + 3)(x + 2)}$

C $\frac{x^2 + 22x}{(x - 3)(x + 3)(x + 2)}$

D $\frac{9x^2 - 2x}{(x - 3)(x + 3)(x + 2)}$

2. If x is a real number, for what values of x is the equation $\frac{2x - 8}{4x^{-1}} = \frac{x^2 - 4x}{2}$ true?

F all values of x

G some values of x

H no values of x

I impossible to determine

558 Chapter 8 Cumulative Standards Review

Answers

Cumulative Standards Review

A. V

B. II

C. I

D. III

E. IV

1. C

2. F

3. Which expression represents the solution to $4^x = 13$?

Ⓐ $\dfrac{\log 13}{\log 4}$

Ⓑ $\log_4 + \log_{13}$

Ⓒ $\dfrac{\log 4}{\log 13}$

Ⓓ $\log_{13} 4$

4. If $f(x) = x^2$ and $g(x) = x - 1$, which statement is true?

Ⓕ $f(x) \cdot g(x) = 2x^3 - 1$

Ⓖ $f(x) - g(x) = x - 1$

Ⓗ $f(x) - g(x) = x^2 - x + 1$

Ⓘ $f(x) + g(x) = x^3 - 1$

5. Which expression is a simpler form of the complex fraction $\dfrac{\frac{1}{x} + \frac{3}{y}}{\frac{2}{xy}}$?

Ⓐ $\dfrac{3xy}{2}$ Ⓒ $\dfrac{3}{2}$

Ⓑ $\dfrac{3x + y}{2xy}$ Ⓓ $\dfrac{3x + y}{2}$

6. Which is the first *incorrect* step in simplifying $\log_9 243$?

Step 1: $\log_9 243 = x$

Step 2: $9^x = 243$

Step 3: $x = 243 \div 9$

Step 4: $= 27$

Ⓕ Step 1

Ⓖ Step 2

Ⓗ Step 3

Ⓘ Step 4

7. Which is/are the solution(s) of the equation $\sqrt{2x + 2} = 2x - 4$?

Ⓐ $x = 3.5$ and $x = 1$

Ⓑ $x = 3.5$ and $x = -1$

Ⓒ $x = 3.5$

Ⓓ $x = 1$

8. Which is the simplest form of the expression?
$4\sqrt{18x^4} - 3\sqrt{72x^4}$

Ⓕ $-6x^2\sqrt{2}$ Ⓗ -6

Ⓖ $-6x^2$ Ⓘ none of the above

9. If $g(x) = x^2 - 4$ and $h(x) = 4x - 6$, which expression is equal to $\left(\frac{g}{h}\right)(x)$?

Ⓐ $\dfrac{4x - 6}{x^2 - 4}$

Ⓑ $\dfrac{x^2 - 2}{4x - 3}$

Ⓒ $x^2 - 4 - (4x - 6)$

Ⓓ $\dfrac{(x + 2)(x - 2)}{2(2x - 3)}$

10. If $i = \sqrt{-1}$, what is the value of $-i^4$?

Ⓕ i Ⓗ 1

Ⓖ $-i$ Ⓘ -1

11. The graph below shows the transformation of the function $f(x) = (x + 3)^2$. Which quadratic function models this graph?

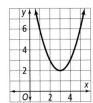

Ⓐ $f(x) = (x - 1)^2$ Ⓒ $f(x) = (x - 3)^2 - 2$

Ⓑ $f(x) = 2(x - 3)^2$ Ⓓ $f(x) = (x - 3)^2 + 2$

12. What is the solution of $3e^{2x} + 1 = 5$?

Ⓕ $x \approx 0.131$ Ⓗ $x \approx 0.187$

Ⓖ $x \approx 0.151$ Ⓘ $x \approx 0.144$

3. A
4. H
5. D
6. H
7. C
8. F
9. D
10. I
11. D
12. I

Answers

Cumulative Standards Review (continued)

13. 5   **14.** 1003   **15.** 1

16. 21   **17.** −12   **18.** −0.89

19. −1   **20.** 4   **21.** 2

22. [2] 35;

$$
\begin{array}{r|rrrr}
2 & 3 & -2 & 1 & 0 & -1 \\
  &   & 6 & 8 & 18 & 36 \\
\hline
  & 3 & 4 & 9 & 18 & 35
\end{array}
$$

    [1] correct method with one computational error.

23. [2] $\dfrac{2g^2}{d} - c = 3x$

$$\dfrac{2g^2}{d} = 3x + c$$

$$2g^2 = d(3x + c)$$

$$g^2 = \tfrac{1}{2}d(3x + c)$$

$$g = \pm\sqrt{\dfrac{d(3x + c)}{2}}$$

    [1] appropriate method with one computational error

24. [2] Since the highest degree of the polynomial is even, the graph does not have up and down end behavior.

    [1] incomplete explanation

25. [2]

    [1] axes are not labeled

26. $\dfrac{\log 13}{\log 4}$

27. $\dfrac{(x + 2)(x - 2)}{2(2x - 3)}$

28. [4] The graph of $y = \frac{3}{x}$ is translated 13 units to the left and 5 units up to get the graph of the eq. $y = \frac{3}{x + 13} + 5$.

    [3] appropriate method, one careless error

    [2] correct eq., incomplete explanation

    [1] correct eq., without explanation

29. [4] $x = y^2 + 15$

    $y = \pm\sqrt{x - 15}$; no; it does not pass the vert. line test.

    [3] one computational error

    [2] incomplete or incorrect explanation

    [1] correct inv., no other questions answered or explained.

30. [4] $\dfrac{-4 \pm \sqrt{4^2 - 24}}{2(3)} = \dfrac{-4 \pm \sqrt{-8}}{6}$

    $x = \dfrac{-2 + 4i}{3}, \dfrac{-2 - 4i}{3}$

    [3] one computational error

    [2] incomplete solution

    [1] correct answer without work shown

---

13. Solve for x: $\dfrac{5}{2x - 2} = \dfrac{15}{x^2 - 1}$.

14. Solve for x: $\log(x - 3) = 3$.

15. What is the value of the x-coordinate of the solution of the system of equations?
$$\begin{cases} 2x + y = 6 \\ y - 3 = x \end{cases}$$

16. What is the remainder when $x^4 - 3x^2 + 7x + 3$ is divided by $x - 2$?

17. The product of three consecutive even integers is −2688. What is the value of the largest integer?

18. What is the smallest zero of $f(x) = 2x^5 - 4x^2 + 3x + 7$? Round your answer to the nearest hundredth.

19. The matrix below represents a linear system of equations. What is the y-coefficient of the first equation of the system?
$$\begin{bmatrix} 3 & -1 & \vline & 5 \\ 1 & 2 & \vline & -1 \end{bmatrix}$$

20. What is the sum of the zeros of the polynomial function $y = x^2 - 4y - 5$?

21. Write the radical expression $\sqrt{50x^5y^3z}$ in simplest form. What is the constant value under the radical sign?

Short Response

22. If $p(x) = 3x^4 - 2x^3 + x^2 - 1$ and $g(x) = x - 2$, what is the remainder of $\dfrac{p(x)}{g(x)}$? Show your work.

23. Solve the equation $\dfrac{2g^2}{d} - c = 3x$ for g. Show your work.

---

24. Explain how you know that the graph of $f(x) = -x^4 - 3x + 7$ does not have up and down end behavior.

25. Graph $y = 3^{x+2} - 5$.

26. How can the solution of $4^x = 13$ be written as a logarithm?

27. If $g(x) = x^2 - 4$ and $h(x) = 4x - 6$, write an expression equivalent to $\left(\frac{g}{h}\right)(x)$ in factored form.

Extended Response

28. Explain how to find an equation for the translation of $y = \frac{3}{x}$ that has asymptotes at $x = -13$ and $y = 5$.

29. What is the inverse of $y = x^2 + 15$? Is the inverse a function? Explain.

30. What are the solutions of $3x^2 + 4x + 2 = 0$? Show your work.

31. You are given the equation $y = 2\,|x - 1| + 3$.

    a. Without graphing, what are the vertex and axis of symmetry of this function?

    b. Describe the transformations from the parent function $y = |x|$.

    c. Sketch the graph.

32. Without solving, explain how you know that the equation $\sqrt{3x - 4} + \sqrt{x + 3} = -2$ has no real solutions.

---

31. [4] a. vertex $(1, 3)$; axis of symmetry $x = 1$

    b. The parent function $y = |x|$ is stretched vertically by a factor of 2 and translated 1 unit to the right and 3 units up.

    c.

    [3] one computational error in one part

    [2] incomplete solution

    [1] incorrect explanation or graph

32. [4] In order for a sum to be negative, one or more of the addends must be negative. Since $\sqrt{3x - 4} \geq 0$ and $\sqrt{x + 3} \geq 0$, the left side of the equation must be positive. Therefore, the equation has no solution.

    [3] minor flaw in logic of explanation

    [2] incorrect use of mathematical language

    [1] incomplete explanation

Get Ready!

Get Ready!

Assign this diagnostic assessment to determine if students have the prerequisite skills for Chapter 9.

Lesson 2-1 ◀ Evaluating Functions

For each function, find $f(1), f(2), f(3),$ and $f(4)$.

1. $f(x) = 2x + 7$

2. $f(x) = 5x - 4$

3. $f(x) = 0.2x + 0.7$

4. $f(x) = -5x + 3$

5. $f(x) = 4x - \frac{2}{3}$

6. $f(x) = -3x - 9$

Lesson 1-1 ◀ Identifying Mathematical Patterns

Identify a pattern and find the next three numbers in the pattern.

7. $9, 4, -1, -6, \ldots$

8. $1, 2, 4, 8, \ldots$

9. $18, 9, 10, 1, 2, \ldots$

10. $7, 10, 13, 16, \ldots$

Lesson 8-5 ◀ Simplifying Complex Fractions

Simplify each complex fraction.

11. $\dfrac{1 - \frac{1}{3}}{\frac{1}{2}}$

12. $\dfrac{\frac{1}{3} + \frac{1}{6}}{\frac{2}{3}}$

13. $\dfrac{1}{1 - \frac{2}{5}}$

14. $\dfrac{1 - \frac{3}{8}}{2 + \frac{1}{4}}$

 Looking Ahead Vocabulary

15. Think of a function and evaluate the function for the input numbers 1, 2, 3, 4, and 5. List the five outputs in order. This list is a *sequence* of numbers. The sequence can be infinitely long.

16. Use a linear function to generate a sequence of five numbers. Beginning with the second number, subtract the number that precedes it. Continue doing this until you have found all four differences. Are the results the same? If so, you have discovered that your sequence has a *common difference*.

17. Now use an exponential function to define your sequence. Instead of subtracting, divide each number by the number that precedes it. Do this until you find all four quotients. Are these four results the same? If so, you have discovered that your sequence has a *common ratio*.

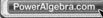

Why Students Need These Skills

Lesson	Skill
2-1	Evaluate Functions
1-1	Identify Mathematical Patterns
8-5	Simplify Complex Fractions

To remediate students, select from these resources (available for every lesson).
- Online Problems (PowerAlgebra.com)
- Reteaching (All-in-One Teaching Resources)
- Practice (All-in-One Teaching Resources)

Why Students Need These Skills
EVALUATING FUNCTIONS
Students will need to evaluate functions when determining the *n*th term in a sequence or series.
IDENTIFYING MATHEMATICAL PATTERNS
Students will need to identify mathematical patterns within sequences to write recursive definitions and explicit formulas for the pattern.
SIMPLIFYING COMPLEX FRACTIONS
Students will need to simplify complex fractions when finding the sum of an infinite geometric series.

Looking Ahead Vocabulary
SEQUENCE Ask students what differentiates a sequence from a set of numbers.
COMMON DIFFERENCE Ask students what it means to have something in common. Have them consider what it means to have a difference in common.
COMMON RATIO Ask students how to find the ratio between two numbers. Have them compare common difference to common ratio.

Answers

Get Ready!

1. 9, 11, 13, 15

2. 1, 6, 11, 16

3. 0.9, 1.1, 1.3, 1.5

4. −2, −7, −12, −17

5. $3\frac{1}{3}, 7\frac{1}{3}, 11\frac{1}{3}, 15\frac{1}{3}$

6. −12, −15, −18, −21

7. subtract 5; −11, −16, −21

8. mult. by 2; 16, 32, 64

9. alternate subtract 9 and add 1; −7, −6, −15

10. add 3; 19, 22, 25

11. $\frac{4}{3}$

12. $\frac{3}{4}$

13. $\frac{5}{3}$

14. $\frac{5}{18}$

15. Answers may vary. Sample: $f(x) = 2x - 1$; 1, 3, 5, 7, 9

16. Answers may vary. Sample: $g(x) = 1 - 2x$; −1, −3, −5, −7, −9; yes; common difference: −2

17. Answers may vary. Sample: $h(x) = 5(2)^x$; 10, 20, 40, 80, 160; yes; common ratio: 2

Chapter 9 Overview

Chapter 9 expands on students' understandings and skills related to sequences and series. In this chapter, students will develop the answers to the Essential Questions posed on the opposite page as they learn the concepts and skills bulleted below.

BIG idea Variable
ESSENTIAL QUESTIONS How can you represent the terms of a sequence explicitly? How can you represent them recursively?
- Students will identify mathematical patterns found in a sequence.
- Students will find a rule to describe a pattern.

BIG idea Equivalence
ESSENTIAL QUESTION What are equivalent explicit and recursive definitions for an arithmetic sequence?
- Students will find the common difference of an arithmetic sequence.

BIG idea Modeling
ESSENTIAL QUESTIONS How can you model a geometric sequence? How can you model its sum?
- Students will find the common ratio of a geometric sequence.
- Students will determine whether a geometric series converges.

© Content Standards

Following are the standards covered in this chapter. Modeling standards are indicated by a star symbol (★)

CONCEPTUAL CATEGORY Algebra
  Domain Seeing Structure in Expressions
    Cluster Write expressions in equivalent forms to solve problems. (Standard A.SSE.4★)
    LESSON 9-5

CONCEPTUAL CATEGORY Functions
  Domain Interpreting Functions
    Cluster Understand the concept of a function and use function notation. (Standard F.IF.3)
    LESSON 9-2

CHAPTER 9

Sequences and Series

Your place to get all things digital

VIDEO
Download videos connecting math to your world.

VOCABULARY
Math definitions in English and Spanish

SOLVE IT!
The online Solve It will get you in gear for each lesson.

DYNAMIC ACTIVITIES
Interactive! Vary numbers, graphs, and figures to explore math concepts.

ONLINE PROBLEMS
Online access to stepped-out problems aligned to Common Core

ONLINE HOMEWORK
Get and view your assignments online.

MathXL FOR SCHOOL
Extra practice and review online

© DOMAINS
- Seeing Structure in Expressions

Arithmetic and geometric sequences are types of patterns. What patterns do you see in these terraced rice fields? You will learn about all kinds of sequences in this chapter.

Vocabulary

English/Spanish Vocabulary Audio Online:

English	Spanish
arithmetic sequence, p. 572	progresión aritmética
arithmetic series, p. 587	serie aritmética
common difference, p. 572	diferencia común
common ratio, p. 580	razón común
converge, p. 598	convergir
diverge, p. 598	divergir
explicit formula, p. 565	fórmula explícita
geometric sequence, p. 580	progresión geométrica
geometric series, p. 595	serie geométrica
limits, p. 589	límites
recursive formula, p. 565	formula recursiva

Chapter 9 Overview

Use these online assets to engage your students. These include support for the Solve It and step-by-step solutions for Problems.

 Show the student-produced video demonstrating relevant and engaging applications of the new concepts in the chapter.

 Find online definitions for new terms in English and Spanish.

 Start each lesson with an attention-getting Problem. View the Problem online with helpful hints.

My Math Video

My Math Video
Use this photo to introduce students to mathematical patterns.

Q What pattern do you see in the planted rice seedlings? **[Samples: rows and columns are the same distance apart; a pattern of squares with seedlings at the vertices]**

Q What pattern do you see in the differences between the heights of the terraced rice fields? **[The difference between the heights of any two consecutive terraces is about the same.]**

Q If a worker is planting a row of rice seedlings 30 cm. apart, how far will the nth seedling be from the first? **[$30(n-1)$ cm.]**

EXTENSION

Have students research how and why rice is planted in this pattern. One method of planting in this pattern is to tie strings to evenly spaced sticks on the edges of the fields. Planting rice in this way increases the production.

BIG ideas

1 **Variable**
Essential Questions How can you represent the terms of a sequence explicitly? How can you represent them recursively?

2 **Equivalence**
Essential Question What are equivalent explicit and recursive definitions for an arithmetic sequence?

3 **Modeling**
Essential Questions How can you model a geometric sequence? How can you model its sum?

Chapter Preview

PowerAlgebra.com   **Chapter 9** Sequences and Series   563

 Increase students' depth of knowledge with interactive online activities.

 Show Problems from each lesson solved step by step. Instant replay allows students to go at their own pace when studying online.

 Assign homework to individual students or to an entire class.

 Prepare students for the Mid-Chapter Quiz and Chapter Test with online practice and review.

SEQUENCES AND SERIES
Math Background ©PROFESSIONAL DEVELOPMENT

Understanding by Design principles were central to the development of the Big Ideas and the Essential Understandings. These will help your students build a structure on which to make connections to prior learning.

Variable

BIG idea Quantities are used to form expressions, equations, and inequalities. An expression refers to a quantity but does not make a statement about it. An equation (or an inequality) is a statement about the quantities it mentions. Using variables in place of numbers in equations (or inequalities) allows the statement of relationships among numbers that are unknown or unspecified.

ESSENTIAL UNDERSTANDINGS

9-1 If the numbers in a list follow a pattern, variables may be used to relate each number in the list to its numerical position in the list.

9-2 In an arithmetic sequence, the difference between any two consecutive terms is always the same number. This number can be represented by a variable.

9-4 When two terms and the number of terms in a finite arithmetic sequence are known, they can be substituted for variables in a formula to find the sum of the terms.

Equivalence

BIG idea A single quantity may be represented by many different expressions. The facts about a quantity may be expressed by many different equations (or inequalities).

ESSENTIAL UNDERSTANDINGS

9-1 If the numbers in a list follow a pattern, each number in the list can be related to its numerical position in the list with more than one equivalent rules.

9-2 In an arithmetic sequence, the difference between any two consecutive terms is always the same number. An arithmetic sequence can be built by adding the same number to each term.

9-4 When two terms and the number of terms in a finite arithmetic sequence are known, one of equivalent formulas can be used to find the sum of the terms.

Modeling

BIG idea Many real-world mathematical problems can be represented algebraically. These representations can lead to algebraic solutions.

ESSENTIAL UNDERSTANDINGS

9-1 If the numbers in a list follow a pattern, a model can relate each number in the list to its numerical position in the list with a rule.

9-3 In a geometric sequence, the ratio of any term (after the first) to its preceding term is a constant value, no matter what two terms are compared. A geometric sequence can be built by multiplying each term by that constant.

9-5 Just as with finite arithmetic series, the sum of a finite geometric series can be found using a formula. The first term, the number of terms, and the common ratio must be known.

Arithmetic Sequences and Series

A **sequence** is an ordered list of numbers. Each number in a sequence is a *term* of the sequence.

An **arithmetic sequence** is a sequence where the difference between consecutive terms is constant. This difference is the common difference d.

Example: Is the sequence 6, 10, 14, 18, . . . arithmetic?

Using consecutive terms:

$10 - 6 = 4$ $14 - 10 = 4$ $18 - 14 = 4$

The difference between consecutive terms is constant, therefore the sequence is arithmetic.

Explicit Formula

An explicit formula can be used to represent terms or find a certain term. For an arithmetic sequence, the nth term is given by the formula $a_n = a_1 + (n - 1)d$, for $n \geq 1$.

Example: Find the 20th term of the arithmetic sequence 8, 11, 14, 17, . . .

$d = 11 - 8 = 3, a = 8, n = 20$

$a_{20} = 8 + (20 - 1)3 = 65$

Arithmetic Series

An arithmetic series is the sum of terms in an arithmetic sequence. The sum of a finite series can be found with the formula $S_n = \frac{n}{2}(a_1 + a_n)$.

Example: Find the sum of $5 + 10 + 15 + . . . + 150$.

$a_1 = 5, a_n = 150, n = \frac{150}{5} = 30$

$S_n = \frac{30}{2}(5 + 150) = 2325$

Summation Notation

Summation notation can be used to represent finite and infinite arithmetic series.

Upper limit $\rightarrow$

Lower limit $\rightarrow$ $\displaystyle\sum_{n=1}^{10} 4n + 1$ $\leftarrow$ Explicit formula

The sum is $S_n = \frac{10}{2}(5 + 41) = 230$.

Common Errors With Arithmetic Sequences and Series

Students should not assume that two terms can be used to determine an explicit formula. For example, the sequence 3, 6, . . . could be arithmetic or geometric.

When using **summation notation**, students must remember to count the actual number of terms rather than looking at the upper limit. For example, if the lower limit is 0 and the upper limit is 10, the number of terms is 11.

©Mathematical Practices

Model with mathematics. Make sense of problems and persevere in solving them. Sequences and series (general, arithmetic, and geometric) are introduced as models of patterned real-world behavior in familiar contexts.

Geometric Sequences and Series

A **geometric sequence** is a sequence in which the ratio of any term (after the first) to its preceding term is a constant value.

Example: Is the sequence 2, 6, 18, 54 geometric?

Using consecutive terms:

$\frac{6}{2} = 3 \qquad \frac{18}{6} = 3 \qquad \frac{54}{18} = 3$

The ratio is constant. This is a geometric sequence in which the common ratio is 3.

Explicit Formula

An explicit formula is used to represent terms or find a term. The nth term of a geometric sequence is given by the formula $a_n = a_1 r^{n-1}$, for $n \geq 1$.

Example: Find the 11th term of the geometric sequence 4, −8, 16, −32, . . .

$r = \frac{-8}{4} = -2, a_1 = 4, n = 11$

$a_{11} = (4)(-2)^{10} = 4096$

Geometric Series

A geometric series is the sum of terms in a geometric sequence. The sum of a **finite series** can be found by:

$S_n = \frac{a_1\left(1 - r^n\right)}{1 - r}$

Example: Find the sum of $1 + 3 + 9 + \ldots + 729$.

Step 1) Use the explicit formula to find the number of terms:

$r = \frac{3}{1} = 3, a_1 = 1$, so $729 = (1)(3)^{n-1}$ and $n = 7$.

Step 2) Use the formula for the sum of a finite series:

$S_7 = \frac{1(1 - 3^7)}{1 - 3} = \frac{-2186}{-2} = 1093$

Common Errors With Geometric Sequences and Series

Geometric sequence errors can occur when the ratio is negative. Remind students that r^n means that the entire value of r (including the negative) is raised to the power.

ⓒ Mathematical Practices

Use appropriate tools strategically. Graphing calculators are used throughout the chapter to analyze the behavior of sequences and series and to simplify tedious computations with large numbers of terms. Technology enables students to solve real-world equations that have been computationally tedious in the past.

Recursive Definitions

A recursive definition specifies the first term and a recursive formula to move from each term to the next.

Recursive Definition for Arithmetic Sequences

$a_n = a_{n-1} + d$, for $n > 1$

Example: Write the next four terms of the sequence given by the recursive formula $a_1 = -6$ and $a_n = a_{n-1} - 2$.

$a_2 = -6 - 2 = -8, a_3 = -8 - 2 = -10,$
$a_4 = -10 - 2 = -12, a_5 = -12 - 2 = -14$

The sequence is −6, −8, −10, −12, −14, . . .

Recursive Definition for Geometric Sequences

$a_n = a_{n-1}r$, for $n > 1$

Example: Write the first four terms of the sequence given by the recursive formula $a_1 = 3, a_n = 2a_{n-1}$.

$a_1 = 3, a_2 = 2(3) = 6, a_3 = 2(6) = 12, a_4 = 2(12) = 24$

The sequence is 3, 6, 12, 24, . . .

Writing Recursive Definitions

To write a recursive definition from a sequence of numbers,
- determine whether the sequence is arithmetic or geometric
- determine the common ratio or common difference
- determine the first term

Example: Write the recursive definition of 12, 16, 20, 24, . . .

The sequence is arithmetic. The common difference is 4. The first term is 12.

$a_1 = 12 \qquad a_n = a_{n-1} + 4$

Example: Write the recursive definition of −8, −16, −32, −64, . . .

The sequence is geometric. The common ratio is 2. The first term is −8.

$a_1 = -8 \qquad a_n = a_{n-1} \cdot 2$

Common Errors When Using Recursive Definitions

Errors can occur as students become familiar with **subscript notation**. Have students write the meanings in words to help them understand the following: a_n means the current term; a_{n-1} means the term before a_n.

ⓒ Mathematical Practices

Reason abstractly and quantitatively. Look for and make use of structure. Students study the structure of sequences to define them recursively.

SEQUENCES AND SERIES
Pacing and Assignment Guide

		TRADITIONAL			BLOCK
Lesson	**Teaching Day(s)**	**Basic**	**Average**	**Advanced**	**Block**
9-1	1	Problems 1–4 Exs. 7–43, 51–55 odd, 65, 71–84	Problems 1–4 Exs. 7–41 odd, 43–65, 71–84	Problems 1–4 Exs. 7–41 odd, 43–84	**Day 1** Problems 1–4 Exs. 7–41 odd, 43–65, 71–84
9-2	1	Problems 1–4 Exs. 7–25, 31–35, 49–53, 61, 75–88	Problems 1–4 Exs. 7–25 odd, 26–62, 75–88	Problems 1–4 Exs. 7–25 odd, 26–88	Problems 1–4 Exs. 7–25 odd, 26–62, 75–88
9-3	1	Problems 1–2 Exs. 7–24, 63–81	Problems 1–2 Exs. 7–23 odd, 63–81	Problems 1–2 Exs. 7–23 odd, 63–81	**Day 2** Problems 1–4 Exs. 7–31 odd, 32–59, 63–81
	2	Problems 3–4 Exs. 25–31, 36–44 even, 48–50, 59	Problems 3–4 Exs. 25–31 odd, 32–59	Problems 3–4 Exs. 25–31 odd, 32–62	
9-4	1	Problems 1–3 Exs. 8–20, 57–70	Problems 1–3 Exs. 9–19 odd, 57–70	Problems 1–3 Exs. 9–19 odd, 57–70	**Day 3** Problems 1–5 Exs. 9–31 odd, 33–50, 57–70
	2	Problems 4–5 Exs. 21–32, 33–41 odd, 46–48	Problems 4–5 Exs. 21–31 odd, 33–50	Problems 4–5 Exs. 21–31 odd, 33–56	
9-5	1	Problems 1–2 Exs. 8–16, 54–69	Problems 1–2 Exs. 9–15 odd, 54–69	Problems 1–3 Exs. 9–31 odd, 32–59	**Day 4** Problems 1–3 Exs. 9–31 odd, 32–51, 54–69
	2	Problem 3 Exs. 17–33, 38–41, 47, 48	Problem 3 Exs. 17–31 odd, 32–51		
Review	1	Chapter 9 Review	Chapter 9 Review	Chapter 9 Review	**Day 5** Chapter 9 Review Chapter 9 Test
Assess	1	Chapter 9 Test	Chapter 9 Test	Chapter 9 Test	
Total		**10 Days**	**10 Days**	**9 Days**	**5 Days**

Note: Pacing does not include Concept Bytes and other feature pages.

Resources

	For the Chapter	9-1	9-2	9-3	9-4	9-5
Planning						
Teacher Center Online Planner & Grade Book	I	I	I	I	I	I
Interactive Learning & Guided Instruction						
My Math Video	I					
Solve It!		I M	I M	I M	I M	I M
Student Companion		P M	P M	P M	P M	P M
Vocabulary Support		I P M	I P M	I P M	I P M	I P M
Got It? Support		I P	I P	I P	I P	I P
Dynamic Activity			I	I		
Online Problems		I	I	I	I	I
Additional Problems		M	M	M	M	M
English Language Learner Support (TR)		E P M	E P M	E P M	E P M	E P M
Activities, Games, and Puzzles		E M	E M	E M	E M	E M
Teaching With TI Technology With CD-ROM						
TI-Nspire™ Support CD-ROM		✓	✓	✓	✓	✓
Lesson Check & Practice						
Student Companion		P M	P M	P M	P M	P M
Lesson Check Support		I P	I P	I P	I P	I P
Practice and Problem Solving Workbook		P	P	P	P	P
Think About a Plan (TR)		E P M	E P M	E P M	E P M	E P M
Practice Form G (TR)		E P M	E P M	E P M	E P M	E P M
Standardized Test Prep (TR)		P M	P M	P M	P M	P M
Practice *Form K* (TR)		E P M	E P M	E P M	E P M	E P M
Extra Practice	E M					
Find the Errors!	M					
Enrichment (TR)		E P M	E P M	E P M	E P M	E P M
Answers and Solutions CD-ROM	✓	✓	✓	✓	✓	✓
Assess & Remediate						
ExamView CD-ROM	✓	✓	✓	✓	✓	✓
Lesson Quiz		I M	I M	I M	I M	I M
Quizzes and Tests *Form G*	E P M			E P M		E P M
Quizzes and Tests *Form K*	E P M			E P M		E P M
Reteaching		E P M	E P M	E P M	E P M	E P M
Performance Tasks	P M					
Cumulative Review	P M					
Progress Monitoring Assessments	I P M					

(TR) Available in All-In-One Teaching Resources

1 Interactive Learning

Solve It!

PURPOSE To identify, continue, and describe a pattern mathematically

PROCESS Students may

- continue drawing the pattern of squares and adding the numbers in the squares.
- find and continue the pattern of differences between the number in the central square of each figure (8, 12, 16, . . .).
- analyze the pattern and write a formula using a variable that corresponds to the figure number.

FACILITATE

Q In Figure 1, $4 \times 1 = 4$. In Figure 2, $4 \times 1 + 4 \times 2 = 12$. What is another way to write $4 \times 1 + 4 \times 2$? **[$4(1 + 2)$ or 4×3]**

Q How can 24 be obtained from the other numbers shown in Figure 3? **[$4(1 + 2 + 3) = 24$]**

Q For the nth figure, the central number will be equal to 4 times what? Use words to describe the relationship. **[4 times the sum of the integers from 1 to n]**

Q How can you write this relationship using numbers? **[$4(1 + 2 + 3 + \ldots + n)$]**

If students know the formula for adding n integers, have them find the formula for this pattern. **[$4\left(\dfrac{n(n + 1)}{2}\right) = 2n(n + 1)$]**

ANSWER See Solve It in Answers on next page.

CONNECT THE MATH This Solve It introduces a new kind of pattern called a *sequence*. In the lesson, students will generate sequences from formulas and write formulas to describe sequences.

Objectives To identify mathematical patterns found in a sequence
To use a formula to find the nth term of a sequence

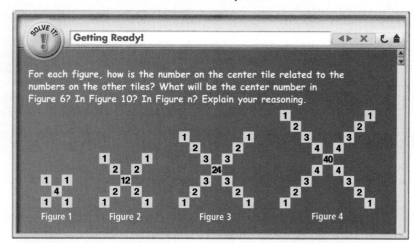

Getting Ready!

For each figure, how is the number on the center tile related to the numbers on the other tiles? What will be the center number in Figure 6? In Figure 10? In Figure n? Explain your reasoning.

Figure 1   Figure 2   Figure 3   Figure 4

Lesson Vocabulary
- sequence
- term of a sequence
- explicit formula
- recursive formula

Sometimes you can state a rule to describe a pattern. At other times, you have to do a bit of work to find a rule.

Essential Understanding If the numbers in a list follow a pattern, you may be able to relate each number in the list to its numerical position in the list with a rule.

A **sequence** is an ordered list of numbers. Each number in a sequence is a **term of a sequence**. You can represent a term of a sequence by using a variable with a subscript number to indicate its position in the sequence. For example, a_5 is the fifth term in the sequence $a_1, a_2, a_3, a_4, \ldots$.

The subscripts of sequence terms are often positive integers starting with 1. If so, you can generalize a term as a_n, the nth term in the sequence.

1st term	2nd term	3rd term	. . .	$n - 1$ term	nth term	$n + 1$ term . . .
↓	↓	↓		↓	↓	↓
a_1	a_2	a_3	. . .	a_{n-1}	a_n	a_{n+1} . . .

9-1 Preparing to Teach

BIG ideas Equivalence
Modeling
Variable

ESSENTIAL UNDERSTANDINGS
- If the numbers in a list follow a pattern, it may be possible to relate each number in the list to its numerical position in the list with a rule.
- A sequence can be defined explicitly by describing its nth term with a formula using n or recursively by stating its first term and a formula for its nth term using the $(n - 1)$ term.

Math Background

A sequence can be represented by an explicit formula or by a recursive definition.

An explicit formula
- allows direct computation of any term for a sequence.
- describes the nth term of a sequence using n.
- is easy to evaluate for the nth term.
- works well for finding terms in a sequence that are far apart.

- can be difficult to find since there is no one method.

A recursive definition
- requires an initial condition to compute the next term with a recursive formula.
- defines each term after the first term using the previous term.
- moves from one term to the next, is easy to evaluate for adjacent terms.
- works well for small segments of a sequence.
- is easy to find given an initial condition, rate of change, and any constant value.

Not all patterns can be expressed mathematically, and not all mathematical patterns can be expressed with a formula.

© Mathematical Practices
Look for and make use of structure.
Students will discern mathematical patterns and describe them with a formula.

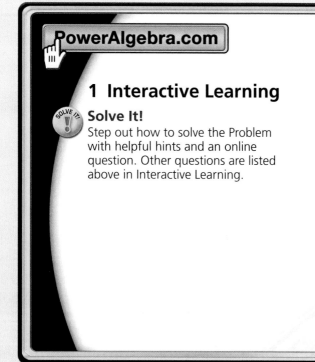

PowerAlgebra.com

1 Interactive Learning

Solve It!
Step out how to solve the Problem with helpful hints and an online question. Other questions are listed above in Interactive Learning.

An **explicit formula** describes the nth term of a sequence using the number n.

For example, in the sequence 2, 4, 6, 8, 10, . . . , the nth term is twice the value of n. You write this as $a_n = 2n$. The table shows how to find a_n by substituting the value of n into the explicit formula.

n	nth term
1	$a_1 = 2(1) = 2$
2	$a_2 = 2(2) = 4$
3	$a_3 = 2(3) = 6$
4	$a_4 = 2(4) = 8$

 Problem 1 Generating a Sequence Using an Explicit Formula

Plan

 How does the explicit formula help you find the value of a term?
Replace n in the formula with the number of the term. Simplify to find the value of the term.

A sequence has an explicit formula $a_n = 3n - 2$. What are the first 10 terms of this sequence?

$a_n = 3n - 2$ Write the formula.

$a_1 = 3(1) - 2 = 1$ Substitute 1 for n and simplify.

$a_2 = 3(2) - 2 = 4$ Substitute 2 for n and simplify.

You can use a table to organize your work for the remaining terms.

n	a_n	
3	$a_3 = 3(3) - 2 = 7$	Substitute 3 for n and simplify.
4	$a_4 = 3(4) - 2 = 10$	
5	$a_5 = 3(5) - 2 = 13$	And so on.
6	$a_6 = 3(6) - 2 = 16$	
7	$a_7 = 3(7) - 2 = 19$	
8	$a_8 = 3(8) - 2 = 22$	
9	$a_9 = 3(9) - 2 = 25$	
10	$a_{10} = 3(10) - 2 = 28$	

The first ten terms are 1, 4, 7, 10, 13, 16, 19, 22, 25, 28.

Got It? **1.** A sequence has an explicit formula $a_n = 12n + 3$. What is term a_{12} in the sequence?

Sometimes you can see the pattern in a sequence by comparing each term to the one that came before it. For example, in the sequence 133, 130, 127, 124, . . . , each term after the first term is equal to three less than the previous term.

A recursive definition for this sequence contains two parts.
(a) an initial condition (the value of the first term): $a_1 = 133$
(b) a **recursive formula** (relates each term after the first term to the one before it):
$a_n = a_{n-1} - 3$, for $n > 1$

2 Guided Instruction

Problem 1
Terms and variables with subscripts are usually read aloud by saying the variable, then "sub," then the subscripted letter or number: "a sub 1," "a sub 2," "a sub n."

Q How can you use a graphing calculator to generate a table with the same values shown in the table on your page? **[Sample: Key the equation $y = 3x - 2$. Then use the Table function with TblStart = 3 and ΔTbl = 1.]**

Q From the formula, would you expect the sequence to have a constant difference of 3? Explain. **[Yes; the variable n has a constant coefficient of 3. The sequence will increase by 3 for each increase of 1 in the variable.]**

Q How are the sequence formula $a_n = 3n - 2$ and the linear function $y = 3x - 2$ the same? How are they different? **[Sample: Both increase by 3 for every increase of 1 in the variable. The linear function has a domain of all real numbers, but the sequence formula has a domain of natural numbers.]**

Got It?   EXTENSION

Q If you knew that $a_{10} = 123$, how could you find a_9 without substituting in the formula? Find a_9. **[The constant coefficient on the variable is 12, so a_9 must be 12 less than a_{10}. Thus $a_9 = 111$.]**

Q What is a_{n-1}? What is a_{n+1}? **[$a_{n-1} = 12n - 9$; $a_{n+1} = 12n + 15$.]**

Q What is the difference between a_{37} and a_{41}? **[48]**

2 Guided Instruction

 Each Problem is worked out and supported online.

Problem 1
Generating a Sequence Using an Explicit Formula
Animated

Problem 2
Writing a Recursive Definition for a Sequence
Animated

Problem 3
Writing an Explicit Formula for a Sequence
Animated

Problem 4
Using Formulas to Find Terms of a Sequence

Support in Algebra 2 Companion
• Vocabulary
• Key Concepts
• Got It?

Answers

Solve It!
It is the sum of the numbers on the other tiles; 84; 220; $2n(n + 1)$

Got It?
1. 147

Problem 2

This problem shows how to write a recursive definition for the triangular numbers examined by students in the Solve It.

> **Q** What is the relationship between the number of the term and the difference from the previous term? **[The number of the term is identical to the difference from the previous term.]**
>
> **Q** Why must you state the initial condition when giving a recursive definition? **[Each term in a recursive definition is defined as an arithmetic operation on the previous term. If a_1 is not given, then no other terms can be found.]**

EXTENSION

> **Q** If the recursive definition of a sequence were $a_1 = 5$ and $a_n = a_{n-1} + n$, what sequence would result? **[5, 7, 10, 14, 19, 25, 32, ...]**

Notice that Problem 2 and practice problem 66 on p. 570 are equivalent. When students are working on problem 66, have them compare the presentations of the pattern. Ask students if the answer to 66c is yes. If so, ask them why the answer is different than the answer for the explicit formula $\frac{1}{2}n(n+1)$ given on p. 567.

Got It?

> **Q** In 2a, is the pattern based on simple addition or on multiplication? Explain. **[Multiplication; there is no pattern in the differences between consecutive terms, but there is a pattern of ratios: $a_2 - a_1 = 1$; $a_3 - a_2 = 4$; $a_4 - a_3 = 18$; $\frac{a_2}{a_1} = 2$; $\frac{a_3}{a_2} = 3$; $\frac{a_4}{a_3} = 4$.]**
>
> **Q** In 2b, what pattern do you see in the differences of successive terms? **[The differences make up the sequence of square numbers.]**

Problem 2 Writing a Recursive Definition for a Sequence

The number of blocks in a two-dimensional pyramid is a sequence that follows a recursive formula. What is a recursive definition for the sequence?

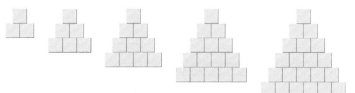

Think	Write
Count the number of blocks in each pyramid.	1, 3, 6, 10, 15, 21
Subtract consecutive terms to find out what happens from one term to the next.	$a_2 - a_1 = 3 - 1 = 2$ $a_3 - a_2 = 6 - 3 = 3$ $a_4 - a_3 = 10 - 6 = 4$ $a_5 - a_4 = 15 - 10 = 5$ $a_6 - a_5 = 21 - 15 = 6$
Use n to express the relationship between successive terms.	$a_n - a_{n-1} = n$
To write a recursive definition, state the initial condition and the recursive formula.	$a_1 = 1$ and $a_n = a_{n-1} + n$.

Got It? 2. What is a recursive definition for each sequence?
(*Hint:* Look for simple addition or multiplication patterns to relate consecutive terms.)
a. 1, 2, 6, 24, 120, 720, ...
b. 1, 5, 14, 30, 55, ...

Additional Problems

1. A sequence has an explicit formula $a_n = n^2 - 10$. What is the term a_8 in the sequence?

ANSWER $a_8 = 54$

2. What is a recursive definition for the sequence 4, 14, 44, 134, ...?

ANSWER $a_1 = 4$ and $a_n = 3a_{n-1} + 2$

3. What is an explicit formula for the sequence 1, −1, 1, −1, 1, ...?

ANSWER $a_n = (-1)^{n-1}$ (or $a_n = (-1)^{n+1}$)

4. In a certain kind of online auction, the price for an item begins high and falls over time until someone purchases the item. If an item begins at $100 and decreases by 25% every 5 minutes, what is the price after a half hour? Round to the nearest cent.

ANSWER $17.80

Answers

Got It? (continued)
2. a. $a_1 = 1$ and $a_n = na_{n-1}$
   b. $a_1 = 1$ and $a_n = a_{n-1} + n^2$

Recursive definitions can be very helpful when you look at a small section of a sequence. However, if you want to know both a_3 and a_{5000} of a sequence, an explicit formula often works better.

 Problem 3 Writing an Explicit Formula for a Sequence

What is the 100th term of the pyramid sequence in Problem 2?

Plan

Why do you use the explicit formula to find a_{100}?
Because starting with a_1, it would take 99 iterations of the formula to get a_{100} using the recursive formula.

To find an explicit formula, expand the first few terms of the pyramid sequence.

a_1	a_2	a_3	a_4	a_5	...	a_n
1	$1+2$	$1+2+3$	$1+2+3+4$	$1+2+3+4+5$	...	$1+2+\ldots+n$
1	3	6	10	15	...	■

Therefore,

$$a_n = 1 + 2 + 3 + \cdots + (n-2) + (n-1) + n,$$

which you can write as

$$a_n = n + (n-1) + (n-2) + \cdots + 3 + 2 + 1.$$

Adding the two previous equations gives the following result:

$$
\begin{array}{rl}
a_n = 1 & + \quad 2 \quad + \quad 3 \quad + \cdots + (n-2) + (n-1) + n \\
+ \ a_n = n & + (n-1) + (n-2) + \cdots + \quad 3 \quad + \quad 2 \quad + 1 \\
\hline
2a_n = (n+1) & + (n+1) + (n+1) + \cdots + (n+1) + (n+1) + (n+1)
\end{array}
$$

$$2a_n = n(n+1)$$

$$a_n = \tfrac{1}{2}n(n+1)$$

The explicit formula for this sequence is $a_n = \tfrac{1}{2}n(n+1)$.

Substitute 100 into the explicit formula to find the 100th term.

$$a_{100} = \tfrac{1}{2}(100)(100+1)$$
$$= \tfrac{1}{2}(100)(101)$$
$$= 5050$$

The 100th term is 5050.

  Got It? 3. a. What is an explicit formula for the sequence 0, 3, 8, 15, 24, . . . ? What is the 20th term?
　　　　b. Reasoning Why is using an explicit formula often more efficient than using a recursive definition?

Problem 3
There are several strategies for finding an explicit formula for the nth term of a sequence. A good starting strategy is to put the terms of the sequence in line with the counting numbers 1, 2, 3, 4, . . . and look for a pattern. The procedure shown in Problem 3 may not work for other sequences.

Q Why was the expanded sum for a_n written forward, then backward, and then added? **[Sample: Writing the expanded sum forward, then backward, and then adding makes each term in the expanded sum equal to $(n + 1)$. Once all the terms are equal to the same number, the sum can be factored to find the explicit formula.]**

Q Does the explicit formula for the triangular numbers remind you of a common geometric formula? If so, which one? **[Yes; the formula for the area of a triangle.]**

Got It?

Q What are the differences between successive terms? Do you know another sequence that has this same pattern of differences? **[The differences are the odd numbers: 3, 5, 7, 9, . . .; Sample: The sequence of square numbers also has this pattern of differences.]**

Q What are two ways to write the formula? **[$n^2 - 1$ or $(n + 1)(n - 1)$]**

---

3. a. $a_n = n^2 - 1$; 399
b. To find the nth term using an explicit formula, you simply substitute for n in the formula. To find the nth term using a recursive definition may require many iterations.

Problem 4

Q Why was a recursive definition used rather than an explicit formula? **[Sample: A recursive definition was easier to fit than an explicit formula. Because a calculator makes repeated operations trivial, a recursive definition is close enough.]**

Q What does the "ANS" you keyed into your calculator mean in the recursive definition? **[ANS means the previous answer or a_{n-1}.]**

Got It?

Q Can you find the answer by solving the equation $1000 = 1.018x + 29$? Explain. **[No. This is a linear function, and Pierre's debt is not accumulating linearly.]**

3 Lesson Check

Do you know HOW?   ERROR INTERVENTION

• If students have trouble getting started on Exercises 1 and 2, suggest they substitute 1, 2, 3, 4, and 5 for n in each formula.

Do you UNDERSTAND?

• If students say there is no error in Exercise 6, clarify that the first term is a_1, not a_0.

Close

Q What are some advantages and disadvantages of recursive definitions and explicit formulas? **[Samples: Recursive definitions are usually easy to find. Recursive definitions cannot calculate any term directly, while explicit formulas can. Explicit formulas can be used to find the number of a term when a value is given.]**

 **Problem 4** Using Formulas to Find Terms of a Sequence

Finance Pierre began the year with an unpaid balance of $300 on his credit card. Because he had not read the credit card agreement, he did not realize that the company charged 1.8% interest each month on his unpaid balance, in addition to a $29 penalty in any month he might fail to make a minimum payment. Pierre ignored his credit card bill for 4 consecutive months before finally deciding to pay off the balance. What did he owe after 4 months of non-payment?

Step 1 Write a recursive definition.
Initial condition: $a_0 = 300$ (Use a_0 so that a_1 represents the balance after 1 month.)
Recursive formula: $a_n = 1.018 \cdot a_{n-1} + 29$, for $n > 1$

 **Think**
Why is it helpful to change FLOAT to 2? This problem involves money, so, real-world solutions will only have 2 decimal places.

Step 2 Use a calculator. In the **MODE** menu, change the digit display from **FLOAT** to 2.

Enter 300 in the home screen. Enter the recursive formula **1.018ANS+29**. Press **enter** for the balance after one month.

Press **enter** three more times until the calculator shows the balance after 4 months.

```
300
               300.00
1.018Ans+29
               334.40
```

```
               369.42
               405.07
               441.36
```

After 4 months, Pierre owes $441.36.

 Got It? 4. If the credit card company were to allow Pierre to continue making no payments, after how many months would his balance exceed $1000?

 Lesson Check

Do you know HOW?

Find the first five terms of each sequence.

1. $a_n = 5n - 3$ **2.** $a_n = n^2 - 2n$

3. What is a recursive definition for the sequence 3, 6, 12, 24, . . . ?

4. What is an explicit formula for the sequence 5, 8, 11, 14, . . . ?

Do you UNDERSTAND?   MATHEMATICAL PRACTICES

5. Vocabulary Explain the difference between an explicit formula and a recursive definition. Give an example of each.

6. Error Analysis A student writes that $a_n = 3n + 1$ is an explicit formula for the sequence 1, 4, 7, 10, ... Explain the student's error and write a correct explicit formula for the sequence.

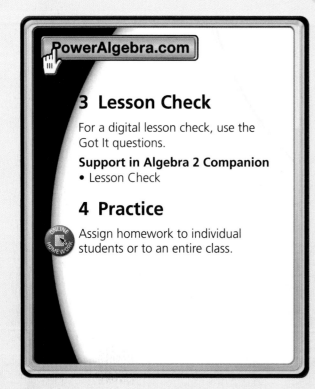

PowerAlgebra.com

3 Lesson Check

For a digital lesson check, use the Got It questions.

Support in Algebra 2 Companion
• Lesson Check

4 Practice

Assign homework to individual students or to an entire class.

Answers

Got It? (continued)
4. 18 months

Lesson Check
1. 2, 7, 12, 17, 22
2. −1, 0, 3, 8, 15
3. $a_1 = 3$ and $a_n = 2a_{n-1}$
4. $a_n = 2 + 3n$
5. A recursive formula defines the terms in a sequence by relating each term after the first term to the one before it and requires that the previous term be known to find a given term. An example of a recursive formula for the sequence 8, 4, 2, 1, . . . is $a_1 = 8$ and $a_n = \frac{1}{2}a_{n-1}$. An explicit formula describes the nth term of a sequence using the variable n and only requires the number of the term to be known. An example of an explicit formula

for the sequence 1, 3, 5, 7, ... is $a_n = 2n - 1$.
6. The "+1" in $a_n = 3n + 1$ is incorrect for the sequence 1, 4, 7, 10, . . . The correct explicit formula is $a_n = -2 + 3n$.

Practice and Problem-Solving Exercises MATHEMATICAL PRACTICES

 Practice Find the first six terms of each sequence.

◀ See Problem 1.

7. $a_n = 3n + 2$ **8.** $a_n = -5n + 1$ **9.** $a_n = \frac{1}{2}n$ **10.** $a_n = n^2 + 1$

11. $a_n = 3n^2 - n$ **12.** $a_n = 2^n - 1$ **13.** $a_n = \frac{1}{2}n^3 - 1$ **14.** $a_n = (-3)^n$

Write a recursive definition for each sequence.

◀ See Problem 2.

15. $80, 77, 74, 71, 68, \ldots$ **16.** $4, 8, 16, 32, 64, \ldots$ **17.** $0, 3, 7, 12, 18, \ldots$

18. $1, 4, 7, 10, 13, \ldots$ **19.** $100, 10, 1, 0.1, 0.01, \ldots$ **20.** $\frac{1}{2}, \frac{1}{4}, \frac{1}{8}, \frac{1}{16}, \frac{1}{32}, \ldots$

21. $4, -8, 16, -32, 64, \ldots$ **22.** $1, 2, 6, 24, 120, \ldots$ **23.** $1, 5, 14, 30, \ldots$

Write an explicit formula for each sequence. Find the tenth term.

◀ See Problem 3.

24. $4, 5, 6, 7, 8, \ldots$ **25.** $4, 7, 10, 13, 16, \ldots$ **26.** $3, 7, 11, 15, 19, \ldots$

27. $-2\frac{1}{2}, -2, -1\frac{1}{2}, -1, \ldots$ **28.** $1, 4, 9, 16, \ldots$ **29.** $2, 5, 10, 17, 26, \ldots$

30. $\frac{1}{2}, \frac{1}{3}, \frac{1}{4}, \frac{1}{5}, \frac{1}{6}, \ldots$ **31.** $1, 3, 9, 27, \ldots$ **32.** $\frac{1}{2}, -\frac{1}{4}, \frac{1}{8}, -\frac{1}{16}, \ldots$

Find the eighth term of each sequence.

33. $-2, -1, 0, 1, 2, \ldots$ **34.** $43, 41, 39, 37, 35, \ldots$ **35.** $40, 20, 10, 5, \frac{5}{2}, \ldots$

36. $6, 1, -4, -9, \ldots$ **37.** $144, 36, 9, \frac{9}{4}, \ldots$ **38.** $\frac{1}{2}, \frac{1}{4}, \frac{1}{8}, \frac{1}{16}, \frac{1}{32}, \ldots$

39. $2, 1, -2, -7, -14, \ldots$ **40.** $\frac{3}{4}, -\frac{3}{2}, 3, -6, \ldots$ **41.** $2, -\frac{3}{2}, \frac{4}{3}, -\frac{5}{4}, \ldots$

42. Exercise You walk 1 mile the first day of your training, 1.2 miles the second day, 1.6 miles the third day, and 2.4 miles the fourth day. If you continue this pattern, how many miles do you walk the seventh day?

◀ See Problem 4.

Apply Determine whether each formula is *explicit* or *recursive*. Then find the first five terms of each sequence.

43. $a_n = 2a_{n-1} + 3$, where $a_1 = 3$ **44.** $a_n = \frac{1}{2}(n)(n - 1)$

45. $a_n = (n - 5)(n + 5)$ **46.** $a_n = -3a_{n-1}$, where $a_1 = -2$

47. $a_n = -4n^2 - 2$ **48.** $a_n = 2n^2 + 1$

Use the given rule to write the 4th, 5th, 6th, and 7th terms of each sequence.

49. $a_n = (n + 1)^2$ **50.** $a_n = 2(n - 1)^3$

51. $a_n = \frac{n^2}{n + 1}$ **52.** $a_n = \frac{n + 1}{n + 2}$

---

4 Practice

ASSIGNMENT GUIDE

Basic: 7–42 all, 43, 51–55 odd, 65

Average: 7–41 odd, 43–65

Advanced: 7–41 odd, 43–70

Standardized Test Prep: 71–75

Mixed Review: 76–84

Mathematical Practices are supported by exercises with red headings. Here are the Practices supported in this lesson:

MP 1: Make Sense of Problems Ex. 53
MP 3: Construct Arguments Ex. 64
MP 3: Critique the Reasoning of Others Ex. 6

Applications exercises have blue headings. Exercise 70 supports MP 4: Model.

EXERCISE 65: Use the Think About a Plan worksheet in the **Practice and Problem Solving Workbook** (also available in the Teaching Resources in print and online) to further support students' development in becoming independent learners.

HOMEWORK QUICK CHECK

To check students' understanding of key skills and concepts, go over Exercises 15, 25, 33, 53, and 65.

Practice and Problem-Solving Exercises

7. 5, 8, 11, 14, 17, 20

8. −4, −9, −14, −19, −24, −29

9. $\frac{1}{2}, 1, \frac{3}{2}, 2, \frac{5}{2}, 3$

10. 2, 5, 10, 17, 26, 37

11. 2, 10, 24, 44, 70, 102

12. 1, 3, 7, 15, 31, 63

13. $-\frac{1}{2}, 3, \frac{25}{2}, 31, \frac{123}{2}, 107$

14. −3, 9, −27, 81, −243, 729

15. $a_1 = 80$ and $a_n = a_{n-1} - 3$

16. $a_1 = 4$ and $a_n = 2a_{n-1}$

17. $a_1 = 0$ and $a_n = a_{n-1} + (n + 1)$

18. $a_1 = 1$ and $a_n = a_{n-1} + 3$

19. $a_1 = 100$ and $a_n = \frac{1}{10}a_{n-1}$

20. $a_1 = \frac{1}{2}$ and $a_n = \frac{1}{2}a_{n-1}$

21. $a_1 = 4$ and $a_n = -2a_{n-1}$

22. $a_1 = 1$ and $a_n = na_{n-1}$

23. $a_1 = 1$ and $a_n = a_{n-1} + n^2$

24. $a_n = n + 3$; 13

25. $a_n = 3n + 1$; 31

26. $a_n = 4n - 1$; 39

27. $a_n = \frac{n - 6}{2}$; 2

28. $a_n = n^2$; 100

29. $a_n = n^2 + 1$; 101

30. $a_n = \frac{1}{n + 1}$; $\frac{1}{11}$

31. $a_n = 3^{n-1}$; 19,683

32. $a_n = -\left(-\frac{1}{2}\right)^n$ or $a_n = (-1)^{n+1}\frac{1}{2^n}$ or $a_n = (-1)^{n-1}\frac{1}{2^n}$; $-\frac{1}{1024}$

33. 5

34. 29

35. $\frac{5}{16}$

36. −29

37. $\frac{9}{1024}$

38. $\frac{1}{256}$

39. −47

40. −96

41. $-\frac{9}{8}$

42. 13.6 mi

43. recursive; 3, 9, 21, 45, 93

44. explicit; 0, 1, 3, 6, 10

45. explicit; −24, −21, −16, −9, 0

46. recursive; −2, 6, −18, 54, −162

47. explicit; −6, −18, −38, −66, −102

48. explicit; 3, 9, 19, 33, 51

49. 25, 36, 49, 64

50. 54, 128, 250, 432

51. $\frac{16}{5}, \frac{25}{6}, \frac{36}{7}, \frac{49}{8}$

52. $\frac{5}{6}, \frac{6}{7}, \frac{7}{8}, \frac{8}{9}$

Answers

Practice and Problem-Solving Exercises
(continued)

53. $140

54. 15; 26; 40

55. 20, 23; $a_n = 3n + 2$, explicit OR
$a_n = a_{n-1} + 3$; $a_1 = 5$, recursive

56. 96, 192; $a_n = 3 \cdot 2^{n-1}$, explicit OR
$a_n = 2a_{n-1}$, $a_1 = 3$, recursive

57. 216, 343; $a_n = n^3$, explicit

58. 4096, 16,384; $a_n = 4^n$, explicit OR
$a_n = 4a_{n-1}$, $a_1 = 4$, recursive

59. 144, 169; $a_n = (n + 6)^2$, explicit OR
$a_n = a_{n-1} + 2n + 11$, $a_1 = 49$, recursive

60. −1, 1; $a_n = (-1)^n$, explicit OR $a_n = -1(a_{n-1})$,
$a_1 = -1$, recursive

61. −1, $-\frac{1}{2}$; $a_n = \frac{-32}{2^n}$, explicit OR $a_n = \frac{a_{n-1}}{2}$,
$a_1 = -16$, recursive

62. −47, −40; $a_n = -82 + 7n$, explicit OR
$a_n = a_{n-1} + 7$, $a_1 = -75$, recursive

63. −11, −19; $a_n = 29 - 8n$, explicit OR
$a_n = a_{n-1} - 8$, $a_1 = 21$, recursive

64. a–c. Answers may vary. Sample:
  a. 1, −2, 4, −8, . . .
  b. $a_n = -2(a_{n-1})$, and
    $a_1 = 1$; $a_n = (-2)^{n-1}$
  c. −524,288

65. a. 25 boxes
  b. 110 boxes
  c. 9 levels

66. a. 10, 15
  b. $a_n = a_{n-1} + n$, $a_1 = 1$
  c. Yes; the formula yields the same values for
    a_n as the recursive formula.

---

 53. Think About a Plan You invested money in a company and each month you receive a payment for your investment. Over the first four months, you received $50, $52, $56, and $62. If this pattern continues, how much do you receive in the tenth month?
- What pattern do you see between consecutive terms?
- Can you write a recursive or explicit formula to describe the pattern?
- How can you use your formula to find the amount you receive in the tenth month?

54. Entertainment Suppose you are building towers of cards with levels as displayed below. Copy and complete the table, assuming the pattern continues.

Number of Levels	Cards Needed
1	2
2	7
3	■
4	■
5	■

Find the next two terms in each sequence. Write a formula for the *n*th term. Identify each formula as *explicit* or *recursive*.

55. 5, 8, 11, 14, 17, . . .

56. 3, 6, 12, 24, 48, . . .

57. 1, 8, 27, 64, 125, . . .

58. 4, 16, 64, 256, 1024, . . .

59. 49, 64, 81, 100, 121, . . .

60. −1, 1, −1, 1, −1, 1, . . .

61. −16, −8, −4, −2, . . .

62. −75, −68, −61, −54, . . .

63. 21, 13, 5, −3, . . .

64. a. Open-Ended Write four terms of a sequence of numbers that you can describe both recursively and explicitly.
  b. Write a recursive definition and an explicit formula for your sequence.
  c. Find the 20th term of the sequence by evaluating one of your formulas. Use the other formula to check your work.

65. Geometry Suppose you are stacking boxes in levels that form squares. The numbers of boxes in successive levels form a sequence. The figure at the right shows the top four levels as viewed from above.
  a. How many boxes of equal size would you need for the next lower level?
  b. How many boxes of equal size would you need to add three levels?
  c. Suppose you are stacking a total of 285 boxes. How many levels will you have?

Challenge

66. Geometry The triangular numbers form a sequence. The diagram represents the first three triangular numbers: 1, 3, 6.
  a. Find the fourth and fifth triangular numbers.
  b. Write a recursive formula for the *n*th triangular number.
  c. Is the explicit formula $a_n = \frac{1}{2}(n^2 + n)$ the correct formula for this sequence? Explain.

$n = 1 \qquad n = 2 \qquad n = 3$

Use each recursive definition to write an explicit formula for the sequence.

67. $a_1 = 10, a_n = 2a_{n-1}$ **68.** $a_1 = -5, a_n = a_{n-1} - 1$ **69.** $a_1 = 1, a_n = a_{n-1} + 4$

Ⓒ 70. Finance Use the information in the ad.

 a. Suppose you start a savings account. Write a recursive definition and an explicit formula for the amount of money you would have in the bank at the end of any week.

 b. How much money would you have in the bank after four weeks?

 c. Assume the bank pays interest every four weeks. To calculate your interest, multiply the balance at the end of the four weeks by 0.005. Then, add that amount to your account on the last day of the four-week period. Write a recursive formula for the amount of money you have after each interest payment.

 d. Reasoning What is the bank's annual interest rate?

Standardized Test Prep

SAT/ACT

71. Scientists determine an object is moving at the rate of $(5 - \sqrt{2})$ ft/s. How many seconds will it take the object to travel 125 ft? Round the answer to the nearest tenth of a second.

72. What is the solution of $\sqrt{4x - 23} - 3 = 2$?

73. Using a calculator, what is the solution of $1080 = 15^{3x-4}$? Round the answer to the nearest hundredth.

74. Using the change of base formula, what is the solution of $\log_5 x = \log_3 20$? Round the answer to the nearest tenth.

75. The battery power available to operate a deep space probe is given by the formula $P = 42e^{-0.005t}$, where P is power in watts and t is time in years. For how many years can the probe run if it requires 35 watts? Round the answer to the nearest tenth year.

Mixed Review

Solve each equation. Check the solution.

◀ See Lesson 8-6.

76. $\dfrac{y}{y+1} = \dfrac{2}{3}$ **77.** $\dfrac{4}{2a} = \dfrac{5}{a+6}$ **78.** $\dfrac{3}{b+2} = \dfrac{6}{b-1}$

Find the slope of the line that passes through the two points.

◀ See Lesson 2-3.

79. $(4, 5)$ and $(1, 8)$ **80.** $(-3, -3)$ and $(2, 2)$ **81.** $(1, 3)$ and $(4, 9)$

Get Ready! **To prepare for Lesson 9-2, do Exercises 82–84.**

Identify the pattern and find the next three terms.

◀ See Lesson 1-1.

82. $10, 8, 6, 4, 2, 0, \ldots$ **83.** $100, 117, 134, 151, 168, \ldots$ **84.** $\dfrac{5}{7}, \dfrac{8}{7}, \dfrac{11}{7}, 2, \ldots$

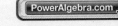

67. $a_n = 10 \cdot 2^{n-1}$

68. $a_n = -n - 4$

69. $a_n = 1 + 4(n - 1)$

70. a. $a_n = a_{n-1} + 5, a_1 = 25$;
  $a_n = 20 + 5n$

 b. $40

 c. $a_n = (a_{n-1} + \$20) \cdot 1.005$,
  $a_1 = \$40.20$

 d. 6.5%

Standardized Test Prep

71. 34.9

72. 12

73. 2.19

74. 80.5

75. 36.5

Mixed Review

76. 2

77. 4

78. −5

79. −1

80. 1

81. 2

82. subtract 2; −2, −4, −6

83. add 17; 185, 202, 219

84. add $\dfrac{3}{7}$; $\dfrac{17}{7}, \dfrac{20}{7}, \dfrac{23}{7}$

Additional Instructional Support

Algebra 2 Companion

Students can use the **Algebra 2 Companion** worktext (4 pages) as you teach the lesson. Use the Companion to support

- New Vocabulary
- Key Concepts
- Got It for each Problem
- Lesson Check

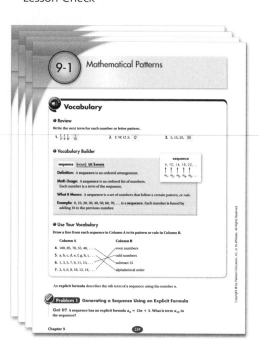

ELL Support

Assess Understanding Divide students into pairs. Have one member of each pair write one recursive definition and one explicit formula. Allow them to consult the textbook. Have the other member of each pair identify which is which and describe how he or she could tell.

"Write your name in cursive." If students do not know cursive script, demonstrate by writing your own name and indicating the letters and how they are connected.

"What are some words that describe cursive writing?" Expected answers include *connected, smooth, curved, looped*.

"In cursive writing, many letters curve or loop back onto themselves. *Recursive* is the same as *cursive* with *re-* added to the front. In English, *re-* added to the front of a verb often means 'going back.' For example, *reset* means 'go back to the original setting.'"

"What do you think *recursive* means? Does this make sense with how a recursive definition works?"

5 Assess & Remediate

Lesson Quiz

1. What are the first five terms of the sequence $a_n = \frac{n}{n+1}$?
2. What is a recursive definition for the sequence $0, -3, -6, -9, \ldots$?
3. What is an explicit formula for the sequence $0, -3, -6, -9, \ldots$?
4. **Do you UNDERSTAND?** Over the last 40 years, the population of a city has increased by roughly 2% each year. If the population was 220,000 at the beginning of this period a_0, what was the population 10 years later?

ANSWERS TO LESSON QUIZ
1. $\frac{1}{2}, \frac{2}{3}, \frac{3}{4}, \frac{4}{5}, \frac{5}{6}$
2. $a_1 = 0$ and $a_n = a_{n-1} - 3$
3. $a_n = -3n + 3$
4. about 268,179

PRESCRIPTION FOR REMEDIATION
Use the student work on the Lesson Quiz to prescribe a differentiated review assignment:

Points	Differentiated Remediation
0–1	Intervention
2–3	On-level
4	Extension

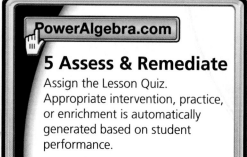

5 Assess & Remediate

Assign the Lesson Quiz. Appropriate intervention, practice, or enrichment is automatically generated based on student performance.

Differentiated Remediation

Intervention

- **Reteaching** (2 pages) Provides reteaching and practice exercises for the key lesson concepts. Use with struggling students or absent students.
- **English Language Learner Support** Helps students develop and reinforce mathematical vocabulary and key concepts.

All-in-One Resources/Online
Reteaching

9-1 Reteaching
Mathematical Patterns

Some patterns are much easier to determine than others. Here are some tips that can help with unfamiliar patterns.
- If the terms become progressively smaller, subtraction or division may be involved.
- If the terms become progressively larger, addition or multiplication may be involved.

Problem
What is the next term in the sequence 6, 8, 11, 15, 20, . . . ?

| 6 | 8 | 11 | 15 | 20 | | Spread the numbers in the sequence apart, leaving space between numbers. |

| +2 | +3 | +4 | +5 | | Beneath each space, write what can be done to get the next number in the sequence. |

In each term, the number that is added to the previous term increases by one. find a pattern.

If the pattern is continued, the next term is 20 + 6, or 26.

Exercises
Describe the pattern that is formed. Find the next three terms.

1. 5, 6, 8, 11, 15   2. 3, 6, 12, 24, 48   3. 1, −2, 4, −8, 16, −32
1. Each term is increased by one more than the previous term; 20, 26, 33
2. Each term is multiplied by 2 to get the next term; 96, 192, 384
3. Each term is multiplied by −2 to get the next term; 64, −128, 256

4. 1, 3, 9, 27, 81   5. 100, 95, 90, 85, 80   6. 15, 18, 21, 24, 27
4. Each term is multiplied by 3 to get the next term; 243, 729, 2187
5. Each term is decreased by 5 to get the next term; 75, 70, 65
6. Each term is increased by 3 to get to the next term; 30, 33, 36

7. 5, 25, 125, 625, 3125   8. 53, 49, 47, 44, 40   9. 240, 120, 60, 30, 15
7. Each term is multiplied by 5 to get the next term; 15,625; 78,125; 390,625
8. Each term is decreased by one more than the previous term; 35, 29, 22
9. Each term is divided by 2 to get the next term; 7.5, 3.75, 1.875

10. 3, 5, 9, 15, 23   11. −80, 120, −180, 270, −405   12. 1, 5, 13, 29, 61
10. In each term, the number is increased by two more than the previous term; 33, 45, 59
11. Each term is multiplied by −1.5 to get the next term; 607.5, −911.25, 1366.875
12. Each term is multiplied by 2 and then 3 is added to get the next term; 125, 253, 509

All-in-One Resources/Online
English Language Learner Support

9-1 Additional Vocabulary Support
Mathematical Patterns

Choose the word or phrase from the list that best matches each sentence.

| explicit formula | recursive formula | sequence | term |

1. an ordered list of numbers _____ sequence
2. a formula that describes the *n*th term of a sequence using the number *n* _____ explicit formula
3. each number in a sequence _____ term
4. a formula that describes the *n*th term of a sequence by referring to preceding terms _____ recursive formula

Choose the word or phrase from the list that best completes each sentence.

| explicit formula | initial condition | recursive formula |
| sequence | subscript number | term |

5. For a sequence that is described by a recursive formula, the first term in the sequence is the _____ initial condition.
6. In the sequence 2, 4, 6, 8, the number 4 is the second _____ term _____ in the sequence.
7. The position of a term in a sequence can be represented by using a(n) _____ subscript number.
8. The formula $a_n = 3n + 2$ is a(n) _____ explicit formula.
9. An ordered list of numbers is called a(n) _____ sequence.
10. The formula $a_{n+1} = a_n + 5$ is a(n) _____ recursive formula.

Differentiated Remediation *continued*

On-Level

- **Practice** (2 pages) Provides extra practice for each lesson. For simpler practice exercises, use the Form K Practice pages found in the All-in-One Teaching Resources and online.
- **Think About a Plan** Helps students develop specific problem-solving skills and strategies by providing scaffolded guiding questions.
- **Standardized Test Prep** Focuses on all major exercises, all major question types, and helps students prepare for the high-stakes assessments.

Extension

- **Enrichment** Provides students with interesting problems and activities that extend the concepts of the lesson.
- **Activities, Games, and Puzzles** Worksheets that can be used for concepts development, enrichment, and for fun!

Practice and Problem Solving Wkbk/ All-in-One Resources/Online
Practice page 1

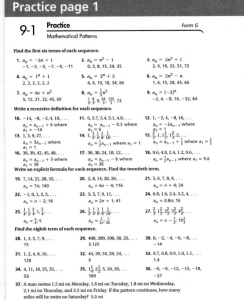

9-1 Practice *Form G*
Mathematical Patterns

Find the first six terms of each sequence.

1. $a_n = -2n + 1$ −1, −3, −5, −7, −9, −11
2. $a_n = n^2 - 1$ 0, 3, 8, 15, 24, 35
3. $a_n = 2n^2 + 1$ 3, 9, 19, 33, 51, 73
4. $a_n = 1^n + 1$ 2, 2, 2, 2, 2, 2
5. $a_n = 2^n + 2$ 4, 6, 10, 18, 34, 66
6. $a_n = 2n^2 - n$ 1, 6, 15, 28, 45, 66
7. $a_n = 4n + n^2$ 5, 12, 21, 32, 45, 60
8. $a_n = \frac{1}{3}n^3$ $\frac{1}{3}, \frac{8}{3}, 9, \frac{64}{3}, \frac{125}{3}, 72$
9. $a_n = (-2)^n$ −2, 4, −8, 16, −32, 64

Write a recursive definition for each sequence.

10. −14, −8, −2, 4, 10, . . . $a_n = a_{n-1} + 6$ where $a_1 = -14$
11. 6, 5.7, 5.4, 5.1, 4.8, . . . $a_n = a_{n-1} - 0.3$ where $a_1 = 6$
12. 1, −2, 4, −8, 16, . . . $a_n = -2a_{n-1}$ where $a_1 = 1$
13. 1, 3, 9, 27, . . . $a_n = 3a_{n-1}$ where $a_1 = 1$
14. $1, \frac{1}{2}, \frac{1}{4}, \frac{1}{8}, \frac{1}{16}, \ldots$ $a_n = \frac{1}{2}a_{n-1}$ where $a_1 = 1$
15. $\frac{2}{3}, 1, 1\frac{1}{3}, 1\frac{2}{3}, 2, \ldots$ $a_n = a_{n-1} + \frac{1}{3}$ where $a_1 = \frac{2}{3}$
16. 36, 39, 42, 45, 48, . . . $a_n = a_{n-1} + 3$ where $a_1 = 36$
17. 36, 30, 24, 18, 12, . . . $a_n = a_{n-1} - 6$ where $a_1 = 36$
18. 9.6, 4.8, 2.4, 1.2, 0.6, . . . $a_n = \frac{1}{2}a_{n-1}$ where $a_1 = 9.6$

Write an explicit formula for each sequence. Find the twentieth term.

19. 7, 14, 21, 28, 35, . . . $a_n = 7n$; 140
20. 2, 8, 14, 20, 26, . . . $a_n = 6n - 4$; 116
21. 5, 6, 7, 8, 9, . . . $a_n = n + 4$; 24
22. −1, 0, 1, 2, 3, . . . $a_n = n - 2$; 18
23. 3, 5, 7, 9, 11, . . . $a_n = 2n + 1$; 41
24. 0.8, 1.6, 2.4, 3.2, 4, . . . $a_n = 0.8n$; 16
25. $\frac{1}{4}, \frac{1}{2}, \frac{3}{4}, 1, \frac{5}{4}, \ldots$ $a_n = \frac{n}{4}$; 5
26. $\frac{1}{2}, \frac{1}{4}, \frac{1}{6}, \frac{1}{8}, \frac{1}{10}, \ldots$ $a_n = \frac{1}{2n}$; $\frac{1}{40}$
27. $\frac{2}{3}, 1\frac{2}{3}, 2\frac{2}{3}, 3\frac{2}{3}, 4\frac{2}{3}, \ldots$ $a_n = n - \frac{1}{3}$; $19\frac{2}{3}$

Find the eighth term of each sequence.

28. 1, 3, 5, 7, 9, . . .   15
29. 400, 200, 100, 50, 25, . . .   3.125
30. 0, −2, −4, −6, −8, . . .   −14
31. 1, 2, 4, 8, 16, . . .   128
32. 44, 39, 34, 29, 24, . . .   9
33. 0.7, 0.8, 0.9, 1.0, 1.1, . . .   1.4
34. 4, 11, 18, 25, 32, . . .   53
35. $1\frac{1}{4}, 2\frac{1}{2}, 5, 10, 20, \ldots$ 160
36. −6, −9, −12, −15, −18,   −27
37. A man swims 1.5 mi on Monday, 1.6 mi on Tuesday, 1.8 mi on Wednesday, 2.1 mi on Thursday, and 2.5 mi on Friday. If the pattern continues, how many miles will he swim on Saturday? 3.0 mi

Practice and Problem Solving Wkbk/ All-in-One Resources/Online
Practice page 2

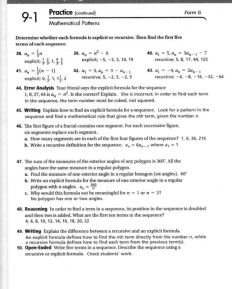

9-1 Practice (continued) *Form G*
Mathematical Patterns

Determine whether each formula is *explicit* or *recursive*. Then find the first five terms of each sequence.

38. $a_n = \frac{1}{3}n$ explicit; $\frac{1}{3}, \frac{2}{3}, 1, \frac{4}{3}, \frac{5}{3}$
39. $a_n = n^2 - 6$ explicit; −5, −2, 3, 10, 19
40. $a_1 = 5, a_n = 3a_{n-1} - 7$ recursive; 5, 8, 17, 44, 125
41. $a_n = \frac{1}{2}(n - 1)$ explicit; $0, \frac{1}{2}, 1, 1\frac{1}{2}, 2$
42. $a_1 = 5, a_n = 3 - a_{n-1}$ recursive; 5, −2, 5, −2, 5
43. $a_1 = -4, a_n = 2a_{n-1}$ recursive; −4, −8, −16, −32, −64
44. **Error Analysis** Your friend says the explicit formula for the sequence 1, 8, 27, 64 is $a_n = n^2$. Is she correct? Explain. She is incorrect; in order to find each term in the sequence, the term number must be cubed, not squared.
45. **Writing** Explain how to find an explicit formula for a sequence. Look for a pattern in the sequence and find a mathematical rule that gives the *n*th term, given the number *n*.
46. The first figure of a fractal contains one segment. For each successive figure, six segments replace each segment.
    a. How many segments are in each of the first four figures of the sequence? 1, 6, 36, 216
    b. Write a recursive definition for the sequence. $a_n = 6a_{n-1}$ where $a_1 = 1$
47. The sum of the measures of the exterior angles of any polygon is 360°. All the angles have the same measure in a regular polygon.
    a. Find the measure of one exterior angle in a regular hexagon (six angles). 60°
    b. Write an explicit formula for the measure of one exterior angle in a regular polygon with *n* angles. $a_n = \frac{360}{n}$
    c. Why would this formula not be meaningful for $n = 1$ or $n = 2$? No polygon has one or two angles.
48. **Reasoning** In order to find a term in a sequence, its position in the sequence is doubled and then two is added. What are the first ten terms in the sequence? 4, 6, 8, 10, 12, 14, 16, 18, 20, 22
49. **Writing** Explain the difference between a recursive and an explicit formula. An explicit formula defines how to find the *n*th term directly from the number *n*, while a recursive formula defines how to find each term from the previous term(s).
50. **Open-Ended** Write five terms in a sequence. Describe the sequence using a recursive or explicit formula. Check students' work.

All-in-One Resources/Online
Enrichment

9-1 Enrichment
Mathematical Patterns

You can define the terms in a sequence using an explicit formula or a recursive definition. You can use another method, called iteration, to form a sequence. The word *iteration* means to repeat an action. In mathematics, a sequence of numbers is generated through iteration when the same procedure is performed on each output.

1. Consider the function $f(x) = 5x + 1$. Let the first term of a sequence be 0. What is $f(0)$? Let $f(0)$ be the second term of the sequence. Write the sequence. 0, 1
2. To create more terms of this sequence through iteration, continue to apply $f(x)$ to each output. The third term in this sequence can be described as $f(f(0))$. What is the third term? $f(f(0)) = f(1) = 6$
3. Determine the first 10 terms of this sequence. You already have the first 3 terms. 0; 1; 6; 31; 156; 781; 3906; 19,531; 97,656; 488,281
4. Determine the first 5 terms of the sequence formed through iterations of $f(x) = \frac{x}{2} + 1$. Begin with $x = 2$. Describe the sequence. 2, 2, 2, 2, 2; all of the terms in the sequence are 2.
5. Will you get the same type of sequence if you start with a different number? No; for example, if you start with $x = 0$, the sequence is 0, 1, 1.5, . . .
6. Iterations have uses other than to form numerical sequences. Consider this iterative process, which forms a sequence of a set of three integers. Make a set of any three integers. Compute the absolute value of the difference between each pair of integers in the set. This produces a new set of three integers. Continue this process on each new set of three integers. Describe what eventually happens. No matter what three integers you choose to start with, the set will eventually repeat itself in combinations of the set {0, *a*, *a*}, where *a* is a positive integer.
7. You can form fractals through iterations. Fractals are geometric figures just like circles or rectangles, but fractals have a special property that these geometric figures do not. You make fractals by iterating the figure itself. For example, start by drawing an equilateral triangle on graph paper. Divide each side into three equal parts. Draw another equilateral triangle on one side of the triangle that has the middle section as its base. Repeat this process on the remaining two sides. You have just created the first two iterations of a fractal called the Koch snowflake.

Practice and Problem Solving Wkbk/ All-in-One Resources/Online
Think About a Plan

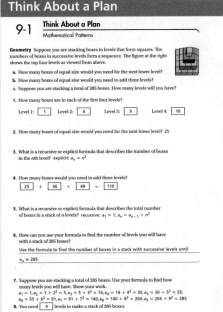

9-1 Think About a Plan
Mathematical Patterns

Geometry Suppose you are stacking boxes in levels that form squares. The numbers of boxes in successive levels form a sequence. The figure at the right shows the top four levels as viewed from above.

a. How many boxes of equal size would you need for the next lower level?
b. How many boxes of equal size would you need to add three levels?
c. Suppose you are stacking a total of 285 boxes. How many levels will you have?

1. How many boxes are in each of the first four levels?
   Level 1: [1] Level 2: [4] Level 3: [9] Level 4: [16]
2. How many boxes of equal size would you need for the next lower level? 25
3. What is a recursive or explicit formula that describes the number of boxes in the *n*th level? explicit: $a_n = n^2$
4. How many boxes would you need to add three levels?
   [25] + [36] + [49] = [110]
5. What is a recursive or explicit formula that describes the total number of boxes in a stack of *n* levels? recursive: $a_1 = 1$; $a_n = a_{n-1} + n^2$
6. How can you use your formula to find the number of levels you will have with a stack of 285 boxes?
   Use the formula to find the number of boxes in a stack with successive levels until $a_n \geq 285$.
7. Suppose you are stacking a total of 285 boxes. Use your formula to find how many levels you will have. Show your work.
   $a_1 = 1, a_2 = 1 + 2^2 = 5, a_3 = 5 + 3^2 = 14, a_4 = 14 + 4^2 = 30, a_5 = 30 + 5^2 = 55,$
   $a_6 = 55 + 6^2 = 91, a_7 = 91 + 7^2 = 140, a_8 = 140 + 8^2 = 204, a_9 = 204 + 9^2 = 285$
8. You need [9] levels to make a stack of 285 boxes.

Practice and Problem Solving Wkbk/ All-in-One Resources/Online
Standardized Test Prep

9-1 Standardized Test Prep
Mathematical Patterns

Multiple Choice

For Exercises 1–6, choose the correct letter.

1. What are the first five terms of the sequence? C
   $$a_n = 3^n - 1$$
   (A) 2, 5, 8, 11, 14   (C) 2, 8, 26, 80, 242
   (B) 3, 9, 27, 81, 243   (D) 2, 4, 8, 16, 32
2. The formula $a_n = 3n + 2$ best represents which sequence? G
   (F) 3, 6, 9, 12, 15   (H) 4, 7, 10, 13, 16
   (G) 5, 8, 11, 14, 17   (I) 5, 9, 29, 83, 245
3. Which pattern can be represented by $a_n = n^2 - 3$? D
   (A) −1, 0, 5, 12, 21   (B) 4, 7, 12, 19, 28   (C) 1, 4, 9, 16, 25   (D) −2, 1, 6, 13, 22
4. The sequence 4, 16, 36, 64, 100, . . . can best be represented by which formula? G
   (F) $a_n = 4n$ (G) $a_n = 4n^2$ (H) $a_n = 4n^3$ (I) $a_n = 2n^4$
5. For the sequence 0, 6, 16, 30, 48, . . . , what is the 40th term? A
   (A) 3198   (B) 3200   (C) 4000   (D) 16,000
6. A student sets up a savings plan to transfer money from his checking account to his savings account. The first week \$10 is transferred, the second week \$12 is transferred, the third week \$16 is transferred, and the fourth week \$24 is transferred. If this pattern continues and he starts with \$100 in his checking account, how many weeks will pass before his balance is zero? G
   (F) 4   (G) 5   (H) 6   (I) 7

Short Response

7. After training for and running a marathon, an athlete wants to reduce her daily run by half each day. The marathon is about 26 mi. How many days will it take after the marathon before she runs less than a mile a day? Show your work.
   [2] 5 days; Day 1: 13 mi, Day 2: 6.5 mi, Day 3: 3.25 mi, Day 4: 1.625 mi, Day 5: 0.8125 mi
   [1] correct answer, without work shown OR incorrect answer with correct sequence
   [0] incorrect answers and no work shown OR no answers given

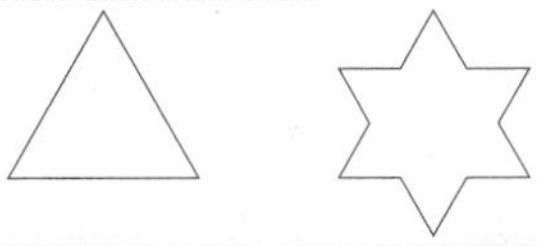

Online Teacher Resource Center
Activities, Games, and Puzzles

9-1 Game: De-"Term"-ining the Answer
Mathematical Patterns

Provide the host with the following list of explicit formulas or recursive formulas with initial term and corresponding terms for twenty sequences.

Formula	Next 10 Terms
$a_n = \frac{1}{n}$	$1, \frac{1}{2}, \frac{1}{3}, \frac{1}{4}, \frac{1}{5}, \frac{1}{6}, \frac{1}{7}, \frac{1}{8}, \frac{1}{9}, \frac{1}{10}$
$a_n = n + 2$	3, 4, 5, 6, 7, 8, 9, 10, 11, 12
$a_n = n - 7$	−6, −5, −4, −3, −2, −1, 0, 1, 2, 3
$a_n = 4n$	4, 8, 12, 16, 20, 24, 28, 32, 36, 40
$a_n = 2n - 1$	1, 3, 5, 7, 9, 11, 13, 15, 17, 19
$a_n = 3n + 5$	8, 11, 14, 17, 20, 23, 26, 29, 32, 35
$a_n = n^3$	1, 8, 27, 64, 125, 216, 343, 512, 729, 1000
$a_n = n^2 + n + 1$	3, 7, 13, 21, 31, 43, 57, 73, 91, 111
$a_{n+1} = a_n + 6; a_1 = -1$	5, 11, 17, 23, 29, 35, 41, 47, 53, 59
$a_{n+1} = a_n + n; a_1 = 1$	2, 4, 7, 11, 16, 22, 29, 37, 46, 56
$a_{n+1} = a_n + 2n; a_1 = 1$	3, 7, 13, 21, 31, 43, 57, 73, 91, 111
$a_{n+1} = a_n + n^2; a_1 = 1$	2, 6, 15, 31, 56, 92, 141, 205, 286, 386
$a_{n+1} = a_n + 2^n; a_1 = 1$	3, 7, 15, 31, 63, 127, 255, 511, 1023, 2047
$a_{n+1} = a_n + n + 4^n; a_1 = 0$	5; 23; 90; 350; 1379; 5481; 21,872; 87,416; 349,569; 1,398,155
$a_{n+1} = a_n + 5(-3)^n; a_1 = 0$	−15; 30; −105; 300; −915; 2730; −8205; 24,600; −73,815; 221,430
$a_{n+1} = 3a_n; a_1 = 2$	6; 18; 54; 162; 486; 1458; 4374; 13,122; 39,366; 118,098
$a_{n+1} = na_n; a_1 = 1$	1; 2; 6; 24; 120; 720; 5040; 40,320; 362,880; 3,628,800
$a_{n+1} = \frac{1}{2}a_n; a_1 = 1$	$\frac{1}{2}, \frac{1}{4}, \frac{1}{8}, \frac{1}{16}, \frac{1}{32}, \frac{1}{64}, \frac{1}{128}, \frac{1}{256}, \frac{1}{512}, \frac{1}{1024}$
$a_{n+1} = 3a_n - n; a_1 = 1$	2; 4; 9; 23; 64; 186; 551; 1645; 4926; 14,768
$a_{n+1} = 1 + \frac{1}{a_n}; a_1 = 1$	$2, \frac{3}{2}, \frac{5}{3}, \frac{8}{5}, \frac{13}{8}, \frac{21}{13}, \frac{34}{21}, \frac{55}{34}, \frac{89}{55}, \frac{144}{89}$

1 Interactive Learning

Solve It!

PURPOSE To write an arithmetic sequence
PROCESS Students may
- subtract 4 km from 10 km and divide by 8 to find the constant value.
- use trial-and-error to find the daily running distance between 4 km and 10 km.

FACILITATE

Q What is the least and most you will run in a day during the training? **[4 km; 10 km]**

Q How many training weeks are left after week 1? **[8]**

Q How many km must be divided in the remaining weeks? **[6]**

Q What expression will determine the equal amount of increase? $[\frac{10-4}{8}]$

Q How are the terms of the sequence generated? **[Add 0.75 to 4 and continue adding 0.75 to the next term until the sum is 10.]**

ANSWER See Solve It in Answers on next page.
CONNECT THE MATH In the Solve It, students write an arithmetic sequence. In the lesson, they will define, identify, and analyze arithmetic sequences.

2 Guided Instruction

Take Note   SYNTHESIZING

If the explicit formula for the nth term in summation notation is a *linear* function of n, then the sequence is arithmetic. The slope of the linear function is the common difference between terms of the sequence.

© **Content Standard**
F.IF.3 Recognize that sequences are functions, sometimes defined recursively, whose domain is a subset of the integers.

Objective To define, identify, and apply arithmetic sequences

 Getting Ready!

To train for a 10-km race ten weeks from now, you plan to begin by running 4 km each day for one week. Each week after that you will increase your distance by a fixed amount. How many kilometers should you add each week to complete your chart? Explain.

Training Schedule

Week 1	Week 2	Week 3	Week 4	Week 5
4 km				
Week 6	Week 7	Week 8	Week 9	Week 10
				10 k

Dynamic Activity Arithmetic Sequences

Lesson Vocabulary
- arithmetic sequence
- common difference
- arithmetic mean

It sometimes is helpful to represent a situation with a sequence of numbers. There are different types of numerical sequences.

Essential Understanding In an *arithmetic sequence*, the difference between any two consecutive terms is always the same number. You can build an arithmetic sequence by adding the same number to each term.

An **arithmetic sequence** is a sequence where the difference between consecutive terms is constant. This difference is the **common difference**.

take note

Key Concept   Arithmetic Sequence

An arithmetic sequence with a starting value a and common difference d is a sequence of the form

$$a, a + d, a + 2d, a + 3d, \ldots.$$

A recursive definition for this sequence has two parts:

$a_1 = a$ \qquad\qquad initial condition
$a_n = a_{n-1} + d$, for $n > 1$ \quad recursive formula

An explicit definition for this sequence is a single formula:

$a_n = a + (n - 1)d$, for $n \geq 1$

BIG ideas **Equivalence**
              Variable

ESSENTIAL UNDERSTANDINGS
- In an arithmetic sequence, the difference between any two consecutive terms is always the same number. An arithmetic sequence can be built by adding the same number to each term.
- A sequence can be defined explicitly by describing its nth term with a formula using n or recursively by stating its first term and a formula for its nth term using the $(n - 1)$ term.
- $a_n = a + (n - 1)d$ and $a_1 = a$, $a_n = a_{n-1} + d$ for $n > 1$ define the same arithmetic sequence, $a, a + d, a + 2d, \ldots$.

Math Background

An arithmetic sequence has a constant difference or common difference between consecutive terms. An arithmetic sequence is related to a special case of a linear function whose domain is the set of

natural numbers. The slope of the graph of this corresponding linear function is equal to the common difference of the sequence.

Any missing term of an arithmetic sequence can be found if any of the following information is known:
- the first term and the common difference,
- the first term and another term.

Note that an arithmetic sequence can be finite or infinite and can have positive and negative terms.

© **Mathematical Practices**
Attend to precision. Students will define the term "arithmetic sequence" and learn to identify arithmetic sequences.

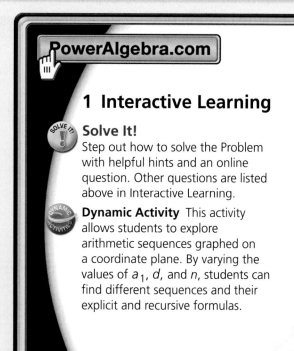

PowerAlgebra.com

1 Interactive Learning

Solve It!
Step out how to solve the Problem with helpful hints and an online question. Other questions are listed above in Interactive Learning.

Dynamic Activity This activity allows students to explore arithmetic sequences graphed on a coordinate plane. By varying the values of a_1, d, and n, students can find different sequences and their explicit and recursive formulas.

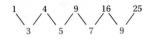 **Problem 1** Identifying Arithmetic Sequences

Plan

How do you know whether a sequence is arithmetic?
The differences between consecutive terms are the same in an arithmetic sequence.

Is the sequence an arithmetic sequence?

A 3, 6, 9, 12, 15, . . .

Find the differences between consecutive terms.

$$3 \quad 6 \quad 9 \quad 12 \quad 15$$
$$\quad 3 \quad 3 \quad 3 \quad 3$$

Each difference is 3. The sequence has a common difference. The sequence is an arithmetic sequence.

B 1, 4, 9, 16, 25, . . .

Find the difference between consecutive terms.

$$1 \quad 4 \quad 9 \quad 16 \quad 25$$
$$\quad 3 \quad 5 \quad 7 \quad 9$$

There is no common difference. The sequence is not an arithmetic sequence.

✔ **Got It?** **1.** Is the sequence an arithmetic sequence?
  a. 2, 4, 8, 16, . . . **b.** 1, 5, 9, 13, 17, . . .

 Problem 2 Analyzing Arithmetic Sequences

A What is the 100th term of the arithmetic sequence that begins 6, 11, . . . ?

The first term a is 6. The common difference d is $11 - 6 = 5$.

$a_n = a + (n - 1)d$	Use the explicit formula.
$a_{100} = 6 + (100 - 1)5$	Substitute 100 for n, 6 for a, and 5 for d.
$a_{100} = 501$	Simplify.

The 100th term is 501.

Plan

What do you need to find the second term given the first term?
You need to know the common difference of the arithmetic sequence.

B What are the second and third terms of the arithmetic sequence 100, ■, ■, 82, . . . ?

The first term a is 100. The fourth term a_4 is 82. There are 3 common differences between 100 and 82.

$82 = 100 + 3d$	Add $3d$ to move from 100 to 82.
$-18 = 3d$	Solve for d.
$-6 = d$	

The common difference is -6. The terms are 100, 94, 88, 82, ...

The second and third terms are 94 and 88.

✔ **Got It?** **2. a.** What is the 46th term of the arithmetic sequence that begins 3, 5, 7, . . . ?
  b. What are the second and third terms of this arithmetic sequence?
    80, ■, ■, 125, . . .

---

2 Guided Instruction

 Each Problem is worked out and supported online.

Problem 1
Identifying Arithmetic Sequences
Animated

Problem 2
Analyzing an Arithmetic Sequence
Animated

Problem 3
Using the Arithmetic Mean

Problem 4
Using an Explicit Formula for an Arithmetic Sequence
Animated

Support in Algebra 2 Companion
• Vocabulary
• Key Concepts
• Got It?

Problem 1 SYNTHESIZING

Q What is the common difference in 1A? **[3]**
Q What is a description in words of the arithmetic sequence elements in 1A? **[multiples of 3, beginning with 3]**
Q How would you describe the values in the sequence 1B? **[squares of 1, 2, 3, 4, 5 ...]**

Got It? ERROR PREVENTION

Q What are the differences between consecutive terms in 1a? **[2, 4, 8]**
Q Is there a common difference in 1b? If so, what is it? **[yes; 4]**

Problem 2 SYNTHESIZING

Q What does n represent in the explicit definition? **[the number of the term]**
Q What equation would you write in 2A if you were asked for the 150th term? **[$a_{150} = 6 + (150 - 1)5$]**
Q If there were 3 terms between 100 and 82 in 2B, what equation would you write to find d? **[$82 = 100 + 4d$]**

Got It?

Q What information do you need to find additional terms of an arithmetic sequence? **[Samples: first term and common difference; at least two terms.]**
Q What equation would you write in 2a? **[$a_{46} = 3 + (46 - 1)2$]**
Q What is the sign of the common difference in 2b? Why? **[Positive, because the terms of the sequence are increasing.]**

Answers

Solve It!
0.75 km; $10 = 4 + (9 - 1)d$

Got It?
1. a. no
  b. yes
2. a. 93
  b. 95, 110

Problem 3

Q Can you use the arithmetic mean to find a missing term given any two terms? Explain. **[No; the three terms involved must be consecutive and the missing term must be the middle term.]**

Got It?   ERROR PREVENTION

Q What must be true about the 10th term? **[It must be less than 132, greater than 98, and the average of 132 and 98.]**

Q Is it possible to get a negative term? Explain. **[yes, if the sequence has negative terms]**

Problem 4

Q Could you use the explicit definition to find the number of seats in any of the 13 rows? Explain. **[Yes; you have the first term and common difference.]**

Got It?   EXTENSION

Q What explicit formula gives the number of seats in the third row? **[$a_3 = 20 + (3 - 1)3$]**

The **arithmetic mean**, or average, of two numbers x and y is $\frac{x + y}{2}$.

In an arithmetic sequence, the middle term of any three consecutive terms is the arithmetic mean of the other two terms.

 Problem 3 Using the Arithmetic Mean   GRIDDED RESPONSE

What is the missing term of the arithmetic sequence $\dots, 15, \blacksquare, 59, \dots$?

$$\text{arithmetic mean} = \frac{15 + 59}{2} = 37$$

The missing term is 37.

Think
To use the formula for arithmetic mean, what are x and y? x is 15 and y is 59.

Got It? **3. a.** The 9th and 11th terms of an arithmetic sequence are 132 and 98. What is the 10th term?

    b. Reasoning If you know the 5th and 6th terms of an arithmetic sequence, how can you find term 7 using the arithmetic mean?

 Problem 4 Using an Explicit Formula for an Arithmetic Sequence

Sports Arena The numbers of seats in the first 13 rows in a section of an arena form an arithmetic sequence. Rows 1 and 2 are shown in the diagram below. How many seats are in Row 13?

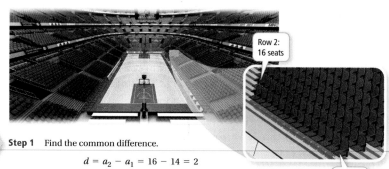

Row 2: 16 seats

Row 1: 14 seats

Plan
What two terms should you use to find the common difference? Use the consecutive terms given.

Step 1 Find the common difference.

$$d = a_2 - a_1 = 16 - 14 = 2$$

Step 2 Write an explicit formula for the arithmetic sequence.

$a_n = a + (n - 1)d$ Use the explicit formula.

$a_{13} = 14 + (13 - 1)2$ Substitute 13 for n, 14 for a, and 2 for d.

$= 38$ Simplify.

There are 38 seats in Row 13.

Got It? **4.** The numbers of seats in the first 16 rows in a curved section of another arena form an arithmetic sequence. If there are 20 seats in Row 1 and 23 seats in Row 2, how many seats are in Row 16?

Additional Problems

1. Is the sequence an arithmetic sequence?

  a. 12, 22, 32, 42, 52, …

  b. 1, 1, 2, 3, 5, …

  ANSWERS a. yes **b.** no

2. What are the indicated terms of the arithmetic sequence?

  a. the 110th term of the sequence that begins 5, 9, …

  b. the second and third terms of the sequence 90, ■, ■, 12, …

  ANSWERS a. 441 **b.** 64, 38

3. What is the missing term of the arithmetic sequence …35, ■, 53, …?

  ANSWER 44

4. Over the last ten years the amount of snow a town received formed an arithmetic sequence. If 21 in. of snow fell 10 years ago and 19 in. fell 9 years ago, how many inches fell 2 years ago?

  ANSWER 5 in.

Answers

Got It? (continued)

  3. a. 115

    b. Use the formula for arithmetic mean and solve for a_7: $a_7 = 2a_6 - a_5$.

4. 65 seats

Lesson Check

Do you know HOW?

Find the tenth term of each arithmetic sequence.

1. 2, 8, 14, 20, . . .   **2.** 15, 23, 31, . . .

Find the missing term of each arithmetic sequence.

3. . . . 4, ■, 22, . . .   **4.** . . . 25, ■, 53, . . .

Do you UNDERSTAND? MATHEMATICAL PRACTICES

5. Vocabulary Explain what it means for a sequence to be an arithmetic sequence.

6. Open-Ended Give an example of a sequence that is not an arithmetic sequence.

 Practice and Problem-Solving Exercises MATHEMATICAL PRACTICES

Ⓐ Practice

Determine whether each sequence is arithmetic. If so, identify the common difference.   ◆ See Problem 1.

7. 10, 20, 30, 40, . . .   **8.** 1, 1, 2, 3, 5, 8, . . .   **9.** −21, −18, −15, −12, . . .

10. 97, 86, 75, 64, . . .   **11.** 3, 7, 11, 15, . . .   **12.** 100, 10, 1, 0.1, . . .

Find the 32nd term of each sequence.   ◆ See Problem 2.

13. 34, 37, 40, 43, . . .   **14.** −9, −8.7, −8.4, . . .   **15.** 23, 30, 37, 44, . . .

16. 9, 4, −1, −6, −11, . . .   **17.** 0.1, 0.5, 0.9, 1.3, . . .   **18.** 101, 105, 109, 113, . . .

Find the missing term of each arithmetic sequence.   ◆ See Problem 3.

19. −15, ■, 1, . . .   **20.** 14, ■, 28, . . .   **21.** . . . 5, ■, 21, . . .

22. . . . 98, ■, 66, . . .   **23.** 25, ■, −10, . . .   **24.** . . . 65, ■, −60, . . .

25. Savings A student deposits the same amount of money into her bank account each week. At the end of the second week she has $30 in her account. At the end of the third week she has $45 in her account. How much will she have in her bank account at the end of the ninth week?   ◆ See Problem 4.

Ⓑ Apply

Find the 17th term of each sequence.

26. $a_{16} = 18, d = 5$ **27.** $a_{16} = 21, d = -3$ **28.** $a_{18} = -5, d = 12$

29. $a_{18} = 32, d = -4$ **30.** $a_{16} = \frac{1}{5}, d = \frac{1}{2}$ **31.** $a_{18} = -9, d = -11$

32. Think About a Plan The arithmetic mean of the monthly salaries of two employees is $3210. One employee earns $3470 per month. What is the monthly salary of the other employee?
   • What is the given information and what is the unknown?
   • What equation can you use to find the other monthly salary?

33. Error Analysis A student claims that the next term of the arithmetic sequence 0, 2, 4, . . . is 8. Explain and correct the student's error.

Lesson Check

1. 56   **2.** 87

3. 13   **4.** 39

5. In an arithmetic sequence, the diff. between any two consecutive terms is always the same number.

6. Answers may vary. Sample: 2, 4, 8, 16, 32, . . .

Practice and Problem-Solving Exercises

7. yes; 10   **8.** no

9. yes; 3   **10.** yes; −11

11. yes; 4   **12.** no

13. 127   **14.** 0.3

15. 240   **16.** −146

17. 12.5   **18.** 225

19. −7   **20.** 21

21. 13   **22.** 82

23. 7.5   **24.** 2.5

25. $135   **26.** 23

27. 18   **28.** −17

29. 36   **30.** $\frac{7}{10}$

31. 2   **32.** $2950

33. The student multiplied the third term by 2 instead of adding 2. The correct answer is 6.

---

3 Lesson Check

Do you know HOW?

• For Exercises 3 and 4, students can use the arithmetic mean to find the term since the missing term is one of three consecutive terms.

Do you UNDERSTAND? ERROR INTERVENTION

• For Exercise 6, review that the difference between terms of a non-arithmetic sequence is not constant.

Close

> **Q** How do you identify an arithmetic sequence and find its missing terms? **[Sample: A sequence is an arithmetic sequence if the difference between the terms is constant. You can use the explicit formula if you have the first term and either another term or the common difference. You can use the arithmetic mean to find a missing term if the proceeding and following term are given.]**

PowerAlgebra.com

3 Lesson Check

For a digital lesson check, use the Got It questions.

Support in Algebra 2 Companion
• Lesson Check

4 Practice

Assign homework to individual students or to an entire class.

4 Practice

ASSIGNMENT GUIDE

Basic: 7–25 all, 31–35, 49–53, 61

Average: 7–25 odd, 26–62

Advanced: 7–25 odd, 26–74

Standardized Test Prep: 75–77

Mixed Review: 78–88

Ⓒ **Mathematical Practices** are supported by exercises with red headings. Here are the Practices supported in this lesson:

MP 1: Make Sense of Problems Ex. 32
MP 2: Reason Quantitatively Ex. 50
MP 3: Communicate Ex. 5, 40b, 51
MP 3: Construct Arguments Ex. 6
MP 3: Critique the Reasoning of Others Ex. 33
MP 4: Model with Mathematics Ex. 62
MP 5: Use Appropriate Tools Ex. 40a

Applications exercises have blue headings. Exercises 25, 52, and 61 support MP 4: Model.

EXERCISE 52: Use the Think About a Plan worksheet in the **Practice and Problem Solving Workbook** (also available in the Teaching Resources in print and online) to further support students' development in becoming independent learners.

HOMEWORK QUICK CHECK

To check students' understanding of key skills and concepts, go over Exercises 7, 13, 32, 50, and 52.

Find the arithmetic mean a_n of the given terms.

34. $a_{n-1} = 7, a_{n+1} = 1$ **35.** $a_{n-1} = 100, a_{n+1} = 140$ **36.** $a_{n-1} = 4, a_{n+1} = -3$

37. $a_{n-1} = 0.3, a_{n+1} = 1.9$ **38.** $a_{n-1} = r, a_{n+1} = s$ **39.** $a_{n-1} = -2x, a_{n+1} = 2x$

 40. a. Graphing Calculator Use your calculator to generate an arithmetic sequence with a common difference of -7. How could you use a calculator to find the 6th term? The 8th term? The 20th term?

Ⓒ **b. Reasoning** Explain how your answer to part (a) relates to the explicit formula $a_n = a + (n - 1)d$.

Write an explicit and a recursive formula for each sequence.

41. 2, 4, 6, 8, 10, . . .   **42.** 0, 6, 12, 18, 24, . . .   **43.** $-5, -4, -3, -2, -1, \ldots$

44. $-4, -8, -12, -16, -20, \ldots$ **45.** $-5, -3.5, -2, -0.5, 1, \ldots$ **46.** $-32, -20, -8, 4, 16, \ldots$

47. $1, 1\frac{1}{3}, 1\frac{2}{3}, 2, \ldots$ **48.** $0, \frac{1}{8}, \frac{1}{4}, \frac{3}{8}, \ldots$ **49.** $27, 15, 3, -9, -21, \ldots$

Ⓒ **50. Reasoning** What information do you need to find a term of a sequence using an explicit formula?

Ⓒ **51. Writing** Describe some advantages and some disadvantages of a recursive formula and an explicit formula. When is it appropriate to use each formula?

52. Transportation Suppose a trolley stops at a certain intersection every 14 min. The first trolley of the day gets to the stop at 6:43 A.M. How long do you have to wait for a trolley if you get to the stop at 8:15 A.M.? At 3:20 P.M.?

Find the missing terms of each arithmetic sequence. (*Hint:* The arithmetic mean of the first and fifth terms is the third term.)

53. $2, a_2, a_3, a_4, -22, \ldots$ **54.** $10, a_2, a_3, a_4, -11.6, \ldots$ **55.** $1, a_2, a_3, a_4, -35, \ldots$

56. $\ldots \frac{13}{5}, a_6, a_7, a_8, \frac{37}{5}, \ldots$ **57.** $17, a_2, a_3, a_4, 17, \ldots$ **58.** $660, a_2, a_3, a_4, 744, \ldots$

59. $\ldots -17, a_4, a_5, a_6, 1, \ldots$ **60.** $\ldots a + 1, a_3, a_4, a_5, a + 17, \ldots$

61. Income The arithmetic mean of the monthly salaries of two people is \$4475. One person earns \$3895 per month. What is the monthly salary of the other person?

Ⓒ **62. Reasoning** Suppose you turn the water on in an empty bathtub with vertical sides. After 20 s, the water has reached a level of 1.15 in. You then leave the room. You want to turn the water off when the level in the bathtub is 8.5 in. How many minutes later should you return? (*Hint:* Begin by identifying two terms of an arithmetic sequence.)

Ⓒ **Challenge**   **63.** In an arithmetic sequence with $a_1 = 4$ and $d = 9$, which term is 184?

64. In an arithmetic sequence with $a_1 = 2$ and $d = -2$, which term is -82?

65. The arithmetic mean of two terms in an arithmetic sequence is 42. One term is 30. Find the other term.

Answers

Practice and Problem-Solving Exercises (continued)

34. 4   **35.** 120   **36.** $\frac{1}{2}$

37. 1.1   **38.** $\frac{r + s}{2}$ **39.** 0

40. a. Answers may vary. Sample: 25, 18, 11, 4, −3, −10, . . . ; to find the 6th term, multiply 5 times (−7) and add to a_1; to find the 8th term, multiply 7 times (−7) and add to a_1; to find the 20th term, multiply 19 times (−7) and add to a_1

b. Answers may vary. Sample: Start with the first term and continue to subtract 7 for each term. For each term, you subtract 7 · (term number − 1) from the first term.

41. $a_n = 2 + 2(n - 1)$; $a_n = a_{n-1} + 2, a_1 = 2$

42. $a_n = 0 + 6(n - 1)$; $a_n = a_{n-1} + 6, a_1 = 0$

43. $a_n = -5 + 1(n - 1)$; $a_n = a_{n-1} + 1, a_1 = -5$

44. $a_n = -4 - 4(n - 1)$; $a_n = a_{n-1} - 4, a_1 = -4$

45. $a_n = -5 + 1.5(n - 1)$; $a_n = a_{n-1} + 1.5, a_1 = -5$

46. $a_n = -32 + 12(n - 1)$; $a_n = a_{n-1} + 12, a_1 = -32$

47. $a_n = 1 + \frac{1}{3}(n - 1)$; $a_n = a_{n-1} + \frac{1}{3}, a_1 = 1$

48. $a_n = \frac{1}{8}(n - 1)$; $a_n = a_{n-1} + \frac{1}{8}, a_1 = 0$

49. $a_n = 27 - 12(n - 1)$; $a_n = a_{n-1} - 12, a_1 = 27$

50. All you need is the term number, since you have an explicit formula.

51. Answers may vary. Sample: An advantage of a recursive formula is that only the preceding term must be known to find the next term; a disadvantage is that many calculations may be required to find a term. An advantage of an explicit formula is that it is easy to find any term. Use the recursive formula when the previous term and common diff. are known. Use the explicit formula when the term number and common diff. are known.

52. 6 min; 1 min

53. −4, −10, −16

54. 4.6, −0.8, −6.2

55. −8, −17, −26

56. $\frac{19}{5}, 5, \frac{31}{5}$

57. 17, 17, 17

58. 681, 702, 723

59. −12.5, −8, −3.5

60. $a + 5, a + 9, a + 13$

61. \$5055

62. 2.13 min or 2 min 8 s

63. 21st term

64. 43rd term

65. 54

66. The arithmetic mean of two terms in an arithmetic sequence is -6. One term is -20. Find the other term.

Given two terms of each arithmetic sequence, find a_1 and d.

67. $a_3 = 5$ and $a_5 = 11$ **68.** $a_4 = 8$ and $a_7 = 20$ **69.** $a_3 = 32$ and $a_7 = -8$

70. $a_{10} = 17$ and $a_{14} = 34$ **71.** $a_4 = -34.5$ and $a_5 = -12.5$ **72.** $a_4 = -2.4$ and $a_6 = 2$

Find the indicated term of each arithmetic sequence.

73. $a_1 = k$, $d = k + 4$; a_9 **74.** $a_1 = k + 7$, $d = 2k - 5$; a_{11}

Standardized Test Prep

SAT/ACT

75. The equation $X(t) = t^4 - 5t^2 + 6$ gives the position of a comet relative to a fixed point, measured in millions of miles, at time t, measured in days. Solve the equation $X(t) = 0$. At what times is the position zero?

(A) $2, 3$ (C) $\pm 2, \pm 3$

(B) $-2, -3$ (D) $\pm\sqrt{2}, \pm\sqrt{3}$

76. Simplify $\dfrac{3 - \frac{1}{x}}{\frac{1}{2x} - 5}$.

(F) $\dfrac{6x - 2}{1 - 10x}$ (H) $\dfrac{4}{1 - 10x}$

(G) $\dfrac{3x - 1}{1 - 10x}$ (I) $\dfrac{3x - 1}{1 - 5x}$

Extended Response

77. What are all the solutions of $\dfrac{3}{x^2 - 1} + \dfrac{4x}{x + 1} = \dfrac{1.5}{x - 1}$? Show your work.

Mixed Review

Determine whether each formula is *explicit* or *recursive*. Then find the first five terms of each sequence.    See Lesson 9-1.

78. $a_1 = -2, a_n = a_{n-1} - 5$ **79.** $a_n = 3n(n + 1)$

80. $a_n = n^2 - 1$ **81.** $a_1 = -121, a_n = a_{n-1} + 13$

Write an equation in point-slope form for each pair of points.   See Lesson 2-4.

82. $(0, 3)$ and $(3, 11)$ **83.** $(4, 6)$ and $(10, 30)$ **84.** $(1, 10)$ and $(5, 42)$

85. Geometry The formula for volume V of a sphere with radius r is $V = \frac{4}{3}\pi r^3$. Find the radius of a sphere as a function of its volume. Rationalize the denominator.   See Lesson 6-2.

Get Ready!   To prepare for Lesson 9-3, do Exercises 86–88.

Find the next term in each sequence.   See Lesson 9-1.

86. $2, 4, 8, 16, \ldots$ **87.** $1, 5, 25, 125, \ldots$ **88.** $-1, -3, -9, -27, \ldots$

---

[3] appropriate methods, but with one computational error

[2] both 1 and $\frac{3}{8}$ are given as solutions

[1] correct solution, without work shown

Mixed Review

78. recursive; $-2, -7, -12, -17, -22$

79. explicit; $6, 18, 36, 60, 90$

80. explicit; $0, 3, 8, 15, 24$

81. recursive; $-121, -108, -95, -82, -69$

82. $y - 3 = \frac{8}{3}x$ or $y - 11 = \frac{8}{3}(x - 3)$

83. $y - 6 = 4(x - 4)$ or $y - 30 = 4(x - 10)$

84. $y - 10 = 8(x - 1)$ or $y - 42 = 8(x - 5)$

85. $r = \dfrac{\sqrt[3]{6\pi^2 V}}{2\pi}$

86. 32

87. 625

88. -81

---

66. 8   **67.** $a_1 = -1, d = 3$

68. $a_1 = -4, d = 4$

69. $a_1 = 52, d = -10$

70. $a_1 = -21\frac{1}{4}, d = 4\frac{1}{4}$

71. $a_1 = -100.5, d = 22$

72. $a_1 = -9, d = 2.2$

73. $9k + 32$ **74.** $21k - 43$

Standardized Test Prep

75. D   **76.** F

77. [4] $\dfrac{3}{(x - 1)(x + 1)} + \dfrac{4x(x - 1)}{(x - 1)(x + 1)} = \dfrac{1.5(x + 1)}{(x - 1)(x + 1)}, x \neq \pm 1$

$$3 + 4x^2 - 4x = 1.5x + 1.5$$
$$4x^2 - 5.5x + 1.5 = 0$$
$$x^2 - \frac{11}{8}x + \frac{3}{8} = 0$$
$$(x - 1)\left(x - \frac{3}{8}\right) = 0$$
$$x = \frac{3}{8}$$

(reject $x = 1$ because 1 is not in the domain)

Lesson Resources

Differentiated Remediation

Additional Instructional Support

Algebra 2 Companion

Students can use the **Algebra 2 Companion** worktext (4 pages) as you teach the lesson. Use the Companion to support

- New Vocabulary
- Key Concepts
- Got It for each Problem
- Lesson Check

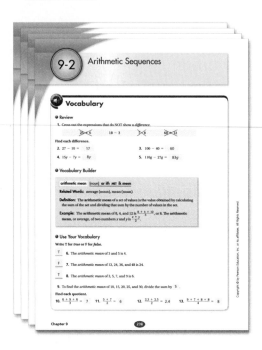

ELL Support

Focus on Language Have one pair of students sit with another pair. Have one pair write an arithmetic sequence and pose questions like the following to the other pair:

- Why is this an arithmetic sequence?
- What is the common difference?
- Give an example of a sequence that is not arithmetic.
- Given the first two terms, how would you find the 50th term?
- Can you explain more than one way to find the missing terms of a sequence?
- What is the arithmetic mean, and how do you use it with a sequence?

Have pairs reverse roles and play again. Travel from group to group and answer questions. Point out that the common *difference* is always the *same* amount.

5 Assess & Remediate

Lesson Quiz

1. Is the sequence an arithmetic sequence? 1, 4, 12, 16, 20, ...
2. What are the second and third terms of the arithmetic sequence 30, ■, ■, 51, ...?
3. What is the missing term of the arithmetic sequence ... 24, ■, 48, ...?
4. **Do you UNDERSTAND?** The number of toy rockets made by an assembly line for 8 hours forms an arithmetic sequence. If the line produced 40 rockets in hour one and 43 rockets in hour two, how many rockets will be produced in hour seven?

ANSWERS TO LESSON QUIZ

1. no
2. 37, 44
3. 36
4. 58

PRESCRIPTION FOR REMEDIATION
Use the student work on the Lesson Quiz to prescribe a differentiated review assignment:

Points	Differentiated Remediation
0–1	Intervention
2–3	On-level
4	Extension

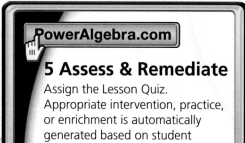

PowerAlgebra.com

5 Assess & Remediate

Assign the Lesson Quiz. Appropriate intervention, practice, or enrichment is automatically generated based on student performance.

Intervention

- **Reteaching** (2 pages) Provides reteaching and practice exercises for the key lesson concepts. Use with struggling students or absent students.
- **English Language Learner Support** Helps students develop and reinforce mathematical vocabulary and key concepts.

All-in-One Resources/Online
Reteaching

9-2 Reteaching
Arithmetic Sequences

The explicit formula for the *n*th term of an arithmetic sequence is $a_n = a + (n-1)d$.
- *a* is the starting value and *d* is the common difference.
- *n* is always greater than or equal to 1.
- You can write the sequence as $a, a + d, a + 2d, a + 3d, \ldots$

Problem

Find the 15th term of an arithmetic sequence whose first three terms are 20, 16.5, and 13.

$20 - 16.5 = 3.5$ First, find the common difference. The difference between
$16.5 - 13 = 3.5$ consecutive terms is 3.5. The sequence decreases. The common
                      difference is −3.5.

$a_n = a + (n-1)d$ Use the explicit formula.
$a_{15} = 20 + (15-1)(-3.5)$ Substitute a = 20, n = 15, and d = −3.5.
$= 20 + (14)(-3.5)$ Subtract within parentheses.
$= 20 + -49$ Multiply.
$= -29$ The 15th term is −29.

Check the answer. Write $a_1, a_2, \ldots, a_{15}$ down the left side of your paper. Start with $a_1 = 20$. Subtract 3.5 and record 16.5 next to a_2. Continue until you find a_{15}.

Exercises

Find the 25th term of each sequence.

1. 20, 18, 16, 14, ... −28   2. 0.0057, 0.0060, 0.0063, ... 0.0129

3. 4, 0, −4, −8, ... −92   4. 0.2, 0.7, 1.2, 1.7, ... 12.2

5. −10, −8.8, −7.6, −6.4, ... 18.8 6. 22, 26, 30, 34, ... 118

All-in-One Resources/Online
English Language Learner Support

9-2 Additional Vocabulary Support
Arithmetic Sequences

Arithmetic Sequence

An arithmetic sequence is a sequence where the difference between consecutive terms is constant.

$$a, a + d, a + 2d, a + 3d, \ldots$$

Sample 2, 5, 8, 11, 14, ...

Determine whether or not each sequence is arithmetic.

1. 1, 4, 7, 9, 11, ...   not arithmetic

2. 3, 9, 15, 21, 27, ...   arithmetic

3. 0, 15, 30, 45, 60, ...   arithmetic

4. 0, 1, 3, 6, 10, ...   not arithmetic

Use the formula $a_n = a + (n-1)d$ to find the indicated term in each arithmetic sequence.

5. Find the 12th term in the sequence that begins 3, 6, 9, ...   36

6. Find the 38th term in the sequence that begins 4, 10, 16, ...   226

7. Find the 104th term in the sequence that begins 5, 9, 13, ...   417

Arithmetic Mean

The arithmetic mean is the average of a set of numbers. The arithmetic mean of two numbers *x* and *y* is found using the formula displayed below.

$$\frac{x+y}{2}$$

Sample The arithmetic mean of 4 and 6 is $\frac{4+6}{2} = \frac{10}{2} = 5$.

Find the missing number in the arithmetic sequence. This number is the arithmetic mean of the two given numbers.

8. ..., 13, ___, 37, ...   25

9. ..., 26, ___, 42, ...   34

10. ..., 45, ___, 99, ...   72

Differentiated Remediation *continued*

On-Level

- **Practice** (2 pages) Provides extra practice for each lesson. For simpler practice exercises, use the Form K Practice pages found in the All-in-One Teaching Resources and online.
- **Think About a Plan** Helps students develop specific problem-solving skills and strategies by providing scaffolded guiding questions.
- **Standardized Test Prep** Focuses on all major exercises, all major question types, and helps students prepare for the high-stakes assessments.

Practice and Problem Solving Wkbk/ All-in-One Resources/Online

Practice page 1

9-2 Practice *Form G*
Arithmetic Sequences

Determine whether each sequence is arithmetic. If so, identify the common difference.

1. 2, 3, 5, 8, . . . no
2. 0, −3, −6, −9, . . . yes; −3
3. 0.9, 0.5, 0.1, −0.3, . . . yes; −0.4
4. 3, 8, 13, 18, . . . yes; 5
5. 14, −15, −44, −73, . . . yes; −29
6. 3.2, 3.5, 3.8, 4.1, . . . yes; 0.3
7. −34, −28, −22, −16, . . . yes; 6
8. 2.3, 2.5, 2.7, 2.9, . . . yes; 0.2
9. 127, 140, 153, 166, . . . yes; 13
10. 11, 13, 17, 25, . . . no

Find the 43rd term of each sequence.

11. 12, 14, 16, 18, . . . 96
12. 13.1, 3.1, −6.9, −16.9, . . . −406.9
13. 19.5, 19.9, 20.3, 20.7, . . . 36.3
14. 27, 24, 21, 18, . . . −99
15. 2, 13, 24, 35, . . . 464
16. 21, 15, 9, 3, . . . −231
17. 1.3, 1.4, 1.5, 1.6, . . . 5.5
18. −2.1, −2.3, −2.5, −2.7, . . . −10.5
19. 45, 48, 51, 54, . . . 171
20. −0.073, −0.081, −0.089, . . . −0.409

Find the missing term of each arithmetic sequence.

21. . . . 23, ■, 49, . . . 36
22. 14, ■, 28, . . . 21
23. . . . 29, ■, 33, . . . 31
24. . . . 14, ■, 15, . . . 14.5
25. . . . −45, ■, −39, . . . −42
26. . . . −5, ■, −2, . . . −3.5
27. −2, ■, 2, . . . 0
28. . . . −6, ■, 2, . . . −2
29. −34, ■, 77, . . . 21.5
30. . . . −45, ■, −12, . . . −28.5
31. −2, ■, 456, . . . 227
32. . . . 34, ■, 345, . . . 189.5

33. A teacher donates the same amount of money each year to help protect the rainforest. At the end of the second year, she has donated enough money to protect 8 acres. At the end of the third year, she has donated enough money to protect 12 acres. How many acres will the teacher's donations protect at the end of the tenth year? 40 acres

34. **Writing** Explain how you know that the sequence 109, 105, 101, 97, 93, . . . is arithmetic. The sequence has a common difference between terms of −4.

Practice and Problem Solving Wkbk/ All-in-One Resources/Online

Practice page 2

9-2 Practice (continued) *Form G*
Arithmetic Sequences

Find the arithmetic mean a_n of the given terms.

35. $a_{n-1} = 5, a_{n+1} = 11$ 8
36. $a_{n-1} = 17, a_{n+1} = 3$ 10
37. $a_{n-1} = -8, a_{n+1} = -9$ −8.5
38. $a_{n-1} = -0.6, a_{n+1} = 3.8$ 1.6
39. $a_{n-1} = y - z, a_{n+1} = y$ $y - \frac{z}{2}$
40. $a_{n-1} = 2t + 3, a_{n+1} = 4t - 1$ $3t + 1$

41. **Open-Ended** Write an arithmetic sequence of at least five terms with a positive common difference. a five-term sequence with a positive common difference

42. **Error Analysis** On your homework, you write that the missing term in the arithmetic sequence 31, ___, 41, . . . is $35\frac{1}{2}$. Your friend says the missing term is 36. Who is correct? What mistake was made? Your friend is correct. You did not take the average of 31 and 41 correctly to find the missing term of 36.

43. **Reasoning** Explain why 84 is the missing term in the sequence 89, 86.5, ___, 81.5, ... The common difference in the arithmetic sequence is −2.5, which means the missing term must be 84 as that is 2.5 less than the term before it and 2.5 more than the term after it.

44. **Writing** Describe the general process of finding a missing term in an arithmetic sequence. If the term that is missing occurs between two other terms that are consecutive to the missing term, you can take the arithmetic mean of the two terms. If the term that is missing is not consecutive, use the formula $a_n = a + (n - 1)d$.

45. You are making an arrangement of cubes in concentric rings for a sculpture. The number of cubes in each ring follows the pattern below.

    1, 9, 17, 25, 33, . . .

    a. Is this an arithmetic sequence? Explain. Yes; there is a common difference of 8.
    b. What are the next three terms? 41, 49, 57
    c. If the sequence continues to the 100th term in this pattern, what will that term be? 793

46. Each year, a volunteer organization expects to add 5 more people to the number of shut-ins for whom the group provides home maintenance services. This year, the organization provides the service for 32 people.
    a. Write a recursive formula for the number of people the organization expects to serve each year. $a_n = a_{n-1} + 5$ where $a_1 = 32$
    b. Write the first five terms of the sequence. 32, 37, 42, 47, 52
    c. Write an explicit formula for the number of people the organization expects to serve each year. $a_n = 32 + 5(n - 1)$
    d. How many people would the organization expect to serve in the 20th year? 127 people

Practice and Problem Solving Wkbk/ All-in-One Resources/Online

Think About a Plan

9-2 Think About a Plan
Arithmetic Sequences

Transportation Suppose a trolley stops at a certain intersection every 14 min. The first trolley of the day gets to the stop at 6:43 A.M. How long do you have to wait for a trolley if you get to the stop at 8:15 A.M.? At 3:20 P.M.?

Know

1. If you define 12:00 A.M. as minute 0, then 6:43 A.M. is [403 min] from 0.
2. 8:15 A.M. is [495 min] from 0 and 3:20 P.M. is [920 min] from 0.
3. The trolley stops every [14 min].

Need

4. To solve the problem I need to find: the closest times that the trolley gets to the stop that are after 8:15 A.M. and 3:20 P.M.

Plan

5. What is an explicit formula for the number of minutes after 12:00 A.M. that the trolley gets to the stop? $a_n = 403 + (n - 1)14$
6. Use your formula to find the smallest n that gives the minutes just after 8:15 A.M. that the trolley arrives at the stop. 8
7. Using this n in your formula, when does the trolley stop? at 501 min How long do you have to wait for this trolley? 6 min
8. Use your formula to find the smallest n that gives the minutes just after 3:20 P.M. that the trolley arrives at the stop. 38
9. Using this n in your formula, when does the trolley stop? at 921 min How long do you have to wait for this trolley? 1 min

Practice and Problem Solving Wkbk/ All-in-One Resources/Online

Standardized Test Prep

9-2 Standardized Test Prep
Arithmetic Sequences

Multiple Choice

For Exercises 1–6, choose the correct letter.

1. Which sequence is an arithmetic sequence? A
   A. 7, 10, 13, 16, 19, . . .
   B. 7, 8, 10, 13, 17, . . .
   C. 7, 14, 28, 56, 112, . . .
   D. 1, 7, 14, 22, 31, 41, . . .
2. An arithmetic sequence begins 4, 9, ... What is the 20th term? I
   F. 76 G. 80 H. 84 I. 99
3. What are the missing terms of the arithmetic sequence 5, __, __, 62, . . . ? C
   A. 19, 24 B. 19, 34 C. 24, 43 D. 43, 62
4. What is the missing term of the arithmetic sequence 25, __, 45, . . . ? G
   F. 30 G. 35 H. 37 I. 40
5. The seventh and ninth terms of an arithmetic sequence are 197 and 173. What is the eighth term? C
   A. 161 B. 180 C. 185 D. 221
6. An artist is creating a tile mosaic. She uses 4 green tiles in the first row, 11 green tiles in the second row, 18 green tiles in the third row, and 25 green tiles in the fourth row. If she continues the pattern, how many green tiles will she use in the 20th row? I
   F. 32 G. 58 H. 134 I. 137

Extended Response

7. What is the 100th term in the arithmetic sequence beginning with 3, 19, . . . ? Show your work.

[4] 1587; $a = 3$, $n = 100$, $d = 16$, $a_n = a + (n - 1)d$; $a_{100} = 3 + (100 - 1)16 = 3 + 1584 = 1587$
[3] appropriate method shown, with one computational error
[2] appropriate method shown, with several computational errors OR correct term found incorrectly with work shown
[1] incorrect term, without work shown
[0] incorrect answers and no work shown OR no answers given

Extension

- **Enrichment** Provides students with interesting problems and activities that extend the concepts of the lesson.
- **Activities, Games, and Puzzles** Worksheets that can be used for concepts development, enrichment, and for fun!

All-in-One Resources/Online

Enrichment

9-2 Enrichment
Arithmetic Sequences

There are many types of sequences. One interesting type of sequence is the *Farey sequence*. The first four Farey sequences are:

F_1: $\left\{\frac{0}{1}, \frac{1}{1}\right\}$

F_2: $\left\{\frac{0}{1}, \frac{1}{2}, \frac{1}{1}\right\}$

F_3: $\left\{\frac{0}{1}, \frac{1}{3}, \frac{1}{2}, \frac{2}{3}, \frac{1}{1}\right\}$

F_4: $\left\{\frac{0}{1}, \frac{1}{4}, \frac{1}{3}, \frac{1}{2}, \frac{2}{3}, \frac{3}{4}, \frac{1}{1}\right\}$

Each Farey sequence is a list of fractions in increasing order between 0 and 1, written in simplest form with a denominator less than or equal to the integer n. For any n greater than 1, there are an odd number of terms in the sequence and the middle term is $\frac{1}{2}$.

Problem

What are the terms of the Farey sequence for $n = 5$?

The Farey sequence for $n = 5$ contains all the terms of the Farey sequence F_4 plus the fractions between 0 and 1 which have a denominator of 5 when written in simplest form.

The fractions $\frac{0}{5}$ and $\frac{5}{5}$ will not be added because they simplify to $\frac{0}{1}$ and $\frac{1}{1}$. Insert the fractions $\frac{1}{5}$, $\frac{2}{5}$, $\frac{3}{5}$, and $\frac{4}{5}$ in the Farey sequence F_4.

F_5: $\left\{\frac{0}{1}, \frac{1}{5}, \frac{1}{4}, \frac{1}{3}, \frac{2}{5}, \frac{1}{2}, \frac{3}{5}, \frac{2}{3}, \frac{3}{4}, \frac{4}{5}, \frac{1}{1}\right\}$

Exercises

1. How many terms are in each of the first five Farey sequences? 2, 3, 5, 7, 11
2. What are the terms for the Farey sequence F_6? $\left\{\frac{0}{1}, \frac{1}{6}, \frac{1}{5}, \frac{1}{4}, \frac{1}{3}, \frac{2}{5}, \frac{1}{2}, \frac{3}{5}, \frac{2}{3}, \frac{3}{4}, \frac{4}{5}, \frac{5}{6}, \frac{1}{1}\right\}$
3. What will be the new terms in the Farey sequence F_7? $\left\{\frac{1}{7}, \frac{2}{7}, \frac{3}{7}, \frac{4}{7}, \frac{5}{7}, \text{and } \frac{6}{7}\right\}$
4. Since 11 is a prime number, how many more terms will be in the sequence F_{11} compared to the sequence F_{10}? 10
5. Is there any limit to how large n can be? No, n can be any positive integer although the computations become tedious.
6. Can you give examples of any other sequences? Answers may vary. Sample: arithmetic, geometric, and Fibonacci

Online Teacher Resource Center

Activities, Games, and Puzzles

9-2 Game: Four Thought
Arithmetic Sequences

This is a game for two players.

To begin the game, roll a number cube twice. The first roll gives the column of your number on the board, and the second roll gives the row of your number on the board. You get to keep that number by writing it down and crossing it off the board. Then your opponent rolls a number cube twice and keeps another number from the board, but only if that number has not already been taken. Otherwise, the player rolls the number cube twice more. If a player rolls two 1's or two 6's, the player gets a FREE PICK! and may choose any number on the board that has not been taken.

The object of the game is to be the first player to collect four numbers that form an arithmetic sequence. You can recognize arithmetic sequences by looking for a constant difference in any four numbers you have taken from the board.

Example: Four of your numbers are 2, 13, 24, and 35.

This is an arithmetic sequence because consecutive numbers have a common difference d equal to 11.

2 13 24 35
11 11 11

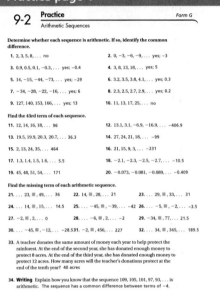

The first player to collect an arithmetic sequence of four numbers wins! Check students' work.

30 FREE PICK!	5	32	3	16	22
10	28	12	34	27	8
35	17	31	6	15	33
21	1	13	24	18	4
7	20	9	26	2	11
19	36	14	29	23	25 FREE PICK!

Guided Instruction

PURPOSE To define and examine the Fibonacci sequence

PROCESS Students will
- use the recursive formula to generate terms of the Fibonacci sequence.
- solve problems about this sequence.

DISCUSS This Concept Byte introduces the Fibonacci sequence, which is related to many natural phenomena.

Example

Q What are always the first two terms of the Fibonacci sequence? **[1,1]**

Q Is this sequence arithmetic? Explain. **[No; there is no common difference.]**

Q How can you find the next term of the sequence? **[Add the two previous terms.]**

Q Is this sequence finite or infinite? **[infinite]**

Exercises

Q For Exercise 2, why are the diagonals formed from the left the same as the diagonals formed from the right of the triangle? **[The triangle is symmetric.]**

Q For Exercise 4, describe the fourth line using math terminology. **[Sample: The sum of the squares of the first five Fibonacci numbers equals the product of the fifth and sixth Fibonacci numbers.]**

Ⓒ **Mathematical Practices** This Concept Byte supports students in looking for patterns, Mathematical Practice 7.

Concept Byte
For Use With Lesson 9-2
EXTENSION

The Fibonacci Sequence

Ⓒ **Content Standard**
F.IF.3 Recognize that sequences are functions, sometimes defined recursively, whose domain is a subset of the integers.

One famous mathematical sequence is the Fibonacci sequence. You can find each term of the sequence using addition, but the sequence is not arithmetic.

Example

The recursive formula for the Fibonacci sequence is $F_n = F_{n-2} + F_{n-1}$, with $F_1 = 1$ and $F_2 = 1$. Using the formula, what are the first five terms of the sequence?

$F_1 = 1$
$F_2 = 1$
$F_3 = F_1 + F_2 = 1 + 1 = 2$
$F_4 = F_2 + F_3 = 1 + 2 = 3$
$F_5 = F_3 + F_4 = 2 + 3 = 5$

The first five terms of the Fibonacci sequence are 1, 1, 2, 3, 5.

Exercises

1. **Nature** The numbers of the Fibonacci sequence are often found in other areas, especially nature. Which term of the Fibonacci sequence does each picture represent?

2. Find "diagonals" in Pascal's triangle at the right by starting with the first 1 in each row and moving one row up and one number to the right. For example, the diagonal starting in the fifth row is 1, 3, 1. The diagonal starting in the sixth row is 1, 4, 3. For each diagonal, write the sum of its entries. What pattern do the sums form?

```
          1
        1   1
      1   2   1
    1   3   3   1
  1   4   6   4   1
1   5  10  10   5   1
1  6  15  20  15   6   1
```

Ⓒ 3. **a.** Generate the first ten terms of the Fibonacci sequence.
  b. Find the sum of the first ten terms of the Fibonacci sequence. Divide the sum by 11. What do you notice?
  c. **Open-Ended** Choose two numbers other than 1 and 1. Generate a Fibonacci-like sequence from them. Write the first ten terms of your sequence, find the sum, and divide the sum by 11. What do you notice?
  d. **Make a Conjecture** What is the sum of the first ten terms of any Fibonacci-like sequence?

4. **a.** Study the pattern at the right. Write the next line.
  b. Without calculating, use the pattern to predict the sum of the squares of the first ten terms of the Fibonacci sequence.
  c. Verify the prediction you made in part (b).

$1^2 + 1^2 = \ \ 2 = 1 \cdot 2$
$1^2 + 1^2 + 2^2 = \ \ 6 = 2 \cdot 3$
$1^2 + 1^2 + 2^2 + 3^2 = 15 = 3 \cdot 5$
$1^2 + 1^2 + 2^2 + 3^2 + 5^2 = 40 = 5 \cdot 8$

Answers

Exercises

1. a. fifth
   b. seventh
   c. sixth
   d. fourth

2. 1st row diagonal: 1
   2nd row diagonal: 1
   3rd row diagonal: 2
   4th row diagonal: 3
   5th row diagonal: 5
   6th row diagonal: 8
   7th row diagonal: 13
   The sums replicate the Fibonacci Sequence.

3. a. 1, 1, 2, 3, 5, 8, 13, 21, 34, 55
   b. 143; 13; the answer is the seventh term
   c. Check students' work; the answer is the seventh term.
   d. It will be 11 times the seventh term.

4. a. $1^2 + 1^2 + 2^2 + 3^2 + 5^2 + 8^2$
       $= 104 = 8 \cdot 13$
   b. 4895
   c. $1^2 + 1^2 + 2^2 + 3^2 + 5^2 + 8^2$
       $+ 13^2 + 21^2 + 34^2 + 55^2$
       $= 55 \cdot 89 = 4895$

Do you know HOW?

Find the first five terms of each sequence.

1. $a_n = 3n + 1$

2. $a_n = -2n - 1$

3. $a_n = n^2 + 2n$

4. $a_n = 3a_{n-1}$, where $a_1 = 2$

5. $a_n = 5 - a_{n-1}$, where $a_1 = 1$

6. $a_n = a_{n-1} + 2n$, where $a_1 = 1$

Write a recursive definition for each sequence.

7. $2, -4, 8, -16, \ldots$

8. $1, 4, 7, 10, \ldots$

9. $4, 2, 5, 1, 6, \ldots$

Write an explicit formula for each sequence.

10. $2, 4, 8, 16, \ldots$

11. $5, 2, -1, -4, \ldots$

12. $2, 5, 10, 17, \ldots$

Find the ninth and tenth terms of each arithmetic sequence.

13. $1, 8, 15, 22, \ldots$

14. $4, 10, 16, 22, \ldots$

15. $6, 3, 0, -3, \ldots$

Determine whether each sequence is arithmetic. If so, identify the common difference.

16. $1, 3, 9, 27, \ldots$

17. $11, 22, 33, 44, \ldots$

18. $1, -1, -3, -5, -7, \ldots$

19. $0, 2, 5, 9, 14, \ldots$

Find the missing term of each arithmetic sequence.

20. $\ldots, 3, \blacksquare, 17, \ldots$

21. $\ldots, 25, \blacksquare, -15, \ldots$

22. $\ldots, -3, \blacksquare, 8, \ldots$

23. $\ldots, 66, \blacksquare, 48, \ldots$

Find the missing terms of each arithmetic sequence.

24. $4, a_2, a_3, a_4, 32, \ldots$

25. $10, a_2, a_3, a_4, -20, \ldots$

26. $5, a_2, a_3, a_4, 35, \ldots$

Do you UNDERSTAND?

 27. **Open-Ended** Write the first four terms of an arithmetic sequence with a common difference of 3 and a third term of 10. Then write both a recursive definition and an explicit formula for this sequence.

28. **Investments** You invested money in a fund and each month you receive a payment for your investment. Over the first four months, you received $50, $52, $55, and $59. If this pattern continues, how much will you receive in the tenth month?
   a. Write a formula to describe this sequence.
   b. Identify your formula as explicit or recursive.
   c. **Writing** Explain the difference between an explicit formula and a recursive formula. Use your formula from part (a) as part of your explanation.

29. **Open-Ended** Write the first five terms of a sequence that is not an arithmetic sequence. Then give both an explicit and recursive formula to describe this sequence.

30. **Sports** A tennis club charges players a $20 court fee plus a $10 hourly charge with a 5-hour maximum. A posted list of the total charges for 1, 2, 3, 4, or 5 hours forms an arithmetic sequence. What is the first term and what is the common difference?

28. 104;
   a. recursive: $a_n = a_{n-1} + n, a_1 = 50$ OR
      explicit: $a_n = 49 + \dfrac{n(n+1)}{2}$
   b. See answer (a).
   c. A recursive formula would have the initial term, a_1, and a formula for the nth term involving the previous term and the common difference, d. The formula $a_n = a_{n-1} + n$ is a recursive formula. An explicit formula would have a formula for the nth term involving the initial term, the common difference, and the term number, n. The formula $a_n = a_1 + (n-1)d$ is an explicit formula.

29. Answers may vary. Sample: 10, 11, 13, 16, 20; $a_n = a_{n-1} + (n-1)$, $a_1 = 10$; $a_n = 10 + \dfrac{n(n-1)}{2}$

30. 30; 10

Answers

1. 4, 7, 10, 13, 16
2. $-3, -5, -7, -9, -11$
3. 3, 8, 15, 24, 35
4. 2, 6, 18, 54, 162
5. 1, 4, 1, 4, 1
6. 1, 5, 11, 19, 29
7. $a_n = -2a_{n-1}, a_1 = 2$
8. $a_n = a_{n-1} + 3, a_1 = 1$
9. $a_n = a_{n-1} + (-1)^{n-1}n, a_1 = 4$
10. $a_n = 2^n$
11. $a_n = 8 - 3n$
12. $a_n = n^2 + 1$
13. 57, 64

14. 52, 58
15. $-18, -21$
16. no
17. yes; 11
18. yes; -2
19. no
20. 10
21. 5
22. 2.5
23. 57
24. 11, 18, 25
25. $2.5, -5, -12.5$
26. 12.5, 20, 27.5
27. $4, 7, 10, 13; a_n = a_{n-1} + 3,$ $a_1 = 4; a_n = 4 + 3(n-1)$

1 Interactive Learning

Solve It!

PURPOSE To extend and compare geometric sequences

PROCESS Students may divide successive terms to find the ratio and then multiply the fourth term by that ratio. They may look for and apply a rule for the relationship between the first term and each successive term.

FACILITATE

Q How can you express division by 10 and division by -3 as multiplication? **[multiplication by 0.1 and $-\frac{1}{3}$]**

Q What is the mathematical relationship between the consecutive terms of each sequence? **[A: multiply by two; B: multiply by 0.1; C: multiply by $-\frac{1}{3}$]**

ANSWER See Solve It in Answers on next page.

CONNECT THE MATH In the Solve It, students use ratios to find terms in geometric sequences. In the lesson, they find and use common ratios to express geometric sequences recursively and explicitly.

2 Guided Instruction

Take Note

Notice that both sequence definitions use the common ratio r. However, the recursive definition uses the previous term in the sequence, and the explicit definition uses the first term in the sequence.

Problem 1

Q In 1A, how would the common ratio change if all the terms were negative? if every other term was negative? **[It would not change; it would be negative.]**

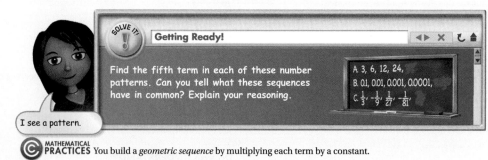

© Content Standard
Prepares for A.SSE.4 Derive the formula for the sum of a geometric series (when the common ratio is not 1), and use the formula to solve problems.

9-3 Geometric Sequences

Objective To define, identify, and apply geometric sequences

Getting Ready!

Find the fifth term in each of these number patterns. Can you tell what these sequences have in common? Explain your reasoning.

A. 3, 6, 12, 24,

B. 0.1, 0.01, 0.001, 0.0001,

C. $\frac{1}{3}, -\frac{1}{9}, \frac{1}{27}, -\frac{1}{81}$

I see a pattern.

© MATHEMATICAL PRACTICES You build a *geometric sequence* by multiplying each term by a constant.

Dynamic Activity Geometric Sequences

Lesson Vocabulary
- geometric sequence
- common ratio
- geometric mean

Essential Understanding In a *geometric sequence*, the ratio of any term to its preceding term is a constant value.

take note

Key Concept Geometric Sequence

A **geometric sequence** with a starting value a and a **common ratio** r is a sequence of the form
$$a, ar, ar^2, ar^3, \ldots$$

A recursive definition for the sequence has two parts:
$$a_1 = a \qquad \text{initial condition}$$
$$a_n = a_{n-1} \cdot r, \text{ for } n > 1 \qquad \text{recursive formula}$$

An explicit definition for this sequence is a single formula:
$$a_n = a_1 \cdot r^{n-1}, \text{ for } n \geq 1$$

© Problem 1 Identifying Geometric Sequences

Is the sequence geometric? If it is, what are a_1 and r?

Ⓐ 3, 6, 12, 24, 48, ...

Think

How do I find the ratios between consecutive terms? Divide the second term by the first term, then the third term by the second term, and so on.

Find the ratios between consecutive terms.

3　6　12　24　48

$$\frac{6}{3} = \frac{12}{6} = \frac{24}{12} = \frac{48}{24} = 2$$

The common ratio is 2. The sequence is geometric with $a_1 = 3$ and $r = 2$.

580　Chapter 9　Sequences and Series

9-3 Preparing to Teach

BIG idea Modeling

ESSENTIAL UNDERSTANDINGS

- In a geometric sequence, the ratio of any term (after the first) to its preceding term is a constant value, no matter what two terms are compared. A geometric sequence can be built by multiplying each term by that constant.
- A geometric sequence can be modeled explicitly or recursively.

Math Background

- Between consecutive terms, a geometric sequence has a common ratio with each term given by a constant multiple of the previous term; an arithmetic sequence has a common difference.
- A geometric sequence is built by multiplying each term by a constant; an arithmetic sequence is built by adding a constant to each term.
- A geometric sequence is an exponential function with a base equal to the common ratio. An arithmetic sequence is a linear function with a slope equal to the common difference.

- The second of 3 consecutive terms in a geometric sequence is the square root of the product of the proceeding and following terms. The second of 3 consecutive terms in an arithmetic sequence is the mean of the preceding and following terms.

For 2 terms x and y, $\sqrt{xy}$ is the geometric mean. The geometric mean provides the value of the term between x and y in a geometric sequence and has other mathematical and real-world applications (e.g. calculating average rates of growth).

© Mathematical Practices

Attend to precision. Students will define the term "geometric sequence" and write formulas to determine terms within sequences.

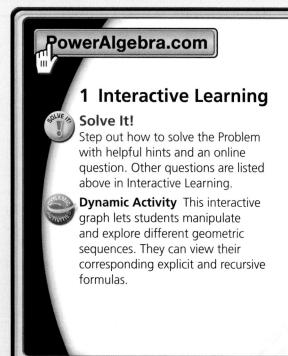

PowerAlgebra.com

1 Interactive Learning

Solve It!

Step out how to solve the Problem with helpful hints and an online question. Other questions are listed above in Interactive Learning.

Dynamic Activity This interactive graph lets students manipulate and explore different geometric sequences. They can view their corresponding explicit and recursive formulas.

B $3, 6, 9, 12, 15, \ldots$

Find the ratio between consecutive terms.

$$3 \quad 6 \quad 9 \quad 12 \quad 15$$

$$\frac{6}{3} \neq \frac{9}{6} \neq \frac{12}{9} \neq \frac{15}{12}$$

The ratios are different. With no common ratio, the sequence is not geometric.

C $3^5, 3^{10}, 3^{15}, 3^{20}, \ldots$

Use the properties of exponents to simplify the ratios of successive terms.

$$3^5 \quad 3^{10} \quad 3^{15} \quad 3^{20}$$

$$\frac{3^{10}}{3^5} = \frac{3^{15}}{3^{10}} = \frac{3^{20}}{3^{15}} = 3^5$$

The common ratio is 3^5. The sequence is geometric with $a_1 = 3^5$ and $r = 3^5$.

 Got It? **1.** Is the sequence geometric? If it is, what are a_1 and r?

  a. $2, 4, 8, 16, \ldots$ **b.** $1, 5, 9, 13, 17, \ldots$ **c.** $2^3, 2^7, 2^{11}, 2^{15}, \ldots$

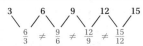 **Problem 2** Analyzing Geometric Sequences

What are the indicated terms of the geometric sequence?

A the 10th term of the geometric sequence $4, 12, 36, \ldots$

The first term a_1 is 4. The common ratio r is $12 \div 4 = 3$.

 $a_n = a_1 r^{n-1}$ Use the explicit formula.

 $a_{10} = 4 \cdot 3^{10-1}$ Substitute 10 for n, 4 for a_1, and 3 for r.

 $a_{10} = 78{,}732$ Simplify.

The 10th term is 78,732.

B the second and third terms of the geometric sequence $2, \blacksquare, \blacksquare, -54, \ldots$

The first term a_1 is 2. The fourth term a_4 is -54.

 $a_n = a_1 r^{n-1}$ Use the explicit formula.

 $a_4 = 2r^{4-1}$ Substitute 2 for a_1 and 4 for n.

 $-54 = 2r^3$ Substitute -54 for a_4. Simplify.

 $-27 = r^3$ Solve for r.

 $-3 = r$

The common ratio is -3. Begin with 2 and multiply by -3.

 $2, -6, 18, -54, \ldots$

The second and third terms are -6 and 18.

 Got It? **2.** What is the 2nd term of the geometric sequence $3, \blacksquare, 12, \ldots$?

Got It?

Q How many pairs of successive terms must you divide to determine whether a sequence is geometric? Give an example to show why this is important. **[The ratios between all of the successive pairs of terms must be checked. Samples: 2, 4, 8, 14 … and 2, 4, 8, 16 …]**

Problem 2

Q Why is the explicit formula easier to use than the recursive definition for 2A? Is there ever a time that the recursive definition would be more convenient? **[Sample: To find the tenth term, you also have to find terms four through nine when you use the recursive definition. The recursive definition is more convenient when you know terms very close to the term you want to find.]**

Q In 2B, what do you know about the signs of the successive terms of the sequence? Will this always be true when r is negative? Explain. **[The signs alternate. Yes because even powers will be positive and odd powers will be negative.]**

Got It?

Q Why could the common ratio be either 2 or -2? Does it change the value of the fifth term? Explain. **[Both 6 and -6 are solutions to the equation $x^2 = 36$. The sign of the ratio does not change the value of the fifth term. It will have the same sign as the first and third term, regardless of the sign of the common ratio.]**

Plan

What do you need to find the second term given the first term?
You need the common ratio.

---

2 Guided Instruction

Each Problem is worked out and supported online.

Problem 1
Identifying Geometric Sequences
       Animated

Problem 2
Analyzing Geometric Sequences
       Animated

Problem 3
Using a Geometric Sequence

Problem 4
Using the Geometric Mean
       Animated

Support in Algebra 2 Companion
• Vocabulary
• Key Concepts
• Got It?

Answers

Solve It!

A. 48

B. 0.00001

C. $\frac{1}{243}$

Each seq. is generated by multiplying the previous term by a common ratio.

Got It?

 1. a. yes; $a_1 = 2, r = 2$

  b. no

  c. yes; $a_1 = 2^3, r = 2^4$

 2. 6 or -6

Problem 3

Q When you find the common ratio for the sequence of the ball bounce heights, what does the value of the ratio represent in the context of the ball bounce height? **[The value represents the portion of the height of a bounce that the next bounce will reach.]**

EXTENSION

Q Would the sequence that represents the changes in heights from bounce to bounce also form a geometric sequence? What would r be for that sequence? Explain. **[Yes, it would also have a common ratio of 0.7, or $\frac{7}{10}$. To show this, the changes in height are −30, −21, −14.7 …]**

Q Is it necessary to start with a to find the heights of the fourth and fifth bounces recursively? Explain. **[No; you can use a recursive definition on any term in a sequence. Beginning with the height of the third bounce creates fewer calculations.]**

Got It?

Q What criteria will you use to determine whether to use an explicit formula or a recursive definition? Is either formula less valid as a method to find terms in a geometric sequence? **[Samples: the known terms, the number of the term to be found, the format of the answer, and the manner of calculation; both formulas are equally valid as methods to find terms in a geometric sequence.]**

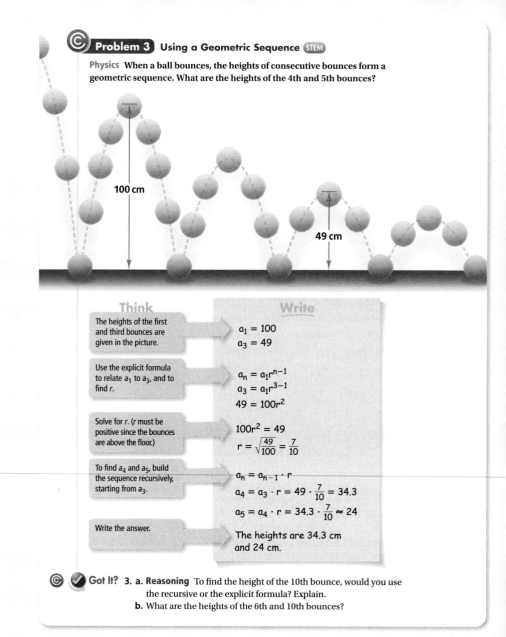

Problem 3 Using a Geometric Sequence STEM

Physics When a ball bounces, the heights of consecutive bounces form a geometric sequence. What are the heights of the 4th and 5th bounces?

100 cm

49 cm

Think

The heights of the first and third bounces are given in the picture.

$a_1 = 100$
$a_3 = 49$

Use the explicit formula to relate a_1 to a_3, and to find r.

$a_n = a_1 r^{n-1}$
$a_3 = a_1 r^{3-1}$
$49 = 100 r^2$

Solve for r. (r must be positive since the bounces are above the floor.)

$100 r^2 = 49$
$r = \sqrt{\frac{49}{100}} = \frac{7}{10}$

To find a_4 and a_5, build the sequence recursively, starting from a_3.

$a_n = a_{n-1} \cdot r$
$a_4 = a_3 \cdot r = 49 \cdot \frac{7}{10} = 34.3$
$a_5 = a_4 \cdot r = 34.3 \cdot \frac{7}{10} \approx 24$

Write

Write the answer.

The heights are 34.3 cm and 24 cm.

Got It? 3. a. Reasoning To find the height of the 10th bounce, would you use the recursive or the explicit formula? Explain.
b. What are the heights of the 6th and 10th bounces?

Additional Problems

1. Is the sequence geometric? If it is, what are a and r?
  a. 5, 10, 50, …
  b. −10, 6, −3.6, …
  ANSWERS
  a. no
  b. yes; $a = -10$, $r = -0.6$

2. What are the 2nd and 3rd terms of the geometric sequence 2, ■, ■, 128, …?
  ANSWER 8, 32

3. You work as a store manager and need to clear some inventory. You decide to discount each item by 30% of the previous week's price until the entire inventory is

sold. The original price of one item was $60. What will be the cost of the item during the fifth week of the sale?
  ANSWER $10.08

4. What are the possible values of the missing term of the geometric sequence 28, ■, 7?
  ANSWER 14 and −14

Answers

Got It? (continued)
  3. a. explicit; it is easier to use because only one calculation is needed.
  b. about 16.8 cm, about 0.11 cm

In a geometric sequence, the square of the middle term of any three consecutive terms is equal to the product of the other two terms. For example, examine the sequence $2, -6, 18, -54, \ldots$.

$$(-6)^2 = 2 \cdot 18 = 36$$
$$2, -6, 18, -54, \ldots$$
$$18^2 = (-6)(-54) = 324$$

In an arithmetic sequence, recall that the middle term of any three consecutive terms is the arithmetic mean of the other two terms.

The **geometric mean** of two positive numbers x and y is $\sqrt{xy}$.

Note that the geometric mean is positive by definition. While there are two possible values for the missing term in the geometric sequence $3, \blacksquare, 12, \ldots$, there is only one geometric mean. The geometric mean is one possible value to fill in the geometric sequence. The opposite of the geometric mean is the other.

 Problem 4 Using the Geometric Mean

Multiple Choice What are the possible values of the missing term of the geometric sequence?

$$48, \blacksquare, 3, \ldots$$

Ⓐ ± 4 Ⓑ ± 9 Ⓒ ± 12 Ⓓ ± 20

Find the geometric mean of 48 and 3.

$$\sqrt{48 \cdot 3} = \sqrt{144}$$
$$= 12$$

The possible values for the missing term are ± 12. The correct answer choice is C.

Think

Why would this question ask for "possible values" rather than "the value"?

The geometric mean and its opposite are both possible values.

✔ **Got It?** **4.** The 9th and 11th terms of a geometric sequence are 45 and 80. What are possible values for the 10th term?

✔ **Lesson Check**

Do you know HOW?

Determine whether each sequence is geometric. If so, find the common ratio.

1. $5, 10, 15, \ldots$

2. $10, 20, 40, \ldots$

Find the seventh term of each geometric sequence.

3. $1, -3, 9, \ldots$

4. $100, 20, 4, \ldots$

Do you UNDERSTAND? Ⓒ MATHEMATICAL PRACTICES

Ⓒ **5. Error Analysis** To find the third term of the geometric sequence $5, 10, \blacksquare, \blacksquare, 80$, your friend says that there are two possible answers—the geometric mean of 5 and 80, and its opposite. Explain your friend's error.

Ⓒ **6. Compare and Contrast** How is finding a missing term of a geometric sequence using the geometric mean similar to finding a missing term of an arithmetic sequence using the arithmetic mean? How is it different?

Problem 4   **EXTENSION**

Q Does the geometric mean give a possible value for the missing term? Explain. **[Yes; sample: Consider the terms 4, x, 36 ... $\frac{x}{4}$ and $\frac{36}{x}$ are equal ratios. Solve $\frac{x}{4} = \frac{36}{x}$; $x^2 = 4 \cdot 36$, so $x = \pm\sqrt{4 \cdot 36}$.]**

Q If the missing term is 12, what is r? If the missing term is -12, what is r? **[$\frac{1}{4}$; $-\frac{1}{4}$]**

Got It?

Q Is it necessary to find a? Would the solution change if you had to find the eighth term and the seventh and ninth terms were 45 and 80? Explain. **[No; the answers would be the same, because the geometric mean of 45 and 80 remains the same.]**

3 Lesson Check

Do you know HOW?

• Students can check their answers for Exercises 3 and 4 by using both a recursive definition and an explicit formula.

Do you UNDERSTAND?

• If students have trouble with Exercise 6, suggest that they work out an example of each type and compare the steps.

Close

Q How can you find a specific term of a geometric sequence when you know a term and the common ratio? **[Sample: Use an explicit formula or a recursive formula, depending on the term you have to find.]**

---

4. ± 60

Lesson Check

1. no

2. yes; 2

3. 729

4. 0.0064

5. The third term would be the geometric mean of 5 and 80 which is 20. Since a is pos. and r^2 is always pos., the third term, ar^2, cannot be neg.

6. For both the arithmetic mean and the geometric mean, the middle term of any three consecutive terms can be determined using the first and last of the three terms. The arithmetic mean is the sum of the first and last terms divided by 2, whereas the geometric mean is the square root (or its opposite) of the product of the first and the last terms.

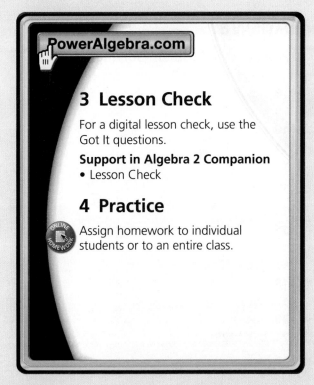

PowerAlgebra.com

3 Lesson Check

For a digital lesson check, use the Got It questions.

Support in Algebra 2 Companion
• Lesson Check

4 Practice

Assign homework to individual students or to an entire class.

4 Practice

ASSIGNMENT GUIDE

Basic: 7–31 all, 36–44 even, 48–50, 59

Average: 7–31 odd, 32–59

Advanced: 7–31 odd, 32–62

Standardized Test Prep: 63–67

Mixed Review: 68–81

ⓒ Mathematical Practices are supported by exercises with red headings. Here are the Practices supported in this lesson:

MP 1: Make Sense of Problems Ex. 48

MP 2: Reason Quantitatively Ex. 50

MP 3: Communicate Ex. 59

MP 3: Compare Arguments Ex. 6

MP 3: Critique the Reasoning of Others Ex. 5

Applications exercises have blue headings. Exercise 25 supports MP 4: Model.

STEM exercises focus on science or engineering applications.

EXERCISE 49: Use the Think About a Plan worksheet in the **Practice and Problem Solving Workbook** (also available in the Teaching Resources in print and online) to further support students' development in becoming independent learners.

HOMEWORK QUICK CHECK

To check students' understanding of key skills and concepts, go over Exercises 9, 19, 48, 49, and 59.

Practice and Problem-Solving Exercises   MATHEMATICAL PRACTICES

Ⓐ Practice Determine whether each sequence is geometric. If so, find the common ratio. ◀ See Problem 1.

7. $1, 2, 4, 8, \ldots$ **8.** $1, 2, 3, 4, \ldots$ **9.** $1, -2, 4, -8, \ldots$

10. $-1, 1, -1, 1, \ldots$ **11.** $10, 4, 1.6, 0.64, \ldots$ **12.** $7, 0.7, 0.07, 0.007, \ldots$

13. $18, -6, 2, -\frac{2}{3}, \ldots$ **14.** $1, \frac{1}{2}, \frac{1}{3}, \frac{1}{4}, \ldots$ **15.** $10, 15, 22.5, 33.75, \ldots$

16. $2, -10, 50, -250, \ldots$ **17.** $-1, -6, -36, -216, \ldots$ **18.** $\frac{1}{2}, \frac{1}{4}, \frac{1}{6}, \frac{1}{8}, \ldots$

Find the eighth term of each geometric sequence. ◀ See Problem 2.

19. $3, 9, 27, \ldots$ **20.** $-3, 6, -12, \ldots$ **21.** $10, 5, 2.5, \ldots$

22. $\frac{2}{3}, \frac{4}{9}, \frac{8}{27}, \ldots$ **23.** $24, -6, \frac{3}{2}, \ldots$ **24.** $-30, 7.5, -1.875, \ldots$

STEM 25. Science When radioactive substances decay, the amount remaining will form a ◀ See Problem 3. geometric sequence when measured over constant intervals of time. The table shows the amount of Np-240, a radioactive isotope of Neptunium, initially and after 2 hours. What are the amounts left after 1 hour, 3 hours, and 4 hours?

Hours Elapsed	0	1	2	3	4
Grams of Np-240	1244	■	346	■	■

Find the missing term of each geometric sequence. It could be the geometric ◀ See Problem 4. mean or its opposite.

26. $5, ■, 911.25, \ldots$ **27.** $9180, ■, 255, \ldots$ **28.** $\frac{2}{5}, ■, \frac{8}{45}, \ldots$

29. $3, ■, 0.75, \ldots$ **30.** $5, ■, 2.8125, \ldots$ **31.** $12, ■, 3, \ldots$

Ⓑ Apply Write an explicit formula for each sequence. Then generate the first five terms.

32. $a_1 = 1, r = 0.5$ **33.** $a_1 = 100, r = -20$ **34.** $a_1 = 7, r = 1$

35. $a_1 = 1024, r = 0.5$ **36.** $a_1 = 4, r = 0.1$ **37.** $a_1 = 10, r = -1$

Identify each sequence as *arithmetic, geometric,* or *neither.* Then find the next two terms.

38. $45, 90, 180, 360, \ldots$ **39.** $25, 50, 75, 100, \ldots$ **40.** $3, -3, 3, -3, \ldots$

41. $-5, 10, -20, 40, \ldots$ **42.** $2, 1, 0.5, 0.25, \ldots$ **43.** $1, 4, 9, 16, \ldots$

Find the missing terms of each geometric sequence. (*Hint:* The geometric mean of the first and fifth terms is the third term. Some terms might be negative.)

44. $972, ■, ■, ■, 12, \ldots$ **45.** $2.5, ■, ■, ■, 202.5, \ldots$

46. $12.5, ■, ■, ■, 5.12, \ldots$ **47.** $-4, ■, ■, ■, -30\frac{3}{8}, \ldots$

Answers

Practice and Problem-Solving Exercises

7. yes; 2

8. no

9. yes; −2

10. yes; −1

11. yes; 0.4

12. yes; 0.1

13. yes; $-\frac{1}{3}$

14. no

15. yes; 1.5

16. yes; −5

17. yes; 6

18. no

19. 6561

20. 384

21. 0.078125

22. $\frac{256}{6561}$

23. $\frac{-3}{2048}$

24. $\frac{15}{8192}$

25. about 656.1 g; about 182.5 g; about 96.2 g

26. ±67.5

27. ±1530

28. $\pm\frac{4}{15}$

29. ±1.5

30. ±3.75

31. ±6

32. $a_n = 0.5^{n-1}$; 1, 0.5, 0.25, 0.125, 0.0625

33. $a_n = 100(-20)^{n-1}$; 100, −2000, 40,000, −800,000, 16,000,000

34. $a_n = 7 \cdot 1^{n-1}$; 7, 7, 7, 7, 7

35. $a_n = 1024(0.5)^{n-1}$; 1024, 512, 256, 128, 64

36. $a_n = 4(0.1)^{n-1}$; 4, 0.4, 0.04, 0.004, 0.0004

37. $a_n = 10(-1)^{n-1}$; 10, −10, 10, −10, 10

38. geometric; 720, 1440

39. arithmetic; 125, 150

40. geometric; 3, −3

41. geometric; −80, 160

42. geometric; 0.125, 0.0625

43. neither; 25, 36

44. 324, 108, 36 or −324, 108, −36

45. 7.5, 22.5, 67.5 or −7.5, 22.5, −67.5

46. 10, 8, 6.4 or −10, 8, −6.4

47. −6.64, −11.02, −18.30 or 6.64, −11.02, 18.30

48. Think About a Plan Suppose a balloon is filled with 5000 cm³ of helium. It then loses one fourth of its helium each day. How much helium will be left in the balloon at the start of the tenth day?
- How can you write a sequence of numbers to represent this situation?
- Is the sequence arithmetic, geometric, or neither?
- How can you write a formula for this sequence?

49. Athletics During your first week of training for a marathon, you run a total of 10 miles. You increase the distance you run each week by twenty percent. How many miles do you run during your twelfth week of training?

50. a. Open-Ended Choose two positive numbers. Find their geometric mean.
b. Find the common ratio for a geometric sequence that includes the terms from part (a) as its first three terms.
c. Find the 9th term of the geometric sequence from part (b).
d. Find the geometric mean of the term from part (c) and the first term of your sequence. What term of the sequence have you just found?

For the geometric sequence 3, 12, 48, 192, . . . , find the indicated term.

51. 5th term   **52.** 17th term   **53.** 20th term   **54.** nth term

Find the 10th term of each geometric sequence.

55. $a_9 = 8, r = \frac{1}{2}$ **56.** $a_9 = -5, r = -\frac{1}{2}$

57. $a_{11} = -5, r = -\frac{1}{2}$ **58.** $a_9 = -\frac{1}{3}, r = \frac{1}{2}$

59. Writing Describe the similarities and differences between a common difference and a common ratio.

Challenge

60. Banking Copy and complete the table below. Use the geometric mean. Assume compound interest is earned and no withdrawals are made.

Period 1	Period 2	Period 3
$140.00		$145.64
$600.00		$627.49
$25.00		$32.76
$57.50		$60.37
$100.00		$111.98
$250.00		$276.55

Find a_1 for a geometric sequence with the given terms.

61. $a_5 = 112$ and $a_7 = 448$ **62.** $a_9 = \frac{1}{2}$ and $a_{12} = \frac{1}{16}$

48. about 375.42 cm³
49. about 74.3 mi
50. a–d. Answers may vary. Sample:
  a. 3 and 12; 6
  b. 3, 6, 12; 2
  c. 768
  d. 48; 5th term
51. 768
52. 3×4^{16} or 12,884,901,888
53. 3×4^{19} or 824,633,720,832
54. $3(4^{n-1})$
55. 4
56. 2.5
57. 10
58. $-\frac{1}{6}$

59. Both the common diff. and the common ratio are used to find the next term in a sequence, but a common diff. is added and a common ratio is multiplied.
60. $142.79, $613.59, $28.62, $58.92, $105.82, $262.94
61. 7
62. 128

Answers

Standardized Test Prep

63. B
64. H
65. C
66. G
67. [2] $x \neq -1, -5$; there's a hole in the graph at $x = -1$. There's a vert. asymptote at $x = -5$.

[1] only one pt. of discontinuity is given

Mixed Review
68. $a_n = -3 + 3(n - 1)$; $a_n = a_{n-1} + 3$, $a_1 = -3$
69. $a_n = 17 - 9(n - 1)$; $a_n = a_{n-1} - 9$, $a_1 = 17$
70. $a_n = -2 - 11(n - 1)$; $a_n = a_{n-1} - 11$, $a_1 = -2$
71. $7\sqrt{14}$
72. $\dfrac{3\sqrt{3x}}{7x}$
73. $\dfrac{x}{y}$
74. $5\sqrt[3]{6}$
75. vert. asymptote: $x = -3$
76. vert. asymptote: $x = -1$
77. vert. asymptotes: $x = 0, 1$
78. vert. asymptote: $x = 3$; hole at $x = -3$
79. $a_n = a_{n-1} + n$, $a_1 = 1$
80. $a_n = a_{n-1} + (2n - 1)$, $a_1 = 1$
81. $a_n = a_{n-1} + n^2$, $a_1 = 1$

Standardized Test Prep

SAT/ACT

63. What is the common ratio in the geometric sequence 4, 10, 25, 62.5, . . . ?
  Ⓐ 0.4   Ⓒ 15
  Ⓑ 2.5   Ⓓ 25

64. The first term of a geometric sequence is 1 and its common ratio is 6. What is the sixth term?
  Ⓕ 31   Ⓗ 7776
  Ⓖ 3176   Ⓘ 46,656

65. Determine by inspection the end behavior of the graph of $y = -2x^3 + 5x - 4$.
  Ⓐ falls to the left, falls to the right: ($\swarrow$, $\searrow$)
  Ⓑ falls to the left, rises to the right: ($\swarrow$, $\nearrow$)
  Ⓒ rises to the left, falls to the right: ($\nwarrow$, $\searrow$)
  Ⓓ rises to the left, rises to the right: ($\nwarrow$, $\nearrow$)

66. What are the asymptotes of the graph of $y = \frac{10}{x-5}$?
  Ⓕ $x = 0, y = 5$
  Ⓖ $x = 5, y = 0$
  Ⓗ $x = 5, y = 10$
  Ⓘ $x = 10, y = 5$

Short Response

67. What are the points of discontinuity of $y = \frac{x(2x - 1)(x + 1)}{(x + 5)(x + 1)}$?

Mixed Review

Write an explicit and a recursive formula for each arithmetic sequence.   ◀ See Lesson 9-2.

68. $-3, 0, 3, 6, \ldots$ **69.** $17, 8, -1, \ldots$ **70.** $-2, -13, -24, \ldots$

Simplify each expression. Rationalize all denominators. Assume that all variables are positive.   ◀ See Lesson 6-2.

71. $\left(\sqrt{7}\right)\left(\sqrt{98}\right)$ **72.** $\dfrac{3\sqrt{6}}{7\sqrt{2x}}$ **73.** $\dfrac{\sqrt{6x^4y}}{\sqrt{6x^2y^3}}$ **74.** $\left(\sqrt[3]{5}\right)\left(\sqrt[3]{150}\right)$

Find the vertical asymptotes and holes for the graph of each rational function.   ◀ See Lesson 8-3.

75. $y = \frac{x-3}{x+3}$ **76.** $y = \frac{x-3}{x+1}$

77. $y = \frac{x-3}{x(x-1)}$ **78.** $y = \frac{x(x+3)}{(x-3)(x+3)}$

Get Ready! To prepare for Lesson 9-4, do Exercises 79–81.

Write a recursive formula for each sequence.   ◀ See Lesson 9-1.

79. $1, 3, 6, 10, \ldots$ **80.** $1, 4, 9, 16, \ldots$ **81.** $1, 5, 14, 30, \ldots$

Additional Instructional Support

Algebra 2 Companion

Students can use the **Algebra 2 Companion** worktext (4 pages) as you teach the lesson. Use the Companion to support

- New Vocabulary
- Key Concepts
- Got It for each Problem
- Lesson Check

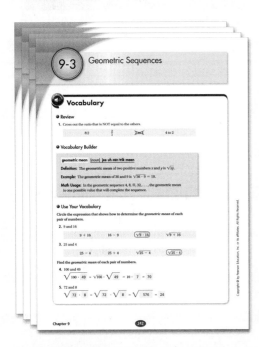

ELL Support

Use Graphic Organizers Have students make a chart summarizing recursive definitions and explicit formulas for both arithmetic and geometric sequences. Students should label the rows of the chart *arithmetic* and *geometric* and should label the columns *recursive*, *explicit*, and *example*. Have students choose a value for *a* and a value to use for both *r* and *d*. In the example column, have students generate the first 5 terms of the arithmetic and geometric sequences. To help students see the difference, have them graph the sequences using the sequence term number for *x* and the sequence term for *y*.

Focus on Language One student in a small group states a recursion or explicit rule for a sequence. Partner(s) identify it as recursive or explicit, arithmetic or geometric.

5 Assess & Remediate

Lesson Quiz

1. Is the sequence geometric? If it is, what are *a* and *r*? 1.5, −4.5, 13.5, . . .

2. What is the 8th term of the geometric sequence 3, . . . , . . . , 81, . . .?

3. **Do you UNDERSTAND?** You drop a ball from a staircase that is 36 ft high. By the time you get down the stairs to measure the height of the bounce, the ball has bounced four times and has a height of 2.25 ft after its fourth bounce. How high did the ball bounce after it first hit the floor?

4. What are the possible values of the missing term of the geometric sequence 6, . . . , 13.5?

ANSWERS TO LESSON QUIZ

1. yes; $a = 1.5$, $r = -3$
2. 6561
3. 18 feet
4. 9 and −9

PRESCRIPTION FOR REMEDIATION

Use the student work on the Lesson Quiz to prescribe a differentiated review assignment:

Points	Differentiated Remediation
0–1	Intervention
2–3	On-level
4	Extension

PowerAlgebra.com

5 Assess & Remediate

Assign the Lesson Quiz. Appropriate intervention, practice, or enrichment is automatically generated based on student performance.

Intervention

- **Reteaching** (2 pages) Provides reteaching and practice exercises for the key lesson concepts. Use with struggling students or absent students.

- **English Language Learner Support** Helps students develop and reinforce mathematical vocabulary and key concepts.

All-in-One Resources/Online
Reteaching

All-in-One Resources/Online
English Language Learner Support

Differentiated Remediation *continued*

On-Level

- **Practice** (2 pages) Provides extra practice for each lesson. For simpler practice exercises, use the Form K Practice pages found in the All-in-One Teaching Resources and online.

- **Think About a Plan** Helps students develop specific problem-solving skills and strategies by providing scaffolded guiding questions.

- **Standardized Test Prep** Focuses on all major exercises, all major question types, and helps students prepare for the high-stakes assessments.

Extension

- **Enrichment** Provides students with interesting problems and activities that extend the concepts of the lesson.

- **Activities, Games, and Puzzles** Worksheets that can be used for concepts development, enrichment, and for fun!

Practice and Problem Solving Wkbk/ All-in-One Resources/Online
Practice page 1

9-3 Practice — Form G
Geometric Sequences

Determine whether each sequence is geometric. If so, find the common ratio.

1. 3, 9, 27, 81, . . . yes; 3   2. 4, 8, 16, 32, . . . yes; 2   3. 4, 8, 12, 16, . . . no

4. 4, −8, 16, −32, . . . yes; −2   5. 1, 0.5, 0.25, 0.125, . . . yes; 0.5   6. 100, 30, 9, 2.7, . . . yes; 0.3

7. −5, 0, 5, 10, . . . no   8. 64, −32, 16, −8, . . . yes; −0.5   9. 1, 4, 9, 16, . . . no

Find the tenth term of each geometric sequence.

10. 2, 4, 8, . . . 1024   11. 1, 3, 9, . . . 19,683   12. −2, 6, −18, . . . 39,366

13. −3, 9, −27, . . . 59,049   14. −3, −12, −48, . . . −786,432   15. −5, 25, −125, . . . 9,765,625

16. $\frac{1}{9}, \frac{1}{3}, 1, \ldots$ 59,049   17. 0.3, 0.6, 1.2, . . . 153.6   18. $\frac{1}{4}, \frac{1}{2}, 1, \ldots$ 128

19. When a pendulum swings freely, the length of its arc decreases geometrically. Find each missing arc length.
a. 20th arc is 20 in.; 22nd arc is 18.5 in. about 19.2 in.
b. 8th arc is 27 mm; 10th arc is 3 mm 9 mm
c. 5th arc is 25 cm; 7th arc is 1 cm 5 cm
d. 100th arc is 18 ft; 98th arc is 2 ft 6 ft

Find the missing term of each geometric sequence. It could be the geometric mean or its opposite.

20. 4, ▧, 16, . . . ±8   21. 9, ▧, 16, . . . ±12   22. 2, ▧, 8, . . . ±4

23. 3, ▧, 12, . . . ±6   24. 2, ▧, 50, . . . ±10   25. 4, ▧, 5.76, . . . ±4.8

26. 625, ▧, 25, . . . ±125   27. $\frac{1}{9}$, ▧, 3, . . . ±1   28. 0.5, ▧, 0.125, . . . ±0.25

29. **Writing** Explain how you know that the sequence 400, 200, 100, 50 is geometric.
The sequence has a common ratio of $\frac{1}{2}$ or 0.5 between terms.

30. **Open-Ended** Write a geometric sequence of at least seven terms.
any seven-term sequence with a common ratio

31. **Error Analysis** A student says that the geometric sequence 30, __, 120 can be completed with 90. Is she correct? Explain.
No; the sequence can be completed with 60 with a common ratio of 2.

Practice and Problem Solving Wkbk/ All-in-One Resources/Online
Practice page 2

9-3 Practice (continued) — Form G
Geometric Sequences

Identify each sequence as *arithmetic, geometric,* or *neither.* Then find the next two terms.

32. 9, 3, 1, $\frac{1}{3}$, . . . geometric; $\frac{1}{9}, \frac{1}{27}$ 33. 1, 0, −2, −5, . . . neither; −9, −14   34. 2, −2, 2, −2, . . . geometric; 2, −2

35. −3, 2, 7, 12, . . . arithmetic; 17, 22   36. 1, −2, −5, −8, . . . arithmetic; −11, −14   37. 1, −2, 3, −4, . . . neither; 5, −6

Write an explicit formula for each sequence. Then generate the first five terms.

38. $a_1 = 3, r = -2$; $a_n = 3(-2)^{n-1}$; 3, −6, 12, −24, 48
39. $a_1 = 5, r = 3$; $a_n = 5(3)^{n-1}$; 5, 15, 45, 135, 405
40. $a_1 = -1, r = 4$; $a_n = -1(4)^{n-1}$; −1, −4, −16, −64, −256
41. $a_1 = -2, r = -3$; $a_n = -2(-3)^{n-1}$; −2, 6, −18, 54, −162
42. $a_1 = 32, r = -0.5$; $a_n = 32(-0.5)^{n-1}$; 32, −16, 8, −4, 2
43. $a_1 = 2187, r = \frac{1}{3}$; $a_n = 2187(\frac{1}{3})^{n-1}$; 2187, 729, 243, 81, 27
44. $a_1 = 9, r = 2$; $a_n = 9(2)^{n-1}$; 9, 18, 36, 72, 144
45. $a_1 = -4, r = 4$; $a_n = -4(4)^{n-1}$; −4, −16, −64, −256, −1024
46. $a_1 = 0.1, r = -2$; $a_n = 0.1(-2)^{n-1}$; 0.1, −0.2, 0.4, −0.8, 1.6

47. The deer population in an area is increasing. This year, the population was 1.025 times last year's population of 2537.
a. Assuming the population increases at the same rate for the next few years, write an explicit formula for the sequence. $a_n = 2537(1.025)^{n-1}$
b. Find the expected deer population for the fourth year of the sequence. about 2732

48. You enlarge the dimensions of a picture to 150% several times. After the first increase, the picture is 1 in. wide.
a. Write an explicit formula to model the width after each increase. $a_n = 1(1.5)^{n-1}$
b. How wide is the photo after the 2nd increase? 1.5 in.
c. How wide is the photo after the 3rd increase? 2.25 in.
d. How wide is the photo after the 12th increase? about 86.5 in.

Find the missing terms of each geometric sequence. (*Hint:* The geometric mean of positive first and fifth terms is the third term. Some terms might be negative.)

49. 12, ▧, ▧, ▧, 0.75   6, 3, 1.5 or −6, 3, −1.5
50. −9, ▧, ▧, ▧, −2304   −36, −144, −576 or 36, −144, 576

For the geometric sequence 6, 18, 54, 162, . . . , find the indicated term.

51. 6th term 1458   52. 19th term 2,324,522,934   53. *n*th term $6(3)^{n-1}$

Practice and Problem Solving Wkbk/ All-in-One Resources/Online
Think About a Plan

9-3 Think About a Plan
Geometric Sequences

Athletics During your first week of training for a marathon, you run a total of 10 miles. You increase the distance you run each week by twenty percent. How many miles do you run during your twelfth week of training?

Understanding the Problem

1. How can you write a sequence of numbers to represent this situation?
Answers may vary. Sample: Start with 10, and multiply it and each successive term by 120% or 1.2

2. Is the sequence arithmetic, geometric, or neither? geometric

3. What is the first term of the sequence? 10

4. What is the common ratio of the sequence? 1.2

5. What is the problem asking you to determine?
the 12th term of a geometric sequence that represents the number of miles you run each week

Planning the Solution

6. Write a formula for the sequence.
$a_n = 10(1.2)^{n-1}$

Getting an Answer

7. Evaluate your formula to find the number of miles you run during your twelfth week of training.
about 74.3 miles

Practice and Problem Solving Wkbk/ All-in-One Resources/Online
Standardized Test Prep

9-3 Standardized Test Prep
Geometric Sequences

Multiple Choice

For Exercises 1–6, choose the correct letter.

1. What is the 10th term of the geometric sequence 1, 4, 16, . . . ? C
Ⓐ 40   Ⓑ 180,224   Ⓒ 262,144   Ⓓ 2,883,584

2. Which sequence is a geometric sequence? H
Ⓕ 1, 3, 5, 7, 9, . . .   Ⓖ 2, 4, 8, 16, 32, . . .
Ⓖ 12, 9, 6, 3, 0, . . .   Ⓘ −2, −6, −10, −14, −18, . . .

3. Which could be the missing term of the geometric sequence 5, __, 125, . . . ? A
Ⓐ 25   Ⓑ 50   Ⓒ 75   Ⓓ 100

4. What could be the missing term of the geometric sequence −12, __, −$\frac{3}{4}$, . . . ? H
Ⓕ −4   Ⓖ −6.375   Ⓗ 3   Ⓘ 4

5. In the explicit formula for the 9th term of the geometric sequence 1, 6, 36, . . . what number is *a*? A
Ⓐ 1   Ⓑ 6   Ⓒ 36   Ⓓ 1,679,616

6. In each successive round of a backgammon tournament, the number of players decreases by half. If the tournament starts with 32 players, which rule could predict the number of players in the *n*th round? I
Ⓕ 32 = (0.5)^n Ⓖ 32 = 0.5^{n-1} Ⓗ $a_n = 15^{n-1}$ Ⓘ $a_n = (32)(0.5)^{n-1}$

Short Response

7. What is the 6th term of the geometric sequence 100, 50, . . . ? Show your work using the explicit formula.
[2] 3.125; $a_n = ar^{n-1}$; $a_6 = 100(\frac{1}{2})^{n-1}$; $a_6 = 100(\frac{1}{2})^5 = 3.125$; correct term with work shown
[1] incorrect term OR correct answer, without work shown
[0] incorrect answers and no work shown OR no answers given

All-in-One Resources/Online
Enrichment

9-3 Enrichment
Geometric Sequences

Doubling Periods in Geometric Sequences

Consider the geometric sequence 3, $4\frac{1}{2}$, $6\frac{3}{4}$, $10\frac{1}{8}$, ...

1. Describe how the terms of the sequence are related. Each term is $1\frac{1}{2}$ times the preceding term.

2. For any term of the sequence, how many terms does it take before the value of the term has at least doubled? 2

The doubling period of a geometric sequence is the number of terms needed to reach a term at least twice as large as a given term. What is the doubling period for the given sequence? 2 terms

3. Write the first ten terms of the geometric sequence $a_1 = 3, r = 1.1$ to two decimal places. 3, 3.3, 3.63, 3.99, 4.39, 4.83, 5.31, 5.85, 6.43, 7.07

4. What is the doubling period for $a_1 = 3$? for $a_2 = 3.3$? 8 terms; 8 terms

Although the doubling period does not depend on which term is given, it does depend on the common ratio. For what value(s) of *r* is the doubling period of a geometric sequence greater than 1? 1 < |r| < 2

The idea of a *doubling period* applies to certain everyday situations. For example, under optimum conditions, bacteria reproduce by splitting in two. Their numbers increase geometrically over time. Suppose at noon on a certain day, there are 1000 bacteria in a dish. At 6 P.M. on the same day, there are 8000 bacteria.

5. If a count is taken every hour, how many terms are in the geometric sequence? What is the common ratio? What is the doubling period? 7; $\sqrt[3]{2}$; 3 terms

6. If a count is taken every 40 min, how many terms are in the sequence? What is the common ratio? What is the doubling period? 10; $\sqrt[9]{2}$; 3 terms

7. In both cases, how many hours does it take the bacteria to double? 2

Online Teacher Resource Center
Activities, Games, and Puzzles

9-3 Activity: Finding the Next Term
Geometric Sequences

Work with a partner for this activity.

Select one of the geometric sequences in the top grid and cross it out. Your partner has to locate the next term of that sequence in the bottom grid and cross it out. Take turns selecting the sequence and locating the next term.

The activity ends when all entries in both grids have been crossed out.

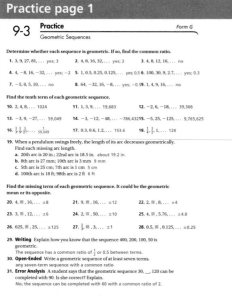

9-4 Arithmetic Series

© **Content Standard**
Extends F.IF.3 Recognize that sequences are functions, sometimes defined recursively, whose domain is a subset of the integers.

Objective To define arithmetic series and find their sums

Getting Ready!

The first four rows of chairs are set up for a meeting. The seating pattern is to continue through 20 rows. How many chairs will there be in all 20 rows? Explain your reasoning.

Be sure you understand the problem. How many chairs are in the 20th row?

© MATHEMATICAL PRACTICES

Just as you found formulas for terms of sequences, you can find formulas for the sums of the terms of sequences.

Essential Understanding When you know two terms and the number of terms in a finite arithmetic sequence, you can find the sum of the terms.

A **series** is the indicated sum of the terms of a sequence. A **finite series**, like a finite sequence, has a first term and a last term, while an **infinite series** continues without end.

Finite sequence	**Finite series**
$6, 9, 12, 15, 18$	$6 + 9 + 12 + 15 + 18$ (The sum is 60.)
Infinite sequence	**Infinite series**
$3, 7, 11, 15, \ldots$	$3 + 7 + 11 + 15 + \ldots$

An **arithmetic series** is a series whose terms form an arithmetic sequence (as shown above). When a series has a finite number of terms, you can use a formula involving the first and last term to evaluate the sum.

take note

> **Property** Sum of a Finite Arithmetic Series
>
> The sum S_n of a finite arithmetic series $a_1 + a_2 + a_3 + \cdots + a_n$ is
> $$S_n = \frac{n}{2}(a_1 + a_n)$$
> where a_1 is the first term, a_n is the nth term, and n is the number of terms.

1 Interactive Learning

Solve It!

PURPOSE To use a pattern to find a sum
PROCESS Students may
• recognize the number of seats in each row as an arithmetic sequence and sum the rows to find the total.
• use number patterns to rearrange the rows to a simpler configuration, then find the sum.

FACILITATE

Q How many chairs are in the last row? Explain. **[23; the number of chairs in each row increases by the same amount, so this is an arithmetic sequence with a common difference of 1.]**

Q Can the chairs be grouped in a different way to make your calculations easier? Explain. **[Yes; sample: Combine rows to get equal sums. The first and last row will sum to 27 chairs. The second row and next-to-last row will sum to 27 chairs, and so on.]**

ANSWER See Solve It in Answers on next page.
CONNECT THE MATH In the Solve It, students use mathematical patterns and arithmetic sequences to find a sum. In this lesson, students will use explicit formulas or a graphing calculator to find the sum of a finite arithmetic series.

2 Guided Instruction

Take Note

Q When you divide the formula for the sum of a finite arithmetic series by n, you get $\frac{a_1 + a_n}{2}$. What does this imply about the mean of all the terms in the series? **[The mean of all the terms in the series is the same as the mean of the first and last terms.]**

9-4 Preparing to Teach

BIG ideas **Equivalence**
Variable

ESSENTIAL UNDERSTANDINGS
• When two terms and the number of terms in a finite arithmetic sequence are known, the sum of the terms can be found.
• A sequence can be defined explicitly by describing its nth term with a formula using n or recursively by stating its first term and a formula for its nth term using the $(n - 1)$ term.

Math Background

A series is the sum of the terms in a sequence. If an arithmetic sequence is infinite, it follows that an arithmetic series is also infinite. However, it is often useful to find the partial sum of an arithmetic series. In this lesson, the partial sum of an

arithmetic series is referred to as a finite arithmetic series.

Finding the sum of a finite arithmetic sequence requires knowing two of the terms and the number of terms in the sequence. This sum can be thought of as the average of the first and last terms times the number of terms.

Students are introduced to summation notation using $\sum$ when writing arithmetic series. Index limits may vary, although most lower limits in this lesson will begin at 0 or 1. The limit values will affect the explicit formula. The number of terms of a finite sequence is one more than the difference of the limits.

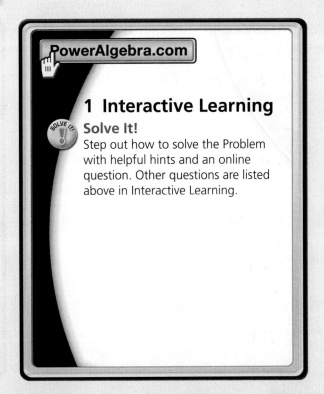

PowerAlgebra.com

1 Interactive Learning

Solve It!

Step out how to solve the Problem with helpful hints and an online question. Other questions are listed above in Interactive Learning.

Problem 1

> **Q** Is it necessary to know the common difference when using the formula to find the value of a finite arithmetic series? Explain. **[Sometimes; the common difference is necessary to find the number of terms or the *n*th term. If the number of terms and the *n*th term are given, the common difference is not needed.]**

Got It?

> **Q** How can the terms be paired to help find the sum? Explain. **[4 + 99 = 103, 9 + 94 = 103, and so on. The sum of each pair times the number of pairs is equal to the total sum.]**

> **Q** How can you find the number of terms using subtraction? Explain your reasoning. **[The difference between 99 and 4 is 95. Dividing 95 by the common difference of 5 gives 19. Because the first term must also be counted, the number of terms is 20.]**

Problem 2

> **Q** How many sales must a sales person make during each of the first five weeks to earn the bonus? Explain. **[10, 12, 14, 16, 18; 10 sales made the first week. The common difference is 2 so 12, 14, 16, and 18.]**

Got It?

> **Q** Which variables are different from Problem 2? How will this affect your answer? **[The bonus decreases from $10,000 to $5000, but this is not used. The common difference decreases from 2 to 1 so the sum will decrease.]**

 Problem 1 Finding the Sum of a Finite Arithmetic Series

What is the sum of the even integers from 2 to 100?

Think

How many even integers are there from 2 to 100? Double 1, 2, 3,..., 50, and you get 2, 4, 6,..., 100, the even integers from 2 to 100. There are 50 even integers.

The series $2 + 4 + 6 + \cdots + 100$ is arithmetic with first term 2, last (and 50th) term 100, and common difference 2. The sum is
$$S_{50} = \frac{50}{2}(2 + 100) = 25(102) = 2550.$$

Got It? 1. a. What is the sum of the finite arithmetic series
$$4 + 9 + 14 + 19 + 24 + \cdots + 99?$$

b. Reasoning Will the sum of a sequence of even numbers always be an even number? Will the sum of a sequence of odd numbers always be an odd number? Explain.

 Problem 2 Using the Sum of a Finite Arithmetic Series

Bonus A company pays a $10,000 bonus to salespeople at the end of their first 50 weeks if they make 10 sales in their first week, and then improve their sales numbers by two each week thereafter. One salesperson qualified for the bonus with the minimum possible number of sales. How many sales did the salesperson make in week 50? In all 50 weeks?

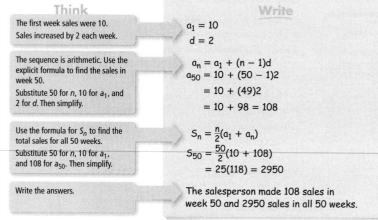

Think	Write
The first week sales were 10. Sales increased by 2 each week.	$a_1 = 10$ $d = 2$
The sequence is arithmetic. Use the explicit formula to find the sales in week 50. Substitute 50 for *n*, 10 for a_1, and 2 for *d*. Then simplify.	$a_n = a_1 + (n - 1)d$ $a_{50} = 10 + (50 - 1)2$ $= 10 + (49)2$ $= 10 + 98 = 108$
Use the formula for S_n to find the total sales for all 50 weeks. Substitute 50 for *n*, 10 for a_1, and 108 for a_{50}. Then simplify.	$S_n = \frac{n}{2}(a_1 + a_n)$ $S_{50} = \frac{50}{2}(10 + 108)$ $= 25(118) = 2950$
Write the answers.	The salesperson made 108 sales in week 50 and 2950 sales in all 50 weeks.

Got It? 2. The company in Problem 2 has an alternative bonus plan. It pays a $5000 bonus if a new salesperson makes 10 sales in the first week and then improves by *one* sale per week each week thereafter. One salesperson qualified for this bonus with the minimum number of sales. How many sales did the salesperson make in week 50? In all 50 weeks?

Answers

Solve It!

270 chairs; continue the pattern and add the number of chairs in each row.

Got It?

1. a. 1030

b. Yes; no; the sum of any number of even numbers is always even. The sum of an odd number of odd numbers is odd, but the sum of an even number of odd numbers is even.

2. 59 sales; 1725 sales

3. a. $\displaystyle\sum_{n=1}^{40}(-12 + 7n)$

b. $\displaystyle\sum_{n=1}^{50}(510 - 10n)$

 PowerAlgebra.com

2 Guided Instruction

Each Problem is worked out and supported online.

Problem 1
Finding the Sum of a Finite Arithmetic Series

Alternative Problem 1
Finding the Sum of a Finite Arithmetic Series
Animated

Problem 2
Using the Sum of a Finite Arithmetic Series
Animated

Problem 3
Writing a Series in Summation Notation

Problem 4
Finding the Sum of a Series
Animated

Problem 5
Using a Graphing Calculator to Find the Sum of a Series

Support in Algebra 2 Companion
• Vocabulary
• Key Concepts
• Got It?

You can use the Greek capital letter sigma, Σ, to indicate a sum. With it, you use *limits* to indicate how many terms you are adding. **Limits** are the least and greatest values of n in the series. You write the limits below and above the Σ to indicate the first and last terms of the series.

For example, you can write the series

$$3^2 + 4^2 + 5^2 + \cdots + 108^2 \text{ as } \sum_{n=3}^{108} n^2.$$

Upper limit: the series ends with $n = 108$.

The explicit formula for each term is n^2.

$$\sum_{n=3}^{108} n^2$$

Lower limit: the series begins with $n = 3$.

For an infinite series, summation notation shows ∞ as the upper limit.

To find the number of terms in a series written in Σ form, subtract the lower limit from the upper limit and add 1.

The number of terms in the series above is $108 - 3 + 1 = 106$.

 Problem 3 Writing a Series in Summation Notation

Multiple Choice What is summation notation for the series?

$7 + 11 + 15 + \cdots + 203 + 207$

Ⓐ $\displaystyle\sum_{n=1}^{51} (4n + 3)$ Ⓑ $\displaystyle\sum_{n=1}^{50} (4n + 3)$ Ⓒ $\displaystyle\sum_{n=1}^{50} (7n)$ Ⓓ $\displaystyle\sum_{n=1}^{51} (7n)$

Plan

What do you need to write a series in summation notation?
You need an explicit formula for the nth term and the lower and upper limits.

The sequence $7, 11, 15, \ldots, 203, 207$ is arithmetic with first term $a = 7$ and common difference $d = 4$.

$a_n = a_1 + (n - 1)d$	Use the explicit formula for an arithmetic sequence.
$a_n = 7 + (n - 1)4$	Substitute 7 for a_1, and 4 for d.
$= 4n + 3$	Simplify.

An explicit formula for the nth term is $4n + 3$.

$a_n = 4n + 3$	Use the explicit formula to find the value of n for the term 207.
$207 = 4n + 3$	Substitute 207 for a_n.
$204 = 4n$	Solve for n.
$51 = n$	

The upper limit is 51. You can write the series as $\displaystyle\sum_{n=1}^{51}(4n + 3)$. The correct answer is A.

 Got It? **3.** What is summation notation for the series?
a. $-5 + 2 + 9 + 16 + \cdots + 261 + 268$
b. $500 + 490 + 480 + \cdots + 20 + 10$

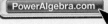

Key Concept Summation Notation and Linear Functions

If the explicit formula for the nth term in summation notation is a *linear* function of n, then the series is arithmetic. The slope of the linear function is the common difference between terms of the series.

Problem 3   AUDITORY LEARNERS
Practice reading the summation notation out loud so students understand the necessary parts.

For example, $\displaystyle\sum_{n=1}^{51}(4n + 3)$ is read as "The sum of $4n + 3$ for values of n from 1 to 51."

EXTENSION

> **Q** How would the summation notation for this problem be different if the lower limit began with $n = 0$? State the new summation notation. [**The explicit formula and the upper and lower limits would change. The summation notation would be $\displaystyle\sum_{n=0}^{50}(4n + 7)$.**]

Got It?   ERROR PREVENTION
Watch for students who confuse n and a_n when writing a series using summation notation. The lower limit to the upper limit is the *number* of terms, not the *values* of the terms.

> **Q** Can the series be written correctly in summation notation in more than one way? Explain. [**Yes; for example, the first series can be written as $\displaystyle\sum_{n=0}^{39}(-5 + 7n)$ or as $\displaystyle\sum_{n=1}^{40}(-12 + 7n)$.**]

Take Note

> **Q** What are the similarities and differences between the graphs of the explicit formulas in Got It 3a and 3b? [**Both graphs are linear with different y-intercepts and different slopes. The graph of 3a increases while the graph of 3b decreases because the positive and negative common differences relate to slope.**]

Additional Problems

1. What is the sum of the finite arithmetic series $14 + 17 + 20 + 23 + \ldots + 116$?

ANSWER 2275

2. There are 30 rows of seats in a large arena. The first row contains 10 seats. Each successive row increases by 3 seats. How many seats are in the last row? How many seats are there in all?

ANSWER 97; 1605

3. What is summation notation for the series?
a. $-19 + -14 + -9 + \ldots + 221 + 226$
b. $20 + 18 + 16 + \ldots + -24 + -26$

ANSWERS
a. $\displaystyle\sum_{n=1}^{50}(5n - 24)$
b. $\displaystyle\sum_{n=1}^{24}(-2n + 22)$

4. What is the sum of the series written in summation notation?
a. $\displaystyle\sum_{n=1}^{27}(-2n + 1)$
b. $\displaystyle\sum_{n=1}^{5}(n^2 + 5)$
c. $\displaystyle\sum_{n=0}^{5}(10^n)$

ANSWERS
a. -729,
b. 80,
c. 111,111

5. What is the sum of the series written in summation notation? $\displaystyle\sum_{n=1}^{85}(n^2 + 4n + 3)$?

ANSWER 223,210

Problem 4

Although the lower limit in summation notation is commonly 0 or 1, it can be any number less than or equal to the upper limit.

> **Q** How can you find the sum of the series in 4A if the lower limit is $n = 20$? What is this new sum? **[Sample: Find the sum of the first 19 terms and subtract the sum from S_{70}: $S_{70} - S_{19} = 12,635 - 1007 = 11,628$.]**

Got It?   ERROR PREVENTION

Have students check whether a series is arithmetic before using the formula for finding the sum of a finite arithmetic series. If a series is not arithmetic, look for a pattern in the terms.

> **Q** Which finite series is arithmetic? Explain. **[The series in 4a contains a first-degree variable, so the explicit formula is linear, and the series is arithmetic. The series in 4b and 4c do not contain variables of the first-degree, therefore, they are not arithmetic.]**

Problem 5   EXTENSION

Some graphing calculators allow an extra parameter representing the index increments. For example, the entry "sum(seq(5N+3, N, 1, 70, 2)" represents the sum of the series using index increments of 2. That is, $n = 1$, $n = 3$, $n = 5$, etc. If this parameter is not entered, the calculator defaults to 1.

Got It?

> **Q** Is this series arithmetic? Explain. **[No; the variable is squared, so the explicit formula is not linear.]**

Think

Is the function $f(n) = (n - 1)^2$ linear?
No; the function is quadratic.

Plan

What calculator commands do you use to find the sum of a series?
Use the sum and sequence commands.

© **Problem 4** Finding the Sum of a Series

What is the sum of the series written in summation notation?

A $\sum_{n=1}^{70}(5n + 3)$

Since the formula is a linear function of n, the series is arithmetic.

$a_1 = 5(1) + 3 = 8$ Find a_1.

$a_{70} = 5(70) + 3 = 353$ Find a_{70}.

$S_n = \frac{n}{2}(a_1 + a_n)$ Use the formula for the sum of a finite arithmetic series.

$S_{70} = \frac{70}{2}(8 + 353) = 12,635$ There are 70 terms, so $n = 70$.

B $\sum_{n=1}^{7}(n - 1)^2$

This series is not arithmetic. However, you can evaluate by adding the terms.

$\sum_{n=1}^{7}(n - 1)^2$

$= (1 - 1)^2 + (2 - 1)^2 + (3 - 1)^2 + (4 - 1)^2 + (5 - 1)^2 + (6 - 1)^2 + (7 - 1)^2$

$= 0 + 1 + 4 + 9 + 16 + 25 + 36 = 91$

✓ **Got It? 4.** What is the sum of each finite series?

     a. $\sum_{n=1}^{40}(3n - 8)$ **b.** $\sum_{n=1}^{4}n^3$ **c.** $\sum_{n=0}^{100}(-1)^n$

On a graphing calculator, you can find the sum of a finite series by using commands from the **LIST** menu.

© **Problem 5** Using a Graphing Calculator to Find the Sum of a Series

What is the sum of the series written in summation notation? $\sum_{n=1}^{70}(5n + 3)$

Input the sum command.   Input the sequence command.   Input the formula, N, and the lower and upper limits.

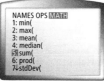

```
NAMES OPS MATH
1: min(
2: max(
3: mean(
4: median(
5: sum(
6: prod(
7: stdDev(
```

```
NAMES OPS MATH
1: SortA(
2: SortD(
3: dim(
4: Fill(
5: seq(
6: cumSum(
7: ΔList(
```

```
sum(seq(5N+3,N,1,70))
                 12635
```

The sum is 12,635.

✓ **Got It? 5.** Use a graphing calculator. What is $\sum_{n=1}^{50}(n^2 - n)$?

Answers

Got It? (continued)

   4. a. 2140

      b. 100

      c. 1

   5. 41,650

Lesson Check

Do you know HOW?

Find the sum of each finite arithmetic series.

1. $4 + 7 + 10 + 13 + 16 + 19 + 22$

2. $10 + 20 + 30 + \cdots + 110 + 120$

Write each arithmetic series in summation notation.

3. $3 + 6 + 9 + 12 + 15 + 18 + 21$

4. $1 + 5 + 9 + \cdots + 41 + 45$

Do you UNDERSTAND?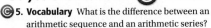

 5. Vocabulary What is the difference between an arithmetic sequence and an arithmetic series?

6. Error Analysis A student writes the arithmetic series $3 + 8 + 13 + \ldots + 43$ in summation notation as $\sum_{n=3}^{8} (3 + 5n)$. Describe and correct the error.

7. Reasoning Is it possible to have more than one arithmetic series with four terms whose sum is 44? Explain.

Practice and Problem-Solving Exercises

Ⓐ Practice

Find the sum of each finite arithmetic series.   ◀ See Problem 1.

8. $2 + 4 + 6 + 8$

9. $8 + 9 + 10 + \cdots + 15$

10. $5 + 6 + 7 + \cdots + 11$

11. $1 + 4 + 7 + \cdots + 31$

12. $7 + 14 + 21 + \cdots + 105$

13. $(-3) + (-6) + (-9) + \cdots + (-30)$

14. Grades A student has taken three math tests so far this semester. His scores for the first three tests were 75, 79, and 83.   ◀ See Problem 2.
 a. Suppose his test scores continue to improve at the same rate. What will be his grade on the sixth (and final) test?
 b. What will be his total score for all six tests?

Write each arithmetic series in summation notation.   ◀ See Problem 3.

15. $4 + 8 + 12 + 16 + 20$

16. $7 + 9 + 11 + \cdots + 21$

17. $5 + 8 + 11 + \cdots + 38$

18. $100 + 90 + 80 + \cdots + 10$

19. $(-3) + (-6) + (-9) + \cdots + (-30)$

20. $105 + 97 + 89 + \cdots + (-71)$

Find the sum of each finite series.   ◀ See Problem 4.

21. $\sum_{n=1}^{5} (2n - 1)$

22. $\sum_{n=1}^{10} (3n - 4)$

23. $\sum_{n=1}^{8} (7 - n)$

24. $\sum_{n=1}^{4} 2^n$

25. $\sum_{n=1}^{9} (-1)^n \cdot 2$

26. $\sum_{n=5}^{10} (20 - n)$

Use a graphing calculator to find the sum of each series.   ◀ See Problem 5.

27. $\sum_{n=1}^{50} (2n - 3)$

28. $\sum_{n=1}^{26} (n^2 - 3n)$

29. $\sum_{n=1}^{10} (-2)^n$

30. $\sum_{n=1}^{20} (n^3 - 10n^2)$

31. $\sum_{n=5}^{73} (-4n + 32)$

32. $\sum_{n=5}^{25} (n^2 - 14n + 32)$

3 Lesson Check

Do you know HOW?
• If students have difficulty getting started with Exercises 3 and 4, ask them to name the components they need to write the series in summation notation. Then ask them to identify which of those components are given.

Do you UNDERSTAND?
• For Exercise 5, if students have difficulty remembering the difference between a sequence and a series, encourage them to come up with some device to help them remember. For example, a series is the sum of a sequence. Both "series" and the phrase "sum of a sequence" contain the letter *s* twice.

Close

> **Q** How are arithmetic series and sequences the same? How are they different? [Sample: **Both an arithmetic series and an arithmetic sequence consist of terms that change by a common difference. A sequence is the list of these terms, while a series is the sum of these terms.**]
>
> **Q** How can the formula for the sum of a finite arithmetic series be explained using the concept of mean? [Sample: **The sum of any arithmetic sequence can be found by multiplying the mean value times the number of values. The mean of the first and last term is multiplied by the number of terms.**]

Lesson Check

1. 91   **2.** 780

3. $\sum_{n=1}^{7} 3n$ **4.** $\sum_{n=1}^{12} (-3 + 4n)$

5. An arithmetic sequence is a list of numbers for which successive numbers have a common difference. An arithmetic series is an expression for the sum of the terms of an arithmetic sequence.

6. The lower limit should not be 3, it should be zero. The correct summation notation is $\sum_{n=0}^{8} (3 + 5n)$.

7. Yes; $44 = 2(a_1 + a_4)$, so any combination of a_1 and a_4 with a sum of 22 is a possible series.

Practice and Problem-Solving Exercises

8. 20   **9.** 92   **10.** 56
11. 176   **12.** 840   **13.** −165

14. a. 95
 b. 510

15. $\sum_{n=1}^{5} 4n$ **16.** $\sum_{n=1}^{8} (5 + 2n)$

17. $\sum_{n=1}^{12} (2 + 3n)$ **18.** $\sum_{n=1}^{10} (110 - 10n)$

19. $\sum_{n=1}^{10} (-3n)$ **20.** $\sum_{n=1}^{23} (113 - 8n)$

21. 25   **22.** 125   **23.** 20
24. 30   **25.** −2   **26.** 75
27. 2400   **28.** 5148   **29.** 682
30. 15,400   **31.** −8556   **32.** 1757

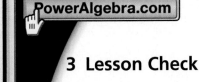

3 Lesson Check

For a digital lesson check, use the Got It questions.

Support in Algebra 2 Companion
• Lesson Check

4 Practice

 Assign homework to individual students or to an entire class.

4 Practice

ASSIGNMENT GUIDE

Basic: 8–32 all, 33–41 odd, 46–48

Average: 9–31 odd, 33–50

Advanced: 9–31 odd, 33–56

Standardized Test Prep: 57–61

Mixed Review: 62–70

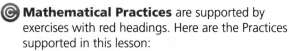 **Mathematical Practices** are supported by exercises with red headings. Here are the Practices supported in this lesson:

MP 1: Make Sense of Problems Ex. 33

MP 2: Reason Quantitatively Ex. 50a

MP 3: Construct Arguments Ex. 7, 47d

MP 3: Critique the Reasoning of Others Ex. 6

Applications exercises have blue headings. Exercises 14 and 46 support MP 4: Model.

EXERCISE 46: Use the Think About a Plan worksheet in the **Practice and Problem Solving Workbook** (also available in the Teaching Resources in print and online) to further support students' development in becoming independent learners.

HOMEWORK QUICK CHECK

To check students' understanding of key skills and concepts, go over Exercises 9, 15, 33, 46, and 47.

B Apply   **33. Think About a Plan** A meeting room is set up with 16 rows of seats. The number of seats in a row increases by two with each successive row. The first row has 12 seats. What is the total number of seats?
- How can you find the number of seats in each row using an explicit formula?
- What is the number of seats in the 16th row?
- How can you find the sum of the seats in 16 rows?

Determine whether each list is a *sequence* or a *series* and *finite* or *infinite*.

34. $1, 2, 4, 8, 16, 32, \ldots$

35. $1, 0.5, 0.25, 0.125, 0.0625$

36. $5 + 10 + \cdots + 25$

37. $-0.5 - 0.25 - 0.125 - \ldots$

38. $\frac{4}{3}, \frac{7}{3}, \frac{10}{3}, \frac{13}{3}, \frac{16}{3}, \ldots$

39. $2.3 + 4.6 + 9.2 + 18.4$

Each sequence has eight terms. Evaluate each related series.

40. $\frac{1}{2}, \frac{3}{2}, \frac{5}{2}, \ldots, \frac{15}{2}$

41. $1, -1, -3, \ldots, -13$

42. $5, 13, 21, \ldots, 61$

43. $-3.5, -1.25, 1, \ldots, 12.25$

44. $1765, 1414, 1063, \ldots, -692$

45. $-13, -14.5, -16, \ldots, -23.5$

STEM **46. Architecture** In a 20-row theater, the number of seats in a row increases by three with each successive row. The first row has 18 seats.
- **a.** Write an arithmetic series to represent the number of seats in the theater.
- **b.** Find the total seating capacity of the theater.
- **c.** Front-row tickets for a concert cost \$60. After every 5 rows, the ticket price goes down by \$5. What is the total amount of money generated by a full house?

47. a. Grocery A supermarket displays cans in a triangle. Write an explicit formula for the sequence of the number of cans.
- **b.** Use summation notation to write the related series for a triangle with 10 cans in the bottom row.
- **c.** Suppose the triangle had 17 rows. How many cans would be in the 17th row?
- **d. Reasoning** Could the triangle have 110 cans? 140 cans? Explain.

Evaluate each series to the given term.

48. $2 + 4 + 6 + 8 + \ldots$; 10th term

49. $-5 - 25 - 45 - \ldots$; 9th term

50. a. Open-Ended Write two explicit formulas for arithmetic sequences.
- **b.** Write the first five terms of each related series.
- **c.** Use summation notation to rewrite each series.
- **d.** Evaluate each series.

Challenge **Use the values of a_1 and S_n to find the value of a_n.**

51. $a_1 = 4$ and $S_{40} = 6080$; a_{40}

52. $a_1 = -6$ and $S_{50} = -5150$; a_{50}

Answers

Practice and Problem-Solving Exercises
(continued)

33. 432 seats

34. sequence; infinite

35. sequence; finite

36. series; finite

37. series; infinite

38. sequence; infinite

39. series; finite

40. 32

41. −48

42. 264

43. 35

44. 4292   **45.** −146

46. a. $\sum\limits_{n=1}^{20}(3n + 15)$

   b. 930

   c. \$46,950

47. a. $a_n = n + 1$

   b. $\sum\limits_{n=1}^{9}(n + 1)$

   c. 18 cans

   d. No; no; 13 rows have 104 cans, 14 rows have 119 cans, 15 rows have 135 cans, and 16 rows have 152 cans. The number of rows would not be an integer for 110 cans or 140 cans.

48. 110

49. −765

50. a–d. Check students' work.

51. 300

52. −200

Find a_1 for each arithmetic series.

53. $S_8 = 440$ and $d = 6$

54. $S_{30} = 240$ and $d = -2$

55. Evaluate S_{10} for the series $x + (x + y) + (x + 2y) + \ldots$

56. Evaluate S_{15} for the series $3x + (3x - 2y) + (3x - 4y) + \ldots$

Standardized Test Prep

SAT/ACT

57. Which expression represents the series $14 + 20 + 26 + 32 + 38 + 44 + 50$?

   Ⓐ $\displaystyle\sum_{n=2}^{8}(7n - 1)$ Ⓒ $\displaystyle\sum_{n=3}^{8}(6n - 4)$

   Ⓑ $\displaystyle\sum_{n=3}^{9}(6n - 4)$ Ⓓ $\displaystyle\sum_{n=8}^{14}(n + 6)$

58. What is the common ratio in the geometric sequence $\frac{9}{2}, 3, 2, \frac{4}{3}, \ldots$?

   Ⓕ $\frac{3}{2}$ Ⓖ $\frac{9}{2}$ Ⓗ $\frac{2}{3}$ Ⓘ $\frac{27}{2}$

59. Which expression is NOT equivalent to $\sqrt[4]{4n^2}$?

   Ⓐ $\left(4n^2\right)^{\frac{1}{4}}$ Ⓑ $2n^{\frac{1}{2}}$ Ⓒ $\left(2|n|\right)^{\frac{1}{2}}$ Ⓓ $\sqrt{2|n|}$

60. The graph shows the inverse of which function?

   Ⓕ $y = 3x$ Ⓗ $y = 3^x$

   Ⓖ $y = -3^{2x}$ Ⓘ $y = 2^{3x}$

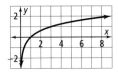

Short Response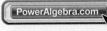

61. Solve the equation $x^2 + 10x + 40 = 5$ by completing the square.

Mixed Review

Write an explicit formula for each geometric sequence. Then find the first three terms.

🔵 See Lesson 9-3.

62. $a_1 = 1, r = 2$ **63.** $a_1 = -1, r = -1$ **64.** $a_1 = 3, r = \frac{3}{2}$

Simplify each rational expression. State any restrictions on the variable.

🔵 See Lesson 8-4.

65. $\dfrac{x^2 + 4x + 3}{x^2 - 3x - 4}$ **66.** $\dfrac{c^2 - 8c + 12}{c^2 - 11c + 30}$ **67.** $\dfrac{3z^4 + 36z^3 + 60z^2}{3z^3 - 3z^2}$

Get Ready! To prepare for Lesson 9-5, do Exercises 68–70.

Find the common ratio for each geometric sequence.

🔵 See Lesson 9-3.

68. $90, -30, 10, \ldots$ **69.** $64, 48, 36, \ldots$ **70.** $-9, 4.5, -2.25, \ldots$

53. 34

54. 37

55. $10x + 45y$

56. $45x - 210y$

Standardized Test Prep

57. C

58. H

59. B

60. H

61. [2] $\left(\dfrac{b}{2}\right)^2 = \left(\dfrac{10}{2}\right)^2 = 25$

         $x^2 + 10x + 25 = -35 + 25$

             $(x + 5)^2 = -10$

               $x + 5 = \pm i\sqrt{10}$

                  $x = -5 \pm i\sqrt{10}$

   [1] appropriate method, but with one computational error

Mixed Review

62. $a_n = 2^{n-1}$; 1, 2, 4

63. $a_n = -1(-1)^{n-1}$; -1, 1, -1

64. $a_n = 3\left(\frac{3}{2}\right)^{n-1}$; 3, $\frac{9}{2}$, $\frac{27}{4}$

65. $\dfrac{x + 3}{x - 4}$; $x \neq 4$, $x \neq -1$

66. $\dfrac{c - 2}{c - 5}$; $c \neq 5$, $c \neq 6$

67. $\dfrac{z^2 + 12z + 20}{z - 1}$; $z \neq 1$, $z \neq 0$

68. $-\frac{1}{3}$

69. $\frac{3}{4}$

70. $-\frac{1}{2}$

Additional Instructional Support

Algebra 2 Companion

Students can use the **Algebra 2 Companion** worktext (4 pages) as you teach the lesson. Use the Companion to support

• New Vocabulary
• Key Concepts
• Got It for each Problem
• Lesson Check

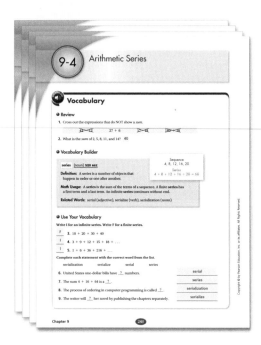

5 Assess & Remediate

Lesson Quiz

1. What is the sum of the finite arithmetic series $-10 + (-8) + (-6) + (-4) + \ldots + 24$?

2. **Do you UNDERSTAND?** You are trying to save $1500. You begin with $5 and save $3 more than the previous amount each week for 30 weeks. Will you meet your goal? Explain.

3. What is the summation notation for the series $-3 + 1 + 5 + \ldots + 169 + 173$?

4. What is $\sum_{n=1}^{105} -2n + 10$?

ANSWERS TO LESSON QUIZ

1. 126

2. No; the first term is 5, and the common difference is 3. The amount saved in week 30 is $a_{30} = 5 + (30 - 1)3 = 92$. The sum for all 30 weeks is $S_{30} = \frac{30}{2}(5 + 92) = \$1455$.

3. $\sum_{n=1}^{45} 4n - 7$

4. $-10,080$

PRESCRIPTION FOR REMEDIATION
Use the student work on the Lesson Quiz to prescribe a differentiated review assignment:

Points	Differentiated Remediation
0–1	Intervention
2–3	On-level
4	Extension

PowerAlgebra.com

5 Assess & Remediate
Assign the Lesson Quiz. Appropriate intervention, practice, or enrichment is automatically generated based on student performance.

Intervention

• **Reteaching** (2 pages) Provides reteaching and practice exercises for the key lesson concepts. Use with struggling students or absent students.

• **English Language Learner Support** Helps students develop and reinforce mathematical vocabulary and key concepts.

All-in-One Resources/Online
Reteaching

All-in-One Resources/Online
English Language Learner Support

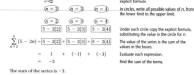

ELL Support

Focus on Language Have students use a dictionary to look up the terms *sequence* and *series*. A sequence is commonly defined as "a following of one thing after another." Students may have heard of the Fibonacci sequence. A series is commonly defined as "similar things happening one after the other." For example, several books are often printed as a series. Television shows are also referred to as series. Encourage students to discuss other examples of sequences and series in real life. Confirm that *sequence* and *series* are often used interchangeably outside of mathematics.

Explain that in mathematics, *sequence* and *series* cannot be used interchangeably. A sequence is an ordered list of numbers, while a series is the sum of the terms in a sequence. Write the words *sequence* and *series* on the board with examples of each. Point to each example, and have students practice saying the words.

Differentiated Remediation *continued*

On-Level

- **Practice** (2 pages) Provides extra practice for each lesson. For simpler practice exercises, use the Form K Practice pages found in the All-in-One Teaching Resources and online.

- **Think About a Plan** Helps students develop specific problem-solving skills and strategies by providing scaffolded guiding questions.

- **Standardized Test Prep** Focuses on all major exercises, all major question types, and helps students prepare for the high-stakes assessments.

Extension

- **Enrichment** Provides students with interesting problems and activities that extend the concepts of the lesson.

- **Activities, Games, and Puzzles** Worksheets that can be used for concepts development, enrichment, and for fun!

Practice and Problem Solving Wkbk/All-in-One Resources/Online
Practice page 1

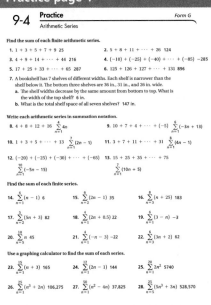

Practice and Problem Solving Wkbk/All-in-One Resources/Online
Practice page 2

9-4 Practice (continued) — Arithmetic Series — Form G

Determine whether each list is a *sequence* or a *series* and *finite* or *infinite*.

29. 7, 12, 17, 22, 27 **sequence; finite**
30. 3 + 5 + 7 + 9 + ... **series; infinite**
31. 8, 8.2, 8.4, 8.6, 8.8, 9.0, ... **sequence; infinite**
32. 1 + 5 + 9 + ... + 21 **series; finite**
33. 40, 20, 10, 5, 2.5, 1.25, ... **sequence; infinite**
34. 10 + 20 + 30 + 40 + 50 **series; finite**

35. An embroidery pattern calls for five stitches in the first row and for three more stitches in each successive row. The 25th row, which is the last row, has 77 stitches. Find the total number of stitches in the pattern. **1025 stitches**

36. A marching band formation consists of 6 rows. The first row has 9 musicians, the second has 11, the third has 13 and so on. How many musicians are in the last row and how many musicians are there in all? **19 musicians; 84 musicians**

37. **Writing** Explain how you can identify the difference between a series and a sequence.
A series is the sum of terms in a sequence, which is indicated by summation notation or addition signs.

38. a. **Open-Ended** Write three explicit formulas for arithmetic sequences.
   b. Write the first seven terms of each related series.
   c. Use summation notation to rewrite the series.
   d. Evaluate each series.
   Check students' work. Sequences should be arithmetic and contain seven terms.

39. **Error Analysis** A student identifies the series 10 + 15 + 20 + 25 + 30 as an infinite arithmetic series. Is he correct? Explain.
No; the series is a finite arithmetic series. An infinite arithmetic series would continue indefinitely.

40. **Mental Math** Use mental math to evaluate $\sum_{1}^{5}(2n+1)$. **15**

41. To train new employees, an employer offers a bonus after 30 work days as follows. An employee must turn in one report on the first day; the number of reports for each subsequent day must increase by two. What is the minimum number of reports an employee will have to turn in over the 30 days to earn the bonus? **900**

All-in-One Resources/Online
Enrichment

9-4 Enrichment — Arithmetic Series

The Gauss Trick

If your teacher asked you to add the numbers from 1 to 100, you would probably begin by adding $1 + 2 + 3 + \cdots + 100$, term by term from left to right. Karl Friedrich Gauss (1777–1855) found another way. Let S represent the finite series whose sum you are trying to find. Since addition is commutative, both equations below represent this series.

$$S = 1 + 2 + 3 + \cdots + 98 + 99 + 100$$
$$S = 100 + 99 + 98 + \cdots + 3 + 2 + 1$$

1. What is the sum of the left side of the first equation and the left side of the second equation? **25**
2. What is the sum of each vertically-aligned pair of quantities on the right side of the equal signs? **101**
3. How may such pairs are there? **100**
4. Because each pair has the same sum, use multiplication to express the sum of all the pairs on the right side. **100 × 101 = 10,100**
5. Write an equation that states that the sum of the left sides must equal the sum of the right sides. Solve your equation for S. **2S = 10,100; S = 5050**

Use the technique outlined above to derive the formula for the sum of n terms of any arithmetic series. Suppose that the series starts with the term a_1 and has a common difference of d.

6. What is the nth term, in terms of a_1, d, and n? $a_1 + (n-1)d$
7. Write the sum S of the n terms of the series, where each number is written in terms of a_1 and d. Then write the sum in reverse order, lining up terms.
$S = a_1 + (a_1 + d) + \cdots + [a_1 + (n-1)d]; S = [a_1 + (n-1)d] + \cdots + (a_1 + d) + a_1$
8. What is the sum of each vertical pair of quantities on the right side? $2a_1 + (n-1)d$
9. How many such pairs are there? n
10. Express the sum of all the pairs using multiplication. $n[2a_1 + (n-1)d]$
11. Write an equation that states that the sum of the left sides must equal the sum of the right sides. Solve your equation for S. $2S = n[2a_1 + (n-1)d]; S = \frac{n[2a_1 + (n-1)d]}{2}$
12. Show that your equation is equivalent to $S = \frac{n}{2}(a_1 + a_n)$. *Hint:* Use your answer to Exercise 6.
$S = \frac{n[2a_1 + (n-1)d]}{2}$
$= \frac{n[a_1 + a_1 + (n-1)d]}{2}$
$= \frac{n[a_1 + a_1 + (n-1)d]}{2}$
$= \frac{n(a_1 + a_n)}{2} = \frac{n}{2}(a_1 + a_n)$

Practice and Problem Solving Wkbk/All-in-One Resources/Online
Think About a Plan

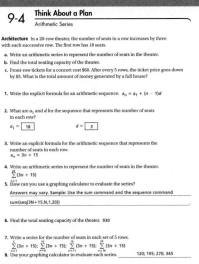

Practice and Problem Solving Wkbk/All-in-One Resources/Online
Standardized Test Prep

9-4 Standardized Test Prep — Arithmetic Series

Multiple Choice

For Exercises 1–6, choose the correct letter.

1. What is the sum of the odd integers 1 to 99? **B**
   (A) 2450 (B) 2500 (C) 2550 (D) 4950

2. Which of the following is an infinite series? **H**
   (F) 3, 8, 13, 18, 23 (H) 3 + 8 + 13 + 18 + 23 + ...
   (G) 3 + 8 + 13 + 18 + 23 (I) 3, 8, 13, 18, 23, ...

3. The high school choir is participating in a fundraising sales contest. The choir will receive a bonus if they make 20 sales in their first week and improve their sales by 3 in every subsequent week. What is the minimum number of sales the choir could make in the first 12 weeks to qualify for the bonus? **C**
   (A) 13 (B) 53 (C) 438 (D) 5015

4. What is summation notation for the series 5 + 7 + 9 + ... + 105? **F**
   (F) $\sum_{n=1}^{51}(2n+3)$ (G) $\sum_{n=1}^{50}(n+3)$ (H) $\sum_{n=1}^{51}(2n+3)$ (I) $\sum_{n=7}^{51}(n+3)$

5. What is the upper limit of the summation $\sum_{n=1}^{100}(n-2)$? **D**
   (A) 1 (B) 2 (C) 98 (D) 100

6. What is the sum of the series $\sum_{n=1}^{30}(2n+2)$? **H**
   (F) 62 (G) 66 (H) 990 (I) 1980

Short Response

7. What is the sum of the finite arithmetic series 2 + 4 + 6 + ... + 50? Show your work.
[2] 650; $S_n = \frac{n}{2}(a_1 + a_n)$; $S_{25} = \frac{25}{2}(2 + 50) = (12.5)(52) = 650$
[1] incorrect sum OR correct sum, without work shown
[0] incorrect answer and no work shown OR no answer given

Online Teacher Resource Center
Activities, Games, and Puzzles

9-4 Activity: Summing a Sequence — Arithmetic Series

The nth term of an arithmetic sequence is given by the formula
$$a_n = a_1 + (n-1) \cdot d.$$
The sum of the first n terms of an arithmetic series is given by the formula
$$S_n = \left(\frac{n}{2}\right) \cdot (a_1 + a_n).$$

Cut out six markers of any shape. These represent terms of a series. Choose an initial value a_1 for the series and write this on a marker. Then choose a value for d, the difference between successive terms in the sequence. On another marker, write the value of $a_1 + d$. Write the next four terms of the sequence on the remaining markers and lay out all six markers in order.

Now rearrange the markers into pairs so that the first and last terms, the second and fifth terms, and the third and fourth terms are together.

1. What is the sum of each pair? Check students' work.

2. Why does each pair have the same sum?
   (*Hint:* $a_2 = a_1 + d$ and $a_5 = a_6 - d$. What is $a_2 + a_5$?) $a_2 + a_5 = (a_1 + d) + (a_6 - d) = a_1 + a_6$

The sum of the first six terms of a series is the number of pairs multiplied by the sum of each pair.

3. Number of pairs: **3**
4. Sum of each pair: Check students' work.
5. S_6: Check students' work.

What happens if you want to compute the sum of an odd number of terms? Cut out another marker and write the seventh term of your sequence on it.

6. Rearrange your markers into pairs so that the first and last terms are together, the second and sixth terms are together, and so on. There is one extra term that does not fit into a pair. Which term is it? a_4
7. Now what is the sum of each pair? Check students' work.
8. There are still three pairs, but if the sum of each pair is multiplied by the number of pairs, you do not get the right sum. What must you add to this result to get the right answer? a_4
9. The extra term can be thought of as half of a pair. What is two times the extra term? Check students' work.
10. Add $\left(\frac{1}{2}\right) \cdot$ (sum of each pair) to the sum of the first three pairs.
    What is the result? S_7

Guided Instruction

PURPOSE To use geometry to model and write an infinite geometric series

PROCESS Students will
- apply their knowledge of series and sequences to geometric terms.
- use area of a geometric figure to write and evaluate an infinite geometric series.

DISCUSS This Concept Byte introduces geometric series. Remind students that a geometric sequence consists of terms multiplied by a constant. Elicit the following:
- A series is the sum of terms in the sequence. Therefore, a geometric series is the sum of terms in a geometric sequence.
- It may be possible to find the sum of an infinite geometric series if each subsequent term decreases.

Activity 1

> **Q** How does the first increase compare to the ninth? **[When the second term is added, the sum increases greatly, from $\frac{1}{2}$ to $\frac{3}{4}$. The tenth term is very small, so the ninth increase is small.]**

Activity 2

> **Q** What part is shaded in each figure? What is the sum of the shaded area for the three figures? **[$\frac{1}{4}$, $\frac{1}{16}$, $\frac{1}{64}$; for a sum of $\frac{21}{64}$]**

 Mathematical Practices This Concept Byte supports students in looking for and making use of structure, Mathematical Practice 7.

Concept Byte
For Use With Lesson 9-5

Geometry and Infinite Series

© **Content Standard**
A.SSE.4 Derive the formula for the sum of a geometric series (when the common ratio is not 1), and use the formula to solve problems.

You can use geometric figures to model some infinite series.

Activity 1

Geometry Draw a geometric figure to model the series.

$$\frac{1}{2} + \left(\frac{1}{2}\right)^2 + \left(\frac{1}{2}\right)^3 + \cdots + \left(\frac{1}{2}\right)^n + \cdots$$

Draw a square. Shade one half of the square. Then shade one half of the remaining unshaded region. Continue until the square is full.

So the series appears to have a sum of 1.

You can write an infinite series from a geometric model.

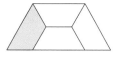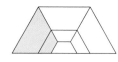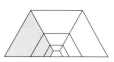

Activity 2

Geometry Write the series modeled by the trapezoids. Estimate the sum of the series. Explain your reasoning.

$$\frac{1}{4} \qquad + \qquad \left(\frac{1}{4}\right)^2 \qquad + \qquad \left(\frac{1}{4}\right)^3 + \cdots$$

The shaded region approaches one third of the figure.

So the series $\frac{1}{4} + \left(\frac{1}{4}\right)^2 + \left(\frac{1}{4}\right)^3 + \cdots + \left(\frac{1}{4}\right)^n + \cdots$ appears to have a sum of $\frac{1}{3}$.

Exercises

1. **a.** Write the series modeled by the figure at the right.
   b. Evaluate the series. Explain your reasoning.

2. Draw a figure to model the series.
$$\frac{1}{5} + \left(\frac{1}{5}\right)^2 + \left(\frac{1}{5}\right)^3 + \cdots + \left(\frac{1}{5}\right)^n + \cdots$$

© 3. **Make a Conjecture** Consider the series.
$$\frac{1}{c} + \left(\frac{1}{c}\right)^2 + \left(\frac{1}{c}\right)^3 + \cdots + \left(\frac{1}{c}\right)^n + \cdots, c > 1$$
What is the sum of the series? Explain your reasoning.

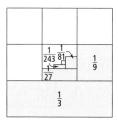

Answers

Concept Byte

1. a. $\frac{1}{3} + \left(\frac{1}{3}\right)^2 + \left(\frac{1}{3}\right)^3 + \cdots + \left(\frac{1}{3}\right)^n + \cdots$

b. $\frac{1}{2}$; The shaded area approximates one half of the figure.

2. Answers may vary. Sample:

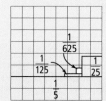

3. Answers may vary. Sample: Where $c > 1$, the sum of the series is $\frac{1}{c-1}$; the examples and the other exercises suggest that pattern.

9-5 Geometric Series

© Content Standard
A.SSE.4 Derive the formula for the sum of a geometric series (when the common ratio is not 1), and use the formula to solve problems.

Objective To define geometric series and find their sums

> The symbol ∞ means there is no upper limit on the values of n. They go on forever.

SOLVE IT!

Getting Ready! ◀▶ ✕ ↻ 🏠

What number

0, 1, 2, 3, 4, 5, 6, 7, 8, or 9

goes into the box to make the sum 1? What sums do the other nine numbers give? Explain your reasoning.

$$\sum_{n=1}^{\infty} \boxed{?}(0.1)^n$$

MATHEMATICAL PRACTICES You can write any whole number that has the same digit in every place as the sum of the terms of a geometric sequence. For example,

Lesson Vocabulary
- geometric series
- converge
- diverge

$$4444 = 4(10)^0 + 4(10)^1 + 4(10)^2 + 4(10)^3$$

You can write any rational number as an infinite repeating decimal. For example, $\frac{47}{90} = 0.5222\ldots$

Therefore, you can write any rational number as a number plus the sum of an infinite geometric sequence.

$$0.5222\ldots = 0.5 + 2(0.1)^2 + 2(0.1)^3 + 2(0.1)^4 + \ldots$$

Essential Understanding Just as with finite arithmetic series, you can find the sum of a finite geometric series using a formula. You need to know the first term, the number of terms, and the common ratio.

A **geometric series** is the sum of the terms of a geometric sequence.

> **take note**
>
> ### Key Concept Sum of a Finite Geometric Series
>
> The sum S_n of a finite geometric series $a_1 + a_1 r + a_1 r^2 + \cdots + a_1 r^{n-1}, r \neq 1$, is
>
> $$S_n = \frac{a_1(1 - r^n)}{1 - r}$$
>
> where a_1 is the first term, r is the common ratio, and n is the number of terms.

PowerAlgebra.com | Lesson 9-5 Geometric Series | 595

---

1 Interactive Learning

Solve It!
PURPOSE To use summation notation to find the sum of an infinite series
PROCESS Students may
- use a calculator to substitute a large value for the upper limit of the series.
- substitute each index value into the explicit formula to determine a pattern.

FACILITATE

Q What is ∞? **[the infinity symbol]**

Q Instead of 9, try 3 in the box. What pattern is in the sequence of the first four terms? What is their sum? **[0.3, 0.03, 0.003, 0.0003; 0.3333.]**

Q How do you write this pattern as a repeated decimal? **[$0.\overline{3}$]**

Q What fraction represents $0.\overline{3}$? **[$\frac{1}{3}$]**

ANSWER See Solve It in Answers on next page.
CONNECT THE MATH Students use their knowledge of series and geometric sequences to find the sum of the series in the Solve It. In this lesson, students will find the sum of finite and infinite geometric series when possible.

2 Guided Instruction

Take Note

Q For the sum S_n, why is the last term of the series $a_1 r^{n-1}$ and not $a_1 r^n$? **[The first term is a_1 and can also be written as $a_1 r^0$. Because the 0th term is counted as the first term, the last term must be to the power $n - 1$.]**

9-5 Preparing to Teach

BIG idea Modeling

ESSENTIAL UNDERSTANDINGS
- Just as with finite arithmetic series, the sum of a finite geometric series can be found using a formula. It is necessary to know the first term, the number of terms, and the common ratio.
- A geometric sequence can be modeled explicitly or recursively. The sum of its first n terms is $\frac{a_1(1 - r^n)}{1 - r}$.

Math Background
As with an arithmetic series, a geometric series is infinite. The sum of a finite number of terms can be found given the first term, the number of terms, and the common ratio. It is also possible to find the sum of an infinite geometric series when the series converges, when $|r| < 1$.

The sum of an infinite series is the number that the sequence of partial sums approaches. Find the sum of the first term, then the first two terms, then the first three terms, etc. The number approached by these partial sums as the number of terms increases is the sum of the infinite series. The sum of a finite series of real numbers is always a real number. The sum of an infinite series may be a real number; the series must converge.

A convergent series approaches a number similar to the way a graph approaches a horizontal asymptote. An arithmetic series always diverges because it is linear.

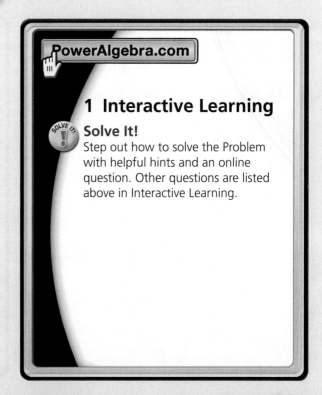

PowerAlgebra.com

1 Interactive Learning

SOLVE IT!

Solve It!
Step out how to solve the Problem with helpful hints and an online question. Other questions are listed above in Interactive Learning.

Problem 1

> **Q** How can you find the number of terms in the geometric series for 1A using a calculator? **[Enter 3, then Ans*2, and count the number of times you hit enter before getting the last term.]**
>
> **Q** Will the terms of the geometric series in 1B increase or decrease? Explain. **[Decrease; the common ratio is $\frac{1}{2}$. This is less than 1, so the terms in the sequence will decrease.]**
>
> **Q** Is it possible to write the series in 1B with a lower limit of 1? Explain. **[Yes; the power in the explicit formula must be reduced by 1 to get the correct first term. The series is $\sum_{n=1}^{21} 4\left(\frac{1}{2}\right)^{n-1}$.]**

ERROR PREVENTION

Because of rounding, there is little difference between $\left(\frac{1}{2}\right)^{20}$ and $\left(\frac{1}{2}\right)^{21}$ when using the formula to find the sum of the series in 1B. Have students state the first term, common ratio, number of terms, and the sum of the series to be sure their methods are correct.

Got It?

> **Q** How is finding the common ratio for 1a different than for 1b? **[In 1a, the common ratio is found by dividing the second term by the first term. In 1b, the common ratio is the value in the explicit formula that is raised to the index power.]**

What is the sum of the finite geometric series?

Plan

What do you need to find the sum?
You need the first term, the common ratio, and the number of terms in the series.

Ⓐ $3 + 6 + 12 + 24 + \cdots + 3072$

The first term is 3. The common ratio is $\frac{6}{3} = \frac{12}{6} = \frac{24}{12} = 2$. The nth term is 3072.

$$a_n = a_1 r^{n-1} \qquad \text{Use the explicit formula.}$$
$$3072 = 3 \cdot 2^{n-1} \qquad \text{Substitute 3 for } a_1\text{, 2 for } r\text{, and 3072 for } a_n.$$
$$1024 = 2^{n-1} \qquad \text{Divide each side by 3.}$$

1024 is 2^{10}, so $n - 1 = 10$ and $n = 11$.

$$S_n = \frac{a_1(1 - r^n)}{1 - r} \qquad \text{Use the sum formula.}$$
$$S_{11} = \frac{3(1 - 2^{11})}{1 - 2} \qquad \text{Substitute 3 for } a_1\text{, 2 for } r\text{, and 11 for } n.$$
$$= 6141 \qquad \text{Simplify.}$$

The sum of the series is 6141.

Think

When the lower limit on n is not 1, how can you find the number of terms?
The number of terms always equals upper limit − lower limit + 1.

Ⓑ $\sum_{n=0}^{20} 4\left(\frac{1}{2}\right)^n$

The first term is $a_1 = 4\left(\frac{1}{2}\right)^0 = 4$. The common ratio is $r = \frac{1}{2}$. The lower limit is 0 and the upper limit is 20, so the number of terms is $n = 21$.

$$S_n = \frac{a_1(1 - r^n)}{1 - r} \qquad \text{Use the sum formula.}$$
$$S_{21} = \frac{4\left(1 - \left(\frac{1}{2}\right)^{21}\right)}{1 - \frac{1}{2}} \qquad \text{Substitute 4 for } a_1\text{, }\frac{1}{2}\text{ for } r\text{, and 21 for } n.$$
$$\approx 8 \qquad \text{Use a calculator.}$$

The sum of the series is approximately 8.

Got It? 1. What is the sum of the finite geometric series?

a. $-15 + 30 - 60 + 120 - 240 + 480$ **b.** $\sum_{n=1}^{10} 5 \cdot (-2)^{n-1}$

The Soldier's Reasonable Request A famous story involves a soldier who rescues his king in battle. The king grants him any prize "within reason" from the riches of the kingdom. The soldier asks for a chessboard with a single kernel of wheat on the first square, two kernels of wheat on the second square, then four, then eight, and so on for all 64 squares of the chessboard. The king decides that the request is reasonable.

See Problem 2 for the outcome.

Answers

Solve It!
9

$0.\overline{8}, 0.\overline{7}, 0.\overline{6}, 0.\overline{5}, 0.\overline{4}, 0.\overline{3}, 0.\overline{2}, 0.\overline{1}, 0$

Got It?
1. **a.** 315
   b. −1705
2. about $2138.43

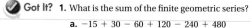

2 Guided Instruction

 Each Problem is worked out and supported online.

Problem 1
Finding the Sums of Finite Geometric Series
Animated

Alternative Problem 1
Finding the Sums of Finite Geometric Series
Animated

Problem 2
Using the Geometric Series Formula

Problem 3
Analyzing Infinite Geometric Series
Animated

Alternative Problem 3
Analyzing Infinite Geometric Series

Support in Algebra 2 Companion
• Vocabulary
• Key Concepts
• Got It?

Problem 2 Using the Geometric Series Formula

According to the story on the preceding page, how many total kernels of wheat did the soldier request?

Know	Need	Plan
The amount of wheat in the first 4 squares	The total amount of wheat	Use the sum formula to find the total amount of wheat.

Step 1 Identify the first term, common ratio, and the number of terms.

$$a_1 = 1, r = 2, n = 64$$

Step 2 Use the sum formula.

$$S_n = \frac{a_1(1 - r^n)}{1 - r}$$ Write the sum formula.

$$S_{64} = \frac{1(1 - 2^{64})}{1 - 2}$$ Substitute for a_1, r, and n.

$$= 2^{64} - 1 \approx 1.845 \times 10^{19}$$ Simplify.

There will be approximately 1.845×10^{19} kernels of wheat.

Got It? **2.** To save money for a vacation, you set aside $100. For each month thereafter, you plan to set aside 10% more than the previous month. How much money will you save in 12 months?

The Rest of the Story A bushel of wheat contains about a million kernels. The total US output of wheat in a recent year was just over 2.1 billion bushels. How many years of production at that level would it take the United States to produce enough wheat to satisfy the soldier's "reasonable" request?

The terms of a geometric series grow rapidly when the common ratio is greater than 1. Likewise, they diminish rapidly when the common ratio is between 0 and 1. In fact, they diminish so rapidly that an *infinite geometric series* has a finite sum.

 Key Concept Infinite Geometric Series

An infinite geometric series with first term a_1 and common ratio $|r| < 1$ has a finite sum

$$S = \frac{a_1}{1 - r}.$$

An infinite geometric series with $|r| \geq 1$ does not have a finite sum.

Problem 2   EXTENSION

Q How can this series be written using summation notation? [$\sum_{n=0}^{63} 2^n$ or $\sum_{n=1}^{64} 2^{n-1}$]

Q How many grains are on the last square? Explain. [**Because the first term is $2^0 = 1$, the last term is $2^{63} \approx 9.22 \times 10^{18}$.**]

Got It?   ERROR PREVENTION

Students sometimes think that because the increase is 10%, the value of r is 0.1. Point out that an r value of 0.1 would result in a decreasing sequence of terms or a lesser amount being put aside each month. Remind students to be sure their values make sense.

Take Note

Q As the value of r gets close to 1, what happens to the value of the denominator? The value of the sum? [**As r gets close to 1, the value of the denominator decreases; the value of the sum increases.**]

SYNTHESIZING

It is sometimes difficult for students to understand how an infinite series can have a sum. Point out that you are finding partial sums and then finding the number approached by an increasing number of partial sums. Refer to Concept Byte 9-5a for models.

Additional Problems

1. What is the sum of the geometric series?

  a. $4 + 12 + 36 + 108 + 324 + 972 + 2916$

  b. $\sum_{n=0}^{11} 3(-1.5)^n$

ANSWERS

  a. 4372

  b. about -154.50

2. A game show is offering a prize of 1¢ on the first day, 3¢ on the second day, 9¢ on the third day, etc. What is the total amount of money earned from this prize in two weeks?

ANSWER $23,914.84

3. Does the infinite series *converge* or *diverge*? If it converges, what is the sum?

  a. $-5 - \frac{5}{2} - \frac{5}{4} - \frac{5}{8} - \frac{5}{16} - \cdots$

  b. $\frac{1}{4} - \frac{3}{8} + \frac{9}{16} - \frac{27}{32} + \cdots$

  c. $\sum_{n=0}^{\infty} (0.8)^n$

ANSWERS

  a. converges; -10

  b. diverges

  c. converges; 5

Problem 3

Q How can you check that the sum of 2 is a reasonable answer for 3A? Explain. **[As the number of terms increases, the partial sums converge to 2. For example, $S_2 = 1.5$; $S_3 = 1.75$; $S_4 = 1.875$; $S_{10} \approx 1.9980$.]**

Got It?

Q Will the convergence or divergence of 3b change if all the terms are positive? Explain. **[No; the absolute value of r determines convergence or divergence, so changing the sign has no effect.]**

3 Lesson Check

Do you know HOW? ERROR INTERVENTION

• If students have difficulty solving Exercises 1 and 2, remind them that they must find the common ratio by dividing the second term by the first.

Do you UNDERSTAND?

• If students have trouble answering Exercise 5, review the definitions of convergence and divergence. A series will converge only if r is between -1 and 1. The ratio must be checked before applying the formula for infinite series.

Close

Q What is the difference between finding the sum of a finite and infinite geometric series? **[A finite series is found by adding each term. An infinite series is found by adding the partial sums and then finding the number approached by the sequence of partial sums.]**

To say that an infinite series $a_1 + a_2 + a_3 + \ldots$, has a sum means that the *sequence of partial sums* $S_1 = a_1, S_2 = a_1 + a_2, S_3 = a_1 + a_2 + a_3, \ldots,$ $S_n = a_1 + a_2 + \cdots + a_n, \ldots$ **converges** to a number S as n gets very large.

When an infinite series does not converge to a sum, the series **diverges**. An infinite geometric series with $|r| \geq 1$ diverges.

 **Problem 3** Analyzing Infinite Geometric Series

Does the series *converge* or *diverge*? If it converges, what is the sum?

A $1 + \frac{1}{2} + \frac{1}{4} + \ldots$

Think
When does an infinite geometric series converge?
An infinite geometric series converges when the absolute value of the common ratio is less than 1.

$r = \frac{1}{2} \div 1 = \frac{1}{2}$

Since $|r| = \left|\frac{1}{2}\right| < 1$, the series converges.

$S = \frac{a_1}{1 - r} = \frac{1}{1 - \frac{1}{2}} = \frac{1}{\frac{1}{2}} = 2$

B $\sum_{n=0}^{\infty} \left(\frac{2}{3}\right)\left(-\frac{5}{4}\right)^n$

Since $|r| = \left|-\frac{5}{4}\right| = \frac{5}{4} > 1$, the series diverges.

Got It? 3. Does the infinite series *converge* or *diverge*? If it converges, what is the sum?

a. $\frac{1}{2} + \frac{3}{4} + \frac{9}{8} + \ldots$　　**b.** $\frac{1}{3} - \frac{1}{9} + \frac{1}{27} - \frac{1}{81} + \ldots$　　**c.** $\sum_{n=1}^{\infty} \left(\frac{2}{3}\right)^n$

d. Reasoning Will an infinite geometric series either converge or diverge? Explain.

Lesson Check

Do you know HOW?

Evaluate each finite geometric series.

1. $\frac{1}{5} + \frac{1}{10} + \frac{1}{20} + \frac{1}{40} + \frac{1}{80}$

2. $9 - 6 + 4 - \frac{8}{3} + \frac{16}{9}$

Determine whether each infinite geometric series *diverges* or *converges*.

3. $1 - \frac{1}{6} + \frac{1}{36} - \frac{1}{216} + \ldots$

4. $\frac{1}{64} + \frac{1}{32} + \frac{1}{16} + \ldots$

Do you UNDERSTAND? MATHEMATICAL PRACTICES

5. Error Analysis A classmate uses the formula for the sum of an infinite geometric series to evaluate $1 + 1.1 + 1.21 + 1.331 + \ldots$ and gets -10. What error did your classmate make?

6. Writing Explain how you can determine whether an infinite geometric series has a sum.

7. Compare and Contrast How are the formulas for the sum of a finite arithmetic series and the sum of a finite geometric series similar? How are they different?

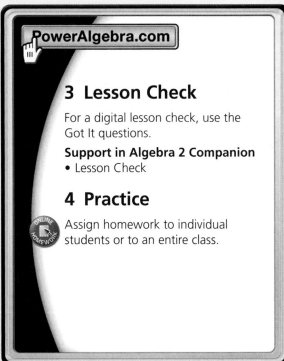

3 Lesson Check

For a digital lesson check, use the Got It questions.

Support in Algebra 2 Companion
• Lesson Check

4 Practice

ONLINE HOMEWORK

Assign homework to individual students or to an entire class.

Answers

Got It? (continued)

3. a. diverges

b. converges; $\frac{1}{4}$

c. converges; 2

d. Yes; if $|r| < 1$, the series converges. If $|r| \geq 1$, the series diverges.

Lesson Check

1. $\frac{31}{80}$

2. $\frac{55}{9}$

3. converges

4. diverges

5. Since $r = 1.1 > 1$, the series diverges and does not have a sum.

6. An infinite geometric series has a sum only when $|r| < 1$.

7. The sum of a finite arithmetic series is $S_n = \frac{n}{2}(a_1 + a_n)$. The sum of finite geometric series is $S_n = \frac{a_1(1 - r^n)}{1 - r}$. The formulas are similar in that each sum requires the first term and the number of terms in the series. The formulas are different in that the sum of a finite arithmetic series needs the last term, while the sum of a finite geometric series needs the common ratio.

Practice and Problem-Solving Exercises

 MATHEMATICAL PRACTICES

Evaluate the sum of the finite geometric series.

See Problem 1.

8. $1 + 2 + 4 + 8 + \cdots + 128$

9. $4 + 12 + 36 + 108 + \cdots + 972$

10. $3 + 6 + 12 + 24 + 48 + \cdots + 768$

11. $-5 - 10 - 20 - 40 - \cdots - 2560$

12. $\sum_{n=1}^{5} 3^n$

13. $\sum_{n=1}^{4} \left(\frac{1}{2}\right)^{n+1}$

14. $\sum_{n=1}^{4} \left(\frac{2}{3}\right)^{n-1}$

15. $\sum_{n=1}^{5} \left(\frac{1}{3}\right)^{n-1}$

16. Financial Planning In March, a family starts saving for a vacation they are planning for the end of August. The family expects the vacation to cost $1375. They start with $125. Each month they plan to deposit 20% more than the previous month. Will they have enough money for their trip? If not, how much more do they need?

See Problem 2.

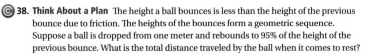

Determine whether each infinite geometric series *diverges* or *converges*. If the series converges, state the sum.

See Problem 3.

17. $1 + \frac{1}{4} + \frac{1}{16} + \ldots$

18. $1 - \frac{1}{2} + \frac{1}{4} - \ldots$

19. $4 + 2 + 1 + \ldots$

20. $1 + 2 + 4 + \ldots$

21. $6 + 18 + 54 + \ldots$

22. $-54 - 18 - 6 - \ldots$

23. $1 - 1 + 1 - \ldots$

24. $1 + \frac{1}{5} + \frac{1}{25} + \ldots$

25. $\frac{1}{4} + \frac{1}{2} + 1 + 2 + \ldots$

Evaluate each infinite geometric series.

26. $1.1 + 0.11 + 0.011 + \ldots$

27. $1.1 - 0.11 + 0.011 - \ldots$

28. $1 - \frac{1}{5} + \frac{1}{25} - \frac{1}{125} + \ldots$

29. $3 + 1 + \frac{1}{3} + \frac{1}{9} + \ldots$

30. $3 + 2 + \frac{4}{3} + \frac{8}{9} + \ldots$

31. $3 - 2 + \frac{4}{3} - \frac{8}{9} + \ldots$

B Apply

Determine whether each series is *arithmetic* or *geometric*. Then evaluate the finite series for the specified number of terms.

32. $2 + 4 + 8 + 16 + \ldots ; n = 10$

33. $2 + 4 + 6 + 8 + \ldots ; n = 20$

34. $-5 + 25 - 125 + 625 - \ldots ; n = 9$

35. $6.4 + 8 + 10 + 12.5 + \ldots ; n = 7$

36. $1 + 2 + 3 + 4 + \ldots ; n = 1000$

37. $81 + 27 + 9 + 3 + \ldots ; n = 200$

38. Think About a Plan The height a ball bounces is less than the height of the previous bounce due to friction. The heights of the bounces form a geometric sequence. Suppose a ball is dropped from one meter and rebounds to 95% of the height of the previous bounce. What is the total distance traveled by the ball when it comes to rest?
- Does the problem give you enough information to solve the problem?
- How can you write the general term of the sequence?
- What formula should you use to calculate the total distance?

ASSIGNMENT GUIDE

Basic: 8–31 all, 32, 33, 38–41, 47, 48

Average: 9–31 odd, 32–51

Advanced: 9–31 odd, 32–53

Standardized Test Prep: 54–58

Mixed Review: 59–69

Mathematical Practices are supported by exercises with red headings. Here are the Practices supported in this lesson:

MP 1: Make Sense of Problems Ex. 38
MP 2: Reason Quantitatively Ex. 46, 47
MP 3: Communicate Ex. 6, 48
MP 3: Compare Arguments Ex. 7
MP 3: Critique the Reasoning of Others Ex. 5, 49a
MP 5: Use Appropriate Tools Ex. 40

Applications exercises have blue headings. Exercises 16, 39, and 50 support MP 4: Model.

STEM exercises focus on science or engineering applications.

EXERCISE 39: Use the Think About a Plan worksheet in the **Practice and Problems Solving Workbook** (also available in the Teaching Resources in print and online) to further support students' development in becoming independent learners.

HOMEWORK QUICK CHECK

To check students' understanding of key skills and concepts, go over Exercises 9, 17, 38, 39, and 48.

Practice and Problem-Solving Exercises

8. 255

9. 1456

10. 1533

11. −5115

12. 363

13. $\frac{15}{32}$

14. $\frac{65}{27}$

15. $\frac{121}{81}$

16. no; $133.76

17. converges; $\frac{4}{3}$

18. converges; $\frac{2}{3}$

19. converges; 8

20. diverges

21. diverges

22. converges; −81

23. diverges

24. converges; $\frac{5}{4}$

25. diverges

26. $1.\overline{2}$

27. 1

28. $\frac{5}{6}$

29. $\frac{9}{2}$

30. 9

31. $\frac{9}{5}$

32. geometric; 2046

33. arithmetic; 420

34. geometric; −1,627,605

35. geometric; about 96.47

36. arithmetic; 500,500

37. geometric; about 121.5

38. 39 m

Answers

Practice and Problem-Solving Exercises
(continued)

39. a.

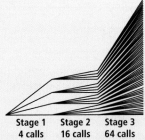

Stage 1	Stage 2	Stage 3
4 calls	16 calls	64 calls

b. $4 + 16 + 64 + 256 + 1024 + 4096$

c. 5460 employees

40. a. 20, 18, 16.2, 14.58

b. about 198.59

c. $S = \dfrac{20}{1 - 0.9} = 200$

d. Check students' work.

41. $\dfrac{5}{4}$

42. 4

43. $\dfrac{3}{4}$

44. no sum

45. $0.8\overline{3}$

46. Check students' work.

47. a. $\dfrac{7}{8}$

b. 10

48. choice (b); (a) yields $26,000; using the formula for finding the sum of a finite geometric series, (b) yields $1,342,177.26.

49. a. Answers may vary. Sample: The student used $r - 1$ instead of $1 - r$ in the formula for the sum of an infinite geometric series.

b. $\dfrac{1}{2}$

50. a. 70th swing

b. 10,000 cm

51. a. $rS_n = r(a_1 + a_1r + \cdots + a_1r^{n-1})$
$= a_1r + a_1r^2 + \cdots + a_1r^n$

b. $S_n - rS_n = a_1 + a_1r + a_1r^2 + \cdots +$
$+ a_1r^{n-1} - a_1r - a_1r^2$
$- \cdots - a_1r^{n-1} - a_1r^n$
$= a_1 - a_1r^n$

c. $S_n - rS_n = a_1 - a_1r^n$
$S_n(1 - r) = a_1 - a_1r^n$
$S_n = \dfrac{a_1 - a_1r^n}{1 - r} = \dfrac{a_1(1 - r^n)}{1 - r}$

---

39. Communications Many companies use a telephone chain to notify employees of a closing due to bad weather. Suppose a company's CEO (Chief Executive Officer) calls four people. Then each of these people calls four others, and so on.
  a. Make a diagram to show the first three stages in the telephone chain. How many calls are made at each stage?
  b. Write the series that represents the total number of calls made through the first six stages.
  c. How many employees have been notified after stage six?

40. Graphing Calculator The graph models the sum of the first n terms in the geometric series with $a_1 = 20$ and $r = 0.9$.
  a. Write the first four sums of the series.
  b. Use the graph to evaluate the series to the 47th term.
  c. Write and evaluate the formula for the sum of the series.
  d. Graph the formula using the window values shown. Use the graph to verify your answer to part (b).

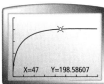

X=47   Y=198.58607

Xmin=0   Ymin=0
Xmax=94   Ymax=250
Xscl=10   Yscl=50

Evaluate each infinite series that has a sum.

41. $\displaystyle\sum_{n=1}^{\infty}\left(\frac{1}{5}\right)^{n-1}$
42. $\displaystyle\sum_{n=1}^{\infty}3\left(\frac{1}{4}\right)^{n-1}$
43. $\displaystyle\sum_{n=1}^{\infty}\left(-\frac{1}{3}\right)^{n-1}$
44. $\displaystyle\sum_{n=1}^{\infty}7(2)^{n-1}$
45. $\displaystyle\sum_{n=1}^{\infty}(-0.2)^{n-1}$

46. Open-Ended Write an infinite geometric series that converges to 3. Use the formula to evaluate the series.

47. Reasoning Find the specified value for each infinite geometric series.
  a. $a_1 = 12$, $S = 96$; find r **b.** $S = 12$, $r = \frac{1}{6}$; find a_1

48. Writing Suppose you are to receive an allowance each week for the next 26 weeks. Would you rather receive (a) $1000 per week or (b) $.02 the first week, $.04 the second week, $.08 the third week, and so on for the 26 weeks? Justify your answer.

49. The sum of an infinite geometric series is twice its first term.
  a. Error Analysis A student says the common ratio of the series is $\frac{3}{2}$. What is the student's error?
  b. Find the common ratio of the series.

STEM **50. Physics** Because of friction and air resistance, each swing of a pendulum is a little shorter than the previous one. The lengths of the swings form a geometric sequence. Suppose the first swing of a pendulum has a length of 100 cm and the return swing is 99 cm.
  a. On which swing will the arc first have a length less than 50 cm?
  b. What is the total distance traveled by the pendulum when it comes to rest?

51. Where did the formula for summing finite geometric series come from? Suppose the geometric series has first term a_1 and constant ratio r, so that $S_n = a_1 + a_1r + a_1r^2 + \cdots + a_1r^{n-1}$.
  a. Show that $rS_n = a_1r + a_1r^2 + a_1r^3 + \cdots + a_1r^n$.
  b. Use part (a) to show that $S_n - rS_n = a_1 - a_1r^n$.
  c. Use part (b) to show that $S_n = \dfrac{a_1 - a_1r^n}{1 - r} = \dfrac{a_1(1 - r^n)}{1 - r}$.

Challenge

52. The function $S(n) = \frac{10(1 - 0.8^n)}{0.2}$ represents the sum of the first n terms of an infinite geometric series.
  a. What is the domain of the function?
  b. Find $S(n)$ for $n = 1, 2, 3, \ldots, 10$. Sketch the graph of the function.
  c. Find the sum S of the infinite geometric series.

53. Use the formula for the sum of an infinite geometric series to show that $0.\overline{9} = 1$.
(*Hint*: $0.\overline{9} = \frac{9}{10} + \frac{9}{100} + \frac{9}{1000} = \ldots$)

68.

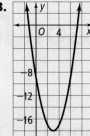

Standardized Test Prep

GRIDDED RESPONSE

SAT/ACT

54. What is the value of $\sum_{n=1}^{5} (2n - 3)$?

55. Evaluate the infinite geometric series $\frac{2}{5} + \frac{4}{25} + \frac{8}{125} + \ldots$. Enter your answer as a fraction.

56. Use $\log_5 2 \approx 0.43$ and $\log_5 7 \approx 1.21$ and the properties of logarithms to approximate $\log_5 \sqrt{14}$ without using a calculator.

57. Use a calculator to solve the equation $7^{2x} = 75$. Round the answer to the nearest hundredth.

58. Use the Change of Base Formula and a calculator to solve $\log_9 x = \log_6 15$. Round the answer to the nearest tenth.

69.

Mixed Review

Evaluate each series to the given term.

See Lesson 9-4.

59. $12.5 + 15 + 17.5 + 20 + 22.5 + \ldots$; 7th term

60. $-100 - 95 - 90 - 85 - \ldots$; 11th term

Add or subtract. Simplify where possible.

See Lesson 8-5.

61. $\frac{7}{2c} - \frac{2}{c^2}$
            62. $\frac{5}{y+3} + \frac{15}{y-3}$
            63. $\frac{4}{x^2-36} + \frac{x}{x-6}$

Use the properties of logarithms to evaluate each expression.

See Lesson 7-4.

64. $\log_2 \frac{1}{8} + \log_2 8$
         65. $\log_{15} 25 + \log_{15} 9$
       66. $3 \log_9 3 - \frac{1}{4} \log_9 81$

Get Ready! To prepare for Lesson 10-1, do Exercises 67–69.

Graph each function.

See Lesson 4-2.

67. $y = x^2 - 4$
            68. $y = x^2 - 6x - 9$
          69. $y = -4x^2 + 1$

52. a. all integers ≥ 1 and $\leq n$
    b. 10; 18; 24.4; 29.52; 33.62; 36.89; 39.51; 41.61; 43.29; 44.63

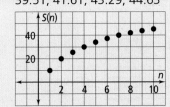

    c. 50

53. $a_1 = \frac{9}{10}, r = \frac{1}{10}; S = \frac{\frac{9}{10}}{1 - \frac{1}{10}} = 1$

Standardized Test Prep

54. 15

55. $\frac{2}{3}$

56. 0.82

57. 1.11

58. 27.7

Mixed Review

59. 140

60. -825

61. $\frac{7c - 4}{2c^2}$

62. $\frac{10(2y + 3)}{(y + 3)(y - 3)}$

63. $\frac{x^2 + 6x + 4}{(x + 6)(x - 6)}$

64. 0

65. 2

66. 1

67.

Differentiated Remediation

Additional Instructional Support

Algebra 2 Companion

Students can use the **Algebra 2 Companion** worktext (4 pages) as you teach the lesson. Use the Companion to support

- New Vocabulary
- Key Concepts
- Got It for each Problem
- Lesson Check

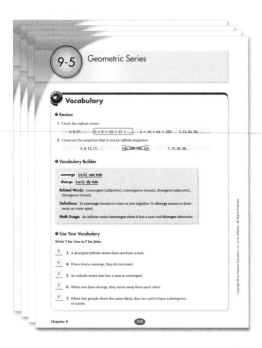

ELL Support

Focus on Graphic Organizer Write the words *finite*, *infinite*, *converge*, and *diverge* with definitions on the board. Then draw rectangles around the words *finite* and *infinite* and ovals around the words *converge* and *diverge*. Next have students copy the graphic organizer below.

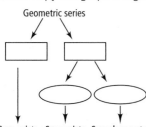

Geometric series

Sum exists   Sum exists   Sum does not exist

Have students fill in the organizer with the vocabulary words and state the information shown. For example, a student may say "I can look at a finite or infinite geometric series. A finite series has a sum. If an infinite series converges, it has a sum. If an infinite series diverges, the sum cannot be found."

5 Assess & Remediate

Lesson Quiz

1. What is the sum of the geometric series $\sum_{n=0}^{18} 3\left(\frac{3}{4}\right)^n$?

2. **Do you UNDERSTAND?** You saved $500 this year. Each year you plan to save 5% more than the previous year. How much do you expect to save after 8 more years?

3. Does the series *converge* or *diverge*? If it converges, what is the sum?
$2 + \frac{1}{2} + \frac{1}{8} + \frac{1}{32} + \cdots$

ANSWERS TO LESSON QUIZ

1. about 11.95
2. $5513.28;
3. converge; $\frac{8}{3}$

PRESCRIPTION FOR REMEDIATION
Use the student work on the Lesson Quiz to prescribe a differentiated review assignment:

Points	Differentiated Remediation
0–1	Intervention
2	On-level
3	Extension

PowerAlgebra.com

5 Assess & Remediate

Assign the Lesson Quiz. Appropriate intervention, practice, or enrichment is automatically generated based on student performance.

Intervention

- **Reteaching** (2 pages) Provides reteaching and practice exercises for the key lesson concepts. Use with struggling students or absent students.

- **English Language Learner Support** Helps students develop and reinforce mathematical vocabulary and key concepts.

All-in-One Resources/Online
Reteaching

9-5 Reteaching
Geometric Series

- The **sum of a finite geometric series** is $S_n = \frac{a_1(1 - r^n)}{1 - r}$, where a_1 is the first term, r is the common ratio, and n is the number of terms.
- The **sum of an infinite geometric series** with $|r| < 1$ is $S = \frac{a_1}{1 - r}$, where a_1 is the first term and r is the common ratio. If $|r| \geq 1$, then the series has no sum.

Problem
What is the sum of the first ten terms of the geometric series
$8 + 16 + 32 + 64 + 128 + \ldots$?

$a_1 = 8$ — a_1 is the first term in the series.

$r = \frac{16}{8} = \frac{32}{16} = \frac{64}{32} = \frac{128}{64} = 2$ — Simplify the ratio formed by any two consecutive terms to find r.

$n = 10$ — n is the number of terms in the series to be added together.

$S_{10} = \frac{8(1 - 2^{10})}{1 - 2}$ — Substitute $a_1 = 8$, $r = 2$, and $n = 10$ into the formula for the sum of a finite geometric series.

$= \frac{8(-1023)}{-1}$ — Simplify inside the parentheses.

$= 8184$ — Simplify.

Exercises
Evaluate the finite series for the specified number of terms.

1. $3 + 12 + 48 + 192 + \ldots$; $n = 6$ 4095
2. $8 + 2 + \frac{1}{2} + \frac{1}{8} + \ldots$; $n = 5$ $\frac{341}{32}$
3. $-10 - 5 - 2.5 - 1.25 - \ldots$; $n = 7$ $-\frac{635}{32}$
4. $10 + (-5) + \frac{5}{2} + \left(-\frac{5}{4}\right) + \ldots$; $n = 11$ $\frac{3415}{512}$

Evaluate each infinite geometric series.

5. $10 + 5 + 2.5 + \ldots$ 20
6. $-1 + \frac{2}{11} - \frac{4}{121} + \ldots$ $-\frac{11}{13}$
7. $\frac{1}{4} + \frac{7}{32} + \frac{49}{256} + \ldots$ 2
8. $\frac{1}{2} - \frac{1}{5} + \frac{64}{25} - \ldots$ $\frac{5}{14}$
9. $-\frac{1}{6} + \frac{1}{12} - \frac{1}{24} + \ldots$ $-\frac{1}{9}$
10. $20 + 16 + \frac{64}{5} + \ldots$ 100
11. $12 + 4 + \frac{4}{3} + \ldots$ 18
12. $\frac{1}{4} - \frac{1}{8} + \frac{1}{16} - \ldots$ $\frac{1}{6}$
13. $\frac{2}{3} + \frac{2}{15} + \frac{2}{75} + \ldots$ $\frac{5}{6}$

All-in-One Resources/Online
English Language Learner Support

9-5 Additional Vocabulary Support
Geometric Series

Problem
What is the sum of the geometric series $2 + 6 + 18 + 54 + \cdots + 1458$?

$\frac{6}{2} = \frac{18}{6} = \frac{54}{18} = 3$ — Identify the common ratio and the nth term.

nth term = 1458

$a_n = a_1 r^{n-1}$ — Use the explicit formula.

$1458 = 2 \cdot 3^{n-1}$ — Substitute 2 for a_1, 3 for r, and 1458 for a_n.

$729 = 3^{n-1}$ — Divide each side by 2.

729 is 3^6, so $n - 1 = 6$ and $n = 7$ — Use a calculator.

$S_n = \frac{a_1(1 - r^n)}{1 - r}$ — Use the sum formula.

$S_7 = \frac{2(1 - 3^7)}{1 - 3}$ — Substitute 2 for a_1, 3 for r, and 7 for n.

$S_7 = 2186$

Exercise
What is the sum of the geometric series $1 + 4 + 16 + 64 + \cdots + 1024$?

$\frac{4}{1} = \frac{16}{4} = \frac{64}{16} = 4$ — Identify the common ratio and the nth term.

nth term = 1024

$a_n = a_1 r^{n-1}$ — Use the explicit formula.

$1024 = 1 \cdot 4^{n-1}$ — Substitute 1 for a_1, 4 for r, and 1024 for a_n.

$1024 = 4^{n-1}$ — Divide each side by 1.

1024 is 4^5, so $n - 1 = 5$ and $n = 6$ — Use a calculator.

$S_n = \frac{a_1(1 - r^n)}{1 - r}$ — Use the sum formula.

$S_6 = \frac{1(1 - 4^6)}{1 - 4}$ — Substitute 1 for a_1, 4 for r, and 6 for n.

$S_6 = 1365$

Differentiated Remediation *continued*

On-Level

- **Practice** (2 pages) Provides extra practice for each lesson. For simpler practice exercises, use the Form K Practice pages found in the All-in-One Teaching Resources and online.

- **Think About a Plan** Helps students develop specific problem-solving skills and strategies by providing scaffolded guiding questions.

- **Standardized Test Prep** Focuses on all major exercises, all major question types, and helps students prepare for the high-stakes assessments.

Extension

- **Enrichment** Provides students with interesting problems and activities that extend the concepts of the lesson.

- **Activities, Games, and Puzzles** Worksheets that can be used for concepts development, enrichment, and for fun!

Practice and Problem Solving Wkbk/All-in-One Resources/Online
Practice page 1

9-5 Practice — Form G
Geometric Series

Evaluate each finite series for the specified number of terms.

1. $40 + 20 + 10 + \ldots; n = 10$ 79.921875
2. $4 + 12 + 36 + \ldots; n = 15$ 28,697,812
3. $15 + 12 + 9.6 + \ldots; n = 40$ about 74.99
4. $27 + 9 + 3 + \ldots; n = 100$ about 40.5
5. $0.2 + 0.02 + 0.002 + \ldots; n = 8$ 0.22222222
6. $100 + 200 + 400 + \ldots; n = 6$ 6300

7. This month, your friend deposits $400 to save for a vacation. She plans to deposit 10% more each successive month for the next 11 months. How much will she have saved after the 12 deposits? $8553.71

Determine whether each infinite geometric series *diverges* or *converges*. State whether each series has a sum.

8. $3 + \frac{3}{2} + \frac{3}{4} + \ldots$ converges; yes
9. $4 + 2 + 1 + \ldots$ converges; yes
10. $17 + 15.3 + 13.77 + \ldots$ converges; yes
11. $6 + 11.4 + 21.66 + \ldots$ diverges; no
12. $-20 - 8 - 3.2 - \ldots$ converges; yes
13. $50 + 70 + 98 + \ldots$ diverges; no

Evaluate each infinite geometric series.

14. $8 + 4 + 2 + 1 + \ldots$ 16
15. $1 + \frac{1}{3} + \frac{1}{9} + \frac{1}{27} + \ldots$ 1.5
16. $120 + 96 + 76.8 + 61.44 + \ldots$ 600
17. $1000 + 750 + 562.5 + 421.875 + \ldots$ 4000

18. Suppose your business made a profit of $5500 the first year. If the profit increased 20% per year, find the total profit over the first 5 yr. $40,928.80

19. The end of a pendulum travels 50 cm on its first swing. Each swing after the first, it travels 99% as far as the preceding swing. How far will the pendulum travel before it stops? 5000 cm

20. A seashell has chambers that are each 0.82 times the length of the enclosing chamber. The outer chamber is 32 mm around. Find the total length of the shell's spiraled chambers. about 177.78 mm

21. The first year a toy manufacturer introduces a new toy, its sales total $495,000. The company expects its sales to drop 10% each succeeding year. Find the total expected sales in the first 6 years. Find the total expected sales if the company offers the toy for sale for as long as anyone buys it. $2,319,367.05; $4,950,000

Practice and Problem Solving Wkbk/All-in-One Resources/Online
Practice page 2

9-5 Practice (continued) — Form G
Geometric Series

Determine whether each series is *arithmetic* or *geometric*. Then evaluate the series for the specified number of terms.

22. $2 + 5 + 8 + 11 + \ldots; n = 9$ arithmetic; 126
23. $\frac{1}{8} + \frac{1}{16} + \frac{1}{32} + \frac{1}{64} + \ldots; n = 8$ geometric; $\frac{255}{1024}$
24. $-3 + 6 - 12 + 24 - \ldots; n = 10$ geometric; 1023
25. $-2 + 2 + 6 + 10 + \ldots; n = 12$ arithmetic; 240
26. $4 + 8 + 16 + 32 + \ldots; n = 15$ geometric; 131,068
27. $5 + 10 + 15 + 20 + \ldots; n = 20$ arithmetic; 1050

Evaluate each infinite series that has a sum.

28. $\sum_{n=1}^{\infty} 5\left(\frac{2}{3}\right)^{n-1}$ 15
29. $\sum_{n=1}^{\infty} (-2.1)^{n-1}$ no sum
30. $\sum_{n=1}^{\infty} \left(-\frac{1}{2}\right)^{n-1}$ $\frac{2}{3}$
31. $\sum_{n=1}^{\infty} 2\left(\frac{5}{3}\right)^{n-1}$ no sum

32. **Open Ended** Write an infinite geometric series that converges to 2. Show your work. Check students' work.

Find the specified value for each infinite geometric series.

33. $a_1 = 5, S = \frac{25}{3}$, find r $\frac{2}{5}$
34. $S = 108, r = \frac{1}{3}$, find a_1 72
35. $a_1 = 3, S = 12$, find r 0.75
36. $S = 840, r = 0.5$, find a_1 420

37. **Error Analysis** Your friend says that an infinite geometric series cannot have a sum because it is infinite. You say that it is possible for an infinite geometric series to have a sum. Who is correct? Explain.
You are correct; an infinite geometric series with $|r|$ less than 1 has a series of partial sums that converges towards a number.

38. **Writing** Describe in general terms how you would find the sum of a finite geometric series. Identify the first term, common ratio, and nth term. Use the explicit formula to find n. Then, use the sum formula with the first term, common ratio, and n to find the sum of the series.

All-in-One Resources/Online
Enrichment

9-5 Enrichment
Geometric Series

An infinite geometric series converges if the absolute value of the common ratio is less than 1 ($|r| < 1$). A *power series* is an infinite series where each term depends on a variable x. Each value of x will give you a specific infinite series, which may converge or diverge.

1. Evaluate the expression $\frac{1}{1-x}$ for $x = 2$ and for $x = \frac{1}{2}$. -1; 2

2. You can evaluate many expressions with a power series called a Taylor series. To evaluate $\frac{1}{1-x}$, you use the Taylor series $1 + x + x^2 + x^3 + \ldots$. What is this infinite series written in summation notation? $\sum_{n=0}^{\infty} x^n$

3. Determine the sum of the first five terms of the Taylor series $1 + x + x^2 + x^3 + \ldots$ for $x = 2$ and for $x = \frac{1}{2}$. 31; 1.9375

4. For which value of x is your computation above a better approximation for the value of the expression $\frac{1}{1-x}$? What might need to be true about the value of x in order for this Taylor series to converge to the value of this expression? $\frac{1}{2}; |x| < 1$

5. You can use a different Taylor series to evaluate e^x. Write the Taylor series $1 + \frac{x}{1!} + \frac{x^2}{2!} + \frac{x^3}{3!} + \ldots$ in summation notation. $\sum_{n=0}^{\infty} \frac{x^n}{n!}$

6. Evaluate e^x for $x = \frac{1}{2}$. Evaluate the first four terms of the Taylor series $1 + \frac{x}{1!} + \frac{x^2}{2!} + \frac{x^3}{3!} + \ldots$ for $x = \frac{1}{2}$. Round your answers to the nearest thousandth. 1.649; 1.646

7. Does the Taylor series for e^x still converge if $|x| \geq 1$? Does it give you the same value as the function $y = e^x$? Explain your reasoning.
Answers may vary. Sample: Yes; yes; for any value of x, the terms eventually decrease rapidly to 0. If you add up enough terms, you will get a good approximation.

Practice and Problem Solving Wkbk/All-in-One Resources/Online
Think About a Plan

9-5 Think About a Plan
Geometric Series

Communications Many companies use a telephone chain to notify employees of a closing due to bad weather. Suppose a company's CEO calls three people. Then each of these people call three others, and so on.
a. Make a diagram to show the first three stages in the telephone chain. How many calls are made at each stage?
b. Write the series that represents the total number of calls made through the first six stages.
c. How many employees have been notified after stage six?

1. What type of diagram can you make to represent the telephone chain? tree diagram

2. Make a diagram to show the first three stages in the telephone chain.

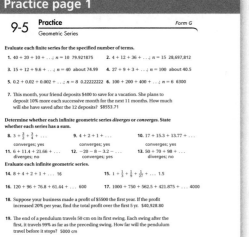

3. What expression represents the number of calls made at stage n? 3^n

4. Write the series that represents the total number of calls made through the first six stages. $3 + 9 + 27 + 81 + 243 + 729$

5. What is the sum of this series? 1092

6. Write the sum formula. $S_n = \frac{a_1(1 - r^n)}{1 - r}$

7. Use the sum formula to find how many employees have been notified after stage six. $S_n = \frac{a_1(1 - r^n)}{1 - r} = \frac{3(1 - 3^6)}{1 - 3} = 1092$

8. Does your answer agree with your sum from Exercise 5? yes

Practice and Problem Solving Wkbk/All-in-One Resources/Online
Standardized Test Prep

9-5 Standardized Test Prep
Geometric Series

Gridded Response

Solve each exercise and enter your answer in the grid provided.

1. What is the value of a_1 in the series $\sum_{n=0}^{40} 3\left(\frac{1}{2}\right)^n$?

2. What is the sum of the geometric series $2 + 6 + 18 + \cdots + 486$?

3. A community organizes a phone tree in order to alert each family of emergencies. In the first stage, one person calls five families. In the second stage, each of the five families calls another five families, and so on. How many stages need to be reached before 600 families or more are called?

4. What is the approximate whole number sum for the finite geometric series $\sum_{n=0}^{8} 8\left(\frac{1}{4}\right)^n$?

5. What is the sum of the geometric series $1 + \frac{1}{3} + \frac{1}{9} + \ldots$? Enter your answer as a fraction.

Answers

Online Teacher Resource Center
Activities, Games, and Puzzles

9-5 Puzzle: Sum Find!
Geometric Series

Calculate the sum S_n of each geometric series. In the space provided, write the sum. Then find and circle the spelled-out answer in the word search below.

1. $S_8 = \frac{-1}{17}(1 - 2 + 4 - \cdots - 128)$ 5
2. $S_6 = \frac{1}{217}(-1 + 5 - 25 + \cdots + 3125)$ 12
3. $S_9 = \frac{-1}{205}(1 - 3 + 9 - \cdots - 2187)$ 8
4. $S_8 = \frac{1}{164}(1 + 3 + 9 + \cdots + 2187)$ 20
5. $S_4 = \frac{-1}{185}(1 - 6 + 36 - 216)$ 1
6. $S_{12} = \frac{1}{273}(1 + 2 + 4 + \cdots + 2048)$ 15
7. $S_4 = \frac{1}{30}(-1 - 7 - 49 - 343)$ 10
8. $S_8 = \frac{1}{85}(1 + 2 + 4 + \cdots + 128)$ 3
9. $S_6 = \frac{1}{651}(1 + 5 + 25 + \cdots + 3125)$ 6
10. $S_4 = \frac{1}{52}(-1 - 5 - 25 + 125)$ 2

Performance Task

Pull It All Together
Understanding by Design principles indicate the importance of performance tasks that assess understanding.
- Make sense of problems and persevere in solving them.
- Look for and make use of structure.

The following questions are designed to
- Help support students as they do the Performance Tasks.
- Help you gauge their progress toward becoming mathematically proficient.

Ⓒ Performance Task 1
Derive algebraic formulas from other formulas and expressions.
- If you know the first term and the common difference of an arithmetic sequence, what formula would you use to find the nth term of the sequence?
- If you group all of the a_1 terms, how many are there? If you factor d from the remaining terms, how would you write the sum of what was left?

Ⓒ Performance Task 2
Express a rational number as a sum of an infinite geometric sequence and use the formula for the sum of an infinite geometric series in a proof.
- How can you write $0.999\ldots$ as a sum of a geometric sequence?

Ⓒ Performance Task 3
Identify what quantities specific formula variables represent.
- Does a subscript correspond to any mathematical operation?

To solve these problems, you will pull together concepts and skills related to sequences and series.

BIG idea Variable
You can represent quantities using variables and algebraic expressions.

Ⓒ Performance Task 1
The sum S_n of a finite arithmetic series of n terms is $S_n = \frac{n}{2}(a_1 + a_n)$ where a_1 is the first term and a_n is the nth term.

a. Show that $S_n = na_1 + \frac{n(n-1)}{2}d$ by replacing a_n with its value in terms of a_1, n, and d in the above formula.

b. Explain why $S_n = na_1 + \frac{n(n-1)}{2}d$ makes sense by explaining how you can extract each of na_1 and $\frac{n(n-1)}{2}d$ from the sum $a_1 + (a_1 + d) + (a_1 + 2d) + \cdots + (a_1 + (n-1)d)$.

BIG idea Equivalence
You can often prove equivalence in a variety of ways.

Ⓒ Performance Task 2
You can find many different proofs to prove that $0.999\ldots = 1$. How can you use the formula for the sum of a geometric series to show that $0.999\ldots = 1$?

BIG idea Modeling
You can represent many real-world mathematical problems algebraically. These representations can lead to algebraic solutions.

Ⓒ Performance Task 3
Each of these sequence or series formulas involves four quantities that are represented by a variable. For each formula, describe the four quantities.

a. $a_n = a_1 + (n-1)d$ **b.** $S_n = \frac{n}{2}(a_1 + a_n)$

c. $a_n = a_1 r^{n-1}$ **d.** $S_n = \frac{a_1(1-r^n)}{1-r}$

Assess Performance

Pull It All Together
See p. 49 for a holistic scoring rubric to gauge a student's progress on Understanding the Problem, Planning a Solution, Getting an Answer, and assessing autonomy.

Performance Task 1
a. First step: Substitute $a_1 + (n-1)d$ for a_n in $S_n = \frac{n}{2}(a_1 + a_n)$.

$\left(S_n = \frac{n}{2}[a_1 + (a_1 + (n-1)d]\right)$

Second step: Simplify $S_n = \frac{n}{2}[a_1 + (a_1 + (n-1)d]$.

$\left[S_n = \frac{n}{2}[a_1 + a_1 + (n-1)d]\right.$

$= \frac{n}{2}(2a_1 + (n-1)d$

$\left. = na_1 + \frac{n(n-1)}{2}d\right]$

b. Possible plan: Evaluate $S_n = na_1 + \frac{n(n-1)}{2}$ for $n = 1$, $n = 2$ and $n = 3$. Look for a pattern that will help you to extract na_1 and $\frac{n(n-1)}{2}$ from each term of the sum.

[When $n = 1$, $S_n = a_1 + \frac{1(0)}{2}d$
$= a_1$
When $n = 2$, $S_n = 2a_1 + \frac{2(1)}{2}d =$
$2a_1 + d = a_1 + (a_1 + d)$.
When $n = 3$, $S_n = 3a_1 +$
$3d = a_1 + (a_1 + d) + (a_1 + 2d)$.
And so on.]

Performance Task 2
First, write $0.999\ldots$ as a sum of an infinite geometric sequence.

$0.999\ldots = 9\left(\frac{1}{10}\right) + 9\left(\frac{1}{10}\right)^2$
$+ 9\left(\frac{1}{10}\right)^3 + \cdots$

In this series, $a_1 = \frac{9}{10}$ and $r = \frac{1}{10}$. Substitute these values into the formula for the sum of an infinite geometric series, $S = \frac{a_1}{1-r}$.

$S = \frac{\frac{9}{10}}{1 - \frac{1}{10}} = \frac{\frac{9}{10}}{\frac{9}{10}} = 1$

So, $0.999\ldots = 1$.

Performance Task 3
a. This formula is used to find nth term of an arithmetic sequence. a_n is the nth term, a_1 is the first term, d is the common difference, and n is the number of the term you are looking for. To find a_n, you need to know a_1, d and n.

b. This formula is used to find the sum of a finite arithmetic series. S_n is the sum, n is the number of terms, a_1 is the first term and a_n is the last term. You need to know a_1, a_n, and n to find S_n.

9 Chapter Review

Connecting BIG ideas and Answering the Essential Questions

1 Variable
You can define a sequence
- by describing its nth term with a formula using n.
- by stating its first term and a formula that relates the $n - 1$ and nth terms.

2 Equivalence
$a_n = a + (n - 1)d$ and $a_1 = a$, $a_n = a_{n-1} + d$ for $n > 1$ define the same arithmetic sequence, $a, a + d, a + 2d, \ldots$

3 Modeling
You can model a geometric sequence explicitly or recursively. The sum of its first n terms is $\frac{a_1(1 - r^n)}{1 - r}$.

Mathematical Patterns and Arithmetic Sequences (Lessons 9-1 and 9-2)
$a_n = 2 - \frac{3}{4}(n - 1)$ and $a_1 = 2$, so
$a_n = a_{n-1} - \frac{3}{4}$ represents the arithmetic sequence $2, \frac{5}{4}, \frac{2}{4}, -\frac{1}{4}, -1, \ldots$.

Mathematical Patterns and Geometric Sequences (Lessons 9-1 and 9-3)
$a_n = 2\left(-\frac{1}{2}\right)^{n-1}$ and $a_1 = 2$, so
$a_n = \left(-\frac{1}{2}\right)a_{n-1}$ represents the geometric sequence $2, -1, \frac{1}{2}, -\frac{1}{4}, \frac{1}{8}, \ldots$.

Arithmetic Series (Lesson 9-4)
The sum $S_n = a_1 + a_2 + \cdots + a_n$ of an arithmetic series is $S_n = \frac{n}{2}(a_1 + a_n)$. The sum
$S_6 = 2 + \frac{5}{4} + \frac{2}{4} - \frac{1}{4} - 1 - \frac{7}{4}$
$= 3\left(2 - \frac{7}{4}\right) = \frac{3}{4}$.

Geometric Series (Lesson 9-5)
$S_n = \frac{a_1(1 - r^n)}{1 - r}$ is the sum of the first n terms of a geometric series. If the series is infinite with $|r| < 1$, the sum is $S = \frac{a_1}{1 - r}$.
For the geometric series,
$a_1 = 2$, $a_n = \left(-\frac{1}{2}\right)a_{n-1}$,
$S_6 = \frac{2\left(1 - \left(-\frac{1}{2}\right)^6\right)}{1 - \left(-\frac{1}{2}\right)}$, or $\frac{21}{16}$, and
$S = \frac{2}{1 - \left(-\frac{1}{2}\right)} = \frac{4}{3}$.

Chapter Vocabulary

- arithmetic mean (p. 574)
- arithmetic sequence (p. 572)
- arithmetic series (p. 587)
- common difference (p. 572)
- common ratio (p. 580)
- converge (p. 598)
- diverge (p. 598)
- explicit formula (p. 565)
- finite series (p. 587)
- geometric mean (p. 583)
- geometric sequence (p. 580)
- geometric series (p. 595)
- infinite series (p. 587)
- limits (p. 589)
- recursive formula (p. 565)
- sequence (p. 564)
- series (p. 587)
- term of a sequence (p. 564)

Choose the vocabulary term that correctly completes each sentence.

1. When you use Σ to write a series, you can use _?_ to indicate how many terms you are adding.

2. An ordered list of terms is a _?_.

3. If an infinite geometric series _?_, then it must have a sum.

4. There is a constant _?_ between consecutive terms in a geometric sequence.

5. A formula that expresses the nth term of a sequence in terms of n is a(n) _?_.

Essential Questions

BIG idea Variable
ESSENTIAL QUESTIONS How can you represent the terms of a sequence explicitly? How can you represent them recursively?
ANSWER You can define a sequence
- by describing its nth term with a formula using n.
- by stating its first term and a formula that relates the $n - 1$ and nth terms.

BIG idea Equivalence
ESSENTIAL QUESTION What are equivalent explicit and recursive definitions for an arithmetic sequence?
ANSWER $a_n = a + (n - 1)d$ and $a_1 = a$, $a_n = a_{n-1} + d$ for $n > 1$ define the same arithmetic sequence, $a, a + d, a + 2d, \ldots$

BIG idea Modeling
ESSENTIAL QUESTIONS How can you model a geometric sequence? How can you model its sum?
ANSWER You can model a geometric sequence explicitly or recursively. The sum of its first n terms is $\frac{a_1(1 - r^n)}{1 - r}$.

Pull It All Together (continued)

c. This formula is used to find the nth term of a geometric sequence. a_n is the nth term, a_1 is the first term, r is the common ratio, and n is the number of the term you are looking for. To find a_n, you need to know a_1, r and n.

d. This formula is used to find the sum of a finite geometric series. S_n is the sum, n is the number of terms, a_1 is the first term and r is the common ratio. You need to know a_1, r and n to find S_n.

Answers

Chapter Review

1. limits
2. sequence
3. converges
4. common ratio
5. explicit formula

Summative Questions

Use the following prompts as you review this chapter with your students. The prompts are designed to help you assess your students' understanding of the Big Ideas they have studied.

- Compare and contrast explicit formula and recursive definition. If you knew the first term, which would you use to find the 100th term?
- How can you find the common difference of a sequence? common ratio?
- When is it possible to find the sum of an arithmetic or geometric series?
- What does it mean for an infinite series to diverge? converge? Could an infinite arithmetic series ever converge?

Answers

Chapter Review (continued)

6. $1, -1, -3, -5, -7$

7. $1, 0, -3, -8, -15$

8. $2, 3, 5, 9, 17$

9. $20, 10, 5, 2.5, 1.25$

10. $a_n = a_{n-1} + 17, a_1 = 5$

11. $a_n = a_{n-1} + 9, a_1 = -2$

12. $a_n = 3n - 2$

13. $a_n = 6.5 - 2.5n$

14. no

15. yes; $d = 15, a_{32} = 468$

16. yes; $d = 3, a_{32} = 100$

17. no

18. 5

19. 101.5

20. 5

21. -4.9

22. $-10.5, -8, -5.5$

23. $1.4, 0.8, 0.2$

24. $a_n = -2 + 9(n - 1)$

25. $a_n = 62 - 3(n - 1)$

9-1 Mathematical Patterns

Quick Review

A **sequence** is an ordered list of numbers called **terms**.

A **recursive definition** gives the first term and defines the other terms by relating each term after the first term to the one before it.

An **explicit formula** expresses the nth term in a sequence in terms of n, where n is a positive integer.

Example

A sequence has an explicit formula $a_n = n^2$. What are the first three terms of this sequence?

$a_1 = (1)^2 = 1$ Substitute 1 for n and evaluate.

$a_2 = (2)^2 = 4$ Substitute 2 for n and evaluate.

$a_3 = (3)^2 = 9$ Substitute 3 for n and evaluate.

The first three terms are 1, 4, and 9.

Exercises

Find the first five terms of each sequence.

6. $a_n = -2n + 3$

7. $a_n = -n^2 + 2n$

8. $a_n = 2a_{n-1} - 1$, where $a_1 = 2$

9. $a_n = \frac{1}{2} a_{n-1}$, where $a_1 = 20$

Write a recursive definition for each sequence.

10. $5, 22, 39, 56, \ldots$ **11.** $-2, 7, 16, 25, \ldots$

Write an explicit formula for each sequence.

12. $1, 4, 7, 10, \ldots$ **13.** $4, 1.5, -1, -3.5, \ldots$

9-2 Arithmetic Sequences

Quick Review

In an **arithmetic sequence**, the difference between consecutive terms is constant. This difference is the **common difference**.

For an arithmetic sequence, a is the first term, a_n is the nth term, n is the number of the term, and d is the common difference.

An explicit formula is $a_n = a + (n - 1)d$.

A recursive formula is $a_n = a_{n-1} + d$, with $a_1 = a$.

The **arithmetic mean** of two numbers x and y is the average of the two numbers $\frac{x + y}{2}$.

Example

What is the missing term of the arithmetic sequence $11, \blacksquare, 27, \ldots$?

arithmetic mean $= \frac{11 + 27}{2} = \frac{38}{2} = 19$

The missing term is 19.

Exercises

Determine whether each sequence is arithmetic. If so, identify the common difference and find the 32nd term of the sequence.

14. $2, 4, 7, 10, \ldots$ **15.** $3, 18, 33, 48, \ldots$

16. $7, 10, 13, 16, \ldots$ **17.** $2, 5, 9, 14, \ldots$

Find the missing term(s) of each arithmetic sequence.

18. $1, \blacksquare, 9, \ldots$ **19.** $104, \blacksquare, 99, \ldots$

20. $-1, \blacksquare, 11, \ldots$ **21.** $-4.6, \blacksquare, -5.2, \ldots$

22. $-13, \blacksquare, \blacksquare, \blacksquare, -3, \ldots$ **23.** $2, \blacksquare, \blacksquare, \blacksquare, -0.4, \ldots$

Write an explicit formula for each arithmetic sequence.

24. $-2, 7, 16, 25, \ldots$ **25.** $62, 59, 56, 53, \ldots$

9-3 Geometric Sequences

Quick Review

In a **geometric sequence**, the ratio of consecutive terms is constant. This ratio is the **common ratio**.

For a geometric sequence, a is the first term, a_n is the nth term, n is the number of the term, and r is the common ratio.

An explicit formula is $a_n = a \cdot r^{n-1}$.

A recursive formula is $a_n = a_{n-1} \cdot r$, with $a_1 = a$.

The geometric mean of two positive numbers x and y is $\sqrt{xy}$.

Example

What is the sixth term of the geometric sequence that begins $2, 6, 18, \ldots$?

$a_1 = 2$ and $r = 6 \div 2 = 3$

$a_6 = 2 \cdot 3^{6-1} = 486$ Substitute 6 for n, 2 for a_1, and 3 for r.

The sixth term is 486.

Exercises

Determine whether each sequence is geometric. If so, identify the common ratio and find the next two terms.

26. $1, \frac{1}{2}, \frac{1}{4}, \frac{1}{8}, \ldots$

27. $1, 3, 5, 7, \ldots$

28. $3, 3.6, 4.32, 5.184, \ldots$

Find the missing term(s) of each geometric sequence.

29. $3, \blacksquare, 12, \ldots$

30. $0.004, \blacksquare, 0.4, \ldots$

31. $-20, \blacksquare, \blacksquare, \blacksquare, -1.25, \ldots$

Write an explicit formula for each geometric sequence.

32. $1, 2, 4, 8, \ldots$

33. $25, 5, 1, \frac{1}{5}, \ldots$

Use an explicit formula to find the 10th term of each geometric sequence.

34. $5, 10, 20, 40, \ldots$ **35.** $-3, 6, -12, 24, \ldots$

9-4 Arithmetic Series

Quick Review

A **series** is the expression for the sum of the terms of a sequence.

An **arithmetic series** is the sum of the terms of an arithmetic sequence. The sum S_n of the first n terms of an arithmetic series is $S_n = \frac{n}{2}(a_1 + a_n)$. You can use a summation symbol, Σ, and lower and upper **limits** to write a series. The lower limit is the least value of n and the upper limit is the greatest value of n.

Example

What is the sum of the arithmetic series?

$2 + 5 + 8 + 11 + 14 + 17 + 20$

$a_1 = 2, a_7 = 20,$ and $n = 7$.

$S_7 = \frac{7}{2}(2 + 20)$ Substitute 7 for n, 2 for a_1, and 20 for a_7.

$= 77$ Evaluate.

Exercises

Use summation notation to write each arithmetic series for the specified number of terms. Then evaluate the sum.

36. $10 + 7 + 4 + \ldots; n = 5$

37. $50 + 55 + 60 + \ldots; n = 7$

38. $6 + 7.4 + 8.8 + \ldots; n = 11$

39. $21 + 19 + 17 + \ldots; n = 8$

Find the number of terms in each series, the first term, and the last term. Then evaluate the sum.

40. $\displaystyle\sum_{n=1}^{3}(17n - 25)$ **41.** $\displaystyle\sum_{n=2}^{10}\left(\frac{1}{2}n + 3\right)$

26. yes; $r = \frac{1}{2}$; $\frac{1}{16}, \frac{1}{32}$

27. no

28. yes; $r = 1.2$; $6.2208, 7.46496$

29. ± 6

30. ± 0.04

31. $\pm 10, -5, \pm 2.5$

32. $a_n = 2^{n-1}$

33. $a_n = 25\left(\frac{1}{5}\right)^{n-1}$

34. 2560

35. 1536

36. $\displaystyle\sum_{n=1}^{5}(13 - 3n); 20$

37. $\displaystyle\sum_{n=1}^{7}(45 + 5n); 455$

38. $\displaystyle\sum_{n=1}^{11}(4.6 + 1.4n); 143$

39. $\displaystyle\sum_{n=1}^{8}(23 - 2n); 112$

40. $3; -8, 26; 27$

41. $9; 4, 8; 54$

Answers

Chapter Review (continued)

42. 31

43. $53\frac{1}{8}$

44. $14\frac{7}{18}$

45. converges; $S = 187.5$

46. diverges

47. diverges

48. converges; $S = 2$

9-5 Geometric Series

Quick Review

A **geometric series** is the sum of the terms of a geometric sequence. The sum S_n of the first n terms of a geometric series is $S_n = \frac{a_1(1 - r^n)}{1 - r}, r \neq 1$.

When an infinite series has a finite sum, the series **converges**. When the series does not converge, the series **diverges**.

In a geometric series, when $|r| < 1$, the series converges to $S = \frac{a_1}{1 - r}$. When $|r| \geq 1$, the series diverges.

Example

What is the sum of the geometric series?

$5 + 10 + 20 + 40 + 80 + 160$

$n = 6, a_1 = 5,$ and $r = 10 \div 5 = 2$.

$S_6 = \frac{5(1 - 2^6)}{1 - 2}$ Substitute 6 for n, 5 for a_1, and 2 for r.

$\quad = 315$ Evaluate.

The sum is 315.

Exercises

Evaluate each finite series for the specified number of terms.

42. $1 + 2 + 4 + \ldots; n = 5$

43. $80 - 40 + 20 - \ldots; n = 8$

44. $12 + 2 + \frac{1}{3} + \ldots; n = 4$

Determine whether each infinite geometric series *converges* or *diverges*. If the series converges, state the sum.

45. $150 + 30 + 6 + \ldots$

46. $2.2 + 2.42 + 2.662 + \ldots$

47. $-10 - 20 - 40 - \ldots$

48. $\frac{2}{3} + \frac{4}{9} + \frac{8}{27} + \ldots$

MathXL® for School
Go to PowerAlgebra.com

Do you know HOW?

Write a recursive definition and an explicit formula for each sequence. Then find a_{12}.

1. 7, 13, 19, 25, 31, ...

2. 10, 20, 40, 80, 160, ...

Determine whether each sequence is *arithmetic, geometric,* or *neither*. Then find the tenth term.

3. 23, 27, 31, 35, 39, ...

4. −12, −5, 2, 9, 16, ...

5. −5, 15, −45, 135, −405, ...

6. $\frac{1}{4}$, 1, 4, 16, ...

Find the missing term of each arithmetic sequence.

7. 4, ■, 12, ...

8. −11, ■, 23, ...

Determine whether each sequence is *arithmetic* or *geometric*. Then identify the common difference or common ratio.

9. 1620, 540, 180, 60, 20, ...

10. 78, 75, 72, 69, 66, 63, 60, ...

11. $\frac{3}{32}$, $\frac{3}{16}$, $\frac{3}{8}$, $\frac{3}{4}$, $\frac{3}{2}$, 3, 6, ...

a_1 is the first term of a sequence, r is a common ratio, and d is a common difference. Write the first five terms.

12. $a_1 = 2, r = -2$ **13.** $a_1 = 3, d = 7$

14. $a_1 = -100, r = \frac{1}{5}$ **15.** $a_1 = 19, d = -4$

Find the missing term of each geometric sequence.

16. 2, ■, 0.5, ...

17. 2, ■, 8, ...

Find the sum of each infinite geometric series.

18. 0.5 + 0.05 + 0.005 + ...

19. $1 - \frac{1}{2} + \frac{1}{4} - ...$

20. $6 + 5 + \frac{25}{6} + ...$

Determine whether each series is *arithmetic* or *geometric*. Then evaluate the finite series for the specified term number.

21. 2 + 7 + 12 + ...; n = 8

22. 5000 + 1000 + 200 + ...; n = 5

23. 1 + 0.01 − 0.98 − ...; n = 5

24. 2 + 6 + 18 + ...; n = 6

Find the sum of each series.

25. $\sum_{n=1}^{5}(3n + 1)$ **26.** $\sum_{n=1}^{8}\frac{2n}{3}$

27. $\sum_{n=4}^{10}(0.8n - 0.4)$ **28.** $\sum_{n=2}^{6}(-2)^{n-1}$

Do you UNDERSTAND?

29. You have saved $50. Each month you add $10 more to your savings.
   a. Write an explicit formula to model the amount you have saved after n months.
   b. How much have you saved after six months?

30. Open-Ended Write an arithmetic sequence. Then write an explicit formula for it.

31. Reasoning How can you tell if a geometric series converges or diverges? Include examples of both types of series. Evaluate the series that converges.

32. A diamond is purchased for $2500. Suppose its value increases 5% each year.
   a. What is the value of diamond after 8 years?
   b. Writing Explain how you can write an explicit formula for a geometric sequence to answer the question.

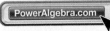 PowerAlgebra.com | **Chapter 9** Chapter Test | 607

29. a. $S = 50 + 10n$ where S represents savings.
   b. $110
30. Answers may vary. Sample answer:
   3, 5, 7, 9, ...; $a_n = 1 + 2n$
31. If the absolute value of the common ratio is less than 1, then it will converge; check students' work.
32. a. $3693.64
   b. $A_n = 2500(1.05)^n$;
   $A_8 = 2500(1.05)^8 \approx 3693.64$

Answers

Chapter Test

1. $a_n = a_{n-1} + 6, a_1 = 7$;
   $a_n = 1 + 6n$; 73
2. $a_n = a_{n-1} \cdot 2, a_1 = 10$;
   $a_n = 10 \cdot 2^{n-1}$; 20,480
3. arithmetic; 59
4. arithmetic; 51
5. geometric; 98,415
6. geometric; 65,536
7. 8
8. 6
9. geometric; $r = \frac{1}{3}$
10. arithmetic; $d = -3$
11. geometric; $r = 2$
12. 2, −4, 8, −16, 32
13. 3, 10, 17, 24, 31

14. $-100, -20, -4, -\frac{4}{5}, -\frac{4}{25}$
15. 19, 15, 11, 7, 3
16. ±1
17. ±4
18. $\frac{5}{9}$
19. $\frac{2}{3}$
20. 36
21. arithmetic; 156
22. geometric; 6248
23. arithmetic; −4.9
24. geometric; 728
25. 50
26. 24
27. 36.4
28. −22

PowerAlgebra.com

MathXL for School
Prepare students for the Mid-Chapter Quiz and Chapter Test with online practice and review.

Item Number	Lesson	Content Standard
1	4-5	A.APR.3
2	9-2	F.IF.3
3	9-5	A.SSE.4
4	5-3	A.SSE.2
5	4-5	A.APR.3
6	4-5	A.APR.3
7	8-4	A.SSE.2
8	9-5	A.SSE.4
9	6-6	F.BF.1.b
10	7-5	F.LE.4
11	8-4	A.SSE.2
12	4-4	A.SSE.2
13	8-6	A.APR.7
14	6-6	F.BF.1.b
15	4-5	A.CED.1
16	9-5	A.SSE.4
17	6-5	A.REI.2
18	3-2	A.CED.2
19	6-6	F.BF.1.b
20	4-4	A.SSE.2
21	4-1	F.BF.3
22	4-8	N.CN.1
23	2-4	A.CED.2
24	9-3	A.SSE.4
25	6-7	F.BF.4.a
26	9-3	A.SSE.4
27	5-3	A.REI.11

TIPS FOR SUCCESS

Read the question at the right. Then follow the tips to answer the sample question.

TIP 1

Find where $y = 0$. These are the x-intercepts of the graph.

TIP 2

Check your solutions in the original equation.

The graph below shows the quadratic function $y = 2x^2 + 2x - 4$. Use the graph to find the solutions of $2x^2 + 2x - 4 = 0$.

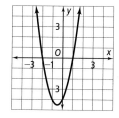

Ⓐ −4 and 0   Ⓒ −1 and 2
Ⓑ −2 and 1   Ⓓ 2 and −1

Think It Through

The x-intercepts of the graph are at $x = -2$ and $x = 1$.

Substitute to verify your answers.

$$2(-2)^2 + 2(-2) - 4$$
$$= 2(4) - 4 - 4$$
$$= 0$$
$$2(1)^2 + 2(1) - 4$$
$$= 2 + 2 - 4$$
$$= 0$$

The correct answer is B.

Vocabulary Builder

As you solve test items, you must understand the meanings of mathematical terms. Match each term with its mathematical meaning.

A. recursive formula

B. limit

C. explicit formula

D. sequence

I. a formula that expresses the nth term in terms of n

II. an ordered list of numbers

III. the least or greatest integer value of n in a series

IV. a formula that gives the first term in a sequence and defines the other terms by relating each term to the one before it

Multiple Choice

Read each question. Then write the letter of the correct answer on your paper.

1. What is the solution set of the equation $(2x - 4)(x + 6) = 0$?

Ⓐ $\{-4, 6\}$ Ⓒ $\{2, -6\}$
Ⓑ $\{-4, 6\}$ Ⓓ $\{-2, -6\}$

2. What are the first five terms of the sequence $a_n = 2n - 1$?

Ⓕ $0, 1, 2, 3, 4$ Ⓗ $2, 4, 6, 8, 10$
Ⓖ $1, 3, 5, 7, 9$ Ⓘ $3, 5, 7, 9, 11$

3. What is the common ratio in a geometric series if $a_2 = \frac{2}{5}$ and $a_5 = \frac{16}{135}$?

Ⓐ $\frac{2}{5}$ Ⓒ $\frac{6}{65}$
Ⓑ $\frac{2}{3}$ Ⓓ $\frac{8}{27}$

Answers

Cumulative Standards Review

A. IV

B. III

C. I

D. II

1. C

2. G

3. B

4. The total area of a sheet of paper can be represented by $27x^3 + 64y^3$. Which factors could represent the length times the width?

F $(3x + 4y)(3x^2 + 4y^2)$

G $(3x + 4y)(9x^2 - 12xy + 16y^2)$

H $(3x - 4y)(9x^2 - 12xy + 16y^2)$

I $(3x + 4y)(3x^2 - 3xy + 4y^2)$

5. The graph below shows the quadratic function $y = x^2 + 2x - 3$. Use the graph to find all the solutions of $x^2 + 2x - 3 = 0$.

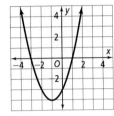

A -3

B -1

C -3 and 1

D 3 and -1

6. The table shows ordered pairs that satisfy the equation $y = -x^2 + 2x + 15$.

x	-3	0	2	3	5
y	0	15	15	12	0

Based on this table, what is the solution set of the equation $-x^2 + 2x + 15 = 0$?

F $\{0, 15\}$

G $\{-3, 15\}$

H $\{5, 0\}$

I $\{-3, 5\}$

7. What is the product of $\frac{x^2 + 5x + 4}{(x - 1)(x + 1)}$ and $\frac{x^2 - 5x + 6}{x - 2}$?

A $\frac{x^2 + 7x + 12}{x - 1}$ for $x \neq 1$

B $\frac{x^2 + x - 12}{x - 1}$ for $x \neq -1, 1,$ or 2

C $\frac{x^2 + x - 12}{x - 1}$ for $x \neq 1$

D $\frac{x^2 + 7x + 12}{x - 1}$ for $x \neq -1, 1,$ or 2

8. What is the sum of the infinite geometric series $\frac{1}{4} + \frac{1}{16} + \frac{1}{64} + \frac{1}{256} + \ldots$?

F $\frac{1}{4}$

G $\frac{1}{3}$

H $\frac{1}{2}$

I 3

9. If $f(x) = 4x^4 - 9$ and $g(x) = 2x^2 + 3$, what is $\left(\frac{f}{g}\right)(x)$?

A $2x^2 - 3$

B $2x + 3$

C $2x - 3$

D $2x^2 + 3$

10. What is the solution of $\log x - \log 3 = 8$?

F 10^8

G 8×10^3

H 3×10^3

I 3×10^8

11. What is $\frac{4x^2 - 1}{2x^2 - 5x - 3} \cdot \frac{x^2 - 6x + 9}{2x^2 + 5x - 3}$?

A 1

B $x + 3$

C $x - 3$

D $\left(\frac{x - 3}{x + 3}\right)$

12. Which is the factored form of $0.81p^2 - 0.09$?

F $(0.9p + 0.045)(0.9p - 0.045)$

G $(0.9p + 0.3)(0.9p - 0.3)$

H $(0.9p + 0.03)(0.9p - 0.03)$

I $(0.9p + 0.81)(0.9p - 0.81)$

13. Which sum is equal to $\frac{x^2 + 4x - 3}{x^2 - 9}$?

A $\frac{1}{x - 3} + \frac{x}{x + 3}$

B $\frac{x - 3}{x + 3} + \frac{x - 1}{x - 3}$

C $\frac{x^2}{x - 3} + \frac{4x - 3}{x + 3}$

D $\frac{1}{x + 3} + \frac{x}{x - 3}$

4. G
5. C
6. I
7. B
8. G
9. A
10. I
11. D
12. G
13. D

Answers

Cumulative Standards Review
(continued)

14. 175.64

15. 2.4

16. 341

17. 1

18. 20

19. 9

20. $(3x + 2)(3x - 2)$

21. $y = x^2 - 3$

22. [2]
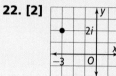

$|-3 + 2i| = \sqrt{(-3)^2 + (2)^2} = \sqrt{13}$

[1] correct graph, but incorrect abs. value OR correct abs. value, but incorrect graph

23. [2] $m = \dfrac{(1 - 5)}{(7 - 3)} = -1$, $y - 5 = -(x - 3)$ OR equivalent eq.

[1] correct eq., without work shown

24. [2] $a_n = 6\left(\dfrac{1}{2}\right)^{n-1}$; $6, 3, \dfrac{3}{2}, \dfrac{3}{4}, \dfrac{3}{8}$

[1] one of the five terms is incorrect

25. [2] $x = \sqrt{y - 5}$, $x^2 = y - 5$, $y = x^2 + 5$, $x \geq 0$

[1] correct inverse function, without work shown

26. [4] $a_3 = \sqrt{a_1 \cdot a_5} = \sqrt{2(162)} = 18$
Likewise, $a_2 = \pm\sqrt{a_1 \cdot a_3} = \pm\sqrt{2(18)} = \pm 6$ and $a_4 = \pm\sqrt{a_3 \cdot a_5} = \pm\sqrt{18(162)} = \pm 54$

[3] one computational error

[2] only pos. values are found for a_2 and a_4.

[1] correct values, without work shown

27. [4] **a.** $x = -1, 3$

b. If the graphs of $f(x)$ and $g(x)$ intersect when $x = a$, then $(a, f(a)) = (a, g(a))$. Therefore, $f(a) = g(a)$.

[3] partial correct solution for part (a) with correct explanation for part (b)

[2] partial correct solution for part (a) with incorrect explanation for part (b)

[1] incorrect solution for part (a) with correct explanation for part (b)

---

14. Marisol wants to start saving money for college. She sees the advertisement below in her local newspaper.

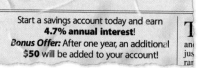

Start a savings account today and earn **4.7% annual interest**!
Bonus Offer: After one year, an additional **$50** will be added to your account!

For x dollars in this savings account, $I(x) = 1.047x$ is the value of the account after one year. $B(x) = x + 50$ is the value of the account after the one-year bonus. $(B \circ I)(x)$ models the value of this account after one year of investment time and the one-year bonus. Marisol opens a savings account by depositing \$120. What is the value of the account after one year?

15. The area of the parallelogram is 35 square units. What is the value of x?

$(2x - 1)$

$(3x + 2)$

16. What is the sum of the following finite geometric series?
$$1 + 4 + 16 + 64 + 256$$

17. What is the solution to $\sqrt{x - 1} = \sqrt{x} - 1$?

18. Rita works a part-time job at a clothing store and earns \$7 per hour. Juan works at another clothing store and earns \$6 per hour plus a 10% commission on sales. How many sales, in dollars, would Juan have to make in two hours to earn the same amount as Rita in a two-hour shift?

19. Let $f(x) = x + 1$ and $g(x) = x^2$. What is $(g \circ f)(2)$?

Short Response

20. What is the factored form of $9x^2 - 4$?

21. Write the equation represented by the graph.

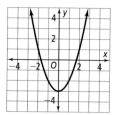

22. What is the graph and absolute value of $-3 + 2i$?

23. What is an equation of the line passing through points $(3, 5)$ and $(7, 1)$?

24. Write an explicit formula for the geometric sequence for which $a_1 = 6$ and $r = \frac{1}{2}$. Then generate the first five terms.

25. What is the inverse of $y = \sqrt{x - 5}$?

Extended Response

26. In a geometric sequence, $a_1 = 2$ and $a_5 = 162$. Explain how to use the geometric mean to find the missing terms a_2, a_3, and a_4.

27. a. Use a graphing calculator to find the points of intersection of the functions $f(x) = x^2 - 2x - 3$ and $g(x) = x^3 - 3x^2 - x + 3$.

b. Explain why the x-coordinates of the points of intersection are the solutions to the equation $f(x) = g(x)$.

Get Ready!

CHAPTER 10

Lesson 4-1 ◀ **Graphing Quadratic Functions**

Graph each function.

1. $y = -x^2$ **2.** $y = \frac{1}{3}x^2$

3. $y = 2x^2 + 5$ **4.** $y = x^2 + 6x + 8$

Lesson 4-3 ◀ **Identifying Quadratic Functions**

Determine whether each function is *linear* or *quadratic*. Identify the quadratic, linear, and constant terms.

5. $y = 6x - x^2 + 1$ **6.** $f(x) = -2(3 + x)^2 + 2x^2$ **7.** $y = 2x - y - 13$

8. $y = 4x(7 - 2x)$ **9.** $g(x) = -2x^2 - 3(x - 2)$ **10.** $y = x - 2(x + 5)$

Lesson 4-6 ◀ **Completing the Square**

Complete the square.

11. $x^2 + 8x +$ ■   **12.** $x^2 - 5x +$ ■   **13.** $x^2 + 14x +$ ■

Rewrite each equation in vertex form. Then graph the function.

14. $y = x^2 + 6x + 7$ **15.** $y = 2x^2 - 4x + 10$ **16.** $y = -3x^2 + x$

Lesson 4-1 ◀ **Graphing Quadratic Functions in Vertex Form**

Graph each function.

17. $y = 2(x - 3)^2 + 1$ **18.** $y = -1(x + 7)^2 - 4$

Lesson 2-7 ◀ **Graphing Absolute Value Functions**

Graph each function.

19. $y = 2|x|$ **20.** $y = |x| + 2$

 Looking Ahead Vocabulary

21. The word *radius* is a Latin word for the spoke of a wheel. It is also the source of the word "radio" because electromagnetic rays radiate from a radio in every direction. Why do you think mathematicians use the term radius to label any line segment from the center of a circle to any point on the circle?

22. In geometry, you learned that a *vertex* is typically a corner or point where two lines intersect. The four corners of a square are called vertices. Using this information, what can you conclude about the vertex of a parabola?

PowerAlgebra.com   **Chapter 10**   Quadratic Relations and Conic Sections   **611**

Get Ready!

Assign this diagnostic assessment to determine if students have the prerequisite skills for Chapter 10.

Lesson	Skill
4-1	Graph Quadratic Functions
4-3	Identify Quadratic Functions
4-6	Complete the Square
4-1	Graph Quadratic Functions in Vertex Form
2-7	Graph Absolute Value Functions

To remediate students, select from these resources (available for every lesson).
- Online Problems (PowerAlgebra.com)
- Reteaching (All-in-One Teaching Resources)
- Practice (All-in-One Teaching Resources)

Why Students Need These Skills

GRAPHING QUADRATIC FUNCTIONS
Graphing quadratic functions is essential to graphing conic sections.

IDENTIFYING QUADRATIC FUNCTIONS
Students will extend their skills identifying quadratic functions to identifying functions of various conic sections.

COMPLETING THE SQUARE
Completing the square is essential to writing the equations of some conic sections in standard form.

GRAPHING QUADRATIC FUNCTIONS IN VERTEX FORM
Students will graph quadratic functions in vertex from when graphing parabolas.

GRAPHING ABSOLUTE VALUE FUNCTIONS
Students will extend graphing absolute value functions to graphing conic section functions.

Looking Ahead Vocabulary

RADIUS Ask students what is true about all of the radii in any circle.

VERTEX A parabola is neither made up of lines nor does it contain a corner. However, like the vertex of a square, the vertex of a parabola is the most protruding point.

Answers

Get Ready!

1.
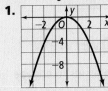

2.
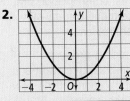

3.
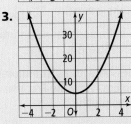

4.

5. quadratic; $-x^2$, $6x$, 1

6. linear; none, $-12x$, -18

7. linear; none, x, $-\frac{13}{2}$

8. quadratic; $-8x^2$, $28x$, none

9. quadratic; $-2x^2$, $-3x$, 6

10. linear; none, $-x$, -10

11. 16   **12.** $\frac{25}{4}$ **13.** 49

14. $y = (x + 3)^2 - 2$

15–22. See back of book.

Get Ready!   611

Chapter 10 Overview

BIG idea Modeling

ESSENTIAL QUESTION What is the intersection of a cone and a plane parallel to a line along the side of a cone?

- Students will identify the possible conic sections formed depending on the angle of intersection of the cone and plane.

BIG idea Equivalence

ESSENTIAL QUESTION What is the graph of $\frac{x^2}{9} + \frac{y^2}{9} = 1$?

- Students will graph functions of circles.
- Students will identify conic sections based on their equations.

BIG idea Coordinate Geometry

ESSENTIAL QUESTION What is the difference between the algebraic representations of ellipses and hyperbolas?

- Students will differentiate between ellipses and hyperbolas algebraically and graphically.

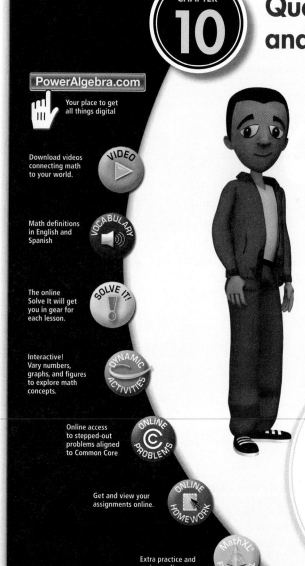

Quadratic Relations and Conic Sections

PowerAlgebra.com
Your place to get all things digital

Download videos connecting math to your world.
VIDEO

Math definitions in English and Spanish
VOCABULARY

The online Solve It will get you in gear for each lesson.
SOLVE IT!

Interactive! Vary numbers, graphs, and figures to explore math concepts.
DYNAMIC ACTIVITIES

Online access to stepped-out problems aligned to Common Core
ONLINE PROBLEMS

Get and view your assignments online.
ONLINE HOMEWORK

Extra practice and review online
MathXL FOR SCHOOL

DOMAINS
- Expressing Geometric Properties with Equations
- Interpreting Functions

I'm going to help you learn how to work with curves that you can trace along the surface of a cone. These curves are called conic sections.

People can manufacture these curves to make beautiful architecture, as shown on the next page.

Vocabulary

English/Spanish Vocabulary Audio Online:

English	Spanish
center of a circle, *p. 630*	centro de un círculo
circle, *p. 630*	círculo
conic section, *p. 614*	sección cónica
directrix, *p. 622*	directriz
ellipse, *p. 638*	elipse
hyperbola, *p. 645*	hipérbola
radius, *p. 630*	radio
standard form of an equation of a circle, *p. 630*	forma normal de la ecuación de un círculo

Content Standards

Following are the standards covered in this chapter.

CONCEPTUAL CATEGORY Functions

Domain Interpreting Functions F.IF

Cluster Analyze functions using different representations. (Standard F.IF.8)
LESSON 10-6

CONCEPTUAL CATEGORY Geometry

Domain Expressing Geometric Properties with Equations G.GPE

Cluster Translate between the geometric description and the equation for a conic section. (Standards G.GPE.1, G.GPE.2, G.GPE.3)
LESSONS 10-1, 10-2, 10-3, 10-4, 10-5, 10-6

PowerAlgebra.com

Chapter 10 Overview

Use these online assets to engage your students. These include support for the Solve It and step-by-step solutions for Problems.

Show the student-produced video demonstrating relevant and engaging applications of the new concepts in the chapter.

Find online definitions for new terms in English and Spanish.

Start each lesson with an attention-getting Problem. View the Problem online with helpful hints.

My Math Video

00:04:04

My Math Video
Use this photo to introduce students to the shapes of some conic sections. The photo depicts the Webb Bridge in Australia. It is a bridge for pedestrians and cyclists.

Q This bridge was designed to be symbolic of reconciliation with the area's indigenous history. How would you describe the resemblance to aboriginal eel traps, baskets, and the flow of the water? **[The curves recall the rounded shape of a netted trap or basket and the smooth flow of water.]**

Q How would you describe the curves depicted? Can you name any of them? **[From the photo shown, the curves resemble parabolas connected by straight segments. If they curve all the way around, they would be circles or ellipses.]**

EXTENSION

Have students research other cases where conic sections have been incorporated into architecture or structural engineering. Have them identify the shapes used, and if possible, the reasons behind choosing those shapes.

BIG ideas

1 Modeling
Essential Question What is the intersection of a cone and a plane parallel to a line along the side of the cone?

2 Equivalence
Essential Question What is the graph of $\frac{x^2}{9} + \frac{y^2}{9} = 1$?

3 Coordinate Geometry
Essential Question What is the difference between the algebraic representations of ellipses and hyperbolas?

Chapter Preview

PowerAlgebra.com | Chapter 10 Quadratic Relations and Conic Sections | 613

Increase students' depth of knowledge with interactive online activities.

Show Problems from each lesson solved step by step. Instant replay allows students to go at their own pace when studying online.

Assign homework to individual students or to an entire class.

Prepare students for the Mid-Chapter Quiz and Chapter Test with online practice and review.

Understanding by Design principles were central to the development of the Big Ideas and the Essential Understandings. These will help your students build a structure on which to make connections to prior learning.

PROGRAM ORGANIZATION · BIG IDEA · ESSENTIAL UNDERSTANDING · ESSENTIAL UNDERSTANDING · PROGRAM ORGANIZATION

Modeling

BIG idea Many real-world mathematical problems can be represented algebraically. These representations can lead to algebraic solutions. A function that models a real-world situation can then be used to make estimates or predictions about future occurrences.

ESSENTIAL UNDERSTANDINGS

10-2   Each point of a parabola is equidistant from a point called the focus and a line called the directix.

10-6   In an $x-y$ relationship, replacing x by $x - h$ and y by $y - k$ (with $h > 0$ and $k > 0$) translates the graph of the relation h units to the right and k units up.

Equivalence

BIG idea A single quantity may be represented by many different expressions. The facts about a quantity may be expressed by many different equations (or inequalities).

ESSENTIAL UNDERSTANDINGS

10-3   An equation of a circle with center (0, 0) and radius r in the coordinate plane is $x^2 + y^2 = r^2$.

10-6   In an $x-y$ relationship, replacing x by $x - h$ and y by $y - k$ (with $h > 0$ and $k > 0$) translates the graph of the relation h units to the right and k units up.

Coordinate Geometry

BIG idea A coordinate system in a plane is formed by two perpendicular number lines, called the x- and y- axes, and the quadrants they form. The coordinate plane can be used to graph many functions and relations.

ESSENTIAL UNDERSTANDINGS

10-1   There are four types of curves known as conic sections: parabolas, circles, ellipses, and hyperbolas. Each curve has its own distinct shape and properties.

10-4   A circle is a set of points a fixed distance from one point. An ellipse "stretches" a circle and is the set of points that have a total fixed distance from two points.

10-5   The shape of a hyperbola is guided by asymptotes.

10-6   In an $x-y$ relationship, replacing x by $x - h$ and y by $y - k$ (with $h > 0$ and $k > 0$) translates the graph of the relation h units to the right and k units up.

Parabolas and Circles

Parabolas

A parabola is formed when a plane intersects a cone parallel to a side of the cone.

Parabola With Vertex (h, k)

Equation: $y = \frac{1}{4c}(x - h)^2 + k$

focus: $(h, k + c)$

directrix: $y = k - c$

The parabola with the form $y = ax^2 + bx + c$ can be changed to an equation in vertex form by completing the square.

Example: What are the vertex, focus, and directrix of the parabola with equation $y = x^2 - 6x + 11$? Sketch the graph.

Step 1)   Complete the square.

$$y = (x^2 - 6x + 9) + 11 - 9$$
$$y = (x - 3)^2 + 2$$

Step 2)   Find the vertex, focus, and directrix.

Because $\frac{1}{4c} = 1$, $c = \frac{1}{4}$, so

vertex: (3, 2)

focus: $\left(3, 2\frac{1}{4}\right)$

directrix: $y = 1\frac{3}{4}$

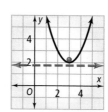

Circles

A circle is formed when a plane intersects a cone perpendicular to the axis of the cone.

Circle With Center (h, k)

Equation: $(x - h)^2 + (y - k)^2 = r^2$

center: (h, k)

radius: r

Example: What is the graph of $(x - 2)^2 + (y - 4)^2 = 9$?

• center: (2, 4)

• radius: 3

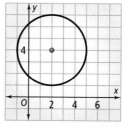

©Mathematical Practices

Model with mathematics. Make sense of problems and persevere in solving them. Conic sections are introduced as models of real-world behavior in familiar contexts, and each conic section is analyzed separately for applications of its particular focal properties.

Ellipses

An ellipse is formed when a plane intersects a cone making a closed curve, while not being perpendicular to its axis.

Ellipse With Center (0, 0)

Horizontal Ellipse

Equation: $\frac{x^2}{a^2} + \frac{y^2}{b^2} = 1$, $a > b > 0$

vertices: $(\pm a, 0)$

co-vertices: $(0, \pm b)$

foci: $(\pm c, 0)$ where $c^2 = a^2 - b^2$

Vertical Ellipse

Equation: $\frac{x^2}{b^2} + \frac{y^2}{a^2} = 1$, $a > b > 0$

vertices: $(0, \pm a)$

co-vertices: $(\pm b, 0)$

foci: $(0, \pm c)$ where $c^2 = a^2 - b^2$

Example: What are the vertices and foci of the ellipse with equation $9x^2 + 16y^2 = 144$? Sketch the graph.

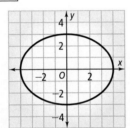

• standard form: $\frac{x^2}{16} + \frac{y^2}{9} = 1$
• major axis is horizontal
• vertices: $(4, 0)$ and $(-4, 0)$
• co-vertices: $(0, 3)$ and $(0, -3)$
• foci: $(\sqrt{7}, 0)$ and $(-\sqrt{7}, 0)$

Horizontal Ellipse With Center (h, k)

Equation: $\frac{(x - h)^2}{a^2} + \frac{(y - k)^2}{b^2} = 1$

vertices: $(h \pm a, k)$

co-vertices: $(h, k \pm b)$

foci: $(h \pm c, k)$, where $c^2 = a^2 - b^2$

Example: What are vertices and foci of the ellipse with equation $\frac{(x - 3)^2}{16} + \frac{(y - 1)^2}{9} = 1$? Sketch the graph.

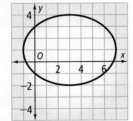

• $h = 3, k = 1, a = 4, b = 3$
• vertices: $(7, 1)$ and $(-1, 1)$
• co-vertices: $(3, 4)$ and $(3, -2)$
• foci: $(3 + \sqrt{7}, 1)$ and $(3 - \sqrt{7}, 1)$

ⓒMathematical Practices

Use appropriate tools strategically. Graphing calculators are used throughout the chapter to analyze the behavior of parabolas, circles, ellipses, and hyperbolas, and to simplify tedious computations involving quadratic equations. Technology enables students to solve real-world problems that would have been computationally tedious in the past.

Hyperbolas

A hyperbola is formed when a plane intersects a cone parallel to the axis.

Horizontal Hyperbola With Center (0, 0)

Equation: $\frac{x^2}{a^2} - \frac{y^2}{b^2} = 1$

vertices: $(\pm a, 0)$

foci: $(\pm c, 0)$, where $c^2 = a^2 + b^2$

asymptotes: $y = \pm \frac{b}{a}x$

Example: What are the vertices, foci, and asymptotes of the hyperbola with equation $4x^2 - 9y^2 = 36$? Sketch the graph.

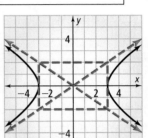

• standard form: $\frac{x^2}{9} - \frac{y^2}{4} = 1$
• vertices: $(3, 0)$ and $(-3, 0)$
• foci: $(\sqrt{13}, 0)$ and $(-\sqrt{13}, 0)$
• asymptotes: $y = \pm \frac{2}{3}x$
• use the central rectangle and asymptotes to graph.

Vertical Hyperbola With Center (0, 0)

Equation: $\frac{y^2}{a^2} - \frac{x^2}{b^2} = 1$

vertices: $(0, \pm a)$

foci: $(0, \pm c)$, where $c^2 = a^2 + b^2$

asymptotes: $y = \pm \frac{a}{b}x$

Example: What are the vertices, foci, and asymptotes of the hyperbola with equation $9y^2 - 16x^2 = 144$? Sketch the graph.

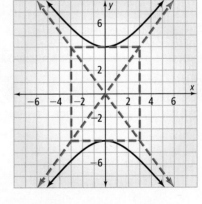

• standard form: $\frac{y^2}{16} - \frac{x^2}{9} = 1$
• vertices: $(0, 4)$ and $(0, -4)$
• foci: $(0, 5)$ and $(0, -5)$
• asymptotes: $y = \pm \frac{4}{3}x$
• use the central rectangle and asymptotes to graph

ⓒMathematical Practices

Reason abstractly and quantitatively. Look for and make use of structure. The conic sections are studied analytically, graphically, and numerically with tables. Students study their distinguishing characteristics and their common origins as graphs of second degree equations in x and y.

QUADRATIC RELATIONS AND CONIC SECTIONS
Pacing and Assignment Guide

Lesson	Teaching Day(s)	Basic	Average	Advanced	Block
		TRADITIONAL			**BLOCK**
10-1	1	Problems 1–3 Exs. 7–21, 54–69	Problems 1–3 Exs. 7–21 odd, 54–69	Problems 1–3 Exs. 7–21 odd, 54–69	**Day 1** Problems 1–5 Exs. 7–33 odd, 34–51, 54–69
	2	Problems 4–5 Exs. 22–33, 34–38 even, 39, 40, 50	Problems 4–5 Exs. 23–33 odd, 34–51	Problems 4–5 Exs. 23–33 odd, 34–53	
10-2	1	Problems 1–5 Exs. 7–33, 38–42 even, 45, 55, 59–69	Problems 1–5 Exs. 7–33 odd, 34–55, 59–69	Problems 1–5 Exs. 7–33 odd, 34–69	**Day 2** Problems 1–5 Exs. 7–33 odd, 34–55, 59–69
10-3	1	Problems 1–5 Exs. 7–33, 43–45, 52–58 even, 67–84	Problems 1–5 Exs. 7–33 odd, 34–62, 67–84	Problems 1–5 Exs. 7–33 odd, 34–84	Problems 1–5 Exs. 7–33 odd, 34–62, 67–84
10-4	1	Problems 1–2 Exs. 7–22, 63–76	Problems 1–2 Exs. 7–21 odd, 63–76	Problems 1–2 Exs. 7–21 odd, 63–76	**Day 3** Problems 1–4 Exs. 7–35 odd, 36–60, 63–76
	2	Problems 3–4 Exs. 23–35, 40–44 even, 47, 56–60 even	Problems 3–4 Exs. 23–35 odd, 36–60	Problems 3–4 Exs. 23–35 odd, 36–62	
10-5	1	Problem 1 Exs. 8–13, 43–55	Problem 1 Exs. 9–13 odd, 43–55	Problem 1 Exs. 9–13 odd, 43–55	**Day 4** Problems 1–3 Exs. 9–23 odd, 24–40, 43–55
	2	Problems 2–3 Exs. 14–23, 24–30 even, 36–40 even	Problems 2–3 Exs. 15–23 odd, 24–40	Problems 2–3 Exs. 15–23 odd, 24–42	
10-6	1	Problems 1–2 Exs. 8–14, 38–53	Problems 1–2 Exs. 9–13 odd, 38–53	Problems 1–2 Exs. 9–13 odd, 38–53	**Day 5** Problems 1–4 Exs. 9–21 odd, 22–35, 38–53
	2	Problems 3–4 Exs. 15–22, 24–30 even	Problems 3–4 Exs. 15–21 odd, 22–35	Problems 3–4 Exs. 15–21 odd, 22–37	
Review	1	Chapter 10 Review	Chapter 10 Review	Chapter 10 Review	**Day 6** Chapter 10 Review Chapter 10 Test
Assess	1	Chapter 10 Test	Chapter 10 Test	Chapter 10 Test	
Total		**12 Days**	**12 Days**	**12 Days**	**6 Days**

Note: Pacing does not include Concept Bytes and other feature pages.

Resources

	For the Chapter	10-1	10-2	10-3	10-4	10-5	10-6
Planning							
Teacher Center Online Planner & Grade Book	I	I	I	I	I	I	I
Interactive Learning & Guided Instruction							
My Math Video	I						
Solve It!		I M	I M	I M	I M	I M	I M
Student Companion		P M	P M	P M	P M	P M	
Vocabulary Support		I P M	I P M	I P M	I P M	I P M	I P
Got It? Support		I P	I P	I P	I P	I P	I P
Dynamic Activity		I	I	I	I		
Online Problems		I	I	I	I	I	I
Additional Problems		M	M	M	M	M	M
English Language Learner Support (TR)		E P M	E P M	E P M	E P M	E P M	E P M
Activities, Games, and Puzzles		E M	E M	E M	E M	E M	E M
Teaching With TI Technology With CD-ROM							
TI-Nspire™ Support CD-ROM		✓	✓	✓	✓	✓	✓
Lesson Check & Practice							
Student Companion		P M	P M	P M	P M	P M	P M
Lesson Check Support		I P	I P	I P	I P	I P	I P
Practice and Problem Solving Workbook		P	P	P	P	P	P
Think About a Plan (TR)		E P M	E P M	E P M	E P M	E P M	E P M
Practice Form G (TR)		E P M	E P M	E P M	E P M	E P M	E P M
Standardized Test Prep (TR)		P M	P M	P M	P M	P M	P M
Practice *Form K* (TR)		E P M	E P M	E P M	E P M	E P M	E P M
Extra Practice	E M						
Find the Errors!	M						
Enrichment (TR)		E P M	E P M	E P M	E P M	E P M	E P M
Answers and Solutions CD-ROM	✓	✓	✓	✓	✓	✓	✓
Assess & Remediate							
ExamView CD-ROM	✓	✓	✓	✓	✓	✓	✓
Lesson Quiz		I M	I M	I M	I M	I M	I M
Quizzes and Tests *Form G* (TR)	E P M			E P M			E P M
Quizzes and Tests *Form K* (TR)	E P M			E P M			E P M
Reteaching (TR)		E P M	E P M	E P M	E P M	E P M	E P M
Performance Tasks (TR)	P M						
Cumulative Review (TR)	P M						
Progress Monitoring Assessments	I P M						

(TR) Available in All-In-One Teaching Resources

1 Interactive Learning

Solve It!

PURPOSE To visualize the intersection of a plane and a cone

PROCESS Students may
- use a foam cup or paper model and scissors to determine the shapes formed.
- list possible shapes and use visualization to determine if any of the shapes can be formed.

FACILITATE

Q What is a planar cut? Give an example. **[slicing something with a plane, for example, using a large flat knife to cut a block of cheese]**

Q What shapes do the ends of the foam cup form? **[They both form circles.]**

Q Is it possible to get a line segment using a plane and the foam cup? Explain. **[Answers may vary. Samples: Yes, theoretically a plane tangent to the cone will form a line.]**

Q Is it possible to create a polygon using the plane and cone? Explain. **[No; a polygon is a closed figure made of a finite number of line segments. Because the cone is curved, it is not possible to create a polygon.]**

ANSWER See Solve It in Answers on next page.
CONNECT THE MATH In the Solve It, students visualize the intersection of a plane and cone. These shapes are conic sections, which students will identify and graph in this lesson.

10-1 Exploring Conic Sections

© Content Standards
Prepares for G.GPE.1 Derive the equation of a circle . . .
Prepares for G.GPE.2 Derive the equation of a parabola . . .
Prepares for G.GPE.3 Derive the equations of ellipses and hyperbolas . . .

Objective To graph and identify conic sections

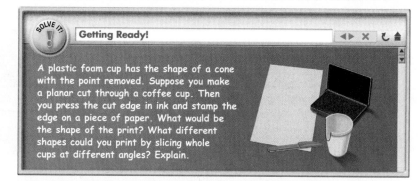

SOLVE IT! **Getting Ready!**

A plastic foam cup has the shape of a cone with the point removed. Suppose you make a planar cut through a coffee cup. Then you press the cut edge in ink and stamp the edge on a piece of paper. What would be the shape of the print? What different shapes could you print by slicing whole cups at different angles? Explain.

Lesson Vocabulary
- conic section

In Chapter 4, you studied parabolas. Geometrically, a parabola has the shape of a cross section of a cone that you cut in a particular way. Parabolas form a family of curves that belong to a larger family known as *conic sections*.

Essential Understanding There are four types of curves known as conic sections: parabolas, circles, ellipses, and hyperbolas. Each curve has its own distinct shape and properties.

take note

Key Concept   Conic Sections

A **conic section** is a curve you get by intersecting a plane and a double cone. By changing the inclination of the plane, you can get a circle, a parabola, an ellipse, or a hyperbola.

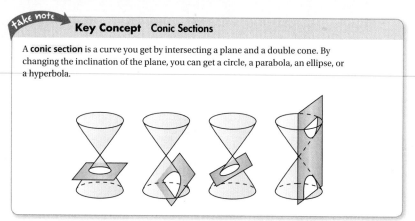

You can use lines of symmetry to graph a conic section.

10-1 Preparing to Teach

BIG idea Coordinate Geometry

ESSENTIAL UNDERSTANDINGS
- There are four types of curves known as conic sections: parabolas, circles, ellipses, and hyperbolas. Each curve has its own distinct shape and properties.
- A conic section is a curve obtained by intersecting a plane and a double cone.

Math Background

Although students may be familiar with parabolas, ellipses, circles, and hyperbolas, this lesson reintroduces these shapes as *conic sections*. Conic sections are shapes formed by the intersection of a plane and a double cone. The angle at which the plane intersects the cone determines the shape.

In a coordinate plane, the graph of a quadratic equation in two variables is always a conic section. The signs of the equations and the coefficients of the variable terms determine the shape.

Future lessons go into greater detail for each conic section. This lesson focuses on using a table of values to graph each conic section in the coordinate plane. From there it is possible to identify lines of symmetry, the center of the figure, domain and range, and the *x*- and *y*-intercepts.

© Mathematical Practices

Make sense of problems and persevere in solving them. With conic sections, students will explain correspondences between graphs, tables, and equations.

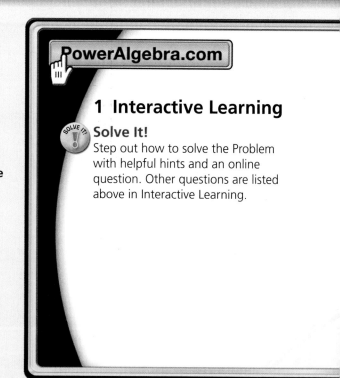

PowerAlgebra.com

1 Interactive Learning

SOLVE IT! Solve It!
Step out how to solve the Problem with helpful hints and an online question. Other questions are listed above in Interactive Learning.

Problem 1 Graphing a Circle

What is the graph of $x^2 + y^2 = 25$? What are its lines of symmetry? What are the domain and range?

Know	Need	Plan
An equation	The lines of symmetry of the graph, the domain and range of the relation	• Plot points and connect them with a smooth curve. • Look for lines of symmetry on the graph. • Determine the domain and range.

Think

Can you find values of x and y that satisfy the equation? Yes; find the x- and y-intercepts. Then look for other values of x and y that make the calculations easy.

Make a table of values. Plot the points and connect them with a smooth curve.

x	−5	−4	−3	0	3	4	5
y	0	±3	±4	±5	±4	±3	0

The graph is a circle with radius 5. Its center is the origin. Every line through the center is a line of symmetry.

The domain is the set of real numbers x with $-5 \le x \le 5$. The range is the set of real numbers y with $-5 \le y \le 5$.

Got It? **1. a.** What is the graph of $x^2 + y^2 = 9$? What are its lines of symmetry? What are the domain and range?
  b. Reasoning In Problem 1, why is there no point on the graph with x-coordinate 6?

Its many lines of symmetry make a circle a special kind of an *ellipse*. In general, an ellipse has only two lines of symmetry.

 Problem 2 Graphing an Ellipse

What is the graph of $9x^2 + 16y^2 = 144$? What are its lines of symmetry? What are the domain and range?

Think

What values should you substitute for x? Substitute both positive and negative values for x.

Make a table of values. Plot the points and connect them with a smooth curve.

x	−4	−3	0	3	4
y	0	±2	±3	±2	0

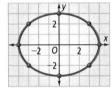

The graph is an ellipse. The center is the origin. The ellipse has two lines of symmetry, the x-axis and the y-axis.

The domain is the set of real numbers x with $-4 \le x \le 4$. The range is the set of real numbers y with $-3 \le y \le 3$.

Got It? **2.** What is the graph of $2x^2 + y^2 = 18$? What are its lines of symmetry? What are the domain and range?

PowerAlgebra.com | Lesson 10-1 Exploring Conic Sections | 615

---

2 Guided Instruction

Problem 1

Q Can you solve for y to help find values? Explain. **[Yes; solve the equation for y, and then substitute values of x to determine y.]**

Q What is the definition of line of symmetry? How can you check that a line of symmetry is correct? **[A line of symmetry divides an object into 2 congruent parts. To check, fold the graph along the line of symmetry and verify that all parts match.]**

Got It?

Q Can you use algebra to check that your domain is correct in 1a? Explain. **[Sample: Yes; solve the equation for y to get $y = \pm\sqrt{9 - x^2}$. The radicand cannot be negative, so $-3 \le x \le 3$.]**

Problem 2

Q How are the domain and range related to the x- and y-intercepts? **[The greatest and least values of the domain are the x-intercepts. The greatest and least values of the range are the y-intercepts.]**

Q Are the points in the table exact values? Explain. **[The x- and y-intercepts are exact values. For $x = \pm3$, $y = \pm\sqrt{\dfrac{144 - 9(\pm3)^2}{16}} \approx \pm1.9843$, so the y-values ±2.0 are approximations.]**

Got It?

Q How can you use the equation to determine whether the longest part of the ellipse will lie on the x- or y-axis? **[The x^2 term has a greater coefficient, so the value of x will be less than the value of y. Thus, the ellipse will be longer along the y-axis.]**

---

2 Guided Instruction

 Each Problem is worked out and supported online.

Problem 1
Graphing a Circle
Animated

Problem 2
Graphing an Ellipse
Animated

Problem 3
Graphing a Hyperbola
Animated

Problem 4
Identifying Graphs of Conic Sections

Problem 5
Using Models

Support in Algebra 2 Companion
• Vocabulary
• Key Concepts
• Got It?

Answers

Solve It!

If you cut the cup in a plane parallel to the base of the cup, you will get a circle; if the plane is not quite parallel to the base of the cup, you will get an ellipse; if you tilt the plane a little bit more, so that it is parallel to one of the sides of the cup, you will get a parabola; if you tilt the plane even further, so that it is perpendicular to the base of the cup, you will get one branch of a hyperbola.

Got It?

1. a. 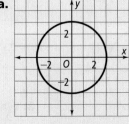 The graph is a circle with center $(0, 0)$ and radius 3. lines of sym.: every line through the origin; domain: $-3 \le x \le 3$, range: $-3 \le y \le 3$

b. 6 is outside the domain of x.

2. See page 617.

Lesson 10-1 **615**

Problem 3

Q What figure would be represented by the equation if it were changed to a sum? How would the domain and range change? **[The equation would represent a circle. The domain would be the set of real numbers $-3 \le x \le 3$, and the range would be the set of real numbers $-3 \le y \le 3$.]**

Q How are the domain and range of a hyperbola different from that of an ellipse? Explain. **[Depending on the orientation of the hyperbola, either the domain or range is the set of all real numbers. The domain and range of an ellipse are bounded.]**

Q What other conic section has a domain or range that is the set of all real numbers? **[Parabola; for example, the domain of $y = x^2$ is all real numbers.]**

Got It?   VISUAL LEARNERS

When students make the table of values by solving for a variable, they sometimes forget to take the negatives into account. Solving for y yields the equation $y = \pm\sqrt{x^2 - 16}$.

Problem 4   EXTENSION

Q What are the lines of symmetry of the graphs in 4A and 4B? **[The lines of symmetry of both the hyperbola and the ellipse are the x- and y-axes.]**

Not all conic sections consist of one smooth curve. The hyperbola consists of two separate curves called branches.

 Problem 3 Graphing a Hyperbola

What is the graph of $x^2 - y^2 = 9$? What are its lines of symmetry? What are the domain and range?

Make a table of values.

x	-5	-4	-3	-2	-1	0	1	2	3	4	5
y	±4	±2.6	0	—	—	—	—	—	0	±2.6	±4

Think

How will you know which points to connect?
Plot enough points so you see a pattern. Only connect points if you know that the points between them satisfy the equation.

Plot the points and connect them with smooth curves.

The graph is a hyperbola that consists of two branches. Its center is the origin. It has two lines of symmetry, the x-axis and the y-axis.

The domain is the set of real numbers x with $x \le -3$ or $x \ge 3$. The range is the set of real numbers.

Got It? **3.** What is the graph of $x^2 - y^2 = 16$? What are its lines of symmetry? What are the domain and range?

In this chapter, there is a separate lesson for each of the conic sections. You should already be able to identify each curve by its shape and features such as the vertex of a parabola, the center of an ellipse, circle, or hyperbola, and the intercepts of each curve.

 Problem 4 Identifying Graphs of Conic Sections

What are the center and intercepts of each conic section? What are the domain and range?

Think

What do you observe from the graph of the hyperbola?
The graph of this hyperbola extends forever but has no x-values between -2 and 2.

The center of the hyperbola is $(0, 0)$. The x-intercepts are $(-2, 0)$ and $(2, 0)$. There are no y-intercepts. The domain is the set of real numbers x with $x \le -2$ or $x \ge 2$. The range is the set of real numbers.

The center of the ellipse is $(0, 0)$. The x-intercepts are $(-6, 0)$ and $(6, 0)$. The y-intercepts are $(0, -4)$ and $(0, 4)$. The domain is the set of real numbers x with $-6 \le x \le 6$. The range is the set of real numbers y with $-4 \le y \le 4$.

Additional Problems

1. What is the graph of $x^2 + y^2 = 16$? What are its lines of symmetry? What are the domain and range?

ANSWER Every line through the center is a line of symmetry.
Domain: the set of real numbers with $-4 \le x \le 4$
Range: the set of real numbers with $-4 \le y \le 4$

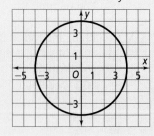

2. What is the graph of $27x^2 + 3y^2 = 27$? What are its lines of symmetry? What are the domain and range?

ANSWER Lines of symmetry: x- and y-axis
Domain: the set of real numbers with $-1 \le x \le 1$
Range: the set of real numbers with $-3 \le y \le 3$

3. What is the graph of $y^2 - x^2 = 36$? What are its lines of symmetry? What are the domain and range?

ANSWER Lines of symmetry: x- and y-axis
Domain: all real numbers
Range: the set of real numbers with $y \le -6$ or $y \ge 6$

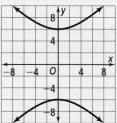

4. What are the center and intercepts of the conic section in Additional Problem 3?

ANSWER Center $(0, 0)$; no x-intercept, y-intercepts: $(0, -6)$, $(0, 6)$

5. Two types of conic sections are represented in this figure. Equations that are possible models for this figure include $36x^2 + 9y^2 = 324$, $x^2 - y^2 = 49$, and $x^2 + y^2 = 196$.

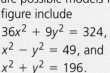

a. Which equation is a possible model for the object in the middle of the figure?

b. Which equation is a possible model for the paths of the small circles?

ANSWERS

a. $x^2 + y^2 = 196$

b. $36x^2 + 9y^2 = 324$

Got It? 4. What are the center and intercepts of the conic section? What are the domain and range?

Q Can the center of this hyperbola be found algebraically? Explain. **[Yes; find the midpoint of the y-intercepts.]**

© Problem 5 Using Models

Design Two patterns, such as arrays of dots or lines, can overlap to form moiré patterns. In the diagram, what pattern do the intersecting ripples form? Which of these equations is a possible model for the pattern: $x^2 - y^2 = 1$, $x^2 + y^2 = 16$, or $25x^2 + 9y^2 = 225$?

Think

How can you identify a possible model?
Find the type of conic section represented by each equation.

The intersecting ripples form a circle.

The equation $x^2 + y^2 = 16$ represents a conic section with two sets of intercepts, $(\pm 4, 0)$ and $(0, \pm 4)$. Each intercept is 4 units from the center. The equation models a circle.

✓ Got It? 5. Unintended moiré patterns cause problems for printers. Describe the unintended pattern. Which equation in Problem 5 is a possible model for each pattern?

a. 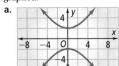 b.

Problem 5

Q How do equations for hyperbolas differ from equations for circles and ellipses? **[In the equation of a hyperbola, the variable terms are subtracted. In equations of circles and ellipses, they are added.]**

Got It?   **VISUAL LEARNERS**

Q What shape is formed by the intersecting lines and circles in 5a? **[ellipse]**

---

3 Lesson Check

Do you know HOW?   ERROR INTERVENTION

• If students have difficulty solving Exercises 1 and 2, have them make a list of the characteristics of the conic sections and their equations.

Do you UNDERSTAND?

• If students have trouble comparing domains in Exercise 6, graph an ellipse and a hyperbola as a class.

Close

Q What are two conic sections formed when a plane intersects a cone? Explain a way each can be formed. **[Sample: Circle: plane intersects the cone perpendicular to the axis of the cone. Hyperbola: the plane is parallel to the axis.]**

✓ Lesson Check

Do you know HOW?

Graph each equation. Find the lines of symmetry, the domain, and the range.

1. $x^2 + 4y^2 = 36$ **2.** $4x^2 - 9y^2 = 36$

Identify the domain and range.

3. 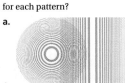   **4.**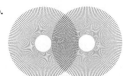

Do you UNDERSTAND? © MATHEMATICAL PRACTICES

© 5. Vocabulary Identify the type of conic section graphed.

a.   b.

© 6. Compare and Contrast How is the domain of an ellipse different from the domain of a hyperbola?

Answers

Got It? (continued)

2.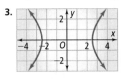

The graph is an ellipse with center (0, 0).
lines of sym.: x-axis and y-axis; domain: $-3 \leq x \leq 3$, range: $-3\sqrt{2} \leq y \leq 3\sqrt{2}$

3.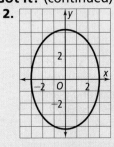

The graph is a hyperbola with center (0, 0).
lines of sym.: x-axis and y-axis;

domain: $x \leq -4$ or $x \geq 4$, range: all real numbers

4. center of hyperbola: (0, 0); no x-intercepts, y-intercepts: (0, 1), (0, −1); domain: all real numbers, range: $y \leq -1$ or $y \geq 1$

5. a. Ellipse; the eq. $25x^2 + 9y^2 = 225$ represents a conic section with two sets of intercepts, $(\pm 3, 0)$ and $(0, \pm 5)$. Since the intercepts are not equidistant from the center, the eq. models an ellipse.

b. Hyperbola; the eq. $x^2 - y^2 = 1$ represents a conic section with one set of intercepts, $(\pm 1, 0)$, so the eq. must model a hyperbola.

Lesson Check

1–6. See next page.

PowerAlgebra.com

3 Lesson Check

For a digital lesson check, use the Got It questions.

Support in Algebra 2 Companion
• Lesson Check

4 Practice

Assign homework to individual students or to an entire class.

4 Practice

ASSIGNMENT GUIDE

Basic: 7–33 all, 34–38 even, 39, 40, 50

Average: 7–33 odd, 34–51

Advanced: 7–33 odd, 34–53

Standardized Test Prep: 54–58

Mixed Review: 59–69

 **Mathematical Practices** are supported by exercises with red headings. Here are the Practices supported in this lesson:

MP 1: Make Sense of Problems Ex. 38

MP 2: Reason Abstractly Ex. 44–49

MP 3: Communicate Ex. 39a

MP 3: Construct Arguments Ex. 39b, 51

MP 3: Compare Arguments Ex. 6

MP 5: Use Appropriate Tools Ex. 53

Applications exercises have blue headings.

STEM exercises focus on science or engineering applications.

EXERCISE 50: Use the Think About a Plan worksheet in the **Practice and Problem Solving Workbook** (also available in the Teaching Resources in print and online) to further support students' development in becoming independent learners.

HOMEWORK QUICK CHECK

To check students' understanding of key skills and concepts, go over Exercises 9, 23, 38, 39, and 50.

Ⓐ Practice Graph each equation. Identify the conic section and describe the graph ◀ See Problems 1, 2, and 3. and its lines of symmetry. Then find the domain and range.

7. $3y^2 - x^2 = 25$ 8. $2x^2 + y^2 = 36$ 9. $x^2 + y^2 = 16$

10. $3y^2 - x^2 = 9$ 11. $4x^2 + 25y^2 = 100$ 12. $x^2 + y^2 = 49$

13. $x^2 - y^2 + 1 = 0$ 14. $x^2 - 2y^2 = 4$ 15. $6x^2 + 6y^2 = 600$

16. $x^2 + y^2 - 4 = 0$ 17. $6x^2 + 24y^2 - 96 = 0$ 18. $4x^2 + 4y^2 - 20 = 0$

19. $x^2 + 9y^2 = 1$ 20. $4x^2 - 36y^2 = 144$ 21. $4y^2 - 36x^2 = 1$

Identify the conic section. Then give the center, intercepts, domain, and range ◀ See Problem 4. of each graph.

22. 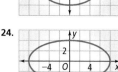   23.

24. 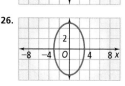   25.

26.   27.

Match each equation with a graph in Exercises 22–27. ◀ See Problem 5.

28. $x^2 - y^2 = 9$ 29. $4x^2 + 9y^2 = 36$ 30. $y^2 - x^2 = 4$

31. $x^2 + 4y^2 = 64$ 32. $25x^2 + 9y^2 = 225$ 33. $y^2 - x^2 = 9$

Ⓑ Apply Graph each equation. Describe the graph and its lines of symmetry. Then find the domain and range.

34. $9x^2 - y^2 = 144$ 35. $11x^2 + 11y^2 = 44$

36. $-8x^2 + 32y^2 - 128 = 0$ 37. $25x^2 + 16y^2 - 320 = 0$

Answers

Lesson Check

1.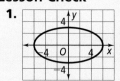

lines of sym.: x-axis and y-axis; domain: $-6 \le x \le 6$, range: $-3 \le y \le 3$

2.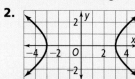

lines of sym.: x-axis and y-axis; domain: $x \le -3$ or $x \ge 3$, range: all real numbers

3. domain: $x \le -2.5$ or $x \ge 2.5$, range: all real numbers

4. domain: $-6 \le x \le 6$, range: $-1.5 \le y \le 1.5$

5. **a.** hyperbola   **b.** circle

6. Answers may vary. Sample answer: The domain of an ellipse is an interval of two real numbers, such as $-a \le x \le a$. The domain of a hyperbola is two intervals, such as $x \le -a$ or $x \ge a$, if there are x-intercepts, or all real numbers if there are no x-intercepts.

Practice and Problem-Solving Exercises

7.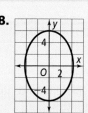

hyperbola; center: (0, 0); no x-intercepts, y-intercepts: $(0, \pm\frac{5\sqrt{3}}{3})$; lines of sym.: x-axis and y-axis; domain: all real numbers, range: $y \le -\frac{5\sqrt{3}}{3}$ or $y \ge \frac{5\sqrt{3}}{3}$

8.

ellipse; center: (0, 0); x-intercepts: $(\pm3\sqrt{2}, 0)$, y-intercepts: $(0, \pm6)$; lines of sym.: x-axis and y-axis; domain: $-3\sqrt{2} \le x \le 3\sqrt{2}$, range: $-6 \le y \le 6$

38. Think About a Plan The light emitted from a lamp with a shade forms a shadow on the wall. How can you turn the lamp in relation to the wall so that the shadow cast by the shade forms a parabola and a circle?
- How can a drawing or model help you solve this problem?
- Can you form a hyperbola and an ellipse? If so, explain how.

39. a. Writing Describe the relationship between the center of a circle and the axes of symmetry of the circle.
   b. Make a Conjecture Where is the center of an ellipse or a hyperbola located in relation to the axes of symmetry? Verify your conjecture with examples.

Graph each circle with the given radius or diameter so that the center is at the origin. Then write the equation for each graph.

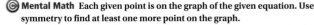

40. radius 6   **41.** radius $\frac{1}{2}$ **42.** diameter 8   **43.** diameter 2.5

Mental Math Each given point is on the graph of the given equation. Use symmetry to find at least one more point on the graph.

44. $(2, -4), y^2 = 8x$
45. $(-\sqrt{2}, 1), x^2 + y^2 = 3$
46. $(2, 2\sqrt{2}), x^2 + 4y^2 = 36$
47. $(-2, 0), 9x^2 + 9y^2 - 36 = 0$
48. $(-3, -\sqrt{51}), 6y^2 - 9x^2 - 225 = 0$
49. $(0, \sqrt{7}), x^2 + 2y^2 = 14$

STEM 50. Sound An airplane flying faster than the speed of sound creates a cone-shaped pressure disturbance in the air. This is heard by people on the ground as a sonic boom. What is the shape of the path on the ground?

51. Open-Ended Describe any other figures you can see that can be formed by the intersection of a plane and another shape, such as a sphere.

Challenge

52. a. Graph the equation $xy = 16$. Use both positive and negative values for x.
   b. Which conic section does the equation appear to model?
   c. Identify any intercepts and lines of symmetry.
   d. Does your graph represent a function? If so, rewrite the equation using function notation.

53. Graphing Calculator An xy-term has an interesting effect on the graph of a conic section. Sketch the graph of each conic section below using your graphing calculator. (*Hint:* To solve for y, you will need to complete a square.)
   a. $4x^2 + 2xy + y^2 = 9$
   b. $4x^2 + 2xy - y^2 = 9$

9.

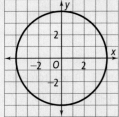

circle; center: (0, 0); radius: 4; x-intercepts: (± 4, 0), y-intercepts: (0, ± 4); infinitely many lines of sym.; domain: $-4 \leq x \leq 4$, range: $-4 \leq y \leq 4$

10.

hyperbola; center: (0, 0); no x-intercepts, y-intercepts: (0, $\pm \sqrt{3}$); lines of sym.: x-axis and y-axis; domain: all real numbers, range: $y \leq -\sqrt{3}$ or $y \geq \sqrt{3}$

11.

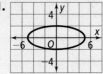

ellipse; center: (0, 0); x-intercepts: (± 5, 0), y-intercepts: (0, ± 2); lines of sym.: x-axis and y-axis; domain: $-5 \leq x \leq 5$, range: $-2 \leq y \leq 2$

12.

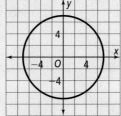

circle; center: (0, 0); radius: 7; x-intercepts: (± 7, 0), y-intercepts: (0, ± 7); infinitely many lines of sym.; domain: $-7 \leq x \leq 7$, range: $-7 \leq y \leq 7$

13.

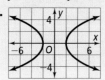

hyperbola; center: (0, 0); no x-intercepts, y-intercepts: (0, ± 1); lines of sym.: x-axis and y-axis; domain: all real numbers, range: $y \leq -1$ or $y \geq 1$

14.

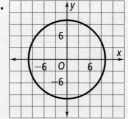

hyperbola; center: (0, 0); x-intercepts: (± 2, 0), no y-intercepts; lines of sym.: x-axis and y-axis; domain: $x \leq -2$ or $x \geq 2$, range: all real numbers

15.

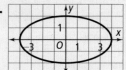

circle; center: (0, 0); radius: 10; x-intercepts: (± 10, 0), y-intercepts: (0, ± 10); infinitely many lines of sym.; domain: $-10 \leq x \leq 10$, range: $-10 \leq y \leq 10$

16.

circle; center: (0, 0); radius: 2; x-intercepts: (± 2, 0), y-intercepts: (0, ± 2); infinitely many lines of sym.; domain: $-2 \leq x \leq 2$, range: $-2 \leq y \leq 2$

17.

ellipse; center: (0, 0); x-intercepts: (± 4, 0), y-intercepts: (0, ± 2); lines of sym.: x-axis and y-axis; domain: $-4 \leq x \leq 4$, range: $-2 \leq y \leq 2$

18.

circle; center: (0, 0); radius: $\sqrt{5}$; x-intercepts: ($\pm \sqrt{5}$, 0), y-intercepts: (0, $\pm \sqrt{5}$); infinitely many lines of sym.; domain: $-\sqrt{5} \leq x \leq \sqrt{5}$, range: $-\sqrt{5} \leq y \leq \sqrt{5}$

19–37. See next page.

Answers

19.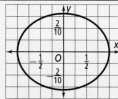

ellipse; center: $(0, 0)$; x-intercepts: $(\pm 1, 0)$, y-intercepts: $\left(0, \pm\frac{1}{3}\right)$; lines of sym.: x-axis and y-axis; domain: $-1 \le x \le 1$, range: $-\frac{1}{3} \le y \le \frac{1}{3}$

20.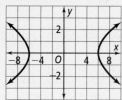

hyperbola; center: $(0, 0)$; x-intercepts: $(\pm 6, 0)$, no y-intercepts; lines of sym.: x-axis and y-axis; domain: $x \le -6$ or $x \ge 6$, range: all real numbers

21.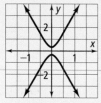

hyperbola; center: $(0, 0)$; no x-intercepts, y-intercepts: $\left(0, \pm\frac{1}{2}\right)$; lines of sym.: x-axis and y-axis; domain: all real numbers, range: $y \le -\frac{1}{2}$ or $y \ge \frac{1}{2}$

22. ellipse; center: $(0, 0)$; x-intercepts: $(\pm 3, 0)$, y-intercepts: $(0, \pm 2)$; domain: $-3 \le x \le 3$, range: $-2 \le y \le 2$

23. hyperbola; center: $(0, 0)$; no x-intercepts, y-intercepts: $(0, \pm 2)$; domain: all real numbers, range: $y \le -2$ or $y \ge 2$

24. ellipse; center: $(0, 0)$; x-intercepts: $(\pm 8, 0)$, y-intercepts: $(0, \pm 4)$; domain: $-8 \le x \le 8$, range: $-4 \le y \le 4$

25. hyperbola; center: $(0, 0)$; x-intercepts: $(\pm 3, 0)$, no y-intercepts; domain: $x \le -3$ or $x \ge 3$, range: all real numbers

26. ellipse; center: $(0, 0)$; x-intercepts: $(\pm 3, 0)$, y-intercepts: $(0, \pm 5)$; domain: $-3 \le x \le 3$, range: $-5 \le y \le 5$

27. hyperbola; center: $(0, 0)$; no x-intercepts, y-intercepts: $(0, \pm 3)$; domain: all real numbers, range: $y \le -3$ or $y \ge 3$

28. 25   **29.** 22

30. 23   **31.** 24

32. 26   **33.** 27

34.

hyperbola; center: $(0, 0)$; x-intercepts: $(\pm 4, 0)$, no y-intercepts; lines of sym.: x-axis and y-axis;

 SAT/ACT

54. Which expression can be simplified to $\frac{x-1}{x-3}$?

 Ⓐ $\frac{x^2 - x - 6}{x^2 - x - 2}$ Ⓑ $\frac{x^2 - 2x + 1}{x^2 + 2x - 3}$ Ⓒ $\frac{x^2 - 3x - 4}{x^2 - 7x + 12}$ Ⓓ $\frac{x^2 - 4x + 3}{x^2 - 6x + 9}$

55. Which is the graph of $4x^2 - y^2 = 4$?

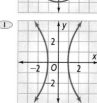

56. Which product is NOT equal to 13?

Ⓐ $(4 + \sqrt{3})(4 - \sqrt{3})$ Ⓒ $(6 + \sqrt{23})(6 - \sqrt{23})$

Ⓑ $(5 - 2\sqrt{3})(5 + 2\sqrt{3})$ Ⓓ $(7 - \sqrt{6})(7 + \sqrt{6})$

57. Which function represents exponential growth?

Ⓕ $y = 35x^{1.35}$ Ⓖ $y = 35 \cdot (0.35)^x$ Ⓗ $y = 35 \cdot (1.35)^x$ Ⓘ $y = 35 \div (1.35)^x$

Short Response

58. What is an explicit formula for the sequence $4, 9, 16, 25, 36, \ldots$? What is the ninth term in this sequence?

Mixed Review

Determine whether each geometric series *diverges* or *converges*. If the series converges, state the sum.   ◀ **See Lesson 9-5.**

59. $1 + 3 + 9 + \ldots$ **60.** $1 + \frac{4}{3} + \frac{16}{9} + \ldots$ **61.** $\frac{1}{2} + \frac{1}{4} + \frac{1}{8} + \ldots$

Expand each binomial.   ◀ **See Lesson 5-7.**

62. $(x - y)^3$ **63.** $(p + q)^6$ **64.** $(x - 2)^4$ **65.** $(3 - x)^5$

Get Ready!   To prepare for Lesson 10-2, do Exercises 66–69.

Make a table of values for each equation. Then graph the equation.   ◀ **See Lesson 2-7.**

66. $y = |x|$ **67.** $y = |x| + 3$ **68.** $y = |x - 2|$ **69.** $y = |x + 1| - 4$

---

domain: $x \le -4$ or $x \ge 4$, range: all real numbers

35.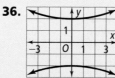

circle; center: $(0, 0)$; radius: 2; x-intercepts: $(\pm 2, 0)$, y-intercepts: $(0, \pm 2)$; infinitely many lines of sym.; domain: $-2 \le x \le 2$, range: $-2 \le y \le 2$

36.

hyperbola; center: $(0, 0)$; no x-intercepts, y-intercepts: $(0, \pm 2)$; lines of sym.: x-axis and y-axis; domain: all real numbers, range: $y \le -2$ or $y \ge 2$

37.

ellipse; center: $(0, 0)$; x-intercepts: $\left(\pm\frac{8\sqrt{5}}{5}, 0\right)$, y-intercepts: $(0, \pm 2\sqrt{5})$; lines of sym.: x-axis and y-axis; domain: $-\frac{8\sqrt{5}}{5} \le x \le \frac{8\sqrt{5}}{5}$, range: $-2\sqrt{5} \le y \le 2\sqrt{5}$

38–69. See back of book.

Additional Instructional Support

Algebra 2 Companion

Students can use the **Algebra 2 Companion** worktext (4 pages) as you teach the lesson. Use the Companion to support

- New Vocabulary
- Key Concepts
- Got It for each Problem
- Lesson Check

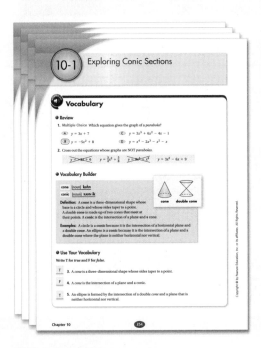

ELL Support

Focus on Language Have students write the words *ellipse*, *circle*, *parabola*, and *hyperbola* on index cards. On the back of each card tell students to draw a representation of each figure in a coordinate plane. If possible, have students write the equation of the figure. Allow students to page through the lesson so they may use equations and graphs from the examples and practice problems if needed. Next, put students in pairs and have one student place his or her cards on the desk with the graphs showing. The other student must take his or her own cards showing only the name of the figure and place them on top of the appropriate shapes. Tell students to state each conic section as they point to the name and the graph. Have students switch partners so they can practice identifying and saying each conic section with several different graphs.

5 Assess & Remediate

Lesson Quiz

1. What is the graph of $25x^2 + 4y^2 = 100$? What are its lines of symmetry? What are the domain and range?
2. Name the conic section in question 1. What are the center and intercepts?
3. **Do you UNDERSTAND?** Of the three equations listed, which equation might be a model for each situation?
   $x^2 + y^2 = 81$; $10x^2 + y^2 = 100$; $x^2 - y^2 = 4$
   a. the path of the Earth around the Sun
   b. the circumference of a dinner plate
   c. a conic section consisting of two smooth curves intersecting the x-axis

ANSWERS TO LESSON QUIZ

1. Lines of symmetry: x- and y-axes; domain: the set of real numbers with $-2 \leq x \leq 2$; range: the set of real numbers with $-5 \leq y \leq 5$

2. ellipse; center: $(0, 0)$; x-intercepts: $(-2, 0)$, $(2, 0)$; y-intercepts: $(0, -5)$, $(0, 5)$

3. a. ellipse; $10x^2 + y^2 = 100$.
   b. circle; $x^2 + y^2 = 81$
   c. hyperbola; $x^2 - y^2 = 4$

PRESCRIPTION FOR REMEDIATION

Use the student work on the Lesson Quiz to prescribe a differentiated review assignment:

Points	Differentiated Remediation
0–1	Intervention
2	On-level
3	Extension

PowerAlgebra.com

5 Assess & Remediate

Assign the Lesson Quiz. Appropriate intervention, practice, or enrichment is automatically generated based on student performance.

Differentiated Remediation

Intervention

- **Reteaching** (2 pages) Provides reteaching and practice exercises for the key lesson concepts. Use with struggling students or absent students.
- **English Language Learner Support** Helps students develop and reinforce mathematical vocabulary and key concepts.

All-in-One Resources/Online
Reteaching

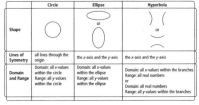

All-in-One Resources/Online
English Language Learner Support

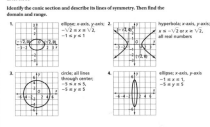

Differentiated Remediation *continued*

On-Level

- **Practice** (2 pages) Provides extra practice for each lesson. For simpler practice exercises, use the Form K Practice pages found in the All-in-One Teaching Resources and online.

- **Think About a Plan** Helps students develop specific problem-solving skills and strategies by providing scaffolded guiding questions.

- **Standardized Test Prep** Focuses on all major exercises, all major question types, and helps students prepare for the high-stakes assessments.

Extension

- **Enrichment** Provides students with interesting problems and activities that extend the concepts of the lesson.

- **Activities, Games, and Puzzles** Worksheets that can be used for concepts development, enrichment, and for fun!

Practice and Problem Solving Wkbk/ All-in-One Resources/Online
Practice page 1

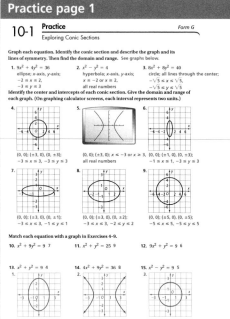

Practice and Problem Solving Wkbk/ All-in-One Resources/Online
Practice page 2

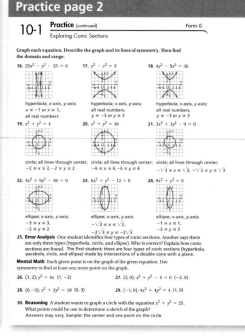

All-in-One Resources/Online
Enrichment

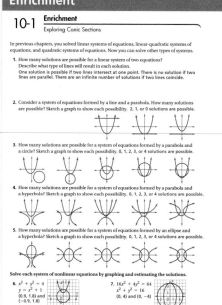

Practice and Problem Solving Wkbk/ All-in-One Resources/Online
Think About a Plan

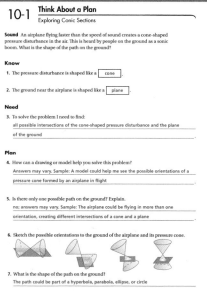

Practice and Problem Solving Wkbk/ All-in-One Resources/Online
Standardized Test Prep

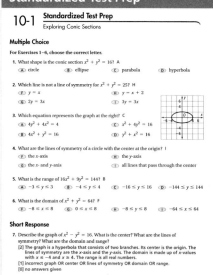

Online Teacher Resource Center
Activities, Games, and Puzzles

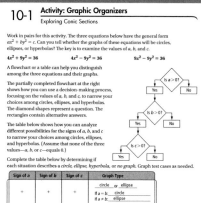

© **Content Standards**
Prepares for G.GPE.1 Derive the equation of a circle . . .
Prepares for G.GPE.2 Derive the equation of a parabola . . .
Prepares for G.GPE.3 Derive the equations of ellipses and hyperbolas . . .

You can use your graphing calculator to graph relations that are not functions.

Example

Graph the ellipse $\frac{x^2}{16} + \frac{y^2}{9} = 1$.

Step 1 Solve the equation for y.

$$\frac{x^2}{16} + \frac{y^2}{9} = 1$$

$$\frac{y^2}{9} = 1 - \frac{x^2}{16}$$

$$y^2 = 9\left(1 - \frac{x^2}{16}\right)$$

$$y = \pm 3\sqrt{1 - \frac{x^2}{16}}$$

Step 2 Enter the equations as Y_1 and Y_2.

```
Plot1  Plot2  Plot3
\Y1 ▪ 3√(1−(X²/16))
\Y2 ▪ −3√(1−(X²/16))
\Y3 = ▪
\Y4 =
\Y5 =
```

Step 3 Select a square window.

```
ZOOM MEMORY
1: ZBOX
2: Zoom In
3: Zoom Out
4: ZDecimal
5: ZSquare
6: ZStandard
7↓ZTrig
```

Step 4 Graph.

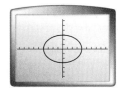

Exercises

Graph each conic section.

1. $x^2 + y^2 = 25$

2. $4x^2 + y^2 = 16$

3. $9x^2 - 16y^2 = 144$

4. $x^2 - y^2 = 3$

5. $\frac{x^2}{4} - \frac{y^2}{9} = 1$

6. $x^2 + \frac{y^2}{4} = 16$

7. **a.** Graph $y = \sqrt{\frac{81}{4} - x^2}$ and $y = -\sqrt{\frac{81}{4} - x^2}$.
   b. Estimate the x-intercepts and find the y-intercepts.
   c. Adjust the window to $-9.3 \le x \le 9.5$. What are the x-intercepts?
   d. What conic section does the graph represent?

Graph each conic section. Find the x- and y-intercepts.

8. $4x^2 + y^2 = 25$

9. $x^2 + y^2 = 30$

10. $9x^2 - 4y^2 = 72$

© 11. **Writing** Explain how to use a graphing calculator to graph $x = |y - 3|$.

© 12. **Reasoning** Which conic sections can you graph using only one equation? Explain.

Answers

Exercises

1.
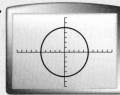

2.
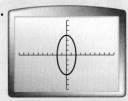

3.
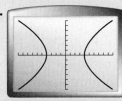

4.
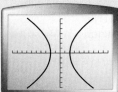

5.
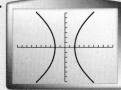

6. (x and y-scales set to two units)
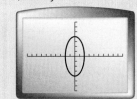

7–12. See back of book.

Guided Instruction

PURPOSE To graph conic sections with a graphing calculator

PROCESS Students will
- solve equations for y.
- find the square roots of polynomials.
- find appropriate windows for viewing the conic sections.

DISCUSS Because a graphing calculator allows you to input only an equation solved for y, it can only graph functions. By separating equations for conic sections into two parts, it is possible to graph conic sections. Elicit that
- graphing two functions can result in a figure that looks like a conic section.
- gaps can appear in the graph of a conic section on a graphing calculator due to rounding.

Example

Q What information is in the table in the graphing calculator but not the graph? **[The trace key can find the y-intercepts, but there are gaps for the x-intercepts in the graph. The table gives values for both.]**

Q Is it possible to write the equation of the ellipse without fractions? Explain. **[Yes; multiplying the entire equation by 144 yields $9x^2 + 16y^2 = 144$.]**

Q What happens when the equations in the calculator are changed to $y = \pm\sqrt{1 + \frac{x^2}{16}}$? Explain. **[The conic section is a hyperbola. The x term is negative on the left side of the equation.]**

© **Mathematical Practices**

This Concept Byte supports students in becoming proficient in using appropriate tools, Mathematical Practice 5.

1 Interactive Learning

Solve It!

PURPOSE To use measurement to explore the definition of a parabola

PROCESS Students may
- measure the distances from point *F* to a point on the parabola and from the point on the parabola to a point directly below.
- work with a partner to determine whether the choice of points affects their conjecture.

FACILITATE

Q The coordinates of which point on the parabola result in the shortest distance between *F* and P_i? **[The shortest distance is between *F* and (0, 0), which is the vertex of the parabola.]**

Q In this activity, what will be true about all the points drawn directly below each point in the parabola? **[The points form a horizontal line.]**

ANSWER See Solve It in Answers on next page.

CONNECT THE MATH In the Solve It, students use measurement and geometry to help them understand the definition of a parabola. In this lesson, students will use the focus and directrix to define parabolas and write their equations.

2 Guided Instruction

Take Note

The previous lesson showed how a parabola was formed by the intersection of a cone and a plane parallel to the side of the cone. This definition uses the focus and directrix to define this conic section in a coordinate plane.

10-2 Parabolas

Content Standard
G.GPE.2 Derive the equation of a parabola given a focus and directrix.

Objective To write the equation of a parabola and to graph parabolas

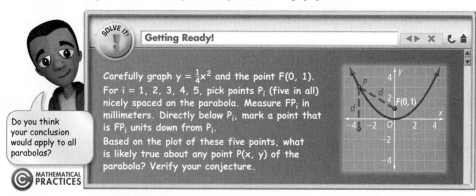

Do you think your conclusion would apply to all parabolas?

Getting Ready!

Carefully graph $y = \frac{1}{4}x^2$ and the point F(0, 1). For i = 1, 2, 3, 4, 5, pick points P_i (five in all) nicely spaced on the parabola. Measure FP_i in millimeters. Directly below P_i, mark a point that is FP_i units down from P_i.
Based on the plot of these five points, what is likely true about any point P(x, y) of the parabola? Verify your conjecture.

MATHEMATICAL PRACTICES

Dynamic Activity Parabolas

Lesson Vocabulary
- focus of a parabola
- directrix
- focal length

From Chapter 4, you know that a parabola has a vertex and an axis of symmetry. A parabola also has other characteristics.

Essential Understanding Each point of a parabola is equidistant from a point called the *focus* and a line called the *directrix*.

take note

Key Concept   Parabola

Definition

A parabola is the set of all points in a plane that are the same distance from a fixed line and a fixed point not on the line.

The fixed point is called the **focus of a parabola**.

The fixed line is called the **directrix**.

The distance between the vertex and the focus is the **focal length** of the parabola.

Graph

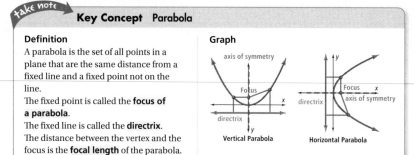

Vertical Parabola

Horizontal Parabola

In this lesson, you will consider vertical parabolas (each of which has a vertical axis of symmetry and a horizontal directrix) and horizontal parabolas (each of which has a horizontal axis of symmetry and a vertical directrix).

BIG idea Modeling

ESSENTIAL UNDERSTANDINGS
- Each point of a parabola is equidistant from a point called the focus and a line called the directrix.
- The intersection of a cone and a plane parallel to a line along its side is a parabola.

Math Background

Students are familiar with parabolas as nonlinear functions. In this lesson parabolas are introduced as conic sections. In this context, the lesson shows that a parabola is not always a function. A parabola can have any orientation. This lesson focuses on horizontal parabolas (which are not functions) and vertical parabolas (which are functions).
- A parabola can be formed by the intersection of a cone and a plane parallel to a side of the cone.
- A parabola is defined as the set of all points in a plane that are the same distance from a fixed line (directrix) and a fixed point not on the line (focus).

The vertex equation for a parabola allows you to determine the vertex, focus, and directrix without graphing.
For a vertical parabola,
- equation: $y = \frac{1}{4c}(x - h)^2 + k$
- focus: $(h, k + c)$
- directrix: $y = k - c$.

When the vertex is at (0, 0), the equation simplifies to $y = \frac{1}{4c}x^2$ so the focus is (0, c), and the directrix is $y = -c$.

Mathematical Practices

Attend to precision. Students will explicitly use the terms "focus" and "directrix" with relation to parabolas and will determine both for a given conic equation.

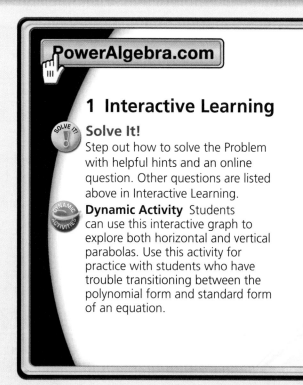

PowerAlgebra.com

1 Interactive Learning

Solve It!
Step out how to solve the Problem with helpful hints and an online question. Other questions are listed above in Interactive Learning.

Dynamic Activity Students can use this interactive graph to explore both horizontal and vertical parabolas. Use this activity for practice with students who have trouble transitioning between the polynomial form and standard form of an equation.

You can find the equation of a vertical parabola with vertex at the origin by using the geometric definition. If you denote the focus by $(0, c)$, the directrix is the line with equation $y = -c$.

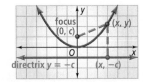

Here's Why It Works Any point (x, y) on the parabola must be equidistant from the focus and the directrix. Use the Distance Formula.

$$\sqrt{(x - 0)^2 + (y - c)^2} = \sqrt{(x - x)^2 + (y - (-c))^2}$$ Distance Formula

$$x^2 + (y - c)^2 = 0^2 + (y + c)^2$$ Square each side.

$$x^2 + y^2 - 2cy + c^2 = y^2 + 2cy + c^2$$ Expand.

$$x^2 - 2cy = 2cy$$ Subtract y^2 and c^2 from each side.

$$x^2 = 4cy$$ Add $2cy$ to each side.

$$y = \frac{1}{4c}x^2$$ Standard quadratic form

Note that the equation has the expected quadratic form $y = ax^2$ for a vertical parabola with vertex at $(0, 0)$. The coefficient $a = \frac{1}{4c}$ determines both the focus $(0, c)$ and the directrix $y = -c$. This is the key to shifting between the algebraic and geometric representations of a parabola.

Problem 1 Parabolas with Equation $y = ax^2$

Plan

How can you tell if this is a vertical or a horizontal parabola?
The focus and the vertex are on the axis of symmetry. They both lie on the y-axis so the parabola is vertical.

A What is an equation of the parabola with vertex at the origin and focus $(0, 2)$?

The focus is directly above the vertex.

This is a vertical parabola with vertex at the origin.

The focus is $(0, c)$, so $c = 2$.

$$y = \frac{1}{4c}x^2 = \frac{1}{4(2)}x^2 = \frac{1}{8}x^2$$

Think

What does the sign of *a* tell you about the graph?
Since *a* is negative, the parabola opens downward.

B What are the focus and directrix of the parabola with equation $y = -\frac{1}{12}x^2$?

This is a vertical parabola with vertex at the origin and $a = -\frac{1}{12}$.

$$a = \frac{1}{4c} = -\frac{1}{12}$$

$$4c = -12$$

$$c = -3$$

Since the vertex is at the origin, knowing c, you can conclude that the focus is the point $(0, -3)$ and the directrix is the line with equation $y = 3$.

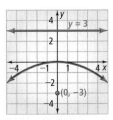

Here's Why It Works   TACTILE LEARNERS

The relationship between the focus and the directrix determines the size and orientation of a parabola. To help students understand this, provide each student with several sheets of folding paper or patty paper and have them follow these steps:
1) Draw one point near the bottom of the paper.
2) Fold the bottom of the paper until it meets the point and make a crease.
3) Unfold and repeat for 20–30 points along the bottom of the paper. When finished, a parabola will be formed by the creases.

Step 1   Step 2   Step 3

Encourage students to change the distance of the point (focus) from the bottom of the paper (directrix) to change the parabola. Point out that each crease represents the perpendicular bisector of the line segment connecting the focus and each point on the directrix.

Problem 1   EXTENSION

Q What is the relationship between the axis of symmetry and the focus and directrix? **[The axis of symmetry is perpendicular to the directrix. The focus is a point on the axis of symmetry.]**

Q In 1B, is it possible to find the vertex of a parabola not at the origin if given the focus and directrix? Explain. **[Yes; the distance from the focus to the vertex is equal to the distance from the vertex to the directrix, so the midpoint formula can be used.]**

---

2 Guided Instruction

 Each Problem is worked out and supported online.

Problem 1
Parabolas with Equation $y = ax^2$
                    Animated

Problem 2
Parabolas with Equation $x = ay^2$

Problem 3
Using Parabolas to Solve Problems
                    Animated

Problem 4
Analyzing a Parabola
                    Animated

Problem 5
Writing an Equation of a Parabola

Support in Algebra 2 Companion
• Vocabulary
• Key Concepts
• Got It?

Answers

Solve It!
Any pt. on the parabola will be equidistant from pt. *F* and the line formed by connecting pts. that are FP_i units down from P_i.

Got It?

Q How can you find the vertex of the parabola in 1b? **[Using the standard form $y = ax^2 + bx + c$, you can use $x = \frac{-b}{2a}$ to find the axis of symmetry. Then substitute the value of x into the equation to find the value of y. The vertex is (x, y).]**

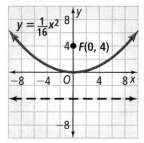
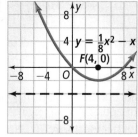

Problem 2

Q Is it possible to graph the parabola in 2A on a graphing calculator? Explain. **[Yes; solving for y, $y = \pm\sqrt{-5x}$, which is defined for negative values of x.]**

 Got It? **1. a.** What is an equation of the parabola with vertex $(0, 0)$ and focus $(0, -1.5)$?
  b. What are the vertex, focus, and directrix of the parabola with equation $y = \frac{x^2}{4}$?
  c. Reasoning How does the distance of the focus from the vertex affect the shape of a parabola?

The quadratic equation $x = ay^2$ determines a *horizontal parabola* with vertex at $(0, 0)$. The coefficient $a = \frac{1}{4c}$ determines both the focus $(c, 0)$ and the directrix $x = -c$.

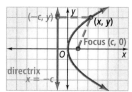

 Problem 2 Parabolas with Equation $x = ay^2$

A What is an equation of a parabola with vertex at the origin and directrix $x = 1.25$?

Plan

How can you tell if this is a vertical or a horizontal parabola?
The directrix is parallel to the y-axis, so this is a horizontal parabola.

The directrix lies directly to the right of the vertex.

The parabola is horizontal.

The directrix has equation $x = -c$, so $c = -1.25$. Thus,
$x = \frac{1}{4c}y^2 = \frac{1}{4(-1.25)}y^2 = -\frac{1}{5}y^2$

Check for Reasonableness

The graph is reasonable since it opens in the negative direction and $a < 0$.

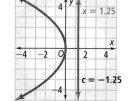

B What are the vertex, focus, and directrix of the parabola with equation $x = 0.75y^2$?

Think

What does the sign of a tell you about the graph?
Since a is positive, the parabola opens to the right.

This is a horizontal parabola. The vertex is at the origin and $a = 0.75$. Thus,

$$a = \frac{1}{4c} = 0.75$$

$$4c = \frac{1}{0.75}$$

$$c = \frac{1}{3}$$

Knowing c, you can conclude that the focus is the point $\left(\frac{1}{3}, 0\right)$. The directrix is the line with equation $x = -\frac{1}{3}$.

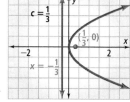

Additional Problems

1. a. What is an equation of the parabola with vertex at the origin and focus $\left(0, \frac{1}{2}\right)$?
  b. What are the focus and directrix of the parabola with equation $y = 6x^2$?

ANSWERS
a. $y = \frac{1}{2}x^2$
b. focus: $\left(0, \frac{1}{24}\right)$; directrix: $y = -\frac{1}{24}$

2. a. What is an equation of a parabola with vertex at the origin and directrix $x = -\frac{1}{8}$?

b. What are the vertex, focus, and directrix of the parabola with equation $x = \frac{3}{5}y^2$?

ANSWERS
a. $x = 2y^2$
b. vertex: $(0, 0)$; focus: $\left(\frac{5}{12}, 0\right)$; directrix: $x = -\frac{5}{12}$

3. The mirrored reflector of a flashlight is 16 cm across and 10 cm deep. How far from the vertex should the light bulb be positioned?

ANSWER 1.6 cm

4. What are the vertex, focus, and directrix of the parabola with equation $y = x^2 - 6x + 15$?

ANSWER vertex: $(3, 6)$; focus: $(3, 6.25)$; directrix: $y = 5.75$

5. Which is an equation of the parabola with vertex $(10, 2)$ and focus $(10, 1)$?

A. $y = -\frac{1}{4}(x + 10)^2 - 2$
B. $y = -\frac{1}{4}(x - 10)^2 + 2$
C. $y = -\frac{1}{4}(x + 10)^2 + 2$
D. $y = -\frac{1}{4}(x - 10)^2 - 2$

ANSWER B

Got It? **2. a.** What is an equation of the parabola with vertex at the origin and directrix $x = -\frac{5}{2}$?

b. What are the vertex, focus, and directrix of the parabola with equation $x = -4y^2$?

The geometry of a parabola implies a very important reflective property that gives real-world meaning to the word "focus."

As the diagram of the *parabolic reflector* shows, lines from the focus reflect off the parabola along lines parallel to the axis of symmetry. This is how a flashlight works. Conversely, lines parallel to the axis of symmetry reflect off the parabola directly into the focus. This is how a satellite dish works.

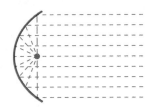

© **Problem 3** Using Parabolas to Solve Problems (STEM)

Solar Reflector The parabolic solar reflector pictured has a depth of 2 feet at the center. How far from the vertex is the focus? (What is the focal length?)

Think
What is the shape of the solar reflector?
A cross section is part of a parabola and is 8 ft across.

Graph the parabola in a coordinate system with vertex $(0, 0)$. The vertical parabola has the form $y = \frac{1}{4c}x^2$. Substitute either the point $(-4, 2)$ or the point $(4, 2)$.

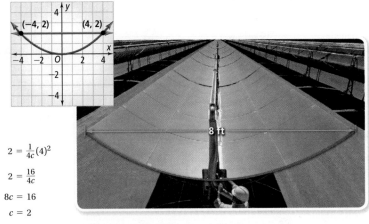

$$2 = \frac{1}{4c}(4)^2$$

$$2 = \frac{16}{4c}$$

$$8c = 16$$

$$c = 2$$

Therefore the focus is at $(0, 2)$, 2 ft from the vertex.
The focal length is 2 ft.

Got It? **3.** The mirrored reflector of a flashlight is 8 cm across and 4 cm deep. How far from the vertex should the light bulb be positioned?

PowerAlgebra.com | Lesson 10-2   Parabolas | **625**

Got It?

Q What can the equation for the directrix tell you about the parabola in 2a? **[The directrix is a vertical line, so the parabola is horizontal.]**

Q Can you describe the orientation of the parabola in 2b before finding the vertex, focus, and directrix? Explain. **[Yes; the x term is linear, so the parabola is horizontal. The a term is negative, so it opens to the left.]**

Problem 3

Q Must the vertex of this parabola be at $(0, 0)$? Explain. **[No; the vertex could be anywhere on the coordinate plane. For ease of computation, the vertex is placed at $(0, 0)$.]**

Q Why can either point be used to find the value of c? **[Because the x-value is squared, the positive or negative x-value will give the same answer.]**

Q What is the equation of the parabola representing the satellite dish? Explain. **[$y = \frac{1}{8}x^2$; the vertex is at the origin and $c = 2$. Substituting into the equation $y = \frac{1}{4c}x^2$ yields the equation of the parabola.]**

Got It?

Q How can you find two ordered pairs on the parabola? **[The reflector is 8 cm across, so the distance between the x-values must be 8 units. Placing the vertex at the origin, the ordered pairs are $(-4, 4)$ and $(4, 4)$.]**

Answers

Got It?

1. a. $y = -\frac{1}{6}x^2$

b. vertex: $(0, 0)$; focus: $(0, 1)$;
directrix: $y = -1$

c. As the distance between the vertex and focus increases, the width of the parabola increases.

2. a. $x = \frac{1}{10}y^2$

b. vertex: $(0, 0)$; focus: $\left(-\frac{1}{16}, 0\right)$;
directrix: $x = \frac{1}{16}$

3. 1 cm

Q What methods can you use to help you remember the equations shown in the box? **[Sample: Use equations for the vertex of a vertical parabola. Substitute 0 for h and k to make an equation for a parabola with vertex at the origin. Horizontal parabola equations are made by switching x and y and switching h and k.]**

Problem 4

Q How can you determine the value of $\frac{1}{4c}$? **[The coefficient of the squared term in the equation is 1, so $\frac{1}{4c} = 1$.]**

Got It?

Q What is the vertex form of the equation? **[$y = (x + 4)^2 + 2$]**

Q How can you algebraically check that your vertex is correct? **[The equation is in standard form, so use $\frac{-b}{2a}$ to find the x-value, then substitute to find y.]**

In Chapter 4, you studied how to translate a parabola from one with vertex $(0, 0)$ to one with vertex (h, k). For such a translation, all of the other features—axis of symmetry, focus, and directrix—translate along with the parabola and its vertex.

take note

Key Concept Transformations of a Parabola

Vertical Parabola	Vertex (0, 0)	Vertex (h, k)
Equation	$y = \frac{1}{4c}x^2$	$y = \frac{1}{4c}(x - h)^2 + k$
Focus	$(0, c)$	$(h, k + c)$
Directrix	$y = -c$	$y = k - c$

Horizontal Parabola	Vertex (0, 0)	Vertex (h, k)
Equation	$x = \frac{1}{4c}y^2$	$x = \frac{1}{4c}(y - k)^2 + h$
Focus	$(c, 0)$	$(h + c, k)$
Directrix	$x = -c$	$x = h - c$

Ⓒ **Problem 4** Analyzing a Parabola

What are the vertex, focus, and directrix of the parabola with equation
$y = x^2 - 4x + 8$?

Know	Need	Plan
The equation of the parabola	• vertex • focus • directrix	• Find c, h, and k • Use these values to find the vertex, focus, and directrix.

Think

How can you change the equation to an equivalent form?
Subtract the same value outside the parentheses that you added inside the parentheses.

First, complete the square to get the equation in vertex form.

$y = x^2 - 4x + 8$	Standard form $y = ax^2 + bx + c$
$y = (x^2 - 4x + 4) + 8 - 4$	Add $\left(\frac{1}{2} \cdot -4\right)^2$ inside parentheses; subtract it outside.
$y = (x - 2)^2 + 4$	Vertex form $y = \frac{1}{4c}(x - h)^2 + k$

Note that, in this case, $\frac{1}{4c} = 1$, so $c = 0.25$.

The vertex (h, k) is $(2, 4)$.

The focus $(h, k + c)$ is $(2, 4.25)$.

The directrix $y = k - c$ is $y = 3.75$.

Got It? 4. What are the vertex, focus, and directrix of the parabola with equation
$$y = x^2 + 8x + 18?$$

Answers

Got It? (continued)

4. vertex: $(-4, 2)$; focus: $\left(-4, 2\frac{1}{4}\right)$;
   directrix: $y = 1\frac{3}{4}$

5. $y = \frac{1}{8}(x - 1)^2 + 4$

Lesson Check

1. $y = \frac{1}{2}x^2$

2. $x = \frac{1}{4}(y - 2)^2 + 3$

3. vertex: $(0, 0)$; focus: $(4, 0)$; directrix:
   $x = -4$

4. vertex: $(-3, -4)$; focus: $(-3, -3.75)$;
   directrix: $y = -4.25$

5. 6 units

6. With the focus one unit away from the vertex of a parabola at the origin, $c = \pm 1$. Given this information, the student cannot tell whether the parabola opens in the vert. direction, with one of the eqs. $y = \frac{1}{4}x^2$ or $y = -\frac{1}{4}x^2$, or whether the parabola opens in the horizontal direction, with one of the eqs. of $x = \frac{1}{4}y^2$ or $x = -\frac{1}{4}y^2$.

Practice and Problem-Solving Exercises

7. $x = \frac{1}{24}y^2$ **8.** $y = -\frac{1}{16}x^2$

9. $y = \frac{1}{28}x^2$ **10.** $x = -\frac{1}{4}y^2$

11. $x = \frac{1}{8}y^2$ **12.** $y = -\frac{1}{20}x^2$

13. vertex: $(0, 0)$
   focus: $\left(0, \frac{1}{16}\right)$
   directrix: $y = -\frac{1}{16}$

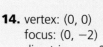

14. vertex: $(0, 0)$
   focus: $(0, -2)$
   directrix: $y = 2$

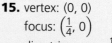

15. vertex: $(0, 0)$
   focus: $\left(\frac{1}{4}, 0\right)$
   directrix: $x = -\frac{1}{4}$

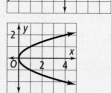

Problem 5 Writing an Equation of a Parabola

Multiple Choice Which is an equation of the parabola with vertex (3, 7) and focus (5, 7)?

Ⓐ $x = \frac{1}{4}(y - 7)^2 + 3$

Ⓒ $x = \frac{1}{8}(y - 7)^2 + 3$

Ⓑ $y = \frac{1}{8}(x - 7)^2 + 3$

Ⓓ $x = \frac{1}{8}(y + 7)^2 - 3$

The focus is to the right of the vertex, so the parabola is horizontal. Also, (h, k) is (3, 7) and $(h + c, k)$ is (5, 7), so $c = 2$. Substitute all this information into the equation for a horizontal parabola, $x = \frac{1}{4c}(y - k)^2 + h$, to get $x = \frac{1}{8}(y - 7)^2 + 3$.
The correct answer is C.

 Got It? 5. What is an equation of the parabola with vertex (1, 4) and focus (1, 6)?

Plan
How do you determine which equation to use?
Use the focus and the vertex to determine the orientation of the parabola.

Lesson Check

Do you know HOW?

Write an equation of a parabola with the given information.

1. vertex (0, 0), focus $\left(0, \frac{1}{2}\right)$

2. vertex (3, 2), focus (4, 2)

Find the vertex, focus, and the directrix of each parabola.

3. $x = \frac{1}{16}y^2$

4. $y = x^2 + 6x + 5$

Do you UNDERSTAND? MATHEMATICAL PRACTICES

5. Vocabulary If the vertex of a parabola is 3 units from the focus, how far is the focus from the directrix?

6. Error Analysis The vertex of a parabola is at the origin, one unit away from the focus. A student concludes that the equation is $y = \frac{1}{4}x^2$. Identify at least two ways in which the student's equation might be in error.

Practice and Problem-Solving Exercises MATHEMATICAL PRACTICES

Ⓐ **Practice** Write an equation of a parabola with vertex at the origin and the given focus. ◆ See Problem 1.

7. focus at (6, 0)

8. focus at (0, −4)

9. focus at (0, 7)

10. focus at (−1, 0)

11. focus at (2, 0)

12. focus at (0, −5)

Identify the vertex, the focus, and the directrix of the parabola with the given equation. Then sketch the graph of the parabola. ◆ See Problems 1 and 2.

13. $y = 4x^2$

14. $y = -\frac{1}{8}x^2$

15. $x = y^2$

16. $x = \frac{1}{2}y^2$

Write an equation of a parabola with vertex at the origin and the given directrix. ◆ See Problem 2.

17. directrix $x = -3$

18. directrix $y = 5$

19. directrix $y = -\frac{1}{3}$

20. directrix $x = 9$

21. directrix $y = 2.8$

22. directrix $x = -3.75$

---

16. vertex: (0, 0)
focus: $\left(\frac{1}{2}, 0\right)$
directrix: $x = -\frac{1}{2}$

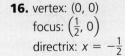

17. $x = \frac{1}{12}y^2$

18. $y = -\frac{1}{20}x^2$

19. $y = \frac{3}{4}x^2$

20. $x = -\frac{1}{36}y^2$

21. $y = -\frac{5}{56}x^2$

22. $x = \frac{1}{15}y^2$

23. Answers may vary. Sample: $y = x^2$. The light produced by the bulb will reflect off the parabolic mirror in parallel rays.

24. vertex: (−2, −1)
focus: $\left(-2, -\frac{3}{4}\right)$
directrix: $y = -\frac{5}{4}$

25. vertex: (3, 2)
focus: $\left(3, \frac{9}{4}\right)$
directrix: $y = \frac{7}{4}$

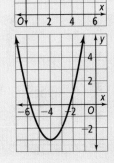

26. vertex: (−4, −3)
focus: $\left(-4, -2\frac{3}{4}\right)$
directrix: $y = -3\frac{1}{4}$

Problem 5

Q How can you use the vertex to help you eliminate one of the answers? **[The vertex is a point on the parabola, so (3, 7) must be a solution to the equation. This point is not a solution to answer D, so D is incorrect.]**

Got It?

Q What is the orientation of this parabola? Explain. **[The focus is above the vertex, so this is a vertical parabola opening upward.]**

3 Lesson Check

Do you know HOW?

• For Exercises 1 and 2, suggest to students that they first determine whether the parabola is vertical or horizontal.

Do you UNDERSTAND?

• If students have trouble with Exercise 6, remind them that a parabola can have any orientation. This lesson focused on vertical and horizontal parabolas facing upward, downward, rightward, or leftward. Have students sketch these four types of parabolas each with vertex at the origin.

Close

Q What is true about the set of points on a parabola, its focus, and its directrix? **[A parabola is the set of all points that are the same distance from the directrix and the focus.]**

Q What can you determine about the orientation of a parabola by looking at its vertex equation? **[If the y-term is linear, the parabola is vertical. If the x-term is linear, the parabola is horizontal. If $\frac{1}{4c}$ is positive, it opens upward or rightward. If negative, it opens downward or leftward.]**

PowerAlgebra.com

3 Lesson Check

For a digital lesson check, use the Got It questions.

Support in Algebra 2 Companion
• Lesson Check

4 Practice

Assign homework to individual students or to an entire class.

4 Practice

ASSIGNMENT GUIDE

Basic: 7–33 all, 38–42 even, 45, 55

Average: 7–33 odd, 34–55

Advanced: 7–33 odd, 34–58

Standardized Test Prep: 59–62

Mixed Review: 63–69

 **Mathematical Practices** are supported by exercises with red headings. Here are the Practices supported in this lesson:

MP 1: Make Sense of Problems Ex. 40
MP 3: Communicate Ex. 55
MP 3: Construct Arguments Ex. 56, 58
MP 3: Critique the Reasoning of Others Ex. 6

Applications exercises have blue headings. Exercises 23 and 45 support MP 4: Model.

STEM exercises focus on science or engineering applications.

EXERCISE 45: Use the Think About a Plan worksheet in the **Practice and Problem Solving Workbook** (also available in the Teaching Resources in print and online) to further support students' development in becoming independent learners.

HOMEWORK QUICK CHECK

To check students' understanding of key skills and concepts, go over Exercises 9, 25, 40, 45, and 55.

STEM 23. Optics A cross section of a flashlight reflector is a parabola. The bulb is located at the focus. Suppose the bulb is located $\frac{1}{4}$ in. from the vertex of the reflector. Model a cross section of the reflector by writing an equation of a parabola that opens upward and has its vertex at the origin. What is an advantage of this parabolic design? ◀ See Problem 3.

Identify the vertex, the focus, and the directrix of the parabola with the given equation. Then sketch the graph of the parabola. ◀ See Problem 4.

24. $y = x^2 + 4x + 3$　　**25.** $y = x^2 - 6x + 11$　　**26.** $y = x^2 + 8x + 13$

27. $y = x^2 - 2x - 4$　　**28.** $y = x^2 - 8x + 17$　　**29.** $y = 2x^2 + 4x - 2$

Write an equation of a parabola with the given vertex and focus. ◀ See Problem 5.

30. vertex $(4, 1)$, focus $(6, 1)$　　　　**31.** vertex $(0, 3)$, focus $(-8, 3)$

32. vertex $(-5, 4)$, focus $(-5, 0)$　　　**33.** vertex $(7, 2)$, focus $(7, -2)$

B Apply Identify the vertex, the focus, and the directrix of a parabola with each equation. Then sketch a graph of the parabola with the given equation.

34. $y^2 - 25x = 0$　　**35.** $x^2 = -4y$　　　**36.** $(x - 2)^2 = 4y$

37. $-8x = y^2$　　　**38.** $y^2 - 6x = 18$　　**39.** $x^2 + 24y - 8x = -16$

40. Think About a Plan In some solar collectors, a mirror with a parabolic cross section is used to concentrate sunlight on a pipe, which is located at the focus of the mirror as shown in the diagram. What is an equation of the parabola that models the cross section of the mirror?
• What information can you get from the diagram?
• What information do you need to be able to write an equation that models the cross section of the mirror?

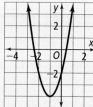

STEM 41. Earth Science The equation $d = \frac{1}{10}s^2$ relates the depth d (in meters) of the ocean to the speed s (in m/s) at which tsunamis travel. What is the graph of the equation?

Use the information in each graph to write the equation for the parabola.

42.

43.

44.

STEM 45. Sound Broadcasters use a parabolic microphone on football sidelines to pick up field audio for broadcasting purposes. A certain parabolic microphone has a reflector dish with a diameter of 28 inches and a depth of 14 inches. If the receiver of the microphone is located at the focus of the reflector dish, how far from the vertex should the receiver be positioned?

Answers

Practice and Problem-Solving Exercises (continued)

23–26. See previous page.

27. vertex: $(1, -5)$
focus: $\left(1, -4\frac{3}{4}\right)$
directrix: $y = -5\frac{1}{4}$

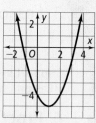

28. vertex: $(4, 1)$
focus: $\left(4, \frac{5}{4}\right)$
directrix: $y = \frac{3}{4}$

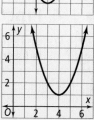

29. vertex: $(-1, -4)$
focus: $\left(-1, -3\frac{7}{8}\right)$
directrix: $y = -4\frac{1}{8}$

30. $x = \frac{1}{8}(y - 1)^2 + 4$

31. $x = -\frac{1}{32}(y - 3)^2$

32. $y = -\frac{1}{16}(x + 5)^2 + 4$

33. $y = -\frac{1}{16}(x - 7)^2 + 2$

34. vertex: $(0, 0)$
focus: $\left(\frac{25}{4}, 0\right)$
directrix: $x = -\frac{25}{4}$

35. vertex: $(0, 0)$
focus: $(0, -1)$
directrix: $y = 1$

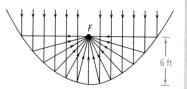

36. vertex: $(2, 0)$
focus: $(2, 1)$
directrix: $y = -1$

37. vertex: $(0, 0)$
focus: $(-2, 0)$
directrix: $x = 2$

38. vertex: $(-3, 0)$
focus: $\left(-\frac{3}{2}, 0\right)$
directrix: $x = -\frac{9}{2}$

Graph each equation.

46. $y^2 - 8x = 0$ **47.** $y^2 - 8y + 8x = -16$ **48.** $2x^2 - y + 20x = -53$

49. $x^2 = 12y$ **50.** $y = 4(x - 3)^2 - 2$ **51.** $(y - 2)^2 = 4(x + 3)$

Write an equation of a parabola with vertex at (1, 1) and the given information.

52. directrix $y = -\frac{1}{2}$ **53.** directrix $x = \frac{3}{2}$ **54.** focus at $(1, 0)$

 55. Writing Explain how to find the distance from the focus to the directrix of the parabola $x = 2y^2$.

Challenge **56. Reasoning** Use the definition of a parabola to show that the parabola with vertex (h, k) and focus $(h, k + c)$ has the equation $(x - h)^2 = 4c(y - k)$.

57. a. What part of a parabola is modeled by the function $y = \sqrt{x}$?
b. State the domain and range for the function in part (a).

 58. Proof If the radius and depth of a satellite dish are equal, prove that the radius is four times the focal length.

Standardized Test Prep

 SAT/ACT **59.** What is the equation of a parabola with vertex at the origin and focus at $\left(0, \frac{5}{2}\right)$?

Ⓐ $x = -\frac{1}{10}y^2$ Ⓑ $x = \frac{1}{10}y^2$ Ⓒ $x = -\frac{1}{10}x^2$ Ⓓ $y = \frac{1}{10}x^2$

60. Use the information in the graph to find the equation for the graph.

Ⓕ $y^2 + 6x = 0$ Ⓗ $x^2 + 6y = 0$
Ⓖ $y^2 - 6x = 0$ Ⓘ $x^2 - 6y = 0$

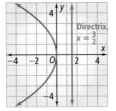

61. Which expression is NOT equivalent to $(25x^4y)^{\frac{1}{3}}$?

Ⓐ $x\sqrt[3]{25xy}$ Ⓒ $\sqrt[3]{25x^4y}$
Ⓑ $5x\sqrt[3]{xy}$ Ⓓ $\sqrt[6]{625x^8y^2}$

Extended Response **62.** Use the properties of logarithms to write log 12 in four different ways. Name each property you use.

Mixed Review

Graph each equation. Identify the conic section and describe the graph and its lines of symmetry. Then find the domain and range.

 ◆ See Lesson 10-1.

63. $x^2 + y^2 = 64$ **64.** $x^2 + 9y^2 = 9$ **65.** $4x^2 - 9y^2 = 36$

Get Ready! To prepare for Lesson 10-3, do Exercises 66–69.

Complete the square. ◆ See Lesson 4-6.

66. $x^2 - 2x + \blacksquare$ **67.** $x^2 + 4x + \blacksquare$ **68.** $x^2 + 10x + \blacksquare$ **69.** $x^2 - 6x + \blacksquare$

---

39. vertex: (4, 0) focus: (4, −6) directrix: $y = 6$

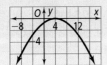

40. $y = \frac{1}{24}x^2$; the focal distance; the focus and the vertex

41.
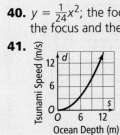
Tsunami Speed (m/s) vs Ocean Depth (m)

42. $x = -\frac{1}{8}y^2$ **43.** $y = \frac{1}{4}x^2$

44. $x = y^2$ **45.** 3.5 in.

46.
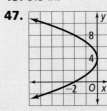
47.

48.
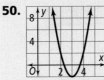
49.
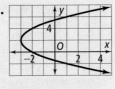

50.
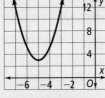
51.

52. $y = \frac{1}{6}(x - 1)^2 + 1$

53. $x = -\frac{1}{2}(y - 1)^2 + 1$

54. $y = -\frac{1}{4}(x - 1)^2 + 1$

55. Answers may vary. Sample: Write the eq. in the form $x = \frac{1}{4\left(\frac{1}{8}\right)}y^2$.

The distance from the focus to the directrix is $2\left(\frac{1}{8}\right)$, or $\frac{1}{4}$.

56. The directrix will have the eq. $y = k - c$. A pt. (x, y) is on

---

the parabola if and only if the distance from (x, y) to the directrix is equal to the distance from (x, y) to the focus. So (x, y) is on the parabola if and only if $|y - (k - c)| = \sqrt{(x - h)^2 + (y - k - c)^2}$. Square and simplify to get the equivalent eq., $4cy - 4kc = (x - h)^2$, or $(x - h)^2 = 4c(y - k)$.

57. a. the top half of the parabola, $y^2 = x$
b. domain: $x \geq 0$, range: $y \geq 0$

58. If $d = r$ and $d = \frac{1}{4c}r^2$, then $r = \frac{1}{4c}r^2$, $r = 4c$.

Standardized Test Prep

59. D **60.** F **61.** B

62. [4]

log 12 = log 3 · 4 = log 3 + log 4; Product Prop.

log 12 = log 3 · 2² = log 3 + 2 log 2; Product and Power Prop.

log 12 = log $\frac{24}{2}$ = log 24 − log 2; Quotient Prop.

log 12 = log $144^{\frac{1}{2}}$ = $\frac{1}{2}$ log 144; Power Prop.

[3] log 12 written in only three diff. ways, correct prop.

[2] log 12 written only in two diff. ways, correct prop. OR log 12 written in four diff. ways, with two incorrect prop.

[1] log 12 written in only two diff. ways, without correct prop.

Mixed Review

63.
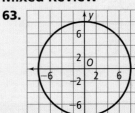
circle: center (0, 0), radius 8; x-intercepts: (±8, 0), y-intercepts: (0, ±8); infinitely many lines of sym.; domain: $-8 \leq x \leq 8$, range: $-8 \leq y \leq 8$

64.

ellipse: center (0, 0); x-intercepts: (±3, 0), y-intercepts: (0, ±1); lines of sym.: x-axis and y-axis; domain: $-3 \leq x \leq 3$, range: $-1 \leq y \leq 1$

65.
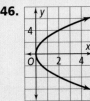
hyperbola: center (0, 0); x-intercepts (±3, 0), no y-intercept; lines of sym.: x-axis and y-axis; domain: $x \leq -3$ or $x \geq 3$, range: all real numbers

66. 1 **67.** 4 **68.** 25 **69.** 9

Additional Instructional Support

Algebra 2 Companion

Students can use the **Algebra 2 Companion** worktext (4 pages) as you teach the lesson. Use the Companion to support

- New Vocabulary
- Key Concepts
- Got It for each Problem
- Lesson Check

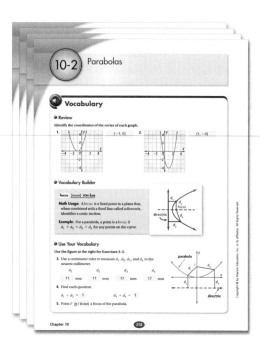

ELL Support

Focus on Language Sketch a parabola on the board. It is not necessary to draw the parabola on a coordinate plane because the focus of this activity is to become familiar with the vocabulary.

Ask, "What is the name of this figure?" [parabola] Place a point at the approximate location of the focus. Point to the focus and ask, "What is the name of this point?" [focus] Draw a line at the approximate location of the directrix. Point to the line and ask, "What is this line?" [directrix]

Next have several students come to the board and sketch parabolas of varying orientations. Parabolas can be vertical, horizontal, or at any angle. Ask each student to draw the approximate focus and directrix. Have students stand in front of their drawing and point to each object saying "parabola, focus, directrix." Next have students move in front of a different sketch and name each part on the new drawing.

5 Assess & Remediate

Lesson Quiz

1. What is an equation of the parabola with vertex at the origin and focus (0, 0.75)?

2. What is an equation of the parabola with vertex at the origin and directrix $x = \frac{1}{8}$?

3. **Do you UNDERSTAND?** A convex lens has a diameter of 30 mm and a depth of 5 mm at the center. How far from the vertex is the focus?

4. What are the vertex, focus, and directrix of the parabola with equation $y = x^2 + 10x + 12$?

5. What is an equation of the parabola with vertex (6, 7) and focus (7, 7)?

ANSWERS TO LESSON QUIZ

1. $y = \frac{1}{3}x^2$
2. $x = -2y^2$
3. 11.25 mm
4. vertex: $(-5, -13)$; focus: $(-5, -12.75)$; directrix: $y = -13.25$
5. $x = \frac{1}{4}(y - 7)^2 + 6$

PRESCRIPTION FOR REMEDIATION
Use the student work on the Lesson Quiz to prescribe a differentiated review assignment:

Points	Differentiated Remediation
0–2	Intervention
3–4	On-level
5	Extension

PowerAlgebra.com

5 Assess & Remediate

Assign the Lesson Quiz. Appropriate intervention, practice, or enrichment is automatically generated based on student performance.

Intervention

- **Reteaching** (2 pages) Provides reteaching and practice exercises for the key lesson concepts. Use with struggling students or absent students.

- **English Language Learner Support** Helps students develop and reinforce mathematical vocabulary and key concepts.

All-in-One Resources/Online
Reteaching

10-2 Reteaching
Parabolas

Problem

What is the graph of the equation $y = -\frac{1}{2}x^2$? Label the vertex, focus, and directrix on your graph.

Step 1
Identify information from the given equation.

$y = -\frac{1}{2}x^2$

$a < 0$ opens downward focus: $(0, -c)$ directrix: $y = c$

| a is negative. When a is negative, the parabola has these characteristics. |

Step 2
Find c.

$|a| = \frac{1}{4c}$

True for all parabolas.

$\left|-\frac{1}{2}\right| = \frac{1}{4c}$ Substitute $-\frac{1}{2}$ for a.

$(2c)\frac{1}{2} = (2c)\frac{1}{4c} = \frac{1}{2}$ Solve for c.

Step 3
Find the vertex, the focus, and the equation of the directrix.

$(0, 0)$ The parabola is of the form $y = ax^2$, so the vertex is at the origin.

$\left(0, -\frac{1}{2}\right)$ The focus is always $(0, -c)$.

$y = \frac{1}{2}$ The directrix is at $y = c$.

Step 4
Locate two more points on the parabola.

$y = -\frac{1}{2}(1)^2$ Substitute 1 for x.

$y = -\frac{1}{2}$ Solve for y.

$\left(1, -\frac{1}{2}\right)$

$y = -\frac{1}{2}(-1)^2$ Substitute -1 for x.

$y = -\frac{1}{2}$ Solve for y.

$\left(-1, -\frac{1}{2}\right)$

Step 5
Graph the parabola using the information you found.

Exercises

Graph each equation. Label the vertex, focus, and directrix on each graph.

1. $y = \frac{1}{4}x^2$
2. $y = -\frac{1}{6}x^2$
3. $x = -\frac{1}{3}y^2$

All-in-One Resources/Online
English Language Learner Support

10-2 Additional Vocabulary Support
Parabolas

What are the vertex, focus, and directrix of the parabola with equation $y = x^2 - 5x + 11$?

You wrote these steps to solve the problem on the note cards, but they got mixed up.

| The vertex is (h, k), so the focus is $(h, k + c)$. | Complete the square to get the equation in vertex form. |

| The directrix is $y = k - c$. | Use $\frac{1}{4c}$ to determine the distance from the vertex to the focus and from the vertex to the directrix. |

Use the note cards to write the steps in order.

1. First, complete the square to get the equation in vertex form

2. Second, use $\frac{1}{4c}$ to determine the distance from the vertex to the focus and from the vertex to the directrix

3. Next, the vertex is (h, k), so the focus is $(h, k + c)$

4. Finally, the directrix is $y = k - c$

Differentiated Remediation *continued*

On-Level

- **Practice (2 pages)** Provides extra practice for each lesson. For simpler practice exercises, use the Form K Practice pages found in the All-in-One Teaching Resources and online.

- **Think About a Plan** Helps students develop specific problem-solving skills and strategies by providing scaffolded guiding questions.

- **Standardized Test Prep** Focuses on all major exercises, all major question types, and helps students prepare for the high-stakes assessments.

Extension

- **Enrichment** Provides students with interesting problems and activities that extend the concepts of the lesson.

- **Activities, Games, and Puzzles** Worksheets that can be used for concepts development, enrichment, and for fun!

Practice and Problem Solving Wkbk/ All-in-One Resources/Online
Practice page 1

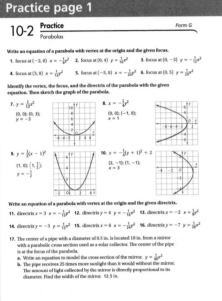

Practice and Problem Solving Wkbk/ All-in-One Resources/Online
Practice page 2

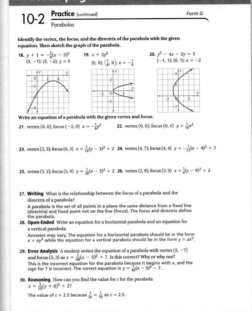

All-in-One Resources/Online
Enrichment

10-2 Enrichment
Parabolas

Quadratic Maxima and Minima

Consider the equation of a parabola in standard form, $y = a(x - h)^2 + k$. If $a > 0$, then the parabola opens upward and the vertex (h, k) represents the lowest point, or minimum value, on the graph. Similarly, if $a < 0$, the parabola opens downward and the vertex (h, k) represents the highest point, or maximum value, on the graph.

Suppose that a rancher has 100 yd of fencing with which to construct a rectangular field in such a way that the total area enclosed is a maximum.

1. If ℓ represents the length of the field and w its width, what equation expresses the area A of the field? $A = \ell w$

2. How would you express the fact that the perimeter P of the field must be 100 yd? $P = 2\ell + 2w = 100$

3. Solve the perimeter equation for ℓ in terms of w, and substitute into the area equation. What is the equation for A in terms of w? $A = (50 - w)w = 50w - w^2$

4. Write your equation in standard form for a parabola. $A = -(w - 25)^2 + 625$

5. For which value of w is the area a maximum? $w = 25$ yd

6. What is the corresponding length ℓ? $\ell = 25$ yd

7. What is the area of the field? 625 yd^2

8. What is its shape? square

Repeat the exercises above assuming that the rancher has 200 yd of fencing.

9. What are the dimensions of the field enclosing the maximum area? 50 yd by 50 yd

10. On the basis of your results, what might you infer? The largest rectangle with a fixed perimeter is a square.

11. What type of geometric figure might enclose the most area given a fixed perimeter? Explain. A circle; its ratio of area to perimeter is even greater than a square's.

Practice and Problem Solving Wkbk/ All-in-One Resources/Online
Think About a Plan

10-2 Think About a Plan
Parabolas

Sound Broadcasters use a parabolic microphone on football sidelines to pick up field audio for broadcasting purposes. A certain parabolic microphone has a reflector dish with a diameter of 28 inches and a depth of 14 inches. If the receiver of the microphone is located at the focus of the reflector dish, how far from the vertex should the receiver be positioned?

Understanding the Problem

1. What is the diameter of the reflector dish? 28 in.

2. What is the depth of the reflector dish? 14 in.

3. What is the problem asking you to determine? the distance between the receiver and the vertex of the dish

Planning the Solution

4. Sketch a graph of a vertical parabola to represent the reflector dish. Place the vertex at the origin.

5. You know the coordinates of two other points on the parabola. Plot and label them on your graph.

6. What is the equation for a vertical parabola with vertex at the origin? $y = \frac{1}{4c}x^2$

7. How can you find the location of the focus from the equation for the parabola? Substitute the point (14, 14) or (−14, 14) into the equation. Solve for c. The focus is at (0, c)

Getting an Answer

8. What is the location of the focus? (0, 3.5)

9. If the receiver of the microphone is located at the focus of the reflector dish, how far from the vertex should the receiver be positioned? 3.5 in.

Practice and Problem Solving Wkbk/ All-in-One Resources/Online
Standardized Test Prep

10-2 Standardized Test Prep
Parabolas

Multiple Choice

For Exercises 1–5, choose the correct letter.

1. Which is an equation of the parabola with the vertex at the origin and focus (0, 3)? B
   Ⓐ $y = \frac{1}{4}x^2$ Ⓑ $y = \frac{1}{12}x^2$ Ⓒ $x = \frac{1}{12}y^2$ Ⓓ $x = \frac{1}{3}y^2$

2. What is the focus of the parabola with the equation $y = -\frac{1}{16}x^2$? F
   Ⓕ (0, −4)   Ⓖ (−4, 0)   Ⓗ $\left(0, -\frac{1}{16}\right)$ Ⓘ $\left(-\frac{1}{16}, 0\right)$

3. Which is the equation of a parabola with vertex at the origin and directrix $x = 2.5$? A
   Ⓐ $x = -\frac{1}{10}y^2$ Ⓑ $x = \frac{1}{10}y^2$ Ⓒ $x = \frac{1}{2.5}y^2$ Ⓓ $x = -\frac{5}{2}y^2$

4. What is the directrix of $x = 2.25y^2$? I
   Ⓕ $x = \frac{1}{4}$ Ⓖ $x = -\frac{1}{4}$ Ⓗ $x = \frac{1}{9}$ Ⓘ $x = -\frac{1}{9}$

5. What is the vertex of $y = x^2 - 8x + 10$? D
   Ⓐ (−4, 8)   Ⓑ (8, 10)   Ⓒ (10, 16)   Ⓓ (4, −6)

Short Response

6. What are the vertex, focus, and directrix of the parabola with equation $y = x^2 - 14x + 5$? Show your work.
   [2] $y = x^2 - 14x + 5$; $y = (x^2 - 14x + 49) + 5 - 49$; $y = (x - 7)^2 - 44$; vertex $(h, k) = (7, -44)$; focus $(h, k + c) = (7, -43.75)$; directrix $(y = k - c)$ is $y = -44.25$
   [1] incorrect vertex OR incorrect focus OR incorrect directrix OR correct answers, without work shown
   [0] incorrect answers and no work shown OR no answers given

Online Teacher Resource Center
Activities, Games, and Puzzles

10-2 Game: A Parabolic Race
Parabolas

This is a game for two players. Each player uses one of the parabolic racetracks provided. For each item below, decide whether the parabola described *opens up, down, to the right,* or *to the left.* Write your answer to the right of each item.

- Move from one point to the next for each correct answer.
- Players must agree on the accuracy of each answer.
- The first player to cross the finish line wins. If neither player crosses, then the player who advances farthest wins.

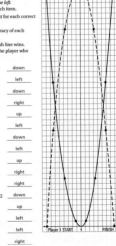

1. focus: $F(-2, 1)$; directrix: $y = 3$ down
2. vertex: $V(2, 7)$; focus: $F(-2, 7)$ left
3. $y = -x^2 + 2x + 5$ down
4. $A(0, 3)$, $B(4, 7)$, $C(4, -7)$ right
5. $y = 3(x - 2)^2 + 1$ up
6. vertex: $V(5, 2)$; directrix: $x = 6$ left
7. vertex: $V(0, 7)$; focus: $F(0, 0)$ down
8. $x = -5y^2 - 2$ left
9. $A(-3, 6)$, $B(0, 1)$, $C(4, 8)$ up
10. $x = 2(y - 1)^2 + 2$ right
11. focus: $F(2, 8)$; directrix: $x = 0$ right
12. vertex: $V(-3, 1)$; directrix: $y = 2$ down
13. $y = 0.3x^2 - 2x + 1$ up
14. focus: $F(2.2, 2)$; vertex: $V(5, 2)$ left
15. $x = -(y + 1)^2 - 3$ left
16. $K(3, 6)$, $L(0, 3)$, $M(3, -6)$ right

1 Interactive Learning

Solve It!

PURPOSE To apply geometric properties of circles, squares, and right triangles

PROCESS Students may

- use the Pythagorean Theorem or distance formula to find the radius of the pond.
- use properties of right triangles, squares, and congruent triangles to find the radius of the feeder pond.

FACILITATE

Q How can the radius of the pond be measured? **[Draw a diameter perpendicular to a tangent line at the point of tangency. The radius is half the length of the diameter.]**

Q Where is the tangency point of the ponds located? **[in the middle of the upper right side of the patch]**

ANSWER See Solve It in Answers on next page.

CONNECT THE MATH In the Solve It, students find the radii of two circles. In the lesson, students will define a circle as the set of points in a plane a fixed distance—the radius—from a center point.

2 Guided Instruction

Take Note

Q What information do you need to write the equation of a circle? **[the center or the horizontal and vertical translations of the center from the origin, and the radius]**

10-3 Circles

Objectives To write and graph the equation of a circle
To find the center and radius of a circle and use them to graph the circle

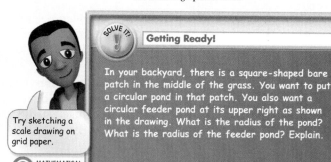

Try sketching a scale drawing on grid paper.

© **MATHEMATICAL PRACTICES**

Getting Ready!

In your backyard, there is a square-shaped bare patch in the middle of the grass. You want to put a circular pond in that patch. You also want a circular feeder pond at its upper right as shown in the drawing. What is the radius of the pond? What is the radius of the feeder pond? Explain.

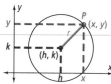

80 ft

Dynamic Activity
Circles in the Coordinate Plane

Lesson Vocabulary
- circle
- center of a circle
- radius
- standard form of an equation of a circle

A **circle** is the set of all points in a plane that are a distance r from a given point, the **center of a circle**. The distance r is the **radius** of the circle. The use of *distance* in these definitions makes the distance formula

$$d = \sqrt{(x_2 - x_1)^2 + (y_2 - y_1)^2}$$ a useful tool for describing a circle in the coordinate plane.

Essential Understanding An equation of a circle with center $(0, 0)$ and radius r in the coordinate plane is $x^2 + y^2 = r^2$.

Not every circle has its center at the origin. Suppose a circle with radius r has center (h, k). Then r is the distance from (h, k) to any point (x, y) on the circle.

$r = \sqrt{(x - h)^2 + (y - k)^2}$ Distance formula
$r^2 = (x - h)^2 + (y - k)^2$ Square each side.

take note

Key Concept   **Standard Form of an Equation of a Circle**

The **standard form of an equation of a circle** with center (h, k) and radius r is
$(x - h)^2 + (y - k)^2 = r^2$.

10-3 Preparing to Teach

BIG idea   **Equivalence**

ESSENTIAL UNDERSTANDINGS

- An equation of a circle with center $(0, 0)$ and radius r in the coordinate plane is $x^2 + y^2 = r^2$.
- Not every circle has its center at the origin. Suppose a circle with radius r has center (h, k). Then r is the distance from (h, k) to any point (x, y) on the circle. The equation is $r^2 = (x - h)^2 + (y - k)^2$.
- $\frac{x^2}{r^2} + \frac{y^2}{r^2} = 1$ is an equation of a circle centered at the origin with radius r. Multiply each side by r^2 to get $x^2 + y^2 = r^2$.

Math Background

A circle is the conic section obtained when a cross section of a cone is taken perpendicularly to the cone's axis.

A circle is defined as the set of all points equidistant from a given point, called the center. In the coordinate plane, the standard form of an equation of a circle is given by $(x - h)^2 + (y - k)^2 = r^2$, where

- h is the horizontal translation of the center from the origin,
- k is the vertical translation of the center from the origin, and
- r is the radius, or the distance from the center to any point on the circle

The lesson shows how to derive the standard equation of a circle from the distance formula. Deriving it using the Pythagorean Theorem is a good activity for interested students. For example, use the same diagram for the distance formula on page 630. Sketch the two legs of a right triangle with r as the hypotenuse and the third vertex as (x, k).

The length of one leg is $x - h$, and the length of the second leg is $y - k$. Thus by the Pythagorean Theorem, $(x - h)^2 + (y - k)^2 = r^2$.

© **Mathematical Practices**
Look for and make use of structure.
Students will find a circle to be defined by two objects, a point and a radius, and will graph using both.

PowerAlgebra.com

1 Interactive Learning

Solve It!
Step out how to solve the Problem with helpful hints and an online question. Other questions are listed above in Interactive Learning.

Dynamic Activity Students can explore a circle in the form $(x - h)^2 + (y - k)^2 = r^2$ by varying the values of h, k, and r. They can also see how the graph of a circle relates to its geometric definition.

You can use the center and the radius of a circle to write an equation for the circle.

 Problem 1 Writing an Equation of a Circle

What is an equation of the circle with center $(-4, 3)$ and radius 4?

$(x - h)^2 + (y - k)^2 = r^2$ Use the standard form.

$(x - (-4))^2 + (y - 3)^2 = 4^2$ Substitute -4 for h, 3 for k, and 4 for r.

$(x + 4)^2 + (y - 3)^2 = 16$ Simplify.

An equation of the circle is $(x + 4)^2 + (y - 3)^2 = 16$.

Check Solve the equation for y. Enter both functions into your graphing calculator.

$(x + 4)^2 + (y - 3)^2 = 16$

$(y - 3)^2 = 16 - (x + 4)^2$

$y - 3 = \pm\sqrt{16 - (x + 4)^2}$

$y = 3 \pm \sqrt{16 - (x + 4)^2}$

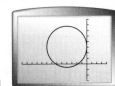

Got It? 1. What is an equation of the circle with center $(5, -2)$ and radius 8? Check your answer.

 Problem 2 Using Translations to Write an Equation

What is an equation for the translation of $x^2 + y^2 = 9$ by 4 units left and 3 units up? Draw the graph.

Know	Need	Plan
The original equation that is translated 4 units left and 3 units up	The equation and graph of the translation	• Use the standard form to write the equation of the translation. • Graph the equation.

$x^2 + y^2 = 9$ Write the given equation.

$(x - (-4))^2 + (y - 3)^2 = 9$ The graph is translated left 4 units and up 3 units.

$(x + 4)^2 + (y - 3)^2 = 3^2$ Simplify inside the parentheses. The form $(x - h)^2 + (y - k)^2 = r^2$ shows the radius r.

Graph the given equation and the translation.

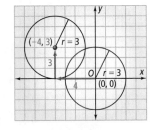

Got It? 2. What is an equation for each translation?
  a. $x^2 + y^2 = 1$; left 5 units and down 3 units
  b. $x^2 + y^2 = 9$; right 2 units and up 3 units

Plan

How do you know which equation to use?
Since this circle is not centered at the origin, use the standard form equation.

Think

How does the translation help you draw the graph?
Use the translation to determine the new center coordinates.

Problem 1

Q Why do you subtract h and k rather than add them? **[Sample: The formula for a circle is derived from the distance formula, in which the variables are subtracted, not added.]**

EXTENSION

Q What does r^2 correspond to in the Pythagorean Theorem? **[r^2 is the square of the length of the hypotenuse.]**

Got It?

Q How can checking the graph of an equation of a circle help you find what errors you may have made in writing the equation? **[Samples: If the center is in the wrong quadrant, one or more signs may be incorrect in the equation; if the radius is too small, it may not have been squared in the equation.]**

Problem 2

Q Does a translation change the radius? Explain. **[No; a translation only relocates the graph of the circle; it does not stretch or shrink the graph of the circle.]**

Got It?

Q How can you check whether your equation for the translation of the circle is correct? **[Sketch the translation without using the translated equation, and then graph the translated equation using your graphing calculator. Compare the graphs.]**

Answers

Solve It!

$20\sqrt{2} \approx 28.28$ ft; $40 - 20\sqrt{2} \approx 11.72$ ft

Got It?

1. $(x - 5)^2 + (y + 2)^2 = 64$

2. a. $(x + 5)^2 + (y + 3)^2 = 1$

  b. $(x - 2)^2 + (y - 3)^2 = 9$

---

2 Guided Instruction

 Each Problem is worked out and supported online.

Problem 1
Writing an Equation of a Circle
Animated

Problem 2
Using Translations to Write an Equation
Animated

Problem 3
Using a Graph to Write an Equation

Problem 4
Finding the Center and Radius
Animated

Problem 5
Graphing a Circle Using Center and Radius

Support in Algebra 2 Companion
• Vocabulary
• Key Concepts
• Got It?

Take Note

Q What are the center and radius of the unit circle? **[(0, 0); 1 unit]**

Q What values of r will stretch the unit circle? What values of r will shrink the unit circle? **[values of $r > 1$; values of r such that $0 < r < 1$]**

Problem 3

Q What reason or reasons can you give to eliminate each of the choices B, C, and D? **[For choice B, the values for h and k are reversed, and the signs on h and k are incorrect; for choice C, the radius is not squared; for choice D, the radius is not squared, and the signs on h and k are incorrect.]**

EXTENSION

Q What would be an equation of the circle representing the edge of the field if it were centered at (0, 0)? **[$x^2 + y^2 = 160,000$]**

Got It?

Q What errors might someone make writing the equation of the circular field described in 3a? **[Samples: You might not square the radius; you might add h and k instead of subtracting them; you might forget the square notation; you might reverse the positions of h and k in the equation.]**

 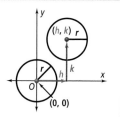

Key Concept Transforming a Circle

You can use the parameter r to stretch or shrink the unit circle $x^2 + y^2 = 1$ to the circle $x^2 + y^2 = r^2$ with radius r.

You can use the parameters h and k to translate the circle $x^2 + y^2 = r^2$ with center $(0, 0)$ to the circle $(x - h)^2 + (y - k)^2 = r^2$ with center (h, k).

Plan

 What information do you need to write an equation for the circle? You need the center and radius of the circle.

Problem 3 Using a Graph to Write an Equation

Multiple Choice Which equation models the circular irrigation field?

Ⓐ $(x - 450)^2 + (y - 500)^2 = 160,000$ Ⓒ $(x - 450)^2 + (y - 500)^2 = 400$

Ⓑ $(x + 500)^2 + (y + 450)^2 = 160,000$ Ⓓ $(x + 450)^2 + (y + 500)^2 = 400$

According to the photograph, this circular irrigation field has radius 400 and center at the point $(450, 500)$.

$(x - h)^2 + (y - k)^2 = r^2$ Use the standard form.

$(x - 450)^2 + (y - 500)^2 = 400^2$ Substitute the values of h, k, and r from the photograph.

$(x - 450)^2 + (y - 500)^2 = 160,000$ Simplify.

The correct answer is A.

Got It? 3. a. What is an equation of the circle for a circular irrigation field that has radius 12 and center $(7, -10)$?

b. Reasoning Will the graph of every equation of the form $(x - h)^2 + (y - k)^2 = r^2$, where h, k, and r are real numbers, be a circle? Explain your reasoning.

(450, 500)

400 ft

Additional Problems

1. What is an equation of a circle with center $(3, -5)$ and radius 2?

ANSWER
$(x - 3)^2 + (y + 5)^2 = 4$

2. What is an equation for the translation of $x^2 + y^2 = 10$ by 2 units right and 5 units down?

ANSWER
$(x - 2)^2 + (y + 5)^2 = 10$

3. You row a boat from the water's edge to the center of a circular pond, located 30 feet north and 80 feet west of your starting point. If the location where you began rowing is the origin, what equation represents

the water's edge around the pond?

ANSWER
$(x + 80)^2 + (y - 30)^2 = 7300$

4. What are the center and radius of the circle with the equation $x^2 + y^2 + 2x - 6y = 6$?

ANSWER center $(-1, 3)$, radius 4

5. What is the graph of $x^2 + (y - 1)^2 = 16$?

ANSWER

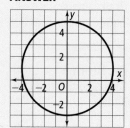

You can find the center and radius of a circle by rewriting the equation in standard form. In some cases, you may need to complete the square.

© **Problem 4** **Finding the Center and Radius**

What are the center and radius of the circle with the given equation?

Ⓐ $(x - 16)^2 + (y + 9)^2 = 144$

$(x - 16)^2 + (y - (-9))^2 = 12^2$ Rewrite the equation in standard form.

$h = 16$ $k = -9$ $r = 12$ Find h, k, and r.

The center of the circle is $(16, -9)$. The radius is 12.

Ⓑ $x^2 + y^2 + 8x - 10y = 8$

$(x^2 + 8x) + (y^2 - 10y) = 8$ Set up to complete the squares.

$(x^2 + 8x + 16) + (y^2 - 10y + 25) = 8 + 16 + 25$ Complete the squares and balance the equation.

$(x + 4)^2 + (y - 5)^2 = 49$ Simplify.

$(x - (-4))^2 + (y - 5)^2 = 7^2$ Rewrite the equation in standard form.

$h = -4$ $k = 5$ $r = 7$ Find h, k, and r.

The center of the circle is $(-4, 5)$. The radius is 7.

✔ **Got It?** **4.** What are the center and radius of the circle with the given equation?

a. $(x + 8)^2 + (y + 3)^2 = 121$ **b.** $x^2 + y^2 - 6x + 14y = 8$

Plan

What do you need to do to the equation to find the center and radius of the circle?
Write the equation in standard form.

You can use the center and the radius to graph a circle.

© **Problem 5** **Graphing a Circle Using Center and Radius**

What is the graph of $(x + 1)^2 + (y - 3)^2 = 25$?

$(x - (-1))^2 + (y - 3)^2 = 5^2$ Rewrite the equation in standard form.

$h = -1$ $k = 3$ $r = 5$ Identify h, k, and r.

center: $(-1, 3)$ radius: $r = 5$ Find the center and the radius of the circle.

Locate the center $(-1, 3)$.

Draw a circle of radius 5.

Plan

What information do you need to graph a circle?
You need the center and radius of the circle.

✔ **Got It?** **5.** What is the graph of $(x - 4)^2 + (y + 2)^2 = 49$?

Problem 4

Q What error can be avoided by writing the equation of the circle in 4A in standard form to find the center and the radius? **[The radius will not be mistaken for 144; and the center will be identified correctly.]**

Q In Problem 4B, why do you add 16 to the x^2 and x terms and 25 to the y^2 and y terms? **[to form perfect square trinomials]**

Q Is $(x + 4)^2 + (y - 5)^2 = 49$ in standard form? Explain. **[No; $(x + 4)^2$ is not written as $(x - h)^2$ (or $(x - (-4))^2$), and 49 is not written as r^2 (or 7^2).]**

Got It?

Q Is the radius of the circle for 4b equal to the square root of 8? Explain. **[No; the value on the right side of the equation changes after you complete the square and balance the equation.]**

Problem 5

Q How can you check your graph? **[Sample: Solve the equation for y and use a graphing calculator.]**

Q How would you describe the translation of the equation from $x^2 + y^2 = 25$? **[left one, up three]**

Got It?

Q How is $(x - 4)^2 + (y + 2)^2 = 49$ translated from $x^2 + y^2 = 49$? **[right 4, down 2]**

Answers

Got It? (continued)

3. a. $(x - 7)^2 + (y + 10)^2 = 144$

b. Yes; the values h and k determine the position of the circle and r determines the size.

4. a. center $(-8, -3)$, radius 11

b. center $(3, -7)$, radius $\sqrt{66}$

5.

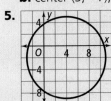

3 Lesson Check

Do you know HOW?

- If students have difficulty writing the equations for Exercises 1–4, have them identify the values of h, k, and r in each problem and then use the standard form of the equation of a circle.

Do you UNDERSTAND?

- If students have difficulty locating the error in Exercise 5, have them identify several translations such as $(x - 4)^2$, $(x - (-4))^2$, and $(x + 4)^2$. Then have them identify the translation in the problem without looking at the student's answer.
- If students have difficulty completing Exercise 6, suggest they sketch a picture of the conditions and then sketch a right triangle with one vertex at the origin, one vertex on the circle, and the right angle on the x-axis.

Close

> **Q** What is the standard form of an equation of a circle, and what do the variables h, k, and r represent? [$(x - h)^2 + (y - k)^2 = r^2$; h and k are the x- and y-coordinates of the center, and r is the radius of the circle.]

 Lesson Check

Do you know HOW?

Use the given information to write an equation of a circle.

1. center at $(-1, -5)$, radius 2

2. center at $(0, 0)$, radius 6

Write an equation for each translation.

3. $x^2 + y^2 = 121$; up 3 units

4. $x^2 + y^2 = 16$; left 5 units and down 3 units

Do you UNDERSTAND? MATHEMATICAL PRACTICES

5. **Error Analysis** A student claims that the circle $(x + 7)^2 + (y - 7)^2 = 8$ is a translation of the circle $x^2 + y^2 = 8$, 7 units right and 7 units down. What is the student's mistake?

6. **Reasoning** Let $P(x, y)$ be any point on the circle with center $(0, 0)$ and radius r. Prove that $x^2 + y^2 = r^2$ is an equation for the circle.

Practice and Problem-Solving Exercises   MATHEMATICAL PRACTICES

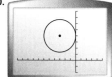 **Practice**   Write an equation of a circle with the given center and radius. Check your answers.   See Problem 1.

7. center $(0, 0)$, radius 10
8. center $(-4, -6)$, radius 7
9. center $(2, 3)$, radius 4.5

10. center $(-6, 10)$, radius 1
11. center $(1, -3)$, radius 10
12. center $(-1.5, -3)$, radius 2

Write an equation for each translation.   See Problem 2.

13. $x^2 + y^2 = 9$; down 1 unit
14. $x^2 + y^2 = 1$; left 1 unit

15. $x^2 + y^2 = 25$; right 2 units and down 4 units
16. $x^2 + y^2 = 81$; left 1 unit and up 3 units

17. $x^2 + y^2 = 100$; down 5 units
18. $x^2 + y^2 = 49$; right 3 units and up 2 units

19. An archery target has a circular bull's-eye (diameter 24 cm) surrounded by four concentric rings, each with a width of 12 cm. Draw the target in a coordinate plane with center at the origin. Write the equations of the circles that form the boundaries of the different regions of the target.

Write an equation for each circle. Each interval represents one unit.   See Problem 3.

20.

21.

For each equation, find the center and radius of the circle.   See Problem 4.

22. $(x - 1)^2 + (y - 1)^2 = 1$
23. $(x + 2)^2 + (y - 10)^2 = 4$

24. $(x - 3)^2 + (y + 1)^2 = 36$
25. $(x + 3)^2 + (y - 5)^2 = 81$

26. $x^2 + (y + 3)^2 = 25$
27. $(x + 6)^2 + y^2 = 121$

3 Lesson Check

For a digital lesson check, use the Got It questions.

Support in Algebra 2 Companion
- Lesson Check

4 Practice

Assign homework to individual students or to an entire class.

Answers

Lesson Check

1. $(x + 1)^2 + (y + 5)^2 = 4$
2. $x^2 + y^2 = 36$
3. $x^2 + (y - 3)^2 = 121$
4. $(x + 5)^2 + (y + 3)^2 = 16$
5. The circle with equation $(x + 7)^2 + (y - 7)^2 = 8$ is a translation of the circle with equation $x^2 + y^2 = 8$ as 7 units left and 7 units up, not right and down.
6. If $P(x, y)$ is one of the pts. $(r, 0)$, $(-r, 0)$, $(0, r)$, or $(0, -r)$, subst. shows that $x^2 + y^2 = r^2$. If $P(x, y)$ is any other pt. on the circle, drop a perpendicular $\overline{PK}$ from P to K on the x-axis. $\triangle OPK$ is a rt. triangle with legs of lengths $|x|$ and $|y|$ and with hypotenuse of length r. By the Pythagorean Thm., $|x|^2 + |y|^2 = r^2$, so $x^2 + y^2 = r^2$.

Practice and Problem-Solving Exercises

7. $x^2 + y^2 = 100$
8. $(x + 4)^2 + (y + 6)^2 = 49$
9. $(x - 2)^2 + (y - 3)^2 = 20.25$
10. $(x + 6)^2 + (y - 10)^2 = 1$
11. $(x - 1)^2 + (y + 3)^2 = 100$
12. $(x + 1.5)^2 + (y + 3)^2 = 4$
13. $x^2 + (y + 1)^2 = 9$
14. $(x + 1)^2 + y^2 = 1$
15. $(x - 2)^2 + (y + 4)^2 = 25$
16. $(x + 1)^2 + (y - 3)^2 = 81$
17. $x^2 + (y + 5)^2 = 100$
18. $(x - 3)^2 + (y - 2)^2 = 49$
19.
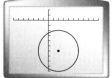 ; $x^2 + y^2 = 144$, $x^2 + y^2 = 576$, $x^2 + y^2 = 1296$, $x^2 + y^2 = 2304$, $x^2 + y^2 = 3600$

Use the center and the radius to graph each circle. See Problem 5.

28. $(x + 4)^2 + (y - 4)^2 = 4$

29. $(x - 6)^2 + y^2 = 64$

30. $x^2 + y^2 = 9$

31. $(x + 3)^2 + (y - 9)^2 = 49$

32. $(x - 7)^2 + (y - 1)^2 = 100$

33. $x^2 + (y + 4)^2 = 144$

B Apply

Write the equation of the circle that passes through the given point and has a center at the origin. (*Hint:* You can use the distance formula to find the radius.)

34. $(0, 4)$ **35.** $(0, -3)$ **36.** $(-5, 0)$

37. $(\sqrt{3}, 0)$ **38.** $(4, -3)$ **39.** $(12, -5)$

40. $(-2, 3)$ **41.** $(1, -5)$ **42.** $(-6, -4)$

© 43. Think About a Plan Three gears of radii 6 in., 4 in., and 2 in. mesh with each other in a motor assembly as shown to the right. What is the equation of each circle in standard form?

• How can the diagram of the gears in the coordinate plane help you solve this problem?
• How can you write an equation for each circle?

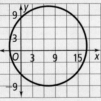

© 44. Open-Ended Write two functions that together represent a circle.

Use the given information to write an equation of the circle.

45. radius 7, center $(-6, 13)$

46. area 25π, center $(5, -3)$

47. center $(-2, 7.5)$, circumference 3π

48. center $(1, -2)$, through $(0, 1)$

49. center $(2, 1)$, through $(6, 4)$

50. center $(6, 4)$, through $(2, 1)$

51. translation of $(x - 1)^2 + (y + 3)^2 = 36$, 2 units left and 4 units down

STEM 52. Machinery Three gears, A, B, and C, mesh with each other in a motor assembly. Gear A has a radius of 4 in., B has a radius of 3 in., and C has a radius of 1 in. If the largest gear is centered at $(-7, 0)$, the smallest gear is centered at $(4, 0)$, and Gear B is centered at the origin, what is the equation of each circle in standard form?

Find the center and the radius of each circle.

53. $x^2 + y^2 = 2$

54. $x^2 + (y + 1)^2 = 5$

55. $x^2 + y^2 = 14$

56. $x^2 + (y - 4)^2 = 11$

57. $(x + 5)^2 + y^2 = 18$

58. $(x + 2)^2 + (y + 4)^2 = 50$

59. $(x + 3)^2 + (y - 5)^2 = 38$

60. $x^2 + 2x + 1 + y^2 = 4$

61. $x^2 + y^2 - 6x - 2y + 4 = 0$

62. $x^2 + y^2 - 4y - 16 = 0$

4 Practice

ASSIGNMENT GUIDE

Basic: 7–33, 43–45, 52–58 even

Average: 7–33 odd, 34–62

Advanced: 7–33 odd, 34–66

Standardized Test Prep: 67–71

Mixed Review: 72–84

© Mathematical Practices are supported by exercises with red headings. Here are the Practices supported in this lesson:

MP 1: Make Sense of Problems Ex. 43

MP 3: Construct Arguments Ex. 6, 44

MP 3: Critique the Reasoning of Others Ex. 5

Applications exercises have blue headings. Exercises 52 and 65 support MP 4: Model.

STEM exercises focus on science or engineering applications.

EXERCISE 52: Use the Think About a Plan worksheet in the **Practice and Problem Solving Workbook** (also available in the Teaching Resources in print and online) to further support students' development in becoming independent learners.

HOMEWORK QUICK CHECK

To check students' understanding of key skills and concepts, go over Exercises 13, 23, 43, 44, and 52.

---

20. $(x + 3)^2 + (y - 4)^2 = 9$

21. $(x - 2)^2 + (y + 6)^2 = 16$

22. center $(1, 1)$, radius 1

23. center $(-2, 10)$, radius 2

24. center $(3, -1)$, radius 6

25. center $(-3, 5)$, radius 9

26. center $(0, -3)$, radius 5

27. center $(-6, 0)$, radius 11

28.

29.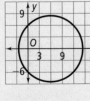

30.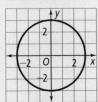

31.

32.

33.

34. $x^2 + y^2 = 16$ **35.** $x^2 + y^2 = 9$

36. $x^2 + y^2 = 25$ **37.** $x^2 + y^2 = 3$

38. $x^2 + y^2 = 25$ **39.** $x^2 + y^2 = 169$

40. $x^2 + y^2 = 13$ **41.** $x^2 + y^2 = 26$

42. $x^2 + y^2 = 52$

43. $x^2 + y^2 = 36$,
$(x - 8)^2 + (y - 6)^2 = 16$,
$(x - 8)^2 + (y)^2 = 4$

44. Answers may vary. Sample:
$y = \sqrt{25 - x^2}$ and $y = -\sqrt{25 - x^2}$.

45. $(x + 6)^2 + (y - 13)^2 = 49$

46. $(x - 5)^2 + (y + 3)^2 = 25$

47. $(x + 2)^2 + (y - 7.5)^2 = 2.25$

48. $(x - 1)^2 + (y + 2)^2 = 10$

49. $(x - 2)^2 + (y - 1)^2 = 25$

50. $(x - 6)^2 + (y - 4)^2 = 25$

51. $(x + 1)^2 + (y + 7)^2 = 36$

52. Gear A: $(x + 7)^2 + y^2 = 16$,
Gear B: $x^2 + y^2 = 9$,
Gear C: $(x - 4)^2 + y^2 = 1$

53. center $(0, 0)$, radius $\sqrt{2}$

54. center $(0, -1)$, radius $\sqrt{5}$

55. center $(0, 0)$, radius $\sqrt{14}$

56. center $(0, 4)$, radius $\sqrt{11}$

57. center $(-5, 0)$, radius $3\sqrt{2}$

58. center $(-2, -4)$, radius $5\sqrt{2}$

59. center $(-3, 5)$, radius $\sqrt{38}$

60. center $(-1, 0)$, radius 2

61. center $(3, 1)$, radius $\sqrt{6}$

62. center $(0, 2)$, radius $2\sqrt{5}$

Answers

Practice and Problem-Solving Exercises (continued)

63.

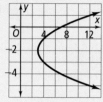

circle; $(x - 4)^2 + (y - 3)^2 = 16$

64.

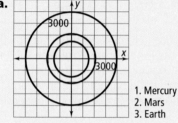

parabola; $x = (y + 2)^2 + 3$

65. a.

1. Mercury
2. Mars
3. Earth

b. Earth: $x^2 + y^2 = 15{,}705{,}369$

Mars: $x^2 + y^2 = 4{,}456{,}321$

Mercury: $x^2 + y^2 = 2{,}296{,}740$

66. a. $(x - 3)^2 + (y - 4)^2 = 25$

b. $y = -\frac{1}{3}x^2 + \frac{10}{3}x$

Standardized Test Prep

67. 12

68. 1.45

69. 5

70. $\frac{2}{3}$

71. 0.42

Mixed Review

72. $x = -\frac{1}{12}y^2$

73. at $x = -1$

74. at $x = 2$ and $x = 3$

75. no points of discontinuity

76. 4

77. 2

78. -3

79. 4

80. $\frac{1}{2}$

81. 1

82. $-2, -9$

83. $0, \pm 4, \pm 4i$

84. $\pm 2, \pm 2\sqrt{2}$

 Graph each pair of equations. Identify the conic section represented by the graph. Then write a single equation for the conic section.

63. $y = 3 + \sqrt{16 - (x - 4)^2}$

$y = 3 - \sqrt{16 - (x - 4)^2}$

64. $y = -2 + \sqrt{x - 3}$

$y = -2 - \sqrt{x - 3}$

STEM 65. Astronomy The table gives the diameters of three planets.

a. Use a center of $(0, 0)$ to graph a circle that represents the size of each planet.

b. Write an equation representing the circular cross section through the center of each planet.

Planet	Diameter (miles)
Mercury	3031
Mars	4222
Earth	7926

66. a. A circle contains the points $(0, 0)$, $(6, 8)$, and $(7, 7)$. Find its equation by solving a system of three equations.

b. Several parabolas contain the three points of part (a), but only one is described by a quadratic function. What is that function?

Standardized Test Prep

GRIDDED RESPONSE

SAT/ACT

67. What is the radius of the circle with equation $(x + 5)^2 + (y - 3)^2 = 144$?

68. Find the positive zero of the function $y = x^2 + 2x - 5$ by graphing. Enter your answer as a decimal to the nearest hundredth.

69. What is the distance between $T(9, -5)$ and the center of the circle with equation $(x - 6)^2 + (y + 1)^2 = 10$?

70. What is the common ratio in a geometric series if $a_2 = \frac{1}{3}$ and $a_5 = \frac{8}{81}$? Enter your answer as a fraction.

71. Evaluate the sum $\sum_{n=1}^{3} \left(\frac{1}{n+1}\right)^2$. Enter your answer as a decimal to the nearest hundredth.

Mixed Review

72. What is an equation of a parabola opening left with vertex $(0, 0)$ and focus $(-3, 0)$?

See Lesson 10-2.

For each rational function, find any points of discontinuity.

See Lesson 8-3.

73. $y = \frac{2}{x + 1}$

74. $y = \frac{1}{x^2 - 5x + 6}$

75. $y = \frac{2x - 1}{x^2 + 4}$

Evaluate each logarithm.

See Lesson 7-3.

76. $\log_2 16$

77. $\log_5 25$

78. $\log_3 \frac{1}{27}$

79. $\log 10{,}000$

80. $\log_{36} 6$

81. $\log_{100} 100$

Get Ready! To prepare for Lesson 10-4, do Exercises 82–84.

Solve each equation.

See Lesson 5-3.

82. $x^2 + 11x = -18$

83. $m^5 - 256m = 0$

84. $p^4 + 32 = 12p^2$

Differentiated Remediation

Additional Instructional Support

Algebra 2 Companion

Students can use the **Algebra 2 Companion** worktext (4 pages) as you teach the lesson. Use the Companion to support

- New Vocabulary
- Key Concepts
- Got It for each Problem
- Lesson Check

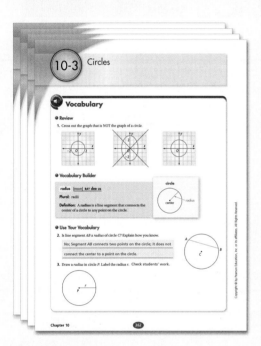

ELL Support

Focus on Language Give students a coordinate plane, and have them write and graph an equation of a circle that fits in the coordinate plane and uses only integers. In pairs, have students try to guess the other person's equation. When a student misses, he or she may ask a question about the horizontal translation, vertical translation, or radius. The other student should answer the question with, for example, "My circle is translated further left than that." The students should take turns until they have both figured out the other student's equation. Monitor to make sure the students are using correct vocabulary to describe the translations and changes in radius.

5 Assess & Remediate

Lesson Quiz

1. What is an equation of a circle with center $(-2, -1)$ and radius 3?

2. What is an equation for the translation of $x^2 + y^2 = 3.6$ by 1 unit left and 2 units down?

3. **Do you UNDERSTAND?** You have a tree in your yard 4 ft to the left of and 5 ft in front of the corner of your porch. A circular fence 3 ft in radius has its center at the tree. If the corner of your porch is the origin and forward is the positive y direction, what equation represents the circle formed by the fence in your yard?

4. What are the center and radius of the circle with equation $x^2 + 12x + y^2 + 4y = -31$?

5. What is the graph of $(x + 1)^2 + (y + 3)^2 = 25$?

ANSWERS TO LESSON QUIZ

1. $(x + 2)^2 + (y + 1)^2 = 9$
2. $(x + 1)^2 + (y + 2)^2 = 3.6$
3. $(x + 4)^2 + (y - 5)^2 = 9$
4. center $(-6, -2)$, radius 3
5.

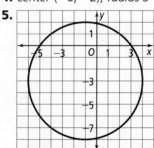

PRESCRIPTION FOR REMEDIATION

Use the student work on the Lesson Quiz to prescribe a differentiated review assignment:

Points	Differentiated Remediation
0–2	Intervention
3–4	On-level
5	Extension

PowerAlgebra.com

👆

5 Assess & Remediate

Assign the Lesson Quiz. Appropriate intervention, practice, or enrichment is automatically generated based on student performance.

Intervention

- **Reteaching** (2 pages) Provides reteaching and practice exercises for the key lesson concepts. Use with struggling students or absent students.

- **English Language Learner Support** Helps students develop and reinforce mathematical vocabulary and key concepts.

All-in-One Resources/Online
Reteaching

10-3 Reteaching
Circles

- When working with circles, begin by writing the equation in standard form:
  $(x - h)^2 + (y - k)^2 = r^2$
- Unlike equations of parabolas, which include either x^2 or y^2, the equation of a circle will include both x^2 and y^2.

Problem

What is the center and radius of the circle with the equation $x^2 + y^2 - 4x + 6y = 12$?

$(x^2 - 4x) + (y^2 + 6y) = 12$ Rearrange and group the terms by variable.

$\frac{b}{2} = \frac{-4}{2} = -2$ $\frac{b}{2} = \frac{6}{2} = 3$ To complete each square, find $\frac{b}{2}$ for each group.

$\left(\frac{b}{2}\right)^2 = (-2)^2 = 4$ $\left(\frac{b}{2}\right)^2 = (3)^2 = 9$ Find $\left(\frac{b}{2}\right)^2$ for each expression.

$(x^2 - 4x + 4) + (y^2 + 6y + 9) = 12 + 4 + 9$ Add $\left(\frac{b}{2}\right)^2$ for each expression to both sides.

$(x - 2)^2 + (y + 3)^2 = 25$ Write the expressions as perfect squares; simplify.

$(x - 2)^2 + (y - (-3))^2 = 5^2$ Write the equation in standard form.

$h = 2, k = -3, r = 5$ Compare the equation to $(x - h)^2 + (y - k)^2 = r^2$.

The center of the circle is $(2, -3)$. The radius of the circle is 5.

Exercises

Find the center and radius of each circle.

1. $x^2 + y^2 - 10y = 0$ (0, 5); 5
2. $x^2 + y^2 = 225$ (0, 0); 15
3. $x^2 + y^2 + 2x - 6y = 15$ (-1, 3); 5
4. $x^2 + y^2 + 12x + 14y = -84$ (-6, -7); 1
5. $x^2 + y^2 + 2x + 8y = 31$ (-1, -2); 6
6. $x^2 + y^2 - 10x - 4y = -20$ (5, 2); 3
7. $x^2 + y^2 + 16x - 8y = -72$ (-8, 4); $2\sqrt{2}$
8. $x^2 + y^2 - 8x + 6y = -5$ (4, -3); $2\sqrt{5}$
9. $x^2 + y^2 - 4x - 6y = -4$ (2, 3); 3
10. $x^2 + y^2 + 8x = 47$ (-4, 0); $3\sqrt{7}$

All-in-One Resources/Online
English Language Learner Support

10-3 Additional Vocabulary Support
Circles

Concept List

center	circle	complete the square
distance formula	parameter	parent graph of a circle
radius	standard from of a circle	translation

Choose the concept from the list above that best represents the item in each box.

1. $x^2 + y^2 = r^2$ parent graph of a circle	2. the set of all points in a plane that are a distance r from a given point circle	3. the method used to change an equation of a circle into standard form complete the square
4. $h, k,$ and r in the equation of a circle parameters	5. $d = \sqrt{(x_2 - x_1)^2 + (y_2 - y_1)^2}$ distance formula	6. the distance r from the center of a circle to a point on the circle radius
7. all points on a circle are equidistant from this point center	8. $(x - h)^2 + (y - k)^2 = r^2$ standard form of a circle	9. movement of the parent graph horizontally or vertically translation

Differentiated Remediation *continued*

On-Level

- **Practice** (2 pages) Provides extra practice for each lesson. For simpler practice exercises, use the Form K Practice pages found in the All-in-One Teaching Resources and online.

- **Think About a Plan** Helps students develop specific problem-solving skills and strategies by providing scaffolded guiding questions.

- **Standardized Test Prep** Focuses on all major exercises, all major question types, and helps students prepare for the high-stakes assessments.

Extension

- **Enrichment** Provides students with interesting problems and activities that extend the concepts of the lesson.

- **Activities, Games, and Puzzles** Worksheets that can be used for concepts development, enrichment, and for fun!

Practice and Problem Solving Wkbk/ All-in-One Resources/Online
Practice page 1

10-3 Practice — *Form G*
Circles

Write an equation of a circle with the given center and radius. Check your answers.

1. center (0, 0), radius 3
$x^2 + y^2 = 9$
2. center (0, 1), radius 2
$x^2 + (y-1)^2 = 4$
3. center (−1, 0), radius 6
$(x+1)^2 + y^2 = 36$
4. center (2, 0), radius 1
$(x-2)^2 + y^2 = 1$
5. center (1, −5), radius 2.5
$(x-1)^2 + (y+5)^2 = 6.25$
6. center (2, 3), diameter 1
$(x-2)^2 + (y-3)^2 = \frac{1}{4}$

Write an equation for each translation.

7. $x^2 + y^2 = 9$; right 4 and down 2
$(x-4)^2 + (y+2)^2 = 9$
8. $x^2 + y^2 = 12$; left 2 and up 5
$(x+2)^2 + (y-5)^2 = 12$
9. $x^2 + y^2 = 49$; right 1 and up 7
$(x-1)^2 + (y-7)^2 = 49$
10. $x^2 + y^2 = 1$; right 5 and up 5
$(x-5)^2 + (y-5)^2 = 1$
11. $x^2 + y^2 = 25$; up 10
$x^2 + (y-10)^2 = 25$
12. $x^2 + y^2 = 36$; left 8 and down 6
$(x+8)^2 + (y+6)^2 = 36$

Write an equation for each circle. Each interval represents one unit.

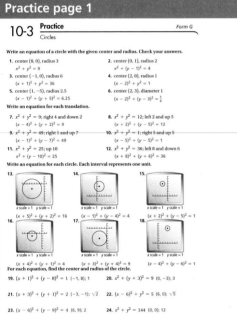

13. x scale = 1 y scale = 1
14. x scale = 1 y scale = 1
15. x scale = 1 y scale = 1
16. x scale = 1 y scale = 1 $(x+5)^2 + (y+2)^2 = 16$
17. x scale = 1 y scale = 1 $(x-1)^2 + (y-4)^2 = 4$
18. x scale = 1 y scale = 1 $(x+2)^2 + (y-5)^2 = 1$

$(x-1)^2 + (y-3)^2 = 1$ $(x+3)^2 + (y+4)^2 = 9$ $(x-4)^2 + (y-6)^2 = 1$

For each equation, find the center and radius of the circle.

19. $(x+1)^2 + (y-8)^2 = 1$ (−1, 8); 1
20. $x^2 + (y+3)^2 = 9$ (0, −3); 3
21. $(x+3)^2 + (y+1)^2 = 2$ (−3, −1); $\sqrt{2}$
22. $(x-6)^2 + y^2 = 5$ (6, 0); $\sqrt{5}$
23. $(x-6)^2 + (y-9)^2 = 4$ (6, 9); 2
24. $x^2 + y^2 = 144$ (0, 0); 12

Practice and Problem Solving Wkbk/ All-in-One Resources/Online
Practice page 2

10-3 Practice (continued) — *Form G*
Circles

Use the center and the radius to graph each circle.

25. $(x+9)^2 + (y-2)^2 = 81$
26. $x^2 + (y+3)^2 = 121$
27. $(x-8)^2 + (y+9)^2 = 64$
28. $x^2 + 8)^2 + y^2 = 49$

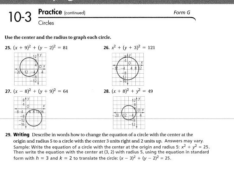

29. **Writing** Describe in words how to change the equation of a circle with the center at the origin and radius 5 to a circle with the center 3 units right and 2 units up. Answers may vary. Sample: Write the equation of a circle with the center at the origin and radius 5: $x^2 + y^2 = 25$. Then write the equation with the center at (3, 2) with radius 5, using the equation in standard form with $h = 3$ and $k = 2$ to translate the circle: $(x-3)^2 + (y-2)^2 = 25$.

30. **Open-Ended** Write an equation for a circle with center at the origin and an equation for another circle that is a translation of the first. Answers may vary. The circle with the center at the origin should be in the form $x^2 + y^2 = r^2$ and the circle that is translated should have the same value for r as the original circle.

31. **Error Analysis** A classmate writes the equation of a circle with the center at (8.5, 0) and diameter 25 as $x + (y - 8.5)^2 = 156.25$. Is she correct? Why or why not? This is the incorrect equation for the circle. The values for h and k are reversed and x should be squared. The correct equation is $(x - 8.5)^2 + y^2 = 156.25$.

32. **Reasoning** How can you determine if the graph of the circle $(x + 8)^2 + (y + 9)^2 = 49$ is correctly drawn? Check that the center of the circle is (−8, −9) and that the radius of the circle is 7.

All-in-One Resources/Online
Enrichment

10-3 Enrichment
Circles

In geometry, you learned that a tangent to a circle is a line that intersects the circle in exactly one point. The tangent is also perpendicular to the radius at the point of tangency. Use these facts, along with what you know about the equation of a circle, to solve the problems below.

1. Write the equation in standard form of a circle with a center at (3, 4) with the y-axis tangent to the circle.
$(x-3)^2 + (y-4)^2 = 9$

2. Write the equation of a circle with radius 2 units with both the x-axis and the y-axis tangent to the circle. Explain why there is more than one equation to describe this circle.
Answers may vary. Sample: $(x-2)^2 + (y-2)^2 = 4$; this circle could be located in any quadrant where the centers could be (2, 2), (2, −2), (−2, 2), or (−2, −2).

3. Write the equation in standard form of a circle that is tangent to the y-axis, tangent to the horizontal line $y = 5$, and tangent to the vertical line $x = −4$.
$(x+2)^2 + (y-3)^2 = 4$

4. Write the equation in standard form of a circle with a diameter that has endpoints (−1, −3) and (3, −3).
$(x-1)^2 + (y+3)^2 = 4$

5. Write the equation in standard form of a circle with center at (−2, 3) that passes through the point (−1, 7).
$(x+2)^2 + (y-3)^2 = 17$

6. Write the equation in standard form of a circle with center in the fourth quadrant with the x-axis, the vertical line $x = 4$, and the vertical line $x = 6$ tangent to the circle.
$(x-5)^2 + (y+1)^2 = 1$

7. Write the equation of a circle with center on the line $y = 2x$, radius 2, and is tangent to the y-axis.
$(x-2)^2 + (y-4)^2 = 4$ or $(x+2)^2 + (y+4)^2 = 4$

Practice and Problem Solving Wkbk/ All-in-One Resources/Online
Think About a Plan

10-3 Think About a Plan
Circles

Machinery Three gears, A, B, and C, mesh with each other in a motor assembly. Gear A has a radius of 4 in., B has a radius of 3 in., and C has a radius of 1 in. If the largest gear is centered at (−4, 0), the smallest gear is centered at (4, 0), and Gear B is centered at the origin, what is the equation of each circle in standard form?

Understanding the Problem

1. The radius of gear $A = \boxed{4}$ in.

2. The radius of gear $B = \boxed{3}$ in.

3. The radius of gear $C = \boxed{1}$ in.

4. The centers of the gears are at what points? (−4, 0), (0, 0), and (4, 0)

5. What is the problem asking you to determine?
an equation for a circle that represents each gear

Planning the Solution

6. What do you need to find an equation for each gear?
the radius and center of each gear

Getting an Answer

7. Fill in the table below to find the equation of the circle that represents each gear.

Gear	(h, k)	r	Equation
A	(−4, 0)	4	$(x + 4)^2 + y^2 = 16$
B	(0, 0)	3	$x^2 + y^2 = 9$
C	(4, 0)	1	$(x − 4)^2 + y^2 = 1$

Practice and Problem Solving Wkbk/ All-in-One Resources/Online
Standardized Test Prep

10-3 Standardized Test Prep
Circles

Multiple Choice

For Exercises 1–5, choose the correct letter.

1. Which is an equation of the circle with center at the origin and radius 3? C
   Ⓐ $x^2 + y^2 = 3$
   Ⓒ $x^2 + y^2 = 9$
   Ⓑ $x^2 + y^2 = 81$
   Ⓓ $(x - 3)^2 + (y - 3)^2 = 9$

2. What is the equation for the translation of $x^2 + y^2 = 16$ two units left and one unit down? I
   Ⓕ $x^2 + y^2 = 16$
   Ⓗ $2x^2 + y^2 = 16$
   Ⓖ $(x - 2)^2 + (y - 1)^2 = 16$
   Ⓘ $(x + 2)^2 + (y + 1)^2 = 16$

3. Which equation represents a circle with a center at (7, −9) and a diameter of 8? C
   Ⓐ $(x - 7)^2 + (y - 9)^2 = 64$
   Ⓒ $(x - 7)^2 + (y + 9)^2 = 16$
   Ⓑ $(x - 7)^2 + (y + 9)^2 = 64$
   Ⓓ $(x + 7)^2 + (y - 9)^2 = 16$

4. What is the center of the circle $(x - 3)^2 + (y + 2)^2 = 81$? G
   Ⓕ (−3, 2)
   Ⓖ (3, −2)
   Ⓗ (3, 2)
   Ⓘ (9, 9)

5. What is the radius of the circle $(x + 8)^2 + (y - 3)^2 = 100$? A
   Ⓐ 10
   Ⓑ 20
   Ⓒ 50
   Ⓓ 100

Short Response

6. What are the radius and center of a circle with the equation $(x + 7)^2 + (y - 8)^2 = 144$?
   [2] The radius is 12; the center is (−7, 8).
   [1] incorrect radius OR center
   [0] no answers given

Online Teacher Resource Center
Activities, Games, and Puzzles

10-3 Puzzle: Circles In Squares
Circles

Here is a puzzle about circles in the coordinate plane. You will need a compass.

Draw circles in the grid that meet all of the conditions described below. Use a compass to lightly draw different combinations of circles until you find a correct answer.

Answers may vary. Sample graph:

- No circle extends beyond the boundary of the puzzle grid.
- All circles have centers whose coordinates are integers.
- There must be two circles with a radius of 3 units, one circle with a radius of 4 units, and one circle with a radius of 5 units.
- No two circles intersect at more than one point.

There are different combinations of circles that can be used to find the solution. Use the space below to write the equation for each circle in your solution.
Answers may vary. Sample: $(x + 3)^2 + (y - 3)^2 = 5^2$; $(x - 4)^2 + (y + 4)^2 = 4^2$; $(x - 5)^2 + (y - 4)^2 = 3^2$; $(x + 4)^2 + (y + 5)^2 = 3^2$

On the grid above, insert a point at the center of each circle. Then form a polygon by drawing segments between the centers of the circles. Classify the polygon by the number of sides. Is the polygon *equilateral*, *equiangular*, *regular*, or *none of these*? Explain.
Answers may vary. Sample: Quadrilateral; the polygon is equilateral because all sides are the same length.

MathXL® for School
Go to PowerAlgebra.com

Do you know HOW?

Describe the graph and identify the domain and range for each equation.

1. $y^2 - 2x^2 = 16$

2. $3x^2 + 3y^2 - 12 = 0$

3. $9x^2 - 25y^2 = 225$

4. $36 - 4x^2 - 9y^2 = 0$

Identify the vertex, focus, and directrix of each parabola. Then graph the parabola.

5. $y = 3x^2$

6. $x = 4(y + 2)^2$

7. $y + 1 = (x - 3)^2$

Write an equation for the parabola with the given vertex and focus.

8. vertex $(-5, 4)$; focus $(-5, 0)$

9. vertex $(7, 2)$; focus $(7, -2)$

10. vertex $(0, 0)$; focus $(-7, 0)$

11. vertex $(2, 4)$; focus $(1, 4)$

12. Write an equation that models the graph below.

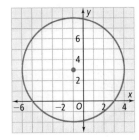

Write an equation in standard form of the circle with the given center and radius.

13. center $(-6, 3)$, radius 8

14. center $(1, 1)$, radius 1.5

Do you UNDERSTAND?

Determine whether each point lies on the graph of the conic section with the given equation.

15. $x^2 + y^2 = 36$
  a. $(-6, 0)$ **b.** $(-2, -\sqrt{3})$ **c.** $(0, \sqrt{2})$

16. $4x^2 - y^2 - 4 = 0$
  a. $(-1, 0)$ **b.** $(2, 2)$ **c.** $(1, 0)$

17. The table below represents points on the graph of a conic section. Identify the conic section.

x	−12	−8	0	12
y	0	±12	±16	0

 18. Writing Suppose that $x^2 = 4py$ and $y = ax^2$ represent the same parabola. Explain how a and p are related.

ⓒ **Reasoning** Without graphing, describe how each graph differs from the graph of $y = x^2$.

19. $y = 2x^2$ **20.** $y = -x^2$

21. $y = x^2 + 2$ **22.** $y = \frac{1}{3}x^2$

23. A circle has center $(0, 0)$ and radius 1. Write an equation that represents the translation of the circle 7 units left and 8 units up. Then graph the equation.

Write the standard form of the equation of the circle that passes through the given point and whose center is at the origin.

24. $(-6, 0)$ **25.** $(0, 5)$

26. $(-11, -11)$ **27.** $(-8, 14)$

8. $y = -\frac{1}{16}(x + 5)^2 + 4$

9. $y = -\frac{1}{16}(x - 7)^2 + 2$

10. $x = -\frac{1}{28}y^2$

11. $x = -\frac{1}{4}(y - 4)^2 + 2$

12. $(x + 1)^2 + (y - 3)^2 = 25$

13. $(x + 6)^2 + (y - 3)^2 = 64$

14. $(x - 1)^2 + (y - 1)^2 = 2.25$

15. a. yes
  b. no
  c. no

16. a. yes
  b. no
  c. yes

17. ellipse

18. Solve $y = ax^2$ for x^2. You get $x^2 = \frac{y}{a}$. Then using the transitive property, you get $4py = \frac{y}{a}$. Solving for a, you will find that $a = \frac{1}{4p}$. So, a and p vary inversely.

19. stretch by a factor of 2

20. reflect across the x-axis

21. translated up 2 units

22. compress by a factor of $\frac{1}{3}$

23. $(x + 7)^2 + (y - 8)^2 = 1$

24. $x^2 + y^2 = 36$

25. $x^2 + y^2 = 25$

26. $x^2 + y^2 = 242$

27. $x^2 + y^2 = 260$

Answers

Mid-Chapter Quiz

1. hyperbola: center: $(0, 0)$; no x-intercept, y-intercepts $(0, \pm 4)$; lines of sym.: x-axis and y-axis; domain: all real numbers, range: $y \le -4$ or $y \ge 4$

2. circle: center: $(0, 0)$, radius 2; x-intercepts: $(\pm 2, 0)$, y-intercepts: $(0, \pm 2)$; infinitely many lines of sym.; domain: $-2 \le x \le 2$, range: $-2 \le y \le 2$

3. hyperbola: center: $(0, 0)$; no y-intercept, x-intercepts $(\pm 5, 0)$; lines of sym.: x-axis and y-axis; domain: $x \le -5$ or $x \ge 5$, range: all real numbers

4. ellipse: center: $(0, 0)$; x-intercepts: $(\pm 3, 0)$, y-intercepts: $(0, \pm 2)$; lines of sym.: x-axis and y-axis; domain: $-3 \le x \le 3$, range: $-2 \le y \le 2$

5. vertex: $(0, 0)$; focus: $\left(0, \frac{1}{12}\right)$; directrix: $y = -\frac{1}{12}$

6. vertex: $(0, -2)$; focus: $\left(\frac{1}{16}, -2\right)$; directrix: $x = -\frac{1}{16}$

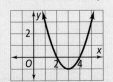

7. vertex: $(3, -1)$; focus: $\left(3, -\frac{3}{4}\right)$; directrix: $y = -\frac{5}{4}$

1 Interactive Learning

Solve It!

PURPOSE To model an ellipse

PROCESS Students may
- solve the problem physically.
- use algebra and the Pythagorean Theorem.

FACILITATE

Q Make a sketch to show the pencil on the positive *x*-axis. What does the string look like? **[It stretches from one tack to the pencil point and then doubles back to the other tack.]**

Q Let *n* equal the length from the tack on the positive *x*-axis to the pencil point when it is on the *x*-axis. Find the length of the string in terms of *n*. What equation can you write to solve for *n*? **[2*n* + 8; 2*n* + 8 = 10]**

Q How can you use the Pythagorean Theorem to find the *y*-intercept? **[When the pencil is on the *y*-axis, the string forms two right triangles. The hypotenuse is half the length of the string, 5. The distance on the *x*-axis is 4, so the distance on the *y*-axis is 3.]**

ANSWER See Solve It in Answers on next page.

CONNECT THE MATH In the Solve It, students use algebra to identify the *x*- and *y*-intercepts of an ellipse. In the lesson, students will use the definition of an ellipse to identify parts of ellipses and write their equations.

2 Guided Instruction

Take Note

You may want to explain the notation. P is any point on the ellipse. The symbol PF_1 refers to the distance from any point P to F_1, and F_1F_2 is the distance between F_1 and F_2.

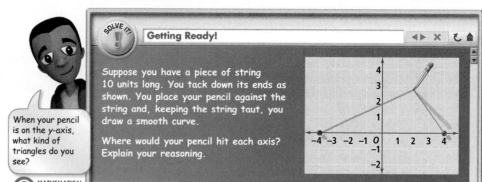

10-4 Ellipses

© Content Standard
G.GPE.3 Derive the equations of ellipses . . . given foci, using the fact that the sum or difference of distances from the foci is constant.

Objectives To write the equation of an ellipse
To find the foci of an ellipse
To graph an ellipse

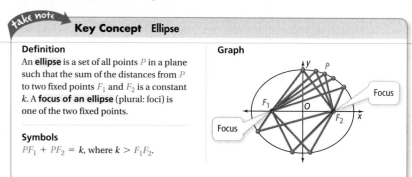

Getting Ready!

Suppose you have a piece of string 10 units long. You tack down its ends as shown. You place your pencil against the string and, keeping the string taut, you draw a smooth curve.

Where would your pencil hit each axis? Explain your reasoning.

When your pencil is on the *y*-axis, what kind of triangles do you see?

© MATHEMATICAL PRACTICES

Lesson Vocabulary
- ellipse
- focus of an ellipse
- major axis
- center of an ellipse
- minor axis
- vertices of an ellipse
- co-vertices of an ellipse

Points on the smooth curve in the Solve It have a total distance of 10 units to the points $(-4, 0)$ and $(4, 0)$. In fact, all of the points on the smooth curve have a total distance of 10 units to the two fixed points. You can describe this smooth curve with an equation.

Essential Understanding A circle is the set of points a fixed distance from one point. An *ellipse* "stretches" a circle in one direction and is the set of points that have a total fixed distance from two points.

take note

Key Concept   Ellipse

Definition
An **ellipse** is a set of all points P in a plane such that the sum of the distances from P to two fixed points F_1 and F_2 is a constant k. A **focus of an ellipse** (plural: foci) is one of the two fixed points.

Graph

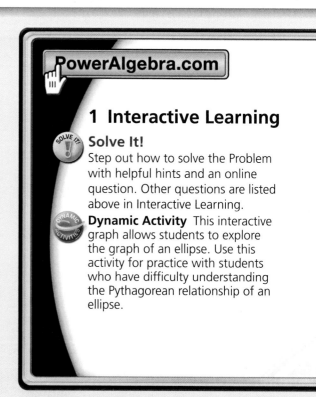

Symbols
$PF_1 + PF_2 = k$, where $k > F_1F_2$.

10-4 Preparing to Teach

BIG idea Coordinate Geometry

ESSENTIAL UNDERSTANDINGS

- A circle is the set of points a fixed distance from one point. An ellipse "stretches" a circle in one direction and is the set of points that have a total fixed distance from two points.
- The x^2 and y^2 terms of the algebraic form of an ellipse are both positive. For a hyperbola, one term is negative.

Math Background

An ellipse is a conic section formed by a plane intersecting a cone at a slant, crossing through both sides to form a bounded figure.

The sum of the distances from any point on an ellipse to both foci is a constant.
By convention, the length of the major axis is 2*a* and the length of the minor axis is 2*b*. Therefore, the standard equation of an ellipse depends on its orientation.

- For a horizontal ellipse, the standard equation is $\frac{x^2}{a^2} + \frac{y^2}{b^2} = 1$ because the major axis is the *x*-axis.
- For a vertical ellipse, the standard equation is $\frac{x^2}{b^2} + \frac{y^2}{a^2} = 1$ because the major axis is the *y*-axis.

A circle is a special case of an ellipse in which the major axis and the minor axis have the same length. Therefore, $a = b$ and $c = 0$, and the foci of a circle centered at the origin coincide at the origin, which is also the center of the circle. The radius of the circle is *a* or *b*.

© Mathematical Practices
Look for and make use of structure. Students will use clear definitions of several geometric terms such as "major axis" and "co-vertex" in relation to ellipses.

PowerAlgebra.com

1 Interactive Learning

Solve It!
Step out how to solve the Problem with helpful hints and an online question. Other questions are listed above in Interactive Learning.

Dynamic Activity This interactive graph allows students to explore the graph of an ellipse. Use this activity for practice with students who have difficulty understanding the Pythagorean relationship of an ellipse.

Dynamic Activity
Ellipses

The **major axis** is the segment that contains the foci and has its endpoints on the ellipse. Its midpoint is the **center of the ellipse**. The **minor axis** is perpendicular to the major axis at the center. The **vertices of an ellipse** (singular: *vertex*) are the endpoints of the major axis. The **co-vertices of an ellipse** are the endpoints of the minor axis.

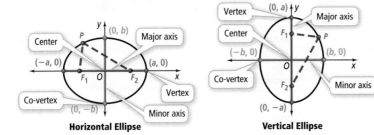

Horizontal Ellipse   **Vertical Ellipse**

take note
Key Concept   Properties of Ellipses with Center (0, 0)

	Horizontal Ellipses	Vertical Ellipses
Standard Equation	$\frac{x^2}{a^2} + \frac{y^2}{b^2} = 1, a > b > 0$	$\frac{x^2}{b^2} + \frac{y^2}{a^2} = 1, a > b > 0$
Major Axis	horizontal	vertical
Vertices	$(\pm a, 0)$	$(0, \pm a)$
Co-vertices	$(0, \pm b)$	$(\pm b, 0)$
Foci	$(\pm c, 0)$ on x-axis	$(0, \pm c)$ on y-axis

The length of the major axis is $2a$ and the length of the minor axis is $2b$.
For any point P on an ellipse, $PF_1 + PF_2 = 2a$.

Think

What is the orientation of the ellipse?
Since the vertices $(-6, 0)$ and $(6, 0)$ are aligned horizontally, the ellipse is horizontal.

Ⓒ **Problem 1**   **Writing an Equation of an Ellipse**

What is an equation in standard form of an ellipse centered at the origin with vertex $(-6, 0)$ and co-vertex $(0, 3)$?

Since one vertex is $(-6, 0)$, the other vertex is $(6, 0)$. The major axis is horizontal.
Since one co-vertex is $(0, 3)$, the other co-vertex is $(0, -3)$. The minor axis is vertical.
So $a = 6, b = 3, a^2 = 36$, and $b^2 = 9$.

$\frac{x^2}{a^2} + \frac{y^2}{b^2} = 1$ Standard form of a horizontal ellipse

$\frac{x^2}{36} + \frac{y^2}{9} = 1$ Substitute for a^2 and b^2.

✓ **Got It?** **1.** What is the equation in standard form of an ellipse centered at the origin with vertex $(0, 5)$ and co-vertex $(2, 0)$?

Q Besides containing the foci, what do you notice about the major axis? **[It is always the longer axis.]**

Take Note

Q How does the orientation of the ellipse affect the vertices? **[For horizontal ellipses, the vertices are x-intercepts. For vertical ellipses, vertices are y-intercepts.]**

Q Why must $a > b > 0$? **[If either a or b were equal to zero, there would be no major or minor axis and thus no ellipse. If $b > a$, the major and minor axes would be reversed. Since the length of the major axis is $2a$ and minor axis is $2b$, a and b cannot be negative.]**

Problem 1

Q What information do you need to find an equation of an ellipse centered at the origin? Explain. **[To write the standard form equation you need a^2 and b^2. Since a is a coordinate of the vertex and b is a coordinate of the co-vertex, you need the vertex and co-vertex.]**

Got It?

Q The foci of this ellipse are on which axis? How do you know? **[The foci are on the y-axis. The foci of an ellipse are always on the major axis. Because $5 > 2$ and the ellipse is centered at the origin, the y-axis must be the major axis.]**

---

2 Guided Instruction

Ⓒ Each Problem is worked out and supported online.

Problem 1
Writing an Equation of an Ellipse
Animated

Problem 2
Finding the Foci of an Ellipse
Animated

Problem 3
Using the Foci of an Ellipse

Problem 4
Using the Foci of an Ellipse
Animated

Support in Algebra 2 Companion
• Vocabulary
• Key Concepts
• Got It?

Answers

Solve It!
It would hit the x-axis at $(\pm 5, 0)$; the distance between the pts. where the string is attached is 8 units. The string can go at most 1 unit past both 4 and -4. It would hit the y-axis at $(0, \pm 3)$.

Got It?
1. $\frac{x^2}{4} + \frac{y^2}{25} = 1$

You may want to show why $PF_1 + PF_2 = 2a$. By definition, the distances from any point on the ellipse to each focus sums to a constant k. Therefore, the sum of the distances from $P(0, b)$ to each focus equals the sum of the distances from $(a, 0)$ to each focus. By inspection, the sum of the distances from $(a, 0)$ to each focus equals $2a$:

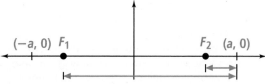

Therefore, $PF_1 + PF_2 = 2a$.

Problem 2

Q In the form of the equation of an ellipse given in the problem, what relationship does the right side of the equation have to the coordinate value of the vertex a and the co-vertex b? **[The right side equals $(ab)^2$.]**

Q Can the distance from the foci to the origin of an ellipse ever be less than the distance from the co-vertices to the origin? Give an example. **[yes; $\frac{x^2}{16} + \frac{y^2}{25} = 1$; $c = 3$ and $b = 4$]**

Got It?   ERROR PREVENTION

In 2a, check to make sure students find
$c = \sqrt{a^2 - b^2} = \sqrt{100 - 36} = 8$ and not
$c = \sqrt{a^2} - \sqrt{b^2} = \sqrt{100} - \sqrt{36} = 4$.

                                              EXTENSION

Q What reflective property do you think a circle has? Explain your reasoning. **[A circle is a special case of an ellipse in which the foci coincide at the center. Thus a line emanating from the center of a circle will be reflected back to the center.]**

Since the co-vertex $P(0, b)$ is on the ellipse, $PF_1 + PF_2 = 2a$. If you denote the distance from each focus to the center of the ellipse by c, then a, b, and c are the lengths of the sides of a right triangle, as shown in the ellipse at the right. Thus, the distances from the center to each vertex, to each co-vertex, and to each focus are related by the Pythagorean Theorem: $a^2 = b^2 + c^2$.

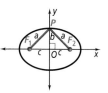

If $(\pm a, 0)$, $(0, \pm b)$, and $(\pm c, 0)$ are the vertices, the co-vertices, and the foci of an ellipse, respectively,

$$c^2 = a^2 - b^2$$

 Problem 2 Finding the Foci of an Ellipse

What are the foci of the ellipse with the equation $25x^2 + 9y^2 = 225$? Graph the foci and the ellipse.

Know	Need	Plan
The equation of an ellipse.	The coordinates of the vertices, co-vertices, and foci.	• Write the equation in standard form to find a^2 and b^2. Use $c^2 = a^2 - b^2$ to find c. • Use a, b, and c to graph the ellipse.

$$25x^2 + 9y^2 = 225$$

$$\frac{25x^2}{225} + \frac{9y^2}{225} = 1 \qquad \text{Divide each side by 225.}$$

$$\frac{x^2}{9} + \frac{y^2}{25} = 1 \qquad \text{Simplify to standard form.}$$

Since $25 > 9$ and 25 is with y^2, the major axis is vertical.

$$a^2 = 25 \text{ and } b^2 = 9$$

$$c^2 = a^2 - b^2 = 25 - 9 = 16$$

$$c = \pm 4$$

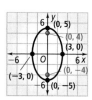

The foci are $(0, 4)$ and $(0, -4)$. Plot points for the vertices, co-vertices, and foci, then graph the ellipse.

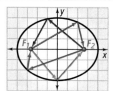 **Got It? 2. a.** What are the coordinates of the foci of the ellipse with the equation $36x^2 + 100y^2 = 3600$? Graph the ellipse.

b. Reasoning What happens to the foci as c gets closer to 0? What would the graph of an ellipse be if $c = 0$?

Like parabolas, ellipses have an important reflective property related to their foci: Any line emanating from one focus of an ellipse will reflect off the ellipse directly into the other focus. This property is related to the two-focus definition of an ellipse and can give a new interpretation to the same picture.

Additional Problems

1. What is an equation in standard form of an ellipse centered at the origin with a vertex at $(8, 0)$ and a co-vertex at $(0, 5)$?

ANSWER $\frac{x^2}{64} + \frac{y^2}{25} = 1$

2. What are the foci of the ellipse with the equation $4x^2 + 36y^2 = 144$? Graph the ellipse.

ANSWER $(-4\sqrt{2}, 0)$ and $(4\sqrt{2}, 0)$

3. Many road-racing tracks in the U.S. are oval, with an asphalt surface in the shape of an ellipse or a flattened ellipse around a grassy infield. If an elliptical track has a major axis of 3400 ft and a minor axis of 1600 ft, how far apart are the foci?

ANSWER 3000 ft

4. What is the standard form equation of the ellipse shown?

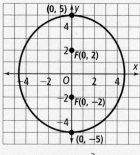

ANSWER $\frac{x^2}{21} + \frac{y^2}{25} = 1$

Answers

Got It? (continued)

2. a. $(\pm 8, 0)$.

b. The vertex and co-vertex approach the same distance from the center of the ellipse; a circle

Problem 3 Using the Foci of an Ellipse STEM

Whispering Gallery A room with an elliptical ceiling (called an *ellipsoid*, since it is 3-dimensional) forms a "whispering gallery." Thanks to the reflective property of the ellipse, a whispered message at one focus can be heard clearly by someone standing across the room at the other focus. If the elliptical ceiling has a major axis of 120 feet and a minor axis of 72 feet, how far apart are the foci?

The major axis has length $2a = 120$, so $a = 60$.

The minor axis has length $2b = 72$, so $b = 36$.

Thus $c = \sqrt{a^2 - b^2} = \sqrt{60^2 - 36^2} = 48$.

The foci are $2c = 96$ feet apart.

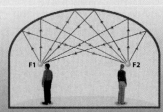

Plan

How can you find the distance between foci, given the major and minor axes?
Find the values of a and b. Then, use a^2 and b^2 to solve for c. The distance between the foci is 2c.

Got It? 3. How far apart are the foci of an ellipse with a major axis of 26 ft and a minor axis of 10 ft?

Problem 4 Using the Foci of an Ellipse

Think

How can you write the equation of an ellipse given a focus and a vertex?
Find the values of a and c. Use a^2 and c^2 to find b^2.

What is the standard form equation of the ellipse shown?

The foci are on the x-axis, so the major axis is horizontal.

Since $c = 5$ and $a = 8$, $c^2 = 25$ and $a^2 = 64$.

$$c^2 = a^2 - b^2$$

$25 = 64 - b^2$ Substitute.

$b^2 = 39$ Solve.

$\dfrac{x^2}{a^2} + \dfrac{y^2}{b^2} = 1$ Standard form of a horizontal ellipse

$\dfrac{x^2}{64} + \dfrac{y^2}{39} = 1$ Substitute.

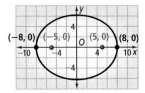

Got It? 4. What is the standard form equation of an ellipse with foci at $(0, \pm\sqrt{17})$ and co-vertices at $(\pm 6, 0)$?

Problem 3

Q How do you know that the foci are 2c apart? **[The calculated value c is the distance from the center to one focus. Thus the distance from one focus to the other is 2c.]**

Got It?

Q Do you need to know whether the ellipse is horizontal or vertical? Explain. **[No; you only need to find the distance between the foci, which does not depend on the orientation.]**

Problem 4

Q What are the coordinates of the co-vertices of this ellipse? Do they make sense looking at the graph? Explain. **[(0, $\sqrt{39}$) and (0, $-\sqrt{39}$); yes; $\sqrt{39}$ is slightly greater than $\sqrt{36} = 6$, and the graph crosses the y-axis just above $y = 6$ and just below $y = -6$.]**

Got It?

Q Is the major axis of this ellipse horizontal or vertical? Explain. **[The foci are on the y-axis, and the co-vertices are on the x-axis, so the major axis is vertical.]**

Q What are the lengths of the major and minor axes of this ellipse? **[major axis = $2\sqrt{53}$ units; minor axis = 12 units]**

---

3. 24 ft

4. $\dfrac{x^2}{36} + \dfrac{y^2}{53} = 1$

3 Lesson Check

Do you know HOW?

- For Exercise 1, students could see that the co-vertices are on the *y*-axis, therefore, the *y*-axis is the minor axis and the *x*-axis is the major axis with vertices $(\pm 8, 0)$.
- For Exercise 2, students should begin by dividing both sides of the equation by 100 to put the equation in standard form. Remind them that in standard form the equation has 1, not zero, on one side.

ERROR INTERVENTION

- If students answer $3\sqrt{23}$ ft (or 14.4 ft) for Exercise 4, point out that the distance between foci and not the distance from a focus to the center is needed.

Do you UNDERSTAND?

- For Exercise 6, challenge students to explain in terms of the standard-form equations and in terms of planes intersecting cones.

Close

> **Q** In a certain ellipse, the distances from the foci to a point on the ellipse are 3 and 5 units. What are other possible whole number values for distances from the foci to points on the ellipse? Are 8 units and 0 units possible values? Explain. **[4 and 4 units; 2 and 6 units; 8 and 0 units are not possible values because a focus cannot lie on the ellipse.]**

 Lesson Check

Do you know HOW?

1. What is an equation in standard form of an ellipse with co-vertices $(0, \pm 6)$ and major axis with length 16?

2. What are the coordinates of the foci of an ellipse with the equation $4x^2 + 25y^2 = 100$?

3. What is an equation in standard form of an ellipse centered at the origin with vertices $(\pm 13, 0)$ and foci $(\pm 12, 0)$?

4. How far apart are the foci of an ellipse with a major axis of 32 ft and minor axis of 14 ft?

Do you UNDERSTAND?

5. **Error Analysis** A student claims that an equation of the ellipse shown is $\frac{x^2}{41} + \frac{y^2}{29} = 1$. Describe the student's error. What is the correct equation in standard form of the ellipse?

6. **Reasoning** Explain why a circle is a special case of an ellipse.

Practice and Problem-Solving Exercises

A Practice

Write an equation of an ellipse in standard form with center at the origin and with the given vertex and co-vertex listed respectively. ● See Problem 1.

7. $(4, 0), (0, 3)$ 8. $(0, 1), (2, 0)$ 9. $(3, 0), (0, -1)$ 10. $(0, 6), (1, 0)$

11. $(0, -7), (4, 0)$ 12. $(-6, 0), (0, 5)$ 13. $(-9, 0), (0, -2)$ 14. $(0, 5), (-3, 0)$

Find the foci for each equation of an ellipse. Then graph the ellipse. ● See Problem 2.

15. $\frac{x^2}{4} + \frac{y^2}{9} = 1$ 16. $\frac{x^2}{9} + \frac{y^2}{25} = 1$ 17. $\frac{x^2}{81} + \frac{y^2}{49} = 1$ 18. $\frac{x^2}{25} + \frac{y^2}{16} = 1$

19. $\frac{x^2}{64} + \frac{y^2}{100} = 1$ 20. $3x^2 + y^2 = 9$ 21. $x^2 + 4y^2 = 16$ 22. $\frac{x^2}{225} + \frac{y^2}{144} = 1$

Find the distance between the foci of an ellipse. The lengths of the major and minor axes are listed respectively. ● See Problem 3.

23. 40 and 24   24. 30 and 18   25. 10 and 8   26. 16 and 10

27. 20 and 16   28. 18 and 14   29. 36 and 12   30. 8 and 6

Write an equation of an ellipse for the given foci and co-vertices. ● See Problem 4.

31. foci $(\pm 6, 0)$, co-vertices $(0, \pm 8)$ 32. foci $(0, \pm 8)$, co-vertices $(\pm 8, 0)$

33. foci $(\pm 5, 0)$, co-vertices $(0, \pm 8)$ 34. foci $(0, \pm 4)$, co-vertices $(\pm 2, 0)$

35. **Miniature Golf** The figure at the right represents a miniature golf green. The green is elliptical with the tee at one focus and the hole at the other.
   a. How far is the hole from the tee?
   b. Knowing that the border is elliptical, how should you aim your putt from the tee?

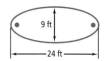

PowerAlgebra.com

3 Lesson Check

For a digital lesson check, use the Got It questions.

Support in Algebra 2 Companion
- Lesson Check

4 Practice

Assign homework to individual students or to an entire class.

Answers

Lesson Check

1. $\frac{x^2}{64} + \frac{y^2}{36} = 1$ 2. $(\pm\sqrt{21}, 0)$

3. $\frac{x^2}{169} + \frac{y^2}{25} = 1$

4. $6\sqrt{23}$ ft ≈ 28.77 ft

5. The student used a and b instead of a^2 and b^2; $\frac{x^2}{1681} + \frac{y^2}{841} = 1$

6. The eq. of an ellipse with center at the origin is $\frac{x^2}{a^2} + \frac{y^2}{b^2} = 1$. For a circle, the major axis and the minor axis are of equal length such that $a = b = r$. Thus, by subst., $\frac{x^2}{r^2} + \frac{y^2}{r^2} = 1$ or $x^2 + y^2 = r^2$.

Practice and Problem-Solving Exercises

7. $\frac{x^2}{16} + \frac{y^2}{9} = 1$ 8. $\frac{x^2}{4} + y^2 = 1$

9. $\frac{x^2}{9} + y^2 = 1$ 10. $x^2 + \frac{y^2}{36} = 1$

11. $\frac{x^2}{16} + \frac{y^2}{49} = 1$ 12. $\frac{x^2}{36} + \frac{y^2}{25} = 1$

13. $\frac{x^2}{81} + \frac{y^2}{4} = 1$ 14. $\frac{x^2}{9} + \frac{y^2}{25} = 1$

15. $(0, \pm\sqrt{5})$ 16. $(0, \pm 4)$

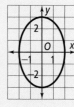

17. $(\pm 4\sqrt{2}, 0)$

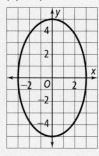

Apply

Find the foci for each equation of an ellipse.

36. $4x^2 + 9y^2 = 36$ **37.** $16x^2 + 4y^2 = 64$ **38.** $4x^2 + 36y^2 = 144$

39. $25x^2 + 4y^2 = 100$ **40.** $36x^2 + 8y^2 = 288$ **41.** $25x^2 + 24y^2 = 600$

 42. Think About a Plan The open area south of the White House is known as the Ellipse, or President's Park South. It is 902 ft wide and 1058 ft long. Assume the origin is at the center of the President's Park South. What is the equation of the ellipse in standard form?
- How does the length and width of the ellipse relate to the equation?
- What does the center at the origin tell you?
- How can you write the equation of the ellipse in standard form?

43. The eccentricity of an ellipse is a measure of how nearly circular it is. Eccentricity is defined as $\frac{c}{a}$, where c is the distance from the center to a focus and a is the distance from the center to a vertex.
- **a.** Find the eccentricity of an ellipse with foci $(\pm 9, 0)$ and vertices $(\pm 10, 0)$.
- **b.** Find the eccentricity of an ellipse with foci $(\pm 1, 0)$ and vertices $(\pm 10, 0)$.
- **c.** Describe the shape of an ellipse that has an eccentricity close to 0.
- **d.** Describe the shape of an ellipse that has an eccentricity close to 1.

Write an equation for each ellipse.

44.  **45.** 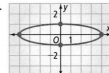 **46.**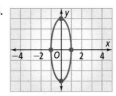

 47. Open-Ended Find a real-world design that uses ellipses. Place a coordinate grid over the design and write an equation of the ellipse.

Write an equation of an ellipse in standard form with center at the origin and with the given characteristics.

48. focus $(1, 0)$, width 4 **49.** $a = 5, b = 2$, width 10

50. vertex $(-11, 0)$, co-vertex $(0, 9)$ **51.** height 29, width 53

52. focus $(-5, 0)$, co-vertex $(0, -12)$ **53.** $c^2 = 68$, vertex $(0, -18)$

54. focus $(0, 3\sqrt{2})$, height 19 **55.** focus $(2, 0)$, x-intercept 4

56. focus $(0, -5)$, y-intercept 8 **57.** focus $(3, 0)$, x-intercept -6

58. $a = 3, b = 2$, width 4 **59.** $a = 2\sqrt{5}, b = 3\sqrt{2}$, width $6\sqrt{2}$

STEM 60. Aerodynamics Scientists used the Transonic Tunnel at NASA Langley Research Center, Virginia, to study the dynamics of air flow. The elliptical opening of the Transonic Tunnel is 82 ft wide and 58 ft high. What is an equation of the ellipse?

PowerAlgebra.com Lesson 10-4 Ellipses **643**

---

4 Practice

ASSIGNMENT GUIDE

Basic: 7–35 all, 40–44 even, 47, 56–60 even

Average: 7–35 odd, 36–60

Advanced: 7–35 odd, 36–62

Standardized Test Prep: 63–66

Mixed Review: 67–76

Mathematical Practices are supported by exercises with red headings. Here are the Practices supported in this lesson:

MP 1: Make Sense of Problems Ex. 42
MP 2: Reason Quantitatively Ex. 47
MP 3: Communicate Ex. 62
MP 3: Construct Arguments Ex. 6
MP 3: Critique the Reasoning of Others Ex. 5

Applications exercises have blue headings. Exercises 60 and 61 support MP4: Model.

STEM exercises focus on science or engineering applications.

EXERCISE 60: Use the Think About a Plan worksheet in the **Practice and Problem Solving Workbook** (also available in the Teaching Resources in print and online) to further support students' development in becoming independent learners.

HOMEWORK QUICK CHECK

To check students' understanding of key skills and concepts, go over Exercises 15, 35, 42, 47, and 60.

---

18. $(\pm 3, 0)$

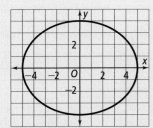

19. $(0, \pm 6)$ **20.** $(0, \pm\sqrt{6})$

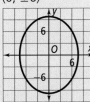 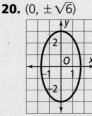

21. $(\pm 2\sqrt{3}, 0)$

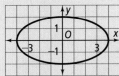

22. $(\pm 9, 0)$

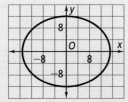

23. 32 **24.** 24

25. 6 **26.** $2\sqrt{39}$

27. 12 **28.** $8\sqrt{2}$

29. $24\sqrt{2}$ **30.** $2\sqrt{7}$

31. $\frac{x^2}{100} + \frac{y^2}{64} = 1$ **32.** $\frac{x^2}{64} + \frac{y^2}{128} = 1$

33. $\frac{x^2}{89} + \frac{y^2}{64} = 1$ **34.** $\frac{x^2}{4} + \frac{y^2}{20} = 1$

35. a. about 22.25 ft
b. Due to the reflective prop. of an ellipse, you can aim your putt at any part of the border. The ball will reflect off the border and go directly into the hole.

36. $(\pm\sqrt{5}, 0)$ **37.** $(0, \pm 2\sqrt{3})$

38. $(\pm 4\sqrt{2}, 0)$ **39.** $(0, \pm\sqrt{21})$

40. $(0, \pm 2\sqrt{7})$ **41.** $(0, \pm 1)$

42. $\frac{x^2}{279,841} + \frac{y^2}{203,401} = 1$

43. a. 0.9 **b.** 0.1
c. The shape is close to a circle.
d. The shape is close to a line segment.

44. $\frac{x^2}{9} + \frac{y^2}{4} = 1$ **45.** $\frac{x^2}{16} + y^2 = 1$

46. $x^2 + \frac{y^2}{9} = 1$ **47.** Check students' work.

48. $\frac{x^2}{4} + \frac{y^2}{3} = 1$ **49.** $\frac{x^2}{25} + \frac{y^2}{4} = 1$

50. $\frac{x^2}{121} + \frac{y^2}{81} = 1$ **51.** $\frac{x^2}{702.25} + \frac{y^2}{210.25} = 1$

52. $\frac{x^2}{169} + \frac{y^2}{144} = 1$ **53.** $\frac{x^2}{256} + \frac{y^2}{324} = 1$

54. $\frac{x^2}{72.25} + \frac{y^2}{90.25} = 1$ **55.** $\frac{x^2}{16} + \frac{y^2}{12} = 1$

56. $\frac{x^2}{39} + \frac{y^2}{64} = 1$ **57.** $\frac{x^2}{36} + \frac{y^2}{27} = 1$

58. $\frac{x^2}{9} + \frac{y^2}{4} = 1$ **59.** $\frac{x^2}{20} + \frac{y^2}{18} = 1$

60. $\frac{x^2}{1681} + \frac{y^2}{841} = 1$

Lesson 10-4 **643**

Answers

Practice and Problem-Solving Exercises (continued)

61. a. 3×10^6 mi

   b. about 0.016

   c. $\dfrac{x^2}{8.649 \times 10^{15}} + \dfrac{y^2}{8.64675 \times 10^{15}} = 1$

62. When c is close to 0, the values of a and b are almost the same. Thus πab is close to πa^2, which is close to the area of a circle with radius a.

Standardized Test Prep

63. B

64. H

65. A

66. [2] $x + 3\overline{)5x + 7}$
$\qquad\quad\dfrac{5x + 15}{-8}$;

$y = 5 - \dfrac{8}{x + 3}$;

horizontal asymptote at $y = 5$

[1] correct asymptote, without work shown

Mixed Review

67. $(x - 1)^2 + (y + 5)^2 = 9$

68. $(x + 2)^2 + (y - 4)^2 = 81$

69. $\dfrac{1}{2x - 3x^4}$; $x \neq 0$ or $\sqrt[3]{\dfrac{2}{3}}$

70. $\dfrac{x - 6}{x - 1}$; $x \neq 1$ or -6

71. $\dfrac{x - 5}{x^2 - 2x + 4}$; $x \neq -2$

72. $\log 15$

73. $\log_3 6$

74. $\log 2$

75. $y = 2x + 4$

76. $y = \dfrac{1}{3}x$

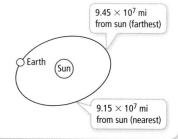

9.45 × 10^7 mi from sun (farthest)

9.15 × 10^7 mi from sun (nearest)

Challenge **61. Astronomy** The sun is at a focus of Earth's elliptical orbit.
   a. Find the distance from the sun to the other focus.
   b. Refer to Exercise 43 for the definition of eccentricity. What is the eccentricity of the orbit?
   c. Write an equation of Earth's orbit. Assume that the major axis is horizontal.

62. Writing The area of a circle is πr^2. The area of an ellipse is πab. Explain the connection.

Standardized Test Prep

SAT/ACT

63. Which equation is represented by the circle shown?
   A $(x - 1)^2 + (y + 2)^2 = 4$ **C** $(x + 2)^2 + (y - 1)^2 = 4$
   B $(x + 1)^2 + (y - 2)^2 = 4$ **D** $(x - 2)^2 + (y + 1)^2 = 4$

64. Solve $\sqrt{x} + \sqrt{2x} = 2$. Check for extraneous solutions.
   F 2, −8   **G** 0, 2   **H** 2   **I** −8, 1

65. The graph of which equation contains all the points in the table below?

x	−4	−2	0	2	4
y	0	$\pm\sqrt{3}$	± 2	$\pm\sqrt{3}$	0

   A $x^2 + 4y^2 = 16$ **B** $4x^2 + 16y^2 = 144$ **C** $4x^2 + 25y^2 = 64$ **D** $9x^2 + 4y^2 = 81$

Short Response

66. Find the horizontal asymptote of $y = \frac{5x + 7}{x + 3}$ by dividing the numerator by the denominator. Explain your steps.

Mixed Review

Write an equation of a circle with the given center and radius.　　◀ See Lesson 10-3.

67. center $(1, -5)$, radius 3　　　　　　　**68.** center $(-2, 4)$, radius 9

Simplify each expression. State any restrictions on the variable.　　◀ See Lesson 8-4.

69. $\dfrac{3x}{6x^2 - 9x^5}$　　　　**70.** $\dfrac{x^2 - 36}{x^2 + 5x - 6}$　　　　**71.** $\dfrac{x^2 - 3x - 10}{x^3 + 8}$

Write each expression as a single logarithm.　　◀ See Lesson 7-4.

72. $\log 3 + \log 5$　　　　**73.** $\log_3 12 - \log_3 2$　　　　**74.** $3 \log 2 - \log 4$

Get Ready! **To prepare for Lesson 10-5, do Exercises 75–76.**

Write an equation of a line in slope-intercept form using the given information.　　◀ See Lesson 2-3.

75. $m = 2$ and the y-intercept is 4　　　　**76.** passes through $(3, 1)$ and $(9, 3)$

Additional Instructional Support

Algebra 2 Companion

Students can use the **Algebra 2 Companion** worktext (4 pages) as you teach the lesson. Use the Companion to support

- New Vocabulary
- Key Concepts
- Got It for each Problem
- Lesson Check

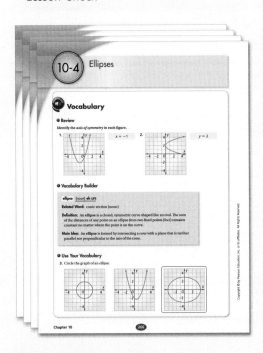

ELL Support

Focus on Language Ask the following questions:

- The plural form of a noun refers to more than one thing. For instance, this is a book. These are books. How did the word *book* change when plural?
- What are two vocabulary words in today's lesson that you do not add an *s* to when making the word plural?
- The plural of *vertex* is *vertices*. The *-ex* becomes *-ices*. With a partner, look through the table of contents of your math textbook to find two other words that end in *-ex*. When you find one, say the word and the plural form to your partner.
- What did you find? What are the plural forms?
- Another math word like this is *axis* and its plural *axes*.
- The plural of *focus* is *foci*. The *-us* becomes *-i*. Try to think of some words that end in *−us*, and say the plural form to your partner. You might think about types of animals.

5 Assess & Remediate

Lesson Quiz

1. What is an equation in standard form of an ellipse centered at the origin with a vertex at $(0, 4)$ and a co-vertex at $(−1, 0)$?

2. What are the foci of the ellipse with the equation $81x^2 + 1681y^2 = 136{,}161$? Graph the ellipse.

3. **Do you UNDERSTAND?** The planets in our solar system have elliptical orbits with the sun at one focus. The major axis of Mercury's orbit is about 11.6 million km long. The foci of Mercury's orbit are about 2.4 million km apart. About how long is the minor axis of Mercury's orbit?

4. What is the standard form equation of the ellipse centered at the origin with co-vertices $(0, ±20)$ and foci $(±15, 0)$?

ANSWERS TO LESSON QUIZ

1. $\dfrac{x^2}{1} + \dfrac{y^2}{16} = 1$

2. $(−40, 0)$ and $(40, 0)$

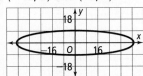

3. about 11.3 million km

4. $\dfrac{x^2}{625} + \dfrac{y^2}{400} = 1$

PRESCRIPTION FOR REMEDIATION

Use the student work on the Lesson Quiz to prescribe a differentiated review assignment:

Points	Differentiated Remediation
0–2	Intervention
3	On-level
4	Extension

PowerAlgebra.com

5 Assess & Remediate

Assign the Lesson Quiz. Appropriate intervention, practice, or enrichment is automatically generated based on student performance.

Intervention

- **Reteaching** (2 pages) Provides reteaching and practice exercises for the key lesson concepts. Use with struggling students or absent students.

- **English Language Learner Support** Helps students develop and reinforce mathematical vocabulary and key concepts.

All-in-One Resources/Online
Reteaching

10-4 Reteaching — Ellipses

To find the standard form of the equation of an ellipse with center at $(0, 0)$, major axis of length $2a$, and minor axis of length $2b$, where $a > b$, use the following:

- When the width is greater than the height, use $\dfrac{x^2}{a^2} + \dfrac{y^2}{b^2} = 1$.
- When the height is greater than the width, use $\dfrac{x^2}{b^2} + \dfrac{y^2}{a^2} = 1$.

Problem

What is the equation of an ellipse that is 10 units wide and 8 units high? Assume that the center is $(0, 0)$.

$\dfrac{x^2}{a^2} + \dfrac{y^2}{b^2} = 1$ Because the width is greater than the height, use the standard form of a horizontal ellipse.

$2a = 10 \quad 2b = 8$ Find a and b.

$a = 5 \qquad b = 4$

$a^2 = 25 \quad b^2 = 16$ Find a^2 and b^2.

$\dfrac{x^2}{25} + \dfrac{y^2}{16} = 1$ Substitute 25 for a^2 and 16 for b^2.

Exercises

Find the equation of the ellipse given the height and width. Assume that the center of the ellipse is $(0, 0)$.

1. height 26 ft, width 24 ft $\dfrac{x^2}{144} + \dfrac{y^2}{169} = 1$
2. height 12 ft, width 4 ft $\dfrac{x^2}{4} + \dfrac{y^2}{36} = 1$
3. height 10 ft, width 6 ft $\dfrac{x^2}{9} + \dfrac{y^2}{25} = 1$
4. height 6 ft, width 18 ft $\dfrac{x^2}{81} + \dfrac{y^2}{9} = 1$
5. height 20 m, width 50 m $\dfrac{x^2}{625} + \dfrac{y^2}{100} = 1$
6. height 10 ft, width 22 ft $\dfrac{x^2}{121} + \dfrac{y^2}{25} = 1$
7. height 16 m, width 18 m $\dfrac{x^2}{81} + \dfrac{y^2}{64} = 1$
8. height 20 ft, width 3 ft $\dfrac{x^2}{2.25} + \dfrac{y^2}{100} = 1$
9. height 3 cm, width 6 cm $\dfrac{x^2}{9} + \dfrac{y^2}{2.25} = 1$
10. height 14 m, width 30 m $\dfrac{x^2}{225} + \dfrac{y^2}{49} = 1$
11. height 12 ft, width 9 ft $\dfrac{x^2}{20.25} + \dfrac{y^2}{36} = 1$
12. height 12 in., width 4 in. $\dfrac{x^2}{4} + \dfrac{y^2}{36} = 1$
13. height 7 m, width 8 m $\dfrac{x^2}{16} + \dfrac{y^2}{12.25} = 1$
14. height 2 in., width 10 in. $\dfrac{x^2}{25} + y^2 = 1$
15. height 16 cm, width 9 cm $\dfrac{x^2}{20.25} + \dfrac{y^2}{64} = 1$
16. Australian Rules Football is played on an elliptical field. One of the fields used for this sport is 174 meters long and 148 meters wide. Find an equation of the ellipse. $\dfrac{x^2}{7569} + \dfrac{y^2}{5476} = 1$

All-in-One Resources/Online
English Language Learner Support

10-4 Additional Vocabulary Support — Ellipses

Complete the vocabulary chart by filling in the missing information.

Word or Word Phrase	Definition	Picture or Example
ellipse	An *ellipse* is the set of all points in a plane such that the sum of the distances from two fixed points is constant.	
focus of an ellipse	A *focus* of an *ellipse* is one of the fixed points.	1.
major axis	2. The *major axis* is the segment that contains the foci and has its endpoints on the ellipse.	
center of an ellipse	The *center* of an *ellipse* is the midpoint of the major axis.	3.
minor axis	4. The *minor axis* is the axis that is perpendicular to the major axis at the center.	
vertices of an ellipse	The *vertices* of an *ellipse* are the end points of the major axis.	5.
co-vertices of an ellipse	6. The *co-vertices* of an *ellipse* are endpoints of the minor axis.	

Differentiated Remediation *continued*

On-Level

- **Practice** (2 pages) Provides extra practice for each lesson. For simpler practice exercises, use the Form K Practice pages found in the All-in-One Teaching Resources and online.

- **Think About a Plan** Helps students develop specific problem-solving skills and strategies by providing scaffolded guiding questions.

- **Standardized Test Prep** Focuses on all major exercises, all major question types, and helps students prepare for the high-stakes assessments.

Extension

- **Enrichment** Provides students with interesting problems and activities that extend the concepts of the lesson.

- **Activities, Games, and Puzzles** Worksheets that can be used for concepts development, enrichment, and for fun!

Practice and Problem Solving Wkbk/ All-in-One Resources/Online
Practice page 1

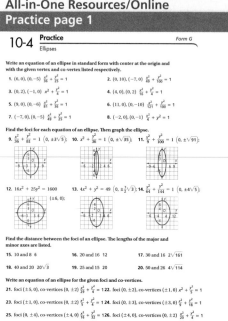

Practice and Problem Solving Wkbk/ All-in-One Resources/Online
Practice page 2

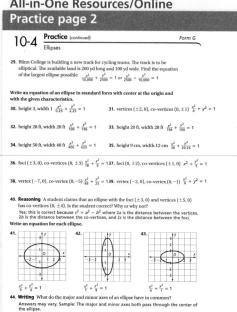

All-in-One Resources/Online
Enrichment

The orbit, or path, of a planet around the sun can be described by an ellipse with the sun as one of the foci. The point in its orbit at which a planet is closest to the sun is called the perihelion. The point at which the planet is farthest from the sun is called the aphelion.

Practice and Problem Solving Wkbk/ All-in-One Resources/Online
Think About a Plan

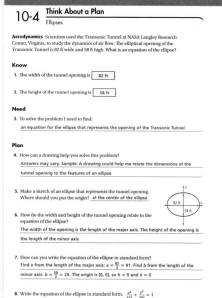

Practice and Problem Solving Wkbk/ All-in-One Resources/Online
Standardized Test Prep

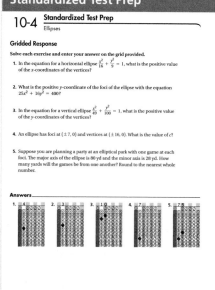

Online Teacher Resource Center
Activities, Games, and Puzzles

10-5 Hyperbolas

Objectives To graph hyperbolas
To find and use the foci of a hyperbola

© **Content Standard**
G.GPE.3 Derive the equations of hyperbolas . . . given foci, using the fact that the sum or difference of distances from the foci is constant.

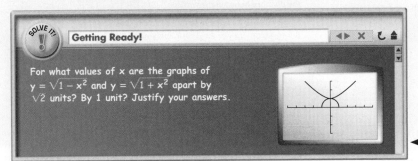

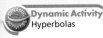

Dynamic Activity
Hyperbolas

Lesson Vocabulary
• hyperbola
• focus of the hyperbola
• vertex of a hyperbola
• transverse axis
• axis of symmetry
• center of a hyperbola
• conjugate axis

In the Solve It, you saw the top halves of two different conic sections. You can complete each conic section by graphing $y = -\sqrt{1 - x^2}$ and $y = -\sqrt{1 + x^2}$ respectively.

Recall from Lesson 10-1, that you can get a variety of conic sections by slicing the double cone with a plane. Changing the angle at which the plane slices the double cone determines the shape of the curve and whether or not the plane will slice both cones. If the plane is parallel to the axis of the double cone, it slices both cones and the result is a *hyperbola*.

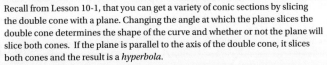

Essential Understanding Like the ellipse, the hyperbola's shape is determined by its distance from two foci.

Key Concept Hyperbola

A **hyperbola** is the set of points P in a plane such that the absolute value of the difference between the distances from P to two fixed points F_1 and F_2 is a constant k.

$$|PF_1 - PF_2| = k, \text{ where } k < F_1F_2$$

Each fixed point F is a **focus of the hyperbola**.

Since F_1 and F_2 are the foci of the hyperbola, the long and short segments in each of the 2 colored paths differ in length by k.

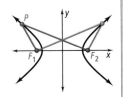

PowerAlgebra.com | Lesson 10-5 Hyperbolas | 645

---

1 Interactive Learning

Solve It!

PURPOSE To find distances between the graphs of one part of a hyperbola and semicircle
PROCESS Students may
• graph the functions on a graphing calculator and use the table feature.
• solve the following equations for x:
$\sqrt{1 + x^2} - \sqrt{2} = \sqrt{1 - x^2}$ and
$\sqrt{1 + x^2} - 1 = \sqrt{1 - x^2}$.

FACILITATE
Q Where would you look for the values on a table? [between $x = 1$ and $x = -1$]
Q What parts of the graph can you ignore? Why? [$x = 0, x > 1, x < -1$; the graphs intersect at $x = 0$, and $y = \sqrt{1 - x^2}$ does not exist at $x > 1, x < -1$]

ANSWER See Solve It in Answers on next page.
CONNECT THE MATH In the Solve It, students find fixed distances between points on a hyperbola and semicircle. In the lesson, students will define, graph and write equations of hyperbolas using fixed points and distances.

2 Guided Instruction

A model can demonstrate the various hyperbolas that are possible at different cutting angles.

Take Note

Q How is the definition of a hyperbola different from the definition of an ellipse? [**For an ellipse, the** *sum* **of the distances from a point to the foci is a constant, while for a hyperbola, the absolute value of the** *difference* **of the distances from a point to the foci is a constant.**]

10-5 Preparing to Teach

BIG idea Coordinate Geometry
ESSENTIAL UNDERSTANDINGS
• The shape of a hyperbola is guided by asymptotes.
• The x^2 and y^2 terms of the algebraic form of an ellipse are both positive. For a hyperbola, one term is negative.

Math Background

It may be helpful to relate the hyperbola to the ellipse and highlight the similarities and differences.

DEFINITION

Instead of the *sum* of the distances from any point to two foci being a constant, the absolute value of the *difference* between the distances from any point to two foci is a constant.

ELEMENTS

For both, the foci and vertices lie on the major axis, called the transverse axis for the hyperbola.

STANDARD EQUATIONS

The standard equations for a horizontal or vertical hyperbola with center (0, 0) are identical to the corresponding ellipse equations with one important exception: the term containing the variable of the conjugate axis is subtracted, not added.

When graphing hyperbolas, make sure students always sketch the central rectangle and asymptotes. The central rectangle guides the location of the asymptotes, and the asymptotes guide the shape of the graph.

© **Mathematical Practices**
Use appropriate tools strategically. Students will use graphing calculators to graph hyperbolas.

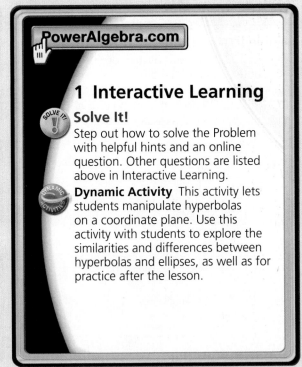

PowerAlgebra.com

1 Interactive Learning

Solve It!
Step out how to solve the Problem with helpful hints and an online question. Other questions are listed above in Interactive Learning.

Dynamic Activity This activity lets students manipulate hyperbolas on a coordinate plane. Use this activity with students to explore the similarities and differences between hyperbolas and ellipses, as well as for practice after the lesson.

While the transverse axis is the axis of symmetry, a hyperbola, like an ellipse, has two lines of symmetry.

Note that for both an ellipse and a hyperbola, the distance between the foci is *by definition* 2c.

> **Q** Which axis of a hyperbola—the transverse axis or the conjugate axis—corresponds to the major axis of an ellipse? Why? **[Transverse axis; like the major axis, it contains the vertices and the foci.]**

Take Note

> **Q** How does the position of the transverse axis determine the orientation of the hyperbola? **[If the transverse axis is along the x-axis, the hyperbola is horizontal. If it is along the y-axis, the hyperbola is vertical.]**
>
> **Q** What are the x-intercepts of a horizontal hyperbola with a center at the origin? y-intercepts? **[(−a, 0) and (a, 0); there are none because the hyperbola does not intersect the y-axis]**
>
> **Q** What are the x-intercepts of a vertical hyperbola with a center at the origin? y-intercepts? **[There are none because the hyperbola does not intersect the x-axis; (0, −a) and (0, a).]**
>
> **Q** Where do the asymptotes intersect the central rectangle of a horizontal hyperbola? vertical hyperbola? **[at the vertices of the rectangle; horizontal: (a, b), (−a, b); (−a, −b), (a, −b); vertical: (b, a), (−b, a), (−b, −a), (b, −a)]**
>
> **Q** How is the relationship between a and c different for a hyperbola than for an ellipse? **[Unlike an ellipse, in a hyperbola, c is greater than a.]**

A hyperbola consists of two smooth branches. The turning point of each branch is a **vertex** of the hyperbola. The segment connecting the two vertices is the **transverse axis**, which lies on the **axis of symmetry**. The two foci also lie on the axis of symmetry. The **center of the hyperbola** is the midpoint between the two vertices, which also is the midpoint between the two foci.

Just as for an ellipse, if the foci are $(\pm c, 0)$, the distance between the two foci is $2c$. If the vertices are $(\pm a, 0)$, the distance between the vertices is $2a$.

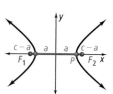

Since vertex P is on the hyperbola, it must satisfy the equation $|PF_1 - PF_2| = k$, but you can also see that

$$|PF_1 - PF_2| = |[2a + (c - a)] - (c - a)|$$
$$= |2a + c - a - c + a|$$
$$= |2a| = 2a$$

Therefore, $k = 2a$.

In a standard hyperbola, c is related to a and b by the equation $c^2 = a^2 + b^2$. The length of the **conjugate axis** is $2b$. The transverse and conjugate axes determine a rectangle that lies between the vertices, and the diagonals of that central rectangle determine the asymptotes of the hyperbola. Recall that an asymptote is a line that a graph approaches. The branches of the hyperbola will approach the asymptotes.

Key Concept Properties of Hyperbolas with Center (0, 0)

Horizontal Hyperbola	Vertical Hyperbola
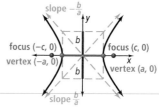	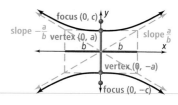

Equation: $\dfrac{x^2}{a^2} - \dfrac{y^2}{b^2} = 1$

Transverse axis: Horizontal

Vertices: $(\pm a, 0)$

Foci: $(\pm c, 0)$, where $c^2 = a^2 + b^2$

Asymptotes: $y = \pm\dfrac{b}{a}x$

Equation: $\dfrac{y^2}{a^2} - \dfrac{x^2}{b^2} = 1$

Transverse axis: Vertical

Vertices: $(0, \pm a)$

Foci: $(0, \pm c)$, where $c^2 = a^2 + b^2$

Asymptotes: $y = \pm\dfrac{a}{b}x$

Answers

Solve It!

± 1; ± 0.93; If you substitute 1 or −1 into both equations the distance between the results will be $\sqrt{2}$. If you substitute 0.93 or −0.93 into both equations, the distance between the results will be 1.

Got It?

1. a. $\dfrac{y^2}{16} - \dfrac{x^2}{9} = 1$

b.

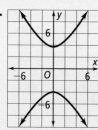

c. when $a = b$

PowerAlgebra.com

2 Guided Instruction

Each Problem is worked out and supported online.

Problem 1
Writing and Graphing the Equation of a Hyperbola
Animated

Problem 2
Analyzing a Hyperbola from Its Equation
Animated

Problem 3
Modeling with a Hyperbola
Animated

Support in Algebra 2 Companion
• Vocabulary
• Key Concepts
• Got It?

Because of symmetry, for both the ellipse and a hyperbola, the value of c is half the distance between the two foci.

 Problem 1 **Writing and Graphing the Equation of a Hyperbola**

A hyperbola centered at $(0, 0)$ has vertices $(\pm 4, 0)$ and one focus $(5, 0)$.

A What is the standard-form equation of the hyperbola?

Think

Is the transverse axis horizontal or vertical?
The vertices and focus are on a horizontal line. The transverse axis is horizontal.

The vertices are $(\pm 4, 0)$, so $a = 4$. One focus is $(5, 0)$, so $c = 5$.

The transverse axis is horizontal.

Use $c^2 = a^2 + b^2$ to find b: $5^2 = 4^2 + b^2$, so $b = 3$.

Write the equation of a horizontal hyperbola in standard form, $\frac{x^2}{a^2} - \frac{y^2}{b^2} = 1$

$\frac{x^2}{4^2} - \frac{y^2}{3^2} = 1$ Substitute values for a and b.

$\frac{x^2}{16} - \frac{y^2}{9} = 1$ Simplify.

B Sketch the hyperbola. Use a graphing calculator to check.

Step 1 Draw the horizontal transverse axis, vertices, and central rectangle. The central rectangle guides the drawing of the graph. It shares a center with the hyperbola and in this case has a height of $2b$ and a width of $2a$. If the hyperbola were vertical the dimensions would be reversed.

Step 2 Extend the diagonals of the rectangle to show the asymptotes.

Step 3 Sketch the branches from the vertices.

Check Solve for y,

$\frac{x^2}{16} - \frac{y^2}{9} = 1$

$\frac{y^2}{9} = \frac{x^2}{16} - 1$

$y^2 = 9\left(\frac{x^2}{16} - 1\right)$

$y = \pm 3\sqrt{\frac{x^2}{16} - 1}.$

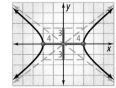

```
Plot1    Plot2    Plot3
\Y1 ▤ 3√(X²/16−1)
\Y2 ▤ ‾Y1
\Y3 =
\Y4 =
\Y5 =
\Y6 =
\Y7 =
```

 Got It? 1. a. What is the standard-form equation of the hyperbola with vertices $(0, \pm 4)$ and foci $(0, \pm 5)$?

    b. Sketch the hyperbola. Use a graphing calculator to check.

    c. Reasoning Under what circumstances are the asymptotes of the graph of a hyperbola perpendicular?

Problem 1   **SYNTHESIZING**

Q What information do you need to write the standard equation of a hyperbola with a center at $(0, 0)$? How does this problem provide it? **[To write the standard equation you need to know a^2 and b^2 and whether it is horizontal or vertical. You are given the vertices and a focus, so you have a and c, and you know the transverse axis is horizontal. To find b^2, solve $b^2 = c^2 - a^2$.]**

Q Is the central rectangle part of the graph of the hyperbola? What is it for? **[No; it defines the asymptotes and assists in graphing.]**

Q Suppose you only graphed Y_1 on the graphing calculator. What would the graph look like? Would it be sufficient to check? **[The graph would not include any points where y is negative. It would look like two curves starting at the x-axis and curving outward. Since the hyperbola is symmetric in the x-axis, it would be sufficient to compare the top part and check for symmetry.]**

Got It?

Q For 1c, how do the dimensions of the rectangle affect the asymptotes? Could the asymptotes ever be parallel? Why or why not? **[The diagonals of the rectangle determine the asymptotes. A long narrow horizontal rectangle would yield asymptotes close together and almost horizontal. However, no rectangle has diagonals that are parallel, so the asymptotes could never be parallel.]**

Additional Problems

1. A hyperbola centered at $(0, 0)$ has vertices $(\pm 2, 0)$ and one focus $(3, 0)$.

   a. What is the standard-form equation of the hyperbola?

   b. Sketch the hyperbola.

   ANSWERS

   a. $\frac{x^2}{4} - \frac{y^2}{5} = 1$

   b.

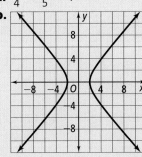

2. What are the vertices, foci, and asymptotes of the hyperbola with equation $4y^2 - x^2 = 16$? Sketch the graph.

   ANSWERS

   vertices: $(0, \pm 2)$

   foci: $(0, \pm 2\sqrt{5})$

   asymptotes: $y = \pm 0.5x$

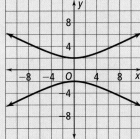

3. If a vertex of a hyperbola is $(0, 10)$ and the equations of the asymptotes are $y = \pm 0.5x$, what is an equation of the hyperbola?

   ANSWER $\frac{y^2}{100} - \frac{x^2}{400} = 1$

Problem 2

Q What information can you get directly from an equation in standard form? How can you use it to find what you need? **[a^2 and b^2 and the transverse axis; use a^2 to find the vertices, a^2 and b^2 to solve for c^2 and find the foci, and $\pm\frac{a}{b}$ to find the equations of the asymptotes.]**

Q What information do you need to graph the hyperbola? Explain. **[You need a to plot the vertices and start the central rectangle, and you need b to finish the central rectangle to sketch the asymptotes. The graph of the hyperbola follows the asymptotes, so you do not need c.]**

EXTENSION

Q Are the asymptotes perpendicular? How could you determine this just by looking at the standard equation? **[No; the asymptotes are perpendicular only if the denominators in the standard equation are equal which happens only when $a = b$.]**

Got It?

Q What are three basic steps for finding the values of a, b, and c for this hyperbola? **[1) Rewrite the equation in standard form, 2) identify a^2 and b^2 and use them to solve for c^2, and 3) take the square root of each to find a, b, and c.]**

 **Problem 2** Analyzing a Hyperbola from Its Equation

What are the vertices, foci, and asymptotes of the hyperbola with equation $9y^2 - 7x^2 = 63$? Sketch the graph. Use a graphing calculator to check your sketch.

Think

Write the equation.

In standard form, the right side must be 1. Divide each side by 63.

Simplify. Since y^2 has the positive coefficient, the hyperbola is vertical. The vertices and foci are on the y-axis.

Compare to $\frac{y^2}{a^2} - \frac{x^2}{b^2} = 1$ to find a^2 and b^2.

Find c^2. Use $c^2 = a^2 + b^2$.

You know a, b, and c. You can answer the questions and draw the graph. $\sqrt{7} \approx 2.65$

Write

$9y^2 - 7x^2 = 63$

$\dfrac{9y^2}{63} - \dfrac{7x^2}{63} = 1$

$\dfrac{y^2}{7} - \dfrac{x^2}{9} = 1$

$a^2 = 7$ and $b^2 = 9$
$a = \pm\sqrt{7}$ $b = \pm 3$

$c^2 = 7 + 9$, so $c = \pm\sqrt{7 + 9} = \pm 4$

Vertices: $(0, \pm\sqrt{7})$, Foci: $(0, \pm 4)$.

Slopes of asymptotes: $m = \pm\dfrac{\sqrt{7}}{3}$

Asymptotes:

$y = \pm\dfrac{\sqrt{7}}{3}x$

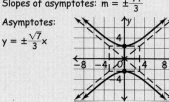

Check

Got It? 2. What are the vertices, foci, and asymptotes of the hyperbola with equation $9x^2 - 4y^2 = 36$? Sketch a graph. Use a graphing calculator to check your sketch.

Answers

Got It? (continued)

2. vertices: $(\pm 2, 0)$; foci: $(\pm\sqrt{13}, 0)$; asymptotes: $y = \pm\dfrac{3}{2}x$

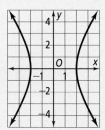

The *reflection property of a hyperbola* is important in optics. As with an ellipse, the reflection property of a hyperbola involves both foci, but only one branch reflects. Any ray on the *external side* of a branch directed at its internal focus will reflect off the branch toward the *external focus*.

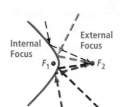

Internal Focus · External Focus · F_1 · F_2

© **Problem 3** Modeling with a Hyperbola **STEM**

Communications The graph shows a 2-dimensional view of a satellite dish. The focus is located at F_1 but the receiving device is located on the bottom of the dish at the point F_2. The rays are reflected by the first reflector (the black curve), toward F_1 and then reflected by the second reflector (the blue curve) toward F_2.

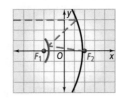

A What kind of curve is the second reflector? How can you tell?

The second reflector is a hyperbola because it reflects rays aimed at its internal focus toward its external focus.

B The vertex of the second reflector is 3 in. from F_1 and 21 in. from F_2. What is an equation for the second reflector? Assume the conic is horizontal and centered at the origin.

Step 1 Determine the standard-form equation of the conic.
The conic is a horizontal hyperbola centered at the origin.
$$\frac{x^2}{a^2} - \frac{y^2}{b^2} = 1$$

Step 2 Find c.
The distance between the foci is $3 + 21 = 24$ in.
Since c is half this distance, $c = 12$.

Step 3 Find a.
The distance from the internal focus to the vertex of the reflector is 3 in.
So, $c - a = 12 - a = 3$ and $a = 9$.

Step 4 Use c and a to find b^2.
$$b^2 = c^2 - a^2$$
$$= 12^2 - 9^2 \quad \text{Substitute and simplify.}$$
$$= 63 \quad \text{Simplify.}$$

Step 5 Use a and b^2 to write the equation.
An equation is $\frac{x^2}{81} - \frac{y^2}{63} = 1$.

 Got It? **3.** Suppose the vertex of the second reflector in Problem 3 were 4 in. from F_1 and 18 in. from F_2. What is the equation for the second reflector? Assume the conic is horizontal and centered at the origin.

PowerAlgebra.com | **Lesson 10-5** Hyperbolas | 649

Think
What information does the diagram give up?
It helps you see the relative positions of the reflectors and foci.

Problem 3

Q How is this reflection different from a reflection within an ellipse? **[Samples: A reflection in an ellipse passes through both foci. The foci are internal in an ellipse.]**

Q On this graph, where is the origin located? **[between the foci]**

Q Is the first reflector part of the graph of the hyperbola? Explain. **[No; it is facing the wrong direction so it could not be part of the second branch.]**

Got It?

Q How does changing the location of the foci and the second reflector change its equation? **[The foci are closer together and the vertex is further from the first focus, so the value of a decreases. The denominator of the x term will be smaller.]**

---

3. $\frac{x^2}{49} - \frac{y^2}{72} = 1$

Lesson Check

1. vertices: $(\pm 6, 0)$; foci: $(\pm \sqrt{61}, 0)$;
slopes of asymptotes: $\pm\frac{5}{6}$

2. vertices: $(0, \pm 4)$; foci: $(0, \pm \sqrt{41})$;
slopes of asymptotes: $\pm\frac{4}{5}$

3. vertices: $(0, \pm 2)$; foci: $(0, \pm 2\sqrt{5})$;
slopes of asymptotes: $\pm\frac{1}{2}$

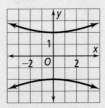

4. vertices: $(\pm 5, 0)$; foci: $(\pm \sqrt{41}, 0)$;
slopes of asymptotes: $\pm\frac{4}{5}$

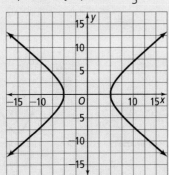

5. $\frac{x^2}{25} - \frac{y^2}{24} = 1$

6. Answers may vary. Sample: Similarities—Both have two axes of sym. that intersect at the center of the figure and two foci that lie on the same line as the two "principal" vertices. Differences—An ellipse consists of pts. whose distances from the foci have a constant sum, whereas a hyperbola consists of pts. whose distances from the foci have a constant diff.

7. Answers may vary. Sample: A hyperbola is vert. or horizontal depending on whether it has a positive coefficient not because the larger denominator is under the y^2 term.

3 Lesson Check

Do you know HOW?
- To assist graphing Exercises 1–4, students should note whether the hyperbola is vertical or horizontal.

Do you UNDERSTAND?
- For Exercise 6, suggest students compare the axes and a and b in both conics.

Close

> **Q** What parts of a hyperbola must be included on its graph? **[the vertices]**

 Lesson Check

Do you know HOW?

Find the vertices and foci of each hyperbola. Write the slopes of the asymptotes. Then sketch the graph.

1. $\frac{x^2}{36} - \frac{y^2}{25} = 1$ **2.** $\frac{y^2}{16} - \frac{x^2}{25} = 1$

3. $4y^2 - x^2 = 16$ **4.** $16x^2 - 25y^2 = 400$

5. What is an equation of a hyperbola with vertices $(\pm 5, 0)$ and focus $(7, 0)$?

Do you UNDERSTAND? MATHEMATICAL PRACTICES

6. Compare and Contrast How is graphing a hyperbola like graphing an ellipse? How is it different?

7. Error Analysis Your friend says that a graph must be a vertical hyperbola because the larger denominator is under the y^2 term. What error did your friend make?

Practice and Problem-Solving Exercises MATHEMATICAL PRACTICES

A Practice

Write an equation of a hyperbola with the given values, foci, or vertices. Assume that the transverse axis is horizontal.   ◀ See Problem 1.

8. $a = 3, b = 4$ **9.** $a = 12, c = 13$

10. $b = 9, c = 10$ **11.** $a = 7, b = 11$

12. foci $(\pm 13, 0)$, vertices $(\pm 12, 0)$ **13.** foci $(\pm 3, 0)$, vertices $(\pm 2, 0)$

Find the vertices, foci, and asymptotes of each hyperbola. Then sketch the graph.   ◀ See Problem 2.

14. $\frac{y^2}{81} - \frac{x^2}{16} = 1$ **15.** $\frac{y^2}{49} - \frac{x^2}{64} = 1$ **16.** $\frac{x^2}{121} - \frac{y^2}{144} = 1$

17. $\frac{x^2}{64} - \frac{y^2}{36} = 1$ **18.** $\frac{y^2}{25} - \frac{x^2}{100} = 1$ **19.** $81y^2 - 9x^2 = 729$

20. $4y^2 - 25x^2 = 100$ **21.** $36x^2 - 8y^2 = 288$ **22.** $14y^2 - 28x^2 = 448$

STEM 23. Satellite Dish The diagram at the right models a satellite dish and the small reflector inside it. Suppose F_1 and F_2 are 7 meters apart, and F_1 is 1 meter from the vertex of the small reflector. What equation best models the small reflector?   ◀ See Problem 3.

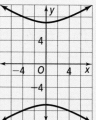

B Apply   **24. Think About a Plan** The path that Voyager 2 made around Jupiter followed one branch of a hyperbola. Find an equation that models the path of Voyager 2 around Jupiter, given that $a = 2{,}184{,}140$ km and $c = 2{,}904{,}906.2$ km. Use the horizontal model.
- What information do you need to write the equation?
- How can you use the given information to find the information you need?

Write an equation of a hyperbola with the given foci and vertices.

25. foci $(\pm 5, 0)$, vertices $(\pm 3, 0)$ **26.** foci $(0, \pm 13)$, vertices $(0, \pm 5)$

27. foci $(0, \pm 2)$, vertices $(0, \pm 1)$ **28.** foci $(\pm \sqrt{5}, 0)$, vertices $(\pm 2, 0)$

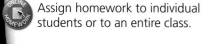

3 Lesson Check

For a digital lesson check, use the Got It questions.

Support in Algebra 2 Companion
- Lesson Check

4 Practice

Assign homework to individual students or to an entire class.

Answers

Practice and Problem-Solving Exercises

1–7. See previous page.

8. $\frac{x^2}{9} - \frac{y^2}{16} = 1$

9. $\frac{x^2}{144} - \frac{y^2}{25} = 1$

10. $\frac{x^2}{19} - \frac{y^2}{81} = 1$

11. $\frac{x^2}{49} - \frac{y^2}{121} = 1$

12. $\frac{x^2}{144} - \frac{y^2}{25} = 1$

13. $\frac{x^2}{4} - \frac{y^2}{5} = 1$

14. vertices: $(0, \pm 9)$; foci: $(0, \pm\sqrt{97})$; asymptotes: $y = \pm\frac{9}{4}x$

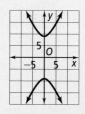

15. vertices: $(0, \pm 7)$; foci: $(0, \pm\sqrt{113})$; asymptotes: $y = \pm\frac{7}{8}x$

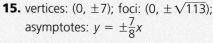

16. vertices: $(\pm 11, 0)$; foci: $(\pm\sqrt{265}, 0)$; asymptotes: $y = \pm\frac{12}{11}x$

Write an equation of a hyperbola from the given information. Assume the center of each hyperbola is (0, 0).

29. Transverse axis is vertical and is 9 units; central rectangle is 9 units by 4 units

30. Perimeter of central rectangle is 16 units; vertices are (0, 3) and (0, −3)

31. (Distance from the center of a hyperbola to a focus)^2 = 96; endpoints of the transverse axis are at $(-\sqrt{32}, 0)$ and $(\sqrt{32}, 0)$.

 Graphing Calculator Solve each equation for y. Graph each relation on your graphing calculator. Use the TRACE feature to locate the vertices.

32. $x^2 - 2y^2 = 4$ **33.** $x^2 - y^2 = 1$ **34.** $3x^2 - y^2 = 2$

Graph each equation.

35. $5x^2 - 12y^2 = 120$ **36.** $16x^2 - 20y^2 = 560$ **37.** $\dfrac{y^2}{20} - \dfrac{x^2}{5} = 1$

STEM 38. Comets The path of a comet around the sun followed one branch of a hyperbola. Find an equation that models its path around the sun, given that a = 40 million miles and c = 250 million miles. Use the horizontal model.

Ⓒ **39. Open-Ended** Choose two points on an axis to be the vertices of a hyperbola. Choose two other points on the same axis to be the foci. Write the equation of your hyperbola and draw its graph.

Ⓒ **40. Error Analysis** On a test, a student found that the foci of the hyperbola with equation $\dfrac{y^2}{100} - \dfrac{x^2}{21} = 1$ were $(0, \pm\sqrt{79})$. The teacher credited the student three points out of a possible five. What did the student do right? What did the student do wrong?

Ⓒ **Challenge** **41.** The function $y = \sqrt{x^2 - 9}$ represents part of a hyperbola. The tables show the coordinates of several points on the graph.

     a. Explain why ERROR appears for some entries.
     b. Describe the relationship between the x- and y-coordinates as x increases.
Ⓒ   **c. Reasoning** Do you think that the x- and y-coordinates will ever be equal? Explain.
Ⓒ   **d. Make a Conjecture** What are the equations of the asymptotes of this hyperbola? Verify your answer by drawing the complete graph.

Lesson 10-5   651

4 Practice

ASSIGNMENT GUIDE
Basic: 8–23 all, 24–30 even, 36–40 even
Average: 9–23 odd, 24–40
Advanced: 9–23 odd, 24–42
Standardized Test Prep: 43–46
Mixed Review: 47–55

Ⓒ **Mathematical Practices** are supported by exercises with red headings. Here are the Practices supported in this lesson:

MP 1: Make Sense of Problems   Ex. 24
MP 2: Reason Quantitatively   Ex. 39
MP 3: Communicate   Ex. 41c
MP 3: Construct Arguments   Ex. 41d
MP 3: Compare Arguments   Ex. 6
MP 3: Critique the Reasoning of Others   Ex. 7, 40
MP 5: Use Appropriate Tools   Ex. 32–34

Applications exercises have blue headings. Exercises 23 and 42 support MP 4: Model.

STEM exercises focus on science or engineering applications.

EXERCISE 38: Use the Think About a Plan worksheet in the **Practice and Problem Solving Workbook** (also available in the Teaching Resources in print and online) to further support students' development in becoming independent learners.

HOMEWORK QUICK CHECK
To check students' understanding of key skills and concepts, go over Exercises 11, 15, 24, 38, and 40.

17. vertices: $(\pm 8, 0)$; foci: $(\pm 10, 0)$; asymptotes: $y = \pm\dfrac{3}{4}x$

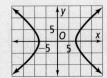

18. vertices: $(0, \pm 5)$; foci: $(0, \pm 5\sqrt{5})$; asymptotes: $y = \pm\dfrac{1}{2}x$

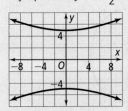

19. vertices: $(0, \pm 3)$; foci: $(0, \pm 3\sqrt{10})$; asymptotes: $y = \pm\dfrac{1}{3}x$

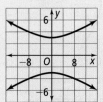

20. vertices: $(0, \pm 5)$; foci: $(0, \pm\sqrt{29})$; asymptotes: $y = \pm\dfrac{5}{2}x$

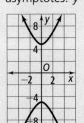

21. vertices: $(\pm 2\sqrt{2}, 0)$; foci: $(\pm 2\sqrt{11}, 0)$; asymptotes: $y = \pm\dfrac{3\sqrt{2}}{2}x$

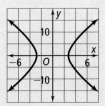

22. vertices: $(0, \pm 4\sqrt{2})$; foci: $(0, \pm 4\sqrt{3})$; asymptotes: $y = \pm\sqrt{2}x$

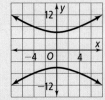

23. $\dfrac{x^2}{6.25} - \dfrac{y^2}{6} = 1$ **24.** $\dfrac{x^2}{4.770 \times 10^{12}} - \dfrac{y^2}{3.668 \times 10^{12}} = 1$

25–41. See next page.

Answers

Practice and Problem-Solving Exercises (continued)

25. $\dfrac{x^2}{9} - \dfrac{y^2}{16} = 1$ **26.** $\dfrac{y^2}{25} - \dfrac{x^2}{144} = 1$

27. $y^2 - \dfrac{x^2}{3} = 1$ **28.** $\dfrac{x^2}{4} - y^2 = 1$

29. $\dfrac{y^2}{20.25} - \dfrac{x^2}{4} = 1$

30. $\dfrac{y^2}{9} - x^2 = 1$ **31.** $\dfrac{x^2}{32} - \dfrac{y^2}{64} = 1$

32. $y = \pm\sqrt{\dfrac{x^2}{2} - 2}$; **33.** $y = \pm\sqrt{x^2 - 1}$;
$(\pm2, 0)$ $(\pm1, 0)$

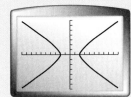 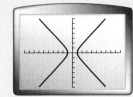

34. $y = \pm\sqrt{3x^2 - 2}$; **35.**
$(\pm0.816, 0)$

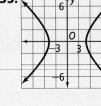

36. 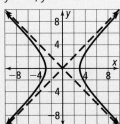 **37.**

38. $\dfrac{x^2}{1.6 \times 10^{15}} - \dfrac{y^2}{6.09 \times 10^{16}} = 1$

39. Check students' work.

40. right: the foci are located on the vert. axis;
wrong: $c^2 = 100 + 21 = 121$, so the foci are
$(0, \pm11)$, not $(0, \pm\sqrt{79})$

41. a. For the x-values in those rows, the value of
$x^2 - 9$ is neg., so $\sqrt{x^2 - 9}$ is not a real
number.

b. As x increases, y increases, but the diff.
between x and y gets closer to zero.

c. No; for positive values of x greater than 3,
$x = \sqrt{x^2}$ and $\sqrt{x^2} \neq \sqrt{x^2 - 9}$.

d. $y = x$, $y = -x$

42. a. your airport

b. 30 km

c. $\dfrac{x^2}{225} - \dfrac{y^2}{351} = 1$

---

42. Air Traffic Control Suppose you are an air traffic controller directing the pilot of a plane on a hyperbolic flight path. You and another air traffic controller from a different airport send radio signals to the pilot simultaneously. The two airports are 48 km apart. The pilot's instrument panel tells him that the signal from your airport always arrives 100 μs (microseconds) before the signal from the other airport.
a. Which airport is the plane closer to?
b. If the signals travel at a rate of 300 m/μs, what is the difference in distances from the plane to the two airports?
c. Write the equation of the flight path. (*Hint:* $k = 2a$)
d. Draw the hyperbola. Which branch represents the flight path?

Standardized Test Prep

SAT/ACT

43. The graph of $\dfrac{x^2}{16} - \dfrac{y^2}{4} = 1$ is a hyperbola. Which set of equations represents the asymptotes of the hyperbola's graph?
Ⓐ $y = \frac{1}{2}x$, $y = -\frac{1}{2}x$ Ⓒ $x = \frac{1}{2}y$, $x = -\frac{1}{2}y$
Ⓑ $y = 2x$, $y = -2x$ Ⓓ $y = \frac{1}{4}x$, $y = -\frac{1}{4}x$

44. Simplify $\dfrac{\frac{1}{y} - \frac{1}{x}}{\frac{1}{xy} - 1}$.
Ⓕ $\dfrac{y - x}{xy - 1}$ Ⓖ $\dfrac{x - y}{1 - xy}$ Ⓗ $\dfrac{x + y}{1 + xy}$ Ⓘ $x + y$

45. How is the graph of $y = 4 \cdot \left(\frac{1}{2}\right)^{x-3}$ translated from the graph of $y = 4 \cdot \left(\frac{1}{2}\right)^{x}$?
Ⓐ 3 units right Ⓑ 3 units left Ⓒ 3 units down Ⓓ 3 units up

Short Response

46. Using sigma notation, what is an expression for the sum of a 6-term arithmetic sequence with first term of 3 and a common difference of 4? What is the sum?

Mixed Review

Find the foci for each equation of an ellipse. Then graph the ellipse. ◀ See Lesson 10-4.

47. $\dfrac{x^2}{34} + \dfrac{y^2}{25} = 1$ **48.** $3x^2 + 2y^2 = 6$ **49.** $25x^2 + 16y^2 = 1600$

Solve each equation. Check your answers. ◀ See Lesson 7-5.

50. $8^{2x} = 4$ **51.** $\log 8x = 3$ **52.** $2\log_3 x - \log_3 4 = 2$

Get Ready! To prepare for Lesson 10-6, do Exercises 53–55.

Rewrite each function in vertex form. ◀ See Lesson 4-2.

53. $y = x^2 - 6x + 1$ **54.** $y = 2x^2 + 12x$ **55.** $y = 3x^2 + 24x - 2$

---

d.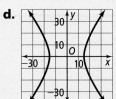

the branch that contains the vertex closest to your airport

Standardized Test Prep

43. A **44.** G **45.** A

46. [2] $\displaystyle\sum_{n=1}^{6}(-1 + 4n)$ OR equivalent expression;
$a_6 = 3 + (6 - 1)4 = 23$,
$S_6 = 6\dfrac{(3 + 23)}{2} = 78$

[1] correct expression, but incorrect sum OR correct sum, but incorrect expression

Mixed Review

47. foci: $(\pm3, 0)$ **48.** foci: $(0, \pm1)$

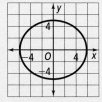 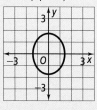

49. foci: $(0, \pm6)$

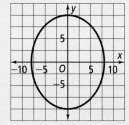

50. $\dfrac{1}{3}$ **51.** 125

52. 6 **53.** $y = (x - 3)^2 - 8$

54. $y = 2(x + 3)^2 - 18$

55. $y = 3(x + 4)^2 - 50$

Differentiated Remediation

Additional Instructional Support

Algebra 2 Companion

Students can use the **Algebra 2 Companion** worktext (4 pages) as you teach the lesson. Use the Companion to support

- New Vocabulary
- Key Concepts
- Got It for each Problem
- Lesson Check

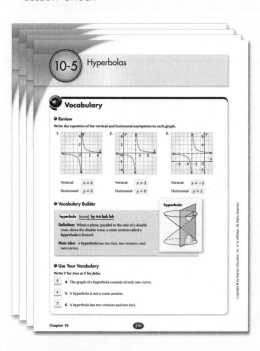

ELL Support

Focus on Language Have one pair of students sit with another pair. Distribute index cards, half with graphs of hyperbolas and the other half with equations. Have each pair work together to match the graph with the equation. Give students additional blank index cards. While one student examines a graph and one student examines an equation, both students discuss how to find a, b, c, vertices, foci, transverse axis and length, conjugate axis and length, dimensions of the central rectangle, and asymptotes. They then record this information on a blank card. If the pair finds that the graph does not match the equation, the graph card is set aside and another graph is chosen. When the activity ends, students should have 3 cards per problem to present to the class.

5 Assess & Remediate

Lesson Quiz

1. What is the standard-form equation of the hyperbola centered at (0, 0) with vertices (0, ±7) and one focus (0, 25)?

2. What are the vertices, foci, and asymptotes of the hyperbola with equation $36x^2 - 25y^2 = 900$? Sketch the graph.

3. **Do you UNDERSTAND?** As a comet shoots through space, it follows a hyperbolic path. The central rectangle is a square, the distance from focus to center is 50, and the hyperbola is horizontal, centered at the origin. What is the equation of the hyperbola?

ANSWERS TO LESSON QUIZ

1. $\dfrac{y^2}{49} - \dfrac{x^2}{576} = 1$;

2. vertices: (±5, 0); foci: (±$\sqrt{61}$, 0); asymptotes: $y = \pm 1.2x$

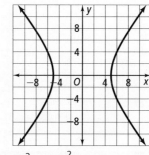

3. $\dfrac{x^2}{1250} - \dfrac{y^2}{1250} = 1$

PRESCRIPTION FOR REMEDIATION

Use the student work on the Lesson Quiz to prescribe a differentiated review assignment:

Points	Differentiated Remediation
1	Intervention
2	On-level
3	Extension

PowerAlgebra.com

5 Assess & Remediate

Assign the Lesson Quiz. Appropriate intervention, practice, or enrichment is automatically generated based on student performance.

Intervention

- **Reteaching** (2 pages) Provides reteaching and practice exercises for the key lesson concepts. Use with struggling students or absent students.

- **English Language Learner Support** Helps students develop and reinforce mathematical vocabulary and key concepts.

All-in-One Resources/Online
Reteaching

All-in-One Resources/Online
English Language Learner Support

Differentiated Remediation *continued*

On-Level

- **Practice** (2 pages) Provides extra practice for each lesson. For simpler practice exercises, use the Form K Practice pages found in the All-in-One Teaching Resources and online.

- **Think About a Plan** Helps students develop specific problem-solving skills and strategies by providing scaffolded guiding questions.

- **Standardized Test Prep** Focuses on all major exercises, all major question types, and helps students prepare for the high-stakes assessments.

Extension

- **Enrichment** Provides students with interesting problems and activities that extend the concepts of the lesson.

- **Activities, Games, and Puzzles** Worksheets that can be used for concepts development, enrichment, and for fun!

Practice and Problem Solving Wkbk/All-in-One Resources/Online
Practice page 1

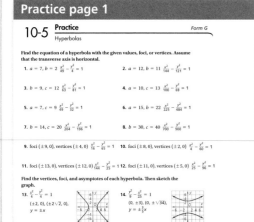

10-5 Practice Form G
Hyperbolas

Find the equation of a hyperbola with the given values, foci, or vertices. Assume that the transverse axis is horizontal.

1. $a = 7$, $b = 2$ $\frac{x^2}{49} - \frac{y^2}{4} = 1$
2. $a = 12$, $b = 11$ $\frac{x^2}{144} - \frac{y^2}{121} = 1$
3. $b = 9$, $c = 12$ $\frac{x^2}{63} - \frac{y^2}{81} = 1$
4. $a = 10$, $c = 13$ $\frac{x^2}{100} - \frac{y^2}{69} = 1$
5. $a = 7$, $c = 9$ $\frac{x^2}{49} - \frac{y^2}{32} = 1$
6. $a = 15$, $b = 22$ $\frac{x^2}{225} - \frac{y^2}{484} = 1$
7. $b = 14$, $c = 20$ $\frac{x^2}{204} - \frac{y^2}{196} = 1$
8. $b = 30$, $c = 40$ $\frac{x^2}{700} - \frac{y^2}{900} = 1$
9. foci $(\pm 9, 0)$, vertices $(\pm 4, 0)$ $\frac{x^2}{16} - \frac{y^2}{65} = 1$
10. foci $(\pm 8, 0)$, vertices $(\pm 2, 0)$ $\frac{x^2}{4} - \frac{y^2}{60} = 1$
11. foci $(\pm 13, 0)$, vertices $(\pm 12, 0)$ $\frac{x^2}{144} - \frac{y^2}{25} = 1$
12. foci $(\pm 11, 0)$, vertices $(\pm 5, 0)$ $\frac{x^2}{25} - \frac{y^2}{96} = 1$

Find the vertices, foci, and asymptotes of each hyperbola. Then sketch the graph.

13. $\frac{x^2}{4} - \frac{y^2}{4} = 1$
$(\pm 2, 0)$, $(\pm 2\sqrt{2}, 0)$,
$y = \pm x$
14. $\frac{y^2}{9} - \frac{x^2}{25} = 1$
$(0, \pm 3)$, $(0, \pm \sqrt{34})$,
$y = \pm \frac{3}{5}x$
15. $\frac{x^2}{25} - \frac{y^2}{4} = 1$
$(\pm 5, 0)$, $(\pm \sqrt{29}, 0)$,
$y = \pm \frac{2}{5}x$
16. $y^2 - \frac{x^2}{9} = 1$
$(0, \pm 1)$, $(0, \pm \sqrt{10})$,
$y = \pm \frac{1}{3}x$
17. $4y^2 - 36x^2 = 144$
$(0, \pm 6)$, $(0, \pm 2\sqrt{10})$,
$y = \pm 3x$
18. $x^2 - 9y^2 = 9$
$(\pm 3, 0)$, $(\pm \sqrt{10}, 0)$,
$y = \pm \frac{1}{3}x$

Practice and Problem Solving Wkbk/All-in-One Resources/Online
Practice page 2

10-5 Practice *(continued)* Form G
Hyperbolas

19. The graph at the right shows a 2-dimensional view of a satellite dish and the small reflector inside it. The vertex of the small reflector is 6 in. from focus F_1 and 20 in. from focus F_2. What equation best models the small reflector? $\frac{x^2}{49} - \frac{y^2}{120} = 1$

Write the equation of a hyperbola with the given foci and vertices.

20. foci $(\pm 7, 0)$, vertices $(\pm 3, 0)$ $\frac{x^2}{9} - \frac{y^2}{40} = 1$
21. foci $(0, \pm 12)$, vertices $(0, \pm 10)$ $\frac{y^2}{100} - \frac{x^2}{44} = 1$
22. foci $(0, \pm 3)$, vertices $(0, \pm 2)$ $\frac{y^2}{4} - \frac{x^2}{5} = 1$
23. foci $(\pm 9, 0)$, vertices $(\pm 5, 0)$ $\frac{x^2}{25} - \frac{y^2}{56} = 1$

Graph each equation.

24. $20x^2 - 8y^2 = 160$
25. $27y^2 - 9x^2 = 243$
26. $6x^2 - 28y^2 = 168$

27. **Writing** How can you tell from the standard form of the equation of a hyperbola whether the hyperbola is horizontal or vertical?
The placement of the x- and y-terms indicates whether the hyperbola is horizontal or vertical. The form $\frac{x^2}{a^2} - \frac{y^2}{b^2} = 1$ indicates a horizontal hyperbola, while the form $\frac{y^2}{a^2} - \frac{x^2}{b^2} = 1$ indicates a vertical hyperbola.

28. **Error Analysis** On a test, a student wrote $(5, 0)$ for the foci of the hyperbola with the equation $\frac{y^2}{9} - \frac{x^2}{16} = 1$. The teacher gave the student partial credit. What did the student do right? What did the student do wrong?
The student correctly identified the value c, but found only one focus and placed it as the x-coordinate rather than the y-coordinate. The foci should be $(0, \pm 5)$.

29. **Reasoning** Describe how you can find the asymptotes when you have the a and c values for a vertical hyperbola.
Use the equation $c^2 = a^2 + b^2$ to find the value of b. Then substitute values of a and b in the equation $y = \pm \frac{a}{b}x$ to find the asymptotes.

Practice and Problem Solving Wkbk/All-in-One Resources/Online
Think About a Plan

10-5 Think About a Plan
Hyperbolas

Comets The path of a comet around the sun followed one branch of a hyperbola. Find an equation for its path around the sun, given that $a = 40$ million miles and $c = 250$ million miles. Use the horizontal model.

Know

1. a is equal to 40×10^6 mi.

2. c is equal to 250×10^6 mi.

Need

3. To solve the problem I need to find:
an equation that models the comet's path around the sun using the
horizontal model

Plan

4. What is the equation for a horizontal hyperbola? $\frac{x^2}{a^2} - \frac{y^2}{b^2} = 1$

5. What do you need in order to write an equation for the hyperbola that models the comet?
a^2 and b^2

6. What is the relationship between a, b, and c in a hyperbola? $c^2 = a^2 + b^2$

7. How can you use the relationship between a, b, and c to find an equation for the hyperbola?
I can solve the equation for b^2 since I know a and c

8. Write an equation for a horizontal hyperbola that models the path of the comet.
$\frac{x^2}{1600 \times 10^{12}} - \frac{y^2}{60,900 \times 10^{12}} = 1$

Practice and Problem Solving Wkbk/All-in-One Resources/Online
Standardized Test Prep

10-5 Standardized Test Prep
Hyperbolas

Multiple Choice

For Exercises 1–4, choose the correct letter.

1. A hyperbola has vertices $(\pm 5, 0)$ and one focus at $(6, 0)$. What is the equation of the hyperbola in standard form? D
   Ⓐ $\frac{x^2}{25} + \frac{y^2}{11} = 1$
   Ⓒ $\frac{x^2}{11} - \frac{y^2}{25} = 1$
   Ⓑ $\frac{x^2}{5} - \frac{y^2}{11} = 1$
   Ⓓ $\frac{x^2}{25} - \frac{y^2}{11} = 1$

2. A hyperbola with a horizontal transverse axis has asymptotes $y = \pm \frac{3}{4}x$. Which of the following could be the equation of the hyperbola in standard form? G
   Ⓕ $\frac{x^2}{3} + \frac{y^2}{4} = 1$
   Ⓗ $\frac{x^2}{4} - \frac{y^2}{3} = 1$
   Ⓖ $\frac{x^2}{16} - \frac{y^2}{9} = 1$
   Ⓘ $\frac{x^2}{25} - \frac{y^2}{16} = 1$

3. What are the vertices of the hyperbola with the equation $8x^2 - 9y^2 = 72$? A
   Ⓐ $(\pm 3, 0)$ Ⓑ $(\pm 2\sqrt{2}, 0)$ Ⓒ $(\pm 8, 0)$ Ⓓ $(\pm 9, 0)$

4. What are the foci of the hyperbola with the equation $\frac{y^2}{12} - \frac{x^2}{5} = 1$? I
   Ⓕ $(0, \pm 5)$ Ⓖ $(0, \pm 12)$ Ⓗ $(0, \pm \sqrt{13})$ Ⓘ $(0, \pm \sqrt{17})$

Short Response

5. What are the vertices, foci, and asymptotes of the hyperbola with the equation $4y^2 - 16x^2 = 64$?
[2] vertices: $(0, \pm 4)$; foci: $(0, \pm 2\sqrt{5})$; asymptotes: $y = \pm 2x$
[1] incorrect vertices OR foci OR asymptotes
[0] no answers given

All-in-One Resources/Online
Enrichment

10-5 Enrichment
Hyperbolas

Rectangular Hyperbolas
The graphs of equations of the form $xy = c$, where c is a nonzero constant, are also hyperbolas, sometimes referred to as rectangular hyperbolas. Graph the following and compare.

1. Draw the graph of $\frac{x^2}{4} - \frac{y^2}{4} = 1$ on the coordinate grid below.
2. Draw the graph of $xy = 2$ on the coordinate grid below.

3. Compare the two graphs. How are they similar? They are the same shape.

4. How are the two graphs different? The second graph is rotated 45° counterclockwise from the first graph.

5. Find the asymptotes for the hyperbola in Exercise 1. $y = x$; $y = -x$

6. Find the asymptotes for the hyperbola in Exercise 2. x-axis; y-axis

7. Describe the graph of $xy = c$ if $c > 0$. What can you say about the x- and y-intercepts? What are the asymptotes? It is a hyperbola with a horizontal transverse axis and equation $x^2 - y^2 = 2c$ rotated 45° counterclockwise; there are no x- or y-intercepts; x- and y-axes are asymptotes.

8. Describe the graph of $xy = c$ if $c < 0$. What can you say about the x- and y-intercepts? What are the asymptotes? It is a hyperbola with a horizontal transverse axis and equation $x^2 - y^2 = 2c$ rotated 45° clockwise; there are no x- or y-intercepts; x- and y-axes are asymptotes.

9. Draw the graph of $xy = -2$ on the coordinate axis at the right.

10. Compare the graph in Exercise 1 to the graph in Exercise 9. What do you notice? It is the same shape but rotated 45° clockwise.

Online Teacher Resource Center
Activities, Games, and Puzzles

10-5 Activity: Closer and Closer . . .
Hyperbolas

Work with a partner. Select one of the three equations and sketch the graph of it on the grid shown.

- Draw the axes and foci.
- Sketch the asymptotes.
- Write the equations for the asymptotes of your hyperbola below.

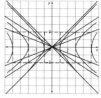

A. $\frac{x^2}{5^2} - \frac{y^2}{2^2} = 1$ $y = \pm \frac{2}{5}x$
B. $\frac{x^2}{3^2} - \frac{y^2}{2^2} = 1$ $y = \pm \frac{2}{3}x$
C. $\frac{x^2}{1^2} - \frac{y^2}{1^2} = 1$ $y = \pm x$

Use a graphing calculator to graph your hyperbola and its asymptotes. Then complete the information for your hyperbola below. The answers to the first row are shown. Record only positive values.

x	A		x	B		x	C	
x	y-value curve	y-value asymptote	x	y-value curve	y-value asymptote	x	y-value curve	y-value asymptote
50	19.90	20	50	33.27	33.33	50	49.99	50
100	39.95	40	100	66.64	66.67	100	99.995	100
200	79.97	80	200	133.32	133.33	200	199.997	200
500	199.99	200	500	333.327	333.333	500	499.999	500
1000	399.995	400	1000	666.664	666.667	1000	999.999	1000

Is there any value of x for which the curve touches the asymptote? Explain.
No; for every value of x, for example when x ≫ 0, the asymptote in the first quadrant is higher up than the curve. But, the distance between them for a given value of x gets smaller and smaller.

What will be the smallest distance between the curve and the asymptote? Where will this distance be found? Explain.
Zero; the distance between the curve and the asymptote becomes zero as x approaches infinity.

As a class, discuss your findings for each of the three given hyperbolas.

Translating Conic Sections

© **Content Standards**
G.GPE.2 Derive the equation of a parabola given a focus and directrix.
Also G.GPE.1, F.IF.8

Objectives To write the equation of a translated conic section
To identify a translated conic section from an equation

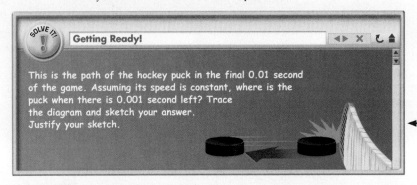

Getting Ready!

This is the path of the hockey puck in the final 0.01 second of the game. Assuming its speed is constant, where is the puck when there is 0.001 second left? Trace the diagram and sketch your answer. Justify your sketch.

In this lesson you will practice translation skills to locate ellipses and hyperbolas when their centers move from $(0, 0)$ to (h, k). You will not need to relearn the geometry of these curves. Each will still depend on the same distances, a, b, and c that relate to their vertices and foci.

Essential Understanding In a relation with an x-y relationship, replacing x by $x - h$ and y by $y - k$ (with $h > 0$ and $k > 0$) translates the graph of the relation h units to the right and k units up.

The summary tables in this lesson are like those from the lesson on parabolas. Notice how each entry in the "Center $(0, 0)$" column relates to the corresponding entry in the "Center (h, k)" column.

take note

Summary   Translating Horizontal Ellipses

Horizontal Ellipse	Center $(0, 0)$	Center (h, k)
Standard-Form Equation	$\dfrac{x^2}{a^2} + \dfrac{y^2}{b^2} = 1$	$\dfrac{(x - h)^2}{a^2} + \dfrac{(y - k)^2}{b^2} = 1$
Vertices	$(\pm a, 0)$	$(h \pm a, k)$
Co-vertices	$(0, \pm b)$	$(h, k \pm b)$
Foci	$(\pm c, 0)$	$(h \pm c, k)$
a, b, c relationship, $a > b > 0$	$c^2 = a^2 - b^2$	$c^2 = a^2 - b^2$

10-6 Preparing to Teach

BIG ideas   Coordinate Geometry
            Equivalence
            Modeling

ESSENTIAL UNDERSTANDINGS
- In an x-y relationship, replacing x by $x - h$ and y by $y - k$ (with $h > 0$ and $k > 0$) translates the graph of the relation h units to the right and k units up.
- The intersection of a cone and a plane parallel to a line along its side is a parabola.
- The x^2 and y^2 terms of the algebraic form of an ellipse are both positive. For a hyperbola, one term is negative.

Math Background
Translating ellipses and hyperbolas is similar to translating circles and parabolas. The techniques for graphing translated ellipses and hyperbolas remain unchanged.

All coordinates of the form (x, y) that satisfy the equation of an ellipse or hyperbola with center $(0, 0)$ are translated to $(x + h, y + k)$, where h represents the horizontal translation and k represents the vertical translation.

The translations can be easily read from the standard form of the equations for conic sections. An equation for a conic in general form, $Ax^2 + Cy^2 + Dx + Ey + F = 0$ can be written in the standard-form equation of a conic section by completing the square and simplifying the resulting equation.

© **Mathematical Practices**
Look for and make use of structure. Students will find the significant elements in conic sections, including foci, co-vertices, etc.

---

1 Interactive Learning

Solve It!
PURPOSE To express a linear translation of an object in one direction
PROCESS Students may
- calculate the distance traveled in 0.01 s and subtract the distance traveled in 0.001 s.
- calculate the distance traveled during a 0.099-second time period.

FACILITATE

Q If the puck is traveling at 95 mi/h, how many feet is it traveling per second? **[$139\frac{1}{3}$ ft/s]**

Q How far did the puck go in 0.001 s? in 0.01 s? **[about 0.14 ft; about 1.39 ft]**

Q How would you define the position and direction of motion of the puck when the last 0.01 second begins? **[ellipse with center at the origin; negative direction along the x-axis.]**

ANSWER See Solve It in Answers on next page.
CONNECT THE MATH In the Solve It, students express the linear motion of an object as a horizontal translation. In the lesson, students will translate ellipses and hyperbolas and express those translations in equation form.

2 Guided Instruction

Take Note
ERROR PREVENTION

Q What fact can you use to remember that $c^2 = a^2 - b^2$ and not $a^2 + b^2$? **[c is the distance from the center to the focus, which is less than the distance from the center to the vertex a; since it is less, you subtract.]**

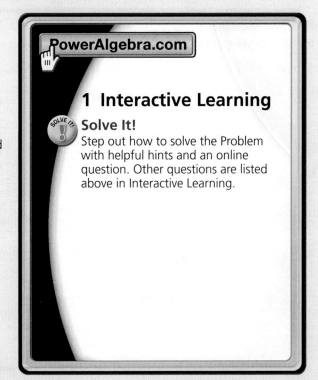

PowerAlgebra.com

1 Interactive Learning

Solve It!
Step out how to solve the Problem with helpful hints and an online question. Other questions are listed above in Interactive Learning.

Take Note

Q Could you tell whether an ellipse is vertical or horizontal just by looking at the equation in standard form? Explain. **[Yes; if the $(x - h)^2$ term has the greater denominator, then the ellipse is horizontal. If the $(y - k)^2$ term has the greater denominator, then the ellipse is vertical.]**

Problem 1

Q Without graphing, how can you tell whether this ellipse is vertical or horizontal? **[The foci and the vertices share the x-coordinate 1, so they all lie on the vertical line $x = 1$. The major axis is vertical, so the ellipse is vertical.]**

Q What are the coordinates of the other focus? **[(1, 8)]**

Q What are two ways to find the value of a? **[Find the length of the major axis and divide by two, or find the distance between one of the vertices and the center of the ellipse.]**

EXTENSION

Q Could you find the equation of the ellipse if you were only given the vertices? Explain. **[No. You could find the center of the ellipse, but there would be no way to find the value for b, the distance of the co-vertices from the center. You could write the equation of a possible ellipse, but there is more than one ellipse with center (1, 11) and vertices of (1, 6) and (1, 16).]**

Got It?

Q Will the a^2 value be under the $(x - h)^2$ term or the $(y - k)^2$ term? Explain. **[The ellipse is horizontal because the vertices and foci share a y term, so a^2 will be under the $(x - h)^2$ term.]**

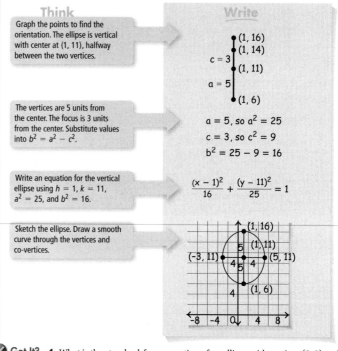

Summary Translating Vertical Ellipses

Vertical Ellipse	Center (0, 0)	Center (h, k)
Standard-Form Equation	$\frac{x^2}{b^2} + \frac{y^2}{a^2} = 1$	$\frac{(x - h)^2}{b^2} + \frac{(y - k)^2}{a^2} = 1$
Vertices	$(0, \pm a)$	$(h, k \pm a)$
Co-vertices	$(\pm b, 0)$	$(h \pm b, k)$
Foci	$(0, \pm c)$	$(h, k \pm c)$
a, b, c relationship, $a > b > 0$	$c^2 = a^2 - b^2$	$c^2 = a^2 - b^2$

Problem 1 Writing an Equation of a Translated Ellipse

What is the standard-form equation of an ellipse with vertices (1, 6) and (1, 16), and one focus at (1, 14)? Sketch the ellipse.

Think

Graph the points to find the orientation. The ellipse is vertical with center at (1, 11), halfway between the two vertices.

The vertices are 5 units from the center. The focus is 3 units from the center. Substitute values into $b^2 = a^2 - c^2$.

Write an equation for the vertical ellipse using $h = 1$, $k = 11$, $a^2 = 25$, and $b^2 = 16$.

Sketch the ellipse. Draw a smooth curve through the vertices and co-vertices.

Write

$a = 5$, so $a^2 = 25$
$c = 3$, so $c^2 = 9$
$b^2 = 25 - 9 = 16$

$\frac{(x - 1)^2}{16} + \frac{(y - 11)^2}{25} = 1$

Got It? **1.** What is the standard-form equation of an ellipse with vertices (2, 3) and (22, 3), and one focus at (6, 3)? Sketch the ellipse.

 PowerAlgebra.com

2 Guided Instruction

Each Problem is worked out and supported online.

Problem 1
Writing an Equation of a Translated Ellipse
Animated

Problem 2
Analyzing a Hyperbola from Its Equation
Animated

Problem 3
Identifying a Translated Conic Section

Problem 4
Modeling With a Conic Section
Animated

Support in Algebra 2 Companion
• Vocabulary
• Key Concepts
• Got It?

Answers

Solve It!

Students' tracings should show the position of the puck at 0.001 s to be about 90% of the way from the puck on the right to the puck on the left.

Got It?

1. $\frac{(x - 12)^2}{100} + \frac{(y - 3)^2}{64} = 1$;

Summary Translating Horizontal and Vertical Hyperbolas

Horizontal Hyperbola	Center (0, 0)	Center (h, k)
Standard-Form Equation	$\frac{x^2}{a^2} - \frac{y^2}{b^2} = 1$	$\frac{(x-h)^2}{a^2} - \frac{(y-k)^2}{b^2} = 1$
Vertices	$(\pm a, 0)$	$(h \pm a, k)$
Foci	$(\pm c, 0)$	$(h \pm c, k)$
Asymptotes	$y = \pm \frac{b}{a}x$	$y - k = \pm \frac{b}{a}(x - h)$
a, b, c relationship	$c^2 = a^2 + b^2$	$c^2 = a^2 + b^2$

Vertical Hyperbola	Center (0, 0)	Center (h, k)
Standard-Form Equation	$\frac{y^2}{a^2} - \frac{x^2}{b^2} = 1$	$\frac{(y-k)^2}{a^2} - \frac{(x-h)^2}{b^2} = 1$
Vertices	$(0, \pm a)$	$(h, k \pm a)$
Foci	$(0, \pm c)$	$(h, k \pm c)$
Asymptotes	$y = \pm \frac{a}{b}x$	$y - k = \pm \frac{a}{b}(x - h)$
a, b, c relationship	$c^2 = a^2 + b^2$	$c^2 = a^2 + b^2$

As with the ellipse, you can identify the characteristics of a hyperbola just by analyzing its equation.

 Problem 2 Analyzing a Hyperbola from Its Equation

What are the center, vertices, foci, and asymptotes of the hyperbola with equation $\frac{(y-1)^2}{25} - \frac{(x-3)^2}{144} = 1$? Sketch the graph.

The equation is of the form $\frac{(y-k)^2}{a^2} - \frac{(x-h)^2}{b^2} = 1$, so the hyperbola is vertical with $h = 3$, $k = 1$, $a^2 = 25$, $b^2 = 144$, and $c^2 = a^2 + b^2 = 25 + 144 = 169$.

Center: $(h, k) = (3, 1)$
Vertices: $(h, k \pm a) = (3, 1 \pm 5)$; $(3, 6)$ and $(3, -4)$
Foci: $(h, k \pm c) = (3, 1 \pm 13)$; $(3, 14)$ and $(3, -12)$

The equations of the asymptotes are $y - 1 = \frac{5}{12}(x - 3)$ and $y - 1 = -\frac{5}{12}(x - 3)$.

To graph the hyperbola, first graph the vertices and central rectangle. Draw the asymptotes. Then sketch the branches through the vertices and along the asymptotes.

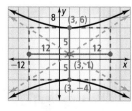

 Got It? 2. What are the center, vertices, foci, and asymptotes of the hyperbola with equation $\frac{(x-2)^2}{36} - \frac{(y+2)^2}{64} = 1$? Sketch the graph.

Take Note EXTENSION

Q In an ellipse, the value of a in a standard-form equation is always greater than b. Is this always true in a hyperbola? Explain using the relationship between a, b, and c. **[No; in an ellipse, $c^2 = a^2 - b^2$ is undefined if the value of b is greater than a. In a hyperbola, $c^2 = a^2 + b^2$ is defined even if the value of a is less than b.]**

Problem 2

Q How can you find the central rectangle? **[The horizontal sides of the central rectangle will be a units above and below the center of the hyperbola, and the vertical sides of the rectangle will be b units left and right of the center of the hyperbola.]**

EXTENSION

Q What one change could you make to the equation of a hyperbola so that it becomes an ellipse? How would the graph of the ellipse be related to the graph of the hyperbola? **[Change the subtraction to addition. The graph of the ellipse would fit in the central rectangle used to graph the hyperbola and would touch all four sides.]**

Got It?

Q Is the hyperbola vertical or horizontal? How do you know? **[Horizontal; the $(x - h)^2$ term is positive.]**

Additional Problems

2. center $(2, -2)$;
vertices: $(-4, -2)$, $(8, -2)$;
foci: $(-8, -2)$, $(12, -2)$;
asymptotes:
$y + 2 = \pm \frac{4}{3}(x - 2)$

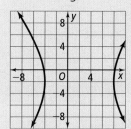

1. What is the standard-form equation of an ellipse with vertices $(-6, -2)$ and $(12, -2)$ and one focus $(3 + 4\sqrt{2}, -2)$? Sketch the ellipse.

ANSWER
$\frac{(x-3)^2}{81} + \frac{(y+2)^2}{49} = 1$

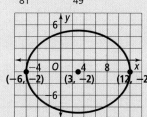

2. What are the center, vertices, foci, and asymptotes of the hyperbola with equation $\frac{y^2}{36} - \frac{(x-4)^2}{16} = 1$? Sketch the hyperbola.

ANSWER center: $(4, 0)$;
vertices: $(4, 6)$ and $(4, -6)$;
foci: $(4, 2\sqrt{13})$ and $(4, -2\sqrt{13})$; asymptotes:
$y = \frac{3}{2}(x - 4)$ and
$y = -\frac{3}{2}(x - 4)$

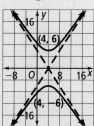

3. Which conic section has the equation $x^2 + 3y^2 + 2x - 18y - 8 = 0$?

ANSWER ellipse with center $(-1, 3)$ and foci $(-1 + 4\sqrt{3}, 3)$ and $(-1 - 4\sqrt{3}, 3)$

4. You set up an electronic fence for a dog by placing two sensor stakes in the yard 60 ft apart. You set the sensor controls so that the total distance from the first sensor to the dog's collar and from the second sensor to the dog's collar is not more than 100 ft. What conic section equation models the border of the area in which the dog can run without getting a warning shock?

ANSWER $\frac{x^2}{2500} + \frac{y^2}{1600} = 1$

Lesson 10-6   655

Q How could writing the general form of an equation for a conic section in standard form help you identify and graph the conic section? **[In standard form, you can easily identify the center and radius of a circle; orientation, center, vertices, and co-vertices of an ellipse; orientation and vertex of a parabola; and orientation, center, and vertices of a hyperbola.]**

Problem 3

Q Are there any answer choices you can eliminate before you complete the square? Explain. **[Yes; you can eliminate choices A and C. The equation is not of a circle because the x^2 and y^2 terms have different coefficients.]**

EXTENSION

Q Are there any characteristics of equations of conic sections in general form that help identify the conic section? Explain. **[Yes; parabolas have only one squared term; the coefficients of the x^2 and y^2 terms of a circle are the same; the coefficients of the x^2 and y^2 terms of an ellipse are different in value but same in sign; the coefficients of the x^2 and y^2 terms of a hyperbola are opposite in sign.]**

Got It?

Q What is the main difference between the standard form equations of an ellipse and of a hyperbola? **[In an ellipse, the left side of the equation is a sum of two expressions, and in a hyperbola the left side is a difference between expressions.]**

All equations for conic sections expand to the general equation form

$$Ax^2 + Bxy + Cy^2 + Dx + Ey + F = 0,$$

where A and C are not both equal to zero. If the conic section is horizontal or vertical, $B = 0$ and the general form becomes

$$Ax^2 + Cy^2 + Dx + Ey + F = 0.$$

To locate the center or the two foci of a conic section, you must first convert the general form equation into the standard form for that conic section. This usually involves completing the square at least once and possibly twice.

© **Problem 3** Identifying a Translated Conic Section

Multiple Choice Which conic section has the equation $4x^2 + y^2 - 24x + 6y + 9 = 0$?

Ⓐ circle; center $(3, -3)$

Ⓒ circle; center $(-3\sqrt{3}, 3\sqrt{3})$

Ⓑ ellipse; foci $(3, -3 - 3\sqrt{3})$ and $(3, -3 + 3\sqrt{3})$

Ⓓ ellipse; foci $(0, 3)$ and $(0, -3)$

Complete the square for the x- and y-terms to write the equation in standard form.

$$4x^2 + y^2 - 24x + 6y + 9 = 0$$

$$4x^2 - 24x + y^2 + 6y = -9 \qquad \text{Group the } x\text{- and } y\text{-terms.}$$

$$4(x^2 - 6x) + (y^2 + 6y) = -9 \qquad \text{Factor.}$$

$$4(x^2 - 6x + (-3)^2) + (y^2 + 6y + 3^2) = -9 + 4(-3)^2 + 3^2 \qquad \text{Complete the square.}$$

$$4(x^2 - 6x + 9) + (y^2 + 6y + 9) = -9 + 36 + 9 \qquad \text{Simplify.}$$

$$4(x - 3)^2 + (y + 3)^2 = 36 \qquad \text{Factor.}$$

$$\frac{4(x - 3)^2}{36} + \frac{(y + 3)^2}{36} = 1 \qquad \text{Divide by 36 so the right side is 1.}$$

$$\frac{(x - 3)^2}{9} + \frac{(y + 3)^2}{36} = 1 \qquad \text{Simplify.}$$

The equation represents a vertical ellipse. The center is $(3, -3)$. Since $a^2 = 36$, $a = 6$. Since $b^2 = 9$, $b = 3$. Use these values to locate the foci.

$$c^2 = a^2 - b^2$$
$$= 36 - 9$$
$$= 27$$
$$c = 3\sqrt{3}$$

The distance from the center $(3, -3)$ of the vertical ellipse to the foci is $3\sqrt{3}$. The foci are at $(3, -3 - 3\sqrt{3})$ and $(3, -3 + 3\sqrt{3})$.

The correct choice is B.

© ✓ **Got It? 3. a.** Which type of conic section has equation $x^2 + y^2 - 12x + 4y = 8$? What is its center? Sketch the graph.
   b. Reasoning Using as few changes as possible, modify the equation $4x^2 + y^2 - 24x + 6y + 9 = 0$ to make it an equation of a hyperbola.

Think

How do you complete the square?
Divide the x (or y) coefficient by 2. Square the result.

Answers

Got It? (continued)

3. a. circle with center $(6, -2)$ and radius $4\sqrt{3}$

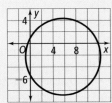

b. Replace $+y^2$ with $-y^2$ to get a new eq., $4x^2 - y^2 - 24x + 6y + 9 = 0$. The standard eq. of the hyperbola is $\frac{(x - 3)^2}{4.5} - \frac{(y - 3)^2}{18} = 1$.

Problem 4 Modeling With a Conic Section

Navigation A lighthouse is on an island 3 miles from a long, straight shoreline. A boat sails around the island; deliberately following a path that always keeps it twice as far from the shoreline as it is from the lighthouse. What is an equation of the conic section describing the boat's path?

Draw a diagram of the situation with the lighthouse at $(0, 0)$, the shore at the line $x = 3$, and the boat at an arbitrary point (x, y) satisfying the given distance condition.

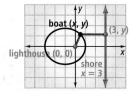

The distance from the boat to the lighthouse is $\sqrt{x^2 + y^2}$ and the distance from the boat to the shore is the horizontal difference $3 - x$. The distance condition translates to:

$$2\sqrt{x^2 + y^2} = 3 - x$$

$$4(x^2 + y^2) = (3 - x)^2 \qquad \text{Square each side.}$$

$$4x^2 + 4y^2 = 9 - 6x + x^2 \qquad \text{Expand.}$$

$$3x^2 + 6x + 4y^2 = 9 \qquad \text{Combine like terms.}$$

$$3(x^2 + 2x + 1) + 4y^2 = 9 + 3(1) \qquad \text{Complete the square.}$$

$$3(x + 1)^2 + 4y^2 = 12 \qquad \text{Simplify.}$$

$$\frac{3(x + 1)^2}{12} + \frac{4y^2}{12} = 1 \qquad \text{Divide each side by 12 so the right side equals 1.}$$

$$\frac{(x + 1)^2}{4} + \frac{y^2}{3} = 1 \qquad \text{Simplify.}$$

This is the standard-form equation for a horizontal ellipse centered at $(-1, 0)$ with major axis of length $2a = 4$ and minor axis of length $2b = 2\sqrt{3}$. Note that $c = \sqrt{a^2 - b^2} = \sqrt{4 - 3} = 1$, so the lighthouse is at one focus of the ellipse.

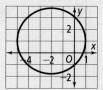

The boat follows an elliptical path modeled by the equation $\frac{(x + 1)^2}{4} + \frac{y^2}{3} = 1$.

Got It? **4.** If the lighthouse were 8 miles from the shore and the boat were to stay 3 times as far from the shore as from the lighthouse, what would be the equation of the conic section describing the boat's path?

Problem 4

Q How can you justify that the <u>distance</u> from the boat to the lighthouse is $\sqrt{x^2 + y^2}$? **[Use the distance formula, or sketch a right triangle and use the Pythagorean Theorem]**

Q Could the diagram be drawn differently? Explain. **[Yes; the ellipse could be vertical or translated vertically, horizontally, or both. The solutions would be the same.]**

Got It?

Q How will the initial equation differ from the one in Problem 4? **[The 2 will be replaced by 3, and the original 3 will be replaced by 8.]**

---

4. $\frac{(x + 1)^2}{9} + \frac{y^2}{8} = 1$

Lesson Check

1. center $(-7, -1)$; vertices: $(-22, -1)$, $(8, -1)$; foci: $(-16, -1)$, $(2, -1)$
2. center $(1, 3)$; vertices: $(4, 3)$, $(-2, 3)$; foci: $(1 \pm \sqrt{13}, 3)$
3. $\frac{x^2}{48} + \frac{(y - 4)^2}{64} = 1$
4. $\frac{(y + 1)^2}{49} - \frac{(x + 3)^2}{51} = 1$
5. ellipse and hyperbola
6. Your friend used the center $(-2, 1)$ instead of $(2, -1)$. The vertices are $(-10, -1)$ and $(14, -1)$.
7. The student didn't write the standard-form equation correctly. The standard-form equation is $(x + 4)^2 + (y - 5)^2 = 0$. This is an equation of a circle with center at $(-4, 5)$ and radius 0. Since the radius is 0, the graph is a single point, $(-4, 5)$.

Practice and Problem-Solving Exercises

8. $\frac{(x + 2)^2}{9} + \frac{(y - 1)^2}{8} = 1$

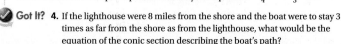

9. $\frac{(x - 3)^2}{21} + \frac{(y + 6)^2}{25} = 1$

10. $\frac{(x - 9)^2}{33} + \frac{(y - 2)^2}{49} = 1$

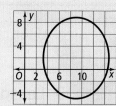

11. $\frac{(x - 1.5)^2}{42.25} + \frac{(y - 4)^2}{12} = 1$

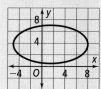

12. center: $(-11, 0)$; vertices: $(-15, 0)$, $(-7, 0)$; foci: $(-16, 0)$, $(-6, 0)$
13. center: $(3, 4)$; vertices: $(3, 1)$, $(3, 7)$; foci: $(3, 4 \pm \sqrt{13})$
14. center: $(-3, -8)$; vertices: $(-3, -6)$, $(-3, -10)$; foci: $(-3, -8 \pm \sqrt{53})$

15. $y = (x - 4)^2 + 3$; parabola; vertex: $(4, 3)$

3 Lesson Check

Do you know HOW?
- If students have difficulty with Exercises 3 and 4, have them plot some points to identify the orientation of the conic sections.

Do you UNDERSTAND?
- If students have difficulty finding the error in Exercise 6, suggest they find the center of the hyperbola described by the equation and the center of the hyperbola that the friend described.

Close

> **Q** Which variables in the standard-form equation of a conic section translate it and how? **[The h translates the conic section h units horizontally, and the k translates the conic section k units vertically.]**

Lesson Check

Do you know HOW?

Identify the center, vertices, and foci of the ellipse or hyperbola.

1. ellipse: $\dfrac{(x+7)^2}{225} + \dfrac{(y+1)^2}{144} = 1$

2. hyperbola: $\dfrac{(x-1)^2}{9} - \dfrac{(y-3)^2}{4} = 1$

3. Write the standard-form equation of the ellipse with vertices $(0, -4)$ and $(0, 12)$ and with a focus $(0, 0)$.

4. Write the standard-form equation of the hyperbola with vertices $(-3, 6)$ and $(-3, -8)$ and with foci $(-3, -11)$ and $(-3, 9)$.

Do you UNDERSTAND? MATHEMATICAL PRACTICES

5. **Vocabulary** Which of the conic sections have more than one focus: circle, parabola, ellipse, hyperbola?

6. **Error Analysis** Your friend said that the points $(-14, 1)$ and $(10, 1)$ are the vertices of the graph of the equation $\dfrac{(x-2)^2}{144} - \dfrac{(y+1)^2}{25} = 1$. What error did your friend make?

7. **Reasoning** A student claims that the graph of the equation $x^2 + y^2 + 8x - 10y + 41 = 0$ is a circle with center at $(-4, 5)$ and radius $\sqrt{41}$. Explain the student's error and describe the correct graph.

Practice and Problem-Solving Exercises MATHEMATICAL PRACTICES

Ⓐ Practice

Write the standard-form equation of an ellipse with the given characteristics. Sketch the ellipse. ◖ See Problem 1.

8. vertices $(-5, 1)$ and $(1, 1)$, focus $(-3, 1)$

9. vertices $(3, -1)$ and $(3, -11)$, focus $(3, -4)$

10. vertices $(9, 9)$ and $(9, -5)$, focus $(9, 6)$

11. vertices $(-5, 4)$ and $(8, 4)$, focus $(-4, 4)$

Identify the center, vertices, and foci of each hyperbola. ◖ See Problem 2.

12. $\dfrac{(x+11)^2}{16} - \dfrac{y^2}{9} = 1$

13. $\dfrac{(y-4)^2}{9} - \dfrac{(x-3)^2}{4} = 1$

14. $\dfrac{(y+8)^2}{4} - \dfrac{(x+3)^2}{49} = 1$

Identify each conic section by writing the equation in standard form and sketching the graph. For a parabola, give the vertex. For a circle, give the center and the radius. For an ellipse or a hyperbola, give the center and the foci. ◖ See Problem 3.

15. $x^2 - 8x - y + 19 = 0$

16. $3x^2 + 6x + y^2 - 6y = -3$

17. $y^2 - x^2 + 6x - 4y = 6$

18. $x^2 - 4y^2 - 2x - 8y = 7$

19. $y^2 - 2x - 4y = -10$

20. $x^2 + y^2 - 4x - 6y - 3 = 0$

21. **Navigation** A lighthouse is on an island 4 miles from a long, straight shoreline. When a boat is directly between the lighthouse and the shoreline, it is 1 mile from the lighthouse and 3 miles from the shore. As it sails away from the shore and lighthouse, it continues so that the difference in distances between boat and lighthouse and between boat and shore is always 2 miles. ◖ See Problem 4.
   a. What conic section models this problem?
   b. What part of the graph does the lighthouse represent? The shoreline?
   c. What equation represents the path of the boat?

Answers

1–15. See previous page.

16. $\dfrac{(x+1)^2}{3} + \dfrac{(y-3)^2}{9} = 1$; ellipse; center: $(-1, 3)$, foci: $(-1, 3 \pm \sqrt{6})$

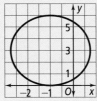

17. $(y-2)^2 - (x-3)^2 = 1$; hyperbola; center: $(3, 2)$, foci: $(3, 2 \pm \sqrt{2})$;

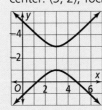

18. $\dfrac{(x-1)^2}{4} - (y+1)^2 = 1$; hyperbola; center: $(1, -1)$, foci: $(1 \pm \sqrt{5}, -1)$

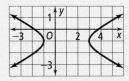

19. $x = \dfrac{1}{2}(y-2)^2 + 3$; parabola; vertex: $(3, 2)$

20. $(x-2)^2 + (y-3)^2 = 16$; circle; center: $(2, 3)$, radius 4

21. a. hyperbola
   b. one focus; the other focus
   c. with the center at the origin, $x^2 - \dfrac{y^2}{3} = 1$

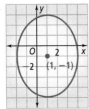 **Apply**

22. Think About a Plan An ellipse has center (3, 2), one vertex (9, 2), and one co-vertex (3, −1). Sketch its graph. Then write its equation.
- How can the sketch help you write the equation?
- What information do you need to write the equation?

23. Reasoning Use the equation $Ax^2 + Bxy + Cy^2 + Dx + Ey + F = 0$ to identify the shape of the graph that results in each case.
a. $A = C = D = E = 0, B \neq 0, F \neq 0$
b. $A = B = C = D = 0, E \neq 0, F \neq 0$

Sketch each conic section. Then write its equation.

24. A parabola has vertex (2, −3) and focus (2, 5).

25. A hyperbola has center (6, −3), one focus (6, 0), and one vertex (6, −1).

26. Theater Arts The director of a stage show asks you to design an elliptical platform. Her sketch shows the platform centered at (9, 7) from the front left corner of the stage. The platform has a 12-ft major axis parallel to the front edge of the stage and extends to within 3 ft of the edge. Write an equation that models the platform.

Write an equation for each graph.

27.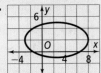

28.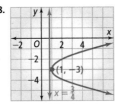

The graph of each equation is to be translated 2 units left and 4 units up. Write each new equation.

29. $(x − 2)^2 + (y + 4)^2 = 16$

30. $\frac{(x − 3)^2}{64} + \frac{(y − 3)^2}{36} = 1$

31. $y = 2x^2$

32. $9x^2 + 3x + 10 = 16y^2 + 154 + 3x$

Graph each pair of functions. Identify the conic section represented by the graph and write the functions as a single equation in standard form.

33. $y = \sqrt{36 − 4x^2}$
$y = −\sqrt{36 − 4x^2}$

34. $y = \sqrt{4x^2 − 36}$
$y = −\sqrt{4x^2 − 36}$

35. $y = 0.5\sqrt{36 − x^2}$
$y = −0.5\sqrt{36 − x^2}$

 Challenge

36. Open-Ended On a graphing calculator, create a design using three translated quadratic relations.

ASSIGNMENT GUIDE
Basic: 8–22 all, 24–30 even
Average: 9–21 odd, 22–35
Advanced: 9–21 odd, 22–37
Standardized Test Prep: 38–41
Mixed Review: 42–53

Mathematical Practices are supported by exercises with red headings. Here are the Practices supported in this lesson:

MP 1: Make Sense of Problems Ex. 22
MP 3: Construct Arguments Ex. 23, 37b
MP 3: Critique the Reasoning of Others Ex. 6, 7
MP 5: Use Appropriate Tools Ex. 36

Applications exercises have blue headings. Exercises 21, 26, and 37 support MP 4: Model.

STEM exercises focus on science or engineering applications.

EXERCISE 26: Use the Think About a Plan worksheet in the **Practice and Problem Solving Workbook** (also available in the Teaching Resources in print and online) to further support students' development in becoming independent learners.

HOMEWORK QUICK CHECK
To check students' understanding of key skills and concepts, go over Exercises 9, 13, 15, 22, and 26.

22.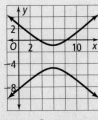

$\frac{(x − 3)^2}{36} + \frac{(y − 2)^2}{9} = 1$

23. a. hyperbola
b. horizontal line

24.

$y = \frac{1}{32}(x − 2)^2 − 3$

25.

$\frac{(y + 3)^2}{4} − \frac{(x − 6)^2}{5} = 1$

26. $\frac{(x − 9)^2}{144} + \frac{(y − 7)^2}{16} = 1$

27. $\frac{(x − 1)^2}{9} + \frac{(y + 1)^2}{16} = 1$

28. $x = (y + 3)^2 + 1$

29. $x^2 + y^2 = 16$

30. $\frac{(x − 1)^2}{64} + \frac{(y − 7)^2}{36} = 1$

31. $y = 2(x + 2)^2 + 4$

32. $\frac{(x + 2)^2}{16} − \frac{(y − 4)^2}{9} = 1$

33.

ellipse; $\frac{x^2}{9} + \frac{y^2}{36} = 1$

34.

hyperbola; $\frac{x^2}{9} − \frac{y^2}{36} = 1$

35.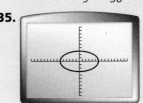

ellipse; $\frac{x^2}{36} + \frac{y^2}{9} = 1$

36. Check students' work.

Answers

Practice and Problem-Solving Exercises (continued)

37. a. Earth: $\dfrac{x^2}{(149.60)^2} + \dfrac{y^2}{(149.58)^2} = 1$;

Mars: $\dfrac{x^2}{(227.9)^2} + \dfrac{y^2}{(226.9)^2} = 1$;

Mercury: $\dfrac{x^2}{(57.9)^2} + \dfrac{y^2}{(56.6)^2} = 1$

```
WINDOW FORMAT
Xmin = -379.0322...
Xmax = 379.03225...
Xscl = 25
Ymin = -250
Xmax = 250
Yscl = 25
```

b. Earth: $\dfrac{a}{b}$ is closest to 1

Standardized Test Prep

38. B

39. I

40. B

41. **[2]** Let a_1, a_2, and a_3 represent the missing terms in the arithmetic sequence: 15, a_1, a_2, a_3, 47. a_2 is the arithmetic mean of 15 and 47, so $a_2 = \dfrac{15 + 47}{2} = 31$. Likewise, $a_1 = \dfrac{15 + a_2}{2} = \dfrac{15 + 31}{2} = 23$, and $a_3 = \dfrac{a_2 + 47}{2} = \dfrac{31 + 47}{2} = 39$. The missing terms are 23, 31, and 39.

[1] incomplete explanation OR correct explanation with one computational error

Mixed Review

42. foci: $(\pm\sqrt{85},\, 0)$

43. foci: $(0,\, \pm\sqrt{21})$

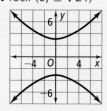

44. foci: $(0,\, \pm 2\sqrt{26})$

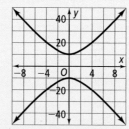

45. $\dfrac{3 \pm \sqrt{17}}{2}$

46. 5

47. $\dfrac{9 \pm \sqrt{201}}{12}$

48. 1

49. 2

50. 3

51. 8

52. -19

53. 6

STEM **37. Astronomy** The dimensions of the elliptical orbits of three planets are given in millions of kilometers in the table. The sun is at one focus. The other focus is on the positive x-axis.

Planet	a	b
Earth	149.60	149.58
Mars	227.9	226.9
Mercury	57.9	56.6

a. Write an equation for each orbit and draw the curves on your graphing calculator. (Remember to adjust the viewing window.)

b. Reasoning Which orbit is most circular? Justify your reasoning.

Standardized Test Prep

SAT/ACT

38. What is the standard form of the equation of the conic given by $2x^2 + 2y^2 + 4x - 12y - 22 = 0$?

Ⓐ $\dfrac{(x + 1)^2}{21} - \dfrac{(y - 3)^2}{21} = 1$

Ⓒ $\dfrac{(x - 3)^2}{21} + \dfrac{(y + 1)^2}{21} = 1$

Ⓑ $\dfrac{(x + 1)^2}{21} + \dfrac{(y - 3)^2}{21} = 1$

Ⓓ $\dfrac{(x - 1)^2}{7} + \dfrac{(y + 3)^2}{3} = 1$

39. Using a calculator, what are the approximate solutions of $x^2 - 7x + 5 = 0$?

Ⓕ $-0.65, 7.65$ Ⓖ $-7.65, 0.65$ Ⓗ $-1.14, 6.14$ Ⓘ $0.81, 6.19$

40. What is the center of the circle with equation $(x + 3)^2 + (y - 2)^2 = 49$?

Ⓐ $(3, -2)$ Ⓑ $(-3, 2)$ Ⓒ $(3, 2)$ Ⓓ $(-3, -2)$

Short Response

41. How can you use the arithmetic mean to find the missing terms in the arithmetic sequence 15, ■, ■, ■, 47, ... ?

Mixed Review

Find the foci of each hyperbola. Draw the graph.   ◀ See Lesson 10-5.

42. $\dfrac{x^2}{49} - \dfrac{y^2}{36} = 1$

43. $8y^2 - 6x^2 = 72$

44. $4y^2 - 100x^2 = 400$

Solve each equation. Check your answers.   ◀ See Lesson 8-6.

45. $\dfrac{1}{3x + 1} = \dfrac{1}{x^2 - 3}$

46. $\dfrac{2}{x + 2} = \dfrac{6}{x^2 - 4}$

47. $\dfrac{5}{x^2 - x} + \dfrac{3}{x - 1} = 6$

Simplify each expression.   ◀ See Lesson 7-6.

48. $\ln e$

49. $2 \ln e$

50. $\ln e^3$

51. $4 \ln e^2$

Get Ready!   To prepare for Lesson 11-1, do Exercises 52–53.

Evaluate each expression for the given value of the variable.   ◀ See Lesson 1-3.

52. $x + 5x - x - 9$; $x = -2$

53. $(n - 4)^2 + n$; $n = 5$

Additional Instructional Support

Algebra 2 Companion

Students can use the **Algebra 2 Companion** worktext (4 pages) as you teach the lesson. Use the Companion to support

- New Vocabulary
- Key Concepts
- Got It for each Problem
- Lesson Check

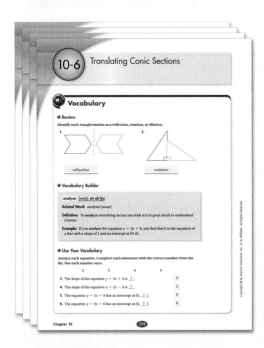

ELL Support

Assess Understanding Pair students and have them discuss the roles of h and k in each line of the Take Note Summaries that contain h and k. Then have students individually write a paragraph summarizing the effects of h and k on the graph of any conic section. Check these to make sure students understand what it means to translate an ellipse and a hyperbola.

5 Assess & Remediate

Lesson Quiz

1. What is the standard-form equation of an ellipse with vertices $(6, -4)$ and $(-2, -4)$ and focus $(4, -4)$? Sketch the ellipse.

2. What are the center, vertices, foci, and asymptotes of the hyperbola with equation $\frac{(x + 1)^2}{9} - \frac{(y + 2)^2}{25} = 1$?

3. Which conic section has the equation $7x^2 - 5y^2 + 14x - 28 = 0$?

4. **Do you UNDERSTAND?** Your mailbox is 4 ft from a straight street. You pace between the mailbox and the street, such that the distance between you and the mailbox is the same as the distance between you and the street. What equation of a conic section describes your path?

ANSWERS TO LESSON QUIZ

1. $\frac{(x - 2)^2}{16} + \frac{(y + 4)^2}{12} = 1$;

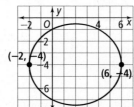

2. center: $(-1, -2)$; vertices: $(2, -2)$ and $(-4, -2)$; foci: $(-1 \pm \sqrt{34}, -2)$; asymptotes: $y + 2 = \pm\frac{5}{3}(x + 1)$

3. hyperbola

4. For vertex at $(0, 0)$, $x = \pm\frac{1}{8}y^2$ or $y = \pm\frac{1}{8}x^2$.

PRESCRIPTION FOR REMEDIATION

Use the student work on the Lesson Quiz to prescribe a differentiated review assignment:

Points	Differentiated Remediation
0–2	Intervention
3	On-level
4	Extension

PowerAlgebra.com

👆

5 Assess & Remediate

Assign the Lesson Quiz. Appropriate intervention, practice, or enrichment is automatically generated based on student performance.

Intervention

- **Reteaching** (2 pages) Provides reteaching and practice exercises for the key lesson concepts. Use with struggling students or absent students.

- **English Language Learner Support** Helps students develop and reinforce mathematical vocabulary and key concepts.

All-in-One Resources/Online
Reteaching

10-6 Reteaching
Translating Conic Sections

Compare the equations and properties of horizontal and vertical ellipses and horizontal and vertical hyperbolas.

	Horizontal Ellipse	Vertical Ellipse	Horizontal Hyperbola	Vertical Hyperbola
Standard-Form Equation	$\frac{(x-h)^2}{a^2} + \frac{(y-k)^2}{b^2} = 1$	$\frac{(x-h)^2}{b^2} + \frac{(y-k)^2}{a^2} = 1$	$\frac{(x-h)^2}{a^2} - \frac{(y-k)^2}{b^2} = 1$	$\frac{(y-k)^2}{a^2} - \frac{(x-h)^2}{b^2} = 1$
Center	(h, k)	(h, k)	(h, k)	(h, k)
Vertices	$(h \pm a, k)$	$(h, k \pm a)$	$(h \pm a, k)$	$(h, k \pm a)$
Foci	$(h \pm c, k)$	$(h, k \pm c)$	$(h \pm c, k)$	$(h, k \pm c)$
a, b, c relationship	$c^2 = a^2 - b^2$ $a > b$	$c^2 = a^2 - b^2$ $a > b$	$c^2 = a^2 + b^2$	$c^2 = a^2 + b^2$

- The centers for horizontal ellipses, vertical ellipses, horizontal hyperbolas, and vertical hyperbolas are always (h, k).
- Finding the vertices always involves adding and subtracting a value of a to either h or k. Horizontal ellipses and horizontal hyperbolas add and subtract a to h, while vertical ellipses and vertical hyperbolas add and subtract a to k.
- Finding the foci always involves adding and subtracting a value of c to h or k. Horizontal ellipses and horizontal hyperbolas add and subtract c to h, while vertical ellipses and vertical hyperbolas add and subtract c to k.
- The relationship between a, b, and c is the same for both horizontal and vertical ellipses.
- The relationship between a, b, and c is the same for both horizontal and vertical hyperbola.

Exercises

Identify the center, vertices, and foci of each horizontal ellipse or hyperbola.

1. $\frac{(x-1)^2}{25} + \frac{(y-2)^2}{16} = 1$
center: (1, 2); vertices: (6, 2); (−4, 2); foci: (4, 2); (−2, 2)

2. $\frac{(x-1)^2}{9} - \frac{(y-2)^2}{16} = 1$
center: (1, 2); vertices: (4, 2); (−2, 2); foci: (6, 2); (−4, 2)

Identify the center, vertices, and foci of each vertical ellipse or hyperbola.

3. $\frac{(y-1)^2}{9} - \frac{(x-2)^2}{16} = 1$
center: (2, 1); vertices: (2, 4); (2, −2); foci: (2, 6); (2, −4)

4. $\frac{(y-1)^2}{25} + \frac{(x-2)^2}{16} = 1$
center: (2, 1); vertices: (2, 6); (2, −4); foci: (2, 4); (2, −2)

All-in-One Resources/Online
English Language Learner Support

10-6 Additional Vocabulary Support
Translating Conic Sections

Problem

Identify the conic that has the equation $x^2 + 4y^2 + 2x - 24y + 33 = 0$. Justify your steps.

$x^2 + 4y^2 + 2x - 24y + 33 = 0$	Write original equation.
$x^2 + 2x + 4y^2 - 24y = -33$	Group the x- and y-terms.
$(x^2 + 2x) + 4(y^2 - 6y) = -33$	Factor.
$(x^2 + 2x + (1)^2) + 4(y^2 - 6y + (3)^2) = -33 + 1^2 + 4(3^2)$	Complete the square.
$(x^2 + 2x + 1) + 4(y^2 - 6y + 9) = -33 + 1 + 36$	Simplify.
$(x + 1)^2 + 4(y - 3)^2 = 4$	Factor.
$\frac{(x+1)^2}{4} + \frac{4(y-3)^2}{4} = 1$	Divide so the right side is 1.
$\frac{(x+1)^2}{4} + \frac{(y-3)^2}{1} = 1$	Simplify.

The conic is a horizontal ellipse.

Exercise

Identify the conic that has the equation $x^2 + y^2 + 4x - 6y + 4 = 0$. Justify your steps.

$x^2 + y^2 + 4x - 6y + 4 = 0$	Write the original equation.
$(x^2 + 4x) + (y^2 - 6y) = -4$	Group the x- and y-terms.
$(x^2 + 4x + (2^2)) + (y^2 - 6y + (3^2)) = -4 + 2^2 + 3^2$	Complete the square.
$(x^2 + 4x + 4) + (y^2 - 6y + 9) = 9$	Simplify.
$(x + 2)^2 + (y - 3)^2 = 9$	Factor.

The conic is a circle.

Differentiated Remediation *continued*

On-Level

- **Practice** (2 pages) Provides extra practice for each lesson. For simpler practice exercises, use the Form K Practice pages found in the All-in-One Teaching Resources and online.

- **Think About a Plan** Helps students develop specific problem-solving skills and strategies by providing scaffolded guiding questions.

- **Standardized Test Prep** Focuses on all major exercises, all major question types, and helps students prepare for the high-stakes assessments.

Extension

- **Enrichment** Provides students with interesting problems and activities that extend the concepts of the lesson.

- **Activities, Games, and Puzzles** Worksheets that can be used for concepts development, enrichment, and for fun!

Practice and Problem Solving Wkbk/ All-in-One Resources/Online
Practice page 1

10-6 Practice *Form G*
Translating Conic Sections

Write the standard-form equation of an ellipse with the given characteristics. Sketch the ellipse.

1. vertices (7, 3) and (−3, 3), focus (5, 3)
$\frac{(x-2)^2}{25} + \frac{(y-3)^2}{16} = 1$

2. vertices (3, 6) and (3, −2), focus (3, 5)
$\frac{(x-3)^2}{7} + \frac{(y-2)^2}{16} = 1$

3. vertices (11, −8) and (−19, −8), focus (5, −8) $\frac{(x+4)^2}{225} + \frac{(y+8)^2}{144} = 1$

4. vertices (2, 7) and (2, −1), focus $\left(2, 3 + \sqrt{7}\right)$ $\frac{(x-2)^2}{9} + \frac{(y-3)^2}{16} = 1$

Identify the center, vertices, and foci of each hyperbola.

5. $\frac{(x-5)^2}{144} - \frac{(y-9)^2}{256} = 1$
center: (5, 9); vertices: (17, 9), (−7, 9); foci: (25, 9); (−15, 9)

6. $\frac{(x-9)^2}{49} - \frac{(x-3)^2}{4} = 1$
center: (3, 9); vertices: (3, 16); (3, 2); foci: (3, 9 + √53); (3, 9 − √53)

7. $\frac{(x-5)^2}{25} - \frac{(y-2)^2}{75} = 1$ center: (5, 2); vertices: (10, 2); (0, 2); foci: (15, 2); (−5, 2)

Identify each conic section by writing the equation in standard form and sketching the graph. For a parabola, give the vertex. For a circle, give the center and the radius. For an ellipse or a hyperbola, give the center and the foci.

8. $3x^2 + 6x + 5y^2 - 20y - 13 = 0$ ellipse; (−1, 2); $\left(-1 \pm \frac{2\sqrt{30}}{5}, 2\right)$

9. $x^2 - 9y^2 + 36y - 45 = 0$ hyperbola; (0, 2); $(\pm\sqrt{10}, 2)$

10. $x^2 + 4y^2 + 8x - 48 = 0$ ellipse; (−4, 0); $\left(-4 \pm 4\sqrt{3}, 0\right)$

11. $x^2 + y^2 - 8x - 4y + 19 = 0$ circle; (4, 2); 1

12. $x^2 + y^2 + 6y - 27 = 0$ circle; (0, −3); 6

13. $x^2 - 10x - 4y^2 + 24y - 15 = 0$ hyperbola; (5, 3); $\left(5 \pm \sqrt{5}, 3\right)$

Practice and Problem Solving Wkbk/ All-in-One Resources/Online
Practice page 2

10-6 Practice *(continued)* *Form G*
Translating Conic Sections

14. Within a telescope, the path that light travels is 12 units closer to the focus of one reflector than the other. The foci are located at (0, 0) and (250, 0).
a. What conic section models this problem? a hyperbola
b. What part of the graph do the foci represent? the foci of the reflector
c. What equation represents the path of the light? $\frac{x - 125)^2}{36} - \frac{y^2}{15,589} = 1$

15. **Writing** A vertical ellipse has center (0, −2), major axis length 5, and minor axis length 3. Describe how you can find the value of a. Then write the equation in standard form. The value of a is half of the length of the major axis length 5; $\frac{x^2}{2.25} + \frac{(y+2)^2}{6.25} = 1$

16. **Error Analysis** A student found that the equation of a hyperbola with center (−4, 5), vertex (−4, 7), and focus (−4, 8) was $\frac{(y-4)^2}{4} - \frac{(x+5)^2}{5} = 1$. Explain why the student is incorrect. Then find the correct answer. The student substituted −k for h and −h for k, respectively. The correct equation is $\frac{(y-5)^2}{4} - \frac{(x+4)^2}{5} = 1$

Mental Math Use mental math to identify the center of each conic section.

17. $\frac{(x+1)^2}{16} - \frac{(y-3)^2}{4} = 1$ (−1, −3)

18. $\frac{(y+2)^2}{4} - \frac{(x-2)^2}{5} = 1$ (2, −2)

19. $\frac{(x-2)^2}{5} + \frac{(y-5)^2}{6} = 1$ (2, 5)

20. $\frac{(x-20)^2}{5} - \frac{(y+11)^2}{6} = 1$ (20, −11)

21. **Reasoning** Explain how you can tell if an ellipse has been translated by looking at the standard form of the equation. Give an example. Answers may vary. Sample: If an ellipse has been translated, there will be values added or subtracted to x and y in the numerators of the first two terms. The equation $\frac{x^2}{9} + \frac{y^2}{12} = 1$ has a center of (0, 0) and is not translated, while the equation $\frac{(x-2)^2}{9} + \frac{(y-5)^2}{12} = 1$ has a center of (2, 5) and is translated.

The graph of each equation is to be translated 3 units right and 1 unit up. Write each new equation.

22. $(x + 3)^2 + (y − 5)^2 = 9$
$x^2 + (y − 6)^2 = 9$

23. $16x^2 − 64x − 9y^2 − 36y − 172 = 0$
$\frac{2(x-5)^2}{25} - \frac{9(y+1)^2}{200} = 1$

Practice and Problem Solving Wkbk/ All-in-One Resources/Online
Think About a Plan

10-6 Think About a Plan
Translating Conic Sections

You designed an elliptical platform that is 12 ft across at its widest point. The choreographer of a play wants to place it on a diagram of her set so it is oriented horizontally with the center at (9, 7) from the front left corner of the stage. She also wants the front edge of the platform to be 3 ft from the front of the stage. Write an equation for your elliptical platform for her diagram.

Understanding the Problem

1. What is the width of the platform? 12 ft

2. Where is the center of the platform on the diagram? (9, 7)

3. How far is the platform from the front of the stage? 3 ft

4. What is the problem asking you to determine?
an equation for an elliptical platform

Planning the Solution

5. How can a sketch help you write the equation?
Answers may vary. Sample: A sketch can help me relate the dimensions and location
of the platform to the features of an ellipse

6. Make a sketch of the stage.

7. What is the general form of the equation of a horizontal ellipse?
$\frac{(x-h)^2}{a^2} + \frac{(y-k)^2}{b^2} = 1$

8. What information do you need to write the equation? a, b, h, and k

Getting an Answer

9. Write an equation for the elliptical platform. $\frac{(x-9)^2}{36} + \frac{(y-7)^2}{16} = 1$

Practice and Problem Solving Wkbk/ All-in-One Resources/Online
Standardized Test Prep

10-6 Standardized Test Prep
Translating Conic Sections

Multiple Choice

For Exercises 1–4, choose the correct letter.

1. A horizontal ellipse has the equation $\frac{(x-2)^2}{25} + \frac{(y-3)^2}{16} = 1$. Which is a vertex? C
Ⓐ (−7, 3) Ⓑ (5, 4) Ⓒ (7, 3) Ⓓ (2, 3)

2. A vertical ellipse has the equation $\frac{(x+8)^2}{81} + \frac{(y-7)^2}{36} = 1$. Which is a vertex? I
Ⓕ (−8, 7) Ⓖ (8, 7) Ⓗ (7, 3) Ⓘ (−8, 13)

3. What is the equation of a horizontal hyperbola with vertices (8, −3) and (2, −3) and focus (10, −3)? A
Ⓐ $\frac{(x-5)^2}{9} - \frac{(y+3)^2}{16} = 1$ Ⓒ $\frac{(x-5)^2}{9} - \frac{(y+3)^2}{9} = 1$
Ⓑ $\frac{(x-8)^2}{4} - \frac{(y-3)^2}{16} = 1$ Ⓓ $\frac{(x+10)^2}{4} - \frac{(y-3)^2}{9} = 1$

4. What are the foci of the hyperbola with the equation $\frac{(y-7)^2}{81} - \frac{(x-2)^2}{144} = 1$? H
Ⓕ (7, 2); (9, 14) Ⓗ (2, 22); (2, −8)
Ⓖ (2, 16); (2, −2) Ⓘ (7, 22); (7, −8)

Extended Response

5. Identify the conic section represented by $25x^2 + 50x - 9y^2 - 18y - 209 = 0$. Give the center and foci. Sketch the graph. Show your work.
hyperbola; (−1, −1); $\left(-1 \pm \sqrt{34}, -1\right)$
[4] Hyperbola, center, and foci are identified correctly. Graph is correct.
[3] Hyperbola, center, and foci are identified correctly. Graph has minor errors.
[2] Conic section OR center or foci identified incorrectly. Graph has errors.
[1] Conic section OR center or foci is identified incorrectly, and graph has major errors; OR correct answers and graph, without work shown.
[0] incorrect answers and no work shown OR no answers given

All-in-One Resources/Online
Enrichment

10-6 Enrichment
Translating Conic Sections

You have used horizontal translations and vertical translations to describe the shape and location of a conic section. Eccentricity is a way to describe the type and shape of a conic section. Eccentricity e is the ratio of the distance c from the center to a focus compared to the distance a from the center to a vertex. Mathematically, eccentricity is the ratio $e = \frac{c}{a}$.

1. Describe how the value of c compares to the value of a for an ellipse.
The value of c is always less than the value of a for an ellipse.

2. Given the relationship between c and a for an ellipse, what will always be true about the eccentricity of an ellipse? Because c < a, $\frac{c}{a}$ < 1.

3. Describe how the value of c compares to the value of a for a hyperbola.
The value of c is always greater than the value of a for a hyperbola.

4. Given the relationship between c and a for a hyperbola, what will always be true about the eccentricity of a hyperbola? Because c > a, $\frac{c}{a}$ > 1.

5. To see how the eccentricity describes the shape of an ellipse, graph the following ellipses and determine the eccentricity $\frac{c}{a}$ as a decimal for each.
a. $\frac{x^2}{25} + \frac{y^2}{4} = 1$ $e \approx 0.92$ b. $\frac{x^2}{9} + \frac{y^2}{4} = 1$ $e = 0.75$ c. $\frac{x^2}{5} + \frac{y^2}{4} = 1$ $e \approx 0.44$

6. Describe how the shape of the ellipse in Exercise 5 part (a) compares to the shape of the ellipse in Exercise 5 part (c). Answers may vary. Sample: The shape of the ellipse in part (c) appears close to the shape of a circle while the shape of the ellipse in part (a) is more elongated.

7. Astronomers use eccentricity to describe how much a space object's orbit deviates from a circle. What can you say about the shape of an orbit if its eccentricity is close to 1? What can you say about the shape of an orbit if its eccentricity is close to 0?
Answers may vary. Sample: The orbit deviates more from a circle as the eccentricity gets closer to 1 and becomes more similar to a circle as the eccentricity gets closer to 0.

Online Teacher Resource Center
Activities, Games, and Puzzles

10-6 Puzzle: Fit 'Em In
Translating Conic Sections

To solve this puzzle, you may want to solve the conic section formulas for y.

Circle	Ellipse	Hyperbola
$x^2 + y^2 = r^2$	$\frac{x^2}{a^2} + \frac{y^2}{b^2} = 1$	$\frac{x^2}{a^2} - \frac{y^2}{b^2} = 1$
$y = \pm\sqrt{r^2 - x^2}$	$y = \pm\sqrt{b^2\left(1 - \frac{x^2}{a^2}\right)}$	$y = \pm\sqrt{b^2\left(\frac{x^2}{a^2} - 1\right)}$

Here is the puzzle. Find an equation in standard form for a hyperbola, an ellipse, and a circle such that the following conditions are met. Sketch the graph of the conic sections on the coordinate grid below.

- All three conic sections have the common center $P(1, 2)$.
- The hyperbola has asymptotes $y - 2 = \frac{5}{4}(x - 1)$ and $y - 2 = -\frac{5}{4}(x - 1)$.
- The hyperbola is externally tangent to rectangle R at exactly two points. These points are the midpoints of the vertical sides of R. (Rectangle R is defined below.)
- The ellipse is internally tangent to rectangle R along a point on each of its sides.
- The circle is internally tangent to rectangle R in exactly two points. These points lie along a pair of opposite sides of R.
- Rectangle R is defined by the lines $x = −3, x = 5, y = −1,$ and $y = 5$.

Hint: Suppose that the common center is the origin $O(0, 0)$. Then use what you know about translations to find the puzzle solution.

$y = -\frac{5}{4}x + \frac{13}{4}$ $y = \frac{5}{4}x + \frac{3}{4}$

Write equations below for each conic section that makes up the puzzle solution.

Circle: $(x - 1)^2 + (y - 2)^2 = 3^2$

Ellipse: $\frac{(x-1)^2}{4^2} + \frac{(y-2)^2}{3^2} = 1$

Hyperbola: $\frac{(x-1)^2}{4^2} - \frac{(y-2)^2}{5^2} = 1$

Solving Quadratic Systems

© **Content Standards**
Extends A.REI.7 Solve a simple system consisting of a linear equation and a quadratic equation in two variables algebraically and graphically.
Also A.REI.11

In Chapter 3, you solved systems of linear equations algebraically and graphically. You can use the same methods to solve systems of quadratic equations.

Example 1

Solve the system algebraically. $\begin{cases} x^2 - y^2 = 9 \\ x^2 + 9y^2 = 169 \end{cases}$

$$x^2 - y^2 = 9$$
$$\underline{x^2 + 9y^2 = 169} \quad \text{Subtract like terms to eliminate the } x^2 \text{ term.}$$
$$-10y^2 = -160$$

$y = 4 \text{ or } y = -4$ Solve for y.

| $x^2 - (4)^2 = 9$ | Substitute the values of y | $x^2 - (-4)^2 = 9$ |
| $x^2 = 25$ | into the original equations. | $x^2 = 25$ |

$x = 5 \text{ or } x = -5$ Solve for x. $x = 5 \text{ or } x = -5$

The ordered pairs $(5, 4), (-5, 4), (5, -4),$ and $(-5, -4)$ are solutions to the system.

Example 2

Solve the system by graphing. $\begin{cases} x^2 + y^2 = 36 \\ y = (x - 2)^2 - 3 \end{cases}$

$$x^2 + y^2 = 36 \quad \text{Solve the first equation for } y.$$
$$y = \pm\sqrt{36 - x^2}$$

Graph the equations and find the point(s) of intersection. The solutions are approximately $(-1, 5.9)$ and $(4.6, 3.8)$.

Exercises

Solve each quadratic system.

1. $\begin{cases} x^2 + 64y^2 = 64 \\ x^2 + y^2 = 64 \end{cases}$

2. $\begin{cases} 2x^2 - y^2 = 2 \\ x^2 + y^2 = 25 \end{cases}$

3. $\begin{cases} 9x^2 + 25y^2 = 225 \\ y = -x^2 + 5 \end{cases}$

© 4. a. **Writing** The system that consists of $y = -3x + 6$ and $y = x^2 - 4x$ is a linear-quadratic system. How would you solve the system algebraically? Graphically?
   b. Solve the system in part (a).

Identify each system as linear-quadratic or quadratic-quadratic. Then solve.

5. $\begin{cases} y = x - 1 \\ x^2 + y^2 = 25 \end{cases}$

6. $\begin{cases} 9x^2 + 4y^2 = 36 \\ x^2 - y^2 = 4 \end{cases}$

7. $\begin{cases} -x + y = 4 \\ y = x^2 - 4x + 2 \end{cases}$

8. $\begin{cases} 4x^2 + 25y^2 = 100 \\ y = x + 2 \end{cases}$

Guided Instruction

PURPOSE To use algebra and graphing to solve quadratic systems of equations in two variables
PROCESS Students will
- use elimination and substitution to find (x, y) pairs that solve a system of quadratic equations.
- use technology to find points of intersection of the graphs of two quadratic equations to solve a system of quadratic equations.

DISCUSS   **VISUAL LEARNERS**
Systems of two quadratic equations can have zero, one, two, three, or four solutions. It may be useful to have students sketch graphs that illustrate each of these cases.

Example 1

> **Q** Once you know the values of one variable, how do you find the values of the other variable to complete the ordered pairs? [**Substitute the values of the variable you have in either original equation and solve for the other variable.**]

Example 2

> **Q** Some quadratic equations are not functions. How do you graph such equations on a graphing calculator? [**You may have to graph two separate equations to graph the entire quadratic equation.**]

Exercises

> **Q** For Exercises 1–3, what are the two figures formed by the equations for each system? [**(1) ellipse and circle, (2) hyperbola and circle, (3) ellipse and parabola**]

© **Mathematical Practices**
This Concept Byte supports students in constructing arguments, Mathematical Practice 3.

Answers

Exercises

1. $(-8, 0), (8, 0)$

2. $(3, 4), (-3, 4), (3, -4), (-3, -4)$

3. $\left(\pm\dfrac{21 + \sqrt{41}}{10}, \dfrac{9 - 21\sqrt{41}}{50}\right),$
   $\left(\pm\dfrac{21 - \sqrt{41}}{10}, \dfrac{9 + 21\sqrt{41}}{50}\right)$ or about
   $(\pm2.74, -2.51), (\pm1.46, 2.87)$

4. a. Algebraically: subst. $-3x + 6$ for y in $y = x^2 - 4x$, solve for x, and then subst. each of the solutions in $y = -3x + 6$ to find corresponding values for y.
   Graphically: Graph both equations and use the Intersect feature to find the coordinates of all pts. of intersection.
   b. $(-2, 12), (3, -3)$

5. linear-quadratic; $(-3, -4), (4, 3)$

6. quadratic-quadratic; $(\pm2, 0)$

7. linear-quadratic;
   $\left(\dfrac{5 + \sqrt{33}}{2}, \dfrac{13 + \sqrt{33}}{2}\right);$
   $\left(\dfrac{5 - \sqrt{33}}{2}, \dfrac{13 - \sqrt{33}}{2}\right)$

8. linear-quadratic; $(0, 2); \left(-\dfrac{100}{29}, -\dfrac{42}{29}\right)$

Performance Task

Pull It All Together

Understanding by Design principles indicate the importance of performance tasks that assess understanding.

- Make sense of problems and persevere in solving them.
- Construct viable arguments
- Look for and make use of structure.

The following questions are designed to
- Help support students as they do the Performance Tasks.
- Help you gauge their progress toward becoming mathematically proficient.

Performance Task 1

Visualize transformations of a conic section and write algebraic representations of the visual transformations.

- If the vertex of the parabola remained constant, which value in the vertex form of the equation of a parabola would effect the transformation described in part b of Task 1?

Performance Task 2

Describe the relationship between an ellipse and a circle in multiple ways.

- What is the shape of the base of a right cone?
- What happens to the shape of an ellipse as the foci move away from the center?

Performance Task 3

Find an equation to represent the distance relationship between the foci of a hyperbola and an ellipse inscribed in the hyperbola's central rectangle.

- What is the distance between $(c_e, 0)$ and $(c_h, 0)$ in terms of c_e and c_h?

BIG idea Modeling

You can represent many real-world mathematical problems algebraically.

Performance Task 1

Imagine a plane and a cone intersecting to form a parabola.

a. Explain why the plane has to intersect the axis of the cone.

b. Imagine the plane moving so that it keeps the same angle with the side of the cone, but its point of intersection with the axis moves in the direction of the apex of the cone and eventually passes through the apex. Describe what happens to the parabola and write equations that describe how the parabola changes.

> To solve these problems, you will pull together concepts and skills related to conic sections.

BIG idea Equivalence

You can represent any relationship in an infinite number of ways, where each representation has the same domain and the same pairing of inputs with outputs.

Performance Task 2

You can define an ellipse using a cone, a set of points, or algebra. For each kind of definition, explain how to describe a circle as a special case of an ellipse.

$$PF_1 + PF_2 = k$$

$$\frac{x^2}{9} + \frac{y^2}{4} = 1$$

BIG idea Coordinate Geometry

You can use a coordinate system to represent and analyze geometric relationships.

Performance Task 3

The focus of the hyperbola $\frac{x^2}{a^2} - \frac{y^2}{b^2} = 1$ is c_h units from $(0, 0)$. Imagine the ellipse inscribed in the central rectangle of the hyperbola. Its focus is c_e units from $(0, 0)$. How far apart are the foci $(c_e, 0)$ and $(c_h, 0)$? Give the distance in terms of a and b.

Assess Performance

Pull It All Together

See p. 49 for a holistic scoring rubric to gauge a student's progress on Understanding the Problem, Planning a Solution, Getting an Answer, and Assessing Autonomy.

SOLUTION OUTLINES

Performance Task 1

a. If the plane does not intersect the axis of the cone, it is parallel to the axis and the conic section formed is a hyperbola.

b. The plane is parallel to the "far edge" of the cone. The plane stays parallel as it moves toward the apex. When the plane intersects the apex, its intersection with the cone is a line—the "far edge" itself. By the continuous nature of the movement, the parabola is getting narrower and narrower with the two branches converging, in a sense, on the line.

If $y = ax^2$ is the equation for a parabola, the above change in the shape of the parabola corresponds to $|a|$ increasing without bound. The equation of the "degenerate" parabola would be $x = 0$. And as the plane proceeds away from the apex after intersecting it, the equation would again be $y = ax^2$ with a having values opposite those for the parabola on the other side of the vertex. (If students have studied Dandelin spheres, point out that the focus is getting close to the vertex of the parabola, and hence to the directrix. The locus description of the parabola thus would force the points of the parabola closer and closer to the parabola's axis.)

Performance Task 2

Using a cone: If the plane intersects the cone perpendicular to the axis, the intersection is a circle.

If the two fixed points used to define an ellipse are the same point, the figure is a circle.

Using algebra: If $\frac{x^2}{a^2} + \frac{y^2}{b^2} = 1$ and $a = b$, the graph is a circle.

Performance Task 3

First step: Write the coordinate of one foci of the hyperbola in terms of a and b. [The foci of the hyperbola are located at $(\pm c, 0)$ and $c = \sqrt{a^2 + b^2}$. So, the focus of the hyperbola is located at $(\sqrt{a^2 + b^2}, 0)$.]

Second step: Write the coordinate of one foci of the ellipse in terms of a and b. [The foci of the ellipse are located at $(\pm c, 0)$ and $c = \sqrt{a^2 - b^2}$. So, the focus of the hyperbola is located at $(\sqrt{a^2 - b^2}, 0)$.]

Third step: Find the distance between $(c_e, 0)$ and $(c_h, 0)$ by subtracting c_e from c_h. ($c_h - c_e = \sqrt{a^2 + b^2} - \sqrt{a^2 - b^2}$)

Using a set of points: (above)

Connecting BIG ideas and Answering the Essential Questions

1 Modeling
The intersection of a cone and a plane parallel to the side of a cone is a parabola.

Parabolas (Lesson 10-2)
Centered at the origin,
• a parabola has equation
$y = ax^2$, or $x = ay^2$.

Translating Conic Sections (Lesson 10-6)
Centered at (h, k),
• substitute $x - h$ for x and $y - k$ for y in the original equation for a conic section.

2 Equivalence
$\frac{x^2}{9} + \frac{y^2}{9} = 1$ is an equation of a circle centered at the origin with radius 3. Multiply each side by 9 to get $x^2 + y^2 = 9$.

Circles (Lesson 10-3)
Centered at the origin,
• a circle with radius r has equation
$x^2 + y^2 = r^2$.

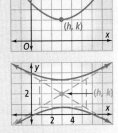

3 Coordinate Geometry
The x^2 and y^2 terms of the algebraic form of an ellipse are both positive. For a hyperbola, one term is negative.

Ellipses and Hyperbolas (Lessons 10-4 and 10-5)
Centered at the origin,
• an ellipse has equation $\frac{x^2}{a^2} + \frac{y^2}{b^2} = 1$
• a hyperbola has equation $\frac{x^2}{a^2} - \frac{y^2}{b^2} = 1$ or $\frac{y^2}{a^2} - \frac{x^2}{b^2} = 1$.

Chapter Vocabulary

- axis of symmetry (p. 646)
- center of a circle (p. 630)
- center of a hyperbola (p. 646)
- center of an ellipse (p. 639)
- circle (p. 630)
- conic section (p. 614)
- conjugate axis (p. 646)
- co-vertices of an ellipse (p. 639)
- directrix (p. 622)
- ellipse (p. 638)
- focal length (p. 622)
- focus of a parabola (p. 622)
- foci of an ellipse (p. 638)
- foci of a hyperbola (p. 645)
- hyperbola (p. 645)
- major axis (p. 639)
- minor axis (p. 639)
- radius (p. 630)
- standard form of an equation of a circle (p. 630)
- transverse axis (p. 646)
- vertices of an ellipse (p. 639)
- vertices of a hyperbola (p. 646)

Fill in the blanks.

1. In the definition of a parabola, a point on the curve is equidistant from the focus and the __?__.

2. The vertices of an ellipse are on its __?__.

3. $(x - h)^2 + (y - k)^2 = r^2$ is the __?__.

4. The distance from a point on a circle to its center is the __?__ of the circle.

5. The vertices of a hyperbola are on its __?__.

Essential Questions

BIG idea Modeling
ESSENTIAL QUESTIONS What is the intersection of a cone and a plane parallel to a line along the side of a cone?
ANSWER The intersection of a cone and a plane parallel to the side of the cone is a parabola.

BIG idea Equivalence
ESSENTIAL QUESTION What is the graph of $\frac{x^2}{9} + \frac{y^2}{9} = 1$?
ANSWER $\frac{x^2}{9} + \frac{y^2}{9} = 1$ is an equation of a circle centered at the origin with radius 3. Multiply each side by 9 to get $x^2 + y^2 = 9$.

BIG idea Coordinate Geometry
ESSENTIAL QUESTIONS What is the difference between the algebraic representations of ellipses and hyperbolas?
ANSWER The x^2 and y^2 terms of the algebraic form of an ellipse are both positive. For a hyperbola, one term is negative.

Answers

Chapter Review

1. directrix
2. major axis
3. standard form of an eq. of a circle
4. radius
5. transverse axis

Summative Questions

Use the following prompts as you review this chapter with your students. The prompts are designed to help you assess your students' understanding of the Big Ideas they have studied.

- Does the graph of a conic section ever intersect its focus or foci?
- Which conic sections are symmetric? How can you identify their axes of symmetry?
- Which is the only conic section without a center? Why does it not have one?
- Compare the standard-form equations of the conic sections. How can you identify each type of conic from the equation?

Answers

Chapter Review (continued)

6.

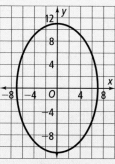

ellipse; lines of sym.: x-axis and y-axis; domain: $-7 \le x \le 7$, range: $-11 \le y \le 11$

7.

circle; lines of sym.: every line through the center; domain: $-2 \le x \le 2$, range: $-2 \le y \le 2$

8.

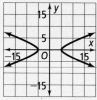

hyperbola; lines of sym.: x-axis and y-axis; domain: $x \le -5$ or $x \ge 5$, range: all real numbers

9.

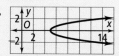

parabola; line of sym.: x-axis; domain: $x \ge 5$, range: all real numbers

10. center $(0, 0)$; domain: $x \le -4$ or $x \ge 4$, range: all real numbers

11. center $(0, 0)$; domain: $-3 \le x \le 3$, range: $-2 \le y \le 2$

12. $x = \frac{1}{20}y^2$

13. $y = -\frac{1}{20}x^2$

14. $y = \frac{1}{24}x^2$

15. $y = \frac{1}{10}x^2$

16. $y = 3x^2$

17. $y = \frac{1}{8}x^2 + 1$

18. $x = -\frac{1}{12}y^2 + 1$

19. focus: $\left(0, \frac{1}{20}\right)$, directrix: $y = -\frac{1}{20}$

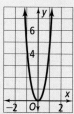

10-1 Exploring Conic Sections

Quick Review

A **conic section** is formed by the intersection of a plane and a double cone. Circles, ellipses, parabolas, and hyperbolas are all conic sections.

Example

Graph the equation $x^2 + y^2 = 9$. Identify the conic section, the domain and range.

Plot points that satisfy the equation. Connect them with a smooth curve.

The graph is a circle with center $(0, 0)$ and radius 3.

The domain is $-3 \le x \le 3$.

The range is $-3 \le y \le 3$.

Exercises

Graph each equation. Identify the conic section, any lines of symmetry, and the domain and range.

6. $\frac{x^2}{49} + \frac{y^2}{121} = 1$ **7.** $x^2 + y^2 = 4$

8. $\frac{x^2}{25} - \frac{y^2}{4} = 1$ **9.** $x = 2y^2 + 5$

Identify the center and domain and range of each graph.

10.

11.

10-2 Parabolas

Quick Review

In a plane, a parabola is the set of all points that are the same distance, c, from a fixed point, the **focus** and a fixed line, the **directrix**.

For $y = ax^2$, if $a > 0$, the parabola opens up, and has focus $(0, c)$ and directrix $y = -c$; if $a < 0$, the parabola opens down, and has focus $(0, -c)$ and directrix $y = c$.

For $x = ay^2$, if $a > 0$, the parabola opens right, and has focus $(c, 0)$ and directrix $x = -c$; if $a < 0$, the parabola opens left, and has focus $(-c, 0)$ and directrix $x = c$. In all cases, $a = \frac{1}{4c}$.

Example

Write an equation of a parabola that opens up, with vertex at the origin and focus 1 unit from the vertex.

Since the parabola opens up, use $y = ax^2$. Since the focus is 1 unit from the vertex, $c = 1$.

$$a = \frac{1}{4c} = \frac{1}{4(1)} = \frac{1}{4}$$

An equation for the parabola is $y = \frac{1}{4}x^2$.

Exercises

Write an equation of a parabola with vertex at the origin and the given focus.

12. $(5, 0)$ **13.** $(0, -5)$ **14.** $(0, 6)$

Write an equation of a parabola that opens up, with vertex at the origin and a focus as described.

15. focus is 2.5 units from the vertex

16. focus is $\frac{1}{12}$ of a unit from the vertex

Write an equation of a parabola with the given focus and directrix.

17. focus: $(0, 3)$; directrix: $y = -1$

18. focus: $(-2, 0)$; directrix: $x = 4$

Find the focus and the directrix of the graph of each equation. Sketch the graph.

19. $y = 5x^2$ **20.** $x = 2y^2$ **21.** $x = -\frac{1}{8}y^2$

20. focus: $\left(\frac{1}{8}, 0\right)$, directrix: $x = -\frac{1}{8}$

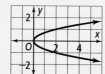

21. focus: $(-2, 0)$, directrix: $x = 2$

10-3 Circles

Quick Review

In a plane, a **circle** is the set of all points that are a given distance, the **radius**, r, from a given point, the **center**, (h, k).

Example

Write an equation in standard form of a circle with center $(-3, 4)$ and radius 2.

Use the standard form of the equation of a circle.
Substitute -3 for h, 4 for k, and 2 for r.

$(x - h)^2 + (y - k)^2 = r^2$
$(x - (-3))^2 + (y - 4)^2 = 2^2$
$(x + 3)^2 + (y - 4)^2 = 4$

An equation for the circle is $(x + 3)^2 + (y - 4)^2 = 4$.

Exercises

Write an equation in standard form of a circle with the given center and radius.

22. center $(0, 0)$; radius 4

23. center $(8, 1)$; radius 5

Write an equation for each translation of $x^2 + y^2 = r^2$ with the given radius.

24. left 3 units, up 2 units; radius 10

25. right 5 units, down 3 units; radius 8

Find the center and the radius of each circle. Graph each circle. Describe the translation from center $(0, 0)$.

26. $(x - 1)^2 + y^2 = 64$

27. $(x + 7)^2 + (y + 3)^2 = 49$

10-4 Ellipses

Quick Review

An **ellipse** is the set of all points P, where the sum of the distances between P and two fixed points, the **foci**, is constant. The **major axis** contains the foci, and its endpoints are the **vertices of the ellipse**. For $a > b$, there are two standard forms of ellipses centered at the origin. If $\frac{x^2}{a^2} + \frac{y^2}{b^2} = 1$, the major axis is horizontal with vertices $(\pm a, 0)$, foci $(\pm c, 0)$, and co-vertices $(0, \pm b)$. If $\frac{x^2}{b^2} + \frac{y^2}{a^2} = 1$, the major axis is vertical with vertices $(0, \pm a)$, foci $(0, \pm c)$, and co-vertices $(\pm b, 0)$. In either case, $c^2 = a^2 - b^2$.

Example

Write an equation of an ellipse with foci $(\pm 5, 0)$ and co-vertices $(0, \pm 3)$.

Since the foci are $(\pm 5, 0)$, the major axis is horizontal. Since $c = 5$ and $b = 3$, $c^2 = 25$ and $b^2 = 9$. Using the equation $c^2 = a^2 - b^2$, $a^2 = 34$.

An equation of the ellipse is $\frac{x^2}{34} + \frac{y^2}{9} = 1$.

Exercises

Write an equation of an ellipse centered at the origin, satisfying the given conditions.

28. foci $(\pm 1, 0)$; co-vertices $(0, \pm 4)$

29. vertex $(0, \sqrt{29})$; co-vertex $(-5, 0)$

30. focus $(0, 1)$; vertex $(0, \sqrt{10})$

31. foci $(\pm 2, 0)$; co-vertices $(0, \pm 6)$

32. Write an equation of an ellipse centered at the origin with height 8 units and width 16 units.

33. Find the foci of the graph of $\frac{x^2}{4} + \frac{y^2}{9} = 1$. Graph the ellipse.

---

30. $\frac{x^2}{9} + \frac{y^2}{10} = 1$

31. $\frac{x^2}{40} + \frac{y^2}{36} = 1$

32. $\frac{x^2}{64} + \frac{y^2}{16} = 1$

33. foci: $(0, \pm\sqrt{5})$

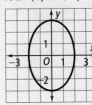

---

22. $x^2 + y^2 = 16$

23. $(x - 8)^2 + (y - 1)^2 = 25$

24. $(x + 3)^2 + (y - 2)^2 = 100$

25. $(x - 5)^2 + (y + 3)^2 = 64$

26. center $(1, 0)$, radius 8

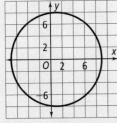

circle with radius 8 translated 1 unit to the rt.

27. center $(-7, -3)$, radius 7

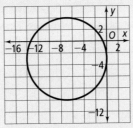

circle with radius 7 translated 7 units to the left and 3 units down

28. $\frac{x^2}{17} + \frac{y^2}{16} = 1$

29. $\frac{x^2}{25} + \frac{y^2}{29} = 1$

Answers

Chapter Review (continued)

34. foci: $(\pm 3\sqrt{29}, 0)$

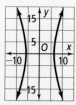

35. foci: $(0, \pm\sqrt{569})$

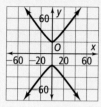

36. foci: $(\pm\sqrt{202}, 0)$

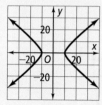

37. $\dfrac{x^2}{64} - \dfrac{y^2}{225} = 1$

38. $\dfrac{y^2}{49} - \dfrac{x^2}{576} = 1$

39. $\dfrac{x^2}{1.148 \times 10^{10}} - \dfrac{y^2}{3.395 \times 10^{10}} = 1$

40. $(x-1)^2 + (y-1)^2 = 25$

41. $\dfrac{(x-3)^2}{4} + \dfrac{(y+2)^2}{9} = 1$

42. $\dfrac{(x-6)^2}{9} - \dfrac{(y-3)^2}{16} = 1$

43. hyperbola; center $(0, -2)$, foci: $(0, -2 \pm 2\sqrt{10})$

44. circle; center $\left(-\dfrac{3}{2}, 2\right)$, radius $\dfrac{\sqrt{61}}{2}$

45. parabola; vertex: $\left(-\dfrac{1}{2}, -\dfrac{169}{4}\right)$

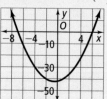

10-5 Hyperbolas

Quick Review

A **hyperbola** is the set of all points P such that the absolute value of the difference of the distances from P to two fixed points, the **foci**, is constant. There are two standard forms of hyperbolas centered at the origin. If $\dfrac{x^2}{a^2} - \dfrac{y^2}{b^2} = 1$, the asymptotes are $y = \pm\dfrac{b}{a}x$, the **transverse axis** is horizontal with vertices $(\pm a, 0)$, and the foci are $(\pm c, 0)$. If $\dfrac{y^2}{a^2} - \dfrac{x^2}{b^2} = 1$, the asymptotes are $y = \pm\dfrac{a}{b}x$, the transverse axis is vertical with vertices $(0, \pm a)$, and the foci are $(0, \pm c)$. In either case, $c^2 = a^2 + b^2$.

Example

Find the foci of the graph of $\dfrac{x^2}{25} - \dfrac{y^2}{9} = 1$.

The equation is in the form $\dfrac{x^2}{a^2} - \dfrac{y^2}{b^2} = 1$, so the transverse axis is horizontal; $a^2 = 25$ and $b^2 = 9$.

Using the Pythagorean Theorem to find c,
$c = \sqrt{25 + 9} = \sqrt{34} \approx 5.8$.

The foci, $(\pm c, 0)$, are approximately $(5.8, 0)$ and $(-5.8, 0)$.

Exercises

Find the foci of each hyperbola. Graph the hyperbola.

34. $\dfrac{x^2}{36} - \dfrac{y^2}{225} = 1$

35. $\dfrac{y^2}{400} - \dfrac{x^2}{169} = 1$

36. $\dfrac{x^2}{121} - \dfrac{y^2}{81} = 1$

Write an equation of a hyperbola with the given foci and vertices.

37. foci $(\pm 17, 0)$, vertices $(\pm 8, 0)$

38. foci $(0, \pm 25)$, vertices $(0, \pm 7)$

39. Find an equation that models the hyperbolic path of a spacecraft around a planet if $a = 107{,}124$ km and $c = 213{,}125.9$ km.

10-6 Translating Conic Sections

Quick Review

Substitute $(x - h)$ for x and $(y - k)$ for y to translate graphs of the conic sections.

Example

Identify and describe the conic section represented by the equation $2x^2 + 3y^2 + 4x + 12y - 22 = 0$.

By completing the square, the equation becomes $\dfrac{(x+1)^2}{18} + \dfrac{(y+2)^2}{12} = 1$, which is an ellipse.

The center is $(-1, -2)$ and the major axis is horizontal.

Using the equation $c^2 = a^2 - b^2$, $c = \sqrt{6}$, so the distance from the center of the ellipse to the foci is $\sqrt{6}$.

Since the ellipse is centered at $(-1, -2)$ and the major axis is horizontal, the foci are located $\sqrt{6}$ to the left and right of this center.

The foci are at $(-1 + \sqrt{6}, -2)$ and $(-1 - \sqrt{6}, -2)$.

Exercises

Write an equation of a conic section with the given characteristics.

40. a circle with center $(1, 1)$; radius 5

41. an ellipse with center $(3, -2)$; vertical major axis of length 6; minor axis of length 4

42. a hyperbola with vertices $(3, 3)$ and $(9, 3)$; foci $(1, 3)$ and $(11, 3)$

Identify the conic section and sketch the graph. If it is a parabola, give the vertex. If it is a circle, give the center and radius. If it is an ellipse or a hyperbola, give the center and foci.

43. $-x^2 + y^2 + 4y - 16 = 0$

44. $x^2 + y^2 + 3x - 4y - 9 = 0$

45. $x^2 + x - y - 42 = 0$

Chapter Test

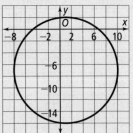
MathXL® for School
Go to PowerAlgebra.com

Do you know HOW?

Identify the type of each conic section. Give the center, domain, and range of each graph.

1.

2.

3.

4.

Identify the focus and the directrix of the graph of each equation.

5. $y = 3x^2$

6. $x = -2y^2$

7. $x + 5y^2 = 0$

8. $9x^2 - 2y = 0$

Write an equation of a parabola with its vertex at the origin and the given characteristics.

9. focus at $(0, -2)$

10. focus at $(3, 0)$

11. directrix $x = 7$

12. directrix $y = -1$

For each equation, find the center and radius of the circle. Graph the circle.

13. $(x - 2)^2 + (y - 3)^2 = 36$

14. $(x + 5)^2 + (y + 8)^2 = 100$

15. $(x - 1)^2 + (y + 7)^2 = 81$

16. $(x + 4)^2 + (y - 10)^2 = 121$

Write an equation of an ellipse for each given height and width. Assume that the center of the ellipse is (0, 0).

17. height 10 units; width 16 units

18. height 2 units; width 12 units

19. height 9 units; width 5 units

Find the foci of each ellipse. Then graph the ellipse.

20. $x^2 + \frac{y^2}{49} = 1$

21. $4x^2 + y^2 = 4$

Find the foci of each hyperbola. Then graph the hyperbola.

22. $\frac{x^2}{64} - \frac{y^2}{4} = 1$

23. $y^2 - \frac{x^2}{225} = 1$

Write an equation of an ellipse with the given characteristics.

24. center $(-2, 7)$; horizontal major axis of length 8; minor axis of length 6

25. center $(3, -2)$; vertical major axis of length 12; minor axis of length 10

Write an equation of a hyperbola with the given characteristics.

26. vertices $(\pm 3, 7)$; foci $(\pm 5, 7)$

27. vertices $(2, \pm 5)$; foci $(2, \pm 8)$

Identify the conic section represented by each equation. If it is a parabola, give the vertex. If it is a circle, give the center and radius. If it is an ellipse or a hyperbola, give the center and foci. Sketch the graph.

28. $3y^2 - x - 6y + 5 = 0$

29. $4x^2 + y^2 - 16x - 6y + 9 = 0$

Do you UNDERSTAND?

30. **Writing** Explain how you can tell what kind of conic section a quadratic equation describes without graphing the equation.

31. **Reasoning** What shape is an ellipse whose height and width are equal?

32. **Open-Ended** Write an equation of a hyperbola whose transverse axis is on the x-axis.

15. center $(1, -7)$, radius 9

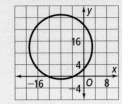

16. center $(-4, 10)$, radius 11

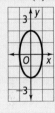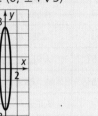

17. $\frac{x^2}{64} + \frac{y^2}{25} = 1$

18. $\frac{x^2}{36} + y^2 = 1$

19. $\frac{x^2}{6.25} + \frac{y^2}{20.25} = 1$

20. foci: $(0, \pm 4\sqrt{3})$

21. foci: $(0, \pm \sqrt{3})$

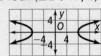

22. foci: $(\pm 2\sqrt{17}, 0)$

23. foci: $(0, \pm \sqrt{226})$

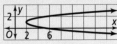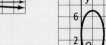

24. $\frac{(x + 2)^2}{16} + \frac{(y - 7)^2}{9} = 1$

25. $\frac{(x - 3)^2}{25} + \frac{(y + 2)^2}{36} = 1$

26. $\frac{x^2}{9} - \frac{(y - 7)^2}{16} = 1$

27. $\frac{y^2}{25} - \frac{(x - 2)^2}{39} = 1$

28. parabola; vertex: (2, 1)

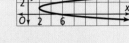

29. ellipse; center (2, 3), foci: $(2, 3 \pm 2\sqrt{3})$

30. Write the eq. in standard form.

31. circle

32. Check students' work.

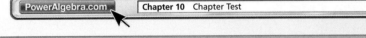

Answers

Chapter Test

1. ellipse: center (0, 0); x-intercepts: $(\pm 2, 0)$, y-intercepts: $(0, \pm 3)$; domain: $-2 \le x \le 2$, range: $-3 \le y \le 3$

2. hyperbola: center (0, 0); x-intercepts $(\pm 2, 0)$, no y-intercept domain: $x \le -2$ or $x \ge 2$, range: all real numbers

3. ellipse: center (0, 0); x-intercepts: $(\pm 2, 0)$, y-intercepts: $(0, \pm 1)$; domain: $-2 \le x \le 2$, range: $-1 \le y \le 1$

4. hyperbola: center (0, 0); no x-intercept, y-intercepts $(0, \pm 2)$; domain: all real numbers, range: $y \le -2$ or $y \ge 2$

5. focus: $\left(0, \frac{1}{12}\right)$, directrix: $y = -\frac{1}{12}$

6. focus: $\left(-\frac{1}{8}, 0\right)$, directrix: $x = \frac{1}{8}$

7. focus: $\left(-\frac{1}{20}, 0\right)$, directrix: $x = \frac{1}{20}$

8. focus: $\left(0, \frac{1}{18}\right)$, directrix: $y = -\frac{1}{18}$

9. $y = -\frac{1}{8}x^2$

10. $x = \frac{1}{12}y^2$

11. $x = -\frac{1}{28}y^2$

12. $y = \frac{1}{4}x^2$

13. center (2, 3), radius 6

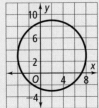

14. center $(-5, -8)$, radius 10

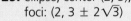
PowerAlgebra.com

MathXL for School

Prepare students for the Mid-Chapter Quiz and Chapter Test with online practice and review.

Item Number	Lesson	© Content Standard
1	10-5	G.GPE.3
2	7-2	F.IF.7.e
3	4-1	F.IF.4
4	7-1	A.CED.2
5	2-6	F.BF.3
6	4-5	A.SSE.1.a
7	10-5	G.GPE.3
8	4-3	F.IF.4
9	8-5	A.APR.7
10	10-4	G.GPE.3
11	3-2	A.REI.6
12	4-9	A.REI.7
13	8-6	A.APR.7
14	10-2	G.GPE.2
15	8-4	A.SSE.2
16	9-5	A.SSE.4
17	6-5	A.REI.2
18	4-5	A.APR.3
19	10-6	F.IF.8
20	10-3	G.GPE.1
21	8-6	A.APR.6
22	6-5	A.REI.2
23	7-2	A.CED.2
24	6-8	F.IF.7.b
25	4-5	A.APR.3
26	7-1	A.SSE.1.b

TIPS FOR SUCCESS

Read the question at the right. Then follow the tips to answer the multiple choice question.

TIP 1
Read the labels on the axes to understand the meaning of a point on the graph.

A stone falls from a 56-foot cliff. The graph shows the height of the stone h, in feet, after t seconds. In about how many seconds does the stone reach the ground?

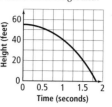

TIP 2
Use the graph to determine when $h = 0$.

Think It Through
Find the point where the graph crosses the horizontal axis.

The graph crosses the horizontal axis at about (1.9, 0). So the stone reaches the ground in about 1.9 seconds.

The correct answer is D.

- (A) 0.9 second
- (B) 1.0 second
- (C) 1.5 seconds
- (D) 1.9 seconds

Vocabulary Builder

As you solve test items, you must understand the meanings of mathematical terms. Match each term with its mathematical meaning.

A. conic section

B. hyperbola

C. directrix

D. ellipse

E. circle

I. a set of points P in a plane such that the absolute value of the difference between the distances from P to two fixed points F_1 and F_2 is a constant k

II. a set of points P in a plane such that the sum of the distances from P to two fixed points F_1 and F_2 is a constant k

III. the set of all points in a plane that are a distance r from a given point

IV. a curve formed by the intersection of a plane and a double cone

V. the fixed line equidistant with the focus from each point on a parabola

Multiple Choice

Read each question. Then write the letter of the correct answer on your paper.

1. Which of the following equations represents the graph of a hyperbola with foci at $(5, 0)$ and $(-5, 0)$?

- (A) $\frac{x^2}{25} - \frac{y^2}{4} = 1$
- (B) $\frac{x^2}{21} + \frac{y^2}{4} = 1$
- (C) $\frac{x^2}{21} - \frac{y^2}{4} = 1$
- (D) $\frac{x^2}{25} + \frac{y^2}{4} = 1$

2. If the equation $y = 4^x$ is graphed, which of the following values of x would produce a point closest to the x-axis?

- (F) 3
- (G) 0
- (H) 1
- (I) 4

Answers

Cumulative Standards Review

A. IV

B. I

C. V

D. II

E. III

1. C

2. G

3. An acrobat landed on a teeterboard and launched his partner into the air. The graph below shows the height h of the partner, in yards, at t seconds after the launch.

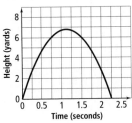

Which value is the best approximation of the maximum height of the partner?

  Ⓐ 6.0 yards   Ⓒ 6.8 yards

  Ⓑ 6.4 yards   Ⓓ 7.2 yards

4. The bacteria in a petri dish are growing exponentially with time, as shown in the table below.

Bacteria Growth

Day	Bacteria
0	50
1	150
2	450

Which of the following equations expresses the number of bacteria y present at day x?

  Ⓕ $y = (3)^x$

  Ⓖ $y = 50 + (3)^x$

  Ⓗ $y = 50 \cdot (3)^x$

  Ⓘ $y = 150 \cdot (3)^x$

5. Which of the following statements is true about the functions $|-2x|$ and $-2|x|$?

  Ⓐ The graphs are the same.

  Ⓑ The graph of $-2|x|$ is a reflection of $|-2x|$ across the x-axis.

  Ⓒ The graph of $-2|x|$ is a reflection of $|-2x|$ across the y-axis.

  Ⓓ The graphs have no similarities.

6. Alex dives from a diving board into a swimming pool. Her distance above the pool, in feet, is given by the equation $h(t) = -16.17t^2 + 13.2t + 33$, where t is the number of seconds after jumping.

What is height of the diving board ?

  Ⓕ -16.17 ft

  Ⓖ 13.2 ft

  Ⓗ 30.03 ft

  Ⓘ 33 ft

7. What is the standard form of the equation of the conic section given below?

$$25x^2 - 49y^2 - 1225 = 0$$

  Ⓐ $\dfrac{x^2}{49} - \dfrac{y^2}{25} = 1$

  Ⓑ $\dfrac{x^2}{49} + \dfrac{y^2}{25} = 1$

  Ⓒ $25x^2 - 49y^2 = 1225$

  Ⓓ $49x^2 - 25y^2 = 1$

8. Owen threw a ball straight up into the air from an initial height of 5 feet. The graph below shows the height h of the ball, in feet, at t seconds after Owen threw it. Of the following times, when was the ball closest to the ground?

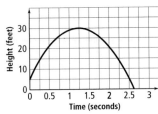

  Ⓕ 0.6 second

  Ⓖ 1 second

  Ⓗ 1.6 seconds

  Ⓘ 2 seconds

3. C

4. H

5. B

6. I

7. A

8. I

Answers

Cumulative Standards Review (continued)

9. 1.50

10. 10

11. 17

12. 29

13. −2

14. 0.25

15. **[2]** Step 4; 4 is not a common factor of the numerator 4 and the denominator $x + 4$.

[1] correct answer with no explanation

16. **[2]** 127

[1] one minor computational error

17. **[2]** $\frac{x}{x-1} - \frac{2}{x} = \frac{1}{x-1}$

$x^2 - 2x - 2 = x$

$x^2 - 3x - 2 = 0$

$(x - 2)(x - 1) = 0$

$x = 1$ is an extraneous solution.

[1] correct answer with no work shown

18. **[2]** $x(x - 2) = 0$

$x = 0, 2$

[1] $x = 0, 2$ with no work shown

19. **[2]** $(3 - \sqrt{21}, 0), (3 + \sqrt{21}, 0)$

[1] one minor computational error

20. **[2]** Circle; the equation follows the parent function for a circle.

[1] correct answer with no explanation

21. **[2]** all real numbers except $x = 2$

[1] one minor computational error

22. **[2]** 9

[1] one minor computational error

23. **[4]** $10,671.59; $13,840.31

[3] $10,671.59 OR $13,840.31

[2] Both answers with minor miscalculations with rounding (such as $10,671 and $13,841).

[1] One of the answers with a minor miscalculation with rounding (such as $13,841).

24. **[4]** The graph of $y = \frac{1}{2}\sqrt{x + 3} - 3$ is the graph of $y = \sqrt{x}$ translated to the left 4, down 3, and compressed vertically, with a scale factor $\frac{1}{2}$.

[3] The graph of $y = \frac{1}{2}\sqrt{x + 3} - 3$ is the graph of $y = \sqrt{x}$ translated left, down, and compressed.

[2] The graph of $y = \frac{1}{2}\sqrt{x + 3} - 3$ is the graph of $y = \sqrt{x}$ translated to the right 4 units, up 3 units, and expanded vertically, with a scale factor $\frac{1}{2}$.

[1] The graph of $y = \frac{1}{2}\sqrt{x + 3} - 3$ is the graph of $y = \sqrt{x}$ translated right, down, and expanded.

---

9. The graph below shows the height h in feet, of an object t seconds after it is tossed from a building. The table shows the height, in feet, of another object t seconds after it is dropped. How long, in seconds, is the first object that hits the ground in the air? Write your answer to the nearest hundredth.

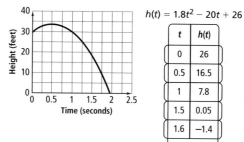

$h(t) = 1.8t^2 - 20t + 26$

t	$h(t)$
0	26
0.5	16.5
1	7.8
1.5	0.05
1.6	−1.4

10. What is the length of the major axis of an ellipse with foci at $(4, 0)$ and $(-4, 0)$, and with a minor axis of length 6?

11. A total of $323 was collected from 40 people to cover the exact cost of their dinners. Some ordered steak at $8.50 per person, others ordered chicken at $7.50 per person. How many people ordered chicken?

12. The height of an acorn falling from the top of a 45-ft tree is modeled by the equation $h = -16t^2 + 45$. Before it can hit the ground a squirrel jumps out and intercepts it. If the squirrel's height is modeled by the equation $h = -3t + 32$, at what height, in feet, did the squirrel intercept the acorn?

13. What is the value of x?

$\frac{10}{x(x-3)} + \frac{4}{x} = \frac{5}{x-3}$

14. What is the y-value of the focus of the parabola?

Short Response

15. Which is the first *incorrect* step in simplifying? Explain.

$$\frac{4}{(x-1)^{-1}(x^2 + 3x - 4)}$$

Step 1: $\dfrac{4(x - 1)}{x^2 + 3x - 4}$

Step 2: $\dfrac{4(x - 1)}{(x + 4)(x - 1)}$

Step 3: $\dfrac{4(x - 1)}{(x + 4)(x - 1)} \div \dfrac{x - 1}{x - 1}$

Step 4: $\dfrac{4}{x + 4} \div \dfrac{4}{4} = \dfrac{1}{x}$

16. What is the sum of the first 7 terms of the geometric series below?

1, 2, 4, 8, . . .

17. What are the extraneous roots of the equation $\frac{x}{x-1} - \frac{2}{x} = \frac{1}{x-1}$?

18. Find the zeros of the function $y = x^2 - 2x$. Show your work.

19. What are the coordinates of the foci of the graph of $4x^2 - 24x = 64 - 25y^2$?

20. Which conic section is represented by the equation $x^2 + y^2 = 6x - 14y - 9$?

21. If x is a real number, for what values of x is the equation $(3x - 6)(x - 2)^{-1} = 3$ true?

22. What is the solution of the equation $\sqrt{x + 5} = \sqrt{2x - 4}$?

Extended Response

23. Suppose you put $10,000 in an account that pays 6.5% annual interest compounded continuously. How much will be in the account after one year? After five years?

24. Explain how to graph $y = \frac{1}{2}\sqrt{x + 3} - 3$ by translating the graph of $y = \sqrt{x}$.

25. Find a nonzero value for k such that the equation $kx^2 - 10x + 25 = 0$ has one solution. Show your work.

26. Explain when the function $y = a \cdot b^x$ models exponential growth and when it models exponential decay.

---

25. **[4]** $100 - 4(k)(25) = 0$;
$100k = 100$; $k = 1$

[3] $100 - 4(k)(25) = 0$; $100k = 100$

[2] $100 - 4(k)(25) = 0$

[1] $100 - 4(k)(25) = 0$;
$100k = 100$; $k = 100$ (contains correct procedure but gives incorrect final response based on a miscalculation error).

26. **[4]** For $y = ab^x$, if $b > 1$, the exponential function represents exponential growth; if $0 < b < 1$, the exponential function represents exponential decay.

[3] For $y = ab^x$, if $b > 1$, the exponential function represents exponential growth.

[2] For $y = ab^x$, if $0 < b < 1$, the exponential function represents exponential growth; if $b > 1$, the exponential function represents exponential decay.

[1] For $y = ab^x$, if $b > 1$, the exponential function represents exponential decay.

Get Ready!

Skills
Handbook,
page 972

◀ **Finding Percent**

Write each number as a percent.

1. $\frac{5}{6}$　　2. $\frac{7}{36}$　　3. $\frac{48}{52}$　　4. 0.3056

Skills
Handbook,
page 975

◀ **Simplifying Expressions**

Simplify each expression.

5. $8 \cdot 7 \cdot 6 \cdot 5 \cdot 4$　　6. $\frac{52 \cdot 51 \cdot 50}{3 \cdot 2 \cdot 1}$　　7. $\frac{5 \cdot 4 \cdot 3 \cdot 2 \cdot 1}{3 \cdot 2 \cdot 1 \cdot 2 \cdot 1}$

Lesson 5-7

◀ **Expanding Binomials**

Use Pascal's Triangle to expand each binomial.

8. $(a + b)^5$　　9. $(j + 3k)^3$　　10. $(m + 0.7)^2$

11. $(2 + t)^4$　　12. $(m + n)^2$　　13. $(x + 3y)^4$

Lesson 6-1

◀ **Finding Real Roots**

Find the real square roots of each number.

14. $\frac{1}{100}$　　15. $\frac{1}{400}$　　16. $\frac{1}{196}$

17. $\frac{1}{4}$　　18. $\frac{1}{9}$　　19. $\frac{1}{576}$

Looking Ahead Vocabulary

20. In driver's education class, students may learn how to drive through a *simulation*. How do you think simulations might be used in a math class?

21. When you describe the likelihood that it will rain tomorrow given that it rained today, you are giving a *conditional probability*. What is the condition in this situation?

22. When you give a value to represent the typical data value in a data set, you are giving a *measure of central tendency* of the data set. What value do you think best represents the following data set? Explain.

$\{1, 3, 3, 3, 4, 10, 20, 30, 40\}$

Get Ready!

Assign this diagnostic assessment to determine if students have the prerequisite skills for Chapter 11.

Lesson	Skill
Skills Handbook, p. T974	Finding Percent
Skills Handbook, p. T977	Simplifying Expressions
5-7	Expanding Binomials
6-1	Finding Real Roots

To remediate students, select from these resources (available for every lesson).
• Online Problems (PowerAlgebra.com)
• Reteaching (All-in-One Teaching Resources)
• Practice (All-in-One Teaching Resources)

Why Students Need These Skills

FINDING PERCENT
Finding percents is essential to expressing probabilities as percents.

SIMPLIFYING EXPRESSIONS
Simplifying expressions is essential for using formulas to calculate probability.

EXPANDING BINOMIALS
Students' skills of expanding binomials are extended with another variation of the Binomial Theorem.

FINDING REAL ROOTS
Finding real roots is essential to finding standard deviation from the variance.

Looking Ahead Vocabulary

SIMULATION Elicit that a simulation can be a way to replay an event or events so that more data can be derived.

CONDITIONAL PROBABILITY Ask students whether the probability is dependent on the given condition.

MEASURE OF CENTRAL TENDENCY Ask students what criteria they are looking for that makes a data value the most typical.

Answers

Get Ready!

1. $83.\overline{3}\%$
2. $19.\overline{4}\%$
3. $\approx 92.308\%$
4. 30.56%
5. 6720
6. $22{,}100$
7. 10
8. $a^5 + 5a^4b + 10a^3b^2 + 10a^2b^3 + 5ab^4 + b^5$
9. $j^3 + 9j^2k + 27jk^2 + 27k^3$
10. $m^2 + 1.4m + 0.49$
11. $16 + 32t + 24t^2 + 8t^3 + t^4$
12. $m^2 + 2mn + n^2$
13. $x^4 + 12x^3y + 54x^2y^2 + 108xy^3 + 81y^4$
14. $\pm\frac{1}{10}$
15. $\pm\frac{1}{20}$
16. $\pm\frac{1}{14}$
17. $\pm\frac{1}{2}$
18. $\pm\frac{1}{3}$
19. $\pm\frac{1}{24}$
20. In a math class, when actual trials are difficult to conduct, you can find the experimental probability by using a simulation which is a model of one or more events.
21. It rained today.
22. The mean, $12.\overline{6}$; the data are fairly evenly distributed around the mean which makes the mean the best representation of the data given.

Chapter 11 Overview

Chapter 11 expands on students' understandings and skills related to probability and statistics. In this chapter, students will develop the answers to the Essential Questions posed on the opposite page as they learn the concepts and skills bulleted below.

BIG idea Probability

ESSENTIAL QUESTION What is the difference between a permutation and a combination?
- Students will find permutations and combinations of data sets using formulas.

BIG idea Probability

ESSENTIAL QUESTION What is the difference between experimental and theoretical probability?
- Students will use simulation to model experimental probability.
- Students will find the theoretical probability of events using a formula.

BIG idea Data Collection and Analysis

ESSENTIAL QUESTION How are measures of central tendency different from standard deviation?
- Students will find and analyze the measures of central tendency of given data sets.
- Students will find the standard deviation of given data sets.

Content Standards

Following are the standards covered in this chapter.

CONCEPTUAL CATEGORY Statistics and Probability

  Domain Making Inferences and Justifying Conclusions S.IC

   Cluster Understand and evaluate random processes underlying statistical experiments. (Standards S.IC.1, S.IC.2)
   LESSONS 11-2, 11-8

   Cluster Make inferences and justify conclusions from sample surveys, experiments. and observational studies. (Standards SIC.3, S.IC.4, S.IC.5, S.IC.6)
   LESSONS 11-6, 11-7, 11-8

  Domain Interpreting Categorical and Quantitative Data S.ID

   Cluster Summarize, represent, and interpret data on a single count or measurement variable. (Standard S.ID.4)
   LESSONS 11-4, 11-10

CHAPTER 11 Probability and Statistics

DOMAINS
- Conditional Probability and the Rules of Probability
- Making Inferences and Justifying Conclusions
- Use Probability to Make Decisions

I'm going to help you learn about probability and statistics.

What's the probability of scoring in soccer on a penalty kick? Do statistics from past games help you decide? How do you apply theoretical and experimental probabilities? How can you compare data sets? You will learn how in this chapter.

Vocabulary

English/Spanish Vocabulary Audio Online:

English	Spanish
combination, *p. 676*	combinación
conditional probability, *p. 696*	probabilidad condicional
experimental probability, *p. 681*	probabilidad experimental
measure of central tendency, *p. 711*	medida de tendencia central
mutually exclusive events, *p. 689*	sucesos mutuamente excluyentes
normal distribution, *p. 739*	distribución normal
permutation, *p. 675*	permutación
simulation, *p. 682*	simulación
theoretical probability, *p. 683*	probabilidad teórica

My Math Video

My Math Video
Use this photo to introduce the concept of probability.

Statistically it is more likely for the kicker to score than for the goalie to save, so the probability of scoring should be greater than 50%, or greater than 0.5.

Q What factors affect the chances of the kicker scoring? **[the skill of the kicker and of the goalie]**

Q How could you examine these factors? **[You could look at the kicker's past percentage of scoring on a penalty kick and the goalie's percentage of saving a penalty kick.]**

Q Statistics show that it is significantly more likely to score on a penalty kick than to save it. What does this tell you about the probabilities of each? **[The probability of scoring on a penalty kick is greater than the probability of saving the penalty kick.]**

EXTENSION

Have students research the statistics of one or more soccer players and compare the likelihood of each scoring.

BIGideas

1 Probability
Essential Question What is the difference between a permutation and a combination?

2 Probability
Essential Question What is the difference between experimental and theoretical probability?

3 Data Collection and Analysis
Essential Question How are measures of central tendency different from standard deviation?

Chapter Preview

 Increase students' depth of knowledge with interactive online activities.

 Show Problems from each lesson solved step by step. Instant replay allows students to go at their own pace when studying online.

 Assign homework to individual students or to an entire class.

 Prepare students for the Mid-Chapter Quiz and Chapter Test with online practice and review.

Content Standards (cont')

Domain Use Probability to Make Decisions S.MD

Cluster Use probability to evaluate outcomes of decisions. (Standards S.MD.6, S.MD.7)
LESSON 11-5

Domain Conditional Probability and the Rules of Probability S.CP

Cluster Understand independence and conditional probability and use them to interpret data. (Standards S.CP.2, S.CP.3, S.CP.4, S.CP.5)
LESSONS 11-3, 11-4

Cluster Use the rules of probability to compute probabilities of compound events in a uniform probability model. (Standards S.CP.6, S.CP.7, S.CP.8, S.CP.9)
LESSONS 11-1, 11-3, 11-4, 11-9

PROBABILITY AND STATISTICS
Math Background

© PROFESSIONAL DEVELOPMENT

Understanding by Design principles were central to the development of the Big Ideas and the Essential Understandings. These will help your students build a structure on which to make connections to prior learning.

Probability

BIG idea Probability expresses the likelihood that a particular event will occur. Data can be used to calculate an experimental probability, and mathematical properties can be used to determine a theoretical probability. Either experimental or theoretical probability can be used to make predictions or decisions about future events. Various counting methods can be used to develop theoretical probabilities.

ESSENTIAL UNDERSTANDINGS

11-1 You can use multiplication to quickly count the number of ways certain things can happen.

11-2 The probability of an impossible event is 0 (or 0%). The probability of a certain event is 1 (or 100%). Otherwise, the probability of an event is a number between 0 and 1 (or a percent between 0% and 100%).

11-3 To find the probability of two events occurring together, you have to decide whether one event occurring affects the other event.

11-4 Conditional probability exists when two events are dependent.

11-5 You can use probability models to analyze situations and make fair decisions.

11-9 You can use binomial probabilities in situations involving two possible outcomes.

Data Collection and Analysis

BIG idea Sampling techniques are used to gather data from real-world situations. If the data are representative of the larger population, inferences can be made about that population. Biased sampling techniques yield data unlikely to be representative of the larger population. Sets of numerical data are described using measures of central tendency and dispersion.

ESSENTIAL UNDERSTANDINGS

11-6 You can describe and compare sets of data using various statistical measures, depending on what characteristics you want to study.

11-7 Standard deviation is a measure of how far the numbers in a data set deviate from the mean.

11-8 You can get good statistical information about a population by studying a sample of the population.

11-9 You can use binomial probabilities in situations involving two possible outcomes.

11-10 Many common statistics (such as human height, weight, and blood pressure) gathered from samples in the natural world tend to have a *normal distribution* about their mean.

Probability

The probability of an event is a number from 0 to 1 that measures how likely it is for the event to occur. If events are equally likely, then the probability of an event A is

$$P(A) = \frac{\text{number of outcomes in event } A}{\text{total number of outcomes}}.$$

Counting Methods

Counting methods help determine the number of events and the number of outcomes.

- The **Fundamental Counting Principle** states that if event A can happen m ways and event B can happen n ways, then Event A followed by Event B can happen in $m \times n$ ways.

- A **permutation** is an arrangement of items in a particular order. For n items arranged r at a time, $_nP_r = \frac{n!}{(n-r)!}$, where $0 \le r \le n$.

- A **combination** is used if the order of the items is not important. $_nC_r = \frac{n!}{r!(n-r)!}$ for $0 \le r \le n$.

Probability Rules

Independent events have no effect on each other. Events are dependent if they do have an effect.

$P(A \text{ and } B) = P(A) \cdot P(B)$ for independent events.

$P(A \text{ or } B) = P(A) + P(B) - P(A \text{ and } B)$

- For the special case of **mutually exclusive events** (events that cannot happen at the same time), then $P(A \text{ and } B) = 0$.

- Conditional probability is the probability that an event will occur given that another event has already occurred.

- $P(B|A) = \frac{P(A \text{ and } B)}{P(A)}$

Common Errors When Finding Probability

Counting errors occur when students choose the wrong counting formula for a situation. Encourage students to begin a list of items to determine whether they are finding permutations or combinations.

Probability rules are used incorrectly when students do not verify conditions. Require students to state whether events are independent, dependent, or mutually exclusive before applying probability rules.

© Mathematical Practices

Model with mathematics. Make sense of problems and persevere in solving them. Basic probability concepts are introduced and then analyzed in statistical contexts, giving students a quick overview of how the laws of probability predictably govern random behavior.

Using Data

Descriptive Measures

The most common measures used to describe data are measures of central tendency and measures of variation.

Measures of Central Tendency

Measures of central tendency include the **mean, median, and mode.** In a normal distribution, these measures are very similar. However, outliers can cause one measure to better represent the data than another measure. An **outlier** is a value substantially different from the rest of the data.

Example: Which measure of central tendency best represents the data? 78, 82, 95, 80, 14, 91, 88

The mean is about 75.4, median is 82, and there is no mode. The value 14 differs greatly from the other values, so it might be considered an outlier. The outlier causes the mean to be much lower than the median, so the median is a better choice.

Measures of Variation

Measures of variation include the **range, quartiles,** and the **interquartile range (IQR).** Quartiles are the values that separate the data into four parts. The IQR is the difference between Q_3 and Q_1.

Standard deviation is a measure of how far the data values in a set deviate from the mean and is given by the formula $\sigma = \sqrt{\frac{\Sigma(x - \bar{x})^2}{n}}$ where $\bar{x}$ is the mean and n is the number of values.

Gathering Data

A **sample** is a subset of a population. A random sample is most representative of a population because each member has an equal chance of being selected. Due to time and cost restraints, convenience samples, self-selected samples, and systematic samples are often used, although they can introduce bias. **Bias** is a systematic error that results in the sample not being a true representation of the population.

ⓒ Mathematical Practices

Use appropriate tools strategically. Graphing calculators are used sparingly to facilitate statistical computations (mean and standard deviation of larger data sets, box plots, binomial probabilities), but only after students have practiced the algebraic manipulations and counting formulas for small distributions.

Binomial and Normal Distributions

A probability distribution is a function that gives the probability of each outcome in a sample space. Two common types of probability distributions are binomial distributions and normal distributions.

Binomial Experiment

A binomial experiment is characterized by:
- trials with exactly two outcomes (success or failure)
- independent trials (probability remains the same)

The individual probability in a binomial experiment can be calculated using the formula $P(x) = {}_nC_x\, p^x q^{n-x}$.

Example: A coin is flipped 6 times. What is the probability of getting exactly 2 heads?

Answer: The 2 outcomes are heads and tails. The trials are independent; probability is always 50%. The number of trials is 6. So $P(2 \text{ heads}) = {}_6C_2\, 0.5^2 0.5^4 \approx 0.23$.

Binomial Distribution

A binomial distribution is a discrete probability distribution because it has a finite number of possible events, or values. It comes from the individual binomial probabilities.

Normal Distribution

A normal distribution is a continuous probability distribution because its values are in an interval of real numbers. Standard deviation is shown on the normal curve and is used to determine what percent of the population falls within certain values.

Example: The average score on a test is 82 with a standard deviation of 4. In a group of 30 students about how many would you expect to score between 78 and 86?

Answer: This is within one standard deviation so 0.68(30) is about 20 students.

ⓒ Mathematical Practices

Reason abstractly and quantitatively. Look for and make use of structure. The emphasis in this brief introduction to probability and statistics is the importance of probability theory as a model for random behavior in the real world. The model is applied in a variety of familiar contexts, including sampling with binomial and normal distributions.

CHAPTER 11

PROBABILITY AND STATISTICS

Pacing and Assignment Guide

Lesson	Teaching Day(s)	TRADITIONAL Basic	Average	Advanced	BLOCK Block
11-1	1	Problems 1–3 Exs. 9–29, 56–68	Problems 1–3 Exs. 9–29 odd, 56–68	Problems 1–3 Exs. 9–29 odd, 56–68	**Day 1** Problems 1–5 Exs. 9–41 odd, 42–53, 56–68
	2	Problems 4–5 Exs. 30–41, 48–52	Problems 4–5 Exs. 31–41 odd, 42–53	Problems 4–5 Exs. 31–41 odd, 42–55	
11-2	1	Problems 1–3 Exs. 8–22, 37–51	Problems 1–3 Exs. 9–21 odd, 37–51	Problems 1–3 Exs. 9–21 odd, 37–51	**Day 2** Problems 1–5 Exs. 9–27 odd, 28–35, 37–51
	2	Problems 4–5 Exs. 23–28, 31–35	Problems 4–5 Exs. 23–27 odd, 28–35	Problems 4–5 Exs. 23–27 odd, 28–36	
11-3	1	Problems 1–2 Exs. 9–17, 45–62	Problems 1–5 Exs. 9–29 odd, 31–42, 45–62	Problems 1–5 Exs. 9–29 odd, 31–62	**Day 3** Problems 1–5 Exs. 9–29 odd, 31–42, 45–62
	2	Problems 3–5 Exs. 18–37			
11-4	1	Problems 1–4 Exs. 8–26, 34–49	Problems 1–4 Exs. 9–19 odd, 20–31, 34–49	Problems 1–4 Exs. 9–19 odd, 20–49	Problems 1–4 Exs. 9–19 odd, 20–31, 34–49
11-5	1	Problems 1–4 Exs. 6–11, 14–16, 19–26	Problems 1–4 Exs. 7–11 odd, 12–17, 19–26	Problems 1–4 Exs. 7–11 odd, 12–26	**Day 4** Problems 1–4 Exs. 7–11 odd, 12–17, 19–26
11-6	1	Problems 1–5 Exs. 7–23, 25, 30–43	Problems 1–5 Exs. 7–15 odd, 16–27, 30–43	Problems 1–5 Exs. 7–15 odd, 16–43	Problems 1–5 Exs. 7–15 odd, 16–27, 30–43
11-7	1	Problems 1–3 Exs. 6–13, 15, 17, 20, 21, 24–27	Problems 1–3 Exs. 7–13 odd, 14–21, 24–37	Problems 1–3 Exs. 7–13 odd, 14–37	**Day 5** Problems 1–3 Exs. 7–13 odd, 14–21, 24–37
11-8	1	Problems 1–3 Exs. 6–12, 15–19, 23, 26–38	Problems 1–3 Exs. 7–11 odd, 15–19, 21–23, 26–38	Problems 1–3 Exs. 7–11 odd, 16–19, 23, 24, 26–38	Problems 1–3 Exs. 7–11 odd, 15–19, 21–23, 26–38
11-9	1	Problems 1–2 Exs. 8–20, 44–60	Problems 1–2 Exs. 9–19 odd, 44–60	Problems 1–2 Exs. 9–19 odd, 44–60	**Day 6** Problems 1–3 Exs. 9–23 odd, 25–39, 44–60
	2	Problem 3 Exs. 21–27, 35, 38	Problem 3 Exs. 21, 23, 25–39	Problem 3 Exs. 21, 23, 25–43	
11-10	1	Problems 1–2 Exs. 7–14, 34–46	Problems 1–2 Exs. 7–13 odd, 34–46	Problems 1–2 Exs. 7–13 odd, 34–46	**Day 7** Problems 1–3 Exs. 7–17 odd, 18–31, 34–46
	2	Problem 3 Exs. 15–17, 18–22 even, 29, 31	Problem 3 Exs. 15–17 odd, 18–31	Problem 3 Exs. 15–17 odd, 18–33	
Review	1	Chapter 11 Review	Chapter 11 Review	Chapter 11 Review	**Day 8** Chapter 11 Review Chapter 11 Test
Assess	1	Chapter 11 Test	Chapter 11 Test	Chapter 11 Test	
Total		**17 Days**	**16 Days**	**16 Days**	**8 Days**

Resources

	For the Chapter	11-1	11-2	11-3	11-4	11-5	11-6	11-7	11-8	11-9	11-10
Planning											
Teacher Center Online Planner & Grade Book	I	I	I	I	I	I	I	I	I	I	I
Interactive Learning & Guided Instruction											
My Math Video	I										
Solve It!		I M	I M	I M	I M	I M	I M	I M	I M	I M	M
Student Companion		P M	P M	P M	P M	P M	P M	P M	P M	P M	P M
Vocabulary Support		I P M	I P M	I P M	I P M	I P M	I P M	I P M	I P M	I P M	I P M
Got It? Support		I P	I P	I P	I P	I P	I P	I P	I P	I P	I P
Dynamic Activity			I	I					I		
Online Problems		I	I	I	I	I	I	I	I	I	
Additional Problems		M	M	M	M	M	M	M	M	M	M
English Language Learner Support (TR)		E P M	E P M	E P M	E P M	E P M	E P M	E P M	E P M	E P M	E P M
Activities, Games, and Puzzles		E M	E M	E M	E M	E M	E M	E M	E M	E M	E M
Teaching With TI Technology With CD-ROM											
TI-Nspire™ Support CD-ROM		✓	✓	✓	✓	✓	✓	✓	✓	✓	✓
Lesson Check & Practice											
Student Companion		P M	P M	P M	P M	P M	P M	P M	P M	P M	P M
Lesson Check Support		I P	I P	I P	I P	I P	I P	I P	I P	I P	I P
Practice and Problem Solving Workbook		P	P	P	P	P	P	P	P	P	P
Think About a Plan (TR)		E P M	E P M	E P M	E P M	E P M	E P M	E P M	E P M	E P M	E P M
Practice Form G (TR)		E P M	E P M	E P M	E P M	E P M	E P M	E P M	E P M	E P M	E P M
Standardized Test Prep (TR)		P M	P M	P M	P M	P M	P M	P M	P M	P M	P M
Practice *Form K* (TR)		E P M	E P M	E P M	E P M	E P M	E P M	E P M	E P M	E P M	E P M
Extra Practice	E M										
Find the Errors!	M										
Enrichment (TR)		E P M	E P M	E P M	E P M	E P M	E P M	E P M	E P M	E P M	E P M
Answers and Solutions CD-ROM	✓	✓	✓	✓	✓	✓	✓	✓	✓	✓	✓
Assess & Remediate											
ExamView CD-ROM	✓	✓	✓	✓	✓	✓	✓	✓	✓	✓	✓
Lesson Quiz		I M	I M	I M	I M	I M	I M	I M	I M	I M	M
Quizzes and Tests *Form G* (TR)	E P M									E P M	
Quizzes and Tests *Form K* (TR)	E P M									E P M	
Reteaching (TR)		E P M	E P M	E P M	E P M	E P M	E P M	E P M	E P M	E P M	E P M
Performance Tasks (TR)	P M										
Cumulative Review (TR)	P M										
Progress Monitoring Assessments	I P M										

(TR) Available in All-In-One Teaching Resources

1 Interactive Learning

Solve It!

PURPOSE To use counting techniques to determine the number of possible lunches

PROCESS Students may make a list or use a tree diagram to list the possible choices.

FACILITATE

Q Can you begin with a simpler problem? Explain. **[Yes; reduce the number of choices for each menu item and calculate the total number of lunch combinations. There are two combinations with 1 sandwich and 2 sides, four combinations with 2 sandwiches and 2 sides, etc.]**

Q Do you notice a pattern? Explain. **[Yes; the number of lunch combinations is the product of the number of options for each menu item.]**

ANSWER See Solve It in Answers on next page.

CONNECT THE MATH Students develop counting techniques to find the number of lunch combinations in the Solve It. In this lesson, students use the Fundamental Counting Principle, permutations, and combinations to count the number of ways certain events can happen.

2 Guided Instruction

Take Note
VISUAL LEARNERS

It may help students to compare the example in the Take Note to the Solve It. Have them explain what the two situations have in common, and what is different about them.

Here's Why It Works

Have students make a similar tree diagram for the Solve It.

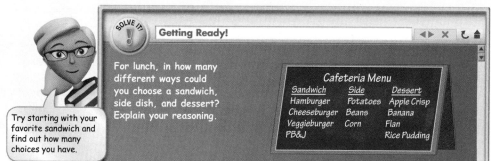

11-1 Permutations and Combinations

© Content Standard
S.CP.9 Use permutations and combinations to compute probabilities of compound events and solve problems.

Objectives To count permutations
To count combinations

Getting Ready!

For lunch, in how many different ways could you choose a sandwich, side dish, and dessert? Explain your reasoning.

Cafeteria Menu		
Sandwich	Side	Dessert
Hamburger	Potatoes	Apple Crisp
Cheeseburger	Beans	Banana
Veggieburger	Corn	Flan
PB&J		Rice Pudding

Try starting with your favorite sandwich and find out how many choices you have.

MATHEMATICAL PRACTICES

Lesson Vocabulary
• Fundamental Counting Principle
• permutation
• n factorial
• combination

It is fairly easy to count the ways you can pick items from a short list. But, sometimes you have so many choices that counting the possibilities is impractical.

Essential Understanding You can use multiplication to quickly count the number of ways certain things can happen.

The **Fundamental Counting Principle** describes the method of using multiplication to count.

> **take note**
>
> **Key Concept**   **Fundamental Counting Principle**
>
> If event M can occur in m ways and is followed by event N that can occur in n ways, then event M followed by event N can occur in $m \cdot n$ ways.
>
> **Example**   3 pants and 2 shirts give $3 \cdot 2 = 6$ possible outfits.

Here's Why It Works Making a tree diagram, you can see that there are 3 groups of 2 outfits, or $3 \cdot 2 = 6$ outfits, starting with the pants.

You can extend the Fundamental Counting Principle to three or more events.

pants 1 — shirt 1 / shirt 2
pants 2 — shirt 1 / shirt 2
pants 3 — shirt 1 / shirt 2

BIG idea Probability

ESSENTIAL UNDERSTANDING

Multiplication can be used to count the number of ways that certain things can happen.

Math Background

This chapter introduces several important counting techniques that are useful in probability, statistics, and combinatorics.

FUNDAMENTAL COUNTING PRINCIPLE

• The number of ways that two or more events can occur is equal to the product of the number of ways each event can occur separately.

NUMBER OF PERMUTATIONS

• Counts the number of ways to order r objects selected from a set of n objects.
• The number of permutations of a set of n items arranged r items at a time is $\frac{n!}{(n-r)!}$ for $0 \leq r \leq n$.

NUMBER OF COMBINATIONS

• Counts the number of ways to choose r items from a set of n items, when the order of the r items does not matter.
• The number of combinations of a set of n items chosen r items at a time is $\frac{n!}{r!(n-r)!}$ for $0 \leq r \leq n$.

The number of permutations is a direct application of the Fundamental Counting Principle. The number of combinations is derived from the number of permutations by dividing by $r!$.

© Mathematical Practice

Attend to precision. Students will state the meaning of the factorial, combination, and permutation symbols, and determine when each is appropriate to a situation.

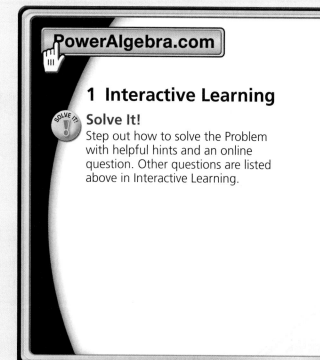

PowerAlgebra.com

1 Interactive Learning

Solve It!

Step out how to solve the Problem with helpful hints and an online question. Other questions are listed above in Interactive Learning.

Problem 1 Using the Fundamental Counting Principle

Motor Vehicles The photos show Maryland license plates in 2004 and 1912. How many more 2004-style license plates were possible than 1912-style plates?

Think

How many digits are in our number system? How many letters are in our alphabet?
There are 10 digits and 26 letters.

For the 2004 license plates, there were places for three letters and three digits. Number of possible 2004 license plates:

$26 \cdot 26 \cdot 26 \cdot 10 \cdot 10 \cdot 10 = 17{,}576{,}000$

For the 1912 license plates, there were places for four digits. Number of possible 1912 license plates:

$10 \cdot 10 \cdot 10 \cdot 10 = 10{,}000$

$17{,}576{,}000 - 10{,}000 = 17{,}566{,}000$ Find the difference.

There were 17,566,000 more 2004-style license plates possible than 1912-style plates.

 Got It? **1.** In 1966, one type of Maryland license plate had two letters followed by four digits. How many of this type of license plate were possible?

A **permutation** is an arrangement of items in a particular order. Suppose you wanted to find the number of ways to order three items. There are 3 ways to choose the first item, 2 ways to choose the second, and 1 way to choose the third. By the Fundamental Counting Principle, there are $3 \cdot 2 \cdot 1 = 6$ permutations.

Using *factorial* notation, you can write $3 \cdot 2 \cdot 1$ as 3!, read "three factorial." For any positive integer n, **n factorial** is $n! = n(n-1) \cdot \ldots \cdot 3 \cdot 2 \cdot 1$. Zero factorial is $0! = 1$.

Plan

What strategy can you use to help you determine the answer?
Act it out and you will see how many options you have at each step.

 Problem 2 Finding the Number of Permutations of n Items

In how many ways can you file 12 folders, one after another, in a drawer?

Use the Fundamental Counting Principle to count the number of permutations of 12 items. There are 12 ways to select the first folder, 11 ways to select the next folder, and so on. The total number of permutations is

$12! = 12 \cdot 11 \cdot \ldots \cdot 2 \cdot 1 = 479{,}001{,}600.$

There are 479,001,600 ways to file 12 folders in a drawer.

 Got It? **2.** In how many ways can you arrange 8 shirts on hangers in a closet?

Sometimes you are interested in the number of permutations possible using all of the objects from a set, but just a few at a time. You can still use the Fundamental Counting Principle or factorial notation.

Problem 1

Q Would the number of possible license plates in 2007 change if the digits were placed in the first three spaces followed by the letters? Explain. **[No; the factors remain the same regardless of the order.]**

Got It?

Q How does the 1966 license plate differ from the 1912 and 2007 license plates? **[The 1912 plate has four digits, the 1966 plate has four digits and two letters, the 2007 plate has one fewer digit but one more letter.]**

Q How can you use the information from Problem 1 to check your answer? **[The 1966 plate should have more possibilities than the 1912 plate but fewer than the 2007 plate.]**

Problem 2   VISUAL LEARNERS

Q If you exchanged the first and second folder in a particular arrangement, would the result be a different permutation of the folders? Explain. **[Yes; two permutations of a set are different if the order of their elements is different.]**

Got It?
To check their work, have students divide their answers into the answer in Problem 2. Discuss why the quotient should equal
$12 \cdot 11 \cdot 10 \cdot 9 = 11{,}880.$

---

2 Guided Instruction

 Each Problem is worked out and supported online.

Problem 1
Using the Fundamental Counting Principle

Problem 2
Finding the Number of Permutations of n Items

Problem 3
Finding $_nP_r$
Animated

Problem 4
Finding $_nC_r$
Animated

Problem 5
Identifying Whether Order is Important
Animated

Support in Algebra 2 Companion
• Vocabulary
• Key Concepts
• Got It?

Answers

Solve It!
48 ways; there are four sandwiches to choose from, three sides, and four desserts; $4 \cdot 3 \cdot 4 = 48$.

Got It?
1. 6,760,000
2. 40,320

Take Note

Q What happens when $r = n$? What is the effect on the formula? **[The formula becomes $\frac{n!}{0!} = \frac{n!}{1} = n!$]**

Q Why must r be less than or equal to n in the formula? **[You cannot order more items than you have.]**

Problem 3

Q How is Method 2 related to Method 1? **[Sample: If you cancel out the common factors in the numerator and denominator in the formula in Method 2, the result is the expression in Method 1.]**

Got It?

Q Is there an advantage to using either the Fundamental Counting Principle or the permutation formula when solving this problem? Explain. **[Sample: using the Fundamental Counting Principle only requires you to multiply three numbers.]**

Take Note

Q What is the difference between the formulas for permutations and combinations? **[The combinations formula has a factor of $r!$ in the denominator.]**

---

take note — Key Concept Number of Permutations

The number of permutations of n items of a set arranged r items at a time is

$$_nP_r = \frac{n!}{(n-r)!} \text{ for } 0 \le r \le n.$$

Example $_{10}P_4 = \frac{10!}{(10-4)!} = \frac{10!}{6!} = 5040$

© Problem 3 Finding $_nP_r$

Track Ten students are in a race. First, second, and third places will win medals. In how many ways can 10 runners finish first, second, and third (no ties allowed)?

Method 1 Use the Fundamental Counting Principle.

$$10 \cdot 9 \cdot 8 = 720$$

Method 2 Use the permutation formula.

There are $n = 10$ runners to arrange taking $r = 3$ at a time.

$_nP_r = \frac{n!}{(n-r)!}$ Use the formula.

$= \frac{10!}{(10-3)!}$ Substitute 10 for n and 3 for r.

$= \frac{10!}{7!} = 720$ Simplify.

There are 720 ways that 10 runners can finish in first, second, and third places.

© **Got It?** **3. a.** In how many ways can 15 runners finish first, second, and third?
     b. Reasoning In Problem 3, is the number of ways for runners to finish first, second, and third the same as the number of ways to finish eighth, ninth, and tenth? Explain.

Suppose in Problem 3 that the first three runners advance to the championship race. In that case, the order in which the first three runners cross the finish line does not matter. A selection in which order does not matter is a **combination**.

As with permutations, you can use a formula to find the number of combinations of n items chosen r at a time.

take note — Key Concept Number of Combinations

The number of combinations of n items of a set chosen r items at a time is

$$_nC_r = \frac{n!}{r!(n-r)!} \text{ for } 0 \le r \le n.$$

Example $_5C_3 = \frac{5!}{3!(5-3)!} = \frac{5!}{3! \cdot 2!} = \frac{120}{6 \cdot 2} = 10$

Plan

If you use the Fundamental Counting Principle, how many numbers will you need to multiply together? You will multiply 3 numbers together to represent the possibilities of finishing first, second, and third.

Additional Problems

1. An old website requires a four-character password consisting of three numbers and one letter. A new website requires a six-character password consisting of three numbers and three letters. How many more passwords can be made for the new website?

ANSWER 17,550,000

2. In how many ways can you arrange nine CDs one after another on a shelf?

ANSWER 362,880

3. In how many ways can a first, second, and third baseman be selected from eight players?

ANSWER 336

4. What is $_{15}C_6$, the number of combinations of 15 items taken six at a time?

ANSWER 5005

5. a. You have 20 songs on your MP3 player. You have time to listen to four of the songs. In how many different ways can you select four songs if order does not matter?

b. A raffle at a school carnival awards prizes of $100, $50, $25, and $10. If 25 raffle tickets are sold, how many different ways can the prizes be distributed?

ANSWERS

a. 4845

b. 303,600

Answers

Got It? (continued)

3. a. 2730

     b. Yes; because $n = 10$ and $r = 3$ in the formula $_nP_r$ for both cases.

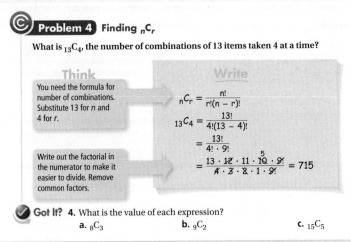

Problem 4 Finding $_nC_r$

What is $_{13}C_4$, the number of combinations of 13 items taken 4 at a time?

Think

You need the formula for number of combinations. Substitute 13 for n and 4 for r.

Write out the factorial in the numerator to make it easier to divide. Remove common factors.

Write

$$_nC_r = \frac{n!}{r!(n-r)!}$$

$$_{13}C_4 = \frac{13!}{4!(13-4)!}$$

$$= \frac{13!}{4! \cdot 9!}$$

$$= \frac{13 \cdot \overset{}{12} \cdot 11 \cdot \overset{5}{10} \cdot 9!}{4 \cdot 3 \cdot 2 \cdot 1 \cdot 9!} = 715$$

✓ Got It? 4. What is the value of each expression?

a. $_8C_3$ b. $_9C_2$ c. $_{15}C_5$

When determining whether to use a permutation or combination, you must decide whether order is important.

Problem 5 Identifying Whether Order Is Important

For each situation, determine whether you should use a permutation or combination. What is the answer to each question?

A A chemistry teacher divides his class into eight groups. Each group submits one drawing of the molecular structure of water. He will select four of the drawings to display. In how many different ways can he select the drawings?

There is no reason why order is important. Use a combination.

$$_nC_r = \frac{n!}{r!(n-r)!}; \qquad _8C_4 = \frac{8!}{4!(8-4)!} = \frac{8 \cdot 7 \cdot 6 \cdot 5 \cdot 4!}{4 \cdot 3 \cdot 2 \cdot 1 \cdot 4!} = 70$$

There are 70 ways to select the drawings.

B You will draw winners from a total of 25 tickets in a raffle. The first ticket wins $100. The second ticket wins $50. The third ticket wins $10. In how many different ways can you draw the three winning tickets?

Values of the tickets depend on the order in which you draw them. Order is important. Use a permutation.

$$_nP_r = \frac{n!}{(n-r)!}; \qquad _{25}P_3 = \frac{25!}{(25-3)!} = \frac{25!}{22!} = 25 \cdot 24 \cdot 23 = 13,800$$

There are 13,800 ways you can draw the winning tickets.

✓ Got It? 5. In Problem 5A, how many ways are possible for the teacher to select and arrange the four drawings from left to right on the wall?

Plan

How will you solve?
If order is important, use the formula $_nP_r = \frac{n!}{(n-r)!}$ and if order is not important, use the formula $_nC_r = \frac{n!}{r!(n-r)!}$.

Problem 4

Q For given values of n and r, are there more combinations or permutations? Explain. **[The number of permutations is greater by a factor of $r!$.]**

Q If $_{13}C_4 = 715$, how can you find $_{13}P_4$ without using a formula? **[The only difference between the formulas is $4!$ in the denominator of $_{13}C_4$. Multiply $715 \times 4! = 17,160$ which equals $_{13}P_4$.]**

Got It?   **ERROR PREVENTION**

Q Is $\frac{15!}{3!}$ equal to 5!? Explain. **[No; $15! = 15 \times 14 \times \ldots \times 2 \times 1$, while $3! = 3 \times 2 \times 1$, so $\frac{15!}{3!}$ equals $15 \times 14 \times \ldots \times 5 \times 4$.]**

Problem 5

Q What is an example of a situation in which order does not matter? **[Sample: In choosing members for a committee, only the final set of members matters. The order in which they are chosen does not matter.]**

Got It?   **ERROR PREVENTION**

Suggest to students that they list a few of the possibilities in each scenario to help them decide whether combinations or permutations should be used. If the order is switched and the outcomes are the same, use combinations. If they are different, use permutations.

4. a. 56
   b. 36
   c. 3003
5. 1680

3 Lesson Check

Do you know HOW? ERROR INTERVENTION

- If students have difficulty with Exercises 1–4, remind them that the only difference between the formulas is a factor of $r!$ in the denominator of a combination.
- For Exercise 5, have students begin making a list by choosing 9 students out of 16 in their class. Ask questions such as "Who is going to bat first?" and "Who is going to bat last?" to help them determine whether combinations or permutations should be used.

Do you UNDERSTAND?

- If students have trouble with Exercise 7, have them substitute numbers for the variables and make $r = n$. Suggest they discuss the meaning in words before determining the meaning of the formula.

Close

> **Q** How are the Fundamental Counting Principle and the formula for permutations related?
> **[The formula for counting permutations is an application of the Fundamental Counting Principle.]**
>
> **Q** Which type of situation requires combinations?
> **[when a certain number of items is chosen from a larger set and order does not matter]**

Lesson Check

Do you know HOW?
Evaluate each expression.

1. $_6P_3$ 2. $_9P_4$ 3. $_5C_2$ 4. $_7C_5$

5. **Sports** How many different nine-player batting orders can be chosen from a baseball team of 16?

Do you UNDERSTAND? MATHEMATICAL PRACTICES

6. **Vocabulary** Explain the difference between permutations and combinations.

7. **Reasoning** Use the definition of permutation to show why $0!$ should equal 1.

8. **Open-Ended** Describe a situation in which the number of outcomes is given by $_9P_2$.

Practice and Problem-Solving Exercises MATHEMATICAL PRACTICES

Ⓐ Practice

9. You have five shirts and four pairs of pants. How many different ways can you arrange your shirts and pants into outfits? ◀ See Problem 1.

10. To create an entry code for a push-button door lock, you need to first choose a letter and then, three single-digit numbers. How many different entry codes can you create?

11. The prom committee has four sites available for the banquet and three sites for the dance. How many arrangements are possible for the banquet and dance?

Evaluate each expression. ◀ See Problem 2.

12. $5!$ 13. $10!$ 14. $13!$ 15. $5!3!$

16. $\frac{12!}{6!}$ 17. $5(4!)$ 18. $\frac{10!}{7!3!}$ 19. $\frac{15!}{10!5!}$

20. **Automobiles** You should rotate tires on a car at regular intervals.
   a. In how many ways can four tires be arranged on a car?
   b. If a spare tire is included, how many arrangements are possible?

Evaluate each expression. ◀ See Problem 3.

21. $_8P_1$ 22. $_8P_2$ 23. $_8P_3$ 24. $_8P_4$

25. $_3P_2$ 26. $_5P_4$ 27. $_9P_6$ 28. $_7P_4$

29. **Scheduling** Fifteen students ask to visit a college admissions counselor. Each scheduled visit includes one student. In how many ways can ten time slots be assigned?

Evaluate each expression. ◀ See Problem 4.

30. $_6C_2$ 31. $_8C_5$ 32. $_4C_4$ 33. $_4C_3$

34. $_7C_3$ 35. $3(_5C_4)$ 36. $_6C_2 + _6C_3$ 37. $\frac{_7C_4}{_9C_4}$

38. **Awards** There are eight swimmers in a competition where the top three swimmers advance. In how many ways can three swimmers advance?

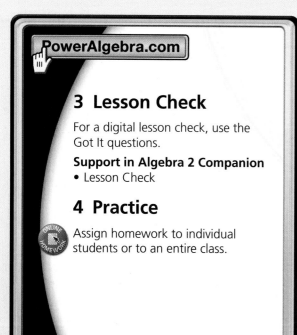

3 Lesson Check

For a digital lesson check, use the Got It questions.

Support in Algebra 2 Companion
- Lesson Check

4 Practice

Assign homework to individual students or to an entire class.

Answers

Lesson Check
1. 120
2. 3024
3. 10
4. 21
5. 4,151,347,200
6. A permutation is an arrangement of items in a particular order; order is important. An arrangement in which order does not matter is a combination.
7. $_nP_r = \frac{n!}{(n-r)!}$; substituting $n = r$, we get $_nP_n = \frac{n!}{(n-n)!} = \frac{n!}{0!}$; but $_nP_n = n! = \frac{n!}{1}$; substituting values again, we get $\frac{n!}{1} = \frac{n!}{(n-n)!}$, and so $0! = 1$.
8. Check students' answers.

Practice and Problem-Solving Exercises
9. 20
10. 26,000
11. 12
12. 120
13. 3,628,800
14. 6,227,020,800
15. 720
16. 665,280
17. 120
18. 120
19. 3003
20. a. 24
    b. 120
21. 8
22. 56
23. 336
24. 1680
25. 6
26. 120
27. 60,480
28. 120
29. 10,897,286,400
30. 15
31. 56
32. 1
33. 4
34. 35
35. 15
36. 35
37. $\frac{5}{18}$
38. 56

For each situation, determine whether to use a permutation or a combination. Then solve the problem.

See Problem 5.

39. How many different teams of 11 players can be chosen from a soccer team of 16?

40. Suppose you find seven equally useful articles related to the topic of your research paper. In how many ways can you choose five articles to read?

41. A salad bar offers eight choices of toppings for a salad. In how many ways can you choose four toppings?

 Apply

Assume *a* and *b* are positive integers. Determine whether each statement is *true* or *false*. If it is true, explain why. If it is false, give a counterexample.

42. $a! + b! = b! + a!$　　　**43.** $a!(b!c!) = (a!b!)c!$　　　**44.** $(a + b)! = a! + b!$

45. $(ab)! = a!b!$　　　**46.** $(a!)! = (a!)^2$　　　**47.** $(a!)^b = a^{(b!)}$

48. Think About a Plan You and your friends are picking up videos at a video store. You have selected 7 videos but will only have time to watch 3 videos together. How many different ways can you select the 3 videos to watch?
 • Does the order in which the videos are selected make a difference?
 • What formula should you use?

49. Security A car door lock has a five-button keypad. Each button has two numerals. The entry code 21914 uses the same button sequence as the code 11023. How many different five-button patterns are possible? You can use a button more than once.

Ⓐ 120　　　Ⓑ 720　　　Ⓒ 3125　　　Ⓓ 5555

50. Consumer Issues A consumer magazine rates televisions by identifying two levels of price, five levels of repair frequency, three levels of features, and two levels of picture quality. How many different ratings are possible?

51. Writing In how many ways is it possible to arrange the two numbers *a* and *b* in an ordered pair? Explain why such a pair is called an *ordered* pair.

52. Reasoning Determine whether the statement $_nC_r = _nP_r$ is *always*, *sometimes*, or *never* true. Explain your reasoning.

53. There are 3!, or 6, arrangements of 3 objects. Consider the number of clockwise arrangements possible for objects placed in a loop, without a beginning or end.

ABC, BCA, and CAB are all parts of one possible clockwise loop arrangement of the letters A, B, and C.

 a. Find the number of clockwise loop arrangements possible for letters A, B, and C.
 b. Use the diagram at the right to help find the number of loop arrangements possible for A, B, C, and D.
 c. Write an expression for the number of clockwise loop arrangements for *n* objects.

ASSIGNMENT GUIDE
Basic: 9–41 all, 48–52
Average: 9–41 odd, 42–53
Advanced: 9–41 odd, 42–55
Standardized Test Prep: 56–60
Mixed Review: 61–68

© **Mathematical Practices** are supported by exercises with red headings. Here are the Practices supported in this lesson:

MP 1: Make Sense of Problems Ex. 48
MP 3: Construct Arguments Ex. 7, 8, 52
MP 3: Communicate Ex. 51, 53, 55

Applications exercises have blue headings. Exercise 29, 50 and 54 support MP 4: Model.

EXERCISE 50: Use the Think About a Plan worksheet in the **Practice and Problem Solving Workbook** (also available in the Teaching Resources in print and online) to further support students' development in becoming independent learners.

HOMEWORK QUICK CHECK
To check students' understanding of key skills and concepts, go over Exercises 9, 39, 48, 50, and 52.

39. combination; 4368

40. combination; 21

41. combination; 70

42. True because of the Comm. Prop. of Add.

43. True because of the Assoc. Prop. of Mult.

44. False; answers may vary. Sample: $(3 + 2)! = 120$ and $3! + 2! = 8$

45. False; answers may vary. Sample: $(3 \cdot 2)! = 6! = 720$ and $3! \cdot 2! = 6 \cdot 2 = 12$

46. False; answers may vary. Sample: $(3!)! = 6! = 720$ and $(3!)^2 = 6^2 = 36$

47. False; answers may vary. Sample: $(3!)^2 = 6^2 = 36$ and $3^{(2!)} = 3^2 = 9$

48. 35

49. C

50. 60

51. Two ways, because order matters.

52. Sometimes; $_nC_r = _nP_r$ when $\dfrac{n!}{r!(n - r)!} = \dfrac{n!}{(n - r)!}$; that is when $r! = 1$, or $r = 1$ or 0.

53. a. 2
 b. 6
 c. $(n - 1)!$

Lesson 11-1　**679**

Answers

Practice and Problem-Solving Exercises (continued)

54. a. 8568

   b. 658,008

55. a. 35

   b. 6

   c. $_7C_3 = \frac{7!}{3!4!}$, so $_7C_3 \cdot 3! = \frac{7!}{4!}$, which is the permutation formula for $_7P_3$.

Standardized Test Prep

56. D

57. H

58. D

59. G

60. [2] $\sum\limits_{n=1}^{\infty}\left(\frac{2}{3}\right)^{n-1} = \frac{1}{1-\frac{2}{3}} = 3$ and $\sum\limits_{n=1}^{\infty}\left(\frac{2}{3}\right)^{n}$

   $= \frac{\frac{2}{3}}{1-\frac{2}{3}} = 2$

   [1] correct sums, without work shown OR only one correct sum

Mixed Review

61. center: (2, 1); vertices: (2, 6), (2, −4); co-vertices: (5, 1), (−1, 1); foci: (2, 5), (2, −3)

62. $(x-1)^2 + (y-1)^2 = 36$ is a circle (not an ellipse) with center (1, 1) and radius 6.

63. $4(x-1)^2$

64. $-(x+3)^2$

65. $3(x-5)(x+5)$

66. 30,240

67. $\frac{4}{5}$

68. 210

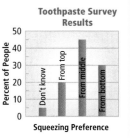

Toothpaste Survey Results

C Challenge **54. Data Analysis** The bar graph at the right shows the results of 40 responses to a survey.

   a. Find the number of possible combinations of five people who squeeze toothpaste from the middle of the tube.

   b. Suppose five people are chosen at random from all the people who responded to the survey. How many combinations of five people are possible?

G **55. a.** In how many ways can you choose three flags from a collection of seven different flags?

   b. In how many different orders can you arrange three flags?

   c. Writing You want to arrange three flags from a group of seven. Explain how you can use $_7C_3 \cdot 3!$ to create the permutation formula.

Standardized Test Prep

SAT/ACT

56. What is the value of $_7C_2$?

   Ⓐ 2520   Ⓑ 49   Ⓒ 42   Ⓓ 21

57. What is the complete solution set of $\frac{3}{x^2-1} + \frac{4x}{x+1} = \frac{1.5}{x-1}$?

   Ⓕ 1, −1   Ⓖ 1, 0.375   Ⓗ 0.375   Ⓘ 0.375, 3

58. Use a calculator to solve $-x^2 - 3x + 7 = 0$. Round to the nearest hundredth.

   Ⓐ −0.76, 4.76   Ⓑ 0.76, 5.76   Ⓒ −1.54, 4.54   Ⓓ −4.54, 1.54

59. What is the center of the circle with equation $(x-5)^2 + (y+1)^2 = 81$?

   Ⓕ (5, 1)   Ⓖ (5, −1)   Ⓗ (−5, 1)   Ⓘ (−5, −1)

Short Response

60. What is the sum of the two infinite series $\sum\limits_{n=1}^{\infty}\left(\frac{2}{3}\right)^{n-1}$ and $\sum\limits_{n=1}^{\infty}\left(\frac{2}{3}\right)^{n}$?

Mixed Review

Identify the center, vertices, and foci for each ellipse.   ◀ See Lesson 10-6.

61. $\frac{(x-2)^2}{9} + \frac{(y-1)^2}{25} = 1$

62. $\frac{(x-1)^2}{49} + \frac{(y-1)^2}{36} = 1$

Factor each expression completely.   ◀ See Lesson 4-4.

63. $4x^2 - 8x + 4$

64. $-x^2 - 6x - 9$

65. $3x^2 - 75$

Get Ready! **To prepare for Lesson 11-2, do Exercises 66–68.**

Simplify each expression.   ◀ See Lesson 11-1.

66. $10 \cdot 9 \cdot 8 \cdot 7 \cdot 6$

67. $\frac{8 \cdot 7 \cdot 5 \cdot 6}{4 \cdot 3 \cdot 2 \cdot 1}$

68. $\frac{7 \cdot 6 \cdot 5 \cdot 4 \cdot 3 \cdot 2 \cdot 1}{4 \cdot 3 \cdot 2 \cdot 1}$

Lesson Resources

Differentiated Remediation

Additional Instructional Support

Algebra 2 Companion

Students can use the **Algebra 2 Companion** worktext (4 pages) as you teach the lesson. Use the Companion to support

- New Vocabulary
- Key Concepts
- Got It for each Problem
- Lesson Check

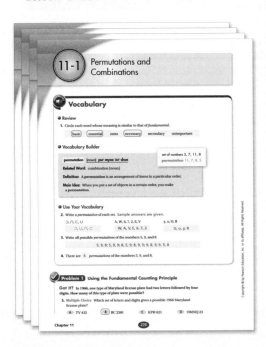

ELL Support

Focus on Language Write the words *permutation*, *combination*, and *order* on the board. Explain to students that *order* refers to how something is arranged. Demonstrate by placing several objects (or people) from tallest to shortest in a line. Then tell students the objects are in order from tallest to shortest. Mix up the objects and tell them the objects are not in order.

Select several students to act out a race. As three students cross the finish line, give them pieces of paper that say first, second, and third. Place the students in order for first, second, and third. Point to the word *permutation* on the board and say: The order matters. Use permutations. Ask students to state the word. Next, have students act out the race again, but give the first three students pieces of paper that say *winner*. Place the students in any order and then switch them around. Point to the word *combination* and say: The order does not matter. Use combinations.

5 Assess & Remediate

Lesson Quiz

1. Students used to have four-digit ID codes. Now ID codes consist of five digits and 1 letter. How many more ID codes are there now than there used to be?

2. In how many ways can you arrange 10 paintings, one after another, on a wall?

3. The drama club has 14 members. Three students are needed to sell tickets, design programs, and handle refreshments. In how many ways can three members be chosen from a group of 14 for tickets, programs, and refreshments?

4. What is $_{15}C_8$, the number of combinations of 15 items taken eight at a time?

5. **Do you UNDERSTAND?** Three students are selected from a class of 12 to be president, vice president, and secretary of the music club. How many ways can these positions be filled?

ANSWERS TO LESSON QUIZ

1. 2,590,000
2. 3,628,800
3. 2184
4. 6435
5. Because the positions are different, the order of the selections matters. This is a permutation, so $_{12}P_3 = 1320$.

A PRESCRIPTION FOR REMEDIATION

Use the student work on the Lesson Quiz to prescribe a differentiated review assignment:

Points	Differentiated Remediation
0–2	Intervention
3–4	On-level
5	Extension

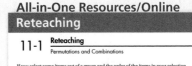

5 Assess & Remediate

Assign the Lesson Quiz. Appropriate intervention, practice, or enrichment is automatically generated based on student performance.

Intervention

- **Reteaching** (2 pages) Provides reteaching and practice exercises for the key lesson concepts. Use with struggling students or absent students.

- **English Language Learner Support** Helps students develop and reinforce mathematical vocabulary and key concepts.

All-in-One Resources/Online
Reteaching

> **11-1 Reteaching**
> Permutations and Combinations
>
> If you select some items out of a group and the order of the items in your selection is important, then your selection is a *permutation* of the items.
>
> For example, suppose Ana, Bob, Cal, and Dan enter a local essay contest. Here are some possible ways for the judges to select the first-prize and second-prize winners.
>
> | First Prize | Second Prize |
> |-------------|--------------|
> | Ana | Bob |
> | Dan | Cal |
> | Bob | Ana |
> | Bob | Dan |
>
> "Ana, Bob" means Ana is first and Bob is second.
> "Bob, Ana" means Bob is first and Ana is second.
> The order of the names in the selection is important. The selection "Ana, Bob" is a *permutation* of the group of contestants.
>
> The number of permutations of *n* items of a set arranged *r* items at a time is
> $$_nP_r = \frac{n!}{(n-r)!}, (0 \le r \le n)$$
>
> **Problem**
>
> In how many ways can the judges select the first-prize and second-prize winners in the essay contest described above?
>
> **Step 1** Is the order of the names in each selection important?
> Yes. "Ana, Bob" is not the same as "Bob, Ana." You are looking for the total number of permutations of 2 items each selected from a group of 4 items.
>
> **Step 2** Describe *n* and *r*.
> There are 4 people in the group of contestants. *n* = 4
> There are 2 people in each selection of prize winners. *r* = 2
>
> **Step 3** Substitute for each variable in the formula.
> $$_nP_r = {_4P_2} = \frac{n!}{(n-r)!} = \frac{4!}{(4-2)!} = \frac{4!}{2!} = \frac{4 \cdot 3 \cdot 2 \cdot 1}{2 \cdot 1} = 12$$
> There are 12 ways for the judges to choose the first-prize and second-prize winners.
>
> **Exercises**
>
> 1. In how many ways can you choose 6 letters for a password from the set A, B, E, L, N, O, S, T, Y? 60,480
>
> 2. In how many ways can a club with 15 members elect a president, vice president, secretary, and treasurer? 32,760
>
> 3. In how many ways can a family of 6 line up in 1 row for a photograph? 720

All-in-One Resources/Online
English Language Learner Support

> **11-1 Additional Vocabulary Support**
> Permutations and Combinations
>
> **Fundamental Counting Principle**
> If event *M* can occur in *m* ways and is followed by event *N* that can occur in *n* ways, then event *M* followed by event *N* can occur in *m* · *n* ways.
>
> **Example** 4 different fruits and 6 different vegetables give 4 · 6 possible fruit and vegetable combinations.
>
> **Solve.**
>
> 1. Hector has 6 computers and 7 printers to choose from. How many possible computer-printer combinations can he make? 42
>
> 2. Raymond and Jasmine have 8 sofas and 14 chairs to choose from. How many possible sofa-chair combinations can they make? 112
>
> **Number of Permutations**
> The number of permutations of *n* items of a set arranged *r* items at a time is
> $$_nP_r = \frac{n!}{(n-r)!} \text{ for } 0 \le r \le n$$
>
> **Example**
> $$_8P_3 = \frac{8!}{(8-3)!} = \frac{8!}{5!} = 336$$
>
> **Evaluate each expression.**
>
> 3. $_7P_4 = $ 840
> 4. $_9P_5 = $ 15,120
>
> **Number of Combinations**
> The number of combinations of *n* items of a set chosen *r* items at a time is
> $$_nC_r = \frac{n!}{r!(n-r)!} \text{ for } 0 \le r \le n$$
>
> **Example**
> $$_7C_3 = \frac{7!}{3!(7-3)!} = \frac{7!}{3! \cdot 4!} = \frac{7!}{6 \cdot 24} = 35$$
>
> **Evaluate each expression.**
>
> 5. $_8C_3 = $ 56
> 6. $_9C_3 = $ 84

Differentiated Remediation *continued*

On-Level

- **Practice** (2 pages) Provides extra practice for each lesson. For simpler practice exercises, use the Form K Practice pages found in the All-in-One Teaching Resources and online.

- **Think About a Plan** Helps students develop specific problem-solving skills and strategies by providing scaffolded guiding questions.

- **Standardized Test Prep** Focuses on all major exercises, all major question types, and helps students prepare for the high-stakes assessments.

Extension

- **Enrichment** Provides students with interesting problems and activities that extend the concepts of the lesson.

- **Activities, Games, and Puzzles** Worksheets that can be used for concepts development, enrichment, and for fun!

Practice and Problem Solving Wkbk/ All-in-One Resources/Online
Practice page 1

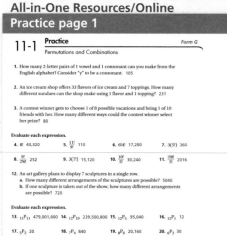

11-1 Practice — Form G
Permutations and Combinations

1. How many 2-letter pairs of 1 vowel and 1 consonant can you make from the English alphabet? Consider "y" to be a consonant. 105

2. An ice cream shop offers 33 flavors of ice cream and 7 toppings. How many different sundaes can the shop make using 1 flavor and 1 topping? 231

3. A contest winner gets to choose 1 of 8 possible vacations and bring 1 of 10 friends with her. How many different ways could the contest winner select her prize? 80

Evaluate each expression.

4. $8!$ 40,320   5. $\frac{11!}{9!}$ 110   6. $6 \cdot 4!$ 17,280   7. $3(5!)$ 360

8. $\frac{9!}{2 \cdot 6!}$ 252   9. $3(7!)$ 15,120   10. $\frac{10!}{5!}$ 30,240   11. $\frac{3!8!}{5!}$ 2016

12. An art gallery plans to display 7 sculptures in a single row.
   a. How many different arrangements of the sculptures are possible? 5040
   b. If one sculpture is taken out of the show, how many different arrangements are possible? 720

Evaluate each expression.

13. $_{12}P_{11}$ 479,001,600   14. $_{12}P_{10}$ 239,500,800   15. $_{12}P_5$ 95,040   16. $_{12}P_1$ 12

17. $_5P_2$ 20   18. $_7P_4$ 840   19. $_8P_6$ 20,160   20. $_6P_2$ 30

21. In how many ways can four distinct positions for a relay race be assigned from a team of nine runners? 3024

Evaluate each expression.

22. $_{12}C_{11}$ 12   23. $_{12}C_{10}$ 66   24. $_{12}C_5$ 792   25. $_{12}C_1$ 12

26. $_{12}C_{12}$ 1   27. $_5C_4 + _5C_3$ 15   28. $\frac{_6C_2}{_4C_2}$ 1   29. $4(_7C_2)$ 84

30. Thirty people apply for 10 job openings as welders. How many different groups of people can be hired? 30,045,015

Practice and Problem Solving Wkbk/ All-in-One Resources/Online
Practice page 2

11-1 Practice (continued) — Form G
Permutations and Combinations

For each situation, determine whether to use a permutation or a combination. Then solve the problem.

31. You draw the names of 5 raffle winners from a basket of 50 names. Each person wins the same prize. How many different groups of winners could you draw? combination: 2,118,760

32. A paint store offers 15 different shades of blue. How many different ways could you purchase 3 shades of blue? combination: 455

33. How many different 5-letter codes can you make from the letters in the word *cipher*? permutation: 720

Assume a and b are positive integers. Determine whether each statement is *true* or *false*. If it is true, explain why. If it is false, give a counterexample.

34. $a!b! = b!a!$ True; Commutative Property of Multiplication
35. $(a^2)! = (a!)^2$ False; let $a = 2$: $(2^2)! = 24$; $(2!)^2 = 4$
36. $a \cdot b! = (ab)!$ False; let $a = 2$ and $b = 3$: $2 \cdot 3! = 12$; $(2 \cdot 3)! = 720$
37. $(a + 0)! = a!$ True; Identity Property of Addition
38. $\frac{a!}{b!} = \left(\frac{a}{b}\right)!$ False; let $a = 4$ and $b = 2$: $\frac{4!}{2!} = \frac{24}{2} = 12$; $\left(\frac{4}{2}\right)! = 2!$ = 2
39. $a!(b! + c!) = a!b! + a!c!$ True; Distributive Property
40. A restaurant offers a fixed-priced meal of 1 appetizer, 1 entrée, 2 sides, and 1 dessert. How many different meals could you choose from 4 appetizers, 5 entrees, 8 sides, and 3 desserts? 1680

41. **Writing** Explain the difference between a permutation and a combination. Answers may vary. Sample: If you choose r items from a group of n items and the order in which the items are chosen is important, then it is a permutation. If the order does not matter, then it is a combination.

42. **Reasoning** Show that for $n = r$, the value of $_nC_r = 1$.
$$_nC_n = \frac{n!}{n!(n-n)!} = \frac{n!}{n!0!} = \frac{n!}{n!(1)} = 1$$

All-in-One Resources/Online
Enrichment

11-1 Enrichment
Permutations and Combinations

Dinner at a Chinese Restaurant

A typical Chinese restaurant will often feature a Special Dinner, in which the customer has the choice of ordering one appetizer and one entree.

1. If there are 8 appetizers and 11 entrees, how many different Special Dinners are there? 88

2. If there are 12 appetizers and 7 entrees, how many different Special Dinners are there? 84

3. If there are A appetizers and E entrees, how many different Special Dinners are there? AE

4. There are 12 appetizers; 4 are soups; 6 contain meat, and 2 do not. In how many different orders can 3 different appetizers be brought to the table? 1320

5. In how many different orders can 5 different appetizers of the 12 be brought to the table? 95,040

6. Do Exercises 1–5 involve permutations or combinations? permutations

7. Assume that 3 customers arrive and order different appetizers to share from a choice of 12 appetizers.
   a. Does this problem involve permutations or combinations? combinations
   b. Why? order doesn't matter
   c. In how many possible ways can this be done? $_{12}C_3 = 220$

8. Suppose that 5 customers arrive, and each orders a different appetizer to share from a choice of 12 appetizers. In how many ways can this be done? $_{12}C_5 = 792$

9. Suppose that 7 customers arrive, and each orders a different appetizer to share from a choice of 12 appetizers.
   a. In how many ways can this be done? $_{12}C_7 = 792$
   b. Why is this answer the same as the number of ways that 5 customers can order different appetizers? $_nC_r = _nC_{n-r}$ or $_{12}C_5 = _{12}C_7$

Practice and Problem Solving Wkbk/ All-in-One Resources/Online
Think About a Plan

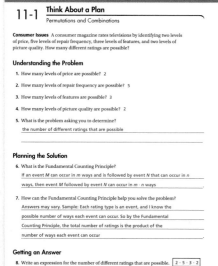

11-1 Think About a Plan
Permutations and Combinations

Consumer Issues A consumer magazine rates televisions by identifying two levels of price, five levels of repair frequency, three levels of features, and two levels of picture quality. How many different ratings are possible?

Understanding the Problem

1. How many levels of price are possible? 2
2. How many levels of repair frequency are possible? 5
3. How many levels of features are possible? 3
4. How many levels of picture quality are possible? 2
5. What is the problem asking you to determine?
   the number of different ratings that are possible

Planning the Solution

6. What is the Fundamental Counting Principle?
   If an event M can occur in m ways and is followed by event N that can occur in n ways, then event M followed by event N can occur in $m \cdot n$ ways

7. How can the Fundamental Counting Principle help you solve the problem?
   Answers may vary. Sample: Each rating type is an event, and I know the possible number of ways each event can occur. So by the Fundamental Counting Principle, the total number of ratings is the product of the number of ways each event can occur

Getting an Answer

8. Write an expression for the number of different ratings that are possible. $2 \cdot 5 \cdot 3 \cdot 2$

9. How many different ratings are possible? 60

Practice and Problem Solving Wkbk/ All-in-One Resources/Online
Standardized Test Prep

11-1 Standardized Test Prep
Permutations and Combinations

Multiple Choice

For Exercises 1–5, choose the correct letter.

1. You choose 5 apples from a case of 24 apples. Which best represents the number of ways you can make your selection? B
   A $_5C_{19}$ B $_{24}C_5$ C $_5P_{24}$ D $_{19}P_5$

2. Which is equivalent to $_7P_3$? H
   F 28   G 35   H 210   I 840

3. A traveler can choose from three airlines, five hotels, and four rental car companies. How many arrangements of these services are possible? B
   A 12   B 60   C 220   D 495

4. Which is equivalent to $a!(b!)$? I
   F $(ab)!$ G $(ab!)!$ H $b \cdot a!$ I $b!(a!)$

5. Which is equivalent to $_9C_3$? A
   A 126   B 3024   C 15,120   D 45,000

Short Response

6. You have a $1 bill, a $5 bill, a $10 bill, a $20 bill, a quarter, a dime, a nickel, and a penny. How many different total amounts can you make by choosing 6 bills and coins? Show your work.
[2] $_8C_6 = \frac{8!}{6!8 - 6!}$
$= \frac{8 \cdot 7 \cdot 6 \cdot 5 \cdot 4 \cdot 3 \cdot 2 \cdot 1}{(6 \cdot 5 \cdot 4 \cdot 3 \cdot 2 \cdot 1)(2 \cdot 1)}$
$= \frac{56}{2}$
$= 28$
[1] incorrect or incomplete work shown
[0] incorrect answer and no work shown OR no answer given

Online Teacher Resource Center
Activities, Games, and Puzzles

11-1 Activity: Word Analysis
Permutations and Combinations

This activity is for groups of two to four students. Parts A and B should be done as a group and Part C should be done individually. Your teacher will determine whether or not you use a calculator.

Part A

1. Find the number of distinct three-letter combinations of the letters that make up the word COMBINE. 35
2. Find the number of distinct three-letter permutations of the letters that make up the word COMBINE. 210
3. Which of these two values is larger? Explain. Support your answer with numbers and actual examples from the word COMBINE.
   Permutations; order matters, and for each three-letter combination, there are six distinct orderings: $35 \cdot 6 = 210$; for example: COM → COM, CMO, OCM, OMC, MCO, and MOC.

Part B

4. Find the number of distinct three-letter combinations of the letters that make up the word PERMUTE. 20
5. Find the number of distinct three-letter permutations of the letters that make up the word PERMUTE. 120
6. How does Part B differ from Part A? Explain what you had to do to resolve the difference. The letter E appears twice in the word PERMUTE. For uniqueness, we can only consider six letters.
7. Write the statement for Part B that parallels $35 \cdot 6 = 210$ from Part A. $20 \cdot 6 = 120$

Part C

Using the letters in your first, middle, and last names, find the following:

8. The number of distinct four-letter combinations. Check students' work.
9. The number of distinct five-letter permutations. Check students' work.
10. Try to find two English words of four or more letters using the distinct letters in your name. Check students' work.

Bonus: How many of the four-letter combinations from Exercise 8 contain a vowel? Check students' work.

11-2 Probability

Objective To find the probability of an event using theoretical, experimental, and simulation methods

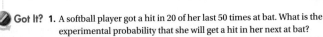

Getting Ready!   ◀▶ ✕ ↻ ⬆

In a probability experiment, you fold an index card slightly off center, as shown at the right. Then you drop the card from a height of several feet. What outcomes are possible? Which do you think is most likely to occur? Explain your reasoning.

Try it out! Find out if the results agree with your prediction.

© **MATHEMATICAL PRACTICES** Probability measures how likely it is for an event to occur.

Essential Understanding The probability of an impossible event is 0 (or 0%). The probability of a certain event is 1 (or 100%). Otherwise, the probability of an event is a number between 0 and 1 (or a percent between 0% and 100%).

When you gather data from observations, you can calculate an *experimental probability*. Each observation is an experiment or a trial.

Lesson Vocabulary
• experimental probability
• simulation
• sample space
• equally likely outcomes
• theoretical probability

Key Concept   Experimental Probability

experimental probability of event: $P(\text{event}) = \dfrac{\text{number of times the event occurs}}{\text{number of trials}}$

© **Problem 1** Finding Experimental Probability

Gridded Response Of the 60 vehicles in a teachers' parking lot today, 15 are pickup trucks. What is the experimental probability that a vehicle in the lot is a pickup truck?

$P(\text{pickup truck}) = \dfrac{\text{number of pickup trucks}}{\text{number of vehicles}} = \dfrac{15}{60} = 0.25$, or 25%

The probability that a vehicle in the lot is a pickup truck is 0.25.

Think
What is a trial? What is an event?
A trial is selecting a vehicle parking in the lot. An event is the vehicle you select being a truck.

✓ **Got It?** 1. A softball player got a hit in 20 of her last 50 times at bat. What is the experimental probability that she will get a hit in her next at bat?

PowerAlgebra.com   Lesson 11-2 Probability   681

---

1 Interactive Learning

Solve It!
PURPOSE To use different strategies to determine the number of possible outcomes
PROCESS Students may replicate the experiment by dropping an index card to determine the possible outcomes or visualize and list the possible outcomes.

FACILITATE
Q What type of outcome is not possible when dropping the index card? **[Sample: The card will not land on a single corner.]**
Q Is it possible to find all possible outcomes? Explain. **[No; although the card can land on different sides, you could also look at the possible orientations of the folded edge.]**

ANSWER See Solve It in Answers on next page.
CONNECT THE MATH Students determine possible outcomes in the Solve It. In this lesson, students find probability using different methods.

2 Guided Instruction

Take Note
Experimental probability is often called *empirical probability*.

Problem 1

Q If the experimental probability was 0%, can you conclude that no teachers ever drive pickup trucks to school? Explain. **[No; 0% means there were no trucks that day.]**

Got It?

Q What is the trial? the event? **[an at bat; a hit]**

11-2 Preparing to Teach

BIG idea Probability

ESSENTIAL UNDERSTANDINGS
• The probability, p, of an event is a number such that $0 \le p \le 1$.
• The probability of an impossible event is 0.
• The probability of a certain event is 1.

Math Background
The probability of an event (experimental or theoretical) is never less than zero or more than one. The experimental probability of an event found using a number of trials or a simulation may differ from the theoretical probability because of randomness. As the number of trials increases, the experimental probability will approach the theoretical probability.

Experimental Probability is determined by dividing the number of times the event occurred by the total number of trials.

Data is gathered from actual trials or a simulation.
Theoretical Probability is determined by dividing the number of outcomes in which an event occurs by the total number of outcomes. It can be used to predict the experimental probability.

Geometric Probability is a type of theoretical probability involved in geometry problems involving length, area, or volume.

© **Mathematical Practices**
Attend to precision. In a study of probability, students will define and calculate experimental probability.

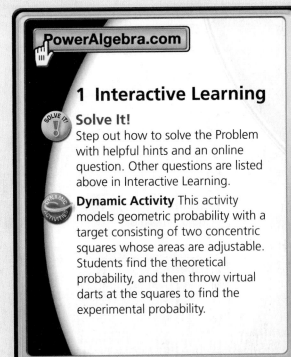

PowerAlgebra.com

1 Interactive Learning

Solve It!
Step out how to solve the Problem with helpful hints and an online question. Other questions are listed above in Interactive Learning.

Dynamic Activity This activity models geometric probability with a target consisting of two concentric squares whose areas are adjustable. Students find the theoretical probability, and then throw virtual darts at the squares to find the experimental probability.

Lesson 11-2   681

Problem 2
ERROR PREVENTION

Q Can other digits be chosen for the simulation? Explain. **[Yes, as long as one digit represents the correct answer and three represent the wrong answer. For example, 5, 6, 7, 8 where 7 represents the correct answer.]**

Q How could you answer this question using experimental probability without a calculator? **[Sample: Use 3 red marbles (wrong answer) and 1 blue marble (correct answer). Randomly select a marble 10 times to determine the number of correct answers. Repeat 20 times.]**

SYNTHESIZING

Students re-creating the simulation may find that none of their tests have six or more correct answers. They might conclude the probability of passing is 0%, although they intuitively know the probability is more than 0%. Explain that simulation and experimental probability yield better results with more trials.

Got It?
EXTENSION

Q How does the simulation change if the passing score is 50% or better? How does it stay the same? **[The digits and number of trials stay the same. The passing test must consist of five or more 1's.]**

Sometimes actual trials are difficult or unreasonable to conduct. In these situations, you can estimate the experimental probability of an event by using a simulation. A **simulation** is a model of the event.

Dynamic Activity
Geometric Probability

Problem 2 Using a Simulation

Testing On a multiple-choice test, each item has 4 choices, but only one choice is correct. How can you simulate guessing the answers? What is the probability that you will pass the test by guessing at least 6 of 10 answers correctly?

Plan

How do you simulate guessing one out of four?
You can pick at random from four numbers, specifying that one of them will be the "correct" answer.

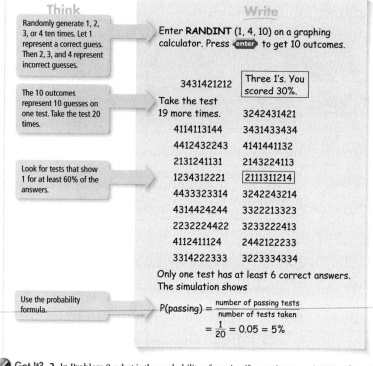

Think

Randomly generate 1, 2, 3, or 4 ten times. Let 1 represent a correct guess. Then 2, 3, and 4 represent incorrect guesses.

The 10 outcomes represent 10 guesses on one test. Take the test 20 times.

Look for tests that show 1 for at least 60% of the answers.

Use the probability formula.

Write

Enter **RANDINT** (1, 4, 10) on a graphing calculator. Press **enter** to get 10 outcomes.

3431421212   *Three 1's. You scored 30%.*

Take the test 19 more times.   3242431421
4114113144   3431433434
4412432243   4141441132
2131241131   2143224113
1234312221   2111311214
4433323314   3242243214
4314424244   3322213323
2232224422   3233222413
4112411124   2442122233
3314222333   3223334334

Only one test has at least 6 correct answers. The simulation shows

$$P(passing) = \frac{number\ of\ passing\ tests}{number\ of\ tests\ taken}$$
$$= \frac{1}{20} = 0.05 = 5\%$$

Got It? 2. In Problem 2, what is the probability of passing if a passing score is 50% or better?

The set of all possible outcomes to an experiment or activity is a **sample space**. When each outcome in a sample space has the same chance of occurring, the outcomes are **equally likely outcomes**.

For one roll of a standard number cube, there are six equally likely outcomes in the sample space. You can calculate *theoretical probability* as a ratio of outcomes.

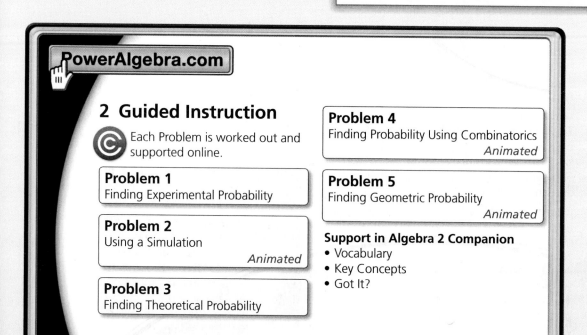

PowerAlgebra.com

2 Guided Instruction

Each Problem is worked out and supported online.

Problem 1
Finding Experimental Probability

Problem 2
Using a Simulation
Animated

Problem 3
Finding Theoretical Probability

Problem 4
Finding Probability Using Combinatorics
Animated

Problem 5
Finding Geometric Probability
Animated

Support in Algebra 2 Companion
• Vocabulary
• Key Concepts
• Got It?

Answers

Solve It!
The index card can fall in various ways, such as on its longer side, shorter side, back, front, like a tent or on one edge, on its top or bottom side.
Answers may vary. Sample: Most likely, the index card will fall on its back, since it has a greater area than any of the other possibilities.

Got It?
1. 0.40, or 40%
2. 0.20, or 20%

Key Concept — Theoretical Probability

If a sample space has n equally likely outcomes and an event A occurs in m of these outcomes, then the **theoretical probability** of event A is $P(A) = \frac{m}{n}$.

Sample space: n outcomes

Event A: m outcomes

© Problem 3 — Finding Theoretical Probability

What is the theoretical probability of each event?

Ⓐ getting a 5 on one roll of a standard number cube

There are six equally likely outcomes, 1, 2, 3, 4, 5, and 6. The number 5 occurs one way.

$$P(5) = \frac{1}{6}$$

Ⓑ getting a sum of 5 on one roll of two standard number cubes

There are 36 possible equally likely outcomes. The favorable outcomes are those with a sum of 5.

$$P(\text{sum } 5) = \frac{4}{36} = \frac{1}{9}$$

✓ Got It? 3. a. What is the theoretical probability of getting a sum that is an odd number on one roll of two standard number cubes?

© b. Reasoning Without calculating the probability, is it more likely to get an even or odd number on one roll of a standard number cube? Explain.

Plan

How many outcomes are there?
Each cube has six numbers on it, so there are $6 \cdot 6 = 36$ outcomes.

It can be easier to use *combinatorics* to find theoretical probability rather than listing and counting all the equally likely outcomes. Combinatorics include the Fundamental Counting Principle, and ways to count permutations and combinations.

© Problem 4 — Finding Probability Using Combinatorics

What is the theoretical probability of being dealt exactly two 7's in a 5-card hand from a standard 52-card deck?

A standard 52-card deck has 4 suits; hearts, diamonds, clubs, and spades. Each suit contains cards numbered 2 though 10, and an ace, jack, queen, and king.

The number of combinations of two 7's from four 7's $= {}_4C_2$.

The number of combinations of 3 non-sevens from 48 other cards $= {}_{48}C_3$.

The number of 5-card hands with two 7's $= {}_4C_2 \cdot {}_{48}C_3$.

The number of possible 5-card hands $= {}_{52}C_5$.

$$P(\text{hand with two 7's}) = \frac{{}_4C_2 \cdot {}_{48}C_3}{{}_{52}C_5} = \frac{103{,}776}{2{,}598{,}960} \approx 0.0399, \text{ or about 4\%}.$$

Think

Should you use permutations or combinations?
Order does not matter. Use combinations.

Take Note

Help students understand the difference between experimental probability and theoretical probability by discussing coin flips. The experimental probability of a coin landing heads is found by flipping a coin many times and recording whether it lands heads or tails. The theoretical probability of a coin landing heads is found by knowing there are two equally likely outcomes, one of which is heads.

Problem 3

Q How can you be sure the sample space consists of equally likely outcomes? [The problem states the number cube is fair. A fair number cube is one in which each side has an equal probability of occurring.]

Got It?

Q What information about summing to odd numbers can help you find the possible favorable outcomes? [The sum of two even numbers is even. The sum of two odd numbers is even. Count only the sums of even and odd numbers.]

Problem 4

Q Why is it necessary to count the number of combinations of three non-seven cards? [Being dealt exactly two 7's means you must also have exactly three non-sevens. Multiply the number of ways to choose 7's by the number of ways to choose non-sevens.]

Additional Problems

1. You observe 119 animals at a zoo, 19 of them have wings. What is the experimental probability that an animal at this zoo has wings?

ANSWER 0.16

2. On a multiple-choice test, each item has three choices, but only one choice is correct. How can you simulate guessing the answers? What is the probability that you will pass the test by guessing at least five of ten answers correctly?

ANSWER Sample: Use digit 1 to represent the correct answer and digits 2 and 3 to represent incorrect answers. Randomly generate 10 numbers, at least 20 times to find the experimental probability of getting at least five 1's, passing the test. Answers may vary. Students' simulation should show approximately 21.3%.

3. What is the theoretical probability of each event?

a. getting a number less than 3 on one roll of a fair number cube

b. getting a sum that is a multiple of 4 on one roll of two fair number cubes

ANSWERS

a. $\frac{1}{3}$ **b.** $\frac{1}{4}$

4. What is the theoretical probability of being dealt exactly three 8's in a 5-card hand from a standard 52-card deck?

ANSWER about 0.0017 or about 0.17%

5. A carnival game consists of throwing darts at a circular board as shown. What is the geometric probability that a dart thrown at random will hit the shaded circle?

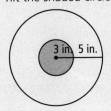

3 in.   5 in.

ANSWER about 14%

Answers

Got It? (continued)

3. a. $\frac{1}{2}$

   b. The likelihood of getting an even or odd is the same, i.e. $\frac{1}{2}$.

Got It?

Q What is the meaning of the denominator when determining this probability? **[The denominator is the sample space or all the possible outcomes. It is all the possible ways to get five cards in a deck of 52.]**

Q How is the Fundamental Counting Principle used to find the probability in this problem? **[The numerator is the number of ways to get four 7's times the number of ways to get one non-seven.]**

Problem 5

"At random" in this problem means that the probability of the ball being thrown to a certain point in the strike zone is the same as the probability of the ball being thrown to any other point in the strike zone.

Q What is the probability that a baseball thrown at random in the strike zone will NOT be in the high-inside strike zone? Explain. **[The probability of not being in that area is 1 − 0.064 or 0.936 which is 93.6%.]**

Q How is area related to sample space? **[Sample space is the set of all possible outcomes. The area can be thought of as the set of all possible points.]**

Got It?

VISUAL LEARNERS

Q If the low inside strike zone is the same area as a high inside strike zone, will the probabilities be different? Explain. **[No; it does not matter where in the total area the event area occurs. If the areas of the different events are the same, the probabilities will be the same.]**

 Got It? 4. What is the theoretical probability of being dealt all four 7's in a 5-card hand?

Sometimes you can use areas to find a theoretical probability.

 Problem 5 Finding Geometric Probability

Geometry A batter's strike zone depends on the height and stance of the batter. What is the geometric probability that a baseball thrown at random within the batter's strike zone, as shown in the figure below, will be a high-inside strike (one of the hardest pitches to hit)?

Think
What are the favorable outcomes? All outcomes?
Favorable outcomes are points in the high-inside region. All outcomes are points in the strike zone.

$$P(\text{high-inside strike}) = \frac{\text{area of high-inside strike zone}}{\text{area of total strike zone}}$$

$$= \frac{4 \cdot 6}{17 \cdot 22}$$

$$\approx 0.064$$

For a baseball thrown at random in the batter's strike zone, the probability that it will be a high-inside strike is about 6.4%.

 Got It? 5. Suppose a batter's strike zone is 15 in.-by-20 in. and the high-inside strike zone is 3 in.-by-5 in. What is the probability that a baseball thrown at random within the strike zone will be a high-inside strike?

Answers

Got It? (continued)

4. $\frac{48}{2,598,960}$ or 0.0000184689 or ≈0.00185%

5. 0.05 or 5%

Lesson Check

Do you know HOW?

1. What is the experimental probability a quarterback will complete his next pass if he has completed 30 of his last 40 passes?

2. What is the experimental probability a quarterback will complete his next pass if he has completed 36 of his last 45 passes?

Find the theoretical probability of each event when rolling a standard number cube.

3. $P(3)$

4. $P(2 \text{ or } 4)$

Do you UNDERSTAND? MATHEMATICAL PRACTICES

5. **Vocabulary** Explain the difference between experimental probability, theoretical probability, and geometric probability.

6. **Writing** Describe three ways you could simulate answering a true-false question.

7. **Reasoning** Why is a simulation better the more times you perform it?

 Practice and Problem-Solving Exercises MATHEMATICAL PRACTICES

Practice

8. A class tossed coins and recorded 161 heads and 179 tails. What is the experimental probability of heads? Of tails?

◆ See Problem 1.

9. Another class rolled number cubes. Their results are shown in the table. What is the experimental probability of rolling each number?

Number	1	2	3	4	5	6
Occurrences	42	44	45	44	47	46

Graphing Calculator For Exercises 10–12, define a simulation by telling how you represent correct answers, incorrect answers, and the quiz. Use your simulation to find each experimental probability.

◆ See Problem 2.

10. If you guess the answers at random, what is the probability of getting at least two correct answers on a five-question true-or-false quiz?

11. If you guess the answers at random, what is the probability of getting at least three correct answers on a five-question true-or-false quiz?

12. A five-question multiple-choice quiz has five choices for each answer. What is the probability of correctly guessing at random exactly one correct answer? Exactly two correct answers? Exactly three correct answers? (*Hint:* You could let any two digits represent correct answers, and the other digits represent wrong answers.)

A jar contains 30 red marbles, 50 blue marbles, and 20 white marbles. You pick one marble from the jar at random. Find each theoretical probability.

◆ See Problem 3.

13. $P(\text{red})$

14. $P(\text{blue})$

15. $P(\text{not white})$

16. $P(\text{red or blue})$

---

3 Lesson Check

Do you know HOW?   ERROR INTERVENTION

• If students have difficulty solving Exercises 1–2, remind them they must determine which number represents the event and which number represents the number of trials.

Do you UNDERSTAND?

• If students have trouble with Exercise 7, have them find the probability in Problem 2 using only the first 5 trials. Point out that using fewer trials does not allow as many possibilities to occur.

Close

Q When might you choose to use experimental probability rather than theoretical probability? Give an example. **[when you do not know the sample space; example: determining the most common color of marble in a bag of marbles when you are unaware of the total number or colors]**

Q What are the maximum and minimum values of a probability? Explain. **[1; 0; the probability of an event is a number between 0 and 1 inclusive.]**

Lesson Check

1. 0.75, or 75%
2. 0.80, or 80%
3. $\frac{1}{6}$
4. $\frac{1}{3}$

5. Experimental probabilities are calculated on the basis of data from an experiment, actual or simulated. Given equally likely outcomes, the basis for calculating theoretical probability is being able to determine the no. of ways that an event can occur within these outcomes. Comparisons of measures such as length and area are the basis of geometric probability.

6. Answers may vary. Samples: Flip a coin; generate random numbers on a calculator; roll a die with odd numbers as true and even numbers as false.

7. Because you are averaging over more samples, you are getting a more accurate average.

Practice and Problem-Solving Exercises

8. $\frac{161}{340} \approx 47\%; \frac{179}{340} \approx 53\%$

9. the number 1: $\frac{21}{134} \approx 15.7\%$;
   the number 2: $\frac{11}{67} \approx 16.4\%$;
   the number 3: $\frac{45}{268} \approx 16.8\%$;
   the number 4: $\frac{11}{67} \approx 16.4\%$;
   the number 5: $\frac{47}{268} \approx 17.5\%$;
   the number 6: $\frac{23}{134} \approx 17.2\%$

10. Sample: Generate random numbers between 0 and 1 using a graphing calculator. Examine the first five digits of each random number. Let even digits represent correct answers and odd digits incorrect answers. If there are two or more even digits, make a tally mark for that number. The total number of tally marks for 100 numbers, as a percent, gives the experimental probability. The simulated probability should be about 0.8.

11–16. See next page.

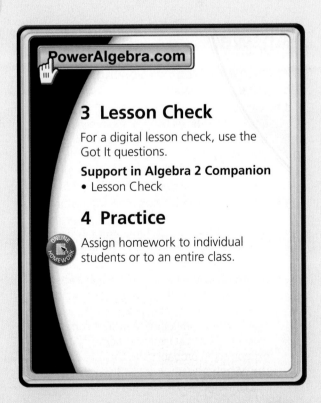

PowerAlgebra.com

3 Lesson Check

For a digital lesson check, use the Got It questions.

Support in Algebra 2 Companion
• Lesson Check

4 Practice

Assign homework to individual students or to an entire class.

4 Practice

ASSIGNMENT GUIDE

Basic: 8–28, 31–35

Average: 9–27 odd, 28–35

Advanced: 9–27 odd, 28–36

Standardized Test Prep: 37–41

Mixed Review: 42–51

Ⓒ **Mathematical Practices** are supported by exercises with red headings. Here are the Practices supported in this lesson:

MP 1: Make Sense of Problems Ex. 28

MP 3: Construct Arguments Ex. 7, 34a

MP 3: Communicate Ex. 6, 34a, 35

MP 5: Use Appropriate Tools Ex. 10–12

Applications exercises have blue headings. Exercises 23 and 33 support MP 4: Model.

EXERCISE 33: Use the Think About a Plan worksheet in the **Practice and Problem Solving Workbook** (also available in the Teaching Resources in print and online) to further support students' development in becoming independent learners.

HOMEWORK QUICK CHECK

To check students' understanding of key skills and concepts, go over Exercises 9, 15, 28, 33, and 35.

A bag contains 36 red blocks, 48 green blocks, 22 yellow blocks, and 19 purple blocks. You pick one block from the bag at random. Find each theoretical probability.

17. P(green) **18.** P(purple) **19.** P(not yellow)

20. P(green or yellow) **21.** P(yellow or not green) **22.** P(purple or not red)

23. Games A group of 30 students from your school is part of the audience for a TV game show. The total number of people in the audience is 150. What is the theoretical probability of 3 students from your school being selected as contestants out of 9 possible contestant spots?   ◀ See Problem 4.

Geometry Suppose that a dart lands at random on the dartboard shown at the right. Find each theoretical probability.   ◀ See Problem 5.

24. The dart lands in the bull's-eye.

25. The dart lands in a green region.

26. The dart scores at least 10 points.

27. The dart scores less than 10 points.

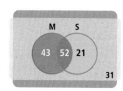

Width of each ring = r.

Ⓑ Apply Ⓒ **28. Think About a Plan** Suppose you roll two standard number cubes. What is the theoretical probability of getting a sum of 7?
- What is the sample space?
- How many outcomes are there?

In a class of 147 students, 95 are taking math (M), 73 are taking science (S), and 52 are taking both math and science. One student is picked at random. Find each probability.

29. P(taking math or science or both)

30. P(not taking math)

31. P(taking math but not science)

32. P(taking neither math nor science)

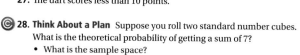

33. Lottery A lottery has 53 numbers from which five are drawn at random. Each number can only be drawn once. What is the probability of your lottery ticket matching all five numbers in any order?

Ⓒ **34. a. Sports** Out of four games, team A has won one game and team B has won three games in a championship series. What is the experimental probability that team A wins the next game? That team B wins the next game?

b. Reasoning Do you think that experimental probability is a good predictor of the winner of the next game? Explain.

Ⓒ **35. Writing** Explain what you would need to know to determine the theoretical probability of a five-digit postal ZIP code ending in 1.

Answers

Practice and Problem-Solving Exercises (continued)

11. Answers may vary. Sample: Toss 5 coins. Keep a tally of the times three or more heads are tossed. (A head represents a correct answer.) Do this 100 times. The total number of tally marks, as a percent, gives the experimental probability. The simulated probability should be about 50%.

12. Answers may vary. Sample: Randomly generate a 1, 2, 3, 4, or 5 five times. Let 1 represent a correct guess and 2–5 represent incorrect guesses. Tally the recorded numbers with exactly one digit that represents a correct answer. Tally the recorded numbers with exactly two digits that represent correct answers. Tally the recorded numbers with exactly three digits that represent correct answers. The tally totals, as percents, give the experimental probabilities. They should be in the neighborhood of 40%, 20%, and 5%, respectively.

13. $\frac{3}{10}$, or 30%

14. $\frac{1}{2}$, or 50%

15. $\frac{4}{5}$, or 80%

16. $\frac{4}{5}$, or 80%

17. $\frac{48}{125}$, or 38.4%

18. $\frac{19}{125}$, or 15.2%

19. $\frac{103}{125}$, or 82.4%

20. $\frac{14}{25}$, or 56%

21. $\frac{77}{125}$, or 61.6%

22. $\frac{89}{125}$, or 71.2%

23. $\frac{_{30}C_3 \cdot {}_{120}C_6}{{}_{150}C_9} \approx 0.17879 \approx 17.9\%$

24. $\frac{1}{16}$, or 6.25%

25. $\frac{5}{8}$, or 62.5%

26. $\frac{1}{4}$, or 25%

27. $\frac{3}{4}$, or 75%

28. $\frac{1}{6}$

29. $\frac{116}{147} \approx 78.9\%$

30. $\frac{52}{147} \approx 35.4\%$

31. $\frac{43}{147} \approx 29.3\%$

32. $\frac{31}{147} \approx 21.1\%$

33. 1 chance in 2,869,685 or $\approx 0.00003485\%$

34. a. $\frac{1}{4}$; $\frac{3}{4}$

b. Answers may vary. Sample: Variables such as injuries make experimental probability a poor predictor.

35. if there are any restrictions on the last digit of a ZIP code

Challenge

36. Assume that an event is neither certain nor impossible. Then the odds in favor of the event are the ratio of the number of favorable outcomes to the number of unfavorable outcomes.

a. If the odds in favor of the event are a to b, or $\frac{a}{b}$, what is the probability of the event?

b. If the probability of the event is $\frac{a}{b}$, what are the odds in favor of the event?

c. Would you rather play a game in which your odds of winning are $\frac{1}{2}$, or a game in which your probability of winning is $\frac{1}{2}$? Explain.

Standardized Test Prep

SAT/ACT

37. What is the theoretical probability of getting a 2 or a 3 when rolling a standard number cube?

Ⓐ $\frac{1}{2}$ Ⓑ $\frac{1}{3}$ Ⓒ $\frac{1}{4}$ Ⓓ $\frac{1}{6}$

38. Which expression is equivalent to $\left(n^{\frac{3}{2}} \div n^{-\frac{1}{6}} \right)^{-3}$?

Ⓕ n^{27} Ⓖ n^{-27} Ⓗ n^{-4} Ⓘ n^{-5}

39. How can you rewrite the equation $x^2 + 12x + 5 = 3$ so the left side of the equation is in the form $(x + a)^2$?

Ⓐ $(x - 6)^2 = 28$ Ⓒ $(x + 6)^2 = 39$

Ⓑ $(x + 6)^2 = 34$ Ⓓ $(x + 12)^2 = -2$

40. How many ways are there to select 25 books from a collection of 27 books?

Ⓕ 702   Ⓖ 5.4×1027 Ⓗ 351   Ⓘ 675

Short Response

41. Use the center and radius to graph the circle with equation $(x + 4)^2 + (y - 2)^2 = 16$.

Mixed Review

Evaluate each expression.   ◀ See Lesson 11-1.

42. $_5P_2$ **43.** $_7P_4$ **44.** $_5C_3$ **45.** $_{10}C_8$

Add or subtract. Simplify where possible.   ◀ See Lesson 8-5.

46. $\frac{5}{a^2 b} - \frac{7a}{5b^2}$ **47.** $\frac{3}{p} + \frac{7}{q}$ **48.** $\frac{x}{x - 5} + \frac{x}{5 - x}$

Get Ready!   To prepare for Lesson 11-3, do Exercises 49–51.

A bag contains 24 green marbles, 22 blue marbles, 14 yellow marbles, and 12 red marbles. Suppose you pick one marble at random. What is each probability?   ◀ See Lesson 11-2.

49. $P(\text{yellow})$ **50.** $P(\text{not blue})$ **51.** $P(\text{green or red})$

---

36. a. $\frac{a}{a + b}$

b. a to $b - a$ or $\frac{a}{b - a}$

c. A game in which the probability of winning is $\frac{1}{2}$; when the odds of winning are $\frac{1}{2}$, the probability of winning is only $\frac{1}{3}$.

Standardized Test Prep

37. B

38. I

39. B

40. H

41. [2]

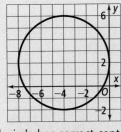

[1] circle has correct center, but incorrect radius

Mixed Review

42. 20

43. 840

44. 10

45. 45

46. $\frac{25b - 7a^3}{5a^2 b^2}$

47. $\frac{3q + 7p}{pq}$

48. 0

49. $\frac{7}{36} = 19.\overline{4}\%$

50. $\frac{25}{36} = 69.\overline{4}\%$

51. $\frac{1}{2}$, or 50%

Additional Instructional Support

Algebra 2 Companion

Students can use the **Algebra 2 Companion** worktext (4 pages) as you teach the lesson. Use the Companion to support

- New Vocabulary
- Key Concepts
- Got It for each Problem
- Lesson Check

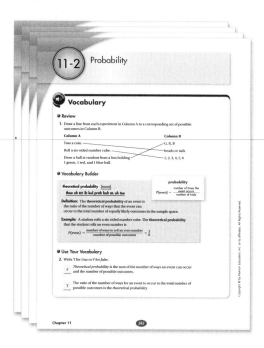

ELL Support

Use Manipulatives Provide students with number cubes and coins to help them learn the difference between experimental and theoretical probability as well as find the sample space of events discussed in this lesson.

Write *experimental probability* on the board. Provide students with one number cube; have them roll the cube 20 times and record their results. Say: This is an experiment. Have students find the experimental probability of rolling a 3. Write the different probabilities found under *experimental probability*.

Next write *theoretical probability* on the board. Have students look at the number cube and record the sample space. Then have them count the number of 3's on the cube. Say: This is theoretical probability. Have the students find the theoretical probability of rolling a 3. Compare the theoretical probabilities with the experimental probabilities if desired.

5 Assess & Remediate

Lesson Quiz

1. Of 24 movies shown in a theater, three are rated G. What is the theoretical probability that a movie at the theater is rated G?

2. **Do you UNDERSTAND?** A multiple-choice test consists of 5 answer choices for each item. How can you use simulation to determine the experimental probability of passing the test with at least 5 out of 10 answers correct?

3. What is the theoretical probability of getting a sum of 7 on one roll of two fair number cubes?

4. What is the theoretical probability of being dealt exactly one ace in a 5-card hand from a standard 52-card deck?

5. A rectangular landing pad measures $20' \times 25'$ with a rectangular target on the pad measuring $6' \times 8'$. What is the geometric probability that a model rocket falling randomly on the pad will land in the target?

ANSWERS TO LESSON QUIZ

1. 12.5%

2. Use random digits 1, 2, 3, 4, 5 ten times with 1 representing the correct answer. Repeat 20 times. Count the number of times the simulation shows 5 or more 1's.

3. $\frac{1}{6}$

4. 29.9%

5. 9.6%

A PRESCRIPTION FOR REMEDIATION

Use the student work on the Lesson Quiz to prescribe a differentiated review assignment:

Points	Differentiated Remediation
0–2	Intervention
3–4	On-level
5	Extension

PowerAlgebra.com

5 Assess & Remediate

Assign the Lesson Quiz. Appropriate intervention, practice, or enrichment is automatically generated based on student performance.

Intervention

- **Reteaching** (2 pages) Provides reteaching and practice exercises for the key lesson concepts. Use with struggling students or absent students.

- **English Language Learner Support** Helps students develop and reinforce mathematical vocabulary and key concepts.

All-in-One Resources/Online
Reteaching

11-2 Reteaching
Probability

Probability is a measure of how likely a specific event is to occur. To find the *experimental probability* of a specific event, you conduct an experiment, or simulation of the experiment, multiple times. Each time you run the experiment or simulation, you are conducting a *trial*. You count the number of times the event you are looking for occurs. The experimental probability is the ratio of the number of times the event occurs to the number of trials.

$$P(\text{event}) = \frac{\# \text{ of times the event occurs}}{\# \text{ of trials}}$$

Problem

You toss a coin 12 times and record each result: H, T, T, H, H, H, T, H, T, H, T, H. What is the experimental probability of tails?

Step 1 Determine the total number of trials, the event you are looking for, and the number of times the event occurred during the trials.
One toss of the coin is one trial. You did 12 trials.
The event you are looking for is tails. Tails occurred 5 times.

Step 2 Use the formula for experimental probability.
$$P(\text{tails}) = \frac{\# \text{ of tails}}{\# \text{ of tosses}} = \frac{5}{12} \approx 0.42, \text{ or } 42\%$$
The experimental probability of tails is about 0.42.

Exercises

In a telephone survey of 150 households, 75 people answered "yes" to a particular question, 50 answered "no", and 25 were "not sure". Find each experimental probability.

1. $P(\text{yes})$ $\frac{1}{2}$, or 50%

2. $P(\text{no})$ $\frac{1}{3} \approx 0.33$, or 33%

3. $P(\text{not sure})$ $\frac{1}{6} \approx 0.17$, or 17%

4. $P(\text{not yes})$ $\frac{1}{2}$, or 50%

5. $P(\text{yes or no})$ $\frac{5}{6} \approx 0.83$, or 83%

6. $P(\text{yes and not sure})$ 0, or 0%

All-in-One Resources/Online
English Language Learner Support

11-2 Additional Vocabulary Support
Probability

Complete the vocabulary chart by filling in the missing information.

Word or Phrase	Definition	Example
experimental probability	1. the number of times the event occurs divided by the number of trials	You take 12 marbles from a bag and 3 of them are blue. The experimental probability of pulling a blue marble from the bag is $\frac{3}{12} = 0.25 = 25\%$.
simulation	2. a *simulation* is a model of an event	You can simulate guessing on a set of true or false questions by flipping a coin.
sample space	a list of all possible outcomes to an experiment or activity	3. The sample space for a flip of a coin is heads or tails.
equally likely sample space	4. a sample space in which each outcome has the same chance of occurring	The sample space for randomly selecting a card from a deck of 52 cards includes all of the cards in the deck, and each outcome has an equal chance of occurring.
theoretical probability	If an event A occurs in m out of n equally likely outcomes, then the theoretical probability of A is $\frac{m}{n}$.	5. The theoretical probability of pulling an Ace from a deck of 52 cards is $\frac{4}{52} = \frac{1}{13}$.

Differentiated Remediation *continued*

On-Level

- **Practice** (2 pages) Provides extra practice for each lesson. For simpler practice exercises, use the Form K Practice pages found in the All-in-One Teaching Resources and online.

- **Think About a Plan** Helps students develop specific problem-solving skills and strategies by providing scaffolded guiding questions.

- **Standardized Test Prep** Focuses on all major exercises, all major question types, and helps students prepare for the high-stakes assessments.

Extension

- **Enrichment** Provides students with interesting problems and activities that extend the concepts of the lesson.

- **Activities, Games, and Puzzles** Worksheets that can be used for concepts development, enrichment, and for fun!

Practice and Problem Solving Wkbk/All-in-One Resources/Online
Practice page 1

11-2 Practice — Form G
Probability

1. A basketball player attempted 24 shots and made 13. Find the experimental probability that the player will make the next shot she attempts. ≈ 0.54 or 54%

2. A baseball player attempted to steal a base 70 times and was successful 47 times. Find the experimental probability that the player will be successful on his next attempt to steal a base. ≈ 0.67, or 67%

Graphing Calculator For Exercises 3–4, define a simulation by telling how you represent correct answers, incorrect answers, and the quiz. Use your simulation to find each experimental probability.

3. If you guess the answers at random, what is the probability of getting at least three correct answers on a four-question true-or-false quiz? Answers may vary. Sample: Let "1" be a correct answer. Let "2" be an incorrect answer. Generate 16 sets of 4 random 1's and 2's. $\frac{5}{16}$ = 0.3125 = 0.31, or 31%.

4. A five-question multiple-choice quiz has four choices for each answer. If you guess the answers at random, what is the probability of getting at least four correct answers? Answers may vary. Sample: Let "1" be a correct answer. Let "2", "3", and "4" be incorrect answers. Generate 64 sets of 5 random 1's, 2's, 3's, and 4's; $\frac{1}{64}$ = 0.015625 ≈ 0.02, or 2%.

A group of five cards are numbered 1–5. You choose one card at random. Find each theoretical probability.

5. P(card is a 2) $\frac{1}{5}$ = 0.20, or 20%

6. P(even number) $\frac{2}{5}$ = 0.40, or 40%

7. P(prime number) $\frac{3}{5}$ = 0.60, or 60%

8. P(less than 5) $\frac{4}{5}$ = 0.80, or 80%

A bucket contains 15 blue pens, 35 black pens, and 40 red pens. You pick one pen at random. Find each theoretical probability.

9. P(black pen) $\frac{35}{90}$ ≈ 0.39, 39%

10. P(blue pen or red pen) $\frac{55}{90}$ ≈ 0.61, 61%

11. P(not a blue pen) $\frac{75}{90}$ ≈ 0.83, 83%

12. P(black pen or not a red pen) $\frac{50}{90}$ ≈ 0.56, 56%

Practice and Problem Solving Wkbk/All-in-One Resources/Online
Practice page 2

11-2 Practice (continued) — Form G
Probability

13. There are 225 juniors and 255 seniors at your school. The school chooses 5 juniors and seniors as Student All-Stars. What is the theoretical probability that exactly 2 of the Student All-Stars will be juniors? ≈ 0.33, or 33%

The rectangular yard shown below has a circular pool and a triangular garden. A ball from an adjacent golf course lands at a random point within the yard. Find each theoretical probability.

14. The ball lands in the pool. ≈ 0.09, or 9%

15. The ball lands in the garden ≈ 0.005, or 5%

16. The ball lands in the garden or the pool. ≈ 0.095, or 9.5%

17. The ball does not land in the pool. ≈ 0.91, or 91%

Five people each flip a coin one time. Find each theoretical probability.

18. P(5 heads) 0.03125, or ≈ 3%

19. P(exactly 2 tails) 0.3125, or ≈ 31%

20. P(at least 3 heads) 0.5, or 50%

21. P(less than 4 tails) 0.8125, or ≈ 81%

22. The spinner shown at the right has four equal-sized sections. Suppose you spin the spinner two times. (1, 1), (1, 2), (1, 3), (1, 4), (2, 1), (2, 2), (2, 3), (2, 4), (3, 1), (3, 2), (3, 3), (3, 4), (4, 1), (4, 2), (4, 3), (4, 4)
   a. What is the sample space?
   b. How many outcomes are there? 16
   c. What is the theoretical probability of getting a sum of 4? 0.1875, or ≈ 19%

23. If x is a real number and x = 0, what is the probability that $\frac{1}{x}$ is undefined? 1

24. If x is a real number and x ≠ 0, what is the probability that $\frac{1}{x}$ is undefined? 0

25. Of the 195 students in the senior class, 104 study Spanish and 86 study French, with 12 studying both Spanish and French. What is the theoretical probability that a student chosen at random is studying Spanish, but not French? ≈ 0.47 or ≈ 47%

All-in-One Resources/Online
Enrichment

11-2 Enrichment
Probability

Biologists use a Punnett Square to predict the gene combinations that are possible for an offspring when the genes of the parents are known. Each parent organism carries two genes, or alleles, for a particular trait. For example, a parent might have the genotype *Bb* for dimples. A capital *B* represents the dominant trait, which is having dimples. A lower case *b* represents the recessive trait, which is not having dimples.

1. Both parents contribute one allele to their offspring. For example, if both parents have the genotype *Bb*, an offspring could inherit the genotype of *BB* with each parent contributing one dominant *B* allele. What are the other possible combinations? *Bb, bB, bb*

2. This information can be displayed in a Punnett Square. Each side of the square represents the genotype of one parent. The Punnett Square for the offspring of the parents who both have the genotype *Bb* is shown at the right. If the dominant allele is present it will be the trait that appears. What is the probability that this offspring will not have dimples? $\frac{1}{4}$

3. Create a Punnett Square to show the possible gene combinations for the offspring if one parent has the genotype *Bb* and the other has the genotype *BB*.

4. What is the probability that the offspring of parents with *Bb* and *BB* will have dimples? 1

5. You can show more complicated crosses when you consider two or more genes that are independent of each other. For example, pea pods can either be round (*R*) or wrinkled (*r*), yellow (*Y*) or green (*y*). What are the possible combinations of shape and color? *RY, Ry, rY, ry*

6. Create a Punnett Square to show the possible gene combinations for the pea pods.

7. What is the probability that a pea pod with both parents *RrYy* will be round and yellow? In other words, what is the probability that there is an *R* and a *Y* present? $\frac{9}{16}$

8. What is the probability that a pea pod with both parents *RrYy* will be wrinkled and yellow? $\frac{3}{16}$

9. What is the probability that a pea pod with both parents *RrYy* will be wrinkled and green? $\frac{1}{16}$

Practice and Problem Solving Wkbk/All-in-One Resources/Online
Think About a Plan

11-2 Think About a Plan
Probability

Lottery A lottery has 53 numbers from which five are drawn at random. Each number can only be drawn once. What is the probability of your lottery ticket matching all five numbers in any order?

Know

1. The lottery has ⬚53 possible numbers that can be drawn.

2. Each number can be drawn ⬚1 time(s).

3. A total of ⬚5 numbers will be drawn.

Need

4. To solve the problem I need to find:
   the theoretical probability of the numbers on a lottery ticket matching the numbers drawn in any order

Plan

5. Because order does not matter, the size of the sample space is a [combination].

6. What is the sample space?
   all combinations of 53 numbers chosen 5 at a time

7. What is the size of the sample space? ₅₃C₅ = 2,869,685

8. How many of the events in the sample space represent your ticket? 1

9. What is the probability of your lottery ticket matching all five numbers in any order? $\frac{1}{2,869,685}$ ≈ 0.00000035

Practice and Problem Solving Wkbk/All-in-One Resources/Online
Standardized Test Prep

11-2 Standardized Test Prep
Probability

Gridded Response

For Exercises 1–3, find each theoretical probability based on one roll of two number cubes. Enter each answer in the grid as a whole percent.

1. P(sum 9)

2. P(one even, one odd)

3. P(sum > 12)

For Exercises 4–5, find each theoretical probability based on one marble drawn at random from a bag of 14 red marbles, 10 pink marbles, 18 blue marbles, and 6 gold marbles. Enter each answer in the grid as a fraction in simplest form.

4. P(not pink)

5. P(blue or gold)

Answers

1. 11   2. 50   3. 0   4. 18/24   5. 1/2

Online Teacher Resource Center
Activities, Games, and Puzzles

11-2 Activity: Colors and Probability
Probability

This activity is best done in groups of two to three students.

Materials
A small container of colored plastic chips. Set up a container with no one color less than 1/20 of the total.

Special Instruction
Do not look inside the container until Part 1 has been completed.

Part 1: Experimental Probability
- Select one member of the group to record the colors drawn.
- Thoroughly mix the chips.
- Draw one chip and record its color.
- Replace the chip and thoroughly mix the chips.
- Repeat 50 times.
- Record your results in the space below.
- Use your results to calculate the experimental probabilities of drawing each color.

Results: Check students' work.

Experimental Probabilities: Check students' work.

Part 2: Theoretical Probability
- Examine the contents of the container and record the number of each color below.
- Calculate the theoretical probabilities of drawing each color.

Results: Check students' work.

Theoretical Probabilities: Check students' work.

Part 3: Compare/Contrast
- Use a separate sheet of paper to write a paragraph comparing and contrasting your results from Parts 1 and 2. Was there any difference in your results? Explain. Which type of probability might be more useful? When? What are the advantages and disadvantages of calculating these different types of probabilities? Check students' work.

1 Interactive Learning

Solve It!

PURPOSE To use counting principles to find probabilities

PROCESS Students may
- make lists to determine the sample spaces.
- find individual probabilities and make predictions about which score is likely.

FACILITATE

Q Can you add the points to find the total number of turns? Why or why not? **[No; some turns do not result in points, so if you only count points, you will undercount the number of turns.]**

ANSWER See Solve It in Answers on next page.

CONNECT THE MATH Students use probability to determine the number of trials and the most likely event in the Solve It. In this lesson, students find probabilities of multiple events that may or may not have an effect on each other.

2 Guided Instruction

Problem 1

Q How does the sample space in 1B change when choosing the first and second cards? **[First sample space is 30. Second is 29.]**

Got It?

Q Does the sample space change for each coin selected? Explain. **[No; since the coin is replaced, the sample space remains the same.]**

Take Note

Emphasize that this rule only applies to independent events.

11-3 Preparing to Teach

BIG idea Probability

ESSENTIAL UNDERSTANDINGS

To find the probability of two events occurring together, it is necessary to determine whether the occurrence of one event affects the probability that the other event will occur.

Math Background

If the occurrence of one event affects the probability that another event will occur, then the events are *dependent*. Otherwise, they are *independent*.

EXAMPLES OF INDEPENDENT EVENTS
- choosing one object each out of two different containers
- choosing an object from a container, replacing it, and then choosing another object

EXAMPLES OF DEPENDENT EVENTS
- choosing two objects out of one container
- choosing an object and then choosing a second object without replacing the first

---

© Content Standards
S.CP.7 Apply the Addition Rule, $P(A \text{ or } B) = P(A) + P(B) - P(A \text{ and } B)$, and interpret the answer in terms of the model.
Also S.CP.2, S.CP.5

Objectives To find the probability of the event *A* and *B*
To find the probability of the event *A* or *B*

SOLVE IT

Getting Ready!

You and your friend take turns rolling two standard number cubes. If you roll a sum that is either odd or a prime number, you score a point. If your friend rolls a sum that is both odd and a prime number, she scores a point. Which score is likely yours? About how many turns have each of you taken? Explain.

PLAYER 1	PLAYER 2
///	

Make sure you understand the game. What is the difference between the words "or" and "and"?

© MATHEMATICAL PRACTICES

VOCABULARY
Lesson Vocabulary
- dependent events
- independent events
- mutually exclusive events

You can find the probabilities of multiple events occurring by using the probabilities of the individual events.

Essential Understanding To find the probability of two events occurring together, you have to decide whether one event occurring affects the other event.

When the occurrence of one event affects how a second event can occur, the events are **dependent events**. Otherwise, the events are **independent events**.

Think

What must you ask yourself?
Does the first event have any effect on the outcome of the second event?

© Problem 1 Classifying Events

Are the outcomes of each trial dependent or independent events?

Ⓐ Roll a number cube. Then spin a spinner.

The two events do not affect each other. They are independent.

Ⓑ Pick one flash card, then another from a stack of 30 flash cards.

Picking the first card affects the possible outcomes of picking the second card. The events are dependent.

 Got It? 1. You select a coin at random from your pocket. You replace the coin and select again. Are your selections independent events? Explain.

Multiply to find the probability that two independent events will both occur.

take note

Key Concept Probability of *A* and *B*

If *A* and *B* are independent events, then $P(A \text{ and } B) = P(A) \cdot P(B)$.

For any two events *A* and *B*, the probability that either *A* or *B* occurs, $P(A \text{ or } B)$, is given by the equation $P(A \text{ or } B) = P(A) + P(B) - P(A \text{ and } B)$. This equation says to add the probability that *A* occurs with the probability that *B* occurs, and then subtract the probability that both *A* and *B* occur.

© Mathematical Practices

Attend to precision. Students will make explicit use of the terms "dependent events" and "independent events." They will also calculate the experimental probability in each circumstance.

PowerAlgebra.com

1 Interactive Learning

Solve It!
Step out how to solve the Problem with helpful hints and an online question. Other questions are listed above in Interactive Learning.

Dynamic Activity Students can model dependent and independent events by choosing different color marbles from a virtual bag. Use this activity with students who have difficulty understanding what makes an event dependent or independent.

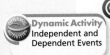

Dynamic Activity
Independent and
Dependent Events

Problem 2 Finding the Probability of Independent Events

Picnic At a picnic there are 10 diet drinks and 5 regular drinks. There are also 8 bags of fat-free chips and 12 bags of regular chips. If you grab a drink and a bag of chips without looking, what is the probability that you get a diet drink and fat-free chips?

Think

Is it important that you don't look?
Yes; probability is based on random events. It is not random if you look.

Event A = picking a diet drink   Event B = picking fat-free chips

A and B are independent. Picking a drink has no effect on picking the chips.

$$P(A \text{ and } B) = P(A) \cdot P(B)$$

$$= \frac{\text{number of diet drinks}}{\text{total number of drinks}} \cdot \frac{\text{number of bags of fat-free chips}}{\text{total number of bags of chips}}$$

$$= \frac{10}{15} \cdot \frac{8}{20} = \frac{4}{15} \approx 0.267, \text{ or } 26.7\%$$

The probability that you get a diet drink and fat-free chips is about 26.7%.

✓ **Got It?** **2.** In Problem 2, what is the probability that you get a regular drink and regular chips?

Two events that cannot happen at the same time are **mutually exclusive events**. If A and B are mutually exclusive events, then $P(A \text{ and } B) = 0$.

Problem 3 Mutually Exclusive Events

You roll a standard number cube. Are the events mutually exclusive? Explain.

Think

Can you roll a 2 and a 3 at the same time?
No; just one number comes up on one roll of one number cube.

Ⓐ rolling a 2 and a 3

You cannot roll a 2 and 3 at the same time. The events are mutually exclusive.

Ⓑ rolling an even number and a multiple of 3

You can roll a 6—an even number and a multiple of 3—at the same time. The events are not mutually exclusive.

✓ **Got It?** **3.** You roll a standard number cube. Are the events mutually exclusive? Explain.
  a. rolling an even number and rolling a prime number
  b. rolling an even number and rolling a number less than 2

To find the probability of either event A or event B occuring, you need to determine whether events A and B are mutually exclusive.

take note

Key Concept Probability of A or B

$$P(A \text{ or } B) = P(A) + P(B) - P(A \text{ and } B)$$

If A and B are mutually exclusive events, then $P(A \text{ or } B) = P(A) + P(B)$.

Problem 2

Q Will the probability be the same for the next person who chooses a drink and bag of chips? Explain. **[No; once a drink and bag of chips have been chosen, the sample space changes.]**

Got It?   EXTENSION

Q Can you find the probability for Got It 2 by taking 1 minus the probability in Problem 2? Explain. **[No; these two situations are not the only possible outcomes.]**

Problem 3   VISUAL LEARNERS

Q Are mutually exclusive events the same as independent events? Explain. **[No; if one mutually exclusive event occurs, the other cannot occur.]**

Got It?

Have students make a Venn diagram to determine whether events are mutually exclusive. For example, the Venn diagram for 3a would be:

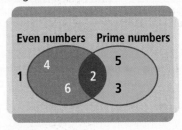

Take Note

Q Why does the equation $P(A \text{ or } B) = P(A) + P(B) - P(A \text{ and } B)$ change if the events are mutually exclusive? **[The events cannot happen at the same time, so $P(A \text{ and } B) = 0$.]**

---

2 Guided Instruction

Each Problem is worked out and supported online.

Problem 1
Classifying Events

Problem 2
Finding the Probability of Independent Events
                                        Animated

Problem 3
Mutually Exclusive Events

Problem 4
Finding Probability for Mutually Exclusive Events
                                        Animated

Problem 5
Finding Probability
                                        Animated

Support in Algebra 2 Companion
• Vocabulary
• Key Concepts
• Got It?

Answers

Solve It!
Your probability of winning is $\frac{19}{36}$. Your friend's is $\frac{14}{36}$. Your scores are likely those on the left. To estimate the number of turns x, solve the equations $18 = \frac{19}{36}x$ and $15 = \frac{14}{36}x$. You each had between 34 and 38 turns.

Got It?
1. Independent; the number of coins is the same after the coin is replaced.

2. 0.20, or 20%

3. a. Not mutually exclusive; 2 is a prime number and an even number.

  b. Mutually exclusive; there is no even number less than 2 in the roll of a number cube.

Problem 4

Q Would the answer be different if students were allowed to take more than one foreign language? Explain. **[Yes; the events would not be mutually exclusive. You would subtract the probability that a student was enrolled in both Spanish and French.]**

Q Is it possible for 50% of the students at the school to be enrolled in Latin? Explain. **[No; because students are limited to one foreign language, the sum of the probabilities cannot exceed 1.]**

Got It?

Q What is the probability a student is not taking Spanish, French, or Mandarin Chinese? Explain your reasoning. **[Students are either taking one of these languages or they are not. These are all possible events, so P(not taking these languages) $= 1 - 0.61 = 0.39 = 39\%$.]**

Problem 5 VISUAL LEARNERS

Q Can you state an event using the same tokens that is mutually exclusive? If so, give an example. **[Yes; a mutually exclusive event would be selecting a token that is yellow or a square.]**

Q Which answer can be eliminated from the choices before solving the problem? Explain. **[Sample: Choice A; it is a smaller probability than choosing a green one alone.]**

Got It?

Q Are the events in 5a mutually exclusive? Explain. **[No; a token can be both square and red.]**

 **Problem 4** Finding Probability for Mutually Exclusive Events

Languages At your high school, a student can take one foreign language each term. About 37% of the students take Spanish. About 15% of the students take French. What is the probability that a student chosen at random is taking Spanish or French?

Know	Need	Plan
• The percentages of students taking Spanish or French. • Students can take one foreign language at a time.	The probability that a student is taking Spanish or French.	Use the correct formula for $P(A$ or $B)$.

"One foreign language each term" means the events are mutually exclusive.

P(Spanish or French) $= P$(Spanish) $+ P$(French) $P(A$ or $B) = P(A) + P(B)$ for mutually exclusive events.

$\approx 0.37 + 0.15$

$= 0.52$

The probability that a student chosen at random is taking Spanish or French is about 0.52, or about 52%.

 Got It? **4. a.** In Problem 4, about 9% of the students take Mandarin Chinese. What is the probability that a student chosen at random is taking Spanish, French, or Mandarin Chinese?

 b. Reasoning Without knowing the number of students in the school in Problem 4, can you determine which language most students take? Explain.

When two events are *not* mutually exclusive, you need to subtract the probability of the common outcomes to find $P(A$ or $B)$.

 **Problem 5** Finding Probability

Multiple Choice Suppose you reach into the dish and select a token at random. What is the probability that the token is round or green?

Ⓐ $\frac{2}{9}$ Ⓑ $\frac{3}{9}$ Ⓒ $\frac{6}{9}$ Ⓓ $\frac{8}{9}$

Think

Are the events mutually exclusive?
No; it is possible to have a round *and* green token.

P(round or green)

$= P$(round) $+ P$(green) $- P$(round and green)

$= \frac{5}{9} + \frac{3}{9} - \frac{2}{9} = \frac{6}{9}$

The probability of selecting a round or green token is $\frac{6}{9}$, or $\frac{2}{3}$. The correct answer is C.

 Got It? **5.** Suppose you select a token at random from the dish above. What is each probability?

 a. the token is square or red   **b.** the token is green or square

---

Additional Problems

1. Is each pair of events dependent or independent?

 a. Flip a coin. Then roll a number cube.

 b. Choose a marble from a bag. Keep the marble, and then choose another marble from the same bag.

 ANSWERS

 a. independent

 b. dependent

2. What is the probability of rolling a 6 on a fair number cube and flipping a coin and getting tails?

 ANSWER about 8.3%

3. You select one card from a standard 52-card deck.

Are the events mutually exclusive? Explain.

 a. choosing a red card or an even numbered card

 b. choosing a red card or a black card

 ANSWERS

 a. not mutually exclusive because a card can be red and an even number at the same time

 b. mutually exclusive because the card cannot be red and black at the same time

4. Students choose one elective each school year. About 18% chose woodworking and about 38% chose music. What is the probability that

a student chosen at random has selected woodworking or music as an elective?

 ANSWER 56%

5. Multiple Choice The numbers 1 through 10 are written on index cards and placed in a box. What is the probability that a card chosen at random has a number that is greater than 7 or even?

 A. 30%

 B. 50%

 C. 60%

 D. 80%

 ANSWER C

Answers

Got It? (continued)

4. a. 0.61, or 61%

 b. Yes; the percentage of students tells which language is chosen by more students.

5. a. $\frac{5}{9}$

 b. $\frac{5}{9}$

Lesson Check

Do you know HOW?

A and *B* are independent events. Find *P(A* and *B)*.

1. $P(A) = \frac{1}{6}, P(B) = \frac{2}{5}$ **2.** $P(A) = \frac{9}{20}, P(B) = \frac{3}{4}$

C and *D* are mutually exclusive events. Find *P(C* or *D)*.

3. $P(C) = \frac{2}{5}, P(D) = \frac{3}{5}$ **4.** $P(C) = \frac{1}{2}, P(D) = \frac{3}{8}$

5. Events *A* and *B* are not mutually exclusive. If $P(A) = \frac{1}{2}$, $P(B) = \frac{1}{4}$, and $P(A$ and $B) = \frac{1}{8}$, find $P(A$ or $B)$.

Do you UNDERSTAND? MATHEMATICAL PRACTICES

 6. Vocabulary Explain the difference between independent events and mutually exclusive events.

7. Error Analysis The weather forecast for the weekend is a 30% chance of rain on Saturday and a 70% chance of rain on Sunday. Your friend says that means there is a 100% chance of rain this weekend. What error did your friend make?

8. Open-Ended Describe two events that are mutually exclusive.

 Practice and Problem-Solving Exercises MATHEMATICAL PRACTICES

 Practice

Tell whether the outcomes of each trial are dependent events or independent events.

See Problem 1.

9. A month is selected at random; a number from 1 to 30 is selected at random.

10. A month is selected at random; a day of that month is selected at random.

11. A letter of the alphabet is selected at random; one of the remaining letters is selected at random.

12. The color of a car is selected at random; the type of transmission is selected at random.

Q and *R* are independent events. Find *P(Q* and *R)*.

See Problem 2.

13. $P(Q) = \frac{1}{4}, P(R) = \frac{2}{3}$ **14.** $P(Q) = \frac{12}{17}, P(R) = \frac{3}{8}$

15. $P(Q) = 0.6, P(R) = 0.9$ **16.** $P(Q) = \frac{1}{3}, P(R) = \frac{6}{7}$

17. Reading Suppose you have five books in your book bag. Three are novels, one is a biography, and one is a poetry book. Today you grab one book out of your bag without looking, and return it later. Tomorrow you do the same thing. What is the probability that you grab a novel both days?

Two fair number cubes are rolled. State whether the events are mutually exclusive. Explain your reasoning.

See Problem 3.

18. The sum is a prime number; the sum is less than 4.

19. The numbers are equal; the sum is odd.

20. The product is greater than 20; the product is a multiple of 3.

---

3 Lesson Check

Do you know HOW?   ERROR INTERVENTION

- If students have difficulty solving Exercises 1–2, remind them that the probabilities of independent events can be multiplied.
- For Exercises 3–4, students might have difficulty choosing between the expressions for *P(A* or *B)*. Remind them that *P(A* and *B)* = 0 for mutually exclusive events. Although the exercise states "mutually exclusive," students should determine this before applying a probability formula.

Do you UNDERSTAND?

- If students have trouble with Exercise 6, remind them that mutually exclusive events cannot happen at the same time. If one event occurs, the other will not occur. Have students apply this fact to the definition of independent events to help them answer the question.

Close

Q In what situation do you multiply probabilities? In what situation do you add them? **[Multiply if finding *P(A* and *B)* and they are independent events. Add if finding *P(A* or *B)* and they are mutually exclusive.]**

Q What is the difference between independent and dependent events? **[Events are dependent if one event affects the probability that another event occurs. Otherwise, they are independent.]**

Lesson Check

1. $\frac{1}{15}$, or $6.\overline{6}\%$ **2.** $\frac{27}{80}$, or 33.75%

3. 1, or 100%   **4.** $\frac{7}{8}$, or 87.5%

5. $\frac{5}{8}$, or 62.5%

6. Events A and B are independent if the outcomes of A do not affect the outcomes of B. The events are mutually exclusive if A and B cannot occur at the same time. For independent events, $P(A$ and $B) = P(A) \cdot P(B)$. For mutually exclusive events, $P(A$ and $B) = 0$. For any events, $P(A$ or $B) = P(A) + P(B) - P(A$ and $B)$.

7. Since these are not mutually exclusive events, $P(A$ and $B) \neq 0$. The student should have calculated $P(A$ or $B) = P(A) + P(B) - P(A$ and $B)$, which is 0.79, or 79%.

8. Check students' work.

Practice and Problem-Solving Exercises

9. independent   **10.** dependent
11. dependent   **12.** independent

13. $\frac{1}{6}$ **14.** $\frac{9}{34}$

15. 0.54   **16.** $\frac{2}{7}$

17. $\frac{9}{25}$

18. not mutually exclusive; 2 is a prime number and less than 4

19. mutually exclusive; if the numbers are equal, then the sum is even

20. not mutually exclusive; $6 \cdot 4 = 24$ which is greater than 20 and a multiple of 3

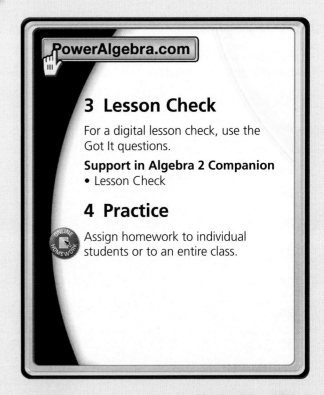

PowerAlgebra.com

3 Lesson Check

For a digital lesson check, use the Got It questions.

Support in Algebra 2 Companion
• Lesson Check

4 Practice

Assign homework to individual students or to an entire class.

4 Practice

S and *T* are mutually exclusive events. Find *P*(*S* or *T*). ◀ See Problem 4.

21. $P(S) = \frac{5}{8}, P(T) = \frac{1}{8}$ **22.** $P(S) = \frac{3}{5}, P(T) = \frac{1}{3}$ **23.** $P(S) = 12\%, P(T) = 27\%$

24. Population About 30% of the U.S. population is under 20 years old. About 17% of the population is over 60. What is the probability that a person chosen at random is under 20 or over 60?

A standard number cube is tossed. Find each probability. ◀ See Problem 5.

25. *P*(3 or odd)   **26.** *P*(4 or even)   **27.** *P*(even or less than 4)

28. *P*(odd or greater than 2)   **29.** *P*(odd or prime)   **30.** *P*(4 or less than 6)

Ⓑ **Apply 31.** Suppose a number from 1 to 100 is selected at random. What is the probability that a multiple of 4 or 5 is chosen?

Ⓒ **32. Think About a Plan** A multiple-choice test has four choices for each answer. Suppose you make a random guess on three of the ten test questions. What is the probability that you will answer all three correctly?
  • Is each guess a dependent event or an independent event?
  • What is the probability that a random guess on one question will yield the correct answer?

Statistics The graph at the right shows the types of jobs held by people in the U.S. Find each probability.

33. A person is in a service occupation.

34. A person is in service or sales and office.

35. A person is not in production, transportation, and material moving.

36. A person is neither in service nor in sales and office.

U.S. Employment, by Occupation

Production, Transportation, and Material Moving

Natural Resources, Construction, and Maintenance 12.4%

10.8% 35.5% Managerial, Professional, and Related

24.8%

Sales and Office 16.5%

Service

SOURCE: U.S. Census Bureau

A jar contains four blue marbles and two red marbles. Suppose you choose a marble at random, and do not replace it. Then you choose a second marble. Find the probability of each event.

37. You select a blue marble and then a red marble.

38. You select a red marble and then a blue marble.

39. One of the marbles you select is blue and the other is red.

40. Both of the marbles you select are red.

For each set of probabilities, determine if the events *A* and *B* are mutually exclusive.

41. $P(A) = \frac{1}{2}, P(B) = \frac{1}{3}, P(A \text{ or } B) = \frac{2}{3}$

42. $P(A) = \frac{1}{6}, P(B) = \frac{3}{8}, P(A \text{ or } B) = \frac{13}{24}$

Answers

Practice and Problem-Solving Exercises (continued)

21. $\frac{3}{4}$

22. $\frac{14}{15}$

23. 39%

24. 47%

25. $\frac{1}{2}$

26. $\frac{1}{2}$

27. $\frac{5}{6}$

28. $\frac{5}{6}$

29. $\frac{2}{3}$

30. $\frac{5}{6}$

31. $\frac{2}{5}$

32. $\frac{1}{64}$; independent; $\frac{1}{4}$

33. 14.5%

34. 38%

35. 87.4%

36. 62%

37. $\frac{4}{15}$

38. $\frac{4}{15}$

39. $\frac{8}{15}$

40. $\frac{1}{15}$

41. not mutually exclusive

42. mutually exclusive

Challenge

43. Two standard number cubes are rolled. What is the probability that the sum is greater than 9 or less than 6?

© 44. Reasoning Tatyana has $x + 2$ pens in the pocket of her backpack. Samuel has $2x - 1$ pens in the pocket of his backpack.
   a. Tatyana has 2 blue pens. Find the probability that she pulls out a blue pen at random.
   b. Samuel has $x - 3$ blue pens. Find the probability that he pulls out a blue pen at random.
   c. Find the probability that either Tatyana or Samuel pulls out a blue pen at random.

Standardized Test Prep

GRIDDED RESPONSE

SAT/ACT

45. A bag contains 5 red marbles, 1 blue marble, 3 yellow marbles, and 2 green marbles. One marble is drawn from the bag. What is the probability that the marble is red or yellow?

46. What is the theoretical probability of getting a 1 or 6 when rolling a standard number cube?

47. The first term of an arithmetic series is 123. The common difference is 12 and the sum 1320. How many terms are in the series?

48. What is the slope of the graph of the equation $6x - 18y = -24$?

49. What is the radius of the circle with equation $x^2 - 4x + y^2 - 21 = 0$?

50. How many five-letter permutations can you form from the letters of the word COMPUTER?

Mixed Review

Find the theoretical probability of each event when rolling a standard number cube.   ◀ See Lesson 11-2.

51. $P(5)$ **52.** $P(\text{an even number})$ **53.** $P(\text{less than 4})$

Solve each equation. Check each solution.   ◀ See Lesson 8-6.

54. $\frac{1}{2} - x = \frac{x}{6}$ **55.** $\frac{2}{2x - 1} = \frac{x}{3}$ **56.** $\frac{3}{2x} - \frac{2}{3x} = 5$

Solve each equation. Check your answers.   ◀ See Lesson 7-6.

57. $\ln 2x = 3$ **58.** $\ln x + \ln 2 = 6$ **59.** $\ln x^2 + 1 = 5$

Get Ready! To prepare for Lesson 11-4, do Exercises 60–62.

A spinner has four equal sections that are red, blue, green, and yellow.   ◀ See Lesson 11-3.
Find each probability for two spins.

60. $P(\text{blue, then blue})$ **61.** $P(\text{red, then yellow})$ **62.** $P(\text{not yellow, then green})$

PowerAlgebra.com   **Lesson 11-3** Probability of Multiple Events   **693**

43. $\frac{4}{9}$

44. a. $\frac{2}{x + 2}$

   b. $\frac{x - 3}{2x - 1}$

   c. $\frac{x - 1}{2x - 1}$

45. $\frac{8}{11}$

46. $\frac{1}{3}$

47. 8

48. $\frac{1}{3}$

49. 5

50. 6720

51. $\frac{1}{6}$

52. $\frac{1}{2}$

53. $\frac{1}{2}$

54. $\frac{3}{7}$

55. $-\frac{3}{2}, 2$

56. $\frac{1}{6}$

57. $\frac{1}{2}e^3 \approx 10.04$

58. $\frac{1}{2}e^6 \approx 201.71$

59. $\pm e^2 \approx \pm 7.39$

60. $\frac{1}{16}$

61. $\frac{1}{16}$

62. $\frac{3}{16}$

Differentiated Remediation

Additional Instructional Support

Algebra 2 Companion
Students can use the **Algebra 2 Companion** worktext (4 pages) as you teach the lesson. Use the Companion to support

- New Vocabulary
- Key Concepts
- Got It for each Problem
- Lesson Check

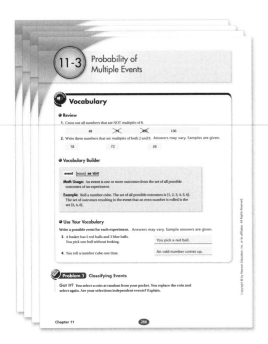

ELL Support
Focus on Language Have students make a vocabulary page for the words *independent* and *dependent*. Direct students to underline the prefix *in-*. Then say: The prefix *in-* sometimes represents the opposite of the root word. The opposite of dependent is independent.

Have students add examples of other words that follow this rule. Examples include *incomplete, incorrect, indirect,* and *informal.*

Explore the meaning of *dependent* by writing sentences using this word. For example: The score on his test was dependent on how much he studied. Her paycheck was dependent on the hours she worked.

5 Assess & Remediate

Lesson Quiz
1. You pick two marbles from a bag and record their color. How can you make your selections independent events? Dependent events?
2. Suppose you toss a coin four times. What is the probability that you get heads on the second, third, and fourth tosses?
3. **Do you UNDERSTAND?** The numbers 20 through 30 are written on cards and placed in a box. Explain whether the events of choosing a number that is a multiple of 3 or choosing a number that is a multiple of 4 are mutually exclusive.
4. Students choose one area of science for a project. About 26% choose biology. About 18% choose botany. What is the probability that a student chosen at random has selected a project in the field of biology or botany?
5. What is the probability of getting an even sum or a sum less than 7 on one roll of two fair number cubes?

ANSWERS TO LESSON QUIZ
1. Replace marbles after picking them; do not replace marbles.
2. 12.5%
3. Not mutually exclusive because 24 is a multiple of 3 and 4.
4. 44%
5. $66.\overline{6}\%$

PRESCRIPTION FOR REMEDIATION
Use the student work on the Lesson Quiz to prescribe a differentiated review assignment:

Points	Differentiated Remediation
0–2	Intervention
3–4	On-level
5	Extension

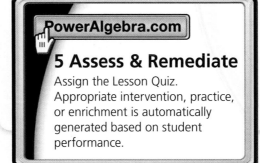

PowerAlgebra.com

5 Assess & Remediate
Assign the Lesson Quiz. Appropriate intervention, practice, or enrichment is automatically generated based on student performance.

Intervention

- **Reteaching** (2 pages) Provides reteaching and practice exercises for the key lesson concepts. Use with struggling students or absent students.
- **English Language Learner Support** Helps students develop and reinforce mathematical vocabulary and key concepts.

All-in-One Resources/Online
Reteaching

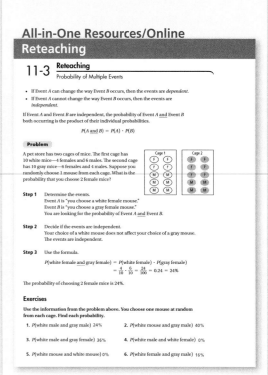

All-in-One Resources/Online
English Language Learner Support

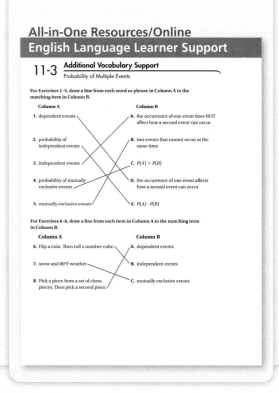

Differentiated Remediation *continued*

On-Level

- **Practice** (2 pages) Provides extra practice for each lesson. For simpler practice exercises, use the Form K Practice pages found in the All-in-One Teaching Resources and online.
- **Think About a Plan** Helps students develop specific problem-solving skills and strategies by providing scaffolded guiding questions.
- **Standardized Test Prep** Focuses on all major exercises, all major question types, and helps students prepare for the high-stakes assessments.

Practice and Problem Solving Wkbk/ All-in-One Resources/Online

Practice page 1

11-3 Practice *Form G*
Probability of Multiple Events

Classify each pair of events as *dependent* or *independent*.

1. A member of the junior class is selected; one of her pets is selected. **dependent**
2. A member of the junior class is selected as junior class president; a freshman is selected as freshman class president. **independent**
3. An odd-numbered problem is assigned for homework; an even-numbered problem is picked for a test. **independent**
4. The sum of two rolls of a number cube is 6; the product of the same two rolls is 8. **dependent**

***Q* and *R* are independent events. Find *P*(*Q* and *R*).**

5. $P(Q) = \frac{1}{8}$, $P(R) = \frac{2}{5}$ **$\frac{1}{20}$**
6. $P(Q) = 0.8$, $P(R) = 0.2$ **0.16**
7. $P(Q) = \frac{1}{4}$, $P(R) = \frac{1}{5}$ **$\frac{1}{20}$**
8. $P(Q) = \frac{3}{4}$, $P(R) = \frac{2}{3}$ **$\frac{1}{2}$**
9. Suppose you have seven CDs in a box. Four are rock, one is jazz, and two are country. Today you choose one CD without looking, play it, and put it back in the box. Tomorrow, you do the same thing. What is the probability that you choose a country CD both days? **$\frac{4}{49}$**

You randomly select an integer from 1 to 100. State whether the events are mutually exclusive. Explain your reasoning.

10. The integer is less than 40; the integer is greater than 50.
Yes; all integers 1–39 are less than 50.
11. The integer is odd; the integer is a multiple of 4.
Yes; all multiples of 4 are even.
12. The integer is less than 50; the integer is greater than 40.
No; the integers 41–49 are less than 50 and greater than 40.

***M* and *N* are mutually exclusive events. Find *P*(*M* or *N*).**

13. $P(M) = \frac{3}{4}$, $P(N) = \frac{1}{6}$ **$\frac{11}{12}$**
14. $P(M) = 10\%$, $P(N) = 45\%$ **55%**
15. $P(M) = 20\%$, $P(N) = 18\%$ **38%**
16. $P(M) = \frac{1}{10}$, $P(N) = \frac{3}{5}$ **$\frac{7}{10}$**

Practice and Problem Solving Wkbk/ All-in-One Resources/Online

Practice page 2

11-3 Practice (continued) *Form G*
Probability of Multiple Events

17. Exactly 62% of the students in your school are under 17 years old. In addition, 4% of the students are over 18. What is the probability that a student chosen at random is under 17 or over 18? **66%**

A fair number cube is tossed. Find each probability.

18. *P*(even or 3) **$\frac{2}{3}$**
19. *P*(less than 2 or even) **$\frac{2}{3}$**
20. *P*(prime or 4) **$\frac{2}{3}$**
21. You randomly choose a natural number from 1 to 10. What is the probability that you choose a multiple of 2 or 3? **$\frac{7}{10}$**

The graph at the right shows the types of bicycles in a bicycle rack. Find each probability.

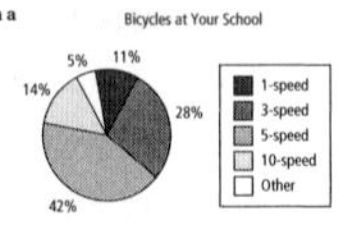

22. A bicycle is a 1-speed. **11%**
23. A bicycle is a 3-speed or a 5-speed. **70%**
24. A bicycle is not a 10-speed. **86%**
25. A bicycle is not a 1-, 3-, or 10-speed. **47%**

You have a drawer with five pairs of white socks, three pairs of black socks, and one pair of red socks. You choose one pair of socks at random each morning, starting on Monday. You do not put the socks you choose back in the drawer. Find the probability of each event.

26. You select black socks on Monday and white socks on Tuesday. **$\frac{5}{24}$**
27. You select red socks on Monday and black socks on Tuesday. **$\frac{1}{24}$**
28. You select white socks on Monday and Tuesday. **$\frac{5}{18}$**
29. You select red socks on Monday. **$\frac{1}{9}$**
30. Only 93% of the airplane parts being examined pass inspection. What is the probability that all of the next 5 parts examined will pass inspection?
≈ 69.6%

Practice and Problem Solving Wkbk/ All-in-One Resources/Online

Think About a Plan

11-3 Think About a Plan
Probability of Multiple Events

Marbles A jar contains four blue marbles and two red marbles. Suppose you choose a marble at random, and do not replace it. Then you choose a second marble. Find the probability that you select a blue marble and then a red marble.

Understanding the Problem

1. How many marbles are blue? **4**
2. How many marbles are red? **2**
3. How many marbles are in the jar? **6**
4. What is the problem asking you to determine?
the probability that you select a blue marble and then a red marble

Planning the Solution

5. What is the probability that you choose a blue marble from the jar? **$\frac{4}{6} = \frac{2}{3}$**
6. Assuming you choose a blue marble and do not replace it, how many marbles of each color remain in the jar? What is the total number of marbles in the jar?
3 blue marbles and 2 red marbles; 5 marbles
7. What is the probability that you now choose a red marble from the jar? **$\frac{2}{5}$**
8. How can you find the probability that you select a blue marble and then a red marble? **Answers may vary. Sample: The probability is the product of the probabilities for each event**.

Getting an Answer

9. What is the probability that you select a blue marble and then a red marble? **$\frac{2}{3} \cdot \frac{2}{5} = \frac{4}{15}$**

Practice and Problem Solving Wkbk/ All-in-One Resources/Online

Standardized Test Prep

11-3 Standardized Test Prep
Probability of Multiple Events

Multiple Choice

For Exercises 1–4, choose the correct letter.

A store display shows two red shirts, one blue shirt, and three shirts with red and white stripes. The display also shows two pairs of blue jeans, one pair of white pants, and one pair of white shorts.

1. What is the probability of randomly selecting an item with white or red on it? **D**
Ⓐ $\frac{1}{4}$ Ⓑ $\frac{3}{10}$ Ⓒ $\frac{1}{2}$ Ⓓ $\frac{7}{10}$
2. What is the probability of randomly selecting two items and getting a pair of blue jeans, putting them back in the display, and then randomly selecting a blue shirt? **F**
Ⓕ $\frac{1}{50}$ Ⓖ $\frac{1}{45}$ Ⓗ $\frac{2}{10}$ Ⓘ $\frac{3}{10}$
3. What is the probability of randomly selecting a complete outfit (one shirt and one pair of jeans, pants, or shorts) on two picks? **D**
Ⓐ $\frac{1}{24}$ Ⓑ $\frac{1}{5}$ Ⓒ $\frac{6}{25}$ Ⓓ $\frac{4}{15}$
4. What is the probability of selecting an item with red or blue on it? **I**
Ⓕ $\frac{3}{20}$ Ⓖ $\frac{3}{10}$ Ⓗ $\frac{3}{5}$ Ⓘ $\frac{4}{5}$

Short Response

5. There is a 50% chance of thunderstorms on Monday, a 50% chance on Tuesday, and a 50% chance on Wednesday. Assume these are independent events. What is the probability that there will be thunderstorms on Monday, Tuesday, and Wednesday? Show your work.
[2] $P(\text{M and T and W}) = P(\text{M}) \cdot P(\text{T}) \cdot P(\text{W})$
$= 0.50 \cdot 0.50 \cdot 0.50$
$= 0.125$
There is a 12.5% probability of thunderstorms on Monday, Tuesday, and Wednesday.
[1] incorrect or incomplete work shown
[0] incorrect answer and no work shown OR no answer given

Extension

- **Enrichment** Provides students with interesting problems and activities that extend the concepts of the lesson.
- **Activities, Games, and Puzzles** Worksheets that can be used for concepts development, enrichment, and for fun!

All-in-One Resources/Online

Enrichment

11-3 Enrichment
Probability of Multiple Events

Tree Diagrams

Complex problems involving probability are often easier to visualize and solve using tree diagrams. For example, suppose that Alice, Bob, and Carol are running for president of the Math Club. Alice has a 0.45 probability of being elected, while Bob has 0.35 probability and Carol has a 0.2 probability of being elected. Sue and Ted are the candidates for vice president. If Alice becomes president, the probability is 0.7 that she will choose Sue as her vice president. If Bob becomes president, the probability that he will choose Sue is 0.4, while if Carol becomes president, the probability is 0.6 that she will choose Sue.

Examine the following tree diagram that represents the given information.

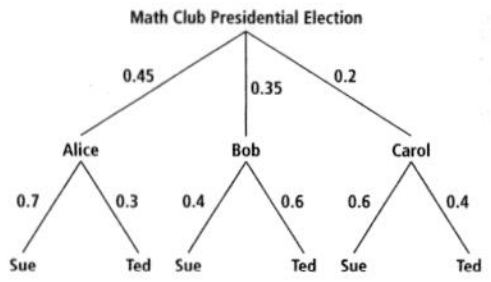

The probability that Alice will be elected president and choose Sue as her vice president can be found by multiplying the probabilities found along the "branches" of the tree. Thus, the Alice-Sue combination has a probability of $0.45 \times 0.7 = 0.315$ of occurring.

1. What is the probability of the Bob-Sue combination? **0.14** of Carol-Sue? **0.12**

Use a tree diagram to compute the probabilities of each of the following events.

2. The probability that a random student at Elmville College is a freshman is 0.3; a sophomore, 0.25; and a junior or senior, 0.45. The probability that a freshman will major in engineering is 0.15; a sophomore, 0.2; and a junior or senior, 0.3. What is the probability that a random student at this college majors in engineering? **0.23**
3. The Adams' restaurant specializes in beef, chicken, and seafood. Of its customers, 32% order beef and 41% order chicken. Of those who order beef, 73% also order dessert. Of those who order chicken, 62% also order dessert. If 65% of the customers order dessert, what is the probability that someone who orders seafood will also order dessert? **about 0.60**

Online Teacher Resource Center

Activities, Games, and Puzzles

11-3 Game: The Probability Path
Probability of Multiple Events

Provide the host with the following questions and answers (shown in brackets).

What is the probability of the following?

1. rolling a 2 on your first turn and a 6 on your second turn **[1/36]**
2. rolling a 3 on your first turn and a 3 on your second turn **[1/36]**
3. rolling an even number on your first turn and a 2 on your second turn **[1/12]**
4. rolling a 1 on your first turn and a 3 or 5 on your second turn **[1/18]**
5. landing on a space with an even denominator **[1/2]**
6. landing on a space with an odd denominator **[2/5]**
7. landing on a $\frac{2}{3}$ or a space with an identical neighbor on each side **[7/15]**
8. landing on a $\frac{1}{12}$ or a space with an identical neighbor on each side **[1/3]**
9. from the $\frac{1}{12}$ in the middle, the next move landing on another $\frac{1}{12}$ **[1/3]**
10. moving "forward two spaces" after being on a $\frac{1}{3}$ **[1/6]**
11. landing on $\frac{1}{2}$ on your second move **[1/12]**
12. landing on $\frac{1}{3}$ on your second move **[1/6]**
13. landing on a $\frac{1}{6}$ or a $\frac{1}{3}$ **[7/30]**
14. landing on a $\frac{1}{4}$ or a $\frac{1}{2}$ **[2/15]**
15. the finishing roll being a 3 **[0]**
16. landing on $\frac{1}{12}$ on your second move **[1/9]**
17. landing on a $\frac{1}{12}$ or "forward two spaces" **[7/30]**
18. landing on a $\frac{2}{3}$ or "back two spaces" **[2/5]**
19. landing on a space with an even denominator or an odd denominator **[9/10]**
20. landing on a space with an even denominator or requiring the piece to move two spaces **[3/5]**
21. landing on a space with an odd denominator or requiring the piece to move two spaces **[1/2]**
22. landing on a space with a 1 or a 2 in the numerator **[9/10]**
23. landing on a $\frac{1}{4}$ after being on a corner space and then landing on a $\frac{1}{12}$ **[1/18]**
24. landing on a "forward two spaces" after being on a $\frac{1}{3}$ and then landing on a $\frac{1}{6}$ on the next turn **[1/18]**
25. landing on a $\frac{1}{6}$ on your first two moves **[1/36]**
26. landing on a $\frac{1}{3}$ on your last two moves **[0]**
27. landing on two $\frac{1}{2}$s in a row **[0]**
28. from the $\frac{1}{12}$ in the right corner landing on $\frac{1}{12}$ **[1/2]**
29. rolling a 4 and landing on a $\frac{1}{6}$ at some point in the game **[1/10]**
30. rolling a 3 and landing on a $\frac{1}{6}$ at some point in the game **[1/6]**

Guided Instruction

PURPOSE To show how individual and cumulative probabilities can be displayed in a table or graph

PROCESS Students will

- use experimental and theoretical probabilities to find individual probabilities.
- sum individual probabilities to find cumulative probabilities.

DISCUSS Probability distributions are used to find probabilities of many different events using the same sample space. Elicit that

- the sum of all possible probabilities in the same sample space is equal to 1.
- cumulative values are found by adding the included value and the values below it.

Activity 1

If time permits, you may suggest that students increase the number of trials so their data will be closer to the theoretical probabilities. Students could also combine data from their experiments.

Q Is this activity using experimental or theoretical probability? Explain. **[Experimental; you are actually rolling the number cubes and collecting the data.]**

Q Might your graph look different if you used theoretical probabilities? Explain. **[Yes; experimental probability might show probabilities of 0%. Theoretically, each of these sums will occur.]**

Q How can you use your table to find the probability that the sum is less than 5? **[Add $P(\text{sum } 2) + P(\text{sum } 3) + P(\text{sum } 4).$]**

Mathematical Practices This Concept Byte supports students in making sense of problems, Mathematical Practice 1.

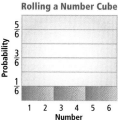

Concept Byte
For Use With Lesson 11-3
ACTIVITY

Probability Distributions

Content Standard
S.IC.2 Decide if a specified model is consistent with results from a given data-generating process, e.g., using simulation.

A **probability distribution** is a function that gives the probability of each outcome in a sample space. You can use a frequency table or a graph to show a probability distribution.

The theoretical probability of rolling each number on a standard number cube is the same: $\frac{1}{6}$. It is a **uniform distribution**, a probability distribution that is equal for each event in the sample space. Here is a table and graph of its probability distribution.

Event: Roll	1	2	3	4	5	6
Frequency	1	1	1	1	1	1
Probability	$\frac{1}{6}$	$\frac{1}{6}$	$\frac{1}{6}$	$\frac{1}{6}$	$\frac{1}{6}$	$\frac{1}{6}$

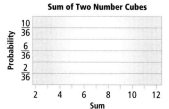

Rolling a Number Cube

Now, suppose you roll two standard number cubes. You can show the probability distribution for the sum of the numbers by making a frequency table and drawing a graph.

Activity 1

Roll a pair of standard number cubes 36 times. Record the sum for each roll.

1. Copy the frequency table below. Use your data to complete your table.

Event: Sum	2	3	4	5	6	7	8	9	10	11	12
Frequency											
Probability											

2. Copy and complete the graph at the right using your data.

3. Make a graph of the probability distribution for the sums of two number cubes rolled 36 times, based on the *theoretical probabilities* of each sum.

4. **a. Reasoning** Compare the graphs. Do you think the number cubes you rolled are fair? Explain.
   b. Explain why there are differences, if any, between the theoretical model and the experimental model.

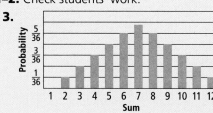

Sum of Two Number Cubes

694 Concept Byte Probability Distributions

Answers

Activity 1

1–2. Check students' work.

3.

4. a–b. Check students' work.

When you can assign numerical values to events, the **cumulative frequency** is the number of times events with values that are less than or equal to a given value occurs. **Cumulative probability** is the probability of events occuring with values that are less than or equal to a given value.

You can use the data you collected in Activity 1 to construct a cumulative probability distribution.

Activity 2

5. Copy and complete the table below. Add the probabilities within each range to find the cumulative probabilites.

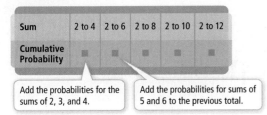

Sum	2 to 4	2 to 6	2 to 8	2 to 10	2 to 12
Cumulative Probability	■	■	■	■	■

Add the probabilities for the sums of 2, 3, and 4.

Add the probabilities for sums of 5 and 6 to the previous total.

6. Reasoning Explain why the cumulative probability in the last interval is 1.

7. Copy the graph below and complete it using the cumulative probabilites you computed.

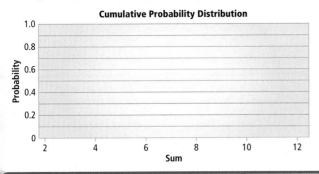

Cumulative Probability Distribution

Exercises

8. a. If you roll a pair of number cubes to model a situation and observe a sum of 7 four times in a row, would you question the model? Explain.
  b. If you observed a sum of 2 four times in a row, would you question the model? Explain.

9. Use a table and a graph to show the probability distribution for the spinner {red, green, blue, yellow}.

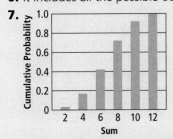

Activity 2

5.

Sum	2 to 4	2 to 6	2 to 8	2 to 10	2 to 12
Cumulative Probability	$\frac{1}{6}$	$\frac{5}{12}$	$\frac{13}{18}$	$\frac{11}{12}$	1

6. It includes all the possible outcomes.

7.

Cumulative Probability vs Sum

8. a. No; there are six ways of rolling a sum of 7. The probability of rolling a sum of 7 four times in a row is $\left(\frac{1}{6}\right)\left(\frac{1}{6}\right)\left(\frac{1}{6}\right)\left(\frac{1}{6}\right) = \frac{1}{1296}$. Although this is unlikely, rolling a sum of 7 four times in a row out of six different ways is possible.
  b. Yes; there is only one way to roll a sum of 2. The probability of rolling a sum of 2 four times in a row is $\left(\frac{1}{36}\right)\left(\frac{1}{36}\right)\left(\frac{1}{36}\right)\left(\frac{1}{36}\right) = \frac{1}{1,679,616}$.
9. See back of book.

1 Interactive Learning

Solve It!

PURPOSE To analyze a conditional probability situation

PROCESS Students may
- act out the situation.
- draw a branching tree diagram.

FACILITATE

Q What is the probability that you originally guessed the correct box? In this case, what wins the prize? $\left[\frac{1}{3}; \text{ not switching boxes}\right]$

Q What is the probability that you did not guess the correct box? In this case, what wins the prize? $\left[\frac{2}{3}; \text{ switching boxes}\right]$

Q How does the probability of winning by switching compare to the probability of winning by not switching? **[The probability of winning by switching is twice that of not switching.]**

ANSWER See Solve It in Answers on next page.

CONNECT THE MATH In the Solve It, students calculate conditional probability based on an initial choice. In the lesson, students will find conditional probability of situations using formulas and tree diagrams.

2 Guided Instruction

Problem 1

Q Multiply the probabilities of selecting a female and selecting a graduate student. Is the product the same as the probability in 1A? Explain. **[No; it is much lower, about 0.11. Selecting a grad student is a given in 1A, so that part of the probability is 100%.]**

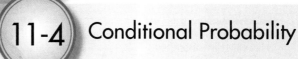

Content Standards

S.CP.6 Find the conditional probability of *A* given *B* as the fraction of *B*'s outcomes that also belong to *A* . . .
Also S.CP.3, S.CP.4, S.CP.5, S.CP.8

11-4 Conditional Probability

Objectives To find conditional probabilities
To use tables and tree diagrams to determine conditional probabilities

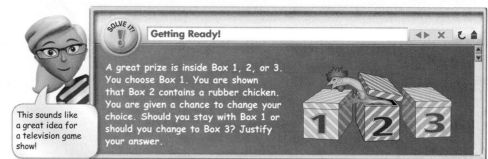

Getting Ready!

A great prize is inside Box 1, 2, or 3. You choose Box 1. You are shown that Box 2 contains a rubber chicken. You are given a chance to change your choice. Should you stay with Box 1 or should you change to Box 3? Justify your answer.

This sounds like a great idea for a television game show!

Lesson Vocabulary
- conditional probability
- contingency table

The probability that an event, *B*, will occur given that another event, *A*, has already occurred is called a **conditional probability**.

Essential Understanding Conditional probability exists when two events are dependent.

You write the conditional probability of event *B*, given that event *A* occurs, as $P(B \mid A)$. You read $P(B \mid A)$ as "the probability of event *B*, given event *A*."

A **contingency table**, or *two-way frequency table*, is a frequency table that contains data from two different categories. Contingency tables and tree diagrams can help you find conditional probabilities.

Problem 1 Finding Conditional Probability

Education The table shows students by gender and by type of school in 2005. You pick a student at random.

A What is $P(\text{female} \mid \text{graduate school})$?

Think

What's the condition?
The student is at a graduate school.

The condition that the person selected is at graduate school limits the sample space to the 3,303,000 graduate students. Of those, 1,954,000 are female.

$$P(\text{female} \mid \text{graduate school}) = \frac{1954}{3303} \approx 0.59$$

Student Genders

	Males (in thousands)	Females (in thousands)
Two-year colleges	1866	2462
Four-year colleges	4324	5517
Graduate schools	1349	1954

SOURCE: U.S. Census Bureau

11-4 Preparing to Teach

BIG idea Probability

ESSENTIAL UNDERSTANDING

A conditional probability is the probability that one event occurs, given that another event has occurred.

Math Background

Conditional probability is the probability that one event will occur given that another event has occurred. For two events *A* and *B*, the conditional probability that *B* will occur, given that *A* has occurred, is written $P(B \mid A)$.

Once it is known that an event *A* has occurred, the sample space is restricted to the subset of events that include *A*. For example, if you are rolling a number cube, then the original sample space is {1, 2, 3, 4, 5, 6}. If *A* is the event that an even number is rolled, and you know that *A* occurs, then the new sample space is {2, 4, 6}. If *B* is the event that a 2 or 4 is rolled, then $P(B) = \frac{1}{3}$. However, $P(B \mid A) = \frac{2}{3}$.

Recall that if two events are independent, then the occurrence of one event does not affect the probability that the second event will occur. Thus, if *C* and *D* are independent events, then $P(D \mid C) = P(D)$.

Mathematical Practices

Attend to precision. Students will use a clear definition of the term "conditional probability" and determine when to calculate it.

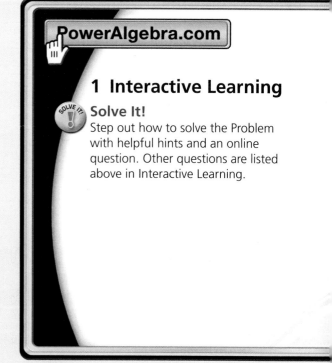

PowerAlgebra.com

1 Interactive Learning

Solve It!

Step out how to solve the Problem with helpful hints and an online question. Other questions are listed above in Interactive Learning.

B What is P(female)?

$$P(\text{F}) = \frac{\text{total number of females}}{\text{total number of students}} = \frac{2462 + 5517 + 1954}{1866 + 2462 + 4324 + 5517 + 1349 + 1954}$$

$$= \frac{9933}{17{,}472} \approx 0.57$$

 Got It? **1. a.** In Problem 1, what is P(Four-year | male)?

b. Reasoning Without calculating, given a student is enrolled in a four-year college, is it more likely for the student to be male or female? Explain.

 Problem 2 **Conditional Probability in Statistics**

Multiple Choice Americans recycle increasing amounts through municipal waste collection. The table shows the collection data for 2007. What is the probability that a sample of recycled waste is paper?

Ⓐ 16%   Ⓒ 33%

Ⓑ 28%   Ⓓ 57%

Municipal Waste Collected (millions of tons)

Material	Recycled	Not Recycled
Paper	45.2	37.8
Metal	7.2	13.6
Glass	3.2	10.4
Plastic	2.1	28.6
Other	21.7	46.3

Source: U.S. Environmental Protection Agency

Think

What's the condition?
The waste sample has to be recycled waste.

The given condition is that the waste is *recycled*. A favorable outcome is that the recycled waste is paper.

$$P(\text{paper | recycled}) = \frac{45.2}{45.2 + 7.2 + 3.2 + 2.1 + 21.7}$$

$$\approx 0.57, \text{ or } 57\%$$

The probability that the recycled waste is paper is about 57%. The correct answer is D.

Got It? **2. a.** What is the probability that a sample of recycled waste is plastic?

b. What is the probability that a sample of recycled waste is glass?

You can use a formula to find conditional probability.

take note

Key Concept **Conditional Probability**

For any two events A and B with $P(A) \neq 0$,

$$P(B \mid A) = \frac{P(A \text{ and } B)}{P(A)}$$

Q In 1B, is 0.57 a reasonable answer? Explain. **[Yes; the number of females is greater than the number of males in every row of the table, so the probability of picking a female must be greater than 50%.]**

Got It?

Q How would you translate 1a into a question using only words? **[What is the probability that a student attends a four-year college, given that the student is male?]**

Problem 2

Q Based on the answer, how would you find the probability that a sample of recycled waste is *not* paper without calculating? **[The probability of recycled waste that is not paper is the probability of all the recycled waste minus the probability of recycled waste that is paper: 100% − 57% = 43%.]**

Got It?

Q Does the question "What is the probability that a sample of waste is recycled glass?" differ from the question in 2b? Explain. **[Yes; in 2b, it is a given that the sample is recycled.]**

Take Note

Q In the formula for conditional probability, is A or B the given condition? **[A is the given condition.]**

Q Why must $P(A)$ not equal zero? **[Division by zero is not allowed.]**

---

2 Guided Instruction

 Each Problem is worked out and supported online.

Problem 1
Finding Conditional Probability
Animated

Problem 2
Conditional Probability in Statistics

Problem 3
Using the Conditional Probability Formula
Animated

Problem 4
Using a Tree Diagram
Animated

Support in Algebra 2 Companion
• Vocabulary
• Key Concepts
• Got It?

Answers

Solve It!
Change to box 3; there is a $\frac{1}{3}$ chance that box 1 has the prize and a $\frac{2}{3}$ chance that box 3 has the prize.

Got It?
1. a. ≈ 0.57355 or $\approx 57.355\%$

b. Female; there are more females enrolled.

2. a. ≈ 0.026448 or $\approx 2.64\%$

b. ≈ 0.040302 or $\approx 4.03\%$

Problem 3

Another approach to Problem 3 is to recognize that once it is given that the customer is male, the sample space is restricted to the first row of the table. To find the size of the new sample space, add the entries in the first column, $12 + 8 = 20$. This is the total number of males in the sample space. The number of males who pay online is 12. Dividing, you get $\frac{12}{20} = 0.6$.

Q Suppose you know that a customer pays by mail. Is it more likely that the customer is male or female? Explain. **[14 customers pay by mail. Of these, eight are male and six are female. Therefore, the probability that a customer is male is $\frac{8}{14} \approx 0.57$. Thus, it is more likely that a customer is male, given that the customer pays by mail, even though there are more females in the original sample space.]**

Got It?

Q What two probabilities do you need to find to solve this problem? **[P(female and directly onto head) and P(female)]**

Q Without using the formula, how would you find $P(\text{Directly on Head} \mid \text{Female})$? **[Divide the number in the female and directly onto head box by the total in the female row.]**

Using the formula for conditional probability, you can calculate a conditional probability from other probabilities.

Problem 3 Using the Conditional Probability Formula

Market Research A utility company asked 50 of its customers whether they pay their bills online or by mail. What is the probability that a customer pays the bill online, given that the customer is male?

Bill Payment

	Online	By Mail
Male	12	8
Female	24	6

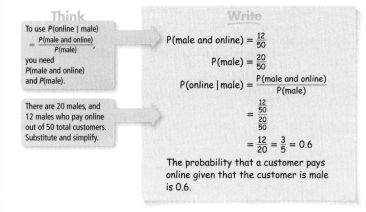

Think

To use $P(\text{online} \mid \text{male})$
$= \frac{P(\text{male and online})}{P(\text{male})}$,
you need $P(\text{male and online})$ and $P(\text{male})$.

There are 20 males, and 12 males who pay online out of 50 total customers. Substitute and simplify.

Write

$P(\text{male and online}) = \frac{12}{50}$

$P(\text{male}) = \frac{20}{50}$

$P(\text{online} \mid \text{male}) = \frac{P(\text{male and online})}{P(\text{male})}$

$= \dfrac{\frac{12}{50}}{\frac{20}{50}}$

$= \frac{12}{20} = \frac{3}{5} = 0.6$

The probability that a customer pays online given that the customer is male is 0.6.

Got It? **3.** Researchers asked shampoo users whether they apply shampoo directly to the head, or indirectly using a hand. What is the probability that a respondent applies shampoo directly to the head, given that the respondent is female?

Applying Shampoo

	Directly Onto Head	Into Hand First
Male	2	18
Female	6	24

It follows from $P(B \mid A) = \frac{P(A \text{ and } B)}{P(A)}$ that $P(A \text{ and } B) = P(A) \cdot P(B \mid A)$.

You can use this rule along with a tree diagram to find probabilities of dependent events.

Additional Problems

1. The table shows the number of male and female freshmen who chose to play one of the three intramural sports offered at a small college.

	Male	Female
Basketball	54	40
Soccer	36	61
Volleyball	10	12

What is $P(\text{soccer} \mid \text{female})$?

ANSWER about 0.54

2. A student compiled the following table comparing the amounts of land area and water area, in square miles, in various U.S. states.

	Land	Water
Alaska	571,936	91,332
Florida	54,018	11,777
Texas	262,100	6721
California	156,002	7694

What is the probability that a point chosen at random on a map is water, given that the map is of Florida?

ANSWER about 17.9%

3. The table shows the number of male and female customers at a café on a certain day. Each customer drank either a soda or an iced tea.

	Soda	Iced Tea
Male	21	29
Female	28	42

What is the probability that a customer drank a soda, given that the customer was male?

ANSWER 0.42

4. The chance of rain for the next evening is 60%. If it rains, the chance of lightning is 80%. If it does not rain, the chance of lighting is 5%. What is the probability that it will not rain and there will be no lightning?

ANSWER 38%

Answers

Got It? (continued)

3. 0.2

Problem 4 Using a Tree Diagram

Education A school system compiled the following information from a survey it sent to people who were juniors 10 years earlier.

- **85% of the students graduated from high school.**
- **Of the students who graduated from high school, 90% are happy with their present jobs.**
- **Of the students who did not graduate from high school, 60% are happy with their present jobs.**

What is the probability that a person from the junior class 10 years ago graduated from high school and is happy with his or her present job?

Make a tree diagram to help organize the information.
Let G = graduated, NG = not graduated, H = happy with present job, and NH = not happy with present job.

Think

What are the branches at each point?
The tree first branches at "graduated" and "not graduated." Each of these branches at "happy" and "not happy."

| This branch represents the students who did graduate. |
| Each first branch represents a simple probability P(G) = 0.85 and P(NG) = 0.15. |
| This branch represents the students who did not graduate. |

G
0.85
0.90 — H
0.10 — NH

NG
0.15
0.60 — H
0.40 — NH

| Each second branch represents a conditional probability P(H | G) = 0.90 and P(NH | NG) = 0.40 |

Think

Which path should you follow?
Follow the path that represents graduates who are happy with their present job.

The blue highlighted path represents P(G and H).

$$P(\text{G and H}) = P(\text{G}) \cdot P(\text{H} \mid \text{G})$$
$$= 0.85 \cdot 0.90$$
$$= 0.765$$

The probability that a person from the junior class 10 years ago graduated and is happy with his or her present job is 0.765, or 76.5%.

 Got It? 4. What is the probability that a student from the junior class 10 years ago in Problem 4 did not graduate and is happy with his or her present job?

Problem 4

A tree diagram is an alternative way to represent a sample space. The advantage of a tree diagram is that you can mark different probabilities for each branch; in an ordered-list sample space the probability of each item in the set is assumed to be equal and it is the number of combinations of items that determines probability.

Q The given information in the problem states the probability a student graduated high school. How was the probability that a student did not graduate found? **[Every student either graduated or did not graduate, so the total probability must be 1, 1 − 0.85 = 0.15.]**

Q The tree diagram shows four paths. What do you think the sum of the probabilities for all four paths should be? Explain and verify your answer. **[The sum of the probabilities for all four paths represents everything that could happen, so the probability should be 100%. P(H and G) + P(NH and G) + P(H and NG) + P(NH and NG) = 0.765 + 0.085 + 0.09 + 0.06 = 1.]**

Got It?

Q Which of the four paths did you follow to answer this question? What is the probability of each section of the path? **[The path is "not graduated" and "is happy." P(NG) = 0.15 and P(H│NG) = 0.6]**

Q If the graduating class contained 600 students, how many students would you expect did not graduate and are happy with their present jobs? **[54 students]**

4. 9%

3 Lesson Check

Do you know HOW?

- For Exercises 1–3, students must understand that it is given that the drawn card is black. That fact does not need to be calculated. Therefore, the denominator for calculating these probabilities should be 26 rather than 52.
- For Exercise 4, students may benefit from drawing a tree diagram. They should determine that the first branch is for illustrated/not-illustrated and the second branches are for hardback/not-hardback.

Do you UNDERSTAND?

- In Exercise 5, students may think that the sum of the probabilities of paired branches should equal the probability of the preceding branch in the diagram. Explain that the smaller branches contain 100% (all) of the preceding branch, which is the same as a part of the entire diagram.
- For Exercise 6, the situation must have at least two choices or events, and the first should be given.

Close

> **Q** What is a simple probability experiment that shows how the probability of an outcome changes when a part is given? **[Answers may vary. Sample: Flipping a coin twice and getting two heads has a probability of one fourth. If the first coin flip is given as heads, then the probability of getting two heads is one half. The probability doubled.]**

Lesson Check

Do you know HOW?

A card is drawn from a standard deck of cards. Find each probability, given that the card drawn is black.

  1. P(club)   **2.** $P(4)$ **3.** P(diamond)

4. The probability that a car has two doors, given that it is red, is 0.6. The probability that a car has two doors *and* is red is 0.2. What is the probability that a car is red?

Do you UNDERSTAND?

5. Reasoning Using the tree diagram in Problem 4, explain why the probabilities on each pair of branches must add up to 1.

6. Open-Ended Describe a situation in which you would use conditional probability to find the answer.

7. Compare and Contrast How are the Fundamental Counting Principle and tree diagrams alike? How are they different?

Practice and Problem-Solving Exercises   MATHEMATICAL PRACTICES

Ⓐ Practice   Use the table to find each probability.   ◀ See Problems 1 and 2.

  8. P(has diploma)

  9. P(has diploma and experience)

  10. P(has experience | has diploma)

  11. P(has no diploma | has experience)

Characteristics of Job Applicants

		Has Experience	
		Yes	No
Has High School Diploma	Yes	54	27
	No	5	4

Use the table to find each probability.

  12. P(The recipient is male.)

  13. P(The degree is a bachelor's.)

  14. P(The recipient is female, given that the degree is an associate's.)

  15. P(The degree is *not* an associate's, given that the recipient is male.)

Projected Number of Degree Recipients in 2010 (thousands)

Degree	Male	Female
Associate's	245	433
Bachelor's	598	858

Source: U.S. National Center for Education Statistics

Use the survey results for Exercises 16 and 17.   ◀ See Problems 3 and 4.

  16. Find the probability that a respondent has a pet, given that the respondent has had a pet.

  17. Find the probability that a respondent has never had a pet, given that the respondent does not have a pet now.

> 39% have a pet now and have had a pet.
>
> 61% do not have a pet now.
>
> 86% have had a pet.
>
> 14% do not have a pet now and have never had a pet.

  18. Sports A football team has a 70% chance of winning when it doesn't snow, but only a 40% chance of winning when it snows. Suppose there is a 50% chance of snow. Make a tree diagram to find the probability that the team will win.

[PowerAlgebra.com]

3 Lesson Check

For a digital lesson check, use the Got It questions.

Support in Algebra 2 Companion
- Lesson Check

4 Practice

Assign homework to individual students or to an entire class.

Answers

Lesson Check

1. $\frac{1}{2}$

2. $\frac{1}{13}$, or about 7.7%

3. 0%

4. 50%

5. The sum of the probability of an event happening and the probability of an event not happening is 1. Each branch represents either the event happening or the event not happening.

6. Check students' work.

7. Answers may vary. Sample: Tree diagrams apply to cases in which more than one event occurs in a sequence. The Fundamental Counting Principle applies to situations in which there are multiple outcomes of a single event. With a tree diagram, but not with the Fundamental Counting Principle, you can determine probabilities of dependent events, or conditional probabilities.

Practice and Problem-Solving Exercises

8. 0.9	**9.** 0.6
10. $0.\overline{6}$	**11.** ≈0.085
12. ≈0.395	**13.** ≈0.682
14. ≈0.639	**15.** ≈0.709
16. ≈45%	**17.** ≈23%

18.

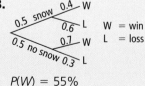

$P(W) = 55\%$

19. Make a tree diagram based on the survey results below. Then find P(a female respondent is left-handed) and P(a respondent is both male and right-handed).
  - Of all the respondents, 17% are male.
  - Of the male respondents, 33% are left-handed.
  - Of female respondents, 90% are right-handed.

 Apply © **20.** Suppose A and B are independent events, with $P(A) = 0.60$ and $P(B) = 0.25$. Find each probability.
  a. $P(A \text{ and } B)$ **b.** $P(A \mid B)$
  c. What do you notice about $P(A)$ and $P(A \mid B)$?
  d. Reasoning One way to describe A and B as independent events is *The occurrence of B has no effect on the probability of A.* Explain how the answer to part (c) illustrates this relationship.

© **21. Think About a Plan** A math teacher gives her class two tests. 60% of the class passes both tests and 80% of the class passes the first test. What percent of those who pass the first test also pass the second test?
  - What conditional probability are you looking for?
  - How can a tree diagram help you solve this problem?

Weather Use probability notation to describe the chance of each event. Let S, C, W, and R represent sunny, cloudy, windy, and rainy weather, respectively.

22. cloudy weather   **23.** sunny and windy weather   **24.** rainy weather if it is windy

25. Transportation You can take Bus 65 or Bus 79. You take the first bus that arrives. The probability that Bus 65 arrives first is 75%. There is a 40% chance that Bus 65 picks up passengers along the way. There is a 60% chance that Bus 79 picks up passengers. Your bus picked up passengers. What is the probability that it was Bus 65?

The tree diagram relates snowfall and school closings. Find each probability. Let H, L, O, and C represent heavy snowfall, light snowfall, schools open, and schools closed, respectively.

26. $P(C)$ **27.** $P(H \text{ and } O)$ **28.** $P(H \mid C)$

29. $P(L \mid O)$ **30.** $P(L \mid C)$ **31.** $P(H \mid O)$

© **Challenge** **32. a. Writing** Explain which branches of the tree diagram at the right represent conditional probabilities. Give a specific example.
  b. Are the event of having a license and the event of being an adult independent events? Justify your answer.
  © **c. Open-Ended** Estimate probabilities for each branch of the tree diagram for your city or town. Then find $P(L)$.

A = adult (21 or older)
M = minor (under 21)
L = licensed driver
N = not licensed to drive

© **33. Reasoning** Sixty percent of a company's sales representatives have completed training seminars. Of these, 80% have had increased sales. Overall, 56% of the representatives (whether trained or not) have had increased sales. Use a tree diagram to find the probability of increased sales, given that a representative has not been trained.

ASSIGNMENT GUIDE
Basic: 8–19 all, 20–26
Average: 9–19 odd, 20–31
Advanced: 9–19 odd, 20–33
Standardized Test Prep: 34–37
Mixed Review: 38–49

© **Mathematical Practices** are supported by exercises with red headings. Here are the Practices supported in this lesson:

MP 1: Make Sense of Problems Ex. 21
MP 2: Reason Quantitatively Ex. 32a
MP 3: Construct Arguments Ex. 5, 6
MP 3: Communicate Ex. 5, 20d, 32a
MP 3: Compare Arguments Ex. 7
MP 4: Model with Mathematics Ex. 33

Applications exercises have blue headings. Exercises 18 and 25 support MP 4: Model.

EXERCISE 25: Use the Think About a Plan worksheet in the **Practice and Problem Solving Workbook** (also available in the Teaching Resources in print and online) to further support students' development in becoming independent learners.

HOMEWORK QUICK CHECK
To check students' understanding of key skills and concepts, go over Exercises 9, 17, 20, 21, and 25.

19.

M = male
F = female
R = right-handed
L = left-handed

$P(L \mid F) = 10\%$, $P(M \text{ and } R) \approx 11.4\%$

20. a. 0.15
  b. 0.60
  c–d. Since $P(A) = P(A \mid B)$, the probability of A is the same, regardless of the occurrence of B.

21. 75%

22. $P(C)$

23. $P(S \text{ and } W)$

24. $P(R \mid W)$

25. $\frac{2}{3}$, or 66.67%

26. 0.50, or 50%

27. 0.08, or 8%

28. 0.64

29. 0.84

30. 0.36

31. 0.16

32. a. The branches labelled L and N represent conditional probabilities dependent upon the person being an adult or a minor. For example, the top branch represents the probability that a person is licensed given that he or she is an adult.

  b. No; the probability of a minor being licensed is not the same as the probability of an adult being licensed.

  c. Check students' work.

33.

T = representative that completed training seminars
R = representative that didn't complete a training seminar
I = representative with increased sales
N = representative without increased sales

$P(I \mid N) = 0.2$

Answers

Standardized Test Prep

34. C

35. H

36. A

37. [2] (1, 1), (1, 2), (1, 3), (2, 1), (2, 2), (2, 3), (3, 1), (3, 2), (3, 3); yes

   [1] correct sample space only

Mixed Review

38. $\frac{1}{3} = 33.\overline{3}\%$

39. $\frac{17}{76} \approx 0.22368 \approx 22.37\%$

40. $x = \frac{1}{4}(y - 2)^2 + 5$

41. $y = \frac{1}{12}(x + 2)^2 + 3$

42. 2

43. 0.830

44. 1.404

45. 3.465

46. $\frac{1}{7}$

47. $\frac{3}{7}$

48. $\frac{2}{7}$

49. $\frac{1}{7}$

Standardized Test Prep

Use the table for Exercises 34–35. A school library classifies its books as hardback or paperback, fiction or nonfiction, and illustrated or non-illustrated.

		Illustrated	Non-Illustrated
Hardback	Fiction	420	780
	Nonfiction	590	250
Paperback	Fiction	150	430
	Nonfiction	110	880

SAT/ACT

34. What is the probability that a book selected at random is a paperback, given that it is illustrated?

  Ⓐ $\frac{260}{3610}$ Ⓑ $\frac{150}{1270}$ Ⓒ $\frac{260}{1270}$ Ⓓ $\frac{110}{150}$

35. What is the probability that a book selected at random is nonfiction, given that it is a non-illustrated hardback?

  Ⓕ $\frac{250}{2040}$ Ⓖ $\frac{780}{1030}$ Ⓗ $\frac{250}{1030}$ Ⓘ $\frac{250}{780}$

36. Which of the following expressions is equivalent to $3(n - 3)(n + 4)$?

  Ⓐ $3n^2 + 3n - 36$ Ⓒ $3n^2 - 3n - 36$
  Ⓑ $3n^2 - 3n + 36$ Ⓓ $3n^2 - 36$

Short Response

37. What is the sample space for spinning the spinner twice? Are all the outcomes equally likely?

Mixed Review

Q and R are independent events. Find $P(Q \text{ and } R)$.   ◀ See Lesson 11-3.

38. $P(Q) = \frac{3}{4}$; $P(R) = \frac{4}{9}$ **39.** $P(Q) = \frac{17}{20}$; $P(R) = \frac{5}{19}$

Write an equation of a parabola with the given vertex and focus.   ◀ See Lesson 10-2.

40. vertex (5, 2); focus (6, 2)   **41.** vertex (−2, 3); focus (−2, 6)

Solve each equation. If necessary, round to the nearest thousandth.   ◀ See Lesson 7-5.

42. $2^x = 4$ **43.** $4^{2x} = 10$ **44.** $4^{x+1} = 28$ **45.** $7 - 3^x = -38$

Get Ready! **To prepare for Lesson 11-5, do Exercises 46–49.**

Find the following theoretical probabilities for the spinner at the right.

46. $P(\text{red})$ **47.** $P(\text{green})$

48. $P(\text{blue})$ **49.** $P(\text{yellow})$

Additional Instructional Support

Algebra 2 Companion

Students can use the **Algebra 2 Companion** worktext (4 pages) as you teach the lesson. Use the Companion to support

- New Vocabulary
- Key Concepts
- Got It for each Problem
- Lesson Check

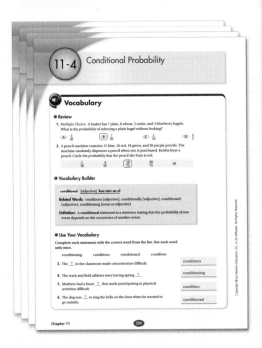

ELL Support

Focus on Communication Divide students into small groups or pairs. Ask each group to develop a table similar to the tables from Problems 1 and 3 in the lesson. Every group should divide its table into columns for "Female" and "Male." Allow each group to pick a way to divide the class into categories based on a single characteristic. Any non-offensive characteristic is acceptable as long as every student in the class will fit into one of the categories in every table.

After each group has decided on a characteristic, allow them to count students and fill in their tables.

Groups should ask each other probability questions of three types about the tables:

- Simple probability: What is the chance a student has brown hair?
- Compound probability: What is the chance a student has brown hair *and* is female?
- Conditional probability: What is the chance a student has brown hair, *given* that the student is female?

5 Assess & Remediate

Lesson Quiz

1. **Do you UNDERSTAND?** The table shows the number of male and female students in a certain classroom who take notes using different methods.

	Male	Female
Laptop Computer	27	33
Voice Recorder	2	1
Pencil and Paper	42	28

What is $P(\text{laptop} \mid \text{male})$?

2. You have two ways to drive home from work: Route A is usually quicker; Route B is scenic but slower. You choose Route A on 80% of your days and this gets you home by 6:00 P.M. 90% of the time. When you choose Route B you get home by 6:00 P.M. only 60% of the time. What is the probability that you choose Route B and get home by 6:00 P.M.?

3. A box contains 10 blue cubes, 5 red cubes, 5 blue marbles, and 10 red marbles. You randomly pick a blue shape out of the box. What is the probability that you picked a cube?

ANSWERS TO LESSON QUIZ

1. about 0.38
2. 12%
3. 0.67, or 67%

PRESCRIPTION FOR REMEDIATION

Use the student work on the Lesson Quiz to prescribe a differentiated review assignment:

Points	Differentiated Remediation
0–1	Intervention
2	On-level
3	Extension

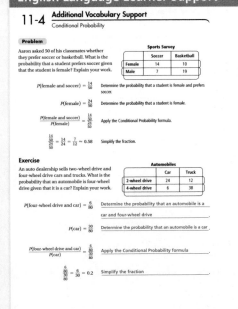

PowerAlgebra.com

5 Assess & Remediate

Assign the Lesson Quiz. Appropriate intervention, practice, or enrichment is automatically generated based on student performance.

Intervention

- **Reteaching** (2 pages) Provides reteaching and practice exercises for the key lesson concepts. Use with struggling students or absent students.

- **English Language Learner Support** Helps students develop and reinforce mathematical vocabulary and key concepts.

All-in-One Resources/Online
Reteaching

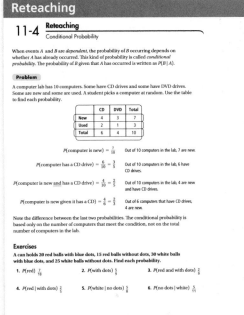

All-in-One Resources/Online
English Language Learner Support

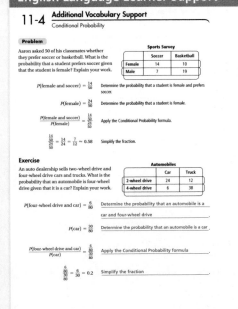

Differentiated Remediation *continued*

On-Level

- **Practice** (2 pages) Provides extra practice for each lesson. For simpler practice exercises, use the Form K Practice pages found in the All-in-One Teaching Resources and online.
- **Think About a Plan** Helps students develop specific problem-solving skills and strategies by providing scaffolded guiding questions.
- **Standardized Test Prep** Focuses on all major exercises, all major question types, and helps students prepare for the high-stakes assessments.

Extension

- **Enrichment** Provides students with interesting problems and activities that extend the concepts of the lesson.
- **Activities, Games, and Puzzles** Worksheets that can be used for concepts development, enrichment, and for fun!

Practice and Problem Solving Wkbk/ All-in-One Resources/Online

Practice page 1

11-4 **Practice** *Form G*
Conditional Probability

Use the table at the right to find each probability.

Education and Salary of Employees

	Under \$20,000	\$20,000 to \$30,000	Over \$30,000
Less than high school	69	36	2
High school	112	98	14
Some college	102	193	143
College degree	13	178	245

1. *P*(has less than high school education) 8.9%
2. *P*(earns over \$30,000 and has less than high school education) 0.2%
3. *P*(earns over \$30,000 | has only high school education) 6.25%
4. *P*(has high school education or less | earns over \$30,000) 4%

Use the table below to find each probability. The table gives information about students at one school.

Favorite Leisure Activities

	Sports	Hiking	Reading	Phoning	Shopping	Other
Female	39	48	85	62	71	29
Male	67	58	76	54	68	39

5. *P*(sports | female) 11.7%
6. *P*(female | sports) 36.8%
7. *P*(reading | male) 21%
8. *P*(male | reading) 47.2%
9. *P*(hiking | female) 14.4%
10. *P*(hiking | male) 16%
11. *P*(male | shopping) 48.9%
12. *P*(female | shopping) 51.1%
13. The senior class is 55% female, and 32% of the class are females who play a competitive sport. What is the probability that a student plays a competitive sport, given that the student is female? 58.2%
14. A softball game has an 80% chance of being cancelled if it rains and a 30% chance of being cancelled if there is fog when there is no rain. There is a 70% chance of fog with no rain and a 30% chance of rain.
    a. Make a tree diagram based on the information above.
    b. Find the probability that there will be fog and the game will be cancelled. 21%
    c. Find the probability that there will be rain and the game will be played. 6%
    d. Find the probability that the game will be cancelled. 45%

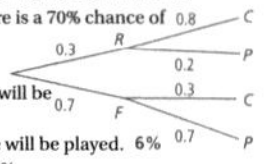

Practice and Problem Solving Wkbk/ All-in-One Resources/Online

Practice page 2

11-4 **Practice** (continued) *Form G*
Conditional Probability

15. The population of a high school is 51% male. 45% of the males and 49% of the females attend concerts.
    a. Make a tree diagram based on the information above.
    b. Find the probability that a student is male and attends concerts. about 23%
    c. Find the probability that a student is female and does not attend concerts. about 25%
    d. Find the probability that a student attends concerts. about 47%

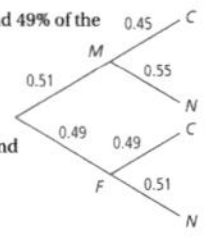

16. **Reasoning** A student says that if $P(A) = P(A \mid B)$, then *A* and *B* must be independent events. Is the student correct? Explain.
    Yes; if *A* and *B* are independent, then the probability of *A* will be the same whether or not *B* occurs.
17. A school's colors are blue and gold. At a pep rally, 65% of the students are wearing both blue and gold, and 90% of the students are wearing blue.
    a. What percent of students wearing blue are also wearing gold? 72%
    b. **Writing** Describe how a tree diagram could help you solve this problem.
    Answers may vary. Sample: A tree diagram can help me determine *P*(B) and *P*(B and G) so that I can use the formula for conditional probability.

You survey a group of juniors and seniors. The tree diagram relates student's class and whether a student is employed after school. Find each probability. Let J, S, E, and U represent junior, senior, employed, and unemployed, respectively.

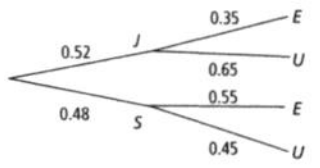

18. *P*(E) 44.6%
19. *P*(J and U) 33.8%
20. *P*(S | E) 59.2%
21. *P*(J | U) 61%
22. *P*(S | U) 39.0%
23. *P*(J | E) 40.8%

All-in-One Resources/Online

Enrichment

11-4 **Enrichment**
Conditional Probability

The Probability of Receiving a Defective Item in a Shipment

Many manufactured items look interchangeable. Examples are ball bearings, light bulbs, and transistors. However, an individual ball bearing may be too large or too small, and a light bulb or a transistor that looks fine may prove to be defective. The following exercises require the computation of certain probabilities based on the number of defective items and the size of the sample. Answers can be given in terms of combination symbols.

1. A shipment contains 50 transistors, 3 of which are defective. What is the probability that a randomly chosen transistor from this shipment works? What is the probability that it is defective?
   $\frac{47}{50}$; $\frac{3}{50}$
2. A sample consisting of 2 transistors is chosen from this shipment. What is the probability that both transistors work? What is the probability that both transistors are defective? $\frac{_{47}C_2}{_{50}C_2}$ or 88.2%; $\frac{_3C_2}{_{50}C_2}$ or 0.2%
3. A shipment contains 80 ball bearings, 5 of which are defective. What is the probability that a randomly selected ball bearing is of an acceptable size? What is the probability that it is defective? $\frac{15}{16}$; $\frac{1}{16}$
4. A sample of three ball bearings is chosen from the above shipment.
   a. What is the probability that all three ball bearings are acceptable? $\frac{_{75}C_3}{_{80}C_3}$; or 82.1%
   b. What is the probability that two ball bearings are acceptable and one is defective? $\frac{_{75}C_2 \times _5C_1}{_{80}C_3}$ or 16.9%
   c. What is the probability that one is acceptable and two are defective? $\frac{_{75}C_1 \times _5C_2}{_{80}C_3}$ or 0.9%
   d. What is the probability that all three ball bearings are defective? $\frac{_5C_3}{_{80}C_3}$ or 0.01%
   e. What is the probability that an odd number of ball bearings are defective? $\frac{_{75}C_2 \times _5C_1 + _5C_3}{_{80}C_3}$ or 16.9%
5. A shipment of toy cars contains 40 red cars and 45 blue cars. Two cars of each color are defective. A sample of three toy cars is chosen from the shipment.
   a. What is the probability that all three toy cars are blue? $\frac{_{45}C_3}{_{85}C_3}$ or 14.4%
   b. What is the probability that two toy cars are blue and one is red? $\frac{_{45}C_2 \times _{40}C_1}{_{85}C_3}$ or 40.1%
   c. What is the probability that two toy cars are acceptable and one is defective? $\frac{_{81}C_2 \times _4C_1}{_{85}C_3}$ or 13.1%
   d. What is the probability that two toy cars are red and acceptable and one is blue and defective? $\frac{_{38}C_2 \times _2C_1}{_{85}C_3}$ or 1.4%
   e. What is the probability that one toy car is an acceptable blue car, another is a defective blue car, and the other is a defective red car? $\frac{_{43}C_1 \times _2C_1 \times _2C_1}{_{85}C_3}$ or 0.2%

Practice and Problem Solving Wkbk/ All-in-One Resources/Online

Think About a Plan

11-4 **Think About a Plan**
Conditional Probability

Transportation You can take Bus 65 or Bus 79. You take the first bus that arrives. The probability that Bus 65 arrives first is 75%. There is a 40% chance that Bus 65 picks up passengers along the way. There is a 60% chance that Bus 79 picks up passengers. Your bus picked up passengers. What is the probability that it was Bus 65?

Understanding the Problem

1. What is the probability that Bus 65 arrives first? 75%
2. What is the probability that Bus 65 picks up passengers? 40%
3. What is the probability that Bus 79 picks up passengers? 60%
4. What is the problem asking you to determine?
   the probability that Bus 65 arrived first

Planning the Solution

5. Let B65 = Bus 65 arrived first, B79 = Bus 79 arrived first, P = passengers, NP = no passengers. What conditional probability are you looking for? *P*(B65 | P)
6. How can a tree diagram help you solve the problem?
   Answers may vary. Sample: A tree diagram can help me organize the information in the problem and see all of the possible probabilities involved.
7. Write an equation you can use to find the probability that your bus was Bus 65.
   $P(\text{B65} \mid \text{P}) = \frac{P(\text{B65 and P})}{P(\text{B65 and P}) + P(\text{B79} + P)}$

Getting an Answer

8. Make a tree diagram for this problem.

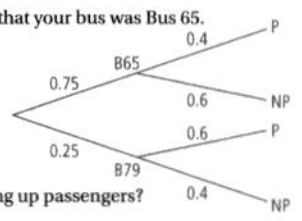

9. Which two branches of the diagram show a bus picking up passengers?
   0.75 × 0.4 and 0.25 × 0.6
10. What is the probability your bus was Bus 65? $\frac{2}{3}$ or 66.67%

Practice and Problem Solving Wkbk/ All-in-One Resources/Online

Standardized Test Prep

11-4 **Standardized Test Prep**
Conditional Probability

Multiple Choice

For Exercises 1–2, choose the correct letter.

A local bookstore classifies its books by type of reader, type of book, and cost. Use the table at the right for Exercises 1–2.

		< \$10	> \$10
Child	Fiction	120	255
	Nonfiction	35	60
Adult	Fiction	200	110
	Nonfiction	75	150

1. What is the probability that a book selected at random is a child's book, given that it costs \$15? C
   A. $\frac{315}{1005}$ B. $\frac{470}{1005}$ C. $\frac{315}{575}$ D. $\frac{470}{575}$
2. What is the probability that a book selected at random is fiction, given that it costs \$6? I
   F. $\frac{320}{1005}$ G. $\frac{430}{1005}$ H. $\frac{120}{430}$ I. $\frac{320}{430}$

Extended Response

3. Of the photographs produced in one day at a photo shop, 25% are black-and-white, and the rest are in color. Portraits make up 65% of the black-and-white photos and 45% of the color photos. Let B, C, P, and N represent black-and-white, color, portrait, and not a portrait, respectively. Draw a tree diagram to represent this situation. What is the probability that a photo chosen at random is not a portrait? Show your work.

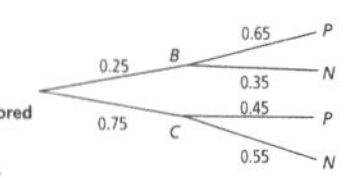

[4] Student used correct tree diagram and conditional probability formula to show $P(N) = 50\%$.
[3] Student used diagram and formula, but misunderstood part of the problem or ignored important information.
[2] Student attempted to use diagram and formula, but did so incorrectly, OR student used inappropriate strategy, but showed some understanding of the problem.
[1] Student attempted to solve problem, but used inappropriate strategy and made little progress toward solution.
[0] incorrect answers and no work shown OR no answers given

Online Teacher Resource Center

Activities, Games, and Puzzles

11-4 **Game: On One Condition**
Conditional Probability

This is a game for two teams of two players. Each team needs nine index cards.

Rules

- Take a few minutes to examine the table below.
- In each round, teams simultaneously write a conditional probability on an index card. Do *not* calculate it at this point.
- Exchange cards and calculate the other team's conditional probability.
- Exchange cards again and calculate your own team's conditional probability, verifying your opponent's result.
- Resolve the difference with your opponent if the probabilities do not match.
- Record your results in the appropriate spaces below.
- The team with the higher-valued probability wins the round.
- A conditional probability can be used only once in the game.
- Do *not* proceed to the probability calculating stage if both teams select the same conditional probability. Both teams must select another conditional probability. This initial one is still available for another round.
- The team that wins the most rounds wins the game.

Number of Fish Stocked in Man-Made Lake

Species	Weight of Fish (lb)					
	0–3.9	4–7.9	8–11.9	12–15.9	16–20	Row Total
Bass	320	250	130	0	0	700
Carp	110	220	310	210	50	900
Catfish	120	340	410	280	50	1200
Trout	150	490	250	110	0	1000
Column Total	700	1300	1100	600	100	3800

	Team 1	Team 2
Round 1	Check students'	work.
Round 2		
Round 3		
Round 4		
Round 5		
Round 6		
Round 7		
Round 8		
Round 9		

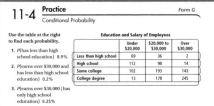

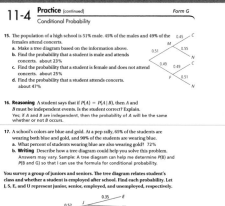

Probability Models

Content Standards
S.MD.6 Students will use probabilities to make fair decisions . . .
S.MD.7 Students will analyze decisions using probability concepts . . .

Objective To use probabilities to make fair decisions and analyze decisions

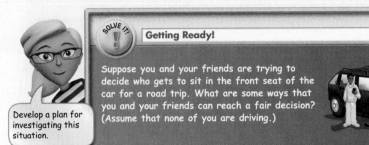

SOLVE IT!

Getting Ready!

Suppose you and your friends are trying to decide who gets to sit in the front seat of the car for a road trip. What are some ways that you and your friends can reach a fair decision? (Assume that none of you are driving.)

Develop a plan for investigating this situation.

MATHEMATICAL PRACTICES

In the Solve It, you may have thought about ways that you have reached fair decisions. In this lesson, you will learn how to use probabilities to make fair decisions.

Essential Understanding You can use probability models to analyze situations and make fair decisions.

A fair game is a game in which all of the participants have an equal chance of winning. For example, two players take turns rolling a number cube. The first player gets a point if an odd number is rolled, and the second player gets a point if an even number is rolled. Each player has the same probability of scoring a point on each roll. Similarly, a fair decision is based on choices that are equally likely to be chosen.

Lesson Vocabulary
• probability model

Problem 1 Making a Fair Decision

A class of 25 students wants to choose 3 students at random to bring food for a class party. Any set of 3 students should have an equal chance of being chosen. Which of the following strategies will result in a fair decision?

A The students line up alphabetically, and each one in succession flips a fair coin. The first three students to flip heads bring the food.

This strategy will not result in a fair decision because all students do not have an equal chance of being chosen. Students at the back of the line will probably never get to flip a coin.

Think
What is required for a decision to be fair?
Each possible outcome must be equally likely.

1 Interactive Learning

Solve It!
PURPOSE To describe ways of making a fair decision.
PROCESS Have students discuss different ways they usually make decisions with their friends or families.

FACILITATE
Q How does probability play a role in making a fair decision? What must be true about the probability that each friend will sit in the front seat? **[The probability of each friend being selected must be the same in order for a fair decision to be reached.]**

ANSWER See Solve It in Answers on next page.
CONNECT THE MATH In the Solve It, students come up with different ways to model a random process that will result in a fair decision. In this lesson, students will learn how to model random situations, conduct simulations, and use probability to analyze decisions.

2 Guided Instruction

Problem 1

In this problem, students will determine whether a method results in a fair decision.

Q What is another method the teacher could use to reach a fair decision? **[Sample answer: Arrange the students in a circle and spin a pencil in the middle 3 times. Choose the 3 students the pencil points at.]**

11-5 Preparing to Teach

BIG ideas Data Collection and Analysis
ESSENTIAL UNDERSTANDINGS
• Probability models can be used to analyze situations and make fair decisions.

Math Background
Learning how to model random situations and make fair decisions is an important skill that can be applied in many areas of life. Students have likely been developing these skills by doing things like flipping a coin to decide who gets the ball first in a game. In this lesson, students will learn how to use probability models to help them make decisions, make predictions, and analyze decisions.

A probability model is a mathematical representation of a random situation. For example, a simulation is a probability model that uses probabilities to make predictions about real-life situations. A probability model can give you insight into what should happen mathematically so that you can make better decisions.

Mathematical Practices
Model with mathematics. Students will analyze and make decisions based on probability models. Sources for the models will be random data and simulations from everyday life, society, and the workplace. Students will determine if decisions made using probability are fair.

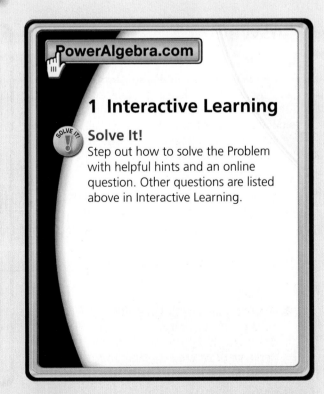

PowerAlgebra.com

1 Interactive Learning

Solve It!
Step out how to solve the Problem with helpful hints and an online question. Other questions are listed above in Interactive Learning.

Got It?

Q Is each sibling likely to have an equal chance of winning the race? Explain. **[No. Unless the siblings are identically suited to the race (which is very unlikely), one sibling is likely to have an advantage over the other.]**

Problem 2

In this problem, students use a random number table to model making a fair decision.

Q Why does this method result in a fair decision? **[Each player is equally likely to be chosen.]**

Q Does the result depend on which line of the random number table you choose? Explain. **[Yes, different lines will result in different players being selected.]**

Got It?

Q Does each student have an equal chance of being selected for either team? Explain. **[Yes, because the digits in the table are random, each student's number is just as likely to be selected for either team.]**

B Each student draws a card from a well-shuffled deck of 52 cards. The teacher shuffles a second deck of cards, spreads them out, and draws cards one by one until he matches the cards of three of the students.

Assuming a good shuffle, this strategy gives any group of three students an equal chance of being selected. So this strategy will result in a fair decision.

 Got It? **1.** Two siblings are trying to decide who has to mow the lawn this weekend. They decide to race, and the winner does not have to mow the lawn. Is the result a fair decision? Explain.

For an event to be random, there is no predetermined pattern or bias toward any particular outcome. You can use random numbers to help you make fair decisions.

A random number table contains randomly-generated digits from 0 to 9. You can use these numbers to model randomness for sampling purposes. Part of a random number table is shown below. Typically, space is inserted between groups of 5 numbers to help with readability.

Random Number						
87494	39707	20525	95704	48361	27556	34599
14164	15888	24997	82392	08525	47551	37304
61249	08241	16243	18371	03349	91759	53613
67868	56747	73521	05975	40411	49493	70904

 Problem 2 Using Random Numbers

A coach wants to select 3 of her 15 basketball players at random to lead warm-ups before practice each week. The coach assigns each player a number from 01 to 15. How can the coach use the random number table to fairly choose the three players?

Step 1 Choose a line of digits from a random number table.

87494 39707 20525 95704 48361 27556 34599

Step 2 Read the digits from the random number table in consecutive pairs until you get the numbers for three of the players. Skip numbers like 87 and 49 because they do not represent any of the 15 players. Also ignore any duplicates that may occur.

87494 39707 20525 95704 48361 27556 34599

The coach chooses the players assigned numbers 07, 04, and 12 to lead warm-ups.

Plan

How do you handle the spaces in the digits?
Ignore the spaces between the digits. For example, the third two-digit number is 43.

 Got It? **2. a.** A teacher wants to organize 10 students into two teams for a math game. The teacher assigns each student a number from 0 to 9. He uses the second line of digits from the random number table above to select the teams. He alternates the assigned team as each student is chosen. Which numbers will be used to create team 1?

b. Reasoning Is this a fair way to determine the teams? Explain.

Answers

Solve It!

Answers will vary. Encourage students to be as creative as possible in their decision methods. Sample method: Have the driver think of a number from 1 to 100. Each friend guesses a number and the closest to the correct number sits up front.

Got It?

1. Answers may vary. Sample: No, it is not likely that both siblings have an equal chance of winning the race.

2. a. 1, 6, 8, 9, 3

   b. Yes, each student has an equal chance of being selected for either team.

3. Answers may vary. Sample: Roll the cube until you get a 6. Keep track of the results. Repeat several times and take the average number of rolls needed.

PowerAlgebra.com

2 Guided Instruction

Each Problem is worked out and supported online.

Problem 1
Making a Fair Decision

Problem 2
Using Random Numbers

Problem 3
Modeling with a Simulation

Problem 4
Using Probability to Analyze Decisions

Support in Algebra 2 Companion
• Vocabulary
• Key Concepts
• Got It?

You can use a **probability model** to assign probabilities to outcomes of a chance process. In Lesson 11-2, you learned that you can use a simulation to estimate the experimental probability of an event. A simulation is an example of a probability model. You can use probability and simulations to make predictions about real-life situations.

© **Problem 3** Modeling with a Simulation

A restaurant gives away 4 different toys in their kids' meals. Each meal contains exactly one toy, and the toys are equally and randomly distributed. About how many kids' meals would a parent expect to have to buy to get all 4 toys?

Know
You know that toys are randomly distributed in each kids' meal. There is 1 toy in each meal.

Need
A probability model that generates four equally-likely events

Plan
You can use a spinner with four equal sections to simulate the random choosing of each toy.

Step 1 Spin the spinner and keep track of the results in a frequency table. Continue spinning until you have simulated getting each toy at least once.

Kids' Meal Simulation

Toy	Tally	Frequency
1	//	2
2	///	3
3	/	1
4	//	2

The results of this trial indicate that you would expect to have to buy
2 + 3 + 1 + 2 = 8 kids' meals in order to get all 4 different toys.

Think
Why do you need to repeat the simulation?
In general, the number of kids' meals you have to buy to collect all four toys will vary.

Step 2 Repeat the simulation several times.
Suppose that you conduct the simulation 24 more times and the results indicate that you can expect to have to buy the meal the following number of times before you get all 4 toys.

7, 9, 12, 6, 15, 5, 8, 10, 7, 13, 11, 6, 8, 9, 12, 13, 9, 10, 12, 7, 11, 5, 6, and 8.

Step 3 Find the average number of kids' meals needed to get all 4 toys.

$$\frac{227}{25} = 9.08$$

On average, you will need to buy about 9 kids' meals in order to get all 4 toys.

✔ **Got It?** **3.** Suppose that you are playing a board game for which you must roll a 6 on a number cube before you are able to move your game piece from start. Describe a simulation you can use to predict the number of times you would expect to have to roll the number cube before you can move from start.

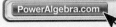

Problem 3 ERROR PREVENTION

When conducting a simulation, be sure students understand that they should conduct several trials and then take an average in order to make an accurate prediction. A single trial or a small number of trials of a simulation will not be predictive.

Q Suppose the spinner lands on Toy 1 three spins in a row. On the next spin, what is *P*(Toy 1)? Explain. **[0.25; the probability of each toy is the same on each spin.]**

Q If the number of trials is increased to 50, do you think the average number of kids' meals needed will be more or less accurate? Explain. **[More accurate; the more trials that are conducted, the better the simulation will model the situation.]**

Got It?

Q Conduct your simulation using at least 20 trials. What is the average number of rolls needed to get a 6? **[Answers will vary.]**

Additional Problems

1. To decide who has to mow the lawn, two brothers flip a coin. If it lands on heads, Tony has to mow the lawn. Otherwise, Chris has to mow the lawn. Will this result in a fair decision? Explain.

ANSWER Yes, each brother has the same chance of having to mow the lawn.

2. A coach wants to choose 2 of her 15 players at random to be team captains each game. She assigns each player a number from 01 to 15 and uses the line from a random number table below.

35737 73449 27032 58113
49598 41862

Which two players will be team captains next game?
ANSWER 03 and 13

3. Suppose a manufacturer is giving away 6 different prizes in boxes of cereal. The prizes are randomly and equally distributed in the cereal boxes. Describe and conduct a simulation to predict how many boxes of cereal you would need to buy to get all 6 prizes.

ANSWER Roll a number cube and let each number represent a different prize. Simulation results will vary.

4. Some junior varsity football players chose to participate in the voluntary weight training program over the summer. The table shows the results of who made the varsity team the following year. Based on these results, would you recommend the weight training program to junior varsity players? Explain.

ANSWER Yes, those who attended the program had a much better chance of making the varsity team.

	Weight Training	No Weight Training	Totals
Made Varsity	7	2	9
Did Not Make Varsity	5	6	11
Totals	12	8	20

Problem 4 ERROR PREVENTION

When using a contingency table to find conditional probabilities, be sure students divide by the correct value. Conditional probabilities limit the sample space to one of the values in the totals row or column. Dividing by the total number of patients (160) will result in incorrect probabilities.

Q In part A, what is the sample space? **[the 80 patients who received the drug]**

Q How is this different from the sample space for the probability P(reported improvements)? Explain. **[The sample space for P(reported improvements) is all 160 patients in the study. The conditional probability "given that he received the test drug" limits the sample space to only those patients who received the drug.]**

Got It?

Q What is P(reported improvements | received the drug)? **[0.46]**

Q What is P(received the placebo | did not report improvements)? **[about 0.53]**

You can use contingency tables to determine conditional probabilities and use those probabilities to evaluate decisions.

 Problem 4 Using Probability to Analyze Decisions

A pharmaceutical company is testing the effectiveness of a new drug for asthma patients. Out of 160 volunteers who suffer from asthma, 80 are given the drug, and 80 are given a placebo, which has no active ingredients. After 2 weeks, the volunteers are asked if they noticed improvement in their asthma symptoms. The results of the survey are shown in the contingency table at the right.

	Improved	Did not Improve	Totals
Received the Drug	67	13	80
Received the Placebo	24	56	80
Totals	91	69	160

A What is the probability that a volunteer reported noticeable improvement in symptoms given that he received the test drug?

The first row represents the total number of volunteers who received the drug. The number of those volunteers that reported improvements in symptoms is 67.

$$P(\text{improvement} \mid \text{drug}) = \frac{\text{number of volunteers who improved}}{\text{number of volunteers who received the drug}} = \frac{67}{80} = 0.8375$$

B What is the probability that a volunteer received the placebo given that he did not report a noticeable improvement in symptoms?

The second column of data shows the total number of volunteers who did not report improvements in symptoms, 69. The second row represents the total number of volunteers who received a placebo.

$$P(\text{placebo} \mid \text{no improvement}) = \frac{56}{69} \approx 0.8116$$

Think

How can you use what you know to analyze the company's decision? You can use the probabilities to analyze whether the drug was actually effective.

C The pharmaceutical company decides to produce and distribute this drug. The drug is marketed as an effective way to improve the symptoms of asthma. Based on the results of the test, did the company make a good decision? Explain.

The probabilities calculated above show that about 8 out of 10 people who are given the drug experience improvements in symptoms. Also, about 7 out of 10 who receive the placebo do not experience improvement in symptoms. Based on this study, the new drug appears to be effective at treating asthma symptoms. The company made a good decision.

Got It? 4. The results of another test are shown in the contingency table below. Should the company produce and distribute the new drug? Explain.

	Reported Improvements	Did not Report Improvements	Totals
Received the Drug	23	27	50
Received the Placebo	19	31	50
Totals	42	58	100

Answers

Got It? (continued)

4. Answers may vary. Sample answer: No, almost as many volunteers who received the placebo reported improvement as received the drug. Fewer than half of those who received the drug reported improvement.

Lesson Check

Do you know HOW?

Use the contingency table for Exercises 1 and 2.

	Passed	Failed	Totals
Studied	8	1	9
Did not Study	3	6	9
Totals	11	7	18

1. Find $P(\text{passed} \mid \text{studied})$.

2. Find $P(\text{did not study} \mid \text{failed})$.

Do you UNDERSTAND? MATHEMATICAL PRACTICES

3. **Open Ended** Give an example of a fair decision and an example of an unfair decision if two brothers are trying to decide who has to wash the dishes.

4. **Error Analysis** A classmate conducted a simulation to predict how many boxes of cereal he would need to buy to get all 5 prizes. After one trial of the simulation, he concluded that he would need to buy 7 boxes of cereal. What was your classmate's error? How should he conduct the simulation?

5. **Vocabulary** Look up the definition of simulation in a dictionary or online. How does this definition relate to the concept of simulation in mathematics?

Practice and Problem-Solving Exercises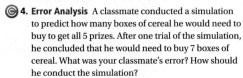

A Practice

For Exercises 6–7, determine whether strategies described result in a fair decision. Explain.

◀ See Problem 1.

6. There are 24 students in math class. The teacher wants to choose 4 students at random to come to the board and work a math problem. She writes each students name on a slip of paper, places them in a hat, and chooses 4 without looking.

7. You and three friends want to choose which two of your group will shovel the snow in the driveway. You are each assigned a number from 1 to 4, and then a spinner to choose the first person. Then that person chooses the second person.

For Exercises 8–9, use the lines from a random number table below.

◀ See Problem 2.

84496 18732 60330 19536 58380 52544 48712
01603 48862 18519 29834 90890 69751 20514

8. The advisor of the Good Citizen's club wants to select 4 of its 25 members to raise and lower the flag each day this week. She assigns a two-digit number from 01 to 25 to each student. What are the numbers that correspond to the members who will raise and lower the flag?

9. **Camp** A coach wants to select 5 of his 16 players at random to help with a youth basketball camp this weekend. He assigns a two-digit number from 01 to 16 to each player. What are the numbers of the players who will help at the camp?

10. **Shopping** A grocery store is giving away scratch-off tickets to each customer when they spend over $50. There are 3 different discount offers randomly and equally distributed among the scratch-off tickets. What is a simulation you could use to find, on average, how many times a customer would have to spend over $50 in order to get all 3 different discount offers?

◀ See Problem 3.

3 Lesson Check

Do you know HOW? ERROR INTERVENTION

• If students have trouble solving Exercises 1 and 2, then refer them to Problem 4.

• If students divide by 18 to find the conditional probabilities, then ask them how the sample space is limited by the condition in each exercise.

Do you UNDERSTAND?

• For Exercise 3, have students share their answers with the class so that they are exposed to a variety of decision-making methods. Ask students whether they have ever used the methods that they chose to make decisions.

• In Exercise 4, point out that a simulation will be much more predictive if several trials are conducted and an average value is found.

Close

Q What does it mean for a decision to be fair? **[Each possible choice is equally likely.]**

Q What is a probability model? How can you use a probability model to make predictions? **[A probability model is a mathematical representation of a random situation. Answers may vary. Sample answer: You can use a simulation to predict how many correct answers you will get on a true-or-false quiz if you guess the answers.]**

Lesson Check

1. about 0.89

2. about 0.86

3. Answers may vary. Sample answer: Flipping a coin to decide who has to wash the dishes is a fair decision. Arm wrestling to see who has to wash the dishes might be unfair if one brother is stronger than the other.

4. Answers may vary. Sample answer: He only conducted 1 trial of the simulation, which is not enough to arrive at an accurate prediction. He should conduct the simulation at least 25 times and find the average number of boxes needed.

5. Answers may vary. Sample answer: A simulation is an imitation or way of acting something out. In a mathematical simulation, a probability model is used to act out a situation that would be difficult or impractical to actually perform.

Practice and Problem-Solving Exercises

6. Answers may vary. Sample answer: Assuming the names are well mixed in the hat, this would result in a fair decision because each name is equally likely to be chosen.

7. Answers may vary. Sample answer: This will not result in a fair decision because the first person chooses the second person and might favor someone over someone else.

8. 01, 05, 25, 20

9. 01, 05, 16, 03, 08

10. Sample answer: Roll a number cube to simulate getting each discount offer. Let rolling a 1 or 2 represent the first offer, rolling a 3 or 4 represent the second offer, and rolling a 5 or 6 represent the third offer. Perform the simulation until each discount offer has been obtained at least once and then stop. Perform 20 or 25 trials of the simulation. Then find the average number needed to get all 3 discount offers.

4 Practice

ASSIGNMENT GUIDE

Basic: 6–11, 14–16

Average: 7–11 odd, 12–17

Advanced: 7–11 odd, 12–18

Standardized Test Prep: 19–22

Mixed Review: 23–26

 Mathematical Practices are supported by exercises with red headings. Here are the Practices supported in this lesson:

MP 1: Make Sense of Problems Ex. 15

MP 3: Compare Arguments Ex. 3

MP 3: Communicate Ex. 16

MP 3: Critique the Reasoning of Others Ex. 4

Applications exercises have blue headings. Exercises 9, 10, 11, and 17 support MP 4: Model.

EXERCISE 12 Use the Think About a Plan worksheet in the **Practice and Problem Solving Workbook** (also available in the Teaching Resources in print and online) to further support students' development in becoming independent learners.

HOMEWORK QUICK CHECK

To check students' understanding of key skills and concepts, go over Exercises 9, 12, 14, 15, and 16.

---

11. Testing The contingency table below shows the number of nursing students who took preparatory class before taking their board exams and the number of students who passed the board exams on their first attempt.

◀ See Problem 4.

	Preparatory Class	No Preparatory Class	Totals
Passed Exams	14	11	25
Did not Pass Exams	3	6	9
Totals	17	17	34

    a. What is the probability that a nursing student passed the board exams given that he or she took the preparatory class?

    b. What is the probability that a nursing student did not pass the board exams given that he or she did not take the preparatory class?

    c. A student decides to take the preparatory class before he takes the board exams. Is this a good decision? Explain.

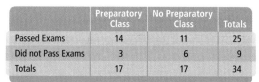 **Apply**

12. Community Service There are 24 members in a school's drama club. The advisor wants to randomly select 8 members to help seat patrons prior to a play at a local theater. How can the advisor choose the 8 members fairly? Explain.

Suppose you take a multiple-choice quiz. There are 4 choices for each question. You do not know the answers to the last 5 questions, so you guess the answers. For Exercises 13–14, use the simulation results below, where 1 represents a correct answer and 2, 3, and 4 represent incorrect answers.

31242 41211 34141 41212 23342 23242 13412
11313 42433 32334 31234 13314 41432 23413
42322 14331 12224 12232 31232 22223 31233
11214 33243 33414 21224 34112 43432 14234

13. How many trials of the simulation were conducted? What was the average number of correct answers for these trials?

14. If you need at least 3 correct answers to earn a passing grade, what is the experimental probability of guessing the answers and getting a passing grade based on this simulation?

© 15. Think About a Plan A delivery company is evaluating the effectiveness of a defensive driving course. The contingency table at the right displays data about drivers who took the course. Based on these results, the company decides to continue to offer the defensive driving course. Is this a good decision? Explain.

	Took Course	Did not Take Course	Totals
No Major Accidents	3	18	21
At least 1 Major Accident	0	4	4
Totals	3	22	25

    • What probabilities do you need to analyze the decision?

    • How do you decide whether the course is effective?

Answers

Practice and Problem-Solving Exercises (continued)

11. a. about 0.82

    b. about 0.35

    c. Sample answer: Yes, a high percentage of students who took the class passed the board exams on their first attempt so the class appears to be beneficial.

12. Answers may vary. Sample answer: Assign each member of the choir a number from 01 to 24 and use a random number table to select the 8 students.

13. 28 trials; about 1.14 correct answers per trial

14. about 10.7%

15. Answers may vary. Sample answer: Yes, the defensive driving course appears to be very effective and should be offered again. None of the drivers who took the course were involved in a major accident in the previous year.

16. Writing What role does probability play in decision-making and problem solving? Support your answer with examples.

17. Sports The local football team's field goal kicker has made 16 out of 20 field goal attempts from less than 30 yards so far this season. So, the experimental probability that the kicker will make his next field goal kick is 80%. What simulation could you use to find the average number of field goals he will make if he has three attempts of less than 30 yards in a game?

C Challenge
18. In some contests, the prizes are randomly distributed, but there may be more of one kind of prize than another. Suppose there are 250 tickets in a raffle. There is 1 grand prize, 5 first prizes, and 20 second prizes available. How can you simulate the results of the raffle?

Standardized Test Prep

SAT/ACT
19. Four customers arrive at a store at the same time to be the first to buy the new release of a video game. Since there are only three copies left, the store manager assigns each customer a number from 1 to 4, and uses the random numbers below to choose which customers get to buy the game. Which customer does NOT get to buy the game?

92352 46423 10770 44286 17178 25060 74858

Ⓐ customer 1   Ⓑ customer 2   Ⓒ customer 3   Ⓓ customer 4

20. Which explicit formula represents the geometric sequence 5, 15, 45, 135, . . . ?

Ⓕ $a_n = 5(3)^{n-1}$ Ⓖ $a_n = 3(5)^{n-1}$ Ⓗ $a_n = 5^{n-1}$ Ⓘ $a_n = 5(3)^n$

21. What is the completely factored form of the expression $3x^2 - 9x - 12$?

Ⓐ $(x - 1)(x + 4)$ Ⓒ $3(x - 4)(x + 1)$
Ⓑ $-3(x + 1)(x - 4)$ Ⓓ $(3x + 3)(x - 4)$

Short Response
22. What is the simplest form of the expression $5\sqrt{50x^5y^3} \cdot 2\sqrt{48xy}$?

Mixed Review

D and F are independent events. $P(D) = 0.35$ and $P(F) = 0.52$.   ◀ See Lesson 11-4.

23. What is $P(D \mid F)$?   **24.** What is $P(F \mid D)$?

Get Ready! To prepare for Lesson 11-6, do Exercises 25–26.   ◀ See p. 983

Find the median of each data set.

25. 0.2 0.3 0.6 1.2 0.7 0.9 0.8   **26.** 11 23 15 17 21 18 21

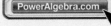

Answers

Practice and Problem-Solving Exercises (continued)

16. Answers may vary. Sample answer: Probability can be used to help make predictions based on simulations. Fair decisions can be reached by making sure the probability of each outcome is equally likely.

17. Answers may vary. Sample answer: Use a graphing calculator to generate random integers from 1 to 5. Let the integers 1, 2, 3, and 4 represent a made field goal, and let 5 represent a missed field goal. Generate random integers in groups of 3 to simulate the attempts in the next game. Perform the simulation at least 20 or 25 times and find the average number of field goals made.

18. Answers may vary. Sample answer: Because the prizes are not equally distributed, the outcomes of the simulation must be proportional to the prize distribution. Let the integer 1 represent winning the grand prize, the integers 2 through 6 represent the 5 first prizes, the integers 7 through 26 represent second prizes, and the integers 27 through 250 represent nonwinning tickets. Use a graphing calculator and the **RANDINT** function to generate random integers from 1 to 250 for each trial.

Standardized Test Prep

19. A

20. F

21. C

22. $200x^3y^2\sqrt{6}$

11-5 Lesson Resources

Additional Instructional Support

Algebra Companion
Students can use the **Algebra Companion** worktext (4 pages) as you teach the lesson. Use the Companion to support

• Solve It!
• New Vocabulary
• Key Concepts

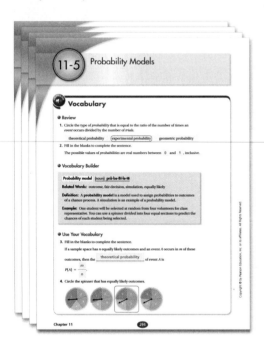

ELL Support
Use Technology In addition to using random number tables, computers and many calculators can be used to produce random numbers for modeling and simulation purposes. The screens below show how one calculator uses a function called **RANDINT** (to produce random integers from 1 to 25.)

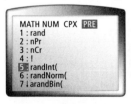

Discuss with students how using a calculator to generate random numbers can be more convenient than using a random number table. Then choose one of the Problems or exercises from the lesson and ask them how they could use a graphing calculator to design a simulation.

5 Assess & Remediate

Lesson Quiz
Use the Lesson Quiz to assess students' mastery of the skills and concepts of this lesson.

1. There are 143 business people attending a conference. Suppose one attendee is selected at random to win a door prize. Using the random numbers below, which attendee will win the prize? Assume they are numbered 001, 002, and so on.
57181 05428 61705 37736 21012

2. So far this season, a basketball player makes 75% of her free throw attempts. Describe a simulation you could use to predict how many of her next 5 free throws she will make.

3. **Do you UNDERSTAND?** The results of an exercise program are shown in the contingency table below. Would you recommend the exercise program? Explain.

	Used the Program	Did Not Use the Program	Totals
Lost Weight	12	7	19
Did not Lose Weight	3	8	11
Totals	15	15	30

ANSWERS TO LESSON QUIZ
1. 101
2. Sample answer: Use a spinner with 4 equal spaces numbered 1, 2, 3, and 4. Let 1, 2, and 3 represent a made free throw and let 4 represent a miss.
Spin the spinner 5 times for each trial and record the results. Conduct several trials and find the average number of made free throws.
3. Sample answer: Yes, the chances of someone losing weight were much higher if they used the weight-loss program.

PRESCRIPTION FOR REMEDIATION
Use the student work on the Lesson Quiz to prescribe a differentiated review assignment:

Points	Differentiated Remediation
0–1	Intervention
2	On-level
3	Extension

Intervention
• **Reteaching** (2 pages) Provides reteaching and practice exercises for the key lesson concepts. Use with struggling students or absent students.

• **English Language Learner Support** Helps students develop and reinforce mathematical vocabulary and key concepts.

All-In-One Resources/Online
Reteaching

All-In-One Resources/Online
English Language Learner Support

On-Level

- **Practice** (2 pages) Provides extra practice for each lesson. For simpler practice exercises, use the Form K Practice pages found in the All-in-One Teaching Resources and online.
- **Think About a Plan** Helps students develop specific problem-solving skills and strategies by providing scaffolded guiding questions.
- **Standardized Test Prep** Focuses on all major exercises, all major question types, and helps students prepare for the high-stakes assessments.

Extension

- **Enrichment** Provides students with interesting problems and activities that extend the concepts of the lesson.
- **Activities, Games, and Puzzles** Worksheets that can be used for concepts development, enrichment, and for fun!

Practice and Problem Solving Wkbk/ All-in-One Resources/Online

Practice page 1

11-5 Practice *Form G*
Probability Models

For Exercises 1 and 2, determine whether the strategies described result in a fair decision. Explain.

1. There are 16 players on a soccer team. The coach wants to choose 3 players at random to demonstrate a kicking drill. She makes a list of the number of goals scored by each player in the past 6 games. Then she chooses the top 3 scorers. Not fair; only the best scorers have a chance to be chosen.
2. There are 84 people in the audience of a theater. The manager wants to choose 5 audience members at random to receive snack coupons. He places all of the ticket stubs in a box and picks 5 of them without looking. Then he calls out the ticket stub numbers to the audience so that they can check whether their tickets have the winning numbers. Fair; each ticket stub has an equal chance of being chosen, so each audience member has an equal chase of winning.

For Exercises 3 and 4, use the lines from a random number table below.

79440	14939	47279	82830	23248	02248	73301
56409	99079	03881	90839	44182	09130	08834

3. A teacher wants to select 4 of the 28 students in her class at random to present their projects on Monday. She assigns a two-digit number from 01 to 28 to each student. What are the numbers of the students who will give their reports on Monday? 01, 27, 28, 23
4. A restaurant owner wants to place survey cards on 4 of the 15 tables in his restaurant at random. He assigns a two-digit number from 01 to 15 to each table. What are the numbers of the tables that will have survey cards? 01, 15, 09, 07
5. A juice company is having a promotion in which one of the letters J, U, I, C, E is printed on the inside of each of their bottle's lids. Customers win a free bottle of juice if they collect all 5 letters. Each lid is printed with exactly one letter, and the letters are equally and randomly distributed. Describe a simulation you can use to predict the number of bottles a customer would expect to buy to collect all 5 letters. Answers may vary. Sample: Make a spinner divided into 5 equal sections, each labeled with one of the letters J, U, I, C, E. Spin the spinner until you have simulated getting each letter at least once, and keep track of the number of spins. Repeat the simulation several times, and average the results.
6. A cereal company is giving away 2 different CDs in its cereal boxes. Each box contains exactly one CD, and the CDs are equally and randomly distributed. Describe a simulation you can use to predict the number of boxes of cereal you would expect to buy to get both CDs. Answers may vary. Sample: Assign "heads" of a coin to one CD and "tails" of the coin to the other CD. Toss the coin until you have simulated getting each CD at least once, and keep track of the number of tosses. Repeat the simulation several times, and average the results.

Practice and Problem Solving Wkbk/ All-in-One Resources/Online

Practice page 2

11-5 Practice (continued) *Form G*
Probability Models

7. The contingency table below shows the number of algebra students who used quiz software to study before a test and the number of students who received an *A* or *B* on the test.

	Quiz software	No quiz software	Totals
Received A or B	8	9	17
Received less than B	5	4	9
Totals	13	13	26

a. What is the probability that a student received an A or a B given that he or she used the quiz software? $\frac{8}{13} \approx 0.6154$

b. What is the probability that a student received an A or a B given that he or she did not use the quiz software? $\frac{9}{13} \approx 0.6923$

c. A school decides to purchase the quiz software for all of its algebra students. Is this a good decision? Explain. Answers may vary. Sample: No; the probability that a student received an A or a B is about the same regardless of whether the student used the quiz software. So, the quiz software does not seem to improve test performance.

8. There are 25 cats at an animal shelter. The shelter manager wants to randomly select 5 of the cats to take to a pet store for an adoption day. How can the shelter manager choose the 5 cats fairly? Explain. Answers may vary. Sample: Write each cat's name on a sheet of paper, place them in a box, and choose 5 without looking.
9. A weather reporter states that there is a 50% chance of rain on each of the next 3 days. Based on this forecast, describe a simulation you could use to determine, on average, the number of days in the next 3 days that it will rain. Answers may vary. Sample: Toss 3 coins, and let heads represent a day with rain and tails represent a day without rain. Count the number of heads. Repeat the simulation several times and average the results.
10. **Writing** Based on a simulation, a classmate concludes that he would have to buy on average 4 packs of trading cards to get all 6 different cards sold in the packs. If your classmate buys 4 packs of trading cards, is he guaranteed to get all 6 different cards? Explain. No; the average number of packs someone will have to buy to get all 6 cards is 4, but the actual number the classmate will have to buy could be less than or greater than 4.

All-in-One Resources/Online

Enrichment

11-5 Enrichment
Probability Models

A teacher has 6 students in her Honors Biology class. She wants to choose one of her students to attend a lecture at a local university. The teacher wants the students with an A average to have twice the chance of being chosen as her students who do not have an A average. She assigns the numbers 1 and 2 to her two students with an A average and the numbers 3–6 to her students who do not have an A average. Then she spins the spinner shown to choose the student who will attend the lecture.

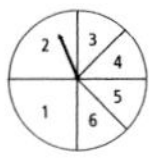

1. Does the process described give each student with an A average twice the chance of being chosen as each of the other students? Explain. Yes; each section on the spinner representing an A student is twice the size of each section representing a student who does not have an A average. So, on each spin, a number representing an A student is twice as likely to be spun as a number representing a student who does not have an A average.
2. What is the probability that a student with an A average will be chosen? $\frac{1}{2} = 0.5$
3. What is the probability that the student assigned the number 4 will be chosen? $\frac{1}{8} = 0.125$
4. Now suppose that 3 of the teacher's 6 students have an A average. Redesign the spinner so that each of the 3 students with an A average have twice the chance of being chosen as each of the students without an A average. Label each section with a number and with its degree measure.

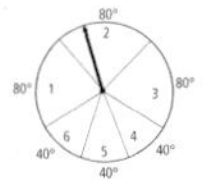

5. Based on the redesigned spinner, what is the probability that a student with an A average will be chosen? $\frac{2}{3} \approx 0.67$
6. Based on the redesigned spinner, what is the probability that the student assigned the number 4 will be chosen? $\frac{1}{9} \approx 0.11$
7. Do the methods described on this page for choosing one of the students result in a fair decision? Explain. Answers may vary. Sample: No; some students have a greater chance of being chosen than others.

Practice and Problem Solving Wkbk/ All-in-One Resources/Online

Think About a Plan

11-5 Think About a Plan
Probability Models

Sports The Redskins' field goal kicker has made 16 out of 20 field goal attempts so far this season. So, the experimental probability that the kicker will make his next field goal kick is 80%. What is a simulation you could use to find, on average, how many field goals he will make next game if he has 3 attempts using this experimental probability?

Know

1. The probability that the kicker will make his next field goal attempt is [80%].
2. What is this probability written as a fraction in simplest form? $\frac{4}{5}$
3. You are to assume that the kicker attempts [3] field goals in his next game.

Need

4. How many equally likely outcomes should your probability model have? Explain. Answers may vary. Sample: 5; the kicker will make a field goal 4 out of 5 times, so the model needs to have 5 equally likely outcomes.
5. Which outcomes will indicate a successful field goal attempt? Explain. Answers may vary. Sample: Outcomes 1–4; the kicker will make a field goal 4 out of 5 times, so 4 of the outcomes will represent a successful attempt.

Plan

6. Describe a probability model you could use to simulate a field goal attempt by the kicker. Answers may vary. Sample: Use a spinner with 5 equal sections numbered 1 to 5. Spinning 1, 2, 3, or 4 represents a successful attempt, and spinning 5 represents an unsuccessful attempt.
7. How could you use your model to simulate the kicker's field goal attempts for the next game? Answers may vary. Sample: Spin the spinner 3 times to represent the 3 attempts.
8. Why is it important to repeat your simulation several times? It is important so you can calculate an average number of field goals made.

Practice and Problem Solving Wkbk/ All-in-One Resources/Online

Standardized Test Prep

11-5 Standardized Test Prep
Probability Models

Multiple Choice

For Exercises 1–3, choose the correct letter.

1. There are 20 contestants in a talent contest. The contest organizer wants to choose 4 contestants at random to appear in the first round. Which strategy would result in the fairest decision? D
   - A The organizer chooses the first 4 contestants to sign up for the contest.
   - B The organizer lists the contestants' names in alphabetical order and chooses the first 4 names.
   - C The organizer writes each contestant's name on a slip of paper and then arranges the names from shortest to longest. Then she chooses the 4 shortest names.
   - D The organizer assigns each contestant a number and spins a spinner numbered 1 to 20. She picks the contestants with the first 4 different numbers that she spins.
2. The head of an astronaut-training program wants to choose 3 of the 32 trainees at random to take a zero-gravity flight. He assigns a two-digit number from 01 to 32 to each trainee. Based on the line of the random number table below, what are the numbers of the trainees who will take the flight? H

   79577 01104 76390 49032 91662 36151 59491 03051 45469 24460

   - F 01, 03, 10
   - G 03, 05, 15
   - H 04, 11, 32
   - I 05, 07, 09
3. A company is testing the effectiveness of a new lotion to fight acne. In the test, 60 volunteers use the new lotion, and 60 volunteers do not use any lotion. Based on the contingency table, what is the approximate probability that a volunteer showed improvement, given that he or she used the lotion? C

	Showed improvement	No improvement	Totals
Used lotion	32	28	60
Did not use lotion	12	48	60
Totals	44	76	120

   - A 27%
   - B 37%
   - C 53%
   - D 73%

Short Response

4. Refer back to Exercise 3. The company decides to sell the lotion as an effective way to treat acne. Based on the results of the test, did the company make a good decision? Explain.
   [2] Student states whether the company made a good decision and clearly and completely supports answer with evidence from the contingency table.
   [1] Incorrect or incomplete explanation given

Online Teacher Resource Center

Activities, Games, and Puzzles

11-5 Puzzle: Can We Set a Data?
Analyzing Data

The table below shows results from the 2008 Summer Olympics in Beijing, China. Use the data to answer the questions below the table, and determine the host countries for the 2012 Summer and 2014 Winter Olympics.

Split Time for First 250 m of Women's Kayak Double (K2), Heat 1									
GER	POL	CZE	FIN	ESP	JPN	SLO	RSA	GBR	
51.05	50.74	50.83	51.50	51.81	52.17	51.41	53.36	53.01	
Men's Handball Scores – Final Day									
CRO	ESP	FRA	ISL	RUS	POL	DEN	KOR		
29	35	28	23	28	29	37	26		
Badminton Mixed Doubles – Medal Round Scores									
CHN	CHN	CHN	INA1	INA1	INA1	KOR	KOR	INA2	INA2
19	21	23	21	17	21	21	21	11	17
Men's Archery Quarterfinals									
UKR	JPN	MAS	RUS	CUB	KOR	MEX	USA		
115	106	104	109	108	108	113	106		
Women's Beach Volleyball – Quarterfinal Scores									
BRA1	USA1	CHN1	AUT	USA2	CHN2	AUS	BRA2		
33	42	42	24	30	42	36	45		
Men's Sailing 470 Finals – Rounded Seconds After Winner (Australia)									
ARG	CRO	FRA	GBR	ITA	JPN	NED	POR	ESP	
24	26	18	6	17	5	24	32	9	
Women's Trampoline – Finals									
CAN1	CAN2	CHN	GEO	GER	RUS	UKR	POR		
37.0	35.5	37.8	36.1	18.9	36.2	36.6	36.9		
Men's Team Sabre – Final Day									
FRA	USA	ITA	RUS	EGY	HUN	BLR	CHN		
45	37	45	44	25	45	45	39		

Summer 2012 Finalists

1. Country with the closest score to the archery mean: RUS, or Russia
2. Country with the median time in sailing: FRA, or France
3. Country with 3 more points than the median of upper part in handball: ESP, or Spain
4. Country with 1.5 fewer points than the median of lower part in volleyball: USA, or the United States of America
5. Country with the lowest time on right whisker of box-and-whisker plot of kayak times: GBR, or Great Britain

Summer 2012 Host Country

6. Country closest to one-third of the mean time in sailing: GBR, or Great Britain

Winter 2014 Finalists

7. Country whose only score in badminton was the mode: KOR, or Korea
8. Country with Sabre score just below the 50th percentile: RUS, or Russia
9. Country with a volleyball score 12.75 points below the mean: AUT, or Austria

Winter 2014 Host Country

10. Country with a trampoline score that was the greatest value less than the median: RUS, or Russia

Answers

Mid-Chapter Quiz

1. 24
2. 720
3. 20
4. 15
5. 35
6. 9
7. 20
8. 19,958,400
9. 1
10. 24
11. 7
12. 21
13. combination; 126 ways
14. combination; 455 groups
15. permutation; 120 ways
16. $\frac{1}{10}$
17. $\frac{1}{5}$
18. $\frac{2}{5}$
19. 0
20. $\frac{3}{5}$
21. $\frac{1}{2}$
22. 1
23. $\frac{5}{8}$
24. $\frac{1}{3}$
25. 1
26. mutually exclusive; $\frac{5}{18}$
27. not mutually exclusive; $\frac{4}{9}$
28. Experimental probabilities are calculated on the basis of data from an experiment, actual or simulated. Given equally likely outcomes, the basis for calculating theoretical probability is being able to determine the no. of ways that an event can occur within these outcomes.
29. **a.** not mutually exclusive since 90 and 96 are both multiples of 2 and 3; independent since each event A or B does not affect the outcome of the other event

MathXL for School

Prepare students for the Mid-Chapter Quiz and Chapter Test with online practice and review.

Do you know HOW?

Evaluate each expression.

1. 4!
2. 6!
3. $\frac{5!}{3!}$
4. $\frac{6!}{4!2!}$
5. $_7C_3$
6. $_9C_8$
7. $_5P_2$
8. $_{11}P_9$
9. $_4C_4$
10. $_4P_4$
11. $2(_5C_4) - {_3}C_2$
12. $3(_3P_2) + {_3}P_1$

Indicate whether each situation involves a combination or permutation. Then solve.

13. How many ways are there to select five actors from a troupe of nine to improvise a scene?

14. How many different three-student study groups can be formed from a class of 15?

15. Your teacher is looking for a new apartment. There are five apartments available. In how many ways can your teacher inspect the apartments?

Suppose you select a number at random from the sample space {5, 6, 7, 8, 9, 10, 11, 12, 13, 14}. Find each probability.

16. $P(7)$
17. $P(5 \text{ or } 13)$
18. $P(\text{greater than } 10)$
19. $P(\text{multiple of } 30)$
20. $P(\text{less than } 7 \text{ or greater than } 10)$
21. $P(\text{greater than } 6 \text{ and less than } 12)$
22. $P(\text{integer})$
23. $P(\text{less than } 10 \mid \text{less than } 13)$
24. $P(\text{greater than } 8 \mid \text{less than } 11)$
25. $P(\text{greater than } 7 \mid \text{greater than } 12)$

Two standard number cubes are tossed. State whether the events are mutually exclusive. Then find $P(A \text{ or } B)$.

26. A means their sum is 12; B means both are odd.

27. A means they are equal; B means their sum is a multiple of 3.

Do you UNDERSTAND?

28. **Vocabulary** Explain the difference between experimental probability and theoretical probability.

29. Suppose you select a number at random from the set $\{90, 91, 92, \ldots, 99\}$. Event A is selecting a multiple of 2. Event B is selecting a multiple of 3.
    a. Writing Are events A and B mutually exclusive? Are they independent? Explain your answers.
    b. Find $P(A)$ and $P(B)$.
    c. Find $P(A \text{ and } B)$.
    d. Find $P(A \text{ or } B)$.
    e. Find $P(A \mid B)$ and $P(B \mid A)$.

30. **Reasoning** Let F and G be mutually exclusive events. Event F occurs more frequently than event G. Write the following in order from least to greatest: $P(F), P(G), P(F \text{ or } G), P(G \mid F)$.

31. **Error Analysis** For two events A and B, a student calculates the probabilities shown. Explain how you can tell that the student made a mistake.

    $P(A \text{ and } B) = 0.35$
    $P(A \mid B) = 0.29$

32. **Writing** A local restaurant owner employs 6 high school students who all want to work the same shift during spring break vacation week. To choose which 2 students will can work the shift, the owner assigns each student employee a number between 1 and 6, and then she rolls a standard number cube twice. The numbers that the number cubes show represent the employees who can work the shift. (If there are doubles, she rolls again.) Is the result a fair decision? Explain.

---

b. $P(A) = \frac{1}{2}$; $P(B) = \frac{2}{5}$

c. $\frac{1}{5}$

d. $\frac{7}{10}$

e. $P(A \mid B) = \frac{1}{2}$; $P(B \mid A) = \frac{2}{5}$

30. $P(G \mid F), P(G), P(F), P(F \text{ or } G)$

31. $P(A \mid B) = \frac{P(B \text{ and } A)}{P(B)}$; If $P(A \text{ and } B) = 0.35$ and $P(A \mid B) = 0.29$, then $0.29 = \frac{0.35}{P(B)}$ and $P(B) = \frac{0.35}{0.29}$. $P(B) > 1$, which is not possible.

32. Yes; each student has an equal chance of being selected.

Content Standards
S.MD.6 Use probabilities to make fair decisions . . .
S.MD.7 Analyze decisions and strategies using probability concepts . . .

Objectives To calculate measures of central tendency
To draw and interpret box-and-whisker plots

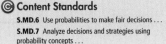

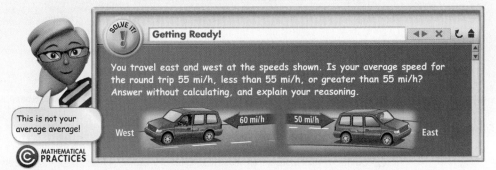

Getting Ready!

You travel east and west at the speeds shown. Is your average speed for the round trip 55 mi/h, less than 55 mi/h, or greater than 55 mi/h? Answer without calculating, and explain your reasoning.

West ← 60 mi/h   50 mi/h → East

This is not your average average!

MATHEMATICAL PRACTICES

Lesson Vocabulary
- measure of central tendency
- mean
- median
- mode
- bimodal
- outlier
- range of a set of data
- quartile
- interquartile range
- box-and-whisker plot
- percentile

People often refer to the mean as the *average*. The mean is only one of the measures considered the average, a measure of the center of a set of data.

Essential Understanding You can describe and compare sets of data using various statistical measures, depending on what characteristics you want to study.

Statistics is the study, analysis, and interpretation of data. One way to analyze data is by finding a *measure of central tendency*. A **measure of central tendency** indicates the "middle" of the data set. The *mean, median,* and *mode* are the most common measures of central tendency.

take note
Key Concepts   Measures of Central Tendency

Measure	Definition	Example, using 1, 2, 3, 3, 4, 5, 5, 9
Mean	$\dfrac{\text{sum of the data values}}{\text{number of data values}}$	$\dfrac{1 + 2 + 3 + 3 + 4 + 5 + 5 + 9}{8} = 4$
Median	for a data set listed in order: the middle value for an odd number of data values; the mean of the two middle values for an even number of data values	For 1, 2, 3, 3, 4, 5, 5, 9, the middle two values are 3 and 4. The median is their mean $\dfrac{3 + 4}{2} = 3.5$.
Mode	the most frequently occurring value(s)	Two modes: In 1, 2, 3, 3, 4, 5, 5, 9, both 3 and 5 occur twice.

1 Interactive Learning

Solve It!
PURPOSE To estimate a weighted average
PROCESS Students may
- draw an annotated diagram showing the number of hours driving each way.
- make a table of distance and number of hours traveling east, west, and in total.

FACILITATE
Q Why is the total average speed different from the average of the two speeds? **[The traveling time in each direction is not the same.]**
Q What is a similar question using the same speeds that would have an answer of 55 mph? **[Answers may vary. Sample: What is the average speed of a car that traveled for 5 hours at 50 mph and for 5 hours at 60 mph?]**

ANSWER See Solve It in Answers on next page.
CONNECT THE MATH Students analyzed the meaning of average in the Solve It. In the lesson, students will analyze data sets and use measures of central tendency.

2 Guided Instruction

Take Note   ELL SUPPORT
The *mode* in statistics is an English word that comes from French and means "fashionable" or "popular." For instance, pie *à la mode* (pie with ice cream) literally means "pie in the popular way." This may help students remember that the mode is the *most frequent* data value.

11-6 Preparing to Teach

BIG idea Probability
ESSENTIAL UNDERSTANDING
Data sets can be described using various statistical measures, depending on what characteristics are being studied.

Math Background
There are numerous statistical measures for describing and comparing sets of data.

Measures of Central Tendency indicate the "middle" of a data set.
- mean: the sum of all the data values divided by the number of terms, commonly called the average
- median: the value in the middle of the ordered data, or the mean of the two middle numbers
- mode: the value that occurs most frequently

Measures of Variation determine the variation within a set of data.
- range: the difference between the greatest and the least values
- interquartile range: the difference between the third and first quartiles
In the next lesson, two more measures of variation are introduced: *variance* and *standard deviation*.

An *outlier* is a value that is significantly greater or less than any other value in the set. Outliers may cause statistical analysis of the data to be misleading.

Mathematical Practices
Attend to precision. In analyzing data, students will make explicit use of the terms "mean," "median," "range" and "mode," and calculate each one.

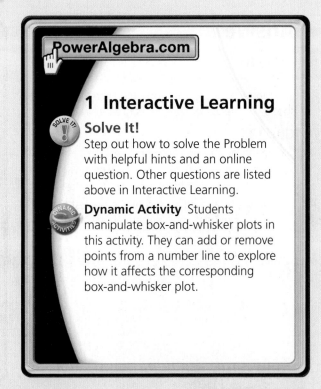

PowerAlgebra.com

1 Interactive Learning

Solve It!
Step out how to solve the Problem with helpful hints and an online question. Other questions are listed above in Interactive Learning.

Dynamic Activity Students manipulate box-and-whisker plots in this activity. They can add or remove points from a number line to explore how it affects the corresponding box-and-whisker plot.

Problem 1

Q About how many job offers do you think a student should expect? Explain your answer. **[Answers may vary. Sample: A student should expect 2 or 3 job offers. The mean is 2.2. A student could not be offered 0.2 of a job, so this can be interpreted as 2 or 3. The median and the mode also indicate 2 or 3 job offers.]**

Got It?

Q In an expression such as "trees per yard," what does *per* mean? **[*Per* means "in each" or "for every."]**

Q The mean of this data set is the ratio of what two quantities? **[the total number of trees to the total number of yards]**

Problem 2

In some situations, you may choose to discard the outliers from the data set.

Q How does finding the difference between values help find an outlier? **[A difference that is much larger than all the other differences may indicate an outlier.]**

Q Can an outlier be a value other than the first or last value in an ordered data set? Explain. **[No; if a possible outlier is not first or last, then there must be more values near it and the value is by definition not an outlier.]**

Got It?

Q What is an explanation for 2a in which 98 might not be an error? **[Answers may vary. Sample: if that data value was recorded at a different time of year]**

A **bimodal** data set has two modes. If a data set has more than two modes, then the modes are probably not statistically useful. If no value occurs more frequently than any other, then there is no mode.

Ⓒ Problem 1 Finding Measures of Central Tendency

Career The frequency table shows the number of job offers received by each student within two months of graduating with a mathematics degree from a small college. What are the mean, median, and mode for the job offers per student?

Job Offers	0	1	2	3	4
Students	2	2	4	5	2

Think

How do you find the total number of job offers?
Add the products of each number of job offers and the number of students with that many job offers.

$$\text{Mean: } \bar{x} = \frac{2(0) + 2(1) + 4(2) + 5(3) + 2(4)}{15}$$

$$= \frac{33}{15} = 2.2$$

The symbol $\bar{x}$, read "*x bar*," represents the mean.

The mean is 2.2.

Median: 0, 0, 1, 1, 2, 2, 2, 2, 3, 3, 3, 3, 4, 4
The median is 2.

List each value the number of times it occurs. Arrange them in order. Find the middle value.

Mode: Five students received 3 job offers each.
The mode is 3.

The mode is the number of job offers received by most students.

 Got It? **1.** The frequency table shows the number of trees in the yard of each house on one street. What are the mean, median, and mode for the trees per yard?

Trees	3	4	5	6	7	8
Yards	1	5	7	4	1	2

An **outlier** is a value that is substantially different from the rest of the data in a set. If the data is in one variable, outliers can occur at the "ends." They can be misleading because they can affect measures of central tendency.

Ⓒ Problem 2 Identifying an Outlier

Multiple Choice Which is an outlier for this data set: 56 65 73 59 98 65 59?

Ⓐ 42　　　　Ⓑ 65　　　　Ⓒ 98　　　　Ⓓ 59

Think

What should you do first?
Put the numbers in order.

```
56   59   59   65   65   73   98      Order the data.
   3    0    6    0    8   25          Find differences between adjacent values.
```

98 appears to be substantially different, so 98 is an outlier. The correct answer is C.

 Got It? **2.** Suppose the values in Problem 2 are the data for the situations below. Would you discard the outlier? Explain.
　　a. water temperature of a lake at seven locations
　　b. the number of customers in a restaurant each night in one week

---

Answers

Solve It!

Average speed will be less than 55 mi/h; it takes you longer to travel the same distance at a lower speed, so the lower speed has greater weight.

Got It?

1. mean: 5.25, median: 5, mode: 5

2. a. Yes; it is unlikely that the water temperature of a lake would change by 25 degrees.

　　b. No; 98 would represent the busiest night of the week, and it may relate to a weekly event.

PowerAlgebra.com

2 Guided Instruction

Ⓒ Each Problem is worked out and supported online.

Problem 1
Finding Measures of a Central Tendency
Animated

Problem 2
Identifying an Outlier
Animated

Problem 3
Comparing Data Sets
Animated

Problem 4
Using a Box-and-Whisker Plot

Problem 5
Finding Percentiles

Support in Algebra 2 Companion
• Vocabulary
• Key Concepts
• Got It?

The **range of a set of data** is the difference between the greatest and least values. If you order data from least value to greatest value, the median divides the data into two parts. The median of each part divides the data further and you have four parts in all. The values separating the four parts are **quartiles**. The **interquartile range** is the difference between the third and first quartiles.

 Problem 3 Comparing Data Sets

Temperature The table shows average monthly water temperatures for four locations on the Gulf of Mexico. How can you compare the 12 water temperatures from St. Petersburg with the 12 water temperatures from Key West?

Gulf of Mexico Eastern Coast Water Temperatures (°F)

Location	J	F	M	A	M	J	J	A	S	O	N	D
St. Petersburg, Florida	62	64	68	74	80	84	86	86	84	78	70	64
Key West, Florida	69	70	75	78	82	85	87	87	86	82	76	72
Dauphin Island, Alabama	51	53	60	70	75	82	84	84	80	72	62	56
Grand Isle, Louisiana	61	61	64	70	77	83	85	85	83	77	70	65

SOURCE: National Oceanographic Data Center

Know
Water temperatures near the two cities

Need
The means, medians, modes, ranges, and interquartile ranges

Plan
Order the data. Find the means, medians, modes, minimums, maximums, quartiles, range, and interquartile range.

Think

What location has a greater range in water temperature?
The range of water temperatures at St. Petersburg is 6°F greater than the range at Key West.

St. Petersburg:

$$\bar{x} = \frac{62 + 64 + 64 + 68 + 70 + 74 + 78 + 80 + 84 + 84 + 86 + 86}{12}$$

$$= \frac{900}{12} = 75 \text{ (mean water temperature)}$$

Modes: 64, 84, and 86

Min.: 62; Max.: 86; Range: $86 - 62 = 24$

Median $(Q_2) = 76$

62 64 (64 68) 70 (74 78) 80 (84 84) 86 86

Median of lower part $(Q_1) = 66$

Median of upper part $(Q_3) = 84$

Interquartile range:
$Q_3 - Q_1 = 84 - 66 = 18$

Key West:

$$\bar{x} = \frac{69 + 70 + 72 + 75 + 76 + 78 + 82 + 82 + 85 + 86 + 87 + 87}{12}$$

$$= \frac{949}{12} \approx 79.1 \text{ (mean water temperature)}$$

Modes: 82 and 87

Min.: 69; Max.: 87; Range: $87 - 69 = 18$

Median $(Q_2) = 80$

69 70 (72 75) 76 (78 82) 82 (85 86) 87 87

Median of lower part $(Q_1) = 73.5$

Median of upper part $(Q_3) = 85.5$

Interquartile range:
$Q_3 - Q_1 = 85.5 - 73.5 = 12$

The range and the interquartile range show the temperatures varying less at Key West than at St. Petersburg. Also, the temperatures at Key West are generally higher.

Problem 3

Note that the median is always the middle value or mean of two middle values of the ordered data, and the quartiles are found by *not* including the median in the "half" data set.

Q Each data set contains 12 values, one for each month of the year. Why is Q_3 of the St. Petersburg data equal to a value in the data set? **[Q_3 of St. Petersburg is the mean of two identical values, 84 and 84.]**

Q Which measure tells the maximum variation in water temperature over the year? **[the range]**

EXTENSION

Q Does it make sense that Key West has a smaller range than St. Petersburg? Explain. **[Answers may vary. Samples: Yes; Key West is 200 miles south of St. Petersburg, and seasonal temperatures vary less towards the equator. Key West is surrounded by the ocean, and large bodies of water tend to resist temperature changes.]**

Q The measures of central tendency tell information about water temperature over a full year. If you wanted to compare how water temperature changes during the year, how would you show the data? **[Answers may vary. Sample: A dual-line plot of the monthly temperature data with one line for St. Petersburg and one line for Key West would show how the temperature changes during a year.]**

Additional Problems

1. The frequency table shows the number of textbooks in several students' book bags.

Textbooks	0	1	2	3	4
Students	1	6	10	4	4

What are the mean, median, and mode for textbooks per student?

ANSWERS mean: 2.16; median: 2; mode: 2

2. Which is an outlier for this data set:
22 35 12 28 46 30 31 15 19?

ANSWER 46

3. The table shows population density by square mile for counties in three of Florida's eight regions, according to the 2000 U.S. Census.

Southwest	Southeast	Central East
204.2	228.1	401.9
13.7	573.0	467.7
548.6	1346.5	224.4
31.4	1157.9	46.4
124.1	79.8	336.6

What are the mean, mode, range, quartiles, and interquartile range for the Southwest and Southeast population density data?

ANSWERS Southwest:
mean = 184.4; mode = none;
range = 534.9; $Q_1 = 22.55$,
$Q_2 = 124.1$, $Q_3 = 376.4$;
IQR = 353.85

Southeast: mean = 677.06;
mode = none; range =
1266.7; $Q_1 = 153.95$,

$Q_2 = 573$, $Q_3 = 1252.2$;
IQR = 1098.25

4. What are the quartiles of the Central East region population density data in the preceding table? Use a graphing calculator box-and-whisker plot.

ANSWERS $Q_1 = 135.4$,
$Q_2 = 336.6$, $Q_3 = 434.8$

5. The data shows the number of hours in a week that students in a class spent doing homework. What value is at the 45th percentile?

0 3 4 4 4 4.25 4.5 4.5 4.75
5 5 5.25 5.5 5.5 6 6.25 6.25
6.5 7 9

ANSWER 4.75

Got It?

Q Is the mode an important measure for these data sets? Why or why not? **[Sample: No; the most common water temperature does not seem to be important. Dauphin Island has one mode, but it is far from the mean and median. Grand Isle has five modes.]**

Take Note

Q What measure of central tendency cannot be read from a box-and-whisker plot? **[mean and mode]**

Problem 4   EXTENSION

Have students repeat the steps from Problem 4, but enter the data for Key West into L2.

Q What are some conclusions about the water temperatures in St. Petersburg and Key West that can be read off the box-and-whisker plots? **[Answers may vary. Samples: St. Petersburg has a greater range than Key West. Every measure of Key West is farther to the right than St. Petersburg.]**

Got It?

Q Do you think any value in the water temperature data is an outlier? Why or why not? **[No; none of the temperatures is very far away from another temperature.]**

Got It? 3. How can you compare the 12 water temperatures in Problem 3 from Dauphin Island with the 12 water temperatures from Grand Isle?

A *box-and-whisker plot* uses minimum and maximum values, the median, and the first and third quartiles to display the spread, or variability, in a data set.

Key Concept Box-and-Whisker Plot

Definition	Graph
A **box-and-whisker plot** is a way to display data that uses • quartiles to bound the center box and • the minimum and maximum values to form the whiskers.	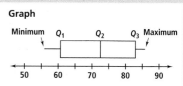

Problem 4 Using a Box-and-Whisker Plot

How can you use a graphing calculator box-and-whisker plot to find quartiles for the water temperature data of St. Petersburg from Problem 3?

Think
What about the appearance of a box-and-whisker plot might suggest an outlier?
If a "whisker" is much longer than the box, it's endpoint may be an outlier.

Step 1 For St. Petersburg, use **STAT EDIT** to enter the temperature data in **L1**.

Step 2 In **STAT PLOT**, select a box-and-whisker plot. Enter **L1** for the St. Petersburg data. Enter the window values. Draw the box-and-whisker plot.

  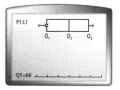

Step 3 Use **TRACE** to find the quartiles: $Q_1 = 66$, $Q_2 = 76$, and $Q_3 = 84$.

Got It? 4. a. How can you use graphing calculator box-and-whisker plots to find water temperature quartiles for other Gulf Coast sites in Problem 3?

b. Reasoning Is a box-and-whisker plot a useful graphical display for data with an outlier? Explain.

A **percentile** is a number from 0 to 100 that you can associate with a value x from a data set. It shows the percent of the data that are less than or equal to x. If x is at the 63rd percentile, then 63% of the data are less than or equal to x.

Answers

Got It? (continued)

3. Dauphin Island: mean: $69.08\overline{3}$, mode: 84, range: 33, $Q_1 = 58$, median: 71, $Q_3 = 81$, interquartile range: 23; Grand Isle: mean: $73.41\overline{6}$, modes: 61, 70, 77, 83, 85, range: 24, $Q_1 = 64.5$, median: 73.5, $Q_3 = 83$, interquartile range: 18.5; The range and the interquartile range show the temperatures varying less at Grand Isle than at Dauphin Island. Also, the temperatures at Grand Isle are generally higher.

4. a. Use STAT PLOT, select a box-and-whisker plot. Enter data for the three remaining Gulf Coast sites. Enter the window values. Draw the box-and-whisker plots. Use TRACE on the plot to find quartiles Q_1, Q_2, and Q_3.

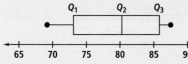

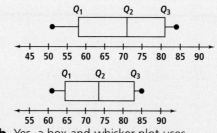

b. Yes, a box-and-whisker plot uses minimum and maximum values, the median, and the first and third quartiles to display the variability in a data set.

Problem 5 Finding Percentiles

Plan

What should you do first to find percentiles?
Put the data in order.

Testing Here is an ordered list of midterm test scores for a Spanish class. What value is at the 65th percentile?

41	54	61	65	67	73	74
77	77	77	79	80	82	88
89	93	97	98	98	100	

Of the 20 values, 65% fall at or below the value at the 65th percentile.

$$20 \cdot 65\% = 20 \cdot 0.65 = 13$$

13 values fall at or below 82, the value at the 65th percentile.

Got It? 5. What are the values at each percentile for the data in Problem 5?
    a. 55th percentile   **b.** 95th percentile

Lesson Check

Do you know HOW?

Identify the outlier in the data set. Then find the mean, median, and mode of the data set when the outlier is included and when it is not.

1. 16 19 21 18 18 54 20 22 23 17

2. 90 100 110 40 98 102 112 90 92

3. Using your results from Exercises 1 and 2, explain which measure of central tendency is most affected by an outlier.

4. Find the values at the 40th and 80th percentiles for the values below.

  58 53 35 60 58 42 57 60 43 44 51 49 58

Do you UNDERSTAND? 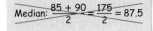 MATHEMATICAL PRACTICES

5. Vocabulary Which measure of central tendency would best represent the values below? Explain your reasoning.

  4 1 5 5 6 8 9 5 5 3 2 7 5 5 1

6. Error Analysis A student found the median of the data set below. Explain the student's error. What is the median?

Score	80	85	90	95
Frequency	6	4	10	1

 Median: $\dfrac{85 + 90}{2} = \dfrac{175}{2} = 87.5$

Practice and Problem-Solving Exercises (C) MATHEMATICAL PRACTICES

(A) **Practice** Find the mean, median, and mode of each set of values.   See Problem 1.

7. Time spent on Internet per day (in minutes): 75 68 43 120 65 180 95 225 140

8.

Age (years)	13	14	15	16	17	18	19
Frequency	7	12	18	9	5	4	2

Problem 5

Q At about what percentiles do you think Q_1, Q_2, and Q_3 are? Verify your answer. **[25th, 50th, and 75th percentile: 25th = 67 and Q_1 = 70; 50th = 77 and Q_2 = 78; 75th = 89 and Q_3 = 91]**

Q Under what condition would Q_1, Q_2, and Q_3 equal the 25th, 50th, and 75th percentiles? **[with an odd number of data]**

Got It?

Q How do you find the value at the 95th percentile? **[Multiply 20 by 0.95, which is 19. Then find the 19th data value.]**

3 Lesson Check

Do you know HOW?

- For Exercise 4, calculating the percentiles will not return an integer value (e.g., $13 \times 0.4 = 5.2$). Students should round to the nearest integer to find the closest data value.

Do you UNDERSTAND?

- If students have trouble spotting the error in Exercise 6, encourage them to write out the full data set.

Close

Q What are situations in which each of the mean, median, and mode would be the most useful measure of central tendency? **[Sample: The mean is most useful when a data set has a small range. The median is most useful when a data set has a larger range or an outlier. The mode is most useful for finding the most common value.]**

---

5. a. 79
   b. 98

Lesson Check

1. outlier: 54; outlier included: mean: 22.8, median: 19.5, mode: 18; outlier not included: mean: $19.\overline{3}$, median: 19, mode: 18

2. outlier: 40; outlier included: mean: $92.\overline{6}$, median: 98, mode: 90; outlier not included: mean: 99.25, median: 99, mode: 90

3. the mean because the sum of the data values is affected and the mean depends on the sum

4. 40%: 51 and below; 80%: 58 and below

5. The mean; when data are somewhat sym, the best representation is the mean.

6. The error is in how to calculate the median. The median is the middle value, or the 11th value, which is 90.

Practice and Problem-Solving Exercises

7. mean: $112.\overline{3}$, median: 95, mode: none

8. mean: ≈ 15.23, median: 15, mode: 15

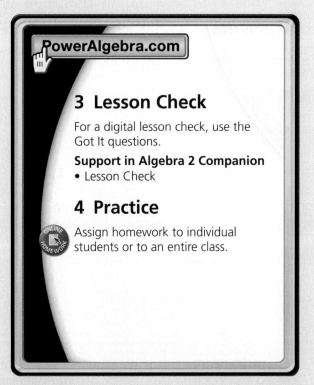

PowerAlgebra.com

3 Lesson Check

For a digital lesson check, use the Got It questions.

Support in Algebra 2 Companion
- Lesson Check

4 Practice

Assign homework to individual students or to an entire class.

4 Practice

ASSIGNMENT GUIDE
Basic: 7–15 all, 18–23, 25
Average: 7–15 odd, 16–27
Advanced: 7–15 odd, 16–29
Standardized Test Prep: 30–33
Mixed Review: 34–43

Ⓒ **Mathematical Practices** are supported by exercises with red headings. Here are the Practices supported in this lesson:

MP 1: Make Sense of Problems Ex. 19
MP 3: Compare Arguments Ex. 28
MP 3: Communicate Ex. 20c
MP 3: Critique the Reasoning of Others Ex. 6, 23

Applications exercises have blue headings.
Exercises 24 and 27 support MP 4: Model.

STEM exercises focus on science or engineering applications.

EXERCISE 20: Use the Think About a Plan worksheet in the **Practice and Problem Solving Workbook** (also available in the Teaching Resources in print and online) to further support students' development in becoming independent learners.

HOMEWORK QUICK CHECK
To check students' understanding of key skills and concepts, go over Exercises 7, 9, 19, 20, and 23.

Identify the outlier of each set of values.   ◄ See Problem 2.

9. 3.4 4.5 2.3 5.9 9.8 3.3 2.1 3.0 2.9

10. 17 21 19 10 15 19 14 0 11 16

11. Weather The table shows average monthly temperatures of two cities.   ◄ See Problems 3 and 4.
How can you compare the temperatures?

	J	F	M	A	M	J	J	A	S	O	N	D
Jacksonville, Florida	52.4	55.2	61.1	67.0	73.4	79.1	81.6	81.2	78.1	69.8	61.9	55.1
Austin, Texas	48.8	52.8	61.5	69.9	75.6	81.3	84.5	84.8	80.2	71.1	60.9	51.6

Make a box-and-whisker plot for each set of values.

12. 12 11 15 12 19 20 19 14 18 15 16

13. 120 145 133 105 117 150 130 136 128

Find the values at the 30th and 90th percentiles for each data set.   ◄ See Problem 5.

14. 6283 5700 6381 6274 5700 5896 5972 6075 5993 5581

15. 7 12 3 14 17 20 5 3 17 4 13 2 15 9 15 18 16 9 1 6

Ⓑ Apply   **Identify the outlier in each data set. Then find the mean, median, and mode of the data set when the outlier is included and when it is not.**

16. 947 757 103 619 661 582 626 900 869 728 1001 596 515

17. 87 104 381 215 174 199 233 186 142 228 9 53 117 129

18. 49 57.5 58 49.2 62 22.2 67 52.1 77 99.9 80 51.7 64

Ⓒ **19. Think About a Plan** Use the water temperature data for the eastern coast of the Gulf of Mexico during the summer months, as shown in the graph below. Find the quartiles by graphing a box-and-whisker plot of the data.

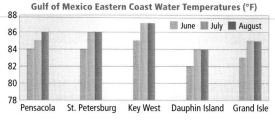

- What information can you get from the graph?
- How can you use that information to make a box-and-whisker plot?
- How can you find the quartiles using your box-and-whisker plot?

Answers

Practice and Problems-Solving Exercises (continued)

9. 9.8

10. 0

11. Jacksonville: mean: 67.991$\overline{6}$, mode: none, range: 29.2, Q_1 = 58.15, median: 68.4, Q_3 = 78.6, interquartile range: 20.45; Austin: mean: 68.58$\overline{3}$, mode: none, range: 36, Q_1 = 56.85, median: 70.5, Q_3 = 80.75, interquartile range: 23.9; the range and the interquartile range show the temperatures varying less at Jacksonville than at Austin.

12.

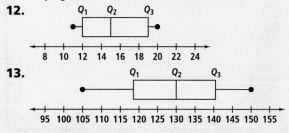

13.

14. 5700; 6283

15. 5; 17

16. outlier: 103; outlier included: mean: ≈684.92, median: 661, mode: none; outlier not included: mean: 733.41$\overline{6}$, median: 694.5, mode: none

17. outlier: 381; outlier included: mean: ≈161.214, median: 158, mode: none; outlier not included: mean: ≈144.308, median: 142, mode: none

18. outliers: 22.2 and 99.9; outliers included: mean: ≈60.74, median: 58, mode: none; both outliers not included: mean: 60.68$\overline{1}$, median: 58, mode: none

19.

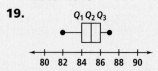

20. Meteorology On May 3, 1999, 59 tornadoes hit Oklahoma in the largest tornado outbreak ever recorded in the state. Sixteen of these were classified as strong (F2 or F3) or violent (F4 or F5).

    a. Make a box-and-whisker plot of the data for length of path.

    b. Identify the outliers. Remove them from the data set and make a revised box-and-whisker plot.

    ⓒ **c. Writing** How does the removal of the outliers affect the box-and-whisker plot? How does it affect the median of the data set?

For Exercises 21–23, use the set of values below.

1 1 1 1 1 1 2 3 5 8 13 21 34 55 89 89 89 89 89 89

21. At what percentile is 1?   **22.** At what percentile is 34?

ⓒ **23. Error Analysis** A student claims that 89 is at the 70th percentile. Explain the student's error.

24. Advertising An electronics store placed an ad in the newspaper showing flat-screen TVs for sale. The ad says "Our flat-screen TVs average $695." The prices of the flat-screen TVs are $1200, $999, $1499, $895, $695, $1100, $1300, and $695.

    a. Find the mean, median, and mode of the prices.

    b. Which measure is the store using in its ad? Why did they choose it?

    c. As a consumer, which measure would you want to see advertised? Explain your reasoning.

ⓒ **25. Reasoning** Which measure better represents a data set with several outliers—the mean or the median? Justify your answer.

26. The table displays the frequency of scores for one Calculus class on the Advanced Placement Calculus exam. The mean of the exam scores is 3.5.

Score	1	2	3	4	5
Frequency	1	3	f	12	3

    a. What is the value of f in the table?

    b. What is the mode of all of the exam scores?

    c. What is the median of all of the exam scores?

27. Grades Some teachers use a *weighted mean* to calculate grades. Each score is assigned a weight based on its importance. To find a weighted mean, multiply each score by its weight and add the results. For example, a student's final chemistry grade is based on four sources: 30% from lab reports, 10% from quizzes, 25% from the midterm exam, and 35% from the final exam. What is the student's weighted mean given the scores shown?

Lab Reports	82
Quizzes	95
Midterm Exam	76
Final Exam	88

Ⓒ **Challenge**

28. Reasoning What effect will adding 10 to every value in a data set have on the mean, median, mode, range, and box-and-whisker plot? What will be the effect if you multiply each value by 10?

Major Tornadoes in Oklahoma, May 3, 1999

Length of Path (miles)	Intensity
6	F3
9	F3
4	F2
37	F5
7	F2
12	F3
8	F2
7	F2
15	F4
39	F4
1	F2
22	F3
15	F3
8	F2
13	F3
2	F2

SOURCE: National Oceanic & Atmospheric Administration

20. a.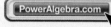

b.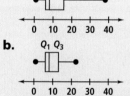

c. The main effect of removing the outlier is a shortening of the long whisker. The median decreases from 8.5 to 8.

21. 30th

22. 65th

23. 89 is at the 100th percentile since 100% of the values are less than or equal to 89.

24. a. mean: $1047.88, median: $1049.50, mode: $695

b. mode; it gives the lowest price

c. median; when extreme values (outliers) are involved ($695 and $1499), the median gives a more accurate measure of central tendency

25. the median; a few outliers can heavily influence the mean without drastically affecting the median.

26. a. 7

b. 4

c. 4

27. 83.9

28. Adding 10 will add 10 to the mean, median, Q_1, Q_3, and mode which translates the box-and-whisker plot to the rt. by 10. The range remains the same.

Multiplying by 10 will multiply the mean, median, Q_1, Q_3, and mode by 10 which translates the box-and-whisker plot to the right by a factor of 10. The range also increases by a factor of 10.

Answers

Practice and Problems-Solving
Exercises (continued)

29. Answers may vary. Sample: The range for women's shot put is greater than that for men's. The men are more consistent, as indicated by the shorter box and whiskers. Overall the men tend to throw farther.

Standardized Test Prep

30. C   **31.** G   **32.** B

33. [2] $P(H|I) = 0.40$, $P(H \text{ and } I) = 0.20$

$$P(H|I) = \frac{P(H \text{ and } I)}{P(I)}$$

$$0.40 = \frac{0.20}{P(I)}$$

$$P(I) = 0.50$$

[1] appropriate method, but with one computational error OR correct probability, without work shown

Mixed Review

34. 0.20

35. 0.56

36. yes; -9

37. yes; 17

38. no

39. yes; 0

40. ± 16

41. ± 0.09

42. $\pm \frac{11}{4}$

43. $\pm \frac{19}{5}$

---

29. Track and Field The box-and-whisker plots show the 36 best qualifying distances for the shot put events for men and women during the 2004 Olympics. Compare box-and-whisker plots. Describe any conclusions you can draw about Olympic-level male and female shot-putters.

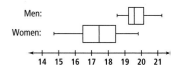

Standardized Test Prep

SAT/ACT

30. Use a calculator to solve $2x^2 - 7x - 5 = 0$. Round answers to the nearest hundredth.

Ⓐ $-1.56, -4.44$ Ⓑ $-5.44, 1.56$ Ⓒ $-0.61, 4.11$ Ⓓ $-5.56, -1.44$

31. Which function generates the table of values below?

x	−2	−1	0	1	2
y	$\frac{27}{8}$	$\frac{9}{2}$	6	8	$\frac{32}{3}$

Ⓕ $27\left(\frac{2}{3}\right)^x$ Ⓖ $6\left(\frac{4}{3}\right)^x$ Ⓗ $\left(\frac{8}{3}\right)^x$ Ⓘ $6\left(\frac{3}{4}\right)^x$

32. A homeroom class consists of 6 boys whose last name begins with S, 8 boys whose last name begins with T, 4 girls whose last name begins with S, and 11 girls whose last name begins with T. A student is chosen at random from the class. What is the probability that the student is a girl or has a last name that begins with S?

Ⓐ $\frac{18}{29}$ Ⓑ $\frac{21}{29}$ Ⓒ $\frac{23}{29}$ Ⓓ $\frac{25}{29}$

Short Response

33. In a library, the probability that a book is a hardback, given that it is illustrated, is 0.40. The probability that a book is hardback *and* illustrated is 0.20. Find the probability that a book is illustrated.

Mixed Review

Of all the respondents to a survey, 59% are girls. Of the girls, 61% read horror stories. Of the boys, 49% read horror stories. Find each probability.   See Lesson 11-4

34. P(boy and reads horror stories)   **35.** P (reads horror stories)

Determine whether each sequence is arithmetic. If it is, identify the common difference.   See Lesson 9-2

36. $16, 7, -2, \ldots$ **37.** $34, 51, 68, \ldots$ **38.** $2, 2.2, 2.22, \ldots$ **39.** $1, 1, 1, \ldots$

Get Ready!   **To prepare for Lesson 11-7, do Exercises 40–43.**

Find all real square roots of each number.   See Lesson 6-1

40. 256   **41.** 0.0081   **42.** $\frac{121}{16}$ **43.** $\frac{361}{25}$

11-6 Lesson Resources

Additional Instructional Support

Algebra 2 Companion

Students can use the **Algebra 2 Companion** worktext (4 pages) as you teach the lesson. Use the Companion to support

- New Vocabulary
- Key Concepts
- Got It for each Problem
- Lesson Check

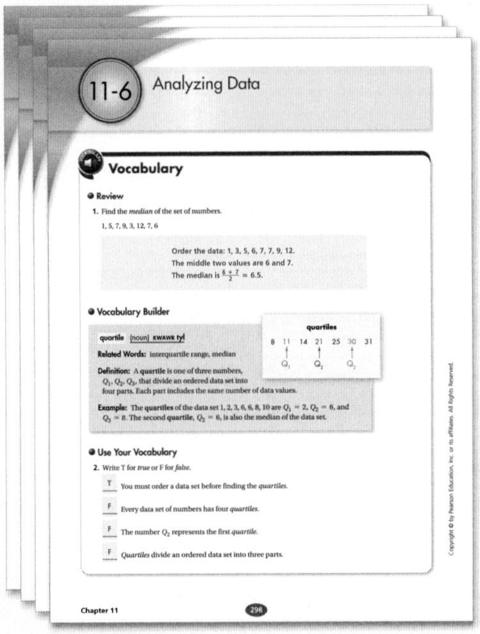

11-6 Analyzing Data

Vocabulary

Review

1. Find the *median* of the set of numbers.

1, 5, 7, 9, 3, 12, 7, 6

Order the data: 1, 3, 5, 6, 7, 7, 9, 12.
The middle two values are 6 and 7.
The median is $\frac{6+7}{2} = 6.5$.

Vocabulary Builder

quartile (noun) KWAWR tyl

Related Words: interquartile range, median

Definition: A quartile is one of three numbers, Q_1, Q_2, Q_3, that divide an ordered data set into four parts. Each part includes the same number of data values.

Example: The quartiles of the data set 1, 2, 3, 6, 6, 8, 10 are $Q_1 = 2$, $Q_2 = 6$, and $Q_3 = 8$. The second quartile, $Q_2 = 6$, is also the median of the data set.

quartiles
8 11 14 21 25 30 31
Q_1 Q_2 Q_3

Use Your Vocabulary

2. Write T for *true* or F for *false*.

T You must order a data set before finding the *quartiles*.

F Every data set of numbers has four *quartiles*.

F The number Q_2 represents the first *quartile*.

F *Quartiles* divide an ordered data set into three parts.

Copyright © by Pearson Education, Inc. or its affiliates. All Rights Reserved.

Chapter 11 298

ELL Support

Use Graphic Organizers Have students work in groups of two or three. Have each group research a small data set with at least eight values. This could be real-world data like the population of South American countries, or data about classmates, like a frequency table of birth months.

Have students make a large table with four rows: *mean*, *median*, *mode*, and *range*. In the first column, students write a brief description of each measure of central tendency. In the second column, students write the data set in order and show the mathematical operations to arrive at the desired measure: adding and dividing for the mean, circling the middle number(s) for the median, underlining the most common numbers for the mode, subtracting greatest and least for the range.

5 Assess & Remediate

Lesson Quiz

1. Which is an outlier for this data set:
170 210 192 105 188 179 195?

2. **Do you UNDERSTAND?** The table shows the heights in inches of men's tennis rosters. Find the mean, mode, range, median, quartiles, and interquartile ranges.

Florida	Florida State
76	69
74	74
74	69
74	73
73	68
74	71
71	71
75	70
70	74

3. The data shows the ages of passengers on a city bus. What value is at the 75th percentile?

8 9 12 15 15 19 22 28 35 35
39 44 45 45 47 48 50 52 55 56

ANSWERS TO LESSON QUIZ

1. 105
2. Florida: mean = 73.4; mode = 74; range = 6; median = 74; $Q_1 = 72$, $Q_2 = 74$, $Q_3 = 74.5$; IQR = 2.5 Florida State: mean = 71; modes = 69, 71, and 74; range = 6; median = 71; $Q_1 = 69$, $Q_2 = 71$, $Q_3 = 73.5$; IQR = 4.5
3. 47

PRESCRIPTION FOR REMEDIATION

Use the student work on the Lesson Quiz to prescribe a differentiated review assignment:

Points	Differentiated Remediation
0–1	Intervention
2	On-level
3	Extension

PowerAlgebra.com

5 Assess & Remediate

Assign the Lesson Quiz. Appropriate intervention, practice, or enrichment is automatically generated based on student performance.

Differentiated Remediation

Intervention

- **Reteaching** (2 pages) Provides reteaching and practice exercises for the key lesson concepts. Use with struggling students or absent students.
- **English Language Learner Support** Helps students develop and reinforce mathematical vocabulary and key concepts.

All-in-One Resources/Online

Reteaching

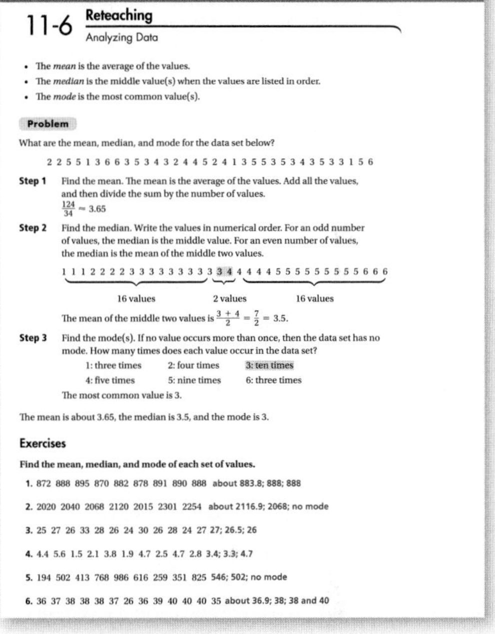

11-6 Reteaching
Analyzing Data

- The *mean* is the average of the values.
- The *median* is the middle value(s) when the values are listed in order.
- The *mode* is the most common value(s).

Problem

What are the mean, median, and mode for the data set below?

2 2 5 5 1 3 6 6 3 5 3 4 3 2 4 4 5 2 4 1 3 5 5 3 5 3 4 3 5 3 3 1 5 6

Step 1 Find the mean. The mean is the average of the values. Add all the values, and then divide the sum by the number of values.
$\frac{124}{34} \approx 3.65$

Step 2 Find the median. Write the values in numerical order. For an odd number of values, the median is the middle value. For an even number of values, the median is the mean of the middle two values.

1 1 1 2 2 2 2 3 3 3 3 3 3 3 3 3 4 4 4 4 4 5 5 5 5 5 5 5 5 5 6 6 6

16 values 2 values 16 values

The mean of the middle two values is $\frac{3+4}{2} = \frac{7}{2} = 3.5$.

Step 3 Find the mode(s). If no value occurs more than once, then the data set has no mode. How many times does each value occur in the data set?

1: three times 2: four times 3: ten times
4: five times 5: nine times 6: three times

The most common value is 3.

The mean is about 3.65, the median is 3.5, and the mode is 3.

Exercises

Find the mean, median, and mode of each set of values.

1. 872 888 895 870 882 878 891 890 888 about 883.8; 888; 888
2. 2020 2040 2068 2120 2015 2301 2254 about 2116.9; 2068; no mode
3. 25 27 26 33 28 26 24 30 26 28 24 27 27; 26.5; 26
4. 4.4 5.6 1.5 2.1 3.8 1.9 4.7 2.5 4.7 2.8 3.4; 3.3; 4.7
5. 194 502 413 768 986 616 259 351 825 546; 502; no mode
6. 36 37 38 38 38 37 26 36 39 40 40 40 35 about 36.9; 38; 38 and 40

All-in-One Resources/Online

English Language Learner Support

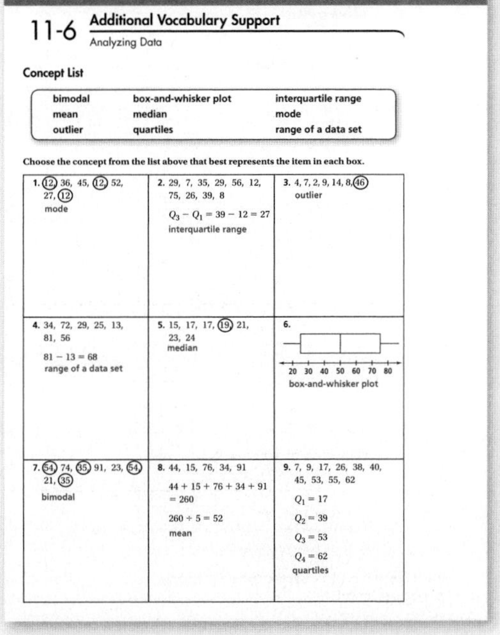

11-6 Additional Vocabulary Support
Analyzing Data

Concept List

bimodal	box-and-whisker plot	interquartile range
mean	median	mode
outlier	quartiles	range of a data set

Choose the concept from the list above that best represents the item in each box.

1. ⑫ 36, 45, ⑫ 52, 27, ⑫ mode	2. 29, 7, 35, 29, 56, 12, 75, 26, 39, 8 $Q_3 - Q_1 = 39 - 12 = 27$ interquartile range	3. 4, 7, 2, 9, 14, 8, ㊻ outlier
4. 34, 72, 29, 25, 13, 81, 56 $81 - 13 = 68$ range of a data set	5. 15, 17, 17, ⑲ 21, 23, 24 median	6. 20 30 40 50 60 70 80 box-and-whisker plot
7. (54) 74, ㉟ 91, 23, (54) 21, ㉟ bimodal	8. 44, 15, 76, 34, 91 $44 + 15 + 76 + 34 + 91 = 260$ $260 \div 5 = 52$ mean	9. 7, 9, 17, 26, 38, 40, 45, 53, 55, 62 $Q_1 = 17$ $Q_2 = 39$ $Q_3 = 53$ $Q_4 = 62$ quartiles

Differentiated Remediation *continued*

On-Level

- **Practice** (2 pages) Provides extra practice for each lesson. For simpler practice exercises, use the Form K Practice pages found in the All-in-One Teaching Resources and online.

- **Think About a Plan** Helps students develop specific problem-solving skills and strategies by providing scaffolded guiding questions.

- **Standardized Test Prep** Focuses on all major exercises, all major question types, and helps students prepare for the high-stakes assessments.

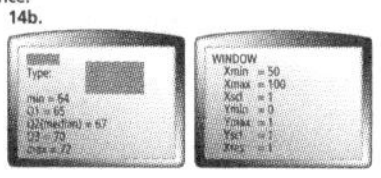

Extension

- **Enrichment** Provides students with interesting problems and activities that extend the concepts of the lesson.

- **Activities, Games, and Puzzles** Worksheets that can be used for concepts development, enrichment, and for fun!

Practice and Problem Solving Wkbk/All-in-One Resources/Online
Practice page 1

11-6 Practice — Form G
Analyzing Data

Find the mean, median, and mode of each set of values.

1. Customers per day: 90 87 79 82 101 99 97 97 102 91 93 about 93.3; 97; 97

2.
Weight (g)	2.3	2.4	2.5	2.6	2.8	2.9
Frequency	1	4	1	1	1	2
2.56; 2.45; 2.4

3.
Length (m)	12	13	14	15	16	17	18
Frequency	2	5	3	1	4	1	1
about 15.2; 15; 17

Identify the outlier of each set of values.

4. 32 35 3 36 37 35 38 40 42 34 3

5. 153 156 176 156 165 110 159 169 172 110

6. The table shows the average monthly rainfall for two cities. How can you City A: mean = 3, compare the rainfall amounts? mode = 3.1, min = 0.8, max = 5, range = 4.2, Q₁ = 2.25,

	J	F	M	A	M	J	J	A	S	O	N	D
City A	3.3	4.5	5.0	4.1	2.9	1.8	0.8	2.2	2.3	3.1	3.0
City B	4.2	4.0	4.7	4.8	4.5	4.3	4.0	3.9	4.3	4.4	4.6	4.5

median = 3.05, Q₃ = 3.65, IQ range = 1.4; City B: mean = 4.35, modes = 4, 4.3, 4.5, min = 3.9, max = 4.8, range = 0.9, Q₁ = 4.1, median = 4.35, Q₃ = 4.6, IQ range = 0.45
7. The list gives the average temperatures in January for several cities in the mid-South. Make a box-and-whisker plot of the data.
49.1 50.8 42.9 44.0 44.2 51.4 45.7
39.9 50.8 46.7 52.4 50.4

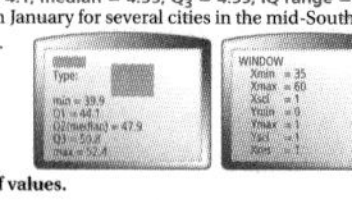

Make a box-and-whisker plot for each set of values.

8. 2 8 3 7 3 6 4 9 10 15 21 29 32 30 5 7 32 4 11 13 11 14 10 12 13 15

9. 1054 1165 1287 1385 1456 1398 1298 1109 1067 1384 1499 1032 1222 1045

8.   9.

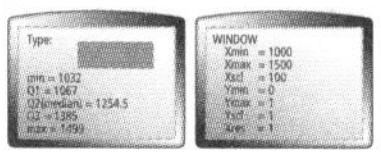

Practice and Problem Solving Wkbk/All-in-One Resources/Online
Practice page 2

11-6 Practice (continued) — Form G
Analyzing Data

Find the values at the 20th and 80th percentiles for each set of values.

10. 188 168 174 198 186 170 180 182 186 176 174; 188

11. 376 324 346 348 350 352 356 368 345 360 346; 368

Identify the outlier in each data set. Then find the mean, median, and mode of the data set when the outlier is included and when it is not.

12. 23 76 79 76 77 74 75 23; about 68.6, 76, 76; about 76.2, 76, 76

13. 43 46 49 50 52 54 78 47 78; about 52.4, 49.5, no mode; about 48.7, 49, no mode

14. The table shows the number of shaved-ice servings sold during the first week of July. See below

Date	7/1	7/2	7/3	7/4	7/5	7/6	7/7
Number Sold	65	70	67	98	72	67	64

a. Make a box-and-whisker plot of the data for the number of shaved-ice servings sold.
b. Find any outliers. Remove them from the data set and make a revised box-and-whisker plot. 98
c. **Writing** How does removing the outliers affect the box-and-whisker plot? How does it affect the measures of central tendency? Answers may vary. Sample: Removing the outliers shortens the right-hand whisker and narrows the box; the mean is reduced from 71.9 to 67.5; the median and mode are unchanged.
For Exercises 15–18, use the set of values below.
1 2 2 2 2 2 2 2 3 3 3 3 4 4 4 5 5 25 26 27
15. At what percentile is 1? 0th   16. At what percentile is 25? 85th
17. Find the mean, median, and mode of the data set. 6.25, 3, 2
18. **Writing** Suppose these values represent years of experience of the accountants at an accounting firm. Which measure(s) of central tendency best describe(s) the experience of the firm's accountants? Explain.
Answers may vary. Sample: median and mode; 60% (12 out of 20) of the accountants have 2 or 3 years of experience, but only 15% (3 out of 20) of them have more than the mean years of experience.
14a.   14b.

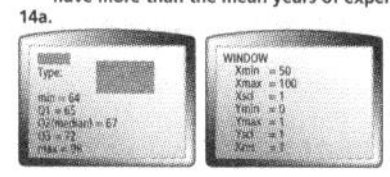

Practice and Problem Solving Wkbk/All-in-One Resources/Online
Think About a Plan

11-6 Think About a Plan
Analyzing Data

Meteorology On May 3, 1999, 59 tornadoes hit Oklahoma in the largest tornado outbreak ever recorded in the state. Sixteen of these were classified as strong (F2 or F3) or violent (F4 or F5).

a. Make a box-and-whisker plot of the data for length of path.
b. Identify the outliers. Remove them from the data set and make a revised box-and-whisker plot.
c. **Writing** How does the removal of the outliers affect the box-and-whisker plot? How does it affect the median of the data set?

Major Tornadoes in Oklahoma, May 3, 1999
Length of path (miles)	Intensity
6	F3
9	F3
4	F2
37	F5
7	F3
12	F3
8	F2
7	F3
15	F4
39	F4
1	F2
22	F3
15	F3
8	F2
13	F3
2	F2

1. Arrange the data in increasing order.
1, 2, 4, 6, 7, 7, 8, 8, 9, 12, 13, 15, 15, 22, 37, 39

2. Minimum value = 1   Q₁ = 6.5
   Maximum value = 39   Q₂ = 8.5
                            Q₃ = 15

3. Use your previous answers to make a box-and-whisker plot of the data for length of path.

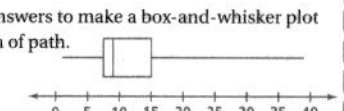

4. How can you identify the outliers in the data set?
Answers may vary. Sample: Look at the ends of the ordered data for values that are substantially different

5. What are the outliers in the data set? 22, 37, 39

6. Remove the outliers from the data set and make a revised box-and-whisker plot.

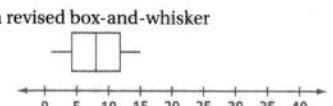

7. How does the removal of the outliers affect the box-and-whisker plot?
Answers may vary. Sample: The box is shifted left and the median moves to almost the center of the box. The whiskers become shorter, especially the right one

8. How does the removal of the outliers affect the median of the data set?
The median shifts from 8.5 to 8

Practice and Problem Solving Wkbk/All-in-One Resources/Online
Standardized Test Prep

11-6 Standardized Test Prep
Analyzing Data

Multiple Choice

For Exercises 1–5, choose the correct letter. Use the data set below.

Day	9/1	9/2	9/3	9/4	9/5	9/6	9/7	9/8	9/9	9/10	9/11	9/12
Deliveries	14	15	19	15	15	16	19	20	21	29	11	17

1. What is the mean of the data set? D
   Ⓐ 12   Ⓑ 15   Ⓒ 16.5   Ⓓ 18

2. How many modes does the data set have? G
   Ⓕ 0   Ⓖ 1   Ⓗ 2   Ⓘ 3

3. What is the interquartile range of the data? C
   Ⓐ 1.5   Ⓑ 3   Ⓒ 4.5   Ⓓ 15

4. What is the median value of the data set *without the outlier*? F
   Ⓕ 16   Ⓖ 17   Ⓗ 19   Ⓘ 29

5. What value is at the 50th percentile? B
   Ⓐ 16   Ⓑ 17   Ⓒ 19   Ⓓ 20

Short Response

6. Make a box-and-whisker plot of the data set. Label the median, minimum, maximum, first quartile, and third quartile.
[2]

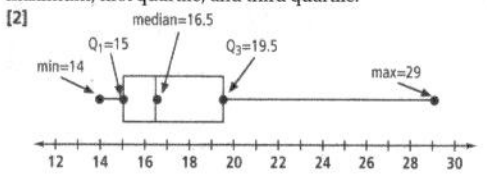

[1] incorrect or incomplete work shown
[0] no answer given

All-in-One Resources/Online
Enrichment

11-6 Enrichment
Analyzing Data

Moments to Remember

You can convey statistical information in several different ways. If you obtain more than 20 or so scores, listing the scores becomes unwieldy. In such cases, you can present the information in a frequency distribution.

Suppose scores range from x_1 through x_n. The frequency of score x_j, written as f_j, is the number of times that score appears in the distribution.

1. Using this notation, express the total of the scores corresponding to x_j. $f_j x_j$

2. Using sigma notation, express the total of the data represented in the distribution. $\sum_{j=1}^{n} f_j x_j$

3. How would you express the mean of the distribution in terms of x_j and f_j? $\bar{x} = \dfrac{\sum_{j=1}^{n} f_j x_j}{\sum_{j=1}^{n} f_j}$

If x is a score in a data set and m is any number, the first moment of x about m is defined as the difference $x - m$. For example, if 73 is a score in a data set, the first moment of 73 about 80 is $73 - 80 = -7$.

4. Suppose a frequency distribution has scores x_1 through x_n and associated frequencies f_1 through f_n. Express the total of the first moments of x_1 about m. $f_1(x_1 - m)$

5. Using sigma notation, express the total of the first moments of the entire distribution about m. $\sum_{j=1}^{n} f_j(x_j - m)$

6. If y is used to represent this sum, express y as a function of m. $y = \sum_{j=1}^{n} f_j x_j - \left(\sum_{j=1}^{n} f_j \right) m$

7. What kind of function is y? linear

8. Let $y = T(m)$. Why is there only one number M such that $T(M) = 0$? Any linear function with nonzero slope meets the x-axis at only one point.

9. Solve the equation $T(M) = 0$ for M. $M = \dfrac{\sum_{j=1}^{n} f_j x_j}{\sum_{j=1}^{n} f_j}$

10. What term describes the value of M? mean

11. Complete the following sentence: The ___mean___ of a distribution is the unique number about which the ___sum___ of the first moments is ___zero___.

The table shows the frequency of five different scores on a challenging 15-point spelling test.

Score	15	14	13	12	11
Frequency	1	4	7	13	18

12. Find the mean for this set of scores. 12

13. Show that the sum of the first moments about the mean is zero.
$\sum_{j=1}^{5} f_j(x_j - m) = 1(15 - 12) + 4(14 - 12) + 7(13 - 12) + 13(12 - 12) + 18(11 - 12) = 0$

Online Teacher Resource Center
Activities, Games, and Puzzles

11-6 Puzzle: Can We Set a Data?
Analyzing Data

The table below shows results from the 2008 Summer Olympics in Beijing, China. Use the data to answer the questions below the table, and determine the host countries for the 2012 Summer and 2014 Winter Olympics.

Split Time for First 250 m of Women's Kayak Double (K2), Heat 1								
GER	POL	CZE	FIN	ESP	JPN	SLO	RSA	GBR
51.05	50.74	50.83	51.50	51.81	52.17	51.41	53.36	53.01

Men's Handball Scores – Final Day				
CRO	ESP	FRA	ISL	POL	DEN	KOR
29	25	28	23	29	37	26

Badminton Mixed Doubles – Medal Round Scores								
CHN	CHN	CHN	INA1	INA1	INA1	KOR	INA2	INA2
19	21	23	21	17	21	21	11	17

Men's Archery Quarterfinals					
UKR	JPN	MAS	RUS	CUB	KOR	MEX	USA
115	106	104	109	108	108	113	106

Women's Beach Volleyball – Quarterfinal Scores					
BRA1	USA1	CHN1	AUT	USA2	CHN2	AUS	BRA2
42	42	24	30	42	24	45	45

Men's Sailing 470 Finals – Rounded Seconds After Winner (Australia)						
ARG	CRO	FRA	GBR	ITA	JPN	NED	ESP
24	26	18	6	17	5	24	9

Women's Trampoline – Finals				
CAN1	CAN2	CHN	GEO	GER	RUS	UKR	POR
37.0	35.5	37.8	36.1	38.9	36.2	36.6	36.9

Men's Team Sabre – Final Day				
FRA	USA	ITA	RUS	EGY	HUN	BLR	CHN
45	37	45	44	25	45	45	39

Summer 2012 Finalists
1. Country with the closest score to the archery mean: RUS, or Russia
2. Country with the median time in sailing: FRA, or France
3. Country with 3 more points than the median of upper part in handball: ESP, or Spain
4. Country with 1.5 fewer points than the median of lower part in volleyball: USA, or the United States of America
5. Country with the lowest time on right whisker of box-and-whisker plot of kayak times: GBR, or Great Britain

Summer 2012 Host Country
6. Country closest to one-third of the mean time in sailing: GBR, or Great Britain

Winter 2014 Finalists
7. Country whose only score in badminton was the mode: KOR, or Korea
8. Country with Sabre score just below the 50th percentile: RUS, or Russia
9. Country with a volleyball score 12.75 points below the mean: AUT, or Austria

Winter 2014 Host Country
10. Country with a trampoline score that was the greatest value less than the median: RUS, or Russia

11-7 Standard Deviation

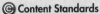

© Content Standards

S.ID.4 Use the mean and standard deviation of a data set to fit it to a normal distribution and to estimate population percentages.
Also S.IC.6

Objectives To find the standard deviation and variance of a set of values
To apply standard deviation and variance

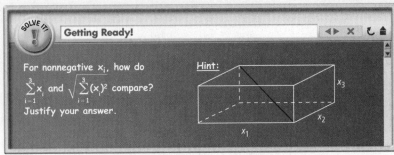

SOLVE IT!

Getting Ready!

For nonnegative x_i, how do $\sum_{i=1}^{3} x_i$ and $\sqrt{\sum_{i=1}^{3} (x_i)^2}$ compare?

Justify your answer.

Hint:

You learned about summation notation in Chapter 9. To find the mean of a data set, you sum the data values and divide by the number of data values. You can use summation to measure how data deviates from the mean.

Essential Understanding Standard deviation is a measure of how far the numbers in a data set deviate from the mean.

In the previous lesson you studied range and interquartile range. Each of these is a **measure of variation**. A measure of variation describes how the data in a data set are spread out.

Variance and **standard deviation** are measures showing how much data values deviate from the mean. The Greek letter σ (sigma) represents standard deviation. σ^2 (sigma squared) is the variance.

Lesson Vocabulary
• measure of variation
• variance
• standard deviation

take note

Key Concepts Finding Variance and Standard Deviation

• Find the mean, $\bar{x}$, of the n values in a data set.
• Find the difference, $x - \bar{x}$, between each value x and the mean.
• Square each difference, $(x - \bar{x})^2$.
• Find the average (mean) of these squares. This is the variance.

$$\sigma^2 = \frac{\sum (x - \bar{x})^2}{n}$$

• Take the square root of the variance. This is the standard deviation.

$$\sigma = \sqrt{\frac{\sum (x - \bar{x})^2}{n}}$$

PowerAlgebra.com | Lesson 11-7 Standard Deviation | 719

1 Interactive Learning

Solve It!

PURPOSE To compare the results of two summations
PROCESS Students may
• substitute the same nonnegative numbers for x in both expressions and compare results.
• find the length of the diagonal of the rectangular prism using $d = \sqrt{\ell^2 + w^2 + h^2}$.

FACILITATE

Q For which summation expression does it matter whether x_i is nonnegative? Explain. **[The first expression; negative numbers affect the sum. In the second expression, squaring negates the effects of negatives.]**

ANSWER See Solve It in Answers on next page.
CONNECT THE MATH In the Solve It, students compare a sum of data values to the square root of the sum of the squares of those data values. In the lesson, students use the square root of the sum of the differences of data values from the mean to find the standard deviation.

2 Guided Instruction

Take Note

Q If all the values in a data set are equal, what is the standard deviation of the set? **[0]**

Q If you increase each data value in the set by the same number, how does it affect the mean and standard deviation of the set? **[The mean increases by that number, but the standard deviation does not change.]**

11-7 Preparing to Teach

BIG idea Probability
ESSENTIAL UNDERSTANDING
Standard deviation is a measure of how far the numbers in a data set deviate from the mean.

Math Background
Measures of variation describe how data in a data set are spread out.

Variance is calculated by finding the average squared deviation of each value from the mean of the data. Because of this, it takes all of the data values into account.

Standard deviation is the positive square root of the variance. It is a measure of spread.

Calculating variance and standard deviation is sometimes difficult for students. Suggest that they write a checklist and use it for each problem

until they are fully comfortable with the process. For example:
• Find the mean of the data set.
• Find the difference between each data value and the above mean. Write them in a list.
• Find and write down the square of each number on the list.
• Find the mean of the list of squares. This is the variance.
• Take the square root of the variance to calculate the standard deviation.

© Mathematical Practices
Look for and express regularity in repeated reasoning. In calculating for variance and standard deviation, students will look for general methods and shortcuts for the many calculations they will have to perform. Students will also use a calculator to determine variance and standard deviation of a set of data.

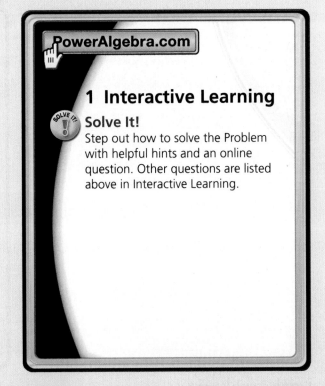

PowerAlgebra.com

1 Interactive Learning

Solve It!
Step out how to solve the Problem with helpful hints and an online question. Other questions are listed above in Interactive Learning.

Lesson 11-7 719

Problem 1 EXTENSION

When calculating variance, squaring each value's difference from the mean serves two purposes:
- It makes each term positive, so values above the mean do not cancel values below.
- It amplifies larger deviations in the data set.

> **Q** What is the sum of the differences from the mean in the third column of the table? **[0]**
>
> **Q** Why is the sum of the differences from the mean of a data set always 0? **[The mean lies at the center of a distribution where the sum of data values above it equals the sum of the data values below it.]**
>
> **Q** Can the variance of a data set be negative? Explain. **[No; the variance is the quotient of two positive numbers—the sum of the squares and the number of data values.]**

Finding the square root of the variance serves two purposes:
- It returns the measurement's unit to the unit of the data values in the set.
- It reduces the size of the measurement so it is easier to use for data analysis.

Got It? ELL SUPPORT

Students can add labels to their tables to help them understand the terms and symbols used: Left to right; "Data Value," "Mean of Data Set," "Difference from Mean," and "Square of Difference."

Problem 2 EXTENSION

> **Q** Does the VAR STATS screen give the variance of the data set? **[no]**
>
> **Q** How can you use the information on the screen to find the variance? **[Square the standard deviation.]**

 Problem 1 Finding Variance and Standard Deviation

What are the mean, variance, and standard deviation of these values?
6.9 8.7 7.6 4.8 9.0

$$\bar{x} = \frac{6.9 + 8.7 + 7.6 + 4.8 + 9.0}{5} = 7.4 \quad \text{Find the mean.}$$

Think
How can you organize you work?
Use a table to record the values.

Make a table.

x	$\bar{x}$	$x - \bar{x}$	$(x - \bar{x})^2$
6.9	7.4	−0.5	0.25
8.7	7.4	1.3	1.69
7.6	7.4	0.2	0.04
4.8	7.4	−2.6	6.76
9.0	7.4	1.6	2.56
		Sum	11.30

Find difference between each value and the mean. Square the differences.

Add the squares of the differences.

$$\sigma^2 = \frac{\sum (x - \bar{x})^2}{n} = \frac{11.3}{5} = 2.26 \qquad \text{Find the variance.}$$

$$\sigma = \sqrt{\sigma^2} = \sqrt{2.26} \approx 1.5 \qquad \text{Find the standard deviation.}$$

The mean is 7.4. The variance is 2.26. The standard deviation is about 1.5.

 Got It? 1. What are the mean, variance, and standard deviation of these values?
52 63 65 77 80 82

 Problem 2 Using a Calculator to Find Standard Deviation **STEM**

Meteorology The table displays the number of U.S. hurricane strikes by decade from the years 1851 to 2000. What are the mean and standard deviation for this data set?

Decade	1	2	3	4	5	6	7	8	9	10	11	12	13	14	15
Strikes	19	15	20	22	21	18	21	13	19	24	17	14	12	15	14

Source: National Hurricane Center

Think
How do you know you are entering all the data values?
The calculator value for n should match the number of table values.

Step 1 Use **STAT EDIT** to enter the data in list **L1**.

Step 2 In **STAT CALC** select the **1– Var Stats** option.

The mean is 17.6; the standard deviation is about 3.5.

```
1 – Var Stats
x̄  = 17.6          ← mean
Σx = 264
Σx² = 4832
Sx = 3.641035959
σx = 3.517574922   ← standard deviation
↓n  = 15
```

Answers

Solve It!

$\sum_{i=1}^{3} x_i$ is the sum of 3 values x_1, x_2, and x_3.

$\sqrt{\sum_{i=1}^{3} (x_i)^2}$ is the square root of the sum of the square of three values i.e. $\sqrt{(x_1)^2 + (x_2)^2 + (x_3)^2}$.

Got It?

1. $\bar{x} = 69.8\overline{3}$, $\sigma^2 = 115.1389$, $\sigma = 10.7303$

 PowerAlgebra.com

2 Guided Instruction

 Each Problem is worked out and supported online.

> **Problem 1**
> Finding Variance and Standard Deviation
> *Animated*

> **Problem 2**
> Using a Calculator to Find Standard Deviation
> *Animated*

> **Problem 3**
> Using Standard Deviation to Describe Data
> *Animated*

Support in Algebra 2 Companion
- Vocabulary
- Key Concepts
- Got It?

✓ **Got It? 2. Meteorology** The table displays the number of hurricanes in the Atlantic Ocean from 1992 to 2006. What are the mean and standard deviation?

Year	1	2	3	4	5	6	7	8	9	10	11	12	13	14	15
Number	4	4	3	11	10	3	10	8	8	9	4	7	9	14	5

SOURCE: National Hurricane Center

In a data list, every value falls within some number of standard deviations of the mean. For example, if the mean is 50 and the standard deviation is 10, then a value x with $40 \leq x \leq 60$ is within one standard deviation of the mean.

© **Problem 3** Using Standard Deviation to Describe Data STEM

Meteorology Use the U.S. hurricane-strike data from Problem 2. Within how many standard deviations from the mean do all of the values fall?

Know	Need	Plan
The data values, their mean, and their standard deviation	The number of standard deviations from the mean that include all the data	• Draw a number line. • Plot the data values and the mean. • Mark off intervals of 3.5 on either side of the mean.

Think

What is a good way to tell which values lie within each σ interval?

Plotting the values on a number line makes it easy to see the σ intervals.

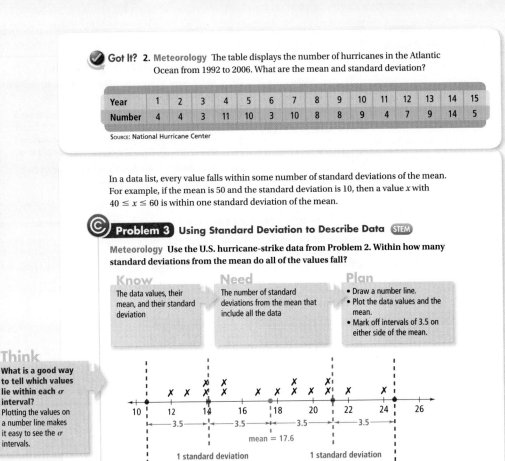

All of the values fall within two standard deviations of the mean. Hurricane watchers can expect that the number of U.S. hurricane strikes in a decade will probably fall within two standard deviations of the 15-decade mean.

© ✓ **Got It? 3. Meteorology** Use the Atlantic Ocean hurricane data from Got It 2.
   a. Within how many standard deviations of the mean do all of the values fall?
   b. Reasoning How might the U.S. Federal Emergency Management Agency (FEMA) use this information?

Got It?   ERROR PREVENTION

Most scientific calculators save entered data sets. To avoid reusing older data sets, students can choose ClrStat to clear the previously used data.

Problem 3   ELL SUPPORT

Explain to students that in general about 95% of all data fall within two standard deviations of the mean.

> **Q** Does this result mean that the U.S. will never have more than 24.6 hurricane strikes in a decade? Explain. **[No; it is only a prediction. It means that having more than 25 hurricanes is unlikely, but still possible.]**
>
> **Q** Do decimals like 10.6 and 24.6 for the data make sense in this problem? Explain. **[No; hurricanes are counted in whole numbers. You do not have 10.6 hurricane strikes in a decade; you have 10 or 11 strikes.]**

Got It?   VISUAL LEARNERS

A bell curve diagram can help students better understand normal distribution of data in a population.

Use a sketch of a bell curve to explain that in a normal distribution:
- about 68% of data values are within 1 standard deviation of the mean.
- about 95% are within 2 standard deviations.
- about 99% are within 3 standard deviations.

Additional Problems

1. What are the mean, variance, and standard deviation of these values?
6.5 5.8 3.9 5.7 4.2

ANSWER mean = 5.22; variance: 0.9976; standard deviation ≈ 0.999

2. The table displays the number of sales a salesperson made each month during the past 15 months. What are the mean and standard deviation?

Month	Sales
1	4
2	3
3	5
4	4
5	6
6	8
7	1
8	3
9	2
10	5
11	6
12	4
13	7
14	5
15	3

ANSWER mean = 4.4; standard deviation ≈ 1.82

3. Use the sales data from Exercise 2. Within how many standard deviations of the mean do all of the values fall?

ANSWER All of the data values fall within two standard deviations of the mean.

Answers

Got It? (continued)

2. $\bar{x} = 7.2\overline{6}$, $\sigma = 3.316$

3. a. within 3 standard deviations of the mean

b. FEMA can expect that the no. of hurricanes for a 15-year period will fall within 3 standard deviations of the mean.

3 Lesson Check

Do you know HOW?
- For Exercise 1, suggest using a table to organize the computations as shown in Problem 1.
- For Exercises 1 and 2, students can use a calculator to verify their answers.

Do you UNDERSTAND?
- For Exercise 3, if necessary, remind students that mean, median, and mode are measures of central tendency, and range, interquartile range, variance, and standard deviation are measures of variation.
- For Exercise 4, students can use graphs to help compare and contrast the data sets. The mean is the peak of each graph's curve, which changes to concave-up at approximately 1 standard deviation greater than and less than the mean.

Close

> **Q** What is standard deviation and how is it used?
> **[Answers may vary. Sample: Standard deviation is a measure of the difference of the data from the mean. It is used to analyze data and to make predictions.]**

Lesson Check

Do you know HOW?
1. Find the mean, variance, and standard deviation for the data set.

   5, 15, 9, 3, 12, 8, 13, 6, 18, 11

2. Within how many standard deviations of the mean do all of the data values fall?

   12, 17, 15, 13, 9, 10, 12, 10, 15, 17

Do you UNDERSTAND? MATHEMATICAL PRACTICES
3. **Vocabulary** Explain the difference between *measures of central tendency* and *measures of variation*.

4. **Compare and Contrast** Three data sets each have a mean of 70. Set A has a standard deviation of 10. Set B has a standard deviation of 5. Set C has a standard deviation of 20. Compare and contrast these 3 sets.

5. **Reasoning** What is the effect of an outlier on the standard deviation of a data set?

Practice and Problem-Solving Exercises MATHEMATICAL PRACTICES

(A) Practice Find the mean, variance, and standard deviation for each data set. *See Problem 1.*

6. 78 90 456 673 111 381 21

7. 13 15 17 18 12 21 10

8. 12 3 2 4 5 7

9. 60 40 35 45 39

Graphing Calculator Find the mean and the standard deviation. *See Problem 2.*

10. The Dow Jones Industrial average for the first 12 weeks of 1988:

1911.31	1956.07	1903.51	1958.22	1910.48	1983.26
2014.59	2023.21	2057.86	2034.98	2087.37	2067.14

11. The Dow Jones Industrial average for the first 12 weeks of 2008:

12800.18	12606.30	12099.3	12207.17	12743.19	12182.13
12348.21	12381.02	12266.39	11893.69	11951.09	11972.25

Determine the whole number of standard deviations from the mean that include all data values. *See Problem 3.*

12. The mean price of the nonfiction books on a best-sellers list is $25.07; the standard deviation is $2.62.
   $26.95, $22.95, $24.00, $24.95, $29.95, $19.95, $24.95, $24.00, $27.95, $25.00

13. The mean length of Beethoven's nine symphonies is 37 minutes; the standard deviation is 12 minutes.
   27 min, 30 min, 47 min, 35 min, 30 min, 40 min, 35 min, 22 min, 65 min

---

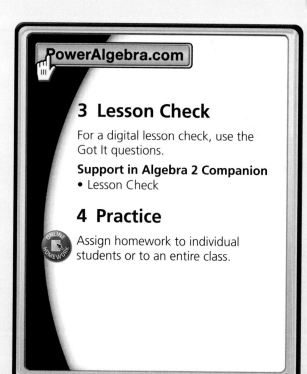

3 Lesson Check

For a digital lesson check, use the Got It questions.

Support in Algebra 2 Companion
- Lesson Check

4 Practice

Assign homework to individual students or to an entire class.

Answers

Lesson Check
1. $\bar{x} = 10$, $\sigma^2 = 19.8$, $\sigma = 4.45$
2. within 2 standard deviations of the mean
3. Measures of central tendency are specific data pts. which give a summary of the middle of the data set, whereas the measures of variation give a summary of the variation of the data set within the range of distribution.
4. Standard deviation measures how widely spread the data values are. If the data pts. are close to the mean, the standard deviation is small; if the data pts. are far from the mean, the standard deviation is large. The data pts. of Set B are closer to the mean of 70 than the data pts. of Sets A and C; likewise, the data pts. of Set A are closer to 70 than the data pts. of Set C.

5. The effect of an outlier on the standard deviation is to increase the standard deviation.

Practice and Problem-Solving Exercises
6. $\bar{x} \approx 258.6$, $\sigma^2 \approx 52{,}136.81$, $\sigma \approx 228.3$
7. $\bar{x} \approx 15.1$, $\sigma^2 \approx 12.4$, $\sigma \approx 3.5$
8. $\bar{x} = 5.5$, $\sigma^2 \approx 10.9$, $\sigma \approx 3.3$
9. $\bar{x} = 43.8$, $\sigma^2 = 75.76$, $\sigma \approx 8.7$
10. $\bar{x} \approx 1984.98$, $\sigma \approx 57.62$
11. $\bar{x} \approx 12{,}320.00$, $\sigma \approx 273.71$
12. 2 standard deviations
13. 3 standard deviations

14. Find the standard deviation for each data set. Use the standard deviations to compare each pair of data sets.

fastest recorded speeds of various large wild cats (miles per hour):
70 50 30 40 35 30 30 40 15

fastest recorded speeds of various birds in flight (miles per hour):
217 106 95 56 65 37 50 31 53 25 25 25

Ⓒ **15. Think About a Plan** Use the data for daily energy usage of a small town during ten days in June. Find the mean and the standard deviation of the data. How many values in the data set fall within one standard deviation from the mean? Within two standard deviations? Within three standard deviations?

| 51.8 MWh | 53.6 MWh | 54.7 MWh | 51.9 MWh | 49.3 MWh |
| 52.0 MWh | 53.5 MWh | 51.2 MWh | 60.7 MWh | 59.3 MWh |

- How is the mean of the data set used in the formula for standard deviation?
- How can a table help you find the standard deviation?
- How can a graph help you decide how many standard deviations a data value is from the mean?

Income Use the chart at the right for Exercises 16–18.

16. Find the mean income for each year.

Ⓒ **17. Writing** Use the standard deviation for each year to describe how farm income varied from 2001 to 2002.

18. For 2001, the farm incomes of which states are not within one standard deviation of the mean?

19. a. Data Collection Make a table showing the number of siblings of each student in your class.
   b. Find the mean and standard deviation of the data.

20. Energy The data for daily energy usage of a small town during ten days in January is shown.

| 83.8 MWh | 87.1 MWh | 92.5 MWh | 80.6 MWh | 82.4 MWh |
| 77.6 MWh | 78.9 MWh | 78.2 MWh | 81.8 MWh | 80.1 MWh |

   a. Find the mean and the standard deviation of the data.
   b. How many values in the data set fall within one standard deviation from the mean? Within two standard deviations? Within three standard deviations?

Ⓒ **21. Error Analysis** One of your friends says that the data below fall within three standard deviations from the mean. Your other friend disagrees, saying that the data fall within six standard deviations from the mean. With whom do you agree? Explain.

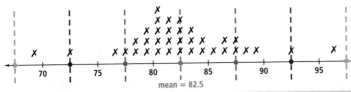

mean = 82.5

Farm Income in Midwestern States (millions of dollars)

State	2001	2002
Iowa	10,653	10,834
Kansas	7979	7862
Minnesota	7537	7478
Missouri	4723	4402
Nebraska	9221	9589
North Dakota	2938	3223
South Dakota	3897	3779

Source: U.S. Department of Agriculture

14. $\sigma_{cats} \approx 14.6$; $\sigma_{birds} \approx 52.3$; the speeds of the birds are more spread out than the speeds of the cats.

15.
$\bar{x} = 53.8$, $\sigma \approx 3.4$; 1σ: 7; 2σ: 9; 3σ: 10

16. year 2001: ≈6707; year 2002: ≈6738

17. Overall farm income increased slightly, but there was less variability among the states in 2002. The income in 2001 clustered more tightly around the mean. (2001: $\sigma_x \approx 2679$, 2002: $\sigma_x \approx 2758$)

18. Iowa, North Dakota, and South Dakota

19. a–b. Check students' work.

20. a. $\bar{x} = 82.3$, $\sigma \approx 4.3$
   b. 1σ: 7; 2σ: 9; 3σ: 10

21. Your first friend; one standard deviation encompasses all values within one standard deviation above and below the mean. The graph shows that all values are within 3 standard deviations of the mean.

4 Practice

ASSIGNMENT GUIDE
Basic: 6–13 all, 15, 17, 20, 21
Average: 7–13 odd, 14–21
Advanced: 7–13 odd, 14–23
Standardized Test Prep: 24–27
Mixed Review: 28–37

Ⓒ **Mathematical Practices** are supported by exercises with red headings. Here are the Practices supported in this lesson:

MP 1: Make Sense of Problems Ex. 15
MP 3: Construct Arguments Ex. 4, 5, 22b
MP 3: Communicate Ex. 17
MP 3: Critique the Reasoning of Others Ex. 21
MP 5: Use Appropriate Tools Ex. 10, 11

Applications exercises have blue headings. Exercises 19 and 20 support MP 4: Model.

STEM exercises focus on science or engineering applications.

EXERCISE 20: Use the Think About a Plan worksheet in the **Practice and Problem Solving Workbook** (also available in the Teaching Resources in print and online) to further support students' development in becoming independent learners.

HOMEWORK QUICK CHECK
To check students' understanding of key skills and concepts, go over Exercises 11, 13, 15, 17, and 20.

Answers

Practice and Problem-Solving Exercises
(continued)

22. a. Men: range: 18 yrs, $\bar{x} \approx 22.44$, $\sigma \approx 3.58$;
Women: range: 13 yrs,
$\bar{x} \approx 25.78$, $\sigma \approx 4.04$

b. No; for the data given, the larger range has the smaller standard deviation.

23. a. no change to σ

b. σ increases by a factor of 10

Standardized Test Prep

24. 194

25. 13

26. 0.8

27. $\frac{5}{6}$

Mixed Review

28.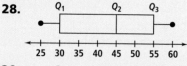

29.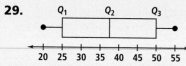

30. center $(2, -1)$; radius 6

31. center $(1, 1)$; radius 2

32. $\frac{1}{2}$

33. $-\frac{1}{3}$

34. $\frac{1}{6}$

35. $-\frac{1}{11}$

36. $-\frac{1}{9}$

37. $\frac{1}{7}$

 Challenge

22. a. Use the table to find the range, the mean, and the standard deviation of the ages for each team.

b. Reasoning For two data sets, does the set with the greater range necessarily have the greater standard deviation? Support your answer with your results from part (a).

23. a. What effect will adding 10 to every value in a data set have on the standard deviation?

b. What will be the effect if you multiply each value by 10?

Ages of the Members of Soccer Teams in an Adult League

Men	19	18	21	22	22	23
	23	23	23	22	36	22
	24	21	21	21	21	22
Women	26	31	22	24	20	22
	20	30	25	26	32	30
	23	33	21	27	24	28

Standardized Test Prep

GRIDDED RESPONSE

SAT/ACT

For Exercises 24–25, use the following bowling scores for six members of a bowling team: 175, 210, 180, 195, 208, 196.

24. What is the mean of the scores?

25. What is the standard deviation of the scores?

26. The 30th term of a finite arithmetic series is 4.4. The sum of the first 30 terms is 78. What is the value of the first term of the series?

27. What is the probability of NOT getting a five when rolling a number cube? Write your answer as a fraction reduced to lowest terms.

Mixed Review

Make a box-and-whisker plot for each set of values.   ◀ See Lesson 11-6.

28. 25, 25, 30, 35, 45, 45, 50, 55, 60, 60   **29.** 20, 23, 25, 36, 37, 38, 39, 50, 52, 55

Find the center and the radius of each circle.   ◀ See Lesson 10-3.

30. $(x - 2)^2 + (y + 1)^2 = 36$ **31.** $(x - 1)^2 + (y - 1)^2 = 4$

Get Ready!   To prepare for Lesson 11-8, do Exercises 32–37.

Simplify each radical expression.   ◀ See Lesson 6-1.

32. $\frac{1}{\sqrt{4}}$ **33.** $-\frac{1}{\sqrt{9}}$ **34.** $\frac{1}{\sqrt{36}}$

35. $-\frac{1}{\sqrt{121}}$ **36.** $-\frac{1}{\sqrt{81}}$ **37.** $\frac{1}{\sqrt{49}}$

Additional Instructional Support

Algebra 2 Companion

Students can use the **Algebra 2 Companion** worktext (4 pages) as you teach the lesson. Use the Companion to support

- New Vocabulary
- Key Concepts
- Got It for each Problem
- Lesson Check

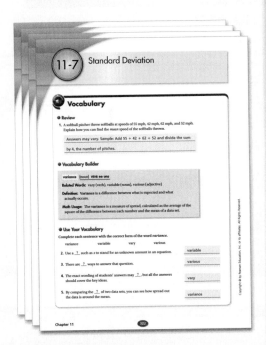

ELL Support

Focus on Language Write *vary*, *variance*, and *variation* on the board. Underline *vary* and explain that it is a verb meaning "to change or to make different." Use a group of different-sized objects to illustrate the meaning. (They vary in size. Some are large; some are small.)

Now circle *variance* and underline its root *vari*. Explain that *variance* is a noun form of *vary* that means "the quality, state, or fact of changing or being different." Repeat the process for *variation* (the act or process of changing or being different). Use both nouns in sentences that show their meanings.

Finally, write *variable* on the board and remind students that a variable is a letter used to stand for an unknown value in an equation. Underline *vari* in *variable* and challenge students to explain how the meaning of *variable* relates to the meaning of its root *vary*.

5 Assess & Remediate

Lesson Quiz

1. What are the mean, variance, and standard deviation of these values?

3.5   4.7   6.4   5.8   4.2

2. Do you UNDERSTAND?

The table at right displays the number of points a basketball player scored in each game last season. What are the mean and standard deviation?

Game	Points
1	11
2	14
3	10
4	8
5	12
6	13
7	12
8	18
9	9
10	12
11	16
12	15
13	11
14	9
15	10

3. Use the basketball points data from Exercise 2. Within how many standard deviations of the mean do all of the values fall?

ANSWERS TO LESSON QUIZ

1. mean = 4.92; variance = 1.1096; standard deviation ≈ 1.05

2. mean = 12; standard deviation ≈ 2.71

3. All the values fall within three standard deviations of the mean.

PRESCRIPTION FOR REMEDIATION

Use the student work on the Lesson Quiz to prescribe a differentiated review assignment:

Points	Differentiated Remediation
0–1	Intervention
2	On-level
3	Extension

PowerAlgebra.com

5 Assess & Remediate

Assign the Lesson Quiz. Appropriate intervention, practice, or enrichment is automatically generated based on student performance.

Intervention

- **Reteaching** (2 pages) Provides reteaching and practice exercises for the key lesson concepts. Use with struggling students or absent students.

- **English Language Learner Support** Helps students develop and reinforce mathematical vocabulary and key concepts.

All-in-One Resources/Online
Reteaching

11-7 Reteaching
Standard Deviation

The mean tells you what the center of a set of data values looks like. But two very different data sets can have the same mean. For example, each of these data sets has a mean of 25.

Set A: {23 24 25 26 27}   Set B: {1 5 25 45 49}

Notice that the data values on the number line for set B are much more spread out from the mean than the data values for set A. *Variance* and *standard deviation* are measures of how widely data values differ from the mean.

The lowercase Greek letter sigma, σ, is the symbol for standard deviation. Variance is the square of the standard deviation, and is written as σ^2. For a set of n data values:

$$\sigma^2 = \frac{\sum(x-\bar{x})^2}{n} \qquad \sigma = \sqrt{\frac{\sum(x-\bar{x})^2}{n}}$$

Problem

What are the variance and standard deviation for the data set {100 158 170 192}?

Step 1 Find the mean of the values.

$$\bar{x} = \frac{100+158+170+192}{4} = 155.$$

Step 2 Subtract the mean from each value in the data set. Then square each difference.

$(100-155)^2 = 3025$ $(158-155)^2 = 9$

$(170-155)^2 = 225$ $(192-155)^2 = 1369$

Step 3 Find the mean of the squared differences. This is the variance.

$$\sigma^2 = \frac{3025+9+225+1369}{4} = 1157$$

Step 4 Find the square root of the variance. This is the standard deviation.

$$\sigma = \sqrt{1157} \approx 34$$

The variance for the data set is 1157 and the standard deviation is about 34.

Exercises

Find the variance and standard deviation for each data set.

1. 6.5 7.0 9.0 8.0 7.5 0.74; about 0.86   **2.** 5.6 5.8 5.9 6.1 0.0325; about 0.18

3. 201 203 208 210 211 15.44; about 3.93   **4.** 12 14 15 17 19 5.84; about 2.42

All-in-One Resources/Online
English Language Learner Support

11-7 Additional Vocabulary Support
Standard Deviation

Rita was studying for a quiz on standard deviation. She wrote the steps to find standard deviation on a set of note cards, but the cards got mixed up.

Calculate the variance by finding the mean of these squares. $\sigma^2 = \frac{\sum(x-\bar{x})^2}{n}$	Find the mean, $\bar{x}$, of the n values in the data set.
Square each difference, $(x_i - \bar{x})^2$.	Take the square root of the variance. $\sigma = \sqrt{\frac{\sum(x-\bar{x})^2}{n}}$
	Find the difference, $x_1 - \bar{x}$, between each value x_1 and the mean.

Use the note cards to write the steps in order.

1. First, find the mean, $\bar{x}$, of the n values in the data set

2. Second, find the difference, $x_1 - \bar{x}$, between each value x_1 and the mean

3. Next, square each difference, $(x_i - \bar{x})^2$

4. Then, calculate the variance by finding the mean of these squares. $\sigma^2 = \frac{\sum(x-\bar{x})^2}{n}$

5. Finally, take the square root of the variance. $\sigma = \sqrt{\frac{\sum(x-\bar{x})^2}{n}}$

Differentiated Remediation *continued*

On-Level

- **Practice** (2 pages) Provides extra practice for each lesson. For simpler practice exercises, use the Form K Practice pages found in the All-in-One Teaching Resources and online.

- **Think About a Plan** Helps students develop specific problem-solving skills and strategies by providing scaffolded guiding questions.

- **Standardized Test Prep** Focuses on all major exercises, all major question types, and helps students prepare for the high-stakes assessments.

Extension

- **Enrichment** Provides students with interesting problems and activities that extend the concepts of the lesson.

- **Activities, Games, and Puzzles** Worksheets that can be used for concepts development, enrichment, and for fun!

Practice and Problem Solving Wkbk/ All-in-One Resources/Online
Practice page 1

11-7 Practice — Form G
Standard Deviation

Find the mean, variance, and standard deviation for each data set.

1. 232 254 264 274 287 298 312 342 398 about 295.7; about 2246.8; about 47.4
2. 26 27 28 28 28 29 30 30 32 35 35 36 about 30.3; about 10.2; about 3.2
3. 2.2 2.2 2.3 2.4 2.4 2.4 2.5 2.5 2.5 2.6 about 2.4; about 0.02; about 0.1
4. 75 73 77 79 79 74 81 74 70 68 70 72 about 74.3; about 15.1; about 3.9

Graphing Calculator Find the mean and the standard deviation.

5. price of XYZ Company stock for the first 12 weeks of 2006 about 5.54; about 0.12

| 5.34 | 5.40 | 5.41 | 5.42 | 5.50 | 5.55 |
| 5.55 | 5.57 | 5.70 | 5.65 | 5.66 | 5.68 |

6. price of XYZ Company stock for the first 12 weeks of 2009 about 5.69; about 0.26

| 6.00 | 5.95 | 5.92 | 5.80 | 5.81 | 5.75 |
| 5.75 | 5.75 | 5.64 | 5.52 | 5.40 | 5.03 |

Determine the whole number of standard deviations that includes all data values.

7. The hours students in your study group study is 66.1 min; the standard deviation is 2.9 min. 3

62 63 65 64 64 68 68 69 72 66

8. The mean weight of your pets is 18.25 lb; the standard deviation is 30.1 lb. 3

0.25 0.25 6 8 10 85

9. Use the data for average daily water usage of a family during the past 10 months. Find the mean and the standard deviation of the data. How many items in the data set fall within one standard deviation of the mean? Within two standard deviations? 249.4; about 162.5; 7; 10

124 gal   113 gal   152 gal   545 gal   150 gal
490 gal   442 gal   207 gal   124 gal   147 gal

10. **Reasoning** In Lesson 11-5 an outlier is defined as a value "substantially different from the rest of the data in a set." How could you use the concept of standard deviation to rewrite this definition? Answers may vary. Sample: An outlier is any data value more than 2 standard deviations from the mean.

Practice and Problem Solving Wkbk/ All-in-One Resources/Online
Think About a Plan

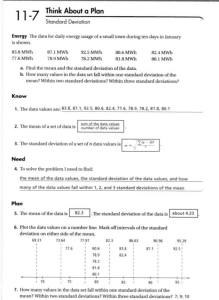

11-7 Think About a Plan
Standard Deviation

Energy The data for daily energy usage of a small town during ten days in January is shown.

83.8 MWh   87.1 MWh   92.5 MWh   80.6 MWh   82.4 MWh
77.6 MWh   78.9 MWh   78.2 MWh   81.8 MWh   80.1 MWh

a. Find the mean and the standard deviation of the data.
b. How many items in the data set fall within one standard deviation of the mean? Within two standard deviations? Within three standard deviations?

Know

1. The data values are: 83.8, 87.1, 92.5, 80.6, 82.4, 77.6, 78.9, 78.2, 81.8, 80.1

2. The mean of a set of data is sum of the data values / number of data values

3. The standard deviation of a set of n data values is $\sigma = \sqrt{\frac{\sum(x-\bar{x})^2}{n}}$

Need

4. To solve the problem I need to find:
the mean of the data values, the standard deviation of the data values, and how many of the data values fall within 1, 2, and 3 standard deviations of the mean

Plan

5. The mean of the data is 82.3 . The standard deviation of the data is about 4.33 .

6. Plot the data values on a number line. Mark off intervals of the standard deviation on either side of the mean.

7. How many values in the data set fall within one standard deviation of the mean? Within two standard deviations? Within three standard deviations? 7; 9; 10

Practice and Problem Solving Wkbk/ All-in-One Resources/Online
Practice page 2

11-7 Practice (continued) — Form G
Standard Deviation

Find the standard deviation for each data set. Use the standard deviations to compare each pair of data sets.

11. prices of the first 10 cars sold at Joe's Used Car Lot in 1998: $\sigma \approx 176.18$
$900 $1300 $1200 $850 $800 $1250 $795 $950 $1020 $975

prices of the first 10 cars sold at Joe's Used Car Lot in 2008: $\sigma \approx 2240.70$
$2500 $2700 $3600 $5000 $1900 $6175 $4000 $7200 $9250 $3000
The 1998 prices are clustered more closely around the mean price than are the 2008 prices.

12. times of boys in 100-m dash state high-school finals in 1998: $\sigma \approx 0.15$
10.43 10.48 10.49 10.51 10.61 10.63 10.66 10.92

times of boys in 100-m dash state high-school finals in 2008: $\sigma \approx 0.21$
10.32 10.38 10.39 10.40 10.70 10.74 10.83 10.90
The 2008 times are slightly more spread out from the mean than the 1998 times.

Use the chart at the right for Exercises 13–17.

13. Find the mean amount of money raised for each year. about $771.88; $1115

14. Find the standard deviation for each year. about $697.70; about $1374.03

15. **Writing** Use the standard deviation for each year to describe how school fundraising varied from 2006–2007 to 2007–2008. Fundraising amounts varied more widely from the mean in 2007–08 than they did in 2006–07.

16. For 2007–2008, the amounts raised by which clubs are not within one standard deviation of the mean? Service Club

17. **Error Analysis** A student says that the amounts raised in 2006–2007 by the Drama Club, Service Club, and Spirit Club are not within one standard deviation of the mean. Do you agree? Explain. No; the Spirit Club's $1000 is within one standard deviation of the mean.

18. a. Make a table showing the heights of ten books in your home. Check students' work.
b. Find the mean and standard deviation of the data. Check students' work.

Fundraising at Smithburg High School

Club	2006–2007	2007–2008
Adventure	$500	$600
Car	$250	$250
Chess	$100	$120
Drama	$1500	$1400
Ecology	$475	$300
Film	$150	$250
Service	$2200	$4500
Spirit	$1000	$1500

Practice and Problem Solving Wkbk/ All-in-One Resources/Online
Standardized Test Prep

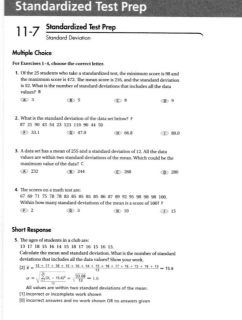

11-7 Standardized Test Prep
Standard Deviation

Multiple Choice

For Exercises 1–4, choose the correct letter.

1. Of the 25 students who take a standardized test, the minimum score is 98 and the maximum score is 472. The mean score is 216, and the standard deviation is 52. What is the number of standard deviations that includes all the data values? B
Ⓐ 3   Ⓑ 5   Ⓒ 7   Ⓓ 9

2. What is the standard deviation of the data set below? F
87 21 90 43 54 23 123 110 90 44 50
Ⓕ 33.1   Ⓖ 47.0   Ⓗ 66.8   Ⓘ 89.0

3. A data set has a mean of 255 and a standard deviation of 12. All the data values are within two standard deviations of the mean. Which could be the maximum value of the data? C
Ⓐ 232   Ⓑ 244   Ⓒ 268   Ⓓ 280

4. The scores on a math test are:
67 69 71 75 78 78 83 85 85 85 85 86 87 89 92 95 98 98 98 100.
Within how many standard deviations of the mean is a score of 100? F
Ⓕ 2   Ⓖ 3   Ⓗ 10   Ⓘ 15

Short Response

5. The ages of students in a club are:
13 17 18 15 16 14 15 18 17 16 15 16 13.
Calculate the mean and standard deviation. What is the number of standard deviations that includes all the data values? Show your work.
[2] $\bar{x} = \frac{13+17+18+15+16+14+15+18+17+16+15+16+13}{13} \approx 15.6$
$\sigma = \sqrt{\frac{\sum(x_i - 15.6)^2}{13}} = \sqrt{\frac{33.08}{13}} \approx 1.6$
All values are within two standard deviations of the mean.
[1] incorrect or incomplete work shown
[0] incorrect answers and no work shown OR no answers given

All-in-One Resources/Online
Enrichment

11-7 Enrichment
Standard Deviation

Speedier Standard Deviations

Standard deviation and variance are both defined in terms of the mean of the distribution. Variance is the square of standard deviation. Using their formulas requires first computing the mean, then using the mean to compute the variance and standard deviation.

Is it possible to compute the variance and standard deviation without first computing the mean? Consider the following reasoning.

1. Write the definition of the mean of the scores x_1 through x_n, using sigma notation. $\bar{x} = \frac{\sum_{i=1}^{n} x_i}{n}$

2. Write the formula for the variance in terms of the mean. $\sigma^2 = \frac{1}{n}\sum_{i=1}^{n}(x_i - \bar{x})^2$

3. Expand the right-hand side of the formula. $\sigma^2 = \frac{1}{n}\sum_{i=1}^{n}(x_i^2 - 2x_i\bar{x} + \bar{x}^2)$

Notice that the middle term has two constants, 2 and $\bar{x}$, so they may be factored outside the sigma symbol. The last term is equivalent to adding the square of the mean n times.

4. What formula results when these substitutions are made? $\sigma^2 = \frac{1}{n}\left(\sum_{i=1}^{n} x_i^2 - 2\bar{x}\sum_{i=1}^{n} x_i + n\bar{x}^2\right)$

5. Now replace the mean, $\bar{x}$, with its sigma notation. What formula results? $\sigma^2 = \frac{1}{n}\left(\sum_{i=1}^{n} x_i^2\right) - \frac{1}{n}\left(\sum_{i=1}^{n} x_i\right)^2$

6. What is the corresponding formula for the standard deviation? $\sigma = \sqrt{\frac{1}{n}\sum_{i=1}^{n} x_i^2 - \frac{1}{n^2}\left(\sum_{i=1}^{n} x_i\right)^2}$

Notice that only the number of scores, the sum of the scores, and the sum of the squares of the scores are needed to find the standard deviation and variance with these formulas.

Suppose the data is presented in terms of the scores x_1 through x_n and their associated frequencies f_1 through f_n.

7. Express the sum of the scores in terms of x_i and f_i. $\sum_{i=1}^{n} f_i x_i$

8. Express the sum of the squares of the scores. $\sum_{i=1}^{n} f_i(x_i)^2$

9. During league play last Friday evening the scores of the last 12 games bowled were 186, 165, 193, 216, 174, 184, 187, 209, 198, 143, 217, and 192. Find the standard deviation of this set of scores without first finding the mean. about 20.4

10. The last 12 games bowled Saturday evening were very close. The score of four games was 186, the score of three games was 184, the score of three games was 187, and the score of two games was 178. Find the standard deviation of this set of scores without first finding the mean. about 3.1

Online Teacher Resource Center
Activities, Games, and Puzzles

11-7 Puzzle: The Usual Suspects
Standard Deviation

Background

On March 14th of last year, a shocking crime was committed. An evil individual set out to crumble the very foundation of Mathtropolis. The villain stated that π is *equal* to 3.14. Fortunately, the Mathtropolis Police Department (MPD) has 10 suspects in custody and they are sure one of them is the culprit.

Goal

Help the MPD determine which of the suspects is guilty. The table shows the suspects' responses to a series of questions whose population mean and standard deviation are given below.

Instructions

- Begin by identifying the five suspects whose responses to Question 1 are more than 1.5 standard deviations from the mean. Suspects B, D, E, G, J
- Of the five, identify those whose responses to Questions 2 and 3 are *both* more than 1.7 standard deviations from the mean. Suspects D, G, J
- Of these three, identify the suspect whose responses to Questions 4, 5, and 6 are all at least 2 standard deviations from the mean. This is the mathematical criminal! Who is it? Suspect G

	A	B	C	D	E	F	G	H	I	J
Q1	14	7	21	28	2	9	5	25	22	27
Q2	0	9	1	8	5	4	2	5	10	1
Q3	77%	96%	89%	56%	59%	32%	100%	92%	86%	60%
Q4	13	1	2	16	12	52	4	13	7	18
Q5	3	4	1	2	2	5	6	3	4	1
Q6	3	5	4	7	2	5	8	3	5	4

Question 1: How many waffles did you eat during this past week?
mean = 17,
standard deviation = 6

Question 2: How many calculators do you and your family own?
mean = 5.1,
standard deviation = 1.3

Question 3: What was your high school algebra average?
mean = 83.2%,
standard deviation = 9.5%

Question 4: How many weeks ago did you last see an action movie?
mean = 10.3,
standard deviation = 2.7

Question 5: How many times a day do you brush your teeth?
mean = 3.9,
standard deviation = 0.8

Question 6: How many digits of π can you recite from memory?
mean = 5.2,
standard deviation = 1.1

Content Standards
S.IC.1 Understand statistics as a process for making inferences about population parameters based on a random sample from that population.
Also S.IC.3, S.IC.4, S.IC.6

Objectives To identify sampling methods
To recognize bias in samples and surveys

SOLVE IT!

Getting Ready!

One day, you catch 100 fish at random from a lake. You tag the fish and then release them back into the lake. The next day you again catch 100 fish at random, as shown on the map. The red dots indicate the fish that have your tags. What can you conclude? Justify your conclusion.

What happened to the other fish you tagged?

MATHEMATICAL PRACTICES

Solve It!
PURPOSE To determine information about a population from a sample
PROCESS Students may consider the minimum number, total number, or possible range of the number of fish.

FACILITATE
Q What is the minimum number of fish that there could be in the pond? How do you know? **[There must be at least 197 fish in the pond, the 97 caught the first day, the three caught twice, and the 97 untagged fish caught the second day.]**

Q If the second day is representative of any catch of one hundred fish, what is the ratio of untagged fish to tagged fish in the pond? **[97 to 3]**

ANSWER See Solve It in Answers on next page.
CONNECT THE MATH In the Solve It, students evaluate a random sample to reach conclusions about a population. In the lesson, students will analyze sampling methods and study methods for validity and bias.

Lesson Vocabulary
• population
• sample
• convenience sample
• self-selected sample
• systematic sample
• random sample
• bias
• observational study
• controlled experiment
• survey

A **population** is all the members of a set. A **sample** is part of a population. If you determine a sample carefully, the statistics for the sample can be used to make general conclusions about the larger population.

Essential Understanding You can get good statistical information about a population by studying a sample of the population.

Suppose you want to know what percent of all voters in your city favor a tax increase to pay for school improvements. It likely would be impossible to ask an opinion of every voter. So instead you select a sample of the voters to estimate the percentage who favor the idea.

You can define different sample types by the methods used to select them.

take note

Key Concepts	Sampling Types and Methods

For a **convenience sample**, select any members of the population who are conveniently and readily available.

For a **self-selected sample**, select only members of the population who volunteer for the sample.

For a **systematic sample**, order the population in some way, and then select from it at regular intervals.

In a **random sample**, all members of the population are equally likely to be chosen.

Take Note

Q Are any of the sampling types and methods random? If a sample is not random, does that mean the conclusions drawn based on the sample are false? Explain. **[The samples are not random because not all members of the population have the same chance of being chosen as part of the sample. The conclusions drawn from such samples may be true, but will likely be suspect.]**

PowerAlgebra.com | Lesson 11-8 Samples and Surveys | 725

BIG idea **Probability**
ESSENTIAL UNDERSTANDING
You can get good statistical information about a population by studying a sample of the population.

Math Background
The statistical information you get about a population depends on the methods you use to sample the population. These methods may cause bias and influence the results of the studies. Understanding these can help to interpret the information more accurately.

SAMPLE METHODS
• Convenience sample: this may have bias when the members of the population who are conveniently and readily available do not represent all groups evenly.
• Self-selected sample: this may have bias when certain groups of people choose not to volunteer.
• Systematic sample: this may have bias when the method used to order the population does not include everyone.

STUDY METHODS
• Observational study: this may introduce bias or inaccuracy depending on the measuring tools and human error.
• Controlled experiment: a double blind can help reduce bias.
• Survey: poorly written survey questions may introduce bias.

Mathematical Practice
Construct viable arguments and critique the reasoning of others. In their study of sampling types and methods, students will distinguish skewed data and offer ways to prevent bias while, in the process, deciding whether certain arguments based on data make sense.

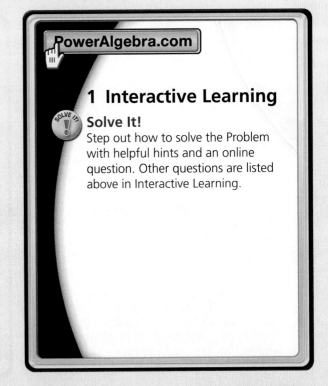

PowerAlgebra.com

1 Interactive Learning

SOLVE IT!
Solve It!
Step out how to solve the Problem with helpful hints and an online question. Other questions are listed above in Interactive Learning.

Problem 1

EXTENSION

Q If the newspaper drew a conclusion about the public's opinion on the proposed property tax in a future issue, why would you want to know what sampling method was used? [**If the sample is random, then the conclusions reached by the newspaper are more reliable than if the sample is not random.**]

Got It?

Q What question could more accurately be answered by the survey sample described in 1a? [**Sample: What food do people choose to eat in the mall food court?**]

Q For 1b, why would someone choose to use a sample instead of a census? [**Sample: It might be too expensive or too time consuming to poll every member of a population.**]

Take Note

Q Which study method would be the best to use to test the effectiveness of a new migraine headache pain reliever? Explain. [**Controlled experiment; administer the new drug to one group of migraine sufferers and another drug to a control group of migraine sufferers, and then compare the effectiveness.**]

Samples vary in how well they reflect a population. A sample has a *bias* when a part of a population is overrepresented or underrepresented. A **bias** is a systematic error introduced by the sampling method.

Problem 1 Analyzing Sampling Methods

Public Opinion A newspaper wants to find out what percent of the city population favors a property tax increase to raise money for local parks. What is the sampling method used for each situation? Does the sample have a bias? Explain.

A A newspaper article on the tax increase invites readers to express their opinions on the newspaper's website.

This is a self-selected sample. It might have a bias, depending on who visits the website. The people who respond may overrepresent or underrepresent some views. For example, some property owners who are against the tax might organize a campaign to get friends and neighbors to visit the website.

B A reporter interviews people leaving the city's largest park.

This is a convenience sample, since it is convenient for the reporter to stay in one place. Because the location is near a park, the sample may overrepresent park supporters and the results will have a bias.

C A survey service calls every 50th listing from the local phone book.

This is a systematic sample because the phone listing is ordered alphabetically. The regular sampling interval is every 50 listings. This sample may have a bias if there is some link between people who are listed (or not listed) in a phone book and people who pay property taxes.

Think
Who are the people in the sample?
The people in the sample are only those who might be selected. In this case, only those who visit the website.

Got It? **1. a.** To survey the eating habits of the community, employees of a local television station interview people visiting a food court in the mall. What sampling method are they using? Does the sample have a bias? Explain.

b. Reasoning A poll of every person in the population is a *census*. What is a situation that requires a census instead of a sample?

One way to collect sample information is to perform a study.

take note

Key Concepts Study Methods

In an **observational study**, you measure or observe members of a sample in such a way that they are not affected by the study.

In a **controlled experiment**, you divide the sample into two groups. You impose a treatment on one group but not on the other "control" group. Then you compare the effect on the treated group to the control group.

In a **survey**, you ask every member of the sample a set of questions.

726   **Chapter 11** Probability and Statistics

Answers

Solve It!

There are about 3333 fish in the lake. You can estimate that for every 3 fish you tagged, there are 97 additional fish. $\frac{100}{3} = 33.\overline{3}$ and $33.\overline{3} \times 100 = 3333$.

Got It?

1. a. Convenience sample; yes; since the location is at the food court, the sample may over-represent fast food supporters.

  b. Sample: population data for the US census

2. Controlled study; if other factors of the volunteers are random, like age, gender, and overall health, the results can be used to make a general conclusion.

3. Answers may vary. Sample: Use a systematic sample. Go to every fifth house in your neighborhood. State the first and last names of the governor and ask a household member to identify the named person. A possible unbiased survey question is, "Who is this person?".

726   **Chapter 11**

PowerAlgebra.com

2 Guided Instruction

Each Problem is worked out and supported online.

Problem 1
Analyzing Sampling Methods
Animated

Problem 2
Analyzing Study Methods

Problem 3
Designing a Survey
Animated

Support in Algebra 2 Companion

• Vocabulary
• Key Concepts
• Got It?

A poorly designed study can result in unreliable statistics. You should always analyze a study's methods before making general conclusions about the population.

Ⓒ Problem 2 Analyzing Study Methods

Which type of study method is described in each situation? Should the sample statistics be used to make a general conclusion about the population?

🅐 **Researchers randomly choose two groups from 10 volunteers. Over a period of 8 weeks, one group eats ice cream before going to sleep, and the other does not. Volunteers wear monitoring devices while sleeping, and researchers record dream activity.**

This is an example of a controlled experiment. The statistics for this study are based on such a small sample that the findings are unreliable as a general conclusion.

🅑 **Students in a science class record the height of bean plants as they grow.**

This is an observational study. The statistics may provide a general conclusion about the growth rate of a bean plant. However, soil type, amount of sunlight and water, fertilizer, and other factors could affect the growth rate.

🅒 **Student council members ask every tenth student in the lunch line if they like the cafeteria food.**

This is a survey. The results are not reliable because people waiting in line are more likely to enjoy the cafeteria food than those who brought their lunch from home.

Think
How can you tell if a sample is a random sample?
In a random sample, each group of the same size is equally likely to be chosen.

✅ **Got It? 2.** A pharmaceutical company asks for volunteers to test a new drug to treat high blood pressure. Half of the volunteers will be given the drug, and half will be given a placebo. The researcher will monitor the blood pressure of each volunteer. Which type of study method is the researcher using? Should the sample statistics be used to make a general conclusion about the effectiveness of the drug in the larger population? Explain.

Ⓒ Problem 3 Designing a Survey

Sports During the 2008 Olympic Games, a U.S. swimmer won more medals than any other swimmer in history. What sampling method could you use to find the percent of students in your school who recognize that swimmer from a photograph? What is an example of a survey question that is likely to yield information that has no bias?

A possible sampling method is to question every 10th student entering school in the morning. This is a systematic sampling. It usually contains the least bias. A possible unbiased survey question is, "Who is pictured in this photograph?".

Think
How do you think of a survey question that has no bias?
Keep it simple. The simplest question is likely to be the least biased.

✅ **Got It? 3.** What sampling method could you use to find the percent of residents in your neighborhood who recognize the governor of your state by name? What is an example of a survey question that is likely to yield information that has no bias?

Problem 2
Review with students the meanings and uses of a control group and placebos in controlled experiments.

Q What factors should you consider to determine if a study method is valid? **[Sample: sample was chosen randomly, sample is the appropriate size, bias in the collection of data]**

Got It?

Q What other factors might be considered when doing medical research on a group of volunteers? **[Sample: Researchers may want a representative sample by age, gender, medical history, and other medical conditions.]**

Problem 3

Q What do you need to be concerned about as you think of a sampling method? **[whether populations are underrepresented or overrepresented and whether all members of the population have an equal opportunity to be chosen]**

Q What conditions in your school would require you to revise the sampling method to avoid bias? **[Sample: Some students do not arrive at school in the morning.]**

Q What should the photograph not depict? **[Sample: a swimming pool, medals, the Olympic symbol]**

Got It?

Q Would mailing a survey to neighbors be a good sampling method? Explain. **[No; residents who do not recognize the name may be less interested and therefore less likely to respond.]**

Additional Problems

1. For each situation, what sampling method is used? Does the sample have a bias?

a. A political candidate wants to know what percent of his constituency favors Referendum A on an upcoming ballot election. His staff asks each person who comes into the candidate's office for three days whether they support Referendum A.

b. The manager of a grocery store wants to determine what percent of shoppers use store coupons. He asks every tenth shopper who passes through the store's door for the next week if he or she intends to use a store coupon on their visit.

ANSWERS

a. convenience sample; visitors to the office of the candidate may share the candidate's opinions more than the population as a whole

b. systematic sample; no

2. Which type of study method is described in each situation? Should the sample statistics be used to make a general conclusion about the population?

a. Scientists study the effects of the phases of the moon on the levels of low tide and high tide in 200 coastal cities in the U.S. for a period of 12 months.

b. A pet food company randomly chooses two groups of 20 puppies for a study. One group eats a new brand of dog food and the other group eats an off-brand dog food for a period of 4 weeks. Researchers record muscular and skeletal growth rates in both groups.

c. For a class project, students in Health class ask every tenth student entering the school if they eat breakfast in the morning.

ANSWERS:

a. observational study; The statistics are reliable since several locations were used and the data were collected for a year.

b. controlled experiment; The statistics are unreliable since a small sample was used. Other factors may include the breeds of the dogs used in the experiment.

c. survey; The results are reliable since a random sample was used.

3 Lesson Check

Do you know HOW?

- If students have difficulty identifying the bias of the survey question in Exercise 2, ask them to identify the adjectives in the question.

Do you UNDERSTAND?

- In Exercise 3, if students do not understand the difference between a population and a sample, use the class as an example of a population and a student as an example of a sample.
- For Exercise 4, if students are unsure what makes a sample unbiased, ask them what makes a sample biased.
- If students have difficulty with the reasoning in Exercise 5, pose questions about the fish pond in the Solve It: If you only caught one fish on the second day, and it was tagged, could you conclude that all the fish in the pond were tagged?

Close

> **Q** What should be considered in determining the reliability of a given sample? **[the sampling type and sampling method, the survey question or questions asked, and the size of the sample]**

 Lesson Check

Do you know HOW?

1. To investigate a community's reading habits, a newspaper conducts a poll from a table near the exit of a history museum.
   a. What is the sampling method?
   b. Does the sampling method have any bias? Explain.

2. A survey asks, "Aren't handmade gifts always better than tacky purchased gifts?" Does this survey question have any bias? Explain.

Do you UNDERSTAND? MATHEMATICAL PRACTICES

3. **Vocabulary** What is the difference between a population and a sample? Give an example of each.

4. **Writing** What does it mean to have an unbiased sample? Why does it matter?

5. **Reasoning** Would a large or small sample tend to give a better estimate of how the total population feels about a topic? Explain.

Practice and Problem-Solving Exercises MATHEMATICAL PRACTICES

A Practice

Identify the sampling method. Then identify any bias in each method. ◀ See Problem 1.

6. A supermarket wants to find the percent of shoppers who use coupons. A manager interviews every shopper entering the greeting card aisle.

7. A maintenance crew wants to estimate how many of 3000 air filters in a 30-story office building need replacing. The crew examines five filters chosen at random on each floor of the building.

8. The student government wants to find out how many students have after-school jobs. A pollster interviews students selected at random as they board buses at the end of the school day.

For Exercises 9–11, identify the type of study method described in each situation and explain whether the sample statistics can be used to make a general conclusion about the population. ◀ See Problem 2.

9. A list of students is randomly generated from the school database. Information for every student is entered into the database, and each student has an equally likely chance of being selected. The students selected are asked how much time they spend on household chores each week.

10. The local librarian collects data about the types of books that are checked out so that she can place a new book order accordingly. She records the type of book checked out by every other person each day for three weeks.

11. **Gardening** A gardener tests a new plant food by planting seeds from the same package in the same soil and location. Each plant is given the same amount of water, but one plant is given food and the other is given no food at all. He records the growth and flowering rates of each plant.

12. **a. Energy** What sampling method could you use to find the percent of adults in your community who support building more nuclear power plants? ◀ See Problem 3.
   b. What is an example of a survey question that is likely to yield unbiased information?

---

3 Lesson Check

For a digital lesson check, use the Got It questions.

Support in Algebra 2 Companion
- Lesson Check

4 Practice

Assign homework to individual students or to an entire class.

Additional Problems (continued)

3. The city planning commission is considering widening a thoroughfare through the center of town to relieve traffic jams. What sampling method could you use to find the percent of city drivers who would favor a change to the thoroughfare? What survey question would you ask to avoid bias?

ANSWER Get a list of licensed drivers for your city and call every twentieth driver on the alphabetical list. A good survey question would be "Would you favor widening the thoroughfare through the center of town?"

Answers

Lesson Check

1. **a.** convenience sample
   b. Yes; since the location is near the exit of a history museum, the sample may overrepresent people who enjoy learning history and the results will have a bias.

2. Yes; the question is leading and loaded. It suggests the person wants a particular answer.

3. All members of the set are the population. A sample is a subset of the population. Answers may vary. Sample: population: students in a high school; sample: students who like to snowboard.

4. It is important to have as little error as possible in a sample, thus giving an unbiased sample. An unbiased sample is more representative of an entire population.

Apply

A university researcher is studying the effect of watching television on residents of the city. Describe a sampling method that can be used for each population.

13. all teenagers

14. all homeowners

15. all women over the age of 21

16. all children under the age of 13

17. Think About a Plan An online advertisement asks you to participate in a survey. The survey asks how much time you spend online each week. What sampling method is the survey using? Identify any bias in the sampling method.
  • What population is likely to see the survey?
  • What population is likely to respond to the survey?

18. Entertainment A magazine publisher mails a survey to every tenth person on a subscriber list. The survey asks for three favorite leisure activities. What sampling method is the survey using? Identify any bias in the sampling method.

19. Student government members survey every tenth student who enters the school building and asks whether students favor the school's new dress code. The sample statistics show that 54% favor the new dress code, 42% oppose the dress code, and 4% have no opinion.
  a. What is the population?
  b. What is the sample?
  c. What general conclusion can be made about the population?

20. Compare and Contrast Describe how a convenience sample and a self-selected sample are alike and how they are different.

21. Elections In a recent election, a survey of randomly selected registered voters was conducted to determine which candidate was likely to win. 48% of respondents said that they would vote for candidate A, 46% would vote for candidate B, and 6% were undecided. Based on the sampling results, can you make a general conclusion that it is more likely that candidate A will win the election? Explain.

22. Customer Satisfaction A car dealership conducts a satisfaction survey. They randomly select a sample of 500 customers from a list of 5000 new customers in the past year. Of the 500 surveys sent, 300 are returned. The statistics show that the dealership is achieving a high level of customer satisfaction. Can the owner of the dealership assume this is true overall? Explain.

23. For a class project, a student studies the likelihood that students turn in their homework each day. For each of her classes, she observes the teacher collect homework. She records the number of students who turn in homework, and the number who do not. The resulting data show that 86% of students turned in homework on time and 5% of students did not turn in any homework at all during the week.
  a. What type of sampling method was used?
  b. What type of study was performed?
  c. Can the student use these statistics to make a general conclusion about all students in her school? Explain.

ASSIGNMENT GUIDE
Basic: 6–12 all, 15–19, 23
Average: 7–11 odd, 15–19, 21–23
Advanced: 7–11 odd, 16–19, 23, 24
Standardized Test Prep: 26–28
Mixed Review: 29–38

Mathematical Practices are supported by exercises with red headings. Here are the Practices supported in this lesson:

MP 1: Make Sense of Problems Ex. 17
MP 2: Reason Abstractly Ex. 12a, 24
MP 2: Reason Quantitatively Ex. 5
MP 3: Compare Arguments Ex. 20
MP 3: Communicate Ex. 4

Applications exercises have blue headings.
Exercise 22 supports MP 4: Model.

EXERCISE 23: Use the Think About a Plan worksheet in the **Practice and Problem Solving Workbook** (also available in the Teaching Resources in print and online) to further support students' development in becoming independent learners.

HOMEWORK QUICK CHECK
To check students' understanding of key skills and concepts, go over Exercises 7, 9, 17, 19, and 23.

5. A large sample size would give a better estimate. The size of the sample is important to the reliability of the sample.

Practice and Problem-Solving Exercises

6. Convenience sampling; This sampling method overrepresents shoppers that buy greeting cards.

7. systematic sampling; no bias

8. convenience sampling; If students walk or drive to school, or are involved in after school activities, they are underrepresented by this sampling method.

9. Survey; the statistics can be used to make a general conclusion about the population because the sample is randomly generated, and the survey question does not introduce a bias into the study.

10. Observational study; the statistics are somewhat unreliable in this study because not all library goers have an equally likely chance of being selected. Although the data collected cannot be used to make a general conclusion about the entire population, it may still give the librarian useful information to make her decision.

11. Controlled experiment; the statistics from this study can be used to make a general conclusion about the effectiveness of the plant food for this particular plant type as compared with giving no plant food at all.

12. a. Answers may vary. Sample: systematic sampling; call every 50th listing in the local phone book.
  b. Check students' work.

13. Answers may vary. Sample: Convenience sampling; interview students at a local high school.

14. Sample: Systematic sampling; contact every 50th homeowner on a list of homeowners in the community.

15. Sample: Self-selected sampling; a newspaper article invites females over the age of 21 to call the paper and express their opinions.

16. Sample: Convenience sampling; contact pediatricians in the community to ask them to have parents of all children under the age of 13 complete a questionnaire.

17. self-selected sampling; biased because only those who spend time online will respond.

18–23. See next page.

Answers

Practice and Problem-Solving Exercises (continued)

18. systematic sampling; This sample may have a bias since people with no strong interest in any leisure-time activity may choose not to respond.

19. a. all students at the school

b. every tenth student who enters the school building the day of the survey

c. Answers may vary. Sample answer: A little over half of students favor the new dress code.

20. Answers may vary. Sample answer: Both samples may introduce bias because respondents are not truly random. A convenience sample may allow for a more representative sample than a self-selected sample, because respondents of a self-selected sample may have strong feelings about the study topic, and other members of the sample may not respond because it is not an important topic to them.

21. Answers will vary. Sample answer: No, because you would have to assume that all registered voters will actually vote on Election Day.

22. Answer will vary. Sample answer: Yes, the sample is randomly determined, a reasonable number of surveys were returned, so the statistics can be used to reliably apply to the entire population.

23. a. convenience sample

b. observational study

c. Answers may vary. Sample answer: The statistics do not necessarily represent the school population because a random sample was not used to conduct the study. Therefore, the statistics are unreliable and should not be used to make a general conclusion about the school population.

24. Check students' responses.

25. Yes, the question is leading the respondent to a particular desired answer, and it gives statistics that may elicit a strong reaction. Also, it requires the respondent to answer a question about whether a person *should* wear a safety belt, which may not necessarily influence whether they support the law.

Standardized Test Prep

26. D

27. G

28. [2] $a = \frac{2}{5}$ and $r = \frac{2}{5}$,

$$\text{Sum} = \frac{\frac{2}{5}}{1 - \frac{2}{5}} = \frac{2}{3}$$

[1] appropriate method, with one computational error

 Challenge

24. Open Ended The government uses a variety of methods to estimate how the general public is feeling about the economy. A researcher wants to conduct a study to determine whether people who live in his state are representative of the latest government results. What type of study should the researcher use? Explain.

25. In a recent telephone survey, respondents were asked questions to determine whether they supported the new law that required every passenger to wear a seat belt while in a moving vehicle. The first question was, "According to the National Highway Traffic Safety Administration, wearing seat belts could prevent 45% of the fatalities suffered in car accidents. Do you think that everyone should wear safety belts?" Does this question introduce a bias into the survey? Explain.

Standardized Test Prep

SAT/ACT

26. To determine the most popular brands of tea consumed by Americans, a survey is conducted in a busy downtown location at lunchtime. Which of the following is NOT a potential bias in the sampling method?

(A) Urban office employees are not representative of the general population.

(B) The results could be influenced by national brand teas available in the area.

(C) A lunchtime survey does not reflect peoples' tastes at other times of the day.

(D) The survey must include call-in and online responses.

27. Which is the equation for the graph of the circle at the right?

(F) $x^2 + (y - 5)^2 = 16$ (H) $(x - 5)^2 + y^2 = 16$

(G) $x^2 + (y + 5)^2 = 16$ (I) $(x + 5)^2 + y^2 = 16$

Short Response

28. What is the sum of the infinite geometric sequence? Show your work.

$$\frac{2}{5}, \frac{4}{25}, \frac{8}{125}, \cdots$$

Mixed Review

Find the mean and the standard deviation for each data set.   ◀ **See Lesson 11-7.**

29. 0, 1, 1, 1, 2, 2, 2, 3, 3, 4, 5, 10

30. 1, 1, 2, 2, 3, 4, 5, 6, 8, 9, 10, 10, 12

Find the inverse of each function. Is the inverse a function?   ◀ **See Lesson 6-7.**

31. $f(x) = 2x + 5$ **32.** $f(x) = x^2$ **33.** $f(x) = \frac{5x^2}{9}$ **34.** $f(x) = 3\sqrt{x}$

Get Ready! To prepare for Lesson 11-9, do Exercises 35–38.

Evaluate each expression.   ◀ **See Lesson 11-1.**

35. $_4C_2$ **36.** $_3C_3$ **37.** $_5C_2$ **38.** $_{12}C_7$

Mixed Review

29. $\bar{x} \approx 2.83$, $\sigma \approx 2.54$

30. $\bar{x} \approx 5.62$, $\sigma \approx 3.67$

31. $y = \frac{1}{2}(x - 5)$; yes

32. $y = \pm\sqrt{x}$; no

33. $y = \pm\sqrt{\frac{9x}{5}}$; no

34. $y = \frac{x^2}{9}$, $x \geq 0$; yes

35. 6

36. 1

37. 10

38. 792

Additional Instructional Support

Algebra 2 Companion

Students can use the **Algebra 2 Companion** worktext (4 pages) as you teach the lesson. Use the Companion to support

- New Vocabulary
- Key Concepts
- Got It for each Problem
- Lesson Check

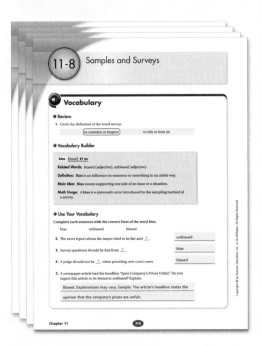

ELL Support

Assess Understanding Have students each write a survey question. In a small group, ask students to revise the questions to remove any bias. Then, have students devise sampling methods for their question and discuss possible sources of bias.

5 Assess & Remediate

Lesson Quiz

1. Identify the sampling method used and any bias the sample might have: A survey is taken by the student council of the first twenty students buying lunch in the cafeteria to see whether students think the cafeteria lunch is a good value.

2. A library asks every tenth person that checks out an item if he or she prefers audio books or printed books. Which study method is described? Should the sample statistics be used to make a general conclusion about the population of library patrons? About the population of the local community?

3. **Do you UNDERSTAND?** The student council is considering petitioning the school board for permission to change the school colors. What sampling method could you use to find the percent of students who would favor a change of school colors? What survey question would you ask to avoid bias?

ANSWERS TO LESSON QUIZ

1. convenience sample; people who are eager for lunch may be overrepresented

2. Sample: survey; The statistics are reliable for a population of the library patrons since a random sample was used. The statistics are not reliable for a population of the local community because it is a convenience sample and is not representative of the community as a whole.

3. Ask every tenth student in the alphabetical directory for a systematic sample. A good survey question would be, "Would you favor a change in school colors?"

PRESCRIPTION FOR REMEDIATION

Use the student work on the Lesson Quiz to prescribe a differentiated review assignment:

Points	Differentiated Remediation
0–1	Intervention
2	On-level
3	Extension

PowerAlgebra.com

5 Assess & Remediate

Assign the Lesson Quiz. Appropriate intervention, practice, or enrichment is automatically generated based on student performance.

Intervention

- **Reteaching** (2 pages) Provides reteaching and practice exercises for the key lesson concepts. Use with struggling students or absent students.

- **English Language Learner Support** Helps students develop and reinforce mathematical vocabulary and key concepts.

All-in-One Resources/Online
Reteaching

11-8 Reteaching
Samples and Surveys

When doing a survey, it usually is not practical to get the opinion of every member of a population. You can get a fairly accurate picture of the opinion of a population by surveying a *sample* of the population. A sample is a smaller group that represents the whole population. There are several ways to choose a sample:

Convenience	choosing any people easily available
Self-selection	having people volunteer to participate in the survey
Systematic	ordering the population and choosing participants at regular intervals (such as choosing every fifth person from the telephone book)
Random	all members of the population have an equal chance of being asked to participate

The way you choose the sample can introduce *bias*, or systematic error, into the survey. When a survey is biased, the results are inaccurate.

Problem

An athletic shoe company wants to learn which brand of athletic shoes is worn most often by local high-school students. The company sets up a booth in a local mall and offers a coupon for a free pair of their athletic shoes to anyone who answers the question, "What is your favorite brand of athletic shoes?"

a. What is the sampling method used? There may be more than one.
b. Is there any bias in the company's sampling method?

a. People in the mall are readily available to the booth. Also, people must volunteer to participate. The sample is a convenience sample and is self-selected.
b. The survey is biased in several ways:
- People who do not shop at the mall are excluded.
- Only people who choose to walk up to the booth participate in the survey.
- People who are not high-school students may participate in the survey.
- People may be more likely to say this company makes their favorite shoes when they are offered a free pair.

Exercises

A politician wants to know what issues are most important to the voters in his district. Identify the sampling method and any bias in the method.

1. The politician spends 9:00 A.M. to 4:00 P.M. on Tuesday talking to people as they enter a grocery store. convenience; excludes people who don't shop during that day

2. The politician sets up a questionnaire on his website. self-selected; excludes people without internet access

All-in-One Resources/Online
English Language Learner Support

11-8 Additional Vocabulary Support
Samples and Surveys

Choose the word from the list that best matches each sentence.

| bias | controlled experiment | observational study |
| population | self-selected sample | |

1. The members of a set. **population**

2. A study method that involves observing members of a sample without affecting them. **observational study**

3. Systematic error caused by the sampling method. **bias**

4. A sample that includes only volunteers. **self-selected sample**

5. A study method that involves a control group and a treated group. **controlled experiment**

Choose the word from the list that best completes each sentence.

| convenience sample | random sample | sample |
| survey | systematic sample | |

6. When conducting a **survey**, you ask members of a sample a set of questions.

7. All members of the population are equally likely to be chosen in a **random sample**.

8. A **convenience sample** includes members of the population who are readily available.

9. A **sample** is a part of the population.

10. To create a **systematic sample**, you must order the population and then select from it at regular intervals.

Differentiated Remediation *continued*

On-Level

- **Practice** (2 pages) Provides extra practice for each lesson. For simpler practice exercises, use the Form K Practice pages found in the All-in-One Teaching Resources and online.
- **Think About a Plan** Helps students develop specific problem-solving skills and strategies by providing scaffolded guiding questions.
- **Standardized Test Prep** Focuses on all major exercises, all major question types, and helps students prepare for the high-stakes assessments.

Practice and Problem Solving Wkbk/ All-in-One Resources/Online

Practice page 1

11-8 Practice *Form G*
Samples and Surveys

Identify the sampling method. Then identify any bias in each method.

1. A teacher committee wants to find how much time students spend reading each week. They ask students as they enter the library. Convenience; the sample is likely to include a disproportionate number of students who spend more time reading.
2. The students planning the junior class party want to know what kinds of pizza to buy. They ask the pizza restaurant what kinds sell the most. Convenience; the restaurant sells to people other than students, and students may prefer something different than the population as a whole.
3. The county road department wants to know which roads cause the most concern among the residents of the county. They ask the local restaurants to hand out survey forms for customers to return by mail. Self-selected; the restaurant patrons are probably not representative of all the different kinds of people who live in the county.

Identify the type of study method described in each situation, and explain whether the sample statistics should be used to make a general conclusion about the population.

4. A company that manufactures light bulbs selects 3 bulbs manufactured each day at random. Then these bulbs are tested to see how many hours they last. observational study; Depending on how many light bulbs the company makes each day, the sample size may be too small to accurately reflect the population.
5. A food product company is researching a new artificial sweetener. The company asks 100 people at a retirement home to rate the taste of a drink on a scale from 1 to 10. Half of the people are given tea sweetened with sugar, and half are given tea sweetened with the artificial sweetener. Then the results from the two groups are averaged. controlled experiment; Because the people in the sample are likely to be older than the general population, the results of the experiment may not accurately reflect the general population.
6. A high-school principal wants to determine what classes students at the school would like to see added next year. He selects every 10th student listed in the school's database and asks each of them to list the 3 classes they would most like to see added to the school's class list. survey; The sample is taken systematically from the member of the population, and the survey question is unbiased. So, the results can be used to make a general conclusion about the population.
7. a. What sampling method could you use to find the percent of people in your community who support tougher penalties for running red lights?
   b. What is an example of a survey question that is likely to yield unbiased information?
   Answers may vary. Sample: Do you think the current penalties for running red lights are appropriate?

Practice and Problem Solving Wkbk/ All-in-One Resources/Online

Practice page 2

11-8 Practice (continued) *Form G*
Samples and Surveys

8. A state's Department of Transportation wants to determine whether the drivers of semi-trailer trucks on an interstate highway would like to have a separate lane for large trucks.
   a. What sampling method could the department use to find the percent of the semi-trailer truck drivers who would like a separate lane? Answers may vary. Sample: Survey the driver of every 20th semi-trailer truck passing through a checkpoint on the interstate highway.
   b. What is an example of a survey question that is likely to yield no bias? Answers may vary. Sample: On a scale of 1 to 5, with 1 being strong support and 5 being strong opposition, what is your opinion of adding a separate lane to the interstate highway for large trucks?

A committee surveys public response to a plan to add bicycle lanes to downtown city streets. Describe a sampling method that can be used for each population.

9. bicyclists Answers may vary. Sample: Interview random people at several city bicycle shops.
10. car drivers Answers may vary. Sample: Call random people from a list of all driver's license holders in the city.
11. downtown business owners
    Answers may vary. Sample: Send surveys to all downtown businesses.
12. a. Write a survey question to find out the number of students in your class who plan to travel out of state after graduation. Check students' work.
    b. Describe the sampling method you would use. Check students' work.
    c. Conduct your survey. Check students' work.
13. A television show's website asks every 20th person who visits the site to name their favorite TV star.
    a. What sampling method is the survey using? convenience or systematic
    b. Describe any bias in the sampling method. People who visit the show's website are more likely than the general television viewer to pick the show's star as their favorite.
14. Biologists test 10 fish selected at random from each tank at a fish hatchery. The sample statistics show that 32% of the fish have a certain chemical present in their bodies and 68% do not have the chemical.
    a. What is the population? all of the fish at the hatchery
    b. What is the sample? 10 fish selected at random from each tank
    c. What general conclusion can be made about the population? Answers may vary. Sample: About $\frac{1}{3}$ of the fish at the hatchery show the presence of the chemical in their bodies.
15. **Reasoning** Explain why the results of a survey could be biased even if the survey sample is selected from the population at random.
    The sample might be too small to accurately reflect the population, or the survey questions might be biased.

Practice and Problem Solving Wkbk/ All-in-One Resources/Online

Think About a Plan

11-8 Think About a Plan
Samples and Surveys

Entertainment A magazine publisher mails a survey to every tenth person on a subscriber list. The survey asks for three favorite leisure activities. What sampling method is the survey using? Identify any bias in the sampling method.

Know

1. The company sending out the survey is a magazine publisher.
2. The surveys are mailed to every tenth person on a subscriber list.
3. The survey asks for three favorite leisure activities.

Need

4. To solve the problem I need to find:
   the sampling method used by the survey and any bias in the sampling method.

Plan

5. What sampling method is the survey using? systematic sampling
6. Do the people who receive the survey represent the general population? Explain.
   Answers may vary. Sample: No; only people who already subscribe to the publisher's magazines receive the survey.
7. Do the people who return the survey represent the general population? Explain.
   Answers may vary. Sample: No; only people who choose to return the survey are represented.
8. Is there any bias in the sampling method? Explain.
   Answers may vary. Sample: Yes; the people who receive the survey subscribe to magazines, so they are likely to list reading magazines as a favorite leisure activity. The sample is also self-selected, depending on who returns the survey. These people may overrepresent or underrepresent some choices of activities.

Practice and Problem Solving Wkbk/ All-in-One Resources/Online

Standardized Test Prep

11-8 Standardized Test Prep
Samples and Surveys

Multiple Choice

For Exercises 1–4, choose the correct letter.

1. The School Dance Committee conducts a survey to find what type of music students would like to hear at the next dance. Which sampling method is *least* likely to result in a biased sample? B
   A. Call 20% of the people in the senior class directory.
   B. Interview every 10th student as they enter the school.
   C. Ask every 5th person leaving a school orchestra concert.
   D. Set up a jazz website where students can list their 3 favorite songs.
2. A news reporter wants to determine what types of movies are most popular in her city. She surveys the first 20 people leaving a movie theater at 8:00 P.M. on a Friday. Which best describes the sampling method used in this situation? F
   F. convenience sample
   G. self-selected sample
   H. random sample
   I. systematic sample
3. A veterinarian monitors a litter of 8 kittens and records their ages in days when they first open their eyes. Which type of study method was used in this situation? B
   A. controlled experiment
   B. observational study
   C. random sample
   D. survey
4. A high-school principal wants to determine how students feel about a new gym that has been proposed for the school. Which survey question is most likely to yield information that has no bias? F
   F. Do you think that the school should build a new gym?
   G. Do you think that building a new gym will be a waste of money?
   H. Shouldn't the school build a new gym to promote healthy exercise?
   I. Should the school build a new gym when the science lab is outdated?
5. The manager of an athletic store selects every tenth name on a list of the players in a city baseball league for middle school students. He asks each selected player what brand of glove he or she uses while playing baseball. Assuming that the sample accurately reflects the population, what is the population in this situation? C
   A. all baseball players in the city
   B. all customers of the athletic store
   C. all baseball players in the league
   D. all middle school students in the city

Short Response

[2] Student describes an appropriate sampling method for the population and correctly explains why the sample is unlikely to be biased.
[1] Incorrect or incomplete sampling method and explanation given

6. Describe a sampling method you could use to find the type of music that is most popular among students at your school. Tell why the sample is unlikely to have a bias.
   [0] Incorrect sampling method and no explanation given OR no answer given

Extension

- **Enrichment** Provides students with interesting problems and activities that extend the concepts of the lesson.
- **Activities, Games, and Puzzles** Worksheets that can be used for concepts development, enrichment, and for fun!

All-in-One Resources/Online

Enrichment

11-8 Enrichment
Samples and Surveys

By choosing a random sample and avoiding bias in survey questions, you can get results that accurately reflect a larger population. However, it is important that the survey be reliable. Reliability is the extent to which a survey will produce the same results on repeated trials. There are three key types of reliability:

Test-retest reliability	the extent to which the same survey given to the same sample gives the same results
Internal consistency	how well items in the same survey measure the same characteristics
Interrater reliability	the extent to which two people conducting a survey get the same results

State which type of reliability is illustrated in each situation.

1. A researcher wants to determine how prepared high school students are for a mathematics class. Several questions in the survey measure the same mathematical concept. internal consistency reliability
2. A group of students were given an IQ test. Each student was given the test twice two weeks apart. test-retest reliability
3. A certain level of communication skills is needed for a telemarketing position. When hiring, an employer gives a communication skills test to each applicant. The interviewer rates the candidate on a scale of 1 to 10. The test is given during the first round of interviews and then again by a second interviewer to all candidates invited back for a second interview. interrater reliability
4. A researcher is designing a survey to find out how satisfied readers are with a particular newspaper. Certain questions are analyzed to make sure that they indicate that the person is satisfied with the newspaper. internal consistency reliability
5. Two researchers are observing an English classroom. The class is discussing a movie the class recently watched as a group. The researchers separately rate each student's level of discussion on a scale of 1 to 5. interrater reliability
6. Before each Olympic wrestling match, each wrestler is weighed twice during the sign-in process. test-retest reliability

Online Teacher Resource Center

Activities, Games, and Puzzles

11-8 Activity: Proportions and Samples
Samples and Surveys

This activity is best for groups of three or four students.

Step 1

Decide as a group on a proportion you would like to estimate using sampling. Here are some ideas.

- What proportion of students prefers sweet-tasting food to sour-tasting food?
- What proportion of students drives his or her own car to school?
- What proportion of students has a cell phone at school?

Step 2

Split your group and poll every student in class. Be sure to include yourselves.

Step 3

Analyze the data your group collected. Use your results to answer the following questions.

1. Which proportion are you estimating?
   Check students' work.
2. Which question did your group ask the other students?
   Check students' work.
3. From which population does your sample come?
   Answers will vary. Sample: all students in school; all juniors in school; all seniors in school
4. What is your sample proportion?
   Check students' work.
5. What is your margin of error?
   Check students' work.
6. How many students would you have to poll to get a margin of error of ±5%?
   400
7. Can you identify any bias in your sampling method?
   Answers will vary. Samples: convenience sample; group members did not use the same question.

Dynamic Activity
Binomial
Probability

Lesson
Vocabulary
• binomial experiment
• binomial probability
• Binomial Theorem

11-9 Binomial Distributions

Content Standard
Extends S.CP.9 Use permutations and combinations to compute probabilities of compound events and solve problems.

Objective To find binomial probabilities and to use binomial distributions

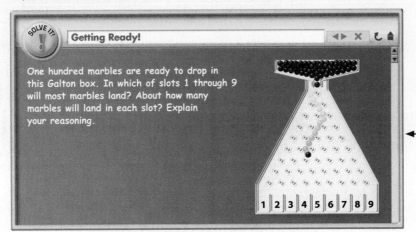

Getting Ready!

One hundred marbles are ready to drop in this Galton box. In which of slots 1 through 9 will most marbles land? About how many marbles will land in each slot? Explain your reasoning.

1 2 3 4 5 6 7 8 9

At each level of a Galton box, a marble can take one of two possible paths.

Essential Understanding You can use binomial probabilities in situations involving two possible outcomes.

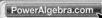

Key Concept Binomial Experiment

A **binomial experiment** has these important features:

• There are a fixed number of trials.
• Each trial has two possible outcomes.
• The trials are independent.
• The probability of each outcome is constant throughout the trials.

Recall from Lesson 11-4, that you can use a tree diagram to find probabilities. The tree diagram on the following page shows different outcomes and probabilities for a basketball player shooting two free throws. It is known that this player is a good shooter, having hit (*H*) about 90% of the free throws so far this season.

PowerAlgebra.com | Lesson 11-9 Binomial Distributions | 731

---

1 Interactive Learning

Solve It!

PURPOSE To analyze an experiment that results in a binomial distribution

PROCESS Students may

• use a Galton box with fewer rows (4 or 5) to understand the probabilities involved.
• make a tree diagram to identify the possible outcomes of each marble's fall and determine the theoretical probabilities of each outcome.

FACILITATE

Q Is each marble's fall an independent event? Explain. **[Yes; the result of a marble's fall does not affect the fall of any other marble.]**

Q When each marble hits any peg, what are the possible outcomes? What is the probability of each outcome? **[The marble goes left or right; $\frac{1}{2}$.]**

ANSWER See Solve It in Answers on next page.
CONNECT THE MATH In the Solve It, students analyzed the theoretical results of binomial experiments. In this lesson, students will calculate and apply binomial probabilities to analyze binomial distributions.

2 Guided Instruction

Take Note

Q How does the Galton box problem illustrate the features of a binomial experiment? **[It has a fixed number of trials—the ball will always hit exactly nine pegs. Each trial has two possible outcomes—left or right. The trials are independent—one trial's outcome cannot affect the probabilities of other trials. The probabilities do not change from trial to trial.]**

11-9 Preparing to Teach

BIG ideas **Probability**
Data Collection and Analysis

ESSENTIAL UNDERSTANDING

Binomial probabilities can be used to model situations in which there are two possible outcomes.

Math Background

A *binomial experiment* is a series of independent trials, each of which has one of two possible outcomes. One example is flipping a fair coin a number of times. Each flip is either heads or tails, and the probability of heads or tails on any given flip is independent of all other flips.

A *binomial probability*, *P(x)*, is a function that gives the probability of *x* successes in *n* trials of a binomial experiment. For example, if you define success as a coin landing heads, and *n* = 10, then *P*(3) gives

the probability that a coin lands heads three times in ten flips of the coin.

Recall that a binomial is a polynomial with two terms. The Binomial Theorem gives a formula for raising a binomial to a power using combinations.

$(a + b)^n = {}_nC_0a^n + {}_nC_1a^{n-1}b + {}_nC_2a^{n-2}b^2 + \ldots + {}_nC_{n-1}ab^{n-1} + {}_nC_nb^n$

Notice in each expansion:

• The powers of *a* decrease by 1 in successive terms and the powers of *b* increase by 1.
• The sum of powers in each term is *n*.
• The coefficients increase and then decrease in a symmetrical pattern.

The coefficients of the expansion are called binomial coefficients and when arranged in a triangular pattern form Pascal's Triangle.

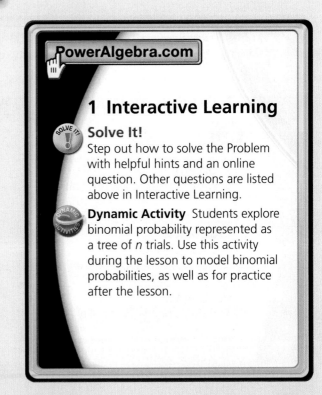

PowerAlgebra.com

1 Interactive Learning

Solve It!
Step out how to solve the Problem with helpful hints and an online question. Other questions are listed above in Interactive Learning.

Dynamic Activity Students explore binomial probability represented as a tree of *n* trials. Use this activity during the lesson to model binomial probabilities, as well as for practice after the lesson.

Lesson 11-9 **731**

Take Note

Students may benefit from a review of the variables used in the binomial formula:

$_nC_x$ = the number of possible combinations of x items from a set of n items (the combination formula)

n = the number of trials

x = the number of successes among n trials

p = the probability of success in one trial

q = the probability of failure in one trial

($q = 1 - p$, the *complement* of the event)

> **Q** For any binomial experiment, what must be the sum $p + q$? **[1]**

Problem 1   ELL SUPPORT

Since the text in the problem might be difficult for English learners, rephrase the information in shorter sentences that are easier to understand.

A school has 3000 students. 40% of the students are in clubs. 5 students in the school are randomly selected. What is the probability that exactly 4 of those students are in clubs?

> **Q** Why is the word *exactly* used in this problem's question? **[The number of successes is 4, not 4 or 5.]**
>
> **Q** What does $_5C_4$ mean in this problem? **[the number of ways 4 students can be selected/ combined out of a group of 5 students]**
>
> **Q** How can you find the value of $_5C_4$ without using a calculator or the combination formula? **[Make a tree diagram to find all the possible combinations.]**

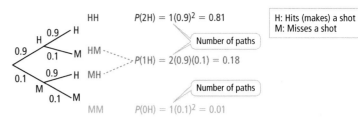

HH $P(2H) = 1(0.9)^2 = 0.81$ H: Hits (makes) a shot
   M: Misses a shot

Number of paths

HM ·········· $P(1H) = 2(0.9)(0.1) = 0.18$

MH ··········

Number of paths

MM $P(0H) = 1(0.1)^2 = 0.01$

Suppose the player needs to make one of two free throws to win a game. The purple and red labels show $P(2 \text{ hits}) + P(1 \text{ hit}) = 0.81 + 0.18 = 0.99$.

The basketball player shoots 2 free throws—each independent of the other (pressure notwithstanding). The player will succeed on 0, 1, or 2 of them. You can compute the probabilities shown in the tree diagram by using the **binomial probability** formula.

take note   Key Concept   Binomial Probability

Suppose you have n repeated independent trials, each with a probability of success p and a probability of failure q (with $p + q = 1$). Then the **binomial probability** of x successes in the n trials can be found by the following formula.

$$P(x) = {_nC_x}p^x q^{n-x}$$

Problem 1   Using a Formula to Find Probabilities

Merchandising As part of a promotion, a store is giving away scratch-off cards. Each card has a 40% chance of awarding a prize. Suppose you have five cards. Find the probability that exactly four of the five cards will reveal a prize.

Know	Need	Plan
• The number of trials n • The number of successes x • The probability of success p	• The probability of failure q • The probability of picking exactly 4 winning cards	• Decide that this is binomial probability. • Find the probability of failure q. • Use the formula for binomial probability.

Determine if this a binomial experiment.

- The situation involves 5 repeated trials—5 cards selected at random.
- Each trial has two possible outcomes: It is a winner or it is not.
- The probability of success is constant, 0.4, throughout the trials.
- The trials are independent. The outcome of scratching one card does not affect the probability of any of the other cards revealing a prize.

PowerAlgebra.com

2 Guided Instruction

Each Problem is worked out and supported online.

Problem 1
Using a Formula to Find Probabilities
Animated

Problem 2
Expanding Binomials
Animated

Problem 3
Applying Binomial Probability
Animated

Support in Algebra 2 Companion

- Vocabulary
- Key Concepts
- Got It?

Answers

Solve It!

Answers may vary. Sample answer: The slots will have the following numbers of marbles, respectively:
0, 3, 11, 22, 28, 22, 11, 3;
more marbles will be in the middle slots, gradually decreasing as the slots approach the edges, because more paths lead to the middle.

Think

How can you find $_nC_x$ using your calculator?

$_nC_x = \dfrac{n!}{x!(n-x)!}$

On a graphing calculator, use **MATH** and $_nC_r$ in the **PRB** menu.

This is a binomial experiment with $n = 5$, $x = 4$, $p = 0.4$, and $q = 1 - p = 0.6$.

$P(x) = {}_nC_x p^x q^{n-x}$

$P(4) = {}_5C_4(0.4)^4(0.6)^1$ Substitute.

$ = 5(0.4)^4(0.6)^1$ Evaluate $_5C_4$.

$ \approx 0.08$ Simplify.

The probability is about 0.08 that exactly 4 of the five cards will reveal a prize.

 Got It? 1. What is the probability that the number of cards that reveal a prize is 0? 1? 2? 3? 5?

The Binomial Theorem (Lesson 5-7) says that for every positive integer n,

$(a + b)^n = P_0 a^n + P_1 a^{n-1} b + P_2 a^{n-2} b^2 + \cdots + P_{n-1} ab^{n-1} + P_n b^n$

where $P_0, P_1, \ldots, P_n$ are the numbers in the nth row of Pascal's Triangle.

For that row, it is possible to show that $P_i = {}_nC_i$. Thus, you can state the **Binomial Theorem** using combinations.

Key Concept   Binomial Theorem

For every positive integer n,

$(a + b)^n = {}_nC_0 a^n + {}_nC_1 a^{n-1} b + {}_nC_2 a^{n-2} b^2 + \cdots + {}_nC_{n-1} ab^{n-1} + {}_nC_n b^n$

© **Problem 2**   Expanding Binomials

Use the Binomial Theorem to solve.

Ⓐ **What is the binomial expansion of $(x + y)^5$?**

Use the Binomial Theorem with $a = x$, $b = y$, and $n = 5$.

$(x + y)^5 = {}_5C_0 x^5 + {}_5C_1 x^4 y + {}_5C_2 x^3 y^2 + {}_5C_3 x^2 y^3$
$ + {}_5C_4 xy^4 + {}_5C_5 y^5$

$ = x^5 + 5x^4 y + 10x^3 y^2 + 10x^2 y^3 + 5xy^4 + y^5$ Substitute for the $_nC_i$.

Think

Which $_4C_i$ do you use in the third term?

You use $_4C_0$, not $_4C_1$, for the first term. Therefore, use $_4C_2$ in the third term.

Ⓑ **What is the third term of $(2x - 3y)^4$?**

The third term of the binomial expansion is $_4C_2 a^{4-2} b^2$.

$_4C_2 a^{4-2} b^2 = {}_4C_2(2x)^2(-3y)^2$ Substitute $a = 2x$ and $b = -3y$.

$\phantom{_4C_2 a^{4-2} b^2} = 6(4x^2)(9y^2)$ Evaluate $_4C_2$.

$\phantom{_4C_2 a^{4-2} b^2} = 216x^2 y^2$ Simplify.

 Got It? 2. What is the binomial expansion of $(3x + y)^4$?

Got It?   EXTENSION

In a binomial distribution, only n and p are needed to determine the mean, variance, and standard deviation.

mean $= np$

variance $= np(1 - p)$ or npq

standard deviation $= \sqrt{np(1 - p)}$ of $\sqrt{npq}$

Challenge students to use these formulas to analyze the binomial experiment in Problem 2.

Take Note

Have students calculate $_nC_0$ and $_nC_n$ for a few values of n. Point out that these values will always be 1 regardless of n.

Problem 2   ERROR PREVENTION

Have students find the sum of the powers of each term in the expansion of $(x + y)^5$. For example, for the third term $_5C_2 x^3 y^2$, the sum of the powers is $3 + 2 = 5$.

Q What pattern do you see in all the sums of the powers in each term? **[They all equal 5, the binomial's power.]**

Q How can you use this pattern to check any binomial expansion? **[If the sum of the powers in one of the expansion's terms does not equal the number of the binomial's power, a mistake was made.]**

Got It?   ERROR PREVENTION

Students sometimes forget to account for a coefficient in binomials like $(3x + y)^4$. Suggest they first write the expansion using a and b:

$(a + b)^4 = {}_4C_0 a^4 + {}_4C_1 a^3 b + {}_4C_2 a^2 b^2 + {}_4C_3 ab^3 + {}_4C_4 b^4$. Then substitute $3x$ for a and y for b.

Additional Problems

1. In a tennis league, 80% of the players are right-handed. The league president is randomly selecting seven players to demonstrate serves. What is the probability that exactly three of the selected players will be right-handed?

ANSWER about 0.029

2. a. What is the binomial expansion of $(4x + 2y)^3$?

    b. What is the fifth term of $(2x - 3y)^7$?

ANSWERS

    a. $(4x + 2y)^3 = 64x^3 + 96x^2 y + 48xy^2 + 8y^3$

    b. $22{,}680x^3 y^4$

3. A spinner has five equal sections. Each section is a different color; red, blue, green, yellow, and orange. You spin the spinner four times. What is the probability that at least two of the spins will land on the red section?

ANSWER 18.08%

Answers

Got It?

1. $P(0) = 0.07776$;
$P(1) = 0.2592$;
$P(2) = 0.3456$;
$P(3) = 0.2304$;
$P(5) = 0.01024$

2. $81x^4 + 108x^3 y + 54x^2 y^2 + 12xy^3 + y^4$

Problem 3

ELL SUPPORT

English learners might be confused by the usage of the terms *success* and *fail* in this problem. Emphasize that in this lesson, *success* means the result you want to test for in a probability. Use a simple example, such as a coin toss, to explain.

Q Why does $p = 0.05$ in this problem? [$p =$ the **probability that a phone will *not* be durable enough, and 95% or 0.95 of them *are* durable enough.**]

Q Why do you find the probability of 4, 3, or 2 phones failing, but not 1? [**The QC only rejects an hour's production if *more than one* phone fails the test.**]

Got It?

You may want to remind students that for this problem, p is the probability of guessing the correct answer on one question, and q is the probability of guessing the wrong answer.

Q Since there are 4 answer choices for each question, what is p? What is q? [$\frac{1}{4}; \frac{3}{4}$]

Q How does the phrase "at least three correct" affect the way this problem is solved? [**You must find the probability of guessing 3, 4, or 5 correct.**]

Now you can apply the Binomial Theorem to binomial probabilities. To find the full probability distribution for a binomial experiment, expand the binomial $(p + q)^n$. For example, suppose you guess on four questions of a five-choice multiple-choice test. For four questions, $n = 4$, P(guessing correctly) $= \frac{1}{5}$, so $p = 0.2$, and $q = 0.8$.

	4 correct	3 correct	2 correct	1 correct	0 correct
$(p + q)^4 =$	$1p^4$	$+ \quad 4p^3q$	$+ \quad 6p^2q^2$	$+ \quad 4pq^3$	$+ \quad 1q^4$
$=$	$(0.2)^4$	$+ \quad 4(0.2)^3(0.8)$	$+ \quad 6(0.2)^2(0.8)^2$	$+ \quad 4(0.2)(0.8)^3 \quad +$	$(0.8)^4$
$=$	0.0016	$+ \quad 0.0256$	$+ \quad 0.1536$	$+ \quad 0.4096$	$+ \quad 0.4096$

You can display the distribution of binomial probabilities as a graph.

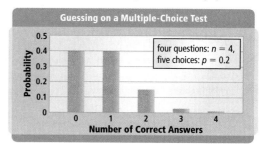

Guessing on a Multiple-Choice Test

four questions: $n = 4$, five choices: $p = 0.2$

Probability (vertical axis: 0, 0.1, 0.2, 0.3, 0.4, 0.5)
Number of Correct Answers (horizontal axis: 0, 1, 2, 3, 4)

 Problem 3 Applying Binomial Probability

Manufacturing Each hour at a cell phone factory, Quality Control (QC) tests the durability of four randomly selected phones. If more than one fails, QC rejects the entire production for that hour. If in one hour, 95% of the phones made are acceptable, what is the probability that QC rejects that hour's phone production?

Write the binomial expansion of $(p + q)^n$ with $n = 4$, $p = 0.05$, and $q = 0.95$.

> **Think**
>
> What is a "success" in one trial of this binomial experiment?
> Success in this experiment means that a phone fails the test.

	4 fail	3 fail	2 fail	1 fail	0 fail

$(p + q)^4 = p^4q^0 + 4p^3q^1 + 6p^2q^2 + 4p^1q^3 + p^0q^4$

$= (0.05)^4 + 4(0.05)^3(0.95)^1 + 6(0.05)^2(0.95)^2 + 4(0.05)^1(0.95)^3 + (0.95)^4$

$\approx 0.000006 + 0.000475 + 0.013538 + 0.171475 + 0.814506$

Probability (4, 3, or 2 phones fail) $\approx 0.000006 + 0.000475 + 0.013538$

≈ 0.014019, or about 1.4%

There is about a 1.4% chance that QC will reject the phones produced in the last hour.

Got It? **3.** A multiple-choice quiz has five questions. Each question has four answer choices. If you guess every answer, what is the probability of getting at least three correct?

Answers

Got It? (continued)

3. ≈ 0.1035, or about 10.4%

Lesson Check

Do you know HOW?

Find the probability of x successes in n trials for the given probability of success p on each trial.

1. $x = 2, n = 6, p = 0.4$

2. $x = 6, n = 9, p = 0.5$

Find the indicated term of each binomial expansion.

3. fourth term of $(c + d)^6$

4. second term of $(x - 2y)^5$

5. What is the probability of 2 successes in 4 trials of an experiment if the probability of success of one trial is 0.3?

Do you UNDERSTAND?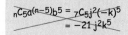

6. Vocabulary Explain how flipping a coin 10 times meets all of the conditions for a binomial experiment.

7. Error Analysis A student finds the fifth term of the binomial expansion $(j - k)^7$. Describe and correct the error the student made.

$$_nC_{5}a^{(n-5)}b^5 = {_7}C_5 j^2(-k)^5$$
$$= -21j^2k^5$$

Practice and Problem-Solving Exercises

MATHEMATICAL PRACTICES

A Practice Find the probability of x successes in n trials for the given probability of success p on each trial.

◆ See Problem 1.

8. $x = 3, n = 8, p = 0.3$

9. $x = 4, n = 8, p = 0.3$

10. $x = 5, n = 10, p = 0.5$

11. $x = 5, n = 10, p = 0.1$

12. Battery Life A calculator contains four batteries. With normal use, each battery has a 90% chance of lasting for one year. What is the probability that all four batteries will last a year?

Expand each binomial.

◆ See Problem 2.

13. $(a + b)^4$

14. $(m + 5n)^3$

15. $(3x + 2y)^5$

16. $(4c - d)^4$

Find the indicated term of each binomial expansion.

17. second term of $(2g + 2h)^7$

18. fifth term of $(x - y)^5$

19. first term of $(e + 3f)^6$

20. eighth term of $(3x - y)^8$

Use the binomial expansion of $(p + q)^n$ to calculate each binomial distribution.

◆ See Problem 3.

21. $n = 6, p = 0.3$

22. $n = 6, p = 0.5$

23. $n = 6, p = 0.9$

24. $n = 8, p = 0.45$

---

3 Lesson Check

Do you know HOW?

- For Exercises 1 and 2, remind students that $q = 1 - p$.
- For Exercises 3 and 4, suggest students first determine the number of terms that will be in each binomial expansion. Encourage students to completely expand each binomial up to the desired term to verify their answers.

Do you UNDERSTAND?

- For Exercise 6, suggest that students ask themselves these questions: *Is there a fixed number of trials? Does each trial have two possible outcomes? Is each trial independent? Is the probability of success constant for each trial?*
- For Exercise 7, some students may find it easier to identify and explain the error by first solving the problem and then comparing steps.

Close

Q What information is needed when using the binomial distribution to determine probability in an experiment? **[Answers may vary. Sample: First, it must be determined that the experiment is binomial. Then the following information is needed: the number of trials, the number of successes among that number of trials, and the probability of success on each trial.]**

Lesson Check

1. ≈ 0.3110, or $\approx 31.10\%$

2. ≈ 0.1641, or $\approx 16.41\%$

3. $20c^3d^3$ **4.** $-10x^4y$

5. 0.2646, or 26.46%

6. Answers may vary. Sample: A binomial experiment has three important features:
- the situation involves repeated trials; flipping a coin 10 times has 10 trials.
- each trial has two possible outcomes; in this case, heads or tails.
- the probability of success is constant throughout the trials; the trials of flipping a coin, are independent.

7. The student wrote "5" instead of "4". It should be:
$$_nC_{(5-1)}a^{n-4}b^4 = {_7}C_4 j^3(-k)^4$$
$$= 35j^3k^4$$

Practice and Problem-Solving Exercises

8. ≈ 0.2541, or $\approx 25.41\%$

9. ≈ 0.1361, or $\approx 13.61\%$

10. ≈ 0.2461, or $\approx 24.61\%$

11. ≈ 0.0015, or $\approx 0.15\%$

12. 0.6561, or 65.61%

13. $a^4 + 4a^3b + 6a^2b^2 + 4ab^3 + b^4$

14. $m^3 + 15m^2n + 75mn^2 + 125n^3$

15. $243x^5 + 810x^4y + 1080x^3y^2 + 720x^2y^3 + 240xy^4 + 32y^5$

16. $256c^4 - 256c^3d + 96c^2d^2 - 16cd^3 + d^4$

17. $896g^6h$ **18.** $5xy^4$

19. e^6 **20.** $-24xy^7$

21. $P(0) \approx 0.1176, P(1) \approx 0.3025, P(2) \approx 0.324, P(3) \approx 0.1852$ $P(4) \approx 0.0595, P(5) \approx 0.010, P(6) \approx 0.0007$

22–24. See next page.

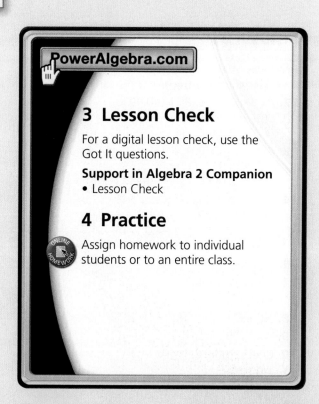

PowerAlgebra.com

3 Lesson Check

For a digital lesson check, use the Got It questions.

Support in Algebra 2 Companion
- Lesson Check

4 Practice

Assign homework to individual students or to an entire class.

4 Practice

ASSIGNMENT GUIDE

Basic: 8–24 all, 25–27, 35, 38

Average: 9–23 odd, 25–39

Advanced: 9–23 odd, 25–43

Standardized Test Prep: 44–48

Mixed Review: 49–60

Ⓒ **Mathematical Practices** are supported by exercises with red headings. Here are the Practices supported in this lesson:

MP 1: Make Sense of Problems Ex. 25
MP 2: Reason Abstractly Ex. 38, 39
MP 3: Construct Arguments Ex. 30, 35
MP 3: Communicate Ex. 34, 35
MP 3: Critique the Reasoning of Others Ex. 7
MP 5: Use Appropriate Tools Ex. 43

Applications exercises have blue headings. Exercises 12, 27–29, 35 support MP 4: Model.

STEM exercises focus on science or engineering applications.

EXERCISE 26: Use the Think About a Plan worksheet in the **Practice and Problem Solving Workbook** (also available in the Teaching Resources in print and online) to further support students' development in becoming independent learners.

HOMEWORK QUICK CHECK

To check students' understanding of key skills and concepts, go over Exercises 9, 21, 25, 26, and 35.

Ⓑ Apply Ⓒ **25. Think About a Plan** One survey found that 80% of respondents eat corn on the cob in circles rather than from side to side. Assume that this sample accurately represents the population. What is the probability that, out of five people you know, at least two of them eat corn on the cob in circles?
- How can you find the probability that one person eats corn on the cob in circles?
- How does a probability distribution help you solve the problem?

STEM **26. Weather** A scientist hopes to launch a weather balloon on one of the next three mornings. For each morning, there is a 40% chance of suitable weather. What is the probability that there will be at least one morning with suitable weather?

Marketing A fruit company guarantees that 90% of the pineapples it ships will ripen within four days of delivery. Find each probability for a case containing 12 pineapples.

27. All 12 are ripe within four days.

28. At least 10 are ripe within four days.

29. No more than 9 are ripe within four days.

Ⓒ **30. Open-Ended** Describe a situation that the graph might represent.

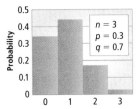

Sociology A study shows that 50% of people in a community watch television during dinner. Suppose you select 10 people at random from this population. Find each probability.

31. P(exactly 5 of the 10 people watch television during dinner)

32. P(exactly 6 of the 10 people watch television during dinner)

33. P(at least 5 of the 10 people watch television during dinner)

Ⓒ **34. Writing** Explain how a binomial experiment is related to a binomial expansion.

STEM **35. Quality Control** A company claims that 99% of its cereal boxes have at least as much cereal by weight as the amount stated on the box.
- **a.** At a quality control checkpoint, one box out of a random sample of ten boxes falls short of its stated weight. What is the probability of this happening due to chance variation in box weights?
- Ⓒ **b. Reasoning** Suppose three of ten boxes fail to have the claimed weight. What would you conclude? Explain.

Answers

Practice and Problem-Solving Exercises (continued)

22. $P(0) \approx 0.0156$, $P(1) \approx 0.0938$,
$P(2) \approx 0.2344$, $P(3) \approx 0.3125$,
$P(4) \approx 0.2344$, $P(5) \approx 0.0938$, $P(6) \approx 0.0156$

23. $P(0) \approx 0.000001$, $P(1) \approx 0.000054$,
$P(2) \approx 0.012$, $P(3) \approx 0.0146$
$P(4) \approx 0.0984$, $P(5) \approx 0.3543$, $P(6) \approx 0.5314$

24. $P(0) \approx 0.0084$, $P(1) \approx 0.0548$,
$P(2) \approx 0.1569$, $P(3) \approx 0.2568$,
$P(4) \approx 0.2627$, $P(5) \approx 0.1719$,
$P(6) \approx 0.0703$, $P(7) \approx 0.0164$, $P(8) \approx 0.0017$

25. 0.99328

26. 0.784, or 78.4%

27. ≈ 0.2824

28. ≈ 0.8891

29. ≈ 0.1109

30. Check students' work.

31. ≈ 0.2461

32. ≈ 0.2051

33. ≈ 0.6230

34. Each term of a binomial expansion $(p + q)^n$ contains a power of p times a power of q. The coefficient of each term is the no. of times that a combination of powers results when $(p + q)^n$ is expanded. In a binomial experiment of n trials, each trial results in success or failure, with probabilities p and q. The probability of each outcome contains n factors, each of which is either p or q. The coefficient of each term is the no. of ways that outcome can be achieved.

35. a. 0.0914

b. The probability that three boxes would be underweight is 0.0001. You can conclude that there might be a malfunction in the machinery or that the company's claim may be false.

36. Basketball Suppose you make 90% of your free throws and you attempt 3 free throws. Use the Binomial Theorem to calculate each probability.
  a. You do not make any of them.
  b. You only make 1 of them.
  c. You only make 2 of them.
  d. You make all of them.

 37. Genetics About 11% of the general population is left-handed. At a school with an average class size of 30, each classroom contains four left-handed desks. Does this seem adequate? Justify your answer.

38. Open-Ended Describe a binomial experiment that can be solved using the expression $_7C_2(0.6)^2(0.4)^5$.

39. Graph each probability distribution for $(p + q)^3$.
  a. $p = 0.9, q = 0.1$ **b.** $p = 0.45, q = 0.55$
  c. Compare and Contrast How are the graphs in parts (a) and (b) similar? How are they different?

Challenge

Statistics A multiple-choice test has ten questions. Each question has five choices, with only one correct answer.

40. Statisticians consider a "rare" event to have less than a 5% chance of occurring. According to this standard, what grades would be rare on this test if you guess? Justify your answer.

41. Design and conduct a simulation to model this situation. Gather results of simulations from your classmates. Do these results confirm the grades you identified as rare in Exercise 40? Explain.

42. Pascal's Triangle The nth row of Pascal's triangle has $n + 1$ terms. Find $_8C_4$. What row and term does this value represent in Pascal's Triangle? Use combinations to find the value of the 8th term of the 13th row of Pascal's triangle.

43. Graphing Calculator Enter the binomial probability formula as shown. Set the window and table shown. (To get integer values of x, you may need to adjust your window.)

  a. Examine the graph of $y = _7C_x(0.5)^x(0.5)^{7-x}$. Describe any symmetry in the graph.
  b. Verify the symmetry by displaying values of the function in table form.
  c. Change the graph to $y = _7C_x(0.6)^x(0.4)^{7-x}$. Does this graph have any symmetry? Explain.

40. Getting 5 or more items correct by guessing would be statistically rare. The probability of getting 10, 9, 8, 7, or 6 correct is each less than 1%. The probability of getting 5 right is 2.6%. The probability of getting 4 right is 8.8%.

41. Check students' work.

42. 70; 8th row 5th term; 1716

43. a. The graph is sym. about the line $x = 3.5$.

b.

x	y
0	0.0078
1	0.0547
2	0.1641
3	0.2734
4	0.2734
5	0.1641
6	0.0547
7	0.0078

c. No; the bulge in the graph has shifted rt.

---

36. a. 0.001   **b.** 0.027
    c. 0.243   **d.** 0.729

37. The probability of a group of 30 students having 4 or fewer left-handed students is about 77.05%. This means that more than three quarters of the classes will have enough left-handed desks; 4 is an adequate no.

38. Answers may vary. Sample: 60% of the summer days in Eastport are sunny. What is the probability of a week containing exactly two sunny days?

39. a. $P(0) = 0.001, P(1) = 0.027,$
$P(2) = 0.243, P(3) = 0.729$

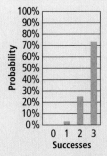

b. $P(0) = 0.166375, P(1) = 0.408375,$
$P(2) = 0.334125, P(3) = 0.091125$

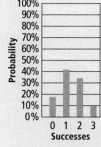

c. The probabilities of each graph sum to 1; $P(0) + P(1) + P(2) + P(3) = 1$. The probabilities of part (a) increase with increasing success numbers; the maximum probability occurring at $P(3)$. The probabilities of part (b) peak with a maximum at $P(1)$ and then decrease with increasing success numbers.

Answers

Standardized Test Prep

44. B

45. G

46. B

47. H

48. [4] $a_n = a_1 r^{n-1}$. Use $a_1 = 3$ and $a_4 = 192$ to find r.

$(192) = (3)r^{(4-1)}$

$4 = r$

Use a_1 and r to find $a_2 = 12$ and $a_3 = 48$.

[3] appropriate method, with one computational error

[2] only a_2 is found correctly OR only a_3 is found correctly

[1] a_2 and a_3 are correct, without work shown

Mixed Review

49. loaded and leading question by the use of the words "beautiful" and "Do you agree"

50. does not provide enough information about the amendments to make a decision

51. vertices: $(0, \pm 7)$; foci: $(0, \pm \sqrt{74})$; asymptotes: $y = \pm \frac{7}{5}x$

52. vertices: $(0, \pm 3)$; foci: $(0, \pm \sqrt{13})$; asymptotes: $y = \pm \frac{3}{2}x$

53. vertices: $(0, \pm 3)$; foci: $(0, \pm 5)$; asymptotes: $y = \pm \frac{3}{4}x$

54. $\frac{2}{3}$

55. $\frac{1}{2}$

56. $\frac{2}{3}$

57. $\bar{x} = 24.4$, $\sigma \approx 5.04$

58. $\bar{x} = 81.8$, $\sigma \approx 4.77$

59. $\bar{x} = 8.6$, $\sigma \approx 0.47$

60. $\bar{x} \approx 24.74$, $\sigma \approx 2.046$

Standardized Test Prep

Standardized Test Prep

 SAT/ACT

44. A survey shows that 60% of adults floss their teeth every day. In a random sample of ten adults, what is the probability that exactly six adults floss every day?

  (A) 11%   (B) 25%   (C) 60%   (D) 100%

45. Which of the statements about the following equation is correct?

$$\frac{b^2 - 4b + 3}{b - 3} = b - 1$$

  (F) The equation is always true.

  (G) The equation is always true, except when $b = 3$.

  (H) The equation is never true.

  (I) The equation is true when $b = 3$.

46. Which is the inverse of $f(x) = (x - 3)^2$?

  (A) $f^{-1}(x) = \frac{x^2}{(3x - 1)^2}$ (C) $f^{-1}(x) = \frac{1}{(3x - 1)^2}$

  (B) $f^{-1}(x) = \pm\sqrt{x} + 3$ (D) $f^{-1}(x) = \pm\sqrt{x - 3}$

47. If $\log 4 \approx 0.60206$ and $\log 5 \approx 0.69897$, what is the approximate value of $\log 80$?

  (F) 0.2534   (G) 0.2914   (H) 1.903   (I) 11.1835

Extended Response

48. In a geometric sequence, $a_1 = 3$ and $a_4 = 192$. Explain how to find a_2 and a_3.

Mixed Review

Identify any bias in each survey question.   See Lesson 11-8.

49. Do you agree that replacing that dog park with a beautiful new library would be better for our town?

50. Do you agree with the amendments to Proposition 39?

Find the vertices, foci, and asymptotes of each hyperbola.   See Lesson 10-5.

51. $\frac{y^2}{49} - \frac{x^2}{25} = 1$ **52.** $4y^2 - 9x^2 = 36$ **53.** $64y^2 - 36x^2 = 576$

A standard number cube is tossed. Find each probability.   See Lesson 11-3.

54. $P(2 \text{ or greater than } 3)$ **55.** $P(6 \text{ or even})$ **56.** $P(\text{prime or } 1)$

Get Ready!   **To prepare for Lesson 11-10, do Exercises 57–60.**

Find the mean and standard deviation for each data set.   See Lessons 11-6 and 11-7.

57. 16, 20, 28, 25, 26, 33, 27, 22, 29, 18   **58.** 81, 78, 79, 80, 76, 88, 83, 90, 87, 76

59. 8.5, 7.9, 8.2, 9.0, 8.3, 9.1, 9.2   **60.** 23.5, 22.4, 25.6, 26.8, 28.1, 22.3, 24.5

Additional Instructional Support

Algebra 2 Companion

Students can use the **Algebra 2 Companion** worktext (4 pages) as you teach the lesson. Use the Companion to support

- New Vocabulary
- Key Concepts
- Got It for each Problem
- Lesson Check

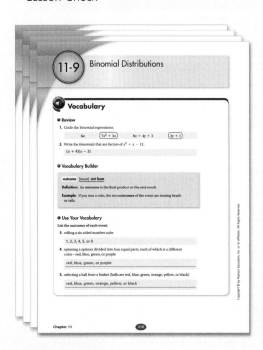

ELL Support

Use Role Playing Have students work in pairs.

Tell students that they are going to do an *experiment* with a coin. Instruct pairs to take turns flipping a coin 10 times and recording the results. Explain that each time they flip the coin it is a *trial* in their experiment. They are "trying" something to see what happens. They are flipping a coin 10 times to see how many times it lands heads up or tails up.

Emphasize that each flip has only two *possible outcomes*—heads or tails. Have one student in each pair flip while the other chooses heads or tails. Explain that the student's choice is *a success*. If the student chooses heads, then heads is a success and tails is a *failure*.

Point out that the chances that a coin will land heads up does not change—*the probability is constant*. For each flip/trial, the probability of success is $\frac{1}{2}$ or 50%.

5 Assess & Remediate

Lesson Quiz

1. **Do you UNDERSTAND?** In a high school, 70% of the 2000 students have cellular phones. The principal is randomly selecting six students to help plan rules for using cell phones in the school. What is the probability that exactly four of the selected students have cellular phones?

2. What is the binomial expansion of $(x + 2y)^4$?

3. What is the fourth term of $(3x - y)^5$?

4. A multiple-choice quiz has four questions. Each question has four answer choices. If you guess every answer, what is the probability of getting at least two correct?

ANSWERS TO LESSON QUIZ

1. about 0.32
2. $(x + 2y)^4 = x^4 + 8x^3y + 24x^2y^2 + 32xy^3 + 16y^4$
3. $-90x^2y^3$
4. about 26.2%

PRESCRIPTION FOR REMEDIATION

Use the student work on the Lesson Quiz to prescribe a differentiated review assignment:

Points	Differentiated Remediation
0–1	Intervention
2–3	On-level
4	Extension

PowerAlgebra.com

5 Assess & Remediate

Assign the Lesson Quiz. Appropriate intervention, practice, or enrichment is automatically generated based on student performance.

Differentiated Remediation

Intervention

- **Reteaching** (2 pages) Provides reteaching and practice exercises for the key lesson concepts. Use with struggling students or absent students.

- **English Language Learner Support** Helps students develop and reinforce mathematical vocabulary and key concepts.

All-in-One Resources/Online
Reteaching

11-9 **Reteaching**
Binomial Distributions

Suppose you repeat an experiment n times, and each time you run the experiment it has a probability of success p and a probability of failure q. Then, the probability of x successes in n trials is:

$$_nC_x \, p^x q^{n-x}, \text{ where } q = 1 - p$$

Problem

What is the probability of two successes in five trials, where the probability of success for each trial is 0.2?

$$_nC_x = {}_5C_2 \qquad \text{Find } {}_5C_2.$$
$$= \frac{5!}{2!(5-2)!}$$
$$= 10$$
$$q = 1 - p \qquad \text{Find } q.$$
$$= 1 - .2$$
$$= 0.8$$
$$P(2 \text{ successes}) = {}_5C_2 (0.2)^2 (0.8)^{5-2} \quad \text{Substitute for } n, x, p, \text{ and } q \text{ in the formula.}$$
$$= 10(0.2)^2(0.8)^3 \qquad \text{Simplify.}$$
$$= 10(0.04)(0.512)$$
$$= .2048$$

The probability of two successes in five trials is about 20%.

Exercises

Find the probability of x successes in n trials for the given probability of success p on each trial. Round to the nearest tenth of a percent.

1. $x = 3, n = 4, p = 0.3$ 7.6%
2. $x = 4, n = 6, p = 0.1$ 0.1%
3. $x = 7, n = 9, p = 0.4$ 2.1%
4. $x = 5, n = 6, p = 0.3$ 1.0%

5. A light fixture contains six light bulbs. With normal use, each bulb has a 95% chance of lasting for 2 yr. What is the probability that all six bulbs last for 2 yr? about 73.5%
6. Use the information from Exercise 5. What is the probability that five of the six bulbs will last for 2 yr? about 23.2%
7. Suppose the bulbs have an 80% chance of lasting for 2 yr. Find the probability that three of the six bulbs will last for 2 yr. 8.2%

All-in-One Resources/Online
English Language Learner Support

11-9 **Additional Vocabulary Support**
Binomial Distributions

In the town of Rainesville, 15% of the 10,000 houses are made of brick. If 7 houses are randomly selected, what is the probability that 4 of them will be made of brick?

There are two sets of cards below that show how to solve the above problem. The set on the left explains the thinking. The set on the right shows the steps. Write the thinking and the steps in the correct order.

Think Cards	Write Cards
Simplify the exponents.	$P(4) = 35(0.0005)(0.6141)$
Evaluate $_7C_4$.	$P(x) = {}_nC_x \, p^x q^{n-x}$
Multiply.	$P(4) = 0.01$
Write the Binomial Probability formula.	$P(4) = {}_7C_4(0.15)^4(0.85)^3$
Substitute values from the problem into the formula.	$P(4) = 35(0.15)^4(0.85)^3$

Think	Write
First, write the Binomial Probability formula.	Step 1 $P(x) = {}_nC_x \, p^x q^{n-x}$
Second, substitute values from the problem into the formula.	Step 2 $P(4) = {}_7C_4(0.15)^4(0.85)^3$
Next, evaluate $_7C_4$.	Step 3 $P(4) = 35(0.15)^4(0.85)^3$
Then, simplify the exponents.	Step 4 $P(4) = 35(0.0005)(0.6141)$
Finally, multiply.	Step 4 $P(4) = 0.01$

Differentiated Remediation *continued*

On-Level

- **Practice (2 pages)** Provides extra practice for each lesson. For simpler practice exercises, use the Form K Practice pages found in the All-in-One Teaching Resources and online.

- **Think About a Plan** Helps students develop specific problem-solving skills and strategies by providing scaffolded guiding questions.

- **Standardized Test Prep** Focuses on all major exercises, all major question types, and helps students prepare for the high-stakes assessments.

Extension

- **Enrichment** Provides students with interesting problems and activities that extend the concepts of the lesson.

- **Activities, Games, and Puzzles** Worksheets that can be used for concepts development, enrichment, and for fun!

Practice and Problem Solving Wkbk/ All-in-One Resources/Online
Practice page 1

11-9 Practice Form G
Binomial Distributions

Find the probability of x successes in n trials for the given probability of success p on each trial.

1. $x = 5$, $n = 5$, $p = 0.4$ about 1%
2. $x = 2$, $n = 8$, $p = 0.9$ about 0.002%
3. $x = 3$, $n = 10$, $p = 0.25$ about 25%
4. $x = 1$, $n = 3$, $p = 0.2$ about 38%

5. A light fixture contains 6 light bulbs. With normal use, each bulb has an 85% chance of lasting for 4 months. What is the probability that all 6 bulbs will last for 4 months? about 38%

Expand each binomial.

6. $(2a + 4b)^3$ $8a^3 + 48a^2b + 96ab^2 + 64b^3$
7. $(m + 3n)^4$ $m^4 + 12m^3n + 54m^2n^2 + 108mn^3 + 81n^4$
8. $(2c - d)^5$ $32c^5 - 80c^4d + 80c^3d^2 - 40c^2d^3 + 10cd^4 - d^5$
9. $(5s + t)^4$ $625s^4 + 500s^3t + 150s^2t^2 + 20st^3 + t^4$

Find the indicated term of each binomial expansion.

10. third term of $(2a - b)^8$ $1792a^6b^2$
11. fifth term of $(r + 3s)^5$ $405rs^4$
12. fourth term of $(-2x + 3y)^6$ $-4320x^3y^3$
13. first term of $(8g + 6h)^3$ $512g^3$

Use the binomial expansion of $(p + q)^n$ to calculate each binomial distribution.

14. $n = 5$, $p = 0.6$
   $P(5) = 0.08$, $P(4) = 0.25$, $P(3) = 0.35$,
   $P(2) = 0.23$, $P(1) = 0.08$, $P(0) = 0.01$
15. $n = 3$, $p = 0.7$
   $P(3) = 0.34$, $P(2) = 0.44$,
   $P(1) = 0.19$, $P(0) = 0.03$

16. The probability that the weather will be acceptable for a launch of a satellite over the next 3 days is 70% each day. What is the probability that the weather will be acceptable at least 1 of the next 3 days? 97.3%

17. A poll shows that 60% of a school district's home owners favor an increase in property tax to fund a new high school. What is the probability that exactly 4 of 5 people chosen at random favor a tax increase? about 26%

Practice and Problem Solving Wkbk/ All-in-One Resources/Online
Practice page 2

11-9 Practice (continued) Form G
Binomial Distributions

There is a 60% probability of rain each of the next 5 days. Find each probability. Round to the nearest whole percent.

18. It will rain on at least 3 of the next 5 days. 68%
19. It will rain on at least 1 of the next 5 days. 99%
20. It will rain on at least 1 of the next 4 days. 97%
21. It will rain on at least 1 of the next 2 days. 84%

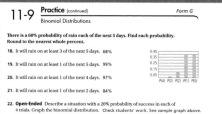

22. **Open-Ended** Describe a situation with a 20% probability of success in each of 4 trials. Graph the binomial distribution. Check students' work. See sample graph above.

23. The probability that an egg from one farm is small is 10%. What is the probability that exactly 1 egg in a sample of 4 eggs is too small? about 29%

In one neighborhood the probability of a power outage during a rainstorm is 4%. Find each probability.

24. P(at least 1 power outage in the next 5 rainstorms) about 18%
25. P(at least 2 power outages in the next 10 rainstorms) about 6%
26. P(at least 1 power outage in the next 20 rainstorms) about 56%

27. **Writing** Explain the relationship between the expansion of $(x + y)^{12}$ and the 12th row of Pascal's triangle. The numbers in the 12th row of Pascal's triangle are the coefficients of the expansion of $(x + y)^{12}$.

28. A newspaper carrier can throw the paper and have it land on a customer's porch 85% of the time. Use the Binomial Theorem to calculate each probability for the deliverer's first 3 throws of the morning.
   a. The carrier does not land any papers on a porch. about 0.34%
   b. The carrier lands only 1 paper on a porch. about 5.7%
   c. The carrier lands exactly 2 papers on a porch. about 32.5%
   d. The carrier lands all 3 papers on a porch. about 61.4%

29. **Reasoning** The probability that a baby born in Scotland has red hair is 13%. A certain Scottish hospital has an average of 20 babies born per week. At the beginning of the week, the hospital has 3 "It's a Redhead!" stickers available to put on the babies' cribs. Does this seem to be an adequate amount? Justify your answer. Yes; the probability that the hospital will have 3 or fewer redheads out of the 20 babies born is about 74%.

All-in-One Resources/Online
Enrichment

11-9 Enrichment
Binomial Distributions

You can use mean and standard deviation to describe a set of data. However, mean and standard deviation each depend on the number of trials in the experiment, which makes comparisons between experiments difficult. Comparisons are possible, however, if you standardize the results and describe them by a z-score. A z-score converts the data to a distribution with a mean of 0 and a standard deviation of 1. Once standardized, you can compare the distributions.

Different binomial distributions can be compared with z-scores. The z-score is found using the formula $z = \frac{X - \overline{X}}{\sigma}$ where X is the data point in the distribution, $\overline{X}$ is the mean, and σ is the standard deviation.

1. Suppose you conduct n independent trials of an event. If the probability of a success on any one trial is p, what is the probability of a failure on any one trial? $1 - p$

2. If there are r successes, how many failures will there be? $n - r$

3. What is the probability that in a sequence of n trials, r are successes? $p^r(1 - p)^{n-r}$

4. Use combinations to express the number of sequences of n trials in which r are successes. $_nC_r$

5. What is the probability of exactly r successes in n trials? $_nC_r p^r(1 - p)^{n-r}$

You might recognize this formula as the binomial distribution with a mean of np and a standard deviation of $\sqrt{np(1 - p)}$.

6. A single number cube is rolled 180 times. What is the probability of rolling a four 28 times? Find the z-score associated with rolling 28 fours. about 0.0754; −0.4

7. A coin is flipped 100 times. What is the probability of getting 55 heads? Find the z-score for 55 heads. about 0.0485; 1

8. The probability of catching a fish on a single cast of a fly rod at your favorite stream is calculated to be 2%. If you make 210 casts, what is the probability of catching 8 fish? Find the number of fish caught that would be associated with a z-score of 0.4. about 0.0354; about 3 fish

Practice and Problem Solving Wkbk/ All-in-One Resources/Online
Think About a Plan

11-9 Think About a Plan
Binomial Distributions

Weather A scientist hopes to launch a weather balloon on one of the next three mornings. For each morning, there is a 40% chance of suitable weather. What is the probability that there will be at least one morning with suitable weather?

Understanding the Problem

1. What is the probability that a morning will have suitable weather? 0.4

2. What is the probability that a morning will have unsuitable weather? 0.6

3. How many chances does the scientist have to launch the balloon? 3

4. What is the problem asking you to determine?
   Answers may vary. Sample: the probability that there will be one, two, or three mornings with suitable weather

Planning the Solution

5. What binomial can help you find the binomial distribution for this problem? $(p + q)^3$

6. Expand your binomial. $p^3 + 3p^2q + 3pq^2 + q^3$

7. What should you substitute for the variables in your binomial expansion?
   $p = 0.4$; $q = 0.6$

8. Which terms of your binomial expansion do you need to solve the problem?
   Explain. Answers may vary. Sample: I need the first three terms because they represent having 3, 2, or 1 successes. A success is a morning with suitable weather

Getting an Answer

9. Use your binomial expansion to find the probability that there will be at least one morning with suitable weather. 0.784 or 78.4%

Practice and Problem Solving Wkbk/ All-in-One Resources/Online
Standardized Test Prep

11-9 Standardized Test Prep
Binomial Distributions

Multiple Choice

For Exercises 1–5, choose the correct letter.

1. The probability that a newborn baby at a certain hospital is male is 50%. What is the probability that exactly 2 of 3 babies born in the hospital on any day are male? A
   A) 37.5% B) 50% C) 66.7% D) 75%

2. The probability that a newborn baby at the hospital is female is 50%. What is the probability that at least 2 babies of 3 children born on a certain day are female? H
   F) 33.3% G) 37.5% H) 50% I) 66.7%

3. What is the fifth term of the expansion of $(2x - y)^8$? D
   A) $-1792x^5y^3$ B) $-448x^3y^5$ C) $256x^4y^4$ D) $1120x^4y^4$

4. A poll shows that 30% of voters favor an earlier curfew. Find the probability that all of five voters chosen at random favor an earlier curfew. F
   F) 0.24% G) 1.5% H) 4.1% I) 16.7%

5. The probability that a machine part is defective is 10%. Find the probability that no more than 2 out of 12 parts tested are defective. C
   A) 28% B) 66% C) 89% D) 98%

Short Response

6. A scientist runs an experiment 4 times. Each run has a 65% chance of success. Calculate and graph the distribution binomial probabilities for the experiment.

   [2] $(p + q)^4 = p^4 + 4p^3q + 6p^2q^2 + 4pq^3 + q^4$
   $= (0.65)^4 + 4(0.65)^3(.35) + 6(.65)^2(.35)^2$
   $+ 4(.65)(.35)^3 + (.35)^4$
   $\approx 0.18 + 0.388 + 0.318 + 0.118 + 0.02$
   [2] correct graph with all work shown
   [1] incorrect or incomplete answer
   [0] incorrect answer and no work shown
   OR no answers given

   Experimental Runs
   (graph: Percent vs. Number of Successes, 0–4)

Online Teacher Resource Center
Activities, Games, and Puzzles

11-9 Puzzle: Right, Then Left, Right?
Binomial Distributions

Bernoulli took a stroll through a garden maze. He used his weighted coin (heads has a probability of 0.3) to get through the maze. Here are the guidelines:

- He will follow the path until he is forced to make a left/right decision. That is, he will not turn of a straight course on his own.
- At a left/right decision, he will repeatedly flip the coin and note the number of heads. His experiments are listed below the maze, in the order he performed them.
- If the probability of getting the number *or* fewer than the number of heads he recorded is less than 25%, he turns left.
- If the probability of getting the number or fewer than the number of heads he recorded is greater than 25%, he turns right.

Trace Bernoulli's path below. Show your work on another sheet of paper.

START

1. 12 flips, 2 heads about 16.8%; left
2. 7 flips, 1 heads about 24.7%; left
3. 8 flips, 2 heads about 29.6%; right
4. 10 flips, 3 heads about 26.7%; right
5. 11 flips, 2 heads about 20.0%; left
6. 10 flips, 2 heads about 23.3%; left
7. 13 flips, 3 heads about 21.8%; left
8. 8 flips, 1 heads about 36.0%; right
9. 7 flips, 2 heads about 31.8%; left
10. 16 flips, 4 heads about 20.4%; left
11. 11 flips, 3 heads about 25.7%; right

11-10 Normal Distributions

Content Standard
S.ID.4 Use the mean and standard deviation of a data set to fit it to a normal distribution and to estimate population percentages. Recognize that there are data sets for which such a procedure is not appropriate . . .

Objective To use a normal distribution

Try it out. Suppose (2, 2) is a point on f(x). If f(x) is even, what other point is on the graph of f(x)?

SOLVE IT!

Getting Ready!

Even and odd functions are defined as follows.
Even function: f(x) = f(−x)
Odd function: −f(x) = f(−x)
Which is the graph of an even function? Of an odd function? Justify your answers.

MATHEMATICAL PRACTICES

A **discrete probability distribution** has a finite number of possible events, or values. The binomial probability distribution you studied in the preceding lesson is a discrete probability distribution.

The events for a **continuous probability distribution** can be any value in an interval of real numbers. If a data set is large, the distribution of its discrete values approximates a continuous distribution.

Essential Understanding Many common statistics (such as human height, weight, or blood pressure) gathered from samples in the natural world tend to have a *normal distribution* about their mean.

A **normal distribution** has data that vary randomly from the mean. The graph of a normal distribution is a normal curve.

Lesson Vocabulary
• discrete probability distribution
• continuous probability distribution
• normal distribution

take note

Key Concept Normal Distribution

−3 deviations   −1 deviation   mean   +1 deviation   +3 deviations
−2 deviations   +2 deviations
2.35%   13.5%   34%   34%   13.5%   2.35%

In a normal distribution,
• 68% of data fall within one standard deviation of the mean
• 95% of data fall within two standard deviations of the mean
• 99.7% of data fall within three standard deviations of the mean

A normal distribution has a symmetric bell shape centered on the mean.

PowerAlgebra.com   Lesson 11-10 Normal Distributions   739

---

1 Interactive Learning

Solve It!

PURPOSE To distinguish between the graphs of even and odd functions using the definitions
PROCESS Students may
• test ordered pairs from the graphs to see whether the graph satisfies the definitions.
• consider how each definition affects the ordered pair given by (x, f(x)).

FACILITATE

Q When the *x*-value of an ordered pair of an even function changes sign, what happens to the *y*-value? **[It stays the same.]**

Q When the *x*-value of an ordered pair of an odd function changes sign, what happens to the *y*-value? **[It changes sign.]**

Q How are even functions symmetric? Odd functions? **[Even functions are symmetric about the y-axis. Odd functions are symmetric about the origin.]**

ANSWER See Solve It in Answers on next page.
CONNECT THE MATH In the Solve It students explore the definitions and symmetry of graphs of even and odd functions. In the lesson, students will explore the graphs of normal distributions that are symmetric about the mean.

2 Guided Instruction

Take Note

Q If a normal distribution had a mean of 50 and a standard deviation of 11, 68 percent of the data points would have to fall between which two values? **[39 and 61]**

11-10 Preparing to Teach

BIG idea Probability
ESSENTIAL UNDERSTANDING
Normal distributions model many common natural phenomena, such as human height, weight, and blood pressure.

Math Background
Normal distributions occur often in real life such as standardized test scores and heights of adults. The normal distribution curve has the following characteristics:
• The graph has its maximum at the center.
• The graph is symmetric about the mean.
• The mean, mode, and median are equal.
• About 68% of the values fall within one standard deviation of the mean, 34% fall within one standard deviation to the right of the mean and 34% fall within one standard deviation to the left of the mean.
• About 95% of the values fall within two standard deviations of the mean, 47.5% fall within two standard deviations to the right of the mean and 47.5% fall within two standard deviations to the left of the mean.
• About 99.7% of the values fall within three standard deviations of the mean, 49.85% fall within three standard deviations to the right of the mean and 49.85% fall within three standard deviations to the left of the mean.

Mathematical Practices
Construct viable arguments and critique the reasoning of others. With knowledge of variance and standard deviation, students will construct arguments about the distribution of a set of data.

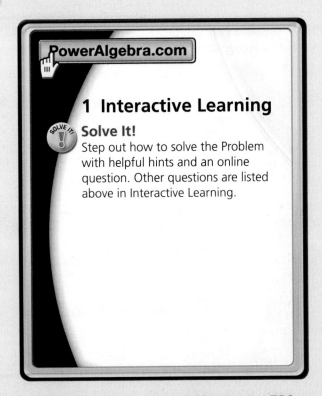

PowerAlgebra.com

1 Interactive Learning

Solve It!
Step out how to solve the Problem with helpful hints and an online question. Other questions are listed above in Interactive Learning.

Problem 1

Q Why do you expect the weights of the female brown bear to be normally distributed? **[Although there may be a few heavy or light bears, most bears are similar in size, so the weights of most of the bears should be close to the average weight of the female brown bears.]**

Q About what percent of the female brown bears weigh less than 100 kg or more than 129 kg? Describe a way to find this value. **[Samples: Since 88% of the bears weigh between 100 kg and 129 kg, 100 − 88 = 12% of the bears weigh less than 100 kg or more than 129 kg. You could also add the percentages for the bars for 80–89, 90–99, 130–139, and 140–149 to get 1 + 5 + 5 + 1 = 12%]**

Q What percent of female brown bears should weigh less than 115 kg? Explain. **[Since the weight is normally distributed, half of the bears, or 50%, should weigh less than the mean and half should weigh more than the mean.]**

Got It?

Q For which intervals on the graph will you add the respective percentages to find the percent for 1a? **[80–89, 90–99, 100–109, and 110–119]**

Q What weight values are 1.5 standard deviations from the mean? How do you find these values? **[130 kg and 100 kg; 115 + 1.5(10) = 130 and 115 − 1.5(10) = 100]**

Sometimes data are not normally distributed. A data set could have a distribution that is *skewed*, an asymmetric curve where one end stretches out further than the other end. When a data set is skewed, the data do not vary predictably from the mean. This means that the data do not fall within the standard deviations of the mean like normally distributed data, and so it is inappropriate to use mean and standard deviation to estimate percentages for skewed data.

Positively Skewed   Normally Distributed   Negatively Skewed

Ⓒ Problem 1 Analyzing Normally Distributed Data **STEM**

Zoology The bar graph gives the weights of a population of female brown bears. The red curve shows how the weights are normally distributed about the mean, 115 kg. Approximately what percent of female brown bears weigh between 100 and 129 kg?

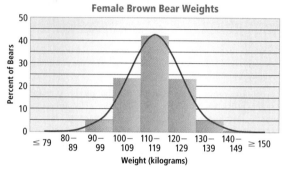

Plan

How do you find this percent?
The percents for each bar are based on the same sample population of bears. You can add the percents.

Estimate and add the percents for the intervals 100–109, 110–119, and 120–129.

$23 + 42 + 23 = 88$

About 88% of female brown bears weigh between 100 and 129 kg.

Got It? **1. a.** Approximately what percent of female brown bears in Problem 1 weigh less than 120 kg?
    b. The standard deviation in the weights of female brown bears is about 10 kg. Approximately what percent of female brown bears have weights that are within 1.5 standard deviations of the mean?

When data are normally distributed, you can sketch the graph of the distribution using the fact that a normal curve has a symmetric bell shape.

 PowerAlgebra.com

2 Guided Instruction

Ⓒ Each Problem is worked out and supported online.

Problem 1
Analyzing Normally Distributed Data
Animated

Problem 2
Sketching a Normal Curve
Animated

Problem 3
Analyzing a Normal Distribution
Animated

Support in Algebra 2 Companion
• Vocabulary
• Key Concepts
• Got It?

Answers

Solve It!
The first graph is of an even function because the *y*-values are the same for *x* and *−x*. The second graph is of an odd function because the *y*-value for *−x* is equal to the opposite of the *y*-value for *x*. The third graph is not of a function.

Got It?
1. a. 71%   **b.** 88%

2.

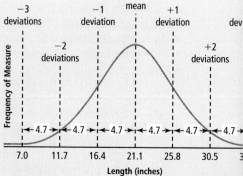

Distribution of Female European Eels

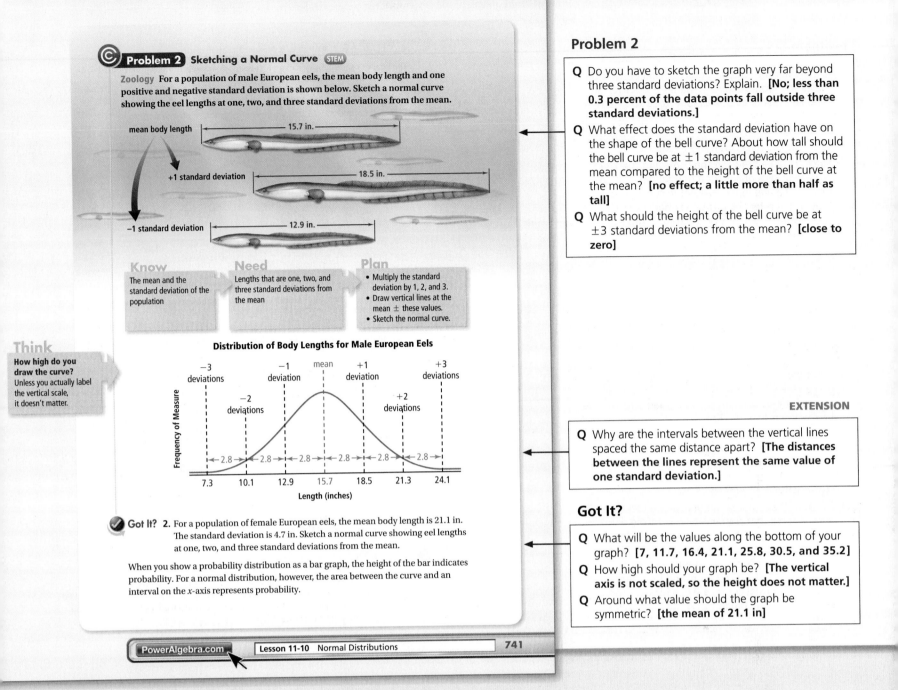

Problem 2 Sketching a Normal Curve STEM

Zoology For a population of male European eels, the mean body length and one positive and negative standard deviation is shown below. Sketch a normal curve showing the eel lengths at one, two, and three standard deviations from the mean.

mean body length ⟵ 15.7 in. ⟶

+1 standard deviation ⟵ 18.5 in. ⟶

−1 standard deviation ⟵ 12.9 in. ⟶

Know
The mean and the standard deviation of the population

Need
Lengths that are one, two, and three standard deviations from the mean

Plan
• Multiply the standard deviation by 1, 2, and 3.
• Draw vertical lines at the mean ± these values.
• Sketch the normal curve.

Think
How high do you draw the curve?
Unless you actually label the vertical scale, it doesn't matter.

Distribution of Body Lengths for Male European Eels

−3 deviations   −2 deviations   −1 deviation   mean   +1 deviation   +2 deviations   +3 deviations

Frequency of Measure

⟵ 2.8 ⟶ ⟵ 2.8 ⟶ ⟵ 2.8 ⟶ ⟵ 2.8 ⟶ ⟵ 2.8 ⟶ ⟵ 2.8 ⟶

7.3   10.1   12.9   15.7   18.5   21.3   24.1

Length (inches)

Got It? 2. For a population of female European eels, the mean body length is 21.1 in. The standard deviation is 4.7 in. Sketch a normal curve showing eel lengths at one, two, and three standard deviations from the mean.

When you show a probability distribution as a bar graph, the height of the bar indicates probability. For a normal distribution, however, the area between the curve and an interval on the x-axis represents probability.

PowerAlgebra.com   Lesson 11-10   Normal Distributions   741

Problem 2

Q Do you have to sketch the graph very far beyond three standard deviations? Explain. **[No; less than 0.3 percent of the data points fall outside three standard deviations.]**

Q What effect does the standard deviation have on the shape of the bell curve? About how tall should the bell curve be at ±1 standard deviation from the mean compared to the height of the bell curve at the mean? **[no effect; a little more than half as tall]**

Q What should the height of the bell curve be at ±3 standard deviations from the mean? **[close to zero]**

EXTENSION

Q Why are the intervals between the vertical lines spaced the same distance apart? **[The distances between the lines represent the same value of one standard deviation.]**

Got It?

Q What will be the values along the bottom of your graph? **[7, 11.7, 16.4, 21.1, 25.8, 30.5, and 35.2]**

Q How high should your graph be? **[The vertical axis is not scaled, so the height does not matter.]**

Q Around what value should the graph be symmetric? **[the mean of 21.1 in]**

Additional Problems

1. You track the number of words in your text messages for a month and sketch the bar graph shown. The number of words is normally distributed about a mean of 10. About what percent of your text messages are between 9 and 11 words long?

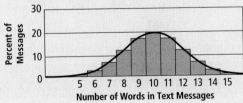

ANSWER 56%

2. For an English class, the average score on a research project was 82 and the standard deviation of the normally distributed scores was 5. Sketch a normal curve showing the project scores and three standard deviations from the mean.

ANSWER

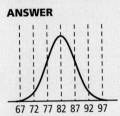

67 72 77 82 87 92 97

3. Using the normal curve from Additional Problem 2, what percent of students scored between 72 and 82 points?
ANSWER 47.5%

Problem 3

> **Q** Is there another way to find out what percent of males you would expect to be taller than 72 in.? **[You could add 13.5 + 2.35 + 0.15 to get 16%.]**

EXTENSION

> **Q** Since the area between the curve and the *x*-axis represents probability for a normal distribution, what is the area under the entire curve? Explain. **[The area under the entire normal curve is one. One hundred percent of the data is represented by the entire curve.]**

Got It?

> **Q** What percent of the scores are below 150? How do you know? **[Since the graph is symmetric, 50% of the data lie above the mean and 50% lie below the mean of 150.]**
>
> **Q** For 3b, what is the most convenient way to divide the graph of the normal curve to find the percent of students scoring above 135? **[Divide the graph into the 34% between 135 and 150 and the 50% scoring above the mean of 150.]**
>
> **Q** For 3c, is there more than one area under the normal curve that contains 13.5% of the data? Which is most likely a B? Explain. **[A grade of B is most likely the area between the first standard deviation and the second deviation. Although an area of 13.5% could be found in other places along the normal curve, a B is a higher grade, and is above the mean but is not the highest grade.]**

Problem 3 Analyzing a Normal Distribution

The heights of adult American males are approximately normally distributed with mean 69.5 in. and standard deviation 2.5 in.

A What percent of adult American males are between 67 in. and 74.5 in. tall?

Draw a normal curve. Label the mean. Divide the graph into sections of standard-deviation widths. Label the percentages for each section.

Plan

How do you divide the graph of the distribution?
Draw vertical lines at intervals that are one standard deviation wide, on both sides of the mean.

Distribution of Heights—Adult American Males

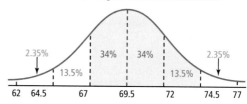

$$P(\,67 < \text{height} < 74.5) = 0.34 + 0.34 + 0.135 = 0.815$$

About 82% of adult American males are between 67 in. and 74.5 in. tall.

B In a group of 2000 adult American males, about how many would you expect to be taller than 6 ft (or 72 in.)?

Because the graph is symmetric about the mean, the right half of the distribution contains 50% of the data. If you subtract everything between 69.5 in. and 72 in. from the right half, only the part of the distribution that is greater than 72 in. remains.

Distribution of Heights—Adult American Males

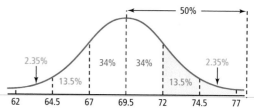

$$P(\text{height} > 72) = 0.50 - 0.34 = 0.16$$

You would expect about 16% of the 2000 adult American males to be taller than 72 in. You would expect about $0.16 \cdot 2000 = 320$ to be over 6 ft tall.

Got It? 3. The scores on the Algebra 2 final are approximately normally distributed with a mean of 150 and a standard deviation of 15.
   a. What percentage of the students who took the test scored above 180?
   b. If 250 students took the final exam, approximately how many scored above 135?
   c. **Reasoning** If 13.6% of the students received a B on the final, how can you describe their scores? Explain.

742 Chapter 11 Probability and Statistics

Answers

Got It? (continued)
3. a. 2.5%
   b. 210 students
   c. The students that received a B had scores between 165 and 180.

Lesson Check

Do you know HOW?

1. Use the graph from Problem 1. What is the approximate percent of female brown bears weighing at least 100 kg?

2. Draw a curve to represent a normally distributed experiment that has a mean of 180 and a standard deviation of 15. Label the *x*-axis and indicate the probabilities.

3. The scores on an exam are normally distributed, with a mean of 85 and a standard deviation of 5. What percent of the scores are between 85 and 95?

Do you UNDERSTAND? MATHEMATICAL PRACTICES

4. **Vocabulary** Why is a normal distribution "normal"?

5. **Compare and Contrast** How do the mean and median compare in a normal distribution?

6. **Reasoning** What is the effect on a normal distribution if each data value increases by 10? Justify your answer.

Practice and Problem-Solving Exercises MATHEMATICAL PRACTICES

Ⓐ Practice

Biology The heights of men in a survey are normally distributed about the mean. Use the graph for Exercises 7–10.

◀ See Problem 1.

7. About what percent of men aged 25 to 34 are 69–71 in. tall?

8. About what percent of men aged 25 to 34 are less than 70 in. tall?

9. Suppose the survey included data on 100 men. About how many would you expect to be 69–71 in. tall?

10. The mean of the data is 70, and the standard deviation is 2.5. Approximately what percent of men are within one standard deviation of the mean height?

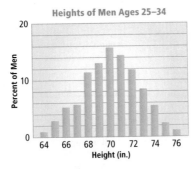

Heights of Men Ages 25–34

Sketch a normal curve for each distribution. Label the *x*-axis values at one, two, and three standard deviations from the mean.

◀ See Problem 2.

11. mean = 45, standard deviation = 5

12. mean = 45, standard deviation = 10

13. mean = 45, standard deviation = 2

14. mean = 45, standard deviation = 3.5

A set of data has a normal distribution with a mean of 50 and a standard deviation of 8. Find the percent of data within each interval.

◀ See Problem 3.

15. from 42 to 58

16. greater than 34

17. less than 50

Lesson Check

1. 94%

2.
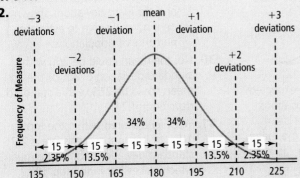

3. 47.5%

4. Normal distribution means that most of the examples in a data set are close to the mean; the distribution of the data is within 1, 2, or 3 standard deviations of the mean.

5. The mean and median are equivalent in a normal distribution.

6. mean increases by 10: the bell curve is translated 10 units to the rt.

7–17. See next page.

---

3 Lesson Check

Do you know HOW?

- If students have difficulty finding the percent in Exercise 1, ask which bars of the bar graph are included by the condition "at least 100 kg."
- If students cannot draw the curve in Exercise 2, remind them that the curve is symmetric about the mean and covers ±3 standard deviations.
- If students have difficulty solving Exercise 3, ask them to draw and label the normal curve that fits the conditions.

Do you UNDERSTAND?

- If students have difficulty comparing the mean and median of a normal distribution for Exercise 5, ask them what percent of the data falls above and below each of the median and mean. Point out that the normal distribution is symmetric about the mean.
- If students have difficulty reasoning the change in the graph of the distribution with an increase in the mean for Exercise 6, then ask what kinds of values increase the mean and where those values occur in a graph.

Close

Q How can the graph of a normal distribution of data help you understand the data? **[Knowing that data fits a normal distribution allows you to calculate what percentage of data falls within various standard deviations of the mean.]**

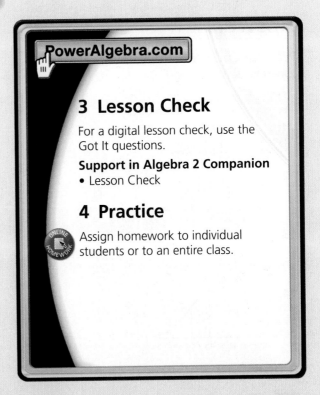

PowerAlgebra.com

3 Lesson Check

For a digital lesson check, use the Got It questions.

Support in Algebra 2 Companion
- Lesson Check

4 Practice

Assign homework to individual students or to an entire class.

4 Practice

ASSIGNMENT GUIDE

Basic: 7–17 all, 18–22 even, 29, 31

Average: 7–17 odd, 18–31

Advanced: 7–17 odd, 18–33

Standardized Test Prep: 34–37

Mixed Review: 38–46

Ⓖ **Mathematical Practices** are supported by exercises with red headings. Here are the Practices supported in this lesson:

MP 1: Make Sense of Problems Ex. 18

MP 3: Construct Arguments Ex. 6, 33

MP 3: Communicate Ex. 6, 20

MP 3: Compare Arguments Ex. 5, 31

MP 3: Critique the Reasoning of Others Ex. 30

Applications exercises have blue headings. Exercises 7–10, 21, 22 support MP 4: Model.

STEM exercises focus on science or engineering applications.

EXERCISE 22: Use the Think About a Plan worksheet in the **Practice and Problem Solving Workbook** (also available in the Teaching Resources in print and online) to further support students' development in becoming independent learners.

HOMEWORK QUICK CHECK

To check students' understanding of key skills and concepts, go over Exercises 9, 13, 18, 22, and 31.

Ⓑ **Apply**

Ⓖ **18. Think About a Plan** The numbers of paper clips per box in a truckload of boxes are normally distributed, with a mean of 100 and a standard deviation of 5. Find the probability that a box will *not* contain between 95 and 105 clips.
- How should you label the vertical lines on the graph of the normal distribution?
- Which parts of the graph are *not* between 95 and 105 clips?

19. a. From the table at the right, select the set of values that appears to be distributed normally.
  b. Using the set you chose in part (a), make a histogram of the values.
  c. Sketch a normal curve over your graph.

Set 1	Set 2	Set 3
1	5	5
10	7	6
5	7	9
19	7	1
2	4	1
7	11	5
1	7	11
7	7	1
2	7	10
10	9	4
6	7	2
9	7	8

Ⓖ **20. Writing** In a class of 25, one student receives a score of 100 on a test. The grades are distributed normally, with a mean of 78 and a standard deviation of 5. Do you think the student's score is an outlier? Explain.

21. Sports To qualify as a contestant in a race, a runner has to be in the fastest 16% of all applicants. The running times are normally distributed, with a mean of 63 min and a standard deviation of 4 min. To the nearest minute, what is the qualifying time for the race?

22. Agriculture To win a prize at the county fair, the diameter of a tomato must be greater than 4 in. The diameters of a crop of tomatoes grown in a special soil are normally distributed, with a mean of 3.2 in. and a standard deviation of 0.4 in. What is the probability that a tomato grown in the special soil will be a winner?

A normal distribution has a mean of 100 and a standard deviation of 10. Find the probability that a value selected at random is in the given interval.

23. from 80 to 100   **24.** from 70 to 130   **25.** from 90 to 120

26. at least 100   **27.** at most 110   **28.** at least 80

STEM **29. Weather** The table at the right shows the number of tornadoes that were recorded in the U.S. in 2008.
  a. Draw a histogram to represent the data.
  b. Does the histogram approximate a normal curve? Explain.
  c. Is it appropriate to use a normal curve to estimate the percent of tornados that occur during certain months of the year? Explain.

Month	Tornadoes
1	84
2	147
3	129
4	189
5	461
6	294
7	93
8	101
9	111
10	21
11	20
12	40

Ⓖ **30. Error Analysis** In a set of data, the value 332 is 3 standard deviations from the mean and the value 248 is 1 standard deviation from the mean. A classmate claims that there is only one possible mean and standard deviation for this data set. Do you agree? Explain.

Ⓖ **31. Reasoning** Jake and Elena took the same standardized test, but are in different classes. They both received a score of 87. In Jake's group, the mean was 80 and the standard deviation was 6. In Elena's group, the mean was 76 and the standard deviation was 4. Did either student score in the top 10% of his or her group? Explain.

Answers

Practice and Problem-Solving Exercises (continued)

7. ≈43%   **8.** ≈39%

9. ≈43 men   **10.** ≈66%

11.
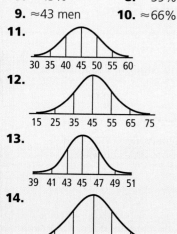
30 35 40 45 50 55 60

12.
15 25 35 45 55 65 75

13.
39 41 43 45 47 49 51

14.
34.5 38 41.5 45 48.5 52 55.5

15. 68%   **16.** 97.5%   **17.** 50%

18. 32%

19. a. Set 2

b–c.

4 5 6 7 8 9 10 11

20. Yes; 99% of all grades are expected to be within 3 standard deviations of the mean, and this score is 4.4 standard deviations above the mean.

21. 59 min   **22.** 2.5%   **23.** 47.5%

24. 99.7%   **25.** 81.5%   **26.** 50%

27. 84%   **28.** 97.5%

29. a.
(histogram: Tornadoes vs. Month, values 500 450 400 350 300 250 200 150 100 50 0 on vertical axis; 0 1 2 3 4 5 6 7 8 9 10 11 12 on horizontal axis labeled Month)

b. No; the curve is skewed to the left.

c. No, because the data are skewed it is not appropriate to use the mean and standard deviations shown on a normal curve to estimate percents of populations.

30. No; the mean could be 206 with standard deviation of 42, or the mean could be 269 with a standard deviation of 21.

31. Yes; Elena scored within the top 10% of her group. Her score is 2.75 standard deviations above the mean, which places her in the top 1%. Jake did not score in the top 10%. His score is 1.16 standard deviations above the mean, or at the 88th percentile.

32. Manufacturing Tubs of yogurt weigh 1.0 lb each, with a standard deviation of 0.06 lb. At a quality control checkpoint, 12 of the tubs taken as samples weighed less than 0.88 lb. Assume that the weights of the samples were normally distributed. How many tubs of yogurt were taken as samples?

33. Reasoning Describe how you can use a normal distribution to approximate a binomial distribution. Draw a binomial histogram and a normal curve to help with your explanation.

Standardized Test Prep

SAT/ACT

34. For a daily airline flight between two cities, the number of pieces of checked luggage has a mean of 380 and a standard deviation of 20. On what percent of the flights would you expect from 340 to 420 pieces of checked luggage?

Ⓐ 34%   Ⓑ 47.5%   Ⓒ 68%   Ⓓ 95%

35. A jar contains 37 pennies, 53 nickels, 29 dimes, and 21 quarters. A coin is drawn at random from the jar. What is the probability that the coin drawn is NOT a quarter?

Ⓕ $\frac{56,869}{2,744,000}$ Ⓖ $\frac{3}{20}$ Ⓗ $\frac{3}{17}$ Ⓘ $\frac{17}{20}$

36. A multiple-choice quiz contains five questions, each with three answer choices. You select all five answer choices at random. What is the best estimate of the probability that you will get at least four answers correct?

Ⓐ 4.1%   Ⓑ 4.5%   Ⓒ 13.2%   Ⓓ 46.1%

Short Response

37. Distribution A has 50 data values with mean 40 and standard deviation 2.4. Distribution B has 30 data values with mean 40 and standard deviation 2.8. Which distribution has more data values at or below 40? Show your work.

Mixed Review

Find the probability of x successes in n trials for the given probability of success p on each trial.   ◀ See Lesson 11-9.

38. $x = 4, n = 7, p = 0.2$ **39.** $x = 2, n = 9, p = 0.4$ **40.** $x = 6, n = 10, p = 0.3$

Graph each equation. Identify the conic section and describe the graph and its lines of symmetry. Then find the domain and range.   ◀ See Lesson 10-1.

41. $x^2 + y^2 = 64$ **42.** $x^2 - y^2 = 9$ **43.** $9x^2 + 25y^2 = 225$

Get Ready! To prepare for Lesson 12-1, do Exercises 44–46.

Write an equation for each horizontal translation of $y = x - 2$. Then graph each translation.   ◀ See Lesson 2-6.

44. 1 unit right   **45.** 2 units left   **46.** $\frac{3}{4}$ unit left

---

42.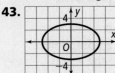

hyperbola; center: (0, 0), foci: ($\pm 3\sqrt{2}$, 0); lines of sym.: $x = 0$, $y = 0$; domain: $x \le -3$ or $x \ge 3$; range: all real numbers

43.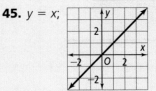

ellipse; center: (0, 0), foci: (± 4, 0); lines of sym.: $x = 0$, $y = 0$; domain: $-5 \le x \le 5$, range: $-3 \le y \le 3$

44. $y = x - 3$;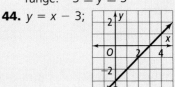

45. $y = x$;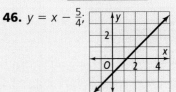

46. $y = x - \frac{5}{4}$;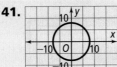

---

32. 480 tubs

33. A binomial distribution has a finite no. of possible probability events which sum to 1 and are a subset of a larger normal distribution. For example using, $n = 6$, $p = 0.5$, the binomial distribution probabilities are $P(0) \approx 0.0156$, $P(1) \approx 0.0938$, $P(2) \approx 0.2344$, $P(3) \approx 0.3125$, $P(4) \approx 0.2344$, $P(5) \approx 0.0938$, $P(6) \approx 0.0156$.

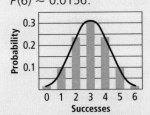

Standardized Test Prep

34. D

35. I

36. B

37. [2] For Distribution A with 50 data values, 25 values are at or below 40, which is the mean. For Distribution B with 30 data values, 15 values are at or below the mean 40. So Distribution A has more values at or below 40.

[1] correct distribution, without explanation or work shown

Mixed Review

38. 0.02867 **39.** 0.1612 **40.** 0.03676

41.

circle; center: (0, 0), radius: 8; lines of sym.: all lines through the center; domain: $-8 \le x \le 8$, range: $-8 \le y \le 8$

Additional Instructional Support

Algebra 2 Companion

Students can use the **Algebra 2 Companion** worktext (4 pages) as you teach the lesson. Use the Companion to support

- New Vocabulary
- Key Concepts
- Got It for each Problem
- Lesson Check

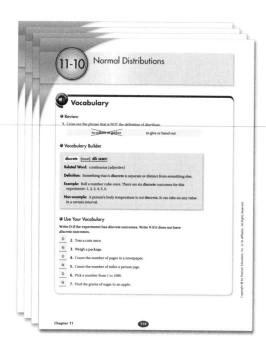

ELL Support

Assess Understanding This section contains several word problems. In small groups, have each student prepare the normal curve graph that would accompany a word problem. Check them and then have each student read the word problem aloud to the group and share the graph with the other group members to aid them in completing the exercises.

Focus on Communication Sketch a normal distribution on the board and draw a line down the middle and the lines representing three standard deviations. Point to each line and ask students to identify what each line represents.

5 Assess & Remediate

Lesson Quiz

1. The bar graph shows the number of minutes that people spent browsing a web site for one week. The curve shows how the time spent is normally distributed about a mean of 4.5 minutes. About what percentage of people spent between 3 and 6 minutes browsing the site?

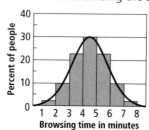

2. The wait times on a computer help line average 4.2 minutes. The standard deviation is 1.3 minutes. Sketch the normal curve showing the wait times at one, two, and three standard deviations from the mean.

3. **Do you UNDERSTAND?** Using the normal curve from Question 2, about what percent of people wait longer than 5.5 minutes?

ANSWERS TO LESSON QUIZ

1. about 76%

2.

0.3   2.9   5.5   8.1

3. about 16%

PRESCRIPTION FOR REMEDIATION

Use the student work on the Lesson Quiz to prescribe a differentiated review assignment:

Points	Differentiated Remediation
0–1	Intervention
2	On-level
3	Extension

PowerAlgebra.com

5 Assess & Remediate

Assign the Lesson Quiz. Appropriate intervention, practice, or enrichment is automatically generated based on student performance.

Intervention

- **Reteaching** (2 pages) Provides reteaching and practice exercises for the key lesson concepts. Use with struggling students or absent students.
- **English Language Learner Support** Helps students develop and reinforce mathematical vocabulary and key concepts.

All-in-One Resources/Online
Reteaching

11-10 Reteaching
Normal Distributions

If a data set has a *normal distribution*:
- 2.35% of the values will be between 2 and 3 standard deviations below the mean.
- 13.5% of the values will be between 1 and 2 standard deviations below the mean.
- 34% of the values will be within 1 standard deviation below the mean.
- 34% of the values will be within 1 standard deviation above the mean.
- 13.5% of the values will be between 1 and 2 standard deviations above the mean.
- 2.35% of the values will be between 2 and 3 standard deviations above the mean.

The graph of a normal distribution is a *normal curve*.
- A normal curve is shaped like a bell, with the highest point at the mean and tapering down evenly on either side of the bell.

Problem

The weight in pounds of newborn calves on a farm is distributed normally, with a mean of 85 and a standard deviation of 4. What percent of newborn calves on the farm weigh between 77 lb and 89 lb?

Step 1 Draw a normal curve. Label the mean.

Step 2 Divide the graph into 6 equal sections. Each section should be one standard deviation wide, which is 4 lb in this problem. Label each section with the appropriate percent for a normal distribution.

Step 3 Add the percents for the sections with weights 77 lb–81 lb, 81 lb–85 lb, and 85 lb–89 lb.
$13.5 + 34 + 34 = 81.5$

About 82% of newborn calves will weigh 77 lb–89 lb.

Exercises

Use the graph above to find the percent of calf weights within each interval.

1. from 73 lb to 81 lb about 16%
2. greater than 81 lb about 84%
3. from 77 lb to 97 lb about 97%
4. less than 85 lb about 50%
5. at most 89 lb about 84%
6. at least 93 lb about 2.5%

All-in-One Resources/Online
English Language Learner Support

11-10 Additional Vocabulary Support
Normal Distributions

Choose the word from the list that best completes each sentence.

continuous probability distribution	discrete probability distribution
normal distribution	normal curve	scatter plot

1. The data vary randomly from the mean in a ___normal distribution___.

2. The graph of a discrete probability distribution is a ___scatter plot___.

3. In a ___continuous probability distribution___, the events can be any value in an interval of real numbers.

4. The graph of a normal distribution is a ___normal curve___.

5. There are a finite number of possible values in a ___discrete probability distribution___.

Identify each of the following graphs as *positively skewed*, *normally distributed*, or *negatively skewed*.

6. normally distributed
7. positively skewed
8. negatively skewed

Multiple Choice

9. In a normal distribution, about what percent of the data are within one standard deviation of the mean? C
   (A) 16%   (B) 34%   (C) 68%   (D) 95%

10. A normal curve is shaped like a symmetric bell centered around the ___. G
   (F) mode   (G) mean   (H) median   (J) range

Differentiated Remediation *continued*

On-Level

- **Practice** (2 pages) Provides extra practice for each lesson. For simpler practice exercises, use the Form K Practice pages found in the All-in-One Teaching Resources and online.

- **Think About a Plan** Helps students develop specific problem-solving skills and strategies by providing scaffolded guiding questions.

- **Standardized Test Prep** Focuses on all major exercises, all major question types, and helps students prepare for the high-stakes assessments.

Extension

- **Enrichment** Provides students with interesting problems and activities that extend the concepts of the lesson.

- **Activities, Games, and Puzzles** Worksheets that can be used for concepts development, enrichment, and for fun!

Practice and Problem Solving Wkbk/ All-in-One Resources/Online
Practice page 1

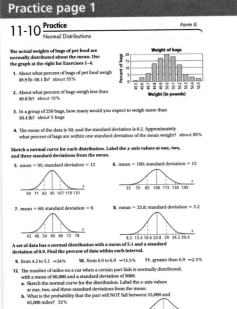

Practice and Problem Solving Wkbk/ All-in-One Resources/Online
Practice page 2

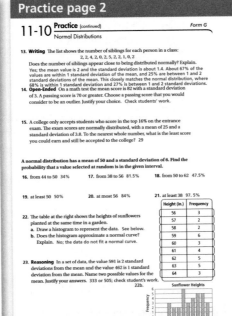

All-in-One Resources/Online
Enrichment

11-10 Enrichment
Normal Distributions

Tchebycheff's Theorem

Tchebycheff's Theorem states that given a number k greater than or equal to 1 and a set of n measurements, at least $\left(1 - \frac{1}{k^2}\right)$ of the measurements will lie within k standard deviations of the mean. Note that the theorem is true for any number you wish to choose for k as long as it is greater than or equal to 1.

The mean and standard deviation of a sample of $n = 25$ measurements are 75 and 10, respectively.

1. Using Tchebycheff's Theorem and $k = 2$, what can you assume? that $\frac{3}{4}$ of data lie within 55 and 95
2. What is the least number of measurements in the sample that will lie in the interval for $k = 2$? 19
3. Using Tchebycheff's Theorem and $k = 3$, what can you assume? that $\frac{8}{9}$ of data lie within 45 and 105
4. What is the least number of measurements in the sample that will lie in the interval for $k = 3$? 23
5. If $k = 1$, do you learn anything about the data? No; it says that at least 0 measurements lie within 65–85.

Consider the following data:
23 45 12 56 34 37 85 26 77 74
15 80 65 47 37 55 26 44 73 86
85 16 37 85 74 57 43 63 37 34
72 65 37 75 77 34

6. Calculate the mean and standard deviation. Round to the nearest whole number. 52; 22
7. Using Tchebycheff's Theorem and $k = 2$, what is the least number of measurements in the sample that will lie within 2 standard deviations of the mean? What interval corresponds to within 2 standard deviations of the mean? 27; between 8 and 96
8. How many measurements in the sample actually lie in that interval? 36
9. Using Tchebycheff's Theorem and $k = 3$, what is the least number of measurements in the sample that will lie within 3 standard deviations of the mean? What interval corresponds to within 3 standard deviations of the mean? 32; between 0 and 118
10. How many measurements in the sample actually lie in that interval? 36

Practice and Problem Solving Wkbk/ All-in-One Resources/Online
Think About a Plan

11-10 Think About a Plan
Normal Distributions

Agriculture To win a prize, a tomato must be greater than 4 in. in diameter. The diameters of a crop of tomatoes grown in a special soil are normally distributed, with a mean of 3.2 in. and a standard deviation of 0.4 in. What is the probability that a tomato grown in the special soil will be a winner?

Know
1. A tomato must have a diameter greater than [4 in.] to win a prize.
2. The mean diameter of the crop of tomatoes is [3.2 in.]
3. The standard deviation of the diameters of the crop of tomatoes is [0.4 in.]

Need
4. To solve the problem I need to find:
   the probability that the diameter of a tomato grown in the special soil is greater than 4 in.

Plan
5. Draw a normal curve. Label the mean and intervals that are multiples of the standard deviation from the mean.
6. What is the percent of the crop with diameters that are greater than the mean? 50%
7. What is the percent of the crop with diameters that are greater than the mean and less than 4 in.? How do you know? 47.5%; I summed the percent of the crop that are between 3.2 in. and 3.6 in. and between 3.6 in. and 4.0 in. in diameter
8. How can you find the percent of the crop with diameters greater than 4 in.? I can subtract the percent of the crop with diameters between 3.2 in. and 4.0 in. from the percent of the crop with diameters greater than the mean
9. What is the probability that a tomato grown in the special soil will be a winner? 2.5%

Practice and Problem Solving Wkbk/ All-in-One Resources/Online
Standardized Test Prep

11-10 Standardized Test Prep
Normal Distributions

Multiple Choice

For Exercises 1–5, choose the correct letter.

1. The mean number of pairs of shoes sold daily by a shoe store is 36, with a standard deviation of 3. On what percent of days would you expect the store to sell from 33 to 42 pairs of shoes? D
   - A 13.5%
   - B 50%
   - C 68%
   - D 81.5%

2. What is the standard deviation for the normal distribution shown at the right? F
   - F 60
   - G 360
   - H 120
   - J 676

   496 556 616 676 736 796 856

3. A normal distribution has a mean of 700 and a standard deviation of 35. What is the probability that a value selected at random is at most 630? B
   - A 0.0235
   - B 0.025
   - C 0.700
   - D 0.975

4. Scores on an exam are distributed normally with a mean of 76 and a standard deviation of 10. Out of 230 tests, about how many students score above 96? H
   - F 2
   - G 4
   - H 6
   - J 8

5. A hardware store sells bags of mixed nails. The number of nails of a given length is distributed normally with a mean length of 5 in. and a standard deviation of 0.03 in. About how many nails in a bag of 120 are between 4.97 in. and 5.03 in. long? C
   - A 34
   - B 41
   - C 68
   - D 82

Short Response

6. The heights of the girls in a school choir are distributed normally, with a mean of 64 and a standard deviation of 1.75. If 38 girls are between 60.5 in. and 67.5 in. tall, how many girls are in the choir? Show your work.
   [2] 64 − 1.75 − 1.75 = 60.5; 64 + 1.75 + 1.75 = 67.5
   The range 60.5 − 67.5 is within two standard deviations of the mean.
   13.5 + 34 + 34 + 13.5 = 95%; 95% of the data is within the range 60.5 − 67.5.
   38 = 0.95x
   x = 40; there are 40 girls in the choir.
   [1] incorrect or incomplete work shown
   [0] incorrect answer and no work shown OR no answer given

Online Teacher Resource Center
Activities, Games, and Puzzles

11-10 Game: Risk and Reward
Normal Distributions

This is a game for five students. One student is the host and the others form two teams.

Host: Your teacher will provide you with a separate sheet of questions and answers. Keep track of the score using the table below.

Players: A gameboard with categories and point values is shown below. Use it to keep track of which questions are still available and your score.

Rules: Decide which team goes first. When it is your turn:
- Select a category. The host will start with the least-points available question.
- If you answer correctly within the time assigned by your teacher, you earn the points for that question. Your turn continues and you select a category again.
- If you answer incorrectly, you lose that number of points and your opponent takes over. In addition, your opponent has 10 seconds to provide the correct answer and earn the points from the missed question. Your group or your teacher can decide to change the response time if needed.
- Play continues in this manner until all the questions have been used. The team with the highest point total wins. See Teacher Instructions page.

	Vocabulary (Define)	What's the z-score?	What's the SAT Score?	How Many Students Scored:	Review
10 pts					
20 pts					
30 pts					
40 pts					
50 pts					

Guided Instruction

PURPOSE To find the margin of error and limits for 95% confidence intervals.

PROCESS Students will

- use the formula $ME = 1.96 \cdot \frac{s}{\sqrt{n}}$ to find the margin of error for 95% confidence intervals.
- calculate the sample proportion for a sampling situation.
- find the margin of error and confidence interval for a population proportion.

DISCUSS Tell students what it means for an estimate to be within a margin of error. Ask, "If you make an estimate of an unknown quantity, would you want the margin of error to be large or small?" Explain that confidence level refers to how sure you are that your estimate is within the margin of error, and that larger margins of error lead to greater confidence levels.

Activity 1

In this activity, students find a 95% confidence interval for the mean from a sample of customer wait times.

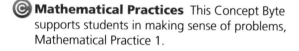

> **Q** Why do the wait times in the table represent a sample and not a population? **[They do not include all wait times.]**
>
> **Q** What is the probability that the actual population mean will lie outside of the confidence interval? **[5%]**

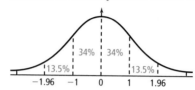 **Mathematical Practices** This Concept Byte supports students in making sense of problems, Mathematical Practice 1.

Concept Byte
For Use With Lesson 11-10

ACTIVITY

Margin of Error

© **Content Standard**
S.IC.4 Use data from a sample survey to estimate a population mean or proportion; develop a margin of error through the use of simulation models for random sampling.

The mean of a sample may or may not be the mean of the population the sample was drawn from. The **margin of error** helps you find the interval in which the mean of the population is likely to be. The margin of error is based on the size of the sample and the *confidence level* desired.

A 95% confidence level means that the probability is 95% that the true population mean is within a range of values called a **confidence interval**. It also means that when you select many different large samples from the same population, 95% of the confidence intervals will actually contain the population mean.

The means of all the samples follow a normal distribution.

The normal distribution above shows that 95% of values are between −1.96 and 1.96 standard deviations from the mean. To find the margin of error based on the mean of a large set of data at a 95% confidence level, you use the formula $ME = 1.96 \cdot \frac{s}{\sqrt{n}}$, where ME is the margin of error, s is the standard deviation of the sample data, and n is the number of values in the sample. The confidence interval for the population mean μ (pronounced *myoo*) is $\bar{x} - ME \leq \mu \leq \bar{x} + ME$, where $\bar{x}$ is the sample mean.

Activity 1

A grocery store manager wanted to determine the wait times for customers in the express lines. He timed customers chosen at random.

Waiting Time (minutes)				
3.3	5.1	5.2	6.7	7.3
7.5	4.6	6.2	5.5	3.6
3.4	3.5	8.2	4.2	3.8
4.7	4.6	4.7	4.5	9.7
5.4	5.9	6.7	6.5	8.2
3.1	3.2	8.2	2.5	4.8

1. What is the mean and stardard deviation of the sample? Round to the nearest tenth of a minute.

2. At a 95% confidence level, what is the approximate margin of error? Round to the nearest tenth of a minute.

3. What is the confidence interval for a 95% confidence level?

4. What is the meaning of the interval in terms of wait times for customers?

Answers

Activity 1

1. 5.4; 1.8
2. 0.6
3. 5.4 ± 0.6
4. At a 95% confidence level, you can say that the waiting time for customers at the grocery store is between 4.8 and 6.0 minutes.

You can also find the margin of error and the confidence interval for a sample proportion. A **sample proporton** $\hat{p}$ is the ratio $\frac{x}{n}$, where x is the number of times an event occurs in a sample of size n.

Activity 2

What is the sample proportion for each situation? Write the ratios as percents rounded to the nearest tenth of a percent.

5. In a poll of 1085 voters selected randomly, 564 favor Candidate A.

6. A coin is tossed 40 times, and it comes up heads 25 times.

To find the margin of error for a sample proportion at a 95% confidence level, use the formula $ME = 1.96 \cdot \sqrt{\dfrac{\hat{p}(1-\hat{p})}{n}}$, where ME is the margin of error, $\hat{p}$ is the sample proportion, and n is the sample size. The confidence interval for the population proportion p is $\hat{p} - ME \le p \le \hat{p} + ME$.

Activity 3

Find (a) the sample proportion, (b) the margin of error, and (c) the 95% confidence interval for the population proportion.

7. In a survey of 530 randomly selected high school students, 280 preferred watching football to watching basketball.

8. In a simple random sample of 500 people, 342 reported using social networking sites on the Internet.

Exercises

For Exercises 9–10, find the 95% confidence interval for the population mean or population proportion, and interpret the confidence interval in context.

9. A consumer research group tested the battery life of 36 randomly chosen batteries to establish the likely battery life for the population of same type of battery.

10. In a poll of 720 likely voters, 358 indicate they plan to vote for Candidate A.

11. **Data Collection** Roll a number cube 30 times. Record the results from each roll. In parts (a) and (b), find the sample proportion, the margin of error for a 95% confidence level, and the 95% confidence interval for the population proportion.

   a. rolling a 2

   b. rolling a 3

   c. Is the 95% confidence intervals for the population proportion about the same for rolling a 2 and for rolling a 3?

   d. Compare your sample proportions to the theoretical proportions for parts (a) and (b). Would you expect the theoretical proportion to be within the confidence intervals you found? Explain.

Battery Life (In Hours)			
63.2	84.6	78.4	85.8
62.1	81.8	63.6	64.2
79.4	75.2	54.1	73.4
66.3	74.5	71.6	60.1
61.2	74.5	72.4	81.3
61.4	83.6	75.6	74.1
68.3	82.2	59.3	47.6
86.2	64.3	72.7	71.8
71.4	63.6	59.6	68.1

Activity 2

In this activity, students calculate the sample proportion for different sampling situations.

> **Q** What is another term for sample proportion? **[relative frequency]**

Activity 3

In this activity, students use a sample proportion to find the margin of error and 95% confidence interval for the population proportion.

> **Q** What does the confidence interval tell you about the actual population proportion? **[That there is a 95% chance that the population proportion is in the confidence interval.]**
>
> **Q** How do you think you would adjust the margin of error to write a 99% confidence interval for the population proportion? **[Increase the margin of error. (The z-score factor is 2.58 for a 99% confidence interval instead of 1.96.)]**

ERROR PREVENTION

Be sure students understand that they need to be consistent in their use of percents and decimals when finding confidence intervals for sample proportions. If they convert the sample proportion from a decimal to a percent, then the margin of error must also be converted to a percent before subtracting and adding to find the limits of the confidence interval.

Activity 2

5. 52.0%

6. 62.5%

Activity 3

7. a. 52.8%

   b. 4.3%

   c. $48.5\% \le P \le$ to 57.1%

8. a. 68.4%

   b. 4.1%

   c. $64.3\% \le P \le 72.5\%$

Exercises

9. The sample mean is 70.5 hours. The 95% confidence interval for the population mean is $67.5 \le \mu \le 73.5$, which tells you that, with 95% probability, the mean life for the battery population is within the stated interval.

10. The sample proportion is 49.7%. The 95% confidence interval for the population proportion is $46.0\% \le P \le 53.4\%$, which tells you that, with 95% probability, the population proportion for voters in the election is within the stated interval.

11a–c. Check students' work.

   d. Answers may vary. Sample: Because the confidence interval is 95%, you would expect the theoretical probability, the ratio $\frac{1}{6}$, to be in the interval.

Guided Instruction

PURPOSE To compare samples and populations using z-scores and determine whether the difference between means or proportions is significant at a 95% confidence level.

PROCESS Students will

- compute z-scores for data values.
- use z-scores and a normal curve to find the probability that a random variable lies within a certain interval.
- determine whether a sample mean or proportion differs significantly from the population mean or proportion.

DISCUSS Students normalize data values by computing z-scores so that they can be compared to a standard normal curve. The mean of a sample is compared to the mean of the population using z-scores. Likewise, a sample proportion is compared to the population proportion. If the z-score is less than −1.96 or greater than 1.96, then there is a significant difference between the sample and population at a 95% confidence level.

Activity 1

In this activity, students compute z-scores for data values and find the probability that a random variable lies within a certain interval.

> **Q** Converting data using z-scores is sometimes called *normalizing* the data set. Why do you suppose this process is known as normalizing? **[Sample answer: the data can then be compared to a standard normal curve with mean 0 and standard deviation 1.]**
>
> **Q** What does it mean if the z-score of a data value is negative? **[The value is less than the mean.]**
>
> **Q** What does it mean if the z-score of a data value is positive? **[The value is greater than the mean.]**

Ⓒ **Mathematical Practices** This Concept Byte supports students in making sense of problems, Mathematical Practice 1.

Drawing Conclusions from Samples

Ⓒ **Content Standard**
S.IC.5 Using data from a randomized experiment to compare two treatments; use simulations to decide if differences between parameters are significant.

You can compare samples to determine if the difference in mean or proportion for a large population, based on a given confidence level, is significant. If a population is large and there are at least 30 data points in a sample, then the means and proportions can be compared using a normal distribution.

An important measure for normally distributed data is the **z-score**, which indicates the number of standard deviations a value lies above or below the mean of a population. When finding the z-score of a data point of a population, the formula is $z = \frac{x - \mu}{\sigma}$, where x is a data point, μ is the mean of a population, and σ is the standard deviation of the population.

Activity 1

In a given population, the weights of newborns are normally distributed about the mean 3250 g. The standard deviation of the population is 500 g.

1. What is the z-score of a newborn weighing 2500 g?

2. What is the z-score of a newborn weighing 4500 g?

3. What is the probability that a newborn weighs between 2270 g and 4230 g? Use z-scores of the weights and the normal curve.

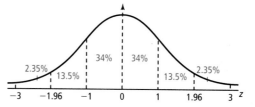

To compare the mean of a sample with the mean of a population, you use the formula $z = \frac{\bar{x} - \mu}{\frac{\sigma}{\sqrt{n}}}$, where $\bar{x}$ is the mean of the sample, μ is the mean of the population, σ is the standard deviation of the population, and n is the sample size. A z-score that is between −1.96 and 1.96 means that at a 95% confidence level, there is not a significant difference between the sample mean and the population mean. A z-score of less than −1.96 or greater than 1.96 indicates that at a 95% confidence level the differences between the sample mean and the population mean is significant and the differences are not simply due to chance.

Answers

Activity 1

1. −1.5
2. 2.5
3. The probability is 95%.

Activity 2

A company that develops fertilizers wants to know whether either of the two new fertilizers they have in development shows a significant difference in the growth of plants based on a 95% confidence level. The company has data on the growth of bean plants without fertilizers. For a growth period of one month, the population of the beans grown without fertilizers have a mean of 20 cm with a standard deviation of 1 cm.

4. A company researcher chooses 30 plants at random and uses fertilizer A for one month. The researcher finds that after using fertilizer A, the mean of the bean plants' growth is 20.4 cm. What is the z-score for the mean of the sample treated with fertilizer A compared to the population of bean plants without fertilizer?

5. Does fertilizer A meet a 95% confidence level for having growth that is significantly different from growth without fertilizer?

6. To test fertilizer B, the researcher chooses 35 plants at random. The bean plants' growth averages 20.3 cm. What is the z-score for the mean of the sample treated with fertilizer B compared to the population of bean plants without fertilizer?

7. Does fertilizer B meet a 95% confidence level for having growth that is significantly different from growth without fertilizer?

8. Based on these data, would you advise the company to market fertilizer A or fertilizer B? Explain.

To compare the proportion of a sample with the proportion of a population, you use the formula for the z-score for a proportion, $z = \dfrac{\hat{p} - p}{\sqrt{\dfrac{p(1 - p)}{n}}}$, where $\hat{p}$ is the sample proportion, p is the population proportion, and n is the sample size. For a 95% confidence level, a z-score between -1.96 and 1.96 means that difference between the sample and the population is not significant. A z-score of less than -1.96 or greater than 1.96 means that the difference in the proportions is significant, and not simply due to chance.

Activity 3

Suppose your teacher accidentally gives you a multiple-choice calculus test, instead of an Algebra 2 test. There are 40 true-false questions, and you and your classmates answer the questions randomly. The probability of getting an answer correct is $\frac{1}{2}$. You can use $\frac{1}{2}$ as the population proportion.

9. Develop a simulation for answering the 40 questions. Record your results.

10. What is the z-score for the sample based on your trials?

11. Compare your results with the results obtained by the rest of the class. At a 95% confidence level, what percentage of the results in the class showed a statistically significant difference from a score you would expect to get by guessing?

Activity 2

In this activity, students determine if there is a significant difference between a sample mean and the population mean at a 95% confidence level.

Q If a z-test score for the mean of a sample were 1.96, would you conclude that the sample mean is significantly different than the population mean at a 95% confidence level? Explain. **[Sample answer: No, the limits of the confidence interval include the endpoints at −1.96 and 1.96. So, the z-test score would still lie in the confidence interval at a 95% confidence level.]**

Activity 3

In this activity, students determine if there is a significant difference between a sample proportion and the population proportion at a 95% confidence level.

Q How many correct answers would you expect to get on the test if you guess at each answer? **[20]**

Activity 2

4. about 2.19
5. Yes, it meets the 95% confidence level.
6. about 1.77
7. No, it does not meet the 95% confidence level.
8. Fertilizer A because it meets the 95% confidence level that it has a significant difference with respect to plant growth.

Activity 3

9. Check students' work.
10. Check students' work.
11. Check students' work.

Performance Task

Pull It All Together

Understanding by Design principles indicate the importance of performance tasks that assess understanding.

- Make sense of problems and persevere in solving them.
- Construct viable arguments.
- Look for and make use of structure.

The following questions are designed to
- Help support students as they do the Performance Tasks.
- Help you gauge their progress toward becoming mathematically proficient.

Performance Task 1

Explain the relationship between permutations and combinations.

- How many ways can you permute r items chosen r at a time?

Performance Task 2

Solve a counting problem by breaking the problem into simpler parts.

- How many ways can you stack three number cubes so that all four sides show all the same number?
- Is it possible for two adjacent sides of the stack to show the same numbers without the other two sides also showing the same two numbers?

Performance Task 3

Demonstrate how outliers can affect the standard deviation without affecting the mean.

- To have the same mean as two standard number cubes, the sum of the numbers on the new number cube would have to total to what number?

To solve these problems, you will pull together concepts and skills related to probability and statistics.

BIG idea Probability

Various counting methods (such as permutations and combinations) can help you analyze situations and develop theoretical probabilities.

© Performance Task 1

Suppose you have n items from which you choose r at a time. Explain why you must divide the number of permutations $\frac{n!}{(n-r)!}$ by $r!$ to find the number of combinations $\frac{n!}{r!(n-r)!}$.

© Performance Task 2

Suppose you stack three identical number cubes. It is possible to have no sides, two sides, or all four sides of the stack showing all the same number. (Note that if one side of a stack shows all the same number, then the opposite side must as well.)

How many ways are there to stack three standard number cubes so that at least two sides of the stack show all the same number? If you can rotate a stack so that it is the same as another, count them as the same arrangement. Explain your solution.

0 sides   2 sides   4 sides

BIG idea Data Collection and Analysis

Standard measures that describe data from a real-world situation can help you make estimates or decisions about the situation, or predictions about future occurrences.

© Performance Task 3

Show all of your work and explain your steps.

a. Find the mean and standard deviation of the sums you should get when you roll two standard number cubes.

b. Suppose you can replace one number cube with a nonstandard number cube, where any of the numbers 1 through 6 can appear on multiple faces. How can you arrange the numbers on the nonstandard cube so that the mean of the rolls is the same as that of two standard number cubes, but the standard deviation is as large as possible? What is this value?

Assess Performance

Pull It All Together

See p. 49 for a holistic scoring rubric to gauge a student's progress on Understanding the Problem, Planning a Solution, Getting an Answer, and Assessing Autonomy.

SOLUTION OUTLINES

Performance Task 1

When counting permutations, order is important so you must count every arrangement of n items taken r at a time. But with combinations, order is not important so you don't need to count every arrangement of r out of n items ($r!$). Using $\frac{n!}{(n-r)!}$ over counts the combinations by a factor of $r!$. Dividing this expression by $r!$ leaves you with the number of combinations of n items taken r at a time.

Performance Task 2

Possible Plan: One strategy would be to count all stacks showing all 6's on one side and all 1's on the opposite side, then to count stacks with all 5's on one side and all 2's on the opposite side, then finally to count stacks with all 4's on one side and all 3's on the opposite side. You must keep track of duplicate stacks and subtract them from the total count.

First Step: Suppose the front of a stack shows all 6's and the back shows all 1's. You can find another arrangement by rotating the top cube so that the 6 stays in the front and the 1 stays in the back. There are four ways to do this. Next, rotate the middle cube and the bottom cube each four ways to generate a new stack with all 6's in the fronts and 1's in the back. There are 4^3 stacks with 6's in the front and 1's in the back.

Second Step: Repeat the first step but with all 5's in the front and all 2's in the back. However, one of these stacks will have all 6's on the left and all 1's on the right. Another will have all 1's on the right and all 6's on the left. There are $4^3 - 2$ stacks with all 5's in the front and all 2's in the back that have not already been counted in Step 1.

Third Step: Repeat the first step but with all 4's in the front and all 3's in the back. Two of these stacks have all 6's and all 1's on the other two sides of the stack, and two stacks have all 5's and all 2's on the other two sides of the stack. So, there are $4^3 - 4$ stacks with all 4's in the front and all 3's in the back that have not already been counted in Steps 1 or 2.

The total will be $4^3 + (4^3 - 2) + (4^3 - 4) = 186$.

Connecting **BIG** ideas and Answering the Essential Questions

1 Probability
A combination is a collection. A permutation is an ordered collection.

Permutations and Combinations (Lesson 11-1)
For n items chosen r at a time, $0 \le r \le n$,
- $_nP_r = \dfrac{n!}{(n-r)!}$
- $_nC_r = \dfrac{n!}{r!(n-r)!}$

Probability of Multiple Events and Conditional Probability (Lessons 11-3 and 11-4)
If A and B are independent events,
- $P(A \text{ and } B) = P(A) \cdot P(B)$
- $P(A \text{ or } B) = P(A) + P(B)$
The probability of event B, given event A is $P(B \mid A) = \dfrac{P(A \text{ and } B)}{P(A)}$.

2 Probability
You base experimental probability on *past*—and theoretical probability on *possible*—occurrences.

Probability (Lesson 11-2)
Experimental probability:
$P(\text{event}) = \dfrac{\text{number of times the event occurs}}{\text{number of trials}}$
Theoretical probability:
For n equally likely outcomes, if event A occurs in m of these outcomes, then $P(A) = \dfrac{m}{n}$.

Probability Models (Lesson 11-5)
You can use probability models to simulate how equally likely outcomes may occur for actual events.

3 Data Collection and Analysis
Probability concepts can be used to analyze data and make decisions. Standard deviation describes how data spread out from a particular middle (central tendency) value.

Analyzing Data and Standard Deviation (Lessons 11-6 and 11-7)
- $\bar{x}$, the mean, $= \dfrac{\sum x}{n}$
- σ, standard deviation $= \sqrt{\dfrac{\sum(x - \bar{x})^2}{n}}$

Binomial Distributions and Normal Distributions (Lessons 11-9 and 11-10)
In a normal distribution, about 68% (95%) of data are within one (two) standard deviation(s) of the mean.

Chapter Vocabulary

- binomial probability (p. 732)
- conditional probability (p. 696)
- continuous probability distribution (p. 739)
- dependent events (p. 688)
- discrete probability distribution (p. 739)
- equally likely outcomes (p. 682)
- independent events (p. 688)
- interquartile range (p. 713)
- mean (p. 711)
- median (p. 711)
- mode (p. 711)
- mutually exclusive events (p. 689)
- normal distribution (p. 739)
- outlier (p. 712)
- percentile (p. 714)
- probability distribution (p. 694)
- probability model (p. 705)
- random sample (p. 725)
- range of a set of data (p. 713)
- sample (p. 725)
- sample space (p. 682)
- standard deviation (p. 719)
- survey (p. 726)
- variance (p. 719)

Fill in the blanks.

1. A(n) __?__ is part of a population.

2. A(n) __?__ has a value substantially different from other data in the set.

3. A function that gives the probability of each event in a sample space is a(n) __?__.

4. The __?__ is the simplest measure of variation.

Essential Questions

BIG idea **Probability**
ESSENTIAL QUESTION What is the difference between a permutation and a combination?
ANSWER A combination is a collection. A permutation is an ordered collection.

BIG idea **Probability**
ESSENTIAL QUESTION What is the difference between experimental and theoretical probability?
ANSWER You base experimental probability on past—and theoretical probability on possible—occurences.

BIG idea **Data Collection and Analysis**
ESSENTIAL QUESTION How are measures of central tendency different from standard deviation?
ANSWER Standard deviation describes how data spread out from a particular middle (central tendency) value.

Performance Task 3

a. First Step: Make a table to find all the possible sums.
(There 36 possible sums.)
Second Step: Find the mean of all the sums. (mean = 7)
Third Step: Find the standard deviation. ($s = 2.415$)

b. Possible Plan: To increase the standard deviation, you want to increase the number of 6's. You need the sum of opposite sides of the nonstandard cube to be 7. So, the nonstandard cube should have sides, 1, 1, 1, 6, 6, and 6. The mean will be 7 and the standard deviation will be about 3.54.

Answers

Chapter Review
1. sample
2. outlier
3. probability distribution
4. range of a set of data

Summative Questions

Use the following prompts as you review this chapter with your students. The prompts are designed to help you assess your students' understanding of the BIG ideas they have studied.

- Compare and contrast combinations and permutations. For a given set of data, are there more combinations or permutations?
- Can mutually exclusive events be independent?
- What can you determine about data using the measures of central tendency? of variance?
- How can sample and study methods influence the results of a study?
- What is the difference between a discrete probability distribution and a continuous probability distribution? Give an example of each.

Answers

Chapter Review (continued)

5. 6

6. 362,880

7. 12

8. 30

9. 21

10. 10

11. 30

12. 744

13. 220; 84; 20; 1

14. 3.315312×10^9

15. 216

16. $\frac{47}{70}$

17. 0

18. $\frac{2}{5}$

19. Not necessarily; you may pick a 5 zero times, one time, or more than once. Each time you pick, the prob. that it will be a 5 is $\frac{1}{20}$.

11-1 Permutations and Combinations

Quick Review

If event M can occur in m ways and event N can occur in n ways, then M followed by N can occur in $m \cdot n$ ways. The notation $n!$ (**n factorial**) means $n(n-1) \cdot \ldots \cdot 3 \cdot 2 \cdot 1$. The number of ways to choose r items from a set of n items, without regard to order, is $_nC_r = \frac{n!}{r!(n-r)!}$. The number of ways to choose r items from a set of n items and place those items in some order is $_nP_r = \frac{n!}{(n-r)!}$.

Example

A vacationer making travel preparations chooses three books from a shelf containing 15 books. How many ways are there to choose three books without regard to order? How many ways are there to choose one book for the trip to the destination, one for the stay, and one for the homeward trip?

Ignoring order, there are $_{15}C_3 = \frac{15!}{3!\,12!} = 455$ ways to choose three books.

There are $_{15}P_3 = \frac{15!}{12!} = 2730$ to choose three books to read in a particular order.

Exercises

Evaluate each of the following.

5. $3!$

6. $9!$

7. $\frac{4!}{2!}$

8. $\frac{5!}{2!\,2!}$

9. $_7C_2$

10. $_4C_3 + {_6C_5}$

11. $_6P_2$

12. $_4P_3 + {_6P_5}$

13. Camping On a camping trip, you bring 12 food items for 4 dinners. For each dinner, you use 3 items. In how many ways can you choose the 3 items for the first dinner? For the second? For the third? For the fourth?

14. Advertising A newspaper ad includes a telephone number 1-555-DIAL VSW. How many seven-letter arrangements are possible for the phone number using the 26 letters of the alphabet if no letter is used more than once? Express your answer using scientific notation.

11-2 Probability

Quick Review

Experimental probability is based on successes during repeated trials, while **theoretical probability** is based on number of occurrences in a **sample space** of equally likely outcomes. When an actual event cannot easily be repeated through numerous trials, a **simulation** can be used to obtain an experimental probability.

Example

What is the probability that you were born on a Thursday?

Since you had an equal chance of being born on any one of the 7 days of the week, the probability that you were born on a Thursday is $\frac{1}{7}$.

Exercises

15. How many possible outcomes are there when a standard number cube is rolled three times?

16. You flipped a coin 70 times and recorded 23 heads. What is the experimental probability of flipping tails?

Find the probability of each event.

17. A standard number cube is rolled and comes up 13.

18. A number picked at random from the numbers 1 through 15 is prime.

19. Writing Suppose you have 20 tiles with the numbers 1 through 20. The theoretical probability that a tile chosen at random is a 5 is $\frac{1}{20}$. If you pick a tile randomly, 20 times, replacing the chosen tile each time, will you get a 5 once? Explain.

11-3 Probability of Multiple Events

Quick Review

For any events A and B,
$P(A \text{ or } B) = P(A) + P(B) - P(A \text{ and } B)$. When the occurrence of one event affects how a second event can occur, the events are **dependent**. When A and B are **independent**, $P(A \text{ and } B) = P(A) \cdot P(B)$. For **mutually exclusive events**, $P(A \text{ and } B) = 0$ so $P(A \text{ or } B) = P(A) + P(B)$.

Example

You roll a standard number cube. Are the events "roll a 1" and "roll an even number" mutually exclusive? Explain.

You cannot roll a 1 and an even number at the same time. The events are mutually exclusive.

Exercises

Classify each pair of events as *dependent* or *independent*.

20. A student in your algebra class is selected at random. One of the remaining students is selected at random.

21. You select a number 1 through 6 by tossing a standard number cube. You select a second number by tossing the number cube again.

Calculate each probability, given that $P(A) = 0.3$, $P(B) = 0.7$, and A and B are independent.

22. $P(A \text{ and } B)$

23. $P(A \text{ or } B)$

11-4 Conditional Probability

Quick Review

The probability that event B will occur, given that A has already occured, is the **conditional probability** $P(B \mid A) = \frac{P(A \text{ and } B)}{P(A)}$.

Example

A standard number cube is rolled twice. If the first number rolled is a and the second is b, find $P(a \text{ is even and } b > 2)$ and $P(b \text{ is even} \mid b > 3)$.

Since number cube rolls are independent events,

$P(a \text{ is even and } b > 2) = P(a \text{ is even}) \cdot P(b > 2)$
$\qquad = \frac{1}{2} \cdot \frac{2}{3} = \frac{1}{3}$

$P(b \text{ is even} \mid b > 3) = \frac{P(b > 3 \text{ and } b \text{ is even})}{P(b > 3)}$

$\qquad = \frac{P(4 \text{ or } 6)}{P(4 \text{ or } 5 \text{ or } 6)} = \frac{\frac{2}{6}}{\frac{3}{6}} = \frac{2}{3}.$

Exercises

Calculate each probability, given that $P(A) = 0.3$, $P(B) = 0.7$, and A and B are independent.

24. $P(A \mid B)$

25. $P(B \mid A)$

Calculate each probability, given that $P(A) = 0.5$, $P(B) = 0.4$, and $P(A \text{ and } B) = 0.1$.

26. $P(A \mid B)$

27. $P(B \mid A)$

28. $P(A \text{ and } B \mid A \text{ or } B)$

20. dependent

21. independent

22. 0.21

23. 0.79

24. 0.3

25. 0.7

26. $\frac{1}{4}$

27. $\frac{1}{5}$

28. $\frac{1}{8}$

Answers

Chapter Review (continued)

29. This will not necessarily result in a fair decision, because the principal may aim at a particular name, which means that not all students have an equally likely chance of being chosen.

30. Yes, this will result in a fair decision, because the probabilities of each goalie being chosen are the same.

31. Answers may vary. Check students' responses.

32. 9

33. mean: 6, median: 6, mode: 9

34. mean: $10.\overline{6}$, median: 7, modes: 3 and 7

35. mean: 15, median: 15, mode: 18

36. mean: 9.5, median: 9.5, mode: none

37. range: 35; $Q_1 = 30$; $Q_3 = 55$

38. range: 35; $Q_1 = 25$; $Q_3 = 50$

39. range: 65; $Q_1 = 42$; $Q_3 = 87$

11-5 Probability Models

Quick Review

Probability models and simulations with equally likely outcomes can be used to make fair decisions. It is important to simulate the event so that the likelihood of each outcome is represented correctly. Random number tables, number cubes, and coin flips, are commonly used to generate the random data in a simulation.

Example

Suppose that there are an equal number of red, green, blue, purple, and orange gumballs in a gumball machine. How many gumballs you would expect to buy before you got a red gumball?

Use random numbers and let red = 1, green = 2, blue = 3, purple = 4, and orange = 5.

27629 73963 08403 31642 08807 03871 92122

You had to buy 8 gumballs before getting a red one. Do several more trials and find the average value.

Exercises

Determine whether the following strategies will result in a fair decision. Explain.

29. Four students are eligible to deliver the morning announcements for the following week. The principal folds the paper in four equal square sections and writes each name in one of the sections. Then she tosses a coin onto the paper. The name closest to the coin will deliver the morning announcements.

30. **Sports** There are 3 equally talented goalies on your soccer team. Your coach assigns each goalie a number 1–3, and uses a spinner to choose which player will play goalie in each game this season. Assume the players are uninjured and eligible to play the entire season.

31. **Reasoning** In the gumball example at the left, each gumball costs $.25. Your friend decides to try for the red gumball. Is this a good decision? Explain.

11-6 Analyzing Data

Quick Review

You can use **measures of central tendency** to analyze data. The **mean**, $\bar{x}$, equals the sum of the values divided by the number of values. The **median** is the middle value of a data set in numerical order. The **mode** is the most frequently occurring value. A data value substantially different from the rest of the data is an **outlier**. A **box-and-whisker plot** summarizes information about the **range**, the median, and the first and third **quartiles** of a data set.

Example

Find the mean, median, mode, and range of the following set of numbers, and identify any outliers.

  3, 3, 4, 6, 19

The mean is $\frac{3 + 3 + 4 + 6 + 19}{5} = 7$.

The median is the middle data value, which is 4.

The mode is 3, which occurs twice.

The range is $19 - 3 = 16$.

The value 19 is very different from the others and is an outlier.

Exercises

32. Identify the outlier of this set of values.
  17, 15, 16, 15, 9, 18, 16

Find the mean, median, and mode for each set of values.

33. 1, 1, 3, 3, 5, 5, 6, 7, 9, 9, 9, 10, 10

34. 0, 3, 3, 7, 7, 8, 21, 22, 25

35. 8, 9, 11, 12, 13, 15, 16, 18, 18, 18, 27

36. 11, 6, 9, 4, 19, 10, 15, 2

Find the range, Q_1, and Q_3 for each set of values.

37. 25, 25, 30, 35, 45, 45, 50, 55, 60, 60

38. 20, 23, 25, 36, 37, 38, 39, 50, 52, 55

39. 36, 36, 48, 65, 75, 82, 92, 101

11-7 Standard Deviation

Quick Review

The range of a data set is one **measure of variation**, used to describe the spread of data. Another measure of variation is the **standard deviation**, defined as

$$\sigma = \sqrt{\frac{\sum (x - \bar{x})^2}{n}}$$

where $\bar{x}$ is the mean of the data set and n is the number of values. The **variance** is σ^2.

Example

Find the mean, variance, and standard deviation for the following data values: 1, 3, 4, 6, 8, 11, 23.

The mean is $\bar{x} = \frac{1 + 3 + 4 + 6 + 8 + 11 + 23}{7} = 8$.
The sum of the squares of the differences is
$(-7)^2 + (-5)^2 + (-4)^2 + (-2)^2 + 0^2 + 3^2 + 15^2 = 328$.
So the variance is $\sigma^2 = \frac{328}{7} \approx 46.9$, and the standard deviation is $\sigma \approx \sqrt{46.9} \approx 6.8$.

Exercises

For each pair of data sets, which is likely to have the greater standard deviation?

40. heights of three people
heights of twenty people

41. ages of thirty college students
ages of thirty high school students

42. gas mileages of eighteen sport utility vehicles
gas mileages of eighteen automobiles of various types

Find the mean and the standard deviation for each set of values.

43. 1, 1, 2, 2, 3, 4, 5, 6, 8, 9, 10, 10, 12, 20

44. 15, 17, 19, 20, 14, 23, 12

45. 3.1, 4.5, 7.8, 7.9, 8.0, 9.6, 11.6

11-8 Samples and Surveys

Quick Review

A **sample** is part of a **population**. For a **random sample**, all members of the population are equally likely to be chosen. A **bias** is a systematic error introduced by the sampling method.

Example

Identify any bias in the survey question "Do you think the school day should be extended even longer than it already is?". Explain.

There is bias because the question is leading. It implies that the school day is already too long and should not be extended.

Exercises

Determine if each of the following is a random sample. Explain your answer.

46. The first 50 names in the telephone directory

47. Twelve jurors chosen through examination by opposing lawyers

48. Two class representatives chosen by drawing names from a hat

49. Five newspapers picked on the basis of circulation size

50. The city council is trying to determine if the city's residents support the building of a new parking garage. They poll 200 people at the local bus station. Identify any bias in the sampling method.

40. heights of 3 people

41. ages of thirty college students

42. gas mileage of 18 automobiles of various types

43. $\bar{x} \approx 6.64$, $\sigma \approx 5.12$

44. $\bar{x} \approx 17.14$, $\sigma \approx 3.52$

45. $\bar{x} = 7.5$, $\sigma \approx 2.67$

46. not a random sample; they will all begin with the letter "a"

47. not a random sample; the lawyers will choose jurors that are likely to support their side

48. random sample; all students have an equal chance to be chosen

49. not a random sample; the five with the largest (or smallest) circulation size will be picked

50. People at the bus station may be less likely to own a car and therefore less likely to be in favor of a new garage.

Answers

Chapter Review (continued)

51. $\frac{1}{2}$

52. $\frac{1}{3}$

53. ≈ 0.14

54. ≈ 0.0710

55. ≈ 0.2066

56. ≈ 0.1766

57. $21a^5b^2$

58. $56a^3b^5$

59. continuous

60. discrete

61. discrete

62. continuous

63. 16%; 2.5%

11-9 Binomial Distributions

Quick Review

A **binomial experiment** has repeated independent trials with each trial having two possible outcomes. In a binomial experiment with probability of success p and of failure q (so $p + q = 1$), the probability of exactly x successes in n trials is $_nC_x\,p^x q^{n-x}$. This value is the **binomial probability**. The **Binomial Theorem** says that for every positive integer n,
$(a + b)^n = _nC_0 a^n + _nC_1 a^{n-1}b + _nC_2 a^{n-2}b^2 + \cdots + _nC_{n-1}ab^{n-1} + _nC_n b^n$.

Example

In a binomial trial, the probability of success is 0.8 for each trial. Find the probability of exactly 4 successes in 7 trials.

$p = 0.8, q = 0.2, x = 4$, and $n = 7$

$P(4) = _7C_4(0.8)^4(0.2)^3$

$ = \frac{7!}{3!4!}(0.8)^4(0.2)^3$

$ \approx 0.115$

The probability of 4 successes in 7 trials is 0.115.

Exercises

For each of the following binomial experiments, state the value of p, the probability of success.

51. A series of coin flips, where success is "heads."

52. A series of number cube rolls, where success is "2 or 4."

In a binomial trial, the probability of success is 0.6 for each trial. Find the probability of each of the following.

53. 13 successes in 24 trials

54. 9 successes in 20 trials

55. 9 successes in 15 trials

56. 6 failures in 12 trials

Use the Binomial Theorem to write each of the following.

57. the third term in the expansion of $(a + b)^7$

58. the sixth term in the expansion of $(a + b)^8$

11-10 Normal Distributions

Quick Review

A **normal distribution** shows data that vary from the mean in a random, continuous manner. The pattern they form is a bell-shaped curve called a normal curve.

Example

Sketch a curve for a normal distribution with mean 10 and standard deviation 4. Label the x-axis at one, two, and three standard deviations from the mean.

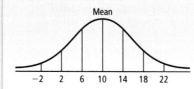

Exercises

For each of the following, state whether the probability distribution would be *discrete* or *continuous*.

59. distance from an arrow's impact point to the center of the bullseye

60. shoe sizes on a softball team

61. price of a gallon of premium unleaded gasoline at a randomly selected gas station

62. time a customer spends on hold during a call to a computer manufacturer's tech support

63. **Auto Maintenance** Suppose the time required for an auto shop to do a tune-up is normally distributed, with a mean of 102 minutes and a standard deviation of 18 minutes. What is the probability that a tune-up will take more than two hours? Under 66 minutes?

MathXL® for School
Go to PowerAlgebra.com

Do you know HOW?

Evaluate each expression.

1. 6!   **2.** $_7C_3$ **3.** $_{11}P_9$

Q and R are independent events. Find $P(Q \text{ and } R)$.

4. $P(Q) = 0.5, P(R) = 0.4$

5. $P(Q) = \frac{1}{3}, P(R) = \frac{3}{8}$

Use the table below for Exercises 6–8.

Age of Respondent	Number of Groups	
	0–4	5 or more
< 30	7	18
≥ 30	12	12

6. Find $P(5 \text{ or more})$.

7. Find $P(5 \text{ or more} \mid \text{age} < 30)$.

8. Find $P(\text{age} \geq 30 \mid 0-4)$.

Two standard number cubes are tossed. State whether the events are mutually exclusive.

9. One of the numbers is 1 less than the other. The sum is odd.

10. The sum is greater than 10. Six is one of the numbers.

11. Find Q_1 and Q_3 for this set of values:
36, 38, 42, 47, 51, 56, 62, 69, 70, 74.

12. Open-Ended At a local high school, there are 150 student parking spaces in the parking lot. There are 200 applications for parking permits. Describe a way that the permits can be assigned fairly.

A set of data has a normal distribution with a mean of 29 and a standard deviation of 4. Find the percent of data within each interval.

13. from 25 to 33   **14.** greater than 29

A newspaper wants to take a poll about which candidate voters prefer for President. Identify any bias in each sampling method.

15. The newspaper interviews people at a political debate.

16. The newspaper calls people selected at random from the local telephone book.

17. At a high school, 30% of the students buy class rings. You select five students at random. Find $P(\text{exactly two buy rings})$ and $P(\text{at least two buy rings})$.

Do you UNDERSTAND?

18. Indicate whether each situation involves a combination or a permutation.
  a. A team of 6 chosen from a class of 36
  b. An 8-digit code chosen for a lock

19. A data set is normally distributed with a mean of 37 and a standard deviation of 8.1. Sketch a normal curve for the distribution. Label the x-axis values at one, two, and three standard deviations from the mean.

© 20. Open-Ended A student guesses the answers to three questions on a true-false test. Design and describe a simulation to find the probability that the student guesses at least one of the questions correctly.

© 21. Writing Describe how a situation can have more than one sample space. Include an example.

22. Airline Ticket Pricing The table contains information from a study of the prices of comparable airline tickets. Which sample most likely was greater in size, A or B? Explain.

Sample	Standard deviation
A	$10.81
B	$3.97

22. Sample B; in the standard deviation formula you divide by n, so the greater the value of n, the smaller the standard deviation.

Answers

Chapter Test

1. 720

2. 35

3. 19,958,400

4. 0.2

5. $\frac{1}{8}$

6. $\frac{30}{49}$

7. $\frac{18}{25}$

8. $\frac{12}{19}$

9. not mutually exclusive

10. not mutually exclusive

11. $Q_1 = 42$, $Q_3 = 69$

12. Answers will vary. Sample: Since $\frac{150}{200}$ reduces to $\frac{3}{4}$, assign each student a 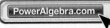 number from 1–4. Then spin a spinner with four equal spaces, numbered 1–4. The first three numbers that are spun get a parking permit.

13. 68%

14. 50%

15. bias toward active voters

16. bias toward voters with listed numbers

17. 0.309; 0.472

18. a. combination
     b. permutation

19.

12.7 20.8 28.9 37 45.1 53.2 61.3

20. Check students' work.

21. Sample: Suppose two hybrid Aa parent plants are crossed. The offspring can be described by the sample space {AA, Aa, aa} or by the sample space {dominant, recessive}.

Item Number	Lesson	© Content Standard
1	11-3	S.CP.7
2	7-2	F.IF.7.c
3	2-4	F.IF.8
4	4-2	F.IF.4
5	4-5	A.APR.3
6	10-3	G.GPE.1
7	11-6	S.ID.2
8	9-5	A.SSE.4
9	3-2	A.REI.5
10	4-5	A.APR.3
11	6-6	F.IF.1.b
12	6-6	F.BF.1.b
13	9-4	F.BF.2
14	4-5	A.APR.3
15	3-4	A.CED.3
16	5-4	A.APR.2
17	4-2	F.IF.6
18	7-5	F.LE.4
19	9-5	A.SSE.4
20	11-3	S.CP.2
21	10-3	G.GPE.1
22	8-1	A.CED.2
23	11-4	S.CP.6
24	6-2	A.SSE.2
25	5-7	A.APR.5
26	11-1	S.CP.9
27	8-6	A.APR.7
28	7-4	F.LE.4
29	8-3	F.IF.7.d
30	10-5	G.GPE.3
31	9-5	A.SSE.4
32	11-10	S.IC.4

TIPS FOR SUCCESS

Some questions on standardized tests ask you to use data analysis concepts like mean, outlier, and percentile. Read the question at the right. Then follow the tips to answer the sample question.

Find the third quartile for the data set.

2 6 8 5 9 3 5 7 1 8 4 4 5

- (A) 6.5
- (B) 7
- (C) 7.5
- (D) 8

TIP 1

If necessary, rewrite the data values in order, from least to greatest.

TIP 2

Make sure you clearly understand the definition of the concept you are applying. The third quartile is the median of the upper half of the data, not including the median.

Think It Through

In order, the data values are as follows.

1 2 3 4 4 5 5 5 6 7 8 8 9

The upper half of the data contains the values 5 6 7 8 8 9

The median of the upper half is $\frac{7 + 8}{2} = 7.5$.

The correct answer is C.

Vocabulary Review

As you solve test items, you must understand the meanings of mathematical terms. Match each term with its mathematical meaning.

A. normal distribution

B. standard deviation

C. quartile

D. median

E. mutually exclusive events

I. one of three values that separate a finite data set into 4 equal parts

II. a measure of how much the values in a data set vary from the mean

III. the middle value of a data set

IV. shows data that vary randomly from the mean in a bell-shaped curve

V. events that cannot happen at the same time

Multiple Choice

Read each question. Then write the letter of the correct answer on your paper.

1. A and B are mutually exclusive events. $P(A) = \frac{1}{3}$ and $P(B) = \frac{1}{2}$. What is $P(A \text{ or } B)$?

- (A) $\frac{1}{6}$
- (B) $\frac{2}{3}$
- (C) $\frac{5}{6}$
- (D) 1

2. Which of the following relationships is best represented by the graph at the right?

- (F) $y = -2^x$
- (G) $y = 2(3)^{-x}$
- (H) $y = -2(3)^x$
- (I) $y = (-6)^x$

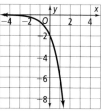

Answers

Cumulative Standards Review

A. IV

B. II

C. I

D. III

E. V

1. C

2. H

3. Which is the equation $5x - 7y = 25$ written in slope-intercept form?

Ⓐ $y = \frac{-5}{7}x + 5$

Ⓑ $y = \frac{5}{7}x - \frac{25}{7}$

Ⓒ $y = \frac{5}{7}x + 5$

Ⓓ $y = \frac{7}{5}x + \frac{25}{7}$

4. What is the vertex of the graph of $y = 2x^2 - 4x + 5$?

Ⓕ $(1, 5)$ Ⓗ $(1, 3)$

Ⓖ $(3, 1)$ Ⓘ $(5, 0)$

5. Which equation has $2 - \sqrt{3}$ as one of its solutions?

Ⓐ $x^2 + 4x + 1 = 0$

Ⓑ $x^2 - 4x + 1 = 0$

Ⓒ $x^2 + 4x - 1 = 0$

Ⓓ $x^2 - 4x - 1 = 0$

6. The equation for the circle below is $x^2 + y^2 = 9$. If the graph is translated one unit up and two units to the left, what is the new equation?

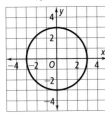

Ⓕ $(x - 1)^2 + (y + 2)^2 = 9$

Ⓖ $(x + 1)^2 + (y - 2)^2 = 9$

Ⓗ $(x - 2)^2 + (y + 1)^2 = 9$

Ⓘ $(x + 2)^2 + (y - 1)^2 = 9$

7. In six basketball games, you scored the following points per game. What is the approximate standard deviation of points scored?

8 11 14 7 12 18

Ⓐ 1.0   Ⓒ 4.0

Ⓑ 2.0   Ⓓ 5.0

8. What is the sum of the geometric series $5 + 10 + 20 + 40$?

Ⓕ $S = \frac{2(1 - 5^4)}{1 - 5}$ Ⓗ $S = \frac{5(1 - 4^2)}{1 - 4}$

Ⓖ $S = \frac{5(1 - 2^4)}{1 - 2}$ Ⓘ $S = \frac{2(1 - 4^5)}{1 - 4}$

9. What is the solution of the system of equations?

$$\begin{cases} 3x - 2y = 8 \\ x + 3y = -1 \end{cases}$$

Ⓐ $(-1, 2)$ Ⓒ $(-5, 2)$

Ⓑ $(7, -22)$ Ⓓ $(2, -1)$

10. What are the solutions to $9x^2 + 4 = 0$?

Ⓕ ± 2 Ⓗ $\pm \frac{2}{3}$

Ⓖ $\pm \frac{2}{3}i$ Ⓘ $\pm \sqrt{\frac{2}{3}}$

11. If $f(x) = x^2 - 1$ and $g(x) = |2x + 3|$, which has the greatest value?

Ⓐ $f(3) + g(3)$ Ⓒ $f(3) - g(3)$

Ⓑ $\frac{f(3)}{g(3)}$ Ⓓ $f(3) \cdot g(3)$

12. If $f(x) = 2x^2$ and $g(x) = 3(x + 1)$, which is an equivalent form of $f(x) + g(x)$?

Ⓕ $2x^2 + 3x + 1$

Ⓖ $2x^2 + 3x + 3$

Ⓗ $2x^2 + 3x - 3$

Ⓘ $5x^3 + 3$

13. The first term of an arithmetic series is 123. The common difference is 12 and the sum is 1113. How many terms are in the series?

Ⓐ 7   Ⓒ 9

Ⓑ 8   Ⓓ 10

14. In the equation $y = 2x^2 - x - 21$, which is a value of x when $y = 0$?

Ⓕ -21 Ⓗ 3

Ⓖ $1\frac{1}{2}$ Ⓘ $3\frac{1}{2}$

3. B
4. H
5. B
6. I
7. C
8. G
9. D
10. G
11. D
12. G
13. A
14. I

Answers

Cumulative Standards Review (continued)

15. 16

16. −5

17. −9

18. 59.1

19. 54

20. $\frac{5}{22}$

21. 5

22. 3

23. $\frac{17}{52}$

24. 15

25. 240

26. [2] **a.** combination; order is not important; the employer can select four employees in any order

    b. 27,405 selections

    [1] only part(a) or part(b) is correct

27. [2] $\frac{x}{6} = \frac{x+4}{9}$

$9x = 6x + 24$

$3x = 24$

$x = 8$

Check: $\frac{8}{6} = \frac{8+4}{9} = \frac{12}{9}$

$\frac{4}{3} = \frac{4}{3}$

    [1] correct solution; without work shown

28. [2] Power Prop. and Quotient Prop.

    [1] only one prop. stated correctly

29. [2] vertical asymptotes
when $x^2 + 2x − 3 = 0$.
$(x + 3)(x − 1) = 0$, $x = −3$ and $x = 1$,
horizontal asymptote at $y = 3$

    [1] correct horizontal asymptote, but incorrect vert. asymptote

30. [4] vertices: $(\pm 4, 0)$, intercepts: $(\pm 4, 0)$,
asymptotes: $y = \pm\frac{3}{4}x$, foci: $(\pm 5, 0)$

    [3] three correctly found, but one incorrect

    [2] two correctly found, but two incorrect

    [1] one correctly found, but three incorrect

31. [4] geometric;

$$S_n = \frac{a_1(1 − r^n)}{1 − r} = \frac{10,000\left(1 − \left(\frac{1}{10}\right)^8\right)}{1 − \frac{1}{10}}$$

$$= 11,111.111$$

    [3] appropriate method, but with one computational error

    [2] correct sum, but the series is not identified as geometric

    [1] correct sum, without work shown

---

15. What is the maximum value of the objective function $P = 3x + 4y$ within the feasible region described by the constraints at the right? $\begin{cases} x \geq 0,\ y \geq 0 \\ x + y \leq 4 \\ 2x + y \leq 5 \end{cases}$

16. What is the remainder when $x^2 + 3x − 5$ is divided by $x + 3$?

17. For the function $f(x) = x^2 − 2x + 15$, what is the average rate of change in the interval from $x = 1$ to $x = 2$?

18. Solve $\log_7 x = \log_3 10$. Round your answer to the nearest tenth.

19. Evaluate $\sum\limits_{n=1}^{8} \frac{3n}{2}$.

20. For a school play, six 9th graders and six 10th graders volunteer to be ushers. If two ushers are chosen at random by drawing names from a bowl, what is the probability that both ushers will be 10th graders? Write your answer as a fraction.

21. What is the radius of the circle with equation $x^2 − 6x + y^2 − 4y − 12 = 0$? If necessary, round your answer to the nearest hundredth.

22. Suppose x and y vary inversely and $x = 4$ when $y = 9$. What is x when $y = 12$?

Short Response

23. Students were asked in a survey whether they had been to a movie theater in the last month. The table below shows the results.

	Yes	No
Male	35	17
Female	28	20

What is the probability that a student has not gone to the movies recently, given that the student is a male?

24. Simplify the expression $(2\sqrt{6} − 3)(2\sqrt{6} + 3)$. Show all your work.

25. What is the coefficient of x^2y^4 in the expansion of $(x + 2y)^6$?

26. An employer is selecting 4 out of 30 workers as employees of the month.

    a. Does this situation involve a combination or a permutation? Explain.

    b. How many different selections are possible?

27. Solve the equation $\frac{x}{6} = \frac{x+4}{9}$. Check your solution. Show your work.

28. State the property or properties used to justify the identity $9 \log 3 − 3 \log 9 = \log 27$.

29. Find all asymptotes of the graph of $y = \frac{3x^2 + 1}{x^2 + 2x − 3}$.

Extended Response

30. Find the vertices, intercepts, asymptotes, and foci of the hyperbola $\frac{x^2}{16} − \frac{y^2}{9} = 1$.

31. Is the series $10,000 + 1000 + 100 + 10 + \ldots$ *arithmetic* or *geometric*? Find the sum of the first eight terms.

32. The following data set is a sample of the ages of students in an art school.

13 12 15 18 14 16 18 12 13 14 14 17 15 8 17 16
12 16 14 15 13 13 17 15 14 18 16 12 12 13

Find the mean and standard deviation. Then find the margin of error with a 95% confidence level by using the formula $ME = 1.96 \frac{s}{\sqrt{n}}$. Round to the nearest hundredth. Explain what this information tells you about the ages of students in the entire art school.

---

32. [4] mean: 14.4; standard deviation: 2.24; $ME = 0.80$; The true mean of the ages of the students in the entire art school is within the interval 13.60 and 15.20 with a 95% confidence level.

    [3] correct statistics with no explanation

    [2] one computational error

    [1] incomplete explanation

Get Ready!

Lesson 1-3

 Evaluating Expressions

Evaluate $ad - bc$ for the given values of the variables.

1. $a = -1, b = -2, c = 5, d = 4$

2. $a = \frac{1}{2}, b = -1, c = -\frac{2}{3}, d = 2$

3. $a = 2, b = \frac{1}{2}, c = \frac{1}{4}, d = -\frac{1}{8}$

4. $a = -\frac{1}{3}, b = \frac{1}{2}, c = \frac{1}{4}, d = -\frac{2}{3}$

Lesson 3-6

 Identifying Matrix Elements

Identify the indicated element.

$$A = \begin{bmatrix} 2 & -1 & 3 \\ 5 & 7 & -9 \\ 4 & 11 & 21 \end{bmatrix}$$

5. a_{23} **6.** a_{32} **7.** a_{13}

Lessons 3-2 and 3-6

 Solving Systems of Equations

Solve each system.

8. $\begin{cases} -2x + y = -5 \\ 4x + y = -2 \end{cases}$

9. $\begin{cases} 4x - y = -2 \\ -\frac{1}{2}x - y = 1 \end{cases}$

10. $\begin{cases} 3x + y = 5 \\ -x + y = 2 \end{cases}$

11. $\begin{cases} x + y + z = 10 \\ 2x - y = 5 \\ y - z = 15 \end{cases}$

12. $\begin{cases} -x + y + 2z = 16 \\ 2x - 2y - 2z = -16 \\ x + y = 0 \end{cases}$

13. $\begin{cases} -2x + 3y + z = 1 \\ x - 3z = 7 \\ -y + z = -5 \end{cases}$

Looking Ahead Vocabulary

14. The local museum store sells books, postcards, and gifts. There are different prices for museum members and nonmembers. At the end of each month, the numbers of items sold in each category are recorded in a table, or *matrix*. Make a sketch of what one of these might look like for one month.

15. Suppose you have the twelve tables, one for each month, of the museum's sales in the previous problem. These can be combined using *matrix addition* to determine the total number of items sold in each category during the year. Describe how this is done. Use several examples like the one you made in the previous problem to see if your method works.

Get Ready!

Assign this diagnostic assessment to determine if students have the prerequisite skills for Chapter 12.

Lesson	Skill
1-3	Evaluate Expressions
3-6	Identify Matrix Elements
3-2 and 3-6	Solve Systems of Equations

To remediate students, select from these resources (available for every lesson).
- Online Problems (PowerAlgebra.com)
- Reteaching (All-in-One Teaching Resources)
- Practice (All-in-One Teaching Resources)

Why Students Need These Skills

EVALUATING EXPRESSIONS

Evaluating expressions is essential to finding determinants and inverse matrices.

IDENTIFYING MATRIX ELEMENTS

Identifying matrix elements is essential to performing operations on them.

SOLVING SYSTEMS OF EQUATIONS

Students will extend solving systems of linear equations with matrix row operations to matrix equations.

Looking Ahead Vocabulary

MATRIX Like a table, a matrix is divided into rows and columns and can be used to organize, store, and display data.

MATRIX ADDITION Ask students to consider whether the sum of two matrices is another matrix or a number.

Answers

Get Ready!

1. 6

2. $\frac{1}{3}$

3. $-\frac{3}{8}$

4. $\frac{7}{72}$

5. -9

6. 11

7. 3

8. $\left(\frac{1}{2}, -4\right)$

9. $\left(-\frac{2}{3}, -\frac{2}{3}\right)$

10. $\left(\frac{3}{4}, \frac{11}{4}\right)$

11. $(7, 9, -6)$

12. $(0, 0, 8)$

13. $(7, 5, 0)$

14. Check students' work.

15. Check students' work.

Chapter 12 Overview

Chapter 12 expands on students' understandings and skills related to matrices and systems of equations. In this chapter, students will develop the answers to the Essential Questions posed on the opposite page as they learn the concepts and skills bulleted below.

BIG idea **Data Representation**
ESSENTIAL QUESTION How can you use a matrix to organize data?
• Students will use matrices to compare data.

BIG idea **Modeling**
ESSENTIAL QUESTION How can you use a matrix equation to model a real-world situation?
• Students will solve systems of equations with matrix equations.

BIG idea **Transformations**
ESSENTIAL QUESTION How can a matrix represent a transformation of a geometric figure in the plane?
• Students will use matrix operations to transform geometric figures.

© Content Standards

Following are the standards covered in this chapter.

CONCEPTUAL CATEGORY Numbers and Quantity

Domain Vector and Matrix Quantities N.VM
Cluster Represent and model with vector quantities.
(Standards N.VM.1, N.VM.2, N.VM.3)
LESSON 12-6

Cluster Perform operations on vectors.
(Standards N.VM.4.a, N.VM.4.b, N.VM.4.c, N.VM.5.a, N.VM.5.b)
LESSON 12-6

Cluster Perform operations on matrices and use matrices in applications.
(Standards N.VM.6, N.VM.7, N.VM.8, N.VM.9, N.VM.10, N.VM.11, N.VM.12)
LESSONS 12-1, 12-2, 12-3, 12-4, 12-5, 12-6

CONCEPTUAL CATEGORY Geometry

Domain Congruence G.CO
Cluster Experiment with transformations in the plane. (Standards G.CO.2, G.CO.5)
LESSON 12-5

CHAPTER
12

Matrices

PowerAlgebra.com
Your place to get all things digital

VIDEO
Download videos connecting math to your world.

VOCABULARY
Math definitions in English and Spanish

SOLVE IT!
The online Solve It will get you in gear for each lesson.

DYNAMIC ACTIVITIES
Interactive! Vary numbers, graphs, and figures to explore math concepts.

ONLINE PROBLEMS
Online access to stepped-out problems aligned to Common Core

ONLINE HOMEWORK
Get and view your assignments online.

MathXL FOR SCHOOL
Extra practice and review online

© DOMAINS
• Vector and Matrix Quantities
• Congruence

Matrices are used to do encryption. The sculpture <u>Kryptos</u> pictured on the next page contains encrypted messages.

How can you add, subtract, and multiply arrays of numbers? How can you use a matrix to represent and solve systems of equations? And how can you use matrices to make transformations of geometric objects? You will learn how in this chapter.

🔊 Vocabulary

English/Spanish Vocabulary Audio Online:

English	Spanish
determinant, *p. 784*	determinante
dilation, *p. 802*	dilatación
equal matrices, *p. 767*	matrices equivalentes
image, *p. 801*	imagen
matrix equation, *p. 765*	ecuación matricial
preimage, *p. 801*	preimagen
scalar multiplication, *p. 772*	multiplicación escalar
variable matrix, *p. 793*	matriz variable
zero matrix, *p. 765*	matriz cero

PowerAlgebra.com

Chapter 12 Overview

Use these online assets to engage your students. These include support for the Solve It and step-by-step solutions for Problems.

 Show the student-produced video demonstrating relevant and engaging applications of the new concepts in the chapter.

 Find online definitions for new terms in English and Spanish.

 Start each lesson with an attention-getting Problem. View the Problem online with helpful hints.

My Math Video

00:04:04

VIDEO

BIG ideas

1 Data Representation
Essential Question How can you use a matrix to organize data?

2 Modeling
Essential Question How can you use a matrix equation to model a real-world situation?

3 Transformations
Essential Question How can a matrix represent a transformation of a geometric figure in the plane?

Chapter Preview

PowerAlgebra.com | Chapter 12 Matrices | 763

My Math Video

Use this photo to introduce the concept of using math for encryption. The Kryptos sculpture contains four different messages that have been encrypted with polyalphabetic substitution and transposition ciphers.

Q What are some codes or ciphers you are familiar with? **[Samples: pig latin, Morse code, secret languages]**

Q What must a person on the receiving end of a code or cipher be able to do? How? **[Sample: Decode or decipher the message to understand it; use a key or work backwards.]**

Q How might you use math to encrypt a message? **[Sample: Assign numerical values to letters and perform specific operations on the values.]**

EXTENSION

Have students invent their own codes or ciphers using mathematical operations.

 Increase students' depth of knowledge with interactive online activities.

 Show Problems from each lesson solved step by step. Instant replay allows students to go at their own pace when studying online.

 Assign homework to individual students or to an entire class.

 Prepare students for the Mid-Chapter Quiz and Chapter Test with online practice and review.

Math Background © PROFESSIONAL DEVELOPMENT

Understanding by Design principles were central to the development of the Big Ideas and the Essential Understandings. These will help your students build a structure on which to make connections to prior learning.

Data Representation

BIG idea The most appropriate data representations depend on the type of data—quantitative or qualitative, and univariate or bivariate. Line plots, box plots, and histograms are different ways to show distribution of data over a possible range of values.

ESSENTIAL UNDERSTANDINGS

12-1 You can extend the addition and subtraction of numbers to matrices.

12-2 The product of two matrices is a matrix. To find an element in the product matrix, you multiply the elements of a row from the first matrix to the corresponding elements of a column from the second matrix. Then add the products.

12-6 A vector is a mathematical object that has both magnitude and direction.

Modeling

BIG idea Many real-world mathematical problems can be represented algebraically. These representations can lead to algebraic solutions. A function that models a real-world situation can then be used to make estimates or predictions about future occurrences.

ESSENTIAL UNDERSTANDINGS

12-3 The product of a matrix and its inverse matrix is the multiplicative identity matrix. Not all matrices have inverse matrices.

12-4 You can solve some matrix equations $AX = B$ by multiplying each side of the equation by A^{-1}, the inverse of matrix A.

12-5 You can multiply a 2×1 matrix representing a point by a 2×2 matrix to rotate the point about the origin or reflect the point across a line.

Transformations

BIG idea Transformations are mathematical functions that model concrete operations with figures. Transformations may be described geometrically or by coordinates. Symmetries of figures may be defined and classified by transformations.

ESSENTIAL UNDERSTANDING

12-5 You can multiply a 2×1 matrix representing a point by a 2×2 matrix to rotate the point an amount about the origin or reflect the point across a line.

Operations with Matrices

Operations that are defined for matrices include addition, subtraction, scalar multiplication, and matrix multiplication.

Addition, Subtraction, and Scalar Multiplication

The properties of equality for real numbers hold for these operations since all operations occur between two elements that are real numbers.

- **Matrix addition** is performed by adding corresponding elements in two or more matrices of the same dimensions:

$$\begin{bmatrix} a & b \\ c & d \end{bmatrix} + \begin{bmatrix} e & f \\ g & h \end{bmatrix} = \begin{bmatrix} a+e & b+f \\ c+g & d+h \end{bmatrix}$$

- **Matrix subtraction** is performed by subtracting corresponding elements in two matrices of the same dimensions.

- **Matrix scalar multiplication** is performed by multiplying each element in the matrix by the scalar. Scalar multiplication can be performed on matrices of any dimensions.

$$k\begin{bmatrix} a & b \\ c & d \end{bmatrix} = \begin{bmatrix} ka & kb \\ kc & kd \end{bmatrix}$$

Matrix Multiplication

The properties of equality for real numbers do not all hold for matrix multiplication, though some properties do hold for square matrix multiplication. One matrix can be multiplied by a second matrix only if the number of columns of the first matrix equals the number of rows of the second.

Common Errors With Matrix Operations

- **Errors in dimensions** occur when students try to add or subtract matrices of different dimensions, or multiply matrices that cannot be multiplied under defined matrix multiplication.

- **Properties of equality** may be taken for granted even though matrices are not real numbers. Make sure students understand that matrix multiplication is not commutative, and show some examples.

- **Errors in matrix multiplication** may occur when students multiply columns by rows instead or rows by columns. Suggest students sketch lines as a reminder:

$$\begin{bmatrix} a_{11} & a_{12} \\ a_{21} & a_{22} \\ a_{31} & a_{32} \end{bmatrix} \times \begin{bmatrix} b_{11} & b_{12} & b_{13} \\ b_{21} & b_{22} & b_{23} \end{bmatrix}$$

© Mathematical Practices

Model with mathematics. Make sense of problems and persevere in solving them. Matrices are introduced first as models of patterns and tabular data, and then as objects with algebraic properties.

"Understanding by Design" is registered as a trademark with the Patent and Trademark Office by the Association for Supervision of Curriculum Development (ASCD). ASCD has not authorized or sponsored this work and is in no way affiliated with Pearson or its products.

Applications of Matrices

Besides organizing and comparing data, matrices are used for several other purposes.

Finding the Area of Polygons

The area of any triangle with vertices (x_1, y_1), (x_2, y_2) and (x_3, y_3) equals $\frac{1}{2} \det \begin{bmatrix} x_1 & y_1 & 1 \\ x_2 & y_2 & 1 \\ x_3 & y_3 & 1 \end{bmatrix}$. The determinant may be negative, and area can only be nonnegative, so any negative sign must be dropped.

Because any polygon can be divided into two or more triangles, this formula can be used to find the area of any polygon.

Solving Systems of Equations

Previously, students used matrix row operations to solve systems of linear equations. Another method uses inverse matrices and matrix multiplication to apply the following relationship:

For matrices A and B, where A is invertible, if $AX = B$, then $X = A^{-1}B$.

For example, for the system $\begin{cases} ax + by = c \\ dx - ey = f \end{cases}$, the matrix equation is $\begin{bmatrix} a & b \\ d & -e \end{bmatrix}\begin{bmatrix} x \\ y \end{bmatrix} = \begin{bmatrix} c \\ f \end{bmatrix}$ and is solved using the equivalent matrix equation: $\begin{bmatrix} x \\ y \end{bmatrix} = \begin{bmatrix} a & b \\ d & -e \end{bmatrix}^{-1}\begin{bmatrix} c \\ f \end{bmatrix}$.

Note that if the coefficient matrix is not invertible, there will not be a unique solution.

Geometric Transformations

You can define a vertex matrix to represent a geometric figure. Then, you can use matrix operations and certain matrices to transform the figure. The figure before any translation is called the **preimage** and the transformed figure is called the **image**.

For **translations**, add the vertex matrix to a matrix whose elements are the amount you want to translate by.

For **dilations**, multiply the vertex matrix by a scalar.

For **rotations** and **reflections**, use matrix multiplication. Certain matrices can be used to rotate a figure by a specific number of degrees or reflect a figure.

©Mathematical Practices

Use appropriate tools strategically. Graphing calculators are used throughout the chapter to reinforce the use of matrices as a tool for problem solving while sparing students the necessity of time-consuming computations. This enables students to use the structure of matrices to solve real-world problems that would have been prohibitively tedious in the past.

Vectors

A vector is a mathematical object that has both magnitude and direction.

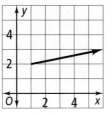

Unlike a ray, the arrowhead does not indicate that the vector continues indefinitely; instead, it reveals the direction of the vector.

Component Form

Vectors exist in all dimensions. One way to represent a vector is component form. For 2-dimensional vectors, the component form is $\langle \triangle x, \triangle y \rangle$. The size of the components indicates the magnitude of the vector, and the sign indicates the direction.

Operations with Vectors

Several operations are defined for vectors.

Addition Add corresponding components.

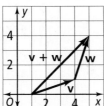

Subtraction Subtract corresponding components.

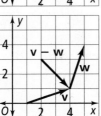

Scalar Multiplication Multiply each component by the scalar.

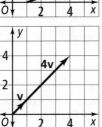

Dot Product Find the products of the corresponding components and add the products.

©Mathematical Practices

Reason abstractly and quantitatively. Look for and make use of structure. Students see how the multi-dimensional structure of matrices is useful for modeling multivariate behavior in a variety of algebraic and geometric settings, including that of two-dimensional vectors.

MATRICES
Pacing and Assignment Guide

| | | TRADITIONAL | | | BLOCK |
Lesson	Teaching Day(s)	Basic	Average	Advanced	Block
12-1	1	Problems 1–2 Exs. 7–14, 33–45	Problems 1–4 Exs. 7–17 odd, 19–29, 33–45	Problems 1–4 Exs. 7–17 odd, 19–45	**Day 1** Problems 1–4 Exs. 7–17 odd, 19–29, 33–45
	2	Problems 3–4 Exs. 15–18, 22–26 even, 27			
12-2	1	Problems 1–3 Exs. 7–27, 49–57	Problems 1–5 Exs. 7–33 odd, 34–44, 49–57	Problems 1–5 Exs. 7–33 odd, 34–57	Problems 1–5 Exs. 7–33 odd, 34–44, 49–57
	2	Problems 4–5 Exs. 28–36, 44			
12-3	1	Problems 1–3 Exs. 7–27, 62–76	Problems 1–3 Exs. 7–27 odd, 62–76	Problems 1–3 Exs. 7–27 odd, 62–76	**Day 2** Problems 1–5 Exs. 7–37 odd, 38–59, 62–76
	2	Problems 4–5 Exs. 28–37, 45–50	Problems 4–5 Exs. 29–37 odd, 38–59	Problems 4–5 Exs. 29–37 odd, 38–61	
12-4	1	Problems 1–3 Exs. 7–22, 59–72	Problems 1–3 Exs. 7–21 odd, 59–72	Problems 1–4 Exs. 7–25 odd, 27–72	**Day 3** Problems 1–4 Exs. 7–25 odd, 27–50, 59–72
	2	Problem 4 Exs. 23–29, 39, 48, 49	Problem 4 Exs. 23–25 odd, 27–50		
12-5	1	Problems 1–2 Exs. 7–13, 42–52	Problems 1–2 Exs. 7–13 odd, 42–52	Problems 1–4 Exs. 7–25 odd, 26–52	**Day 4** Problems 1–4 Exs. 7–25 odd, 26–37, 42–52
	2	Problems 3–4 Exs. 14–25, 32–36	Problems 3–4 Exs. 15–25 odd, 26–37		
12-6	1	Problems 1–2 Exs. 7–19, 54–71	Problems 1–2 Exs. 7–19 odd, 54–71	Problems 1–2 Exs. 7–19 odd, 54–71	**Day 5** Problems 1–5 Exs. 7–31 odd, 32–49, 54–71
	2	Problems 3–5 Exs. 20–31, 35–38, 42	Problems 3–5 Exs. 21–31 odd, 32–49	Problems 3–5 Exs. 21–31 odd, 32–53	
Review	1	Chapter 12 Review	Chapter 12 Review	Chapter 12 Review	**Day 6** Chapter 12 Review Chapter 12 Test
Assess	1	Chapter 12 Test	Chapter 12 Test	Chapter 12 Test	
Total		**14 Days**	**12 Days**	**10 Days**	**6 Days**

Note: Pacing does not include Concept Bytes and other feature pages.

Resources

	For the Chapter	12-1	12-2	12-3	12-4	12-5	12-6
Planning							
Teacher Center Online Planner & Grade Book	I	I	I	I	I	I	I
Interactive Learning & Guided Instruction							
My Math Video	I						
Solve It!		I M	I M	I M	I M	I M	I M
Student Companion		P M	P M	P M	P M	P M	
Vocabulary Support		I P M	I P M	I P M	I P M	I P M	I P M
Got It? Support		I P	I P	I P	I P	I P	I P
Dynamic Activity						I	
Online Problems		I	I	I	I	I	I
Additional Problems		M	M	M	M	M	M
English Language Learner Support (TR)		E P M	E P M	E P M	E P M	E P M	E P M
Activities, Games, and Puzzles		E M	E M	E M	E M	E M	E M
Teaching With TI Technology With CD-ROM							
TI-Nspire™ Support CD-ROM		✓	✓	✓	✓	✓	✓
Lesson Check & Practice							
Student Companion		P M	P M	P M	P M	P M	P M
Lesson Check Support		I P	I P	I P	I P	I P	I P
Practice and Problem Solving Workbook		P	P	P	P	P	P
Think About a Plan (TR)		E P M	E P M	E P M	E P M	E P M	E P M
Practice Form G (TR)		E P M	E P M	E P M	E P M	E P M	E P M
Standardized Test Prep (TR)		P M	P M	P M	P M	P M	P M
Practice *Form K* (TR)		E P M	E P M	E P M	E P M	E P M	E P M
Extra Practice	E M						
Find the Errors!	M						
Enrichment (TR)		E P M	E P M	E P M	E P M	E P M	E P M
Answers and Solutions CD-ROM	✓	✓	✓	✓	✓	✓	✓
Assess & Remediate							
ExamView CD-ROM	✓	✓	✓	✓	✓	✓	✓
Lesson Quiz		I M	I M	I M	I M	I M	I M
Quizzes and Tests *Form G* (TR)	E P M			E P M			E P M
Quizzes and Tests *Form K* (TR)	E P M			E P M			E P M
Reteaching (TR)		E P M	E P M	E P M	E P M	E P M	E P M
Performance Tasks (TR)	P M						
Cumulative Review (TR)	P M						
Progress Monitoring Assessments	I P M						

(TR) Available in All-In-One Teaching Resources

1 Interactive Learning

Solve It!

PURPOSE To find and complete a pattern among square arrays of numbers

PROCESS Students may
- compare numbers within an array to determine a pattern.
- compare numbers in the same position of different arrays to find a pattern.

FACILITATE

Q Is each array identical? Explain. **[No; notice the center terms.]**

Q What is the pattern of the center squares? **[Sample: multiples of 5]**

Q What number goes in the center of the first square? **[5]**

Q What could be the pattern for the numbers in the first row third column? **[Sample: multiples of 3]**

ANSWER See Solve It in Answers on next page.

CONNECT THE MATH In the Solve It, students compare ordered arrays of numbers, or matrices. In the lesson, students will add and subtract matrices and use them to compare data.

2 Guided Instruction

Take Note

Q How do you know which are the corresponding elements in two matrices? **[Samples: they have the same position, row and column; they have the same subscript.]**

© **Content Standards**
N.VM.8 Add, subtract, and multiply matrices of appropriate dimensions.
N.VM.10 Understand that the zero and identity matrices play a role in matrix addition and multiplication similar to the role of 0 and 1 . . .

Objective To add and subtract matrices and to solve matrix equations

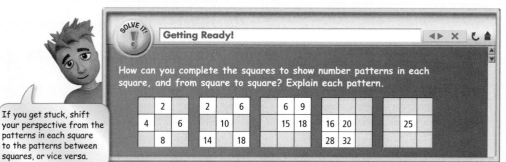

Getting Ready!

How can you complete the squares to show number patterns in each square, and from square to square? Explain each pattern.

	2	
4		6
	8	

	2	6
	10	
	14	18

	6	9
	15	18

16	20	
	28	32

	25	

If you get stuck, shift your perspective from the patterns in each square to the patterns between squares, or vice versa.

MATHEMATICAL PRACTICES

Lesson Vocabulary
- corresponding elements
- matrix equation
- zero matrix
- equal matrices

In Lesson 3-6, you solved a system of equations by expressing it as a single matrix. Now you will learn how to work with more than one matrix at a time.

Essential Understanding You can extend the addition and subtraction of numbers to matrices.

Recall that the *dimensions* of a matrix are the numbers of rows and columns. A matrix with 2 rows and 3 columns is a 2×3 matrix. Each number in a matrix is a *matrix element*. In matrix A, a_{12} is the element in row 1 and column 2.

Sometimes you want to combine matrices to get new information. You can combine two matrices with equal dimensions by adding or subtracting the corresponding elements. **Corresponding elements** are elements in the same position in each matrix.

take note

Key Concept **Matrix Addition and Subtraction**

To add matrices A and B with the same dimensions, add corresponding elements. Similarly, to subtract matrices A and B with the same dimensions, subtract corresponding elements.

$$A = \begin{bmatrix} a_{11} & a_{12} \\ a_{21} & a_{22} \end{bmatrix} \qquad B = \begin{bmatrix} b_{11} & b_{12} \\ b_{21} & b_{22} \end{bmatrix}$$

$$A + B = \begin{bmatrix} a_{11} + b_{11} & a_{12} + b_{12} \\ a_{21} + b_{21} & a_{22} + b_{22} \end{bmatrix} \qquad A - B = \begin{bmatrix} a_{11} - b_{11} & a_{12} - b_{12} \\ a_{21} - b_{21} & a_{22} - b_{22} \end{bmatrix}$$

BIG idea Data Representation

ESSENTIAL UNDERSTANDINGS
- The addition and subtraction of numbers can be extended to matrices.
- Matrices can be added or subtracted by adding or subtracting corresponding elements.

Math Background

To add or subtract two matrices, you add or subtract the corresponding elements of each matrix. Therefore, it is only possible to add or subtract matrices of the same dimensions.

The definition of matrix addition and subtraction allows you to extend the properties of addition and subtraction of real numbers to matrices.

It follows that, like any real number, each matrix has an additive inverse, which is a matrix with each element the opposite of the corresponding matrix element. Like real numbers, the sum of a matrix

and its additive inverse is the identity. The identity matrix is a matrix of the same dimensions with all elements equal to zero.

Two other properties include the following:
- Closure: Adding or subtracting matrices results in a matrix with the same dimensions.
- Commutative: Like real numbers, matrix addition is commutative, while matrix subtraction is not.

© **Mathematical Practices**
Look for and express regularity in repeated reasoning. In adding and subtracting matrices, students will look for general methods and shortcuts to the several minor calculations they will have to perform.

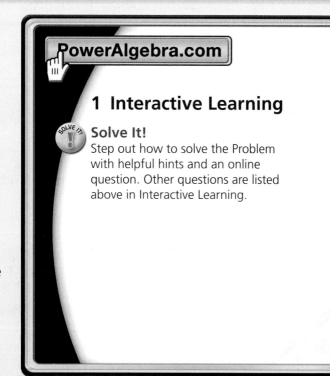

PowerAlgebra.com

1 Interactive Learning

Solve It!
Step out how to solve the Problem with helpful hints and an online question. Other questions are listed above in Interactive Learning.

Think
To add matrices they need to have the same dimensions. What are the dimensions of C?
C has 2 rows and 3 columns, so it's a 2×3 matrix.

 Problem 1 Adding and Subtracting Matrices

Given $C = \begin{bmatrix} 3 & 2 & 4 \\ -1 & 4 & 0 \end{bmatrix}$ and $D = \begin{bmatrix} 1 & 4 & 3 \\ -2 & 2 & 4 \end{bmatrix}$, what are the following?

A $C + D$

$$\begin{bmatrix} 3 & 2 & 4 \\ -1 & 4 & 0 \end{bmatrix} + \begin{bmatrix} 1 & 4 & 3 \\ -2 & 2 & 4 \end{bmatrix}$$

$$= \begin{bmatrix} 3+1 & 2+4 & 4+3 \\ -1+(-2) & 4+2 & 0+4 \end{bmatrix}$$

$$= \begin{bmatrix} 4 & 6 & 7 \\ -3 & 6 & 4 \end{bmatrix}$$

B $C - D$

$$\begin{bmatrix} 3 & 2 & 4 \\ -1 & 4 & 0 \end{bmatrix} - \begin{bmatrix} 1 & 4 & 3 \\ -2 & 2 & 4 \end{bmatrix}$$

$$= \begin{bmatrix} 3-1 & 2-4 & 4-3 \\ -1-(-2) & 4-2 & 0-4 \end{bmatrix}$$

$$= \begin{bmatrix} 2 & -2 & 1 \\ 1 & 2 & -4 \end{bmatrix}$$

 Got It? **1.** Given $A = \begin{bmatrix} -12 & 24 \\ -3 & 5 \\ -1 & 10 \end{bmatrix}$ and $B = \begin{bmatrix} -3 & 1 \\ 2 & -4 \\ -1 & 5 \end{bmatrix}$, what are the following?

a. $A + B$
b. $A - B$
c. Reasoning Is matrix addition commutative? Explain.

A **matrix equation** is an equation in which the variable is a matrix. You can use the addition and subtraction properties of equality to solve a matrix equation. An example of a matrix equation is shown below.

$$\begin{bmatrix} 1 & 0 & 12 \\ 3 & 5 & 9 \\ 7 & 8 & -2 \end{bmatrix} + A = \begin{bmatrix} 8 & 11 & 9 \\ -5 & 5 & 2 \\ 10 & 7 & 8 \end{bmatrix}$$

Problem 2 Solving a Matrix Equation

Sports The first table shows the teams with the four best records halfway through their season. The second table shows the full season records for the same four teams. Which team had the best record during the second half of the season?

Records for the First Half of the Season

Team	Wins	Losses
Team 1	30	11
Team 2	29	12
Team 3	25	16
Team 4	24	17

Records for Season

Team	Wins	Losses
Team 1	53	29
Team 2	67	15
Team 3	58	24
Team 4	61	21

Problem 1

Q Which number in matrix D corresponds to the element with value 4 in matrix C? **[Matrix C contains two elements with value 4, so this question does not have a single answer. The element with value 4 in row one corresponds to the 3 in matrix D; the element with value 4 in row two corresponds to the 2 in matrix D.]**

Q Which value in matrix C corresponds to d_{21}? **[c_{21} has a value of -1.]**

EXTENSION

Q If the elements in matrix C are input values and the elements in matrix D are output values, do the matrices show a function? Why or why not? **[No; the input value of 4 would map to two different output values.]**

Got It?

Q Your answers to 1a and 1b will be matrices of what size? **[3×2]**

Q Does $A - B$ equal $B - A$? Explain. **[No; matrix addition or subtraction is a series of individual additions or subtractions of corresponding elements. Because subtraction is not a commutative operation, matrix subtraction is not commutative either.]**

Problem 2   ERROR PREVENTION

Q How many rows and columns do the tables contain? If you made a matrix for each of the tables, how many rows and columns would the matrices contain? Explain. **[The tables each have 5 rows and 3 columns. A matrix for each table would have 4 rows and 2 columns because matrices contain values, not names and descriptions.]**

2 Guided Instruction

 Each Problem is worked out and supported online.

Problem 1
Adding and Subtracting Matrices
Animated

Problem 2
Solving a Matrix Equation
Animated

Problem 3
Using Identity and Inverse Matrices

Problem 4
Finding Unknown Matrix Values
Animated

Support in Algebra 2 Companion
• Vocabulary
• Key Concepts
• Got It?

Answers

Solve It!
Answers may vary. Sample:

1	2	3		2	4	6		3	6	9
4	5	6,		8	10	12,		12	15	18,
7	8	9		14	16	18		21	24	27

4	8	12		5	10	15
16	20	24,		20	25	30
28	32	36		35	40	45

Each 3-by-3 square has 9 elements. The first square contains the first 9 multiples of 1, the second contains the first 9 multiples of 2, and so on. Within each square, the top row contains the first 3 multiples, the middle row contains the fourth through the sixth multiples, and the bottom row contains the seventh through the ninth multiples.

Got It?

1. a. $\begin{bmatrix} -15 & 25 \\ -1 & 1 \\ -2 & 15 \end{bmatrix}$ **b.** $\begin{bmatrix} -9 & 23 \\ -5 & 9 \\ 0 & 5 \end{bmatrix}$

c. Yes; it does not matter in which order you add matrices.

Q Did all four teams play the same number of games during the second half of the season? How can you find out? **[Yes; the first column of each matrix shows games won, and the second column shows games lost, so totaling each row in a single matrix gives total games.]**

Got It?

Q How do you solve the literal equation? **[Add B to both sides: A = C + B.]**

Q What other equation will also give the correct answer? Why? **[A = B + C, because matrix addition is commutative.]**

Problem 3

Q What do you think a subtractive identity matrix might look like? Explain. **[A subtractive identity matrix would be the same as an additive identity matrix. Neither adding zero to a number nor subtracting zero from a number changes a value.]**

Got It?

Q In 3a, name the left-hand matrix A and name the right-hand matrix B. Which matrix is the additive inverse of the other? Explain. **[−A = B and −B = A, so each matrix is the additive inverse of the other.]**

Know	Need	Plan
• Records for the first half of the season • Records for the full season	Records for the second half of the season	• Use the equation: first half records + second half records = season records. • Solve the matrix equation.

Step 1 Write 4×2 matrices to show the information from the two tables.

Let $A =$ the first half records
$B =$ the second half records
$F =$ the final records

$$A = \begin{bmatrix} 30 & 11 \\ 29 & 12 \\ 25 & 16 \\ 24 & 17 \end{bmatrix} \quad F = \begin{bmatrix} 53 & 29 \\ 67 & 15 \\ 58 & 24 \\ 61 & 21 \end{bmatrix}$$

Think

What are the dimensions of matrix B?
B will have 4 rows and 2 columns. It is a 4×2 matrix.

Step 2 Solve $A + B = F$ for B.

$B = F - A$

$$B = \begin{bmatrix} 53 & 29 \\ 67 & 15 \\ 58 & 24 \\ 61 & 21 \end{bmatrix} - \begin{bmatrix} 30 & 11 \\ 29 & 12 \\ 25 & 16 \\ 24 & 17 \end{bmatrix} = \begin{bmatrix} 53-30 & 29-11 \\ 67-29 & 15-12 \\ 58-25 & 24-16 \\ 61-24 & 21-17 \end{bmatrix} = \begin{bmatrix} 23 & 18 \\ 38 & 3 \\ 33 & 8 \\ 37 & 4 \end{bmatrix}$$

Team 2 had the best record (38 wins and 3 losses) during the second half of the season.

Got It? **2.** If $B = \begin{bmatrix} 1 & 6 & -1 \\ 2 & 6 & 1 \\ -1 & -2 & 4 \end{bmatrix}$, $C = \begin{bmatrix} 2 & 0 & 0 \\ -1 & -3 & 6 \\ 2 & 3 & -1 \end{bmatrix}$, and $A - B = C$, what is A?

For $m \times n$ matrices, the additive identity matrix is the **zero matrix** O, or $O_{m \times n}$, with all elements zero. The *opposite*, or *additive inverse*, of an $m \times n$ matrix A is $-A$ where each element is the opposite of the corresponding element of A.

© **Problem 3** Using Identity and Opposite Matrices

What are the following sums?

Think

How is this like adding real numbers?
Adding zero leaves the matrix unchanged. Adding opposites give you zero.

A $\begin{bmatrix} 1 & 2 \\ 5 & -7 \end{bmatrix} + \begin{bmatrix} 0 & 0 \\ 0 & 0 \end{bmatrix}$

$= \begin{bmatrix} 1+0 & 2+0 \\ 5+0 & -7+0 \end{bmatrix} = \begin{bmatrix} 1 & 2 \\ 5 & -7 \end{bmatrix}$

B $\begin{bmatrix} 2 & 8 \\ -3 & 0 \end{bmatrix} + \begin{bmatrix} -2 & -8 \\ 3 & 0 \end{bmatrix}$

$= \begin{bmatrix} 2+(-2) & 8+(-8) \\ -3+3 & 0+0 \end{bmatrix} = \begin{bmatrix} 0 & 0 \\ 0 & 0 \end{bmatrix}$

Got It? **3.** What are the following sums?

a. $\begin{bmatrix} 14 & 5 \\ 0 & -2 \end{bmatrix} + \begin{bmatrix} -14 & -5 \\ 0 & 2 \end{bmatrix}$

b. $\begin{bmatrix} 0 & 0 & 0 \\ 0 & 0 & 0 \end{bmatrix} + \begin{bmatrix} -1 & 10 & -5 \\ 0 & 2 & -3 \end{bmatrix}$

Additional Problems

1. Given $A = \begin{bmatrix} -9 & -3 \\ 9 & 0 \\ 4 & 3 \end{bmatrix}$ and

$B = \begin{bmatrix} -7 & -2 \\ 4 & 6 \\ 9 & -3 \end{bmatrix}$, what is $B + A$?

ANSWER $\begin{bmatrix} -16 & -5 \\ 13 & 6 \\ 13 & 0 \end{bmatrix}$

2. The tables show the number of hours two students spent on homework in Math and Science classes.

Fall Semester Hours

	Math	Science
Student A	166	133
Student B	140	120

Fall and Spring Semester Hours

	Math	Science
Student A	300	227
Student B	282	231

Which student spent more hours on homework in the Spring Semester?

ANSWER Student B

3. What is the sum of the matrices $[-6 \quad 7 \quad 0]$ and $[6 \quad -7 \quad 0]$?

ANSWER $[0 \quad 0 \quad 0]$

4. What values of x and y make the equation true?

$$\begin{bmatrix} 8 & -2x \\ 3 & 7 \end{bmatrix} + \begin{bmatrix} 0 & -7 \\ 8 & 2 \end{bmatrix}$$

$$= \begin{bmatrix} 8 & -5 \\ 11 & 3y \end{bmatrix}$$

ANSWER $x = -1; y = 3$

Answers

Got It? (continued)

2. $A = \begin{bmatrix} 3 & 6 & -1 \\ 1 & 3 & 7 \\ 1 & 1 & 3 \end{bmatrix}$

3. a. $\begin{bmatrix} 0 & 0 \\ 0 & 0 \end{bmatrix}$

b. $\begin{bmatrix} -1 & 10 & -5 \\ 0 & 2 & -3 \end{bmatrix}$

Properties Properties of Matrix Addition

If A, B, and C are $m \times n$ matrices, then

Example	Property
$A + B$ is an $m \times n$ matrix	**Closure Property of Addition**
$A + B = B + A$	**Commutative Property of Addition**
$(A + B) + C = A + (B + C)$	**Associative Property of Addition**
There is a unique $m \times n$ matrix O such that $O + A = A + O = A$	**Additive Identity Property**
For each A, there is a unique opposite, $-A$, such that $A + (-A) = O$	**Additive Inverse Property**

Equal matrices have the same dimensions and equal corresponding elements. For example, $\begin{bmatrix} 0.25 & 1.5 \\ -3 & \frac{4}{5} \end{bmatrix}$ and $\begin{bmatrix} \frac{1}{4} & 1\frac{1}{2} \\ -3 & 0.8 \end{bmatrix}$ are equal matrices. You can use the definition of equal matrices to find unknown values in matrix elements.

 Problem 4 Finding Unknown Matrix Values

Multiple Choice What values of x and y make the equation true?

$$\begin{bmatrix} 9 & 3x + 1 \\ 2y - 1 & 10 \end{bmatrix} = \begin{bmatrix} 9 & 16 \\ -5 & 10 \end{bmatrix}$$

Ⓐ $x = 3, y = 5$ Ⓒ $x = 5, y = -2$

Ⓑ $x = \frac{17}{3}, y = 5$ Ⓓ $x = 5, y = -3$

Think
How can you solve the equation?
For the two matrices to be equal, the corresponding elements must be equal.

$3x + 1 = 16$ Set corresponding elements equal.	$2y - 1 = -5$
$3x = 16 - 1$ Isolate the variable term.	$2y = -5 + 1$
$3x = 15$ Simplify.	$2y = -4$
$x = 5$ Solve for x and y.	$y = -2$

The correct answer is C.

Got It? **4.** What values of x, y, and z make the following equations true?

a. $\begin{bmatrix} x + 3 & -2 \\ y - 1 & x + 1 \end{bmatrix} = \begin{bmatrix} 9 & -2 \\ 2y + 5 & 7 \end{bmatrix}$

b. $\begin{bmatrix} z & -3 \\ 3x & 0 \end{bmatrix} - \begin{bmatrix} 10 & -4 \\ x & 2y + 6 \end{bmatrix} = \begin{bmatrix} 2 & 1 \\ 8 & 4y + 12 \end{bmatrix}$

Q What does $m \times n$ mean in the Take Note box? Does it have anything to do with multiplication? [$m \times n$ **is the generic size of a matrix, with m rows and n columns. This does not mean multiplication inside the matrix, but the product mn is the total number of elements in the matrix.**]

Q What do you think the Closure Property means? Does this property also apply to matrix subtraction? [**The Closure Property means that the sum of two equal-sized matrices is a matrix of the same size. This property also applies to matrix subtraction.**]

Problem 4

Q If you replaced each matrix with a variable, what could the equation look like? [**Sample: $A = B$**]

Q How could you rewrite the left-hand matrix as the sum of two matrices to isolate the variable terms in a single matrix? How would this help you solve the problem? [**Answers may vary. Sample: Write a sum of two 2×2 matrices with elements 0, $3x$, $2y$, 0 and 9, 1, -1, and 10. The matrix that does not contain variables can be subtracted from both sides.**]

Got It?

Q In 4b, what three equations did you write to solve for the variables? [**Sample: $z - 10 = 2$; $3x - x = 8$; $0 - (2y + 6) = 4y + 12$**]

4. a. $x = 6, y = -6$
b. $x = 4, y = -3, z = 2$

3 Lesson Check

Do you know HOW?

- To solve Exercises 1–4, students must understand that the sum of two matrices of the same size is another matrix of the same size. The solution to Exercises 1, 3, and 4 is a 2 × 2 matrix; the solution to Exercise 2 is a 2 × 3 matrix.
- If students have trouble getting started with Exercises 1 and 2, describe matrix addition and subtraction as a series of simple additions or subtractions of corresponding elements.

Do you UNDERSTAND?

- To start on Exercise 5, students should convert all elements to either fractional or decimal form.
- In Exercise 6, challenge students to name and define the property of matrix addition the student disregarded.

Close

> **Q** How does matrix addition compare with real-number addition? **[Matrix addition and real-number addition involve the same basic operations. Matrix addition is a way of performing many real-number additions at once.]**

Lesson Check

Do you know HOW?

Find each sum or difference.

1. $\begin{bmatrix} 1 & -1 \\ 2 & 3 \end{bmatrix} + \begin{bmatrix} 0 & 2 \\ -4 & 5 \end{bmatrix}$

2. $\begin{bmatrix} 5 & -3 & 7 \\ -1 & 0 & 8 \end{bmatrix} - \begin{bmatrix} 4 & 6 & -1 \\ 2 & 1 & 0 \end{bmatrix}$

Solve each matrix equation.

3. $\begin{bmatrix} 6 & 1 \\ 4 & -2 \end{bmatrix} + X = \begin{bmatrix} 3 & 5 \\ -1 & 9 \end{bmatrix}$

4. $X - \begin{bmatrix} 2 & 0 \\ 5 & -1 \end{bmatrix} = \begin{bmatrix} 4 & 10 \\ 8 & -3 \end{bmatrix}$

Do you UNDERSTAND?

5. **Vocabulary** Are the two matrices equal? Explain.

$\begin{bmatrix} \frac{1}{2} & \frac{3}{8} \\ 0.2 & \sqrt[3]{27} \end{bmatrix}$ and $\begin{bmatrix} 0.5 & 0.375 \\ \frac{1}{5} & 3 \end{bmatrix}$

6. **Error Analysis** Describe and correct the error made in subtracting the two matrices.

Practice and Problem-Solving Exercises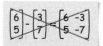

Practice   Find each sum or difference.   ◀ See Problem 1.

7. $\begin{bmatrix} 5 & 4 & 3 \\ 1 & -2 & 6 \end{bmatrix} + \begin{bmatrix} 1 & 1 & 1 \\ 1 & 1 & 1 \end{bmatrix}$

8. $\begin{bmatrix} 2 & 1 & 2 \\ 1 & 2 & 1 \end{bmatrix} - \begin{bmatrix} 2 & 3 & 2 \\ 3 & 2 & 3 \end{bmatrix}$

9. $\begin{bmatrix} 6.4 & -1.9 \\ -6.4 & 0.8 \end{bmatrix} + \begin{bmatrix} -2.5 & -0.4 \\ 5.8 & 8.3 \end{bmatrix}$

10. $\begin{bmatrix} 1.5 & -1.9 \\ 0 & 4.6 \end{bmatrix} - \begin{bmatrix} 8.3 & -3.2 \\ 2.1 & 5.6 \end{bmatrix}$

Solve each matrix equation.   ◀ See Problem 2.

11. $\begin{bmatrix} 1 & 2 \\ 2 & 1 \\ -3 & 4 \end{bmatrix} + X = \begin{bmatrix} 5 & -6 \\ 1 & 0 \\ 8 & 5 \end{bmatrix}$

12. $\begin{bmatrix} 2 & 1 & -1 \\ 0 & 2 & 1 \end{bmatrix} - X = \begin{bmatrix} 11 & 3 & -13 \\ 15 & -9 & 8 \end{bmatrix}$

13. $X - \begin{bmatrix} 1 & 4 \\ -2 & 3 \end{bmatrix} = \begin{bmatrix} 5 & -2 \\ 1 & 0 \end{bmatrix}$

14. $X + \begin{bmatrix} 6 & 1 \\ -2 & 3 \end{bmatrix} = \begin{bmatrix} 2 & 0 \\ -3 & 1 \end{bmatrix}$

Find each sum.   ◀ See Problem 3.

15. $\begin{bmatrix} 2 & -3 & 4 \\ 5 & 6 & -7 \end{bmatrix} + \begin{bmatrix} 0 & 0 & 0 \\ 0 & 0 & 0 \end{bmatrix}$

16. $\begin{bmatrix} 6 & -3 \\ -7 & 2 \end{bmatrix} + \begin{bmatrix} -6 & 3 \\ 7 & -2 \end{bmatrix}$

Find the value of each variable.   ◀ See Problem 4.

17. $\begin{bmatrix} 2 & 2 \\ -1 & 6 \end{bmatrix} - \begin{bmatrix} 4 & -1 \\ 0 & 5 \end{bmatrix} = \begin{bmatrix} x & y \\ -1 & z \end{bmatrix}$

18. $\begin{bmatrix} 2 & 4 \\ 8 & 4.5 \end{bmatrix} = \begin{bmatrix} 4x - 6 & -10t + 5 \\ 4x & 15t + 1.5x \end{bmatrix}$

Answers

Lesson Check

1. $\begin{bmatrix} 1 & 1 \\ -2 & 8 \end{bmatrix}$

2. $\begin{bmatrix} 1 & -9 & 8 \\ -3 & -1 & 8 \end{bmatrix}$

3. $\begin{bmatrix} -3 & 4 \\ -5 & 11 \end{bmatrix}$

4. $\begin{bmatrix} 6 & 10 \\ 13 & -4 \end{bmatrix}$

5. Yes; the elements in each of the corresponding positions are equal.

6. The elements were not subtracted. The correct answer is
$\begin{bmatrix} 6 \\ 5 \end{bmatrix} - \begin{bmatrix} 3 \\ 7 \end{bmatrix} = \begin{bmatrix} 3 \\ -2 \end{bmatrix}$

Practice and Problem-Solving Exercises

7. $\begin{bmatrix} 6 & 5 & 4 \\ 2 & -1 & 7 \end{bmatrix}$

8. $\begin{bmatrix} 0 & -2 & 0 \\ -2 & 0 & -2 \end{bmatrix}$

9. $\begin{bmatrix} 3.9 & -2.3 \\ -0.6 & 9.1 \end{bmatrix}$

10. $\begin{bmatrix} -6.8 & 1.3 \\ -2.1 & -1 \end{bmatrix}$

11. $\begin{bmatrix} 4 & -8 \\ -1 & -1 \\ 11 & 1 \end{bmatrix}$

12. $\begin{bmatrix} -9 & -2 & 12 \\ -15 & 11 & -7 \end{bmatrix}$

13. $\begin{bmatrix} 6 & 2 \\ -1 & 3 \end{bmatrix}$

14. $\begin{bmatrix} -4 & -1 \\ -1 & -2 \end{bmatrix}$

15. $\begin{bmatrix} 2 & -3 & 4 \\ 5 & 6 & -7 \end{bmatrix}$

16. $\begin{bmatrix} 0 & 0 \\ 0 & 0 \end{bmatrix}$

17. $x = -2, y = 3, z = 1$

18. $x = 2, t = \frac{1}{10}$

---

3 Lesson Check

For a digital lesson check, use the Got It questions.

Support in Algebra 2 Companion
- Lesson Check

4 Practice

Assign homework to individual students or to an entire class.

Apply **Find each matrix sum or difference if possible. If not possible, explain why.**

$$A = \begin{bmatrix} 3 & 4 \\ 6 & -2 \\ 1 & 0 \end{bmatrix} \quad B = \begin{bmatrix} -3 & 1 \\ 2 & -4 \\ -1 & 5 \end{bmatrix} \quad C = \begin{bmatrix} 1 & 2 \\ -3 & 1 \end{bmatrix} \quad D = \begin{bmatrix} 5 & 1 \\ 0 & 2 \end{bmatrix}$$

19. $A + B$ **20.** $B + D$ **21.** $C + D$ **22.** $B - A$ **23.** $C - D$

24. Think About a Plan The table shows the number of beach balls produced during one shift at two manufacturing plants. Plant 1 has two shifts per day and Plant 2 has three shifts per day. Write matrices to represent one day's total output at the two plants. Then find the difference between daily production totals at the two plants.
- How can you use the number of shifts to find the total daily production totals at each plant?
- What matrix equation can you use to solve this problem?

Beach Ball Production Per Shift

	1-color		3-color	
	Plastic	Rubber	Plastic	Rubber
Plant 1	500	700	1300	1900
Plant 2	400	1200	600	1600

25. Sports The modern pentathlon is a grueling all-day competition. Each member of a team competes in five events: target shooting, fencing, swimming, horseback riding, and cross-country running. Here are scores for the U.S. women at the 2004 Olympic Games.
a. Write two 5×1 matrices to represent each woman's scores for each event.
b. Find the total score for each athlete.

U.S. Women's Pentathlon Scores, 2004 Olympics

Event	Anita Allen	Mary Beth Iagorashvili
Shooting	952	760
Fencing	720	832
Swimming	1108	1252
Riding	1172	1144
Running	1044	1064

Source: Athens 2004 Olympic Games

26. Data Analysis Refer to the table at the right.
a. Add two matrices to find the total number of people participating in each activity.
b. Subtract two matrices to find the difference between the numbers of males and females in each activity.
c. Reasoning In part (b), does the order of the matrices matter? Explain.

U.S. Participation (millions) in Selected Leisure Activities

Activity	Male	Female
Movies	59.2	65.4
Exercise Programs	54.3	59.0
Sports Events	40.5	31.1
Home Improvement	45.4	41.8

Source: U.S. National Endowment for the Arts

27. Writing Given a matrix A, explain how to find a matrix B such that $A + B = 0$.

Solve each equation for each variable.

28. $\begin{bmatrix} 4b + 2 & -3 & 4d \\ -4a & 2 & 3 \\ 2f - 1 & -14 & 1 \end{bmatrix} = \begin{bmatrix} 11 & 2c - 1 & 0 \\ -8 & 2 & 3 \\ 0 & 3g - 2 & 1 \end{bmatrix}$

29. $\begin{bmatrix} 4c & 2 - d & 5 \\ -3 & -1 & 2 \\ 0 & -10 & 15 \end{bmatrix} = \begin{bmatrix} 2c + 5 & 4d & g \\ -3 & h & f - g \\ 0 & -4c & 15 \end{bmatrix}$

4 Practice

ASSIGNMENT GUIDE
Basic: 7–18 all, 22–26 even, 27
Average: 7–17 odd, 19–29
Advanced: 7–17 odd, 19–32
Standardized Test Prep: 33–36
Mixed Review: 37–45

(C) **Mathematical Practices** are supported by exercises with red headings. Here are the Practices supported in this lesson:
MP 1: Make Sense of Problems Ex. 24
MP 2: Reason Quantitatively Ex. 26c
MP 3: Communicate Ex. 5, 27
MP 3: Critique the Reasoning of Others Ex. 6
Model With Mathematics Ex. 26

Applications exercises have blue headings. Exercises 25 support MP 4: Model.

EXERCISE 26: Use the Think About a Plan worksheet in the **Practice and Problem Solving Workbook** (also available in the Teaching Resources in print and online) to further support students' development in becoming independent learners.

HOMEWORK QUICK CHECK
To check students' understanding of key skills and concepts, go over Exercises 11, 17, 24, 26, and 27.

19. $\begin{bmatrix} 0 & 5 \\ 8 & -6 \\ 0 & 5 \end{bmatrix}$

20. B and D cannot be added because they do not have the same dimensions.

21. $\begin{bmatrix} 6 & 3 \\ -3 & 3 \end{bmatrix}$

22. $\begin{bmatrix} -6 & -3 \\ -4 & -2 \\ -2 & 5 \end{bmatrix}$

23. $\begin{bmatrix} -4 & 1 \\ -3 & -1 \end{bmatrix}$

24.

Plant 1

	Plastic	Rubber
1-color	1000	1400
3-color	2600	3800

Plant 2

	Plastic	Rubber
1-color	1200	3600
3-color	1800	4800

Plant 1 − Plant 2 = $\begin{bmatrix} -200 & -2200 \\ 800 & -1000 \end{bmatrix}$, where the top row represents 1-color balls and the bottom represents 3-color balls.

25. a. $\begin{bmatrix} 952 \\ 720 \\ 1108 \\ 1172 \\ 1044 \end{bmatrix}$; $\begin{bmatrix} 760 \\ 832 \\ 1252 \\ 1144 \\ 1064 \end{bmatrix}$

b. Allen: 4996; Iagorashvili: 5052

26. a. $\begin{bmatrix} 124.6 \\ 113.3 \\ 71.6 \\ 87.2 \end{bmatrix}$

b. $\begin{bmatrix} -6.2 \\ -4.7 \\ 9.4 \\ 3.6 \end{bmatrix}$

c. Yes; order matters because subtraction is not comm.

27. Matrix B would have the same dimensions as A. Its elements would be the opposites of the corresponding elements in A.

28. $a = 2$, $b = \frac{9}{4}$, $c = -1$, $d = 0$, $f = \frac{1}{2}$, $g = -4$

29. $c = \frac{5}{2}$, $d = \frac{2}{5}$, $f = 7$, $g = 5$, $h = -1$

Answers

Practice and Problem-Solving Exercises (continued)

30. $\begin{bmatrix} 5 \\ 4 \\ 2 \end{bmatrix}$

31. Consider any two 2×2 matrices, $A = \begin{bmatrix} a & b \\ c & d \end{bmatrix}$ and $B = \begin{bmatrix} w & x \\ y & z \end{bmatrix}$. By the definition of matrix addition and the Comm. Prop. of Add.

$A + B = \begin{bmatrix} a & b \\ c & d \end{bmatrix} + \begin{bmatrix} w & x \\ y & z \end{bmatrix} = \begin{bmatrix} a+w & b+x \\ c+y & d+z \end{bmatrix}$

$\quad = \begin{bmatrix} w+a & x+b \\ y+c & z+d \end{bmatrix} = \begin{bmatrix} w & x \\ y & z \end{bmatrix} + \begin{bmatrix} a & b \\ c & d \end{bmatrix}$

$\quad = B + A$

32. Consider any three 2×2 matrices, $A = \begin{bmatrix} a & b \\ c & d \end{bmatrix}$, $B = \begin{bmatrix} e & f \\ g & h \end{bmatrix}$, and $C = \begin{bmatrix} w & x \\ y & z \end{bmatrix}$. By the definition of matrix addition and the Assoc. Prop. of Add.

$A + (B + C) = \begin{bmatrix} a & b \\ c & d \end{bmatrix} + \left(\begin{bmatrix} e & f \\ g & h \end{bmatrix} + \begin{bmatrix} w & x \\ y & z \end{bmatrix} \right)$

$\quad = \begin{bmatrix} a & b \\ c & d \end{bmatrix} + \begin{bmatrix} e+w & f+x \\ g+y & h+z \end{bmatrix}$

$\quad = \begin{bmatrix} a+(e+w) & b+(f+x) \\ c+(g+y) & d+(h+z) \end{bmatrix}$

$\quad = \begin{bmatrix} (a+e)+w & (b+f)+x \\ (c+g)+y & (d+h)+z \end{bmatrix}$

$\quad = \begin{bmatrix} (a+e) & (b+f) \\ (c+g) & (d+h) \end{bmatrix} + \begin{bmatrix} w & x \\ y & z \end{bmatrix}$

$\quad = \left(\begin{bmatrix} a & b \\ c & d \end{bmatrix} + \begin{bmatrix} e & f \\ g & h \end{bmatrix} \right) + \begin{bmatrix} w & x \\ y & z \end{bmatrix}$

$\quad = (A + B) + C$

Standardized Test Prep

33. B

34. I

35. B

36. [2] 440 pieces of luggage; since 3 standard deviations is $3 \cdot 20 = 60$ pieces of luggage, 3 standard deviations above the mean is $380 + 60 = 440$ pieces of luggage.

[1] incomplete explanation OR one computational error

Mixed Review

37. 68%

38. 97.5%

39. 47.5%

40. 2, −6

41. $\frac{2}{3}$, 2

42. $-\frac{1}{2}$, −6

43. 5, 0

44. $\begin{bmatrix} 9 & 15 \\ 6 & 24 \end{bmatrix}$

45. $\begin{bmatrix} -20 \\ 35 \end{bmatrix}$

Challenge

30. Find the sum of $E = \begin{bmatrix} 3 \\ 4 \\ 7 \end{bmatrix}$ and the additive inverse of $G = \begin{bmatrix} -2 \\ 0 \\ 5 \end{bmatrix}$.

31. Prove that matrix addition is commutative for 2×2 matrices.

32. Prove that matrix addition is associative for 2×2 matrices.

Standardized Test Prep

SAT/ACT

33. What is the sum $\begin{bmatrix} 5 & 7 & 3 \\ -1 & 0 & -4 \end{bmatrix} + \begin{bmatrix} -7 & 4 & 2 \\ 1 & -2 & -3 \end{bmatrix}$?

Ⓐ The matrices cannot be added.

Ⓑ $\begin{bmatrix} -2 & 11 & 5 \\ 0 & -2 & -7 \end{bmatrix}$ Ⓒ $\begin{bmatrix} 12 & 3 & 1 \\ -2 & 2 & -1 \end{bmatrix}$ Ⓓ $\begin{bmatrix} -35 & 28 & 6 \\ -1 & 0 & 12 \end{bmatrix}$

34. Which arithmetic sequence includes the term 27?

I. $a_1 = 7, a_n = a_{n-1} + 5$ II. $a_n = 3 + 4(n - 1)$ III. $a_n = 57 - 6n$

Ⓕ I only   Ⓖ I and II only   Ⓗ II and III only   Ⓘ I, II, and III

35. Which equation is graphed at the right?

Ⓐ $(x + 3)^2 + (y - 2)^2 = 25$

Ⓑ $(x - 2)^2 + (y + 3)^2 = 25$

Ⓒ $(x + 2)^2 + (y - 3)^2 = 25$

Ⓓ $(x - 3)^2 + (y + 2)^2 = 25$

Short Response

36. For a daily airline flight to Denver, the numbers of checked pieces of luggage are normally distributed with a mean of 380 and a standard deviation of 20. What number of checked pieces of luggage is 3 standard deviations above the mean?

Mixed Review

A set of data with a mean of 62 and a standard deviation of 5 is normally distributed. Find the percent of data within each interval. ◀ See Lesson 11-10.

37. from 57 to 67   **38.** greater than 52   **39.** from 62 to 72

Find the slope and y-intercept of each line. ◀ See Lesson 2-3.

40. $y = 2x - 6$ **41.** $3y = 6 + 2x$ **42.** $-x - 2y = 12$ **43.** $y = 5x$

Get Ready! To prepare for Lesson 12-2, do Exercises 44–45.

Find each sum. ◀ See Lesson 12-1.

44. $\begin{bmatrix} 3 & 5 \\ 2 & 8 \end{bmatrix} + \begin{bmatrix} 3 & 5 \\ 2 & 8 \end{bmatrix} + \begin{bmatrix} 3 & 5 \\ 2 & 8 \end{bmatrix}$

45. $\begin{bmatrix} -4 \\ 7 \end{bmatrix} + \begin{bmatrix} -4 \\ 7 \end{bmatrix} + \begin{bmatrix} -4 \\ 7 \end{bmatrix} + \begin{bmatrix} -4 \\ 7 \end{bmatrix} + \begin{bmatrix} -4 \\ 7 \end{bmatrix}$

Additional Instructional Support

Algebra 2 Companion

Students can use the **Algebra 2 Companion** worktext (4 pages) as you teach the lesson. Use the Companion to support

- New Vocabulary
- Key Concepts
- Got It for each Problem
- Lesson Check

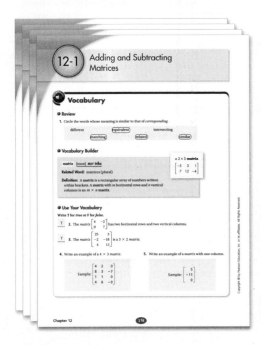

ELL Support

Focus on Communication Although few ideas are simple for every student to learn, the concepts presented in this lesson are fairly elementary.

Ask: Rows go across and columns go up and down. How many rows of desks are in the classroom? How many columns of desks are in the classroom?

Have students draw a rectangular matrix of seating positions in the classroom and label it with position numbers similar to the matrix in the Take Note box on p. 756. Make sure the positions are labeled with numbers in the order row-column.

Have students ask each other (or the whole group) questions about the positions on their matrix, such as,

- How many rows are in the matrix?
- Which student sits at position 23? (Note: say "23" as "two three" not "twenty-three.")
- At which position is [student's name] sitting?
- What are the dimensions of the matrix?

5 Assess & Remediate

Lesson Quiz

1. Given $A = \begin{bmatrix} 2 & -4 \\ 0 & 3 \end{bmatrix}$ and $B = \begin{bmatrix} 5 & 6 \\ 7 & 8 \end{bmatrix}$, what is $B - A$?

2. What is the sum of the matrices $\begin{bmatrix} 0 & 0 \\ 0 & 0 \end{bmatrix}$ and $\begin{bmatrix} 2 & -4 \\ -4 & 8 \end{bmatrix}$?

3. **Do you UNDERSTAND?** What values of x and y make the equation true?

$$\begin{bmatrix} 2x - 1 & 0 \\ -3y & 4 \end{bmatrix} = \begin{bmatrix} 1 & 0 \\ y + 2 & 4 \end{bmatrix}$$

ANSWERS TO LESSON QUIZ

1. $\begin{bmatrix} 3 & 10 \\ 7 & 5 \end{bmatrix}$

2. $\begin{bmatrix} 2 & -4 \\ -4 & 8 \end{bmatrix}$

3. $x = 1; y = -0.5$

PRESCRIPTION FOR REMEDIATION

Use the student work on the Lesson Quiz to prescribe a differentiated review assignment:

Points	Differentiated Remediation
0–1	Intervention
2	On-level
3	Extension

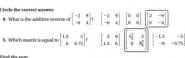

5 Assess & Remediate

Assign the Lesson Quiz. Appropriate intervention, practice, or enrichment is automatically generated based on student performance.

Differentiated Remediation

Intervention

- **Reteaching** (2 pages) Provides reteaching and practice exercises for the key lesson concepts. Use with struggling students or absent students.
- **English Language Learner Support** Helps students develop and reinforce mathematical vocabulary and key concepts.

All-in-One Resources/Online
Reteaching

All-in-One Resources/Online
English Language Learner Support

Differentiated Remediation *continued*

On-Level

- **Practice** (2 pages) Provides extra practice for each lesson. For simpler practice exercises, use the Form K Practice pages found in the All-in-One Teaching Resources and online.

- **Think About a Plan** Helps students develop specific problem-solving skills and strategies by providing scaffolded guiding questions.

- **Standardized Test Prep** Focuses on all major exercises, all major question types, and helps students prepare for the high-stakes assessments.

Extension

- **Enrichment** Provides students with interesting problems and activities that extend the concepts of the lesson.

- **Activities, Games, and Puzzles** Worksheets that can be used for concepts development, enrichment, and for fun!

Practice and Problem Solving Wkbk/ All-in-One Resources/Online
Practice page 1

12-1 Practice — Form G
Adding and Subtracting Matrices

(worksheet thumbnail)

Practice and Problem Solving Wkbk/ All-in-One Resources/Online
Practice page 2

12-1 Practice (continued) — Form G
Adding and Subtracting Matrices

(worksheet thumbnail)

All-in-One Resources/Online
Enrichment

12-1 Enrichment
Adding and Subtracting Matrices

(worksheet thumbnail)

Practice and Problem Solving Wkbk/ All-in-One Resources/Online
Think About a Plan

12-1 Think About a Plan
Adding and Subtracting Matrices

(worksheet thumbnail)

Practice and Problem Solving Wkbk/ All-in-One Resources/Online
Standardized Test Prep

12-1 Standardized Test Prep
Adding and Subtracting Matrices

(worksheet thumbnail)

Online Teacher Resource Center
Activities, Games, and Puzzles

12-1 Activity: Board With Matrices
Adding and Subtracting Matrices

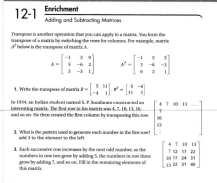

Concept Byte

For Use With Lesson 12-1

TECHNOLOGY

Working with Matrices

© **Content Standard**
N.VM.8 Add, subtract, and multiply matrices of appropriate dimensions.

You can use a graphing calculator to work with matrices. First you need to know how to enter a matrix into the calculator.

MATHEMATICAL PRACTICES

Example 1

Enter matrix $A = \begin{bmatrix} -3 & 4 \\ 7 & -5 \\ 0 & -2 \end{bmatrix}$ into your graphing calculator.

Select the **EDIT** option of the (matrix) feature to edit matrix **[A]**. Specify a 3×2 matrix by pressing **3** (enter) **2** (enter). Enter the matrix elements one row at a time, pressing (enter) after each element. Then use the (quit) feature to return to the main screen.

Example 2

Given $A = \begin{bmatrix} -3 & 4 \\ 7 & -5 \\ 0 & -2 \end{bmatrix}$ and $B = \begin{bmatrix} 10 & -7 \\ 4 & -3 \\ -12 & 11 \end{bmatrix}$, find $A + B$ and $A - B$.

Enter both matrices into the calculator. Use the **NAMES** option of the (matrix) feature to select each matrix. Press (enter) to see the sum. Repeat the corresponding steps to find the difference $A - B$.

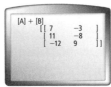

Exercises

Find each sum or difference.

1. $\begin{bmatrix} 0 & -3 \\ 5 & -7 \end{bmatrix} - \begin{bmatrix} -5 & 3 \\ 4 & 10 \end{bmatrix}$

2. $\begin{bmatrix} 3 & 5 & -7 \\ 0 & -2 & 0 \end{bmatrix} - \begin{bmatrix} -1 & 6 & 2 \\ -9 & 4 & 0 \end{bmatrix}$

3. $\begin{bmatrix} 3 \\ 5 \end{bmatrix} - \begin{bmatrix} -6 \\ 7 \end{bmatrix}$

4. $[3 \quad 5 \quad -8] + [-6 \quad 4 \quad 1]$

5. $\begin{bmatrix} 17 & 8 & 0 \\ 3 & -5 & 2 \end{bmatrix} - \begin{bmatrix} 4 & 6 & 5 \\ 2 & -2 & 9 \end{bmatrix}$

6. $[-9 \quad 6 \quad 4] + [-3 \quad 8 \quad 4]$

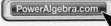

Answers

Concept Byte

1. $\begin{bmatrix} 5 & -6 \\ 1 & -17 \end{bmatrix}$

2. $\begin{bmatrix} 4 & -1 & -9 \\ 9 & -6 & 0 \end{bmatrix}$

3. $\begin{bmatrix} 9 \\ -2 \end{bmatrix}$

4. $[-3 \quad 9 \quad -7]$

5. $\begin{bmatrix} 13 & 2 & -5 \\ 1 & -3 & -7 \end{bmatrix}$

6. $[-12 \quad 14 \quad 8]$

Guided Instruction

PURPOSE To use a graphing calculator to work with matrices

PROCESS Students will
- enter and edit matrices in their graphing calculators.
- perform simple operations on matrices using a graphing calculator.

DISCUSS To enter the matrix correctly in Example 1, point out that on some graphing calculators the negative sign key is different from the subtraction key. This is the key used when entering numbers in the matrix.

The keystrokes to move from screen to screen and within a screen are not always apparent. Encourage students to try several times. If they get stuck, they can use the QUIT feature to return to the start screen and try again.

Make sure students enter [B] in the EDIT matrix menu when entering B in Example 2. They should not re-edit the matrix they entered in Example 1, although they should use similar steps.

Example 1

Q What do you think will happen if you add $A + A$?
[Answers will vary. Sample: $A + A$ might be a matrix of the same size but with each element doubled.]

Example 2

Q What do you think $A - B + (B - A)$ will equal? Check your answer on your calculator.
[$A - B + (B - A)$ should equal the zero matrix with 3 rows and 2 columns of zeros.]

© **Mathematical Practices** This Concept Byte supports students in becoming proficient in using appropriate tools, Mathematical Practice 5.

1 Interactive Learning

Solve It!

PURPOSE To use information from a table to solve a percentage problem

PROCESS Students may calculate the entire fat allowance for the family and the fat content of the cake and then divide the fat content of the cake by the total fat allowance to find the percentage.

FACILITATE

Q Do you need to know how much cake each person had? Explain. **[No; even if the pieces were not the same size, the total grams of fat of the consumed 500 g cake will remain the same.]**

Q What expression will calculate the total grams of fat in the cake? **[500 × 0.2]**

Q What expression will calculate the total grams of fat the family is allowed to consume? Explain. **[2 · 65 + 3 · 80; there are two parents who are each allowed 65 g and three children who are each allowed 80 g.]**

ANSWER See Solve It in Answers on next page.

CONNECT THE MATH In the Solve It, students multiply elements of the table by a number as a step to solve the problem. In the lesson, students will multiply elements of a matrix by a scalar.

2 Guided Instruction

Take Note

Q What algebraic property of real numbers does scalar multiplication resemble? **[Distributive Property]**

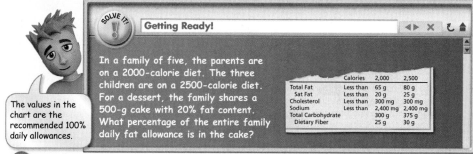

Content Standards

N.VM.6 Use matrices to represent and manipulate data . . .

N.VM.7 Multiply matrices by scalars to produce new matrices . . .

Also N.VM.8, N.VM.9

Objective To multiply matrices using scalar and matrix multiplication

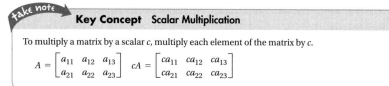

In the Solve It, you may have found the sum of products. Finding the sum of products is essential to matrix multiplication.

Essential Understanding The product of two matrices is a matrix. To find an element in the product matrix, you multiply the elements of a row from the first matrix by the corresponding elements of a column from the second matrix. Then add the products.

Before you learn how to multiply two matrices, however, you should learn a simpler type of multiplication. This type of multiplication allows you to scale, or resize, the elements of the matrix.

$$3\begin{bmatrix} 5 & -1 \\ 3 & 7 \end{bmatrix} = \begin{bmatrix} 3(5) & 3(-1) \\ 3(3) & 3(7) \end{bmatrix} = \begin{bmatrix} 15 & -3 \\ 9 & 21 \end{bmatrix}$$

The real number factor (such as 3 in the example) is a **scalar**. Multiplication of a matrix A by a scalar c is **scalar multiplication**. To find the resulting matrix cA, you multiply each element of A by c.

Key Concept Scalar Multiplication

To multiply a matrix by a scalar c, multiply each element of the matrix by c.

$$A = \begin{bmatrix} a_{11} & a_{12} & a_{13} \\ a_{21} & a_{22} & a_{23} \end{bmatrix} \quad cA = \begin{bmatrix} ca_{11} & ca_{12} & ca_{13} \\ ca_{21} & ca_{22} & ca_{23} \end{bmatrix}$$

Lesson Vocabulary
- scalar
- scalar multiplication

BIG idea Data Representation

ESSENTIAL UNDERSTANDINGS

- To multiply a matrix by a scalar, multiply each element of the matrix by the scalar.
- If A is an $m \times n$ matrix, and B is an $n \times p$ matrix, then AB is an $m \times p$ matrix.

Math Background

It is important to clearly differentiate between the two different kinds of multiplication with matrices.

Scalar multiplication is the product of a constant (called a scalar) and a matrix. Each element of the matrix is multiplied by the scalar. It can be thought of as changing the scale of the matrix.

- Scalar multiplication does not change the dimensions of the matrix. The product of a scalar and an $m \times n$ matrix is an $m \times n$ matrix.
- The product of a matrix and a scalar always exists.
- Scalar multiplication is commutative.

Matrix multiplication is the product of two matrices. To find element c_{ij}, each element in the ith row of the first matrix is multiplied by the corresponding element in the jth row of the second matrix. The sum of the products is c_{ij}.

- Matrix multiplication changes the dimensions of non-square matrices. The product of an $m \times n$ matrix by an $n \times p$ matrix is an $m \times p$ matrix.
- The product only exists if the number of columns of the first matrix equals the number of rows of the second.
- Therefore, matrix multiplication is not commutative.

Mathematical Practices

Look for and express regularity in repeated reasoning. Students will look for a general method for multiplying two matrices. They will also check to see if the resulting matrix makes sense.

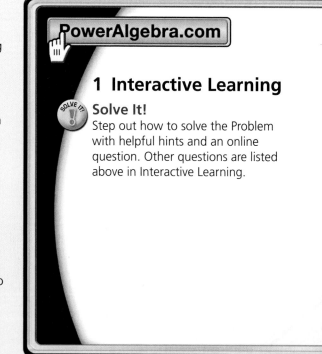

PowerAlgebra.com

1 Interactive Learning

Solve It!

Step out how to solve the Problem with helpful hints and an online question. Other questions are listed above in Interactive Learning.

Problem 1 Using Scalar Products

Think

What operation should you do first?
You should first multiply by the scalars, 4 and 3.

If $A = \begin{bmatrix} 2 & 8 & -3 \\ -1 & 5 & 2 \end{bmatrix}$ and $B = \begin{bmatrix} -1 & 0 & 5 \\ 0 & 3 & -2 \end{bmatrix}$, what is $4A + 3B$?

$$4A + 3B = 4\begin{bmatrix} 2 & 8 & -3 \\ -1 & 5 & 2 \end{bmatrix} + 3\begin{bmatrix} -1 & 0 & 5 \\ 0 & 3 & -2 \end{bmatrix}$$

$$= \begin{bmatrix} 8 & 32 & -12 \\ -4 & 20 & 8 \end{bmatrix} + \begin{bmatrix} -3 & 0 & 15 \\ 0 & 9 & -6 \end{bmatrix}$$

$$= \begin{bmatrix} 5 & 32 & 3 \\ -4 & 29 & 2 \end{bmatrix}$$

Got It? **1.** Using matrices A and B from Problem 1, what is $3A - 2B$?

 Properties Scalar Multiplication

If A and B are $m \times n$ matrices, c and d are scalars, and O is the $m \times n$ zero matrix, then

Example	Property
cA is an $m \times n$ matrix	**Closure Property**
$(cd)A = c(dA)$	**Associative Property of Multiplication**
$c(A + B) = cA + cB$ $(c + d)A = cA + dA$	**Distributive Properties**
$1 \cdot A = A$	**Multiplicative Identity Property**
$0 \cdot A = O$ and $cO = O$	**Multiplicative Properties of Zero**

 Problem 2 Solving a Matrix Equation With Scalars

Think

Where have you seen problems that look like this before?
You saw problems like this when you solved one variable equations like $2x + 3(5) = 20$.

What is the solution of $2X + 3\begin{bmatrix} 2 & -1 \\ 3 & 4 \end{bmatrix} = \begin{bmatrix} 8 & 5 \\ 11 & 0 \end{bmatrix}$?

$$2X + \begin{bmatrix} 6 & -3 \\ 9 & 12 \end{bmatrix} = \begin{bmatrix} 8 & 5 \\ 11 & 0 \end{bmatrix} \qquad \text{Multiply by the scalar 3.}$$

$$2X = \begin{bmatrix} 8 & 5 \\ 11 & 0 \end{bmatrix} - \begin{bmatrix} 6 & -3 \\ 9 & 12 \end{bmatrix} \qquad \text{Subtract } \begin{bmatrix} 6 & -3 \\ 9 & 12 \end{bmatrix} \text{ from each side.}$$

$$2X = \begin{bmatrix} 2 & 8 \\ 2 & -12 \end{bmatrix} \qquad \text{Simplify.}$$

$$X = \begin{bmatrix} 1 & 4 \\ 1 & -6 \end{bmatrix} \qquad \text{Multiply each side by } \tfrac{1}{2} \text{ and simplify.}$$

Got It? **2.** What is the solution of $3X - 2\begin{bmatrix} -1 & 5 \\ 7 & 0 \end{bmatrix} = \begin{bmatrix} 17 & -13 \\ -7 & 0 \end{bmatrix}$?

Problem 1

Q Do you have to follow the order of operations with matrices? Explain using Problem 1. **[Yes; in Problem 1, you have to multiply before adding.]**

Got It?

Q Does it matter whether you multiply B by 2 or -2? Explain. **[No; but if you multiply B by 2, you will have to subtract B from A, and if you multiply B by -2, you will have to add A and B.]**

Take Note   EXTENSION

Q Does the Commutative Property hold for scalar multiplication? Explain. **[Yes; You are simply multiplying elements that are real numbers by a real number, so order does not matter.]**

Problem 2

Q Are the steps you use to solve for matrix X any different than the steps you used when solving simple equations of one variable? Explain. **[No; you still use the inverse operations and order of operations to solve for the unknown variable.]**

Got It?

Q What steps should you take and in what order to solve the equation? **[Sample: Multiply the matrix by the scalar and then use the inverse operation to isolate $3X$. Then divide each side by 3 to solve for matrix X.]**

Q What will be the dimensions of the solution for matrix X? **[2×2]**

---

2 Guided Instruction

Each Problem is worked out and supported online.

Problem 1
Using Scalar Products

Problem 2
Solving a Matrix Equation With Scalars
Animated

Problem 3
Multiplying Matrices
Animated

Problem 4
Applying Matrix Multiplication
Animated

Problem 5
Determining Whether Product Matrices Exist

Support in Algebra 2 Companion
• Vocabulary
• Key Concepts
• Got It?

Answers

Solve It!
27%; the cake contains $(0.2)(500 \text{ g}) = 100 \text{ g}$ of fat. Altogether, the family's maximum daily allowance of fat is $2(65) + 3(80) = 370 \text{ g}$. The cake contains $\frac{100}{370} = 27\%$ of the family's daily allowance of fat.

Got It?

1. $\begin{bmatrix} 8 & 24 & -19 \\ -3 & 9 & 10 \end{bmatrix}$

2. $\begin{bmatrix} 5 & -1 \\ \frac{7}{3} & 0 \end{bmatrix}$

Take Note

Q Where in the final product of two matrices would the result of multiplying row two by column one be located? **[in row two, column one]**

Problem 3

Q Why do the number of elements in each row of the first matrix have to equal the number of elements in each column of the second matrix in order to multiply the two matrices? **[each row element of the first matrix must be multiplied by a corresponding column element of the second matrix]**

Q Is it possible for two matrices A and B to exist so that AB has an answer and BA does not? Explain. **[Yes; if the number of elements in each row of matrix A equals the number of elements in each column of matrix B, but the number of elements in each row of matrix B does not equal the number of elements in each column of matrix A. For example, A is 2×3 and B is 3×3.]**

Got It?

Q What would have to be true about AB and BA for multiplication of A and B to be commutative? **[AB would have to equal BA.]**

EXTENSION

Q If matrices A and B were exactly the same and could be multiplied, would $AB = BA$? Explain. **[Yes; the dimensions would allow for multiplication, and the elements would be identical in both products.]**

The product of two matrices is a matrix. To find an element in the product matrix, multiply the elements of a row from the first matrix by the corresponding elements of a column from the second matrix. Then add the products.

   Key Concept   Matrix Multiplication

To find element c_{ij} of the product matrix AB, multiply each element in the ith row of A by the corresponding element in the jth column of B. Then add the products.

$$AB = \begin{bmatrix} a_{11} & a_{12} \\ a_{21} & a_{22} \end{bmatrix} \begin{bmatrix} b_{11} & b_{12} \\ b_{21} & b_{22} \end{bmatrix} = \begin{bmatrix} a_{11}b_{11} + a_{12}b_{21} & a_{11}b_{12} + a_{12}b_{22} \\ a_{21}b_{11} + a_{22}b_{21} & a_{21}b_{12} + a_{22}b_{22} \end{bmatrix}$$

 Problem 3 **Multiplying Matrices**

If $A = \begin{bmatrix} 2 & 1 \\ -3 & 0 \end{bmatrix}$ and $B = \begin{bmatrix} -1 & 3 \\ 0 & 4 \end{bmatrix}$, what is AB?

Think

What relationship must exist between the numbers of elements in a row of A and a column of B?
They must be equal.

Step 1 Multiply the elements in the first row of A by the elements in the first column of B. Add the products and place the sum in the first row, first column of AB.

$$\begin{bmatrix} 2 & 1 \\ -3 & 0 \end{bmatrix} \begin{bmatrix} -1 & 3 \\ 0 & 4 \end{bmatrix} = \begin{bmatrix} -2 & \_ \\ \_ & \_ \end{bmatrix} \qquad 2(-1) + 1(0) = -2$$

Step 2 Multiply the elements in the first row of A by the elements in the second column of B. Add the products and place the sum in the first row, second column of AB.

$$\begin{bmatrix} 2 & 1 \\ -3 & 0 \end{bmatrix} \begin{bmatrix} -1 & 3 \\ 0 & 4 \end{bmatrix} = \begin{bmatrix} -2 & 10 \\ \_ & \_ \end{bmatrix} \qquad 2(3) + 1(4) = 10$$

Repeat Steps 1 and 2 with the second row of A to fill in row two of the product matrix.

Step 3 $\begin{bmatrix} 2 & 1 \\ -3 & 0 \end{bmatrix} \begin{bmatrix} -1 & 3 \\ 0 & 4 \end{bmatrix} = \begin{bmatrix} -2 & 10 \\ 3 & \_ \end{bmatrix} \qquad (-3)(-1) + 0(0) = 3$

Step 4 $\begin{bmatrix} 2 & 1 \\ -3 & 0 \end{bmatrix} \begin{bmatrix} -1 & 3 \\ 0 & 4 \end{bmatrix} = \begin{bmatrix} -2 & 10 \\ 3 & -9 \end{bmatrix} \qquad (-3)(3) + 0(4) = -9$

The product of $\begin{bmatrix} 2 & 1 \\ -3 & 0 \end{bmatrix}$ and $\begin{bmatrix} -1 & 3 \\ 0 & 4 \end{bmatrix}$ is $\begin{bmatrix} -2 & 10 \\ 3 & -9 \end{bmatrix}$.

 Got It? 3. If $A = \begin{bmatrix} 2 & -1 \\ 3 & 4 \end{bmatrix}$ and $B = \begin{bmatrix} -3 & 1 \\ 0 & 2 \end{bmatrix}$, what are the following products?
     a. AB **b.** BA
     c. Reasoning Is matrix multiplication commutative? Explain.

Additional Problems

1. If $A = \begin{bmatrix} 4 & -3 \\ 1 & 2 \end{bmatrix}$ and $B = \begin{bmatrix} 7 & 3 \\ -2 & -4 \end{bmatrix}$, what is $3A - B$?

ANSWER $\begin{bmatrix} 5 & -12 \\ 5 & 10 \end{bmatrix}$

2. What is the solution of $-2\begin{bmatrix} 2 & 3 \\ 1 & 0 \end{bmatrix} + 2T = \begin{bmatrix} -2 & -14 \\ -2 & 6 \end{bmatrix}$?

ANSWER $\begin{bmatrix} 1 & -4 \\ 0 & 3 \end{bmatrix}$

3. If $V = \begin{bmatrix} -4 & 0 \\ 3 & 5 \end{bmatrix}$ and $W = \begin{bmatrix} 2 & 2 \\ -1 & 3 \end{bmatrix}$, what is VW?

ANSWER $\begin{bmatrix} -8 & -8 \\ 1 & 21 \end{bmatrix}$

4. A library has three printers. The cost of printing from printer A is 3 cents per page, from printer B is 6 cents per page, and from printer C is 14 cents per page. During October and November, the librarian recorded the number of pages printed on each printer, as shown in the table. Using matrix multiplication, what was the monthly cost of operating the printers for October and November?

	Oct	Nov
Printer A	584	598
Printer B	549	610
Printer C	159	185

ANSWER October: $72.72
November: $80.44

5. Does either product AB or BA exist?
$A = \begin{bmatrix} -5 & 0 \\ 3 & -2 \end{bmatrix}$
$B = \begin{bmatrix} -2 & 1 & -1 \\ 4 & 2 & 5 \end{bmatrix}$

ANSWER AB is a 2×3 matrix; BA does not exist.

Answers

Got It? (continued)

3. a. $\begin{bmatrix} -6 & 0 \\ -9 & 11 \end{bmatrix}$

b. $\begin{bmatrix} -3 & 7 \\ 6 & 8 \end{bmatrix}$

c. No; explanations may vary. Sample: For the matrices in parts (a) and (b), $AB = \begin{bmatrix} -6 & 0 \\ -9 & 11 \end{bmatrix}$ and $BA = \begin{bmatrix} -3 & 7 \\ 6 & 8 \end{bmatrix}$, so $AB \neq BA$.

Problem 4 Applying Matrix Multiplication

Sports In 1966, Washington and New York (Giants) played the highest scoring game in National Football League history. The table summarizes the scoring. A touchdown (TD) is worth 6 points, a field goal (FG) is worth 3 points, a safety (S) is worth 2 points, and a point after touchdown (PAT) is worth 1 point. Using matrix multiplication, what was the final score?

	TD	FG	S	PAT
WASHINGTON	10	1	0	9
NEW YORK	6	0	0	5

Know
- The number of each type of score
- The point value of each score

Need
The scoring summary and point values as matrices

Plan
Multiply the matrices to find each team's final score.

Think

What is the meaning of each number in matrix *P*?
They are the point values for each type of score.

Step 1 Enter the information in matrices.

$$S = \begin{bmatrix} 10 & 1 & 0 & 9 \\ 6 & 0 & 0 & 5 \end{bmatrix} \qquad P = \begin{bmatrix} 6 \\ 3 \\ 2 \\ 1 \end{bmatrix}$$

Step 2 Use matrix multiplication. The final score is the product *SP*.

$$SP = \begin{bmatrix} 10 & 1 & 0 & 9 \\ 6 & 0 & 0 & 5 \end{bmatrix} \begin{bmatrix} 6 \\ 3 \\ 2 \\ 1 \end{bmatrix}$$

$$= \begin{bmatrix} 10(6) + 1(3) + 0(2) + 9(1) \\ 6(6) + 0(3) + 0(2) + 5(1) \end{bmatrix} = \begin{bmatrix} 72 \\ 41 \end{bmatrix}$$

Step 3 Interpret the product matrix.

The first row of *SP* shows scoring for Washington, so the final score was Washington 72, New York 41.

Got It? **4.** There are three ways to score in a basketball game: three-point field goals, two-point field goals, and one-point free throws. In 1994, suppose a high school player scored 36 two-point field goals and 28 free throws. In 2006, suppose a high school player scored 7 three-point field goals, 21 two-point field goals, and 18 free throws. Using matrix multiplication, how many points did each player score?

You can multiply two matrices *A* and *B* only if the number of columns of *A* is equal to the number of rows of *B*.

Problem 4

Q In matrix *S*, how would you label each row? How would you label each row of the product matrix? **[Both would be labeled with the team names.]**

Q In matrix *P*, how would you label the column? How would you label the column of the product matrix? **[Both would be labeled with point values.]**

Q How would you label the columns of matrix *S* and the rows of matrix *P*? **[Both would be labeled with score type.]**

Got It?

Q What matrix would represent the total count of types of scores for the 1994 and 2006 players?

$$\begin{bmatrix} 0 & 36 & 28 \\ 7 & 21 & 18 \end{bmatrix}$$

Q What matrix would represent the point values for each type of score? $\begin{bmatrix} 3 \\ 2 \\ 1 \end{bmatrix}$

Q What will be the dimensions of the matrix product? **[2 × 1]**

4. player from 1994: 100 pts., player from 2006: 81 pts.

Take Note

Q Can all matrices be squared? Explain. **[No; only square matrices can be squared, because for the inside dimensions to match, the number of rows must equal the number of columns.]**

Problem 5

Q If the dimensions of two matrices are 2 × 4 and 4 × 3, can they be multiplied? In what order? What would the dimensions of the product matrix be? **[Yes; you can only multiply the 2 × 4 matrix times the 4 × 3 matrix to get a 2 × 3 matrix.]**

Q Is it possible for two matrices A and B of different dimensions to be multiplied to get products for AB and BA? What would their dimensions be? **[yes; $n \times m$ and $m \times n$]**

Got It?

Q What are the dimensions of matrices A, B, and C? **[Matrix A: 2 × 2; matrix B: 1 × 2; matrix C: 2 × 3]**

Q Where the product exists, what would be the dimensions of the product matrix? **[5b: 1 × 2; 5c: 2 × 3; 5e: 1 × 3]**

Take Note

Q Why must the matrices be square matrices ($n \times n$) for these properties to be true? **[so that multiplication is defined for the three matrices no matter what order you multiply them and so that addition is defined no matter how you add the matrices or products]**

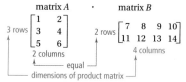

Property Dimensions of a Product Matrix

If A is an $m \times n$ matrix and B is an $n \times p$ matrix, then the product matrix AB is an $m \times p$ matrix.

matrix A $\cdot$ matrix B

$$3 \text{ rows} \begin{bmatrix} 1 & 2 \\ 3 & 4 \\ 5 & 6 \end{bmatrix} \qquad 2 \text{ rows} \begin{bmatrix} 7 & 8 & 9 & 10 \\ 11 & 12 & 13 & 14 \end{bmatrix}$$

2 columns   4 columns

equal

dimensions of product matrix

Product matrix AB is a 3 × 4 matrix.

Ⓒ Problem 5 Determining Whether Product Matrices Exist

Does either product AB or BA exist?

$$A = \begin{bmatrix} -2 & 1 \\ 3 & -2 \\ 0 & 1 \end{bmatrix} \qquad B = \begin{bmatrix} -1 & 0 & 2 & 1 \\ 2 & 0 & 0 & 3 \end{bmatrix}$$

AB BA

$(3 \times 2)(2 \times 4) \rightarrow 3 \times 4$ product matrix $(2 \times 4)(3 \times 2) \rightarrow$ no product

equal   Product AB exists.   not equal

Think
How can you tell if a product matrix exists without computing it? Compare the dimensions of the matrices.

✓ **Got It? 5.** Do the following products exist?

$$A = \begin{bmatrix} 1 & 4 \\ -3 & 5 \end{bmatrix} \qquad B = \begin{bmatrix} -1 & 1 \end{bmatrix} \qquad C = \begin{bmatrix} 4 & 2 & 0 \\ 1 & 3 & 5 \end{bmatrix}$$

a. AB **b.** BA **c.** AC **d.** CA **e.** BC

Matrix multiplication of square ($n \times n$) matrices has some of the properties of real number multiplication.

Properties Matrix Multiplication

If A, B, and C are $n \times n$ matrices, and O is the $n \times n$ zero matrix, then

Example	Property
AB is an $n \times n$ matrix	Closure Property
$(AB)C = A(BC)$	Associative Property of Multiplication
$A(B + C) = AB + AC$ $(B + C)A = BA + CA$	Distributive Property
$OA = AO = O$	Multiplicative Property of Zero

Answers

Got It? (continued)

5. a. no

b. yes

c. yes

d. no

e. yes

Lesson Check

Do you know HOW?

Let $A = \begin{bmatrix} 3 & -1 \\ 2 & 0 \end{bmatrix}$ and $B = \begin{bmatrix} 1 & 3 \\ -2 & 2 \end{bmatrix}$.

Find each of the following.

1. $2A$

2. $3B - 2A$

3. AB

4. BA

Do you UNDERSTAND?

5. Vocabulary Which type of multiplication, *scalar* or *matrix*, can help you with a repeated matrix addition problem? Explain.

6. Error Analysis Your friend says there is a right order and a wrong order when multiplying A (a 2×4 matrix) and B (a 3×6 matrix). Explain your friend's error.

Practice and Problem-Solving Exercises

Practice Use matrices A, B, C, and D. Find each product, sum, or difference.   ◀ **See Problem 1.**

$$A = \begin{bmatrix} 3 & 4 \\ 6 & -2 \\ 1 & 0 \end{bmatrix} \qquad B = \begin{bmatrix} -3 & 1 \\ 2 & -4 \\ -1 & 5 \end{bmatrix} \qquad C = \begin{bmatrix} 1 & 2 \\ -3 & 1 \end{bmatrix} \qquad D = \begin{bmatrix} 5 & 1 \\ 0 & 2 \end{bmatrix}$$

7. $3A$

8. $4B$

9. $-3C$

10. $-D$

11. $A - 2B$

12. $3A + 2B$

13. $4C + 3D$

14. $2A - 5B$

Solve each matrix equation. Check your answers.   ◀ **See Problem 2.**

15. $3\begin{bmatrix} 2 & 0 \\ -1 & 5 \end{bmatrix} - 2X = \begin{bmatrix} -10 & 5 \\ 0 & 17 \end{bmatrix}$

16. $4X + \begin{bmatrix} 1 & 3 \\ -7 & 9 \end{bmatrix} = \begin{bmatrix} -3 & 11 \\ 5 & -7 \end{bmatrix}$

17. $\frac{1}{2}X + \begin{bmatrix} 4 & -3 \\ 12 & 1 \end{bmatrix} = \begin{bmatrix} 2 & 1 \\ 1 & 2 \end{bmatrix}$

18. $5X - \begin{bmatrix} 1.5 & -3.6 \\ -0.3 & 2.8 \end{bmatrix} = \begin{bmatrix} 0.2 & 1.3 \\ -5.6 & 1.7 \end{bmatrix}$

Find each product.   ◀ **See Problem 3.**

19. $\begin{bmatrix} -3 & 4 \\ 5 & 2 \end{bmatrix}\begin{bmatrix} 1 & 0 \\ 2 & -3 \end{bmatrix}$

20. $\begin{bmatrix} 1 & 0 \\ 2 & -3 \end{bmatrix}\begin{bmatrix} -3 & 4 \\ 5 & 2 \end{bmatrix}$

21. $\begin{bmatrix} 0 & 2 \\ -4 & 0 \end{bmatrix}\begin{bmatrix} 0 & 2 \\ -4 & 0 \end{bmatrix}$

22. $\begin{bmatrix} -3 & 5 \end{bmatrix}\begin{bmatrix} -3 \\ 5 \end{bmatrix}$

23. $\begin{bmatrix} -3 & 5 \end{bmatrix}\begin{bmatrix} -3 & 0 \\ 5 & 0 \end{bmatrix}$

24. $\begin{bmatrix} -3 & 5 \end{bmatrix}\begin{bmatrix} 0 & -3 \\ 0 & 5 \end{bmatrix}$

25. $\begin{bmatrix} 0 & -3 \\ 0 & 5 \end{bmatrix}\begin{bmatrix} -3 & 0 \\ 5 & 0 \end{bmatrix}$

26. $\begin{bmatrix} 1 & 0 \\ -1 & -5 \\ 0 & 3 \end{bmatrix}\begin{bmatrix} -1 & 0 \\ 0 & -1 \end{bmatrix}$

27. $\begin{bmatrix} -1 & 3 & -3 \\ 2 & -2 & 1 \end{bmatrix}\begin{bmatrix} 5 \\ 4 \\ 3 \end{bmatrix}$

28. Business A florist makes three special floral arrangements. One uses three lilies.   ◀ **See Problem 4.**
The second uses three lilies and four carnations. The third uses four daisies and three carnations. Lilies cost \$2.15 each, carnations cost \$.90 each, and daisies cost \$1.30 each.
  a. Write a matrix to show the number of each type of flower in each arrangement.
  b. Write a matrix to show the cost of each type of flower.
  c. Find the matrix showing the cost of each floral arrangement.

---

3 Lesson Check

Do you know HOW?

- If students have difficulty evaluating Exercises 1 and 2, remind them that scalar multiplication means they have to multiply every element of the matrix by the scalar.
- If students think that Exercises 3 and 4 are the same problem, remind them that multiplication of matrices is not commutative.

Do you UNDERSTAND?

- In Exercise 5, if students have difficulty determining which is more appropriate to do repeated matrix addition, ask them what expression they would use to add five 3's.
- If students have difficulty explaining the error in Exercise 6, ask them to write out both possibilities and compare the inside dimensions.

Close

Q How do you multiply a matrix by a scalar? **[Multiply each element of the matrix by the scalar.]**

Q When can you multiply two matrices, and how? **[If the number of columns of the first matrix equals the number of rows of the second matrix, multiply the elements of each row of the first matrix by the corresponding elements of each of the columns of the second matrix, add the results, and place the new element in the corresponding row and column of the product matrix.]**

Lesson Check

1. $\begin{bmatrix} 6 & -2 \\ 4 & 0 \end{bmatrix}$

2. $\begin{bmatrix} -3 & 11 \\ -10 & 6 \end{bmatrix}$

3. $\begin{bmatrix} 5 & 7 \\ 2 & 6 \end{bmatrix}$

4. $\begin{bmatrix} 9 & -1 \\ -2 & 2 \end{bmatrix}$

5. Scalar; repeated matrix addition is repeated addition of each element of the matrix, which is the same as scalar multiplication of the matrix.

6. The product of two matrices A and B exists only if the number of columns of A is equal to the number of rows of B. Since A is a 2×4 matrix with 4 columns and B is a 3×6 matrix with 3 rows and $4 \neq 3$, the product AB does not exist. Likewise, since $6 \neq 2$, the product BA does not exist.

Practice and Problem-Solving Exercises

7. $\begin{bmatrix} 9 & 12 \\ 18 & -6 \\ 3 & 0 \end{bmatrix}$

8. $\begin{bmatrix} -12 & 4 \\ 8 & -16 \\ -4 & 20 \end{bmatrix}$

9. $\begin{bmatrix} -3 & -6 \\ 9 & -3 \end{bmatrix}$

10. $\begin{bmatrix} -5 & -1 \\ 0 & -2 \end{bmatrix}$

11. $\begin{bmatrix} 9 & 2 \\ 2 & 6 \\ 3 & -10 \end{bmatrix}$

12. $\begin{bmatrix} 3 & 14 \\ 22 & -14 \\ 1 & 10 \end{bmatrix}$

13. $\begin{bmatrix} 19 & 11 \\ -12 & 10 \end{bmatrix}$

14. $\begin{bmatrix} 21 & 3 \\ 2 & 16 \\ 7 & -25 \end{bmatrix}$

15. $\begin{bmatrix} 8 & -2.5 \\ -1.5 & -1 \end{bmatrix}$

16. $\begin{bmatrix} -1 & 2 \\ 3 & -4 \end{bmatrix}$

17. $\begin{bmatrix} -4 & 8 \\ -22 & 2 \end{bmatrix}$

18. $\begin{bmatrix} 0.34 & -0.46 \\ -1.18 & 0.9 \end{bmatrix}$

19. $\begin{bmatrix} 5 & -12 \\ 9 & -6 \end{bmatrix}$

20. $\begin{bmatrix} -3 & 4 \\ -21 & 2 \end{bmatrix}$

21. $\begin{bmatrix} -8 & 0 \\ 0 & -8 \end{bmatrix}$

22. $\begin{bmatrix} 34 \end{bmatrix}$

23. $\begin{bmatrix} 34 & 0 \end{bmatrix}$

24. $\begin{bmatrix} 0 & 34 \end{bmatrix}$

25. $\begin{bmatrix} -15 & 0 \\ 25 & 0 \end{bmatrix}$

26. $\begin{bmatrix} -1 & 0 \\ 1 & 5 \\ 0 & -3 \end{bmatrix}$

27–28. See next page.

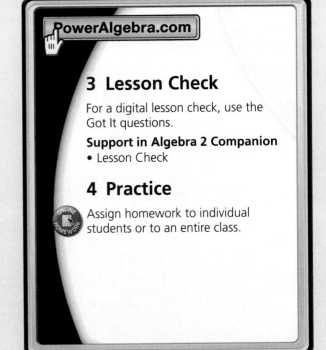

PowerAlgebra.com

3 Lesson Check

For a digital lesson check, use the Got It questions.

Support in Algebra 2 Companion
- Lesson Check

4 Practice

Assign homework to individual students or to an entire class.

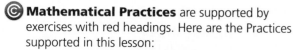

4 Practice

ASSIGNMENT GUIDE

Basic: 7–36, 44

Average: 7–33 odd, 34–44

Advanced: 7–33 odd, 34–48

Standardized Test Prep: 49–53

Mixed Review: 54–57

Ⓒ **Mathematical Practices** are supported by exercises with red headings. Here are the Practices supported in this lesson:

MP 1: Make Sense of Problems Ex. 34

MP 2: Reason Abstractly Ex. 5

MP 3: Communicate Ex. 44

MP 3: Critique the Reasoning of Others Ex. 6

Applications exercises have blue headings. Exercise 35 supports MP 4: Model.

EXERCISE 35: Use the Think About a Plan worksheet in the **Practice and Problem Solving Workbook** (also available in the Teaching Resources in print and online) to further support students' development in becoming independent learners.

HOMEWORK QUICK CHECK

To check students' understanding of key skills and concepts, go over Exercises 15, 19, 34, 35, and 44.

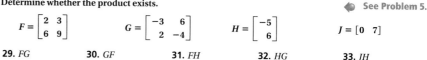

Determine whether the product exists.

◄ See Problem 5.

$$F = \begin{bmatrix} 2 & 3 \\ 6 & 9 \end{bmatrix} \qquad G = \begin{bmatrix} -3 & 6 \\ 2 & -4 \end{bmatrix} \qquad H = \begin{bmatrix} -5 \\ 6 \end{bmatrix} \qquad J = \begin{bmatrix} 0 & 7 \end{bmatrix}$$

29. *FG*   **30.** *GF*   **31.** *FH*   **32.** *HG*   **33.** *JH*

Ⓑ **Apply**

Ⓒ **34. Think About a Plan** A hardware store chain sells hammers for $3, flashlights for $5, and lanterns for $7. The store manager tracks the daily purchases at three of the chain's stores in a 3 × 3 matrix. What is the total gross revenue from the flashlights sold at all three stores?

Number of Items Sold

	Store A	Store B	Store C
Hammers	10	9	8
Flashlights	3	14	6
Lanterns	2	5	7

- How can you use matrix multiplication to solve this problem?
- What does the product matrix represent?

35. Sports Two teams are competing in a two-team track meet. Points for individual events are awarded as follows: 5 points for first place, 3 points for second place, and 1 point for third place. Points for team relays are awarded as follows: 5 points for first place and no points for second place.

a. Use matrix operations to determine the score in the track meet.

Team	Individual Events			Relays	
	First	Second	Third	First	Second
West River	8	5	2	8	5
River's Edge	6	9	12	6	9

b. Who would win if the scoring was changed to 5 points for first place, 2 points for second place, and 1 point for third place in each individual event and 5 points for first place and 0 points for second place in a relay?

For Exercises 36–43, use matrices D, E, and F. Perform the indicated operations if they are defined. If an operation is not defined, label it *undefined*.

$$D = \begin{bmatrix} 1 & 2 & -1 \\ 0 & 3 & 1 \\ 2 & -1 & -2 \end{bmatrix} \qquad E = \begin{bmatrix} 2 & -5 & 0 \\ 1 & 0 & -2 \\ 3 & 1 & 1 \end{bmatrix} \qquad F = \begin{bmatrix} -3 & 2 \\ -5 & 1 \\ 2 & 4 \end{bmatrix}$$

36. *DE*   **37.** $-3F$ **38.** $(DE)F$ **39.** $D(EF)$

40. $D - 2E$ **41.** $(E - D)F$ **42.** $(DD)E$ **43.** $(2D)(3F)$

Ⓒ **44. Writing** Suppose *A* is a 2 × 3 matrix and *B* is a 3 × 2 matrix with elements not all being equal. Are *AB* and *BA* equal? Explain your reasoning. Include examples.

Answers

Practice and Problem-Solving Exercises (continued)

27. $\begin{bmatrix} -2 \\ 5 \end{bmatrix}$

28. a.

	Lilies	Carnations	Daisies
Arrangement 1	3	0	0
Arrangement 2	3	4	0
Arrangement 3	0	3	4

b.

	Cost
Lilies	$2.15
Carnations	$0.90
Daisies	$1.30

c.

	Cost
Arrangement 1	$6.45
Arrangement 2	$10.05
Arrangement 3	$7.90

29. yes

30. yes

31. yes

32. no

33. yes

34. $115

35. a. River's Edge: 99 pts.; West River: 97 pts.

b. West River

36. $\begin{bmatrix} 1 & -6 & -5 \\ 6 & 1 & -5 \\ -3 & -12 & 0 \end{bmatrix}$

37. $\begin{bmatrix} 9 & -6 \\ 15 & -3 \\ -6 & -12 \end{bmatrix}$

38. $\begin{bmatrix} 17 & -24 \\ -33 & -7 \\ 69 & -18 \end{bmatrix}$

39. $\begin{bmatrix} 17 & -24 \\ -33 & -7 \\ 69 & -18 \end{bmatrix}$

40. $\begin{bmatrix} -3 & 12 & -1 \\ -2 & 3 & 5 \\ -4 & -3 & -4 \end{bmatrix}$

41. $\begin{bmatrix} 34 & -1 \\ 6 & -13 \\ -7 & 16 \end{bmatrix}$

42. $\begin{bmatrix} 16 & 8 & -15 \\ 15 & -9 & -15 \\ 2 & 11 & -5 \end{bmatrix}$

43. $\begin{bmatrix} -90 & 0 \\ -78 & 42 \\ -30 & -30 \end{bmatrix}$

44. No; *AB* will be a 2 × 2 matrix, *BA* will be a 3 × 3 matrix, and equal matrices must have the same dimensions. Answers may vary. Sample:

Let *A* be the matrix $\begin{bmatrix} 0 & 1 & 2 \\ 3 & 0 & 0 \end{bmatrix}$, and let *B* be the matrix $\begin{bmatrix} 1 & 0 \\ 2 & 4 \\ 3 & 1 \end{bmatrix}$.

Then $AB = \begin{bmatrix} 8 & 6 \\ 3 & 0 \end{bmatrix}$ and

$BA = \begin{bmatrix} 0 & 1 & 2 \\ 12 & 2 & 4 \\ 3 & 3 & 6 \end{bmatrix}$.

For Exercises 45–48, use matrices P, Q, R, S, and I. Determine whether the two expressions in each pair are equal.

$$P = \begin{bmatrix} 3 & 4 \\ 1 & 2 \end{bmatrix} \qquad Q = \begin{bmatrix} 1 & 0 \\ 3 & -2 \end{bmatrix} \qquad R = \begin{bmatrix} 1 & 4 \\ -2 & 1 \end{bmatrix} \qquad S = \begin{bmatrix} 0 & 1 \\ 2 & 0 \end{bmatrix} \qquad I = \begin{bmatrix} 1 & 0 \\ 0 & 1 \end{bmatrix}$$

45. $(P + Q)R$ and $PR + QR$

46. $(P + Q)I$ and $PI + QI$

47. $(P + Q)(R + S)$ and $(P + Q)R + (P + Q)S$

48. $(P + Q)(R + S)$ and $PR + PS + QR + QS$

Standardized Test Prep

49. Which product is NOT defined?

Ⓐ $\begin{bmatrix} -1 \\ 2 \end{bmatrix} \begin{bmatrix} -1 & 2 \end{bmatrix}$ Ⓑ $\begin{bmatrix} -1 & 2 \\ -1 & 2 \end{bmatrix} \begin{bmatrix} -1 & 2 \end{bmatrix}$ Ⓒ $\begin{bmatrix} -1 & 2 \\ -1 & 2 \end{bmatrix} \begin{bmatrix} 2 & -1 \\ 2 & -1 \end{bmatrix}$ Ⓓ $\begin{bmatrix} -1 & 2 \end{bmatrix} \begin{bmatrix} -1 \\ 2 \end{bmatrix}$

50. What is the geometric mean of 8 and 18?

Ⓕ 12 Ⓖ 13 Ⓗ 26 Ⓘ 36

51. The random number table simulates an experiment where you toss a coin 90 times. Even digits represent heads and odd digits represent tails. What is the experimental probability, to the nearest percent, of the coin coming up heads?

Ⓐ 45% Ⓑ 50% Ⓒ 54% Ⓓ 56%

Random Number Table		
31504	51648	40613
79321	80927	42404
15594	84675	68591
34178	00460	31754
49676	58733	00884
85400	72294	22551

52. Four percent of the tenants in an apartment building live alone. Suppose five tenants are selected randomly. Which expression represents $P(\text{all live alone})$?

Ⓕ $(0.04)^5$ Ⓖ $(0.4)^5$ Ⓗ $(0.96)^5$ Ⓘ $(5)^{0.04}$

53. Explain how to find an equation for the ellipse, centered at the origin, that is 50 units wide and 40 units high.

Mixed Review

Add or subtract.

◀ See Lesson 12-1.

54. $\begin{bmatrix} -1 & 2 \\ 0 & 17 \end{bmatrix} - \begin{bmatrix} 32 & 14 \\ 6 & -10 \end{bmatrix}$

55. $\begin{bmatrix} 0 & -1 & 5 \\ 6 & 10 & 12 \end{bmatrix} + \begin{bmatrix} 9 & -5 & 7 \\ -4 & 10 & 0 \end{bmatrix}$

Get Ready! To prepare for Lesson 12-3, do Exercises 56–57.

Simplify each group of expressions.

◀ See p. 975.

56. a. $3(4)$ **b.** $2(6)$ **c.** $3(4) - 2(6)$

57. a. $3(-4)$ **b.** $2(-6)$ **c.** $3(-4) - 2(-6)$

45. yes

46. yes

47. yes

48. yes

Standardized Test Prep

49. B

50. F

51. C

52. F

53. [2] Since the center is at the origin, the vertices are $\left(\pm\frac{50}{2}, 0\right)$ and the co-vertices are $\left(0, \pm\frac{40}{2}\right)$. Using $\frac{x^2}{a^2} + \frac{y^2}{b^2} = 1$, $a = \pm 25$ and $b = \pm 20$, so $\frac{x^2}{625} + \frac{y^2}{400} = 1$.

[1] correct vertices and co-vertices, but incorrect eq. OR incomplete explanation

Mixed Review

54. $\begin{bmatrix} -33 & -12 \\ -6 & 27 \end{bmatrix}$

55. $\begin{bmatrix} 9 & -6 & 12 \\ 2 & 20 & 12 \end{bmatrix}$

56. a. 12

b. 12

c. 0

57. a. −12

b. −12

c. 0

Additional Instructional Support

Algebra 2 Companion

Students can use the **Algebra 2 Companion** worktext (4 pages) as you teach the lesson. Use the Companion to support

- New Vocabulary
- Key Concepts
- Got It for each Problem
- Lesson Check

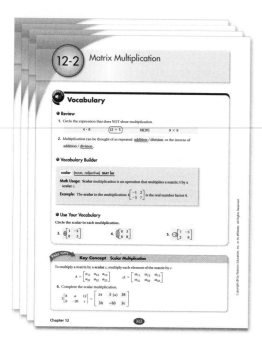

ELL Support

Graphic Organizers To help students understand the process of multiplying two matrices, put two matrices on the board: a 2×2 and a 2×3. Label the elements a, b, c, d in the first matrix and the elements e, f, g, h, j, k in the second matrix. Model the thinking for multiplying one or two rows times columns. Then ask students to multiply the remainder and record their results on paper and on the board. The resulting matrix shows clearly the pattern of elements being multiplied. Point out to students that the elements in the row of the first matrix do not appear in any of the expressions outside of that row in the product matrix and that the elements of the first column of the second matrix do not appear outside the first column of the product matrix. This will provide a graphic for the students to refer to as they multiply matrices in the exercises.

5 Assess & Remediate

Lesson Quiz

1. If $A = \begin{bmatrix} 3 & 6 \\ -1 & 0 \\ 2 & -7 \end{bmatrix}$ and $B = \begin{bmatrix} 0 & -3 \\ 8 & 2 \\ 1 & -4 \end{bmatrix}$, what is $A - 3B$?

2. Solve $\begin{bmatrix} -2 & 1 \\ 4 & 3 \end{bmatrix} - 4X = \begin{bmatrix} -6 & -7 \\ 0 & 3 \end{bmatrix}$.

3. If $G = \begin{bmatrix} -1 & 2 & -3 \\ 2 & 0 & 1 \end{bmatrix}$ and $H = \begin{bmatrix} -1 & -2 \\ 0 & 2 \\ 3 & 1 \end{bmatrix}$, what is GH?

4. Do you UNDERSTAND? Can you multiply $\begin{bmatrix} -1 & 3 \\ 2 & 0 \end{bmatrix}\begin{bmatrix} -3 \\ 5 \end{bmatrix}$? Explain.

ANSWERS TO LESSON QUIZ

1. $\begin{bmatrix} 3 & 15 \\ -25 & -6 \\ -1 & 5 \end{bmatrix}$

2. $\begin{bmatrix} 1 & 2 \\ 1 & 0 \end{bmatrix}$

3. $\begin{bmatrix} -8 & 3 \\ 1 & -3 \end{bmatrix}$

4. Yes; Sample: a 2×2 matrix times a 2×1 matrix is a 2×1 matrix.

PRESCRIPTION FOR REMEDIATION

Use the student work on the Lesson Quiz to prescribe a differentiated review assignment:

Points	Differentiated Remediation
0–2	Intervention
3	On-level
4	Extension

PowerAlgebra.com

5 Assess & Remediate

Assign the Lesson Quiz. Appropriate intervention, practice, or enrichment is automatically generated based on student performance.

Intervention

- **Reteaching** (2 pages) Provides reteaching and practice exercises for the key lesson concepts. Use with struggling students or absent students.

- **English Language Learner Support** Helps students develop and reinforce mathematical vocabulary and key concepts.

All-in-One Resources/Online
Reteaching

12-2 Reteaching
Matrix Multiplication

- To multiply a matrix by a real number, multiply each element in the matrix by the real number. This is *scalar multiplication*. The real number is the *scalar*.
- Solving matrix equations with scalars is like solving other kinds of equations. Isolate the variable on one side of the equal sign and simplify the other side.

Problem

What is the solution of $-3\begin{bmatrix} 1 & 3 \\ 6 & 4 \end{bmatrix} + 2X = \begin{bmatrix} -3 & 1 \\ -20 & -6 \end{bmatrix}$?

$\begin{bmatrix} -3\cdot1 & -3\cdot3 \\ -3\cdot6 & -3\cdot4 \end{bmatrix} + 2X = \begin{bmatrix} -3 & 1 \\ -20 & -6 \end{bmatrix}$ — Multiply $\begin{bmatrix} 1 & 3 \\ 6 & 4 \end{bmatrix}$ by the scalar -3.

$\begin{bmatrix} -3 & -9 \\ -18 & -12 \end{bmatrix} + 2X = \begin{bmatrix} -3 & 1 \\ -20 & -6 \end{bmatrix}$ — Simplify.

$2X = \begin{bmatrix} -3 & 1 \\ -20 & -6 \end{bmatrix} - \begin{bmatrix} -3 & -9 \\ -18 & -12 \end{bmatrix}$ — Subtract $\begin{bmatrix} -3 & -9 \\ -18 & -12 \end{bmatrix}$ from each side.

$2X = \begin{bmatrix} 0 & 10 \\ -2 & 6 \end{bmatrix}$ — Subtract corresponding elements.

$\frac{1}{2}(2X) = \frac{1}{2}\begin{bmatrix} 0 & 10 \\ -2 & 6 \end{bmatrix}$ — Multiply each side by $\frac{1}{2}$ to isolate X.

$X = \begin{bmatrix} \frac{1}{2}\cdot0 & \frac{1}{2}\cdot10 \\ \frac{1}{2}\cdot(-2) & \frac{1}{2}\cdot6 \end{bmatrix}$ — Multiply $\begin{bmatrix} 0 & 10 \\ -2 & 6 \end{bmatrix}$ by the scalar $\frac{1}{2}$.

$X = \begin{bmatrix} 0 & 5 \\ -1 & 3 \end{bmatrix}$ — Simplify.

Exercises

Solve each matrix equation.

1. $\begin{bmatrix} 5 & -1 \\ 0 & 3 \end{bmatrix} + X = 2\begin{bmatrix} -3 & 4 \\ 4 & 3 \end{bmatrix}$ $\begin{bmatrix} -11 & 9 \\ 8 & 3 \end{bmatrix}$

2. $\frac{2}{3}\begin{bmatrix} 9 & 12 \\ -3 & 9 \end{bmatrix} = 4X + \begin{bmatrix} -6 & 0 \\ 0 & -3 \end{bmatrix}\begin{bmatrix} 3 & 2 \\ \frac{1}{2} & -4 \end{bmatrix}$

3. $\begin{bmatrix} 1 & 2 & 0 \\ 0 & 0 & 3 \end{bmatrix} - 3X = \begin{bmatrix} -2 & -7 & 6 \\ 3 & -3 & 9 \end{bmatrix}\begin{bmatrix} 1 & 3 & -2 \\ -1 & 1 & -2 \end{bmatrix}$

4. $2\begin{bmatrix} 3 \\ 8 \end{bmatrix} = \begin{bmatrix} 14 \\ 20 \end{bmatrix} - 4X \begin{bmatrix} 2 \\ 1 \end{bmatrix}$

All-in-One Resources/Online
English Language Learner Support

12-2 Additional Vocabulary Support
Matrix Multiplication

Kerri is learning how to multiply matrices. She wrote the steps to multiply $A = \begin{bmatrix} 3 & 7 \\ 1 & -2 \end{bmatrix}$ by $B = \begin{bmatrix} 0 & 2 \\ 3 & 4 \end{bmatrix}$ on note cards, but the cards got mixed up.

- Multiply the elements in the first row of A by the elements in the second column of B. Add the products and place the sum in the first row, second column of AB.
- Multiply the elements in the second row of A by the elements in the second column of B. Add the products and place the sum in the second row, second column of AB.
- Multiply the elements in the second row of A by the elements in the first column of B. Add the products and place the sum in the second row, first column of AB.
- Multiply the elements in the first row of A by the elements in the first column of B. Add the products and place the sum in the first row, first column of AB.

Use the note cards to write the steps in the order that you would use.

1. First, multiply the elements in the first row of A by the elements in the first column of B. Place the sum in the first row, first column of AB

2. Second, multiply the elements in the first row of A by the elements in the second column of B. Place the sum in the first row, second column of AB

3. Then, multiply the elements in the second row of A by the elements in the first column of B. Place the sum in the second row, first column of AB

4. Finally, multiply the elements in the second row of A by the elements in the second column of B. Place the sum in the second row, second column of AB

Differentiated Remediation *continued*

On-Level

- **Practice** (2 pages) Provides extra practice for each lesson. For simpler practice exercises, use the Form K Practice pages found in the All-in-One Teaching Resources and online.
- **Think About a Plan** Helps students develop specific problem-solving skills and strategies by providing scaffolded guiding questions.
- **Standardized Test Prep** Focuses on all major exercises, all major question types, and helps students prepare for the high-stakes assessments.

Extension

- **Enrichment** Provides students with interesting problems and activities that extend the concepts of the lesson.
- **Activities, Games, and Puzzles** Worksheets that can be used for concepts development, enrichment, and for fun!

Practice and Problem Solving Wkbk/ All-in-One Resources/Online

Practice page 1

12-2 Practice *Form G*
Matrix Multiplication

Use matrices *A*, *B*, *C*, and *D*. Find each product, sum, or difference.

$A = \begin{bmatrix} 1 & -1 \\ 3 & -2 \end{bmatrix}$ $B = \begin{bmatrix} 0 & 2 \\ -2 & 1 \\ -1 & 0 \end{bmatrix}$ $C = \begin{bmatrix} 3 & -3 & -1 \\ 2 & -2 & 4 \end{bmatrix}$ $D = \begin{bmatrix} 1 & 0 \\ 0 & 1 \end{bmatrix}$

1. $2D$ $\begin{bmatrix} 2 & 0 \\ 0 & 2 \end{bmatrix}$
2. $0.2B$ $\begin{bmatrix} 0 & 0.4 \\ -0.4 & 0.2 \\ -0.2 & 0 \end{bmatrix}$
3. $\frac{1}{4}C$ $\begin{bmatrix} \frac{3}{4} & -\frac{3}{4} & -\frac{1}{4} \\ \frac{1}{2} & -\frac{1}{2} & 1 \end{bmatrix}$
4. DC $\begin{bmatrix} 3 & -3 & -1 \\ 2 & -2 & 4 \end{bmatrix}$
5. BD $\begin{bmatrix} 0 & 2 \\ -2 & 1 \\ -1 & 0 \end{bmatrix}$
6. $2A + 4D$ $\begin{bmatrix} 6 & -2 \\ 6 & 0 \end{bmatrix}$
7. $5D - A$ $\begin{bmatrix} 4 & 1 \\ -3 & 7 \end{bmatrix}$
8. $3D + A$ $\begin{bmatrix} 4 & -1 \\ 3 & 1 \end{bmatrix}$
9. $3C - 2DC$ $\begin{bmatrix} 3 & -3 & -1 \\ 2 & -2 & 4 \end{bmatrix}$

Solve each matrix equation. Check your answers.

10. $2\begin{bmatrix} 0 & 1 \\ 3 & -4 \end{bmatrix} - 3X = \begin{bmatrix} 9 & -6 \\ 1 & -2 \end{bmatrix}$ $\begin{bmatrix} -3 & \frac{8}{3} \\ \frac{5}{3} & -2 \end{bmatrix}$
11. $\frac{1}{2}X + \begin{bmatrix} 5 & -1 \\ 0 & \frac{2}{3} \end{bmatrix} = 2\begin{bmatrix} 3 & 0 \\ 1 & 2 \end{bmatrix}$ $\begin{bmatrix} 2 & 2 \\ 4 & \frac{20}{3} \end{bmatrix}$

Find each product.

12. $\begin{bmatrix} 2 & -1 \\ 5 & 3 \end{bmatrix}\begin{bmatrix} 0 & 4 \\ -3 & 1 \end{bmatrix}$ $\begin{bmatrix} 3 & 7 \\ -9 & 23 \end{bmatrix}$
13. $\begin{bmatrix} 0 & 4 \\ -3 & 1 \end{bmatrix}\begin{bmatrix} 2 & -1 \\ 5 & 3 \end{bmatrix}$ $\begin{bmatrix} 20 & 12 \\ -1 & 6 \end{bmatrix}$
14. $\begin{bmatrix} 2 & -1 & 6 \end{bmatrix}\begin{bmatrix} 2 \\ -1 \\ 6 \end{bmatrix}$ $[41]$
15. $\begin{bmatrix} 2 & -1 & 6 \end{bmatrix}\begin{bmatrix} 0 & 2 \\ 0 & -1 \\ 0 & 6 \end{bmatrix}$ $[0 \;\; 41]$
16. $\begin{bmatrix} 2 & -1 & 6 \end{bmatrix}\begin{bmatrix} 2 & 0 \\ -1 & 0 \\ 6 & 0 \end{bmatrix}$ $[41 \;\; 0]$
17. $\begin{bmatrix} 0 & 0 & 0 \\ 2 & -1 & 6 \end{bmatrix}\begin{bmatrix} 2 & 0 \\ -1 & 0 \\ 6 & 0 \end{bmatrix}$ $\begin{bmatrix} 0 & 0 \\ 41 & 0 \end{bmatrix}$
18. $\begin{bmatrix} -5 & 0 \\ 0 & -4 \end{bmatrix}\begin{bmatrix} -5 & 0 \\ 0 & -4 \end{bmatrix}$ $\begin{bmatrix} 25 & 0 \\ 0 & 16 \end{bmatrix}$
19. $\begin{bmatrix} 4 & 3 \\ 9 & 7 \end{bmatrix}\begin{bmatrix} 6 & 3 \\ 9 & 4 \end{bmatrix}$ $\begin{bmatrix} 51 & 24 \\ 117 & 55 \end{bmatrix}$
20. $\begin{bmatrix} 3 & 1 \\ -2 & 4 \\ -1 & 0 \end{bmatrix}\begin{bmatrix} -1 & 0 \\ 0 & -1 \end{bmatrix}$ $\begin{bmatrix} -3 & -1 \\ 2 & -4 \\ 1 & 0 \end{bmatrix}$
21. $\begin{bmatrix} 0 & 4 & 1 \\ 2 & -2 & -1 \end{bmatrix}\begin{bmatrix} 1 \\ 6 \\ 3 \end{bmatrix}$ $\begin{bmatrix} 27 \\ -13 \end{bmatrix}$

Practice and Problem Solving Wkbk/ All-in-One Resources/Online

Practice page 2

12-2 Practice (continued) *Form G*
Matrix Multiplication

22. A carpenter builds three boxes. One box uses 12 nails. The second box uses 6 nails and 6 screws. The third box uses 8 screws and 2 hinges. Nails cost \$.04 each, screws cost \$.06 each, and hinges cost \$.12 each.
    a. Write a matrix to show the number of each type of hardware in each box.
    b. Write a matrix to show the cost of each type of hardware.
    c. Find the matrix showing the cost of hardware for each box.
    $\begin{bmatrix} 12 & 0 & 0 \\ 6 & 6 & 0 \\ 0 & 8 & 2 \end{bmatrix}$; $\begin{bmatrix} 0.04 \\ 0.06 \\ 0.12 \end{bmatrix}$; $\begin{bmatrix} 0.48 \\ 0.60 \\ 0.72 \end{bmatrix}$ or $\begin{bmatrix} 12 & 6 & 0 \\ 0 & 6 & 8 \\ 0 & 0 & 2 \end{bmatrix}$; $[0.04 \;\; 0.06 \;\; 0.12]$; $[0.48 \;\; 0.60 \;\; 0.72]$

Determine whether the product exists.

$P = \begin{bmatrix} 4 & -5 \\ 0 & 1 \end{bmatrix}$ $Q = \begin{bmatrix} 5 \\ 9 \end{bmatrix}$ $R = [-3 \;\; 2]$ $S = \begin{bmatrix} 0 & -1 \\ 4 & 6 \end{bmatrix}$

23. SP yes
24. QS no
25. PR no
26. QR yes

27. A rugby game consists of two 40-min halves. In rugby, a try (T) is 5 points, a conversion kick (C) is 2 points, a penalty kick (PK) is 3 points, and a drop goal (DG) is 3 points.
    a. Use matrix operations to determine the score in a game between the Austin Huns and the Dallas Harlequins. Austin 33, Dallas 29

Austin Huns vs. Dallas Harlequins

	First Half				Second Half			
Team	T	C	PK	DG	T	C	PK	DG
Austin	2	2	1	0	2	0	2	0
Dallas	1	0	3	0	2	1	0	1

    b. Many years ago, a try was worth only 4 points and a conversion was worth 3 points. If the second half were scored by the old rules, which team would win the game? Austin

28. **Reasoning** Real-number multiplication is commutative. Is the same true for matrix multiplication? Explain your reasoning. No; answers may vary. Sample: Changing the order of the factors changes the product. For example, if *A* and *B* are 2 × 2 matrices, $(ab)_{11} = a_{11}b_{11} + a_{12}b_{21}$, but $(ba)_{11} = a_{11}b_{11} + a_{21}b_{12}$.
29. **Error Analysis** A student says $\begin{bmatrix} 1 & 1 \\ 1 & 1 \end{bmatrix}$ is the multiplicative identity for a 2 × 2 matrix. Do you agree? If not, what is the correct matrix? No; answers may vary. Sample: The multiplicative identity for a 2 × 2 matrix is $\begin{bmatrix} 1 & 0 \\ 0 & 1 \end{bmatrix}$.

All-in-One Resources/Online

Enrichment

12-2 Enrichment
Matrix Multiplication

Nilpotent Matrices

A matrix *A* is said to be nilpotent if there is an integer *n* such that $A^n = 0$, the zero matrix.

1. What can you say about the dimensions of a nilpotent matrix? Why? If $A = \begin{bmatrix} 0 & 1 \\ 0 & 0 \end{bmatrix}$, find A^2 and A^3. What can you conclude? The number of rows must be the same as the number of columns, so it can be multiplied by itself; $\begin{bmatrix} 0 & 0 \\ 0 & 0 \end{bmatrix}$; $\begin{bmatrix} 0 & 0 \\ 0 & 0 \end{bmatrix}$; Matrix *A* is nilpotent.

The *order* of a nilpotent matrix *A* is the least integer *n* such that $A^n = 0$. In the example above, although both $A^2 = 0$ and $A^3 = 0$, the order of matrix *A* is 2.

2. Examine the conditions under which a nonzero 2 × 2 matrix of order 2 is nilpotent. Suppose $A = \begin{bmatrix} a & b \\ c & d \end{bmatrix}$. Find A^2. $\begin{bmatrix} a^2 + bc & ab + bd \\ ac + cd & bc + d^2 \end{bmatrix}$

If *A* is nilpotent of order 2, then $A^2 = 0$. Therefore, each element of the matrix A^2 must be equal to zero.

3. Write four equations that show that the elements in the corresponding rows and columns of matrix A^2 from exercise 2 are zero. $a^2 + bc = 0$; $ab + bd = 0$; $ac + cd = 0$; $bc + d^2 = 0$
   Equation (1, 1): Equation (1, 2):
   Equation (2, 1): Equation (2, 2):
4. Factor equation (1, 2). $b(a + d) = 0$
5. Find two possible solutions. $b = 0$; $a + d = 0$
6. If $b = 0$, what can you conclude from equation (1, 1)? From equation (2, 2)? $a^2 = 0$, so $a = 0$; $d^2 = 0$, so $d = 0$
7. Use this information to write matrix *A*. Verify that this matrix is nilpotent of order 2. $A = \begin{bmatrix} 0 & 0 \\ c & 0 \end{bmatrix}$; $A^2 = \begin{bmatrix} 0 & 0 \\ 0 & 0 \end{bmatrix}$
8. Using equations (2, 1), (1, 1), and (2, 2), and substituting in matrix *A*, find another nilpotent matrix of order 2. $\begin{bmatrix} 0 & b \\ 0 & 0 \end{bmatrix}$

Practice and Problem Solving Wkbk/ All-in-One Resources/Online

Think About a Plan

12-2 Think About a Plan
Matrix Multiplication

Sport Two teams are competing in a track meet. Points for individual events are awarded as follows: 5 points for first place, 3 points for second place, and 1 point for third place. Points for team relays are awarded as follows: 5 points for first place and no points for second place.

a. Use matrix operations to determine the score in the track meet.
b. Who would win if the scoring were changed to 5 points for first place, 2 points for second place, and 1 point for third place in each individual event with relay scoring remaining 5 points for first place?

	Individual Events			Relays	
Team	First	Second	Third	First	Second
West River	8	5	2	8	5
River's Edge	6	9	12	6	9

Know

1. What is the given information? The number of first, second, and third place wins for each school and the point value of each place.

Need

2. To solve the problem I need to: write the number of wins and the point values as matrices, then multiply the matrices.

Plan

3. Write the number of wins as a 2 × 5 matrix and the original and alternate point values as 5 × 1 matrices. $\begin{bmatrix} 8 & 5 & 2 & 8 & 5 \\ 6 & 9 & 12 & 6 & 9 \end{bmatrix}$, $\begin{bmatrix} 5 \\ 3 \\ 1 \\ 5 \\ 0 \end{bmatrix}$, $\begin{bmatrix} 5 \\ 2 \\ 1 \\ 5 \\ 0 \end{bmatrix}$
4. Use matrix multiplication to find the original total team scores and the alternate total team scores for the track meet.
   $\begin{bmatrix} 8 & 5 & 2 & 8 & 5 \\ 6 & 9 & 12 & 6 & 9 \end{bmatrix}\begin{bmatrix} 5 \\ 3 \\ 1 \\ 5 \\ 0 \end{bmatrix} = \begin{bmatrix} 97 \\ 99 \end{bmatrix}$ $\begin{bmatrix} 8 & 5 & 2 & 8 & 5 \\ 6 & 9 & 12 & 6 & 9 \end{bmatrix}\begin{bmatrix} 5 \\ 2 \\ 1 \\ 5 \\ 0 \end{bmatrix} = \begin{bmatrix} 92 \\ 90 \end{bmatrix}$
5. What was the score in the track meet? West River: 97, River's Edge: 99
6. Who would win if the scoring were changed? West River

Practice and Problem Solving Wkbk/ All-in-One Resources/Online

Standardized Test Prep

12-2 Standardized Test Prep
Matrix Multiplication

Multiple Choice

For Exercises 1–3, choose the correct letter.

1. Which matrix is equivalent to $-2\begin{bmatrix} 1 & 5 & -3 \\ 0 & 2 & 4 \\ 7 & -2 & 0 \end{bmatrix}$? A
   (A) $\begin{bmatrix} -2 & -10 & 6 \\ 0 & -4 & -8 \\ -14 & 4 & 0 \end{bmatrix}$ (C) $\begin{bmatrix} -2 & -10 & 6 \\ 0 & 2 & 4 \\ 7 & -2 & 0 \end{bmatrix}$
   (B) $\begin{bmatrix} 1 & 5 & -3 \\ 0 & -4 & -8 \\ 7 & -2 & 0 \end{bmatrix}$ (D) $\begin{bmatrix} -1 & 3 & -5 \\ -2 & 0 & 2 \\ 5 & -4 & -2 \end{bmatrix}$
2. What is the product $\begin{bmatrix} 6 & -1 \\ 3 & 9 \end{bmatrix}\begin{bmatrix} 3 \\ -6 \end{bmatrix}$? H
   (F) $\begin{bmatrix} 18 & -3 \\ -18 & -54 \end{bmatrix}$ (G) $[24 \;\; -45]$ (H) $\begin{bmatrix} 24 \\ -45 \end{bmatrix}$ (I) $\begin{bmatrix} 15 & 36 \\ -30 & -72 \end{bmatrix}$
3. Which matrix is the solution of $\begin{bmatrix} 1 & -1 & 2 \\ 2 & 0 & -1 \end{bmatrix} - 2X = \begin{bmatrix} 4 & 5 & 6 \\ 6 & 5 & 4 \end{bmatrix}$? D
   (A) $\begin{bmatrix} 3 & 6 & 4 \\ 4 & 5 & 5 \end{bmatrix}$ (C) $\begin{bmatrix} \frac{3}{2} & 3 & 2 \\ 2 & \frac{5}{2} & \frac{5}{2} \end{bmatrix}$
   (B) $\begin{bmatrix} -6 & -12 & -8 \\ -8 & -10 & -10 \end{bmatrix}$ (D) $\begin{bmatrix} -\frac{3}{2} & -3 & -2 \\ -2 & -\frac{5}{2} & -\frac{5}{2} \end{bmatrix}$

Extended Response \$107 for Bath 1, \$67 for Bath 2, \$220 for the kitchen, so \$394 total.

$T = \begin{bmatrix} 20 & 50 & 10 \\ 15 & 30 & 5 \\ 25 & 100 & 50 \end{bmatrix}\begin{bmatrix} 1.20 \\ 1.50 \\ 0.80 \end{bmatrix} = \begin{bmatrix} 20(1.20) + 50(1.50) + 10(0.80) \\ 15(1.20) + 30(1.50) + 5(0.80) \\ 25(1.20) + 100(1.50) + 50(0.80) \end{bmatrix} = \begin{bmatrix} 107 \\ 67 \\ 220 \end{bmatrix}$

4. The table shows the number of tiles used in a house. Blue tiles cost \$1.20 each, white cost \$1.50 each, and green cost \$.80 each. Write and solve a matrix equation to find the total cost of the tile. Show your work.

Tiles Used

	Blue	White	Green
Bath #1	20	50	10
Bath #2	15	30	5
Kitchen	25	100	50

[3] appropriate solution strategy with a minor computational or copying error
[2] correct equation solved incorrectly OR incorrect equation solved correctly; total cost correct based on previous work
[1] correct total cost with no work shown
[0] incorrect answers and no work shown OR no answers given

Online Teacher Resource Center

Activities, Games, and Puzzles

12-2 Activity: Matrix "Eggsperiment"
Matrix Multiplication

For this activity you will need some empty egg cartons, pennies, dimes, and tape.

- Use scissors to divide the cartons into 2-by-1, 2-by-2, and 2-by-3 sections.
- Decide each section's orientation to obtain a matrix. For instance, a 2-by-3 section can give you a 2 × 3 matrix or 3 × 2 matrix.
- Place anywhere from 0 to 5 coins in each space for every matrix. Use dimes to represent negative numbers. Leave some of the spaces empty.

Activity Directions

The number of pennies minus the number of dimes in each position of the carton represents the value of that entry in the matrix. Pick a partner and compare your matrices to your classmates' matrices. Decide whether or not you can add your matrix to another matrix or multiply your matrix with another matrix.

Add or multiply your matrix with your partner's to make a new resulting matrix. Decide whether or not a different size matrix or additional coins are required. You can use tape to put smaller matrices together and create larger ones. If time permits, change partners and repeat the activity.

1. Which size matrices could be added to your matrix? matrices with the same dimension as your matrix
2. Which size matrices could be multiplied with your matrix? Does the way the carton was oriented make a difference? To multiply two matrices, the number of columns in the first matrix must equal the number of rows in the second matrix. Orientation makes a difference; a 2 × 3 matrix is different from a 3 × 2 matrix.
3. How do you find the size of a matrix resulting from the multiplication of two matrices? Explain by giving an example. An $n \times m$ matrix multiplied by an $m \times p$ matrix gives an $n \times p$ matrix.
4. Is the size of the product of two matrices always different from the original matrices? Explain by giving an example. Not necessarily; multiplying two square matrices gives a square matrix of the same size.
5. Is the size of the sum of two matrices always the same as the original matrices? yes

Guided Instruction

PURPOSE To apply matrices to finite and directed graphs

PROCESS Students will
- make matrices to represent sketches of finite and directed graphs.
- sketch directed graphs from matrices.
- use a matrix and a sketch to model a real-world problem.

DISCUSS Matrices can represent various networks, even social networks. For example, a matrix could represent friendships among a group of people.

Example 1

Q Why are there zeros in a_{11}, a_{22}, a_{33}, and a_{44}?
[These represent the path from a vertex to itself, which does not exist in the finite graph.]

Example 2   VISUAL LEARNERS

Ask students to trace a path on the directed graph from S to T. Then have students circle the 1's in the matrix that show the path they traced is possible.

Q What would a row of zeros indicate about the vertex that had the row of zeros? **[There is no path from the vertex to any other vertex.]**

Q What would the matrix look like that represented the directed graph for the fire department, F, the hospital, H, the school, S, and the apartment building, A?

$$
\begin{array}{c c}
& \begin{array}{cccc} F & H & S & A \end{array} \\
\begin{array}{c} F \\ H \\ S \\ A \end{array} &
\left[\begin{array}{cccc}
0 & 1 & 1 & 1 \\
1 & 0 & 0 & 0 \\
1 & 0 & 0 & 1 \\
0 & 1 & 1 & 0
\end{array} \right]
\end{array}
$$

©️ Mathematical Practices This Concept Byte supports students in modeling with mathematics, Mathematical Practice 4.

780   Chapter 12

©️ **Content Standard**

N.VM.6 Use matrices to represent and manipulate data . . .

A finite graph is a set of points, called vertices, connected by curves, or paths.

You can use a matrix to describe a finite graph. The digit "1" indicates a path between two vertices or one vertex and itself. The digit "0" indicates that no path exists between two vertices or from one vertex to itself.

Example 1

Write a matrix A to represent the finite graph. Explain the significance of element a_{41}.

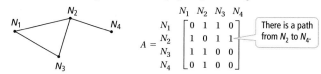

$$
A = \begin{array}{c c}
& \begin{array}{cccc} N_1 & N_2 & N_3 & N_4 \end{array} \\
\begin{array}{c} N_1 \\ N_2 \\ N_3 \\ N_4 \end{array} &
\left[\begin{array}{cccc}
0 & 1 & 1 & 0 \\
1 & 0 & 1 & 1 \\
1 & 1 & 0 & 0 \\
0 & 1 & 0 & 0
\end{array} \right]
\end{array}
$$

There is a path from N_2 to N_4.

Element a_{41} is 0. It indicates that there is no path between N_4 and N_1.

Directed graphs are finite graphs that indicate the direction of a path. The directed graph below represents the information in the map.

You can use a matrix to represent the information in a directed graph.

Example 2

Write a matrix B to represent the information from the directed graph. Compare elements b_{12} and b_{21}.

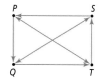

$$
B = \begin{array}{c c}
\text{To} \rightarrow & \begin{array}{cccc} P & Q & S & T \end{array} \\
\text{From} \rightarrow \begin{array}{c} P \\ Q \\ S \\ T \end{array} &
\left[\begin{array}{cccc}
0 & 1 & 0 & 1 \\
0 & 0 & 1 & 1 \\
1 & 1 & 0 & 0 \\
1 & 0 & 1 & 0
\end{array} \right]
\end{array}
$$

Element b_{12} is 1 and b_{21} is 0. The path between P and Q is one way, from P to Q.

Answers

Concept Byte

1.
$$
\begin{array}{c c}
& \begin{array}{cccc} N_1 & N_2 & N_3 & N_4 \end{array} \\
\begin{array}{c} N_1 \\ N_2 \\ N_3 \\ N_4 \end{array} &
\left[\begin{array}{cccc}
0 & 1 & 0 & 1 \\
1 & 0 & 1 & 1 \\
0 & 1 & 0 & 1 \\
1 & 1 & 1 & 0
\end{array} \right]
\end{array}
$$

2.
$$
\begin{array}{c c}
& \begin{array}{cccc} S & T & U & V \end{array} \\
\begin{array}{c} S \\ T \\ U \\ V \end{array} &
\left[\begin{array}{cccc}
0 & 0 & 1 & 0 \\
0 & 0 & 1 & 0 \\
1 & 1 & 0 & 1 \\
0 & 0 & 1 & 0
\end{array} \right]
\end{array}
$$

3.
$$
\begin{array}{c c}
& \begin{array}{ccccc} V_1 & V_2 & V_3 & V_4 & V_5 \end{array} \\
\begin{array}{c} V_1 \\ V_2 \\ V_3 \\ V_4 \\ V_5 \end{array} &
\left[\begin{array}{ccccc}
0 & 1 & 0 & 0 & 0 \\
1 & 0 & 1 & 0 & 0 \\
0 & 1 & 0 & 1 & 1 \\
0 & 0 & 1 & 0 & 1 \\
0 & 0 & 1 & 1 & 0
\end{array} \right]
\end{array}
$$

4. From →
$$
\begin{array}{c c}
\text{To} \rightarrow & \begin{array}{ccccc} A & B & C & D & E \end{array} \\
\begin{array}{c} A \\ B \\ C \\ D \\ E \end{array} &
\left[\begin{array}{ccccc}
0 & 1 & 0 & 0 & 1 \\
1 & 0 & 1 & 0 & 0 \\
0 & 1 & 0 & 1 & 0 \\
0 & 0 & 0 & 0 & 1 \\
0 & 0 & 0 & 1 & 0
\end{array} \right]
\end{array}
$$

5. From →
$$
\begin{array}{c c}
\text{To} \rightarrow & \begin{array}{cccc} A & B & C & D \end{array} \\
\begin{array}{c} A \\ B \\ C \\ D \end{array} &
\left[\begin{array}{cccc}
0 & 1 & 0 & 0 \\
0 & 0 & 0 & 0 \\
0 & 1 & 1 & 1 \\
1 & 1 & 0 & 1
\end{array} \right]
\end{array}
$$

6. From →
$$
\begin{array}{c c}
\text{To} \rightarrow & \begin{array}{ccccc} R & S & T & U & V \end{array} \\
\begin{array}{c} R \\ S \\ T \\ U \\ V \end{array} &
\left[\begin{array}{ccccc}
0 & 1 & 0 & 1 & 0 \\
1 & 0 & 1 & 0 & 1 \\
0 & 1 & 0 & 1 & 0 \\
1 & 0 & 1 & 0 & 0 \\
0 & 1 & 0 & 0 & 0
\end{array} \right]
\end{array}
$$

780   Chapter 12

Example 3

Draw a directed graph to represent the information in the matrix.

$$C = \begin{array}{c} \text{From} \rightarrow \\ A \\ B \\ C \end{array} \begin{array}{c} \text{To} \rightarrow \\ \begin{bmatrix} 1 & 1 & 1 \\ 1 & 0 & 1 \\ 0 & 0 & 0 \end{bmatrix} \end{array} \begin{array}{ccc} A & B & C \end{array}$$

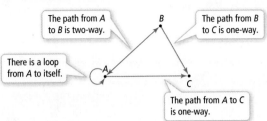

The path from A to B is two-way.

The path from B to C is one-way.

There is a loop from A to itself.

The path from A to C is one-way.

Example 3

Q Is the path from B to A described by the element in c_{12} or c_{21}? **[c_{21}]**

Q Why is it important to designate *from* and *to* consistently in the matrix representing a directed graph? **[to indicate the one-way paths correctly]**

Exercises

Write a matrix to represent each finite or directed graph.

1.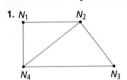

2.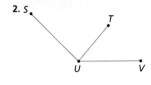

3.

4.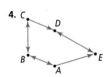

5.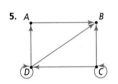

6.

Exercises

Q What will the dimensions of the matrices be for Exercises 1–6? **[Exercises 1, 2, and 5 will be 4 × 4 matrices, and Exercises 3, 4, and 6 will be 5 × 5 matrices.]**

ERROR PREVENTION

Q How can you tell how many ones will appear in the matrix without making the matrix for Exercises 4–6? Explain. **[Count the arrowheads. Each arrowhead indicates a valid path, which will be represented by a one in the matrix.]**

Q How many vertices will each graph have for Exercises 7–9? **[four]**

Q How many vertices do you need to represent the problem in Exercise 10? Explain. **[four; one for each residence or intersection]**

ERROR INTERVENTION

If students have difficulty interpreting T^2 for Exercise 10c, ask them to check the paths where the ones appear in the squared matrix.

Draw a directed graph to represent the information in each matrix.

7.
$$\begin{array}{c} J \\ K \\ L \\ M \end{array} \begin{array}{c} \begin{array}{cccc} J & K & L & M \end{array} \\ \begin{bmatrix} 0 & 0 & 0 & 1 \\ 0 & 0 & 1 & 1 \\ 0 & 1 & 0 & 1 \\ 1 & 1 & 1 & 0 \end{bmatrix} \end{array}$$

8.
$$\begin{array}{c} A \\ B \\ C \\ D \end{array} \begin{array}{c} \begin{array}{cccc} A & B & C & D \end{array} \\ \begin{bmatrix} 0 & 0 & 1 & 1 \\ 1 & 1 & 0 & 0 \\ 0 & 1 & 0 & 1 \\ 1 & 0 & 1 & 0 \end{bmatrix} \end{array}$$

9.
$$\begin{array}{c} N_1 \\ N_2 \\ N_3 \\ N_4 \end{array} \begin{array}{c} \begin{array}{cccc} N_1 & N_2 & N_3 & N_4 \end{array} \\ \begin{bmatrix} 1 & 1 & 1 & 1 \\ 0 & 0 & 1 & 1 \\ 1 & 0 & 0 & 0 \\ 0 & 0 & 1 & 0 \end{bmatrix} \end{array}$$

Ⓒ 10. Travel Alice and Becky live on Parkway East, at the intersections of Owens Bridge and Bay Bridge, respectively. Carl and David live on Parkway West, at the intersections of Bay Bridge and Owens Bridge, respectively. Parkway East is a one-way street running east. Parkway West is one-way running west. Both bridges are two-way.
  a. Draw a directed graph indicating road travel between the houses.
  b. Write a matrix T to represent the information in the directed graph.
  c. Writing Calculate T^2. What does the matrix model? Explain.

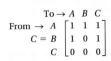   **Concept Byte** Networks   781

1–6. See previous page.

7.

8.

9.

10. a.

(directed graph A, B, C, D)

b. $T = \begin{array}{c} A \\ B \\ C \\ D \end{array} \begin{array}{c} \begin{array}{cccc} A & B & C & D \end{array} \\ \begin{bmatrix} 0 & 1 & 0 & 1 \\ 0 & 0 & 1 & 0 \\ 0 & 1 & 0 & 1 \\ 1 & 0 & 0 & 0 \end{bmatrix} \end{array}$

c. $\begin{bmatrix} 1 & 0 & 1 & 0 \\ 0 & 1 & 0 & 1 \\ 1 & 0 & 1 & 0 \\ 0 & 1 & 0 & 1 \end{bmatrix}$ The matrix models trips from one house to another that can be traveled using exactly two paths.

1 Interactive Learning

Solve It!

PURPOSE To find the area of a triangle using the vertices of the triangle

PROCESS Students may

- find the area of the rectangle containing the triangle and subtract the areas of the right triangles formed between the given triangle and the sides of the rectangles.
- find the lengths of the sides using the distance formula and then use Heron's formula to find the area.

FACILITATE

Q What are the coordinates of the vertices of the triangle? **[(−2, 1), (3, 4), and (4, −1)]**

Q What are the dimensions of the smallest rectangle that has sides parallel to the axes and contains the triangle? **[6 by 5 units]**

Q How many triangles are in your rectangle? Which can you find the area of? **[four, the given triangle and the three that contain the area between the sides of the given triangle and the rectangle; all four]**

ANSWER See Solve It in Answers on next page.
CONNECT THE MATH In the Solve It, students find the area of a triangle by comparing surrounding areas. In the lesson, students will use a formula using this same idea to calculate area of a triangle from the coordinates of the vertices.

2 Guided Instruction

Take Note

Q Why must *A* and *B* be square matrices? **[so that *AB* and *BA* are defined]**

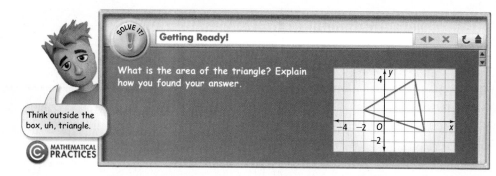

© **Content Standards**
N.VM.10 . . . The determinant of a square matrix is nonzero if and only if the matrix has a multiplicative inverse.
N.VM.12 Work with 2 × 2 matrices as a transformation of the plane . . .

12-3 Determinants and Inverses

Objective To find the inverse of a matrix

> **Getting Ready!**
>
> What is the area of the triangle? Explain how you found your answer.

Think outside the box, uh, triangle.

© **MATHEMATICAL PRACTICES**

Lesson Vocabulary

- square matrix
- multiplicative identity matrix
- multiplicative inverse matrix
- determinant
- singular matrix

This lesson will prepare you to use matrices to solve problems, including how to find the area of a triangle with vertices anywhere in the coordinate plane.

Essential Understanding The product of a matrix and its *multiplicative inverse matrix* is the *multiplicative identity matrix*. Not all matrices have inverse matrices.

A **square matrix** is a matrix with the same number of rows and columns. While there is a multiplicative identity matrix for any square matrix, not all square matrices have multiplicative inverses.

> ### Key Concepts Identity and Multiplicative Inverse Matrices
>
> For an $n \times n$ matrix, the **multiplicative identity matrix** is an $n \times n$ matrix I, or I_n, with 1's along the main diagonal and 0's elsewhere.
>
> $$I_2 = \begin{bmatrix} 1 & 0 \\ 0 & 1 \end{bmatrix}, \quad I_3 = \begin{bmatrix} 1 & 0 & 0 \\ 0 & 1 & 0 \\ 0 & 0 & 1 \end{bmatrix}, \quad \text{and so forth.}$$
>
> If A and B are square matrices and $AB = BA = I$, then B is the **multiplicative inverse matrix** of A, written A^{-1}.

12-3 Preparing to Teach

BIG idea Modeling

ESSENTIAL UNDERSTANDINGS

- The product of a matrix and its inverse matrix is the multiplicative identity matrix. Not all matrices have inverse matrices.
- A matrix has an inverse if and only if its determinant does not equal 0.

Math Background

All square matrices have a multiplicative identity matrix. It contains 1's along the main diagonal and 0's elsewhere. Students might expect the multiplicative identity matrix to have all elements equal to one, since the multiplicative identity of real numbers is 1. You may wish to have them multiply such a matrix by another matrix to see what happens.

Unlike real numbers, not all matrices have multiplicative inverses. One way to determine whether a matrix has a multiplicative inverse is to calculate its determinant. If the determinant is 0,

the matrix does not have an inverse. The determinant is only defined for square matrices.

Students may be confused by the concept of the determinant. It is a number, not a matrix. It has many uses beyond determining whether a matrix has a multiplicative inverse. It can also be used to determine the inverse and to find areas of polygons. It has applications in calculus, linear algebra, and elsewhere.

© Mathematical Practices

Attend to precision. Students will define, make explicit use of, and calculate the inverse of a matrix, the determinant of a matrix, and the identity matrix.

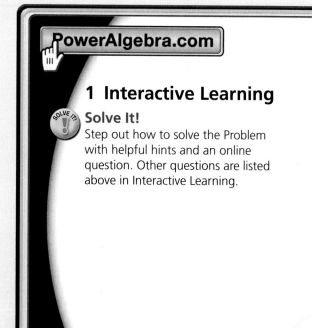

PowerAlgebra.com

1 Interactive Learning

Solve It!
Step out how to solve the Problem with helpful hints and an online question. Other questions are listed above in Interactive Learning.

Think

How do you determine whether *A* and *B* are inverses?
Find *AB* and *BA*. Each product must equal *I*.

© **Problem 1** Determining Whether Matrices are Inverses

For each of the following, are matrices *A* and *B* inverses?

A $A = \begin{bmatrix} 1 & 2 \\ 3 & 4 \end{bmatrix}$ $B = \begin{bmatrix} -2 & 1 \\ \frac{3}{2} & -\frac{1}{2} \end{bmatrix}$

Since $AB = I$ and $BA = I$, matrices *A* and *B* are inverses.

B $A = \begin{bmatrix} 1 & 0 & 2 \\ -2 & 1 & 1 \\ -1 & 1 & 2 \end{bmatrix}$ $B = \begin{bmatrix} -1 & -2 & 2 \\ -3 & -4 & 5 \\ 1 & 1 & -1 \end{bmatrix}$

Since $AB = I$ and $BA = I$, matrices *A* and *B* are inverses.

C $A = \begin{bmatrix} 2 & 4 \\ 2 & 2 \end{bmatrix}$ $B = \begin{bmatrix} 2 & 5 \\ -1 & -3 \end{bmatrix}$

Since $AB \neq I$ (and $BA \neq I$), matrices *A* and *B* are not inverses.

© ✓ **Got It?** **1.** For each of the following, are *A* and *B* inverses?

a. $A = \begin{bmatrix} 1 & 1 \\ 5 & 4 \end{bmatrix}$ $B = \begin{bmatrix} -4 & 1 \\ 5 & -1 \end{bmatrix}$ **b.** $A = \begin{bmatrix} 3 & 2 \\ 5 & 4 \end{bmatrix}$ $B = \begin{bmatrix} 2 & -1 \\ -\frac{5}{2} & \frac{3}{2} \end{bmatrix}$

c. Reasoning Does the matrix $\begin{bmatrix} 0 & 0 \\ 0 & 0 \end{bmatrix}$ have an inverse? Explain.

Every square matrix with real-number elements has a number associated with it.

The number is its *determinant*. Given $A = \begin{bmatrix} a & b \\ c & d \end{bmatrix}$,

Write	Read	Evaluate
↓	↓	↓
det *A*	the determinant of *A*	$\det \begin{bmatrix} a & b \\ c & d \end{bmatrix} = ad - bc$

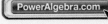
Problem 1

Q Could *A* and *B* be square matrices with $AB = BA$, but not be inverses? Explain using an example. **[Yes; samples: if *A* and *B* are the same matrix;** $\begin{bmatrix} 2 & 4 \\ 4 & 2 \end{bmatrix}$ **and** $\begin{bmatrix} 3 & -1 \\ -1 & 3 \end{bmatrix}$**, whose product is** $\begin{bmatrix} 2 & 10 \\ 10 & 2 \end{bmatrix}$ **for *AB* or *BA*]**

Q If $AB \neq I$, do you have to check *BA* to see if *A* and *B* are inverses? Explain. **[No; a failure in any part of the conditions that must be satisfied for *B* to be a multiplicative inverse of *A* means that *B* is not the multiplicative inverse of *A*. You still might want to check *BA* in case you made an error in calculation for *BA*.]**

Got It?

Q What conditions must be met for *A* and *B* to be multiplicative inverses? **[*A* and *B* must be square matrices, and $AB = BA = I$.]**

Q What is the result if you multiply any square matrix by the same size matrix filled with zeros? Explain. **[The resulting matrix will be the zero matrix; each element of the square matrix will equal zero when multiplied by zero.]**

2 Guided Instruction

 Each Problem is worked out and supported online.

Problem 1
Determining Whether Matrices are Inverses
Animated

Problem 2
Evaluating the Determinants of Matrices
Animated

Problem 3
Finding the Area of a Polygon

Problem 4
Finding the Inverse of a Matrix
Animated

Problem 5
Encoding and Decoding With Matrices

Support in Algebra 2 Companion
• Vocabulary
• Key Concepts
• Got It?

Answers

Solve It!
≈14 units², enclose the triangle in the rectangle with vertices (−2, −1), (4, −1), (4, 4), and (−2, 4). The area of the triangle is the area of the rectangle minus the areas of three right triangles:
$6 \cdot 5 - \frac{1}{2} \cdot 6 \cdot 2 - \frac{1}{2} \cdot 5 \cdot 1 - \frac{1}{2} \cdot 5 \cdot 3 = 14.$

Got It?
1. a. yes
   b. yes
   c. No; no matrix that is multiplied by the zero matrix will give an identity matrix.

Q Gather together terms that contain a_1, b_1, and c_1, and factor these terms out, factoring out -1 with the b_1. What is the result? **[$a_1(b_2c_3 - b_3c_2) - b_1(a_2c_3 - a_3c_2) + c_1(a_2b_3 - a_3b_2)$]**

Q What do you notice about the expressions in parentheses after you factor out a_1, $-b_1$, and c_1? **[They are the determinants of the matrices formed by the elements not in the columns or rows of each factored-out element.]**

Q Does the pattern for finding the determinant of a 3×3 matrix work for a 4×4 matrix? Use your calculator to check if this is true. **[no]**

Problem 2

Q What would be different about the determinant if you subtracted the down diagonal products from the up diagonal products? **[The sign of the answer would be reversed, but the numerical value would be the same.]**

Got It?

Q What are the expanded expressions that will give the value of the determinant for 2a, 2b, and 2c? **[$(3)(5) - (6)(2)$; $(-2)(0) - (3)(0)$; and $(1)(4)(3) + (0)(6)(5) + (3)(2)(-1) - ((5)(4)(3) + (-1)(6)(1) + (3)(2)(0))$]**

Take Note

Q What does the area of the triangle in the Solve It equal when you apply the formula? Is this the same as the value you calculated by subtracting area? **[14 square units; the value is the same.]**

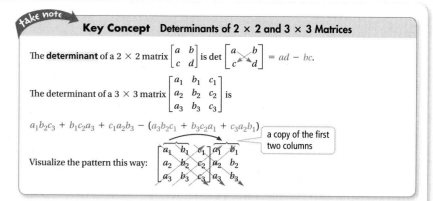

Key Concept **Determinants of 2 × 2 and 3 × 3 Matrices**

The **determinant** of a 2×2 matrix $\begin{bmatrix} a & b \\ c & d \end{bmatrix}$ is $\det \begin{bmatrix} a & b \\ c & d \end{bmatrix} = ad - bc$.

The determinant of a 3×3 matrix $\begin{bmatrix} a_1 & b_1 & c_1 \\ a_2 & b_2 & c_2 \\ a_3 & b_3 & c_3 \end{bmatrix}$ is

$a_1b_2c_3 + b_1c_2a_3 + c_1a_2b_3 - (a_3b_2c_1 + b_3c_2a_1 + c_3a_2b_1)$

a copy of the first two columns

Visualize the pattern this way: $\begin{bmatrix} a_1 & b_1 & c_1 \\ a_2 & b_2 & c_2 \\ a_3 & b_3 & c_3 \end{bmatrix} \begin{matrix} a_1 & b_1 \\ a_2 & b_2 \\ a_3 & b_3 \end{matrix}$

Problem 2 Evaluating the Determinants of Matrices

What are the following determinants?

A $\det \begin{bmatrix} 3 & -1 \\ 2 & 5 \end{bmatrix} = (3)(5) - (-1)(2) = 15 - (-2) = 17$

B $\det \begin{bmatrix} 1 & 0 & -2 \\ 0 & 4 & -1 \\ 3 & 5 & 2 \end{bmatrix} = (1)(4)(2) + (0)(-1)(3) + (-2)(0)(5)$
$- [(3)(4)(-2) + (5)(-1)(1) + (2)(0)(0)]$
$= 8 + 0 + 0 - (-24 - 5 + 0)$
$= 37$

Check Use a graphing calculator.

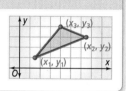

Got It? **2.** What are the determinants of the following matrices?

a. $\begin{bmatrix} 3 & 6 \\ 2 & 5 \end{bmatrix}$ **b.** $\begin{bmatrix} -2 & 0 \\ 3 & 0 \end{bmatrix}$ **c.** $\begin{bmatrix} 1 & 0 & 3 \\ 2 & 4 & 6 \\ 5 & -1 & 3 \end{bmatrix}$

You can use determinants to find the areas of polygons. Since all polygons can be divided into triangles, all you need is a way to find the area of a triangle.

Key Concept **Area of a Triangle**

The area of a triangle with vertices (x_1, y_1), (x_2, y_2), and (x_3, y_3) is

Area $= \frac{1}{2} |\det A|$ where $A = \begin{bmatrix} x_1 & y_1 & 1 \\ x_2 & y_2 & 1 \\ x_3 & y_3 & 1 \end{bmatrix}$

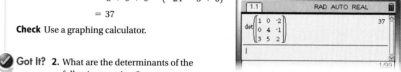

Think

What can you do first to evaluate a 3 × 3 determinant?
Copy the first two columns to the right of the matrix.

$\begin{bmatrix} 1 & 0 & -2 \\ 0 & 4 & -1 \\ 3 & 5 & 2 \end{bmatrix} \begin{matrix} 1 & 0 \\ 0 & 4 \\ 3 & 5 \end{matrix}$

Additional Problems

1. If $A = \begin{bmatrix} 2 & 0 & 1 \\ 1 & 3 & -1 \\ 2 & 1 & 1 \end{bmatrix}$ and

$B = \begin{bmatrix} \frac{4}{3} & \frac{1}{3} & -1 \\ -1 & 0 & 1 \\ -\frac{5}{3} & -\frac{2}{3} & 2 \end{bmatrix}$, are

A and B inverses?

ANSWER yes

2. What is the determinant of $\begin{bmatrix} 3 & 5 & -1 \\ 1 & 0 & -2 \\ 2 & 3 & 1 \end{bmatrix}$?

ANSWER -10

3. As part of a remodeling project, you want to paint a triangular area on a cement floor that is marked along the wall with decorative stones every meter. Using the stones as a reference, you determine the coordinates of the vertices of the area you want to paint are (4, 6), (12, 9), and (7, 11). What is the area of the triangle?

ANSWER 15.5 sq m

4. Does the matrix

$A = \begin{bmatrix} 4 & -4 \\ -3 & 6 \end{bmatrix}$ have an

inverse? If it does, what is A^{-1}?

ANSWER yes; $\begin{bmatrix} \frac{1}{2} & \frac{1}{3} \\ \frac{1}{4} & \frac{1}{3} \end{bmatrix}$

5. You stored your credit card numbers in a file after they were coded by the matrix

$\begin{bmatrix} -5 & 3 \\ 3 & -7 \end{bmatrix}$. One of the

numbers in the file is -1, -14, -16, -22, 10, 10, -31, -29, -15, -2, -6, 8, -32, -32, 3, 7. What is the original credit card number?

ANSWER 2455 1187 3231 5532

Answers

Got It? (continued)

2. a. 3

b. 0

c. -48

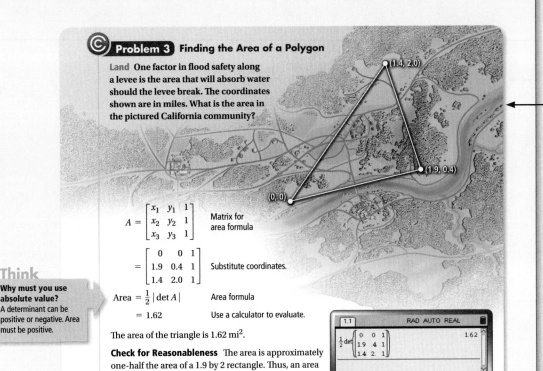

Problem 3   Finding the Area of a Polygon

Land One factor in flood safety along a levee is the area that will absorb water should the levee break. The coordinates shown are in miles. What is the area in the pictured California community?

$$A = \begin{bmatrix} x_1 & y_1 & 1 \\ x_2 & y_2 & 1 \\ x_3 & y_3 & 1 \end{bmatrix} \quad \text{Matrix for area formula}$$

$$= \begin{bmatrix} 0 & 0 & 1 \\ 1.9 & 0.4 & 1 \\ 1.4 & 2.0 & 1 \end{bmatrix} \quad \text{Substitute coordinates.}$$

Area $= \frac{1}{2} |\det A|$ Area formula

$= 1.62$ Use a calculator to evaluate.

The area of the triangle is 1.62 mi².

Check for Reasonableness The area is approximately one-half the area of a 1.9 by 2 rectangle. Thus, an area of about 1.6 units² is reasonable.

> | 1.1 | | RAD AUTO REAL | |
> |---|---|---|---|
> | $\frac{1}{2} \det \left(\begin{smallmatrix} 0 & 0 & 1 \\ 1.9 & .4 & 1 \\ 1.4 & 2. & 1 \end{smallmatrix} \right)$ | | | 1.62 |
> | | | | 1/99 |

Think

Why must you use absolute value?
A determinant can be positive or negative. Area must be positive.

✔ **Got It?**   **3.** What is the area of the triangle with the given vertices?
     a. $(1, 3), (-3, 0), (5, 0)$ **b.** $(1, 3), (5, 8), (9, -1)$

The determinant of a matrix can help you determine whether the matrix has an inverse and, if it exists, to find the inverse.

take note

Key Concept   Inverse of a 2 × 2 Matrix

Let $A = \begin{bmatrix} a & b \\ c & d \end{bmatrix}$.

If $\det A = 0$, then A is a **singular matrix** and has no inverse.

If $\det A \neq 0$, then the inverse of A, written A^{-1}, is

$$A^{-1} = \frac{1}{\det A} \begin{bmatrix} d & -b \\ -c & a \end{bmatrix} = \frac{1}{ad - bc} \begin{bmatrix} d & -b \\ -c & a \end{bmatrix}.$$

Problem 3

Q Does it matter in which order you list the points? Explain. **[No, as long as you list the coordinates of each point in their own row. The naming of the vertices as (x_1, y_1), (x_2, y_2), and (x_3, y_3) is arbitrary.]**

Q How would you check for reasonableness if none of the vertices were located at $(0, 0)$? **[Use half of the area of the rectangle with dimensions of (greatest x-coordinate − least x-coordinate) and (greatest y-coordinate − least y-coordinate).]**

Got It?

Q What matrices would you use to find the area of the triangles in 3a and 3b?
$$\left[\begin{bmatrix} 1 & 3 & 1 \\ -3 & 0 & 1 \\ 5 & 0 & 1 \end{bmatrix} ; \begin{bmatrix} 1 & 3 & 1 \\ 5 & 8 & 1 \\ 9 & -1 & 1 \end{bmatrix} \right]$$

Q What values for reasonableness would you use to check the areas you find for 3a and 3b? What expressions would you use to find these values? **[half the area of the rectangle formed by the difference of the greatest and least x- and y-coordinates; 3a: $(5 - (-3)) \cdot (3 - 0) \cdot 0.5 = 12$; 3b: $(9 - 1) \cdot (8 - (-1)) \cdot 0.5 = 36$]**

Take Note

Q Why does a matrix not have an inverse if its determinant is zero? **[A determinant of zero would cause division by zero when you tried to find the inverse, and division by zero is not defined.]**

---

3. a. 12 units²
    b. 28 units²

Problem 4 ERROR PREVENTION

Q If when you check the inverse you find that your matrix is not the correct matrix, what are the possible errors you might have made? **[Samples: You may have calculated the determinant incorrectly; one or more signs may have been changed incorrectly; you may have forgotten to switch the numbers on the diagonal; you may have forgotten to multiply by the scalar; the inverse matrix may have been simplified incorrectly.]**

Q If you do not have access to a graphing calculator, what would you have to do to check if the matrix you found is the inverse? **[Multiply the original matrix by the matrix you found to see if you get the identity matrix, *I*.]**

EXTENSION

Q If you forget to change the diagonals of the matrix when calculating the determinant, how will the matrix you find be different from the inverse matrix? **[The elements on the main diagonal will be in the wrong corners and the elements on the other diagonal will have the wrong sign.]**

Got It?

Q What are the determinants of 4a, 4b, and 4c? **[2, 0 and 1]**

Q What matrices will you multiply by the scalar $\frac{1}{\det A}$ to find the inverse if it exists for 4a, 4b, and 4c? $\left[\begin{array}{cc} 2 & -2 \\ -3 & 4 \end{array}\right]; \left[\begin{array}{cc} -10 & -5 \\ 4 & 2 \end{array}\right];$ and $\left[\begin{array}{cc} 3 & -4 \\ -5 & 7 \end{array}\right]$]

 Problem 4 Finding the Inverse of a Matrix

Does the matrix $A = \left[\begin{array}{cc} -3 & 6 \\ -1 & 3 \end{array}\right]$ have an inverse? If it does, what is A^{-1}?

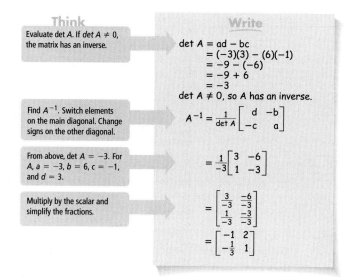

Think	Write
Evaluate det A. If $\det A \neq 0$, the matrix has an inverse.	$\det A = ad - bc$ $= (-3)(3) - (6)(-1)$ $= -9 - (-6)$ $= -9 + 6$ $= -3$ $\det A \neq 0$, so A has an inverse.
Find A^{-1}. Switch elements on the main diagonal. Change signs on the other diagonal.	$A^{-1} = \frac{1}{\det A}\left[\begin{array}{cc} d & -b \\ -c & a \end{array}\right]$
From above, det A = −3. For A, $a = -3$, $b = 6$, $c = -1$, and $d = 3$.	$= \frac{1}{-3}\left[\begin{array}{cc} 3 & -6 \\ 1 & -3 \end{array}\right]$
Multiply by the scalar and simplify the fractions.	$= \left[\begin{array}{cc} \frac{3}{-3} & \frac{-6}{-3} \\ \frac{1}{-3} & \frac{-3}{-3} \end{array}\right]$ $= \left[\begin{array}{cc} -1 & 2 \\ -\frac{1}{3} & 1 \end{array}\right]$

Check Use a graphing calculator.

Method 1

Check that $AA^{-1} = I$.

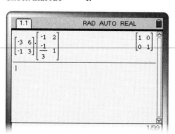

Method 2

Find A^{-1}.

Got It? **4.** Does the matrix have an inverse? If so, what is it?

a. $A = \left[\begin{array}{cc} 4 & 2 \\ 3 & 2 \end{array}\right]$ **b.** $B = \left[\begin{array}{cc} 2 & 5 \\ -4 & -10 \end{array}\right]$ **c.** $C = \left[\begin{array}{cc} 7 & 4 \\ 5 & 3 \end{array}\right]$

Answers

Got It? (continued)

4. a. yes; $\left[\begin{array}{cc} 1 & -1 \\ -\frac{3}{2} & 2 \end{array}\right]$

  b. no

  c. yes; $\left[\begin{array}{cc} 3 & -4 \\ -5 & 7 \end{array}\right]$

Problem 5 Encoding and Decoding With Matrices

A How can you use matrix multiplication to encode the account number from the credit card?

Step 1 Select a coding matrix. $C = \begin{bmatrix} 2 & -1 \\ 3 & 5 \end{bmatrix}$

Step 2 Place the card information in a matrix with appropriate dimensions for multiplication by the coding matrix.

$$A = \begin{bmatrix} 4 & 1 & 7 & 3 & 1 & 2 & 3 & 4 \\ 9 & 8 & 7 & 6 & 1 & 3 & 5 & 7 \end{bmatrix}$$

Step 3 Multiply the coding matrix and the information matrix to encode the information. Use a calculator.

$$CA = \begin{bmatrix} 2 & -1 \\ 3 & 5 \end{bmatrix}\begin{bmatrix} 4 & 1 & 7 & 3 & 1 & 2 & 3 & 4 \\ 9 & 8 & 7 & 6 & 1 & 3 & 5 & 7 \end{bmatrix}$$

$$= \begin{bmatrix} -1 & -6 & 7 & 0 & 1 & 1 & 1 & 1 \\ 57 & 43 & 56 & 39 & 8 & 21 & 34 & 47 \end{bmatrix}$$

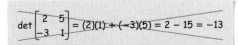

Step 4 The coded account number is
$-1, -6, 7, 0, 1, 1, 1, 1, 57, 43, 56, 39, 8, 21, 34, 47.$

B How do you use a decoding matrix to recover the account number?

Multiply the coded information by the inverse of the coding matrix.

$$\begin{bmatrix} 2 & -1 \\ 3 & 5 \end{bmatrix}^{-1}\begin{bmatrix} -1 & -6 & 7 & 0 & 1 & 1 & 1 & 1 \\ 57 & 43 & 56 & 39 & 8 & 21 & 34 & 47 \end{bmatrix} = \begin{bmatrix} 4 & 1 & 7 & 3 & 1 & 2 & 3 & 4 \\ 9 & 8 & 7 & 6 & 1 & 3 & 5 & 7 \end{bmatrix}$$

Got It? 5. a. How can you use matrix multiplication and the coding matrix $\begin{bmatrix} 4 & 8 \\ -2 & 4 \end{bmatrix}$ to encode the credit card account number in Problem 5?

  b. How can you use the inverse of the coding matrix to recover the credit card number?

Lesson Check

Do you know HOW?

Evaluate the determinant of each matrix.

1. $\begin{bmatrix} 4 & -1 \\ 8 & 2 \end{bmatrix}$ **2.** $\begin{bmatrix} 1 & 0 & 0 \\ -1 & 2 & 3 \\ 4 & -1 & 2 \end{bmatrix}$

Find the inverse of each matrix, if it exists.

3. $\begin{bmatrix} 4 & 2 \\ 10 & 5 \end{bmatrix}$ **4.** $\begin{bmatrix} 5 & 2 \\ 7 & 3 \end{bmatrix}$

Do you UNDERSTAND? MATHEMATICAL PRACTICES

5. Error Analysis What mistake did the student make when finding the determinant of $\begin{bmatrix} 2 & 5 \\ -3 & 1 \end{bmatrix}$?

$$\det\begin{bmatrix} 2 & 5 \\ -3 & 1 \end{bmatrix} = (2)(1) + (-3)(5) = 2 - 15 = -13$$

6. Reasoning Explain why a 2×3 matrix does not have a multiplicative inverse.

Q Could you use a coding matrix with three columns? Explain. **[No; the credit card has sixteen digits, which cannot be divided evenly into three rows.]**

Got It?

Q Would you alter matrix A in any way to code the credit card number using the new coding matrix? Explain. **[No; since the coding matrix still has two columns, matrix A does not have to be altered to allow multiplication.]**

3 Lesson Check

Do you know HOW?
- If students are unsure whether the matrix they found for Exercise 4 is the inverse, remind them that they can check the answer by multiplying the matrix by the inverse.

Do you UNDERSTAND?
- For Exercise 6, if students cannot figure out why a 2×3 matrix does not have a multiplicative inverse, ask them what kinds of matrices have determinants.

Close

Q What steps do you take to find the inverse of a 2×2 matrix A? **[Find the determinant, if it exists. Switch the elements of the main diagonal of the matrix, and switch the signs of the elements of the other diagonal. Multiply the new matrix by the scalar $\frac{1}{\det A}$, and simplify the resulting matrix. Check.]**

Plan

What size array should you use for the card information? Since the coding matrix has two columns, the information matrix must have two rows, so they can be multiplied.

---

5. a. 88, 68, 84, 60, 12, 32, 52, 72, 28, 30, 14, 18, 2, 8, 14, 20

  b. Multiply the coded information by the inverse of the coding matrix and get the following:
$$\begin{bmatrix} 4 & 1 & 7 & 3 & 1 & 2 & 3 & 4 \\ 9 & 8 & 7 & 6 & 1 & 3 & 5 & 7 \end{bmatrix}$$

Lesson Check

1. 16

2. 7

3. does not exist

4. $\begin{bmatrix} 3 & -2 \\ -7 & 5 \end{bmatrix}$

5. The student did not subtract correctly.
$$\det\begin{bmatrix} 2 & 5 \\ -3 & 1 \end{bmatrix} = (2)(1) - (-3)(5)$$
$$= 2 - (-15)$$
$$= 2 + 15 = 17$$

6. Answers may vary. Sample: A 2×3 matrix does not have a multiplicative inverse because the set of 2×3 matrices has no multiplicative identity.

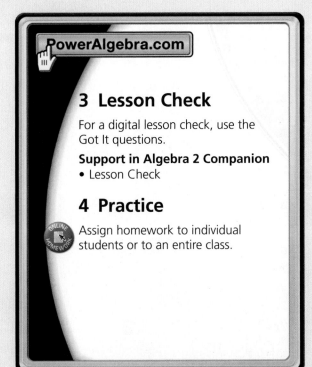

PowerAlgebra.com

3 Lesson Check

For a digital lesson check, use the Got It questions.

Support in Algebra 2 Companion
- Lesson Check

4 Practice

Assign homework to individual students or to an entire class.

4 Practice

ASSIGNMENT GUIDE
Basic: 7–37 all, 45–50
Average: 7–37 odd, 38–59
Advanced: 7–37 odd, 38–61
Standardized Test Prep: 62–66
Mixed Review: 67–76

 Mathematical Practices are supported by exercises with red headings. Here are the Practices supported in this lesson:

MP 1: Make Sense of Problems Ex. 46
MP 2: Reason Quantitatively Ex. 58, 59
MP 3: Construct Arguments Ex. 59
MP 3: Communicate Ex. 6, 47, 58
MP 3: Critique the Reasoning of Others Ex. 5, 36
MP 5: Use Appropriate Tools Ex. 24–26

Applications exercises have blue headings.
Exercise 49 supports MP 4: Model.

EXERCISE 49: Use the Think About a Plan worksheet in the **Practice and Problem Solving Workbook** (also available in the Teaching Resources in print and online) to further support students' development in becoming independent learners.

HOMEWORK QUICK CHECK
To check students' understanding of key skills and concepts, go over Exercises 7, 29, 46, 47, and 49.

 Practice and Problem-Solving Exercises MATHEMATICAL PRACTICES

Practice Determine whether the matrices are multiplicative inverses.   *See Problem 1.*

7. $\begin{bmatrix} 3 & 2 \\ 4 & 3 \end{bmatrix}, \begin{bmatrix} 3 & -2 \\ -4 & 3 \end{bmatrix}$

8. $\begin{bmatrix} -3 & 7 \\ -2 & 5 \end{bmatrix}, \begin{bmatrix} -5 & 7 \\ -2 & 3 \end{bmatrix}$

9. $\begin{bmatrix} \frac{1}{5} & -\frac{1}{10} \\ 0 & \frac{1}{4} \end{bmatrix}, \begin{bmatrix} 5 & 2 \\ 0 & 4 \end{bmatrix}$

10. $\begin{bmatrix} 1 & 2 & -1 \\ -1.5 & -3 & 1.75 \\ 0 & -1 & 0.5 \end{bmatrix}, \begin{bmatrix} 1 & 0 & 2 \\ 3 & 2 & -1 \\ 6 & 4 & 0 \end{bmatrix}$

11. $\begin{bmatrix} 2 & 2 & 2 \\ -2 & 2 & -2 \\ -2 & -2 & -2 \end{bmatrix}, \begin{bmatrix} 2 & 2 & 2 \\ -2 & 2 & -2 \\ -2 & -2 & -2 \end{bmatrix}$

Evaluate the determinant of each matrix.   *See Problems 2, 3, and 4.*

12. $\begin{bmatrix} 7 & 2 \\ 0 & -3 \end{bmatrix}$

13. $\begin{bmatrix} 6 & 2 \\ -6 & -2 \end{bmatrix}$

14. $\begin{bmatrix} 0 & 0.5 \\ 1.5 & 2 \end{bmatrix}$

15. $\begin{bmatrix} \frac{1}{2} & \frac{2}{3} \\ \frac{3}{5} & \frac{1}{4} \end{bmatrix}$

16. $\begin{bmatrix} -1 & 3 \\ 5 & 2 \end{bmatrix}$

17. $\begin{bmatrix} 5 & 3 \\ -2 & 1 \end{bmatrix}$

18. $\begin{bmatrix} 2 & -1 \\ 5 & -4 \end{bmatrix}$

19. $\begin{bmatrix} -4 & 3 \\ 2 & 0 \end{bmatrix}$

20. $\begin{bmatrix} 1 & 2 & 5 \\ 3 & 1 & 0 \\ 1 & 2 & 1 \end{bmatrix}$

21. $\begin{bmatrix} 1 & 4 & 0 \\ 2 & 3 & 5 \\ 0 & 1 & 0 \end{bmatrix}$

22. $\begin{bmatrix} -2 & 4 & 1 \\ 3 & 0 & -1 \\ 1 & 2 & 1 \end{bmatrix}$

23. $\begin{bmatrix} 2 & 3 & 0 \\ 1 & 2 & 5 \\ 7 & 0 & 1 \end{bmatrix}$

Graphing Calculator Evaluate the determinant of each 3 × 3 matrix.

24. $\begin{bmatrix} 1 & 0 & 0 \\ 0 & 1 & 0 \\ 0 & 0 & 1 \end{bmatrix}$

25. $\begin{bmatrix} 0 & -2 & -3 \\ 1 & 2 & 4 \\ -2 & 0 & 1 \end{bmatrix}$

26. $\begin{bmatrix} 12.2 & 13.3 & 9 \\ 1 & -4 & -17 \\ 21.4 & -15 & 0 \end{bmatrix}$

27. Use the map to determine the approximate area of the Bermuda Triangle.

Determine whether each matrix has an inverse. If an inverse matrix exists, find it.

28. $\begin{bmatrix} 2 & -1 \\ 1 & 0 \end{bmatrix}$

29. $\begin{bmatrix} 2 & 3 \\ 1 & 1 \end{bmatrix}$

30. $\begin{bmatrix} 2 & 3 \\ 2 & 4 \end{bmatrix}$

31. $\begin{bmatrix} 1 & 3 \\ 2 & 0 \end{bmatrix}$

32. $\begin{bmatrix} 6 & -8 \\ -3 & 4 \end{bmatrix}$

33. $\begin{bmatrix} 4 & 8 \\ -3 & -2 \end{bmatrix}$

34. $\begin{bmatrix} -1.5 & 3 \\ 2.5 & -0.5 \end{bmatrix}$

35. $\begin{bmatrix} 1 & -2 \\ 3 & 0 \end{bmatrix}$

36. **Error Analysis** A student wrote $\begin{bmatrix} 1 & \frac{1}{2} \\ \frac{1}{3} & \frac{1}{4} \end{bmatrix}$ as the inverse of $\begin{bmatrix} 1 & 2 \\ 3 & 4 \end{bmatrix}$. What mistake did the student make? Explain your reasoning.

37. Use the coding matrix in Problem 5 to encode the phone number (555) 358-0001.   *See Problem 5.*

Answers

Practice and Problem-Solving Exercises

7. yes
8. yes
9. yes
10. yes
11. no
12. −21
13. 0
14. −0.75
15. $-\frac{11}{40}$
16. −17
17. 11
18. −3
19. −6
20. 20
21. −5
22. −14

23. 106
24. 1
25. 6
26. −7314.14
27. 466,250 mi²

28. yes; $\begin{bmatrix} 0 & 1 \\ -1 & 2 \end{bmatrix}$

29. yes; $\begin{bmatrix} -1 & 3 \\ 1 & -2 \end{bmatrix}$

30. yes; $\begin{bmatrix} 2 & -1.5 \\ -1 & 1 \end{bmatrix}$

31. yes; $\begin{bmatrix} 0 & \frac{1}{2} \\ \frac{1}{3} & -\frac{1}{6} \end{bmatrix}$

32. no

33. yes; $\begin{bmatrix} -\frac{1}{8} & -\frac{1}{2} \\ \frac{3}{16} & \frac{1}{4} \end{bmatrix}$

34. yes; $\begin{bmatrix} \frac{2}{27} & \frac{4}{9} \\ \frac{10}{27} & \frac{2}{9} \end{bmatrix}$

35. yes; $\begin{bmatrix} 0 & \frac{1}{3} \\ -\frac{1}{2} & \frac{1}{6} \end{bmatrix}$

36. The student found the inverse of each individual element of the matrix and NOT the inverse of the entire matrix.

The inverse of $\begin{bmatrix} 1 & 2 \\ 3 & 4 \end{bmatrix}$ is $\begin{bmatrix} -2 & 1 \\ \frac{3}{2} & -\frac{1}{2} \end{bmatrix}$.

37. 2, 10, 10, 6, 9, 55, 15, 15, 9, 20

Evaluate each determinant.

38. $\begin{bmatrix} 4 & 5 \\ -4 & 4 \end{bmatrix}$

39. $\begin{bmatrix} -3 & 10 \\ 6 & 20 \end{bmatrix}$

40. $\begin{bmatrix} -\frac{1}{2} & 2 \\ -2 & 8 \end{bmatrix}$

41. $\begin{bmatrix} 6 & 9 \\ 3 & 6 \end{bmatrix}$

42. $\begin{bmatrix} 0 & 2 & -3 \\ 1 & 2 & 4 \\ -2 & 0 & 1 \end{bmatrix}$

43. $\begin{bmatrix} 5 & 1 & 0 \\ 0 & 2 & -1 \\ -2 & -3 & 1 \end{bmatrix}$

44. $\begin{bmatrix} 4 & 6 & -1 \\ 2 & 3 & 2 \\ 1 & -1 & 1 \end{bmatrix}$

45. $\begin{bmatrix} -3 & 2 & -1 \\ 2 & 5 & 2 \\ 1 & -2 & 0 \end{bmatrix}$

46. **Think About a Plan** Use matrices to find the area of the figure at the right.
    - What shapes do you know how to find the area of?
    - Can the polygon be broken into these shapes?
    - How many shapes will you need to break the polygon into?

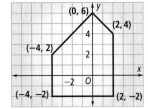

47. **Writing** Suppose $A = \begin{bmatrix} a & b \\ c & d \end{bmatrix}$ has an inverse. In your own words, describe how to switch or change the elements of A to write A^{-1}.

48. If matrix A has an inverse, what must be true?

    I. $AA^{-1} = I$ II. $A^{-1}A = I$ III. $A^{-1}I = A^{-1}$

    Ⓐ I only   Ⓒ I and II only

    Ⓑ II only   Ⓓ I, II, and III

49. **Geometry** Use matrices to find the area of the figure at the right. Check your result by using standard area formulas.

Determine whether each matrix has an inverse. If an inverse matrix exists, find it. If it does not exist, explain why not.

50. $\begin{bmatrix} 1 & 4 \\ 1 & 3 \end{bmatrix}$

51. $\begin{bmatrix} 4 & 7 \\ 3 & 5 \end{bmatrix}$

52. $\begin{bmatrix} -3 & 11 \\ 2 & -7 \end{bmatrix}$

53. $\begin{bmatrix} 2 & 0 \\ 0 & 2 \end{bmatrix}$

54. $\begin{bmatrix} -2 & 1 & -1 \\ 2 & 0 & 4 \\ 0 & 2 & 5 \end{bmatrix}$

55. $\begin{bmatrix} 2 & 0 & -1 \\ -1 & -1 & 1 \\ 3 & 2 & 0 \end{bmatrix}$

56. $\begin{bmatrix} 0 & 0 & 2 \\ 1 & 4 & -2 \\ 3 & -2 & 1 \end{bmatrix}$

57. $\begin{bmatrix} 1 & 2 & 6 \\ 1 & -1 & 0 \\ 1 & 0 & 2 \end{bmatrix}$

38. 36
39. −120
40. 0
41. 9
42. −30
43. −3
44. 25
45. 1
46. 44 units²
47. Answers may vary. Sample: Form a new matrix by switching the element in row 1, column 1 with the element in row 2, column 2. Then replace the other two elements with their opposites. Finally, divide each element by the determinant of the original matrix.
48. D
49. 38 units²
50. yes; $\begin{bmatrix} -3 & 4 \\ 1 & -1 \end{bmatrix}$

51. yes; $\begin{bmatrix} -5 & 7 \\ 3 & -4 \end{bmatrix}$

52. yes; $\begin{bmatrix} 7 & 11 \\ 2 & 3 \end{bmatrix}$

53. yes; $\begin{bmatrix} 0.5 & 0 \\ 0 & 0.5 \end{bmatrix}$

54. yes; $\begin{bmatrix} -4 & -3.5 & 2 \\ -5 & -5 & 3 \\ 2 & 2 & -1 \end{bmatrix}$

55. yes; $\begin{bmatrix} 0.4 & 0.4 & 0.2 \\ -0.6 & -0.6 & 0.2 \\ -0.2 & 0.8 & 0.4 \end{bmatrix}$

56. yes; $\begin{bmatrix} 0 & \frac{1}{7} & \frac{2}{7} \\ \frac{1}{4} & \frac{3}{14} & -\frac{1}{14} \\ \frac{1}{2} & 0 & 0 \end{bmatrix}$

57. no inverse because the determinant equals zero

Answers

Practice and Problem-Solving Exercises (continued)

58. a. 0

   b. 0

   c. 0

   d. 0

Answers may vary. Sample: When the top row and bottom row are identical and the middle row has the same numbers as both rows, then the determinant is zero.

59. 6

60. Answers may vary. Sample: when
$ad - bc = -1$ and $a = -d$

61. $MN = \begin{bmatrix} ae + bg & af + bh \\ ce + dg & cf + dh \end{bmatrix}$

$$\det MN = (ae + bg)(cf + dh)$$
$$- (af + bh)(ce + dg)$$
$$= acef + adeh + bcfg + bdgh$$
$$- acef - adfg - bceh - bdgh$$
$$= adeh + bcfg - adfg - bceh$$

Also, $\det M \cdot \det N = (ad - bc)(eh - fg)$
$$= adeh - adfg$$
$$- bceh + bcfg.$$

So, $\det M \cdot \det N = \det MN$

Standardized Test Prep

62. 15

63. $\frac{1}{2}$

64. $\frac{1}{56}$

65. 15

66. 4

Mixed Review

67. $\begin{bmatrix} 2 & 5 \\ 1 & 1 \end{bmatrix}$

68. $\begin{bmatrix} -10 & 19 \\ -20 & 7 \end{bmatrix}$

69. 720

70. 362,880

71. $1.08972864 \times 10^{10}$

72. 110,880

73. no solution

74. $(6, 0, -3)$

75. $(3, -3, 9)$

76. $(-2, -1, -3)$

---

58. Writing Evaluate the determinant of each matrix. Describe any patterns.

   a. $\begin{bmatrix} 1 & 2 & 3 \\ 1 & 2 & 3 \\ 1 & 2 & 3 \end{bmatrix}$
   b. $\begin{bmatrix} -1 & -2 & -3 \\ -3 & -2 & -1 \\ -1 & -2 & -3 \end{bmatrix}$
   c. $\begin{bmatrix} 1 & 2 & 3 \\ 2 & 3 & 1 \\ 1 & 2 & 3 \end{bmatrix}$
   d. $\begin{bmatrix} -1 & 2 & -3 \\ 2 & -3 & -1 \\ -1 & 2 & -3 \end{bmatrix}$

59. Reasoning For what value of x will matrix A have no inverse? $A = \begin{bmatrix} 1 & 2 \\ 3 & x \end{bmatrix}$

Challenge

60. Reasoning Suppose $A = \begin{bmatrix} a & b \\ c & d \end{bmatrix}$. For what values of a, b, c, and d will A be its own inverse? (*Hint:* There is more than one correct answer.)

61. Let $M = \begin{bmatrix} a & b \\ c & d \end{bmatrix}$ and $N = \begin{bmatrix} e & f \\ g & h \end{bmatrix}$. Prove that the product of the determinants of M and N equals the determinant of the matrix product MN.

Standardized Test Prep

GRIDDED RESPONSE

SAT/ACT

62. What is the determinant of $\begin{bmatrix} -2 & -3 \\ 5 & 0 \end{bmatrix}$?

63. If $A = \begin{bmatrix} 4 & 2 \\ -3 & -1 \end{bmatrix}$, and the inverse of A is $x\begin{bmatrix} -1 & -2 \\ 3 & 4 \end{bmatrix}$, what is the value of x? Enter your answer as a fraction.

64. What is the value of $\frac{6!}{8!}$? Give your answer as a fraction in simplest terms.

65. If $\log(7y - 5) = 2$, what is the value of y?

66. If the equation for a circle is $x^2 + y^2 - 2x + 6y - 6 = 0$, what is its radius?

Mixed Review

Solve each matrix equation.   See Lesson 12-2.

67. $2\begin{bmatrix} -1 & 3 \\ -2 & 0 \end{bmatrix} - 3X = \begin{bmatrix} -8 & -9 \\ -7 & -3 \end{bmatrix}$
   68. $2X + 3\begin{bmatrix} 4 & -6 \\ 8 & -3 \end{bmatrix} = \begin{bmatrix} -8 & 20 \\ -16 & 5 \end{bmatrix}$

Evaluate each expression.   See Lesson 11-1.

69. $6!$
   70. $9!$
   71. $\frac{15!}{5!}$
   72. $\frac{12!}{6!3!}$

Get Ready! To prepare for Lesson 12-4, do Exercises 73–76.

Solve each system.   See Lesson 3-5.

73. $\begin{cases} x = 5 \\ x - y + z = 5 \\ x + y - z = -5 \end{cases}$
   74. $\begin{cases} x - y - z = 9 \\ 3x + 2z = 12 \\ x = y - 2z \end{cases}$

75. $\begin{cases} -x + 2y + z = 0 \\ y = -2x + 3 \\ z = 3x \end{cases}$
   76. $\begin{cases} 5x - 4y - 3z = 3 \\ z = y + x \\ x = 3y + 1 \end{cases}$

Differentiated Remediation

Additional Instructional Support

Algebra 2 Companion

Students can use the **Algebra 2 Companion** worktext (4 pages) as you teach the lesson. Use the Companion to support

- New Vocabulary
- Key Concepts
- Got It for each Problem
- Lesson Check

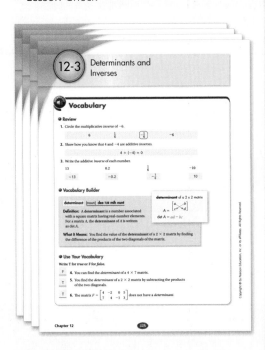

ELL Support

Use Graphic Organizers To aid student understanding of the process of finding the determinant, refer to the diagonal multiplications by their physical directions as you use the board in instruction. Draw the arrows indicating the directions of multiplication, and use real numbers instead of the notation for the elements. In addition, as you draw the arrows through the diagonals whose values are being multiplied, place the product value at the end of each arrow tip. Show the sums of the product results above and below the matrix for a 3×3 matrix to indicate the source of the values.

5 Assess & Remediate

Lesson Quiz

1. If $A = \begin{bmatrix} 1 & 3 \\ -1 & 4 \end{bmatrix}$ and $B = \begin{bmatrix} 4 & -3 \\ 1 & 1 \end{bmatrix}$, are A and B inverses?

2. What is the determinant of $\begin{bmatrix} -4 & 3 \\ 1 & 2 \end{bmatrix}$?

3. **Do you UNDERSTAND?** You want to buy a corner lot shaped like a triangle. You use the scale of a map to measure the coordinates of the lot in feet. They are (0, 0), (50, 45), and (−25, 90). What is the area of the lot?

4. Find the inverse of the matrix $\begin{bmatrix} -3 & -6 \\ 1 & 3 \end{bmatrix}$ if it exists.

5. What would the credit card number 3087 2377 1988 3579 be coded by the matrix $\begin{bmatrix} -1 & 4 \\ 2 & 1 \end{bmatrix}$?

ANSWERS TO LESSON QUIZ

1. no

2. −11

3. 2812.5 sq ft

4. $\begin{bmatrix} -1 & -2 \\ \frac{1}{3} & 1 \end{bmatrix}$

5. 1, 36, 24, 25, 10, 17, 21, 29, 7, 9, 24, 22, 7, 11, 21, 23

PRESCRIPTION FOR REMEDIATION

Use the student work on the Lesson Quiz to prescribe a differentiated review assignment:

Points	Differentiated Remediation
0–2	Intervention
3–4	On-level
5	Extension

PowerAlgebra.com

5 Assess & Remediate

Assign the Lesson Quiz. Appropriate intervention, practice, or enrichment is automatically generated based on student performance.

Intervention

- **Reteaching** (2 pages) Provides reteaching and practice exercises for the key lesson concepts. Use with struggling students or absent students.
- **English Language Learner Support** Helps students develop and reinforce mathematical vocabulary and key concepts.

All-in-One Resources/Online
Reteaching

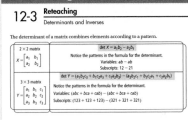

All-in-One Resources/Online
English Language Learner Support

Differentiated Remediation *continued*

On-Level

- **Practice** (2 pages) Provides extra practice for each lesson. For simpler practice exercises, use the Form K Practice pages found in the All-in-One Teaching Resources and online.

- **Think About a Plan** Helps students develop specific problem-solving skills and strategies by providing scaffolded guiding questions.

- **Standardized Test Prep** Focuses on all major exercises, all major question types, and helps students prepare for the high-stakes assessments.

Extension

- **Enrichment** Provides students with interesting problems and activities that extend the concepts of the lesson.

- **Activities, Games, and Puzzles** Worksheets that can be used for concepts development, enrichment, and for fun!

Practice and Problem Solving Wkbk/ All-in-One Resources/Online
Practice page 1

12-3 Practice — Form G
Determinants and Inverses

Determine whether the matrices are multiplicative inverses.

1. yes 2. yes 3. yes

4. no 5. yes

Evaluate the determinant of each matrix.

6. -1 7. -21 8. 14

9. -29 10. 9 11. 36

12. 21 13. 42 14. -210

Graphing Calculator Evaluate the determinant of each 3 × 3 matrix.

15. -1 16. 268 17. 617.578

18. The area between the North Carolina cities of Raleigh, Durham, and Chapel Hill is called the Research Triangle. Use the map to determine the approximate area of the Research Triangle. The coordinates are given in miles. Answers may vary. Sample: about 32 mi²

Practice and Problem Solving Wkbk/ All-in-One Resources/Online
Practice page 2

12-3 Practice (continued) — Form G
Determinants and Inverses

Determine whether each matrix has an inverse. If an inverse matrix exists, find it.

19. 20. no inverse 21.

22. 23. 24. no inverse

25. Use the coding matrix [[3, 6],[9, 12]] to encode the serial number 45-8-62-4-31-10.
159-210-246-453-444-678

Evaluate the determinant of each matrix.

26. 46 27. -49 28. 4

29. 37 30. 0 31. 576

32. **Writing** Describe how to use matrices to find the area of a polygon.
Answers may vary. Sample: Divide the polygon into triangles. Name the coordinates of each vertex. Find the area of each triangle using the formula
$Area = \frac{1}{2}\left|\det\begin{bmatrix} x_1 & y_1 & 1 \\ x_2 & y_2 & 1 \\ x_3 & y_3 & 1 \end{bmatrix}\right|$. Add the areas.

33. Find the area of the figure at the right.
25.5 square units

Determine whether each matrix has an inverse. If an inverse matrix exists, find it. If it does not exist, explain why not.

34. 35. 36.

All-in-One Resources/Online
Enrichment

12-3 Enrichment
Determinants and Inverses

Suppose A and B are 2 × 2 matrices as follows:
$A = \begin{bmatrix} a & b \\ c & d \end{bmatrix}$, $B = \begin{bmatrix} e & f \\ g & h \end{bmatrix}$

1. What is the value of the determinant of A, det A? $ad - bc$

2. Evaluate det B. $eh - fg$

3. Evaluate det A · det B. $adeh + bcfg - bceh - adfg$

4. Compute matrix AB. $\begin{bmatrix} ae + bg & af + bh \\ ce + dg & cf + dh \end{bmatrix}$

5. Evaluate det(AB). $(ae + bg)(cf + dh) - (af + bh)(ce + dg) = adeh + bcfg - bceh - adfg$

6. What can you conclude? $\det(AB) = \det A \cdot \det B$

7. Explain your results.
The determinant of the product of two matrices is equal to the product of the determinants.

8. Suppose that a 2 × 2 matrix A has an inverse A^{-1}. Use the product rule to investigate how the determinant of A^{-1} is related to the determinant of A. $\det A = 1$; $\frac{1}{\det A}$
$\det(A \cdot A^{-1}) = \det A \cdot \det A^{-1}$
_____ $= \det A \cdot \det A^{-1}$
_____ $= \det A \cdot \det A^{-1}$
_____ $= \det A^{-1}$

9. Explain your results.
The determinant of the inverse of a matrix is equal to the reciprocal (inverse) of the determinant of the original matrix.

Practice and Problem Solving Wkbk/ All-in-One Resources/Online
Think About a Plan

12-3 Think About a Plan
Determinants and Inverses

Geometry Find the area of the figure to the right.

Understanding the Problem

1. You know how to find the area of what shape using matrices? triangle

2. Can you divide the figure into these shapes? Explain.
Answers may vary. Sample: Yes; by picking a vertex and drawing two segments from it to the other two nonadjacent vertices, I can divide the figure into 3 triangles.

3. What is the problem asking you to find?
the area of the figure by dividing it into triangles and adding the areas of the triangles

Planning the Solution

4. Divide the figure into these shapes. List the vertices of the shapes.
Answers may vary. Sample: (0, 6), (2, 4), (−4, 2); (2, 4), (−2, −2), (−4, 2); (2, −2), (−4, −2), (−4, 2)

5. Write an expression to find the area of the figure. Answers may vary. Sample:
$\frac{1}{2}\left|\det\begin{bmatrix} 0 & 6 & 1 \\ 2 & 4 & 1 \\ -4 & 2 & 1 \end{bmatrix}\right| + \frac{1}{2}\left|\det\begin{bmatrix} 2 & 4 & 1 \\ -2 & -2 & 1 \\ -4 & 2 & 1 \end{bmatrix}\right| + \frac{1}{2}\left|\det\begin{bmatrix} 2 & -2 & 1 \\ -4 & -2 & 1 \\ -4 & 2 & 1 \end{bmatrix}\right|$

Getting an Answer

6. Simplify your expression to find the area of the figure. 38 units²

7. Is your answer reasonable? Explain.
Answers may vary. Sample: Yes; the figure fits within a rectangle that is 6 units wide and 8 units high, so an area somewhat less than 48 units² is reasonable.

Practice and Problem Solving Wkbk/ All-in-One Resources/Online
Standardized Test Prep

12-3 Standardized Test Prep
Determinants and Inverses

Gridded Response

Solve each exercise and enter your answer in the grid provided.

1. What is the determinant of $\begin{bmatrix} 4 & -2 \\ 5 & -3 \end{bmatrix}$?

2. If $A = \begin{bmatrix} 2 & 1 \\ -9 & 3 \end{bmatrix}$ and the inverse of A is $x \cdot \begin{bmatrix} 3 & -1 \\ 9 & 2 \end{bmatrix}$, what is the value of x?

3. If $\begin{bmatrix} 6 & 2 \\ 4 & 1 \end{bmatrix}$ and $A^{-1} = \begin{bmatrix} x & 1 \\ 2 & -3 \end{bmatrix}$, what is the value of x?

4. What is the determinant of $\begin{bmatrix} 1 & 0 & 2 \\ -1 & 2 & 3 \\ 0 & 3 & 2 \end{bmatrix}$?

5. What is the area of a triangle with vertices at (−5, 0), (3, −1), and (2, 6)?

Answers

Online Teacher Resource Center
Activities, Games, and Puzzles

12-3 Puzzle: That's Sum Matrix!
Determinants and Inverses

Match each exercise to its answer. Write the exercise number of the corresponding letter into the empty puzzle grid at the bottom of the page. All of your grid entries are correct if the sum of each column, row, and diagonal is 34.

1. Find the inverse of $\begin{bmatrix} 2 & 3 \\ 1 & 4 \end{bmatrix}$. H   A. -2

2. Evaluate $\begin{vmatrix} 3 & 4 \\ 1 & 5 \end{vmatrix}$. B   B. 11

3. Evaluate the determinant of $\begin{bmatrix} 6 & 7 \\ 8 & 9 \end{bmatrix}$. A   C. 0

4. Find $\begin{bmatrix} 3 & 5 \\ 1 & 2 \end{bmatrix}^{-1}$. G   D. -9

5. Evaluate $\det\begin{bmatrix} 3 & 4 \\ 6 & 8 \end{bmatrix}$. C   E. $\begin{bmatrix} 5 & -11 \\ -4 & 9 \end{bmatrix}$

6. If $M = \begin{bmatrix} 9 & 11 \\ 4 & 5 \end{bmatrix}$, find M^{-1}. E   F. $\begin{bmatrix} 0.3 & -0.7 \\ -0.2 & 0.8 \end{bmatrix}$

7. Find the inverse of $\begin{bmatrix} 8 & 7 \\ 2 & 3 \end{bmatrix}$. F   G. $\begin{bmatrix} 2 & -5 \\ -1 & 3 \end{bmatrix}$

8. Evaluate $\begin{vmatrix} -1 & 4 \\ 0 & 9 \end{vmatrix}$. D   H. $\begin{bmatrix} 0.8 & -0.6 \\ -0.2 & 0.4 \end{bmatrix}$

16	A. 3	B. 2	13
C. 5	10	11	D. 8
9	E. 6	F. 7	12
G. 4	15	14	H. 1

MathXL® for School
Go to PowerAlgebra.com

Do you know HOW?

Use matrices *A*, *B*, *C*, and *D*. Perform each operation.

$A = \begin{bmatrix} 3 & 1 \\ 5 & 7 \end{bmatrix}$ $B = \begin{bmatrix} 4 & 6 \\ 1 & 0 \end{bmatrix}$

$C = \begin{bmatrix} -5 & 3 \\ 1 & 9 \end{bmatrix}$ $D = \begin{bmatrix} 1.5 & 2 \\ 9 & -6 \end{bmatrix}$

1. $A + C$ **2.** $B - A$

3. $3D$ **4.** BA

5. $C(DB)$ **6.** $(AB)C$

Solve each matrix equation.

7. $X + \begin{bmatrix} -3 & 2 \\ 9 & -7 \end{bmatrix} = \begin{bmatrix} -3 & 5 \\ 4 & -5 \end{bmatrix}$

8. $\begin{bmatrix} 4 & -6 \\ -7 & 2 \end{bmatrix} - X = \begin{bmatrix} -1 & -7 \\ 3 & -2 \end{bmatrix}$

9. $X - \begin{bmatrix} -3 & 2 & -1 \\ 6 & -7 & 8 \end{bmatrix} = \begin{bmatrix} -2 & 3 & 5 \\ 1 & -3 & 7 \end{bmatrix}$

10. $3X + \begin{bmatrix} -2 & 1 \\ 7 & -3 \end{bmatrix} = \begin{bmatrix} 4 & -5 \\ -8 & 9 \end{bmatrix}$

11. $\begin{bmatrix} -3 & 2 \\ 5 & -1 \end{bmatrix} = \begin{bmatrix} 4 & 5 \\ -1 & 3 \end{bmatrix} - \frac{1}{2}X$

Solve each equation for *x* and *y*.

12. $\begin{bmatrix} -3 + 2x & 2 \\ 4 & -7y \end{bmatrix} = \begin{bmatrix} x - 4 & 2 \\ 4 & -35 \end{bmatrix}$

13. $\begin{bmatrix} 2x & 3 \\ -3 & -7x + y \end{bmatrix} = \begin{bmatrix} 3x + 2 & 3 \\ -3 & -4x \end{bmatrix}$

Evaluate the determinant of each matrix.

14. $\begin{bmatrix} -5 & 3 \\ 1 & 2 \end{bmatrix}$ **15.** $\begin{bmatrix} 3 & -1 \\ 4 & 2 \end{bmatrix}$

16. $\begin{bmatrix} -3 & 2 & 0 \\ -2 & 1 & 5 \\ -1 & 0 & 3 \end{bmatrix}$ **17.** $\begin{bmatrix} 5 & -1 & 1 \\ -3 & 0 & 2 \\ 7 & -8 & 4 \end{bmatrix}$

Find the inverse of each matrix, if it exists.

18. $\begin{bmatrix} -5 & 2 \\ 3 & -1 \end{bmatrix}$

19. $\begin{bmatrix} 4 & -5 \\ 1 & -6 \end{bmatrix}$

20. $\begin{bmatrix} -1 & 3 & 3 \\ 1 & 5 & 1 \\ 2 & 4 & -3 \end{bmatrix}$

21. $\begin{bmatrix} 3 & -1 & 2 \\ -1 & 0 & 2 \\ 1 & 3 & -1 \end{bmatrix}$

Given the vertices, find the area of each triangle.

22. $(-4, 1)$, $(5, 2)$, and $(2, -3)$

23. $(-2, -3)$, $(-5, 4)$, and $(4, 1)$

Do you UNDERSTAND?

© 24. Writing How can you decide whether you can multiply two matrices?

© 25. Open-Ended Write a matrix equation with solution $\begin{bmatrix} 12 & 7 & -3 & 8 \\ 9 & 0 & -11 & 1 \end{bmatrix}$.

© 26. Reasoning Suppose the product of two matrices has dimensions 4×3. If one of the matrices in the multiplication has dimensions 4×5, what are the dimensions of the other matrix?

27. Sales A store sells three kinds of pencils and the first matrix below shows the prices, in dollars, for each type. The second matrix shows the quantity sold for each type. Explain how you can find the total sales using the two matrices.

Type
Type A B C $\begin{matrix} A \\ B \\ C \end{matrix}\begin{bmatrix} 20 \\ 10 \\ 15 \end{bmatrix}$
$\begin{bmatrix} 3 & 4 & 2 \end{bmatrix}$

20. $\begin{bmatrix} \frac{19}{16} & \frac{21}{16} & -\frac{3}{4} \\ \frac{5}{16} & -\frac{3}{16} & \frac{1}{4} \\ -\frac{3}{8} & \frac{5}{8} & -\frac{1}{2} \end{bmatrix}$

21. $\begin{bmatrix} \frac{6}{25} & -\frac{1}{5} & \frac{2}{25} \\ -\frac{1}{25} & \frac{1}{5} & \frac{8}{25} \\ \frac{3}{25} & \frac{2}{5} & \frac{1}{25} \end{bmatrix}$

22. 21 units²

23. 27 units²

24. The number of columns of the first matrix must equal the number of rows of the second matrix.

25. Answers may vary. Sample:
$\begin{bmatrix} 23 & 10 & 0 & -2 \\ 14 & 3 & 0 & 5 \end{bmatrix} - \begin{bmatrix} 11 & 3 & 3 & -10 \\ 5 & 3 & 11 & 4 \end{bmatrix} = x$

26. 5×3

27. Multiply the first matrix (price for each type of pencil) by the second matrix (quantity sold for each type of pencil) to find the total sales. $3(20) + 4(10) + 2(15) = 130$.

Answers

Mid-Chapter Quiz

1. $\begin{bmatrix} -2 & 4 \\ 6 & 16 \end{bmatrix}$

2. $\begin{bmatrix} 1 & 5 \\ -4 & -7 \end{bmatrix}$

3. $\begin{bmatrix} 4.5 & 6 \\ 27 & -18 \end{bmatrix}$

4. $\begin{bmatrix} 42 & 46 \\ 3 & 1 \end{bmatrix}$

5. $\begin{bmatrix} 50 & 117 \\ 278 & 495 \end{bmatrix}$

6. $\begin{bmatrix} -47 & 201 \\ -105 & 351 \end{bmatrix}$

7. $\begin{bmatrix} 0 & 3 \\ -5 & 2 \end{bmatrix}$

8. $\begin{bmatrix} 5 & 1 \\ -10 & 4 \end{bmatrix}$

9. $\begin{bmatrix} -5 & 5 & 4 \\ 7 & -10 & 15 \end{bmatrix}$

10. $\begin{bmatrix} 2 & -2 \\ -5 & 4 \end{bmatrix}$

11. $\begin{bmatrix} 14 & 6 \\ -12 & 8 \end{bmatrix}$

12. $x = -1$, $y = 5$

13. $x = -2$, $y = -6$

14. -13

15. 10

16. -7

17. 78

18. $\begin{bmatrix} 1 & 2 \\ 3 & 5 \end{bmatrix}$

19. $\begin{bmatrix} \frac{6}{19} & -\frac{5}{19} \\ \frac{1}{19} & -\frac{4}{19} \end{bmatrix}$

1 Interactive Learning

Solve It!
PURPOSE To write and solve a system of linear equations in two variables

PROCESS Students may
- choose two variables to represent the number of each type of coin and write and solve a system of linear equations.
- guess and check.

FACILITATE

Q What system of equations can you write to represent the unknown number of nickels and dimes in the machine? **[If n and d represent the number of nickels and dimes respectively, then two equations are 0.05n + 0.10d = 14.35 and n + d = 184]**

Q What two methods can you use to solve this system of equations algebraically? **[substitution and elimination]**

ANSWER See Solve It in Answers on next page.

CONNECT THE MATH In the Solve It, students solve a system of linear equations in two variables algebraically. In this lesson, students will solve systems of linear equations in two or three variables by writing equivalent matrix equations and using matrix operations and properties.

2 Guided Instruction

Problem 1

Q How do the elements in matrix A compare with the elements in matrix A^{-1}? **[The elements on the main diagonal are switched, and the elements on the other diagonal have opposite signs.]**

© Content Standard
N.VM.8 Add, subtract, and multiply matrices of appropriate dimensions.

Objective To solve systems of equations using matrix inverses and multiplication

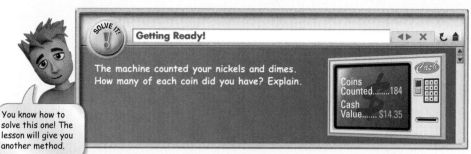

Getting Ready!

The machine counted your nickels and dimes. How many of each coin did you have? Explain.

Coins Counted........184
Cash Value....... $14.35

You know how to solve this one! The lesson will give you another method.

© **MATHEMATICAL PRACTICES** In Chapter 3, you used row operations on a matrix to solve a system of equations. Now you will solve systems by solving a matrix equation.

Lesson Vocabulary
- coefficient matrix
- variable matrix
- constant matrix

Essential Understanding You can solve some matrix equations $AX = B$ by multiplying each side of the equation by A^{-1}, the inverse of matrix A.

If matrix A has an inverse, you can use it to solve the matrix equation $AX = B$. Multiply each side of the equation by A^{-1} to find X.

$$AX = B$$
$$A^{-1}AX = A^{-1}B \quad \text{Multiply each side by } A^{-1}.$$
$$IX = A^{-1}B \quad A^{-1}A = I, \text{ the identity matrix.}$$
$$X = A^{-1}B \quad IX = X$$

© **Problem 1** Solving a Matrix Equation Using an Inverse Matrix

What is the solution of each matrix equation?

 A $\begin{bmatrix} 5 & 3 \\ 3 & 2 \end{bmatrix} X = \begin{bmatrix} 1 \\ -3 \end{bmatrix}$

Think
How do you know the equation has a solution?
Check det A. If det $A \neq 0$, you can solve the equation.

Step 1 Evaluate det A and find A^{-1}.

$$\det A = (5)(2) - (3)(3) = 1$$

$$A^{-1} = \frac{1}{\det A}\begin{bmatrix} d & -b \\ -c & a \end{bmatrix} = \frac{1}{1}\begin{bmatrix} 2 & -3 \\ -3 & 5 \end{bmatrix} = \begin{bmatrix} 2 & -3 \\ -3 & 5 \end{bmatrix}$$

12-4 Preparing to Teach

BIG idea Modeling

ESSENTIAL UNDERSTANDINGS
- Systems of linear equations can be modeled by matrix equations.
- Some matrix equations of the form $AX = B$ can be solved by multiplying each side of the equation on the left by A^{-1}, the inverse of matrix A.

Math Background

In 3-6, students solved systems of linear equations using matrix row operations. In this lesson, they apply what they know about inverse matrices and determinants to solve systems of linear equations.

If you write a system of linear equations as a matrix equation with a coefficient matrix, variable matrix, and constant matrix, you can solve for the variables by multiplying both sides of the equation on the left by the inverse coefficient matrix.

If the determinant is zero, the inverse coefficient matrix does not exist, and the associated system of linear equations does not have a unique solution.

© **Mathematical Practices**
Make sense of problems and persevere in solving them. Students will solve systems of equations using matrices and will check their solutions using substitution.

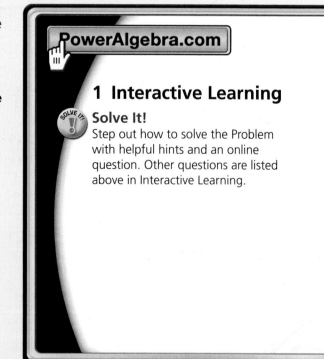

PowerAlgebra.com

1 Interactive Learning

Solve It!
Step out how to solve the Problem with helpful hints and an online question. Other questions are listed above in Interactive Learning.

Think

Does it matter if you multiply by A^{-1} on the left or right side of A?
Even though $A^{-1}A = AA^{-1} = I$, you must multiply each side of the equation by A^{-1} on the left.

Step 2 Multiply each side of the equation by A^{-1}.

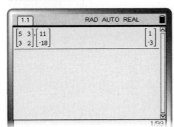

$$\begin{bmatrix} 2 & -3 \\ -3 & 5 \end{bmatrix}\begin{bmatrix} 5 & 3 \\ 3 & 2 \end{bmatrix}X = \begin{bmatrix} 2 & -3 \\ -3 & 5 \end{bmatrix}\begin{bmatrix} 1 \\ -3 \end{bmatrix}$$

$$\begin{bmatrix} (2)(5)+(-3)(3) & (2)(3)+(-3)(2) \\ (-3)(5)+(5)(3) & (-3)(3)+(5)(2) \end{bmatrix}X = \begin{bmatrix} (2)(1)+(-3)(-3) \\ (-3)(1)+(5)(-3) \end{bmatrix}$$

$$\begin{bmatrix} 1 & 0 \\ 0 & 1 \end{bmatrix}X = \begin{bmatrix} 11 \\ -18 \end{bmatrix}$$

$$X = \begin{bmatrix} 11 \\ -18 \end{bmatrix}$$

Check

Method 1

Use paper and pencil.

$$\begin{bmatrix} 5 & 3 \\ 3 & 2 \end{bmatrix}X \stackrel{?}{=} \begin{bmatrix} 1 \\ -3 \end{bmatrix}$$

$$\begin{bmatrix} 5 & 3 \\ 3 & 2 \end{bmatrix}\begin{bmatrix} 11 \\ -18 \end{bmatrix} \stackrel{?}{=} \begin{bmatrix} 1 \\ -3 \end{bmatrix}$$

$$\begin{bmatrix} (5)(11)+(3)(-18) \\ (3)(11)+(2)(-18) \end{bmatrix} \stackrel{?}{=} \begin{bmatrix} 1 \\ -3 \end{bmatrix}$$

$$\begin{bmatrix} 1 \\ -3 \end{bmatrix} = \begin{bmatrix} 1 \\ -3 \end{bmatrix} ✔$$

Method 2

Use a calculator.

B $\begin{bmatrix} 3 & -9 \\ -2 & 6 \end{bmatrix}X = \begin{bmatrix} 2 \\ 5 \end{bmatrix}$

Evaluate det A.

$\det A = (3)(6) - (-2)(-9) = 18 - 18 = 0.$

Matrix A has no inverse. The matrix equation has no solution.

✓ **Got It?** **1.** What is the solution of each matrix equation?

a. $\begin{bmatrix} 4 & 3 \\ 2 & 2 \end{bmatrix}X = \begin{bmatrix} -5 \\ 2 \end{bmatrix}$ **b.** $\begin{bmatrix} 7 & 5 \\ 4 & 3 \end{bmatrix}X = \begin{bmatrix} -3 & 0 \\ 1 & 4 \end{bmatrix}$ **c.** $\begin{bmatrix} 2 & 3 \\ 4 & 6 \end{bmatrix}X = \begin{bmatrix} 3 \\ -7 \end{bmatrix}$

You can write a system of equations as a matrix equation $AX = B$, using a **coefficient matrix**, a **variable matrix**, and a **constant matrix**.

System of Equations
$$\begin{cases} 2x + 3y = 1 \\ 5x - 2y = 13 \end{cases}$$

Matrix Equation
$$\begin{bmatrix} 2 & 3 \\ 5 & -2 \end{bmatrix}\begin{bmatrix} x \\ y \end{bmatrix} = \begin{bmatrix} 1 \\ 13 \end{bmatrix}$$

coefficient matrix, A | variable matrix, X | constant matrix, B

Q In Step 2 of 1A, can you write the matrix product on the right side of the equation as $\begin{bmatrix} 1 \\ -3 \end{bmatrix}\begin{bmatrix} 2 & -3 \\ -3 & 5 \end{bmatrix}$ instead of $\begin{bmatrix} 2 & -3 \\ -3 & 5 \end{bmatrix}\begin{bmatrix} 1 \\ -3 \end{bmatrix}$? Why or why not? **[No, because matrix multiplication is not commutative: $A^{-1}B \neq BA^{-1}$.]**

Q In 1B, why does a value of 0 for the determinant of A mean that there is no solution for this equation? **[The formula to calculate A^{-1} includes the scalar $\frac{1}{ab - cd}$, where $ab - cd$ is the determinant of A. If it is 0, then the factor becomes $\frac{1}{0}$, which is undefined.]**

Got It? SYNTHESIZING

The first step in solving a matrix equation is to evaluate $ab - cd$, the determinant of A in the equation $AX = B$. Since a, b, c, and d are real numbers, by the Law of Trichotomy, the determinant is either equal to 0, which means that there is no unique solution to the equation, or it is less than or greater than 0, which means that there is a unique solution to the equation.

Q In 1c, what does it mean that the equation has no solution? **[Sample: The lines that the system represents are parallel.]**

---

2 Guided Instruction

 Each Problem is worked out and supported online.

Problem 1
Solving Matrix Equations Using an Inverse Matrix
Animated

Problem 2
Writing Systems as a Matrix Equation
Animated

Problem 3
Solving a System of Two Equations
Animated

Problem 4
Solving a System of Three Equations

Support in Algebra 2 Companion
• Vocabulary
• Key Concepts
• Got It?

Answers

Solve It!
81 nickels and 103 dimes; write a system of eqs. to represent the problem and then solve the system using either substitution or elimination.
$n + d = 184$
$0.05n + 0.1d = 14.35$
Using substitution, solve the first eq. for n and plug it into the second.
$0.05(184 - d) + 0.1d = 14.35$
Solving for d, we get $d = 103$. Since $n + d = 184$, $n = 81$.

Got It?

1. a. $\begin{bmatrix} -8 \\ 9 \end{bmatrix}$

b. $\begin{bmatrix} -14 & -20 \\ 19 & 28 \end{bmatrix}$

c. Since matrix A has no inverse, the eq. has no solution.

Problem 2

To write a system of two (or three) linear equations as a matrix equation, each equation should be in standard form: $Ax + By = C$, where A, B, and C are real numbers.

> **Q** In Step 1 of 2A, what is the relationship between the elements in each row of the coefficient matrix and each equation of the system? **[The elements in each row are the coefficients of the variables x and y in each equation written in standard form.]**
>
> **Q** In Step 1 of 2B, can matrix A be written as
> $$\begin{bmatrix} 5 & 0 & -3 \\ 0 & 7 & 2 \\ 3 & 5 & -12 \end{bmatrix}\begin{bmatrix} a \\ b \\ c \end{bmatrix} = \begin{bmatrix} 1 \\ 8 \\ 6 \end{bmatrix};$$ that is can the rows in A and B be rearranged? Explain. **[Yes; rows in a matrix can be switched without changing the value of the matrix.]**
>
> **Q** In Step 2 of 2B, can the matrix equation be written as $$\begin{bmatrix} 6 \\ 8 \\ 1 \end{bmatrix} = \begin{bmatrix} 3 & 5 & -12 \\ 0 & 7 & 2 \\ 5 & 0 & -3 \end{bmatrix}\begin{bmatrix} a \\ b \\ c \end{bmatrix}$$? Explain.
>
> **[Yes, because matrix equations are symmetric; $AX = B \Leftrightarrow B = AX$. When solving $B = AX$, both sides would still be multiplied on the left by A^{-1}.]**

Got It?

ERROR PREVENTION

Students should know that the row dimension of a coefficient matrix corresponds to the number of variables in the system. They should also know that if the coefficient of a missing variable term in an equation of the system is 0 (e.g., $0x = 0$), the number 0 is inserted as an element in the corresponding row of A to represent the missing term in the equation.

 **Problem 2** Writing a System as a Matrix Equation

What is the matrix equation that corresponds to each system?

A $\begin{cases} 4x + 7y = 6 \\ -5x + 3y = 1 \end{cases}$

Step 1 Identify the coefficient, variable, and constant matrices.

coefficient matrix, A variable matrix, X constant matrix, B

$\begin{bmatrix} 4 & 7 \\ -5 & 3 \end{bmatrix}$ $\begin{bmatrix} x \\ y \end{bmatrix}$ $\begin{bmatrix} 6 \\ 1 \end{bmatrix}$

Step 2 Write the matrix equation.

$$\begin{bmatrix} 4 & 7 \\ -5 & 3 \end{bmatrix}\begin{bmatrix} x \\ y \end{bmatrix} = \begin{bmatrix} 6 \\ 1 \end{bmatrix}$$

B $\begin{cases} 3a + 5b - 12c = 6 \\ 7b + 2c = 8 \\ 5a = 3c + 1 \end{cases}$

> **Plan**
>
> **How is this system different from the one in part A?**
> There are three variables. Some terms have coefficients of 0, and the third equation has a variable on the right side of the = sign.

Step 1 Rewrite the system so the variables are in the same order in each equation.

$\begin{cases} 3a + 5b - 12c = 6 \\ 7b + 2c = 8 \\ 5a = 3c + 1 \end{cases}$ → $\begin{cases} 3a + 5b - 12c = 6 \\ 7b + 2c = 8 \\ 5a \quad\quad - 3c = 1 \end{cases}$

Step 2 Identify the coefficient, variable, and constant matrices.

coefficient matrix, A variable matrix, X constant matrix, B

$\begin{bmatrix} 3 & 5 & -12 \\ 0 & 7 & 2 \\ 5 & 0 & -3 \end{bmatrix}$ $\begin{bmatrix} a \\ b \\ c \end{bmatrix}$ $\begin{bmatrix} 6 \\ 8 \\ 1 \end{bmatrix}$

Step 3 Write the matrix equation.

$$\begin{bmatrix} 3 & 5 & -12 \\ 0 & 7 & 2 \\ 5 & 0 & -3 \end{bmatrix}\begin{bmatrix} a \\ b \\ c \end{bmatrix} = \begin{bmatrix} 6 \\ 8 \\ 1 \end{bmatrix}$$

✓ **Got It? 2.** What is the matrix equation that corresponds to each system?

a. $\begin{cases} 3x - 7y = 8 \\ 5x + y = -2 \end{cases}$ **b.** $\begin{cases} x + 3y + 5z = 12 \\ -2x + y - 4z = -2 \\ 7x - 2y \quad\quad = 7 \end{cases}$ **c.** $\begin{cases} 2x + 3 = 8y \\ -x + y = -4 \end{cases}$

If the coefficient matrix has an inverse, you can use it to find a unique solution to a system of equations.

Additional Problems

1. What is the solution of this matrix equation?
$$\begin{bmatrix} 2 & 1 \\ 1 & -1 \end{bmatrix} X = \begin{bmatrix} 6 \\ 3 \end{bmatrix}$$

ANSWER $\begin{bmatrix} 3 \\ 0 \end{bmatrix}$

2. What is a matrix equation that corresponds to each system?

a. $\begin{cases} 2x - y = -1 \\ x + 3y = 17 \end{cases}$

b. $\begin{cases} 3a + 2b = 5 \\ 4a = 3c + 7 \\ 6b - 6c = -5 \end{cases}$

ANSWERS

a. $\begin{bmatrix} 2 & -1 \\ 1 & 3 \end{bmatrix}\begin{bmatrix} x \\ y \end{bmatrix} = \begin{bmatrix} -1 \\ 17 \end{bmatrix}$

b. $\begin{bmatrix} 3 & 2 & 0 \\ 4 & 0 & -3 \\ 0 & 6 & -6 \end{bmatrix}\begin{bmatrix} a \\ b \\ c \end{bmatrix} = \begin{bmatrix} 5 \\ 7 \\ -5 \end{bmatrix}$

3. What is the solution of the system $\begin{cases} 4x + 5y = -8 \\ x + \frac{3}{4}y = 2 \end{cases}$? Solve using matrices.

ANSWER $(8, -8)$

4. Multiple Choice A baseball field has 6200 seats in the lower three tiers. Seats sell for $120 in section A, $100 in section B, and $75 in section C. If tickets are sold for all of the seats, the total in sales is $604,000. The number of seats in section C is 500 fewer than those in section B. How many seats are in each section of the field?

A. 1600 seats in section A, 2550 seats in section B, and 2050 seats in section C

B. 1700 seats in section A, 2000 seats in section B, and 2500 seats in section C

C. 2000 seats in section A, 2350 seats in section B, and 1850 seats in section C

D. 1700 seats in section A, 2500 seats in section B, and 2000 seats in section C

ANSWER D

Answers

Got It? (continued)

2. a. $\begin{bmatrix} 3 & -7 \\ 5 & 1 \end{bmatrix}\begin{bmatrix} x \\ y \end{bmatrix} = \begin{bmatrix} 8 \\ -2 \end{bmatrix}$

b. $\begin{bmatrix} 1 & 3 & 5 \\ -2 & 1 & -4 \\ 7 & -2 & 0 \end{bmatrix}\begin{bmatrix} x \\ y \\ z \end{bmatrix} = \begin{bmatrix} 12 \\ -2 \\ 7 \end{bmatrix}$

c. $\begin{bmatrix} 2 & -8 \\ -1 & 1 \end{bmatrix}\begin{bmatrix} x \\ y \end{bmatrix} = \begin{bmatrix} -3 \\ -4 \end{bmatrix}$

What is the solution of the system $\begin{cases} 5x - 4y = 4 \\ 3x - 2y = 3 \end{cases}$? Solve using matrices.

Think

Write the system as a matrix equation. Write the coefficient, variable, and constant matrices.

Write

$$\underset{A}{\begin{bmatrix} 5 & -4 \\ 3 & -2 \end{bmatrix}} \underset{X}{\begin{bmatrix} x \\ y \end{bmatrix}} = \underset{B}{\begin{bmatrix} 4 \\ 3 \end{bmatrix}}$$

You need to find A^{-1}. Since det $A = 2$, A^{-1} exists.

$$A^{-1} = \frac{1}{\det A}\begin{bmatrix} -2 & 4 \\ -3 & 5 \end{bmatrix}$$

$$= \frac{1}{(5)(-2) - (3)(-4)}\begin{bmatrix} -2 & 4 \\ -3 & 5 \end{bmatrix}$$

$$= \frac{1}{2}\begin{bmatrix} -2 & 4 \\ -3 & 5 \end{bmatrix}$$

$$= \begin{bmatrix} -1 & 2 \\ -\frac{3}{2} & \frac{5}{2} \end{bmatrix}$$

Multiply each side of the matrix equation by A^{-1} on the left.

$$\begin{bmatrix} -1 & 2 \\ -\frac{3}{2} & \frac{5}{2} \end{bmatrix}\begin{bmatrix} 5 & -4 \\ 3 & -2 \end{bmatrix}\begin{bmatrix} x \\ y \end{bmatrix} = \begin{bmatrix} -1 & 2 \\ -\frac{3}{2} & \frac{5}{2} \end{bmatrix}\begin{bmatrix} 4 \\ 3 \end{bmatrix}$$

Solve for $\begin{bmatrix} x \\ y \end{bmatrix}$ and check.

$$\begin{bmatrix} x \\ y \end{bmatrix} = \begin{bmatrix} (-1)(4) + (2)(3) \\ \left(-\frac{3}{2}\right)(4) + \left(\frac{5}{2}\right)(3) \end{bmatrix} = \begin{bmatrix} 2 \\ \frac{3}{2} \end{bmatrix}$$

The solution is $x = 2$, $y = \frac{3}{2}$.

$5(2) - 4\left(\frac{3}{2}\right) = 4$ ✔

$3(2) - 2\left(\frac{3}{2}\right) = 3$ ✔

Got It? 3. What is the solution of each system of equations? Solve using matrices.

a. $\begin{cases} 9x + 2y = 3 \\ 3x + y = -6 \end{cases}$
b. $\begin{cases} 4x - 6y = 9 \\ -10x + 15y = 8 \end{cases}$

The system $\begin{cases} -6x + 3y = 8 \\ 4x - 2y = 10 \end{cases}$ has coefficient matrix A with det $A = 0$. There is no inverse matrix and the system has no unique solution. Recall that this means the system either has no solutions (graphs are parallel lines in the 2×2 case) or infinitely many solutions (graphs are the same line in the 2×2 case). For the system above, the lines are parallel.

Problem 3

Q What would be the matrix equation if the system of equations were written as $\begin{cases} 3x - 2y = 3 \\ 5x - 4y = 4 \end{cases}$?
$[\begin{bmatrix} 3 & -2 \\ 5 & -4 \end{bmatrix}\begin{bmatrix} x \\ y \end{bmatrix} = \begin{bmatrix} 3 \\ 4 \end{bmatrix}]$

Q What matrix is equivalent to A^{-1}? $[\begin{bmatrix} -1 & 2 \\ -1.5 & 2.5 \end{bmatrix}]$

Q What does the solution of this matrix equation and system of linear equations represent in the rectangular coordinate plane? **[Each equation represents a linear function, and the values of x and y represent the coordinates of the point of intersection between the two lines.]**

Got It?   SYNTHESIZING

Q How could writing the equations in slope-intercept form help you anticipate whether a system of two linear equations has a solution? **[If the resulting equations have the same slope, you can determine whether the lines are parallel or coincident by comparing the y-intercepts of both lines and whether the system has no solution or an infinite number of solutions.]**

To see whether the matrix solution of the system in 3a is reasonable, have students graph the lines and determine the coordinates of the point of intersection of the two lines.

3. a. $(5, -21)$
b. no solution

Problem 4

Students should recognize that there are three variables and three relationships among them: the total number of calories expended every other day, the number of minutes to be spent exercising every other day, and the relationship between the time spent running versus jogging. Expressing these relationships in words may help students translate them into equations.

Q What does the equation $2x = y$ represent in terms of the variables x and y? **[The time spent jogging y is twice that spent running x.]**

Q What units correspond to each constant in the constant matrix? **[310 is the number of calories burned each session; 40 is the total time in minutes spent exercising every other day; 0 is the difference in minutes between twice the time spent running and the time spent jogging every other day.]**

Q How would you check this solution? **[Samples: Find the matrix product of the coefficient matrix and the matrix solution to see if they equal the constant matrix; substitute the values 10, 20, and 10 for the variables x, y, and z in each equation of the system.]**

You can use a graphing calculator to solve a system of three equations.

© Problem 4 Solving a System of Three Equations

Multiple Choice On a new exercise program, your friend plans to do a run-jog-walk routine every other day for 40 min. She would like to burn 310 calories during each session. The table shows how many calories a person your friend's age and weight burns per minute of each type of exercise.

Calories Burned

Running (8 mi/h)	Jogging (5 mi/h)	Walking (3.5 mi/h)
12.5 cal/min	7.5 cal/min	3.5 cal/min

If your friend plans on jogging twice as long as she runs, how many minutes should she exercise at each rate?

Ⓐ run 10, jog 5, walk 25   Ⓒ run 5, jog 10, walk 25

Ⓑ run 30, jog 15, walk 5   Ⓓ run 10, jog 20, walk 10

Think

How many equations do you need to solve this problem?
Since there are three variables you need three equations.

Step 1 Define the variables.

Let x = number of minutes running.
y = number of minutes jogging.
z = number of minutes walking.

Step 2 Write a system of equations for the problem.

$$\begin{cases} 12.5x + 7.5y + 3.5z = 310 \\ x + y + z = 40 \\ 2x = y \end{cases} \rightarrow \begin{cases} 12.5x + 7.5y + 3.5z = 310 \\ x + y + z = 40 \\ 2x - y + 0z = 0 \end{cases}$$

Step 3 Write the system as a matrix equation.

$$\begin{bmatrix} 12.5 & 7.5 & 3.5 \\ 1 & 1 & 1 \\ 2 & -1 & 0 \end{bmatrix} \begin{bmatrix} x \\ y \\ z \end{bmatrix} = \begin{bmatrix} 310 \\ 40 \\ 0 \end{bmatrix}$$

Step 4 Use a calculator. Solve for the variable matrix.

Step 5 Interpret the solution.

Your friend should run for 10 min, jog for 20 min, and walk for 10 min. The correct answer is D.

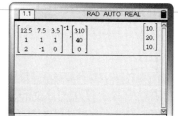

Answers

Got It? (continued)
4. run: 32 min; jog: 8 min

Lesson Check

1. $\begin{bmatrix} -6 & 3 \\ 4 & -2 \end{bmatrix} \begin{bmatrix} x \\ y \end{bmatrix} = \begin{bmatrix} 8 \\ 10 \end{bmatrix}$

2. $\begin{bmatrix} 2 & 3 & 0 \\ 1 & -2 & 1 \\ 0 & 6 & -4 \end{bmatrix} \begin{bmatrix} x \\ y \\ z \end{bmatrix} = \begin{bmatrix} 12 \\ 9 \\ 8 \end{bmatrix}$

3. (5, 3)

4. (−6, −6)

5. The student did not separate the coefficient matrix and the variable matrix. The matrix eq. should be written as $\begin{bmatrix} 2 & 3 \\ -4 & 5 \end{bmatrix} \begin{bmatrix} x \\ y \end{bmatrix} = \begin{bmatrix} 5 \\ 1 \end{bmatrix}$.

6. Use matrix multiplication to combine the coefficient matrix and the variable matrix into a product matrix. Then set the first element in

the product matrix equal to the first element in the constant matrix and set the second element in the product matrix equal to the second element in the constant matrix. The result will be a system of equations.;
$-2p + 3q = 2$
$4p + q = -5$

Practice and Problem-Solving Exercises

7. $\begin{bmatrix} -15 & -17 \\ 26 & 29 \end{bmatrix}$

8. No solution; the determinant of $\begin{bmatrix} 0 & -4 \\ 0 & -1 \end{bmatrix}$ is 0.

9. $\begin{bmatrix} \frac{29}{31} \\ -\frac{66}{217} \\ \frac{34}{217} \end{bmatrix}$

10. $\begin{bmatrix} \frac{2487}{253} \\ \frac{1192}{253} \\ -\frac{430}{253} \end{bmatrix}$

11. $\begin{bmatrix} 1 & 1 \\ 1 & -2 \end{bmatrix} \begin{bmatrix} x \\ y \end{bmatrix} = \begin{bmatrix} 5 \\ -4 \end{bmatrix}$; coefficient matrix: $\begin{bmatrix} 1 & 1 \\ 1 & -2 \end{bmatrix}$, variable matrix: $\begin{bmatrix} x \\ y \end{bmatrix}$, constant matrix: $\begin{bmatrix} 5 \\ -4 \end{bmatrix}$

Got It? **4.** After following her exercise program from Problem 4 for a month, your friend plans to increase the calories she burns with each session. She still wants to exercise for 40 min every other day, but now she wants to burn 460 calories during each session. If she only runs and jogs, how many minutes of each exercise type should she do now?

Lesson Check

Do you know HOW?

Write each system as a matrix equation.

1. $\begin{cases} -6x + 3y = 8 \\ 4x - 2y = 10 \end{cases}$

2. $\begin{cases} 2x + 3y = 12 \\ x - 2y + z = 9 \\ 6y - 4z = 8 \end{cases}$

Solve each system using a matrix equation. Check your answer.

3. $\begin{cases} x + 2y = 11 \\ x + 4y = 17 \end{cases}$

4. $\begin{cases} 2x - 3y = 6 \\ x + y = -12 \end{cases}$

Do you UNDERSTAND? MATHEMATICAL PRACTICES

5. Error Analysis A student is trying to use the matrix equation below to solve a system of equations. What error did the student make? What matrix equation should the student use?

6. Reasoning Explain how to write the matrix equation $\begin{bmatrix} -2 & 3 \\ 4 & 1 \end{bmatrix} \begin{bmatrix} p \\ q \end{bmatrix} = \begin{bmatrix} 2 \\ -5 \end{bmatrix}$ as a system of linear equations.

Practice and Problem-Solving Exercises MATHEMATICAL PRACTICES

A Practice Solve each matrix equation. If an equation cannot be solved, explain why. *See Problem 1.*

7. $\begin{bmatrix} 12 & 7 \\ 5 & 3 \end{bmatrix} X = \begin{bmatrix} 2 & -1 \\ 3 & 2 \end{bmatrix}$

8. $\begin{bmatrix} 0 & -4 \\ 0 & -1 \end{bmatrix} X = \begin{bmatrix} 0 \\ 4 \end{bmatrix}$

9. $\begin{bmatrix} 5 & 1 & 4 \\ 2 & -3 & -5 \\ 7 & 2 & -6 \end{bmatrix} X = \begin{bmatrix} 5 \\ 2 \\ 5 \end{bmatrix}$

10. $\begin{bmatrix} 6 & 10 & 13 \\ 4 & -2 & 7 \\ 0 & 9 & -8 \end{bmatrix} X = \begin{bmatrix} 84 \\ 18 \\ 56 \end{bmatrix}$

Write each system as a matrix equation. Identify the coefficient matrix, the variable matrix, and the constant matrix. *See Problem 2.*

11. $\begin{cases} x + y = 5 \\ x - 2y = -4 \end{cases}$

12. $\begin{cases} y = 3x - 7 \\ x = 2 \end{cases}$

13. $\begin{cases} 3a + 5b = 0 \\ a + b = 2 \end{cases}$

14. $\begin{cases} x + 3y - z = 2 \\ x + 2z = 8 \\ 2y - z = 1 \end{cases}$

15. $\begin{cases} r - s + t = 150 \\ 2r + t = 425 \\ s + 3t = 0 \end{cases}$

16. $\begin{cases} x + 2y = 11 \\ 2x + 3y = 18 \end{cases}$

PowerAlgebra.com | **Lesson 12-4** Inverse Matrices and Systems | **797**

Got It? ERROR PREVENTION

Q How many variables need to be represented in writing a system of equations that represents this situation and why? **[Two: x represents the time spent running, and y represents the time spent jogging.]**

Q What are the dimensions of the constant matrix for this situation? **[2 × 1]**

3 Lesson Check

Do you know HOW?
- In Exercise 2, check that students insert a 0 in two of the three rows of the coefficient matrix, representing the missing variable terms.
- In Exercises 3 and 4, suggest that students first check to be sure that the determinant of each coefficient matrix is not 0. Then they can use matrix operations to solve the equation. The solution represents the coordinates of the points of intersection of each pair of lines represented by each system.

Do you UNDERSTAND?
- For Exercise 5, suggest students write what they think was the original system and then use it to write the matrix equation. They should recognize that the variables should be removed.

Close

Q When does the matrix equation $AX = B$ have no solution? **[when the determinant of A, the coefficient matrix, is 0]**

Q How do you solve a matrix equation of the form $AX = B$? **[Multiply both sides of the equation on the left by A^{-1}, the inverse of the coefficient matrix.]**

---

12. $\begin{bmatrix} -3 & 1 \\ 1 & 0 \end{bmatrix} \begin{bmatrix} x \\ y \end{bmatrix} = \begin{bmatrix} -7 \\ 2 \end{bmatrix}$; coefficient matrix: $\begin{bmatrix} -3 & 1 \\ 1 & 0 \end{bmatrix}$, variable matrix: $\begin{bmatrix} x \\ y \end{bmatrix}$, constant matrix: $\begin{bmatrix} -7 \\ 2 \end{bmatrix}$

13. $\begin{bmatrix} 3 & 5 \\ 1 & 1 \end{bmatrix} \begin{bmatrix} a \\ b \end{bmatrix} = \begin{bmatrix} 0 \\ 2 \end{bmatrix}$; coefficient matrix: $\begin{bmatrix} 3 & 5 \\ 1 & 1 \end{bmatrix}$, variable matrix: $\begin{bmatrix} a \\ b \end{bmatrix}$, constant matrix: $\begin{bmatrix} 0 \\ 2 \end{bmatrix}$

14. $\begin{bmatrix} 1 & 3 & -1 \\ 1 & 0 & 2 \\ 0 & 2 & -1 \end{bmatrix} \begin{bmatrix} x \\ y \\ z \end{bmatrix} = \begin{bmatrix} 2 \\ 8 \\ 1 \end{bmatrix}$; coefficient matrix: $\begin{bmatrix} 1 & 3 & -1 \\ 1 & 0 & 2 \\ 0 & 2 & -1 \end{bmatrix}$, variable matrix: $\begin{bmatrix} x \\ y \\ z \end{bmatrix}$, constant matrix: $\begin{bmatrix} 2 \\ 8 \\ 1 \end{bmatrix}$

15. $\begin{bmatrix} 1 & -1 & 1 \\ 2 & 0 & 1 \\ 0 & 1 & 3 \end{bmatrix} \begin{bmatrix} r \\ s \\ t \end{bmatrix} = \begin{bmatrix} 150 \\ 425 \\ 0 \end{bmatrix}$; coefficient matrix: $\begin{bmatrix} 1 & -1 & 1 \\ 2 & 0 & 1 \\ 0 & 1 & 3 \end{bmatrix}$, variable matrix: $\begin{bmatrix} r \\ s \\ t \end{bmatrix}$, constant matrix: $\begin{bmatrix} 150 \\ 425 \\ 0 \end{bmatrix}$

16. $\begin{bmatrix} 1 & 2 \\ 2 & 3 \end{bmatrix} \begin{bmatrix} x \\ y \end{bmatrix} = \begin{bmatrix} 11 \\ 18 \end{bmatrix}$; coefficient matrix: $\begin{bmatrix} 1 & 2 \\ 2 & 3 \end{bmatrix}$, variable matrix: $\begin{bmatrix} x \\ y \end{bmatrix}$, constant matrix: $\begin{bmatrix} 11 \\ 18 \end{bmatrix}$

PowerAlgebra.com

3 Lesson Check

For a digital lesson check, use the Got It questions.

Support in Algebra 2 Companion
- Lesson Check

4 Practice

Assign homework to individual students or to an entire class.

Lesson 12-4 **797**

4 Practice

ASSIGNMENT GUIDE

Basic: 7–29, 39, 48, 49

Average: 7–25 odd, 27–50

Advanced: 7–25 odd, 27–58

Standardized Test Prep: 59–62

Mixed Review: 63–72

Ⓒ Mathematical Practices are supported by exercises with red headings. Here are the Practices supported in this lesson:

MP 1: Make Sense of Problems Ex. 27

MP 2: Reason Abstractly Ex. 50

MP 3: Communicate Ex. 6

MP 3: Critique the Reasoning of Others Ex. 5

Applications exercises have blue headings. Exercises 26, 28 support MP 4: Model.

EXERCISE 28: Use the Think About a Plan worksheet in the **Practice and Problem Solving Workbook** (also available in the Teaching Resources in print and online) to further support students' development in becoming independent learners.

HOMEWORK QUICK CHECK

To check students' understanding of key skills and concepts, go over Exercises 9, 13, 27, 28, and 48.

Solve each system of equations using a matrix equation. Check your answers. See Problem 3.

17. $\begin{cases} x + 3y = 5 \\ x + 4y = 6 \end{cases}$

18. $\begin{cases} p - 3q = -1 \\ -5p + 16q = 5 \end{cases}$

19. $\begin{cases} 300x - y = 130 \\ 200x + y = 120 \end{cases}$

20. $\begin{cases} x + 5y = -4 \\ x + 6y = -5 \end{cases}$

21. $\begin{cases} 2x + 3y = 12 \\ x + 2y = 7 \end{cases}$

22. $\begin{cases} 2x + 3y = 5 \\ x + 2y = 6 \end{cases}$

23. $\begin{cases} x + y + z = 4 \\ 4x + 5y = 3 \\ y - 3z = -10 \end{cases}$

24. $\begin{cases} 9y + 2z = 18 \\ 3x + 2y + z = 5 \\ x - y = -1 \end{cases}$

25. $\begin{cases} 9y + 2z = 14 \\ 3x + 2y + z = 5 \\ x - y = -1 \end{cases}$

26. Fitness Your classmate is starting a new fitness program. He is planning to ride his bicycle 60 minutes every day. He burns 7 Calories per minute bicycling at 11 mph and 11.75 Calories per minute bicycling at 15 mph. How long should he bicycle at each speed to burn 600 calories per hour? See Problem 4.

Ⓑ Apply

Ⓒ 27. Think About a Plan Suppose you want to fill nine 1-lb tins with a snack mix. You plan to buy almonds for $2.45/lb, peanuts for $1.85/lb, and raisins for $.80/lb. You want the mix to contain twice as much nuts as raisins by weight. If you spend exactly $15, how much of each ingredient should you buy?
- How many equations do you need to represent this situation?
- How can you represent this system using a matrix equation?

28. Nutrition Suppose you are making a trail mix for your friends and want to fill three 1-lb bags. Almonds cost $2.25/lb, peanuts cost $1.30/lb, and raisins cost $.90/lb. You want each bag to contain twice as much nuts as raisins by weight. If you spent $4.45, how much of each ingredient did you buy?

Solve each system.

29. $\begin{cases} -3x + 4y = 2 \\ x - y = -1 \end{cases}$

30. $\begin{cases} x + 2y = 10 \\ 3x + 5y = 26 \end{cases}$

31. $\begin{cases} x - 3y = -1 \\ -6x + 19y = 6 \end{cases}$

32. $\begin{cases} x = 5 - y \\ 3y = z \\ x + z = 7 \end{cases}$

33. $\begin{cases} -x = -4 - z \\ 2y = z - 1 \\ x = 6 - y - z \end{cases}$

34. $\begin{cases} -b + 2c = 4 \\ a + b - c = -10 \\ 2a + 3c = 1 \end{cases}$

35. $\begin{cases} x + y + z = 4 \\ 4x + 5y = 4 \\ y - 3z = -9 \end{cases}$

36. $\begin{cases} x + y + z = 4 \\ 4x + 5y = 3 \\ y - 3z = -10 \end{cases}$

37. $\begin{cases} -2w + x + y = 0 \\ -w + 2x - y + z = 1 \\ -2w + 3x + 3y + 2z = 6 \\ w + x + 2y + z = 5 \end{cases}$

38. $\begin{cases} -2w + x + y = -2 \\ -w + 2x - y + z = -4 \\ -2w + 3x + 3y + 2z = 2 \\ w + x + 2y + z = 6 \end{cases}$

Solve each matrix equation. If the coefficient matrix has no inverse, write *no unique solution*.

39. $\begin{bmatrix} 1 & 1 \\ 1 & 2 \end{bmatrix}\begin{bmatrix} x \\ y \end{bmatrix} = \begin{bmatrix} 8 \\ 10 \end{bmatrix}$

40. $\begin{bmatrix} 2 & -3 \\ -4 & 6 \end{bmatrix}\begin{bmatrix} a \\ b \end{bmatrix} = \begin{bmatrix} 1 \\ -2 \end{bmatrix}$

41. $\begin{bmatrix} 2 & 1 \\ 4 & 3 \end{bmatrix}\begin{bmatrix} x \\ y \end{bmatrix} = \begin{bmatrix} 10 \\ -2 \end{bmatrix}$

Answers

Practice and Problem-Solving Exercises (continued)

17. (2, 1)

18. (−1, 0)

19. $\left(\frac{1}{2}, 20\right)$

20. (1, −1)

21. (3, 2)

22. (−8, 7)

23. (2, −1, 3)

24. (−3, −2, 18)

25. (1, 2, −2)

26. about 22 min at 11 mph and about 38 min at 15 mph

27. 2.5 lb of almonds, 3.5 lb of peanuts, and 3 lb of raisins

28. 1 lb of almonds, 1 lb of peanuts, and 1 lb of raisins

29. (−2, −1)

30. (2, 4)

31. (−1, 0)

32. (4, 1, 3)

33. (5, 0, 1)

34. (−19, 22, 13)

35. (1, 0, 3)

36. (2, −1, 3)

37. (1, 1, 1, 1)

38. (2, 0, 2, 0)

39. (6, 2)

40. no unique solution

41. (16, −22)

Determine whether each system has a unique solution. If it has a unique solution, find it.

42. $\begin{cases} 20x + 5y = 240 \\ y = 20x \end{cases}$

43. $\begin{cases} 20x + 5y = 145 \\ 30x - 5y = 125 \end{cases}$

44. $\begin{cases} y = 2000 - 65x \\ y = 500 + 55x \end{cases}$

45. $\begin{cases} y = \frac{2}{3}x - 3 \\ y = -x + 7 \end{cases}$

46. $\begin{cases} 3x + 2y = 10 \\ 6x + 4y = 16 \end{cases}$

47. $\begin{cases} x + 2y + z = 4 \\ y = x - 3 \\ z = 2x \end{cases}$

48. **Coordinate Geometry** The coordinates (x, y) of a point in a plane are the solution of the system $\begin{cases} 2x + 3y = 13 \\ 5x + 7y = 31 \end{cases}$. Find the coordinates of the point.

49. **Geometry** A rectangle is twice as long as it is wide. The perimeter is 840 ft. Find the dimensions of the rectangle.

50. **Reasoning** Substitute each point $(-3, 5)$ and $(2, -1)$ into the slope-intercept form of a linear equation to write a system of equations. Then use the system to find the equation of the line containing the two points. Explain your reasoning.

 Challenge   Solve each matrix equation.

51. $-2\begin{bmatrix} -2 & 0 \\ 0 & -1 \end{bmatrix} + \begin{bmatrix} 0 & -3 \\ 5 & -4 \end{bmatrix}X + \begin{bmatrix} 0 & -3 \\ 5 & -4 \end{bmatrix} = \begin{bmatrix} 19 & -27 \\ 10 & -24 \end{bmatrix}$

52. $\begin{bmatrix} 0 & -6 \\ 1 & 2 \end{bmatrix} - \begin{bmatrix} 5 & 2 \\ 4 & 3 \end{bmatrix}X - \begin{bmatrix} 2 & -26 \\ 3 & -18 \end{bmatrix} = \begin{bmatrix} 3 & 25 \\ 2 & 24 \end{bmatrix}$

53. $\begin{bmatrix} 7 & -5 & 3 \\ 0 & 1 & 3 \\ 8 & 4 & -2 \end{bmatrix}X + \begin{bmatrix} 5 \\ -9 \\ 0 \end{bmatrix} = \begin{bmatrix} 54 \\ -12 \\ 96 \end{bmatrix}$

54. $\begin{bmatrix} -1 & 0 & 2 \\ -6 & -5 & 0 \\ 1 & 4 & 1 \end{bmatrix} - \begin{bmatrix} -4 & 0 & 2 \\ 0 & 3 & 6 \\ 0 & 5 & 0 \end{bmatrix}X = \begin{bmatrix} -21 & 10 & 26 \\ -54 & 1 & -15 \\ 1 & 4 & -24 \end{bmatrix}$

Open-Ended Complete each system for the given number of solutions.

55. infinitely many
$\begin{cases} x + y = 7 \\ 2x + 2y = \blacksquare \end{cases}$

56. one solution
$\begin{cases} x + y + z = 7 \\ y + z = \blacksquare \\ z = \blacksquare \end{cases}$

57. no solution
$\begin{cases} x + y + z = 7 \\ y + z = \blacksquare \\ y + z = \blacksquare \end{cases}$

58. **Nutrition** A caterer combines ingredients to make a paella, a Spanish fiesta dish. The paella weighs 18 lb, costs $29.50, and supplies 850 g of protein.
   a. Write a system of three equations to find the weight of each ingredient that the caterer uses.
   b. Solve the system. How many pounds of each ingredient did she use?

Paella Nutrition Chart

Food	Cost/lb	Protein/lb
Chicken	$1.50	100 g
Rice	$.40	20 g
Shellfish	$6.00	50 g

42. $(2, 40)$

43. $(5.4, 7.4)$

44. $(12.5, 1187.5)$

45. $(6, 1)$

46. no unique solution

47. $(2, -1, 4)$

48. $(2, 3)$

49. length = 280 ft, width = 140 ft

50. $6x + 5y = 7$; There are 2 eqs. in the system: $5 = -3m + b$ and $-1 = 2m + b$, where m = slope and b = y-intercept Solving the system, the eq. of the line is $y = -1.2x + 1.4$ or, in standard form, $6x + 5y = 7$.

51. $\begin{bmatrix} -3 & 2 \\ -5 & 8 \end{bmatrix}$

52. $\begin{bmatrix} -1 & -1 \\ 0 & 0 \end{bmatrix}$

53. $\begin{bmatrix} 10 \\ 3 \\ -2 \end{bmatrix}$

54. $\begin{bmatrix} -1 & 2 & 6 \\ 0 & 0 & 5 \\ 8 & -1 & 0 \end{bmatrix}$

55. 14

56. Answers may vary. Sample:
$y + z = 0; z = 0$

57. Answers may vary. Sample:
$y + z = 0; y + z = 1$

58. a. Let c = lb of chicken, r = lb of rice, and s = lb of shellfish.
$c + r + s = 18$
$1.50c + 0.40r + 6.00s = 29.50$
$100c + 20r + 50s = 850$
   b. $(5, 10, 3)$; 5 lb of chicken, 10 lb of rice, 3 lb of shellfish

Answers

59. B

60. H

61. A

62. [2] First, write each eq. in standard form. Then place the coefficients in a matrix with the coefficients of x in the first column, the coefficients of y in the second column, and the coefficients of z in the third column:

$$\begin{bmatrix} 2 & -3 & 1 \\ 1 & 4 & -2 \\ -3 & -2 & 3 \end{bmatrix}$$. Finally, put this in an eq.

with the variable matrix $\begin{bmatrix} x \\ y \\ z \end{bmatrix}$ and the

constant matrix $\begin{bmatrix} -10 \\ 11 \\ -7 \end{bmatrix}$, to get

$$\begin{bmatrix} 2 & -3 & 1 \\ 1 & 4 & -2 \\ -3 & -2 & 3 \end{bmatrix}\begin{bmatrix} x \\ y \\ z \end{bmatrix} = \begin{bmatrix} -10 \\ 11 \\ -7 \end{bmatrix}.$$

[1] incomplete explanation OR mistake in arrangement of coefficient matrix.

Mixed Review

63. −44

64. 4913

65. −218

66. 34.$\overline{4}$; 30.9; 5.56

67. 4.17; 1.32; 1.15

68. 19.$\overline{6}$ m; 22.$\overline{2}$ m; 4.7 m

69. 57.4 mi; 345.44 mi^2; 18.6 mi

70. 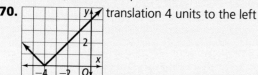 translation 4 units to the left

71. 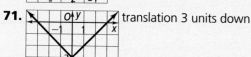 translation 3 units down

72. 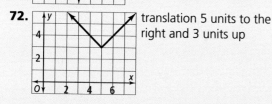 translation 5 units to the right and 3 units up

---

Standardized Test Prep

SAT/ACT

59. Which matrix equation represents the system $\begin{cases} 2x - 3y = -3 \\ -5x + y = 14 \end{cases}$?

Ⓐ $\begin{bmatrix} x \\ y \end{bmatrix}\begin{bmatrix} 2 & -3 \\ -5 & 1 \end{bmatrix} = \begin{bmatrix} -3 \\ 14 \end{bmatrix}$

Ⓒ $\begin{bmatrix} 2 & -3 \\ -5 & 1 \end{bmatrix}\begin{bmatrix} -3 \\ 14 \end{bmatrix} = \begin{bmatrix} x \\ y \end{bmatrix}$

Ⓑ $\begin{bmatrix} 2 & -3 \\ -5 & 1 \end{bmatrix}\begin{bmatrix} x \\ y \end{bmatrix} = \begin{bmatrix} -3 \\ 14 \end{bmatrix}$

Ⓓ $\begin{bmatrix} -3 \\ 14 \end{bmatrix}[x \ \ y] = \begin{bmatrix} 2 & -3 \\ -5 & 1 \end{bmatrix}$

60. What is the value of x if $17e^{4x} = 85$?

Ⓕ $\frac{5}{4}$ Ⓖ $\frac{\ln 85}{17 \cdot \ln 4}$ Ⓗ $\frac{\ln 5}{4}$ Ⓘ $\frac{\ln 85 - \ln 17}{\ln 4}$

61. A set of data is normally distributed with a mean of 44 and a standard deviation of 3.2. Which statements are NOT true?

I. 68% of the values are between 37.6 and 50.4

II. 13.5% of the values are less than 40.8

III. 5% of the values are lower than 37.6 or higher than 50.4

Ⓐ I and II only   Ⓒ II and III only

Ⓑ I and III only   Ⓓ I, II, and III

Short Response

62. How can you write the three equations below as a matrix equation for a system? Explain your steps.

$2x - 3y + z + 10 = 0$

$x + 4y = 2z + 11$

$-2y + 3z + 7 = 3x$

Mixed Review

Evaluate the determinant of each matrix.   ◀ See Lesson 12-3.

63. $\begin{bmatrix} -1 & 3 & 7 \\ 5 & -4 & -2 \\ 0 & 2 & 10 \end{bmatrix}$ **64.** $\begin{bmatrix} 17 & 0 & 0 \\ 0 & 17 & 0 \\ 0 & 0 & 17 \end{bmatrix}$ **65.** $\begin{bmatrix} -3 & 0 & 5 \\ 5 & -3 & 2 \\ -3 & -5 & -2 \end{bmatrix}$

Find the mean, variance, and standard deviation for each data set.   ◀ See Lesson 11-7.

66. 29, 35, 44, 25, 36, 30, 40, 33, 38   **67.** 5.2, 6.0, 3.5, 4.4, 2.5, 3.0, 4.6

68. 14 m, 18 m, 22 m, 28 m, 15 m, 21 m   **69.** 71 mi, 60 mi, 82 mi, 30 mi, 44 mi

Get Ready!   To prepare for Lesson 12-5, do Exercises 70–72.

Graph each equation. Then describe the transformation from the parent function $f(x) = |x|$.   ◀ See Lesson 2-7.

70. $f(x) = |x + 4|$ **71.** $f(x) = |x| - 3$ **72.** $f(x) = |x - 5| + 3$

Additional Instructional Support

Algebra 2 Companion

Students can use the **Algebra 2 Companion** worktext (4 pages) as you teach the lesson. Use the Companion to support

- New Vocabulary
- Key Concepts
- Got It for each Problem
- Lesson Check

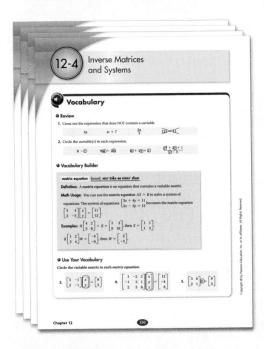

ELL Support

Assess Understanding Have students compare the solution of simple linear equations like $ax = b$ and the solution of matrix equations $AX = B$. In the first case, a is a non-zero real number, and x can be found by multiplying both sides of the equation by a^{-1}, or $\frac{1}{a}$. If $a = 2$, $a^{-1} = \frac{1}{2}$. However, in the second case, A^{-1} is the scalar product:

$$\frac{1}{ab - cd}\begin{bmatrix} d & -b \\ -c & a \end{bmatrix},$$ so to solve $A^{-1}B$

without using a calculator, students must follow three steps:

(1) determine the value of the non-zero determinant of the coefficient matrix;
(2) write its (multiplicative) inverse; and
(3) find the corresponding scalar product described above.

5 Assess & Remediate

Lesson Quiz

1. What is the solution of this matrix equation?
$$\begin{bmatrix} 2 & -3 \\ 1 & 1 \end{bmatrix} X = \begin{bmatrix} 6 \\ -12 \end{bmatrix}$$

2. What is a matrix equation that corresponds to the system
$$\begin{cases} 5p - 3q + r = 5 \\ 4p - 3r = 1 \\ 2q = 3r - 2 \end{cases} ?$$

3. What is the solution of the system
$$\begin{cases} 4x + 3y = 4 \\ 2x - y = 7 \end{cases} ?$$
Solve using matrices.

4. **Do you UNDERSTAND?** There are 34 coins in your friend's piggy bank made up of nickels, dimes, and quarters. The total value of the coins in the bank is $3. If the number of nickels is 6 more than the number of dimes and the number of quarters put together, how many coins of each type are in the bank?

ANSWERS TO LESSON QUIZ

1. $$\begin{bmatrix} -6 \\ -6 \end{bmatrix}$$

2. $$\begin{bmatrix} 5 & -3 & 1 \\ 4 & 0 & -3 \\ 0 & 2 & -3 \end{bmatrix}\begin{bmatrix} p \\ q \\ r \end{bmatrix} = \begin{bmatrix} 5 \\ 1 \\ -2 \end{bmatrix}$$

3. $(2.5, -2)$

4. 20 nickels, 10 dimes, 4 quarters

PRESCRIPTION FOR REMEDIATION

Use the student work on the Lesson Quiz to prescribe a differentiated review assignment:

Points	Differentiated Remediation
0–2	Intervention
3	On-level
4	Extension

PowerAlgebra.com

5 Assess & Remediate

Assign the Lesson Quiz. Appropriate intervention, practice, or enrichment is automatically generated based on student performance.

Intervention

- **Reteaching** (2 pages) Provides reteaching and practice exercises for the key lesson concepts. Use with struggling students or absent students.

- **English Language Learner Support** Helps students develop and reinforce mathematical vocabulary and key concepts.

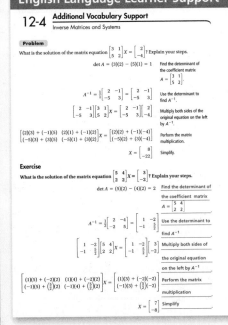

Differentiated Remediation *continued*

On-Level

- **Practice** (2 pages) Provides extra practice for each lesson. For simpler practice exercises, use the Form K Practice pages found in the All-in-One Teaching Resources and online.
- **Think About a Plan** Helps students develop specific problem-solving skills and strategies by providing scaffolded guiding questions.
- **Standardized Test Prep** Focuses on all major exercises, all major question types, and helps students prepare for the high-stakes assessments.

Extension

- **Enrichment** Provides students with interesting problems and activities that extend the concepts of the lesson.
- **Activities, Games, and Puzzles** Worksheets that can be used for concepts development, enrichment, and for fun!

Practice and Problem Solving Wkbk/ All-in-One Resources/Online

Practice page 1

12-4 Practice — Form G

Inverse Matrices and Systems

Solve each matrix equation. If an equation cannot be solved, explain why.

1. $\begin{bmatrix} 0.25 & -0.75 \\ 3.5 & 2.25 \end{bmatrix} X = \begin{bmatrix} 1.5 \\ -3.75 \end{bmatrix}$ $\begin{bmatrix} \frac{3}{17} \\ -\frac{33}{17} \end{bmatrix}$

2. $\begin{bmatrix} 3 & -9 \\ 1 & -6 \end{bmatrix} X = \begin{bmatrix} 12 \\ 0 \end{bmatrix}$ $\begin{bmatrix} 8 \\ \frac{4}{3} \end{bmatrix}$

3. $\begin{bmatrix} 3 & -6 \\ -1 & 2 \end{bmatrix} X = \begin{bmatrix} 4 \\ 9 \end{bmatrix}$ no sol.; det $A = 0$

4. $\begin{bmatrix} 1 & 0 & -1 \\ 3 & 2 & 1 \\ -1 & 2 & 2 \end{bmatrix} X = \begin{bmatrix} 2 \\ 2 \\ -2 \end{bmatrix}$ $\begin{bmatrix} \frac{2}{3} \\ \frac{2}{3} \\ -\frac{4}{3} \end{bmatrix}$

Write each system as a matrix equation. Identify the coefficient matrix, the variable matrix, and the constant matrix.

5. $\begin{cases} 6x + 9y = 36 \\ 4x + 13y = 2 \end{cases}$ $\begin{bmatrix} 6 & 9 \\ 4 & 13 \end{bmatrix}\begin{bmatrix} x \\ y \end{bmatrix} = \begin{bmatrix} 36 \\ 2 \end{bmatrix}$; $\begin{bmatrix} 6 & 9 \\ 4 & 13 \end{bmatrix}$; $\begin{bmatrix} x \\ y \end{bmatrix}$; $\begin{bmatrix} 36 \\ 2 \end{bmatrix}$

6. $\begin{cases} 3x - 4y = -9 \\ 7y = 24 \end{cases}$ $\begin{bmatrix} 3 & -4 \\ 0 & 7 \end{bmatrix}\begin{bmatrix} x \\ y \end{bmatrix} = \begin{bmatrix} -9 \\ 24 \end{bmatrix}$; $\begin{bmatrix} 3 & -4 \\ 0 & 7 \end{bmatrix}$; $\begin{bmatrix} x \\ y \end{bmatrix}$; $\begin{bmatrix} -9 \\ 24 \end{bmatrix}$

7. $\begin{cases} 3a = 5 \\ b = 12 + a \end{cases}$ $\begin{bmatrix} 3 & 0 \\ -1 & 1 \end{bmatrix}\begin{bmatrix} a \\ b \end{bmatrix} = \begin{bmatrix} 5 \\ 12 \end{bmatrix}$; $\begin{bmatrix} 3 & 0 \\ -1 & 1 \end{bmatrix}$; $\begin{bmatrix} a \\ b \end{bmatrix}$; $\begin{bmatrix} 5 \\ 12 \end{bmatrix}$

8. $\begin{cases} 4x - z = 9 \\ 12x + 2y = 17 \\ x - y + 12z = 3 \end{cases}$ $\begin{bmatrix} 4 & 0 & -1 \\ 12 & 2 & 0 \\ 1 & -1 & 12 \end{bmatrix}\begin{bmatrix} x \\ y \\ z \end{bmatrix} = \begin{bmatrix} 9 \\ 17 \\ 3 \end{bmatrix}$; $\begin{bmatrix} 4 & 0 & -1 \\ 12 & 2 & 0 \\ 1 & -1 & 12 \end{bmatrix}$; $\begin{bmatrix} x \\ y \\ z \end{bmatrix}$; $\begin{bmatrix} 9 \\ 17 \\ 3 \end{bmatrix}$

Solve each system of equations using a matrix equation. Check your answers.

9. $\begin{cases} x + 3y = 5 \\ x + 4y = 6 \end{cases}$ $x = 2, y = 1$

10. $\begin{cases} 2x + 3y = 12 \\ x + 2y = 7 \end{cases}$ $x = 3, y = 2$

11. $\begin{cases} x - 3y = -1 \\ -6x + 19y = 6 \end{cases}$ $x = -1, y = 0$

12. $\begin{cases} 4x - 3y = 55 \\ x + y = 5 \end{cases}$ $x = 10, y = -5$

13. $\begin{cases} 6x + 7y = -12 \\ 3x - 4y = -6 \end{cases}$ $x = -2, y = 0$

14. $\begin{cases} 3x - y = 6 \\ -2x + 3y = 10 \end{cases}$ $x = 4, y = 6$

15. $\begin{cases} -3x + 4y - z = -5 \\ x - y - z = -8 \\ 2x + y + 2z = 9 \end{cases}$ $x = -2, y = -1, z = 7$

16. $\begin{cases} x + y + z = 31 \\ x - y + z = 1 \\ x - 2y + 2z = 7 \end{cases}$ $x = -5, y = 15, z = 21$

17. $\begin{cases} x + 2y - z = 8 \\ -2x + 3z = -4 \\ y + z = 3 \end{cases}$ $x = 2, y = 3, z = 0$

18. $\begin{cases} 3x - 2y + 4z = -10 \\ y - 3z = 1 \\ 2x + z = -3 \end{cases}$ $x = -2, y = 4, z = 1$

Practice and Problem Solving Wkbk/ All-in-One Resources/Online

Practice page 2

12-4 Practice (continued) — Form G

Inverse Matrices and Systems

19. An apartment building has 50 units. All have one or two bedrooms. One-bedroom units rent for $425/mo. Two-bedroom units rent for $550/mo. When all units are occupied, the total monthly rent collected is $25,000. How many units of each type are in the building? 20 one-bedroom, 30 two-bedroom

20. The difference between twice Bill's age and Carlos's age is 26. The sum of Anna's age, three times Bill's age, and Carlos's age is 92. The total of the three ages is 52.
    a. Write a matrix equation to represent this situation. $\begin{bmatrix} 0 & 2 & -1 \\ 1 & 3 & 1 \\ 1 & 1 & 1 \end{bmatrix}\begin{bmatrix} a \\ b \\ c \end{bmatrix} = \begin{bmatrix} 26 \\ 92 \\ 52 \end{bmatrix}$
    b. How old is each person? Anna: 18, Bill: 20, Carlos: 14

Solve each system.

21. $\begin{cases} x + 2y - 3z = 18 \\ -3x - z = -20 \\ y + 3z = -13 \end{cases}$ $x = 8, y = -1, z = -4$

22. $\begin{cases} x + y + 3z = 9 \\ 2y - 5z = -21 \\ 2x - 5y = 21 \end{cases}$ $x = 3, y = -3, z = 3$

23. $\begin{cases} w + 2x - 3y + z = -2 \\ 2w - x - y + 3z = 3 \\ -w + 3x + y - z = 0 \\ 3w - x - 2y + 2z = -1 \end{cases}$ $w = -1, x = 0, y = 1, z = 2$

24. $\begin{cases} 2w + 3x - y + z = -11 \\ w + x + y + z = 0 \\ -3w - 2x - y - z = -3 \\ -2w + x + 3y + 2z = -5 \end{cases}$ $w = 3, x = -3, y = 4, z = -4$

Solve each matrix equation. If the coefficient matrix has no inverse, write *no unique solution*.

25. $\begin{bmatrix} 12 & -3 \\ 16 & 4 \end{bmatrix}\begin{bmatrix} x \\ y \end{bmatrix} = \begin{bmatrix} 144 \\ -64 \end{bmatrix}$ $x = 4, y = -32$

26. $\begin{bmatrix} 3 & 1 \\ 12 & 4 \end{bmatrix}\begin{bmatrix} x \\ y \end{bmatrix} = \begin{bmatrix} 9 \\ 10 \end{bmatrix}$ no unique solution

Determine whether each system has a unique solution.

27. $\begin{cases} 4d + 2e = 4 \\ d + 3e = 6 \end{cases}$ yes

28. $\begin{cases} 3x - 2y = 43 \\ 9x - 6y = 40 \end{cases}$ no

29. $\begin{cases} -y - z = 3 \\ x + 2y + 3z = 1 \\ 4x - 5y - 6z = -50 \end{cases}$ yes

30. **Reasoning** Explain how you could use a matrix equation to show that the lines represented by $y = -3x + 4$ and $y = -4x - 8$ intersect. Write the matrix equation $\begin{bmatrix} 3 & 1 \\ 4 & 1 \end{bmatrix}\begin{bmatrix} x \\ y \end{bmatrix} = \begin{bmatrix} 4 \\ -8 \end{bmatrix}$ to solve the system. If the equation has a solution (x, y), then the lines intersect at that point. A solution exists if the determinant of the coefficient matrix $\begin{bmatrix} 3 & 1 \\ 4 & 1 \end{bmatrix}$ does not equal zero.

All-in-One Resources/Online

Enrichment

12-4 Enrichment

Inverse Matrices and Systems

You can find the determinant of a 3×3 matrix $\begin{bmatrix} a_1 & b_1 & c_1 \\ a_2 & b_2 & c_2 \\ a_3 & b_3 & c_3 \end{bmatrix}$ by using submatrices that you form by removing rows and columns.

You can form the submatrix M_{ij} by removing the ith row and the jth column. For example, M_{12} is the submatrix formed by removing the first row and the second column.

$$\begin{bmatrix} \not{a_1} & \not{b_1} & \not{c_1} \\ a_2 & \not{b_2} & c_2 \\ a_3 & \not{b_3} & c_3 \end{bmatrix}$$

So $M_{12} = \begin{bmatrix} a_2 & c_2 \\ a_3 & c_3 \end{bmatrix}$.

The determinant of a 3×3 matrix A is $\det A = a_1 \det M_{11} - b_1 \det M_{12} + c_1 \det M_{13}$.

1. Find the determinant of $C = \begin{bmatrix} -1 & 3 & 5 \\ 2 & -4 & 6 \\ 0 & 1 & -1 \end{bmatrix}$ using the formula above. 18

The determinant of a 4×4 matrix A can be found in a similar manner:

$\det A = a_1 \det M_{11} - b_1 \det M_{12} + c_1 \det M_{13} - d_1 \det M_{14}$

2. Find the determinant of $B = \begin{bmatrix} 1 & 2 & 3 & 4 \\ 0 & 1 & 2 & 3 \\ 4 & 0 & 1 & 2 \\ 3 & 4 & 0 & 1 \end{bmatrix}$ using the formula above. 25

3. The matrix $A = \begin{bmatrix} 1 & 2 & 3 & 4 \\ 1 & 2 & 3 & 4 \\ 4 & 5 & 6 & 7 \\ 3 & 4 & 5 & 6 \end{bmatrix}$ has two identical rows. Calculate det A. 0

4. Write a 3×3 matrix with two identical rows. Calculate its determinant. Answers may vary. Sample: $\begin{bmatrix} 1 & 2 & 3 \\ 1 & 2 & 3 \\ 4 & 5 & 6 \end{bmatrix}$; 0

5. Write a 2×2 matrix with two identical rows. Calculate its determinant. Answers may vary. Sample: $\begin{bmatrix} 1 & 2 \\ 1 & 2 \end{bmatrix}$; 0

6. What do you think the determinant of an $n \times n$ matrix with two identical rows will be? Its determinant is zero.

Practice and Problem Solving Wkbk/ All-in-One Resources/Online

Think About a Plan

12-4 Think About a Plan

Inverse Matrices and Systems

Nutrition Suppose you are making a trail mix for your friends and want to fill three 1-lb bags. Almonds cost $2.25/lb, peanuts cost $1.30/lb, and raisins cost $.90/lb. You want each bag to contain twice as much nuts as raisins by weight. If you spent $4.45, how much of each ingredient did you buy?

Know

1. I need [3 lb] of ingredients that cost a total of [$4.45].
2. Almonds cost $2.25/lb, peanuts cost $1.30/lb, and raisins cost $.90/lb.
3. Each bag will contain twice as much nuts as raisins by weight.

Need

4. To solve the problem I need to: write and solve 3 equations for three unknowns.

Plan

5. Let x = the number of pounds of almonds, y = the number of pounds peanuts, and z = the number of pounds of raisins. Write a system of equations to solve the problem.
   $x + y + z = 3$
   $x + y - 2z = 0$
   $2.25x + 1.3y + 0.9z = 4.45$
6. Write the system as a matrix equation. $\begin{bmatrix} 1 & 1 & 1 \\ 1 & 1 & -2 \\ 2.25 & 1.3 & 0.9 \end{bmatrix}\begin{bmatrix} x \\ y \\ z \end{bmatrix} = \begin{bmatrix} 3 \\ 0 \\ 4.45 \end{bmatrix}$
7. Use a calculator. Solve for the variable matrix. $\begin{bmatrix} x \\ y \\ z \end{bmatrix} = \begin{bmatrix} 1 \\ 1 \\ 1 \end{bmatrix}$
8. How much of each ingredient did you buy? 1 lb of almonds, 1 lb of peanuts, and 1 lb of raisins
9. How can you check your solution? Does your solution check? Substitute $x = 1$, $y = 1$, and $z = 1$ into the system of equations. The solution checks.

Practice and Problem Solving Wkbk/ All-in-One Resources/Online

Standardized Test Prep

12-4 Standardized Test Prep

Inverse Matrices and Systems

Multiple Choice

For Exercises 1–4, choose the correct letter.

1. Which matrix equation represents the system $\begin{cases} 2x - y = 11 \\ x + 3y = 2 \end{cases}$? C
   (A) $\begin{bmatrix} x \\ y \end{bmatrix}\begin{bmatrix} 2 & -1 \\ 1 & 3 \end{bmatrix} = \begin{bmatrix} 11 \\ 2 \end{bmatrix}$
   (B) $\begin{bmatrix} 2 & -1 & 11 \\ 1 & 3 & 2 \end{bmatrix} = \begin{bmatrix} x \\ y \end{bmatrix}$
   (C) $\begin{bmatrix} 2 & -1 \\ 1 & 3 \end{bmatrix}\begin{bmatrix} x \\ y \end{bmatrix} = \begin{bmatrix} 11 \\ 2 \end{bmatrix}$
   (D) $\begin{bmatrix} 2 & -1 \\ 1 & 3 \end{bmatrix} = \begin{bmatrix} x \\ y \end{bmatrix}\begin{bmatrix} 11 \\ 2 \end{bmatrix}$

2. Let $\begin{bmatrix} 3 & 5 \\ -4 & -1 \end{bmatrix}\begin{bmatrix} x \\ y \end{bmatrix} = \begin{bmatrix} -4 \\ -6 \end{bmatrix}$. What values of x and y make the equation true? I
   (F) $(-12, -1)$ (G) $(-4, -6)$ (H) $(-3, -20)$ (I) $(2, -2)$

3. Which system has a unique solution? C
   (A) $\begin{cases} 3x - 2y = 43 \\ 9x - 6y = 40 \end{cases}$
   (B) $\begin{cases} 6x + 8y = 16 \\ -3x - 4y = 12 \end{cases}$
   (C) $\begin{cases} 2x - 5y = 6 \\ 4x + 7y = 12 \end{cases}$
   (D) $\begin{cases} 4x + 2y = 10 \\ 8x + 4y = 18 \end{cases}$

4. Let $\begin{bmatrix} 5 & 1 \\ 2 & -1 \end{bmatrix} X = \begin{bmatrix} 0 \\ -14 \end{bmatrix}$. What value of X makes the equation true? F
   (F) $\begin{bmatrix} -2 \\ 10 \end{bmatrix}$ (G) $\begin{bmatrix} -6 \\ -15 \end{bmatrix}$ (H) $\begin{bmatrix} 0 \\ 14 \end{bmatrix}$ (I) $\begin{bmatrix} -5 \\ 2 \end{bmatrix}$

Short Response

5. The Spirit Club sold buttons for $1, hats for $4, and t-shirts for $8. They sold 3 times as many buttons as hats. Together, the number of hats and t-shirts sold was equal to the number of buttons sold. They earned a total of $460. Write and solve a matrix equation to find how many buttons, hats, and t-shirts the club sold.
   [2] Possible Answer: $\begin{bmatrix} 1 & 4 & 8 \\ 1 & -3 & 0 \\ 1 & -1 & -1 \end{bmatrix}\begin{bmatrix} b \\ h \\ t \end{bmatrix} = \begin{bmatrix} 460 \\ 0 \\ 0 \end{bmatrix}$; $\begin{bmatrix} b \\ h \\ t \end{bmatrix} = \begin{bmatrix} 1 & 4 & 8 \\ 1 & -3 & 0 \\ 1 & -1 & -1 \end{bmatrix}^{-1}\begin{bmatrix} 460 \\ 0 \\ 0 \end{bmatrix} = \begin{bmatrix} 60 \\ 20 \\ 40 \end{bmatrix}$
   They sold 60 buttons, 20 hats, and 40 t-shirts.
   [1] incorrect or incomplete work shown
   [0] incorrect answers and no work shown OR no answers given

Online Teacher Resource Center

Activities, Games, and Puzzles

12-4 Puzzle: A Four-Word and Down-Word Puzzle

Inverse Matrices and Systems

Solve the following linear systems by using inverse matrices. Write the letter of each answer in the table below. Note that you may have to write some answers more than once. The letters of your answers should spell a word across each row and down each column.

1. $x + y = 5$, $x - 2y = -4$ L
2. $\begin{bmatrix} 1 & -3 \\ -5 & 16 \end{bmatrix}\begin{bmatrix} x \\ y \end{bmatrix} = \begin{bmatrix} -1 \\ 5 \end{bmatrix}$ I
3. $2x + 3y = 5$, $x + 2y = 6$ M
4. $\begin{bmatrix} 2 & -3 \\ -4 & 6 \end{bmatrix}\begin{bmatrix} x \\ y \end{bmatrix} = \begin{bmatrix} 1 \\ -2 \end{bmatrix}$ B
5. $3x - y = 5$, $x + 4y = 6$ C
6. $\begin{bmatrix} 2 & -5 \\ 1 & -3 \end{bmatrix}\begin{bmatrix} x \\ y \end{bmatrix} = \begin{bmatrix} 0 \\ -1 \end{bmatrix}$ O
7. $x - 5y = -2$, $3x + 2y = 11$ K
8. $\begin{bmatrix} 1 & 2 \\ 2 & -1 \end{bmatrix}\begin{bmatrix} x \\ y \end{bmatrix} = \begin{bmatrix} 11 \\ 2 \end{bmatrix}$ N

B. no solution
C. $x = 2, y = 1$
I. $x = -1, y = 0$
K. $x = 3, y = 1$
L. $x = 2, y = 3$
M. $x = -8, y = 7$
N. $x = 3, y = 4$
O. $x = 5, y = 2$

1. L	2. I	3. M	4. B
A	R	E	A
5. C	6. O	R	7. K
7. K	8. N	E	E

12-5 Geometric Transformations

© **Content Standards**
G.CO.5 Given a geometric figure and a rotation, reflection, or translation, draw the transformed figure . . . Specify a sequence of transformations . . .
Also G.CO.2, N.VM.6, N.VM.7, N.VM.8

Objective To transform geometric figures using matrix operations

The first column in R is the point (1, 0).

© MATHEMATICAL PRACTICES

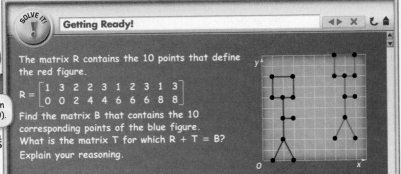

SOLVE IT! **Getting Ready!**

The matrix R contains the 10 points that define the red figure.

$$R = \begin{bmatrix} 1 & 3 & 2 & 2 & 3 & 1 & 2 & 3 & 1 & 3 \\ 0 & 0 & 2 & 4 & 4 & 6 & 6 & 6 & 8 & 8 \end{bmatrix}$$

Find the matrix B that contains the 10 corresponding points of the blue figure. What is the matrix T for which R + T = B? Explain your reasoning.

Dynamic Activity
Translations
Dilations

Lesson Vocabulary
• image
• preimage
• dilation
• rotation
• center of rotation

Matrix *T* in the Solve It *translates* the figure. Other transformations *dilate*, *rotate*, and *reflect* such geometric figures.

Essential Understanding You can multiply a 2 × 1 matrix representing a point by a 2 × 2 matrix to rotate the point about the origin or reflect the point across a line.

You can write the *n* points that define a figure as a 2 × *n* matrix. For example, you can represent the four vertices of kite *ABCD* with the 2 × 4 matrix shown.

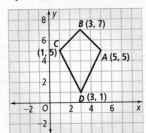

x-coordinate
y-coordinate
$$\begin{array}{cccc} A & B & C & D \\ \begin{bmatrix} 5 & 3 & 1 & 3 \\ 5 & 7 & 5 & 1 \end{bmatrix} \end{array}$$

A change to a figure is a transformation of the figure. The transformed figure is the **image**. The original figure is the **preimage**. In the Solve It, the red figure is the preimage. The blue figure is the image.

---

1 Interactive Learning

Solve It!

PURPOSE Use a matrix to describe a translation
PROCESS Students may
• identify the coordinates of the corresponding points in the blue figure to identify *B*.
• compare the points on the figures and identify the translation and use it to identify *T*.

FACILITATE

Q What is the horizontal distance and what is the vertical distance between corresponding points represented in matrix *R* and matrix *B*? **[Each *x* coordinate in *B* is 6 units to the right of the corresponding *x*-coordinate in *R*; each *y* coordinate in *B* is 2 units up from the corresponding *y*-coordinate in *R*.]**

Q What does the equation *R* + *T* = *B* represent? **[the result of adding each element in *T* to each *x*- and *y*-element in *R* to produce the coordinates of points in the image, represented by *B*]**

ANSWER See Solve It in Answers on next page.
CONNECT THE MATH In the Solve It, students determine that when a figure is represented by a matrix, adding another matrix can result in a translation of the figure. In the lesson, students will use matrices to transform geometric figures.

12-5 Preparing to Teach

BIG ideas Modeling
Transformations

ESSENTIAL UNDERSTANDINGS
• Transformations that can be performed using matrices include translations, dilations, rotations, and reflections.
• A 2 × 1 matrix representing a point can be multiplied by a 2 × 2 matrix to rotate the point about the origin or reflect the point across a line.

Math Background

Matrices can be used to represent a set of *x*- and *y*-coordinates of points in the coordinate plane, as well as different transformations that can be applied to them. Using specific matrix operations related to each transformation, a matrix of the coordinates of corresponding points on an image could be obtained.

Translations use matrix addition and subtraction. If matrix *R* represents coordinates of *n* points on a preimage and matrix *T* represents an *x*–*y*-translation of those points, then *R* + *T* is a third matrix *B* containing the corresponding coordinates of points in the image.

Dilations use scalar multiplication. If matrix *R* represents coordinates of *n* points on a preimage, and *c* is the scale factor for a dilation, then *cR* is a second matrix *B* containing the corresponding coordinates of points in the image.

Rotations and reflections use matrix multiplication. If matrix *R* represents coordinates of *n* points on a preimage, and matrix *T* represents rotation or reflection of those points, then *R* × *T* is a third matrix *B* containing the corresponding coordinates of points in the image.

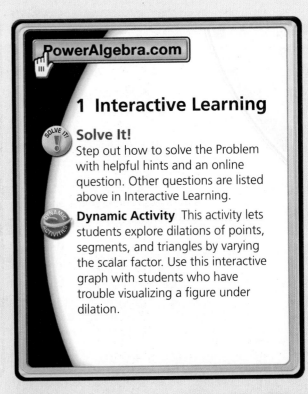

PowerAlgebra.com

1 Interactive Learning

Solve It!
Step out how to solve the Problem with helpful hints and an online question. Other questions are listed above in Interactive Learning.

Dynamic Activity This activity lets students explore dilations of points, segments, and triangles by varying the scalar factor. Use this interactive graph with students who have trouble visualizing a figure under dilation.

2 Guided Instruction

Problem 1

> **Q** What are the image vertices of kite $A'D'C'B'$ under the same translation? Explain. $\begin{bmatrix} 13 & 11 & 9 & 11 \\ 0 & -4 & 0 & 2 \end{bmatrix}$
> **The order of the points was obtained by moving clockwise around the perimeter of kite *ABCD*.]**
>
> **Q** How does the image matrix representing kite $A'D'C'B'$ differ from the image matrix representing kite $A'B'C'D'$? **[Both matrices represent the same set of points but are written in a different order. One matrix starts at *A'* and lists the vertices in counterclockwise order, and the other starts at *A'* and lists the vertices in clockwise order around the figure.]**
>
> **Q** What would be the image matrix of kite $A'B'C'D'$ if the translation of kite *ABCD* were 8 units to the left and 5 units up? $\begin{bmatrix} -3 & -5 & -7 & -5 \\ 10 & 12 & 10 & 6 \end{bmatrix}$]

Got It?   SYNTHESIZING

> **Q** Given a matrix representing points on a figure, like *ABCD*, and a matrix representing corresponding points on its image, $A'B'C'D'$, how could you determine the translation matrix? **[Subtract the elements in the preimage matrix from the corresponding elements in the image matrix.]**
>
> **Q** If the pentagon in 1b is translated 3 units left and 2 units down, what is the translation from the image to the preimage? **[3 units right and 2 units up]**

The transformation of the figure in the Solve It is a translation—moving a figure to a new location without changing its size, shape, or orientation. You can use matrix addition to translate all the vertices of a figure in one step.

©️ Problem 1 Translating a Figure

Kite *ABCD* has vertices (5, 5), (3, 7), (1, 5), and (3, 1). If you translate it 8 units to the right and 5 units down, what are the coordinates of the vertices of its image $A'B'C'D'$? Use matrix addition. Draw *ABCD* and its image.

Think
To translate 8 units to the right, what must you do to each *x*-coordinate?
Add 8 to each *x*-coordinate to translate 8 units to the right.

Preimage Vertices		Translation Matrix		Image Vertices

$$\begin{array}{c} A\ \ B\ \ C\ \ D \\ \begin{bmatrix} 5 & 3 & 1 & 3 \\ 5 & 7 & 5 & 1 \end{bmatrix} \end{array} + \begin{bmatrix} 8 & 8 & 8 & 8 \\ -5 & -5 & -5 & -5 \end{bmatrix} = \begin{array}{c} A'\ \ B'\ \ C'\ \ D' \\ \begin{bmatrix} 13 & 11 & 9 & 11 \\ 0 & 2 & 0 & -4 \end{bmatrix} \end{array}$$

Add 8 to each *x*-coordinate.
Subtract 5 from each *y*-coordinate.

The vertices of the preimage, $A(5, 5)$, $B(3, 7)$, $C(1, 5)$, and $D(3, 1)$ translate to the vertices $A'(13, 0)$, $B'(11, 2)$, $C'(9, 0)$, and $D'(11, -4)$ of the image.

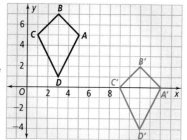

> ©️ ✔️ **Got It?** **1. a. Reasoning** How would you translate the kite image $A'B'C'D'$ to the kite preimage *ABCD*?
>
> **b.** A pentagon has vertices (0, −5), (−1, −1), (−5, 0), (1, 3), and (4, 0). Use matrix addition to translate the pentagon 3 units left and 2 units up. What are the vertices of the image? Graph the preimage and the image.

You enlarge or reduce a figure with a **dilation**. You use scalar multiplication to dilate a figure with center of dilation at the origin. In this book, dilations have their centers at the origin.

$$2\begin{array}{c} A\ \ \ B\ \ \ \ C \\ \begin{bmatrix} -1 & 3 & 2 \\ 0 & 2 & -1 \end{bmatrix} \end{array} = \begin{array}{c} A'\ \ B'\ \ \ C' \\ \begin{bmatrix} -2 & 6 & 4 \\ 0 & 4 & -2 \end{bmatrix} \end{array}$$

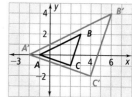

Answers

Solve It!

$$B = \begin{bmatrix} 7 & 9 & 8 & 8 & 9 & 7 & 8 & 9 & 7 & 9 \\ 2 & 2 & 4 & 6 & 6 & 8 & 8 & 8 & 10 & 10 \end{bmatrix}$$

$$T = B - R = \begin{bmatrix} 6 & 6 & 6 & 6 & 6 & 6 & 6 & 6 & 6 & 6 \\ 2 & 2 & 2 & 2 & 2 & 2 & 2 & 2 & 2 & 2 \end{bmatrix}$$

T represents a translation of the blue figure 6 units to the right of and 2 units up from the red figure.

Got It?

1. a. Subtract 8 from each *x*-coordinate and add 5 to each *y*-coordinate.
  b. See page 804.
2. See page 804.

 PowerAlgebra.com

2 Guided Instruction

©️ Each Problem is worked out and supported online.

Problem 1
Translating a Figure
Animated

Problem 2
Dilating a Figure

Problem 3
Rotating a Figure
Animated

Problem 4
Reflecting a Figure
Animated

Support in Algebra 2 Companion
• Vocabulary
• Key Concepts
• Got It?

Problem 2 Dilating a Figure (STEM)

Digital Media The width of the digital picture is presently 800 pixels (approximately 11.1 in.). Its height is 600 pixels (approximately 8.3 in.). You want to reduce its width as shown. This will allow the picture to fit on any computer screen without scrolling. Using a dilation, what are the coordinates of the vertices of the reduced image?

Know
- Current picture size
- Dilated picture width

Need
- Scale factor
- Dilated picture height

Plan
- Find the scale factor.
- Write a preimage matrix of the photo coordinates.
- Use scalar multiplication.

Step 1 Find the scale factor.

Dilated picture width: 640 pixels

Current picture width: 800 pixels

Scale factor $= \dfrac{\text{Dilated Width}}{\text{Current Width}} = \dfrac{640}{800}$, or 0.8.

Step 2 Multiply the preimage matrix by the scale factor, 0.8.

$$0.8 \begin{bmatrix} 0 & 800 & 800 & 0 \\ 0 & 0 & 600 & 600 \end{bmatrix} = \begin{bmatrix} 0 & 640 & 640 & 0 \\ 0 & 0 & 480 & 480 \end{bmatrix}$$

The coordinates of the vertices of the reduced image are
(0, 0), (640, 0), (640, 480), and (0, 480).

Got It? 2. You are to enlarge a picture by the factor 2. The preimage is 5 in. by 3 in.
a. Write a matrix of coordinates of the preimage vertices. Make one vertex (0, 0).
b. What are the coordinates of the vertices of the image? Show the multiplication that you used for the dilation.
c. **Reasoning** You enlarged the picture by the factor 2. By what factor did you increase its area?

Problem 2
Dilation is a transformation that does not preserve lengths of segments. If the scale factor is greater than 1, corresponding lengths of segments in an image are greater than those in the preimage; if the scale factor is less than 1, lengths of corresponding segments in the image are less than those in the preimage.

Q In Step 1, why does the scale factor have to be less than 1? **[The picture is being reduced.]**

Q In Step 2, what is the intermediate step in the multiplication of the scale factor and the preimage matrix?
$$\begin{bmatrix} 0.8 \times 0 & 0.8 \times 800 & 0.8 \times 800 & 0.8 \times 0 \\ 0.8 \times 0 & 0.8 \times 0 & 0.8 \times 600 & 0.8 \times 600 \end{bmatrix}$$

Q What are the approximate width and height of the image photo in inches? **[approximately 8.88 in. by 6.64 in.]**

Got It?   ELL SUPPORT
Some students may not remember the relationship between the areas of similar figures and assume that it is also 2:1. A quick calculation should help.

Q What is the area of the original picture? **[15 in²]**
Q What is the area of the enlarged image? **[60 in²]**
Q What is the ratio between the areas of the original picture and its image? **[$\frac{60 \text{ in}^2}{15 \text{ in}^2} = \frac{4}{1}$]**

Additional Problems

1. Kite *ABCD* has vertices (4, 2), (2, 4), (0, 2), and (2, −3). If you translate it 5 units to the left and 3 units down, what are the coordinates of the vertices of its image *A′B′C′D′*? Use matrix addition. Draw *ABCD* and its image.

ANSWER
A′(−1, −1), *B′*(−3, 1), *C′*(−5, −1) and *D′*(−3, −6)

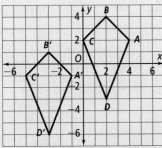

2. The width of a photograph is 8 in. and its height is 10 in. You want to reduce it so its width is 5 in. Using a dilation, what are the coordinates of the vertices of the reduced image?

ANSWER
$$\begin{bmatrix} 0 & 5 & 5 & 0 \\ 0 & 0 & 6.25 & 6.25 \end{bmatrix}$$

3. Rotate the triangle with vertices *A*(2, −1), *B*(−1, 3), and *C*(2, 5) 180° about the origin. What are the vertices of the image? Graph the preimage and the image in the same coordinate plane.

ANSWER
A′(−2, 1), *B′*(1, −3), and and *C′*(−2, −5)

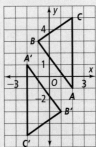

4. Reflect the quadrilateral with vertices *A*(2, 5), *B*(−2, 4), *C*(−3, 1) and *D*(4, 3) across the *x*-axis. What are the vertices of the image? Graph the preimage and the image in the same coordinate plane.

ANSWER
A′(2, −5), *B′*(−2, −4), *C′*(−3, −1), and *D′*(4, −3)

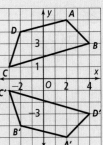

Take Note

Q What is the determinant of each rotation matrix? Where does the image of a figure after a 360° rotation end up? Explain. **[1; a 360° rotation is the identity matrix, so an image maps onto its preimage.]**

Problem 3

Q What is center of rotation for the problems in 3A and 3B? **[the origin]**

Q In 3A and 3B, what is the distance between the center of rotation and each pair of corresponding vertices in the preimage and image? Explain. **[$\sqrt{2}$, $\sqrt{29}$ and $\sqrt{13}$ respectively. In a rotation, each pair of corresponding points is equidistant from the origin, and their x- and y-coordinates are the lengths of the legs in a right triangle. So the distance is the length of the hypotenuse in each triangle, which you can calculate using the Pythagorean Theorem.]**

Q What is the vertex matrix of the image if the triangle is rotated 360° about the origin?

$$\left[\begin{array}{ccc} 1 & 5 & -2 \\ 1 & 2 & 3 \end{array}\right]$$

Got It?   EXTENSION

Just as you can work backwards from the image of a figure translated in the coordinate plane to its preimage, you can also work backwards from the image in a rotation to its preimage.

Q What rotation matrix could you apply to the image in 3a to get back to its preimage? **[a 90° rotation matrix]**

A **rotation** turns a figure about a fixed point—the **center of rotation**. You can multiply a figure's vertex matrix by a rotation matrix to find the vertices of the rotation image. In this book, rotations are counterclockwise about the origin.

The matrix $\left[\begin{array}{cc} 0 & -1 \\ 1 & 0 \end{array}\right]$ rotates a figure 90°. A 90° rotation followed by another 90° rotation, or

$$\left[\begin{array}{cc} 0 & -1 \\ 1 & 0 \end{array}\right]\left[\begin{array}{cc} 0 & -1 \\ 1 & 0 \end{array}\right] = \left[\begin{array}{cc} 0 & -1 \\ 1 & 0 \end{array}\right]^2 = \left[\begin{array}{cc} -1 & 0 \\ 0 & -1 \end{array}\right],$$

is a 180° rotation. Rotate another 90° for a 270° rotation.

take note **Properties**   **Rotation Matrices for the Coordinate Plane**

90° Rotation	180° Rotation	270° Rotation	360° Rotation
$\left[\begin{array}{cc} 0 & -1 \\ 1 & 0 \end{array}\right]$	$\left[\begin{array}{cc} -1 & 0 \\ 0 & -1 \end{array}\right]$	$\left[\begin{array}{cc} 0 & 1 \\ -1 & 0 \end{array}\right]$	$\left[\begin{array}{cc} 1 & 0 \\ 0 & 1 \end{array}\right]$

Ⓒ **Problem 3** **Rotating a Figure**

Rotate the triangle with vertices $A(1, 1)$, $B(5, 2)$, and $C(-2, 3)$ by the indicated amount. What are the vertices of the image? Graph the preimage and the image in the same coordinate plane.

Plan

How do you rotate the triangle?
Multiply the 2 × 3 triangle matrix by the appropriate rotation matrix to get the 2 × 3 image matrix.

Ⓐ 90°

$$\left[\begin{array}{cc} 0 & -1 \\ 1 & 0 \end{array}\right]\left[\begin{array}{ccc} 1 & 5 & -2 \\ 1 & 2 & 3 \end{array}\right]$$
$$= \left[\begin{array}{ccc} -1 & -2 & -3 \\ 1 & 5 & -2 \end{array}\right]$$

The vertices of the image are $(-1, 1)$, $(-2, 5)$, and $(-3, -2)$.

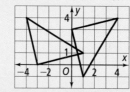

Ⓑ 180°

$$\left[\begin{array}{cc} -1 & 0 \\ 0 & -1 \end{array}\right]\left[\begin{array}{ccc} 1 & 5 & -2 \\ 1 & 2 & 3 \end{array}\right]$$
$$= \left[\begin{array}{ccc} -1 & -5 & 2 \\ -1 & -2 & -3 \end{array}\right]$$

The vertices of the image are $(-1, -1)$, $(-5, -2)$, and $(2, -3)$.

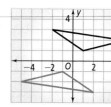

✓ **Got It?** **3.** Rotate the triangle with vertices $D(-3, 0)$, $E(-4, 4)$, and $F(1, 1)$ the indicated amount. What are the vertices of the image? Graph the preimage and the image in the same coordinate plane.

  a. 270°   **b.** 360°

Answers

Got It? (continued)

1. b. $\left[\begin{array}{ccccc} 0 & -1 & -5 & 1 & 4 \\ -5 & -1 & 0 & 3 & 0 \end{array}\right] +$
$\left[\begin{array}{ccccc} -3 & -3 & -3 & -3 & -3 \\ 2 & 2 & 2 & 2 & 2 \end{array}\right] =$
$\left[\begin{array}{ccccc} -3 & -4 & -8 & -2 & 1 \\ -3 & 1 & 2 & 5 & 2 \end{array}\right]$;

$(-3, -3)$, $(-4, 1)$, $(-8, 2)$, $(-2, 5)$, $(1, 2)$

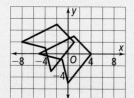

2. Answers may vary. Samples:

a. $\left[\begin{array}{cccc} 0 & 5 & 5 & 0 \\ 0 & 0 & 3 & 3 \end{array}\right]$

b. $2\left[\begin{array}{cccc} 0 & 5 & 5 & 0 \\ 0 & 0 & 3 & 3 \end{array}\right] = \left[\begin{array}{cccc} 0 & 10 & 10 & 0 \\ 0 & 0 & 6 & 6 \end{array}\right]$;

$(0, 0)$, $(10, 0)$, $(10, 6)$, $(0, 6)$

c. 4

3. a. $(0, 3)$, $(4, 4)$, $(1, -1)$;

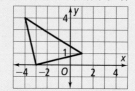

b. $(-3, 0)$, $(-4, 4)$, $(1, 1)$;

A *reflection* maps a point or figure in the coordinate plane to its mirror image using a specific line as its line of reflection. In this book, the lines of reflection are $y = 0$ (the x-axis), $x = 0$ (the y-axis), $y = x$, and $y = -x$.

take note

Properties   Reflection Matrices for the Coordinate Plane

across x-axis	across y-axis	across $y = x$	across $y = -x$
$\begin{bmatrix} 1 & 0 \\ 0 & -1 \end{bmatrix}$	$\begin{bmatrix} -1 & 0 \\ 0 & 1 \end{bmatrix}$	$\begin{bmatrix} 0 & 1 \\ 1 & 0 \end{bmatrix}$	$\begin{bmatrix} 0 & -1 \\ -1 & 0 \end{bmatrix}$

© **Problem 4** Reflecting a Figure

Reflect the quadrilateral with vertices $A(2, 1)$, $B(8, 1)$, $C(8, 4)$, and $D(5, 5)$ across the indicated line. What are the vertices of the image? Graph the preimage and the image in the same coordinate plane.

Think

Does it matter what order you list the points in the preimage matrix?
Yes; you should list them in order as you move around the outside of the figure.

A y-axis

$$\begin{bmatrix} -1 & 0 \\ 0 & 1 \end{bmatrix}\begin{bmatrix} 2 & 8 & 8 & 5 \\ 1 & 1 & 4 & 5 \end{bmatrix}$$

$$= \begin{bmatrix} -2 & -8 & -8 & -5 \\ 1 & 1 & 4 & 5 \end{bmatrix}$$

The vertices of the image are
$(-2, 1)$, $(-8, 1)$, $(-8, 4)$, and $(-5, 5)$.

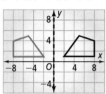

B $y = -x$

$$\begin{bmatrix} 0 & -1 \\ -1 & 0 \end{bmatrix}\begin{bmatrix} 2 & 8 & 8 & 5 \\ 1 & 1 & 4 & 5 \end{bmatrix}$$

$$= \begin{bmatrix} -1 & -1 & -4 & -5 \\ -2 & -8 & -8 & -5 \end{bmatrix}$$

The vertices of the image are
$(-1, -2)$, $(-1, -8)$, $(-4, -8)$, and $(-5, -5)$.

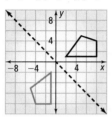

✓ **Got It?** **4.** Reflect the quadrilateral with vertices $E(1, 1)$, $F(3, 1)$, $G(6, 4)$, and $H(1, 3)$ across the indicated line. What are vertices of the image? Graph the preimage and the image in the same coordinate plane.
   a. x-axis   **b.** $y = x$

Take Note

Q What is the determinant of each reflection matrix? Does any reflection produce an image that maps onto its preimage? Explain. **[−1; no; none of the reflection matrices are the identity matrix.]**

Problem 4

Q In 4A, how would you describe the elements in the image matrix that represent the x- and y-coordinates of the image? **[The x-coordinates are the opposites of those in the preimage matrix, and the y-coordinates are the same as those in the preimage matrix.]**

Q What do the elements in the reflection matrix across the x-axis suggest about the relationship between the x- and y-coordinates in the preimage matrix and in the image matrix? **[The x-coordinates will be the same as those in the preimage matrix, but the y-coordinates will be the opposite.]**

Q In 4B, how would you describe the relationship between the x- and y-coordinates in the preimage matrix and in the image matrix? **[The elements in the rows have been switched and the elements are opposites.]**

Got It?   ERROR PREVENTION

Q When using either a rotation or a reflection matrix T to determine the image coordinates of a preimage matrix R, in what order should the matrices in the multiplication step be written and why? **[TR, not RT: the number of columns in the first matrix must equal the number of rows in the second matrix.]**

4. a. $(1, -1)$, $(3, -1)$, $(6, -4)$, $(1, -3)$

b. $(1, 1)$, $(1, 3)$, $(4, 6)$, $(3, 1)$

3 Lesson Check

Do you know HOW?

- In Exercise 1, students need to recognize that a reduction is a dilation involving the product of the scale factor $\frac{1}{2}$ and the preimage matrix $\begin{bmatrix} 1 & 2 & 4 \\ 1 & 4 & -1 \end{bmatrix}$. The corresponding elements of the image matrix are equal to one-half those in the preimage matrix.

- In Exercise 2, students can multiply the preimage matrix by the 270° rotation matrix, and in Exercise 3, multiply it by the $y = x$ reflection matrix. In each case, students are solving the matrix equation $TR = B$, where T is a transformation matrix, R is a preimage matrix of coordinates, and B is the image matrix of corresponding coordinates.

Do you UNDERSTAND?

- For Exercise 4, students should recognize that a dilation by a factor other than 1 does not preserve the lengths of segments in a figure. If the scalar is a positive number less than 1, the preimage is reduced; if the scalar is greater than 1, the preimage is enlarged.

Close

Q Which transformation of a preimage matrix of coordinates does not involve multiplication? **[translation]**

Q Which transformations always preserve the lengths of segments in a preimage? **[translations, reflections, and rotations]**

 Lesson Check

Do you know HOW?

Use matrices to perform the following transformations on the triangle with vertices $A(1, 1)$, $B(2, 4)$, and $C(4, -1)$. State the coordinates of the vertices of the image.

1. Reduce by a factor of $\frac{1}{2}$.

2. Rotate 270°.

3. Reflect across the line $y = x$.

Do you UNDERSTAND?

 4. **Reasoning** Which transformations, translation, dilation, rotation, or reflection, leave the size of a figure unchanged? Explain.

 5. **Writing** Describe two ways that the point $(3, 7)$ can be transformed to the point $(7, 3)$.

6. **Reasoning** What is true about $\begin{bmatrix} -3 & 0 \\ 0 & -3 \end{bmatrix}\begin{bmatrix} 1 & -2 & 4 \\ 1 & -1 & 2 \end{bmatrix}$ and $-3\begin{bmatrix} 1 & -2 & 4 \\ 1 & -1 & 2 \end{bmatrix}$? Explain.

Practice and Problem-Solving Exercises

A Practice

Use matrix addition to find the coordinates of each image after a translation 3 units left and 5 units up. If possible, graph each pair of figures on the same coordinate plane. — See Problem 1.

7. $A(1, -3)$, $B(1, 1)$, $C(5, 1)$, $D(5, -3)$
8. $G(0, 0)$, $H(4, 4)$, $I(8, 0)$, $J(4, -4)$
9. $J(-10, 2)$, $K(-16, 1)$, $L(12, -5)$
10. $R(9, 3)$, $S(3, 6)$, $T(3, 3)$, $U(6, -3)$

Find the coordinates of each image after the given dilation. — See Problem 2.

11. $\begin{bmatrix} 0 & 2 & 5 & 8 \\ 0 & 4 & 5 & 1 \end{bmatrix}, 2$

12. $\begin{bmatrix} -7 & -3 & 4 \\ -5 & 4 & 0 \end{bmatrix}, 0.5$

13. $\begin{bmatrix} -8 & 2 & 3 & 1 & -2 \\ 6 & 4 & 0 & -4 & 0 \end{bmatrix}, 1.5$

Graph each figure and its image after the given rotation. — See Problem 3.

14. $\begin{bmatrix} 0 & -3 & 5 \\ 0 & 1 & 2 \end{bmatrix}; 90°$

15. $\begin{bmatrix} -1 & 0 & 5 \\ -1 & 5 & 0 \end{bmatrix}; 180°$

16. $\begin{bmatrix} -5 & 6 & 0 \\ -1 & 2 & 4 \end{bmatrix}; 90°$

Find the coordinates of each image after the given rotation.

17. $\begin{bmatrix} 3 & 6 & 3 & 6 \\ -3 & 3 & 3 & -3 \end{bmatrix}; 270°$

18. $\begin{bmatrix} 0 & 4 & 8 & 6 \\ 0 & 4 & 4 & 2 \end{bmatrix}; 360°$

19. $\begin{bmatrix} 1 & 2 & 3 & 4 & 2.5 \\ 3 & 2 & 2 & 3 & 5 \end{bmatrix}; 180°$

Graph each figure and its image after reflection across the given line. — See Problem 4.

20. $\begin{bmatrix} 0 & -3 & 5 \\ 0 & 1 & 2 \end{bmatrix}; y = x$

21. $\begin{bmatrix} -1 & 0 & 5 \\ -1 & 5 & 0 \end{bmatrix}; y\text{-axis}$

22. $\begin{bmatrix} -3 & -5 & -10 \\ 4 & 7 & 1 \end{bmatrix}; x\text{-axis}$

Find the coordinates of each image after reflection across the given line.

23. $\begin{bmatrix} 3 & 6 & 3 & 6 \\ -3 & 3 & 3 & -3 \end{bmatrix}; y = -x$

24. $\begin{bmatrix} 0 & 4 & 8 & 6 \\ 0 & 4 & 4 & 2 \end{bmatrix}; x\text{-axis}$

25. $\begin{bmatrix} 1 & 2 & 3 & 4 & 2.5 \\ 3 & 2 & 2 & 3 & 5 \end{bmatrix}; y = x$

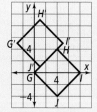

3 Lesson Check

For a digital lesson check, use the Got It questions.

Support in Algebra 2 Companion
- Lesson Check

4 Practice

Assign homework to individual students or to an entire class.

Answers

Lesson Check

1. $A'\left(\frac{1}{2}, \frac{1}{2}\right)$, $B'(1, 2)$, $C'\left(2, -\frac{1}{2}\right)$

2. $A'(1, -1)$, $B'(4, -2)$, $C'(-1, -4)$

3. $A'(1, 1)$, $B'(4, 2)$, $C'(-1, 4)$

4. Translations, rotations and reflections leave the size of the figure unchanged. Translation moves the figure to a new location. Rotation turns the figure about a fixed pt. Reflection maps a figure in the coordinate plane to its mirror image using a specific line as its mirror.

5. Answers may vary. Sample: reflection across $y = x$; translation 4 units right and 4 units down

6. They are equal.; $\begin{bmatrix} -3 & 0 \\ 0 & -3 \end{bmatrix}\begin{bmatrix} 1 & -2 & 4 \\ 1 & -1 & 2 \end{bmatrix}$

$= -3\begin{bmatrix} 1 & 0 \\ 0 & 1 \end{bmatrix}\begin{bmatrix} 1 & -2 & 4 \\ 1 & -1 & 2 \end{bmatrix}$

$= -3\begin{bmatrix} 1 & -2 & 4 \\ 1 & -1 & 2 \end{bmatrix}$

Practice and Problem-Solving Exercises

7. $(-2, 2)$, $(-2, 6)$, $(2, 6)$, $(2, 2)$;

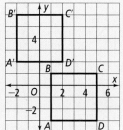

8. $(-3, 5)$, $(1, 9)$, $(5, 5)$, $(1, 1)$;

B Apply

Geometry Each matrix represents the vertices of a polygon. Translate each figure 5 units left and 1 unit up. Express your answer as a matrix.

26. $\begin{bmatrix} -3 & -3 & 2 & 2 \\ -2 & -4 & -2 & -4 \end{bmatrix}$　　27. $\begin{bmatrix} -3 & 0 & 3 & 0 \\ -9 & -6 & -9 & -12 \end{bmatrix}$　　28. $\begin{bmatrix} 0 & 1 & -4 \\ 0 & 3 & 5 \end{bmatrix}$

For Exercises 29–32, use △*ABC*. Write the coordinates of each image in matrix form.

29. a translation 2 units left and 3 units down

30. a dilation half the original size

31. a rotation of 180°

32. a reflection across the *x*-axis

© 33. **Think About a Plan** In an upcoming cartoon, the hero is a gymnast. In one scene he swings around a high bar. Describe the rotation matrices that would be needed so four frames of the movie would show the illustrated motion (below), one frame after the other.
- What do you need to do first to describe the motion?
- Can you use just one rotation matrix, or do you need three?

Frame 1　　　　Frame 2　　　　Frame 3　　　　Frame 4

  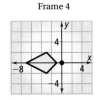

34. **Animation** Suppose you want the cartoon of the gymnast in the previous exercise to show two revolutions around the bar. What rotation matrices are needed so eight frames of the movie would show the illustrated motion, one frame after the other.

© 35. **Writing** Explain why you might want to represent a transformation as a matrix.

Use matrices to represent the vertices of graph *f* and graph *g*. Name each transformation.

36.
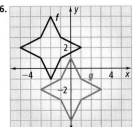

37.
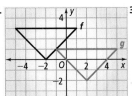

38.

---

4 Practice

ASSIGNMENT GUIDE
Basic: 7–25 all, 32–36
Average: 7–25 odd, 26–37
Advanced: 7–25 odd, 26–41
Standardized Test Prep: 42–46
Mixed Review: 47–52

© **Mathematical Practices** are supported by exercises with red headings. Here are the Practices supported in this lesson:

MP 1: Make Sense of Problems Ex. 3
MP 2: Reason Abstractly Ex. 4, 21
MP 2: Reason Quatitatively Ex. 6
MP 3: Communicate Ex. 5, 35

Applications exercises have blue headings. Exercise 34 supports MP 4: Model.

EXERCISE 34: Use the Think About a Plan worksheet in the **Practice and Problem Solving Workbook** (also available in the Teaching Resources in print and online) to further support students' development in becoming independent learners.

HOMEWORK QUICK CHECK
To check students' understanding of key skills and concepts, go over Exercises 11, 21, 33, 34, and 35.

---

9. (−13, 7), (−19, 6), (9, 0);

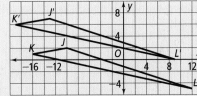

10. (6, 8), (0, 11), (0, 8), (3, 2);

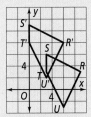

11. (0, 0), (4, 8), (10, 10), (16, 2)

12. (−3.5, −2.5), (−1.5, 2), (2, 0)

13. (−12, 9), (3, 6), (4.5, 0), (1.5, −6), (−3, 0)

14.

15.
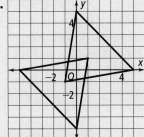

16.

17. (−3, −3), (3, −6), (3, −3), (−3, −6)

18. (0, 0), (4, 4), (8, 4), (6, 2)

19. (−1, −3), (−2, −2), (−3, −2), (−4, −3), (−2.5, −5)

20.
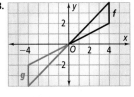

21.
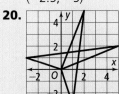

22.
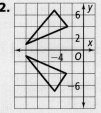

23. (3, −3), (−3, −6), (−3, −3), (3, −6)

24. (0, 0), (4, −4), (8, −4), (6, −2)

25. (3, 1), (2, 2), (2, 3), (3, 4), (5, 2.5)

26–38. See next page.

Answers

Practice and Problem-Solving Exercises (continued)

26. $\begin{bmatrix} -8 & -8 & -3 & -3 \\ -1 & -3 & -1 & -3 \end{bmatrix}$

27. $\begin{bmatrix} -8 & -5 & -2 & -5 \\ -8 & -5 & -8 & -11 \end{bmatrix}$

28. $\begin{bmatrix} -5 & -4 & -9 \\ 1 & 4 & 6 \end{bmatrix}$

29. $\begin{bmatrix} -5 & -1 & -3 \\ -2 & -1 & 1 \end{bmatrix}$

30. $\begin{bmatrix} -1.5 & 0.5 & -0.5 \\ 0.5 & 1 & 2 \end{bmatrix}$

31. $\begin{bmatrix} 3 & -1 & 1 \\ -1 & -2 & -4 \end{bmatrix}$

32. $\begin{bmatrix} -3 & 1 & -1 \\ -1 & -2 & -4 \end{bmatrix}$

33. Apply a 90° rotation matrix $\begin{bmatrix} 0 & -1 \\ 1 & 0 \end{bmatrix}$ three times to determine the image matrix for each frame. The fourth application of the 90° rotation matrix would show the gymnast at the starting position of Frame 1.

34. Apply a 90° rotation matrix $\begin{bmatrix} 0 & -1 \\ 1 & 0 \end{bmatrix}$ eight times.

35. Check students' work.

36. f: $\begin{bmatrix} -5 & -3 & -2 & -1 & 1 & -1 & -2 & -3 \\ 2 & 1 & -1 & 1 & 2 & 3 & 5 & 3 \end{bmatrix}$
g: $\begin{bmatrix} -3 & -1 & 0 & 1 & 3 & 1 & 0 & -1 \\ -2 & -3 & -5 & -3 & -2 & -1 & 1 & -1 \end{bmatrix}$
translation

37. f: $\begin{bmatrix} -5 & -2 & 1 \\ 3 & 0 & 3 \end{bmatrix}$, g: $\begin{bmatrix} -1 & 2 & 5 \\ 1 & -2 & 1 \end{bmatrix}$ translation

38. f: $\begin{bmatrix} 0 & 4 & 4 \\ 0 & 2 & 4 \end{bmatrix}$, g: $\begin{bmatrix} 0 & -4 & -4 \\ 0 & -2 & -4 \end{bmatrix}$ rotation

39. $\begin{bmatrix} -1.5 & 0.25 & -2.5 \\ 0 & 1.5 & 1.5 \end{bmatrix}$

40. $\begin{bmatrix} 3 & 1.5 & 2 & 4 \\ -3 & -4.5 & -5 & -3.5 \end{bmatrix}$

41. Check students' work. The reflection of a matrix of pts. from a function table across the line $y = x$ interchanges the values of y and x in the function table. Finding the inverse of the matrix of pts. of a function from a function table also results in the interchanging of the values of y and x.

Standardized Test Prep

42. B

43. H

44. D

45. G

Geometry Each matrix represents the vertices of a transformed polygon. Write a matrix to represent the vertices of the image before each transformation.

39. $\begin{bmatrix} -3 & 0.5 & -5 \\ 0 & 3 & 3 \end{bmatrix}$; dilation of 2

40. $\begin{bmatrix} 3 & 4.5 & 5 & 3.5 \\ 3 & 1.5 & 2 & 4 \end{bmatrix}$; rotation of 90°

ⓒ **41. Writing** Explain why a reflection of a matrix of points from a function table across the line $y = x$ is equivalent to finding the inverse of the function.

Standardized Test Prep

SAT/ACT

42. What are the coordinates of $X(5, 1)$, $Y(-5, -3)$, and $Z(-1, 3)$ reflected across the line $y = x$?

Ⓐ $X'(-5, -1)$, $Y'(5, 3)$, $Z'(1, -3)$

Ⓒ $X'(-1, -5)$, $Y'(3, 5)$, $Z'(-3, 1)$

Ⓑ $X'(1, 5)$, $Y'(-3, -5)$, $Z'(3, -1)$

Ⓓ $X'(5, 1)$, $Y'(-5, -3)$, $Z'(-1, 3)$

43. Given $P = \begin{bmatrix} 4 & 3 & -2 \\ -1 & 0 & 5 \end{bmatrix}$ and $Q = \begin{bmatrix} 3 & -2 & -5 \\ -1 & -2 & -1 \end{bmatrix}$, what is $2P - 3Q$?

Ⓕ $\begin{bmatrix} 1 & -5 & 3 \\ 0 & -2 & 6 \end{bmatrix}$

Ⓖ $\begin{bmatrix} 17 & 0 & 19 \\ -5 & 6 & 7 \end{bmatrix}$

Ⓗ $\begin{bmatrix} -1 & 12 & 11 \\ 1 & 6 & 13 \end{bmatrix}$

Ⓘ $\begin{bmatrix} 1 & 5 & 3 \\ 0 & 2 & 6 \end{bmatrix}$

44. What is the solution to the matrix equation $\begin{bmatrix} 3 & -1 \\ -1 & 2 \end{bmatrix} \begin{bmatrix} a \\ b \end{bmatrix} = \begin{bmatrix} 7 \\ -9 \end{bmatrix}$?

Ⓐ $a = 7, b = -9$ Ⓑ $a = 2, b = 1$ Ⓒ $a = \frac{7}{3}, b = \frac{9}{2}$ Ⓓ $a = 1, b = -4$

45. What is the determinant of $\begin{bmatrix} -5 & 4 \\ -9 & 7 \end{bmatrix}$?

Ⓕ -71 Ⓖ 1 Ⓗ -3 Ⓘ 71

Short Response

46. The results of a college entrance exam are shown at the right. What is the probability that a student's score on the verbal section is from 401 to 514?

Section	Mean	Standard Deviation
Math	505	111
Verbal	514	113

Mixed Review

Solve each system of equations. Check your answers.   ◀ See Lesson 12-4.

47. $\begin{cases} 3x + 2y = 5 \\ -x + y = -5 \end{cases}$

48. $\begin{cases} x + 4y + 3z = 3 \\ 2x - 5y - z = 5 \\ 3x + 2y - 2z = -3 \end{cases}$

49. $\begin{cases} x + y + z = -1 \\ y + 3z = -5 \\ x + z = -2 \end{cases}$

Get Ready!   To prepare for Lesson 12-6, do Exercises 50–52.

Find each product.   ◀ See Lesson 12-2.

50. $0.8\begin{bmatrix} 20 \\ 15 \end{bmatrix}$

51. $\begin{bmatrix} 1 & -2 \end{bmatrix}\begin{bmatrix} 2 \\ -5 \end{bmatrix}$

52. $\begin{bmatrix} -3 & -5 \end{bmatrix}\begin{bmatrix} -4 \\ -2 \end{bmatrix}$

---

46. [2] 0.34; $514 - 401 = 113$, or one standard deviation. Assuming a normal distribution, 34% of the data points fall between the mean and one standard deviation below the mean. So, the probability that a student chosen at random got between a 401 and 514 is 34% $= \frac{34}{100} = 0.34$.

[1] answer given only in terms of normal distribution, and not probability

50. $\begin{bmatrix} 16 \\ 12 \end{bmatrix}$

51. $[12]$

52. $[22]$

Mixed Review

47. $(3, -2)$

48. $(1, -1, 2)$

49. $(0, 1, -2)$

Additional Instructional Support

Algebra 2 Companion

Students can use the **Algebra 2 Companion** worktext (4 pages) as you teach the lesson. Use the Companion to support

- New Vocabulary
- Key Concepts
- Got It for each Problem
- Lesson Check

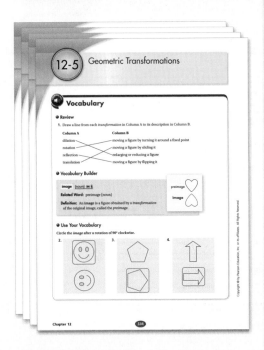

ELL Support

Connect to Prior Knowledge Students have studied transformational geometry in previous courses. In this lesson, they extend that knowledge to applying matrix operations to represent and generate reflections (flips), rotations (turns), translations (slides), and dilations (shrinks or stretches). Have students verify answers to transformation problems solved using matrices by reviewing and applying skills they learned earlier.

5 Assess & Remediate

Lesson Quiz

1. Kite *ABCD* has vertices (0, 3), (−2, 5), (−4, 3), and (−2, −2). If you translate it 5 units to the left and 3 units up, what are the coordinates of the vertices of its image *A′B′C′D′*? Use matrix addition.

2. **Do you UNDERSTAND?** The width of a digital picture is 1280 pixels. Its height is 960 pixels. You want to reduce it so its width is 800 pixels. Using a dilation, what are the coordinates of the vertices of the reduced image?

3. Rotate the triangle with vertices *A* (−2, 4), *B* (4, 2), and *C* (−3, 1) 270° about the origin. What are the vertices of the image?

4. Reflect the quadrilateral with vertices *A* (3, 4), *B* (6, −1), *C* (4, −3) and *D* (−1, 0) across the line $y = -x$. What are the vertices of the image?

ANSWERS TO LESSON QUIZ

1. *A′*(−5, 6), *B′*(−7, 8), *C′*(−9, 6), *D′*(−7, 1)

2. $\begin{bmatrix} 0 & 800 & 800 & 0 \\ 0 & 0 & 600 & 600 \end{bmatrix}$

3. *A′*(4, 2), *B′*(2, −4), *C′*(1, 3)

4. *A′*(−4, −3), *B′*(1, −6), *C′*(3, −4), *D′*(0, 1)

PRESCRIPTION FOR REMEDIATION

Use the student work on the Lesson Quiz to prescribe a differentiated review assignment:

Points	Differentiated Remediation
0–2	Intervention
3	On-level
4	Extension

PowerAlgebra.com

5 Assess & Remediate

Assign the Lesson Quiz. Appropriate intervention, practice, or enrichment is automatically generated based on student performance.

Intervention

- **Reteaching** (2 pages) Provides reteaching and practice exercises for the key lesson concepts. Use with struggling students or absent students.

- **English Language Learner Support** Helps students develop and reinforce mathematical vocabulary and key concepts.

All-in-One Resources/Online
Reteaching

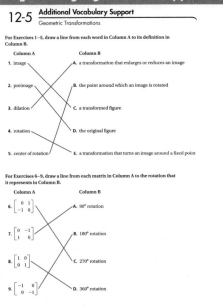

All-in-One Resources/Online
English Language Learner Support

Differentiated Remediation *continued*

On-Level

- **Practice** (2 pages) Provides extra practice for each lesson. For simpler practice exercises, use the Form K Practice pages found in the All-in-One Teaching Resources and online.

- **Think About a Plan** Helps students develop specific problem-solving skills and strategies by providing scaffolded guiding questions.

- **Standardized Test Prep** Focuses on all major exercises, all major question types, and helps students prepare for the high-stakes assessments.

Extension

- **Enrichment** Provides students with interesting problems and activities that extend the concepts of the lesson.

- **Activities, Games, and Puzzles** Worksheets that can be used for concepts development, enrichment, and for fun!

Practice and Problem Solving Wkbk/ All-in-One Resources/Online
Practice page 1

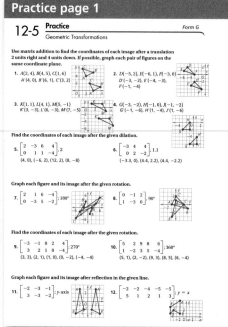

Practice and Problem Solving Wkbk/ All-in-One Resources/Online
Practice page 2

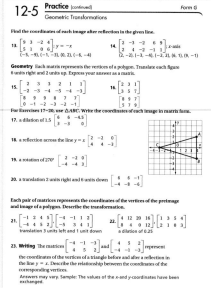

All-in-One Resources/Online
Enrichment

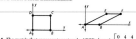

Practice and Problem Solving Wkbk/ All-in-One Resources/Online
Think About a Plan

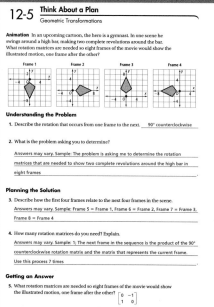

Practice and Problem Solving Wkbk/ All-in-One Resources/Online
Standardized Test Prep

Online Teacher Resource Center
Activities, Games, and Puzzles

12-6 Vectors

© **Content Standards**
N.VM.5a Represent scalar multiplication graphically by scaling vectors . . . perform scalar multiplication component-wise.
N.VM.11 Multiply a vector . . . by a matrix of suitable dimension to produce another vector.
Also N.VM.1-4, N.VM.5b, N.VM.12

Objective To use basic vector operations and the dot product

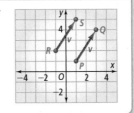

SOLVE IT!

Getting Ready!

A young sailor maintains a constant speed of 12 knots. Starting from a pier, she sails for 20 min on the heading shown. Then she turns and sails for 15 min on the next heading. On her next turn, the sailboat capsizes. The Coast Guard immediately sends a rescue boat, traveling at 50 knots, from the same pier. How long does it take the rescue boat to reach her? Explain.

N 45° W

N 45° E

1 **knot** is a speed of 1 nautical mile (about 6076 ft) per hour. 1 knot is faster than 1 mi/h.

© **MATHEMATICAL PRACTICES**

In the Solve It, the Coast Guard had to know both distance and direction to rescue the sailor.

Essential Understanding A *vector* is a mathematical object that has both *magnitude* (size) and direction.

 Lesson Vocabulary
• vector
• magnitude
• initial point
• terminal point
• dot product
• normal vectors

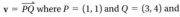

Key Concept   Vectors in Two Dimensions

A vector has magnitude and direction. You can describe a vector as a directed line segment with initial and terminal points. Two such segments with the same magnitude and direction represent the same vector.

$\mathbf{v} = \overrightarrow{PQ}$ where $P = (1, 1)$ and $Q = (3, 4)$ and
$\mathbf{v} = \overrightarrow{RS}$ where $R = (-1, 2)$ and $S = (1, 5)$

represent the same vector.

A **vector** has both magnitude and direction. You often use an arrow to represent a vector. The **magnitude** of a vector $\mathbf{v}$ is the length of the arrow. You can denote it as $|\mathbf{v}|$. You show the direction of the vector by the **initial point** and the **terminal point** of the arrow.

1 Interactive Learning

Solve It!

PURPOSE To solve a problem involving vectors
PROCESS Students may
• draw and label a diagram, using right triangle to find distances.
• write the path as a series of coordinate pairs.

FACILITATE

Q The sailor is traveling at a speed of 12 knots for some period of time. What distance units can you use to solve the problem? **[nautical miles, because one knot is equal to one nautical mile per hour]**

Q The sailor first travels for 20 minutes at N⁺ 45°E. What distance has she traveled? How can you find her *x*- and *y*-coordinates at that point? **[She traveled 4 nautical miles. Her *x*- and *y*- coordinates are the legs of 45°-45°-90° triangle with hypotenuse 4.]**

Q How can you find the position where she capsized? **[Find the distance she traveled after she turned. To find her position, sum the *x*- and *y*-distances of the two paths.]**

ANSWER See Solve It in Answers on next page.
CONNECT THE MATH The Solve It activates prior knowledge of coordinate distance and slope while introducing vectors. In the lesson, students will perform basic operations on vectors.

2 Guided Instruction

Take Note

Q How is the slope of a segment similar to the direction of a vector? **[Slope shows the angle a segment makes in relation to the *x*- and *y*-axes, as does the direction of a vector.]**

12-6 Preparing to Teach

BIG idea **Data Representation**
ESSENTIAL UNDERSTANDINGS
• A *vector* is a mathematical object that has both magnitude and direction.
• Vectors can be added or subtracted by adding or subtracting corresponding elements.
• The dot product of two vectors is the sum of the products of corresponding elements.

Math Background

A vector's magnitude and direction can be described geometrically by a directed line segment and algebraically in component form or matrix form.

Because vectors can be represented as matrices, some properties of matrices can be applied. The same matrices used to rotate and reflect geometric figures can be

used to rotate and reflect vectors. Several other operations are defined for vectors.
• Addition and subtraction: For real number components, add or subtract the corresponding numbers in component form using the properties of real numbers.
• Scalar multiplication: Like a matrix, a vector can be multiplied by a constant or scalar. Each component is multiplied by the scalar. Scalar multiplication can change the magnitude and reverse the direction of a vector.
• Vector multiplication: Many kinds of vector multiplication are defined. This chapter examines the dot product, which is the sum of the products of corresponding components. The dot product is a scalar, not a vector. If it is zero, the vectors are normal (perpendicular).

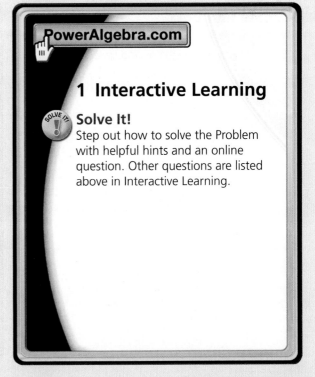

PowerAlgebra.com

1 Interactive Learning

SOLVE IT! Solve It!
Step out how to solve the Problem with helpful hints and an online question. Other questions are listed above in Interactive Learning.

Problem 1

Q How do you know that the vector shows a movement from *P* to *Q*? **[Samples: The segment has an arrowhead that ends at point *Q*; the arrowhead is over *Q* in $\overrightarrow{PQ}$.]**

Q Component form is a way of thinking about a vector as combination of two separate movements. What are the two components of a vector? Why do you think this is a useful way to think about vectors? **[The two components are movement in the *x*-direction and movement in the *y*-direction. This is useful when adding vectors, such as in the Solve It.]**

Got It?

Q When you found the slope of a segment or a line, you subtracted coordinates of points and it did not matter which way you subtracted. Does it matter for vectors? Explain. **[Yes; the direction of the vector is determined by subtracting the coordinates of the initial point from the coordinates of the terminal point.]**

Problem 2

Q How could you rotate a vector 90° counterclockwise without a rotation matrix? **[For any vector $\langle x, y \rangle$ a rotation by 90° counterclockwise makes new vector $\langle -y, x \rangle$.]**

The position of a vector is not important. For this reason, a vector **v** in standard position has initial point $(0, 0)$ and is completely determined by its terminal point (a, b). You can represent **v** in component form as $\langle a, b \rangle$. Use the Pythagorean theorem to find the magnitude of **v**, $|\mathbf{v}| = \sqrt{a^2 + b^2}$.

 **Problem 1** Representing a Vector

What is the component form of the vector $\mathbf{v} = \overrightarrow{PQ}$ shown here?

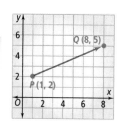

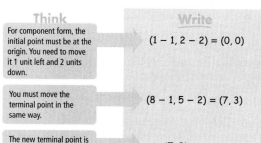

Think	Write
For component form, the initial point must be at the origin. You need to move it 1 unit left and 2 units down.	$(1 - 1, 2 - 2) = (0, 0)$
You must move the terminal point in the same way.	$(8 - 1, 5 - 2) = (7, 3)$
The new terminal point is the component form.	$\mathbf{v} = \langle 7, 3 \rangle$

 Got It? **1.** What are the component forms of the two vectors shown here?

You can also write a vector $\mathbf{v} = \langle a, b \rangle$ in matrix form, $\mathbf{v} = \begin{bmatrix} a \\ b \end{bmatrix}$. By writing in matrix form, you can use matrix transformations to transform a vector.

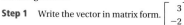 **Problem 2** Rotating a Vector

Rotate the vector $\mathbf{w} = \langle 3, -2 \rangle$ by 90°. What is the component form of the resulting vector?

Think

How can you rotate points in the coordinate plane? You can multiply by a rotation matrix.

Step 1 Write the vector in matrix form. $\begin{bmatrix} 3 \\ -2 \end{bmatrix}$

Step 2 Multiply the vector by the 90° rotation matrix.
$$\begin{bmatrix} 0 & -1 \\ 1 & 0 \end{bmatrix}\begin{bmatrix} 3 \\ -2 \end{bmatrix} = \begin{bmatrix} 2 \\ 3 \end{bmatrix}$$

Step 3 The resulting vector is $\langle 2, 3 \rangle$.

Answers

Solve It!
6 min; the sailor's headings and speed describe a 3-4-5 right triangle. Her boat thus capsizes at a point reached in 25 min at 12 knots, or 6 min at 50 knots.

Got It?
1. $\mathbf{u} = \langle 3, 4 \rangle$; $\mathbf{v} = \langle -1, -6 \rangle$

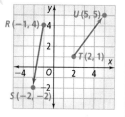

PowerAlgebra.com

2 Guided Instruction

© Each Problem is worked out and supported online.

Problem 1
Representing a Vector
Animated

Problem 2
Rotating a Vector

Problem 3
Adding and Subtracting Vectors
Animated

Problem 4
Scalar Multiplication
Animated

Problem 5
Finding Dot Products

Support in Algebra 2 Companion
• Vocabulary
• Key Concepts
• Got It?

Got It? **2. a.** Rotate the vector $\mathbf{v} = \langle -3, 5 \rangle$ by 270°. What is the component form of the resulting vector?

      b. Reasoning What other matrix transformations can you apply to vectors in matrix form?

You can use real number operations to define operations involving vectors.

Properties Operations With Vectors

Given $\mathbf{v} = \langle v_1, v_2 \rangle$, $\mathbf{w} = \langle w_1, w_2 \rangle$, and any real number k:

$\mathbf{v} + \mathbf{w} = \langle v_1 + w_1, v_2 + w_2 \rangle$
$\mathbf{v} - \mathbf{w} = \langle v_1 - w_1, v_2 - w_2 \rangle$
$k\mathbf{v} = \langle kv_1, kv_2 \rangle$

Note that
$\mathbf{w} + (\mathbf{v} - \mathbf{w}) = \mathbf{v}$
and $(\mathbf{v} - \mathbf{w}) + \mathbf{w} = \mathbf{v}$.

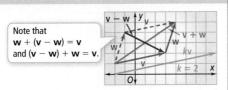

Problem 3 Adding and Subtracting Vectors   **GRIDDED RESPONSE**

Let $\mathbf{u} = \langle -2, 3 \rangle$ and $\mathbf{v} = \langle 5, -2 \rangle$. What is $|\mathbf{u} + \mathbf{v}|$, rounded to the nearest hundredth?

To find $\mathbf{u} + \mathbf{v}$, use the tip-to-tail method shown above.

Step 1 Draw $\mathbf{u} = \langle -2, 3 \rangle$ in standard position.

Step 2 At the tip of $\mathbf{u}$, draw $\mathbf{v} = \langle 5, -2 \rangle$ from $(-2, 3)$ to $(3, 1)$.

Step 3 Draw $\mathbf{u} + \mathbf{v}$ to have the initial point of $\mathbf{u}$ and the terminal point of $\mathbf{v}$.

Step 4 Express $\mathbf{u} + \mathbf{v}$ in component form. $\mathbf{u} + \mathbf{v} = \langle 3, 1 \rangle$

Step 5 $|\mathbf{u} + \mathbf{v}| = \sqrt{3^2 + 1^2} = \sqrt{10} \approx 3.16$

Check $\mathbf{u} + \mathbf{v} = \langle -2, 3 \rangle + \langle 5, -2 \rangle = \langle -2 + 5, 3 + (-2) \rangle = \langle 3, 1 \rangle$

Got It? **3.** Using the vectors given in Problem 3, what is $|\mathbf{u} - \mathbf{v}|$?

Scalar multiplication of a vector by a positive number (other than 1) changes only the magnitude. Multiplication by a negative number (other than −1) changes the magnitude and reverses the direction of the vector.

Got It?

Q What is the rotation matrix you used in 2a?
$\left[\begin{matrix} 0 & 1 \\ -1 & 0 \end{matrix}\right]$

Take Note

The diagram shows that vectors have a direction and a magnitude but no set position. If the initial point of a vector is the origin, the terminal point has coordinates equal to the components of the vector.

Q Subtracting is the same as adding the opposite, so $\mathbf{v} - \mathbf{w}$ is the same as $\mathbf{v} + -\mathbf{w}$. How does $-\mathbf{w}$ compare to $\mathbf{w}$? **[$-\mathbf{w}$ looks like the same vector but with the arrowhead on the opposite end. The magnitude is the same, but the direction is opposite.]**

Problem 3

Q How would you describe the tip-to-tail method of vector addition geometrically? **[Each vector describes a motion. Move to the terminal point of the first vector. That terminal point is the initial point for the second vector, and the terminal point of the second motion is the sum.]**

Q What is an algebraic way to solve this problem? **[Add the x-components of the vectors. Add the y-components of the vectors. The sums are the components of the resultant vector.]**

Got It?

Q Why is the magnitude of the resultant vector found by taking the square root of the sum of the squares of the x- and y-components? **[The x- and y-components show perpendicular distances, which are the legs of a right triangle. The Pythagorean Theorem can be used to find the length of the hypotenuse.]**

Additional Problems

1. What is the component form of the vector $\mathbf{v} = \overrightarrow{GH}$ shown here?

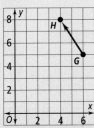

ANSWER $\langle -2, 3 \rangle$

2. Rotate the vector $\mathbf{t} = \langle -8, 2 \rangle$ by 270°. What is the component form of the resulting vector?

ANSWER $\langle 2, 8 \rangle$

3. Let $\mathbf{v} = \langle -5, -3 \rangle$ and $\mathbf{w} = \langle -7, -6 \rangle$. What is

$|\mathbf{v} - \mathbf{w}|$, rounded to the nearest hundredth?

ANSWER 3.61

4. For $\mathbf{u} = \langle 2, -1 \rangle$, what is the graph of $-2\mathbf{u}$?

ANSWER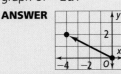

5. Let $\mathbf{w} = \langle 2, 7 \rangle$ and $\mathbf{u} = \langle -8, 9 \rangle$. Are $\mathbf{w}$ and $\mathbf{u}$ normal vectors?

ANSWER no

Answers

Got It? (continued)
2. a. $\langle 5, 3 \rangle$
  b. translation, reflection and dilation
3. $\sqrt{74} \approx 8.60$

Problem 4

Q Does scalar multiplication change the direction of a vector? Explain. **[Sample: No, unless the scaler is negative; a negative scalar makes the direction exactly opposite.]**

Q What is the sum of a vector, **v**, and its opposite, −**v**? **[The vector would have x- and y-components of zero.]**

Q Do you think that scalar multiplication is distributive over vector addition? Explain. **[Yes; it does not matter whether the scalar multiplication is done before or after the addition.]**

Got It?   EXTENSION

Q Without graphing, what do you think $-\mathbf{u} + \frac{1}{2}\mathbf{u}$ equals? What would be the component form of the resultant vector? $[-\mathbf{u} + \frac{1}{2}\mathbf{u}$ **should equal** $-\frac{1}{2}\mathbf{u}$**; the resultant vector would be** $\langle 1, -2 \rangle$**.]**

Problem 5

Q How does the dot product tell whether vectors are perpendicular? Explain in terms of components and slope. **[A non-vertical vector with components** $\langle x, y \rangle$ **has slope** $\frac{y}{x}$**. A vector perpendicular to it has a slope** $\frac{-x}{y}$**, so it is a vector with components** $\langle y, -x \rangle$**. Using the dot-product, you get** $xy + y(-x)$**, which equals zero.]**

Got It?

Q How do you find the dot product in 5a? **[Multiply the x-components and add them to the product of the y-components:** $-2(-9) + 6(-18) = 18 - 108 = -90$**.]**

For **v** = $\langle 1, -2 \rangle$ and **w** = $\langle 2, 3 \rangle$, what are the graphs of the following vectors?

Ⓐ v and 3v

$3\mathbf{v} = 3\langle 1, -2 \rangle$
$\quad = \langle 3(1), 3(-2) \rangle$
$\quad = \langle 3, -6 \rangle$

Ⓑ w and −2w

$-2\mathbf{w} = -2\langle 2, 3 \rangle$
$\quad = \langle -2(2), -2(3) \rangle$
$\quad = \langle -4, -6 \rangle$

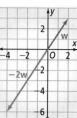

Plan

How should you start?
Begin by finding the component form of the scaled vectors.

Got It? 4. Given **u** = $\langle -2, 4 \rangle$, what are the graphs of the following vectors?

    a. −**u**   **b.** $\frac{1}{2}$**u**

If **v** = $\langle v_1, v_2 \rangle$ and **w** = $\langle w_1, w_2 \rangle$, the **dot product v · w** is $v_1 w_1 + v_2 w_2$.
If **v · w** = 0, the two vectors are **normal**, or perpendicular, to each other.

 Problem 5 Finding Dot Products

Are the following vectors normal?

Ⓐ t = $\langle 2, -5 \rangle$, u = $\langle 7, 3 \rangle$

$\mathbf{t} \cdot \mathbf{u} = (2)(7) + (-5)(3)$
$\quad = 14 + (-15) = -1$

t and u are not normal.

Check

$m_t = \frac{-5 - 0}{2 - 0} = -\frac{5}{2}$

$m_u = \frac{3 - 0}{7 - 0} = \frac{3}{7}$

not perpendicular ✔

Ⓑ v = $\langle 10, -4 \rangle$, w = $\langle 2, 5 \rangle$

$\mathbf{v} \cdot \mathbf{w} = (10)(2) + (-4)(5)$
$\quad = 20 - 20 = 0$

v and w are normal.

Check

$m_v = \frac{-4 - 0}{10 - 0} = -\frac{2}{5}$

$m_w = \frac{5 - 0}{2 - 0} = \frac{5}{2}$

perpendicular ✔

Think

How can you check your results?
If the slopes of the lines containing the vectors are negative reciprocals, the vectors are normal.

Got It? 5. Are the following vectors normal?

    a. $\langle -2, 6 \rangle$, $\langle -9, -18 \rangle$ **b.** $\left\langle 3, \frac{5}{6} \right\rangle$, $\left\langle -\frac{10}{9}, 4 \right\rangle$

Answers

Got It? (continued)

4. a.

b.

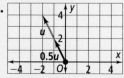

5. a. not normal

    b. normal

Lesson Check

Do you know HOW?

Let $P = (-2, 2)$, $Q = (3, 4)$, $R = (-2, 5)$, and $S = (2, -8)$. What are the component forms of the following vectors?

1. $\overrightarrow{PQ}$

2. $\overrightarrow{RS} + \overrightarrow{PQ}$

3. $\overrightarrow{RS} - \overrightarrow{RQ}$

4. $-5\overrightarrow{PR}$

Do you UNDERSTAND? 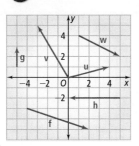 MATHEMATICAL PRACTICES

5. **Vocabulary** Which of the following vectors has the greatest magnitude? Explain.

$$a = \langle 3, 4 \rangle \qquad b = \langle -4, 3 \rangle \qquad c = \langle 4, -3 \rangle$$

6. **Error Analysis** Your friend says that the magnitude of vector $\langle 8, 3 \rangle$ is 4 times that of vector $\langle 2, 3 \rangle$ since 8 is 4 times 2. Explain why your friend's statement is incorrect.

Practice and Problem-Solving Exercises   MATHEMATICAL PRACTICES

A Practice

Referring to the graph, what are the component forms of the following vectors?

See Problem 1.

7. u

8. v

9. w

10. f

11. g

12. h

Transform each vector as described. Write the resulting vector in component form.

See Problem 2.

13. $\langle 5, 1 \rangle$; rotate $90°$

14. $\langle -4, 3 \rangle$; rotate $180°$

15. $\langle 0, 2 \rangle$; rotate $270°$

16. $\langle 11, -4 \rangle$; reflect across x-axis

17. $\langle -3, 0 \rangle$; reflect across y-axis

18. $\langle 4, 5 \rangle$; reflect across $y = x$

19. $\langle 4, -3 \rangle$; reflect across $y = -x$

Let $u = \langle -1, 3 \rangle$, $v = \langle 2, 4 \rangle$, and $w = \langle 2, -5 \rangle$. Find the component forms of the following vectors.

See Problems 3 and 4.

20. $u + v$

21. $v + w$

22. $u - v$

23. $u - w$

24. $2u$

25. $-4w$

26. $\frac{3}{2}v$

27. $-3v$

Determine whether the vectors in each pair are normal to each other.

See Problem 5.

28. $\langle 6, -3 \rangle$ and $\langle 2, 4 \rangle$

29. $\langle 8, -4 \rangle$ and $\langle -2, 4 \rangle$

30. $\begin{bmatrix} 1 \\ 8 \end{bmatrix}$ and $\begin{bmatrix} 4 \\ -2 \end{bmatrix}$

31. $\begin{bmatrix} 0.8 \\ -0.6 \end{bmatrix}$ and $\begin{bmatrix} 0.3 \\ 0.4 \end{bmatrix}$

---

3 Lesson Check

Do you know HOW?

- Before beginning Exercises 1–4, students may write the component forms of the vectors.

ERROR INTERVENTION

- If students find an opposite of the needed vector in Exercises 1–4, remind them that the order of subtraction matters when finding the component form of a vector.

VISUAL LEARNERS

- If a student finds it helpful, allow her or him to plot points and vectors for Exercises 1–4. Ask the student to solve them algebraically as well.

Do you UNDERSTAND?

- Students should be able to solve Exercise 5 by inspection, although calculating may help students understand the concept.
- In Exercise 6, students should find the components of a vector with 4 times the magnitude of $\langle 2, 1 \rangle$.

Close

> **Q** How are segments and vectors similar and different? **[Both segments and vectors can be defined by two points. A segment has a set position in the coordinate plane, two endpoints, a slope (if it is not vertical), and a length. A vector does not have a set position, and has a direction and a magnitude or length.]**
>
> **Q** A vector has an initial point and a terminal point. How can two points be shown with only two numbers, the components of the vector? **[The components are the coordinates of the terminal point of a vector with initial point at the origin.]**

Lesson Check

1. $\langle 5, 2 \rangle$

2. $\langle 9, -11 \rangle$

3. $\langle -1, -12 \rangle$

4. $\langle 0, -15 \rangle$

5. The magnitudes of vectors **a**, **b**, and **c** are the same. Each has magnitude 5.

6. Although the x-component of $\langle 8, 3 \rangle$ is 4 times the x-component of $\langle 2, 1 \rangle$, the y-component and the magnitude of $\langle 8, 3 \rangle$ are not 4 times those of $\langle 2, 1 \rangle$. $3 \neq 4 \times 1$ and $\sqrt{73} \neq 4 \times \sqrt{5}$.

Practice and Problem-Solving Exercises

7. $\langle 4, 1 \rangle$

8. $\langle -3, 5 \rangle$

9. $\langle 4, -2 \rangle$

10. $\langle 6, -2 \rangle$

11. $\langle 0, 2 \rangle$

12. $\langle -5, 0 \rangle$

13. $\langle -1, 5 \rangle$

14. $\langle 4, -3 \rangle$

15. $\langle 2, 0 \rangle$

16. $\langle 11, 4 \rangle$

17. $\langle 3, 0 \rangle$

18. $\langle 5, 4 \rangle$

19. $\langle 3, -4 \rangle$

20. $\langle 1, 7 \rangle$

21. $\langle 4, -1 \rangle$

22. $\langle -3, -1 \rangle$

23. $\langle -3, 8 \rangle$

24. $\langle -2, 6 \rangle$

25. $\langle -8, 20 \rangle$

26. $\langle 3, 6 \rangle$

27. $\langle -6, -12 \rangle$

28. normal

29. not normal

30. not normal

31. normal

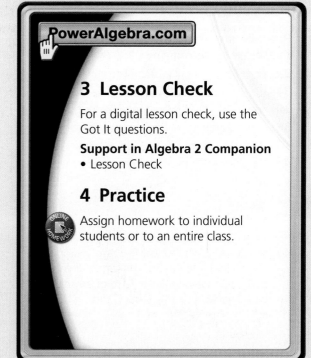

PowerAlgebra.com

3 Lesson Check

For a digital lesson check, use the Got It questions.

Support in Algebra 2 Companion
- Lesson Check

4 Practice

Assign homework to individual students or to an entire class.

4 Practice

ASSIGNMENT GUIDE

Basic: 7–31 all, 35–38, 42

Average: 7–31 odd, 32–49

Advanced: 7–31 odd, 32–53

Standardized Test Prep: 54–59

Mixed Review: 60–71

 Mathematical Practices are supported by exercises with red headings. Here are the Practices supported in this lesson:

MP 1: Make Sense of Problems Ex. 36
MP 2: Reason Quantitatively Ex. 5
MP 3: Construct Arguments Ex. 46–49
MP 3: Communicate Ex. 45
MP 3: Critique the Reasoning of Others Ex. 6

Applications exercises have blue headings. Exercises 37 and 44 support MP 4: Model.

EXERCISE 37: Use the Think About a Plan worksheet in the **Practice and Problem Solving Workbook** (also available in the Teaching Resources in print and online) to further support students' development in becoming independent learners.

HOMEWORK QUICK CHECK

To check students' understanding of key skills and concepts, go over Exercises 15, 29, 36, 37, and 38.

B Apply Let $u = \begin{bmatrix} -5 \\ 3 \end{bmatrix}$, $v = \begin{bmatrix} 4 \\ -3 \end{bmatrix}$, and $w = \begin{bmatrix} 2 \\ 2 \end{bmatrix}$. Find the following vectors.

32. $2u + 3v$ **33.** $2v - 4w$ **34.** $-u - w$ **35.** $-3u + v - \frac{1}{2}w$

36. Think About a Plan A ferry shuttles people from one side of a river to the other. The speed of the ferry in still water is 25 mi/h. The river flows directly south at 7 mi/h. If the ferry heads directly west, what is the ferry's resulting speed?
- How can a sketch help you solve this problem?
- What formula can you use to find the speed?

37. Aviation A twin-engine airplane has a speed of 300 mi/h in still air. Suppose the airplane heads south and encounters a wind blowing 50 mi/h due east. What is the resultant speed of the airplane?

38. Aviation A small airplane lands at a point 216 mi east and 76 mi north of the point from which it took off. How far did the airplane fly?

39. Consider the triangle with vertices at $A(2, 2)$, $B(5, 3)$, and $C(3, 6)$. Express the sides of the triangle as vectors $\overrightarrow{AB}$, $\overrightarrow{BC}$, and $\overrightarrow{CA}$.

Let $a = \langle 6, -1 \rangle$, $b = \langle -4, 3 \rangle$, and $c = \langle 2, 0 \rangle$. Solve each of the following for the unknown vector v.

40. $a + v = b$ **41.** $c - v = b$

42. $v - b = a + c$ **43.** $a + b + c + v = \langle 0, 0 \rangle$

44. Navigation A fishing boat leaves its home port and travels 150 mi directly east. It then changes course and travels 40 mi due north. How long will the direct return trip take if the boat averages 23 mi/h?

45. Writing Subtract any vector from itself. The result is still a vector, but a unique one. Explain what this vector is, and what it means for vector addition.

Reasoning Do the following properties hold for vectors and scalars? Identify each property and make a diagram to support your answers.

46. $u + v = v + u$ **47.** $k(u + v) = ku + kv$

48. $u - v = v - u$ **49.** $(u + v) + w = u + (v + w)$

C Challenge

50. Aviation A helicopter starts at $(0, 0)$ and makes three legs of a flight represented by the vectors $\langle 10, 10 \rangle$, $\langle 5, -4 \rangle$, and $\langle -3, 5 \rangle$, in that order. If another helicopter starts at $(0, 0)$ and flies the same three legs in a different order, would it end in the same place? Justify your answer.

51. Two vectors are parallel if the absolute value of their dot product is equal to the product of their magnitudes. Which of the following vectors are parallel? Which are perpendicular?

$a = \begin{bmatrix} 0.9 \\ 1.2 \end{bmatrix}$ $b = \begin{bmatrix} -2 \\ 1.5 \end{bmatrix}$ $c = \begin{bmatrix} 6 \\ -8 \end{bmatrix}$ $d = \begin{bmatrix} -4.5 \\ -6 \end{bmatrix}$

Answers

Practice and Problem-Solving Exercises (continued)

32. $\langle 2, -3 \rangle$ **33.** $\langle 0, -14 \rangle$

34. $\langle 3, -5 \rangle$ **35.** $\langle 18, -13 \rangle$

36. about 26 mi/h **37.** about 304 mi/h

38. about 229 mi

39. $\overrightarrow{AB} = \langle 3, 1 \rangle$, $\overrightarrow{BC} = \langle -2, 3 \rangle$, $\overrightarrow{CA} = \langle -1, -4 \rangle$

40. $\langle -10, 4 \rangle$

41. $\langle 6, -3 \rangle$

42. $\langle 4, 2 \rangle$

43. $\langle -4, -2 \rangle$

44. 6.75 h

45. $v - v = \langle 0, 0 \rangle$; $\langle 0, 0 \rangle$, the zero vector, is the additive identity for the set of all vectors and $-v$ is the additive inverse of any given vector v; so, $v + \langle 0, 0 \rangle = v$ and $v + (-v) = \langle 0, 0 \rangle$.

46. yes; Comm. Prop. of Add.

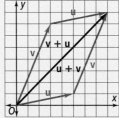

47. yes; Distributive Prop.

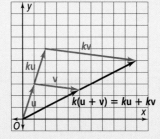

48. No; subtraction of vectors is not commutative.

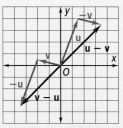

49. yes; Assoc. Prop. of Add.

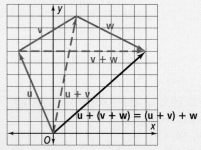

50. Yes; the vector addition of $\langle 10, 10 \rangle$, $\langle 5, -4 \rangle$, and $\langle -3, 5 \rangle$ is comm. and assoc.

51. **a** and **d** are parallel; **a** and **b** are perpendicular; **b** and **d** are perpendicular

52. Given $\mathbf{u} = \langle -4, 3 \rangle$ and $\mathbf{v} = \langle 1, -2 \rangle$, find $\mathbf{w}$ if $\mathbf{u} \cdot \mathbf{w} = 7$ and $\mathbf{v} \cdot \mathbf{w} = -8$.

STEM **53. Physics** When an object is not moving, all the forces acting on it must sum to 0. The object is said to be *in equilibrium*. Two cables of different lengths hold a stoplight over an intersection. The force vectors being applied along the two cables are $\langle 20, 18 \rangle$ and $\langle -20, 12 \rangle$. The magnitude of each vector is measured in pounds. A third force vector in this situation is the force due to gravity, and is straight downward. How much does the stoplight weigh?

Standardized Test Prep

GRIDDED RESPONSE

SAT/ACT

54. Let $\mathbf{u} = \langle -3, 2 \rangle$ and $\mathbf{v} = \langle 9, -3 \rangle$. What is $|\mathbf{u} + \mathbf{v}|$?

55. If $x \begin{bmatrix} -2 & 1 \\ 3 & -1 \end{bmatrix} - \begin{bmatrix} 5 & -1 \\ -2 & 4 \end{bmatrix} = \begin{bmatrix} 1 & -2 \\ -7 & -1 \end{bmatrix}$, what is x?

56. What is the determinant of $\begin{bmatrix} \frac{3}{10} & \frac{1}{5} \\ \frac{1}{8} & \frac{1}{3} \end{bmatrix}$? Enter your answer as a fraction.

57. If $B = \begin{bmatrix} 4 & -1 \\ 2 & 0 \end{bmatrix}$, what is $\det B^{-1}$?

58. What is the rotation in degrees that transforms a triangle with vertices $(2, 0)$, $(-3, 5)$, and $(1, -2)$ into a triangle with vertices $(0, 2)$, $(-5, -3)$, and $(2, 1)$?

59. Given $\mathbf{u} = \langle x, 3 \rangle$, $\mathbf{v} = \langle -3, 2 \rangle$, and $\mathbf{u} \cdot \mathbf{v} = -9$, what is x?

Mixed Review

Graph each figure and its image after reflection across the given line. ◀ **See Lesson 12-5.**

60. $\begin{bmatrix} 1 & 5 & 3 \\ 1 & -2 & 3 \end{bmatrix}$; $y = x$

61. $\begin{bmatrix} -3 & 0 & 2 & -1 \\ 2 & 3 & 0 & -2 \end{bmatrix}$; the x-axis

Solve each system of inequalities by graphing. ◀ **See Lesson 3-3.**

62. $\begin{cases} 2 + y < 3 \\ -x - y \geq 1 \end{cases}$

63. $\begin{cases} 2x \leq 0 \\ -x + y > -1 \end{cases}$

64. $\begin{cases} x < 3 \\ y \geq -4 \\ -x + y < 5 \end{cases}$

Write in point-slope form an equation of the line through each pair of points. ◀ **See Lesson 2-4.**

65. $(0, 1)$ and $(2, -5)$

66. $(-9, 3)$ and $(-4, -4)$

67. $(1, 8)$ and $(7, 2)$

Get Ready! **To prepare for Lesson 13-1, do Exercises 68–71.**

Determine whether each relation is a function. ◀ **See Lesson 2-1.**

68. $\{(2, 4), (1, 3), (-3, -1), (4, 6)\}$

69. $\{(2, 6), (-3, 1), (2, 2), (0, 4)\}$

70. $\{(5, 3), (1, 3), (-3, 3), (4, 3)\}$

71. $\{(8, 4), (8, 3), (8, -1), (8, 6)\}$

---

52. $\mathbf{w} = \langle 2, 5 \rangle$ **53.** 30 lb

Standardized Test Prep

54. about 6.08   **55.** -3

56. $\frac{3}{40}$ **57.** $\frac{1}{2}$

58. 90   **59.** 5

Mixed Review

60. $\begin{bmatrix} 1 & -2 & 3 \\ 1 & 5 & 3 \end{bmatrix}$;

61. $\begin{bmatrix} -3 & 0 & 2 & -1 \\ -2 & -3 & 0 & 2 \end{bmatrix}$;

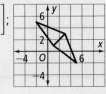

62.

63.

64.

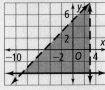

65. $y - 1 = -3x$ OR $y + 5 = -3(x - 2)$

66. $y + 4 = -\frac{7}{5}(x + 4)$ OR

$y - 3 = -\frac{7}{5}(x + 9)$

67. $y - 2 = -(x - 7)$ OR

$y - 8 = -(x - 1)$

68. yes

69. no

70. yes

71. no

Additional Instructional Support

Algebra 2 Companion

Students can use the **Algebra 2 Companion** worktext (4 pages) as you teach the lesson. Use the Companion to support

- New Vocabulary
- Key Concepts
- Got It for each Problem
- Lesson Check

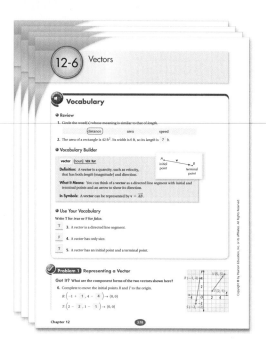

ELL Support

Use Role Playing If students in your classroom sit at desks or tables, you can visualize the seating positions as points on a coordinate plane. Define an origin in the coordinate plane. Have students sketch a grid to represent the seating positions in the classroom centered on the origin. Any questions asked and examples given will have to use fairly small numbers (probably from 0 to 4 or 5) in order to stay within the coordinate grid. Have students draw vectors on their sketches and then ask others to act the vectors out by starting at the origin and completing the motion described by the vector.

Encourage students to pose examples using all the vocabulary in this lesson.

Examples:
- Act out a vector with magnitude $\sqrt{10}$.
- Show vector $\overrightarrow{PQ}$ with $P(1, 1)$ and $Q(2, 0)$.
- Find the terminal point of a vector with components $\langle 3, 1 \rangle$.
- Calculate the sum of the vectors $\langle 2, 2 \rangle$ and $\langle -1, 2 \rangle$ and then act it out.

5 Assess & Remediate

Lesson Quiz

1. What is the component form of the vector $\mathbf{v} = \overrightarrow{PQ}$?

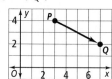

2. Rotate the vector $\mathbf{w} = \langle -5, 3 \rangle$ by 90°. What is the component form of the resulting vector?

3. **Do you UNDERSTAND?** For $\mathbf{u} = \langle -9, 1 \rangle$ and $\mathbf{v} = \langle 8, -7 \rangle$, what is $|\mathbf{u} + \mathbf{v}|$, rounded to the nearest hundredth?

4. Let $\mathbf{w} = \langle 4, 6 \rangle$. What is the graph of $\frac{1}{2}\mathbf{w}$?

5. Let $\mathbf{t} = \langle -9, 3 \rangle$ and $\mathbf{u} = \langle 1, 3 \rangle$. Are $\mathbf{t}$ and $\mathbf{u}$ normal vectors?

ANSWERS TO LESSON QUIZ

1. $\langle 4, -2 \rangle$

2. $\langle -3, -5 \rangle$

3. 6.08

4.

5. yes

PRESCRIPTION FOR REMEDIATION

Use the student work on the Lesson Quiz to prescribe a differentiated review assignment:

Points	Differentiated Remediation
0–2	Intervention
3–4	On-level
5	Extension

PowerAlgebra.com

5 Assess & Remediate

Assign the Lesson Quiz. Appropriate intervention, practice, or enrichment is automatically generated based on student performance.

Intervention

- **Reteaching** (2 pages) Provides reteaching and practice exercises for the key lesson concepts. Use with struggling students or absent students.

- **English Language Learner Support** Helps students develop and reinforce mathematical vocabulary and key concepts.

All-in-One Resources/Online
Reteaching

12-6 Reteaching
Vectors

All-in-One Resources/Online
English Language Learner Support

12-6 Additional Vocabulary Support
Vectors

Differentiated Remediation *continued*

On-Level

- **Practice (2 pages)** Provides extra practice for each lesson. For simpler practice exercises, use the Form K Practice pages found in the All-in-One Teaching Resources and online.

- **Think About a Plan** Helps students develop specific problem-solving skills and strategies by providing scaffolded guiding questions.

- **Standardized Test Prep** Focuses on all major exercises, all major question types, and helps students prepare for the high-stakes assessments.

Extension

- **Enrichment** Provides students with interesting problems and activities that extend the concepts of the lesson.

- **Activities, Games, and Puzzles** Worksheets that can be used for concepts development, enrichment, and for fun!

Practice and Problem Solving Wkbk/ All-in-One Resources/Online

Practice page 1

12-6 Practice   *Form G*
Vectors

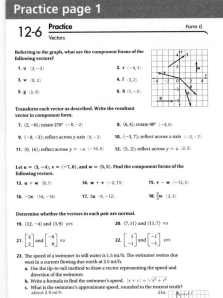

Referring to the graph, what are the component forms of the following vectors?

1. **u** ⟨3, −3⟩   2. **v** ⟨−4, 1⟩

3. **w** ⟨0, 2⟩   4. **f** ⟨3, 2⟩

5. **g** ⟨3, 0⟩   6. **h** ⟨1, −3⟩

Transform each vector as described. Write the resultant vector in component form.

7. ⟨2, −8⟩; rotate 270° ⟨−8, −2⟩   8. ⟨6, 4⟩; rotate 90° ⟨−4, 6⟩

9. ⟨−9, −3⟩; reflect across y-axis ⟨9, −3⟩   10. ⟨−3, 7⟩; reflect across x-axis ⟨−3, −7⟩

11. ⟨0, 16⟩; reflect across $y = -x$ ⟨−16, 0⟩   12. ⟨5, 2⟩; reflect across $y = x$ ⟨2, 5⟩

Let **u** = ⟨3, −4⟩, **v** = ⟨−7, 8⟩, and **w** = ⟨5, 5⟩. Find the component forms of the following vectors.

13. **u** + **w** ⟨8, 1⟩   14. **w** + **v** ⟨−2, 13⟩   15. **v** − **w** ⟨−12, 3⟩

16. −2**v** ⟨14, −16⟩   17. 3**u** ⟨9, −12⟩   18. $\frac{3}{5}$**w** ⟨3, 3⟩

Determine whether the vectors in each pair are normal.

19. ⟨12, −4⟩ and ⟨3, 9⟩ yes   20. ⟨7, 11⟩ and ⟨11, 7⟩ no

21. $\begin{bmatrix} 3 \\ 2 \end{bmatrix}$ and $\begin{bmatrix} -9 \\ 6 \end{bmatrix}$ no   22. $\begin{bmatrix} 1 \\ -1 \end{bmatrix}$ and $\begin{bmatrix} -1 \\ -1 \end{bmatrix}$ yes

23. The speed of a swimmer in still water is 1.5 mi/h. The swimmer swims due west in a current flowing due north at 2.5 mi/h.
   a. Use the tip-to-tail method to draw a vector representing the speed and direction of the swimmer.
   b. Write a formula to find the swimmer's speed. $|s + r| = \sqrt{s^2 + r^2}$
   c. What is the swimmer's approximate speed, rounded to the nearest tenth? about 2.9 mi/h   23a.

Practice and Problem Solving Wkbk/ All-in-One Resources/Online

Practice page 2

12-6 Practice (continued)   *Form G*
Vectors

Let **u** = $\begin{bmatrix} -5 \\ 9 \end{bmatrix}$, **v** = $\begin{bmatrix} 4 \\ 4 \end{bmatrix}$, and **w** = $\begin{bmatrix} -2 \\ 6 \end{bmatrix}$. Find the following vectors.

24. 3**u** + 2**w** $\begin{bmatrix} -19 \\ 39 \end{bmatrix}$ 25. −**v** + 3**w** $\begin{bmatrix} -10 \\ 14 \end{bmatrix}$ 26. **w** − $\frac{3}{2}$**v** − 2**u** $\begin{bmatrix} 2 \\ -18 \end{bmatrix}$

27. A bird flies 16 mi/h in still air. Suppose the bird flies due south with a wind blowing 15 mi/h due east. What is the resultant speed of the bird rounded to the nearest mile per hour? about 22 mi/h

28. A model rocket lands 245 ft west and 162 ft south of the point from which it was launched. How far did the rocket fly? Round your answer to the nearest foot. about 294 ft

29. Consider a polygon with vertices at $A(−3, 5)$, $B(2, 3)$, $C(4, −4)$, and $D(−6, −3)$. Express the sides of the polygon as vectors $\overrightarrow{AB}$, $\overrightarrow{BC}$, $\overrightarrow{CD}$ and $\overrightarrow{DA}$. $\overrightarrow{AB} = ⟨5, −2⟩$, $\overrightarrow{BC} = ⟨2, −7⟩$, $\overrightarrow{CD} = ⟨−10, 1⟩$, $\overrightarrow{DA} = ⟨3, 8⟩$

Let **a** = ⟨7, 5⟩, **b** = ⟨4, −1⟩, and **c** = ⟨0, −3⟩. Solve each of the following for the unknown vector **v**.

30. **b** − **v** = **c** ⟨4, 2⟩   31. **v** + **a** = **b** ⟨−3, −6⟩

32. **a** + **b** = **v** − **c** ⟨11, 1⟩   33. **a** − **v** + **b** − **c** = ⟨1, 1⟩ ⟨10, 6⟩

34. A train leaves Dawson station and travels 360 mi due north. Then it turns and travels 120 mi due west to reach New Port. If the train travels 75 mi/h on a straight route directly back to Dawson, how long will the return trip take? Round your answer to the nearest hour. about 5 h

35. **Reasoning** Identify the additive identity vector **v**, if it exists. Explain your reasoning. $\begin{bmatrix} 0 \\ 0 \end{bmatrix}$; if $\begin{bmatrix} v_1 \\ v_2 \end{bmatrix} + \begin{bmatrix} a_1 \\ a_2 \end{bmatrix} = \begin{bmatrix} a_1 \\ a_2 \end{bmatrix}$, then $\begin{bmatrix} v_1 \\ v_2 \end{bmatrix} = \begin{bmatrix} a_1 \\ a_2 \end{bmatrix} - \begin{bmatrix} a_1 \\ a_2 \end{bmatrix} = \begin{bmatrix} 0 \\ 0 \end{bmatrix}$.

Let **u** = $\begin{bmatrix} -2 \\ 2 \end{bmatrix}$ and **v** = $\begin{bmatrix} 3 \\ -1 \end{bmatrix}$. Graph the following vectors.

36. 3**u**   37. −**v**   38. $-\frac{1}{2}$**u**

All-in-One Resources/Online

Enrichment

12-6 Reteaching
Vectors

A vector shows *magnitude* (length) and *direction*, but does NOT represent location. You can name a vector using its initial and terminal points, or you can write it in *component form*. The component form gives you the coordinates of the terminal point when the initial point is translated to the origin.

Problem

What is the component form of vector **v** = $\overrightarrow{PQ}$ in the graph above?
Step 1 Translate the vector so that the initial point becomes (0, 0). The translation is 3 units right and 1 unit down.

Step 2 Find the coordinates of the translated terminal point. The original terminal point was (2, 4). The translated terminal point is (2 + 3, 4 − 1) = (5, 3)

The component form is **v** = ⟨5, 3⟩.

You can add, subtract, and do scalar multiplication with vectors in component form.

Problem

Let **u** = ⟨5, −8⟩ and **v** = ⟨3, 1⟩. What is 2**u** + **v** in component form?

$2u = 2⟨5, −8⟩$ Substitute the component form for u.
$= ⟨(2)(5), (2)(−8)⟩ = ⟨10, −16⟩$ Multiply each coordinate by the scalar 2.
$2u + v = ⟨10, −16⟩ + ⟨3, 1⟩$ Substitute the component forms for 2u and v.
$= ⟨(10 + 3), (−16 + 1)⟩ = ⟨13, −15⟩$ Add the x-coordinates. Add the y-coordinates.

The component form is 2**u** + **v** = ⟨13, −15⟩.

Exercises

Let **r** = ⟨−6, 3⟩, **s** = ⟨4, 7⟩, and **t** = ⟨2, −5⟩. Find the component forms of the following vectors.

1. **r** − **s** ⟨−10, −4⟩   2. 3**t** + 2**r** ⟨−6, −9⟩   3. $\frac{3}{2}$**r** − 4**s** + **t** ⟨−18, −31⟩

Practice and Problem Solving Wkbk/ All-in-One Resources/Online

Think About a Plan

12-6 Think About a Plan
Vectors

Aviation A twin-engine airplane has a speed of 300 mi/h in still air. Suppose the airplane heads south and encounters a wind blowing 50 mi/h due east. What is the resultant speed of the airplane?

Know

1. The airplane is traveling | south | at a speed of | 300 mi/h |.

2. The wind is blowing | east | at a speed of | 50 mi/h |.

Need

3. To solve the problem I need to find: the sum of the vectors that represent the speed of the airplane and the speed of the wind

Plan

4. Sketch the speed of the airplane and the speed of the wind as vectors. Then use the tip-to-tail method to sketch **a** + **w**.

5. What is the component form of the vector for the speed of the airplane? **a** = ⟨0, −300⟩

6. What is the component form of the vector for the speed of the wind? **w** = ⟨50, 0⟩

7. Express **a** + **w** in component form. **a** + **w** = ⟨50, −300⟩

8. What equation can you use to find the magnitude of **a** + **w**? |**a** + **w**| = $\sqrt{(50)^2 + (−300)^2}$

9. What is the resultant speed of the airplane? about 304 mi/h in a S/SE direction

Practice and Problem Solving Wkbk/ All-in-One Resources/Online

Standardized Test Prep

12-6 Standardized Test Prep
Vectors

Multiple Choice

For Exercises 1–5, choose the correct letter.

1. Let **u** = ⟨4, −7⟩ and **v** = ⟨−1, 3⟩. What is |**u** + **v**|? D
   Ⓐ −5   Ⓑ −1   Ⓒ 1   Ⓓ 5

2. What is the component form of vector **v**? F
   Ⓕ ⟨−2, 6⟩   Ⓗ ⟨−1, 3⟩
   Ⓖ ⟨0, 0⟩   Ⓘ ⟨1, −3⟩

3. Which represents the vector **u** = ⟨16, −9⟩ rotated 180°? C
   Ⓐ $\begin{bmatrix} -9 \\ -16 \end{bmatrix}$ Ⓑ $\begin{bmatrix} -9 \\ 16 \end{bmatrix}$ Ⓒ $\begin{bmatrix} -16 \\ 9 \end{bmatrix}$ Ⓓ $\begin{bmatrix} 16 \\ 9 \end{bmatrix}$

4. Let **u** = $\begin{bmatrix} 5 \\ 8 \end{bmatrix}$ and **v** = $\begin{bmatrix} -2 \\ -4 \end{bmatrix}$. What is the vector −2**u** − $\frac{5}{2}$**v**? G
   Ⓕ $\begin{bmatrix} -15 \\ -26 \end{bmatrix}$ Ⓖ $\begin{bmatrix} -5 \\ -6 \end{bmatrix}$ Ⓗ $\begin{bmatrix} 0 \\ 8 \end{bmatrix}$ Ⓘ $\begin{bmatrix} 10 \\ 4 \end{bmatrix}$

5. Which represents the vector **w** = $\begin{bmatrix} 8 \\ 14 \end{bmatrix}$ reflected across $y = x$? B
   Ⓐ $\begin{bmatrix} -14 \\ 8 \end{bmatrix}$ Ⓑ $\begin{bmatrix} 14 \\ 8 \end{bmatrix}$ Ⓒ $\begin{bmatrix} -8 \\ 14 \end{bmatrix}$ Ⓓ $\begin{bmatrix} -8 \\ -14 \end{bmatrix}$

Short Response

6. Let **p** = ⟨6, −1⟩ and **q** = ⟨3, 5⟩. Are **p** and **q** normal? Show your work.
   [2] **p** · **q** = (6)(3) + (−1)(5) = 18 − 5 = 13 The dot product does not equal zero. The vectors are not normal.
   [1] incorrect or incomplete work shown
   [0] incorrect answer and no work shown OR no answer given

Online Teacher Resource Center

Activities, Games, and Puzzles

12-6 Game: Last Will Be First
Vectors

Provide the host with the following questions and answers.

Questions	Answers
• the magnitude of the vector ⟨20, 21⟩	29
• the dot product of ⟨4, 7⟩ and ⟨9, −5⟩	1
• the sum of ⟨2, 3⟩ and ⟨−1, 4⟩	⟨1, 7⟩
• the magnitude of the vector ⟨3, −4⟩	5
• the dot product of ⟨6, −9⟩ and ⟨7, 5⟩	−3
• the sum of ⟨1, 5⟩ and ⟨−3, −8⟩	⟨−4, −3⟩
• the magnitude of the vector ⟨−5, 14⟩	14.9
• the dot product of ⟨8, 6⟩ and ⟨−3, 4⟩	0
• the sum of ⟨−2, 7⟩ and ⟨5, 0⟩	⟨3, 7⟩
• the magnitude of the vector ⟨5, 6⟩	7.8
• the dot product of ⟨−2, 5⟩ and ⟨8, 4⟩	4
• the sum of ⟨4, −1⟩ and ⟨3, 2⟩	⟨7, 1⟩
• the magnitude of the vector ⟨−3, −3⟩	4.2
• the dot product of ⟨5, 6⟩ and ⟨−3, 4⟩	9
• the sum of ⟨8, −5⟩ and ⟨−5, 9⟩	⟨3, 4⟩
• the magnitude of the vector ⟨8, 15⟩	17
• the dot product of ⟨6, −4⟩ and ⟨5, 7⟩	2
• the sum of ⟨2, −3⟩ and ⟨−4, −1⟩	⟨−6, −4⟩
• the magnitude of the vector ⟨−7, −8⟩	10.6
• the dot product of ⟨7, 3⟩ and ⟨−4, 6⟩	−10
• the sum of ⟨8, −7⟩ and ⟨−6, 5⟩	⟨2, −2⟩
• the magnitude of the vector ⟨−5, −12⟩	13
• the dot product of ⟨7, 4⟩ and ⟨−5, 7⟩	−7
• the sum of ⟨9, −5⟩ and ⟨−4, 3⟩	⟨5, −2⟩

Performance Task

Pull It All Together

Understanding by Design principles indicate the importance of performance tasks that assess understanding.
- Make sense of problems and persevere in solving them.
- Model with mathematics.
- Attend to precision.

The following questions are designed to
- Help support students as they do the Performance Tasks.
- Help you gauge their progress toward becoming mathematically proficient.

Performance Task 1

Assign values under specific conditions to undefined elements in a matrix equation and then explain the matrix equation.
- What do r_1 and r_2 represent?

Performance Task 2

Use the determinant of a matrix to show that a system of equations must either have no solutions or many solutions.
- What matrix represents A?
- What is the determinant of A? What value can you set the determinant equal to?

Performance Task 3

Use matrices to determine what transformation results from the application of two transformations to a point or a set of points.
- If you rotated a set of points 90° and then reflected the set of points across the line $y = x$, what two matrices would you be multiplying by?

To solve these problems, you will pull together concepts and skills related to matrices.

BIG idea Data Representation
You can represent data in a variety of ways.

Performance Task 1

The first matrix represents inventory (how many there are) of four types of objects. The second matrix is a price matrix. The third matrix is the product of the first two matrices. Give an example of real inventory and real prices for which the product matrix makes sense. Explain the meaning of the product.

$$\begin{bmatrix} a_1 & a_2 \\ b_1 & b_2 \end{bmatrix}\begin{bmatrix} p_1 \\ p_2 \end{bmatrix} = \begin{bmatrix} r_1 \\ r_2 \end{bmatrix}$$

BIG idea Modeling
You can represent many real-world mathematical problems algebraically. These representations can lead to algebraic solutions.

Performance Task 2

Suppose the matrix equation $AX = B$ represents the system $\begin{cases} a_1x + a_2y = b_1 \\ a_3x + a_4y = b_2 \end{cases}$ and det $A = 0$. Show that the system is either dependent (has many solutions) or inconsistent (has no solutions). (*Hint:* First show that a_3 and a_4 are proportional to a_1 and a_2.)

BIG idea Transformations
Translations, reflections, rotations, and dilations can help you understand relationships within objects and between objects.

Performance Task 3

Each entry in a multiplication table, as shown in the 2-by-2 table at the right, is the product of the factor shown at the left and the factor shown at the top.

Let $ROT = \{r_{90°}, r_{180°}, r_{270°}, r_{360°}\}$

$REF = \{R_{x\text{-axis}}, R_{y\text{-axis}}, R_{y=x}, R_{y=-x}\}$

be the sets of rotations and reflections, respectively, as described in Lesson 12-5. Build each 4-by-4 multiplication table.

×	c	d
a	ac	ad
b	bc	bd

a.   b.   c.   d.

Assess Performance

Pull It All Together

See p. 49 for a holistic scoring rubric to gauge a student's progress on Understanding the Problem, Planning a Solution, Getting an Answer, and Assessing Autonomy.

SOLUTION OUTLINES

1. Possible Plan: You are buying supplies for two art classes. For each class you will need markers, and drawing tablets. The first matrix will be the number of items needed. The second matrix will be the cost of each item. The product matrix will be the total cost of the supplies.

2. First step: Write a matrix equation to represent the system.

$$\left(\begin{bmatrix} a_1 & a_2 \\ a_3 & a_4 \end{bmatrix} \cdot \begin{bmatrix} x \\ y \end{bmatrix} = \begin{bmatrix} b_1 \\ b_2 \end{bmatrix}\right)$$

Second step: The determinant is equal to 0. So,

$$a_1a_4 - a_2a_3 = 0$$
$$a_1a_4 = a_2a_3$$
$$\frac{a_1}{a_2} = \frac{a_3}{a_4}$$

Third step: Since a_1 and a_2 are proportional to a_3 and a_4, there is no inverse matrix and the system has no unique solution. Depending on the values of b_1 and b_2 the graphs will be either parallel lines (no solutions) or the same line (infinitely many solutions).

b.

	$Ref_{x\text{-axis}}$	$Ref_{y\text{-axis}}$	$Ref_{y=x}$	$Ref_{y=-x}$
$Ref_{x\text{-axis}}$	$\begin{bmatrix} 1 & 0 \\ 0 & 1 \end{bmatrix}$	$\begin{bmatrix} -1 & 0 \\ 0 & -1 \end{bmatrix}$	$\begin{bmatrix} 0 & 1 \\ -1 & 0 \end{bmatrix}$	$\begin{bmatrix} 0 & -1 \\ 1 & 0 \end{bmatrix}$
$Ref_{y\text{-axis}}$	$\begin{bmatrix} -1 & 0 \\ 0 & -1 \end{bmatrix}$	$\begin{bmatrix} 1 & 0 \\ 0 & 1 \end{bmatrix}$	$\begin{bmatrix} 0 & -1 \\ 1 & 0 \end{bmatrix}$	$\begin{bmatrix} 0 & 1 \\ -1 & 0 \end{bmatrix}$
$Ref_{y=x}$	$\begin{bmatrix} 0 & -1 \\ 1 & 0 \end{bmatrix}$	$\begin{bmatrix} 0 & 1 \\ -1 & 0 \end{bmatrix}$	$\begin{bmatrix} 1 & 0 \\ 0 & 1 \end{bmatrix}$	$\begin{bmatrix} -1 & 0 \\ 0 & -1 \end{bmatrix}$
$Ref_{y=-x}$	$\begin{bmatrix} 0 & 1 \\ -1 & 0 \end{bmatrix}$	$\begin{bmatrix} 0 & -1 \\ 1 & 0 \end{bmatrix}$	$\begin{bmatrix} -1 & 0 \\ 0 & -1 \end{bmatrix}$	$\begin{bmatrix} 1 & 0 \\ 0 & 1 \end{bmatrix}$

3a.

	$Rot_{90°}$	$Rot_{180°}$	$Rot_{270°}$	$Rot_{360°}$
$Rot_{90°}$	$\begin{bmatrix} -1 & 0 \\ 0 & -1 \end{bmatrix}$	$\begin{bmatrix} 0 & 1 \\ -1 & 0 \end{bmatrix}$	$\begin{bmatrix} 1 & 0 \\ 0 & 1 \end{bmatrix}$	$\begin{bmatrix} 0 & -1 \\ 1 & 0 \end{bmatrix}$
$Rot_{180°}$	$\begin{bmatrix} 0 & 1 \\ -1 & 0 \end{bmatrix}$	$\begin{bmatrix} 1 & 0 \\ 0 & 1 \end{bmatrix}$	$\begin{bmatrix} 0 & -1 \\ 1 & 0 \end{bmatrix}$	$\begin{bmatrix} -1 & 0 \\ 0 & -1 \end{bmatrix}$
$Rot_{270°}$	$\begin{bmatrix} 0 & 1 \\ 1 & 0 \end{bmatrix}$	$\begin{bmatrix} 0 & -1 \\ 1 & 0 \end{bmatrix}$	$\begin{bmatrix} -1 & 0 \\ 0 & -1 \end{bmatrix}$	$\begin{bmatrix} 0 & 1 \\ -1 & 0 \end{bmatrix}$
$Rot_{360°}$	$\begin{bmatrix} 0 & -1 \\ 1 & 0 \end{bmatrix}$	$\begin{bmatrix} -1 & 0 \\ 0 & -1 \end{bmatrix}$	$\begin{bmatrix} 0 & 1 \\ -1 & 0 \end{bmatrix}$	$\begin{bmatrix} 1 & 0 \\ 0 & 1 \end{bmatrix}$

12 Chapter Review

Connecting BIG ideas and Answering the Essential Questions

1 Data Representation
You can organize data in a matrix in exactly the same way that you organize data in a rectangular table.

2 Modeling
If you can model a real-world situation with a system of equations, you can represent the system with a matrix equation.

3 Transformations
You can use matrix operations to transform points in a plane:
- addition for translating
- multiplication for rotating and reflecting
- scalar multiplication for dilating.

Adding, Subtracting, and Multiplying Matrices (Lessons 12-1 and 12-2)
To add or subtract matrices, add or subtract corresponding elements.

To multiply two matrices:
$$\begin{bmatrix} a & b \\ c & d \end{bmatrix}\begin{bmatrix} e & f \\ g & h \end{bmatrix} = \begin{bmatrix} ae + bg & af + bh \\ ce + dg & cf + dh \end{bmatrix}$$

Determinants and Inverses (Lesson 12-3)
Let A be an $n \times n$ matrix. If $\det A \neq 0$, then A^{-1} exists and $AA^{-1} = A^{-1}A = I_n$ (the $n \times n$ identity matrix).

Geometric Transformations (Lesson 12-5)
$$\begin{bmatrix} 0 & -1 \\ 1 & 0 \end{bmatrix}, \begin{bmatrix} -1 & 0 \\ 0 & -1 \end{bmatrix}, \begin{bmatrix} 0 & 1 \\ -1 & 0 \end{bmatrix}, \text{and}$$
$$\begin{bmatrix} 1 & 0 \\ 0 & 1 \end{bmatrix} \text{ rotate } 90°, 180°, 270°, \text{ and } 360°.$$

Vectors (Lesson 12-6)
You can add two vectors as matrices, or graphically.

Inverse Matrices and Systems (Lesson 12-4)
The matrix equation $AX = B$ represents a system of linear equations.

A is the coefficient matrix,
X is the variable matrix,
B is the constant matrix.

If $\det A \neq 0$, then multiply each side by A^{-1} to find X.
$$A^{-1}AX = A^{-1}B$$
$$X = A^{-1}B$$

Chapter Vocabulary

- center of rotation (p. 804)
- coefficient matrix (p. 793)
- constant matrix (p. 793)
- corresponding elements (p. 764)
- determinant (p. 784)
- dilation (p. 802)
- dot product (p. 812)
- equal matrices (p. 767)
- image (p. 801)
- initial point (p. 809)
- magnitude (p. 809)
- matrix equation (p. 765)
- multiplicative identity matrix (p. 782)
- multiplicative inverse matrix (p. 782)
- normal vectors (p. 812)
- preimage (p. 801)
- rotation (p. 804)
- scalar (p. 772)
- scalar multiplication (p. 772)
- singular matrix (p. 785)
- square matrix (p. 782)
- terminal point (p. 809)
- variable matrix (p. 793)
- vector (p. 809)
- zero matrix (p. 766)

Choose the correct term to complete each sentence.

1. If corresponding elements of matrices are equal, the matrices are   ? .

2. The additive identity of a matrix is the   ? .

3. A(n)   ?   consists of a coefficient matrix, a variable matrix, and a constant matrix.

4. An $n \times n$ matrix is called a(n)   ? .

Essential Questions

BIG idea Data Representation
ESSENTIAL QUESTION How can you use a matrix to organize data?
ANSWER You can organize data in a matrix in exactly the same way that you organize data in a rectangular table.

BIG idea Modeling
ESSENTIAL QUESTION How can you use a matrix equation to model a real-world situation?
ANSWER If you can model a real situation with a system of equations, you can represent the system with a matrix equation.

BIG idea Transformations
ESSENTIAL QUESTION How can a matrix represent a transformation of a geometric figure in the plane?
ANSWER You can use matrix operations to transform points in a plane:
- addition for translating
- multiplication for rotating and reflecting
- scalar multiplication for dilating.

---

c.

	$Rot_{90°}$	$Rot_{180°}$	$Rot_{270°}$	$Rot_{360°}$
$Ref_{x\text{-axis}}$	$\begin{bmatrix} 0 & -1 \\ -1 & 0 \end{bmatrix}$	$\begin{bmatrix} -1 & 0 \\ 0 & 1 \end{bmatrix}$	$\begin{bmatrix} 0 & 1 \\ 1 & 0 \end{bmatrix}$	$\begin{bmatrix} 1 & 0 \\ 0 & -1 \end{bmatrix}$
$Ref_{y\text{-axis}}$	$\begin{bmatrix} 0 & 1 \\ 1 & 0 \end{bmatrix}$	$\begin{bmatrix} 1 & 0 \\ 0 & -1 \end{bmatrix}$	$\begin{bmatrix} 0 & -1 \\ -1 & 0 \end{bmatrix}$	$\begin{bmatrix} -1 & 0 \\ 0 & 1 \end{bmatrix}$
$Ref_{y=x}$	$\begin{bmatrix} 1 & 0 \\ 0 & -1 \end{bmatrix}$	$\begin{bmatrix} 0 & -1 \\ -1 & 0 \end{bmatrix}$	$\begin{bmatrix} -1 & 0 \\ 0 & 1 \end{bmatrix}$	$\begin{bmatrix} 0 & 1 \\ 1 & 0 \end{bmatrix}$
$Ref_{y=-x}$	$\begin{bmatrix} -1 & 0 \\ 0 & 1 \end{bmatrix}$	$\begin{bmatrix} 0 & 1 \\ 1 & 0 \end{bmatrix}$	$\begin{bmatrix} 1 & 0 \\ 0 & -1 \end{bmatrix}$	$\begin{bmatrix} 0 & -1 \\ -1 & 0 \end{bmatrix}$

d.

	$Ref_{x\text{-axis}}$	$Ref_{y\text{-axis}}$	$Ref_{y=x}$	$Ref_{y=-x}$
$Rot_{90°}$	$\begin{bmatrix} 0 & 1 \\ 1 & 0 \end{bmatrix}$	$\begin{bmatrix} 0 & -1 \\ -1 & 0 \end{bmatrix}$	$\begin{bmatrix} -1 & 0 \\ 0 & 1 \end{bmatrix}$	$\begin{bmatrix} 1 & 0 \\ 0 & -1 \end{bmatrix}$
$Rot_{180°}$	$\begin{bmatrix} -1 & 0 \\ 0 & 1 \end{bmatrix}$	$\begin{bmatrix} 1 & 0 \\ 0 & -1 \end{bmatrix}$	$\begin{bmatrix} 0 & -1 \\ -1 & 0 \end{bmatrix}$	$\begin{bmatrix} 0 & 1 \\ 1 & 0 \end{bmatrix}$
$Rot_{270°}$	$\begin{bmatrix} 0 & -1 \\ -1 & 0 \end{bmatrix}$	$\begin{bmatrix} 0 & 1 \\ 1 & 0 \end{bmatrix}$	$\begin{bmatrix} 1 & 0 \\ 0 & -1 \end{bmatrix}$	$\begin{bmatrix} -1 & 0 \\ 0 & 1 \end{bmatrix}$
$Rot_{360°}$	$\begin{bmatrix} 1 & 0 \\ 0 & -1 \end{bmatrix}$	$\begin{bmatrix} -1 & 0 \\ 0 & 1 \end{bmatrix}$	$\begin{bmatrix} 0 & 1 \\ 1 & 0 \end{bmatrix}$	$\begin{bmatrix} 0 & -1 \\ -1 & 0 \end{bmatrix}$

Answers

Chapter Review

1. equal matrices
2. zero matrix
3. matrix equation
4. square matrix

Summative Questions

Use the following prompts as you review this chapter with your students. The prompts are designed to help you assess your students' understanding of the BIG ideas they have studied.

- Could you add an $m \times n$ matrix and an $m \times p$ matrix? Could you multiply them?
- Compare and contrast matrix multiplication and scalar multiplication. Can they both change the dimensions of a matrix?
- Why is matrix multiplication not commutative?
- How can you use a determinant to analyze a system of linear equations?
- If you want to translate a geometric figure, which matrix operation would you use?
- What is a dot product of two vectors? Is it a vector itself? What can it tell you about the two vectors?

Answers

Chapter Review (continued)

5. $\begin{bmatrix} -1 & 9 & -8 \\ 4 & 0 & 6 \end{bmatrix}$

6. $\begin{bmatrix} 5 & -4 \\ 5 & 0 \end{bmatrix}$

7. $\begin{bmatrix} 1 & -8 & 12 \end{bmatrix}$

8. $\begin{bmatrix} -3 & 10 \\ -3 & 3 \end{bmatrix}$

9. $x = -2, w = 8, r = 4, t = -1$

10. $t = -4, y = \dfrac{11}{2}, r = 4, w = 4$

11. $\begin{bmatrix} 18 & 3 & 0 & 24 \\ -12 & 9 & 21 & 33 \end{bmatrix}$

12. undefined

13. undefined

14. $\begin{bmatrix} -6 & 10 & 21 & 41 \\ -28 & 10 & 28 & 28 \end{bmatrix}$

15. $\begin{bmatrix} -14 & -2 \\ 43 & -7 \end{bmatrix}$

16. $\begin{bmatrix} -11 & 18 \\ -17 & -2 \end{bmatrix}$

12-1 Adding and Subracting Matrices

Quick Review

To perform matrix addition or subtraction, add or subtract the corresponding elements in the matrices.

Two matrices are **equal matrices** when they have the same dimensions and corresponding elements are equal. This principle is used to solve a **matrix equation**.

Example

If $A = \begin{bmatrix} 2 & 1 & -2 \\ 1 & 4 & 3 \\ -2 & -1 & 5 \end{bmatrix}$ and $B = \begin{bmatrix} 1 & -2 & 4 \\ -3 & -2 & 1 \\ 0 & 0 & 5 \end{bmatrix}$,

what is $A + B$?

$A + B = \begin{bmatrix} 2+1 & 1+(-2) & -2+4 \\ 1+(-3) & 4+(-2) & 3+1 \\ -2+0 & -1+0 & 5+5 \end{bmatrix}$

$= \begin{bmatrix} 3 & -1 & 2 \\ -2 & 2 & 4 \\ -2 & -1 & 10 \end{bmatrix}$

Exercises

Find each sum or difference.

5. $\begin{bmatrix} 1 & 2 & -5 \\ 3 & -2 & 1 \end{bmatrix} + \begin{bmatrix} -2 & 7 & -3 \\ 1 & 2 & 5 \end{bmatrix}$

6. $\begin{bmatrix} 0 & 2 \\ -4 & -1 \end{bmatrix} - \begin{bmatrix} -5 & 6 \\ -9 & -1 \end{bmatrix}$

Solve each matrix equation.

7. $\begin{bmatrix} 2 & -6 & 8 \end{bmatrix} + \begin{bmatrix} -1 & -2 & 4 \end{bmatrix} = X$

8. $\begin{bmatrix} 7 & -1 \\ 0 & 8 \end{bmatrix} + X = \begin{bmatrix} 4 & 9 \\ -3 & 11 \end{bmatrix}$

Find the value of each variable.

9. $\begin{bmatrix} x-5 & 9 \\ 4 & t+2 \end{bmatrix} = \begin{bmatrix} -7 & w+1 \\ 8-r & 1 \end{bmatrix}$

10. $\begin{bmatrix} -4+t & 2y \\ r & w+5 \end{bmatrix} = \begin{bmatrix} 2t & 11 \\ -2r+12 & 9 \end{bmatrix}$

12-2 Matrix Multiplication

Quick Review

To obtain the product of a matrix and a **scalar**, multiply each matrix element by the scalar. Matrix multiplication uses both multiplication and addition. The element in the ith row and the jth column of the product of two matrices is the sum of the products of each element of the ith row of the first matrix and the corresponding element of the jth column of the second matrix. The first matrix must have the same number of columns as the second has rows.

Example

If $A = \begin{bmatrix} 1 & -3 \\ -2 & 0 \end{bmatrix}$ and $B = \begin{bmatrix} 1 & 4 \\ 0 & 2 \end{bmatrix}$, what is AB?

$AB = \begin{bmatrix} (1)(1)+(-3)(0) & (1)(4)+(-3)(2) \\ (-2)(1)+(0)(0) & (-2)(4)+(0)(2) \end{bmatrix}$

$= \begin{bmatrix} 1 & -2 \\ -2 & -8 \end{bmatrix}$

Exercises

Use matrices A, B, C, and D to find each scalar product and sum, or difference, if possible. If an operation is not defined, label it *undefined*.

$A = \begin{bmatrix} 6 & 1 & 0 & 8 \\ -4 & 3 & 7 & 11 \end{bmatrix}$ $\quad B = \begin{bmatrix} 1 & 3 \\ -2 & 4 \end{bmatrix}$

$C = \begin{bmatrix} -2 & 1 \\ 4 & 0 \\ 2 & 2 \\ 1 & 1 \end{bmatrix}$ $\quad D = \begin{bmatrix} 5 & -2 \\ 3 & 6 \end{bmatrix}$

11. $3A$ **12.** $B - 2A$

13. AB **14.** BA

15. $AC - BD$ **16.** $4B - 3D$

12-3 Determinants and Inverses

Quick Review

A **square matrix** with 1's along its main diagonal and 0's elsewhere is the **multiplicative identity matrix**, I. If A and X are square matrices such that $AX = I$, then X is the **multiplicative identity matrix** of A, A^{-1}.

You can use a calculator to find the inverse of a matrix. You can find the inverse of a 2×2 matrix $A = \begin{bmatrix} a & b \\ c & d \end{bmatrix}$ by using its **determinant**.

$$A^{-1} = \frac{1}{\det A} \begin{bmatrix} d & -b \\ -c & a \end{bmatrix} = \frac{1}{ad - bc} \begin{bmatrix} d & -b \\ -c & a \end{bmatrix}$$

Example

What is the determinant of $\begin{bmatrix} 2 & -3 \\ 3 & -4 \end{bmatrix}$?

$$\det \begin{bmatrix} 2 & -3 \\ 3 & -4 \end{bmatrix} = (2)(-4) - (-3)(3)$$
$$= -8 - (-9) = 1$$

Exercises

Evaluate the determinant of each matrix and find the inverse, if possible.

17. $\begin{bmatrix} 6 & 1 \\ 0 & 4 \end{bmatrix}$

18. $\begin{bmatrix} 5 & -2 \\ 10 & -4 \end{bmatrix}$

19. $\begin{bmatrix} 10 & 1 \\ 8 & 5 \end{bmatrix}$

20. $\begin{bmatrix} 1 & 0 & 2 \\ -1 & 0 & 1 \\ -1 & -2 & 0 \end{bmatrix}$

12-4 Inverse Matrices and Systems

Quick Review

You can use inverse matrices to solve some matrix equations and systems of equations. When equations in a system are in standard form, the product of the **coefficient matrix** and the **variable matrix** equals the **constant matrix**. You solve the equation by multiplying both sides of the equation by the inverse of the coefficient matrix. If that inverse does not exist, the system does not have a unique solution.

Example

What is the matrix equation that corresponds to the following system? $\begin{cases} 2x - y = 12 \\ x + 4y = 15 \end{cases}$

Identify $A = \begin{bmatrix} 2 & -1 \\ 1 & 4 \end{bmatrix}$, $X = \begin{bmatrix} x \\ y \end{bmatrix}$, and $B = \begin{bmatrix} 12 \\ 15 \end{bmatrix}$.

The matrix equation is $AX = B$ or $\begin{bmatrix} 2 & -1 \\ 1 & 4 \end{bmatrix}\begin{bmatrix} x \\ y \end{bmatrix} = \begin{bmatrix} 12 \\ 15 \end{bmatrix}$.

Exercises

Use an inverse matrix to solve each equation or system.

21. $\begin{bmatrix} 3 & 5 \\ 6 & 2 \end{bmatrix} X = \begin{bmatrix} -2 & 6 \\ 4 & 12 \end{bmatrix}$

22. $\begin{cases} x - y = 3 \\ 2x - y = -1 \end{cases}$

23. $\begin{bmatrix} 4 & 1 \\ 2 & 1 \end{bmatrix}\begin{bmatrix} x \\ y \end{bmatrix} = \begin{bmatrix} 10 \\ 6 \end{bmatrix}$

24. $\begin{bmatrix} -6 & 0 \\ 7 & 1 \end{bmatrix} X = \begin{bmatrix} -12 & -6 \\ 17 & 9 \end{bmatrix}$

25. $\begin{cases} x + 2y = 15 \\ 2x + 4y = 30 \end{cases}$

26. $\begin{cases} a + 2b + c = 14 \\ b = c + 1 \\ a = -3c + 6 \end{cases}$

17. $24;\ \begin{bmatrix} \frac{1}{6} & -\frac{1}{24} \\ 0 & \frac{1}{4} \end{bmatrix}$

18. 0; does not exist

19. $42;\ \begin{bmatrix} \frac{5}{42} & -\frac{1}{42} \\ -\frac{4}{21} & \frac{5}{21} \end{bmatrix}$

20. $6;\ \begin{bmatrix} \frac{1}{3} & -\frac{2}{3} & 0 \\ -\frac{1}{6} & \frac{1}{3} & -\frac{1}{2} \\ \frac{1}{3} & \frac{1}{3} & 0 \end{bmatrix}$

21. $\begin{bmatrix} 1 & 2 \\ -1 & 0 \end{bmatrix}$

22. $(-4, -7)$

23. $\begin{bmatrix} 2 \\ 2 \end{bmatrix}$

24. $\begin{bmatrix} 2 & 1 \\ 3 & 2 \end{bmatrix}$

25. no unique solution

26. no unique solution

Answers

Chapter Review (continued)

27. $\begin{bmatrix} 0 & -5 & -2 \\ 5 & 4 & 9 \end{bmatrix}$

28. $\begin{bmatrix} -3 & 2 & -1 \\ 1 & 0 & 5 \end{bmatrix}$

29. $\begin{bmatrix} 1 & 0 & 5 \\ 3 & -2 & 1 \end{bmatrix}$

30. $\begin{bmatrix} 1.5 & -1 & 0.5 \\ 0.5 & 0 & 2.5 \end{bmatrix}$

31. $\begin{bmatrix} 6 & -4 & 2 \\ 2 & 0 & 10 \end{bmatrix}$

32. $\begin{bmatrix} 1 & 0 & 5 \\ -3 & 2 & -1 \end{bmatrix}$

33. $\langle -1, 8 \rangle$; about 8.1

34. $\langle 7, -5 \rangle$; about 8.6

35. $\langle -9, 12 \rangle$; 15

36. $\langle -2, 14 \rangle$; about 14.1

37. $\langle -8, 14 \rangle$; about 16.1

38. $\langle -4, 21 \rangle$; about 21.4

39. 0; normal

40. 0; normal

12-5 Geometric Transformations

Quick Review

A change made to a figure is a transformation. The original figure is the **preimage**, and the transformed figure is the **image**. A translation slides a figure without changing its size or shape. A **dilation** changes the size of a figure. You can use matrix addition to translate a figure and scalar multiplication to dilate a figure.

You can use multiplication by the appropriate matrix to perform transformations that are specific reflections or **rotations**. For example, to reflect a figure across the y-axis, multiply by $\begin{bmatrix} -1 & 0 \\ 0 & 1 \end{bmatrix}$.

Example

A triangle has vertices $A(3, 2)$, $B(1, -2)$, and $C(1, 2)$. What are the coordinates after a 90° rotation?

$$\begin{bmatrix} 0 & -1 \\ 1 & 0 \end{bmatrix}\begin{bmatrix} 3 & 1 & 1 \\ 2 & -2 & 2 \end{bmatrix} = \begin{bmatrix} -2 & 2 & -2 \\ 3 & 1 & 1 \end{bmatrix}$$

The coordinates are $(-2, 3)$, $(2, 1)$, and $(-2, 1)$.

Exercises

In matrix form, write the coordinates of each image of the triangle with vertices $A(3, 1)$, $B(-2, 0)$, and $C(1, 5)$.

27. a translation 3 units left and 4 units up

28. a reflection across the y-axis

29. a reflection across the line $y = x$

30. a dilation half the original size

31. a dilation twice the original size

32. a rotation of 270°

12-6 Vectors

Quick Review

A **vector** has both **magnitude** and **direction**. It is a directed line segment that you can describe using a pair of **initial** and **terminal** points. If a vector were in standard position with the initial point at $(0, 0)$, the component form would be $\langle a, b \rangle$ and the magnitude $|v| = \sqrt{a^2 + b^2}$ would give you the length.

Given two vectors $v = \langle v_1, v_2 \rangle$ and $w = \langle w_1, w_2 \rangle$, the **dot product** $v \cdot w$ is $v_1 w_1 + v_2 w_2$. If the dot product equals 0, then v and w are **normal**, or perpendicular, to each other.

Example

Are the vectors $\langle -1, 2 \rangle$ and $\langle 4, 2 \rangle$ normal?

$\langle -1, 2 \rangle \cdot \langle 4, 2 \rangle = (-1)(4) + (2)(2)$
$\qquad\qquad\qquad = -4 + 4 = 0$

The vectors are normal.

Exercises

Let $u = \langle -3, 4 \rangle$, $v = \langle 2, 4 \rangle$, and $w = \langle 4, -1 \rangle$. Write each resulting vector in component form and find the magnitude.

33. $u + v$ **34.** $w - u$

35. $3u$ **36.** $-2w + 3v$

37. $\frac{1}{2}v + 3u$ **38.** $-w + 3v + 2u$

Find the dot product of each pair of vectors and determine whether they are normal.

39. $\langle 4, -3 \rangle$ and $\langle -3, -4 \rangle$

40. $\begin{bmatrix} 1 \\ 7 \end{bmatrix}$ and $\begin{bmatrix} 14 \\ -2 \end{bmatrix}$

Chapter Test

 MathXL° for School
Go to PowerAlgebra.com

Do you know HOW?

Find each sum or difference.

1. $\begin{bmatrix} 4 & 7 \\ -2 & 1 \end{bmatrix} - \begin{bmatrix} -9 & 3 \\ 6 & 0 \end{bmatrix}$

2. $\begin{bmatrix} 4 & -5 & 1 \\ 10 & 7 & 4 \\ 21 & -9 & -6 \end{bmatrix} + \begin{bmatrix} -7 & -10 & 4 \\ 17 & 0 & 3 \\ -2 & -6 & 1 \end{bmatrix}$

Find each product.

3. $\begin{bmatrix} 2 & 6 \\ 1 & 0 \end{bmatrix}\begin{bmatrix} -1 & 5 \\ 3 & 1 \end{bmatrix}$ **4.** $2\begin{bmatrix} -8 & 5 & -1 \\ 0 & 9 & 7 \end{bmatrix}$

5. $\begin{bmatrix} 0 & 3 \\ -4 & 9 \end{bmatrix}\begin{bmatrix} -4 & 6 & 1 & 3 \\ 9 & -8 & 10 & 7 \end{bmatrix}$

Find the determinant of each matrix.

6. $\begin{bmatrix} 1 & 0 & 0 \\ 0 & 1 & 0 \\ 0 & 0 & 1 \end{bmatrix}$ **7.** $\begin{bmatrix} 2 & 3 & 0 \\ -1 & 1 & 0 \\ 4 & 2 & 1 \end{bmatrix}$

8. $\begin{bmatrix} 8 & -3 \\ 2 & 9 \end{bmatrix}$ **9.** $\begin{bmatrix} \frac{1}{2} & -3 \\ 1 & 0 \end{bmatrix}$

Find the inverse of each matrix, if it exists.

10. $\begin{bmatrix} 3 & 8 \\ -7 & 10 \end{bmatrix}$ **11.** $\begin{bmatrix} 0 & -5 \\ 9 & 6 \end{bmatrix}$

12. $\begin{bmatrix} 3 & 1 & 0 \\ 1 & -1 & 2 \\ 1 & 1 & 1 \end{bmatrix}$ **13.** $\begin{bmatrix} 1 & 1 & 2 \\ 2 & 1 & 3 \\ 2 & 1 & 1 \end{bmatrix}$

Solve each matrix equation.

14. $\begin{bmatrix} 3 & -8 \\ 10 & 5 \end{bmatrix} - X = \begin{bmatrix} 2 & 8 \\ -1 & 12 \end{bmatrix}$

15. $\begin{bmatrix} 3 & 2 \\ -1 & 5 \end{bmatrix}X = \begin{bmatrix} -10 & -11 \\ 26 & -36 \end{bmatrix}$

16. $2X - \begin{bmatrix} -2 & 0 \\ 1 & 4 \end{bmatrix} = \begin{bmatrix} 5 & 10 \\ -15 & 9 \end{bmatrix}$

Find the area of each triangle with the given vertices.

17. vertices at $(2, 3), (-3, -1), (0, 4)$

18. vertices at $(-2, -3), (5, 0), (-1, 4)$

Parallelogram $ABCD$ **has coordinates** $A(2, -1)$, $B(4, 3)$, $C(1, 5)$, **and** $D(-1, 1)$**. Write a matrix for the vertices after each transformation.**

19. a dilation by a factor of $\frac{2}{3}$

20. a translation 2 units right and 4 units down

21. a rotation of 270°   **22.** a reflection across $y = x$

Let $u = \langle -2, 1 \rangle$, $v = \langle 1, 5 \rangle$, **and** $w = \langle -1, -3 \rangle$**. Find each of the following.**

23. $u - v$ **24.** $3v$

25. $3w + 2u - 2w$ **26.** $3v - 2u$

27. $u \cdot v$ **28.** $v \cdot w$

Determine whether each pair of vectors is normal.

29. $\langle 3, -4 \rangle, \langle -8, 6 \rangle$ **30.** $\langle 5, -2 \rangle, \langle 3, 4 \rangle$

Do you UNDERSTAND?

31. Open-Ended Write a matrix that has no inverse.

32. Writing Explain how to determine whether two matrices can be multiplied and what the dimensions of the product matrix will be.

33. Shopping A local store is having a special promotion where all movies sell at the same price and all video games sell at another price. Suppose you buy 5 movies and 4 video games for $97.50 and your friend buys 3 movies and 6 video games for $103.50. Write a matrix equation to describe the purchases. Then solve the matrix equation to find the price of a movie and the price of a video game.

34. Writing Describe the advantages and disadvantages of writing a vector in matrix form instead of component form.

 PowerAlgebra.com   Chapter 12   Chapter Test   821

Answers

Chapter Test

1. $\begin{bmatrix} 13 & 4 \\ -8 & 1 \end{bmatrix}$

2. $\begin{bmatrix} -3 & -15 & 5 \\ 27 & 7 & 7 \\ 19 & -15 & -5 \end{bmatrix}$

3. $\begin{bmatrix} 16 & 16 \\ -1 & 5 \end{bmatrix}$

4. $\begin{bmatrix} -16 & 10 & -2 \\ 0 & 18 & 14 \end{bmatrix}$

5. $\begin{bmatrix} 27 & -24 & 30 & 21 \\ 97 & -96 & 86 & 51 \end{bmatrix}$

6. 1

7. 5

8. 78

9. 3

10. $\begin{bmatrix} \frac{5}{43} & -\frac{4}{43} \\ \frac{7}{86} & \frac{3}{86} \end{bmatrix}$

11. $\begin{bmatrix} \frac{2}{15} & \frac{1}{9} \\ -\frac{1}{5} & 0 \end{bmatrix}$

12. $\begin{bmatrix} \frac{3}{8} & \frac{1}{8} & -\frac{2}{8} \\ \frac{1}{8} & -\frac{3}{8} & \frac{6}{8} \\ \frac{2}{8} & \frac{2}{8} & \frac{4}{8} \end{bmatrix}$

13. $\begin{bmatrix} -1 & 0.5 & 0.5 \\ 2 & -1.5 & 0.5 \\ 0 & 0.5 & -0.5 \end{bmatrix}$

14. $\begin{bmatrix} 1 & -16 \\ 11 & -7 \end{bmatrix}$

15. $\begin{bmatrix} -6 & 1 \\ 4 & -7 \end{bmatrix}$

16. $\begin{bmatrix} \frac{3}{2} & 5 \\ -7 & \frac{13}{2} \end{bmatrix}$

17. $\frac{13}{2}$ units^2 or 6.5 units^2

18. 23 units^2

19. $\begin{bmatrix} \frac{4}{3} & \frac{8}{3} & \frac{2}{3} & -\frac{2}{3} \\ -\frac{2}{3} & 2 & \frac{10}{3} & \frac{2}{3} \end{bmatrix}$

20. $\begin{bmatrix} 4 & 6 & 3 & 1 \\ -5 & -1 & 1 & -3 \end{bmatrix}$

21. $\begin{bmatrix} -1 & 3 & 5 & 1 \\ 2 & 4 & 1 & -1 \end{bmatrix}$

22. $\begin{bmatrix} -1 & 3 & 5 & 1 \\ -2 & -4 & -1 & 1 \end{bmatrix}$

23. $\langle -3, -4 \rangle$

24. $\langle 3, 15 \rangle$

25. $\langle -5, -1 \rangle$

26. $\langle 7, 13 \rangle$

27. 3

28. −16

29. not normal

30. not normal

31. Answers may vary. Sample: $\begin{bmatrix} 1 & 2 \\ 1 & 2 \end{bmatrix}$

32. Answers may vary. Sample: Two matrices can be multiplied if and only if the number of columns of the first matrix equals the number of rows of the second matrix. The product matrix will have the same number of rows as the first matrix and the same number of columns as the second matrix.

33. $\begin{bmatrix} 5 & 4 \\ 3 & 6 \end{bmatrix}\begin{bmatrix} m \\ v \end{bmatrix} = \begin{bmatrix} 97.50 \\ 103.50 \end{bmatrix}$; movie: $9.50; video game: $12.50

34. Writing a vector in matrix form makes it easier to manipulate the vector mathematically; writing the vector in component form makes it easier to visualize the vector in space.

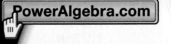 PowerAlgebra.com

MathXL for School

Prepare students for the Mid-Chapter Quiz and Chapter Test with online practice and review.

Item Number	Lesson	Content Standard
1	1-6	A.SSE.1.b
2	2-7	F.BF.3
3	2-8	F.IF.7.b
4	1-5	A.CED.1
5	3-3	A.REI.12
6	4-2	F.IF.8
7	4-2	F.IF.4
8	5-4	A.APR.1
9	6-7	F.BF.4.a
10	6-6	F.BF.1.b
11	8-6	A.REI.2
12	11-1	S.CP.9
13	12-3	N.VM.10
14	7-4	F.LE.4
15	9-5	A.SSE.4
16	11-3	S.CP.7
17	12-4	N.VM.8
18	7-3	F.BF.4
19	10-2	G.GPE.2
20	10-3	G.GPE.1
21	8-3	F.IF.7.d
22	10-4	G.GPE.3
23	8-3	F.IF.7.d
24	5-7	A.APR.5
25	9-5	F.IF.5
26	12-2	N.VM.6
27	11-5	S.MD.6

TIPS FOR SUCCESS

Some problems require you to find the equations of lines.

Which matrix equation is represented by the graph below?

TIP 1

Use the equation $y = mx + b$, where m represents the slope and b is the y-intercept.

A $\begin{bmatrix} 1 & -1 \\ 2 & -1 \end{bmatrix}\begin{bmatrix} x \\ y \end{bmatrix} = \begin{bmatrix} 1 \\ -2 \end{bmatrix}$

B $\begin{bmatrix} -1 & -1 \\ 1 & -1 \end{bmatrix}\begin{bmatrix} x \\ y \end{bmatrix} = \begin{bmatrix} 1 \\ -2 \end{bmatrix}$

C $\begin{bmatrix} -1 & -1 \\ 2 & -1 \end{bmatrix}\begin{bmatrix} x \\ y \end{bmatrix} = \begin{bmatrix} 1 \\ -2 \end{bmatrix}$

D $\begin{bmatrix} -1 & -1 \\ 2 & -1 \end{bmatrix}\begin{bmatrix} x \\ y \end{bmatrix} = \begin{bmatrix} 2 \\ 1 \end{bmatrix}$

TIP 2

Rewrite the equations as matrices in standard form.

Think It Through

The slope of line a is -1 and its y-intercept is $(0, -1)$.

The equation of line a is $y = -x - 1$.

As a matrix equation in standard form, the equation of line a is

$[-1 \quad -1]\begin{bmatrix} x \\ y \end{bmatrix} = [1]$.

The slope of line b is 2 and its y-intercept is $(0, 2)$.

The equation of line b is $y = 2x + 2$.

As a matrix equation in standard form, the equation of line b is

$[2 \quad -1]\begin{bmatrix} x \\ y \end{bmatrix} = [-2]$.

The correct answer is C.

Vocabulary Review

As you solve test items, you must understand the meanings of mathematical terms. Match each term with its mathematical meaning.

A. image

B. dilation

C. preimage

D. determinant

E. square matrix

I. a matrix with the same number of rows and columns

II. a figure after a transformation

III. a transformation that enlarges or reduces a figure

IV. a real number computed from the elements of a square matrix

V. a figure before a transformation

Multiple Choice

Read each question. Then write the letter of the correct answer on your paper.

1. If a person walks toward you, and the expression $|13 - 3t|$ represents their distance from you at time t, what does the 3 represent?

    A number of steps
    B total distance
    C the walking rate
    D number of minutes

2. The graph of $y = |x - 1|$ is translated up 4 units and to the right 3 units. Which equation represents the translated graph?

    F $y = |x - 3| + 4$
    G $y = |x - 4| + 4$
    H $y = |x - 4| - 3$
    I $y = |x + 2| + 4$

822 Chapter 12 Cumulative Standards Review

Answers

Cumulative Standards Review
A. II
B. III
C. V
D. IV
E. I
1. C
2. G

3. Which inequality is described by the graph below?

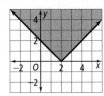

Ⓐ $y \le |x - 2|$ Ⓒ $y \ge |x - 2|$

Ⓑ $y \ge |x + 2|$ Ⓓ $y \ge |x| + 2$

4. Which of the following is the compound inequality that describes the range of the following function?

Ⓕ $-3 < y \le 0$

Ⓖ $-3 \le y < 3$

Ⓗ $0 \le y \le 3$

Ⓘ $5 \le y \le 6$

5. Which system is represented by the graph below?

Ⓐ $\begin{cases} 2y + 6 \ge x \\ y < -\frac{3}{2}x + 5 \end{cases}$ Ⓒ $\begin{cases} 2y - 6 \ge x \\ y < -\frac{3}{2}x + 5 \end{cases}$

Ⓑ $\begin{cases} 2y + 6 \ge x \\ y > -\frac{3}{2}x + 5 \end{cases}$ Ⓓ $\begin{cases} 2y + 6 \ge x \\ -y < \frac{3}{2}x + 5 \end{cases}$

6. The graph below shows a quadratic function. Which of the following equations is represented by the graph?

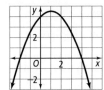

Ⓕ $y = x^2 - 2x - 8$

Ⓖ $y = -x^2 + x + 4$

Ⓗ $y = \frac{1}{2}x^2 + x + 8$

Ⓘ $y = -\frac{1}{2}x^2 + x + 4$

7. The graph of a quadratic function in the xy-plane opens downward and has x-intercepts at $x = -3$ and $x = 5$. For what x-value is the value of this function greatest?

Ⓐ $x = -3$ Ⓒ $x = 2$

Ⓑ $x = 1$ Ⓓ $x = 5$

8. The area of a rectangle is $6x^3 - 22x^2 + 23x - 5$. The width is $3x - 5$. What is the length?

Ⓕ $2x^2 - 4x + 1$

Ⓖ $2x^2 + 4x - 1$

Ⓗ $2x^2 + 1$

Ⓘ $2x^2 - x - 4$

9. Which relation is the inverse of $f(x) = (x - 3)^2$?

Ⓐ $g(x) = \dfrac{x^2}{(3x - 1)^2}$

Ⓑ $g(x) = \dfrac{1}{(3x - 1)^2}$

Ⓒ $g(x) = \pm\sqrt{x} + 3$

Ⓓ $g(x) = \pm\sqrt{x - 3}$

3. C
4. H
5. A
6. I
7. B
8. F
9. C

Answers

Cumulative Standards Review (continued)

10. 13

11. 1

12. 120

13. 17

14. 1.9

15. -255

16. $\frac{1}{20}$

17. 1

18. $f^{-1}(x) = \log_2 x + 1$

19. $x = \frac{1}{12} y^2$

20. $(x - 3)^2 + y^2 = 16$

21. [2] hole: $x = 1$; vertical asymptote: $x = -1$;
the factors of the denominator are
$x^2 - 1 = (x + 1)(x - 1)$, so there
are pts. of discontinuity at $x = \pm 1$.
Since the factors of the numerator are
$3x^2 - 2x - 1 = (3x + 1)(x - 1)$, and the
factor $(x - 1)$ is common and the factor
$(x + 1)$ is not, there is an asymptote at
$x = -1$ and a hole at $x = 1$.

   [1] asymptote mistaken for hole or vice versa
OR only one of the two found correctly OR
incomplete explanation

22. [2] $\frac{x^2}{4} + y^2 = 1$; since the center is at
the origin, the vertices are $(\pm\frac{4}{2}, 0)$
and the co-vertices are $(0, \pm\frac{2}{2})$. Using
$\frac{x^2}{a^2} + \frac{y^2}{b^2} = 1$, $a = \pm 2$ and $b = \pm 1$, so
$\frac{x^2}{4} + y^2 = 1$.

   [1] correct vertices and co-vertices, but
incorrect eq. OR incomplete explanation.

23. [2] vertical asymptotes: $x = 5$, $x = -3$;
horizontal asymptote: $y = 0$;
the factors of the denominator are
$x^2 - 2x - 15 = (x - 5)(x + 3)$ and there
are vertical asymptotes at the zeros, 5 and
-3. Since the degree of the numerator is
greater than that of the denominator, there
is also a horizontal asymptote at $y = 0$.

   [1] only two of the three asymptotes found OR
incomplete explanation

24. [2] $4320a^3$; using the Binomial Theorem and
Pascal's Triangle:

```
          1
        1   1
      1   2   1
    1   3   3   1
  1   4   6   4   1
1   5  10  10   5   1
```

$(3a + (-4))^5 = (3a)^5 + 5(3a)^4(-4)^1$
     $+ 10(3a)^3(-4)^2 + 10(3a)^2(-4)^3$
     $+ 5(3a)^1(-4)^4 + 1(-4)^5$
    $= 243a^5 - 1620a^4 + 4320a^3$
     $- 5760a^2 + 3840a - 1024$

---

10. Let $f(x) = 2x^2 + 3x - 1$ and $g(x) = x - 1$.
Evaluate $(g \cdot f)(2)$.

11. How many roots does the equation $\frac{2}{x^2} + \frac{1}{x} = 0$ have?

12. A box has 10 items inside. What is the number of
combinations possible when selecting 3 of the items?

13. What is the value of $\det\begin{bmatrix} 7 & -1 \\ 3 & 2 \end{bmatrix}$?

14. If $\log a = 0.6$, and $\log b = 0.7$, what is $\log a^2 b$?

15. What is the sum of the geometric series below?

$$\sum_{n=1}^{8} 3 \cdot (-2)^{n-1}$$

16. A and B are independent but not mutually exclusive
events. If $P(A) = \frac{1}{4}$ and $P(B) = \frac{1}{5}$, what is $P(A \text{ and } B)$?

17. What is the value of x in the solution of the matrix
equation below?

$$\begin{bmatrix} 5 & -3 \\ 2 & -1 \end{bmatrix}\begin{bmatrix} x \\ y \end{bmatrix} = \begin{bmatrix} 2 \\ 1 \end{bmatrix}$$

Short Response

18. Determine the function that is the inverse of
$f(x) = 2^{x-1}$.

19. Write the equation for the parabola with a focus of
$(3, 0)$ and a directrix $x = -3$.

20. What is the equation of the circle below?

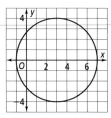

21. Describe the vertical asymptotes and holes for the
graph of the function $y = \frac{3x^2 - 2x - 1}{x^2 - 1}$.

---

22. What is an equation of an ellipse with height 2 meters
and width 4 meters? Assume that the center of the
ellipse is $(0, 0)$.

23. What are the asymptotes of the graph of
$y = \frac{x - 3}{x^2 - 2x - 15}$?

24. Use the binomial theorem to find the third term in
the expansion of $(3a - 4)^5$.

Extended Response

25. In a geometric sequence, $a_1 = 3$ and $a_5 = 768$.
Explain how to find a_2 and a_3.

26. A dietician wants to prepare a meal with 24 g of
protein, 27 g of fat, and 20 g of carbohydrates using the
three foods shown in the table.

Food	Protein	Fat	Carbohydrates
A	2 g/oz	3 g/oz	4 g/oz
B	3 g/oz	3 g/oz	1 g/oz
C	3 g/oz	3 g/oz	2 g/oz

   a. Set up a matrix equation for the data.
   b. Solve the matrix equation.
   c. How many ounces of each food are needed?

27. The coach of a high school debate team must choose 4
of the 6 members to represent the team at a state-wide
competition. Each of the team members is equally
qualified for the competition. Use probability concepts
to describe how the coach can make his decision fairly.
Describe why your method is fair.

---

   [1] one error in transcribing the
theorem

25. [4] $a_2 = \pm 12$, $a_3 = \pm 48$; find a_3
by calculating the geometric
mean of a_1 and a_5:
$a_3 = \pm\sqrt{768 \cdot 3} = \pm\sqrt{2304} = \pm 48$.
Next, find a_2 by calculating the
geometric mean of a_1 and a_3:
$a_2 = \pm\sqrt{3 \cdot 48} = \pm\sqrt{144} = \pm 12$.

   [3] correct method, but with one
computational error

   [2] only one of the values found

   [1] correct answers, without work
shown

26. [4] a. $\begin{bmatrix} 2 & 3 & 3 \\ 3 & 3 & 3 \\ 4 & 1 & 2 \end{bmatrix}\begin{bmatrix} A \\ B \\ C \end{bmatrix} = \begin{bmatrix} 24 \\ 27 \\ 20 \end{bmatrix}$

   b. $(3, 4, 2)$

   c. 3 oz of Food A, 4 oz of Food
B, 2 oz of Food C

   [3] correct method, but with one
computational error

---

   [2] matrix equation solved correctly,
but given improper set-up in (a)

   [1] correct answer, without work
shown

27. [4] Student describes a simulation
that simulates a random drawing
where there are 6 equally likely
outcomes, like rolling a number
cube or assigning the team
members a digit between 1 and
6 and using a random number
table to choose the 4 team
members.

   [3] describes a correct random
method, but the method does
not include at least six equally
likely events

   [2] describes a method that does not
use equally likely events

   [1] makes a simple statement
like "use a die," but does not
describe a method of use

Get Ready!

Lesson 8-3 ◆ **Analyzing Graphs of Rational Functions**

Find the vertical asymptotes and holes for the graph of each rational function.

1. $y = \dfrac{2}{x - 3}$

2. $y = \dfrac{x + 2}{(2x + 1)(x - 4)}$

Lesson 8-4 ◆ **Simplifying Complex Fractions**

Simplify each complex fraction.

3. $\dfrac{\frac{2}{a}}{\frac{1}{b}}$

4. $\dfrac{5 + \frac{1}{2}}{2 - \frac{1}{5}}$

5. $\dfrac{\frac{3}{c + d}}{2}$

6. $\dfrac{\frac{1}{4}}{\frac{4}{c}}$

7. $\dfrac{\frac{2}{3}}{\frac{6}{c + 4}}$

8. $\dfrac{\frac{4}{x}}{\frac{2}{8}}$

9. $\dfrac{3 - \frac{1}{2}}{\frac{7}{6}}$

10. $\dfrac{\frac{9}{m - n}}{\frac{3}{2m - 2n}}$

Lesson 9-1 ◆ **Writing Formulas for Sequences**

Find the next two terms in each sequence. Write a formula for the *n*th term. Identify each formula as *explicit* or *recursive*.

11. 16, 13, 10, 7, . . .

12. −1, −8, −27, −64, −125, . . .

Lesson 10-6 ◆ **Translating Conic Sections**

Write an equation for each conic section. Then sketch the graph.

13. circle with center at $(1, -4)$ and radius 4

14. ellipse with center at $(2, 5)$, vertices at $(5, 5)$ and $(-1, 5)$, and co-vertices at $(2, 3)$ and $(2, 7)$

15. parabola with vertex at $(0, -3)$ and focus at $(0, 5)$

16. hyperbola with center at $(6, 1)$, one focus at $(6, 6)$, and one vertex at $(6, -2)$

 Looking Ahead Vocabulary

17. If you were to graph the average monthly rainfall for your community for the past 5 years, you would very likely graph a *periodic function*. Why do you think it is called a periodic function?

18. Graph the month-by-month attendance at one of these larger National Parks—The Everglades, Grand Canyon, Yellowstone, Yosemite—for several years. The pattern that results may resemble a *sine curve*. Describe the features of this curve.

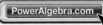

Get Ready!

Assign this diagnostic assessment to determine if students have the prerequisite skills for Chapter 13.

Lesson	Skill
8-3	Analyzing Graphs of Rational Functions
8-5	Simplifying Complex Fractions
9-1	Writing Formulas for Sequences
10-6	Translating Conic Sections

To remediate students, select from these resources (available for every lesson).
- Online Problems (PowerAlgebra.com)
- Reteaching (All-in-One Teaching Resources)
- Practice (All-in-One Teaching Resources)

Why Students Need These Skills

ANALYZING GRAPHS OF RATIONAL FUNCTIONS
Students apply techniques for analyzing graphs of rational functions to analyze graphs of trigonometric functions and other periodic functions.

SIMPLIFYING COMPLEX FRACTIONS
Simplifying complex fractions is essential to finding the exact value of reciprocal trigonometric functions.

WRITING FORMULAS FOR SEQUENCES
Students will extend their skill of writing formulas for sequences by finding formulas for trigonometric functions.

TRANSLATING CONIC SECTIONS
Translating conic sections is closely related to translating trigonometric functions.

Looking Ahead Vocabulary

PERIODIC FUNCTION Ask students what they understand by the word *periodic* or by its root word *period*.

CYCLE Ask students what they understand by the word *cycle*, or *cyclic*.

Answers

Get Ready!

1. vert. asymptote: $x = 3$

2. vert. asymptotes: $x = -\frac{1}{2}$ and $x = 4$

3. $\frac{2b}{a}$ **4.** $\frac{55}{18}$ **5.** $\frac{3}{2(c + d)}$ **6.** $\frac{c}{16}$

7. $\frac{c + 4}{9}$ **8.** $\frac{16}{x}$ **9.** $\frac{15}{7}$ **10.** 6

11. 4, 1; $a_n = 19 - 3n$, explicit or $a_1 = 16$, $a_n = a_{n-1} - 3$, recursive

12. −216, −343; $a_n = -n^3$, explicit

13. $(x - 1)^2 + (y + 4)^2 = 16$;

14. $\dfrac{(x - 2)^2}{9} + \dfrac{(y - 5)^2}{4} = 1$;

15. $y = \frac{1}{32}x^2 - 3$;

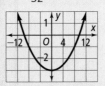

16. $\dfrac{(y - 1)^2}{9} - \dfrac{(x - 6)^2}{16} = 1$;

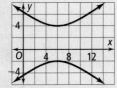

17. Answers may vary. Sample: Similar data tends to recur after a certain period has lapsed. In this case, 12 months.

18. Check students' work.

Chapter 13 Overview

Chapter 13 expands on students' understandings and skills related to periodic functions and trigonometry. In this chapter, students will develop the answers to the Essential Questions posed on the opposite page as they learn the concepts and skills bulleted below.

BIG idea **Modeling**

ESSENTIAL QUESTION How can you model periodic behavior?
- Students will identify and explore periodic behavior.
- Students will graph periodic functions.

BIG idea **Function**

ESSENTIAL QUESTION What function has as its graph a sine curve with amplitude 4, period π, and a minimum at the origin?
- Students will write the formulas of trigonometric functions.
- Students will find amplitude, period, minimums, and maximums of trigonometric functions.

BIG idea **Function**

ESSENTIAL QUESTION If you know the value of $\sin \theta$, how can you find $\cos \theta$, $\tan \theta$, $\csc \theta$, $\sec \theta$, and $\cot \theta$?
- Students will find the value of the reciprocal trigonometric functions based on the corresponding trigonometric functions.

My Math Video

@ Content Standards

Following are the standards covered in this chapter. Modeling standards are indicated by a star symbol (★)

CONCEPTUAL CATEGORY Functions

  Domain Interpreting Functions F.IF

    Cluster Interpret functions that arise in applications in terms of the context. (Standard F.IF.4)
    LESSONS 13-1, 13-4, 13-5

    Cluster Analyze functions using different representations (Standard F.IF.7.e★)
    LESSONS 13-4, 13-5, 13-6, 13-7, 13-8

  Domain Trigonometric Functions F.TF

    Cluster Extend the domain of trigonometric functions using the unit circle. (Standards F.TF.1, F.TF.2)
    LESSONS 13-3, 13-4, 13-5, 13-6

    Cluster Model periodic phenomena with trigonometric functions (Standard F.TF.5★)
    LESSONS 13-1, 13-4, 13-5, 13-6, 13-7

CHAPTER 13 Periodic Functions and Trigonometry

PowerAlgebra.com

Your place to get all things digital

VIDEO Download videos connecting math to your world.

VOCABULARY Math definitions in English and Spanish

SOLVE IT! The online Solve It will get you in gear for each lesson.

DYNAMIC ACTIVITIES Interactive! Vary numbers, graphs, and figures to explore math concepts.

ONLINE PROBLEMS Online access to stepped-out problems aligned to Common Core

ONLINE HOMEWORK Get and view your assignments online.

MathXL FOR SCHOOL Extra practice and review online

@ DOMAINS
- Trigonometric Functions
- Interpreting Functions

I'm going to help you learn about periodic functions and trigonometry. You have already seen periodic phenomena, like the phases of the moon.

How does geometric measurement relate to trigonometry? What is a radian, and how do you use radian measure? How do you write and graph functions to describe periodic data? You will learn how in this chapter.

Vocabulary

English/Spanish Vocabulary Audio Online:

English	Spanish
amplitude, *p. 830*	amplitud
central angle, *p. 844*	ángulo central
cosine, *p. 838*	coseno
cycle, *p. 828*	ciclo
midline, *p. 830*	línea media
period, *p. 828*	período
periodic function, *p. 828*	función periódica
phase shift, *p. 875*	cambio de fase
radian, *p. 844*	radián
sine, *p. 838*	seno
tangent, *p. 868*	tangente
unit circle, *p. 838*	círculo unitario

PowerAlgebra.com

Chapter 13 Overview

Use these online assets to engage your students. These include support for the Solve It and step-by-step solutions for Problems.

 Show the student-produced video demonstrating relevant and engaging applications of the new concepts in the chapter.

 Find online definitions for new terms in English and Spanish.

 Start each lesson with an attention-getting Problem. View the Problem online with helpful hints.

My Math Video

Use this photo to introduce the concept of periodic functions. The lunar cycle is the moon's continuous orbit around the earth. The pattern of phase changes is the following:

New
Waxing Crescent
First Quarter
Waxing Gibbous
Full
Waning Gibbous
Third Quarter
Waning Crescent
New

Q Why can you use the pattern of phase changes to predict which phase change will occur next? **[Since the phases occur in a cycle, they always happen in the same order.]**

EXTENSION

Have students research the phases of the moon to determine how the relationships among the earth, sun, and moon cause the lunar cycle.

BIG ideas

1 Modeling

Essential Question How can you model periodic behavior?

2 Function

Essential Question What function has as its graph a sine curve with amplitude 4, period π, and a minimum at the origin?

3 Function

Essential Question If you know the value of $\sin\theta$, how can you find $\cos\theta$, $\tan\theta$, $\csc\theta$, $\sec\theta$, and $\cot\theta$?

Chapter Preview

PowerAlgebra.com   Chapter 13 Periodic Functions and Trigonometry   827

 Increase students' depth of knowledge with interactive online activities.

 Show Problems from each lesson solved step by step. Instant replay allows students to go at their own pace when studying online.

 Assign homework to individual students or to an entire class.

 Prepare students for the Mid-Chapter Quiz and Chapter Test with online practice and review.

Understanding by Design principles were central to the development of the Big Ideas and the Essential Understandings. These will help your students build a structure on which to make connections to prior learning.

Modeling

BIG idea Many real-world mathematical problems can be represented algebraically. These representations can lead to algebraic solutions. A function that models a real-world situation can then be used to make estimates or predictions about future occurrences.

ESSENTIAL UNDERSTANDINGS

13-1 Periodic behavior is behavior that repeats over intervals of constant length.

13-2 The measure of an angle in standard position is the input for two important functions. The outputs are the coordinates (called *cosine* and *sine*) of the point on the terminal side of the angle that is 1 unit from the origin.

13-3 An angle with a full circle rotation measures 2π radians. An angle with a semicircle rotation measures π radians.

13-7 You can translate periodic functions in the same way that you translate other functions.

Function

BIG idea A function is a relationship between variables in which each value of the input variable is associated with a unique value of the output variable. Functions can be represented in a variety of ways, such as graphs, tables, equations, or words. Each representation is particularly useful in certain situations. Some important families of functions are developed through transformations of the simplest form of the function.

ESSENTIAL UNDERSTANDINGS

13-2 The measure of an angle in standard position is the input for two important functions. The outputs are the coordinates (called *cosine* and *sine*) of the point on the terminal side of the angle that is 1 unit from the origin.

13-3 An angle with a full circle rotation measures 2π radians. An angle with a semicircle rotation measures π radians.

13-4 As the terminal side of an angle rotates about the origin (beginning at 0°), its sine value on the unit circle increases from 0 to 1, decreases from 1 to −1, and then increases back to 0.

13-5 As the terminal side of an angle rotates about the origin (beginning at 0°), its cosine value on the unit circle decreases from 1 to −1, and then increases back to 1.

13-6 The tangent function has infinitely many points of discontinuity with a vertical asymptote at each point. Its range is all real numbers. Its period is π, half that of both the sine and cosine functions.

13-7 You can translate periodic functions in the same way that you translate other functions.

13-8 Cosine, sine, and tangent have reciprocals. Cosine and *secant* are reciprocals as are sine and *cosecant*. Tangent and *cotangent* are also reciprocals.

Periodic Functions

A **periodic function** repeats a pattern of outputs at regular intervals.

Example: The graph below is the graph of a periodic function.

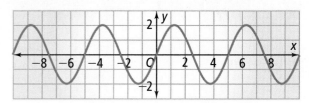

A **cycle** is a complete pattern of outputs of a periodic function. A cycle may begin at any point on the graph of a function.

Example: One cycle of the function above is the set of *y*-values that correspond to the *x*-values between $x = 0$ and $x = 5$.

The **period** of a periodic function is the horizontal length of one cycle.

Example: One cycle of the function above begins and ends at $x = 0$ and $x = 5$, respectively, so the period of the function is $5 - 0 = 5$.

The **amplitude** of a periodic function is half the difference between the maximum and minimum output values of the function.

Example: The maximum value of the function above is 2 and the minimum value is −2.

$$\text{amplitude} = \tfrac{1}{2}(\text{maximum value} - \text{minimum value})$$

$$= \tfrac{1}{2}(2 - (-2))$$

$$= \tfrac{1}{2}(4)$$

$$= 2$$

Common Errors With Periodic Functions

- Students sometimes think that a function whose graph repeats a shape is periodic even if the *y*-values are different. Emphasize that the pattern of *y*-values must repeat.
- When finding the amplitude, students sometimes find the difference between the maximum and minimum values but forget to divide them in half. Explain that the amplitude is half the distance between the values.
- Make sure students understand the difference between a cycle and the period: the cycle is the pattern of *y*-values, while the period is the horizontal length of the cycle.

© Mathematical Practices

Use appropriate tools strategically. Graphing calculators are used throughout the chapter to facilitate graphing and to solve trigonometric equations in real-world problems, but there is still a strong emphasis on paper-and-pencil computations using triangle ratios and unit circle coordinates.

The Sine Function

Definition

The sine function is a periodic function with a period of 2π and amplitude of 1. It can be defined as a ratio of sides of a right triangle (shown in the next chapter), as a Taylor polynomial function (in advanced math and calculus) and as the y-value of the terminal side of angles rotating about the origin of the unit circle.

Transformations

Transformations of the sine function affect the period and amplitude of the function.

For $y = a \sin b\theta$, with $a \neq 0$ and $b > 0$, θ in radians,
- $|a|$ is the amplitude
- b is the number of cycles in the interval from 0 to 2π
- $\frac{2\pi}{b}$ is the period.

Example: Graph $y = 2 \sin \frac{1}{2}\theta$ on the interval from 0 to 4π. What are the amplitude and period?

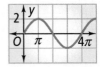

The amplitude is 2 and the period is 4π.

Translations

The sine function can be translated like other functions. A horizontal translation is called a **phase shift**. Translations do not change either the period or amplitude of a function.

For $y = a \sin b(x - h) + k$,
- h is a phase shift (horizontal shift)
- k is a vertical shift.

Example: Identify the translations of $y = 3 \sin 2(x - \pi) + 1$ from the parent function. What is the phase shift?

The function is translated up one unit vertically and π units to the right. The phase shift is π.

Common Errors With the Sine Function

Translating Sine Functions Students sometimes get confused over which directions to translate sine functions. Draw parallels between translating sine functions and other functions that they are more familiar with, such as linear and quadratic functions.

© Mathematical Practices

Reason abstractly and quantitatively. Look for and make use of structure. Function transformations are revisited with families of trigonometric functions, which are analyzed algebraically, graphically, and numerically with tables. Sine and cosine functions are used to model periodic behavior.

Finding Values of Trigonometric Functions Geometrically

You can use the unit circle to find the exact value of a trigonometric function at some values.

Sine and Cosine Functions

For an angle in standard position with measure θ, the sine of θ is the y-coordinate of the point at which the terminal side of the angle intersects the unit circle. The cosine of θ is the x-coordinate. You can find the exact value for angles that are multiples of 30° or 45° ($\frac{\pi}{6}$ or $\frac{\pi}{4}$ radians).

To find the sine and cosine of an angle, sketch the angle in standard position on the unit circle and determine where the terminal side intersects the circle.

Example: What are sin 120° and cos 120°?

Sketch the unit circle and identify $P(x, y)$:

In a 30°-60°-90° triangle, the shorter leg is half the hypotenuse and the longer leg is $\sqrt{3}$ times the shorter leg, so $\sin 120° = \frac{\sqrt{3}}{2}$ and $\cos 120° = -\frac{1}{2}$.

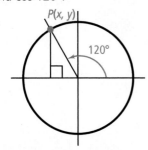

Tangent Functions

For an angle θ in standard position whose terminal side intersects the unit circle at (x, y), the tangent of θ is defined as the ratio $\frac{y}{x}$. Thus to find $\tan \theta$, sketch the unit circle and identify $P(x, y)$. $\tan \theta = \frac{y}{x}$.

Reciprocal Trigonometric Functions

The reciprocal trigonometric functions are defined using the reciprocals of sine, cosine, and tangent.

By definition,
$\csc \theta = \frac{1}{\sin \theta}$, $\sec \theta = \frac{1}{\cos \theta}$, and $\cot \theta = \frac{1}{\tan \theta}$.
Thus the exact values as found on the unit circle are:
$\csc \theta = \frac{1}{y}$, $\sec \theta = \frac{1}{x}$, and $\cot \theta = \frac{x}{y}$.

Common Errors Finding Values of Trigonometric Functions Graphically

Errors occur when students try to find the exact value of trigonometric functions for angles other than multiples of 30° or 45°. To find good estimates they should use a calculator.

© Mathematical Practices

Attend to precision. Look for and express regularity in repeated reasoning. A rich variety of exercises gives students ample familiarity with unit circle computations and with the analysis of the six trigonometric functions and their families.

PERIODIC FUNCTIONS AND TRIGONOMETRY
Pacing and Assignment Guide

		TRADITIONAL			BLOCK
Lesson	Teaching Day(s)	Basic	Average	Advanced	Block
13-1	1	Problems 1–2 Exs. 7–15, 37–49	Problems 1–2 Exs. 7–13 odd, 37–49	Problems 1–2 Exs. 7–17 odd, 19–49	**Day 1** Problems 1–4 Exs. 7–17 odd, 19–34, 37–49
	2	Problems 3–4 Exs. 16–18, 21–26, 28–34 even	Problems 3–4 Exs. 15, 17, 19–34		
13-2	1	Problems 1–3 Exs. 7–25, 60–74	Problems 1–3 Exs. 7–25 odd, 60–74	Problems 1–3 Exs. 7–25 odd, 60–74	**Day 2** Problems 1–5 Exs. 7–33 odd, 34–52, 60–74
	2	Problems 4–5 Exs. 26–33, 37–41, 47–52	Problems 4–5 Exs. 27–33 odd, 34–52	Problems 4–5 Exs. 27–33 odd, 34–59	
13-3	1	Problems 1–2 Exs. 6–25, 54–68	Problems 1–2 Exs. 7–25 odd, 54–68	Problems 1–2 Exs. 7–25 odd, 54–68	**Day 3** Problems 1–4 Exs. 7–33 odd, 35–50, 54–68
	2	Problems 3–4 Exs. 26–34, 35–49 odd	Problems 3–4 Exs. 27–33 odd, 35–50	Problems 3–4 Exs. 27–33 odd, 35–53	
13-4	1	Problems 1–3 Exs. 6–14, 55–69	Problems 1–3 Exs. 7–13 odd, 55–69	Problems 1–3 Exs. 7–13 odd, 55–69	**Day 4** Problems 1–6 Exs. 7–29 odd, 31–47, 55–69
	2	Problems 4–6 Exs. 15–30, 33–39 odd, 47	Problems 4–6 Exs. 15–29 odd, 31–47	Problems 4–6 Exs. 15–29 odd, 31–54	
13-5	1	Problems 1–2 Exs. 7–15, 46–65	Problems 1–4 Exs. 7–25 odd, 27–42, 46–65	Problems 1–4 Exs. 7–25 odd, 27–65	**Day 5** Problems 1–4 Exs. 7–25 odd, 27–42, 46–65
	2	Problems 3–4 Exs. 16–26, 34–37, 42			
13-6	1	Problems 1–3 Exs. 8–29, 35–47 odd, 52–68	Problems 1–3 Exs. 9–29 odd, 30–48, 52–68	Problems 1–3 Exs. 9–29 odd, 30–68	Problems 1–3 Exs. 9–29 odd, 30–48, 52–68
13-7	1	Problems 1–3 Exs. 6–26, 55–71	Problems 1–6 Exs. 7–39 odd, 40–48, 55–71	Problems 1–6 Exs. 7–39 odd, 40–71	**Day 6** Problems 1–6 Exs. 7–39 odd, 40–48, 55–71
	2	Problems 4–6 Exs. 27–40, 42–44, 46			
13-8	1	Problems 1–3 Exs. 9–28, 65–80	Problems 1–5 Exs. 9–37 odd, 38–61, 65–80	Problems 1–5 Exs. 9–37 odd, 38–80	Problems 1–5 Exs. 9–37 odd, 38–61, 65–80
	2	Problems 4–5 Exs. 29–37, 38–42 even, 48–52			
Review	1	Chapter 13 Review	Chapter 13 Review	Chapter 13 Review	**Day 7** Chapter 13 Review Chapter 13 Test
Assess	1	Chapter 13 Test	Chapter 13 Test	Chapter 13 Test	
Total		**17 Days**	**14 Days**	**13 Days**	**7 Days**

Note: Pacing does not include Concept Bytes and other feature pages.

Resources

KEY

I = Interactive asset at PowerAlgebra.com
E = Editable master at PowerAlgebra.com
P = Available in Print
M = Master at PowerAlgebra.com
✓ = CD-ROM

	For the Chapter	13-1	13-2	13-3	13-4	13-5	13-6	13-7	13-8
Planning									
Teacher Center Online Planner & Grade Book	I	I	I	I	I	I	I	I	I
Interactive Learning & Guided Instruction									
My Math Video	I								
Solve It!		I M	I M	I M	I M	I M	I M	I M	I M
Student Companion		P M	P M	P M	P M	P M	P M	P M	P M
Vocabulary Support		I P M	I P M	I P M	I P M	I P M	I P M	I P M	I P M
Got It? Support		I P	I P	I P	I P	I P	I P	I P	I P
Dynamic Activity					I	I	I	I	
Online Problems		I	I	I	I	I	I	I	I
Additional Problems		M	M	M	M	M	M	M	M
English Language Learner Support (TR)		E P M	E P M	E P M	E P M	E P M	E P M	E P M	E P M
Activities, Games, and Puzzles		E M	E M	E M	E M	E M	E M	E M	E M
Teaching With TI Technology With CD-ROM					✓ P			✓ P	
TI-Nspire™ Support CD-ROM		✓	✓	✓	✓	✓	✓	✓	✓
Lesson Check & Practice									
Student Companion		P M	P M	P M	P M	P M	P M	P M	P M
Lesson Check Support		I P	I P	I P	I P	I P	I P	I P	I P
Practice and Problem Solving Workbook		P	P	P	P	P	P	P	P
Think About a Plan (TR)		E P M	E P M	E P M	E P M	E P M	E P M	E P M	E P M
Practice Form G (TR)		E P M	E P M	E P M	E P M	E P M	E P M	E P M	E P M
Standardized Test Prep (TR)		P M	P M	P M	P M	P M	P M	P M	P M
Practice *Form K* (TR)		E P M	E P M	E P M	E P M	E P M	E P M	E P M	E P M
Extra Practice	E M								
Find the Errors!	M								
Enrichment (TR)		E P M	E P M	E P M	E P M	E P M	E P M	E P M	E P M
Answers and Solutions CD-ROM	✓	✓	✓	✓	✓	✓	✓	✓	✓
Assess & Remediate									
ExamView CD-ROM	✓	✓	✓	✓	✓	✓	✓	✓	✓
Lesson Quiz		I M	I M	I M	I M	I M	I M	I M	I M
Quizzes and Tests *Form G* (TR)	E P M				E P M				E P M
Quizzes and Tests *Form K* (TR)	E P M				E P M				E P M
Reteaching (TR)		E P M	E P M	E P M	E P M	E P M	E P M	E P M	E P M
Performance Tasks (TR)	P M								
Cumulative Review (TR)	P M								
Progress Monitoring Assessments	I P M								

(TR) Available in All-In-One Teaching Resources

1 Interactive Learning

Solve It!

PURPOSE To recognize and describe predictable and repeatable behaviors

PROCESS Students may imagine each situation and look for patterns.

FACILITATE

Q How long does it take Earth to complete one orbit about the Sun? [$365\frac{1}{4}$ days]

Q What is the function of the heart? [**Its rhythmic contractions pump blood.**]

Q What factors determine the repetitive behavior of ocean waves? [**constant pull of moon's gravity on Earth, interaction of wind and water, water and land**]

ANSWER See Solve It in Answers on next page.

CONNECT THE MATH The images in the Solve It capture four behaviors that have unique cyclical patterns. In this lesson students will identify a cyclical function from its graph and describe its cyclical nature in terms of its period and amplitude.

2 Guided Instruction

Problem 1

Q What is another way to determine the period of this function? [**Start at a minimum value and find the next minimum value that completes the cycle.**]

Q If the x-coordinate of the start of one period of this function is x_1, what is the x-coordinate of the end of that period in terms of x_1? [$x_1 + 4$]

Objectives To identify cycles and periods of periodic functions
To find the amplitude of periodic functions

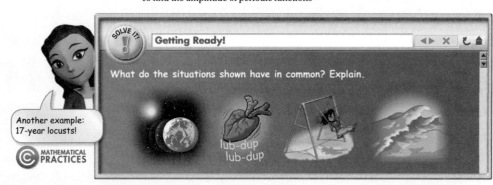

Another example: 17-year locusts!

© MATHEMATICAL PRACTICES

Getting Ready!

What do the situations shown have in common? Explain.

lub-dup
lub-dup

Lesson Vocabulary
• periodic function
• cycle
• period
• amplitude

A **periodic function** is a function that repeats a pattern of y-values (outputs) at regular intervals. One complete pattern is a **cycle**. A cycle may begin at any point on the graph of the function. The **period** of a function is the horizontal length—the distance along the x-axis—of one cycle. The x-value in a periodic function often represents time.

Essential Understanding Periodic behavior is behavior that repeats over intervals of constant length.

© **Problem 1** Identifying Cycles and Periods

Analyze the periodic function below. Identify the cycle in two different ways. What is the period of the function?

Think
Is there a good point at which to start the cycle?
If you start at the maximum value, it is easy to tell when you have completed the cycle.

Begin at any point on the graph. Trace one complete cycle.

one cycle   one cycle

period   period

The beginning and ending x-values of each cycle determine the period of the function.

One cycle begins at $x = 2$ and ends at $x = 6$; $6 - 2 = 4$, so the period of the function is 4.

13-1 Preparing to Teach

BIG idea Modeling
ESSENTIAL UNDERSTANDINGS

• Periodic behavior repeats over intervals of constant length.
• The amplitude of a periodic function is half the difference of the maximum and minimum values of the function.

Math Background

The graph of a periodic function repeats itself after a fixed interval, known as the period.

• Algebraically, as x changes at a constant rate, there is a pattern of y-values that repeats at regular intervals.
• Graphically, the graph is formed by repeated horizontal translations of the period.

Once a graph's function is identified as periodic, the period can be found by finding the difference in x-values of one whole period. Although the x-value of any point on the graph can be used, it is often easier to use a maximum or minimum value.

Another important characteristic of periodic functions is *amplitude*. The amplitude is half the difference between the maximum and minimum values of the function.

There are many real-world examples of periodic functions, including trigonometric functions, which students will analyze and graph later in this chapter.

© **Mathematical Practices**
Attend to precision. Students will define and make explicit use of terms relating to periodic functions. They will also identify periodic functions based on graphs of data.

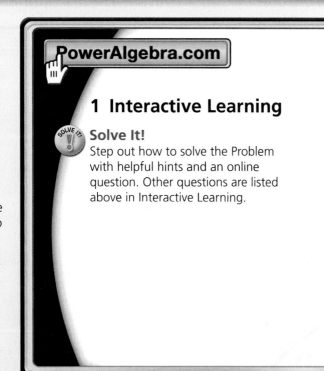

PowerAlgebra.com

1 Interactive Learning

Solve It!
Step out how to solve the Problem with helpful hints and an online question. Other questions are listed above in Interactive Learning.

Got It? **1.** Analyze each periodic function. Identify the cycle in two different ways. What is the period of the function?

a.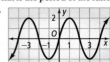

b.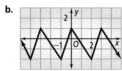

You can analyze the graph of a function to determine if the function is periodic.

Think

Do the *y*-values of the function repeat?
No; there is a repeating pattern but the actual *y*-values do not repeat.

© **Problem 2** **Identifying Periodic Functions**

Is the function periodic? If it is, what is its period?

Ⓐ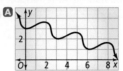

Although the graph shows similar curves, the *y*-values from one section do not repeat in other sections. The function is not periodic.

Ⓑ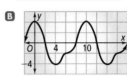

The pattern of *y*-values in one section repeats exactly in other sections. The function is periodic.

Find points at the beginning and end of one cycle. Subtract the *x*-values of the points: $10 - 0 = 10$. The pattern in the graph repeats every 10 units, so its period is 10.

 Got It? **2.** Is the function periodic? If it is, what is its period?

a.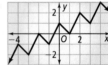

b.

c. Reasoning If the period of a function is 4 seconds, how many cycles does it have in a minute? What is the period of a function that has 180 cycles per minute (for example, a point on a spinning wheel)? That has 440 cycles per second (for example, a point on the end of a tuning fork)?

Got It?

There are at least two ways to determine the period of the function in 1a. Either calculate the absolute value of the difference of the *x*-coordinates of two consecutive maximum points: $|-3 - (1)| = 4$, or two consecutive minimum points: $|-1 - (3)| = 4$.

Problem 2

One way to determine whether a continuous or a discontinuous function is periodic is to see whether its graph is a horizontal translation of a basic cycle. If a function is continuous, check whether each cycle has the same maximum and minimum values for all *x* in the domain of the function.

Q The graph in 2A shows a repeating pattern; why is it not periodic? **[The function values do not actually repeat. They are continually decreasing]**

Q What are the coordinates of the endpoints of each interval within a cycle of the graph in 2B in terms of *x* and its period? **[*x* and (*x* + 10), or *x* and (*x* − 10)]**

Got It? ERROR PREVENTION

Students should recognize that the amplitude and period of a periodic function are always positive numbers. To avoid negative values, calculate the absolute value of the difference between corresponding *x*- or *y*-coordinates.

---

2 Guided Instruction

 Each Problem is worked out and supported online.

Problem 1
Identifying Cycles and Periods

Problem 2
Identifying Periodic Functions
Animated

Problem 3
Finding Amplitude and Midline of a Periodic Function
Animated

Problem 4
Using a Periodic Function to Solve a Problem
Animated

Support in Algebra 2 Companion
• Vocabulary
• Key Concepts
• Got It?

Answers

Solve It!

All these situations have a repeated pattern at regular intervals. The earth orbits the sun. A heart contracts and expands. A swing moves forward and back. The ocean moves up and down as waves pass.

Got It?

1. a. from $x = -3$ to $x = 1$ or from $x = 0$ to $x = 4$; 4

   b. from $x = -4$ to $x = -1$ or from $x = 0$ to $x = 3$; 3

2. a. no

   b. yes; 4

   c. 15 cycles; $\frac{1}{3}$ s; $\frac{1}{440}$ s

Problem 3 — VISUAL LEARNERS

Imagine drawing the line that is parallel to and equidistant from both lines through the maximum and minimum values of the graph in Problem 3. The amplitude of the function is the distance between the midline and either of the other two lines.

> **Q** What are the equations of the horizontal lines through the maximum and minimum values of this periodic function? **[$y = 4$ and $y = -2$]**
>
> **Q** What is the length of a vertical segment between the lines through the maximum and minimum values of the function? **[$|4 - (-2)| = 6$]**
>
> **Q** What is half the length of a vertical segment between the lines through the maximum and minimum values of this function? **[3, which is also the amplitude of the function.]**
>
> **Q** Once you find the amplitude of the function, can you think of another way to find the equation of the midline? **[Subtract the amplitude from the maximum value or add the amplitude to the minimum value.]**

Got It? — VISUAL LEARNERS

Have students line up the edge of a piece of paper to mark off the distance between one set of maximum values for one of the graphs. Then have them line up the marked paper with one set of minimum values so they can see that the distance is the same and is the period. Then have them line up the paper with some other point such as an x-intercept so they can see that no matter where you start, the function will be in the same position at the end of the length of the period.

The *amplitude* of a periodic function measures the amount of variation in the function values.

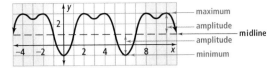

The **midline** is the horizontal line midway between the maximum and minimum values of a periodic function. The **amplitude** is half the difference between the maximum and minimum values of the function.

$$\text{amplitude} = \tfrac{1}{2}(\text{maximum value} - \text{minimum value})$$

 Problem 3 Finding Amplitude and Midline of a Periodic Function

What is the amplitude of the periodic function at the right? What is the equation of the midline?

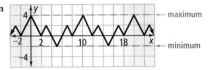

Think	Write
Use the definition of amplitude.	$\text{amplitude} = \tfrac{1}{2}(\text{maximum value} - \text{minimum value})$
Substitute 4 for the maximum and -2 for the minimum.	$= \tfrac{1}{2}[4 - (-2)]$
Subtract within parentheses and simplify.	$= \tfrac{1}{2}(6) = 3$
The midline is the horizontal line through the average of the maximum and minimum values.	$y = \tfrac{1}{2}(\text{maximum value} + \text{minimum value})$
Substitute the values and solve.	$= \tfrac{1}{2}[4 + (-2)]$ $= \tfrac{1}{2}(2) = 1$

✓ **Got It? 3.** What is the amplitude of each periodic function? What is the equation of the midline?

a. 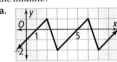 b.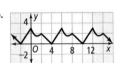

Additional Problems

1. Analyze the periodic function below. What is the period of this function?

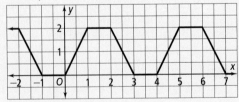

ANSWER 4

2. Is the function periodic? If it is periodic, what is its period?

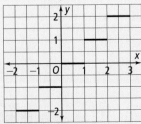

ANSWER no

3. What is the amplitude of this periodic function? What is the equation of the midline?

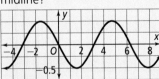

ANSWER 0.5; $y = 0$

4. Hours of Daylight The approximate number of hours of sunlight in a location can be predicted by knowing how many hours of sunshine occur on the summer and winter solstices. This graph shows the approximate number of hours of sunshine in a certain city given the two solstice values for a year. What are the amplitude, period, and the equation of the midline for this function?

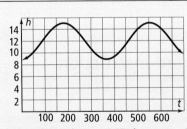

ANSWER 3 hours, 365 days, $y = 12$

You can model some data with periodic functions. The rotation of a Ferris wheel, the beating of a heart, and the movement of sound waves are all examples of real-world events that generate periodic data.

 Problem 4 Using a Periodic Function to Solve a Problem STEM

Sound Waves Sound is produced by periodic changes in air pressure called sound waves. The yellow graph in the digital wave display at the right shows the graph of a pure tone from a tuning fork. What are the period and the amplitude of the sound wave?

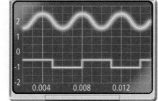

One cycle of the sound wave occurs from 0.004 s to 0.008 s. The maximum value of the function is 2.5, and the minimum value is 1.5.

Find the period.   Find the amplitude.

period = 0.008 − 0.004   amplitude = $\frac{1}{2}$(2.5 − 1.5)

= 0.004   = $\frac{1}{2}$(1) = $\frac{1}{2}$

The period of the sound wave is 0.004 s. The amplitude is $\frac{1}{2}$.

 Got It? 4. What are the period, the amplitude, and the equation of the midline of the green graph in the digital wave display in Problem 4?

Plan

How does identifying the cycle help you? The period is the horizontal length of the cycle. The amplitude is half the vertical length of the cycle.

 Lesson Check

Do you know HOW?

Determine if the function *is* or *is not* periodic. If it is, find the period.

1.
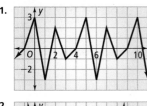

2.
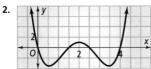

Do you UNDERSTAND?   MATHEMATICAL PRACTICES

3. **Writing** A sound wave can be graphed as a periodic function. Name two more real-world examples of periodic functions.

4. **Error Analysis** A student looked at the following function and wrote that the amplitude was 2. Describe and correct the student's error.

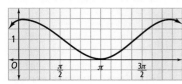

5. **Reasoning** Suppose f is a periodic function. The period of f is 5 and $f(1) = 2$. What are $f(6)$ and $f(11)$? Explain your reasoning.

6. A wave has a maximum of 6. If its midline is at $y = 1$, what is its minimum?

Problem 4

Q In the yellow graph, what is the value of x at the end of the cycle beginning at $x = 0.012$? **[0.012 + 0.004 = 0.016]**

Q How many times does the cycle repeat in one second? Explain. **[250 cycles per second, 1 ÷ 0.004 = 250]**

Got It?   EXTENSION

Q What are the period, amplitude, and equation of the midline of the graph of a pure-tone sound wave if one cycle of the sound wave occurs from 0.0016 s to 0.0101 s and its maximum and minimum are 6 and −6 respectively? **[period: 0.0085 s; amplitude: 6; midline: $y = 0$]**

3 Lesson Check

Do you know HOW?

• In Exercises 1 and 2, students may just try to calculate the period. Tell them to first identify the cycle to make sure it is periodic.

Do you UNDERSTAND?

• For Exercise 3, encourage students to brainstorm various applications that may exist as periodic functions; for example, the graphs of alternating current circuits and biorhythm functions.

Close

Q How does the graph of a function help you determine whether it is periodic? **[If there is a repeating pattern or cycle in the graph of a function, you can find its maximum and minimum values, period, and amplitude.]**

Answers

Got It? (continued)
3. a. 1.5; $y = -0.5$
   b. 1.5; $y = 0.5$
4. period: 0.006; amplitude: 0.25; $y = -0.75$

Lesson Check
1. periodic; 5
2. no
3. Answers may vary. Sample: hands of a clock, phases of the moon
4. The amplitude is not 2, but $\frac{2}{2} = 1$.
5. $f(6) = f(11) = 2$; for any x, $f(x + 5)$ will always equal $f(x)$ because the period is 5.
6. −4

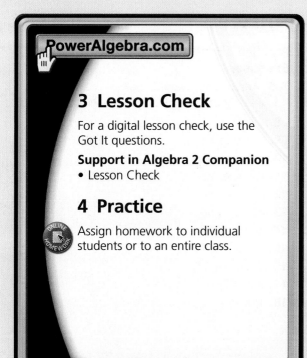

PowerAlgebra.com

3 Lesson Check

For a digital lesson check, use the Got It questions.

Support in Algebra 2 Companion
• Lesson Check

4 Practice

Assign homework to individual students or to an entire class.

4 Practice

ASSIGNMENT GUIDE

Basic: 7–18 all, 21–26, 28–34 even

Average: 7–17 odd, 19–34

Advanced: 7–17 odd, 19–36

Standardized Test Prep: 37–41

Mixed Review: 42–49

© **Mathematical Practices** are supported by exercises with red headings. Here are the Practices supported in this lesson:

MP 1: Make Sense of Problems Ex. 24
MP 2: Reason Abstractly Ex. 5, 26
MP 3: Construct Arguments Ex. 36d
MP 3: Communicate Ex. 3, 23
MP 3: Critique the Reasoning of Others Ex. 4

Applications exercises have blue headings. Exercise 36 supports MP 4: Model.

EXERCISE 25: Use the Think About a Plan worksheet in the **Practice and Problem Solving Workbook** (also available in the Teaching Resources in print and online) to further support students' development in becoming independent learners.

HOMEWORK QUICK CHECK

To check students' understanding of key skills and concepts, go over Exercises 8, 12, 24, 25, and 26.

 Practice and Problem-Solving Exercises © MATHEMATICAL PRACTICES

Ⓐ Practice Identify one cycle in two different ways. Then determine the period of the function. ◀ See Problem 1.

7. **8.** **9.**

Determine whether each function *is* or *is not* periodic. If it is, find the period. ◀ See Problem 2.

10. **11.** 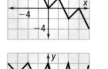 **12.**

13. **14.** 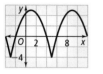 **15.**

Find the amplitude of each periodic function, and midline. ◀ See Problems 3 and 4.

16. 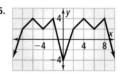 **17.** 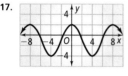 **18.**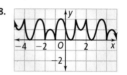

Ⓑ Apply Sketch the graph of a sound wave with the given period, amplitude, and midline.

19. period 0.02, amplitude 4, midline 6   **20.** period 0.005, amplitude 9, midline –5

21. Complete each statement with *x* or *y*.
 a. You use ■-values to compute the amplitude of a function.
 b. You use ■-values to compute the period of a function.

22. Which of the following could be represented by a periodic function? Explain.
 a. the average monthly temperature in your community, recorded every month for three years
 b. the population in your community, recorded every year for the last 50 years
 c. the number of cars per hour that pass through an intersection near where you live, recorded for two consecutive work days

---

Answers

Practice and Problem-Solving Exercises

7–9. Answers may vary. Samples:

7. $x = -2$ to $x = 3$, $x = 2$ to $x = 7$; 5

8. $x = 0$ to $x = 4$, $x = 5$ to $x = 9$; 4

9. $x = 0$ to $x = 4$, $x = 2$ to $x = 6$; 4

10. not periodic

11. periodic; 12

12. not periodic

13. not periodic

14. periodic; 8

15. periodic; 7

16. 4; $y = 0$

17. 3; $y = -1$

18. 1; $y = 1$

19.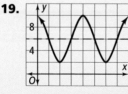

1 unit on the *x*-axis is 0.005 s.

20.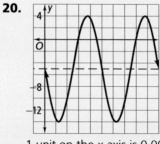

1 unit on the *x*-axis is 0.001 s.

21. a. y
  b. x

22. a–c. Answers may vary. Samples:
 a. This could be; average monthly temperatures for three years should be cyclical due to the variation of the seasons.
 b. Probably not; population usually increases or decreases, but is not usually cyclical.
 c. This could be; traffic that passes through an intersection should be at similar levels at the same times of day on each of the two consecutive work days.

23. Writing What do all periodic functions have in common?

24. Think About a Plan
A person's pulse rate is the number of times his or her heart beats in one minute. Each cycle in the graph represents one heartbeat. What is the pulse rate?
- Will you compute the period or the amplitude, or both?
- Does the graph provide information you do NOT need?

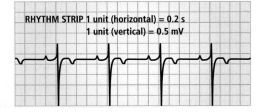

RHYTHM STRIP 1 unit (horizontal) = 0.2 s
1 unit (vertical) = 0.5 mV

25. Health An electrocardiogram (EKG or ECG) measures the electrical activity of a person's heart in millivolts over time. Refer to the graph in the previous exercise.
   a. What is the period of the EKG shown above?
   b. What is the amplitude of the EKG?

26. Open-Ended Sketch a graph of a periodic function that has a period of 3 and an amplitude of 2.

Find the maximum, minimum, and period of each periodic function. Then copy the graph and sketch two more cycles.

27.   **28.**   **29.**

Language Arts Functions that repeat over time are common in everyday life. The English language has many words that stand for common periods of time. State the period of time from which each term derives.

30. annual   **31.** biweekly   **32.** quarterly   **33.** hourly   **34.** circadian

Challenge

35. Suppose g is a periodic function. The period of g is 24, $g(3) = 67$, and $g(8) = 70$. Find each function value.
   a. $g(27)$ **b.** $g(80)$ **c.** $g(-16)$ **d.** $g(51)$

36. Calendar A day is a basic measure of time. A solar year is about 365.2422 days. We try to keep our calendar in step with the solar year.
   a. If every calendar year has 365 days, by how many days would the calendar year and the solar year differ after 100 years?
   b. If every fourth year has an extra "leap" day added, by how many days would the two systems differ after 100 years?
   c. If every hundred years the "leap" day is omitted, by how many days would the two systems differ after 100 years?
   d. Reasoning Why is it important for the difference between the calendar year and the solar year to be zero?

---

36. a. 24.22 days
   b. 0.78 day
   c. 0.22 day
   d. Answers may vary. Sample: The calendar year is meant to predict events in the solar year. Minimizing the difference between the two is necessary for the calendar year to be useful.

---

23. repeating of a pattern at regular intervals

24. 60 beats per minute

25. a. 1 s
   b. 1.5 mV

26. Check students' work.

27. 3, −3, 4;

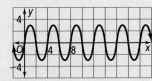

28. 5, 0, 8;

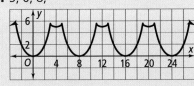

29. 4, −4, 8;

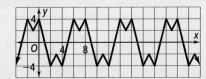

30. 1 yr

31. 2 weeks

32. 3 months

33. 1 hr

34. 1 day

35. a. 67
   b. 70
   c. 70
   d. 67

Answers

Standardized Test Prep

37. C

38. G

39. B

40. I

41. [4] 64 s; The first two functions are at the beginning of their cycles together every $6 \cdot 7 = 42$ seconds: 42, 84, 126, . . . The third function is at the beginning of its cycle every 8 seconds, starting at 20 seconds: 62, 70, 78, 86, 94, 102, 110, 118, 126, . . . The three functions are all at the beginning of their cycles at 126 seconds, which is 64 seconds after the third function achieves its first maximum.

[3] appropriate reasoning, but with one computational error

[2] only took two of the functions into account OR attempted to take all three into account, but only reasoned correctly for one pair

[1] correct answer, without work shown

Mixed Review

42. about 302 mi/h

43.

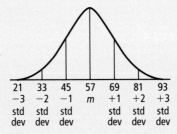

21	33	45	57	69	81	93
−3	−2	−1	*m*	+1	+2	+3
std dev	std dev	std dev		std dev	std dev	std dev

44. $x^2 + y^2 = 1$

45. $x^2 + y^2 = 13$

46. $x^2 + y^2 = 25$

47. $x^2 + y^2 = 2$

48. $x^2 + y^2 = 1$

49. $x^2 + y^2 = 1$

Standardized Test Prep

37. A periodic function goes through 5 complete cycles in 4 min. What is the period of the function?

- Ⓐ $\frac{1}{5}$ min
- Ⓑ $\frac{1}{4}$ min
- Ⓒ 48 s
- Ⓓ 75 s

38. The period of a periodic function is 8 s. How many cycles does it go through in 30 s?

- Ⓕ $\frac{4}{15}$ cycle
- Ⓖ 3.75 cycles
- Ⓗ 22 cycles
- Ⓘ 240 cycles

39. Which graph is NOT the graph of a periodic function?

- Ⓐ I only
- Ⓑ II only
- Ⓒ III only
- Ⓓ II and III only

40. The amplitude of a periodic function is 2.5 and its minimum value is 0. What is the function's maximum value?

- Ⓕ −2.5
- Ⓖ 0
- Ⓗ 2.5
- Ⓘ 5.0

Extended Response

41. Two periodic functions have periods of 6 s and 7 s. A machine records the two functions reaching their maximum values at the same time. Twenty seconds later, the machine records a new periodic function reaching its maximum value. The new function has a period of 8 s. How many seconds after that will all the functions reach their maximum values at the same time? Explain.

Mixed Review

42. An airplane has a speed of 300 mi/h in still air. Suppose the airplane flies due north and encounters a wind blowing 35 mi/h due west. What is the resultant speed of the airplane?

See Lesson 12-6.

43. Sketch a normal curve for a distribution that has mean 57 and standard deviation 12. Label the *x*-axis values at one, two, and three standard deviations from the mean.

See Lesson 11-9.

Get Ready! To prepare for Lesson 13-2, do Exercises 44–49.

Write an equation of the circle that passes through the given point and has its center at the origin. (*Hint:* Use the distance formula to find the radius.)

See Lesson 10-3.

44. $(0, 1)$

45. $(2, 3)$

46. $(3, 4)$

47. $(-1, -1)$

48. $\left(\frac{\sqrt{3}}{2}, \frac{1}{2}\right)$

49. $\left(\frac{\sqrt{2}}{2}, \frac{\sqrt{2}}{2}\right)$

Additional Instructional Support

Algebra 2 Companion

Students can use the **Algebra 2 Companion** worktext (4 pages) as you teach the lesson. Use the Companion to support

- New Vocabulary
- Key Concepts
- Got It for each Problem
- Lesson Check

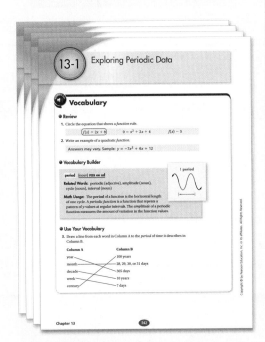

ELL Support

Assess Understanding Have students examine the graphs of the three periodic functions in Problem and Got It 3. For each one, ask students to describe the scale along the horizontal axis and to start anywhere on the graph and use their fingers to trace one complete cycle of the graph. Have students identify the periods of the graphs and explain how they determined those values. Then, ask volunteers to define in their own words what is meant by the period of a function.

5 Assess & Remediate

Lesson Quiz

1. Is the function periodic? If so, what is its period?

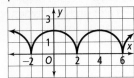

2. **Do you UNDERSTAND?** Alternating current (AC) is a form of electricity whose direction switches back and forth 60 times each second. The graph shows an AC current. What are the period, amplitude, and equation of the midline of this periodic function?

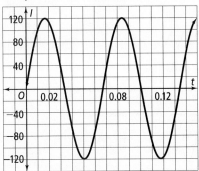

ANSWERS TO LESSON QUIZ

1. Yes, its period is 4.
2. about 0.066; 120; $y = 0$.

PRESCRIPTION FOR REMEDIATION

Use the student work on the Lesson Quiz to prescribe a differentiated review assignment:

Points	Differentiated Remediation
0	Intervention
1	On-level
2	Extension

PowerAlgebra.com

5 Assess & Remediate

Assign the Lesson Quiz. Appropriate intervention, practice, or enrichment is automatically generated based on student performance.

Intervention

- **Reteaching** (2 pages) Provides reteaching and practice exercises for the key lesson concepts. Use with struggling students or absent students.
- **English Language Learner Support** Helps students develop and reinforce mathematical vocabulary and key concepts.

All-in-One Resources/Online
Reteaching

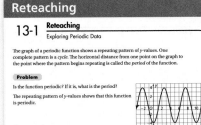

All-in-One Resources/Online
English Language Learner Support

Differentiated Remediation *continued*

On-Level

- **Practice** (2 pages) Provides extra practice for each lesson. For simpler practice exercises, use the Form K Practice pages found in the All-in-One Teaching Resources and online.

- **Think About a Plan** Helps students develop specific problem-solving skills and strategies by providing scaffolded guiding questions.

- **Standardized Test Prep** Focuses on all major exercises, all major question types, and helps students prepare for the high-stakes assessments.

Extension

- **Enrichment** Provides students with interesting problems and activities that extend the concepts of the lesson.

- **Activities, Games, and Puzzles** Worksheets that can be used for concepts development, enrichment, and for fun!

Practice and Problem Solving Wkbk/ All-in-One Resources/Online
Practice page 1

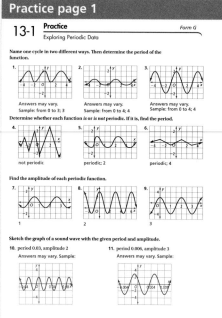

Practice and Problem Solving Wkbk/ All-in-One Resources/Online
Practice page 2

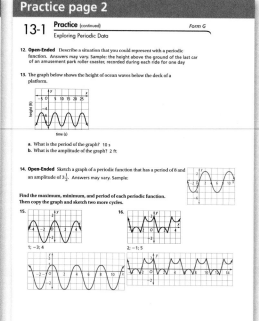

All-in-One Resources/Online
Enrichment

13-1 Enrichment
Exploring Periodic Data

A periodic function repeats a pattern of outputs at regular intervals. There are several ways to describe this pattern. You have already learned that a cycle is one complete pattern. The period is the horizontal length of one cycle and the amplitude measures the amount of variation in the function values. One additional way to describe a periodic function is by its *frequency*.

1. Determine the period and the amplitude for the graph at the right. 2; 1

2. The frequency is defined as the number of cycles completed in one unit. For this graph, what part of a cycle is completed in 1 unit? $\frac{1}{2}$

Determine the period and the frequency of each graph.

3. 8; $\frac{1}{8}$ 4. $\frac{2}{3}$; $\frac{3}{2}$

5. Describe the relationship between the period and the frequency. Answers may vary. Sample: They are reciprocals of each other.

6. If a graph has a period of 12 units, what is its frequency? $\frac{1}{12}$

7. If a graph has a frequency of $\frac{3}{4}$, what is the period? $\frac{4}{3}$

8. The period of visible light ranges from 1.27×10^{-15} to 2.54×10^{-15} s.
   a. What is the range of frequencies for visible light? approximately 3.94×10^{14} to 7.87×10^{14} cycles per s
   b. What is the physical meaning of this range? Answers may vary. Sample: Visible light is periodic and oscillates approximately 3.94×10^{14} to 7.87×10^{14} times while traveling 1 s.

Practice and Problem Solving Wkbk/ All-in-One Resources/Online
Think About a Plan

13-1 Think About a Plan
Exploring Periodic Data

Health An electrocardiogram (EKG or ECG) measures the electrical activity of a person's heart in millivolts over time.

RHYTHM STRIP 1 unit (horizontal) = 0.2 s
1 unit (vertical) = 0.5 mV

a. What is the period of the EKG shown above?
b. What is the amplitude of the EKG?

Know

1. One horizontal unit on the graph represents [0.2 s].

2. One vertical unit on the graph represents [0.5 mV].

3. The EKG represents a periodic function.

Need

4. To solve the problem, I need to find the period and amplitude of the periodic function represented by the graph.

Plan

5. One cycle of the function has a length of [5 units].

6. What is the period of the function? 1 s

7. What is the definition of amplitude? amplitude = $\frac{1}{2}$ (maximum value − minimum value)

8. The amplitude of the function is [1.5 mV].

Practice and Problem Solving Wkbk/ All-in-One Resources/Online
Standardized Test Prep

13-1 Standardized Test Prep
Exploring Periodic Data

Multiple Choice

For Exercises 1–3, choose the correct letter.

1. Which pair of coordinates names one complete cycle of the periodic function? D
   Ⓐ $(-5, -3)$ to $(-2, 2)$ Ⓒ $(-2, 2)$ to $(-1, -3)$
   Ⓑ $(-5, -3)$ to $(5, 0)$ Ⓓ $(-1, -3)$ to $(3, -3)$

2. Which graph is NOT the graph of a periodic function? G

3. A periodic function has a period of 12 s. How many cycles does it go through in 40 s? A
   Ⓐ $3\frac{1}{3}$ cycles   Ⓑ $\frac{3}{10}$ cycle   Ⓒ 28 cycles   Ⓓ 480 cycles

Short Response

4. The graph at the right represents a periodic function.
   a. What is the period of the function?
   b. What is the amplitude of the function?
   [2] a. 2.5 b. 1.75
   [1] incorrect period OR incorrect amplitude
   [0] no answers given

Online Teacher Resource Center
Activities, Games, and Puzzles

13-1 Game: Repeating Myself
Exploring Periodic Data

The graphs of five periodic functions over one cycle are shown below. The functions are a, m, d, n, and p.

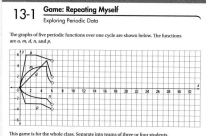

This game is for the whole class. Separate into teams of three or four students.
- Your job is to predict the value of each function based on the graphs. Remember that each function is periodic and one cycle is shown.
- Each correct response earns 3 points.
- The team that earns the most points wins.

1. $a(6) = $ __0__   2. $m(5) = $ __4__   3. $p(1) = $ __−3__
4. $n(12) = $ __0__   5. $m(12) = $ __0__   6. $a(13) = $ __6__
7. $m(11) = $ __4__   8. $p(13) = $ __−3__   9. $n(17) = $ __−2__
10. $d(11) = $ __5__   11. $n(18) = $ __0__   12. $a(15) = $ __6__
13. $p(7) = $ __−3__   14. $a(18) = $ __0__   15. $d(23) = $ __5__
16. $n(24) = $ __0__   17. $n(24) = $ __0__   18. $d(23) = $ __5__
19. $a(19) = $ __6__   20. $p(10) = $ __−3__   21. $n(11) = $ __−2__
22. $d(18) = $ __0__   23. $p(28) = $ __−3__   24. $m(29) = $ __4__
25. $n(29) = $ __−2__   26. $d(30) = $ __0__   27. $a(27) = $ __6__

Special Right Triangles

© **Content Standard**
Reviews G.SRT.6 Understand that by similarity, side ratios in right triangles . . . lead to definitions of trigonometric ratios for acute angles.

In Geometry, you learned about two special right triangles, the 45°-45°-90° triangle and the 30°-60°-90° triangle. The figures at the right summarize the relationships among the lengths of the sides of each triangle.

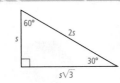

Example 1

Find the missing side lengths in each 45°-45°-90° triangle.

Ⓐ

$y = \sqrt{2} \cdot 5$ hypotenuse $= \sqrt{2} \cdot$ leg

$y = 5\sqrt{2}$ Simplify.

Ⓑ

$5 = \sqrt{2} \cdot x$

$x = \dfrac{5}{\sqrt{2}} = \dfrac{5\sqrt{2}}{2}$

Example 2

Find the missing side lengths in the 30°-60°-90° triangle at the right.

$4 = \sqrt{3} \cdot x$ longer leg $= \sqrt{3} \cdot$ shorter leg

$x = \dfrac{4}{\sqrt{3}} = \dfrac{4\sqrt{3}}{3}$ Divide and simplify.

$y = 2x$ hypotenuse $= 2 \cdot$ shorter leg

$y = 2 \cdot \dfrac{4\sqrt{3}}{3} = \dfrac{8\sqrt{3}}{3}$ Substitute $\dfrac{4\sqrt{3}}{3}$ for x and simplify.

Exercises

Use the given information to find the missing side length(s) in each 45°-45°-90° triangle. Rationalize any denominators.

1. hypotenuse 1 in.   **2.** leg 2 cm   **3.** hypotenuse $\sqrt{3}$ ft   **4.** leg $2\sqrt{5}$ m

Use the given information to find the missing side lengths in each 30°-60°-90° triangle. Rationalize any denominators.

5. shorter leg 3 in.   **6.** longer leg 1 cm   **7.** hypotenuse 1 ft   **8.** shorter leg $\sqrt{3}$ cm

Guided Instruction

PURPOSE To review the relationship between sides and angles of special right triangles

PROCESS Students will
- identify special right triangles.
- find side lengths of 30°-60°-90° triangles and 45°-45°-90° triangles given one side length.

DISCUSS Students are familiar with the Pythagorean Theorem. They know that special right triangles show a particular relationship between sides. Elicit that
- the Pythagorean Theorem applies to right triangles only and is given by the formula $a^2 + b^2 = c^2$ where a and b are legs and c is the hypotenuse.
- an isosceles right triangle has congruent legs and base angles. Therefore, the angle measures are 45°-45°-90°.

Example 1

Q How can you use the Pythagorean Theorem to show the special relationship in any 45°-45°-90° triangle? **[Because base angles are congruent, the legs are also congruent. Letting a equal the measure of one leg, you have $a^2 + a^2 = c^2$ or $c = \sqrt{2a^2} = a\sqrt{2}$.]**

Example 2

Q If only the longer leg of a 30°-60°-90° triangle is marked, how do you determine the angle measures in the triangle? **[The longest side of any triangle will always be opposite the angle with the greatest measure. In a right triangle, the hypotenuse is opposite the 90° angle and the longer leg is opposite the 60° angle.]**

© **Mathematical Practices** This Concept Byte supports students in using repeated reasoning, Mathematical Practice 8.

Answers

Geometry Review

1. $\dfrac{\sqrt{2}}{2}$ in.

2. $2\sqrt{2}$ cm

3. $\dfrac{\sqrt{6}}{2}$ ft

4. $2\sqrt{10}$ m

5. hypotenuse: 6 in., longer leg: $3\sqrt{3}$ in.

6. shorter leg: $\dfrac{\sqrt{3}}{3}$ cm,

    hypotenuse: $\dfrac{2\sqrt{3}}{3}$ cm

7. shorter leg: $\dfrac{1}{2}$ ft, longer leg: $\dfrac{\sqrt{3}}{2}$ ft

8. hypotenuse: $2\sqrt{3}$ cm,
    longer leg: 3 cm

1 Interactive Learning

Solve It!
PURPOSE To compare the measures of angles with a vertex at the origin on a coordinate grid
PROCESS Students may
- plot each point and use a ruler and protractor to draw the angle and measure.
- use points and their positions in each quadrant or on each axis to determine the greatest angle.

FACILITATE
Q At what angle are the red and blue arrows if the red arrow contains the point (0, 1)? Explain. **[The arrows lie on the *x*-and *y*-axes, so they are perpendicular and form a 90° angle.]**

Q How is the position of the red arrow and the measure of the angle related to the quadrant in which the point is plotted? **[An angle going through a point in the first quadrant has lesser measure than an angle in the second quadrant.]**

Q Does the angle through (5, 5) have greater measure than the angle through (2, 2)? Explain. **[No; in fact, they are the same angle. The ray from the origin through (2, 2) also passes through (5, 5).]**

ANSWER See Solve It in Answers on next page.
CONNECT THE MATH Students use their knowledge of angles on a coordinate grid to find the angle with the greatest measure in the Solve It. In this lesson, students sketch angles of a certain degree and find values for the sine and cosine of these angles.

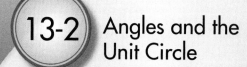
© **Content Standard**
Prepares for F.TF.2 Explain how the unit circle . . . enables the extension of trigonometric functions to all real numbers, interpreted as radian measures of angles traversed counterclockwise around the unit circle.

Objectives To work with angles in standard position
To find coordinates of points on the unit circle

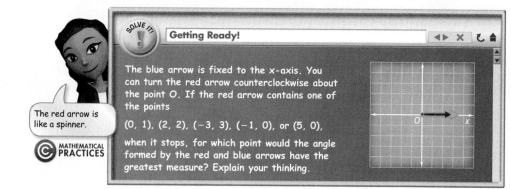

The red arrow is like a spinner.

© MATHEMATICAL PRACTICES

Getting Ready!

The blue arrow is fixed to the x-axis. You can turn the red arrow counterclockwise about the point O. If the red arrow contains one of the points

(0, 1), (2, 2), (−3, 3), (−1, 0), or (5, 0),

when it stops, for which point would the angle formed by the red and blue arrows have the greatest measure? Explain your thinking.

Lesson Vocabulary
- standard position
- initial side
- terminal side
- coterminal angles
- unit circle
- cosine of θ
- sine of θ

An angle in the coordinate plane is in **standard position** when the vertex is at the origin and one ray is on the positive *x*-axis. The ray on the *x*-axis is the **initial side** of the angle. The other ray is the **terminal side** of the angle.

The measure of an angle in standard position is the amount of rotation from the initial side to the terminal side.

Standard Position

Essential Understanding The measure of an angle in standard position is the input for two important functions. The outputs are the coordinates (called *cosine* and *sine*) of the point on the terminal side of the angle that is 1 unit from the origin.

The measure of an angle is positive when the rotation from the initial side to the terminal side is in the counterclockwise direction. The measure is negative when the rotation is clockwise.

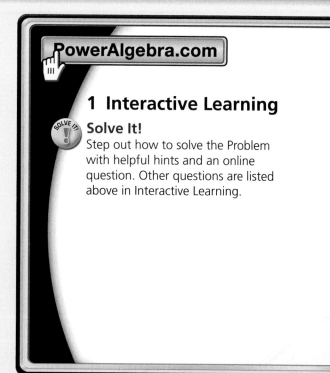

13-2 Preparing to Teach

BIG ideas Modeling
Function
ESSENTIAL UNDERSTANDINGS
- The measure of an angle in standard position is the input for two important functions. The outputs are the coordinates (called cosine and sine) of the point on the terminal side of the angle that is 1 unit from the origin.
- Two angles in standard position are coterminal angles if they have the same terminal side.

Math Background
Many students are not familiar with the idea of angles being greater than 180 degrees or less than 0 degrees.

This lesson prepares students for trigonometry, where it is more helpful to relate angle measure to the concept of rotations and to allow for angles of any measure, positive or negative.

For angles in standard position, a counterclockwise rotation is positive, and a clockwise rotation is negative.

Angles that share a terminal side when drawn in standard position are called *coterminal angles*. An unlimited number of coterminal angles of a given angle can be identified by adding or subtracting 360 degrees.

The unit circle definitions of the sine and cosine functions reveal that these are periodic functions. These definitions are new to students who associate trigonometric functions only with triangles.

PowerAlgebra.com

1 Interactive Learning

Solve It!
Step out how to solve the Problem with helpful hints and an online question. Other questions are listed above in Interactive Learning.

Problem 1 Measuring Angles in Standard Position

What are the measures of each angle?

A

This angle is a counterclockwise rotation that makes a right angle, so its measure is 90°.

B

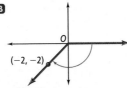
(−2, −2)

This angle is a clockwise rotation that goes 45° beyond a right angle, so its measure is −135°.

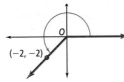
(−2, −2)

 Got It? 1. What is the measure of the angle shown?

Problem 2 Sketching Angles in Standard Position

What is a sketch of each angle in standard position?

A 36°

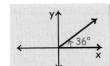

36° Counterclockwise

B 315°

315° Counterclockwise

C −150°

150° Clockwise

 Got It? 2. What is a sketch of each angle in standard position?

a. 85°   b. −320°   c. 180°

Two angles in standard position are **coterminal angles** if they have the same terminal side.

Angles in standard position that have measures 135° and −225° are coterminal.

135°
−225°

2 Guided Instruction

Problem 1

Point out that in a unit circle, angles formed by clockwise movements are negative. Angles formed by counterclockwise movements are positive.

Q What is the terminal side of an angle measuring −90°? **[The terminal side is along the negative part of the *y*-axis.]**

Q How do you know that the angle in 1B goes 45° beyond a right angle? **[Sample: Draw a line from a point on the terminal side perpendicular to the *y*-axis. This forms an isosceles right triangle with angle measures 45°-45°-90°.]**

Got It?

Q How can you check that your answer is reasonable? **[The terminal side of the angle is in Quadrant III and the angle is counterclockwise. Therefore, the measure should be between 180° and 270°.]**

Problem 2

Q What are the possible positive and negative angle measures if the terminal side of an angle in standard position is in Quadrant II? **[from 90° to 180° or from −180° to −270°]**

Got It?

Q What is the position of an angle when sketching it in standard position? **[The vertex of the angle is at the origin, and the initial side is on the positive *x*-axis.]**

2 Guided Instruction

 Each Problem is worked out and supported online.

Problem 1
Measuring Angles in Standard Position

Problem 2
Sketching Angles in Standard Position

Problem 3
Identifying Coterminal Angles
Animated

Problem 4
Finding Cosines and Sines of Angles
Animated

Problem 5
Finding Exact Values of Cosine and Sine
Animated

Support in Algebra 2 Companion
• Vocabulary
• Key Concepts
• Got It?

Answers

Solve It!
(−1, 0); the largest angle is 180°.

Got It?

1. 225°

2. a.

85°

b.

−320°

c.

180°

Problem 3

Q Without using the graph, how can you show that an angle of 300° is coterminal with an angle of −60°? **[300° − 360° = −60°]**

Q How many coterminal angles are possible for an angle of 60°? Explain. **[An infinite number because any coterminal angle can be found by adding or subtracting multiples of 360°.]**

Got It?

Q What is the first step to determine whether angles are coterminal? Explain. **[Sample: Choose one angle and add or subtract 360°. For example, because 45° + 360° = 405°, the angles 45° and 405° are coterminal.]**

Take Note

Q For what values of θ is the sine increasing? decreasing? Explain. **[The sine will increase as θ goes from 0° to 90° because the y-values are increasing. It will decrease from 90° to 270°, then increase from 270° to 360°.]**

Multiple Choice Which of the following angles is not coterminal with any of the other three?

Ⓐ 300°   Ⓑ −60°   Ⓒ 60°   Ⓓ −420°

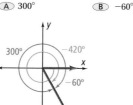 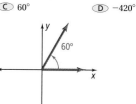

Think
How do you know if two angles are coterminal?
Two angles are coterminal if they differ by a multiple of 360°.

Angles of 300° and −60° are coterminal. An angle of −420° is coterminal with both, since it is a full 360° rotation beyond −60°.

An angle of 60° is not coterminal with any of the other three.

Angles of 300°, −60°, and −420° all have the same terminal side and are coterminal. The 60° angle has a different terminal side. The correct answer is C.

✓ **Got It? 3.** Which angles are coterminal?
    a. −315°   **b.** 45°   **c.** 315°   **d.** 405°

In a 360° angle, a point 1 unit from the origin on the terminal ray makes one full rotation about the origin. The resulting circle is a unit circle. The **unit circle** has a radius of 1 unit and its center at the origin of the coordinate plane. Any right triangle formed by the radius of the unit circle has a hypotenuse of 1. Points on the unit circle are related to periodic functions.

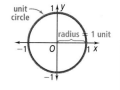

You can use the symbol θ for the measure of an angle in standard position.

take note   **Key Concepts**   **Cosine and Sine of an Angle**

Suppose an angle in standard position has measure θ. The **cosine of θ** (cos θ) is the x-coordinate of the point at which the terminal side of the angle intersects the unit circle. The **sine of θ** (sin θ) is the y-coordinate.

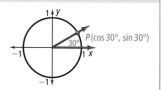

Additional Problems

1. What is the measure of each angle?

a.

b.

ANSWERS
a. 45°   **b.** −270°

2. What is a sketch of each angle in standard position?
a. 100°   **b.** −215°

ANSWERS
a.

b.

3. Multiple Choice Which of the following angles is not coterminal with the other three?
A. 750°   **B.** 30°
C. −330°   **D.** −540°

ANSWER D

4. What are cos θ and sin θ for θ = −360°, θ = 180°, and θ = 450°?

ANSWER
cos −360° = 1, sin −360° = 0;
cos 180° = −1, sin 180° = 0;
cos 450° = 0, sin 450° = 1

5. What are the cosine and sine of the angle?
a. 135°   **b.** 300°

ANSWERS
a. $\cos 135° = -\frac{\sqrt{2}}{2}$, $\sin 135° = \frac{\sqrt{2}}{2}$

b. $\cos 300° = \frac{1}{2}$, $\sin 300° = -\frac{\sqrt{3}}{2}$

Answers

Got It? (continued)

3. 315°

Problem 4 Finding Cosines and Sines of Angles

What are $\cos \theta$ and $\sin \theta$ for $\theta = 90°$, $\theta = -180°$, and $\theta = 270°$?

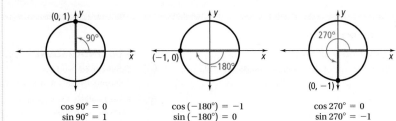

$\cos 90° = 0$
$\sin 90° = 1$

$\cos(-180°) = -1$
$\sin(-180°) = 0$

$\cos 270° = 0$
$\sin 270° = -1$

✔ **Got It? 4. a.** What are $\cos \theta$ and $\sin \theta$ for $\theta = -90°$, $\theta = 360°$, and $\theta = 540°$?
b. In a triangle, sine and cosine are ratios between side lengths. What ratios produce the values in (a)?

You can find the exact value of sine and cosine for angles that are multiples of 30° or 45°.

Problem 5 Finding Exact Values of Cosine and Sine

What are the cosine and sine of the angle?

A $\theta = 60°$

Know	Need	Plan
An angle	The x- and y-coordinates of the point where the angle intersects the unit circle	• Sketch the angle on the unit circle. • Use the angle to draw a right triangle with one leg on the x-axis.

The cosine of 60° is the length of the shorter leg of the triangle. The sine of 60° is the length of the longer leg of the triangle. In a 30°-60°-90° triangle, the shorter leg is half the hypotenuse and the longer leg is $\sqrt{3}$ times the shorter leg.

$\cos 60° = x = \text{length of shorter leg} = \dfrac{1}{2}$

$\sin 60° = y = \text{length of longer leg} = \dfrac{\sqrt{3}}{2}$

B $\theta = 225°$

Draw the angle in standard position to determine the point $P(x, y)$ on the unit circle. P is in the third quadrant, so the signs of x and y will be negative. Form a right triangle with hypotenuse 1. In a 45°-45°-90° triangle, the lengths of the legs of the triangle are $\dfrac{\sqrt{2}}{2}$ times the hypotenuse.

$\cos 225° = x = -\text{length of leg} = -\dfrac{\sqrt{2}}{2}$ $\sin 225° = y = -\text{length of leg} = -\dfrac{\sqrt{2}}{2}$

Problem 4

Q How can knowing the cosine and sine when $x = -180°$ help you find the cosine and sine when $x = 180°$? **[180° is the coterminal angle of −180° because −180° + 360° = 180°, so the sine and cosine will be the same for 180° as it is for −180°.]**

Got It?

Q What coterminal angle can help you find the value of cos 540° and sin 540°? Explain. **[The coterminal angle of 540° − 360° = 180° can be used because they have the same terminal side, so cos 540° = cos 180° and sin 540° = sin 180°.]**

Problem 5

Q How do you know the measure of the hypotenuse is 1? **[The circle is a unit circle, which by definition has a radius of 1 unit. Therefore, the hypotenuse is 1 unit.]**

Q How can the information from 5A be used to determine the cosine of 30°? Explain. **[The same 30°-60°-90° triangle relationship is used with an angle of 30° at the origin. If cos 60° is the length of the shorter leg, then cos 30° must be the length of the longer leg.]**

Q How can you check that the answer in 5B is reasonable? **[Using a calculator, $\dfrac{\sqrt{2}}{2} \approx 0.707$, so the approximate value of $P(x, y)$ is (−0.707, −0.707) which is in Quadrant III so the answer is reasonable.]**

---

4. a. $\cos(-90°) = 0$, $\sin(-90°) = -1$;
$\cos(360°) = 1$, $\sin(360°) = 0$;
$\cos(540°) = -1$, $\sin(540°) = 0$

b. $\cos -90° = \dfrac{0}{1} = 0$, $\sin -90° = \dfrac{-1}{1} = -1$

$\cos 360° = \dfrac{1}{1} = 1$, $\sin 360° = \dfrac{0}{1} = 0$

$\cos 540° = \dfrac{-1}{1} = -1$, $\sin 540° = \dfrac{0}{1} = 0$

Got It?

VISUAL LEARNERS

Q For 5a, does the negative angle indicate negative values for sine and cosine? Explain. **[No; the negative angle indicates a clockwise direction. An angle of −45° is in Quadrant IV, so the cosine is positive and sine is negative.]**

3 Lesson Check

Do you know HOW? ERROR INTERVENTION

• For Exercise 2, suggest students form a right triangle using the terminal side as the hypotenuse and drawing a line perpendicular to the x-axis. The coordinates can be used to find the length of the legs of the right triangle.

• If students have difficulty solving Exercises 3 and 4, remind them that a coterminal angle can be found by adding or subtracting a multiple of 360° to an angle.

Do you UNDERSTAND?

• If students have difficulty with Exercise 6, suggest that they sketch the angle of 50° and the angle of 310° to determine in which quadrants they reside. Then use this information to explain and correct the student's error.

Close

Q What are the meanings of positive and negative angle measures? **[A positive angle measure means the rotation from the initial side to the terminal side is counterclockwise. A negative angle means the rotation is clockwise.]**

Q What are the meanings of sine and cosine? **[Sine is the y-coordinate where the terminal side of an angle intersects the unit circle. The cosine is the x-coordinate.]**

  Got It? 5. What are the cosine and sine of the angle?
  a. $\theta = -45°$ **b.** $\theta = 150°$
  c. Reasoning For an angle θ, can $\cos \theta$ equal $\sin \theta$? Explain.

Lesson Check

Do you know HOW?

Find the measure of each angle in standard position.

1.

2.

Sketch each angle in standard position. Then find the measure of a coterminal angle.

3. 28°   **4.** 325°

Do you UNDERSTAND? **MATHEMATICAL PRACTICES**

5. Open-Ended Find a positive and a negative coterminal angle for an angle that measures 1485°.

6. Error Analysis On a test a student wrote that the measure of an angle coterminal to a 50° angle is 310°. Describe and correct the student's error.

Practice and Problem-Solving Exercises MATHEMATICAL PRACTICES

A Practice Find the measure of each angle in standard position. ◀ See Problem 1.

7. (2, 2)

8. (−5, −5)

9. (−1, −√3)

10. 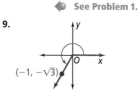 $\left(-\frac{\sqrt{3}}{2}, \frac{1}{2}\right)$

11. $(2\sqrt{3}, -2)$

12. 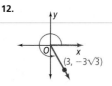 (3, −3√3)

Sketch each angle in standard position. ◀ See Problem 2.

13. 40°   **14.** −130°   **15.** −270°   **16.** 120°   **17.** 95°

Find the measure of an angle between 0° and 360° coterminal with each given angle. ◀ See Problem 3.

18. 385°   **19.** 575°   **20.** −405°   **21.** −356°

22. 500°   **23.** −210°   **24.** 415°   **25.** −180°

---

3 Lesson Check

For a digital lesson check, use the Got It questions.

Support in Algebra 2 Companion
• Lesson Check

4 Practice

Assign homework to individual students or to an entire class.

Answers

Got It?

5. a. $\frac{\sqrt{2}}{2}, -\frac{\sqrt{2}}{2}$ **b.** $-\frac{\sqrt{3}}{2}, \frac{1}{2}$

c. Yes; for example, when $\theta = 45°$, $\sin \theta = \cos \theta$.

Lesson Check

1. 135°   **2.** 240°

3. 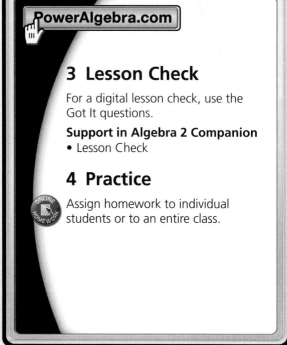 ; −332°

4. 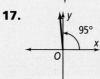 ; −35°

5. Answers may vary. Sample: 45° and −315°

6. The measure of the coterminal angle is not 310°; the measure of the coterminal angle is $50° - 360° = -310°$.

Practice and Problem-Solving Exercises

7. −315°   **8.** −135°   **9.** 240°
10. 150°   **11.** −30°   **12.** 300°

13. 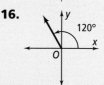   **14.**

15.   **16.**

17.

18. 25°   **19.** 215°
20. 315°   **21.** 4°
22. 140°   **23.** 150°
24. 55°   **25.** 180°

Find the exact values of the cosine and sine of each angle. Then find the decimal values. Round your answers to the nearest hundredth.

◀ See Problems 4 and 5.

26.

27.

28.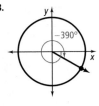

29. $-240°$ 30. $390°$ 31. $315°$ 32. $-30°$ 33. $-225°$

B Apply **Graphing Calculator** For each angle θ, find the values of $\cos \theta$ and $\sin \theta$. Round your answers to the nearest hundredth.

34. $-95°$ 35. $-10°$ 36. $154°$ 37. $90°$ 38. $210°$

ⓒ 39. **Think About a Plan** On an analog clock, the minute hand has moved 128° from the hour. What number will it pass next?
- How can a drawing help you understand the problem?
- How can you find the number of degrees between every two consecutive numbers?

ⓒ **Open-Ended** Find a positive and a negative coterminal angle for the given angle.

40. $45°$ 41. $10°$ 42. $-675°$ 43. $400°$ 44. $213°$

Determine the quadrant or axis where the terminal side of each angle lies.

45. $150°$ 46. $210°$ 47. $540°$ 48. $-60°$ 49. $0°$

50. **Time** The time is 2:46 P.M. What is the measure of the angle that the minute hand swept through since 2:00 P.M.?

ⓒ 51. a. Copy and complete the chart at the right.
   b. Suppose you know that $\cos \theta$ is negative and $\sin \theta$ is positive. In which quadrant does the terminal side of the angle lie?
   c. **Writing** Summarize how the quadrant in which the terminal side of an angle lies affects the sign of the sine and cosine of that angle.

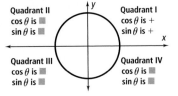

52. a. **Graphing Calculator** Use a calculator to find the value of each expression: $\cos 40°$, $\cos 400°$, and $\cos (-320°)$.
   ⓒ b. **Reasoning** What do you notice about the values you found in part (a)? Explain.

4 Practice

ASSIGNMENT GUIDE
Basic: 7–33 all, 37–41, 47–52

Average: 7–33 odd, 34–52

Advanced: 7–33 odd, 34–59

Standardized Test Prep: 60–63

Mixed Review: 64–74

ⓒ **Mathematical Practices** are supported by exercises with red headings. Here are the Practices supported in this lesson:

MP 1: Make Sense of Problems   Ex. 39
MP 2: Reason Abstractly   Ex. 5, 52b
MP 2: Reason Quantitatively   Ex. 58
MP 3: Construct Arguments   Ex. 59
MP 3: Communicate   Ex. 51c
MP 3: Critique the Reasoning of Others   Ex. 6
MP 5: Use Tools Appropriately   Ex. 34–38, 52

Applications exercises have blue headings.

EXERCISE 50: Use the Think About a Plan worksheet in the **Practice and Problem Solving Workbook** (also available in the Teaching Resources in print and online) to further support students' development in becoming independent learners.

HOMEWORK QUICK CHECK
To check students' understanding of key skills and concepts, go over Exercises 9, 19, 39, 50, and 51.

26. $\frac{1}{2}, -\frac{\sqrt{3}}{2}$; 0.50, −0.87

27. $-\frac{\sqrt{2}}{2}, \frac{\sqrt{2}}{2}$; −0.71, 0.71

28. $\frac{\sqrt{3}}{2}, -\frac{1}{2}$; 0.87, −0.50

29. $-\frac{1}{2}, \frac{\sqrt{3}}{2}$; −0.50, 0.87

30. $\frac{\sqrt{3}}{2}, \frac{1}{2}$; 0.87, 0.50

31. $\frac{\sqrt{2}}{2}, -\frac{\sqrt{2}}{2}$; 0.71, −0.71

32. $\frac{\sqrt{3}}{2}, -\frac{1}{2}$; 0.87, −0.50

33. $-\frac{\sqrt{2}}{2}, \frac{\sqrt{2}}{2}$; −0.71, 0.71

34. −0.09, −1.00   35. 0.98, −0.17

36. −0.90, 0.44   37. 0.00, 1.00

38. −0.87, −0.5   39. 5

40–44. Answers may vary. Samples:

40. $405°, -315°$ 41. $370°, -350°$

42. $45°, -315°$ 43. $40°, -320°$

44. $573°, -147°$ 45. II

46. III   47. negative x-axis

48. IV   49. positive x-axis

50. $-276°$

51. a.
   Quadrant II $\cos \theta$ is − $\sin \theta$ is +
   Quadrant I $\cos \theta$ is + $\sin \theta$ is +
   Quadrant III $\cos \theta$ is − $\sin \theta$ is −
   Quadrant IV $\cos \theta$ is + $\sin \theta$ is −

   b. II

   c. If the terminal side of an angle is in Quadrants I or II, then the sine of the angle is positive. If the terminal side of an angle is in Quadrants I or IV, then the cosine of the angle is positive.

52. a. 0.77, 0.77, 0.77
   b. The cosines of the three angles are equal because the angles are coterminal.

53.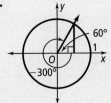
   $\frac{1}{2}, \frac{\sqrt{3}}{2}$

Answers

Practice and Problem-Solving Exercises (continued)

53. See page 841.

54.

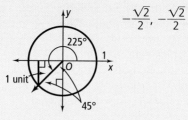

$-\frac{1}{2}, \frac{\sqrt{3}}{2}$

55.

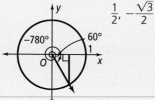

$-\frac{\sqrt{2}}{2}, -\frac{\sqrt{2}}{2}$

56.

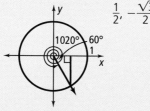

$\frac{1}{2}, -\frac{\sqrt{3}}{2}$

57.

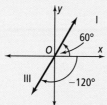

$\frac{1}{2}, -\frac{\sqrt{3}}{2}$

58. Answers may vary. Sample:
30°, 150°, −210°, 390°

59. No; yes; if the sine and cosine are both negative, the angle is in Quadrant III. 60° is in Quadrant I and −120° is in Quadrant III;

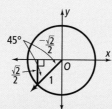

Standardized Test Prep

60. A   **61.** H   **62.** D

63. [2]

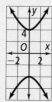

The terminal side forms an angle of 45° with the negative x-axis, so:
$\sin(-135°) = -\frac{\sqrt{2}}{2}$ and
$\cos(-135°) = -\frac{\sqrt{2}}{2}$. Then
$[\sin(-135°)]^2 + [\cos(-135°)]^2$
$= \left(-\frac{\sqrt{2}}{2}\right)^2 + \left(-\frac{\sqrt{2}}{2}\right)^2 =$
$\frac{2}{4} + \frac{2}{4} = \frac{4}{4} = 1.$

Challenge   Sketch each angle in standard position. Use the unit circle and a right triangle to find exact values of the cosine and the sine of the angle.

53. −300°   **54.** 120°   **55.** 225°   **56.** −780°   **57.** 1020°

58. Open-Ended Find the measures of four angles in standard position that have a sine of 0.5. (*Hint:* Use the unit circle and right triangles.)

59. Reasoning Suppose θ is an angle in standard position and $\cos\theta = -\frac{1}{2}$ and $\sin\theta = -\frac{\sqrt{3}}{2}$. Can the value of θ be 60°? Can it be −120°? Draw a diagram and justify your reasoning.

Standardized Test Prep

SAT/ACT

60. Which angle, in standard position, is NOT coterminal with the others?
Ⓐ −570°   Ⓑ −170°   Ⓒ 190°   Ⓓ 550°

61. An angle drawn in standard position has a terminal side that passes through the point $(\sqrt{2}, -\sqrt{2})$. What is one possible measure of the angle?
Ⓕ 45°   Ⓖ 225°   Ⓗ 315°   Ⓘ 330°

62. An angle of 120° is in standard position. What are the coordinates of the point at which the terminal side intersects the unit circle?
Ⓐ $\left(\frac{1}{2}, \frac{\sqrt{3}}{2}\right)$ Ⓑ $\left(-\frac{1}{2}, \frac{\sqrt{3}}{-2}\right)$ Ⓒ $\left(\frac{-\sqrt{3}}{2}, \frac{1}{2}\right)$ Ⓓ $\left(-\frac{1}{2}, \frac{\sqrt{3}}{2}\right)$

Short Response

63. Use an angle in standard position to find the exact value of $[\sin(-135°)]^2 + [\cos(-135°)]^2$. Show your work.

Mixed Review

Determine whether each function *is* or *is not* periodic. If it is, find the period.   ◆ **See Lesson 13-1.**

64.   **65.**   **66.**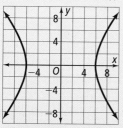

Find the foci of each hyperbola. Draw the graph.   ◆ **See Lesson 10-5.**

67. $\frac{y^2}{16} - \frac{x^2}{4} = 1$ **68.** $\frac{y^2}{25} - \frac{x^2}{100} = 1$ **69.** $\frac{x^2}{36} - \frac{y^2}{49} = 1$ **70.** $\frac{x^2}{81} - \frac{y^2}{64} = 1$

Get Ready!   To prepare for Lesson 13-3, do Exercises 71–74.

Find the area of a circle with the given radius or diameter. Use 3.14 for π.   ◆ **See p. 976.**

71. radius 4 in.   **72.** diameter 70 m   **73.** radius 8 mi   **74.** diameter 3.4 ft

---

[1] no diagram OR incorrect explanation

Mixed Review

64. periodic; 3   **65.** not periodic

66. periodic; 6

67. $(0, 2\sqrt{5}), (0, -2\sqrt{5})$;

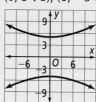

68. $(0, 5\sqrt{5}), (0, -5\sqrt{5})$;

69. $(\sqrt{85}, 0), (-\sqrt{85}, 0)$;

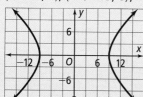

70. $(\sqrt{145}, 0), (-\sqrt{145}, 0)$;

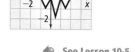

71. 50.24 in.²   **72.** 3846.5 m²

73. 200.96 mi²   **74.** 9.0746 ft²

13-2 Lesson Resources

Differentiated Remediation

Additional Instructional Support

Algebra 2 Companion
Students can use the **Algebra 2 Companion** worktext (4 pages) as you teach the lesson. Use the Companion to support

- New Vocabulary
- Key Concepts
- Got It for each Problem
- Lesson Check

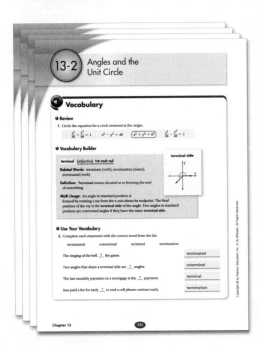

ELL Support
Focus on Language Have students write new terms on one side of an index card and picture definitions on the other. For example, cosine and sine could look like this:

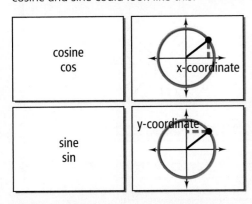

| cosine cos | x-coordinate |
| sine sin | y-coordinate |

Continue with initial side, terminal side, coterminal angles, and any other terms needed. Place the cards with picture side up, and have students practice saying the appropriate term. Then direct students to flip the card over and check their answers.

5 Assess & Remediate

Lesson Quiz
1. What is a sketch of each angle in standard position?
   a. 225°   **b.** −90°
2. **Do you UNDERSTAND?** What are some examples of angles that are coterminal and not coterminal to an angle measuring 540°? Explain.
3. What are the sine and cosine of −270°?
4. What are the sine and cosine of −150°?

ANSWERS TO LESSON QUIZ

1. a.   **b.**
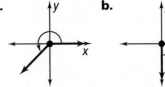

2. A multiple of 360° must be added or subtracted from an angle to find a coterminal angle. A coterminal angle would be 540° − 360° = 180°. An angle that is not coterminal is 540° − 100° = 340°.
3. sin (−270°) = 1, cos (−270°) = 0
4. sin (−150°) = $-\frac{1}{2}$; cos (−150°) = $-\frac{\sqrt{3}}{2}$

PRESCRIPTION FOR REMEDIATION
Use the student work on the Lesson Quiz to prescribe a differentiated review assignment:

Points	Differentiated Remediation
0–2	Intervention
3	On-level
4	Extension

PowerAlgebra.com

5 Assess & Remediate
Assign the Lesson Quiz. Appropriate intervention, practice, or enrichment is automatically generated based on student performance.

Intervention

- **Reteaching** (2 pages) Provides reteaching and practice exercises for the key lesson concepts. Use with struggling students or absent students.
- **English Language Learner Support** Helps students develop and reinforce mathematical vocabulary and key concepts.

All-in-One Resources/Online
Reteaching

All-in-One Resources/Online
English Language Learner Support

Differentiated Remediation *continued*

On-Level

- **Practice** (2 pages) Provides extra practice for each lesson. For simpler practice exercises, use the Form K Practice pages found in the All-in-One Teaching Resources and online.

- **Think About a Plan** Helps students develop specific problem-solving skills and strategies by providing scaffolded guiding questions.

- **Standardized Test Prep** Focuses on all major exercises, all major question types, and helps students prepare for the high-stakes assessments.

Extension

- **Enrichment** Provides students with interesting problems and activities that extend the concepts of the lesson.

- **Activities, Games, and Puzzles** Worksheets that can be used for concepts development, enrichment, and for fun!

Practice and Problem Solving Wkbk/ All-in-One Resources/Online
Practice page 1

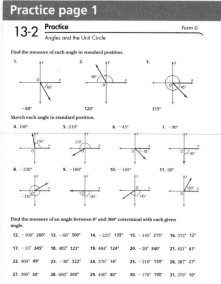

Practice and Problem Solving Wkbk/ All-in-One Resources/Online
Practice page 2

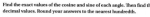
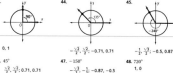

All-in-One Resources/Online
Enrichment

Practice and Problem Solving Wkbk/ All-in-One Resources/Online
Think About a Plan

Practice and Problem Solving Wkbk/ All-in-One Resources/Online
Standardized Test Prep

Online Teacher Resource Center
Activities, Games, and Puzzles

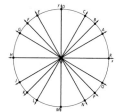

Additional Instructional Support

Algebra 2 Companion

Students can use the **Algebra 2 Companion** worktext (4 pages) as you teach the lesson. Use the Companion to support

- New Vocabulary
- Key Concepts
- Got It for each Problem
- Lesson Check

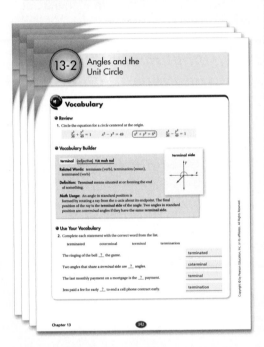

ELL Support

Focus on Language Have students write new terms on one side of an index card and picture definitions on the other. For example, cosine and sine could look like this:

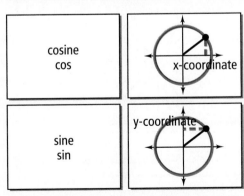

Continue with initial side, terminal side, coterminal angles, and any other terms needed. Place the cards with picture side up, and have students practice saying the appropriate term. Then direct students to flip the card over and check their answers.

5 Assess & Remediate

Lesson Quiz

1. What is a sketch of each angle in standard position?
   a. 225°   **b.** −90°
2. **Do you UNDERSTAND?** What are some examples of angles that are coterminal and not coterminal to an angle measuring 540°? Explain.
3. What are the sine and cosine of −270°?
4. What are the sine and cosine of −150°?

ANSWERS TO LESSON QUIZ

1. a. 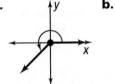   **b.**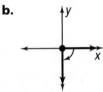

2. A multiple of 360° must be added or subtracted from an angle to find a coterminal angle. A coterminal angle would be 540° − 360° = 180°. An angle that is not coterminal is 540° − 100° = 340°.
3. $\sin(-270°) = 1$, $\cos(-270°) = 0$
4. $\sin(-150°) = -\frac{1}{2}$; $\cos(-150°) = -\frac{\sqrt{3}}{2}$

PRESCRIPTION FOR REMEDIATION

Use the student work on the Lesson Quiz to prescribe a differentiated review assignment:

Points	Differentiated Remediation
0–2	Intervention
3	On-level
4	Extension

PowerAlgebra.com

5 Assess & Remediate

Assign the Lesson Quiz. Appropriate intervention, practice, or enrichment is automatically generated based on student performance.

Intervention

- **Reteaching** (2 pages) Provides reteaching and practice exercises for the key lesson concepts. Use with struggling students or absent students.
- **English Language Learner Support** Helps students develop and reinforce mathematical vocabulary and key concepts.

All-in-One Resources/Online
Reteaching

13-2 Reteaching
Angles and the Unit Circle

A measurement of an angle in standard position is the measurement of the *rotation* from the initial side of the angle to the terminal side of the angle. Coterminal angles have the same terminal side.

Problem

What are two angles that are coterminal with a 140° angle?

Step 1 Sketch a 140° angle in standard position. The rotation from the initial side of the angle to the positive *y*-axis is 90°. So, the rotation from the positive *y*-axis to the terminal side of the angle is 50°. (140 − 90 = 50)

Step 2 Put your finger on the point where the initial side intersects the unit circle. Trace once rotation *counterclockwise* around the circle. Count the degrees of rotation (90°, 180°, 270°, 360°) as you pass each axis. Keep tracing to the positive *y*-axis again. The degree of rotation is now 450°. (360 + 90 = 450)
Continue tracing to the terminal side of the angle. Now the degree of rotation is 500°. (450 + 50 = 500)
A 500° angle is coterminal with a 140° angle.

Step 3 Put your finger on the point where the initial side intersects the unit circle. Trace the circle *clockwise*, counting the *negative* degrees of rotation as you pass each axis. (−90°, −180°)
Keep tracing until you reach the terminal side of the angle. The rotation from the negative *x*-axis to the terminal side of the angle is −40°. (140 − 180 = −40)
So, the total rotation is −220°. (−180 + (−40) = −220)
A −220° angle is coterminal with a 140° angle.

Exercises

Give one positive angle and one negative angle coterminal with the given angle. Answers may vary. Samples are given.

1. 20° 380°, −340°   2. 265° 625°, −95°   3. 305° 665°, −55°

All-in-One Resources/Online
English Language Learner Support

13-2 Additional Vocabulary Support
Angles and the Unit Circle

For Exercises 1–7, draw a line from each word in Column A to the matching item in Column B.

Column A
1. standard position
2. initial side
3. terminal side
4. coterminal angles
5. unit circle
6. cosine of θ
7. sine of θ

Column B
A. two angles in standard position with the same terminal side
B. has a radius of 1 unit and center at the origin
C. the ray on the *x*-axis in an angle in standard position
D. describes an angle with a vertex at the origin and one ray on the positive *x*-axis
E. for 90°, it is 1
F. the ray not on the *x*-axis in an angle in standard position
G. for 90°, it is 0

Circle the angle measure that is *not* coterminal with the other angles.

8. a. 90°   b. −270°   **c. 270°**   d. 450°
9. a. 150°   b. −210°   c. 510°   **d. 210°**
10. a. 25°   **b. 390°**   c. −335°   d. 385°

Use a unit circle to solve the following problems.

11. sin 270° = ⎡−1⎤   12. cos 180° = ⎡−1⎤

Differentiated Remediation *continued*

On-Level

- **Practice** (2 pages) Provides extra practice for each lesson. For simpler practice exercises, use the Form K Practice pages found in the All-in-One Teaching Resources and online.

- **Think About a Plan** Helps students develop specific problem-solving skills and strategies by providing scaffolded guiding questions.
- **Standardized Test Prep** Focuses on all major exercises, all major question types, and helps students prepare for the high-stakes assessments.

Extension

- **Enrichment** Provides students with interesting problems and activities that extend the concepts of the lesson.
- **Activities, Games, and Puzzles** Worksheets that can be used for concepts development, enrichment, and for fun!

Practice and Problem Solving Wkbk/ All-in-One Resources/Online
Practice page 1

13-2 Practice Form G
Angles and the Unit Circle

Find the measure of each angle in standard position.

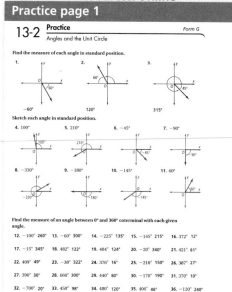

1. −60° 2. 120° 3. 315°

Sketch each angle in standard position.

4. 100° 5. 210° 6. −45° 7. −90°

8. −330° 9. −180° 10. −145° 11. 60°

Find the measure of an angle between 0° and 360° coterminal with each given angle.

12. −100° 260° 13. −60° 300° 14. −225° 135° 15. −145° 215° 16. 372° 12°

17. −15° 345° 18. 482° 122° 19. 484° 124° 20. −20° 340° 21. 421° 61°

22. 409° 49° 23. −38° 322° 24. 376° 16° 25. −210° 150° 26. 387° 27°

27. 390° 30° 28. 660° 300° 29. 440° 80° 30. −170° 190° 31. 370° 10°

32. −700° 20° 33. 458° 98° 34. 480° 120° 35. 406° 46° 36. −120° 240°

37. 460° 100° 38. −222° 138° 39. −330° 30° 40. −127° 233° 41. 377° 17°

Practice and Problem Solving Wkbk/ All-in-One Resources/Online
Practice page 2

13-2 Practice (continued) Form G
Angles and the Unit Circle

42. The spokes shown on the bicycle wheel at the right form an angle. Estimate the measures of two coterminal angles that coincide with the angle at the right. **Answers may vary. Sample: 225°, −135°**

Find the exact values of the cosine and sine of each angle. Then find the decimal values. Round your answers to the nearest hundredth.

43. 0, 1

44. $-\frac{\sqrt{2}}{2}, \frac{\sqrt{2}}{2}$; −0.71, 0.71

45. $-\frac{1}{2}, -\frac{\sqrt{3}}{2}$; −0.5, −0.87

46. 45° $\frac{\sqrt{2}}{2}, \frac{\sqrt{2}}{2}$; 0.71, 0.71

47. −150° $-\frac{\sqrt{3}}{2}, -\frac{1}{2}$; −0.87, −0.5

48. 720° 1, 0

Graphing Calculator For each angle θ, find the values of cos θ and sin θ. Round your answers to the nearest hundredth.

49. 225° (−0.71, −0.71) 50. −225° (−0.71, 0.71) 51. −45° (0.71, −0.71)

52. 330° (0.87, −0.5) 53. −330° (0.87, 0.5) 54. 150° (−0.87, 0.5)

Open-Ended Find a positive and a negative coterminal angle for the given angle.

55. 50° 410°, −310° 56. −130° 230°, −490° 57. −680° 40°, −320°

58. 395° 35°, −325° 59. −38° 322°, −398° 60. −434° 286°, −74°

61. a. Suppose you know the terminal side of angle θ lies in Quadrant II. What is the sign of cos θ? sin θ? **negative, positive**
b. **Writing** Describe the reasoning you followed to answer part (a). **Answers may vary. Sample: Cos θ is the x-coordinate of the point where the terminal side of θ intersects the unit circle, and sin θ is the y-coordinate. In Quadrant II, x-values are negative and y-values are positive.**

All-in-One Resources/Online
Enrichment

13-2 Enrichment
Angles and the Unit Circle

Nautical Miles

Recall that 1° is $\frac{1}{360}$ of a full 360° rotation. You can break down a degree even further. If you divide 1° into 60 equal parts, each one of the parts is called 1 minute, denoted 1′. One minute is $\frac{1}{60}$ of a degree; there are 60 minutes in every degree.

If a central angle with its vertex at the center of the earth has a measure of 1′, then the arc on the surface of the earth that is cut off by this angle has a measure of 1 nautical mile.

For the following problems, assume that the radius of the earth is 4000 miles.

1. Find the number of regular (statute) miles in 1 nautical mile to the nearest hundredth of a mile. **about 1.16 miles**

2. If two ships are 20 nautical miles apart on the ocean, how many statute miles apart are they? Use the result from Exercise 1 in your calculation. **23.2 miles**

3. Two islands are in the ocean. If the central angle with vertex at the center of the earth and rays that pass through these two islands measures 12′, how many statute miles apart are they? Use the result from Exercise 1 in your calculation. **13.92 miles**

4. Los Angeles and San Francisco are approximately 450 miles apart on the surface of the earth. Find the measure of the central angle with its vertex at the center of the earth, one ray that passes through Los Angeles, and another ray that passes through San Francisco. **about 9.113 radians or about 6.5°**

5. Los Angeles and New York City are approximately 2500 miles apart on the surface of the earth. Find the measure of the central angle with its vertex at the center of the earth, one ray that passes through Los Angeles, and another ray that passes through New York City. **0.625 radian or about 35.8°**

Practice and Problem Solving Wkbk/ All-in-One Resources/Online
Think About a Plan

13-2 Think About a Plan
Angles and the Unit Circle

Time The time is 2:46 P.M. What is the measure of the angle that the minute hand swept through since 2:00 P.M.?

Understanding the Problem

1. How many minutes have passed since 2:00 P.M.? **46 min**

2. How many minutes does a full-circle sweep of the minute hand represent? **60 min**

3. How many degrees are in a circle? **360°**

4. What is the problem asking you to determine?
The measure of the angle formed by a minute hand pointing at the 12 and a minute hand pointing at 46 min past the hour

Planning the Solution

5. How can a drawing help you understand the problem?
Answers may vary. Sample: A drawing can help me understand the angles involved

6. Make a drawing that represents the clock and the starting and ending position of the minute hand.

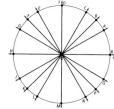

7. Write a proportion that you can use to determine the measure of the angle that the minute hand swept through since 2:00 P.M.
$$\frac{46}{60} = \frac{x}{360}$$

8. Is the angle positive or negative? Explain.
Negative; the minute hand moves clockwise, so the angle it sweeps through is negative

Getting an Answer

9. Solve your proportion to find the measure of the angle. **−276°**

Practice and Problem Solving Wkbk/ All-in-One Resources/Online
Standardized Test Prep

13-2 Standardized Test Prep
Angles and the Unit Circle

Multiple Choice

For Exercises 1–4, choose the correct letter.

1. Which angle, in standard position, is coterminal with an angle in standard position measuring 152°? **D**
   Ⓐ 28° Ⓑ 62° Ⓒ −152° Ⓓ −208°

2. Which could be the measure of an angle θ where sin θ is $-\frac{\sqrt{3}}{2}$? **G**
   Ⓕ −330° Ⓖ 240° Ⓗ 60° Ⓘ 150°

3. An angle in standard position intersects the unit circle at (0, −1). Which could be the measure of the angle? **C**
   Ⓐ 90° Ⓑ −270° Ⓒ −450° Ⓓ 540°

4. What are the coordinates of the point where the terminal side of a 135° angle intersects the unit circle? **F**
   Ⓕ $\left(-\frac{\sqrt{2}}{2}, \frac{\sqrt{2}}{2}\right)$ Ⓖ $\left(\frac{\sqrt{2}}{2}, -\frac{\sqrt{2}}{2}\right)$ Ⓗ $\left(\frac{\sqrt{2}}{2}, \frac{\sqrt{2}}{2}\right)$ Ⓘ $\left(-\frac{\sqrt{2}}{2}, -\frac{\sqrt{2}}{2}\right)$

Short Response

5. What is the exact value of sin (300°)? Show your work.
[2] sin (300°) = $-\frac{\sqrt{3}}{2}$

[1] incorrect answer OR incorrect work OR work not shown
[0] incorrect answers and no work shown OR answers not given

Online Teacher Resource Center
Activities, Games, and Puzzles

13-2 Puzzle: Spinning Around
Angles and the Unit Circle

The points along the circle shown below represent locations of houses. The diameters of the circle with center O determine central angles, whose measures are multiples of 30° and 45°.

- Starting at point G, move along the circle according to these directions: clockwise 60°, counterclockwise 45°, clockwise 135°, counterclockwise 90°, clockwise 60°, counterclockwise 90°, clockwise 180°, clockwise 75°, and counterclockwise 165°.
  What point are you at now? **A**

Three students live in three different houses. Follow the clues to find out where each student lives. Use all the clues below.
- The students live along the shorter arc between G and the point you found above.
- The three homes are "consecutive" points along the circle.
- Student 1 lives on the circle between Student 2 and Student 3.
- None of the students live at point C.
- Student 2 lives closest to point C.

Student 1 lives at point **E**
Student 2 lives at point **D**
Student 3 lives at point **F**

@ **Content Standard**
Prepares for F.TF.1 Understand radian measure of an angle as the length of the arc on the unit circle subtended by the angle.

In the past, you have used degrees to measure angles. When angles are used in periodic functions, they are often measured in larger units called radians.

1. Measure the diameter of a cylinder and calculate its radius. On a piece of string, mark off a "number line" with each unit equal to the radius. Mark at least seven units.

2. Wrap the string around the cylinder. How many radius units are needed to go around the cylinder one time?

3. Use the end of the cylinder to draw a circle on a sheet of paper. Keep the cylinder in place and wrap the string around it on the paper. Mark an arc of the circle equal to one radius unit of length.

4. Remove the cylinder and string. Use paper folding to locate the center of the circle. (Fold the circle onto itself and crease the paper along a diameter. Repeat to get a second diameter.) Draw a central angle that intercepts one radius unit of arc.

The measure of the angle you drew in Question 4 is 1 radian.

5. Use a protractor to measure the angle from Question 4 in degrees.

@ 6. **Reasoning** The formula $C = 2\pi r$ relates the circumference of a circle C to its radius r. *Exactly* how many radians are in a 360° angle? Explain.

The diagram at the right shows that a rotation of 180° is equivalent to π radians.

7. Find the number of degrees in one radian by dividing 180 by π. How does your answer compare to the measurement you made in Question 5?

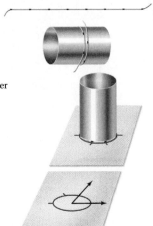

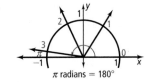

π radians = 180°

Exercises

Use the proportion $\frac{d°}{180°} = \frac{r\,\text{radians}}{\pi\,\text{radians}}$. Find the equivalent degree measure or radian measure.

8. 10°	9. 45°	10. 90°	11. 120°	12. 270°
13. 310°	14. 50°	15. 415°	16. 170°	17. 380°
18. $\frac{13\pi}{18}$ radians	19. $\frac{3\pi}{8}$ radians	20. $\frac{7\pi}{2}$ radians	21. $\frac{11\pi}{4}$ radians	22. $\frac{5\pi}{6}$ radians

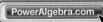

Guided Instruction

PURPOSE To develop a tactile understanding of radian measure

PROCESS Students will
- make a radius measuring tool by marking radius lengths on a string.
- use the measuring tool to draw angles in radian measure.
- use a protractor and reasoning to estimate the degree equivalence of radian measure.

DISCUSS Lengths of string given to students must be about four times the diameter of the cylinder they measure. When students wrap string around the cylinder, have them try to keep the string parallel to the end of the cylinder.

Q The circumference of a cylinder is how many times the radius? About how many lengths on your string do you expect to wrap around the cylinder? **[2π; about $6\frac{1}{4}$]**

Q Will the process you used in 3 and 4 work for other cylinders with your same piece of string? Why or why not? **[The string will work only for cylinders with the same radius. The lengths on the string would not measure a radius length for all cylinders.]**

Q In 4, why does folding the circle back onto itself in two ways find the center? **[A circle is symmetrical across an infinite number of diameters; folding finds diameters. By definition, a diameter of a circle passes through the center. Any two lines can intersect at most once in a plane, and because both must pass through the center, they must intersect at the center.]**

@ **Mathematical Practices** This Concept Byte supports students in making sense of problems, Mathematical Practice 1.

Answers

Concept Byte

1–5. Check students' work.

6. 2π; a circle has an angle measure of 360°. Dividing the circumference, $2\pi r$, by the length of a radius r, we find that there are 2π radians in 360°.

7. about 57.30°; the numbers are very close.

8. $\frac{\pi}{18}$ radians

9. $\frac{\pi}{4}$ radians

10. $\frac{\pi}{2}$ radians

11. $\frac{2\pi}{3}$ radians

12. $\frac{3\pi}{2}$ radians

13. $\frac{31\pi}{18}$ radians

14. $\frac{5\pi}{18}$ radians

15. $\frac{83\pi}{36}$ radians

16. $\frac{17\pi}{18}$ radians

17. $\frac{19\pi}{9}$ radians

18. 130°

19. 67.5°

20. 630°

21. 495°

22. 150°

1 Interactive Learning

Solve It!

PURPOSE To find the degree measure equal to one radian

PROCESS Students may
- approximate the angle by measuring.
- find the angle using geometric formulas.

FACILITATE

Q What is the circumference of the pie? **[2π times the radius]**

Q Arc length is a portion of the circumference. If the arc length were half of the circumference, what would be the central angle? **[180° or π radians]**

Q If the arc length were a quarter of the circumference, what would be the central angle? **[90° or $\frac{\pi}{2}$ radians]**

Q What formula can you use to find the central angle? **[the ratio of the arc length to the circumference times 360° or 2π radians]**

ANSWER See Solve It in Answers on next page.
CONNECT THE MATH The Solve It applies students' knowledge of arcs and central angles. The lesson extends that knowledge to the idea of angle measure written in terms of the circumference, the radian.

2 Guided Instruction

Take Note

Q If the denominator on the left were 360°, what would be the denominator on the right? **[2π radians]**

© Content Standard
F.TF.1 Understand radian measure of an angle as the length of the arc on the unit circle subtended by the angle.

Objectives To use radian measure for angles
To find the length of an arc of a circle

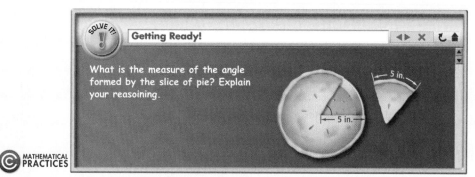

Getting Ready!

What is the measure of the angle formed by the slice of pie? Explain your reasoning.

5 in.

© MATHEMATICAL PRACTICES

Lesson Vocabulary
- central angle
- intercepted arc
- radian

A **central angle** of a circle is an angle with a vertex at the center of a circle. An **intercepted arc** is the portion of the circle with endpoints on the sides of the central angle and remaining points within the interior of the angle.

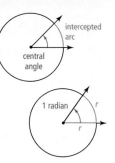
intercepted arc
central angle

A **radian** is the measure of a central angle that intercepts an arc with length equal to the radius of the circle. Radians, like degrees, measure the amount of rotation from the initial side to the terminal side of an angle.

1 radian
r
r

Essential Understanding An angle with a full circle rotation measures 2π radians. An angle with a semicircle rotation measures π radians.

take note **Key Concept** **Proportion Relating Radians and Degrees**

You can use the proportion $\frac{d°}{180°} = \frac{r \text{ radians}}{\pi \text{ radians}}$ to convert between radians and degrees.

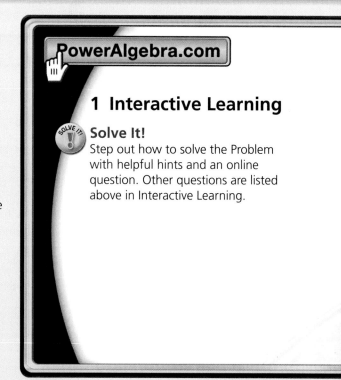

13-3 Preparing to Teach

BIG ideas **Modeling**
Function

ESSENTIAL UNDERSTANDINGS
- An angle with a full circle rotation measures 2π radians. An angle with a semicircle rotation measures π radians.
- To convert degrees to radians, multiply by $\frac{\pi \text{ radians}}{180°}$. To convert radians to degrees, multiply by $\frac{180°}{\pi \text{ radians}}$.
- For a circle of radius r and a central angle of measure θ (in radians), the length of the intercepted arc is $s = r\theta$.

Math Background

Students may not be aware of the advantages radian measure has over degree measure. It is actually a more convenient unit and simplifies calculations in trigonometry, calculus, and other higher-level mathematics and engineering.

The radian measure of an angle is the ratio of the arc length to the radius of the circle. The conversion factor follows directly from this definition; the circumference of a circle is $2\pi r$, so 2π radians is 360 degrees.

The relationship between the angle measure in radians and its arc length s determined by a central angle θ in a circle, $s = r\theta$.

© Mathematical Practices

Attend to precision. Students will define and explicitly use the term "radian" in communicating angle measure. They will also convert from radians to degrees.

PowerAlgebra.com

1 Interactive Learning

Solve It!

Step out how to solve the Problem with helpful hints and an online question. Other questions are listed above in Interactive Learning.

Here's Why It Works

Because the circumference of a circle is $2\pi r$, there are 2π radians in any circle. Since 2π radians $= 360°$, it follows that π radians $= 180°$. This equality leads to the following *conversion factors* for converting between radian measure and degree measure.

> **take note**
>
> #### Key Concept   Converting Between Radians and Degrees
>
> To convert degrees to radians, multiply by $\frac{\pi \text{ radians}}{180°}$.
>
> To convert radians to degrees, multiply by $\frac{180°}{\pi \text{ radians}}$.

You can use the conversion factors and dimensional analysis to convert between angle measurement systems.

© Problem 1   Using Dimensional Analysis

A What is the degree measure of an angle of $-\frac{3\pi}{4}$ radians?

$$-\frac{3\pi}{4} \text{ radians} = -\frac{3\pi}{4} \text{ radians} \cdot \frac{180°}{\pi \text{ radians}} \qquad \text{Multiply by } \frac{180°}{\pi \text{ radians}}.$$

$$= -\frac{3\pi}{1\cancel{4}} \cancel{\text{radians}} \cdot \frac{\overset{45°}{\cancel{180°}}}{\cancel{\pi \text{ radians}}} \qquad \text{Simplify.}$$

$$= -135°$$

An angle of $-\frac{3\pi}{4}$ radians measures $-135°$.

B What is the radian measure of an angle of $27°$?

$$27° = 27° \cdot \frac{\pi \text{ radians}}{180°} \qquad \text{Multiply by } \frac{\pi \text{ radians}}{180°}.$$

$$= {}^{3}\cancel{27°} \cdot \frac{\pi \text{ radians}}{\underset{20}{\cancel{180°}}} \qquad \text{Simplify.}$$

$$= \frac{3\pi}{20} \text{ radians}$$

An angle of $27°$ measures $\frac{3\pi}{20}$ radians.

 Got It? 1. What is the degree measure of each angle expressed in radians? What is the radian measure of each angle expressed in degrees? (Express radian measures in terms of π.)

    a. $\frac{\pi}{2}$ radians   **b.** $225°$ **c.** 2 radians   **d.** $150°$

PowerAlgebra.com   **Lesson 13-3** Radian Measure   845

Think

How do you know which conversion factor to use?
Because radians are in the numerator, use the conversion factor with radians in the denominator.

Here's Why It Works

> **Q** Do radians give the measure of an angle or the length of an intercepted arc? When do these measures have the same value? **[Measure of a central angle of a circle; when the radius is one (unit circle), the radian measure is equal to the length of the intercepted arc.]**

Take Note
When converting between radians and degrees, make sure that the units cancel when multiplying.

> **Q** What are other equalities that could be used to get conversion factors? **[Samples: $360° = 2\pi$ radians; $90° = \frac{\pi}{2}$ radians]**

Problem 1

> **Q** What is a positive coterminal angle measure equivalent to the negative angle measure in 1A? Find the answer in both radians and degrees. Describe your method. **[Sample: A full circle has 2π radians or $360°$, so the coterminal angle must be $2\pi - \frac{3\pi}{4} = \frac{5\pi}{4}$ and $360° - 135° = 225°$.]**
>
> **Q** If the radius of the circle in 1B were one, what would be the length of the arc intercepted by the angle? **[Samples: 0.47; $\frac{3\pi}{20}$]**

Got It?
Before calculating the degree measure of 1c, ask students to estimate a reasonable answer. The thought process should go like this: π radians $= 180°$; $\frac{\pi}{2}$ radians $= 90°$; $\pi \approx 3.14$, so $\frac{\pi}{2} \approx 1.6$. 2 radians must be between $90°$ and $180°$ and closer to $90°$. A good estimate would be between $100°$ and $120°$.

---

2 Guided Instruction

© Each Problem is worked out and supported online.

Problem 1
Using Dimensional Analysis
Animated

Problem 2
Finding Cosine and Sine of a Radian Measure
Animated

Problem 3
Finding the Length of an Arc

Problem 4
Using Radian Measure to Solve a Problem
Animated

Support in Algebra 2 Companion
• Vocabulary
• Key Concepts
• Got It?

Answers

Solve It!
1 radian $\approx 57.3°$; the circumference of the pie is $2\pi r = 10\pi$, so $\frac{5}{10\pi} = \frac{\theta}{2\pi}$. Simplifying, $\theta = 1$ radian. To convert to degrees, $\frac{1 \text{ radian}}{2\pi \text{ radians}} = \frac{x°}{360°}$, so $x \approx 57.3°$.

Got It?
1. a. $90°$

    b. $\frac{5\pi}{4}$ radians

    c. $\frac{360°}{\pi} \approx 114.59°$

    d. $\frac{5\pi}{6}$ radians

Problem 2

Q How many angles have a sine and a cosine that are equal in absolute value? What are the angles? **[An infinite number; from 0 radians to 2π radians, there are four angles: $\frac{\pi}{4}$, $\frac{3\pi}{4}$, $\frac{5\pi}{4}$, and $\frac{7\pi}{4}$.]**

Got It?

Q From 0 radians to 2π radians, how many angles have either a sine or a cosine value with absolute value equal to $\frac{1}{2}$? What are they? **[Eight; $\frac{\pi}{6}$, $\frac{\pi}{3}$, $\frac{2\pi}{3}$, $\frac{5\pi}{6}$, $\frac{7\pi}{6}$, $\frac{4\pi}{3}$, $\frac{5\pi}{3}$, and $\frac{11\pi}{6}$.]**

Take Note

An angle in standard form can have a negative measure. When calculating the length of an intercepted arc, the result is a distance. A negative distance is never a valid solution. Use the absolute value of the angle measure in these cases.

Here's Why It Works

In a unit circle, the length of an arc has the same numerical value as the angle measure of the arc in radians. Students often confuse radians with a unit of length. Radians measure the angle, not length.

Problem 3

Q What is a radius measure of a circle that would return an integer arc length? **[any fraction with an integer numerator and π in the denominator]**

Got It?   **EXTENSION**

Q How can you find the remaining arc length of the circle in Problem 3? **[Samples: Calculate the circumference, C, and subtract the known lengths s and b; subtract the given angles from 2π and use the arc length formula.]**

Think

What kind of angle is π?
It is a straight angle.

Problem 2 Finding Cosine and Sine of a Radian Measure

What are the exact values of $\cos\left(\frac{\pi}{4}\text{ radians}\right)$ and $\sin\left(\frac{\pi}{4}\text{ radians}\right)$?

$\frac{\pi}{4} = \frac{1}{4}\pi = \frac{1}{4}$ of a straight angle or $45°$

Draw the angle on the unit circle.
Complete a $45°$-$45°$-$90°$ triangle. Since the hypotenuse has length 1, both legs have length $\frac{\sqrt{2}}{2}$.
Thus, $\cos\left(\frac{\pi}{4}\text{ radians}\right) = \frac{\sqrt{2}}{2}$ and $\sin\left(\frac{\pi}{4}\text{ radians}\right) = \frac{\sqrt{2}}{2}$.

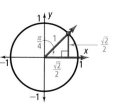

✓ **Got It? 2.** What are the exact values of $\cos\left(\frac{7\pi}{6}\text{ radians}\right)$ and $\sin\left(\frac{7\pi}{6}\text{ radians}\right)$?

If you know the radius and the measure in radians of a central angle, you can find the length of the intercepted arc.

Key Concept Length of an Intercepted Arc

For a circle of radius r and a central angle of measure θ (in radians), the length s of the intercepted arc is $s = r\theta$.

Here's Why It Works The length of the intercepted arc is the same fraction of the circumference of the circle as the central angle is of 2π. So, $\frac{\theta}{2\pi} = \frac{s}{C}$. Since $C = 2\pi r$, then $\frac{\theta}{2\pi} = \frac{s}{2\pi r}$. This simplifies to $\theta = \frac{s}{r}$. Multiplying by r results in $s = r\theta$.

Problem 3 Finding the Length of an Arc

Use the circle at the right. What is length s to the nearest tenth?

$s = r\theta$	Use the formula.
$= 3 \cdot \frac{5\pi}{6}$	Substitute 3 for r and $\frac{5\pi}{6}$ for θ.
$= \frac{5\pi}{2}$	Simplify.
≈ 7.9	Use a calculator.

The arc has a length of about 7.9 in.

Think

What units will the length of the arc have?
Because the radius is in inches, the arc length will be in inches too.

✓ **Got It? 3. a.** What is length b in Problem 3 to the nearest tenth?
b. Reasoning If the radius of the circle doubled, how would the arc length change?

Additional Problems

1. What is the degree measure of an angle of $-\frac{7\pi}{30}$ radians?

ANSWER $-42°$

2. What are the exact measures of $\sin (\pi \text{ radians})$ and $\cos (\pi \text{ radians})$?

ANSWERS 0; -1

3. What is length d to the nearest tenth?

ANSWER 14.1 in.

4. A satellite in geosynchronous orbit travels one Earth circumference in a full day. From a point on the ground, the satellite appears stationary overhead. The orbital height for a geosynchronous satellite is about 36,000 km. The radius of Earth is 6400 km. About how far does the satellite travel in 8 hours? Assume the length of an Earth day is exactly 24 hours.

ANSWER 89,000 km

Answers

Got It? (continued)

2. $-\frac{\sqrt{3}}{2}$, $-\frac{1}{2}$

3. a. 6.3 in.
   b. Arc length would also double.

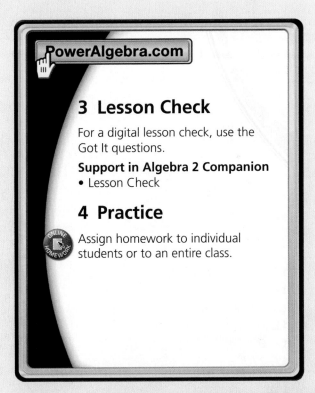

Problem 4 Using Radian Measure to Solve a Problem STEM

Weather Satellite A weather satellite in a circular orbit around Earth completes one orbit every 2 h. How far does the satellite travel in 1 h?

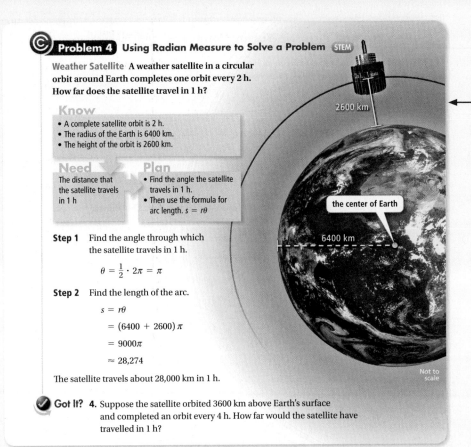

2600 km

the center of Earth

6400 km

Not to scale

Know
- A complete satellite orbit is 2 h.
- The radius of the Earth is 6400 km.
- The height of the orbit is 2600 km.

Need
The distance that the satellite travels in 1 h

Plan
- Find the angle the satellite travels in 1 h.
- Then use the formula for arc length. $s = r\theta$

Step 1 Find the angle through which the satellite travels in 1 h.

$$\theta = \frac{1}{2} \cdot 2\pi = \pi$$

Step 2 Find the length of the arc.

$$s = r\theta$$
$$= (6400 + 2600)\pi$$
$$= 9000\pi$$
$$\approx 28{,}274$$

The satellite travels about 28,000 km in 1 h.

Got It? 4. Suppose the satellite orbited 3600 km above Earth's surface and completed an orbit every 4 h. How far would the satellite have travelled in 1 h?

Lesson Check

Do you know HOW?

1. Find the radian measure of an angle of 300°.

2. Find the degree measure of an angle of $\frac{3\pi}{4}$ radians.

3. Find the length a.

$\frac{4\pi}{3}$

5 in.

a

Do you UNDERSTAND? MATHEMATICAL PRACTICES

4. Vocabulary The radius of a circle is 9 cm. A central angle intercepts an arc that is 9 cm. What is the measure of the central angle in radians?

5. Reasoning A certain baker believes that a perfect slice of pie has a central angle of 1 radian. How many "perfect" slices can he get out of one pie?

PowerAlgebra.com   Lesson 13-3 Radian Measure   847

Problem 4

Q How long does it take the satellite to travel 50,000 km? Explain. **[about 1 hr 46 min; use the arc length formula: 50,000 = 9000 θ. $\theta = \frac{50{,}000}{9000} \approx 5.56$ radians. The satellite travels 2π radians every 2 hours: 5.56 radians $\cdot \frac{2}{2\pi} \approx 1.77$ hr $\approx$ 1 hr 46 min.]**

Got It?

Q What is an alternate way to solve 4? **[Sample: In 1 hour, the satellite completes $\frac{1}{4}$ of a circumference. Calculate the circumference and divide by 4.]**

3 Lesson Check

Do you know HOW? ERROR INTERVENTION
- For Exercises 1 and 2, some students may remember the conversion 360° = 2π more easily than 180° = π. Either conversion will return the correct answer.

Do you UNDERSTAND? ERROR INTERVENTION
- If students answer "9 radians" to Exercise 4, reinforce the definition of a radian by asking analogous questions, such as "What is the measure of a central angle with radius 1 that intercepts an arc with length 1?" "What is the measure of a central angle with radius 2 that intercepts an arc with length 2?"

Close

Q What advantage does radian measure have over degree measure? **[Sample: Radian measure is based on the length of the radius, so it relates to the other important measures of the circle. The "unit" of radian measure is the "unit" of a circle of radius 1.]**

---

4. ≈15,708 km

Lesson Check

1. $\frac{5\pi}{3}$ radians ≈ 5.24 radians

2. 135°

3. $\frac{20\pi}{3}$ ≈ 20.94 in.

4. 1 radian

5. 6 "perfect" slices

PowerAlgebra.com

3 Lesson Check

For a digital lesson check, use the Got It questions.

Support in Algebra 2 Companion
- Lesson Check

4 Practice

Assign homework to individual students or to an entire class.

Lesson 13-3   847

4 Practice

ASSIGNMENT GUIDE

Basic: 6–34 all, 35–49 odd

Average: 7–33 odd, 35–50

Advanced: 7–33 odd, 35–53

Standardized Test Prep: 54–57

Mixed Review: 58–68

ⓒ Mathematical Practices are supported by exercises with red headings. Here are the Practices supported in this lesson:

MP 1: Make Sense of Problems Ex. 35
MP 2: Reason Quantitatively Ex. 4, 5, 34b, 53
MP 2: Reason Abstractly Ex. 46
MP 3: Communicate Ex. 45
MP 3: Critique the Reasoning of Others Ex. 4

Applications exercises have blue headings. Exercises 34, 36, and 50 support MP 4: Model.

STEM exercises focus on science or engineering applications.

EXERCISE 47: Use the Think About a Plan worksheet in the **Practice and Problem Solving Workbook** (also available in the Teaching Resources in print and online) to further support students' development in becoming independent learners.

HOMEWORK QUICK CHECK

To check students' understanding of key skills and concepts, go over Exercises 7, 19, 35, 47, and 49.

Practice and Problem-Solving Exercises   **MATHEMATICAL PRACTICES**

Ⓐ Practice

Write each measure in radians. Express your answer in terms of π and as a decimal rounded to the nearest hundredth.   ◀ See Problem 1.

6. $-300°$ **7.** $150°$ **8.** $-90°$

9. $-60°$ **10.** $160°$ **11.** $20°$

Write each measure in degrees. Round your answer to the nearest degree, if necessary.

12. 3π radians   **13.** $\frac{11\pi}{10}$ radians   **14.** $-\frac{2\pi}{3}$ radians

15. -3 radians   **16.** 1.57 radians   **17.** 4.71 radians

The measure θ of an angle in standard position is given. Find the exact values of $\cos \theta$ and $\sin \theta$ for each angle measure.   ◀ See Problem 2.

18. $\frac{\pi}{6}$ radians   **19.** $\frac{\pi}{3}$ radians   **20.** $\frac{\pi}{2}$ radians   **21.** $-\frac{\pi}{4}$ radians

22. $\frac{2\pi}{3}$ radians   **23.** $-\frac{\pi}{2}$ radians   **24.** $\frac{5\pi}{4}$ radians   **25.** $\frac{7\pi}{6}$ radians

Use each circle to find the length of the indicated arc. Round your answer to the nearest tenth.   ◀ See Problem 3.

26.   **27.**   **28.**

29.   **30.**   **31.**

Find the length of each arc.

32. 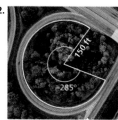   **33.**

848   Chapter 13   Periodic Functions and Trigonometry

Answers

Practice and Problem-Solving Exercises

6. $-\frac{5\pi}{3}$, -5.24

7. $\frac{5\pi}{6}$, 2.62

8. $-\frac{\pi}{2}$, -1.57

9. $-\frac{\pi}{3}$, -1.05

10. $\frac{8\pi}{9}$, 2.79

11. $\frac{\pi}{9}$, 0.35

12. $540°$

13. $198°$

14. $-120°$

15. $-172°$

16. $90°$

17. $270°$

18. $\frac{\sqrt{3}}{2}$, $\frac{1}{2}$

19. $\frac{1}{2}$, $\frac{\sqrt{3}}{2}$

20. 0, 1

21. $\frac{\sqrt{2}}{2}$, $-\frac{\sqrt{2}}{2}$

22. $-\frac{1}{2}$, $\frac{\sqrt{3}}{2}$

23. 0, -1

24. $\frac{-\sqrt{2}}{2}$, $-\frac{\sqrt{2}}{2}$

25. $-\frac{\sqrt{3}}{2}$, $-\frac{1}{2}$

26. 3.1 cm

27. 10.5 m

28. 51.8 ft

29. 25.1 in.

30. 4.7 m

31. 43.2 cm

32. ≈ 746 ft

33. ≈ 32 ft

STEM 34. Space A geostationary satellite is positioned 35,800 km above Earth's surface. It takes 24 h to complete one orbit. The radius of Earth is about 6400 km. ◆ **See Problem 4.**
   a. What distance does the satellite travel in 1 h? 3 h? 2.5 h? 25 h?
   Ⓒ **b. Reasoning** After how many hours has the satellite traveled 200,000 km?

Ⓑ Apply   Ⓒ **35. Think About a Plan** Suppose a windshield wiper arm has a length of 22 in. and rotates through an angle of 110°. What distance does the tip of the wiper travel as it moves once across the windshield?
   • Which formula can help you answer this question?
   • Do you need to convert between degrees and radians?

36. Geography The 24 lines of longitude that approximate the 24 standard time zones are equally spaced around the equator.
   a. Suppose you use 24 central angles to divide a circle into 24 equal arcs. Express the measure of each angle in degrees and in radians.
   b. The radius of the equator is about 3960 mi. About how wide is each time zone at the equator?
   c. The radius of the Arctic Circle is about 1580 mi. About how wide is each time zone at the Arctic Circle?

Determine the quadrant or axis where the terminal side of each angle lies.

37. $\frac{4\pi}{3}$ radians   **38.** $-\frac{5\pi}{4}$ radians   **39.** $-\pi$ radians   **40.** $\frac{6\pi}{5}$ radians

Draw an angle in standard position with each given measure. Then find the values of the cosine and sine of the angle.

41. $\frac{7\pi}{4}$ radians   **42.** $-\frac{2\pi}{3}$ radians   **43.** $\frac{5\pi}{2}$ radians   **44.** $\frac{7\pi}{6}$ radians

Ⓒ **45. Writing** Two angles are measured in radians. Explain how to tell whether the angles are coterminal without rewriting their measures in degrees.

Ⓒ **46. Open-Ended** Draw an angle in standard position. Draw a circle with its center at the vertex of the angle. Find the measure of the angle in radians and degrees.

47. Transportation Suppose the radius of a bicycle wheel is 13 in. (measured to the outside of the tire). Find the number of radians through which a point on the tire turns when the bicycle has moved forward a distance of 12 ft.

Ⓒ **48. Error Analysis** A student wanted to rewrite $\frac{9\pi}{4}$ radians in degrees. The screen shows her calculation. What error did the student make?

9*π/4*360/2*π
           3997.189782

49. Music A CD with diameter 12 cm spins in a CD player. Calculate how much farther a point on the outside edge of the CD travels in one revolution than a point 1 cm closer to the center of the CD.

50. Geography Assume that Earth is a sphere with radius 3960 miles. A town is at latitude 32° N. Find the distance in miles from the town to the North Pole. (*Hint:* Latitude is measured north and south from the equator.)

---

44.   −0.87, −0.50

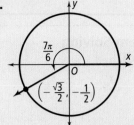

45. If two angles measured in radians are coterminal, the difference of their measures will be evenly divisible by 2π.

46. Check students' work.

47. ≈11 radians

48. The student forgot to include parentheses around 2*π.

49. ≈6.3 cm

50. ≈4008.7 mi

---

34. a. ≈11,048 km, ≈33,144 km, ≈27,620 km, ≈276,198 km

  b. ≈18.1 h

35. ≈42.2 in.

36. a. 15°, $\frac{\pi}{12}$ radians

  b. ≈1036.7 mi

  c. ≈413.6 mi

37. III   **38.** II

39. negative x-axis   **40.** III

41.   0.71, −0.71

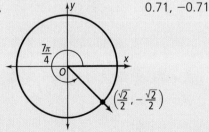

42.   −0.50, −0.87

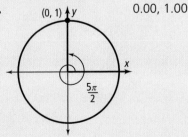

43.   0.00, 1.00

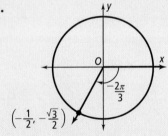

Answers

Practice and Problem-Solving Exercises (continued)

51. $-\frac{3\pi}{2}$ radians

52. $\frac{4\pi}{3}$ radians

53. $\frac{\theta}{s} = \frac{2\pi}{2\pi r}$

$\frac{\theta}{s} = \frac{1}{r}$

$\theta r = s$

$s = \theta r$

Standardized Test Prep

54. C

55. G

56. B

57. [2] For a central angle of 1 radian, the length of the intercepted arc is the length of the radius.

[1] correct description, but does not use the terms "intercepted arc" and "central angle"

Mixed Review

58.

59.

60.

61.

62.

63. mean ≈ 12.9, s.d. ≈ 3.53

64. mean $= 30$, s.d. ≈ 8.09

65. 2

66. all real numbers

67. 1

68. $y = 0$

Challenge The given angle θ is in standard position. Find the radian measure of the angle that results after the given number of revolutions from the terminal side of θ.

51. $\theta = \frac{\pi}{2}$; 1 clockwise revolution

52. $\theta = -\frac{2\pi}{3}$; 1 counterclockwise revolution

53. Reasoning Use the proportion $\frac{\text{measure of central angle}}{\text{length of intercepted arc}} = \frac{\text{measure of one complete rotation}}{\text{circumference}}$ to derive the formula $s = r\theta$. Use θ for the central angle measure and s for the arc length. Measure the rotation in radians.

Standardized Test Prep

SAT/ACT

54. Which pairs of measurements represent the same angle measures?

I. $240°$, $\frac{7\pi}{6}$ radians   II. $135°$, $\frac{3\pi}{4}$ radians   III. $150°$, $\frac{5\pi}{6}$ radians

Ⓐ I and II only   Ⓑ I and III only   Ⓒ II and III only   Ⓓ I, II, and III

55. What is the exact value of $\cos\left(\frac{5\pi}{4} \text{ radians}\right)$?

Ⓕ $-\frac{\sqrt{3}}{2}$ Ⓖ $-\frac{\sqrt{2}}{2}$ Ⓗ $-\frac{1}{2}$ Ⓘ $\frac{\sqrt{2}}{2}$

56. Two arcs have the same length. One arc is intercepted by an angle of $\frac{3\pi}{2}$ radians in a circle of radius 15 cm. If the radius of the other circle is 25 cm, what central angle intercepts the arc?

Ⓐ $\frac{3\pi}{2}$ radians   Ⓑ $\frac{9\pi}{10}$ radians   Ⓒ $\frac{5\pi}{2}$ radians   Ⓓ $\frac{5\pi}{3}$ radians

Short Response

57. For a central angle of one radian, describe the relationship between the radius of the circle and the length of the arc.

Mixed Review

Sketch each angle in standard position.   ◀ See Lesson 13-2.

58. $15°$ **59.** $-75°$ **60.** $150°$ **61.** $-270°$ **62.** $-85°$

Find the mean and the standard deviation for each set of values.   ◀ See Lesson 11-6.

63. 12 13 15 9 16 5 18 16 12 11 15   **64.** 21 29 35 26 25 28 27 51 24 34

Get Ready! To prepare for Lesson 13-4, do Exercises 65–67.

Use the graph. Find each of the following.   ◀ See Lesson 13-1.

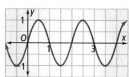

65. the period   **66.** the domain   **67.** the amplitude   **68.** the equation of the midline

Additional Instructional Support

Algebra 2 Companion

Students can use the **Algebra 2 Companion** worktext (4 pages) as you teach the lesson. Use the Companion to support

- New Vocabulary
- Key Concepts
- Got It for each Problem
- Lesson Check

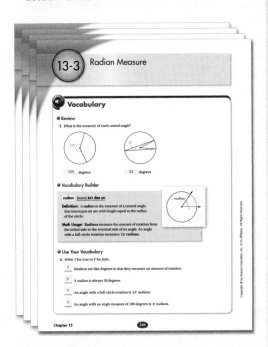

ELL Support

Connect to Prior Knowledge Have students recall and define vocabulary concerning circles and then connect to the new vocabulary in the lesson. Drawing a diagram of a circle showing a radius, diameter, and central angles may help the discussion. Encourage students to talk about any vocabulary. Two scripted sections related to this lesson are below.

- What are some math words that have to do with circles? [*radius, diameter, circumference, center, area,* and *arc*]
- Every point on a circle is the same distance from the *center*. If an angle in a circle has its vertex on the center, what might you call that angle? [*center angle* or *central angle*]
- In this lesson, you learned about the angle measure called the *radian*. What does that word sound like? [*radius*]
- The words *radian* and *radius* sound almost the same. How are they the same in math? [A central angle measures one *radian* when the arc length measures one *radius*.]

5 Assess & Remediate

Lesson Quiz

1. What is the radian measure of an angle of 132°?

2. What are the exact values of $\sin\left(\frac{2\pi}{3}\text{ radians}\right)$ and $\cos\left(\frac{2\pi}{3}\text{ radians}\right)$?

3. What is length a to the nearest tenth?

4. **Do you UNDERSTAND?** In a baseball field, the arc that divides the outfield from the infield has a radius of 95 feet measured from the pitching rubber. The degree measure of the arc is about 145°. What is the length of the arc to the nearest foot?

ANSWERS TO LESSON QUIZ

1. $\frac{11\pi}{15}$

2. $\frac{\sqrt{3}}{2}; -\frac{1}{2}$

3. 23.6 m

4. 240 ft

PRESCRIPTION FOR REMEDIATION

Use the student work on the Lesson Quiz to prescribe a differentiated review assignment:

Points	Differentiated Remediation
0–2	Intervention
3	On-level
4	Extension

PowerAlgebra.com

5 Assess & Remediate

Assign the Lesson Quiz. Appropriate intervention, practice, or enrichment is automatically generated based on student performance.

Intervention

- **Reteaching** (2 pages) Provides reteaching and practice exercises for the key lesson concepts. Use with struggling students or absent students.

- **English Language Learner Support** Helps students develop and reinforce mathematical vocabulary and key concepts.

All-in-One Resources/Online
Reteaching

13-3 Reteaching — Radian Measure

- A central angle that measures π radians intercepts an arc that forms a semicircle. It is a 180° rotation from the initial side to the terminal side of the angle.
- When converting radians to degrees or degrees to radians, use the proportion $\frac{\text{degree measure}}{360} = \frac{\text{radian measure}}{2\pi}$.

Problem

What is the radian measure of an angle of 225°?

$\frac{225}{360} = \frac{x}{2\pi}$ — Substitute 225 for degree measure and a variable for radian measure.

$360x = 450\pi$ — Cross multiply.

$x = \frac{450\pi}{360}$ — Divide both sides by 360.

$x = \frac{5\pi}{4}$ — Simplify.

$x \approx 3.93$ — Use a calculator.

Check $\frac{\theta}{360} = \frac{\frac{5\pi}{4}}{2\pi}$ — Check by substituting the radians into the proportion and solving for degrees.

$\frac{\theta}{360} = \frac{\frac{5}{4}}{2x}$ — Cancel π since it is in the numerator and denominator.

$2\theta = 450$ — Cross multiply.

$\theta = 225$ — Divide both sides by 2. This gives the degree measure.

An angle of 225° measures about 3.93 radians.

Exercises

Write each measure in radians and check.

1. 20° $\frac{\pi}{9} \approx 0.35$ 2. 150° $\frac{5\pi}{6} \approx 2.62$ 3. 45° $\frac{\pi}{4} \approx 0.79$

4. −110° $-\frac{11\pi}{18} \approx -1.92$ 5. 315° $\frac{7\pi}{4} \approx 5.50$ 6. 320° $\frac{16\pi}{9} \approx 5.59$

Write each measure in degrees and check.

7. $-\frac{3\pi}{2} -270°$ 8. $\frac{5\pi}{3} 300°$ 9. $\frac{\pi}{12} 15°$

10. $\frac{8\pi}{5} 288°$ 11. $-\frac{7\pi}{6} -210°$ 12. $\frac{9\pi}{2} 810°$

All-in-One Resources/Online
English Language Learner Support

13-3 Additional Vocabulary Support — Radian Measure

Problem

Use the circle at the right. What is length s to the nearest tenth?

$s = r\theta$ — Use the formula for the length of an intercepted arc.

$s = 6 \cdot \frac{2\pi}{3}$ — Substitute 6 for r and $\frac{2\pi}{3}$ for θ.

$s = \frac{12\pi}{3} = 4\pi$ — Simplify.

$s \approx 12.6$ in. — Use a calculator.

Check $12.6 = r\frac{2\pi}{3}$ — Substitute 12.6 and $\frac{2\pi}{3}$ into the formula.

$12.6 = 2.1r$ — Simplify $\frac{2\pi}{3}$ and round to the nearest tenth.

$r = \frac{12.6}{2.1}$ — Solve for r.

Exercise

Use the circle at the right. What is length s to the nearest tenth?

$s = r\theta$ — Use the formula for the length of an intercepted arc.

$s = 9 \cdot \frac{\pi}{3}$ — Substitute 9 for r and $\frac{\pi}{3}$ for θ.

$s = \frac{9\pi}{3} = 3\pi$ — Simplify.

$s \approx 9.4$ in. — Use a calculator.

Check $9.4 = r\frac{\pi}{3}$ — Substitute 9.4 and $\frac{\pi}{3}$ into the formula.

$9.4 = 1.05r$ — Simplify $\frac{\pi}{3}$ and round to the nearest hundredth.

$r = \frac{9.4}{1.05} \approx 9$ — Solve for r.

Differentiated Remediation *continued*

On-Level

- **Practice** (2 pages) Provides extra practice for each lesson. For simpler practice exercises, use the Form K Practice pages found in the All-in-One Teaching Resources and online.

- **Think About a Plan** Helps students develop specific problem-solving skills and strategies by providing scaffolded guiding questions.

- **Standardized Test Prep** Focuses on all major exercises, all major question types, and helps students prepare for the high-stakes assessments.

Extension

- **Enrichment** Provides students with interesting problems and activities that extend the concepts of the lesson.

- **Activities, Games, and Puzzles** Worksheets that can be used for concepts development, enrichment, and for fun!

Practice and Problem Solving Wkbk/ All-in-One Resources/Online
Practice page 1

13-3 Practice — Form G
Radian Measure

Write each measure in radians. Express your answer in terms of π and as a decimal rounded to the nearest hundredth.

1. 45°   2. 90°   3. 30°   4. −150°
   π/4; 0.79   π/2; 1.57   π/6; 0.52   −5π/6; −2.62

5. 180°   6. −240°   7. 270°   8. 300°
   π; 3.14   −4π/3; −4.19   3π/2; 4.71   5π/3; 5.24

Write each measure in degrees. Round your answer to the nearest degree, if necessary.

9. π/6 radians 30°   10. −7π/6 radians −210°   11. 7π/4 radians 315°

12. −4 radians −229°   13. 1.8 radians 103°   14. 0.45 radians 26°

The measure θ of an angle in standard position is given. Find the exact values of cos θ and sin θ for each angle measure.

15. π/6 √3/2; 1/2   16. π/3 1/2; √3/2   17. −3π/4 −√2/2; −√2/2

18. 7π/4 √2/2; −√2/2   19. 11π/6 √3/2; −1/2   20. −2π/3 −1/2; −√3/2

Use each circle to find the length of the indicated arc. Round your answer to the nearest tenth.

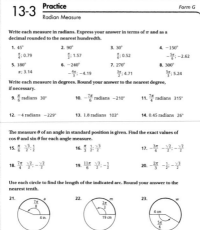

21. 11.0 in.   22. 39.8 cm   23. 10.5 cm

24. 92.2 cm   25. 2.1 ft   26. 15.7 m

Practice and Problem Solving Wkbk/ All-in-One Resources/Online
Practice page 2

13-3 Practice (continued) — Form G
Radian Measure

27. The minute hand of a clock is 8 in. long.
    a. What distance does the tip of the minute hand travel in 10 min? about 8.38 in.
    b. What distance does the tip of the minute hand travel in 40.5 min? about 33.93 in.
    c. What distance does the tip of the minute hand travel in 3.25 h? about 163.36 in.
    d. **Reasoning** After approximately how many hours has the tip of the minute hand traveled 100 ft? about 24 h

28. A 0.8 m pendulum swings through an angle of 86°. What distance does the tip of the pendulum travel? about 1.2 m

29. A scientist studies two islands shown at the right. The distance from the center of the Earth to the equator is about 3960 mi.
    a. What is the measure in radians of the central angle that intercepts the arc along the equator between the islands? π/15 radians
    b. About how far apart are the two islands? about 829.38 mi

Determine the quadrant or axis where the terminal side of each angle lies.

30. π/5 I   31. −5π/2 negative y-axis   32. 5π/3 IV   33. 8π/7 III

Draw an angle in standard position with each given measure. Then find the values of the cosine and sine of the angle to the nearest hundredth.

34. 5π/4   35. −3π   36. 2π/9
    −0.71; −0.71   −1; 0   0.77; 0.64

37. **Error Analysis** A student wanted to convert 75° to radians. His calculation is shown at the right. What error did he make? What is the correct conversion?
    He inverted the conversion factor; 5π/12 radians
    (75 × 180)/π ≈ 4297.18 radians

Practice and Problem Solving Wkbk/ All-in-One Resources/Online
Think About a Plan

13-3 Think About a Plan
Radian Measure

Transportation Suppose the radius of a bicycle wheel is 13 in. (measured to the outside of the tire). Find the number of radians through which a point on the tire turns when the bicycle has moved forward a distance of 12 ft.

Know

1. The radius of the tire is [13 in.].

2. The bicycle moves forward a distance of [12 ft].

3. The formula for the circumference of a circle is [C = 2πr].

Need

4. To solve the problem I need to find the number of radians a point on the tire turns when the bicycle travels forward 12 ft.

Plan

5. The circumference of the tire is [26π in.].

6. The distance the bicycle travels forward is [144] in.

7. The number of radians a point on the tire turns in one complete rotation is [2π].

8. What proportion can you use to find the radians through which the tire turns when the bicycle has moved forward a distance of 12 ft?
   26π in./2π radians = 144 in./x radians

9. Solve your proportion to find the radians through which a point on the tire turns when the bicycle has moved forward a distance of 12 ft. about 11 radians

---

Practice and Problem Solving Wkbk/ All-in-One Resources/Online
Standardized Test Prep

13-3 Standardized Test Prep
Radian Measure

Multiple Choice

For Exercises 1–4, choose the correct letter.

1. Which angle measure is equivalent to 4π/3 radians? D
   Ⓐ 60°   Ⓑ 120°   Ⓒ 135°   Ⓓ 240°

2. If sin θ = √3/2, which could be the value of θ? F
   Ⓕ 2π/3 radians   Ⓖ 3π/4 radians   Ⓗ 4π/3 radians   Ⓘ 3π/2 radians

3. In a circle with a 12 mm radius, a central angle measuring 7π/6 radians intercepts an arc. What is the length of the arc? D
   Ⓐ 6π/7 mm   Ⓑ 72π/7 mm   Ⓒ 12π mm   Ⓓ 14π mm

4. Circle X has a central angle of 3π/8 radians intercepting an arc 3π ft long. Circle Y has a central angle of 3π/4 radians intercepting an arc 3π ft long. Which best describes the radii of circle X and circle Y? G
   Ⓕ The radius of circle X is half as long as the radius of circle Y.
   Ⓖ The radius of circle X is twice as long as the radius of circle Y.
   Ⓗ The radius of circle X is the same length as the radius of circle Y.
   Ⓘ The radius of circle X is more than twice as long as the radius of circle Y.

Short Response

5. Describe the relationship between the total number of radians in a circle and the circumference of the circle.
   [2] A central angle measuring 1 radian intercepts an arc the same length as the radius of the circle. Because the circumference of a circle is 2πr, there are 2π radians in a circle.
   [1] incomplete explanation
   [0] no answer given

All-in-One Resources/Online
Enrichment

13-3 Enrichment
Radian Measure

Conversion Formulas

Radian measure results in an easy-to-remember formula for computing the length of an arc of a circle intercepted by a given angle. Suppose you are given two concentric circles, one of radius r and one of radius 1, and a central angle A.

Let s denote the length of the arc intercepted by ∠A in the circle of radius 1. Let S denote the length of the arc intercepted by ∠A in the circle of radius r.

1. Write an equation involving the ratios of the arc lengths to the radii of the circles. S/r = s/1

2. If A represents the measure of ∠A in radians, express A in terms of s. A = s

3. Express A in terms of S and r. A = S/r

4. Use your results to find S in terms of r and A. S = rA

5. In a circle of radius 3, find the length of the arc intercepted by a central angle of 60°. π

6. Recall that there are 360° or 2π radians in a circle. If A represents the number of radians and D represents the number of degrees in ∠A, write a proportion that can be used to convert between degrees and radians. D/360 = A/2π

7. Derive a formula for the length of the arc S intercepted by ∠A in terms of D. S = π/180 rD

8. What is the length of the arc S intercepted by an angle of V revolutions along a circle of radius r? S = 2πVr

9. Revolutions are often used to express rates of angular rotation. For example, the rate of angular rotation of a long-playing record is 33⅓ rpm. Express this rate in radians per second. 10π/9 radians/s

---

Online Teacher Resource Center
Activities, Games, and Puzzles

13-3 Activity: Revolutions per Minute
Radian Measure

Circles appear everywhere in everyday life. In earlier work, you learned about central angles and how to measure them in degrees. One way to look at the motion of a point around a circle is to measure the degrees traveled over time. Besides using degrees over time, there are other ways to deal with the motion of a point around a circle.

- Begin by working as a class. Think about and list examples in everyday life where you expect to find a point move around a circle. Be as specific as you can. For example, you could list a compact disc or a bicycle wheel. List specific situations below.
  Answers may vary. Samples: merry-go-round, gyroscope, centrifuge, aircraft propeller, circular saw blade, compact disc, fan blade, some water sprinklers, barrel

- As a group, list various situations in which you hear the term *revolutions per minute* (rpm). It is another way to measure the speed at which a point travels around a circle by counting the number of times a point goes around in a circle over time.
  Answers may vary. Samples: circular saw blade, fan blade, automobile crankshaft

- A point travels around a circle at 5400 revolutions per minute. Through how many degrees does that point travel in one minute? 1,944,000°

  Now work in small groups to convert measures of circular motion. For example, you can convert speed in miles per hour to revolutions per minute.

- Suppose a bicycle travels at 10 miles per hour. The wheel of the bicycle has a 14-inch radius. Find how many revolutions a point on the wheel travels in one minute. (In other words, find the wheel's rpm.) Show your work.
  $\frac{10 \text{ mi}}{1 \text{ hr}} = \frac{10}{60 \text{ min}} \times \frac{5280 \text{ ft}}{1} = \frac{10 \times 5280 \times 12 \text{ in.}}{60 \text{ min}} = \frac{10,560 \text{ in.}}{1 \text{ min}}$; circumference is 28π in.;
  $\frac{10,560 \text{ in.}}{1 \text{ min}} \times \frac{1 \text{ revolution}}{28\pi \text{ in.}} \approx 120 \text{ rpm}$

- Now generalize for a driver traveling at m miles per hour on wheels with radius x inches. Use your previous work as a basis to derive a formula that converts m miles per hour on a wheel with radius x inches to revolutions per minute. Show your work.
  $\frac{m \text{ mi}}{1 \text{ hr}} = \frac{m \times 5280 \text{ ft}}{60 \text{ min}} = \frac{m \times 5280 \times 12 \text{ in.}}{60 \text{ min}} = \frac{1056 m \text{ in.}}{1 \text{ min}}$; circumference is 2πx in.;
  $\frac{1056 m \text{ in.}}{1 \text{ min}} \times \frac{1 \text{ revolution}}{2\pi x \text{ in.}} \approx 168\left(\frac{m}{x}\right) \text{ rpm}$

The Sine Function

Content Standards
F.TF.2 Explain how the unit circle . . . enables the extension of trigonometric functions to all real numbers . . .
F.TF.5 Choose trigonometric functions to model periodic phenomena . . .
Also F.IF.4, F.IF.7.e

Objectives To identify properties of the sine function
To graph sine curves

All you need is a plan! How will you start?

MATHEMATICAL PRACTICES

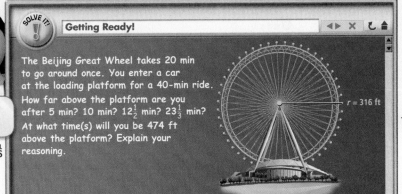

Getting Ready!

The Beijing Great Wheel takes 20 min to go around once. You enter a car at the loading platform for a 40-min ride. How far above the platform are you after 5 min? 10 min? $12\frac{1}{2}$ min? $23\frac{1}{3}$ min? At what time(s) will you be 474 ft above the platform? Explain your reasoning.

$r = 316$ ft

Dynamic Activity
The Sine Curve

Lesson Vocabulary
• sine function
• sine curve

The **sine function**, $y = \sin\theta$, matches the measure θ of an angle in standard position with the y-coordinate of a point on the unit circle. This point is where the terminal side of the angle intersects the unit circle.

You can graph the sine function in radians or degrees. In this book, you should use radians unless degrees are specified. For each and every point along the unit circle, the radian measure of the arc has a corresponding sine value. In the graphs below, the points for 1, 2, and 3 radians are marked on the unit circle. The black bars represent the sine values of the points on the circle translated onto the sine graph.

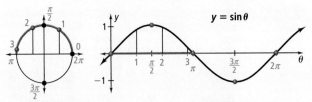

$y = \sin\theta$

Essential Understanding As the terminal side of an angle rotates about the origin (beginning at 0), its sine value on the unit circle increases from 0 to 1, decreases from 1 to −1, and then increases back to 0.

1 Interactive Learning

Solve It!
PURPOSE To find y-coordinates of points on a circle
PROCESS Students may
• draw a diagram of the wheel with points on the wheel for different times in minutes.
• convert minutes to degrees or radians and calculate the sine value.

FACILITATE
Q What function gives the y-value of the position on a circle? **[the sine function]**
Q What is the period of the wheel? How can you convert minutes to radians? **[The period is 20 minutes. In 20 minutes the wheel turns 2π radians, so multiplying by $\frac{\pi}{10}$ converts minutes to radians.]**
Q The wheel turns $\frac{\pi}{10}$ radians every minute, and a passenger travels about 107 ft every minute. These are linear functions. Does the height change by a constant amount for every minute? Explain. **[No. Sample: The height change is greater near the x-axis. The horizontal change is greater near the y-axis.]**

ANSWER See Solve It in Answers on next page.
CONNECT THE MATH The Solve It presents a problem that can be modeled with a periodic function. In the lesson, students will analyze and graph the sine function, which is a periodic function.

13-4 Preparing to Teach

BIG idea Function
ESSENTIAL UNDERSTANDINGS
• As the terminal side of an angle rotates about the origin (beginning at 0°), its sine value on the unit circle increases from 0 to 1, decreases from 1 to −1, and then increases back to 0.
• A nontranslated sine function can be completely described in terms of its amplitude and period.

Math Background
The sine function is a basic periodic function. The period and amplitude of the sine function and its transformations can be found in the same way as other periodic functions.

The parent sine function has a period of 2π and amplitude of 1. Transformations

of the sine function can be represented as $y = a \sin bx$, or $y = a \sin b\theta$.
• The period of a transformation of the sine function is equal to $\frac{2\pi}{b}$.
• The amplitude of a transformation of the sine function is equal to $|a|$.
• For $a < 0$, the graph is a reflection in the x-axis.

Mathematical Practice
Make sense of problems and persevere in solving them. Students will explain correspondences between a representation of sine on a unit circle and a graph of the sine function.

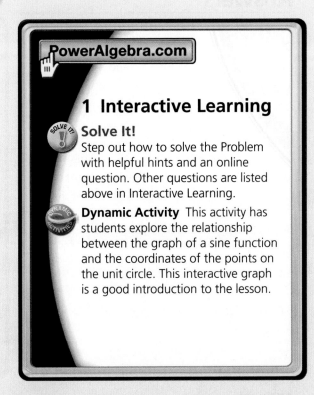

PowerAlgebra.com

1 Interactive Learning
Solve It!
Step out how to solve the Problem with helpful hints and an online question. Other questions are listed above in Interactive Learning.

Dynamic Activity This activity has students explore the relationship between the graph of a sine function and the coordinates of the points on the unit circle. This interactive graph is a good introduction to the lesson.

2 Guided Instruction

Problem 1
Make sure students know how to change their calculator setting between degrees and radians.

Q At which *x*-values can you determine an exact value? **[0, $\frac{\pi}{2}$, π, $\frac{3\pi}{2}$, and 2π]**

Q What is the slope of this graph? Over what range is the slope negative? **[The graph has no single slope; it is always changing. The slope is negative between $\frac{\pi}{2}$ and $\frac{3\pi}{2}$.]**

Got It?

Q What value would you estimate for sin (3 + 2π)? Explain. **[The sine function has a period of 2π, so the value should be the same as for sin 3.]**

Problem 2

Q What is the interval of *x*-values shown on the graph? How many cycles would you expect to see? How many are there actually? **[The interval is 0 to 2π; 1 cycle; 4 cycles.]**

Q How does *y* = sin 4*x* compare with *y* = sin *x*? **[The coefficient of 4 causes a horizontal compression of *y* = sin *x*, changing the period. The amplitude remains the same.]**

Got It?   **ERROR PREVENTION**
Students need to check the *x*-scale in 2a in order to find the correct solution.

Q If the graphs in 2a and 2b have sine as their parent function, what do you think is the coefficient of *x* in each case? **[1 in 2a; $\frac{3}{2}$ in 2b]**

 Think

How accurate should your estimate be?
The *y*-values range from −1 to 1, so the estimate should be to the nearest tenth.

 Plan

How do you find the number of cycles?
Identify the smallest repeating section of the graph and count the number of times it occurs.

 Problem 1 Estimating Sine Values Graphically

What is a reasonable estimate for each value from the graph? Check your estimate with a calculator.

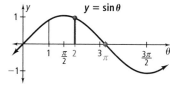

A sin 2

The sine function reaches its maximum value of 1 at $\frac{\pi}{2} \approx 1.57$. The value of the function at 2 is slightly less than 1, or about 0.9.

Check sin 2 ≈ 0.9092974268   Use a calculator in radian mode.

B sin π

The sine function crosses the *x*-axis at π, so sin π = 0.

Check sin π = 0   Use a calculator in radian mode.

Got It? 1. What is a reasonable estimate for each value from the graph above? Check your estimate with a calculator.
 a. sin 3   **b.** sin $\frac{3\pi}{2}$

The graph of a sine function is called a **sine curve**. By varying the period (horizontal length of one cycle), you get different sine curves.

Problem 2 Finding the Period of a Sine Curve

Use the graph of *y* = sin 4*x* at the right.

A How many cycles occur in the graph at the right?

The graph shows 4 cycles.

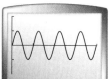

B What is the period of *y* = sin 4*x*?

$$2\pi \div 4 = \frac{\pi}{2}$$ Divide the interval of the graph by the number of cycles.

The period of *y* = sin 4*x* is $\frac{\pi}{2}$.

Got It? 2. How many cycles occur in the graph? What is the period of the sine curve?
 a.   **b.**

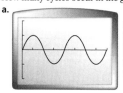   

Answers

Solve It!
Draw a diagram. At 5, 10, 12$\frac{1}{2}$, and 23$\frac{1}{2}$ minutes you are *r*, 2*r*, *r* + $\frac{r}{\sqrt{2}}$, and *r* − $\frac{\sqrt{3}}{2}$ ft high, or 316, 632, 316 + $\frac{316}{\sqrt{2}}$ ≈ 539, and 316 − $\frac{316}{2}$ = 158 ft high. Height of 474 ft = 316 + 158 ft, which is the height after the wheel turns 90° plus an angle with sine = 30°. 90 + 30 = 120, so time = $\frac{120}{360}$ · 20 min = 6$\frac{2}{3}$ min. By symmetry of the circle, you are also at a height 474 ft after the wheel turns 120° + 60° + 60° = 240°. So time = $\frac{240}{360}$ · 20 min = 13$\frac{1}{3}$ min.

Got It?
 1. a. ≈ 0.1411; estimates may vary.
    b. −1
 2. a. 2; 2π
    b. 3; $\frac{4\pi}{3}$

 PowerAlgebra.com

2 Guided Instruction

Each Problem is worked out and supported online.

Problem 1
Estimating Sine Values Graphically

Problem 2
Finding the Period of a Sine Curve
                                   Animated

Problem 3
Finding the Amplitude of a Sine Curve

Problem 4
Sketching a Graph

Problem 5
Graphing From a Function Rule
                                   Animated

Problem 6
Using the Sine Function to Model Light Waves
                                   Animated

Support in Algebra 2 Companion
• Vocabulary
• Key Concepts
• Got It?

You can also vary the amplitude of a sine curve.

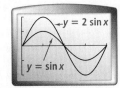 **Problem 3** Finding the Amplitude of a Sine Curve

The graphing calculator screens at the right show four graphs of $y = a \sin x$. Each x-axis shows values from 0 to 2π.

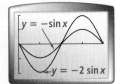

 Think

What is the amplitude?
The amplitude is half the difference of the maximum and minimum values of the periodic function.

A What is the amplitude of each sine curve? How does the value of a affect the amplitude?

The amplitude of $y = \sin x$ is 1, and the amplitude of $y = 2 \sin x$ is 2.
The amplitude of $y = -\sin x$ is 1, and the amplitude of $y = -2 \sin x$ is 2.
In each case, the amplitude of the curve is $|a|$.

B How does a negative value of a affect the position of the curve?

When a is negative, the graph is a reflection across the x-axis.

✓ **Got It?** **3.** The equation of the graph is of the form $y = a \sin x$. What is the amplitude of the sine curve? What is the value of a?

a. 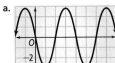   b.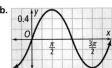

The summary box below lists the properties of sine functions.

take note

Concept Summary   Properties of Sine Functions

Suppose $y = a \sin b\theta$, with $a \neq 0$, $b > 0$, and θ in radians.

- $|a|$ is the amplitude of the function.
- b is the number of cycles in the interval from 0 to 2π.
- $\frac{2\pi}{b}$ is the period of the function.

You can use five points equally spaced through one cycle to sketch a sine curve. For $a > 0$, this five-point pattern is *zero–max–zero–min–zero*.

Problem 3

Q Does the coefficient a stretch the graph vertically or horizontally? **[vertically]**

EXTENSION

Q The function $y = 2 \sin x$ has a range from $+2$ to -2. How could you modify the parent sine function so that its range is $+2$ to 0? **[Add 1 to the parent function: $y = \sin x + 1$]**

Got It?

Q The sine function is periodic, so you can assume it repeats in both directions. How could you write a sine function for 3a using positive 3 as the value for a, assuming the graph has a period of 2π? Explain. **[Answers may vary. Sample: The function $y = 3 \sin (x + \pi)$ would show the graph with a positive a value. Any positive or negative x-shift by an odd-integer multiple of π would work.]**

Take Note

Q Why is b restricted to positive values? **[b needs to be positive in order to use it as the number of cycles from 0 to 2π. A negative number of cycles does not make sense. Since $a \sin (-bx) = -a \sin (bx)$, you can always assume b to be positive and change the sign of a to compensate if necessary.]**

Q If b were zero, what would the graph look like? If b were -1, what would the graph look like? **[If b is zero, the graph is a horizontal line $y = 0$. If b is -1, the graph is reflected across the x-axis; it looks the same as $y = -1 \sin x$.]**

Q For negative values of a, what pattern of five points would you use to sketch a graph? **[zero-min-zero-max-zero]**

Additional Problems

1. Is sin 4 positive or negative? Explain.

ANSWER Negative; 4 is between π and 2π.

2. How many cycles appear in the graph? What is the period of a cycle of the function?

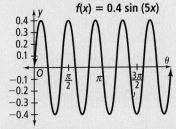

$f(x) = 0.4 \sin (5x)$

ANSWER $5; \frac{2\pi}{5}$

3. The equation of the graph for Additional Problem 2 is of the form $y = a \sin x$. What is the amplitude of this sine curve? What is the value of a?

ANSWER $0.4; a = 0.4$

4. A sine curve has amplitude 0.2, period 8π, and $a > 0$. What is an equation for the sine curve in the form $y = a \sin b\theta$?

ANSWER $y = 0.2 \sin 0.25\theta$

5. What is the graph of one cycle of $y = 10 \sin 4\theta$?

ANSWER

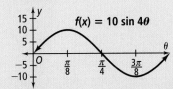

$f(x) = 10 \sin 4\theta$

6. The pattern of ocean tides cannot be modeled by a sine function, but the simpler individual forces that make up tides can. Two such patterns are called diurnal tides, which complete a cycle in a day, and semidiurnal tides, which complete a cycle in half a day. If the semidiurnal tide causes a maximum difference of 4 ft between high tide and low tide, what is the value of a in the function modeling the semidiurnal tide, $y = a \sin \frac{\pi}{6}\theta$?

ANSWER 2

Answers

Got It? (continued)

3. a. $3; -3$
    b. $0.6; 0.6$

Problem 4

Q In Step 2 you divide the period into fourths to find points, but you need 5 points to sketch the graph. How does this make sense? **[Dividing the period into 4 parts does give 5 points: one at the beginning, three in the middle that you mark, and one at the end.]**

Got It?

Q How will your graph compare with the graph in Problem 4? **[The period will be the same. The amplitude will be $1\frac{1}{2}$ times as great.]**

Problem 5

Q What is meant by *critical values* on the θ-axis? **[where the function has max, min, or zero values for y]**

Q What are the units of the θ-axis and the y-axis for this graph? **[The θ-axis has units of radians. The y-axis has an unspecified unit of length.]**

Think

What do you need to find to write the equation?
You need to find a and b.

© **Problem 4** Sketching a Graph

What is the graph of one cycle of a sine curve with amplitude 2, period 4π, midline $y = 0$, and $a > 0$? Using the form $y = a \sin b\,\theta$, what is an equation for the sine curve?

Step 1 Choose scales for the y-axis and the θ-axis that are about equal ($\pi \approx 3$ units). On the θ-axis, mark one period (4π).

Step 2 Mark equal spaces through one cycle by dividing the period into fourths.

Step 3 Since the amplitude is 2, the maximum is 2 and the minimum is -2. Since $a > 0$, the maximum value occurs before the minimum value. Plot the five-point pattern and sketch the curve.

Step 4 The amplitude is 2, and $a > 0$, so $a = 2$. The period is 4π, and $4\pi = \frac{2\pi}{b}$, so $b = \frac{1}{2}$.

An equation for the function is $y = 2 \sin \frac{1}{2}\theta$.

✔ **Got It?** **4.** What is the graph of one cycle of a sine curve with amplitude 3, period 4π, and $a > 0$? Use the form $y = a \sin b\,\theta$. What is an equation with $a > 0$ for the sine curve?

© **Problem 5** Graphing From a Function Rule

What is the graph of one cycle of $y = \frac{1}{2} \sin 2\theta$?

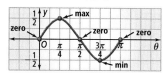

Know	Need	Plan
An equation of the form $y = a \sin b\theta$	The graph of one cycle of the equation	Identify the amplitude and period to find and plot points of the *zero-max-zero-min-zero* pattern.

Step 1 Find the amplitude, number of cycles, and period.

$$|a| = \left|\frac{1}{2}\right| = \frac{1}{2} \text{ and } b = 2, \text{ so it cycles 2 times from 0 to } 2\pi.$$

Period: $\frac{2\pi}{b} = \frac{2\pi}{2} = \pi$

Step 2 Divide the period into fourths. Identify θ-values for the five-point pattern.

$\pi \div 4 = \frac{\pi}{4}$ The θ-values are $0, \frac{\pi}{4}, \frac{\pi}{2}, \frac{3\pi}{4}$, and π.

Step 3 Sketch the graph.

Answers

Got It? (continued)

4.

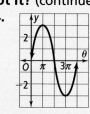

$y = 3 \sin \frac{1}{2}\theta$

Got It? **5.** What is the graph of one cycle of each sine function?
   a. $y = 1.5 \sin 2\theta$ **b.** $y = 3 \sin \frac{\pi}{2}\theta$

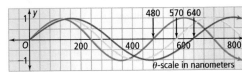 **Problem 6** Using the Sine Function to Model Light Waves

Multiple Choice The graphs at the right model waves of red, blue, and yellow light. Which equation best models blue light?

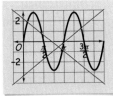

θ-scale in nanometers

Ⓐ $y = \sin 240\pi\theta$ Ⓑ $y = \sin 480\pi\theta$ Ⓒ $y = \sin \frac{\pi}{480}\theta$ Ⓓ $y = \sin \frac{\pi}{240}\theta$

According to the graph, one blue cycle takes 480 nanometers to complete, so the period is 480.

Think

How can you check if you found the correct value for b?
Multiply the value you found for *b* by the number of nanometers where the first cycle ends. The product should be 2π.

To write an equation, first find *b*.

period $= \frac{2\pi}{b}$ Use the relationship between the period and *b*.

$480 = \frac{2\pi}{b}$ Substitute.

$b = \frac{2\pi}{480}$ Multiply each side by $\frac{b}{480}$.

An equation for blue light is $y = \sin \frac{2\pi}{480}\theta$ or $y = \sin \frac{\pi}{240}\theta$. The correct answer is D.

Got It? **6.** What equation best models red light in Problem 6?

Problem 6

Q If period determines color, what might the amplitude determine? **[Answers may vary. Sample: the intensity of the light]**

Got It?

Q How do you find the period of red light? What is it? How did you find *b*? **[The period is one full cycle read off the graph: 640 nm. Divide 2π by 640 to find *b*.]**

Lesson Check

Do you know HOW?

1. a. How many cycles does this graph of a sine function have in the interval from 0 to 2π?
   b. What are the amplitude and period?
   c. Write an equation for the function.

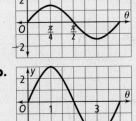

Xmin = 0
Xmax = 2π
Xscl = π/2
Ymin = −3
Ymax = 3
Yscl = 1

2. Sketch one cycle of the sine curve that has amplitude 2 and period $\frac{\pi}{3}$.

Do you UNDERSTAND? Ⓒ MATHEMATICAL PRACTICES

Ⓒ **3. Vocabulary** What is the difference between one cycle and the period of a sine curve?

Ⓒ **4. Open-Ended** Write a sine function that has a period greater than the period for $y = 5 \sin \frac{\theta}{2}$.

Ⓒ **5. Error Analysis** A student drew this graph for the function $y = -3 \sin \pi\theta$. Describe and correct the student's errors.

3 Lesson Check

Do you know HOW?
- In Exercise 2, the student's *y*-axis must run from at least −2 to +2, not from −1 to +1.

Do you UNDERSTAND? ERROR INTERVENTION
- If students write a function with a *b* value greater than $\frac{1}{2}$ for Exercise 4, explain that *b* is inversely proportional to the period. A greater *b* value gives a shorter period.
- In Exercise 5, the graph has *two* errors. Students should examine both the amplitude and the period.

Close

Q How do the coefficients *a* and *b* in $y = a \sin bx$ change the graph of the parent function $y = \sin x$? **[a changes the amplitude of the graph; b changes the period of the graph.]**

5. a.

b.

6. $y = \sin \frac{\pi}{320}\theta$

Lesson Check

1. a. 2
   b. 3; π
   c. $y = 3 \sin 2\theta$

2.

3. *b* is the number of cycles of a sine function in the interval from 0 to 2π; the period of the sine function is $\frac{2\pi}{b}$, or the length of one complete cycle.

4. Answers may vary. Sample:
$y = 5 \sin \frac{\theta}{3}$

5. The amplitude is 3, but since *a* < 0, the graph is reflected across the *x*-axis. Also, the period is 2, not π.

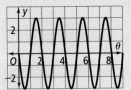

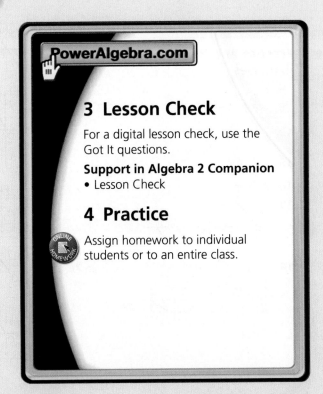

PowerAlgebra.com

3 Lesson Check

For a digital lesson check, use the Got It questions.

Support in Algebra 2 Companion
- Lesson Check

4 Practice

Assign homework to individual students or to an entire class.

4 Practice

ASSIGNMENT GUIDE

Basic: 6–30 all, 33–39 odd, 47

Average: 7–29 odd, 31–47

Advanced: 7–29 odd, 31–54

Standardized Test Prep: 55–59

Mixed Review: 60–69

© **Mathematical Practices** are supported by exercises with red headings. Here are the Practices supported in this lesson:

MP 1: Make Sense of Problems Ex. 39
MP 2: Reason Abstractly Ex. 3, 46
MP 3: Communicate Ex. 4
MP 3: Critique the Reasoning of Others Ex. 5
MP 5: Use Tools Appropriately Ex. 37

Applications exercises have blue headings. Exercises 47, 48 support MP 4: Model.

EXERCISE 47: Use the Think About a Plan worksheet in the **Practice and Problem Solving Workbook** (also available in the Teaching Resources in print and online) to further support students' development in becoming independent learners.

HOMEWORK QUICK CHECK

To check students' understanding of key skills and concepts, go over Exercises 7, 27, 35, 39, and 47.

 Practice and Problem-Solving Exercises **MATHEMATICAL PRACTICES**

A Practice

Use the graph at the right to find the value of $y = \sin\theta$ for each value of θ. ◀ See Problem 1.

6. $\frac{\pi}{2}$ radians **7.** 3 radians

8. 4 radians **9.** 5 radians

10. $\frac{3\pi}{2}$ radians **11.** $\frac{7\pi}{4}$ radians

Determine the number of cycles each sine function has in the interval from 0 to 2π. Find the amplitude and period of each function. ◀ See Problems 2 and 3.

12.   **13.**   **14.**

Sketch one cycle of each sine curve. Assume $a > 0$. Write an equation for each graph. ◀ See Problem 4.

15. amplitude 2, period $\frac{2\pi}{3}$ **16.** amplitude $\frac{1}{3}$, period π **17.** amplitude 4, period 4π

18. amplitude 3, period 2π **19.** amplitude 1, period 2 **20.** amplitude 1.5, period 3

Sketch one cycle of the graph of each sine function. ◀ See Problem 5.

21. $y = \sin \pi\theta$ **22.** $y = \sin 3\theta$ **23.** $y = -\sin\frac{\pi}{2}\theta$

24. $y = 2\sin \pi\theta$ **25.** $y = 4\sin\frac{1}{2}\theta$ **26.** $y = -4\sin\frac{1}{2}\theta$

Find the period of each sine curve. Then write an equation for each sine function. ◀ See Problem 6.

27. 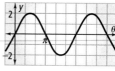 **28.**

29. 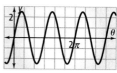 **30.**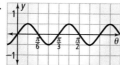

Answers

Practice and Problem-Solving Exercises

6. 1 **7.** ≈0.1 **8.** ≈−0.8

9. ≈−1 **10.** −1 **11.** ≈−0.7

12. 3; 2, $\frac{2\pi}{3}$

13. $\frac{1}{2}$; 1, 4π

14. 2; 3, π

15. 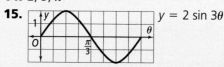 $y = 2\sin 3\theta$

16. 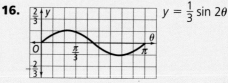 $y = \frac{1}{3}\sin 2\theta$

17. 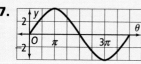 $y = 4\sin\frac{1}{2}\theta$

18. $y = 3\sin\theta$

19. $y = \sin \pi\theta$

20. 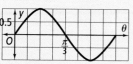 $y = \frac{3}{2}\sin\frac{2\pi}{3}\theta$

21.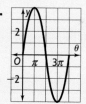

22.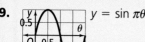

23.

24.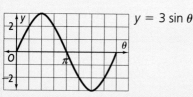

25.

26.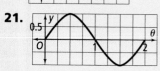

27. 2π; $y = 2\sin\theta$

28. 2π; $y = -3\sin\theta$

29. π; $y = \frac{5}{2}\sin 2\theta$

30. $\frac{\pi}{3}$; $y = \frac{1}{2}\sin 6\theta$

Determine the number of cycles each sine function has in the interval from 0 to 2π. Find the amplitude and period of each function.

31. $y = \sin \theta$ **32.** $y = \sin 5\theta$ **33.** $y = \sin \pi\theta$

34. $y = 3 \sin \theta$ **35.** $y = -5 \sin \theta$ **36.** $y = -5 \sin 2\pi\theta$

37. Graphing Calculator Graph the functions $y = 3 \sin \theta$ and $y = -3 \sin \theta$ on the same screen. How are the two graphs related? How does the graph of $y = a \sin b\theta$ change when a is replaced with its opposite?

38. Use the formula period $= \frac{2\pi}{b}$ to find the period of each sine function.

a. $y = 1.5 \sin 2\theta$ **b.** $y = 3 \sin \frac{\pi}{2}\theta$

39. Think About a Plan The sound wave for the note A above middle C can be modeled by the function $y = 0.001 \sin 880\pi\theta$. Sketch a graph of the sine curve.
- What is the period of the function?
- What is the amplitude of the function?
- How many cycles of the graph are between 0 and 2π?

Find the period and amplitude of each sine function. Then sketch each function from 0 to 2π.

40. $y = -3.5 \sin 5\theta$ **41.** $y = \frac{5}{2} \sin 2\theta$ **42.** $y = -2 \sin 2\pi\theta$

43. $y = 0.4 \sin 3\theta$ **44.** $y = 0.5 \sin \frac{\pi}{3}\theta$ **45.** $y = -1.2 \sin \frac{5\pi}{6}\theta$

46. Open-Ended Write the equations of three sine functions with the same amplitude that have periods of 2, 3, and 4. Then sketch all three graphs.

47. Music The sound wave for a certain pitch fork can be modeled by the function $y = 0.001 \sin 1320\pi\theta$. Sketch a graph of the sine curve.

Challenge

48. Astronomy In Houston, Texas, at the spring equinox (March 21), there are 12 hours and 9 minutes of sunlight. The longest and shortest day of the year vary from the equinox by 1 h 55 min. The amount of sunlight during the year can be modeled by a sine function.
a. Define the independent and dependent variables for a function that models the variation in hours of sunlight in Houston.
b. What are the amplitude and period of the function measured in days?
c. Write a function that relates the number of days away from the spring equinox to the variation in hours of sunlight in Houston.
d. **Estimation** Use your function from part (c). In Houston, about how much less sunlight does February 14 have than March 21?

March 21
equal day and night

June 21
longest day

Dec. 21
shortest day

Sept. 22
equal day and night

43. $\frac{2\pi}{3}$, 0.4;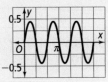

44. 6, 0.5;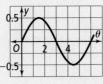

45. $\frac{12}{5}$, 1.2;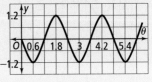

46. Check students' work.

47.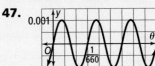

48. a. independent: days from spring equinox, dependent: hours of sunlight

b. $\frac{23}{12}$ h, about 365 days

c. $y = \frac{23}{12} \sin \frac{2\pi x}{365}$

d. 1.1 h

31. 1; 1, 2π

32. 5; 1, $\frac{2\pi}{5}$

33. π; 1, 2

34. 1; 3, 2π

35. 1; 5, 2π

36. 2π; 5, 1

37.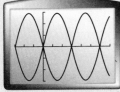

They are reflections of each other across the x-axis.

When a is replaced by its opposite, the graph is a reflection of the original graph across the x-axis.

38. a. π

b. 4

39.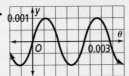

40. $\frac{2\pi}{5}$, 3.5;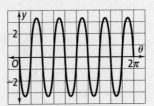

41. π, $\frac{5}{2}$;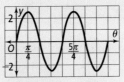

42. 1, 2;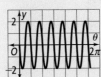

Answers

Practice and Problem-Solving Exercises (continued)

49. $y = \sin 60\pi\theta$

50. $y = \sin 30\pi\theta$

51. $y = \sin 240{,}000\pi\theta$

52. 2π, 1;

53. 2π, 1;

54. π, 1;
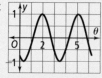

Standardized Test Prep

55. C

56. G

57. C

58. G

59. [2] 120°; consider the point where a 60° angle intersects the unit circle. Reflect this point across the y-axis. The image is the intersection of a 120° angle and the unit circle. These two points have the same y-coordinate. Therefore $\sin 120° = \sin 60°$.

    [1] incorrect explanation

Mixed Review

60. $-\dfrac{4\pi}{9}$ radians, -1.40 radians

61. $\dfrac{5\pi}{6}$ radians, 2.62 radians

62. $-\dfrac{4\pi}{3}$ radians, -4.19 radians

63. $\dfrac{16\pi}{9}$ radians, 5.59 radians

64. $-\dfrac{5\pi}{2}$ radians, -7.85 radians

65. $\approx 49\%$

66. 1

67. 0

68. -1

69. 0

STEM **Sound** For sound waves, the period and the frequency of a pitch are reciprocals of each other: $\text{period} = \frac{\text{seconds}}{\text{cycle}}$ and $\text{frequency} = \frac{\text{cycles}}{\text{second}}$. Write an equation for each pitch. Let θ = time in seconds. Use $a = 1$.

49. the lowest pitch easily heard by humans: 30 cycles per second

50. the lowest pitch heard by elephants: 15 cycles per second

51. the highest pitch heard by bats: 120,000 cycles per second

Find the period and amplitude of each function. Sketch each function from 0 to 2π.

52. $y = \sin(\theta + 2)$ **53.** $y = \sin(\theta - 3)$ **54.** $y = \sin(2\theta + 4)$

Standardized Test Prep

SAT/ACT

55. Which value is NOT the same as the other three values?
  Ⓐ $\sin 100°$ Ⓑ $\sin 80°$ Ⓒ $\sin -80°$ Ⓓ $\sin -260°$

56. What is the amplitude of $y = 3\sin 4\theta$?
  Ⓕ $\frac{4}{3}$ Ⓖ 3   Ⓗ 4   Ⓘ 2π

57. Which answer choice describes $y = -\sin 2\theta$?
  Ⓐ amplitude -1, period 4π Ⓒ amplitude 1, period π
  Ⓑ amplitude 2, period $-\pi$ Ⓓ amplitude 2π, period 1

58. Which function has a period of 4π and an amplitude of 8?
  Ⓕ $y = -8\sin 8\theta$ Ⓖ $y = -8\sin\frac{1}{2}\theta$ Ⓗ $y = 8\sin 2\theta$ Ⓘ $y = 4\sin 8\theta$

Short Response

59. Find the value of θ that is between 90° and 180° such that $\sin\theta = \sin 60°$. Show your work.

Mixed Review

Write each measure in radians. Express the answer in terms of π and as a decimal rounded to the nearest hundredth.
◆ See Lesson 13-3.

60. $-80°$ **61.** $150°$ **62.** $-240°$ **63.** $320°$ **64.** $-450°$

65. A poll of teenagers in one town showed that 43% play a team sport. It also showed that 21% play varsity team sports. Find the probability that a teenager plays varsity sports, given that the teenager plays a team sport.
◆ See Lesson 11-4.

Get Ready! To prepare for Lesson 13-5, do Exercises 66–69.

Find the x-coordinate of each point on the unit circle at the right.
◆ See Lesson 13-2.

66. A **67.** B **68.** C **69.** D

Additional Instructional Support

Algebra 2 Companion

Students can use the **Algebra 2 Companion** worktext (4 pages) as you teach the lesson. Use the Companion to support

- New Vocabulary
- Key Concepts
- Got It for each Problem
- Lesson Check

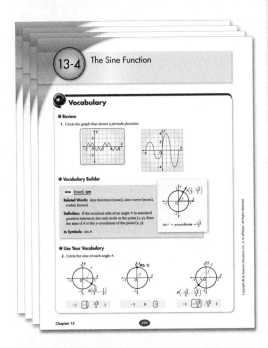

ELL Support

Use Manipulatives For this activity you will need an empty paper towel roll (or some other hollow cylinder) for each group participating, felt-tip pens or markers and tape.

Have each group secure the pen to the *inside* of the paper-towel roll with tape. The writing point of the pen should stick out just past the lip of the roll. Have students tape a piece of graph paper to a firm flat surface like the back of a notebook. While one student holds the notebook perpendicular to a desk or table, another rolls the cylinder with the pen tip touching the graph paper. Have students draw axes on their sine curve so that the maximum and minimum values are equidistant from the horizontal axis. Ask:

- Is this a sine curve or a sine function? [a sine curve]
- What is the difference? [A sine curve is the graph of the sine function.]
- How can you find the amplitude of this curve? the period? [The radius of the cylinder is the amplitude. The period is the circumference of the cylinder.]

Measure both the cylinder and the graph to check.

5 Assess & Remediate

Lesson Quiz

1. The equation of the graph is of the form $y = a \sin x$. What is the amplitude of the sine curve? What is the value of a?

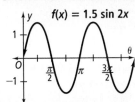

$f(x) = 1.5 \sin 2x$

2. What is the graph of one cycle of a sine curve with amplitude 5, period π, and $a > 0$? What is an equation for the sine curve in the form $y = a \sin b\theta$?

3. **Do you UNDERSTAND?** The musical tone known as "middle C" completes one cycle in 132 cm. The note one half-step higher, D-flat, completes one cycle in 124 cm. Which note could be modeled by the function $y = \sin \frac{\pi}{62}\theta$?

ANSWERS TO LESSON QUIZ

1. 1.5; $a = 1.5$

2.

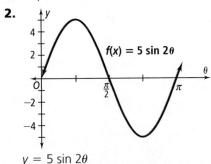

$f(x) = 5 \sin 2\theta$

$y = 5 \sin 2\theta$

3. D-flat

PRESCRIPTION FOR REMEDIATION

Use the student work on the Lesson Quiz to prescribe a differentiated review assignment:

Points	Differentiated Remediation
0–1	Intervention
2	On-level
3	Extension

PowerAlgebra.com

5 Assess & Remediate

Assign the Lesson Quiz. Appropriate intervention, practice, or enrichment is automatically generated based on student performance.

Intervention

- **Reteaching** (2 pages) Provides reteaching and practice exercises for the key lesson concepts. Use with struggling students or absent students.

- **English Language Learner Support** Helps students develop and reinforce mathematical vocabulary and key concepts.

All-in-One Resources/Online
Reteaching

13-4 Reteaching — The Sine Function

A sine curve is the graph of a sine function. You can identify a sine curve by its *amplitude* and *period*. Amplitude is one-half the vertical distance between the maximum and minimum values. The period is the horizontal length of one cycle.

Problem

Use the graph of $y = -3\sin 2x$, where x is measured in radians, at the right. What are the amplitude and period of the sine curve?

Amplitude

The maximum value of the sine curve is 3.

The minimum value of the sine curve is −3.

One-half the difference of these values is $\frac{(3 - (-3))}{2} = \frac{6}{2} = 3$.

The amplitude of the curve is 3.

> The **amplitude** equals the absolute value of the coefficient of the function.

Period

Between 0 and 2π, the graph cycles 2 times.

To get the length of one cycle, divide 2π by the number of cycles between 0 and 2π.

The period of the curve is $\frac{2\pi}{2} = \pi$.

> The **number of cycles** between 0 and 2π equals the coefficient of x in the function.

Summary

For all sine functions written in the form $y = a \sin b\theta$, where $a \neq 0$, $b > 0$, and θ is measured in radians:

$$\text{amplitude} = |a| \qquad \text{period} = \frac{2\pi}{b}$$

Exercises

Find the amplitude and period of each sine function.

1. $y = \frac{1}{2} \sin 3\theta$ $\frac{1}{2}; \frac{2\pi}{3}$
2. $y = \sin 5\theta$ $1; \frac{2\pi}{5}$
3. $y = 4 \sin \frac{4}{5}\theta$ $4; \frac{5}{2}$
4. $y = \frac{3}{2} \sin \theta$ $\frac{3}{2}; 2\pi$
5. $y = -2 \sin \frac{4}{5}\theta$ $2; \frac{5\pi}{2}$
6. $y = \pi \sin 2\theta$ π, π

All-in-One Resources/Online
English Language Learner Support

13-4 Additional Vocabulary Support — The Sine Function

Properties of Sine Functions

Suppose $y = a \sin b\theta$, with $a \neq 0$, $b > 0$, and θ in radians.

- $|a|$ is the amplitude of the function.
- b is the number of cycles in the interval from 0 to 2π.
- $\frac{2\pi}{b}$ is the period of the function.

Find the amplitude, number of cycles in the interval from 0 to 2π, and period of each function.

1. $y = 4 \sin \frac{1}{2}\theta$ amplitude: 4   cycles: $\frac{1}{2}$ period: 4π

2. $y = -3 \sin 2\pi\theta$ amplitude: 3   cycles: 2π period: 1

3. $y = 2 \sin\left(\frac{\pi}{2} \cdot \theta\right)$ amplitude: 2   cycles: $\frac{\pi}{2}$ period: 4

Write sine functions with the following properties.

4. an amplitude of 6 and 4π cycles $y = 6 \sin 4\pi\theta$ or $y = -6 \sin 4\pi\theta$

5. an amplitude of 1 and $\frac{\pi}{2}$ cycles $y = \sin\left(\frac{\pi}{2} \cdot \theta\right)$ or $y = -\sin\left(\frac{\pi}{2} \cdot \theta\right)$

6. an amplitude of 2 and 6 cycles $y = 2 \sin 6\theta$ or $y = -2 \sin 6\theta$

Find the amplitude of each sine curve. Amplitude equals half the difference of the maximum and minimum values of the function.

7. 4
8. 0.9

Differentiated Remediation continued

On-Level

- **Practice** (2 pages) Provides extra practice for each lesson. For simpler practice exercises, use the Form K Practice pages found in the All-in-One Teaching Resources and online.

- **Think About a Plan** Helps students develop specific problem-solving skills and strategies by providing scaffolded guiding questions.

- **Standardized Test Prep** Focuses on all major exercises, all major question types, and helps students prepare for the high-stakes assessments.

Extension

- **Enrichment** Provides students with interesting problems and activities that extend the concepts of the lesson.

- **Activities, Games, and Puzzles** Worksheets that can be used for concepts development, enrichment, and for fun!

Practice and Problem Solving Wkbk/ All-in-One Resources/Online
Practice page 1

Practice and Problem Solving Wkbk/ All-in-One Resources/Online
Practice page 2

All-in-One Resources/Online
Enrichment

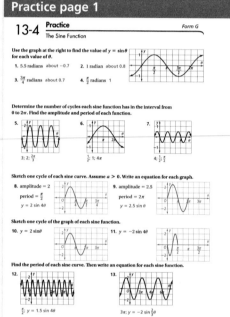

Practice and Problem Solving Wkbk/ All-in-One Resources/Online
Think About a Plan

Practice and Problem Solving Wkbk/ All-in-One Resources/Online
Standardized Test Prep

Online Teacher Resource Center
Activities, Games, and Puzzles

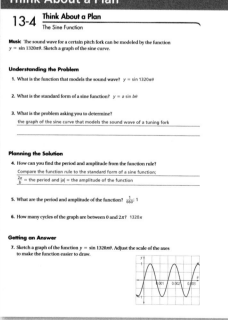

MathXL® for School
Go to PowerAlgebra.com

Do you know HOW?

1. Find the period and amplitude of the periodic function.

2. Find the measure of the angle in standard position.

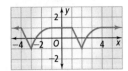

Sketch each angle in standard position.

3. −150°

4. 240°

Write each measure in radians. Express the answer in terms of π and as a decimal rounded to the nearest hundredth.

5. −180°

6. 36°

Write each measure in degrees. Round your answer to the nearest degree if necessary.

7. $\frac{2}{3}\pi$ radians

8. $-\frac{7}{6}\pi$ radians

9. 0.5 radians

10. −2 radians

The measure θ of an angle in standard position is given. Find the exact values of $\cos \theta$ and $\sin \theta$ for each angle measure.

11. −225°

12. 120°

13. $-\frac{4\pi}{3}$ radians

14. $\frac{5\pi}{4}$ radians

15. Find the length of the intercepted arc to the nearest tenth for an arc with a central angle of measure $\theta = \frac{\pi}{3}$ on a circle of radius $r = 10$.

16. Sketch one cycle of a sine function with amplitude 3 and period 2.

17. Find the amplitude, period, and midline of the graph of $y = \frac{1}{4} \sin 3\theta$.

Do you UNDERSTAND?

18. **Open-Ended** Sketch the graph of a periodic function with a period of 10 and an amplitude of 7.

19. **Writing** You are given an angle with a positive angle measure in degrees. Describe how you can find an angle coterminal with that angle that also has a positive angle measure in degrees.

20. **Reasoning** On a merry-go-round, you stand 15 feet from the center while your friend stands 10 feet from the center. How would you find how much further you travel in one revolution than your friend? What is that distance?

21. **Reasoning** Will two sine functions with the same period but different amplitudes intersect? Explain.

22. **Reasoning** In the formula $y = a \sin b\theta$, you know how the values a, b, and θ affect the graph of the sine wave.
   a. Hypothesize how the formula would need to change to allow for a sine wave whose midline was above or below the x-axis.
   b. How would it change to show a wave translated left or right?

20. Find the difference of the circumferences of circles with radii 15 ft and 10 ft. The difference is 10π, or about 31.4 ft.

21. Yes; they will intersect as long as one of the graphs is not translated up or down. For example: $y = \sin(x)$ and $y = 2 \sin(x)$ have the same period and different amplitudes, and they intersect. They will both cross the x-axis at the same pts.

22. a. $y = a \sin b\theta + k$
    b. $y = a \sin b(\theta - h)$

Answers

Mid-Chapter Quiz

1. 51

2. 210°

3.

4.

5. $-\pi \approx -3.14$

6. $\frac{\pi}{5} \approx 0.63$

7. 120°

8. −210°

9. 29°

10. −115°

11. $\frac{-\sqrt{2}}{2}, \frac{\sqrt{2}}{2}$

12. $-\frac{1}{2}, \frac{\sqrt{3}}{2}$

13. $-\frac{1}{2}, \frac{\sqrt{3}}{2}$

14. $-\frac{\sqrt{2}}{2}, -\frac{\sqrt{2}}{2}$

15. ≈10.5

16. 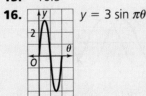 $y = 3 \sin \pi\theta$

17. $\frac{1}{4}, \frac{2\pi}{3}, y = 0$

18. Check students' work.

19. Add a multiple of 360° to the measure of the given angle.

PowerAlgebra.com

MathXL for School
Prepare students for the Mid-Chapter Quiz and Chapter Test with online practice and review.

Guided Instruction

PURPOSE To graph trigonometric functions using a graphing calculator

PROCESS Students will
- graph sign and cosine functions using radian and degree mode.
- determine appropriate window settings so the graphs can be described and compared.

DISCUSS Students are familiar with the shapes of graphs of periodic functions. Elicit that
- it is important to view at least one cycle of a graph to determine domain, range, period, and amplitude.
- the TRACE key can be used to find values on the graph.

Activity 1

> **Q** Why are the Ymin and Ymax values the same for both degrees and radians? **[The cosine value still varies between −1 and +1, regardless of whether the angle measures are expressed in degrees or radians.]**

Activity 2

> **Q** How could you find the same values in radians on the graphing calculator? **[Change the mode to radians and set Xmin = −2π and Xmax = 2π. Press TRACE, enter π/6 for x, press ENTER to find the y-value. Repeat for $\frac{5\pi}{6}$.]**

Teacher Note

The graph of $y = \cos x$ in Degree mode (first graph) and in Radian mode (second graph) appear to be identical. However, they are actually *very different functions*. In fact, the graph you see in Degree mode is a horizontal stretch of the graph in Radian mode by the sizable factor $\frac{180}{\pi}$. The graphs look the same because the scale in the left window (from −360 to 360) is $\frac{180}{\pi}$ times the scale in the right window (from −2π to 2π).

To illustrate the difference, use DEGREE mode and a window with $-360 \le x \le 360$. Graph $y_1 = \cos x$ and $y_2 = \cos\left(\frac{180}{\pi}x\right)$. The portion of the graph of y_2 on the tiny interval $-2\pi \le x \le 2\pi$ is the cosine curve you see in the second graph on this page. Change the window width to $-2\pi \le x \le 2\pi$ and you will see the second graph on this page. You will also see a portion of the graph of y_1.

Using radian values is preferable to using degree values as inputs for the trigonometric functions because, in general, you can see the complete behavior of these functions within a reasonable neighborhood, say $-2\pi \le x \le 2\pi$, of the origin. If you had to work in an interval like $-360 \le x \le 360$, the graph of $y = x$, or $y = x^2$ on the same interval would be virtually indistinguishable from the y-axis. This is why students should learn to work in radians and check the mode key on their calculators when they get unexpectedly bizarre graphs.

Ⓒ Mathematical Practices This Concept Byte supports students in becoming proficient in using appropriate tools, Mathematical Practice 5.

Graphing Trigonometric Functions

Ⓒ Content Standard
Prepares for **F.TF.5** Choose trigonometric functic to model periodic phenomena with specified ampli frequency, and midline.

Activity 1

Ⓒ MATHEMATICAL PRACTICES

Compare the graphs of $y = \cos x$ from $-360°$ to $360°$ and from -2π to 2π radians.

Step 1 Press ⟨mode⟩ to set the mode to degrees. Adjust the window values. Graph the function.

Step 2 Change the mode to radians. Graph the function.

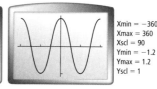
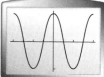

Xmin = −360
Xmax = 360
Xscl = 90
Ymin = −1.2
Ymax = 1.2
Yscl = 1

Xmin = −2π
Xmax = 2π
Xscl = $\frac{\pi}{2}$
Ymin = −1.2
Ymax = 1.2
Yscl = 1

The graphs appear to be identical. The function has a period of $360°$ or 2π radians.

Activity 2

Graph the function $y = \sin x$. Find $\sin 30°$ and $\sin 150°$.

Step 1 Set the mode to degrees and adjust the window values as shown.

Step 2 Graph the function. Use the ⟨trace⟩ key to find the y-values when $x = 30$ and $x = 150$.

WINDOW   FORMAT
Xmin = −470
Xmax = 470
Xscl = 30
Ymin = −1.2
Ymax = 1.2
Yscl = 1

Use these values to trace easily.

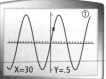
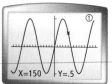

X=30   Y=.5

X=150   Y=.5

Exercises

Use appropriate window values to identify the period of each function in radians and in degrees. Then evaluate each function at 90°.

1. $y = \cos x$ **2.** $y = \sin x$ **3.** $y = \sin 3x$ **4.** $y = -3\sin x$ **5.** $y = \cos(x + 30)$

Ⓒ Writing Graph the two functions in the same window. Compare the graphs. How are they similar? How are they different?

6. $y = \sin x, y = \cos x$ **7.** $y = \sin x, y = \cos\left(x - \frac{\pi}{2}\right)$ **8.** $y = \sin x, y = \cos\left(x + \frac{\pi}{2}\right)$

Answers

Concept Byte
1. 2π radians, 360°; 0
2. 2π radians, 360°; 1
3. $\frac{2\pi}{3}$ radians, 120°; −1
4. 2π radians, 360°; −3
5. 2π radians, 360°; −0.5
6.

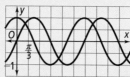

The graphs are horizontal translations of each other by $\frac{\pi}{2}$.

7.

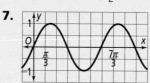

The graphs are the same.

8.

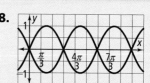

The graphs are reflections of each other across the x-axis or horizontal translations of each other by π.

The Cosine Function

Content Standards
F.TF.5 Choose trigonometric functions to model periodic phenomena . . .
F.IF.4 For a function that models a relationship between two quantities . . . sketch graphs.
Also F.IF.7.e, F.TF.2

Objectives To graph and write cosine functions
To solve trigonometric equations

"cos" is short for cosine.

MATHEMATICAL PRACTICES

Dynamic Activity
The Cosine Curve

Lesson Vocabulary
• cosine function

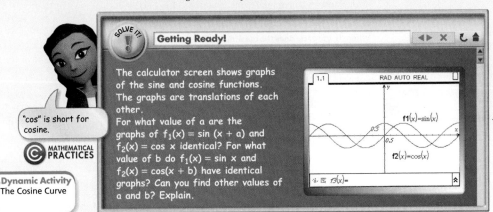

Getting Ready!

The calculator screen shows graphs of the sine and cosine functions. The graphs are translations of each other.
For what value of a are the graphs of $f_1(x) = \sin(x + a)$ and $f_2(x) = \cos x$ identical? For what value of b do $f_1(x) = \sin x$ and $f_2(x) = \cos(x + b)$ have identical graphs? Can you find other values of a and b? Explain.

RAD AUTO REAL
$f1(x) = \sin(x)$
$f2(x) = \cos(x)$

The **cosine function**, $y = \cos \theta$, matches θ with the x-coordinate of the point on the unit circle where the terminal side of angle θ intersects the unit circle. The symmetry of the set of points $(x, y) = (\cos \theta, \sin \theta)$ on the unit circle guarantees that the graphs of sine and cosine are congruent translations of each other.

Essential Understanding For each and every point along the unit circle the radian measure of the arc has a corresponding cosine value. The colored bars represent the cosine values of the points on the circle translated onto the cosine graph. So as the terminal side of an angle rotates about the origin (beginning at $0°$), its cosine value on the unit circle decreases from 1 to -1, and then increases back to 1.

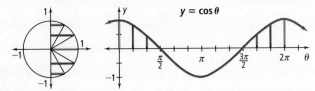

$y = \cos \theta$

1 Interactive Learning

Solve It!
PURPOSE To determine translations of sine and cosine functions
PROCESS Students may
• graph functions on calculators and use guess and check to determine the values of a and b.
• use sine and cosine values from the unit circle to determine when those values are equivalent.

FACILITATE
Q How do you know these functions are translations of each other? **[Translations are shifts. You can see that a shift to the left of the cosine function is the sine function.]**
Q What is a difference between the graphs of the sine and cosine functions? **[Sample: The sine function crosses the y-axis at 0; the cosine function crosses at 1.]**
Q Is it necessary to know the direction in which the sine function shifts to find a translation? Explain. **[No; the sine function is periodic, so you can shift to the right or left.]**

ANSWER See Solve It in Answers on next page.
CONNECT THE MATH Students use their knowledge of periodic functions and sine and cosine values to find the translation of the graphs in the Solve It. In this lesson, students sketch cosine functions, determine cosine models for real-life events, and solve cosine equations.

13-5 Preparing to Teach

BIG idea Function
ESSENTIAL UNDERSTANDINGS
• As the terminal side of an angle rotates about the origin (beginning at 0°), its cosine value on the unit circle decreases from 1 to -1, and then increases back to 1.
• A nontranslated cosine function can be completely described in terms of its amplitude and period.

Math Background
To better understand how the unit circle defines the cosine function, have students sketch and label a large unit circle.

Have them use a pencil as the terminal side of the angle and describe the behavior of the x-values:

The x-value of the terminal side begins at 1, decreases to 0 and then to -1, increases to 0 and then back to 1 again.

Next, have students sketch the terminal sides of the angles 0, $\frac{\pi}{2}$, π, $\frac{3\pi}{2}$, and 2π. Have them identify the cosine value of each on the unit circle.

Be sure students understand how the unit circle makes it easy to calculate the cosine: in a unit circle, the fraction $\frac{\text{adjacent}}{\text{hypotenuse}}$ for any angle always has a denominator of 1.

Ask them to identify the pattern they have found so far.

Point out that if they continue around the unit circle in increments of $\frac{\pi}{2}$ the pattern continues.

Ask them to try moving the terminal side clockwise around the circle to see whether the pattern continues for negative angle values.

Conclude with pointing out how the graph of $y = \cos \theta$ illustrates the pattern. Note that y is a function of θ, and not x.

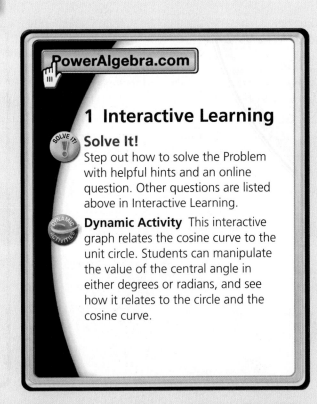

PowerAlgebra.com

1 Interactive Learning

Solve It!
Step out how to solve the Problem with helpful hints and an online question. Other questions are listed above in Interactive Learning.

Dynamic Activity This interactive graph relates the cosine curve to the unit circle. Students can manipulate the value of the central angle in either degrees or radians, and see how it relates to the circle and the cosine curve.

2 Guided Instruction

Problem 1

Remind students that they found the amplitude and period of the sine function in the previous lesson. Explain that the definitions and methods for finding these values remain the same.

> **Q** What is the smallest interval needed to determine the amplitude of this cosine function? Explain. **[2π; you need the maximum and minimum values.]**

Got It?

> **Q** How do the domain and range of the sine and cosine functions compare? **[They are the same since both values are determined from the unit circle. The maximum and minimum values are 1 and -1.]**

Take Note

> **Q** What happens to the cosine graph if $a < 0$? How does this affect the amplitude? **[The graph is reflected in the x-axis. The amplitude does not change because the difference between the maximum and minimum values remains the same.]**

Problem 2   VISUAL LEARNERS

Have students graph the equation in parts along with the parent function to see how the graph is different.

> **Q** Will the graph look different in the interval from π to 2π than 0 to π? Explain. **[No; the graph is periodic so it will have the same values between 0 and π as it does between π and 2π.]**

© **Problem 1** Interpreting a Graph

A What are the domain, period, range, and amplitude of the cosine function?

The domain of the function is all real numbers.

The function goes from its maximum value of 1 to its minimum value of -1 and back again in an interval from 0 to 2π. The period is 2π. The midline is $y = 0$.

The range of the function is $-1 \le y \le 1$.

$$\text{amplitude} = \tfrac{1}{2}(\text{maximum} - \text{minimum}) = \tfrac{1}{2}[1 - (-1)] = 1$$

Think
How do you find a zero of a function?
Zeros are where the graph of a function crosses the x-axis.

B Examine the cycle of the cosine function in the interval from 0 to 2π. Where in the cycle does the maximum value occur? Where does the minimum occur? Where do the zeros occur?

The maximum value occurs at 0 and 2π. The minimum value occurs at π. The zeros occur at $\frac{\pi}{2}$ and $\frac{3\pi}{2}$.

✔ **Got It?** 1. Use the graph. What are the domain, period, range, and amplitude of the sine function? Where do the maximum and minimum values occur? Where do the zeros occur?

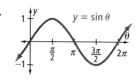

$y = \sin \theta$

---

take note   **Concept Summary**   **Properties of Cosine Functions**

Suppose $y = a \cos b\theta$, with $a \ne 0$, $b > 0$, and θ in radians.

- $|a|$ is the amplitude of the function.
- b is the number of cycles in the interval from 0 to 2π.
- $\frac{2\pi}{b}$ is the period of the function.

To graph a cosine function, locate five points equally spaced through one cycle. For $a > 0$, this five-point pattern is *max-zero-min-zero-max*.

© **Problem 2** Sketching the Graph of a Cosine Function

Plan
What should you find to graph the function?
Find the amplitude, cycle, and period.

Sketch one cycle of $y = 1.5 \cos 2\theta$.

$|a| = 1.5$, so the amplitude is 1.5.

$b = 2$, so the graph has two full cycles from 0 to 2π. One cycle is from 0 to π.

$\frac{2\pi}{b} = \pi$, so the period is π.

Divide the period into fourths. Plot the five-point pattern for one cycle. Use 1.5 for the maximum and -1.5 for the minimum. Sketch the curve.

Choose scales for axes that are about equal ($\frac{\pi}{3} \approx 1$).

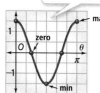

Answers

Solve It!

$a = \frac{\pi}{2}$ and $b = -\frac{\pi}{2}$; yes; add multiples of 2π to the values of a and b.

Got It?

1. domain: all real numbers; period: 2π; range: $-1 \le y \le 1$; amplitude: 1 sine: max at $\frac{\pi}{2}$; min at $\frac{3\pi}{2}$; zeros at 0, π, 2π

 PowerAlgebra.com

2 Guided Instruction

© Each Problem is worked out and supported online.

Problem 1
Interpreting the Graph of Cos θ
Animated

Problem 2
Sketching the Graph of a Cosine Function
Animated

Problem 3
Modeling with a Cosine Function
Animated

Problem 4
Solving a Cosine Equation

Support in Algebra 2 Companion
- Vocabulary
- Key Concepts
- Got It?

Got It? 2. Sketch one cycle of $y = 2\cos\frac{\theta}{3}$.

© **Problem 3** Modeling with a Cosine Function (STEM)

Oceanography The water level varies from low tide to high tide as shown. What is a cosine function that models the water level in inches above and below the average water level? Express the model as a function of time in hours since 10:30 A.M.?

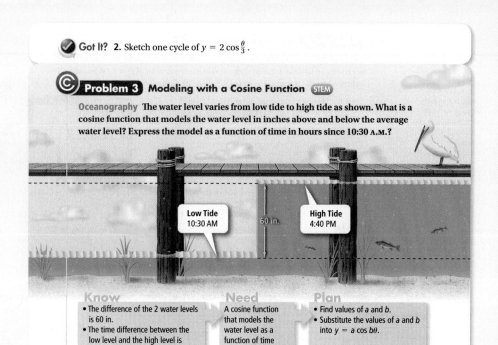

Low Tide
10:30 AM

60 in.

High Tide
4:40 PM

Know
- The difference of the 2 water levels is 60 in.
- The time difference between the low level and the high level is 6 h 10 min.

Need
A cosine function that models the water level as a function of time

Plan
- Find values of a and b.
- Substitute the values of a and b into $y = a\cos b\theta$.

Amplitude is $\frac{1}{2}(60) = 30$. Since the tide is at -30 inches at time zero, the curve follows the *min-zero-max-zero-min* pattern, so $a = -30$.

The cycle is halfway complete after 6 h and 10 min, so the full period is 12 hours and 20 minutes or $12\frac{1}{3}$ hours.

$$12\frac{1}{3} = \frac{2\pi}{b}$$

$$b = \frac{6\pi}{37}$$

So, the function $f(t) = -30\cos\left(\frac{6\pi}{37}t\right)$ models the water level.

Got It? 3. a. Suppose that the water level varies 70 inches between low tide at 8:40 A.M. and high tide at 2:55 P.M. What is a cosine function that models the variation in inches above and below the average water level as a function of the number of hours since 8:40 A.M.?

b. At what point in the cycle does the function cross the midline? What does the midline represent?

You can solve an equation by graphing to find an exact location along a sine or cosine curve.

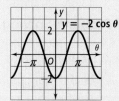

PowerAlgebra.com   Lesson 13-5   The Cosine Function   863

Got It?

Q What is the effect on the graph if $0 < b < 1$? **[The period will be greater than 2π. This means the graph will look stretched out.]**

Problem 3   EXTENSION

Remind students that the Solve It showed how the sine function could be translated to equal the cosine function. This translation can be used to write any cosine equation as a sine equation because $\cos x = \sin\left(x + \frac{\pi}{2}\right)$. The equation in this problem would become $y = -30\sin\left(\frac{6\pi}{37}t + \frac{\pi}{2}\right)$.

Q How do you know the value of a should be -30 and not $+30$? **[The graph must begin the way the problem is described. The model begins at low tide, so the cosine function can be rotated in the x-axis to show this.]**

Q How do you know the cycle is only halfway complete after 6 hours and 10 minutes? **[A complete cycle occurs the first time a value repeats. If the cycle begins at the low-level, it must end at the low-level.]**

Q What is the meaning of b? Explain what this means for the graph. **[The value b is the number of cycles in the interval from 0 to 2π. The decimal approximation is 0.51. You should expect to see about half the cycle between 0 and 2π.]**

Got It?

Q By how much will the amplitude change from Problem 3? Explain. **[The water level variation increases by 10 in., so the amplitude will change by 5.]**

Q What is the period for this function? Explain how to find b. **[Half of the cycle is 6.25 h, so the period is 12.5 h. Set 12.5 equal to $\frac{2\pi}{b}$ and solve for b.]**

Additional Problems

1. a. What are the domain, period, range, and amplitude of this cosine function?

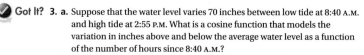
$y = -2\cos\theta$

b. Examine the cycle of the cosine function shown in the interval from 0 to 2π. Where in the cycle do the maximum, minimum, and zeros occur?

ANSWERS

a. domain: all real numbers; period: 2π; range: $-2 \le y \le 2$; amplitude: 2

b. maximum: π; minimum: 0 and 2π; zeros: $\frac{\pi}{2}$ and $\frac{3\pi}{2}$.

2. What is the graph of $y = 0.75\cos 3\theta$ in the interval from 0 to 2π?

ANSWER

3. The average temperature of a certain area varies from $-5°F$ to $60°F$. The highest temperature is in July and the lowest in January. What is a cosine function that models the temperature above and below the average as a function of time in months since July?

ANSWER $y = 32.5\cos\frac{\pi}{6}t$

4. Suppose you want to find the time t in months when the temperature is 20°F below the average temperature represented by $y = 0$. What are all solutions to the equation $y = 32.5\cos\frac{\pi}{6}t$ in terms of months since July in the interval from 0 to 12?

ANSWER about 4.27 months and 7.73 months

Answers

Got It? (continued)

2.
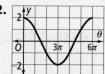

3. a. $f(t) = -35\cos\left(\frac{4\pi}{25}t\right)$

b. The function would cross the midline at 3 hours, 7 minutes, 30 seconds. The midline represents average water level.

Problem 4 — ERROR PREVENTION

Q For which value of y will the function have the fewest solutions in this interval? Explain. **[This interval has 3 min and 2 max values. Using the amplitude the maximum values occur at $y = 30$.]**

Got It?

Q How do you determine window settings when graphing the equation in 4a? **[Use the amplitude plus a little more for y-values. Amplitude is 3, so Ymax = 4 and Ymin = −4. The interval is 0 to 2π so Xmin = 0 and Xmax = 2π.]**

3 Lesson Check

Do you know HOW?   ERROR INTERVENTION
• If students have difficulty solving Exercises 1 and 2, encourage them to visualize the function before graphing so they may anticipate the shape of the graph. Graph the parent function at the same time so students can see the effect of a change in amplitude and period.

Do you UNDERSTAND?
• If students have trouble with Exercise 6a, remind them how to find cosine values on the unit circle. The cosine is represented by the x-coordinate; these values will be positive in Quadrants I and IV.

Close

Q How does knowing properties of $y = \sin \theta$ help you understand the properties of $y = \cos \theta$? **[The cosine function is a translation of the sine function, so the domain, range, amplitude, and period are the same.]**

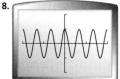

3 Lesson Check
For a digital lesson check, use the Got It questions.

Support In Algebra 2 Companion
• Lesson Check

4 Practice
Assign homework to individual students or to an entire class.

 Problem 4 Solving a Cosine Equation

Suppose you want to find the time t in hours when the water level from Problem 3 is exactly 10 in. above the average level represented by $f(t) = 0$. What are all solutions to the equation $-30 \cos\left(\frac{6\pi}{37}t\right) = 10$ in the interval from 0 to 25?

Plan

How can two equations help find the solutions?
The solutions occur where their graphs intersect.

Step 1 Use two equations. Graph $y = 10$ and $y = -30 \cos\left(\frac{6\pi}{37}t\right)$ on the same screen.

Step 2 Use the **INTERSECT** feature to find the points at which the two graphs intersect.

Xmin = 0
Xmax = 25
Xscl = 5
Ymin = −35
Ymax = 35
Yscl = 5

The graphs show four solutions in the interval. They are $t \approx 3.75, 8.58, 16.08,$ and 20.92.

The water level is 10 in. above the average level at about 3.75 h, 8.58 h, 16.08 h, and 20.92 h after 10:30 A.M.

 Got It? 4. What are all solutions to each equation in the interval from 0 to 2π?
  a. $3 \cos 2t = -2$ **b.** $-2 \cos \theta = 1.2$
  c. Reasoning In the interval from 0 to 2π, when is $-2 \cos \theta$ less than 1.2? Greater than 1.2?

 Lesson Check

Do you know HOW?

Sketch the graph of each function in the interval from 0 to 2π.

1. $y = \cos \frac{1}{2}\theta$ **2.** $y = 2 \cos \frac{\pi}{3}\theta$

Write a cosine function for each description. Assume that $a > 0$.

3. amplitude 3, period 2π **4.** amplitude 1.5, period π

Do you UNDERSTAND? MATHEMATICAL PRACTICES

5. Open-Ended Write a cosine function with amplitude 5 and between 2 and 3 cycles from 0 to 2π.

6. Assume θ is in the interval from 0 to 2π.
  a. For what values of θ is y positive for $y = \cos \theta$?
  b. For what values of θ is y positive for $y = -\sin \theta$?
  c. Reasoning What sine function has the same graph as $y = -3 \cos \frac{2\pi}{3}\theta$?

 Practice and Problem-Solving Exercises MATHEMATICAL PRACTICES

 Practice   Find the period and amplitude of each cosine function. Determine the values of x for $0 \le x \le 2\pi$ where the maximum value(s), minimum value(s), and zeros occur.   ◀ See Problem 1.

7.

Xmin = −2π
Xmax = 2π
Xscl = π
Ymin = −4
Ymax = 4
Yscl = 1

8.

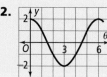

Xmin = −2π
Xmax = 2π
Xscl = π
Ymin = −2
Ymax = 2
Yscl = 1

Answers

Got It? (continued)
4. a. 1.15, 1.99, 4.29, 5.13
  b. 2.21, 4.06
  c. $0 \le \theta < 2.21$ and $4.06 < \theta \le 2\pi$; $2.21 < \theta < 4.06$

Lesson Check

1.

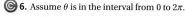

2.

3. $y = 3 \cos \theta$

4. $y = 1.5 \cos 2\theta$

5. Answers may vary. Sample:
$y = 5 \cos\left(\frac{5}{2}\theta\right)$

6. a. $0 \le \theta < \frac{\pi}{2}, \frac{3\pi}{2} < \theta \le 2\pi$
  b. $\pi < \theta < 2\pi$
  c. $y = 3 \sin\left(\frac{2\pi}{3}x - \frac{\pi}{2}\right)$

Practice and Problem-Solving Exercises

7. 2π, 3; max: 0, 2π; min: π; zeros: $\frac{\pi}{2}, \frac{3\pi}{2}$

8. $\frac{2\pi}{3}$, 1; max: 0, $\frac{2\pi}{3}, \frac{4\pi}{3}$, 2π; min: $\frac{\pi}{3}, \pi \frac{5\pi}{3}$; zeros: $\frac{\pi}{6}, \frac{\pi}{2}, \frac{5\pi}{6}, \frac{7\pi}{6}, \frac{3\pi}{2}, \frac{11\pi}{6}$

9.

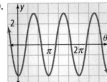

Xmin = -2π
Xmax = 2π
Xscl = π
Ymin = -2
Ymax = 2
Yscl = 1

10.

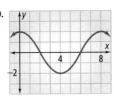

Xmin = -2π
Xmax = 2π
Xscl = π
Ymin = -4
Ymax = 4
Yscl = 1

Sketch one cycle of the graph of each cosine function.

◀ **See Problem 2.**

11. $y = \cos 2\theta$ **12.** $y = -3\cos\theta$ **13.** $y = -\cos 3t$ **14.** $y = \cos\frac{\pi}{2}\theta$ **15.** $y = -\cos\pi\theta$

Write a cosine function for each description. Assume that $a > 0$.

◀ **See Problem 3.**

16. amplitude 2, period π **17.** amplitude $\frac{\pi}{2}$, period 3 **18.** amplitude π, period 2

Write an equation of a cosine function for each graph.

19.

20.

Solve each equation in the interval from 0 to 2π. Round your answer to the nearest hundredth.

◀ **See Problem 4.**

21. $\cos 2t = \frac{1}{2}$ **22.** $20\cos t = -8$ **23.** $-2\cos\pi\theta = 0.3$

24. $3\cos\frac{t}{3} = 2$ **25.** $\cos\frac{1}{4}\theta = 1$ **26.** $8\cos\frac{\pi}{3}t = 5$

 Apply

Identify the period, range, and amplitude of each function.

27. $y = 3\cos\theta$ **28.** $y = -\cos 2t$ **29.** $y = 2\cos\frac{1}{2}t$ **30.** $y = \frac{1}{3}\cos\frac{\theta}{2}$

31. $y = 3\cos\left(-\frac{\theta}{3}\right)$ **32.** $y = -\frac{1}{2}\cos 3\theta$ **33.** $y = 16\cos\frac{3\pi}{2}t$ **34.** $y = 0.7\cos\pi t$

35. Think About a Plan In Buenos Aires, Argentina, the average monthly temperature is highest in January and lowest in July, ranging from 83°F to 57°F. Write a cosine function that models the change in temperature according to the month of the year.
• How can you find the amplitude?
• What part of the problem describes the length of the cycle?

36. Writing Explain how you can apply what you know about solving cosine equations to solving sine equations. Use $-1 = 6\sin 2t$ as an example.

ASSIGNMENT GUIDE
Basic: 7–26 all, 34–37, 42
Average: 7–25 odd, 27–42
Advanced: 7–25 odd, 27–45
Standardized Test Prep: 46–50
Mixed Review: 51–65

ⓒ **Mathematical Practices** are supported by exercises with red headings. Here are the Practices supported in this lesson:

MP 1: Make Sense of Problems Ex. 35
MP 2: Reason Quantitatively Ex. 5, 6c
MP 3: Communicate Ex. 36
MP 5: Use Tools Appropriately Ex. 60–65

Applications exercises have blue headings. Exercise 35 supports MP 4: Model.

STEM exercises focus on science or engineering applications.

EXERCISE 42: Use the Think About a Plan worksheet in the **Practice and Problem Solving Workbook** (also available in the Teaching Resources in print and online) to further support students' development in becoming independent learners.

HOMEWORK QUICK CHECK
To check students' understanding of key skills and concepts, go over Exercises 11, 17, 35, 36, and 42.

---

9. π, 1; max: 0, π, 2π; min: $\frac{\pi}{2}$, $\frac{3\pi}{2}$; zeros: $\frac{\pi}{4}$, $\frac{3\pi}{4}$, $\frac{5\pi}{4}$, $\frac{7\pi}{4}$

10. 2π, 2; max: π; min: 0, 2π; zeros: $\frac{\pi}{2}$, $\frac{3\pi}{2}$

11.

12.

13.

14.

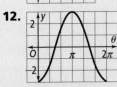

15.

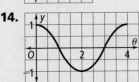

16. $y = 2\cos 2\theta$

17. $y = \frac{\pi}{2}\cos\frac{2\pi}{3}\theta$

18. $y = \pi\cos\pi\theta$

19. $y = -3\cos 2\theta$

20. $y = 2\cos\frac{\pi}{4}x$

21. 0.52, 2.62, 3.67, 5.76

22. 1.98, 4.30

23. 0.55, 1.45, 2.55, 3.45, 4.55, 5.45

24. 2.52

25. 0.00

26. 0.86, 5.14

27. 2π, $-3 \le y \le 3$, 3

28. π, $-1 \le y \le 1$, 1

29. 4π, $-2 \le y \le 2$, 2

30. 4π, $-\frac{1}{3} \le y \le \frac{1}{3}$, $\frac{1}{3}$

31. 6π, $-3 \le y \le 3$, 3

32. $\frac{2\pi}{3}$, $-\frac{1}{2} \le y \le \frac{1}{2}$, $\frac{1}{2}$

33. $\frac{4}{3}$, $-16 \le y \le 16$, 16

34. 2, $-0.7 \le y \le 0.7$, 0.7

35. $y = 70 + 13\cos\frac{\pi}{6}(x - 1)$ where x represents the months of the year with January as 1, February as 2, March as 3, etc.

36. Graph the equations $y = -1$ and $y = 6\sin 2t$ on the same screen. Use the Intersect feature to find the points at which the two graphs intersect. The graph shows 4 solutions in the interval from 0 to 2π. They are: 1.65, 3.06, 4.80, and 6.20.

Answers

Practice and Problem-Solving Exercises (continued)

37. 0.64, 2.50

38. 1.83, 2.88, 4.97, 6.02

39. 0.50, 2.50, 4.50

40. a. 3.79, 5.64

  b. 10.07, 11.92; these values are the sums of the values from part (a) and 2π.

41. a.

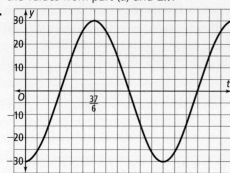

  b. 4:40 P.M., 5:00 A.M. (next day), 5:20 P.M., 5:40 A.M. (two days later)

  c. 6 h 10 min; 6 h 10 min

42. a. 5.5 ft; 1.5 ft

  b. about 12 h 22 min

  c. $y = 1.5 \cos \dfrac{60\pi t}{371}$

  d. 12:17 A.M.–7:49 A.M., 12:40 P.M.–8:11 P.M.

43. On the unit circle, the x-values of $-\theta$ are equal to the x-values of θ, so $\cos(-\theta) = \cos\theta$. $-\cos\theta$ is the opposite of $\cos\theta$, so these graphs are reflections of each other across the x-axis.

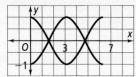

44. $y = \cos\dfrac{\pi}{12}x$ or $y = -\cos\dfrac{\pi}{12}x$

45. a.

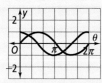

  shift of $\dfrac{\pi}{2}$ units to the right

  b.

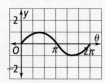

  They are the same.

  c. To write a sine function as a cosine function, replace sin with cos and replace θ with $\theta - \dfrac{\pi}{2}$.

Solve each equation in the interval from 0 to 2π. Round your answers to the nearest hundredth.

37. $\sin\theta = 0.6$ **38.** $-3\sin 2\theta = 1.5$ **39.** $\sin \pi\theta = 1$

40. a. Solve $-2\sin\theta = 1.2$ in the interval from 0 to 2π.

  b. Solve $-2\sin\theta = 1.2$ in the interval $2\pi \le \theta \le 4\pi$. How are these solutions related to the solutions in part (a)?

41. a. Graph the equation $y = -30\cos\left(\frac{6\pi}{37}t\right)$ from Problem 3.

  b. The independent variable θ represents time (in hours). Find four times at which the water level is the highest.

  c. For how many hours during each cycle is the water level above the line $y = 0$? Below $y = 0$?

STEM **42. Tides** The table at the right shows the times for high tide and low tide of one day. The markings on the side of a local pier showed a high tide of 7 ft and a low tide of 4 ft on the previous day.

  a. What is the average depth of water at the pier? What is the amplitude of the variation from the average depth?

  b. How long is one cycle of the tide?

  c. Write a cosine function that models the relationship between the depth of water and the time of day. Use $y = 0$ to represent the average depth of water. Use $t = 0$ to represent the time 4:03 A.M.

  d. Reasoning Suppose your boat needs at least 5 ft of water to approach or leave the pier. Between what times could you come and go?

Tide Table	
High tide	4:03 A.M.
Low tide	10:14 A.M.
High tide	4:25 P.M.
Low tide	10:36 P.M.

Challenge **43.** Graph one cycle of $y = \cos\theta$, one cycle of $y = -\cos\theta$, and one cycle of $y = \cos(-\theta)$ on the same set of axes. Use the unit circle to explain any relationships you see among these graphs.

STEM **44. Biology** A helix is a three-dimensional spiral. The coiled strands of DNA and the edges of twisted crepe paper are examples of helixes. In the diagram, the y-coordinate of each edge illustrates a cosine function. Write an equation for the y-coordinate of one edge.

45. a. Graphing Calculator Graph $y = \cos\theta$ and $y = \cos\left(\theta - \frac{\pi}{2}\right)$ in the interval from 0 to 2π. What translation of the graph of $y = \cos\theta$ produces the graph of $y = \cos\left(\theta - \frac{\pi}{2}\right)$?

  b. Graph $y = \cos\left(\theta - \frac{\pi}{2}\right)$ and $y = \sin\theta$ in the interval from 0 to 2π. What do you notice?

  c. Reasoning Explain how you could rewrite a sine function as a cosine function.

60. 0.866, 0.5, 1.732
61. 0.5, 0.866, 0.577
62. 1, 0, undefined
63. 0.5, −0.866, −0.577
64. 1, 0, undefined
65. 0, 1, 0

Standardized Test Prep

 SAT/ACT

46. Which function has a period of 2π and an amplitude of 4?

ⓐ $f(x) = 2\cos 4\theta$ ⓒ $f(x) = 2\cos\theta$

ⓑ $f(x) = 4\cos 2\theta$ ⓓ $f(x) = 4\cos\theta$

47. Which equation corresponds to the graph shown at the right? The screen dimensions are $-4\pi \le x \le 4\pi$ and $-2 \le y \le 2$.

ⓕ $y = \frac{1}{2}\cos\frac{x}{4}$ ⓗ $y = \frac{1}{2}\cos 4x$

ⓖ $y = 2\cos\frac{x}{4}$ ⓘ $y = 2\cos 4x$

48. Which equation has the same graph as $y = -\cos t$?

ⓐ $y = \cos(-t)$ ⓒ $y = \cos(t - \pi)$

ⓑ $y = \sin(t - \pi)$ ⓓ $y = -\sin t$

49. How many solutions does the equation $1 = -\sin 2t$ have for $0 \le t \le 2\pi$?

ⓕ 1   ⓖ 2   ⓗ 3   ⓘ 4

Short Response

50. What are the amplitude and period of $y = -0.2\cos\frac{\pi}{3}\theta$?

Mixed Review

Sketch one cycle of each sine curve. Assume that $a > 0$. Then write an equation for each graph.   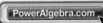 **See Lesson 13-4.**

51. amplitude 1, period $\frac{\pi}{3}$ **52.** amplitude 2.5, period π **53.** amplitude 4, period 1

Find the sample size that produces each margin of error.   **See Lesson 11-7.**

54. ±3%   **55.** ±7%   **56.** ±11%

Write the explicit formula for each geometric sequence. Then, list the first five terms.   **See Lesson 9-3.**

57. $a_1 = 10, r = 3$ **58.** $a_1 = 12, r = -0.3$ **59.** $a_1 = 900, r = -\frac{1}{3}$

Get Ready! To prepare for Lesson 13-6, do Exercises 60–65.

 Graphing Calculator Use a calculator to find the sine and cosine of each value of θ. Then calculate the ratio $\frac{\sin\theta}{\cos\theta}$. Round answers to the nearest thousandth, if necessary.   **See Lesson 13-5.**

60. $\frac{\pi}{3}$ radians   **61.** 30 degrees   **62.** 90 degrees

63. $\frac{5\pi}{6}$ radians   **64.** $\frac{5\pi}{2}$ radians   **65.** 0 degrees

Standardized Test Prep

46. D

47. F

48. C

49. G

50. [2] 0.2, 6; for this function, $a = -0.2$ and $b = \frac{\pi}{3}$. So, the amplitude is $|a| = 0.2$ and the period $\frac{2\pi}{b} = \frac{2\pi}{\left(\frac{\pi}{3}\right)}$, which simplifies to 6.

[1] appropriate method, with one computational error OR incorrect explanation

Mixed Review

51.

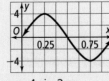

$y = \sin 6\theta$

52.

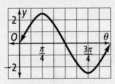

$y = \frac{5}{2}\sin 2\theta$

53.

$y = 4\sin 2\pi x$

54. about 1111

55. about 204

56. about 83

57. $a_n = 10 \cdot 3^{n-1}$; 10, 30, 90, 270, 810

58. $a_n = 12(-0.3)^{n-1}$; 12, −3.6, 1.08, −0.324, 0.0972

59. $a_n = 900\left(-\frac{1}{3}\right)^{n-1}$; 900, −300, 100, $-\frac{100}{3}, \frac{100}{9}$

Differentiated Remediation

Additional Instructional Support

Algebra 2 Companion

Students can use the **Algebra 2 Companion** worktext (4 pages) as you teach the lesson. Use the Companion to support

- New Vocabulary
- Key Concepts
- Got It for each Problem
- Lesson Check

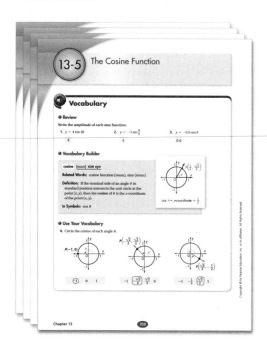

ELL Support

Use Graphic Organizers Tell students to make a 3-column KWL table. The columns are labeled *Know*, *Want to Know*, and *Learned*. In the first column, have students write a declarative sentence about each of the following words: *domain*, *range*, *period*, and *amplitude*. In the second column, have them write a question about each word. After the lesson, ask students to write what they have learned about each word in the third column.

Give the students this example to help them get started:

K: The range of $y = \sin \theta$ is $-1 \leq y \leq 1$

W: What is the range of $y = \cos \theta$?

After the lesson, give the students this example to help them get started on the *Learned* column:

L: The range of $y = \cos \theta$ is the same as the range of $y = \sin \theta$.

5 Assess & Remediate

Lesson Quiz

1. Sketch the graph of $y = \frac{1}{2} \cos 3\theta$ in the interval from 0 to 2π. What are the domain, range, period, and amplitude of the function?

2. A water level varies 50 in. between low tide at 8:30 A.M. and high tide at 3:00 P.M. What cosine function models the variation in inches above and below the average water level as a function of the number of hours since 8:30 A.M.?

3. **Do you UNDERSTAND?** A model of average temperatures in degrees Fahrenheit is given by $y = 40 \cos \frac{\pi}{6} t$. The highest temperature is reached in July. Explain how to find when the temperature is 5°F above average. What are the solutions in terms of months since July over the interval 0 to 12?

ANSWERS TO LESSON QUIZ

1. domain: all real numbers;
   period: $\frac{2\pi}{3}$;
   range: $-\frac{1}{2} \leq y \leq \frac{1}{2}$;
   amplitude: $\frac{1}{2}$

2. $y = -25 \cos \frac{2\pi}{13} t$

3. Find the intersection of $y = 40 \cos \frac{\pi}{6} t$ and $y = 5$. Solutions are about 2.76 and 9.24.

PRESCRIPTION FOR REMEDIATION

Use the student work on the Lesson Quiz to prescribe a differentiated review assignment:

Points	Differentiated Remediation
0–1	Intervention
2	On-level
3	Extension

PowerAlgebra.com

5 Assess & Remediate

Assign the Lesson Quiz. Appropriate intervention, practice, or enrichment is automatically generated based on student performance.

Intervention

- **Reteaching** (2 pages) Provides reteaching and practice exercises for the key lesson concepts. Use with struggling students or absent students.

- **English Language Learner Support** Helps students develop and reinforce mathematical vocabulary and key concepts.

All-in-One Resources/Online
Reteaching

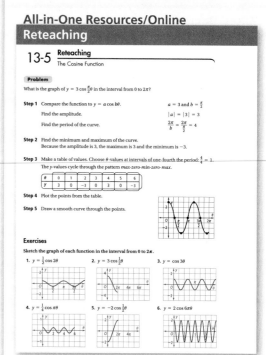

All-in-One Resources/Online
English Language Learner Support

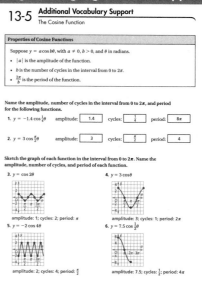

Differentiated Remediation *continued*

On-Level

- **Practice** (2 pages) Provides extra practice for each lesson. For simpler practice exercises, use the Form K Practice pages found in the All-in-One Teaching Resources and online.

- **Think About a Plan** Helps students develop specific problem-solving skills and strategies by providing scaffolded guiding questions.

- **Standardized Test Prep** Focuses on all major exercises, all major question types, and helps students prepare for the high-stakes assessments.

Extension

- **Enrichment** Provides students with interesting problems and activities that extend the concepts of the lesson.

- **Activities, Games, and Puzzles** Worksheets that can be used for concepts development, enrichment, and for fun!

Practice and Problem Solving Wkbk/All-in-One Resources/Online
Practice page 1

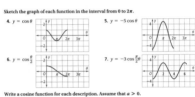
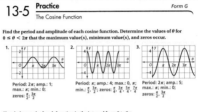

Practice and Problem Solving Wkbk/All-in-One Resources/Online
Practice page 2

All-in-One Resources/Online
Enrichment

Practice and Problem Solving Wkbk/All-in-One Resources/Online
Think About a Plan

Practice and Problem Solving Wkbk/All-in-One Resources/Online
Standardized Test Prep

Online Teacher Resource Center
Activities, Games, and Puzzles

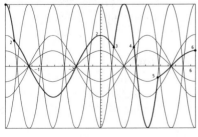

1 Interactive Learning

Solve It!

PURPOSE To analyze graphs of functions built from the sine and cosine functions

PROCESS Students may divide the values of y for the graphs of $\sin x$ and $\cos x$ at the values of x used in the first two dot plots to estimate the dot plot of $\frac{\sin x}{\cos x}$.

FACILITATE

Q What are the y-values of $\sin x$ at $x = 0$, π, and 2π? of $\cos x$? **[Sin x = 0 at all three; cos x = 1 at $x = 0$ and 2π and -1 at $x = \pi$.]**

Q What do you know about the y-values of $\sin x$ and $\cos x$ where the graphs of $\sin x$ and $\cos x$ intersect? **[They are the same; $\frac{\sqrt{2}}{2}$.]**

Q What happens to the values of $\frac{\sin x}{\cos x}$ as the values of $\sin x$ get closer to zero? **[The values get closer to zero.]**

Q What will happen to the values of $\frac{\sin x}{\cos x}$ as the values of $\cos x$ get closer to zero and the values of $\sin x$ get closer to 1 or -1? **[The values get farther from 1, approaching the vertical asymptotes.]**

Q What is the value of $\frac{\sin x}{\cos x}$ when $\cos x = 0$? **[undefined]**

ANSWER See Solve It in Answers on next page.
CONNECT THE MATH In the Solve It, students explore functions that are built from the sine and cosine functions, including $\frac{\sin x}{\cos x}$. In the lesson, students analyze the tangent function, which can be defined, using the unit circle, as $\frac{\sin x}{\cos x}$.

Take Note

Q What is $\tan \theta$ in terms of $\cos \theta$ and $\sin \theta$? **[$\tan \theta = \frac{\sin \theta}{\cos \theta}$]**

Content Standards
F.IF.7.e Graph . . .trigonometric functions, showing period, midline, and amplitude.
F.TF.2 Explain how the unit circle in the coordinate plane enables the extension of trigonometric functions to all real numbers.
Also F.TF.5

Objective To graph the tangent function.

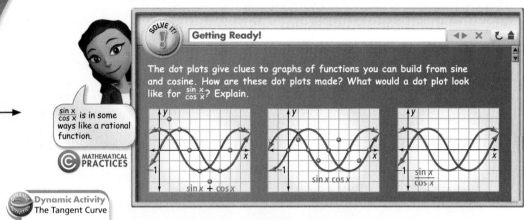

$\frac{\sin x}{\cos x}$ is in some ways like a rational function.

MATHEMATICAL PRACTICES

Getting Ready!

The dot plots give clues to graphs of functions you can build from sine and cosine. How are these dot plots made? What would a dot plot look like for $\frac{\sin x}{\cos x}$? Explain.

$\sin x + \cos x$ $\sin x \cos x$ $\frac{\sin x}{\cos x}$

Dynamic Activity The Tangent Curve

Lesson Vocabulary
• tangent of θ
• tangent function

The tangent function is closely associated with the sine and cosine functions, but it differs from them in three dramatic ways.

Essential Understanding The tangent function has infinitely many points of discontinuity, with a vertical asymptote at each point. Its range is all real numbers. Its period is π, half that of both the sine and cosine functions. Its domain is all real numbers except odd multiples of $\frac{\pi}{2}$.

take note

Key Concept Tangent of an Angle

Suppose the terminal side of an angle θ in standard position intersects the unit circle at the point (x, y). Then the ratio $\frac{y}{x}$ is the **tangent of θ,** denoted $\tan \theta$.

In this diagram, $x = \cos \theta$, $y = \sin \theta$, and $\frac{y}{x} = \tan \theta$.

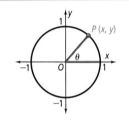

13-6 Preparing to Teach

BIG idea Function

ESSENTIAL UNDERSTANDINGS

• The tangent function has infinitely many points of discontinuity with a vertical asymptote at each point. Its range is all real numbers. Its period is π.
• Suppose $y = a \tan b\theta$, with $b > 0$ and θ measured in radians. Then $\frac{\pi}{b}$ is the period of the function, one cycle occurs in the interval $-\frac{\pi}{2b}$ to $\frac{\pi}{2b}$, and there are vertical asymptotes at each end of the cycle.

Math Background

The relationship between the tangent function and the sine and cosine functions is that the tangent of an angle equals the ratio of the sine of that angle to the cosine of that angle.

Like the graphs of sine and cosine functions, the graph of the tangent function is periodic.

Unlike the sine and cosine functions, the range of the tangent function is all real numbers since it has no maximum or minimum values (no amplitude).

Because the tangent function equals the ratio of the sine function to the cosine function, the critical points for the tangent function can be determined by the points where sine is zero causing the tangent to be zero: 0, π, 2π, and the points where cosine is zero causing the tangent to be undefined: $-\frac{\pi}{2}$, $\frac{\pi}{2}$, and $\frac{3\pi}{2}$. Thus, the tangent function has the pattern asymptote, zero, asymptote and a period of π.

Mathematical Practices

Make sense of problems and persevere in solving them. Students will explain correspondences between the tangent function represented on the unit circle and a graph of the function.

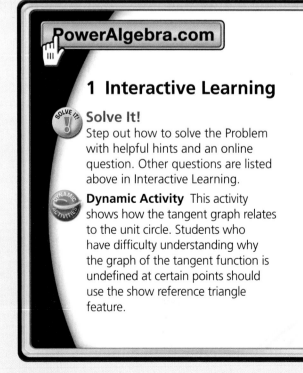

PowerAlgebra.com

1 Interactive Learning

Solve It!
Step out how to solve the Problem with helpful hints and an online question. Other questions are listed above in Interactive Learning.

Dynamic Activity This activity shows how the tangent graph relates to the unit circle. Students who have difficulty understanding why the graph of the tangent function is undefined at certain points should use the show reference triangle feature.

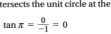**Problem 1** Finding Tangents Geometrically

Think

Will a graph help?
Yes; use a graph of the unit circle to visualize the problem.

What is the value of each expression? Do not use a calculator.

A $\tan \pi$

An angle of π radians in standard position has a terminal side that intersects the unit circle at the point $(-1, 0)$.

$$\tan \pi = \frac{0}{-1} = 0$$

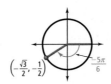
$(-1, 0)$

B $\tan\left(-\frac{5\pi}{6}\right)$

An angle of $-\frac{5\pi}{6}$ radians in standard position has a terminal side that intersects the unit circle at the point $\left(-\frac{\sqrt{3}}{2}, -\frac{1}{2}\right)$.

$$\tan\left(-\frac{5\pi}{6}\right) = \frac{-\frac{1}{2}}{-\frac{\sqrt{3}}{2}} = \frac{1}{\sqrt{3}} = \frac{\sqrt{3}}{3}.$$

$\left(-\frac{\sqrt{3}}{2}, -\frac{1}{2}\right)$ $-\frac{5\pi}{6}$

Got It? **1.** What is the value of each expression? Do not use a calculator.
   a. $\tan\frac{\pi}{2}$ **b.** $\tan\frac{2\pi}{3}$ **c.** $\tan\left(-\frac{\pi}{4}\right)$

There is another way to geometrically define $\tan\theta$.

The diagram shows the unit circle and the vertical line $x = 1$. The angle θ in standard position determines a point $P(x, y)$.

By similar triangles, the length of the vertical red segment divided by the length of the horizontal red segment is equal to $\frac{y}{x}$. The horizontal red segment has length 1 since it is a radius of the unit circle, so the length of the vertical red segment is $\frac{y}{x}$ or $\tan\theta$, which is also the y-coordinate of Q.

If θ is an angle in standard position and *not* an odd multiple of $\frac{\pi}{2}$, then the line containing the terminal side of θ intersects the line $x = 1$ at a point Q with y-coordinate $\tan\theta$.

The graph at the right shows one cycle of the **tangent function**, $y = \tan\theta$, for $-\frac{\pi}{2} < \theta < \frac{\pi}{2}$. The pattern repeats periodically with period π. At $\theta = \pm\frac{\pi}{2}$, the line through P fails to intersect the line $x = 1$, so $\tan\theta$ is undefined.

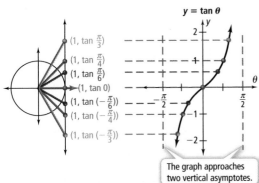

$y = \tan\theta$

$(1, \tan\frac{\pi}{3})$
$(1, \tan\frac{\pi}{4})$
$(1, \tan\frac{\pi}{6})$
$(1, \tan 0)$
$(1, \tan(-\frac{\pi}{6}))$
$(1, \tan(-\frac{\pi}{4}))$
$(1, \tan(-\frac{\pi}{3}))$

The graph approaches two vertical asymptotes.

---

2 Guided Instruction

Problem 1

Q How can you determine the point of intersection of the terminal side of the angle if the point does not fall on the axis? **[The coordinates of the point are given by $(\cos x, \sin x)$.]**

Q The terminal side of the angle of $-\frac{5\pi}{6}$ is the same as the terminal side of what positive angle? **[$\frac{7\pi}{6}$]**

Q How does $\frac{1}{\sqrt{3}}$ become $\frac{\sqrt{3}}{3}$? **[Rationalize the denominator; multiply $\frac{1}{\sqrt{3}}$ by $\frac{\sqrt{3}}{\sqrt{3}}$, and simplify the resulting expression.]**

Got It?

Q What are the points of intersection of the terminal sides of the angles with the unit circle? **[1a: (0, 1); 1b: $(-\frac{1}{2}, \frac{\sqrt{3}}{2})$; 1c: $(\frac{\sqrt{2}}{2}, -\frac{\sqrt{2}}{2})$.]**

Q What kind of triangle is the triangle defined by a line segment from the origin to a point (x, y), the altitude from (x, y), to the x-axis, and the line segment from the origin to the intersection of the altitude and the x-axis? **[right triangle]**

Q How is the tangent of θ defined in this right triangle? **[the ratio of the opposite side and the adjacent side, or as y divided by x]**

---

2 Guided Instruction

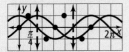
Each Problem is worked out and supported online.

Problem 1
Finding Tangents Geometrically
Animated

Problem 2
Graphing a Tangent Function
Animated

Problem 3
Using the Tangent Function to Solve Problems
Animated

Support in Algebra 2 Companion
• Vocabulary
• Key Concepts
• Got It?

Answers

Solve It!
The dot plots are made by computing distinct values of the new compound functions from corresponding distinct values of sine and cosine; the dot plot would have distinct sections broken up by vertical asymptotes because whenever $\cos\theta = 0$, then $\frac{\sin\theta}{\cos\theta}$ is undefined.

Got It?
1. a. not defined
   b. $\sqrt{3}$
   c. -1

Q If $y = a \tan b\theta$, how many cycles of $\tan \theta$ should fit between $-\frac{\pi}{2}$ and $\frac{\pi}{2}$? **[b cycles]**

Q What effect does the value of a have on the graph of $y = a \tan b\theta$? **[The value of a will vertically stretch ($|a| > 1$) or shrink ($0 < |a| < 1$) or reflect in the x-axis ($a < 0$) the graph of $\tan \theta$.]**

Problem 2

Q Why divide the period into fourths? **[The y-value of the function is one unit at x-values that are one-fourth of the period from the asymptotes, and the y-value in the center of the cycle is zero.]**

Q If you graphed the cycle to the left of the cycle that passes through the origin, where would the zero occur? **[x = −1]**

Got It?

Q What is the period of each tangent curve? **[2a has a period of $\frac{\pi}{3}$; 2b has a period of 2.]**

Q Where do the asymptotes occur for each tangent curve if you graph the cycle passing through the origin? **[2a has asymptotes at $x = -\frac{\pi}{6}$ and $x = \frac{\pi}{6}$. 2b has asymptotes at $x = -1$ and $x = 1$.]**

Q Where would the second zero for each curve be if you graphed the second cycle of the tangent curve to the right of the cycle that passes through the origin? **[for 2a, at $x = \frac{\pi}{3}$; for 2b at $x = 2$]**

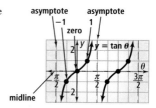

Concept Summary   Properties of Tangent Functions

Suppose $y = a \tan b\theta$, with $a \neq 0$, $b > 0$, and θ in radians.

- $\frac{\pi}{b}$ is the period of the function.
- One cycle occurs in the interval from $-\frac{\pi}{2b}$ to $\frac{\pi}{2b}$.
- There are vertical asymptotes at each end of the cycle.

You can use asymptotes and three points to sketch one cycle of a tangent curve. As with sine and cosine, the five elements are equally spaced through one cycle. Use the pattern *asymptote-(−a)-zero-(a)-asymptote*. In the graph at the right, $a = b = 1$.

The next example shows how to use the period, asymptotes, and points to graph a tangent function.

Problem 2 Graphing a Tangent Function

Sketch two cycles of the graph of $y = \tan \pi\theta$.

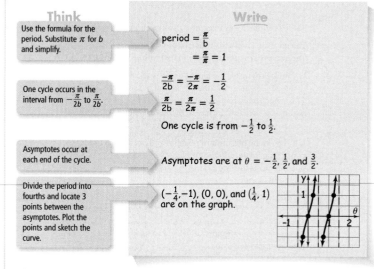

Think

Use the formula for the period. Substitute π for b and simplify.

One cycle occurs in the interval from $-\frac{\pi}{2b}$ to $\frac{\pi}{2b}$.

Asymptotes occur at each end of the cycle.

Divide the period into fourths and locate 3 points between the asymptotes. Plot the points and sketch the curve.

Write

$$\text{period} = \frac{\pi}{b}$$
$$= \frac{\pi}{\pi} = 1$$

$$-\frac{\pi}{2b} = -\frac{\pi}{2\pi} = -\frac{1}{2}$$
$$\frac{\pi}{2b} = \frac{\pi}{2\pi} = \frac{1}{2}$$

One cycle is from $-\frac{1}{2}$ to $\frac{1}{2}$.

Asymptotes are at $\theta = -\frac{1}{2}, \frac{1}{2},$ and $\frac{3}{2}$.

$(-\frac{1}{4}, -1)$, $(0, 0)$, and $(\frac{1}{4}, 1)$ are on the graph.

Got It? **2.** Sketch two cycles of the graph of each tangent curve.

a. $y = \tan 3\theta, 0 \leq \theta \leq \frac{2\pi}{3}$ **b.** $y = \tan \frac{\pi}{2}\theta, 0 \leq \theta \leq 4$

870 Chapter 13 Periodic Functions and Trigonometry

Additional Problems

1. What is the value of each expression? Do not use a calculator.

a. $\tan \frac{5\pi}{4}$

b. $\tan\left(-\frac{\pi}{2}\right)$

c. $\tan \frac{\pi}{6}$

ANSWERS

a. 1

b. undefined

c. $\frac{\sqrt{3}}{3}$

2. Sketch two cycles of the graph of $y = \tan \frac{\pi}{3}\theta$.

ANSWER

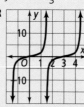

3. An architect wants to place right triangular panels on either side of the double doors of a building. The doors are each 7 ft tall. The function $y = 97 \tan \theta$ models the height of the triangles, where θ is the bottom acute angle. If the architect does not want the panels to be taller than the doors, what is the maximum angle, to the nearest whole degree, for θ?

ANSWER 4°

Answers

Got It? (continued)

2. a.

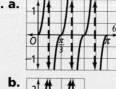

b.

Problem 3 Using the Tangent Function to Solve Problems (STEM)

Design An architect is designing the front facade of a building to include a triangle, similar to the one shown. The function $y = 100 \tan \theta$ models the height of the triangle, where θ is the angle indicated. Graph the function using the degree mode. What is the height of the triangle if $\theta = 16°$? If $\theta = 22°$?

200 ft

Think

How should you graph the function? "Degree mode" suggests that you use a graphing calculator. Then use **TABLE** to show y values for different θ values.

Step 1 Graph the function.

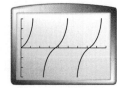

Xmin = 0
Xmax = 470
Xscl = 50
Ymin = −300
Ymax = 300
Yscl = 90

X	Y1
16	28.675
17	30.573
18	32.492
19	34.433
20	36.397
21	38.386
22	40.403

X=16

Step 2 Use the **TABLE** feature.

When $\theta = 16°$, the height of the triangle is about 28.7 ft. When $\theta = 22°$, the height of the triangle is about 40.4 ft.

 Got It? 3. a. What is the height of the triangle when $\theta = 25°$?
 b. Reasoning The architect wants the triangle to be at least one story tall. The average height of a story is 14 ft. What must θ be for the height of the triangle to be at least 14 ft?

 Lesson Check

Do you know HOW?

Find each value without using a calculator.

1. $\tan \frac{\pi}{4}$

2. $\tan \frac{7\pi}{6}$

3. $\tan \left(-\frac{\pi}{4}\right)$

4. $\tan \left(-\frac{3\pi}{3}\right)$

Do you UNDERSTAND? (C) MATHEMATICAL PRACTICES

5. **Vocabulary** Successive asymptotes of a tangent curve are $x = \frac{\pi}{3}$ and $x = -\frac{\pi}{3}$. What is the period?

6. **Error Analysis** A quiz contained a question asking students to solve the equation $8 = -2 \tan 3\theta$ to the nearest hundredth of a radian. One student did not receive full credit for writing $\theta = -1.33$. Describe and correct the student's error.

7. **Writing** Explain how you can write a tangent function that has the same period as $y = \sin 4\theta$.

---

3. a. ≈46.6 ft
 b. ≈8°

Lesson Check
 1. 1
 2. $\frac{\sqrt{3}}{3}$
 3. −1
 4. 0
 5. $\frac{2\pi}{3}$
 6. The student found 3θ instead of θ. Divide each side of $3\theta = -1.33$ by 3 to get $\theta = -0.44$.
 7. $y = \tan 2\theta$; the period of the function $y = \sin 4\theta$ is $\frac{\pi}{2}$. For a tangent function to have the same period, $\frac{\pi}{2}$, b must equal 2.

Problem 3

Q What is the domain of x for the front façade? Explain. **[$0° < x < 90°$; if the angle is 0° or greater than 90°, no triangle will form.]**

Q Why does $y = 100 \tan \theta$ model the height of the triangle? **[$\tan \theta = \frac{\text{height}}{100}$, so $h = 100 \cdot \tan \theta$.]**

Got It?

Q What error might you make in solving 3b? **[You might look for 14 in the x-value column.]**

3 Lesson Check

Do you know HOW?

• If students have difficulty finding the exact value for the tangent of the given θ in Exercises 1–4, ask them to find the point where the terminal side of the angle intersects the unit circle. Ask them to find the sine and cosine of the given θ and identify the relationship between tangent, sine, and cosine.

Do you UNDERSTAND?

• If students have difficulty identifying the error in Exercise 6, ask what the solution to $8 = -2 \tan \theta$ would be and how the original equation differs.

Close

Q How is the tangent of an angle θ related to the sine and cosine of the angle θ? to the unit circle? **[$\tan \theta = \frac{\sin \theta}{\cos \theta}$; if the terminal side of θ in standard position intersects the unit circle in a point (x, y), then $\tan \theta = \frac{y}{x}$.]**

Q What do you need to sketch a graph of a tangent curve? **[a, the period and asymptotes]**

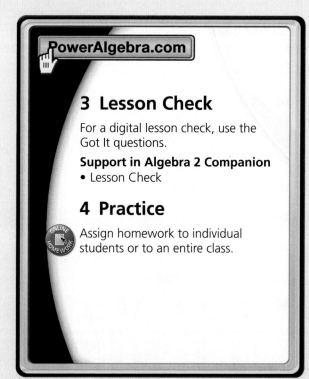

PowerAlgebra.com

3 Lesson Check

For a digital lesson check, use the Got It questions.

Support in Algebra 2 Companion
• Lesson Check

4 Practice

Assign homework to individual students or to an entire class.

4 Practice

ASSIGNMENT GUIDE

Basic: 8–29 all, 35–47 odd

Average: 9–29 odd, 30–48

Advanced: 9–29 odd, 30–51

Standardized Test Prep: 52–56

Mixed Review: 57–68

ⓒ Mathematical Practices are supported by exercises with red headings. Here are the Practices supported in this lesson:

MP 1: Make Sense of Problems Ex. 37
MP 2: Reason Abstractly Ex. 5, 36a
MP 3: Construct Arguments Ex. 50a
MP 3: Communicate Ex. 7, 51
MP 3: Critique the Reasoning of Others Ex. 6
MP 5: Use appropriate tools Ex. 26–28, 33–35

Applications exercises have blue headings. Exercises 38, 47 support MP 4: Model.

EXERCISE 47: Use the Think About a Plan worksheet in the **Practice and Problem Solving Workbook** (also available in the Teaching Resources in print and online) to further support students' development in becoming independent learners.

HOMEWORK QUICK CHECK

To check students' understanding of key skills and concepts, go over Exercises 9, 19, 37, 45, and 47.

  Practice and Problem-Solving Exercises **MATHEMATICAL PRACTICES**

Ⓐ Practice Find each value without using a calculator. ◀ See Problem 1.

8. $\tan(-\pi)$ **9.** $\tan \pi$ **10.** $\tan \frac{3\pi}{4}$ **11.** $\tan \frac{\pi}{2}$

12. $\tan\left(-\frac{7\pi}{4}\right)$ **13.** $\tan 2\pi$ **14.** $\tan\left(-\frac{3\pi}{4}\right)$ **15.** $\tan\left(\frac{3\pi}{2}\right)$

Each graphing calculator screen shows the interval 0 to 2π. What is the period of each graph? ◀ See Problem 2.

16. 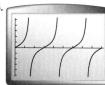   **17.**

Identify the period and determine where two asymptotes occur for each function.

18. $y = \tan 5\theta$ **19.** $y = \tan \frac{3\theta}{2}$ **20.** $y = \tan 4\theta$ **21.** $y = \tan \frac{2}{3\pi}\theta$

Sketch the graph of each tangent curve in the interval from 0 to 2π.

22. $y = \tan \theta$ **23.** $y = \tan 2\theta$ **24.** $y = \tan \frac{2\pi}{3}\theta$ **25.** $y = \tan(-\theta)$

Graphing Calculator Graph each function on the interval $0 \le x \le 2\pi$ and ◀ See Problem 3.
$-200 \le y \le 200$. Evaluate each function at $x = \frac{\pi}{4}, \frac{\pi}{2},$ and $\frac{3\pi}{4}$.

26. $y = 50 \tan x$ **27.** $y = -100 \tan x$ **28.** $y = 125 \tan\left(\frac{1}{2}x\right)$

29. Graphing Calculator Suppose the architect in Problem 3 reduces the length of the base of the triangle to 100 ft. The function that models the height of the triangle becomes $y = 50 \tan \theta$.
 a. Graph the function on a graphing calculator.
 b. What is the height of the triangle when $\theta = 16°$?
 c. What is the height of the triangle when $\theta = 22°$?

Ⓑ Apply Identify the period for each tangent function. Then graph each function in the interval from -2π to 2π.

30. $y = \tan \frac{\pi}{6}\theta$ **31.** $y = \tan 2.5\theta$ **32.** $y = \tan\left(-\frac{3}{2\pi}\theta\right)$

Graphing Calculator Solve each equation in the interval from 0 to 2π. Round your answers to the nearest hundredth.

33. $\tan \theta = 2$ **34.** $\tan \theta = -2$ **35.** $6 \tan 2\theta = 1$

ⓒ 36. a. Open-Ended Write a tangent function.
 b. Graph the function on the interval -2π to 2π.
 c. Identify the period and the asymptotes of the function.

Answers

Practice and Problem-Solving Exercises

8. 0   **9.** 0

10. −1   **11.** undefined

12. 1   **13.** 0

14. 1   **15.** undefined

16. $\frac{2\pi}{3}$ **17.** $\frac{\pi}{2}$

18. $\frac{\pi}{5}$; $\theta = -\frac{\pi}{10}$ and $\theta = \frac{\pi}{10}$

19. $\frac{2\pi}{3}$; $\theta = -\frac{\pi}{3}$ and $\theta = \frac{\pi}{3}$

20. $\frac{\pi}{4}$; $\theta = -\frac{\pi}{8}$ and $\theta = \frac{\pi}{8}$

21. $\frac{3\pi^2}{2}$; $\theta = -\frac{3\pi^2}{4}$ and $\theta = \frac{3\pi^2}{4}$

22.    **23.**

24. 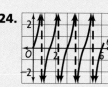   **25.** 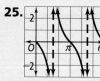   **28.**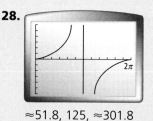

26.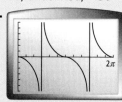

50, undefined, −50

27.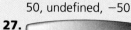

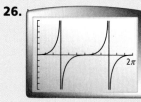

−100, undefined, 100

$\approx 51.8, 125, \approx 301.8$

29. a.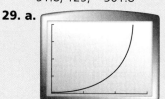

 b. ≈ 14.3 ft
 c. ≈ 20.2 ft

30. 6;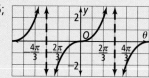

37. Think About a Plan A quilter is making hexagonal placemats by sewing together six quilted isosceles triangles. Each triangle has a base length of 10 in. The function $y = 5 \tan \theta$ models the height of the triangular quilts, where θ is the measure of one of the base angles. Graph the function. What is the area of the placemat if the triangles are equilateral?
- How can a graph of the function help you find the height of each triangle?
- How can you find the area of each triangle?
- What will be the last step in your solution?

38. Ceramics An artist is making triangular ceramic tiles for a triangular patio. The patio will be an equilateral triangle with base 18 ft and height 15.6 ft.
  a. Find the area of the patio in square feet.
  b. The artist uses tiles that are isosceles triangles with base 6 in. The function $y = 3 \tan \theta$ models the height of the triangular tiles, where θ is the measure of one of the base angles. Graph the function. Find the height of the tile when $\theta = 30°$ and when $\theta = 60°$.
  c. Find the area of one tile in square inches when $\theta = 30°$ and when $\theta = 60°$.
  d. Find the number of tiles the patio will require if $\theta = 30°$ and if $\theta = 60°$.

Use the function $y = 200 \tan x$ on the interval $0° \le x \le 141°$. Complete each ordered pair. Round your answers to the nearest whole number.

39. $(45°, \blacksquare)$ **40.** $(\blacksquare°, 0)$ **41.** $(\blacksquare°, -200)$ **42.** $(141°, \blacksquare)$ **43.** $(\blacksquare°, 550)$

Write an equation of a tangent function for each graph.

44. 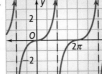 **45.** 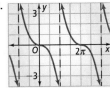 **46.**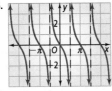

 47. Construction An architect is designing a hexagonal gazebo. The floor is a hexagon made up of six isosceles triangles. The function $y = 4 \tan \theta$ models the height of one triangle, where θ is the measure of one of the base angles and the base of the triangle is 8 ft long.
  a. Graph the function. Find the height of one triangle when $\theta = 60°$.
  b. Find the area of one triangle in square feet when $\theta = 60°$.
  c. Find the area of the gazebo floor in square feet when the triangles forming the hexagon are equilateral.

48. a. The graph of $y = \frac{1 - \cos x}{\sin x}$ suggests a tangent curve of the form $y = a \tan bx$. Graph the function using the window $[-3\pi, 3\pi]$ by $[-4, 4]$.
  b. What is the period of the curve? What is the value of a?
  c. Find the x-coordinate halfway between a removable discontinuity and the asymptote to its right. Find the corresponding y-coordinate.
  d. Find an equivalent function of the form $y = a \tan bx$.

47. a.
  ≈ 6.9 ft
  b. ≈ 27.7 ft^2
  c. ≈ 166.3 ft^2

48. a.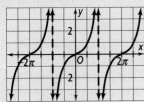
  b. 2π; 1
  c. $\left(\frac{\pi}{2}, 1\right)$
  d. $y = \tan\left(\frac{1}{2}x\right)$

---

31. $\frac{2\pi}{5}$;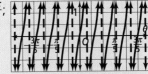

32. $\frac{2\pi^2}{3}$;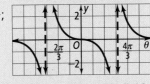

33. 1.11, 4.25   **34.** 2.03, 5.18

35. 0.08, 1.65, 3.22, 4.79

36. a–c. Check students' work.

37.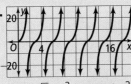
$150\sqrt{3}$ in.$^2 \approx 260$ in.^{2}

38. a. ≈ 140.4 ft^2
  b.
  ≈ 1.7 in., ≈ 5.2 in.
  c. ≈ 5.2 in.^{2}, ≈ 15.6 in.^{2}
  d. ≈ 3888 tiles, ≈ 1296 tiles

39. 200

40. 0

41. 135

42. -162

43. 70

44. $y = \tan\left(\frac{1}{2}x\right)$

45. $y = -\tan\left(\frac{1}{2}x\right)$

46. $y = -\tan x$ or $y = \tan(-x)$

Answers

Practice and Problem-Solving Exercises (continued)

49. Answers may vary. Sample: Triangles *OAP* and *OBQ* both share the angle θ and each triangle has a right angle, so they are similar by AA. $\frac{\sin \theta}{\cos \theta} = \frac{AP}{OA} = \frac{BQ}{OB} = \frac{\tan \theta}{1}$. Thus $\frac{\sin \theta}{\cos \theta} = \tan \theta$.

50. a. Check students' work.

   b. The new pattern is asymptote-$(-a)$-zero-(a)-asymptote.

51. 2; for $0 \le x < 2\pi$, x is nonnegative and there are only 2 sections of the graph of the tangent function on or above the x-axis.

Standardized Test Prep

52. C

53. H

54. B

55. I

56. [2] No, because the tangent function has no maximum or minimum value.

   [1] incorrect explanation

Mixed Review

57. 1.32, 4.97

58. 1.77, 4.51

59. 6.15

60. 0.44, 1.56, 2.44, 3.56, 4.44, 5.56

61. mean ≈ 5.9, median $= 6$, modes $= 4$ and 6

62. 83

63. -227

64. 145

65. -332

66. 2 units to the right and up 5 units

67. 5 units to the left and down 4 units

68. 2 units to the left and up 1 unit

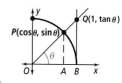

Challenge   **49. Geometry** Use the drawing at the right and similar triangles. Justify the statement that $\tan \theta = \frac{\sin \theta}{\cos \theta}$.

50. a. Graph $y = \tan x$, $y = a \tan x$ (with $a > 0$), and $y = a \tan x$ (with $a < 0$) on the same coordinate plane.

   b. Reasoning Recall the pattern of five elements for graphing a tangent function: *asymptote-(−1)-zero-(1)-asymptote*. How does the value of a affect this pattern?

51. Writing How many solutions does the equation $x = \tan x$ have for $0 \le x < 2\pi$? Explain.

Standardized Test Prep

SAT/ACT

52. Which value is NOT defined?

   Ⓐ $\tan 0$ Ⓑ $\tan \pi$ Ⓒ $\tan \frac{3\pi}{2}$ Ⓓ $\frac{1}{\tan \frac{\pi}{4}}$

53. What is the exact value of $\tan \frac{7\pi}{6}$?

   Ⓕ $-\sqrt{3}$ Ⓖ $-\frac{\sqrt{3}}{3}$ Ⓗ $\frac{\sqrt{3}}{3}$ Ⓘ $\sqrt{3}$

54. Which equation does NOT represent a vertical asymptote of the graph of $y = \tan \theta$?

   Ⓐ $\theta = -\frac{\pi}{2}$ Ⓑ $\theta = 0$ Ⓒ $\theta = \frac{\pi}{2}$ Ⓓ $\theta = \frac{3\pi}{2}$

55. Which function has a period of 4π?

   Ⓕ $y = \tan 4\theta$ Ⓖ $y = \tan 2\theta$ Ⓗ $y = \tan \frac{1}{2}\theta$ Ⓘ $y = \tan \frac{1}{4}\theta$

Short Response

56. Does a tangent function have amplitude? Explain.

Mixed Review

Solve each equation in the interval from 0 to 2π. Round your answer to the nearest hundredth.   ◆ See Lesson 13-5.

57. $\cos t = \frac{1}{4}$ **58.** $10 \cos t = -2$ **59.** $3 \cos \frac{t}{5} = 1$ **60.** $5 \cos \pi t = 0.9$

61. Find the mean, median, and mode for the set of values.   ◆ See Lesson 11-5.

   9 6 8 1 3 4 5 2 6 8 4 9 12 3 4 10 7 6

Find the 27th term of each sequence.   ◆ See Lesson 9-2.

62. 5, 8, 11, . . .   **63.** 59, 48, 37, . . .   **64.** $-11, -5, 1, . . .$ **65.** 6, -7, -20, . . .

Get Ready!   **To prepare for Lesson 13-7, do Exercises 66–68.**

Identify each horizontal and vertical translation of the parent function $y = |x|$.   ◆ See Lesson 2-6.

66. $y = |x - 2| + 5$ **67.** $y = |x + 5| - 4$ **68.** $y = |x + 2| + 1$

Additional Instructional Support

Algebra 2 Companion

Students can use the **Algebra 2 Companion** worktext (4 pages) as you teach the lesson. Use the Companion to support

- New Vocabulary
- Key Concepts
- Got It for each Problem
- Lesson Check

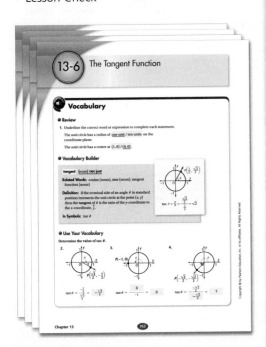

ELL Support

Graphic Organizers Ask students to make a three-column chart. In the first column, have students list the components they need to know in order to sketch a graph of a tangent curve, skipping three to four lines. Have students in small groups or pairs compare lists and discuss these components. In the second column, have students write a description of what each component is and how to find it from the equation of a tangent curve. In the third column, have students label the components on a sketch.

5 Assess & Remediate

Lesson Quiz

1. What is the value of $\tan\left(-\frac{\pi}{3}\right)$? Do not use a calculator.
2. Sketch two cycles of the graph of $y = \tan\frac{1}{2}\theta$.
3. **Do you UNDERSTAND?** A local building code requires that the angle of the pitch on a roof be between 20° and 25°. You are building a 20 ft wide shed, and the height of the roof at its center will be defined by the tangent curve $y = 10\tan\theta$. If you wanted to put a roof that was 5 ft high measured from the top of the wall, would the roof pass the building code? What is the range of heights for the roof that will fall within the building code?

ANSWERS TO LESSON QUIZ

1. $-\sqrt{3}$
2.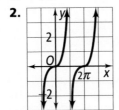
3. no; between about 3.6 and 4.6 ft

PRESCRIPTION FOR REMEDIATION

Use the student work on the Lesson Quiz to prescribe a differentiated review assignment:

Points	Differentiated Remediation
0–1	Intervention
2	On-level
3	Extension

PowerAlgebra.com

5 Assess & Remediate

Assign the Lesson Quiz. Appropriate intervention, practice, or enrichment is automatically generated based on student performance.

Intervention

- **Reteaching** (2 pages) Provides reteaching and practice exercises for the key lesson concepts. Use with struggling students or absent students.
- **English Language Learner Support** Helps students develop and reinforce mathematical vocabulary and key concepts.

All-in-One Resources/Online
Reteaching

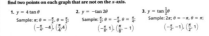

13-6 Reteaching
The Tangent Function

All-in-One Resources/Online
English Language Learner Support

13-6 Additional Vocabulary Support
The Tangent Function

Differentiated Remediation *continued*

On-Level

- **Practice** (2 pages) Provides extra practice for each lesson. For simpler practice exercises, use the Form K Practice pages found in the All-in-One Teaching Resources and online.

- **Think About a Plan** Helps students develop specific problem-solving skills and strategies by providing scaffolded guiding questions.

- **Standardized Test Prep** Focuses on all major exercises, all major question types, and helps students prepare for the high-stakes assessments.

Extension

- **Enrichment** Provides students with interesting problems and activities that extend the concepts of the lesson.

- **Activities, Games, and Puzzles** Worksheets that can be used for concepts development, enrichment, and for fun!

Practice and Problem Solving Wkbk/All-in-One Resources/Online
Practice page 1

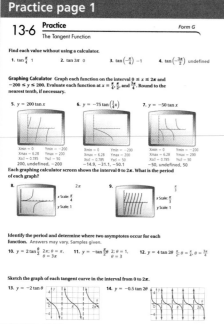

Practice and Problem Solving Wkbk/All-in-One Resources/Online
Practice page 2

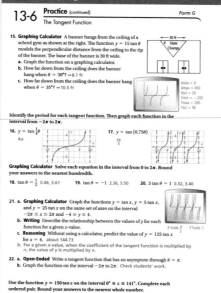

All-in-One Resources/Online
Enrichment

13-6 Enrichment
The Tangent Function

Even and Odd Functions

Practice and Problem Solving Wkbk/All-in-One Resources/Online
Think About a Plan

13-6 Think About a Plan
The Tangent Function

Practice and Problem Solving Wkbk/All-in-One Resources/Online
Standardized Test Prep

13-6 Standardized Test Prep
The Tangent Function

Online Teacher Resource Center
Activities, Games, and Puzzles

13-6 Activity: Steeper and Steeper
The Tangent Function

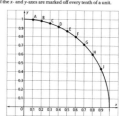

13-7 Translating Sine and Cosine Functions

© Content Standards
F.TF.5 Choose trigonometric functions to model periodic phenomena . . .
F.IF.7.e Graph . . . trigonometric functions, showing period, midline, and amplitude.

Objectives To graph translations of trigonometric functions
To write equations of translations

When in doubt, make a sketch.

MATHEMATICAL PRACTICES

Dynamic Activity
Translating and Scaling Sine and Cosine Functions

Lesson Vocabulary
• phase shift

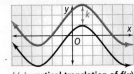

SOLVE IT!

Getting Ready!

Think about riding a bike, and pumping the pedals at a constant rate of one revolution each second. How does the graph of the height of one of your feet compare with the graph of a sine function? How does it compare with the graph of the height of your other foot? Explain.

12 in.

3 in.

Recall that for any function f, you can graph $f(x - h)$ by translating the graph of f by h units horizontally. You can graph $f(x) + k$ by translating the graph of f by k units vertically.

Essential Understanding You can translate periodic functions in the same way that you translate other functions.

Each horizontal translation of certain periodic functions is a **phase shift**.

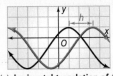

$g(x)$: horizontal translation of $f(x)$
$g(x) = f(x - h)$

$h(x)$: vertical translation of $f(x)$
$h(x) = f(x) + k$

When $g(x) = f(x - h)$, the value of h is the amount of the shift. If $h > 0$, the shift is to the right. If $h < 0$, the shift is to the left. When $h(x) = f(x) + k$, the value of k is the amount of the midline shift. If $k > 0$, the midline shifts up. If $k < 0$, the midline shifts down.

1 Interactive Learning

Solve It!
PURPOSE To compare a function describing a real-world situation to a sine function
PROCESS Students may
• use paper and pencil to graph the height of each foot at different times to see how each graph compares to the sine function.
• graph $y = \sin x$ on a graphing calculator and use the TRACE key to decide how the height of each foot can be represented by this function.

FACILITATE

Q Why is it important that the bike pedal moves at a constant rate? Explain. **[A periodic function requires that a pattern repeats at regular intervals. This can only occur as a function of time if the height of a foot is increasing and decreasing at a constant rate.]**

Q If a sine function represents the heights, how are the maximum and minimum values determined? **[The maximum value is the height of the foot from the ground when the foot is at the highest point. The minimum is the height when the foot is at the lowest point.]**

Q Can the height of a foot be represented by the sine function if the sine function values go below zero? Explain. **[Yes, if the sine function is translated up.]**

ANSWER See Solve It in Answers on next page.
CONNECT THE MATH Students draw comparisons between the sine function and the model of a real world situation in the Solve It. In this lesson, students will graph and write equations and translations of trigonometric functions.

13-7 Preparing to Teach

BIG ideas Modeling
Function
ESSENTIAL UNDERSTANDINGS
• Periodic functions can be translated the same way as other functions.
• All functions in the sine and cosine family of functions can be completely described by their amplitude, period, vertical shift, and horizontal shift (or phase shift).

Math Background
Translations of trigonometric functions behave essentially the same as the other functions studied so far:
• Subtracting a value h from x causes a horizontal translation to the right ($h > 0$) or left ($h < 0$).
• Adding a value k to the function rule causes a vertical translation k units up ($k > 0$) or down ($k < 0$).

For periodic functions, horizontal translations are called *phase shifts*.

Note that phase shifts and vertical translations do not change the period or amplitude of trigonometric functions. They change only the location of the periodic curve, not the shape or maximum or minimum values.

© Mathematical Practices
Look for and make use of structure. In graphing sine and cosine functions, students will find each complicated case of either function to be composed of algebraic adjustments to the basic function. Students will find the phase shift, vertical translation, and other transformations to sine and cosine.

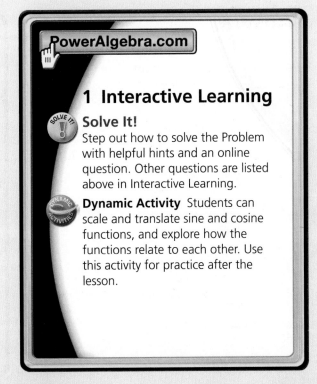

PowerAlgebra.com

1 Interactive Learning

SOLVE IT! **Solve It!**
Step out how to solve the Problem with helpful hints and an online question. Other questions are listed above in Interactive Learning.

Dynamic Activity Students can scale and translate sine and cosine functions, and explore how the functions relate to each other. Use this activity for practice after the lesson.

2 Guided Instruction

Problem 1

Q How are a phase shift and a translation the same? How are they different? **[A translation refers to a function shifting up, down, right, or left. A phase shift refers only to a shift right or left.]**

Q Can a vertical translation of a sine function cause a change in amplitude? Explain. **[No, the translation only shifts the function up or down. The difference between maximum and minimum values remains the same.]**

Got It?

Q How can you rewrite the equation in 1b to help find the value of h? **[Rewrite the addition expression using subtraction, so $x + 3$ becomes $x - (-3)$]**

Problem 2

Point out to students that the equation in 2A does not have parentheses; therefore, the equation indicates you must find the sine of x and then add 3. If students are using a graphing calculator to check their answers, remind them to use parentheses when entering a problem. For example, $y = \sin x + 3$ should be entered as $Y1 = \sin (x) + 3$.

Q How do the graphs of $y = \sin (x + 3)$ and $y = \sin x + 3$ differ from the parent function $y = \sin x$? Explain. **[The graph of $y = \sin (x + 3)$ is a shift to the left of the parent function. The graph of $y = \sin x + 3$ is a shift up.]**

Q How would the graph in Problem 2B change if the parentheses were removed? **[The graph would be a translation of $y = \sin x$ by $\frac{\pi}{2}$ units down.]**

 Problem 1 Identifying Phase Shifts

What is the value of h in each translation? Describe each phase shift (use a phrase such as *3 units to the left*).

Think

Why should you rewrite $x + 4$ as $x - (-4)$?
When the function uses this form, you are less likely to misinterpret the value of h.

Ⓐ $g(x) = f(x - 2)$
  $h = 2$; the phase shift is 2 units to the right.

Ⓑ $y = \cos(x + 4)$
  $= \cos(x - (-4))$
  $h = -4$; the phase shift is 4 units to the left.

✓ **Got It? 1.** What is the value of h in each translation? Describe each phase shift (use a phrase such as *3 units to the left*).
  a. $g(t) = f(t - 5)$
  b. $y = \sin(x + 3)$

You can analyze a translation to determine how it relates to the parent function.

 Problem 2 Graphing Translations

Use the graph of the parent function $y = \sin x$. What is the graph of each translation in the interval $0 \le x \le 2\pi$?

Think

How do trigonometric translations relate to those of other functions?
Translating the graphs of trigonometric functions is similar to translating graphs of other functions.

Ⓐ $y = \sin x + 3$

$k = 3$

Translate the graph of the parent function 3 units up. The midline is $y = 3$.

Ⓑ $y = \sin\left(x - \frac{\pi}{2}\right)$

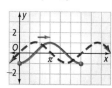

$h = \frac{\pi}{2}$

Translate the graph of the parent function $\frac{\pi}{2}$ units to the right.

Answers

Solve It!

The graph of the height of your foot that starts in the lowest position is the same as the graph of the sine function, but translated up 9 units and with an amplitude of 6. The graph of the other foot is a reflection of the first graph across the line $y = 9$.

Got It?

1. a. 5; 5 units to the right
  b. −3; 3 units to the left

2. a.

  b.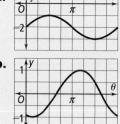

  c. $y = \sin (x - 2)$ **d.** $y = \sin x - 2$

3. See page 878.

 PowerAlgebra.com

2 Guided Instruction

Ⓒ Each Problem is worked out and supported online.

Problem 1
Identifying Phase Shifts

Problem 2
Graphing Translations

Problem 3
Graphing a Combined Translation
Animated

Problem 4
Graphing a Translation of $y = \sin 2x$
Animated

Problem 5
Writing Translations

Problem 6
Writing a Trigonometric Equation to Model a Situation
Animated

Support in Algebra 2 Companion
• Vocabulary
• Key Concepts
• Got It?

Got It? 2. Use the graph of $y = \sin x$ from Problem 2. What is the graph of each translation in the interval $0 \le x \le 2\pi$?

a. $y = \sin x - 2$ b. $y = \sin(x - 2)$

c. Which translation is a phase shift?

d. Which translation gives the graph a new midline?

You can translate both vertically and horizontally to produce combined translations.

 Problem 3 Graphing a Combined Translation

Use the graph of the parent function $y = \sin x$ in Problem 2. What is the graph of the translation $y = \sin(x + \pi) - 2$ in the interval $0 \le x \le 2\pi$?

Think

What are the translations?
Because π is added to x, the horizontal phase shift is π units left. Because -2 is added to the dependent value, the vertical translation is 2 units down.

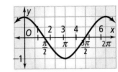

Translate the graph of the parent function 2 units down and π units to the left.

Got It? 3. Use the graph at the right of the parent function $y = \cos x$. What is the graph of each translation in the interval $0 \le x \le 2\pi$?

a. $y = \cos(x - 2) + 5$

b. $y = \cos(x + 1) + 3$

The translations graphed in Problems 2 and 3 belong to the families of the sine and cosine functions.

take note

Concept Summary   Families of Sine and Cosine Functions

Parent Function	Transformed Function
$y = \sin x$	$y = a \sin b(x - h) + k$
$y = \cos x$	$y = a \cos b(x - h) + k$

- $|a|$ = amplitude (vertical stretch or shrink)
- $\frac{2\pi}{b}$ = period (when x is in radians and $b > 0$)
- h = phase shift, or horizontal shift
- k = vertical shift ($y = k$ is the midline)

Got It?

Q To find a translation, does it help to rewrite the equation in 2b as $y = \sin(x + (-2))$? Explain. **[No; the translation is h when the function is in the form $g(x) = f(x - h)$, so the translation can be directly read from the equation in its original form $y = \sin(x - 2)$.]**

Problem 3   **VISUAL LEARNERS**

Q Do the max or min values change during a phase shift? Do the zeros change? Explain. **[The max and min values do not change because the graph is shifted right or left. The zeros might change depending on the amount of the phase shift.]**

Q Does the amplitude or period of the translated graph change? Explain. **[No; amplitude is the difference between max and min, so a shift will not change the amplitude. The period will not change because the graph has not been stretched or compressed horizontally.]**

Got It?

Q How could you describe what you expect to see in the graphs of 3a and 3b after the translation? **[For 3a, the function $y = \cos x$ should shift 2 units to the right and 5 units up. For 3b, the function will shift 1 unit to the left and 3 units up.]**

Take Note   **ERROR PREVENTION**

Be sure students understand that the period is $\frac{2\pi}{b}$ and not b.

Q What happens to the period as b increases? Explain. **[Because b is in the denominator, the period will decrease as b increases.]**

Additional Problems

1. What is the value of h in each translation? Describe each phase shift.

a. $g(x) = f(x - 6)$

b. $y = \cos(x + 1.5)$

ANSWERS

a. $h = 6$; the phase shift is 6 units to the right.

b. $h = -1.5$; the phase shift is 1.5 units to the left.

2. Use the graph of the parent function $y = \sin x$. What is the graph of each translation in the interval $0 \le x \le 2\pi$?

a. $y = \sin x + 4$

b. $y = \sin(x - \pi)$

ANSWER

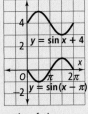

3. Use the graph of the parent function $y = \sin x$. What is the graph of $y = \sin\left(x - \frac{\pi}{2}\right) + 3$ in the interval $0 \le x \le 2\pi$?

ANSWER

4. What is the graph of $y = \sin 2(x - \pi) - 3$ in the interval from 0 to 2π?

ANSWER

5. What is an equation that models each translation?

a. $y = -\sin x$, 5 units up

b. $y = 3 \cos x$, 1 unit to the right

ANSWERS

a. $y = -\sin x + 5$

b. $y = 3 \cos(x - 1)$

6. The table gives the average temperature in Los Angeles, California x months after the start of the calendar year ($0 \le x \le 12$). What cosine function models the temperature as a function of x?

Month	Temp (°F)
1	57
2	58
3	59
4	62
5	64
6	67
7	72
8	73
9	72
10	67
11	64
12	59

ANSWER

$y = 8 \cos \frac{\pi}{6}(x - 8) + 65$

Problem 4   ERROR PREVENTION

Remind students that the phase shift can be read directly from the equation only when the equation is in a certain form. The equation $y = \cos(3x - \pi)$ is not in the form $y = \cos b(x - h)$. It must be rewritten as $y = \cos 3\left(x - \frac{\pi}{3}\right)$ to see that the phase shift is $\frac{\pi}{3}$.

Q How can you use the graph to find the number of cycles of the graph $y = \sin 2x$ in the interval from 0 to 2π? Explain. **[One cycle is complete from 0 to π, so 2 cycles will be shown from 0 to 2π.]**

Got It?

Q How many cycles of the graph are in the interval between 0 and 2π for 4b? Explain. **[About 1.5 cycles because the period is 4, and 2π is approximately 6.28. 6.28 divided by 4 is 1.57.]**

Problem 5

Q Which of the equations in Problem 5 represents a phase shift? Explain what this means when writing the equation. **[The equation in 5B is a phase shift because the function is translated to the left. This means the value of h must be written inside parentheses.]**

Got It?

Q Will the amplitude of the function in 5b change after the translation to the right? Explain. **[No, the translation does not affect the amplitude because the value of a remains the same.]**

Think

Why should you graph the parent function first?
Once you know the relative dimensions of the curve, you can translate it according to the h- and k-values.

Ⓒ **Problem 4** Graphing a Translation of $y = \sin 2x$

What is the graph of $y = \sin 2\left(x - \frac{\pi}{3}\right) - \frac{3}{2}$ in the interval from 0 to 2π?

Since $a = 1$ and $b = 2$, the graph is a translation of $y = \sin 2x$.

Step 1 Sketch one cycle of $y = \sin 2x$. Use five points in the pattern *zero-max-zero-min-zero*.

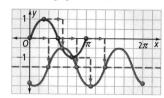

Step 2 Since $h = \frac{\pi}{3}$ and $k = -\frac{3}{2}$, translate the graph $\frac{\pi}{3}$ units to the right and $\frac{3}{2}$ units down. Extend the periodic pattern from 0 to 2π. Sketch the graph.

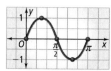

The blue curve above is the graph of $y = \sin 2\left(x - \frac{\pi}{3}\right) - \frac{3}{2}$.

✓ **Got It? 4.** What is the graph of each translation in the interval from 0 to 2π?
  a. $y = -3 \sin 2\left(x - \frac{\pi}{3}\right) - \frac{3}{2}$
  b. $y = 2 \cos \frac{\pi}{2}(x + 1) - 3$

You can write an equation to describe a translation.

Think

What are a, b, h, and k in $y = a \sin b(x - h) + k$?
$a = b = 1$, $h = 0$, and $k = -\pi$.

Ⓒ **Problem 5** Writing Translations

What is an equation that models each translation?

A $y = \sin x$, π units down
  π units down means $k = -\pi$.
  An equation is $y = \sin x - \pi$.

B $y = -\cos x$, 2 units to the left
  2 units to the left means $h = -2$.
  An equation is $y = -\cos(x + 2)$.

✓ **Got It? 5.** What is an equation that models each translation?
  a. $y = \cos x$, $\frac{\pi}{2}$ units up
  b. $y = 2 \sin x$, $\frac{\pi}{4}$ units to the right

Answers

Got It? (continued)

3. a.
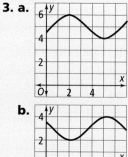

b.

4. a.
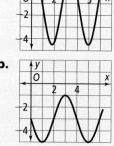

b.

5. a. $y = \cos x + \frac{\pi}{2}$

  b. $y = 2 \sin\left(x - \frac{\pi}{4}\right)$

You can write a trigonometric function to model a situation.

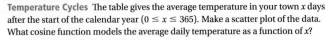 **Problem 6** **Writing a Trigonometric Function to Model a Situation** STEM

Temperature Cycles The table gives the average temperature in your town x days after the start of the calendar year ($0 \leq x \leq 365$). Make a scatter plot of the data. What cosine function models the average daily temperature as a function of x?

Day of Year	16	47	75	106	136	167	198	228	258	289	319	350
Temperature (°F)	33	35	42	52	62	72	77	76	69	58	48	38

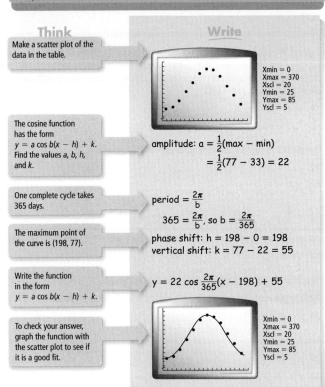

Think

Make a scatter plot of the data in the table.

Write

Xmin = 0
Xmax = 370
Xscl = 20
Ymin = 25
Ymax = 85
Yscl = 5

The cosine function has the form $y = a \cos b(x - h) + k$. Find the values a, b, h, and k.

amplitude: $a = \frac{1}{2}(\text{max} - \text{min})$
$\qquad = \frac{1}{2}(77 - 33) = 22$

One complete cycle takes 365 days.

period = $\frac{2\pi}{b}$

$365 = \frac{2\pi}{b}$, so $b = \frac{2\pi}{365}$

The maximum point of the curve is (198, 77).

phase shift: $h = 198 - 0 = 198$
vertical shift: $k = 77 - 22 = 55$

Write the function in the form $y = a \cos b(x - h) + k$.

$y = 22 \cos \frac{2\pi}{365}(x - 198) + 55$

To check your answer, graph the function with the scatter plot to see if it is a good fit.

Xmin = 0
Xmax = 370
Xscl = 20
Ymin = 25
Ymax = 85
Yscl = 5

© ✓ **Got It? 6. a.** Use the model in Problem 6. What was the average temperature in your town 150 days into the year?
b. What value does the midline of this model represent?
c. Reasoning Can you use this model to predict temperatures for next year? Explain your answer.

Problem 6

Q How would the equation change if the lowest temperature were 27°? Explain. **[Because the minimum would be a different value, the amplitude would be $\frac{1}{2}(77 - 27) = 25$. Also, the vertical shift would be $77 - 25 = 52$.]**

Q Can the equation be written using the sine function? If so, what is this new function? If not, why not? **[Yes; because the sine function is a phase shift of the cosine function by $\frac{1}{4}$ of the period, which is $\frac{365}{4} = 91.25$. $y = 22 \sin\left(\frac{2\pi}{365}(x - 106.75)\right) + 55$.]**

EXTENSION

Students can also determine a sine model using SinReg on a graphing calculator.

EDIT CALC TESTS
7↑QuartReg
8 : LinReg (a+bx)
9 : LnReg
0 : ExpReg
A : PwrReg
B : Logistic
C↓SinReg

SinReg
y = a*sin(bx+c)+d
a = 21.93576525
b = .0170334096
c = −1.948076551
d = 54.98585604

Because the equation in a graphing calculator uses the $(bx + c)$ form rather than the $b(x - c)$ form, students can compare it with the sine function in the question above by multiplying and combining terms in the sine equation. Remind students that an infinite number of equations can be used to model this function, so the equations might differ by a phase shift equal to the period.

Got It?

Q What do x and y represent in the equation? How can you use the equation to find your answer? **[x is the number of days into the year; y is the temperature. Substitute 150 for x in the equation and solve for y.]**

6. a. 69.9°F
b. the average of the highest and lowest temperatures
c. Yes; data can be extrapolated to calculate for next year.

3 Lesson Check

Do you know HOW?   ERROR INTERVENTION
- If students have difficulty solving Exercise 1, have them look at Problem 2 so they understand that this graph is a translation of the parent function by $\frac{\pi}{4}$ units to the left.
- For Exercise 2, students might become confused because the difference between this function and $y = \cos x$ is a translation as well as an amplitude change. Have students review the Take Note: Families of Sine and Cosine Functions and Problem 4 to see which numbers indicate a translation.

Do you UNDERSTAND?
- If students have trouble finding Amberly's error in Exercise 5, remind them that the phase shift can be directly read only from the equation in the form $y = a \sin b(x - h) + k$. Distributing b to the terms in parentheses will not allow you to directly find the phase shift.

Close

> **Q** What is a phase shift? Is every translation a phase shift? Explain. **[A phase shift is a horizontal translation. Because some translations are vertical, every translation is not a phase shift. However, every phase shift is a translation.]**
>
> **Q** Is it better to use a sine function or a cosine function when modeling real-life situations? Explain. **[It does not matter because they are translations of each other.]**

 Lesson Check

Do you know HOW?
1. Graph $y = \sin\left(x + \frac{\pi}{4}\right)$ in the interval from 0 to 2π.
2. Describe any phase shift or vertical shift in the graph of $y = 4 \cos(x - 2) + 9$.
3. What is an equation that shifts $y = \cos x$, 3 units up and $\frac{2\pi}{3}$ units to the right?

Do you UNDERSTAND?   MATHEMATICAL PRACTICES
4. **Vocabulary** Write a sine function that has amplitude 4, period 3π, phase shift π, and vertical shift -5.
5. **Error Analysis** Two students disagree on the translation for $y = \cos 3\left(x + \frac{\pi}{6}\right)$. Amberly says that it is $\frac{\pi}{2}$ units to the left of $y = \cos 3x$. Scott says that it is $\frac{\pi}{6}$ units to the left of $y = \cos 3x$. Is either student correct? Describe any errors of each student.

Practice and Problem-Solving Exercises   MATHEMATICAL PRACTICES

A Practice

Determine the value of h in each translation. Describe each phase shift (use a phrase like *3 units to the left*).   ◀ See Problem 1.

6. $g(x) = f(x + 1)$ 7. $g(t) = f(t + 2)$ 8. $f(z) = g(z - 1.6)$
9. $f(x) = g(x - 3)$ 10. $y = \sin(x + \pi)$ 11. $y = \cos\left(x - \frac{5\pi}{7}\right)$

Use the function $f(x)$ at the right. Graph each translation.   ◀ See Problem 2.

12. $g(x) = f(x) + 1$ 13. $g(x) = f(x) - 3$
14. $g(x) = f(x + 2)$ 15. $g(x) = f(x - 1)$

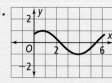

Graph each translation of $y = \cos x$ in the interval from 0 to 2π.

16. $y = \cos(x + 3)$ 17. $y = \cos x + 3$ 18. $y = \cos x - 4$
19. $y = \cos(x - 4)$ 20. $y = \cos x + \pi$ 21. $y = \cos(x - \pi)$

Describe any phase shift and vertical shift in the graph.   ◀ See Problem 3.

22. $y = 3 \sin x + 1$ 23. $y = 4 \cos(x + 1) - 2$
24. $y = \sin\left(x + \frac{\pi}{2}\right) + 2$ 25. $y = \sin(x - 3) + 2$

Graph each function in the interval from 0 to 2π.

26. $y = 2 \sin\left(x + \frac{\pi}{4}\right) - 1$ 27. $y = \sin\left(x + \frac{\pi}{3}\right) + 1$
28. $y = \cos(x - \pi) - 3$ 29. $y = 2 \sin\left(x - \frac{\pi}{6}\right) + 2$

Graph each function in the interval from 0 to 2π.   ◀ See Problem 4.

30. $y = 3 \sin \frac{1}{2}x$ 31. $y = \cos 2\left(x + \frac{\pi}{2}\right) - 2$
32. $y = \frac{1}{2} \sin 2x - 1$ 33. $y = \sin 3\left(x + \frac{\pi}{3}\right)$
34. $y = \sin 2(x + 3) - 2$ 35. $y = 3 \sin \frac{\pi}{2}(x - 2)$

Answers

Lesson Check
1.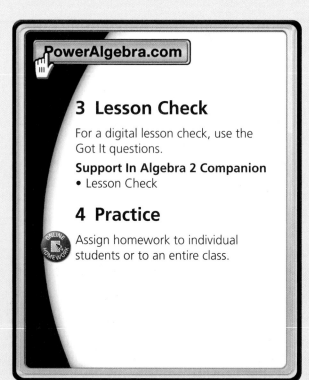

2. phase shift: 2 units to the right; vertical shift: 9 units up
3. $y = \cos\left(x - \frac{2\pi}{3}\right) + 3$
4. Answers may vary. Sample: $y = 4 \sin \frac{2}{3}(x - \pi) - 5$
5. Scott is correct; $y = a \cos b(x - h) + k = \cos 3\left(x + \frac{\pi}{6}\right)$ where $h = -\frac{\pi}{6}$. The phase shift is $\frac{\pi}{6}$ units to the left of $y = \cos 3x$.

Practice and Problem-Solving Exercises
6. -1; 1 unit to the left
7. -2; 2 units to the left
8. 1.6; 1.6 units to the right
9. 3; 3 units to the right
10. $-\pi$; π units to the left
11. $\frac{5\pi}{7}$; $\frac{5\pi}{7}$ units to the right
12.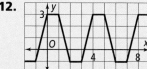
13.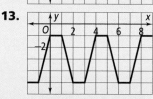
14.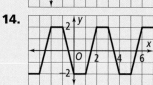

Write an equation for each translation. 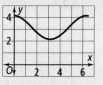 See Problem 5.

36. $y = \sin x$, π units to the left

37. $y = \cos x$, $\frac{\pi}{2}$ units down

38. $y = \sin x$, 3 units up

39. $y = \cos x$, 1.5 units to the right

STEM 40. Temperature The table below shows water temperatures at a buoy in the Gulf of Mexico on several days of the year. 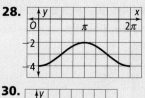 See Problem 6.

Day of Year	16	47	75	106	136	167	198	228	258	289	319	350
Temperature (°F)	71	69	70	73	77	82	85	86	84	82	78	74

  a. Plot the data.   **b.** Write a cosine model for the data.

 Apply Write an equation for each translation.

41. $y = \cos x$, 3 units to the left and π units up

42. $y = \sin x$, $\frac{\pi}{2}$ units to the right and 3.5 units up

43. Think About a Plan The function $y = 1.5 \sin \frac{\pi}{6}(x - 6) + 2$ represents the average monthly rainfall for a town in central Florida, where x represents the number of the month (January $= 1$, February $= 2$, and so on). Rewrite the function using a cosine model.
  • How does the graph of $y = \sin x$ translate to the graph of $y = \cos x$?
  • What parts of the sine function will stay the same? What must change?

Write a cosine function for each graph. Then write a sine function for each graph.

44.
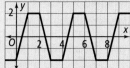

45.

46. The graphs of $y = \sin x$ and $y = \cos x$ are shown at the right.
  a. What phase shift will translate the cosine graph onto the sine graph? Write your answer as an equation in the form $\sin x = \cos(x - h)$.
  b. What phase shift will translate the sine graph onto the cosine graph? Write your answer as an equation in the form $\cos x = \sin(x - h)$.

47. a. Open-Ended Draw a periodic function. Find its amplitude and period. Then sketch a translation of your function 3 units down and 4 units to the left.
  b. Reasoning Suppose your original function is $f(x)$. Describe your translation using the form $g(x) = f(x - h) + k$.

48. a. Write $y = 3\sin(2x - 4) + 1$ in the form $y = a \sin b(x - h) + k$. (*Hint:* Factor where possible.)
  b. Find the amplitude, midline, and period. Describe any translations.

ASSIGNMENT GUIDE
Basic: 6–40 all, 42–44, 46
Average: 7–39 odd, 40–48
Advanced: 7–39 odd, 40–54
Standardized Test Prep: 55–58
Mixed Review: 59–71

Ⓒ Mathematical Practices are supported by exercises with red headings. Here are the Practices supported in this lesson:

MP 1: Make Sense of Problems Ex. 43
MP 2: Reason Abstractly Ex. 4
MP 3: Construct Arguments Ex. 47a, b
MP 3: Critique the Reasoning of Others Ex. 5
MP 5: Use Tools Appropriately Ex. 49–54

Applications exercises have blue headings. Exercise 40 supports MP 4: Model.

STEM exercises focus on science or engineering applications.

EXERCISE 44: Use the Think About a Plan worksheet in the **Practice and Problem Solving Workbook** (also available in the Teaching Resources in print and online) to further support students' development in becoming independent learners.

HOMEWORK QUICK CHECK
To check students' understanding of key skills and concepts, go over Exercises 7, 27, 37, 43, and 44.

15.
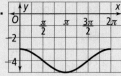

16.
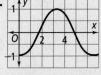

17.
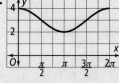

18.

19.
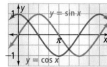

20.

21.
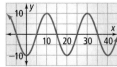

22. 1 unit up
23. 1 unit to the left and 2 units down
24. $\frac{\pi}{2}$ units to the left and 2 units up
25. 3 units to the right and 2 units up

26.
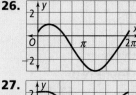

27.
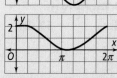

28.
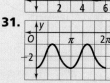

29.
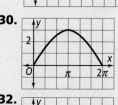

30.
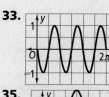

31.
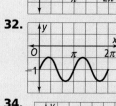

32.
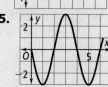

33.

34.
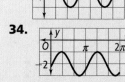

35.

36–48. See next page.

Answers

Practice and Problem-Solving Exercises (continued)

36. $y = \sin(x + \pi)$

37. $y = \cos x - \frac{\pi}{2}$

38. $y = \sin x + 3$

39. $y = \cos(x - 1.5)$

40. a.

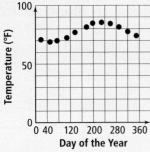

Day of the Year

b. $y = 8.5 \cos \frac{2\pi}{365}(x - 228) + 77.5$

41. $y = \cos(x + 3) + \pi$

42. $y = \sin\left(x - \frac{\pi}{2}\right) + 3.5$

43. $y = 1.5 \cos\left[\frac{\pi}{6}(x - 6) - \frac{\pi}{2}\right] + 2$

44. $y = 2 \cos\left(x - \frac{\pi}{3}\right) - 1$;

$y = 2 \sin\left(x + \frac{\pi}{6}\right) - 1$

45. $y = -10 \cos\frac{\pi}{10}x$;

$y = 10 \sin\left(\frac{\pi}{10}x - \frac{\pi}{2}\right)$

46. a. $\frac{\pi}{2}$; $\sin x = \cos\left(x - \frac{\pi}{2}\right)$

b. $-\frac{\pi}{2}$; $\cos x = \sin\left(x + \frac{\pi}{2}\right)$

47. a. Check students' work.

b. $g(x) = f(x + 4) - 3$

48. a. $y = 3 \sin 2(x - 2) + 1$

b. $3, y = 1, \pi$; translation of $y = 3 \sin 2x$, 2 units to the right and 1 unit up

49.

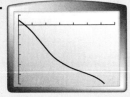

50.

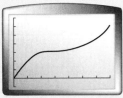

51.

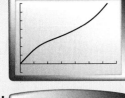

C Challenge 🖩 Use a graphing calculator to graph each function in the interval from 0 to 2π. Then sketch each graph.

49. $y = \sin x + x$

50. $y = \sin x + 2x$

51. $y = \cos x - 2x$

52. $y = \cos x + x$

53. $y = \sin(x + \cos x)$

54. $y = \sin(x + 2 \cos x)$

Standardized Test Prep

SAT/ACT

55. Which function is a phase shift of $y = \sin \theta$ by 5 units to the left?
   - Ⓐ $y = 5 \sin \theta$
   - Ⓒ $y = \sin(\theta + 5)$
   - Ⓑ $y = \sin \theta + 5$
   - Ⓓ $y = \sin 5\theta$

56. Which function is a translation of $y = \cos \theta$ by 5 units down?
   - Ⓕ $y = -5 \cos \theta$
   - Ⓗ $y = \cos(\theta - 5)$
   - Ⓖ $y = \cos \theta - 5$
   - Ⓘ $y = \cos(-5\theta)$

57. Which function is a translation of $y = \sin \theta$ that is $\frac{\pi}{3}$ units up and $\frac{\pi}{2}$ units to the left?
   - Ⓐ $y = \sin\left(\theta + \frac{\pi}{3}\right) + \frac{\pi}{2}$
   - Ⓒ $y = \sin\left(\theta - \frac{\pi}{2}\right) + \frac{\pi}{3}$
   - Ⓑ $y = \sin\left(\theta + \frac{\pi}{2}\right) + \frac{\pi}{3}$
   - Ⓓ $y = \sin\left(\theta - \frac{\pi}{3}\right) - \frac{\pi}{2}$

Short Response

58. Find values of a and b such that the function $y = \sin \theta$ can be expressed as $y = a \cos(\theta + b)$.

Mixed Review

Identify the period of each function. Then tell where two asymptotes occur for each function.

See Lesson 13-6.

59. $y = \tan 6\theta$

60. $y = \tan \frac{\theta}{4}$

61. $y = \tan 1.5\theta$

62. $y = \tan \frac{\theta}{6}$

For the given probability of success P on each trial, find the probability of x successes in n trials.

See Lesson 11-8.

63. $x = 4, n = 5, p = 0.2$

64. $x = 3, n = 5, p = 0.6$

65. $x = 4, n = 8, p = 0.7$

66. $x = 7, n = 8, p = 0.7$

Get Ready! To prepare for Lesson 13-8, do Exercises 67–71.

See p. 973.

Find the reciprocal of each fraction.

67. $\frac{9}{13}$

68. $\frac{-5}{8}$

69. $\frac{1}{2\pi}$

70. $\frac{4m}{15}$

71. $\frac{14}{-t}$

52.

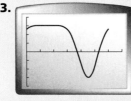

53.

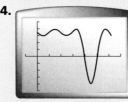

54.

Standardized Test Prep

55. C   **56.** G   **57.** B

58. [2] If the function $y = \cos \theta$ is shifted $\frac{\pi}{2}$ radians to the right, the result is $y = \cos\left(\theta - \frac{\pi}{2}\right)$, which is the same as $y = \sin \theta$. So, $a = 1$, and $b = -\frac{\pi}{2}$.

[1] incorrect explanation OR only one of the two values correct

Mixed Review

59. $\frac{\pi}{6}$; $\theta = -\frac{\pi}{12}, \frac{\pi}{12}$

60. 4π; $\theta = -2\pi, 2\pi$

61. $\frac{2\pi}{3}$; $\theta = -\frac{\pi}{3}, \frac{\pi}{3}$

62. 6π; $\theta = -3\pi, 3\pi$

63. 0.0064   **64.** 0.3456

65. ≈0.136   **66.** ≈0.198

67. $\frac{13}{9}$ **68.** $-\frac{8}{5}$

69. 2π **70.** $\frac{15}{4m}$

71. $-\frac{t}{14}$

Additional Instructional Support

Algebra 2 Companion

Students can use the **Algebra 2 Companion** worktext (4 pages) as you teach the lesson. Use the Companion to support

- New Vocabulary
- Key Concepts
- Got It for each Problem
- Lesson Check

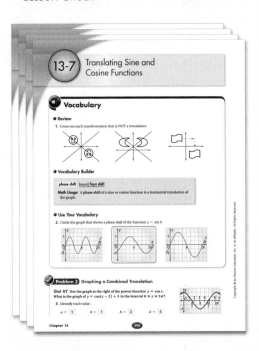

ELL Support

Assess Understanding Have each student write the words *up*, *down*, *left*, and *right* on index cards. Write the equation $y = \sin(x + 2)$ on the board. Have students show the card that says *left* to indicate that this function is a translation to the left of the parent function $y = \sin x$. Write the equation $y = \cos(x - 3) + 2$ on the board. Have students show the cards *right* and *up* to indicate how this function is translated. Use the following equations to start the activity.

$y = \sin(x - 4)$ (*right*)

$y = \cos x + 7$ (*up*)

$y = \sin(x + 2) - 5$ (*left and down*)

$y = \cos(x - \pi) + 2$ (*right and up*)

$y = \sin 3\left(x - \frac{\pi}{2}\right) - 1$ (*right and down*)

Encourage students to come up to the board and write their own equations. The student at the board can be responsible for verifying that the answers shown by students are correct.

5 Assess & Remediate

Lesson Quiz

1. What is the value of h in $y = \sin(x - 3.2)$? Describe the phase shift.

2. **Do you UNDERSTAND?** Describe the translations of the graph $y = \sin(x + \pi) - 2$. What is the graph in the interval $0 \le x \le 2\pi$?

3. A scientist slowly heats and then cools a substance over a period of 6 hours ($0 \le x \le 6$), and then repeats. The table gives the temperature x hours after the start of the experiment. What cosine function models the temperature as a function of x?

h	1	2	3	4	5	6
°F	35	50	55	51	42	36

ANSWERS TO LESSON QUIZ

1. $h = 3.2$; 3.2 units to the right

2. The graph is shifted 2 units down and π units to the left.

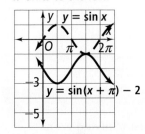

3. $y = 10 \cos \frac{\pi}{3}(x - 3) + 45$

PRESCRIPTION FOR REMEDIATION

Use the student work on the Lesson Quiz to prescribe a differentiated review assignment:

Points	Differentiated Remediation
0–1	Intervention
2	On-level
3	Extension

PowerAlgebra.com

5 Assess & Remediate

Assign the Lesson Quiz. Appropriate intervention, practice, or enrichment is automatically generated based on student performance.

Intervention

- **Reteaching** (2 pages) Provides reteaching and practice exercises for the key lesson concepts. Use with struggling students or absent students.

- **English Language Learner Support** Helps students develop and reinforce mathematical vocabulary and key concepts.

All-in-One Resources/Online
Reteaching

13-7 Reteaching
Translating Sine and Cosine Functions

You can translate the graphs of sine and cosine functions both horizontally and vertically. A horizontal translation is called a *phase shift*. For a function in the form $y = a \sin b(x - h) + k$ or $y = a \cos b(x - h) + k$:

- $|a|$ = amplitude
- $\frac{2\pi}{b}$ = period
- h = phase shift   If $h > 0$, the graph moves to the right.
                        If $h < 0$, the graph moves to the left.
- k = vertical shift   If $k > 0$, the graph moves up.
                        If $k < 0$, the graph moves down.

Problem

What are the amplitude, period, and any phase shift or vertical shift in the graph of the function $y = 2 \sin \frac{1}{3}(x + 5)$?

$y = 2 \sin \frac{1}{3}(x - (-5)) + 0$ Write function as $y = a \sin b(x - h) + k$.

$a = 2, b = \frac{1}{3}, h = -5, k = 0$ Identify a, b, h, and k.

$|a| = |2| = 2$ amplitude = 2

$\frac{2\pi}{b} = \frac{2\pi}{\frac{1}{3}} = 6\pi$ period = 6π

$h = -5$ The phase shift is 5 units to the left.

$k = 0$ There is no vertical shift.

Exercises

Determine the amplitude, period, and any phase shift or vertical shift in the graphs of the functions.

1. $y = 6 \cos 3x + 2$
6; $\frac{2\pi}{3}$; 2 units up

2. $y = -\sin \frac{1}{2}(x - \pi)$
1; 4π; π units right

3. $y = 2 \sin 8\left(x - \frac{\pi}{3}\right) - 5$
2; $\frac{\pi}{4}$; $\frac{\pi}{3}$ right; 5 units down

4. $y = \cos 2(x - 1) + 3.4$
1; π; 1 unit right; 3.4 units up

5. $y = \frac{2}{3} \sin(x + 3\pi) - \pi$
$\frac{2}{3}$; 2π; 3π units left; π units down

6. $y = -3 \cos\left(x + \frac{\pi}{4}\right) + 12$
3; 2π; $\frac{\pi}{4}$ units left; 12 units up

All-in-One Resources/Online
English Language Learner Support

13-7 Additional Vocabulary Support
Translating Sine and Cosine Functions

For Exercises 1–5, draw a line from each item in Column A to the matching item in Column B.

Column A	Column B
1. h	A. vertical shift
2. $|a|$	B. period
3. $y = \sin x$	C. phase shift or horizontal shift
4. k	D. parent function
5. $\frac{2\pi}{b}$	E. amplitude

Name each of the following functions as a *phase shift* or a *vertical shift*.

6. $y = \sin x + 5$
vertical shift

7. $y = \cos(x - 3)$
phase shift

8. $y = 2 \sin(x + 7)$
phase shift

9. $y = 0.5 \cos x - 4$
vertical shift

10. $y = \sin\left(x + \frac{\pi}{6}\right)$
phase shift

11. $y = \cos x - \frac{2\pi}{3}$
vertical shift

Describe any phase shift or vertical shift in the graphs of the following functions.

12. $y = 3 \sin x + 5$
Shift the graph of the parent function up 5 units

13. $y = 0.5 \cos\left(x - \frac{\pi}{4}\right)$
Shift the graph of the parent function $\frac{\pi}{4}$ units to the right

14. $y = \sin(x - \pi) - 7$
Shift the graph of the parent function π units to the right and 7 units down

Differentiated Remediation *continued*

On-Level

- **Practice** (2 pages) Provides extra practice for each lesson. For simpler practice exercises, use the Form K Practice pages found in the All-in-One Teaching Resources and online.

- **Think About a Plan** Helps students develop specific problem-solving skills and strategies by providing scaffolded guiding questions.

- **Standardized Test Prep** Focuses on all major exercises, all major question types, and helps students prepare for the high-stakes assessments.

Extension

- **Enrichment** Provides students with interesting problems and activities that extend the concepts of the lesson.

- **Activities, Games, and Puzzles** Worksheets that can be used for concepts development, enrichment, and for fun!

Practice and Problem Solving Wkbk/ All-in-One Resources/Online
Practice page 1

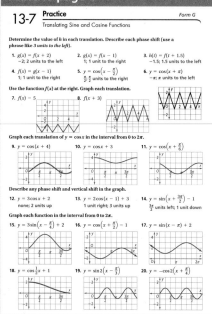

Practice and Problem Solving Wkbk/ All-in-One Resources/Online
Practice page 2

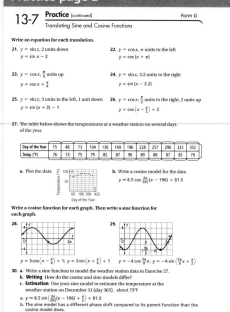

All-in-One Resources/Online
Enrichment

Practice and Problem Solving Wkbk/ All-in-One Resources/Online
Think About a Plan

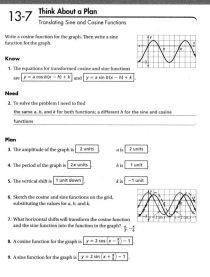

Practice and Problem Solving Wkbk/ All-in-One Resources/Online
Standardized Test Prep

Online Teacher Resource Center
Activities, Games, and Puzzles

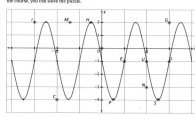

13-8 Reciprocal Trigonometric Functions

Content Standard
F.IF.7.e Graph . . . trigonometric functions, showing period, midline, and amplitude.

Objectives To evaluate reciprocal trigonometric functions
To graph reciprocal trigonometric functions

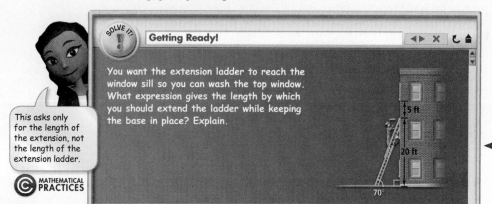

Getting Ready!

You want the extension ladder to reach the window sill so you can wash the top window. What expression gives the length by which you should extend the ladder while keeping the base in place? Explain.

This asks only for the length of the extension, not the length of the extension ladder.

5 ft
20 ft
70°

MATHEMATICAL PRACTICES

Lesson Vocabulary
• cosecant
• secant
• cotangent

To solve an equation $ax = b$, you multiply each side by the reciprocal of a. If a is a trigonometric expression, you need to use its reciprocal.

Essential Understanding Cosine, sine, and tangent have reciprocals. Cosine and *secant* are reciprocals, as are sine and *cosecant*. Tangent and *cotangent* are also reciprocals.

take note

Key Concept Cosecant, Secant, and Cotangent Functions

The **cosecant** (csc), **secant** (sec), and **cotangent** (cot) functions are defined using reciprocals. Their domains do not include the real numbers θ that make the denominator zero.

$$\csc \theta = \frac{1}{\sin \theta} \qquad \sec \theta = \frac{1}{\cos \theta} \qquad \cot \theta = \frac{1}{\tan \theta}$$

($\cot \theta = 0$ at odd multiples of $\frac{\pi}{2}$, where $\tan \theta$ is undefined.)

You can use the unit circle to evaluate the reciprocal trigonometric functions directly. Suppose the terminal side of an angle θ in standard position intersects the unit circle at the point (x, y).

Then $\csc \theta = \frac{1}{y}$, $\sec \theta = \frac{1}{x}$, $\cot \theta = \frac{x}{y}$.

13-8 Preparing to Teach

BIG idea Function
ESSENTIAL UNDERSTANDINGS
• Cosine, sine, and tangent have reciprocals. Cosine and secant are reciprocals, as are sine and cosecant. Tangent and cotangent are also reciprocals.
• Reciprocal trigonometric functions can be evaluated using what you know about sine, cosine, and tangent.
• The graphs of reciprocal trigonometric functions have asymptotes when their denominators equal 0.

Math Background
The secant function is defined as the reciprocal of the cosine function, the cosecant function is defined as the reciprocal of the sine function, and the cotangent function is defined as the reciprocal of the tangent function.

Note that the reciprocal of a function is different from the inverse of a function.

For example, the cosecant function is not $\sin^{-1} x$ (as shown on graphing calculators.) The inverse trigonometric functions will be addressed in the next chapter.

Because of the nature of the functions, the reciprocal trigonometric functions have asymptotes wherever the trigonometric function is equal to zero.

The reciprocal trigonometric functions are equal to the trigonometric functions wherever the trigonometric functions are 1 or −1, since taking the reciprocal does not change these numbers.

Mathematical Practices
Make sense of problems and persevere in solving them. Students will define the reciprocal trigonometric functions and explain correspondences between their values on the unit circle and their graphs.

---

1 Interactive Learning

Solve It!
PURPOSE To use trigonometric functions to solve a problem
PROCESS Students may
• find the expressions for the length of the ladder and extended ladder and subtract.
• find an expression for the length of the extension directly.

FACILITATE
Q What expression relates the ladder length d to the angle with the vertical? **[sin 70° = $\frac{20}{d}$]**
Q What is an expression that relates the ladder length plus the extension, x, to the angle with the vertical? **[sin 70° = $\frac{25}{d + x}$]**
Q How can you divide the triangle representing the position of the longer ladder so that the length of the extension can be found directly? **[Draw a line parallel to the ground at a height of 20 ft. on the side of the building.]**

ANSWER See Solve It in Answers on next page.
CONNECT THE MATH In the Solve It, students write expressions using trigonometric functions in the denominator of a fraction. In the lesson, they will write such fractions as the reciprocal trigonometric functions.

2 Guided Instruction

Take Note
ERROR PREVENTION

Q What error regarding sec θ and csc θ do you think might be easy to make? **[Sample: The error is thinking sec θ is the reciprocal of sin θ and csc θ is the reciprocal of cos θ.]**

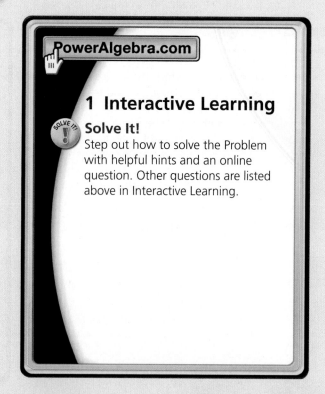

PowerAlgebra.com

1 Interactive Learning

Solve It!
Step out how to solve the Problem with helpful hints and an online question. Other questions are listed above in Interactive Learning.

Problem 1

Q What is another method you could use to find $\cot\left(-\frac{5\pi}{6}\right)$? **[Find tan $\left(-\frac{5\pi}{6}\right)$, and take its reciprocal.]**

Q Will the sign of a reciprocal function for an angle θ be the same as the sign of the original function for that angle? Explain. **[Yes, dividing 1 by a number will not change the sign of the number.]**

Got It?

Q Which of the three original trigonometric functions would you use to solve 1a, 1b, and 1c? **[For 1a use sine, for 1b use tangent, and for 1c use cosine.]**

Q Since $\cot\theta = \frac{1}{\tan\theta}$, what expression would you substitute for $\tan\theta$ to express $\cot\theta$ in terms of the coordinates of the point where the unit circle intersects the terminal side of the angle θ? **[Substitute $\frac{y}{x}$ for tan θ.]**

You can use what you know about the unit circle to find exact values for reciprocal trigonometric functions.

Ⓒ Problem 1 Finding Values Geometrically

What are the exact values of $\cot\left(-\frac{5\pi}{6}\right)$ and $\csc\left(\frac{\pi}{6}\right)$? Do not use a calculator.

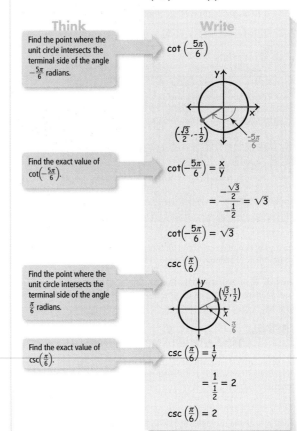

Think	Write
Find the point where the unit circle intersects the terminal side of the angle $-\frac{5\pi}{6}$ radians.	$\cot\left(-\frac{5\pi}{6}\right)$
Find the exact value of $\cot\left(-\frac{5\pi}{6}\right)$.	$\cot\left(-\frac{5\pi}{6}\right) = \frac{x}{y}$ $= \dfrac{-\frac{\sqrt{3}}{2}}{-\frac{1}{2}} = \sqrt{3}$ $\cot\left(-\frac{5\pi}{6}\right) = \sqrt{3}$ $\csc\left(\frac{\pi}{6}\right)$
Find the point where the unit circle intersects the terminal side of the angle $\frac{\pi}{6}$ radians.	
Find the exact value of $\csc\left(\frac{\pi}{6}\right)$.	$\csc\left(\frac{\pi}{6}\right) = \frac{1}{y}$ $= \dfrac{1}{\frac{1}{2}} = 2$ $\csc\left(\frac{\pi}{6}\right) = 2$

Ⓒ ✔ **Got It? 1.** What is the exact value of each expression? Do not use a calculator.

    a. $\csc\frac{\pi}{3}$ **b.** $\cot\left(-\frac{5\pi}{4}\right)$ **c.** $\sec 3\pi$

    d. Reasoning Use the unit circle at the right to find $\cot n$, $\csc n$, and $\sec n$. Explain how you found your answers.

Answers

Solve It!

To find the length by which the ladder should be extended, you must subtract the ladder's original length from its length after extension. Begin by finding the distance d between the bottom of the ladder and the building and the original length ℓ_1 of the ladder: $d = \frac{20}{\tan 70°}$ and $\ell_1 = \frac{20}{\sin 70°}$. Using the Pythagorean Theorem, you can also find the length of the ladder after extension $\ell_2 = \sqrt{\left(\frac{20}{\tan 70°}\right)^2 + 625}$. So, an expression for the amount the ladder must be extended is $\ell_2 - \ell_1 = \sqrt{\left(\frac{20}{\tan 70°}\right)^2 + 625} - \frac{20}{\sin 70°} \approx 4.755$ ft.

PowerAlgebra.com

2 Guided Instruction

Ⓒ Each Problem is worked out and supported online.

Problem 1
Finding Values Geometrically
Animated

Problem 2
Finding Values with a Calculator

Problem 3
Sketching a Graph
Animated

Problem 4
Using Technology to Graph a Reciprocal Function

Problem 5
Using Reciprocal Functions to Solve a Problem
Animated

Support in Algebra 2 Companion
• Vocabulary
• Key Concepts
• Got It?

Use the reciprocal relationships to evaluate secant, cosecant, or cotangent on a calculator, since most calculators do not have these functions as menu options.

Problem 2 Finding Values with a Calculator

What is the decimal value of each expression? Use the radian mode on your calculator. Round to the nearest thousandth.

Think

Can you use the $\sin^{-1}$, $\cos^{-1}$, and $\tan^{-1}$ keys on the calculator for the reciprocal functions?
No; those keys are *inverse functions*, not reciprocal functions.

A sec 2

$$\sec 2 = \frac{1}{\cos 2}$$

1/cos(2)
-2.402997962

$$\sec 2 \approx -2.403$$

B cot 10

$$\cot 10 = \frac{1}{\tan 10}$$

1/tan(10)
1.542351045

$$\cot 10 \approx 1.542$$

C csc 35°

$$\csc 35° = \frac{1}{\sin 35°}$$

To evaluate an angle in degrees in radian mode, use the degree symbol from the ANGLE menu.

1/sin(35°)
1.743446796

$$\csc 35° \approx 1.743$$

D cot π

$$\cot \pi = \frac{1}{\tan \pi}$$

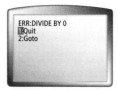

ERR:DIVIDE BY 0
1:Quit
2:Goto

Evaluating cot π results in an error message, because tan π is equal to zero.

Got It? 2. What is the decimal value of each expression? Use the radian mode on your calculator. Round your answers to the nearest thousandth.
 a. cot 13
 b. csc 6.5
 c. sec 15°
 d. sec $\frac{3\pi}{2}$
 e. Reasoning How can you find the cotangent of an angle without using the tangent key on your calculator?

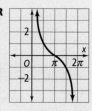
PowerAlgebra.com | Lesson 13-8 Reciprocal Trigonometric Functions | 885

Problem 2 ERROR PREVENTION

Q Why is it important to either check the mode of your calculator or use symbols for the units when evaluating any of the trigonometric functions? **[If you are in the wrong mode or use the wrong units, the solution will be incorrect, unless the angle is zero degrees or zero radians.]**

Q What happens when you try to find the cotangent of 90° or $\frac{\pi}{2}$ radians? Why? What is the actual value of cot $\frac{\pi}{2}$? **[The calculator gives an error message because the tan $\frac{\pi}{2}$ is undefined and the calculator cannot calculate the value to divide by. The actual value is zero.]**

EXTENSION

Q If your graphing calculator is in degree mode, how can you evaluate the trigonometric function of an angle in radians without converting the angle to degrees or changing the mode? **[In the angle menu, use the symbol r.]**

Got It?

Q How can you find the solution to 2c if your calculator is in radian mode? **[Samples: Use the degree symbol from the ANGLE menu to override the mode setting; change the mode from degrees to radians before evaluating; convert 15° to $\frac{\pi}{24}$ radians before evaluating.]**

Q How can you express tan θ in terms of sin θ and cos θ to help you answer 2e? **[tan θ = $\frac{\sin\theta}{\cos\theta}$.]**

Additional Problems

1. What is the exact value of $\sec\left(-\frac{\pi}{6}\right)$? Do not use a calculator.

ANSWER $\frac{2\sqrt{3}}{3}$

2. What is the decimal value of each expression? Use radian mode on your calculator. Round to the nearest thousandth.
 a. cot −34° **b.** csc $\left(\frac{5\pi}{8}\right)$ **c.** sec 1.2
ANSWERS a. −1.483; **b.** 1.082; **c.** 2.760

3. What is the graph of $y = \cot \frac{1}{2}x$ in the interval from 0 to 2π?

ANSWER

4. Graph $y = \csc x$. What is the value of csc 15° to the nearest thousandth?

ANSWER 3.864

5. A seaman is standing atop a ship's watchtower that stands 115 ft above the water's surface in the center of the ship. He is using a spotting scope at that height to search the waters around the ship. The equation that represents the distance, y, from the center of the ship along the water to any object the seaman spots is given by $y = 115 \cot \theta$, where θ is the angle of depression from the seaman to the object. If the seaman spots two objects, one at an angle of depression of 4° and the other at an angle of depression of 11°, how far are the spotted objects from the center of the ship, rounded to the nearest foot?

ANSWER 1645 ft and 592 ft

Answers

Got It?

1. a. $\frac{2\sqrt{3}}{3}$ **b.** −1 **c.** −1

 d. $\frac{3}{4}, \frac{5}{4}, \frac{5}{3}$; by the definition of a unit circle, the length of the hypotenuse of the right triangle is 1. By the Pythag. Thm., the length of the unlabeled leg is $\frac{4}{5}$. So the triangle is similar to a 3-4-5 right triangle.

2. a. ≈2.16

 b. ≈4.649

 c. ≈1.035

 d. undefined

 e. use $\frac{\cos x}{\sin x}$

Lesson 13-8 885

Problem 3

Q Why do you only need to make a table of values from 0 to 2π? **[The cycle of the graph will repeat every 2π units because the period of sin x is 2π.]**

EXTENSION

Q What are the y-coordinates of the points of intersection of the pairs of functions of tan x and cot x, sin x and csc x, and cos x and sec x? Explain. **[Either 1 or −1; 1 and −1 are the only numbers that are reciprocals of themselves.]**

Got It?

Q For what range of values should you make a table to get a complete idea of what the graph of $y = \cot x$ looks like? Explain. **[Sample: A range of values from 0 to π would be enough because the period of $y = \tan x$ is π.]**

Q Where will the asymptotes be for the graph of $y = \cot x$? **[If x is in radians, the asymptotes will be at integer multiples of π.]**

Problem 4

Q Why should you look at the graph of the equation you enter in your calculator even though you are not going to use the graph to evaluate sec 20°? **[to make sure you have entered the equation correctly]**

Got It?

Q What should you enter for y in your graphing calculator to find the value of csc 45° on a graph? **[$Y_1 = 1/\sin(x)$]**

The graphs of reciprocal trigonometric functions have asymptotes where the functions are undefined.

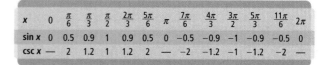

Problem 3 Sketching a Graph

Think
For what values is csc x undefined?
Wherever sin x = 0, its reciprocal is undefined.

What are the graphs of $y = \sin x$ and $y = \csc x$ in the interval from 0 to 2π?

Step 1 Make a table of values.

x	0	$\frac{\pi}{6}$	$\frac{\pi}{3}$	$\frac{\pi}{2}$	$\frac{2\pi}{3}$	$\frac{5\pi}{6}$	π	$\frac{7\pi}{6}$	$\frac{4\pi}{3}$	$\frac{3\pi}{2}$	$\frac{5\pi}{3}$	$\frac{11\pi}{6}$	2π
sin x	0	0.5	0.9	1	0.9	0.5	0	−0.5	−0.9	−1	−0.9	−0.5	0
csc x	—	2	1.2	1	1.2	2	—	−2	−1.2	−1	−1.2	−2	—

Step 2 Plot the points and sketch the graphs.

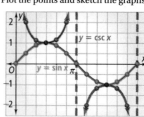

$y = \csc x$ will have a vertical asymptote whenever its denominator (sin x) is 0.

Got It? **3.** What are the graphs of $y = \tan x$ and $y = \cot x$ in the interval from 0 to 2π?

You can use a graphing calculator to graph trigonometric functions quickly.

Problem 4 Using Technology to Graph a Reciprocal Function

Plan
How can you find the value?
Use the table feature of your calculator.

Graph $y = \sec x$. What is the value of sec 20°?

Step 1 Use degree mode.
Graph $y = \frac{1}{\cos x}$.

Step 2 Use the **TABLE** feature.
sec 20° ≈ 1.0642

Xmin = −360
Xmax = 360
Xscl = 30
Ymin = −5
Ymax = 5
Yscl = 1

X	Y₁
20	1.0642
21	1.0711
22	1.0785
23	1.0864
24	1.0946
25	1.1034
26	1.1126

X=20

Got It? **4.** What is the value of csc 45°? Use the graph of the reciprocal trigonometric function.

Answers

Got It? (continued)

3.
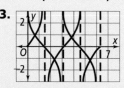

4. ≈1.4142

You can use a reciprocal trigonometric function to solve a real-world problem.

Problem 5 Using Reciprocal Functions to Solve a Problem

A restaurant is near the top of a tower. A diner looks down at an object along a line of sight that makes an angle of θ with the tower. The distance in feet of an object from the observer is modeled by the function $d = 601 \sec \theta$. How far away are objects sighted at angles of 40° and 70°?

Set your calculator to degree mode. Enter the function and construct a table that gives values of d for various angles of θ.

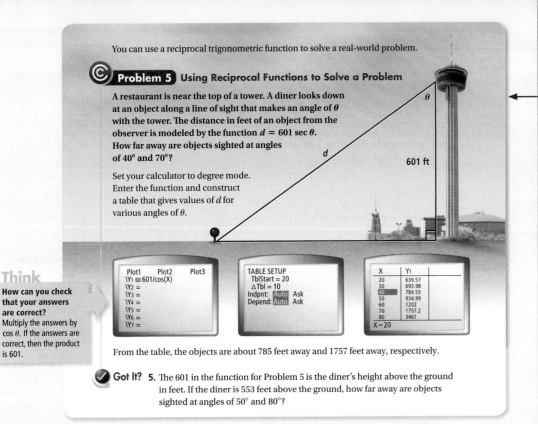

Think

How can you check that your answers are correct?
Multiply the answers by $\cos \theta$. If the answers are correct, then the product is 601.

From the table, the objects are about 785 feet away and 1757 feet away, respectively.

Got It? 5. The 601 in the function for Problem 5 is the diner's height above the ground in feet. If the diner is 553 feet above the ground, how far away are objects sighted at angles of 50° and 80°?

Lesson Check

Do you know HOW?

Find each value without using a calculator.

1. $\csc \frac{\pi}{2}$

2. $\sec\left(-\frac{\pi}{6}\right)$

Use a calculator to find each value. Round your answers to the nearest thousandth.

3. $\csc 1.5$

4. $\sec 42°$

5. An extension ladder leans against a building forming a 50° angle with the ground. Use the function $y = 21 \csc x + 2$ to find y, the length of the ladder. Round to the nearest tenth of a foot.

Do you UNDERSTAND? MATHEMATICAL PRACTICES

6. **Reasoning** Explain why the graph of $y = 5 \sec \theta$ has no zeros.

7. **Error Analysis** On a quiz, a student wrote $\sec 20° + 1 = 0.5155$. The teacher marked it wrong. What error did the student make?

8. **Compare and Contrast** How are the graphs of $y = \sec x$ and $y = \csc x$ alike? How are they different? Could the graph of $y = \csc x$ be a transformation of the graph of $y = \sec x$?

Problem 5

Q Why does the function $d = 601 \sec \theta$ model the distance? **[The triangle formed by the tower, the line of sight, and the ground is a right triangle, so $\cos \theta = \frac{adj}{hyp} = \frac{601}{d}$, so $d = \frac{601}{\cos \theta}$. Since $\sec \theta = \frac{1}{\cos \theta}$, $d = 601 \sec \theta$.]**

Got It?

Q What function models the situation described? **[$y = 553 \sec \theta$]**

3 Lesson Check

Do you know HOW?

- If students have difficulty finding the value without a calculator in Exercises 1 and 2, have them rewrite the expression in terms of the reciprocal function.
- If students are not finding the correct value in Exercises 3, 4 and 5, ask them to check what mode, radians or degrees, their calculator is in.

Do you UNDERSTAND?

- For Exercise 7, if students cannot find the error, ask them if sec 20° could be a negative value.

Close

Q How do you evaluate a reciprocal trigonometric function without a calculator? with a calculator? **[Without a calculator, find the value of the corresponding trigonometric function and take the reciprocal of that value. With a calculator, enter the corresponding trigonometric function as the denominator of the expression in the calculator.]**

---

5. about 860 ft away and 3185 ft away

Lesson Check

1. 1

2. $\frac{2}{\sqrt{3}}$ or $\frac{2\sqrt{3}}{3}$

3. ≈ 1.003

4. ≈ 1.346

5. 29.4 ft

6. $y = 5 \sec \theta = \frac{5}{\cos \theta}$; there is no value of θ that will make $\frac{5}{\cos \theta}$ equal to zero.

7. The student found the reciprocal of $(1 + \cos 20°) = \frac{1}{1 + \cos 20°} \approx 0.5155$. The answer should be: $\sec 20° + 1 = \frac{1}{\cos 20°} + 1 \approx 1.0642 + 1 \approx 2.0642$.

8. The graphs have the same period and range. The domain of $y = \sec x$ is all real numbers except $n\pi + \frac{\pi}{4}$ (where n is an integer), which are its asymptotes. The domain of $y = \csc x$ is all real numbers except $\frac{n\pi}{2}$ (where n is an integer), which are its asymptotes. The graph of $y = \csc x$ can be obtained as a translation of $y = \sec\left(x - \frac{\pi}{4}\right)$ of the parent function $y = \sec x$.

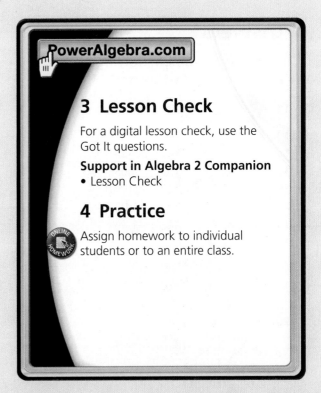

PowerAlgebra.com

3 Lesson Check

For a digital lesson check, use the Got It questions.

Support in Algebra 2 Companion
- Lesson Check

4 Practice

Assign homework to individual students or to an entire class.

4 Practice

ASSIGNMENT GUIDE

Basic: 9–37 all, 38–42 even, 48–52

Average: 9–37 odd, 38–61

Advanced: 9–37 odd, 38–64

Standardized Test Prep: 65–70

Mixed Review: 71–79

Ⓒ **Mathematical Practices** are supported by exercises with red headings. Here are the Practices supported in this lesson:

MP 1: Make Sense of Problems Ex. 38

MP 2: Reason Abstractly Ex. 6, 48, 60e

MP 3: Compare Arguments Ex. 8, 53c, 60d

MP 3: Communicate Ex. 49–51

MP 3: Critique the Reasoning of Others Ex. 7

MP 5: Use appropriate tools Ex. 17–24, 29–36

Applications exercises have blue headings. Exercise 37 supports MP 4: Model.

EXERCISE 52: Use the Think About a Plan worksheet in the **Practice and Problem Solving Workbook** (also available in the Teaching Resources in print and online) to further support students' development in becoming independent learners.

HOMEWORK QUICK CHECK

To check students' understanding of key skills and concepts, go over Exercises 11, 25, 38, 48, and 52.

Ⓐ **Practice**   Find each value without using a calculator. If the expression is undefined, write *undefined*.   ◀ See Problem 1.

9. $\sec(-\pi)$ 10. $\csc\frac{5\pi}{4}$ 11. $\cot\left(-\frac{\pi}{3}\right)$ 12. $\sec\frac{\pi}{2}$

13. $\cot\left(-\frac{3\pi}{2}\right)$ 14. $\csc\frac{7\pi}{6}$ 15. $\sec\left(-\frac{3\pi}{4}\right)$ 16. $\cot(-\pi)$

📱 **Graphing Calculator** Use a calculator to find each value. Round your answers to the nearest thousandth.   ◀ See Problem 2.

17. $\sec 2.5$ 18. $\csc(-0.2)$ 19. $\cot 56°$ 20. $\sec\left(-\frac{3\pi}{2}\right)$

21. $\cot(-32°)$ 22. $\sec 195°$ 23. $\csc 0$ 24. $\cot(-0.6)$

Graph each function in the interval from 0 to 2π.   ◀ See Problem 3.

25. $y = \sec 2\theta$ 26. $y = \cot\theta$ 27. $y = \csc 2\theta - 1$ 28. $y = \csc 2\theta$

📱 **Graphing Calculator** Use the graph of the appropriate reciprocal trigonometric function to find each value. Round to four decimal places.   ◀ See Problem 4.

29. $\sec 30°$ 30. $\sec 80°$ 31. $\sec 110°$ 32. $\csc 30°$

33. $\csc 70°$ 34. $\csc 130°$ 35. $\cot 30°$ 36. $\cot 60°$

37. **Distance** A woman looks out a window of a building. She is 94 feet above the ground. Her line of sight makes an angle of θ with the building. The distance in feet of an object from the woman is modeled by the function $d = 94\sec\theta$. How far away are objects sighted at angles of 25° and 55°?   ◀ See Problem 5.

Ⓑ **Apply** Ⓒ 38. **Think About a Plan** A communications tower has wires anchoring it to the ground. Each wire is attached to the tower at a height 20 ft above the ground. The length y of the wire is modeled with the function $y = 20\csc\theta$, where θ is the measure of the angle formed by the wire and the ground. Find the length of wire needed to form an angle of 45°.
  • Do you need to graph the function?
  • How can you rewrite the function so you can use a calculator?

39. **Multiple Representations** Write a cosecant model that has the same graph as $y = \sec\theta$.

Match each function with its graph.

40. $y = \frac{1}{\sin x}$ 41. $y = \frac{1}{\cos x}$ 42. $y = -\frac{1}{\sin x}$

a.   b.   c.

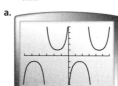      

Answers

Practice and Problem-Solving Exercises

9. -1

10. $-\sqrt{2}$

11. $\frac{-\sqrt{3}}{3}$

12. undefined

13. 0

14. -2

15. $-\sqrt{2}$

16. undefined

17. ≈ -1.248

18. ≈ -5.033

19. ≈ 0.675

20. undefined

21. ≈ -1.6

22. ≈ -1.035

23. undefined

24. ≈ -1.462

25.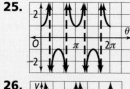

26.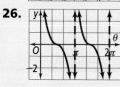

27.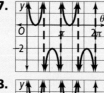

28.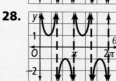

29. 1.1547   30. 5.7588

31. -2.9238 32. 2

33. 1.0642   34. 1.3054

35. 1.7321   36. 0.5774

37. ≈ 104 ft and ≈ 164 ft

38. About 28.28 ft.

39. Answers may vary. Sample:
    $y = \csc\left(\theta + \frac{\pi}{2}\right)$

40. B   41. C

42. A

43.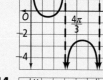

44.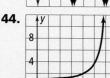

45.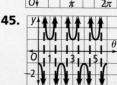

46.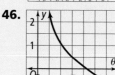

Graph each function in the interval from 0 to 2π.

43. $y = \csc\theta - \frac{\pi}{2}$ **44.** $y = \sec\frac{1}{4}\theta$ **45.** $y = -\sec\pi\theta$ **46.** $y = \cot\frac{\theta}{3}$

47. a. What are the domain, range, and period of $y = \csc x$?
  b. What is the relative minimum in the interval $0 \le x \le \pi$?
  c. What is the relative maximum in the interval $\pi \le x \le 2\pi$?

ⓒ 48. Reasoning Use the relationship $\csc x = \frac{1}{\sin x}$ to explain why each statement is true.
  a. When the graph of $y = \sin x$ is above the x-axis, so is the graph of $y = \csc x$.
  b. When the graph of $y = \sin x$ is near a y-value of -1, so is the graph of $y = \csc x$.

ⓒ Writing Explain why each expression is undefined.

49. $\csc 180°$ **50.** $\sec 90°$ **51.** $\cot 0°$

52. Indirect Measurement The fire ladder forms an angle of measure θ with the horizontal. The hinge of the ladder is 35 ft from the building. The function $y = 35\sec\theta$ models the length y in feet that the fire ladder must be to reach the building.

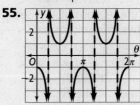

  a. Graph the function.
  b. In the photo, $\theta = 13°$. What is the ladder's length?
  c. How far is the ladder extended when it forms an angle of 30°?
  d. Suppose the ladder is extended to its full length of 80 ft. What angle does it form with the horizontal? How far up a building can the ladder reach when fully extended? (*Hint:* Use the information in the photo.)

ⓒ 53. a. Graph $y = \tan x$ and $y = \cot x$ on the same axes.
  b. State the domain, range, and asymptotes of each function.
  c. Compare and Contrast Compare the two graphs. How are they alike? How are they different?
  d. Geometry The graph of the tangent function is a reflection image of the graph of the cotangent function. Name at least two reflection lines for such a transformation.

Graphing Calculator Graph each function in the interval from 0 to 2π. Describe any phase shift and vertical shift in the graph.

54. $y = \sec 2\theta + 3$ **55.** $y = \sec 2\left(\theta + \frac{\pi}{2}\right)$ **56.** $y = -2\sec(x - 4)$

57. $f(x) = 3\csc(x + 2) - 1$ **58.** $y = \cot 2(x + \pi) + 3$ **59.** $g(x) = 2\sec\left(3\left(x - \frac{\pi}{6}\right)\right) - 2$

ⓒ 60. a. Graph $y = -\cos x$ and $y = -\sec x$ on the same axes.
  b. State the domain, range, and period of each function.
  c. For which values of x does $-\cos x = -\sec x$? Justify your answer.
  d. Compare and Contrast Compare the two graphs. How are they alike? How are they different?
  e. Reasoning Is the value of $-\sec x$ positive when $-\cos x$ is positive and negative when $-\cos x$ is negative? Justify your answer.

54.
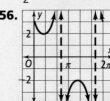
3 units up

55.

$\frac{\pi}{2}$ units to the left

56.
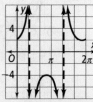
4 units to the right

57.
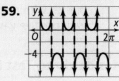
2 units to the left and 1 unit down

58.
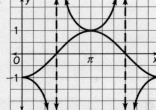
π units to the left and 3 units up

59.
2 units to the left and 1 unit down

$\frac{\pi}{6}$ units to the and 2 units down

60. a.

b. $y = -\cos x$: domain: all real numbers, range: $-1 \le y \le 1$; period: 2π; $y = -\sec x$: domain: all real numbers except odd multiples of $\frac{\pi}{2}$, range: $y \ge 1$ or $y \le -1$; period: 2π

c. Multiples of π; by definition, $\sec x = \frac{1}{\cos x}$, so $-\cos x = -\sec x$ is equivalent to $-\cos x = -\frac{1}{\cos x}$, or $(\cos x)^2 = 1$. The solutions of $(\cos x)^2 = 1$ are the values of x for which $\cos x = 1$ or $\cos x = -1$. These values are multiples of π.

d. Answers may vary. Sample: The graphs have the same period and their signs are always the same. However, they have no range values in common except 1 and −1.

e. The signs of $-\sec x$ and $-\cos x$ are the same because reciprocals have the same sign.

47. a. domain: all real numbers except multiples of π, range: $y \ge 1$ or $y \le -1$; period: 2π
  b. 1
  c. −1

48. a. Reciprocals have the same sign.
  b. The reciprocal of −1 is −1.

49. $\csc 180°$ is undefined because $\sin 180° = 0$ and $\csc\theta = \frac{1}{\sin\theta}$.

50. $\sec 90°$ is undefined because $\cos 90° = 0$ and $\sec\theta = \frac{1}{\cos\theta}$.

51. $\cot 0°$ is undefined because $\sin 0° = 0$ and $\cot\theta = \frac{\cos\theta}{\sin\theta}$.

52. a.
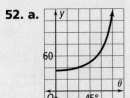
  b. ≈35.9 ft

  c. ≈40.4 ft
  d. ≈64°; 80 ft above the ground

53. a.

  b. The domain of $y = \tan x$ is all real numbers except odd multiples of $\frac{\pi}{2}$, where its asymptotes occur. The domain of $y = \cot x$ is all real numbers except multiples of π, where its asymptotes occur. The range of both functions is all real numbers.
  c. The graphs have the same period and range. Their asymptotes are shifted $\frac{\pi}{2}$ units.
  d. Answers may vary. Sample: $x = \frac{\pi}{4}, x = \frac{3\pi}{4}$

Answers

Practice and Problem-Solving
Exercises (continued)

61. a. II   **b.** I

62. $y = \sec x$ and $y = \csc x$ are not parabolas because parabolas are not restricted by asymptotes, whereas the sections of $y = \sec x$ and $y = \csc x$ are between asymptotes.

63. $y = \cos 3x$ cycles 3 times for each cycle of $y = \cos x$. Thus, for each cycle of $y = \sec x$, $y = \sec 3x$ cycles 3 times, and each cycle of $y = \sec 3x$ is $\frac{1}{3}$ as wide as one cycle of $y = \sec x$.

64. a.

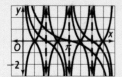

b. Answers may vary. Sample: Given $y = \cot bx$, as $|b|$ decreases, the period increases; as $|b|$ increases, the period decreases. If $b < 0$, $y = \cot bx$ begins each branch with negative y-values and ends with positive y-values; the opposite is true for $b > 0$.

Standardized Test Prep

65. $\frac{4}{3}$

66. $\frac{5}{3}$

67. $\frac{3}{4}$

68. $\frac{5}{4}$

69. 1.4

70. 0.6

Mixed Review

71. $2, 2\pi$; 5 units down

72. $1, 2\pi$; 4 units left, 7 units down

73. $3, 2\pi$; $\frac{\pi}{6}$ units to the left, 4 units up

74. $5, 2$; 1.5 units to the right, 8 units down

75.

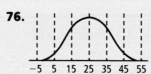

---

61. a. Reasoning Which expression gives the correct value of csc 60°?

     I. $\sin((60^{-1})°)$ II. $(\sin 60°)^{-1}$ III. $(\cos 60°)^{-1}$

b. Which expression in part (a) represents $\sin\left(\frac{1}{60}\right)°$?

Challenge

62. Reasoning Each branch of $y = \sec x$ and $y = \csc x$ is a curve. Explain why these curves cannot be parabolas. (*Hint:* Do parabolas have asymptotes?)

63. Reasoning Consider the relationship between the graphs of $y = \cos x$ and $y = \cos 3x$. Use the relationship to explain the distance between successive branches of the graphs of $y = \sec x$ and $y = \sec 3x$.

64. a. Graph $y = \cot x$, $y = \cot 2x$, $y = \cot(-2x)$, and $y = \cot \frac{1}{2}x$ on the same axes.
b. Make a Conjecture Describe how the graph of $y = \cot bx$ changes as the value of b changes.

Standardized Test Prep

GRIDDED RESPONSE

SAT/ACT

For Exercises 65–68, suppose $\cos \theta = \frac{3}{5}$ and $\sin \theta > 0$. Enter each answer as a fraction.

65. What is $\tan \theta$?   **66.** What is $\sec \theta$?   **67.** What is $\cot \theta$?   **68.** What is $\csc \theta$?

For Exercises 69–70, suppose $\tan \theta = \frac{4}{3}$ and $-\frac{\pi}{2} \le \theta < \frac{\pi}{2}$. Enter each answer as a decimal. Round your answer to the nearest tenth, if necessary.

69. What is $\cot \theta + \cos \theta$?   **70.** What is $(\sin \theta)(\cot \theta)$?

Mixed Review

Find the amplitude and period of each function. Describe any phase shift and vertical shift in the graph.   ◀ See Lesson 13-7.

71. $y = 2 \sin x - 5$ **72.** $y = -\cos(x + 4) - 7$

73. $y = -3 \sin\left(x + \frac{\pi}{6}\right) + 4$ **74.** $y = 5 \cos \pi(x - 1.5) - 8$

Sketch a normal curve for each distribution. Label the x-axis values at one, two, and three standard deviations from the mean.   ◀ See Lesson 11-9.

75. mean = 25, standard deviation = 5   **76.** mean = 25, standard deviation = 10

Get Ready! To prepare for Lesson 14-1, do Exercises 77–79.

Determine whether each equation is true for all real numbers x. Explain your reasoning.   ◀ See Lesson 1-4.

77. $2x + 3x = 5x$ **78.** $-(4x - 10) = 10 - 4x$ **79.** $3x + 15 = 5(x - 3) - 2x$

76.

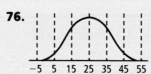

-5 5 15 25 35 45 55

77. true; Add. Prop.

78. true; Dist. Prop. and Comm. Prop. of Add.

79. not true

Differentiated Remediation

Additional Instructional Support

Algebra 2 Companion
Students can use the **Algebra 2 Companion** worktext (4 pages) as you teach the lesson. Use the Companion to support

- New Vocabulary
- Key Concepts
- Got It for each Problem
- Lesson Check

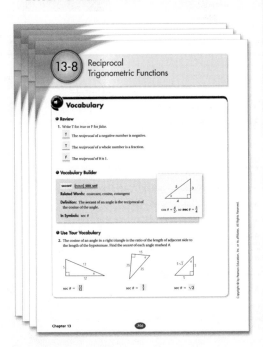

ELL Support
Use Manipulatives Give each student twelve index cards or similarly sized blank pieces of paper. Have students:

- Write the names of the six trigonometric functions on the first six cards and sketch graphs of the six trigonometric functions on the other six cards.
- Mix the cards. Ask students to match the pairs of the trigonometric functions and their reciprocals.
- Mix the cards again. Ask them to match the trigonometric functions with their graphs.

Have two students combine their cards, mix them up and place them face down. Let student play a memory match game, getting a match when they correctly pair a function with its graph in turning over two cards, or when they correctly pair a function with its reciprocal, in name or graphic form.

5 Assess & Remediate

Lesson Quiz

1. What is the exact value of $\csc\left(\frac{3\pi}{4}\right)$? Do not use a calculator.
2. Use your calculator in degree mode to find the decimal value, rounded to the nearest thousandth, of $\sec 59°$.
3. What is the graph of $y = \sec x$ in the interval from 0 to 2π?
4. Graph $y = \cot x$. What is the value of $\cot 50°$?
5. **Do you UNDERSTAND?** A guy wire is stretched from the top of a 38 foot flagpole to the ground so that the length of the wire, y, is given by $y = 38\csc\theta$, where θ is the angle of elevation from the ground to the top of the pole. How long will the guy wire be if the angle of elevation is 60°? if it is 75°?

ANSWERS TO LESSON QUIZ
1. $\sqrt{2}$
2. 1.942
3.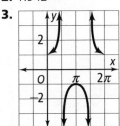
4. 0.839
5. about 43.9 ft and 39.3 ft

PRESCRIPTION FOR REMEDIATION
Use the student work on the Lesson Quiz to prescribe a differentiated review assignment:

Points	Differentiated Remediation
0–2	Intervention
3–4	On-level
5	Extension

PowerAlgebra.com

5 Assess & Remediate
Assign the Lesson Quiz. Appropriate intervention, practice, or enrichment is automatically generated based on student performance.

Intervention

- **Reteaching** (2 pages) Provides reteaching and practice exercises for the key lesson concepts. Use with struggling students or absent students.
- **English Language Learner Support** Helps students develop and reinforce mathematical vocabulary and key concepts.

All-in-One Resources/Online
Reteaching

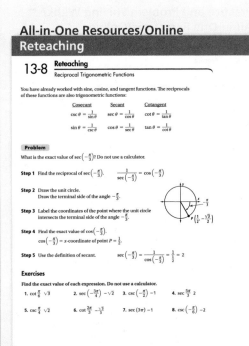

All-in-One Resources/Online
English Language Learner Support

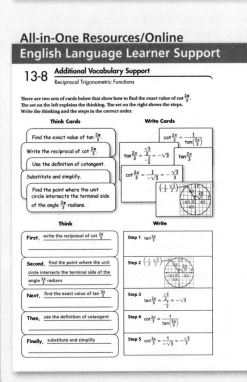

Differentiated Remediation *continued*

On-Level

- **Practice** (2 pages) Provides extra practice for each lesson. For simpler practice exercises, use the Form K Practice pages found in the All-in-One Teaching Resources and online.

- **Think About a Plan** Helps students develop specific problem-solving skills and strategies by providing scaffolded guiding questions.

- **Standardized Test Prep** Focuses on all major exercises, all major question types, and helps students prepare for the high-stakes assessments.

Extension

- **Enrichment** Provides students with interesting problems and activities that extend the concepts of the lesson.

- **Activities, Games, and Puzzles** Worksheets that can be used for concepts development, enrichment, and for fun!

Practice and Problem Solving Wkbk/ All-in-One Resources/Online
Practice page 1

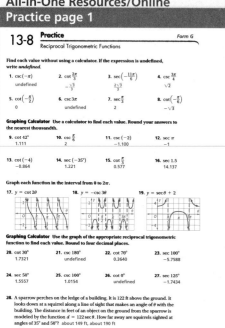

Practice and Problem Solving Wkbk/ All-in-One Resources/Online
Practice page 2

All-in-One Resources/Online
Enrichment

Practice and Problem Solving Wkbk/ All-in-One Resources/Online
Think About a Plan

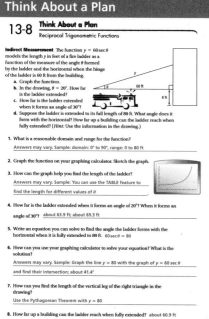

Practice and Problem Solving Wkbk/ All-in-One Resources/Online
Standardized Test Prep

Online Teacher Resource Center
Activities, Games, and Puzzles

Pull It All Together ASSESSMENT

To solve these problems, you will pull together many concepts and skills related to trigonometric functions.

 BIG idea Modeling

You can sometimes use a function to model a real-world situation based on data from the situation.

Performance Task 1

In one year on the Arctic and Antarctic Circles, the amount of daylight each day varies from 0 h to 24 h. Let $Ar(d)$ and $An(d)$ represent the amount of daylight as a function of the day of the year d at the two locations, respectively. Describe the graph of one of the functions. Then tell how the graph of the other function relates to the first graph. Do the graphs resemble patterns you have seen elsewhere? If so, what patterns? How could you predict the future behavior of these functions?

BIG idea Function

You can represent functions in a variety of ways (such as graphs, tables, equations, or words). Each representation is particularly useful in certain situations.

Performance Task 2

The diagram shows how $\cos \theta$, $\sin \theta$, and $\tan \theta$ relate to the unit circle. Copy the diagram and show how $\sec \theta$, $\csc \theta$, and $\cot \theta$ relate to the unit circle.

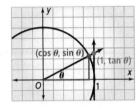

a. First, find in the diagram a segment whose length is $\sec \theta$. Explain why its length is $\sec \theta$.

b. Next, find $\cot \theta$. To do this you must add to the diagram. Use the representation of tangent as a clue for what to show for *cotangent*. Justify your claim for $\cot \theta$.

c. Find $\csc \theta$ in your diagram. Justify your claim for $\csc \theta$.

BIG idea Function

You can derive some functions from a basic parent function by a particular transformation. Functions related through these transformations are called a family of functions.

Performance Task 3

The functions f and g are periodic. You can get the graph of g by changing the amplitude and period of f, and then applying a translation. Find $g(x)$ in terms of $f(x)$.

 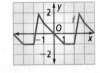

Performance Task

Pull It All Together

Understanding by Design principles indicate the importance of performance tasks that assess understanding.

- Make sense of problems and persevere in solving them.
- Model with mathematics.
- Attend to precision.

The following questions are designed to
- Help support students as they do the Performance Tasks.
- Help you gauge their progress toward becoming mathematically proficient.

Performance Task 1

Express two graphs that are related to each other and model a given real-world situation.

- If $Ar(t)$ is 24, what does the value of $An(t)$ have to be?
- What will the values for $Ar(t)$ and $An(t)$ sum to for a given value of t?

Performance Task 2

Express the secant, cosecant, and cotangent functions in terms of the unit circle.

- How can the similar triangles you used to express $\tan \theta$ in terms of the unit circle be used to express $\sec \theta$?

Performance Task 3

Express transformations of one function to another by analyzing the graphs of both functions.

- How many cycles appear in the graph of g? of f?
- How does the height of g compare to the height of f?

Assess Performance

Pull It All Together

See p. 49 for a holistic scoring rubric to gauge a student's progress on Understanding the Problem, Planning a Solution, Getting an Answer, and Assessing Autonomy.

SOLUTION OUTLINES

1. The graph of the amount of daylight and the amount of night at the Arctic Circle is periodic and can be represented by a sine curve.

   The graph of the amount of daylight and the amount of night at the Antarctic Circle is also periodic and can be represented by a cosine curve.

On any date, the amounts of daylight and night at the Arctic Circle are the converse of those at the Antarctic Circle.

2. **a.** Possible Plan: Use similar triangles and proportions to find secant. $\left(\frac{1}{\cos \theta} = \frac{n}{1}; \text{ So, } \sec \theta = n.\right)$

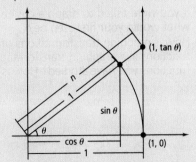

Thus, $\sec \theta$ is the length of the ray from the origin to its intersection with the tangent line.

b. Possible Plan: Use similar triangles and proportions to find cotangent. $\left(\frac{1}{\tan \theta} = \frac{r}{1}; \text{ So, } \cot \theta = r.\right)$

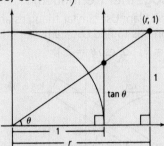

$\cot \theta$ is the length of the line segment tangent to the unit circle from the y-axis to the terminal ray of θ.

2c–3. See next page.

Essential Questions

BIG idea **Modeling**

ESSENTIAL QUESTION How can you model periodic behavior?

ANSWER You can use combinations of circular functions (sine and cosine) to model natural periodic behavior.

BIG idea **Function**

ESSENTIAL QUESTION What function has as its graph a sine curve with amplitude 4, period π, and a minimum at the origin?

ANSWER The graph of $y = 4 \sin 2\left(x - \frac{x}{4}\right) + 4$ has amplitude 4, period π, midline of $y = 4$, and a minimum at the origin.

BIG idea **Function**

ESSENTIAL QUESTION If you know the value of $\sin \theta$, how can you find $\cos \theta$, $\tan \theta$, $\csc \theta$, $\sec \theta$, and $\cot \theta$?

ANSWER If you know the value of $\sin \theta$, find an angle with measure θ in standard position on the unit circle to find values of the other trigonometric functions.

Connecting **BIG** ideas and Answering the Essential Questions

1 Modeling
You can use combinations of circular functions (sine and cosine) to model natural periodic behavior.

2 Function
The graph of $y = 4 \sin 2(x - \frac{\pi}{4}) + 4$ has amplitude 4, period π, midline of $y = 4$, and a minimum at the origin.

3 Function
If you know the value of $\sin \theta$, find an angle with measure θ in standard position on the unit circle to find values of the other trigonometric functions.

Angles, the Unit Circle, and Radian Measure (Lessons 13-2 and 13-3)
One radian is the measure of a central angle of a circle that intercepts an arc of length equal to the radius of the circle.

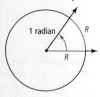

Sine, Cosine, and Tangent Functions (Lessons 13-4, 13-5, and 13-6)

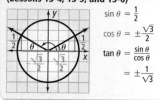

$\sin \theta = \frac{1}{2}$

$\cos \theta = \pm \frac{\sqrt{3}}{2}$

$\tan \theta = \frac{\sin \theta}{\cos \theta}$
$= \pm \frac{1}{\sqrt{3}}$

Translating Sine and Cosine Functions (Lesson 13-7)
For the functions
$$y = a \sin b(x - h) + k,$$
and
$$y = a \cos b(x - h) + k,$$
- $|a|$ is the amplitude
- $\frac{2\pi}{b}$ is the period
- h is the phase shift, or horizontal shift
- k is the vertical shift ($y = k$ is the midline)

Reciprocal Trigonometric Functions (Lesson 13-8)

$\csc \theta = \frac{1}{\sin \theta} = 2$

$\sec \theta = \frac{1}{\cos \theta} = \pm \frac{2}{\sqrt{3}}$

$\cot \theta = \frac{1}{\tan \theta} = \pm \sqrt{3}$

Chapter Vocabulary

- amplitude (p. 830)
- central angle (p. 844)
- cosecant (p. 883)
- cosine function (p. 861)
- cosine of θ (p. 838)
- cotangent (p. 883)
- coterminal angle (p. 837)
- cycle (p. 828)
- initial side (p. 836)
- intercepted arc (p. 844)
- midline (p. 830)
- period (p. 828)
- periodic function (p. 828)
- phase shift (p. 875)
- radian (p. 844)
- secant (p. 883)
- sine curve (p. 852)
- sine function (p. 851)
- sine of θ (p. 838)
- standard position (p. 836)
- tangent function (p. 869)
- tangent of θ (p. 868)
- terminal side (p. 836)
- unit circle (p. 838)

Choose the correct term to complete each sentence.

1. The __?__ of a periodic function is the length of one cycle.

2. Centered at the origin of the coordinate plane, the __?__ has a radius of 1 unit.

3. An asymptote of the __?__ occurs at $\theta = \frac{\pi}{2}$, and repeats every π units.

4. A horizontal translation of a periodic function is a(n) __?__.

5. The __?__ is the reciprocal of the cosine function.

Answers

Pull It All Together (continued)

c. Possible Plan: Use similar triangles and proportions to find cosecant.
$\left(\frac{1}{\sin \theta} = \frac{z}{1}; \text{So, } \csc \theta = z.\right)$

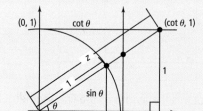

$\csc \theta$ is the length of the ray from the origin to its intersection with the cotangent line.

3. Possible Plan: Check for both vertical and horizontal transformations. Notice that the period of $g(x)$ is smaller than $f(x)$ and that $g(x)$ is deeper than $f(x)$.
$\left(g(x) = \frac{1}{2}f(x) - \frac{3}{2}\right)$.

Summative Questions

Use the following prompts as you review this chapter with your students. The prompts are designed to help you assess your students' understanding of the BIG ideas they have studied.

- How can you determine whether a function is periodic?
- If you were asked to graph a cosine function, what would your first step be?
- How is graphing transformations of trigonometric functions like graphing transformations of other functions you have studied? How is it different?

Answers

Chapter Review

1. period
2. unit circle
3. tangent function
4. phase shift
5. secant function

13-1 Exploring Periodic Data

Quick Review

A **periodic function** repeats a pattern of y-values at regular intervals. One complete pattern is called a **cycle**. A cycle may begin at any point on the graph. The **period** of a function is the length of one cycle. The **midline** is the line located midway between the maximum and the minimum values of the function. The **amplitude** of a periodic function is half the difference between its maximum and minimum values.

Example

What is the period of the periodic function?

One cycle is 5 units long, so the period of the function is 5.

Exercises

6. Determine whether the function below *is* or *is not* periodic. If it is, identify one cycle in two different ways and find the period and amplitude.

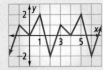

7. Sketch the graph of a wave with a period of 2, an amplitude of 4, and a midline of $y = 1$.

8. Sketch the graph of a wave with a period of 4, an amplitude of 3, and a midline of $y = 0$.

13-2 Angles and the Unit Circle

Quick Review

An angle is in **standard position** if the vertex is at the origin and one ray, the **initial side,** is on the positive x-axis. The other ray is the **terminal side** of the angle. Two angles in standard position are **coterminal** if they have the same terminal side.

The **unit circle** has radius of 1 unit and its center at the origin. The **cosine of** θ ($\cos \theta$) is the x-coordinate of the point where the terminal side of the angle intersects the unit circle. The **sine of** θ ($\sin \theta$) is the y-coordinate.

Example

What are the cosine and sine of $-210°$?

Sketch an angle of $-210°$ in standard position with a unit circle. The terminal side forms a $30°$-$60°$-$90°$ triangle with hypotenuse $= 1$, shorter leg $= \frac{1}{2}$, longer leg $= \frac{\sqrt{3}}{2}$

Since the terminal side lies in Quadrant II, $\cos(-210°)$ is negative and $\sin(-210°)$ is positive.

$\cos(-210°) = -\frac{\sqrt{3}}{2}$ and $\sin(-210°) = \frac{1}{2}$

Exercises

9. Find the measurement of the angle in standard position below.

10. Sketch a $-30°$ angle in standard position.

11. Find the measure of an angle between $0°$ and $360°$ coterminal with a $-120°$ angle.

12. Find the exact values of the sine and cosine of $315°$ and $-315°$. Then find the decimal equivalents. Round your answers to the nearest hundredth.

6. periodic; from 0 to 4 or from 4 to 6; 4; 2

7. Answers may vary. Sample:

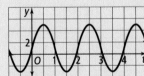

8.

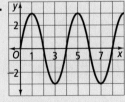

9. $-225°$

10.

11. $240°$

12. $\sin(315°) = -\frac{\sqrt{2}}{2} \approx -0.71$,

$\cos(315°) = \frac{\sqrt{2}}{2} \approx 0.71$;

$\sin(-315°) = \frac{\sqrt{2}}{2} \approx 0.71$,

$\cos(-315°) = \frac{\sqrt{2}}{2} \approx 0.71$

Answers

Chapter Review (continued)

13. a. $\frac{\pi}{3}$

    b. $\frac{1}{2}, \frac{\sqrt{3}}{2}$

14. a. $-\frac{\pi}{4}$

    b. $\frac{\sqrt{2}}{2}, -\frac{\sqrt{2}}{2}$

15. a. π

    b. $-1, 0$

16. a. $360°$

    b. $1, 0$

17. a. $150°$

    b. $-\frac{\sqrt{3}}{2}, \frac{1}{2}$

18. a. $-135°$

    b. $-\frac{\sqrt{2}}{2}, -\frac{\sqrt{2}}{2}$

19. 26.2 ft

20.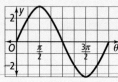

21.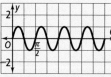

22. $y = 4 \sin 4\theta$

13-3 Radian Measure

Quick Review

A **central angle** of a circle is an angle whose vertex is at the center of a circle and whose sides are radii of the circle. An **intercepted arc** is the portion of the circle whose endpoints are on the sides of the angle and whose remaining points lie in the interior of the angle. A **radian** is the measure of a central angle that intercepts an arc equal in length to a radius of the circle.

Example

What is the radian measure of an angle of −210°?

$$-210° = -210° \cdot \frac{\pi}{180°} \text{ radians} = -\frac{7\pi}{6} \text{ radians}$$

Exercises

The measure θ of an angle in standard position is given.

  a. Write each degree measure in radians and each radian measure in degrees rounded to the nearest degree.

  b. Find the exact values of $\cos \theta$ and $\sin \theta$ for each angle measure.

13. $60°$

14. $-45°$

15. $180°$

16. 2π radians

17. $\frac{5\pi}{6}$ radians

18. $-\frac{3\pi}{4}$ radians

19. Use the circle to find the length of the indicated arc. Round your answer to the nearest tenth.

13-4 The Sine Function

Quick Review

The **sine function** $y = \sin \theta$ matches the measure θ of an angle in standard position with the y-coordinate of a point on the unit circle. This point is where the terminal side of the angle intersects the unit circle. The graph of a sine function is called a **sine curve**.

For the sine function $y = a \sin b\theta$, the amplitude equals $|a|$, there are b cycles from 0 to 2π, and the period is $\frac{2\pi}{b}$.

Example

Determine the number of cycles the sine function $y = -7 \sin 3\theta$ has in the interval from 0 to 2π. Find the amplitude and period of each function.

For $y = -7 \sin 3\theta$, $a = -7$ and $b = 3$. Therefore there are 3 cycles from 0 to 2π. The amplitude is $|a| = |-7| = 7$. The period is $\frac{2\pi}{b} = \frac{2\pi}{3}$.

Exercises

Sketch the graph of each function in the interval from 0 to 2π.

20. $y = 3 \sin \theta$

21. $y = \sin 4\theta$

22. Write an equation of a sine function with $a > 0$, amplitude 4, and period 0.5π.

13-5 The Cosine Function

Quick Review

The **cosine function** $y = \cos\theta$ matches the measure θ of an angle in standard position with the x-coordinate of a point on the unit circle. This point is where the terminal side of the angle intersects the unit circle.

For the cosine function $y = a \cos b\theta$, the amplitude equals $|a|$, there are b cycles from 0 to 2π, and the period is $\frac{2\pi}{b}$.

Example

Find all solutions to $5 \cos\theta = -4$ in the interval from 0 to 2π. Round each answer to the nearest hundredth.

On a graphing calculator graph the equations $y = -4$ and $y = 5 \cos\theta$.

Use the Intersect feature to find the points at which the two graphs intersect. The graph shows two solutions in the interval. They are $\theta \approx 2.50$ and 3.79.

Exercises

Sketch the graph of each function in the interval from 0 to 2π.

23. $y = 2\cos\left(\frac{\pi}{2}\theta\right)$

24. $y = -\cos 2\theta$

25. Write an equation of a cosine function with $a > 0$, amplitude 3, and period π.

Solve each equation in the interval from 0 to 2π. Round your answer to the nearest hundredth.

26. $3\cos 4\theta = -2$

27. $\cos(\pi\theta) = -0.6$

13-6 The Tangent Function

Quick Review

The **tangent** of an angle θ in standard position is the y-coordinate of the point where the terminal side of the angle intersects the tangent line $x = 1$. A **tangent function** in the form $y = a \tan b\theta$ has a period of $\frac{\pi}{b}$. Unlike the graphs of the sine and the cosine, the tangent is periodically undefined. At these points, the graph has vertical asymptotes.

Example

What is the period of $y = \tan\frac{\pi}{4}\theta$? Tell where two asymptotes occur.

$$\text{period} = \frac{\pi}{b} = \frac{\pi}{\frac{\pi}{4}} = 4$$

One cycle occurs in the interval from -2 to 2, so there are asymptotes at $\theta = -2$ and $\theta = 2$.

Exercises

Graph each function in the interval from 0 to 2π. Then evaluate the function at $t = \frac{\pi}{4}$ and $t = \frac{\pi}{2}$. If the tangent is undefined at that point, write *undefined*.

28. $y = \tan\frac{1}{2}t$

29. $y = \tan 3t$

30. $y = 2\tan t$

31. $y = 4\tan 2t$

23.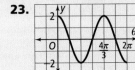

24.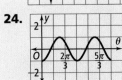

25. $y = 3\cos 2\theta$

26. 0.58, 1.00, 2.15, 2.57, 3.72, 4.14, 5.29, 5.71

27. 0.70, 1.30, 2.70, 3.30, 4.70, 5.30

28.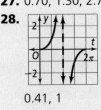

0.41, 1

29.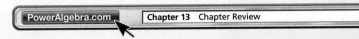

-1, undefined

30.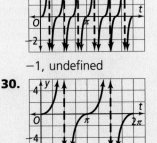

2, undefined

31.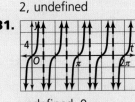

undefined, 0

Answers

Chapter Review (continued)

32.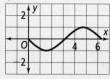

33.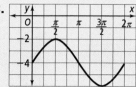

34.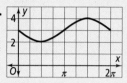

35.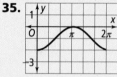

36. $y = \sin\left(x - \dfrac{\pi}{4}\right)$

37. $y = \cos x - 2$

38. $\sqrt{2}$

39. $-\dfrac{\sqrt{3}}{3}$

40. 2

41. $\sqrt{3}$

42.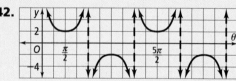

43.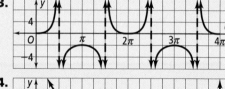

44.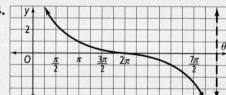

45.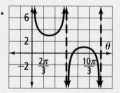

13-7 Translating Sine and Cosine Functions

Quick Review

Each horizontal translation of certain periodic functions is a **phase shift**. When $g(x) = f(x - h) + k$, the value of h is the amount of the horizontal shift and the value of k is the amount of the vertical shift. $y = k$ is the midline of the graph.

Example

What is an equation for the translation of $y = \sin x$, 2 units to the right and 1 unit up?

2 units to the right means $h = 2$ and 1 unit up means $k = 1$.

An equation is $y = \sin(x - 2) + 1$.

Exercises

Graph each function in the inteval from 0 to 2π.

32. $y = \cos\left(x + \dfrac{\pi}{2}\right)$ **33.** $y = 2\sin x - 4$

34. $y = \sin(x - \pi) + 3$ **35.** $y = \cos(x + \pi) - 1$

Write an equation for each translation.

36. $y = \sin x$, $\dfrac{\pi}{4}$ units to the right

37. $y = \cos x$, 2 units down

13-8 Reciprocal Trigonometric Functions

Quick Review

The **cosecant** (csc), **secant** (sec), and **cotangent** (cot) functions are defined as reciprocals for all real numbers θ (except those that make a denominator zero).

$$\csc \theta = \dfrac{1}{\sin \theta} \qquad \sec \theta = \dfrac{1}{\cos \theta} \qquad \cot \theta = \dfrac{1}{\tan \theta}$$

Example

Suppose $\sin \theta = -\dfrac{3}{5}$. Find $\csc \theta$.

$$\csc \theta = \dfrac{1}{\sin \theta} = \dfrac{1}{\frac{-3}{5}} = -\dfrac{5}{3}$$

Exercises

Evaluate each expression. Write your answer in exact form.

38. $\sec(-45°)$ **39.** $\cot 120°$

40. $\csc 150°$ **41.** $\cot(-150°)$

Graph each function in the interval from 0 to 4π.

42. $y = 2\csc \theta$ **43.** $y = \sec \theta - 1$

44. $y = \cot \dfrac{1}{4}\theta$ **45.** $y = \csc \dfrac{1}{2}\theta + 2$

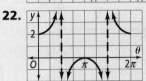
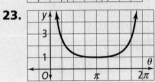
Do you know HOW?

Determine whether each function *is* or *is not* periodic. If it is periodic, find the period and amplitude.

1.
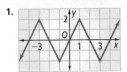

2.
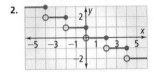

Find the measure of an angle between 0° and 360° coterminal with the given angle.

3. −32° **4.** −229° **5.** 375°

Write each measure in radians. Express your answer in terms of π and also as a decimal rounded to the nearest hundredth.

6. −225° **7.** 120° **8.** 600°

Write each radian measure in degrees. If necessary, round your answer to the nearest degree.

9. $\frac{5\pi}{6}$ **10.** −2.5π **11.** 0.8

12. Using the graph below, determine how many cycles the sine function has in the interval from 0 to 2π. Find the amplitude, period, and midline.

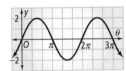

Find the amplitude and period of each function. Then sketch one cycle of the graph of each function.

13. $y = 4\sin(2x)$ **14.** $y = 2\sin(4x)$

Solve each equation in the interval from 0 to 2π. Give an exact answer and an answer rounded to the nearest hundredth.

15. $\cos t = \frac{1}{2}$ **16.** $3\tan 2t = \sqrt{3}$

Graph each function in the interval from 0 to 2π.

17. $y = 2\cos x$ **18.** $y = \cos(x + \pi)$
19. $y = -\cos\frac{\theta}{\pi}$ **20.** $y = \tan\frac{\pi}{3}\theta$
21. $y = \cot x$ **22.** $y = \sec\theta + 1$
23. $y = \csc\frac{\theta}{2}$ **24.** $y = \csc(\theta + 1)$

Write an equation for each translation.

25. $y = \cos x$, 7.5 units to the right
26. $y = \sin x$, 3 units to the left, 1.5 units down

Evaluate each expression. Write your answer in exact form. If the expression is undefined, write *undefined*.

27. $\sin 30°$ **28.** $\sin(-330°)$
29. $\sec 270°$ **30.** $\tan(-60°)$

Do you UNDERSTAND?

31. Open-Ended Sketch a function with period 4, amplitude 7, and midline $y = 3$.

32. Writing Explain how to convert an angle measure in radians to an angle measure in degrees. Include an example.

33. Physics On each swing, a pendulum 18 inches long travels through an angle of $\frac{3\pi}{4}$ radians. How far does the tip of the pendulum travel in one swing? Round your answer to the nearest inch.

34. Reasoning What are the steps you take to find the asymptotes of the function $y = \tan(ax + b)$?

21.
22.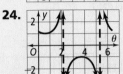
23.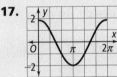
24.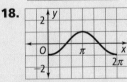

25. $y = \cos(x − 7.5)$
26. $y = \sin(x + 3) − 1.5$
27. $\frac{1}{2}$
28. $\frac{1}{2}$
29. undefined
30. $-\sqrt{3}$
31. Check students' work.
32. Answers may vary. Sample: Multiply the radian measure by $\frac{180°}{\pi}$. Example: $\frac{2\pi}{3}$ radians · $\frac{180°}{\pi} = 120°$
33. 42 in.
34. The asymptotes of $y = \tan\theta$ are at $\theta = \frac{n\pi}{2}$ (for *n* odd). If $\theta = ax + b$, the asymptotes of $y = \tan(ax + b)$ are when $ax + b = \frac{n\pi}{2}$ (for *n* odd) or when $x = \frac{-2b + n\pi}{2a}$ (for *n* odd).

Answers

Chapter Test

1. periodic; 4, 2 **2.** not periodic
3. 328° **4.** 131°
5. 15° **6.** $-\frac{5\pi}{4}$, −3.93
7. $\frac{2\pi}{3}$, 2.09 **8.** $\frac{10\pi}{3}$, 10.47
9. 150° **10.** −450°
11. 46° **12.** 1 cycle; 2, 2π
13. 4, π;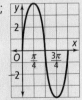
14. 2, $\frac{\pi}{2}$;
15. $\frac{\pi}{3}, \frac{5\pi}{3}$; 1.05, 5.24
16. $\frac{\pi}{12}, \frac{7\pi}{12}, \frac{13\pi}{12}, \frac{19\pi}{12}$; 0.26, 1.83, 3.40, 4.97
17.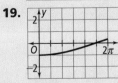
18.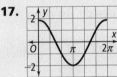
19.
20.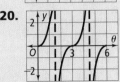

Item Number	Lesson	© Content Standard
1	9-5	A.SSE.4
2	1-4	A.CED.4
3	2-8	A.CED.2
4	2-4	F.IF.9
5	3-4	A.CED.3
6	4-1	F.BF.3
7	5-6	N.CN.7
8	8-1	A.CED.2
9	7-4	F.LE.4
10	5-5	A.APR.3
11	10-3	G.GPE.1
12	11-4	S.CP.8
13	11-4	S.CP.8
14	5-7	A.APR.5
15	4-9B	N.CN.1
16	4-8	N.CN.2
17	11-3	S.IC.2
18	12-3	N.VM.10
19	13-1	F.IF.4
20	8-1	A.CED.2
21	7-5	F.LE.4
22	11-10	S.ID.4
23	12-1	N.VM.8
24	8-5	A.APR.7
25	8-3	F.IF.7d
26	5-7	A.APR.5
27	10-6	G.GPE.2
28	12-3	N.VM.8
29	6-5	A.REI.2
30	12-1	N.VM.8
31	7-1	A.CED.2
32	9-5	A.SSE.4

13 Cumulative Standards Review ASSESSMENT

TIPS FOR SUCCESS

Some problems ask you to use given results to find the probability of independent events.

TIP 1
Find the number of trials for the experiment.

The table below shows the results of spinning a spinner.

Outcome	Frequency
Orange	8
Green	7
Blue	5

What is the probability of landing on orange and then blue?

Ⓐ $\frac{1}{10}$ Ⓒ $\frac{2}{5}$

Ⓑ $\frac{7}{20}$ Ⓓ $\frac{13}{20}$

TIP 2
Find the number of times the events "landing on orange" and "landing on blue" occur.

Think It Through
The number of trials for the experiment is $8 + 7 + 5 = 20$. Of those, 8 are orange.

$\frac{8}{20} = \frac{2}{5}$

The probability of spinning blue is $\frac{5}{20} = \frac{1}{4}$. The probability of spinning orange, then blue is

$\frac{2}{5} \cdot \frac{1}{4} = \frac{2}{20} = \frac{1}{10}$.

The correct answer is A.

Vocabulary Review

As you solve test items, you must understand the meanings of mathematical terms. Match each term with its mathematical meaning.

A. amplitude
B. initial side
C. radian
D. terminal side
E. phase shift

I. the measure of a central angle that intercepts an arc equal in length to a radius of the circle

II. the ray not on the x-axis of an angle in standard position

III. a horizontal translation of certain periodic functions

IV. the ray on the x-axis of an angle in standard position

V. half the difference between the minimum and maximum values of a periodic function

Multiple Choice

Read each question. Then write the letter of the correct answer on your paper.

1. What is the sum of the geometric series $2 + 4 + 8 + \ldots + 64$?

Ⓐ 30   Ⓒ 126
Ⓑ 62   Ⓓ 252

2. Solve the following equation for x.

$y = \frac{1}{\sqrt{x+6}}$

Ⓕ $x = \frac{1}{\sqrt{y-6}}$ Ⓗ $x = \frac{1}{y^2} - 6$

Ⓖ $x = \frac{1}{y^2} + 6$ Ⓘ $x = \frac{1}{y} - 6$

Answers

Cumulative Standards Review

A. V
B. IV
C. I
D. II
E. III
1. C
2. H

3. Which point is *not* a solution of the inequality
$y > 2|x + 3| - 7$?

(A) $(0, 0)$ (C) $(1, 1)$

(B) $(-2, -1)$ (D) $(-1, 1)$

4. Which of the following equations is an equivalent form of $3x - 4y = 36$ that makes it easy to identify the y-intercept?

(F) $y = -\frac{3}{4}x - 9$ (H) $y - 6 = \frac{3}{4}(x + 4)$

(G) $y + 6 = \frac{3}{4}(x - 4)$ (I) $y = \frac{3}{4}x - 9$

5. Which point in the feasible region below maximizes the objective function $C = 2x + 3y$?
$$\begin{cases} x \geq 0, y \geq 0 \\ x + y \leq 8 \\ 3x + 2y \leq 18 \end{cases}$$

(A) $(0, 0)$ (B) $(2, 6)$ (C) $(0, 8)$ (D) $(18, 0)$

6. Which best describes the transformations used to obtain the graph of $y = 3(-x + 3)^3$ from the graph of $y = x^3$?

(F) reflect across the x-axis, shift left 3 units, stretch by a factor of 3

(G) reflect across the y-axis, shift right 3 units, stretch by a factor of 3

(H) reflect across the x-axis, shift right 3 units, stretch by a factor of 3

(I) reflect across the y-axis, shift left 3 units, stretch by a factor of 3

7. A sixth degree polynomial equation with rational coefficients has roots -1, $2i$, and $1 - \sqrt{5}$. Which of the following cannot also be a root of the polynomial?

   I. 1 II. $-2i$ III. $\sqrt{5}$ IV. $1 - i$

(A) I only   (C) III and IV only

(B) II and III only   (D) II, III, and IV only

8. Which equation shows an inverse variation?

(F) $y = 5x$ (H) $6 = \frac{x}{y}$

(G) $xy - 4 = 0$ (I) $y = -4$

9. Which is equivalent to $2^9 = 512$?

(A) $\log_{512} 2 = 9$ (C) $\log_2 9 = 512$

(B) $\log_2 512 = 9$ (D) $\log_9 512 = 2$

10. What are the roots of $5x^4 - 12x^3 - 11x^2 + 6x = 0$?

(F) $-1, \frac{5}{2}, 3$ (H) $0, 1, \frac{5}{2}, 3$

(G) $-1, 0, \frac{2}{5}, 3$ (I) $-1, -\frac{2}{5}, 0, 3$

11. Which equation represents a circle with center $(-3, 8)$ and radius 12?

(A) $(x - 8)^2 + (y + 3)^2 = 144$

(B) $(x - 8)^2 - (y + 3)^2 = 144$

(C) $(x + 3)^2 + (y - 8)^2 = 144$

(D) $(x - 3)^2 - (y - 8)^2 = 144$

12. The table below shows the results of spinning a spinner. What is the probability of the spinner landing on white, then red?

Outcome	Frequency
Red	7
Blue	3
White	5

(F) $\frac{1}{9}$ (H) $\frac{7}{18}$

(G) $\frac{7}{45}$ (I) $\frac{4}{5}$

13. During a promotional event, two customers at a clothing store between 9 and 10 A.M. will be randomly selected to win a gift certificate. Suppose you and a friend visit the store and there are 19 other customers between 9 and 10 A.M. What is the probability you and your friend will NOT both win the gift certificate?

(A) $\frac{1}{210}$ (C) $\frac{2}{21}$

(B) $\frac{2}{19}$ (D) $\frac{209}{210}$

14. What is the sixth term in the expansion of $(2x - 3y)^7$?

(F) $21\, x^2 y^5$

(G) $-126\, x^2 y^5$

(H) $-20{,}412\, x^2 y^5$

(I) $20{,}412\, x^2 y^5$

3. C
4. I
5. C
6. H
7. C
8. G
9. B
10. G
11. C
12. G
13. D
14. H

Answers

Cumulative Standards Review (continued)

15. -1　　　　**16.** 6.4

17. 0.17　　　**18.** 17

19. 25　　　　**20.** 6

21. 1.11　　　**22.** 7.39

23. -3　　　　**24.** 4

25. [2] vertical asymptote: $x = -4$; horizontal asymptote: $y = 3$

$$y = \frac{3x^2 - 5x - 2}{x^2 + 2x - 8} = \frac{(3x + 1)(x - 2)}{(x + 4)(x - 2)}$$

$$= \frac{3x + 1}{x + 4}$$

$x + 4 = 0$ when $x = -4$ and $y = \frac{3}{1} = 3$.

[1] correct answer, without work shown OR appropriate method, but with one computational error OR only one asymptote found

26. [2] $r^4 - 12r^3 + 54r^2 - 108r + 81$

[1] one incorrect coefficient

27. [2] $y = 2$; in standard form, the equation is $y = -\frac{1}{8}x^2 + \frac{3}{4}x - \frac{9}{8}$. Since $|a| = \frac{1}{4c} = \frac{1}{8}$, $c = 2$. Since the vertex lies on the x-axis, the directrix is the line $y = 2$.

[1] correct answer, without work shown OR appropriate method, but with one computational error

28. $\begin{bmatrix} 2 & 1 \\ -3 & -2 \end{bmatrix}$

29. $x = \frac{2}{5}$

30. $\begin{bmatrix} 6 & -1 & 10 \\ 1 & -7 & 2 \\ 14 & 1 & 15 \end{bmatrix}$

31. [4] a. 4%; $780.61 - 750.00 = 30.61$ and $\frac{30.61}{250.00} = 0.04$

b. $y = 750e^{0.04t}$

c. 7 yrs;

$$1000 = 750e^{0.04t}$$
$$1.\overline{3} = e^{0.04t}$$
$$\ln 1.\overline{3} = \ln e^{0.04t}$$
$$\ln 1.\overline{3} = 0.04t$$
$$t = 7.19$$

[3] correct methods, but with one computational error

[2] incorrect equation in (b) solved correctly in (c)

[1] correct answers, without work shown

32. [4] Determine r by using $a_4 = a_1 r^3$:

$$a_4 = a_1 r^3$$
$$r^3 = \frac{a_4}{a_1} = \frac{27}{8}$$
$$r = \frac{3}{2}$$

Substituting $a_1 = 8$ and $r = \frac{3}{2}$:

$$a_7 = a_1 r^6$$
$$a_7 = 8\left(\frac{3}{2}\right)^6 = \frac{729}{8}$$

---

15. What is the integer equivalent of i^6?

16. What is the distance of $4 - 5i$ from the origin?

17. To the nearest hundredth, what is the theoretical probability of rolling a 3 on a standard number cube?

18. What is the determinant of $\begin{bmatrix} 5 & -3 \\ 4 & 1 \end{bmatrix}$?

19. A periodic function has an amplitude of 14 and a minimum value of -3. What is its maximum value?

20. Suppose y varies directly with the square of x. If $y = 20$ when $x = 3$, what is $|x|$ when $y = 80$?

21. What is the solution to the equation $7^{2x} = 75$ to the nearest hundredth?

22. The table below shows a family's daily water usage for 2 weeks. Find the standard deviation of the data to the nearest hundredth.

Daily Water Usage (gal)

92.3	81.3
85.3	81.6
89.7	76.9
101.2	94.0
80.3	89.6
91.4	96.3
88.8	102.1

23. If $A = \begin{bmatrix} 3 & -1 & 0 \\ -5 & 4 & 2 \end{bmatrix}$, what is the entry a_{12} of the matrix $3A$?

24. Find the sum of the rational expressions below. What is the coefficient of the x^2 term in the numerator of the sum? $\frac{x + 1}{x^2 + 2} + \frac{x + 1}{3x + 6}$

Short Response

25. Find all asymptotes of the graph of $y = \frac{3x^2 - 5x - 2}{x^2 + 2x - 8}$.

26. Using Pascal's Triangle, what is the expansion of $(r - 3)^4$?

```
       1
      1 1
     1 2 1
    1 3 3 1
   1 4 6 4 1
```

27. What is the directrix of the graph of $6x = x^2 + 8y + 9$?

28. What is the inverse matrix of $\begin{bmatrix} 2 & 1 \\ -3 & -2 \end{bmatrix}$?

29. Solve $8 + \sqrt{5x + 2} = 10$.

30. If $B = \begin{bmatrix} 2 & -1 & 3 \\ 4 & -8 & 0 \\ 5 & 6 & 9 \end{bmatrix}$ and $C = \begin{bmatrix} 4 & 0 & 7 \\ -3 & 1 & 2 \\ 9 & -5 & 6 \end{bmatrix}$, what is $B + C$?

Extended Response

31. The table shows the values of an investment after the given number of years of continuously compounded interest.

Years	0	1	2	3
Value	$750.00	$780.61	$812.47	$845.62

a. What is the rate of interest?
b. Write an equation to model the growth of the investment.
c. To the nearest year, when will the investment be worth more than $1000?

32. In a geometric sequence, $a_1 = 8$ and $a_4 = 27$. Explain how to find a_7.

[3] correct methods, but with one computational error

[2] r solved for correctly, but not a_7 OR a_7 solved for correctly, given incorrect r

[1] correct answers, without work shown

Get Ready!

Lesson 4-5 ◆ **Solving Quadratic Equations**

Solve each equation.

1. $4x^2 = 25$ **2.** $x^2 - 23 = 0$ **3.** $3x^2 = 80$

4. $8x^2 - 44 = 0$ **5.** $0.5x^2 = 15$ **6.** $6x^2 - 13 = 11$

Lesson 6-7 ◆ **Finding the Inverse of a Function**

For each function f, find f^{-1} and the domain and range of f and f^{-1}. Determine whether f^{-1} is a function.

7. $f(x) = 5x + 2$ **8.** $f(x) = \sqrt{x + 3}$

9. $f(x) = \sqrt{3x - 4}$ **10.** $f(x) = \frac{5}{x}$

11. $f(x) = \frac{10}{x - 1}$ **12.** $f(x) = \frac{10}{x} - 1$

Lesson 7-5 ◆ **Solving Exponential and Logarithmic Equations**

Solve each equation.

13. $4^x = \frac{1}{8}$ **14.** $\log 5x + 1 = -1$

15. $7^{3x} = 500$ **16.** $\log 3x + \log x = 9$

17. $\log(4x + 3) - \log x = 5$ **18.** $3^x = 243$

Lessons 13-4, 13-5, and 13-6 ◆ **Evaluating Trigonometric Functions**

For each value of θ, find the values of $\cos \theta$, $\sin \theta$, and $\tan \theta$. Round your answers to the nearest hundredth.

19. $48°$ **20.** $-105°$ **21.** $16°$ **22.** $\frac{5\pi}{6}$

 Looking Ahead Vocabulary

23. The equation $1 + \tan^2 \theta = \sec^2 \theta$ is a *trigonometric identity*. Use what you know about identities to make a conjecture about this equation.

24. The Pythagorean Theorem is a special case of the *Law of Cosines*. What do you suppose you will use the Law of Cosines to find?

Get Ready!

Assign this diagnostic assessment to determine if students have the prerequisite skills for Chapter 14.

Lesson	Skill
4-5	Solve Quadratic Equations
6-7	Find the Inverse of a Function
7-5	Solve Exponential and Logarithmic Equations
13-4, 13-5, and 13-6	Evaluate Trigonometric Functions

To remediate students, select from these resources (available for every lesson).

- Online Problems (PowerAlgebra.com)
- Reteaching (All-in-One Teaching Resources)
- Practice (All-in-One Teaching Resources)

Why Students Need These Skills

SOLVING QUADRATIC EQUATIONS

Solving quadratic equations is essential to solving some trigonometric equations.

FINDING THE INVERSE OF A FUNCTION

Understanding how to find the inverse of a function is essential to understanding inverse trigonometric functions.

SOLVING EXPONENTIAL AND LOGARITHMIC EQUATIONS

Solving exponential and logarithmic equations by using inverse functions is related to solving trigonometric functions by using inverse functions.

EVALUATING TRIGONOMETRIC FUNCTIONS

Evaluating trigonometric functions is necessary when solving some real-world trigonometric problems.

Looking Ahead Vocabulary

TRIGONOMETRIC IDENTITY Ask students what other identities they studied in Algebra 2.

LAW OF COSINES The Pythagorean Theorem can be used to find missing side lengths of right triangles. It is a special case of the Law of Cosines, which can be used for a triangle of any shape.

Answers

Get Ready!

1. $x = \pm\frac{5}{2}$ **2.** $x = \pm\sqrt{23}$

3. $x = \pm 4\sqrt{\frac{5}{3}}$ **4.** $x = \pm\sqrt{\frac{11}{2}}$

5. $x = \pm\sqrt{30}$ **6.** $x = \pm 2$

7. $f^{-1}(x) = \frac{x - 2}{5}$; domain of f and range of f^{-1}: all real numbers, range of f and domain of f^{-1}: all real numbers; yes

8. $f^{-1}(x) = x^2 - 3$; domain of f and range of f^{-1}: all real numbers ≥ -3, domain of f^{-1}: all real numbers, range of f: all real numbers ≥ 0; yes

9. $f^{-1}(x) = \frac{x^2 + 4}{3}$; domain of f and range of f^{-1}: all real numbers $\geq \frac{4}{3}$, domain of f^{-1}: all real numbers, range of f: all real numbers ≥ 0; yes

10. $f^{-1}(x) = \frac{5}{x}$; domain of f and range of f^{-1}: all real numbers except 0, domain of f^{-1} and range of f: all real numbers except 0; yes

11. $f^{-1}(x) = \frac{10}{x} + 1$; domain of f and range of f^{-1}: all real numbers except 1, domain of f^{-1} and range of f: all real numbers except 0; yes

12. $f^{-1}(x) = \frac{10}{x + 1}$; domain of f and range of f^{-1}: all real numbers except 0, domain of f^{-1} and range of f: all real numbers except -1; yes

13. $x = -\frac{3}{2}$ **14.** $x = 0.002$

15. $x = 1.0646$ **16.** $x = 18257.4$

17. $x = 0.00003$ **18.** $x = 5$

19. 0.67; 0.74; 1.11

20. -0.26; -0.97; 3.73

21. 0.96; 0.28; 0.29

22. -0.87; 0.50; -0.58

23. Answers may vary. Sample: The eq. is true for all values of θ for which $\tan^2 \theta$ and $\sec^2 \theta$ are defined.

24. Answers may vary. Sample: the lengths of the sides of rt. triangles

Chapter 14 Overview

Chapter 14 expands on students' understandings and skills related to periodic functions and trigonometry. In this chapter, students will develop the answers to the Essential Questions posed on the opposite page as they learn the concepts and skills bulleted below.

BIG idea **Equivalence**

ESSENTIAL QUESTION How do you verify that an equation involving the variable *x* is an identity?

• Students will show that trigonometric identities are true for all values of the variable within the domain of validity.

BIG idea **Function**

ESSENTIAL QUESTION A trigonometric function corresponds one number to many, so how can its inverse be a function?

• Students will restrict the domains of trigonometric functions to make their inverses functions.

BIG idea **Equivalence**

ESSENTIAL QUESTION How do the trigonometric *functions* relate to the trigonometric *ratios* for a right triangle?

• Students will restrict the domain of the trigonometric functions so that the function values are equivalent to the trigonometric ratios for a right triangle.

PowerAlgebra.com

 Your place to get all things digital

 VIDEO Download videos connecting math to your world.

VOCABULARY Math definitions in English and Spanish

SOLVE IT! The online Solve It will get you in gear for each lesson.

DYNAMIC ACTIVITIES Interactive! Vary numbers, graphs, and figures to explore math concepts.

ONLINE PROBLEMS Online access to stepped-out problems aligned to Common Core

 ONLINE HOMEWORK Get and view your assignments online.

 MathXL FOR SCHOOL Extra practice and review online

DOMAINS
• Trigonometric Functions
• Similarity, Right Triangles, and Trigonometry

Trigonometric identities and equations are ideas that can help you fly to extraordinary heights.

How do you verify a trigonometric identity? How do you solve a trigonometric equation? How can you solve real-world problems involving right triangles by using trigonometric ratios? You will learn how in this chapter.

Vocabulary

English/Spanish Vocabulary Audio Online:

English	Spanish
Law of Cosines, *p. 936*	Ley de cosenos
Law of Sines, *p. 929*	Ley de senos
trigonometric identity, *p. 904*	identidad trigonométrica
trigonometric ratios for a right triangle, *p. 922*	razones trigonométricas para un triángulo rectángulo

Content Standards

Following are the standards covered in this chapter. Modeling standards are indicated by a star symbol (★).

CONCEPTUAL CATEGORY Functions

Domain Trigonometric Functions F.TF

Cluster Model periodic phenomena with trigonometric functions. (Standards F.TF.6, F.TF.7★)
LESSON 14-2

Cluster Prove and apply trigonometric identities. (Standards F.TF.8, F.TF.9)
LESSONS 14-1, 14-6, 14-7

CONCEPTUAL CATEGORY Geometry

Domain Similarity, Right Triangles, and Trigonometry

Cluster Define trigonometric ratios and solve problems involving right triangles. (Standards G.SRT.6, G.SRT.8)
LESSON 14-3

Cluster Apply trigonometry to general triangles. (Standards G.SRT.9, G.SRT.10, G.SRT.11)
LESSONS 14-4, 14-5

PowerAlgebra.com

Chapter 14 Overview

Use these online assets to engage your students. These include support for the Solve It and step-by-step solutions for Problems.

VIDEO Show the student-produced video demonstrating relevant and engaging applications of the new concepts in the chapter.

VOCABULARY Find online definitions for new terms in English and Spanish.

SOLVE IT! Start each lesson with an attention-getting Problem. View the Problem online with helpful hints.

My Math Video

Use this video to introduce the importance of math, specifically trigonometry, in aerodynamics. The photo shows Swiss pilot Yves Rossy, the first man to fly with jetfuel-powered wings strapped to his back.

Q You can use trigonometry to calculate Yves Rossy's glide angle when he jumps out of the plane before firing up the jetpacks. Why would this be important? **[Sample: as a safety precaution]**

Q You can use math to determine the ideal shape of the wings by analyzing the forces on the wings. What forces would you have to consider? **[Samples: lift, drag, weight, thrust]**

EXTENSION

Have students research the methods the Wright brothers used to analyze the lift and drag on the wings of their airplanes. Although vector analysis is currently used to study those forces, the Wright brothers used trigonometry.

BIG ideas

1 Equivalence

Essential Question How do you verify that an equation involving the variable x is an identity?

2 Function

Essential Question A trigonometric function corresponds one number to many, so how can its inverse be a function?

3 Equivalence

Essential Question How do the trigonometric *functions* relate to the trigonometric *ratios* for a right triangle?

Chapter Preview

PowerAlgebra.com   Chapter 14 Trignometric Identities and Equations   903

 Increase students' depth of knowledge with interactive online activities.

 Show Problems from each lesson solved step by step. Instant replay allows students to go at their own pace when studying online.

 Assign homework to individual students or to an entire class.

 Prepare students for the Mid-Chapter Quiz and Chapter Test with online practice and review.

Math Background

PROFESSIONAL DEVELOPMENT

Understanding by Design principles were central to the development of the Big Ideas and the Essential Understandings. These will help your students build a structure on which to make connections to prior learning.

Equivalence

BIG idea A single quantity may be represented by many different expressions. The facts about a quantity may be expressed by many different equations (or inequalities).

ESSENTIAL UNDERSTANDINGS

14-1 The interrelationships among the six basic trigonometric functions make it possible to write trigonometric expressions in various equivalent forms, some of which can be significantly easier to work with than others in mathematical applications.

14-5 If you know the measures of enough parts of a triangle to completely determine the triangle, you can solve the triangle.

14-6 Several trigonometric identities involve a single angle. Other trigonometric identities involve two angles. No important trigonometric identity is *additive*; for example, $\sin(A + B) \neq \sin A + \sin B$.

14-7 The *double-angle identities* are special cases of the angle-sum identities. Substitute $\frac{\theta}{2}$ for θ in certain double angle identities and you get the *half-angle identities*.

Function

BIG idea A function is a relationship between variables in which each value of the input variable is associated with a unique value of the output variable. Functions can be represented in a variety of ways, such as graphs, tables, equations, or words. Each representation is particularly useful in certain situations. Some important families of functions are developed through transformations of the simplest form of the function.

ESSENTIAL UNDERSTANDINGS

14-2 To solve some trigonometric equations, you can use an inverse trigonometric function to find one solution. Then you can use periodicity to find all solutions.

14-3 If you restrict the domains of the trigonometric functions to angle measures between 0° and 90°, the function values are the trigonometric ratios associated with the acute angles of a right triangle.

14-4 If you know two angles and a side of a triangle, you can use trigonometry to solve the triangle. If you know two sides and the included angle, you can find the area of the triangle.

Trigonometric Identities and Inverse Functions

The properties of real numbers can be used to find relationships between trigonometric function values.

Basic Identities

$$\csc \theta = \frac{1}{\sin \theta} \qquad \sec \theta = \frac{1}{\cos \theta} \qquad \cot \theta = \frac{1}{\tan \theta}$$

$$\sin \theta = \frac{1}{\csc \theta} \qquad \cos \theta = \frac{1}{\sec \theta} \qquad \tan \theta = \frac{1}{\cot \theta}$$

$$\tan \theta = \frac{\sin \theta}{\cos \theta} \qquad \cot \theta = \frac{\cos \theta}{\sin \theta}$$

Example: Verify that $\sec \theta \cot \theta = \csc \theta$.

$$\sec \theta \cot \theta = \frac{1}{\cos \theta} \cdot \frac{\cos \theta}{\sin \theta}$$

$$= \frac{1}{\sin \theta}$$

$$= \csc \theta$$

Pythagorean Identities

$$\cos^2 \theta + \sin^2 \theta = 1 \qquad 1 + \tan^2 \theta = \sec^2 \theta$$

$$1 + \cot^2 \theta = \csc^2 \theta$$

Example: Verify $(1 - \cos^2 \theta) \cot \theta = \sin \theta \cos \theta$.

$$(1 - \cos^2 \theta) \cot \theta = \sin^2 \theta \cdot \left(\frac{\cos \theta}{\sin \theta}\right)$$

$$= \sin \theta \cos \theta$$

Inverse Trigonometric Functions

Inverses can be found for trigonometric functions. These inverses are not functions unless the domains of the trigonometric functions are restricted. The restrictions are:

$$y = \cos \theta \qquad 0 < \theta < \pi$$

$$y = \sin \theta \qquad -\frac{\pi}{2} < \theta < \frac{\pi}{2}$$

$$y = \tan \theta \qquad -\frac{\pi}{2} < \theta < \frac{\pi}{2}$$

Example: What are the radian measures of all angles whose sine is 0.85?

Solution: Using your calculator, $\sin^{-1} 0.85 \approx 1.02$. Since sine is positive in Quadrants I and II, the angle $\pi - 1.02 \approx 2.12$ is also a solution. All of the angles whose sine is 0.85 are $1.02 + 2\pi n$ and $2.12 + 2\pi n$, for n an integer.

Ⓒ Mathematical Practices

Model with mathematics. Make sense of problems and persevere in solving them. The usefulness of trigonometric functions for solving problems is extended in this chapter through the use of various identities.

Measures of Sides and Angles of Triangles

Right Triangles

Trigonometric functions can be used to find measures of sides and angles of right triangles. For example,

$$\sin A = \frac{opp}{hyp}$$

$$\sin 20° = \frac{8}{x} \qquad x \approx 23.4 \text{ ft}$$

Law of Sines

If you know two angles and a side of a triangle, you can use the Law of Sines to find the measure of a side or angle. Specifically it can be used in the cases of AAS or ASA. It can also be used in the case of SSA. However, for SSA, it is possible to get no solution, one solution, or two solutions.

$$\frac{\sin A}{a} = \frac{\sin B}{b} = \frac{\sin C}{c}$$

If you know the measures of two sides and the included angle of a triangle, you can find the **area**.

$$\text{Area} = \tfrac{1}{2} bc \sin A = \tfrac{1}{2} ac \sin B = \tfrac{1}{2} ab \sin C$$

Note that if you find the area of a right triangle using the formula $\frac{1}{2} bh$, you are actually using a special case of $\frac{1}{2} ab \sin C$ in which the sine of C (the 90° angle) is 1.

Law of Cosines

The Law of Cosines relates the length of a side of any triangle to the measure of the opposite angle and the other two sides.

$$a^2 = b^2 + c^2 - 2bc \cos A$$
$$b^2 = a^2 + c^2 - 2ac \cos B$$
$$c^2 = a^2 + b^2 - 2ab \cos C$$

Specifically, the Law of Cosines allows you to find the measure of an angle if you know SSS or a side if you know SAS.

Example: What is the measure of $\angle A$?

$$a^2 = b^2 + c^2 - 2bc \cos A$$
$$3^2 = 5^2 + 7^2 - (2)(5)(7) \cos A$$
$$9 = 25 + 49 - 70 \cos A$$
$$\frac{13}{14} = \cos A$$
$$\cos^{-1}\left(\frac{13}{14}\right) \approx 21.8°$$

© Mathematical Practices

Use appropriate tools strategically. As the emphasis of this chapter is on problem solving, graphing calculators are used throughout the chapter to solve equations in real-world problems. Applications of identities that do not require a calculator are used in some lessons to reinforce special triangle ratios.

Angle Identities

Identities show the relationships between trigonometric functions.

Negative Angle Identities

$$\sin(-\theta) = -\sin\theta \quad \cos(-\theta) = \cos\theta \quad \tan(-\theta) = -\tan\theta$$

Cofunction Angle Identities

$$\sin\left(\frac{\pi}{2} - \theta\right) = \cos\theta \quad \cos\left(\frac{\pi}{2} - \theta\right) = \sin\theta$$
$$\tan\left(\frac{\pi}{2} - \theta\right) = \cot\theta$$

Angle Sum and Angle Difference Identities

$$\sin(A + B) = \sin A \cos B + \cos A \sin B$$
$$\sin(A - B) = \sin A \cos B - \cos A \sin B$$
$$\cos(A + B) = \cos A \cos B - \sin A \sin B$$
$$\cos(A - B) = \cos A \cos B + \sin A \sin B$$
$$\tan(A + B) = \frac{\tan A + \tan B}{1 - \tan A \tan B}$$
$$\tan(A - B) = \frac{\tan A - \tan B}{1 + \tan A \tan B}$$

You can use identities to find exact values.

Example: Find the exact value of $\sin 15°$.

Solution:
$$\sin(A - B) = \sin A \cos B - \cos A \sin B$$
$$\sin(60° - 45°) = \sin 60° \cos 45° - \cos 60° \sin 45°$$
$$= \frac{\sqrt{3}}{2}\left(\frac{\sqrt{2}}{2}\right) - \frac{1}{2}\left(\frac{\sqrt{2}}{2}\right)$$
$$= \frac{\sqrt{6} - \sqrt{2}}{4}$$

Double-Angle Identities

$$\cos 2\theta = \cos^2\theta - \sin^2\theta \qquad \sin 2\theta = 2\sin\theta\cos\theta$$
$$\cos 2\theta = 2\cos^2\theta - 1$$
$$\cos 2\theta = 1 - 2\sin^2\theta \qquad \tan 2\theta = \frac{2\tan\theta}{1 - \tan^2\theta}$$

Half-Angle Identities

Double-angle identities can be used to derive half-angle identities.

$$\sin\frac{A}{2} = \pm\sqrt{\frac{1 - \cos A}{2}} \qquad \cos\frac{A}{2} = \pm\sqrt{\frac{1 + \cos A}{2}}$$
$$\tan\frac{A}{2} = \pm\sqrt{\frac{1 - \cos A}{1 + \cos A}}$$

© Mathematical Practices

Reason abstractly and quantitatively. Look for and make use of structure. Trigonometric identities give students practice in constructing mathematical proofs and then applying abstract results to solve concrete problems. Proofs are given for major identities (e.g., angle addition formulas, Laws of Sines, and Law of Cosines).

TRIGONOMETRIC IDENTITIES AND EQUATIONS
Pacing and Assignment Guide

		TRADITIONAL			BLOCK
Lesson	Teaching Day(s)	Basic	Average	Advanced	Block
14-1	1	Problems 1–4 Exs. 7–15, 68–84	Problems 1–4 Exs. 7–15 odd, 68–84	Problems 1–4 Exs. 7–15 odd, 68–84	**Day 1** Problems 1–5 Exs. 7–27 odd, 28–61, 68–84
	2	Problem 5 Exs. 16–28, 38–60 even	Problem 5 Exs. 17–27 odd, 28–61	Problem 5 Exs. 17–27 odd, 28–67	
14-2	1	Problems 1–3 Exs. 7–18, 67–84	Problems 1–3 Exs. 7–17 odd, 67–84	Problems 1–3 Exs. 7–17 odd, 67–84	**Day 2** Problems 1–6 Exs. 7–33 odd, 35–61, 67–84
	2	Problems 4–6 Exs. 19–34, 35–41 odd, 42, 43	Problems 4–6 Exs. 19–33 odd, 35–61	Problems 4–6 Exs. 19–33 odd, 35–66	
14-3	1	Problems 1–4 Exs. 7–18, 52–65	Problems 1–4 Exs. 7–17 odd, 52–65	Problems 1–6 Exs. 7–25 odd, 26–65	**Day 3** Problems 1–6 Exs. 7–25 odd, 26–46, 52–65
	2	Problems 5–6 Exs. 19–25, 32–38 even, 45	Problems 5–6 Exs. 19–25 odd, 26–46		
14-4	1	Problems 1–4 Exs. 6–16, 17–25 odd, 36–50	Problems 1–4 Exs. 7–15 odd, 17–33, 36–50	Problems 1–4 Exs. 7–15 odd, 17–50	**Day 4** Problems 1–4 Exs. 7–15 odd, 17–33, 36–50
14-5	1	Problems 1–3 Exs. 7–20, 27–29, 33–35, 50, 54–71	Problems 1–3 Exs. 7–19 odd, 21–50, 54–71	Problems 1–3 Exs. 7–19 odd, 21–71	Problems 1–3 Exs. 7–19 odd, 21–50, 54–71
14-6	1	Problems 1–3 Exs. 7–21, 56–69	Problems 1–6 Exs. 7–35 odd, 36–48, 56–69	Problems 1–6 Exs. 7–35 odd, 36–69	**Day 5** Problems 1–6 Exs. 7–35 odd, 36–48, 56–69
	2	Problems 4–6 Exs. 22–36, 40–43, 48			
14-7	1	Problems 1–3 Exs. 7–16, 66–78	Problems 1–5 Exs. 7–31 odd, 33–58, 66–78	Problems 1–5 Exs. 7–31 odd, 33–78	Problems 1–5 Exs. 7–31 odd, 33–58, 66–78
	2	Problems 4–5 Exs. 17–35, 40, 48–54 even			
Review	1	Chapter 14 Review	Chapter 14 Review	Chapter 14 Review	**Day 6** Chapter 14 Review Chapter 14 Test
Assess	1	Chapter 14 Test	Chapter 14 Test	Chapter 14 Test	
Total		**14 Days**	**12 Days**	**11 Days**	**6 Days**

Note: Pacing does not include Concept Bytes and other feature pages.

Resources

	For the Chapter	14-1	14-2	14-3	14-4	14-5	14-6	14-7
Planning								
Teacher Center Online Planner & Grade Book	I	I	I	I	I	I	I	I
Interactive Learning & Guided Instruction								
My Math Video	I							
Solve It!		I M	I M	I M	I M	I M	I M	I M
Student Companion		P M	P M	P M	P M	P M	P M	
Vocabulary Support		I P M	I P M	I P M	I P M	I P M	I P M	I P M
Got It? Support		I P	I P	I P	I P	I P	I P	I P
Dynamic Activity		I					I	
Online Problems		I		I	I	I	I	I
Additional Problems		M	M	M	M	M	M	M
English Language Learner Support (TR)		E P M	E P M	E P M	E P M	E P M	E P M	E P M
Activities, Games, and Puzzles		E M	E M	E M	E M	E M	E M	E M
Teaching With TI Technology With CD-ROM								
TI-Nspire™ Support CD-ROM		✓	✓	✓	✓	✓	✓	✓
Lesson Check & Practice								
Student Companion		P M	P M	P M	P M	P M	P M	P M
Lesson Check Support		I P	I P	I P	I P	I P	I P	I P
Practice and Problem Solving Workbook		P	P	P	P	P	P	P
Think About a Plan (TR)		E P M	E P M	E P M	E P M	E P M	E P M	E P M
Practice Form G (TR)		E P M	E P M	E P M	E P M	E P M	E P M	E P M
Standardized Test Prep (TR)		P M	P M	P M	P M	P M	P M	P M
Practice *Form K* (TR)		E P M	E P M	E P M	E P M	E P M	E P M	E P M
Extra Practice	E M							
Find the Errors!	M							
Enrichment (TR)		E P M	E P M	E P M	E P M	E P M	E P M	E P M
Answers and Solutions CD-ROM	✓	✓	✓	✓	✓	✓	✓	✓
Assess & Remediate								
ExamView CD-ROM	✓	✓	✓	✓	✓	✓	✓	✓
Lesson Quiz		I M	I M	I M	I M	I M	I M	I M
Quizzes and Tests *Form G* (TR)	E P M			E P M				E P M
Quizzes and Tests *Form K* (TR)	E P M			E P M				E P M
Reteaching (TR)		E P M	E P M	E P M	E P M	E P M	E P M	E P M
Performance Tasks (TR)	P M							
Cumulative Review (TR)	P M							
Progress Monitoring Assessments	I P M							

(TR) Available in All-In-One Teaching Resources

1 Interactive Learning

Solve It!

PURPOSE To use trigonometric functions to determine where holes in a function might occur
PROCESS Students may use trigonometric functions as possible denominators or experiment with a graphing calculator.

> **FACILITATE**
>
> **Q** What function describes these graphs if there were no holes? **[*y* = cos *θ*]**
>
> **Q** What would cause a hole in the graph of a function? **[an *x*-value for which the function is undefined]**
>
> **Q** Why would the function $y = \frac{1}{\sec \theta}$ have the same graph as $y = \cos \theta$, except for some holes? Where would these holes occur? **[Since cos *θ* and sec *θ* are reciprocals, $\cos \theta = \frac{1}{\sec \theta}$, except when sec *θ* is undefined; holes occur whenever cos *θ* = 0.]**
>
> **Q** The second graph shows holes at multiples of *π*. Which trigonometric function is zero where these holes occur? **[*y* = sin *x*]**

ANSWER See Solve It in Answers on next page.
CONNECT THE MATH Students use values for trigonometric functions to determine possible functions for graphs in the Solve It. In this lesson, students write trigonometric expressions in equivalent forms and find values of the variable for which all expressions are defined.

2 Guided Instruction

Take Note

The basic identities can be transformed to related identities. For example, multiplying both sides of $\csc \theta = \frac{1}{\sin \theta}$ by sin *θ* yields csc *θ* sin *θ* = 1.

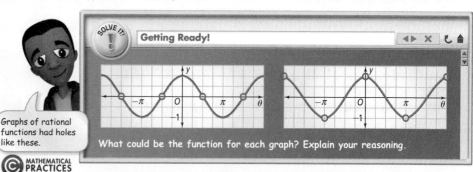

© Content Standard
F.TF.8 Prove the Pythagorean identity $\sin^2(x) + \cos^2(x) = 1$ and use it to find sin(x), cos(x), or tan(x), given sin(x), cos(x), or tan(x), and the quadrant of the angle.

Objective To verify trigonometric identities

Graphs of rational functions had holes like these.

© MATHEMATICAL PRACTICES

Dynamic Activity Trigonometric Identities

Lesson Vocabulary
• trigonometric identity

You may recognize $x^2 = 5x - 6$ as an equation that you are to solve to find the few, if any, values of *x* that make the equation true. On the other hand, you may recognize $\frac{x^5}{x^3} = x^2$, as an *identity*, an equation that is true for all values of *x* for which the expressions in the equation are defined. (Here, $\frac{x^5}{x^3}$ is not defined for *x* = 0.)

A **trigonometric identity** in one variable is a trigonometric equation that is true for all values of the variable for which all expressions in the equation are defined.

Essential Understanding The interrelationships among the six basic trigonometric functions make it possible to write trigonometric expressions in various equivalent forms, some of which can be significantly easier to work with than others in mathematical applications.

Some trigonometric identities are definitions or follow immediately from definitions.

Key Concept	**Basic Identities**		
Reciprocal Identities	$\csc \theta = \frac{1}{\sin \theta}$	$\sec \theta = \frac{1}{\cos \theta}$	$\tan \theta = \frac{1}{\cot \theta}$
	$\sin \theta = \frac{1}{\csc \theta}$	$\cos \theta = \frac{1}{\sec \theta}$	$\cot \theta = \frac{1}{\tan \theta}$
Tangent Identity	$\tan \theta = \frac{\sin \theta}{\cos \theta}$	**Cotangent Identity**	$\cot \theta = \frac{\cos \theta}{\sin \theta}$

The *domain of validity* of an identity is the set of values of the variable for which all expressions in the equation are defined.

14-1 Preparing to Teach

BIG idea Equivalence
ESSENTIAL UNDERSTANDINGS

• The interrelationships among the six basic trigonometric functions make it possible to write trigonometric expressions in various equivalent forms, some of which can be significantly easier to work with than others, in mathematical applications.
• Known identities can be used to verify other identities.
• Trigonometric identities can be used to simplify trigonometric expressions.

Math Background

Unlike the Additive Identity Property and the Multiplicative Identity Property, which are true for all real numbers, the trigonometric identities are true only for the values for which the functions are defined. These values are called the domain of validity.

A trigonometric identity is formed by two equivalent expressions set equal to each other.

• The **basic identities** include the reciprocal, tangent, and cotangent identities. They follow from the definitions of the trigonometric functions.
• The **Pythagorean identities** are derived from the Pythagorean Theorem and the unit circle.

These identities can be used to derive other trigonometric identities. Different equivalent identities make it easier to simplify when working with trigonometric equations.

It is important that students learn the basic identities and at least one Pythagorean identity and use them to derive other identities as needed, rather than try to memorize a number of identities.

© Mathematical Practices
Construct viable arguments and critique the reasoning of others. Using their knowledge of the Pythagorean Theorem, students will construct the Pythagorean identities for trigonometric functions.

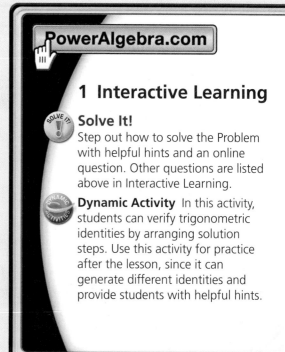

PowerAlgebra.com

1 Interactive Learning

Solve It!
Step out how to solve the Problem with helpful hints and an online question. Other questions are listed above in Interactive Learning.

Dynamic Activity In this activity, students can verify trigonometric identities by arranging solution steps. Use this activity for practice after the lesson, since it can generate different identities and provide students with helpful hints.

Plan

How can an expression be undefined?
An expression could contain a denominator that could be zero or it could contain an expression that is itself undefined for some values.

© **Problem 1** Finding the Domain of Validity

What is the domain of validity of each trigonometric identity?

A $\cos \theta = \frac{1}{\sec \theta}$.

The domain of $\cos \theta$ is all real numbers. The domain of $\frac{1}{\sec \theta}$ excludes all zeros of $\sec \theta$ (of which there are none) and all values θ for which $\sec \theta$ is undefined (odd multiples of $\frac{\pi}{2}$).

Therefore the domain of validity of $\cos \theta = \frac{1}{\sec \theta}$ is the set of real numbers except for the odd multiples of $\frac{\pi}{2}$.

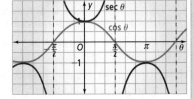

B $\sec \theta = \frac{1}{\cos \theta}$.

The domain of validity is the same as part (a), because $\sec \theta$ is not defined for odd multiples of $\frac{\pi}{2}$, and the odd multiples of $\frac{\pi}{2}$ are the zeros of $\cos \theta$.

✔ **Got It?** **1.** What is the domain of validity of the trigonometric identity $\sin \theta = \frac{1}{\csc \theta}$?

You can use known identities to verify other identities. To verify an identity, you can use previously known identities to transform one side of the equation to look like the other side.

© **Problem 2** Verifying an Identity Using Basic Identities

Plan

What identity do you know that you can use?
Look for a way to write the expression on the left in terms of $\sin \theta$ and $\cos \theta$. The identity $\sec \theta = \frac{1}{\cos \theta}$ does the job.

Verify the identity. What is the domain of validity?

A $(\sin \theta)(\sec \theta) = \tan \theta$

$(\sin \theta)(\sec \theta) = \sin \theta \cdot \frac{1}{\cos \theta}$ Reciprocal Identity

$\qquad\qquad = \frac{\sin \theta}{\cos \theta}$ Simplify.

$\qquad\qquad = \tan \theta$ Tangent Identity

The domain of $\sin \theta$ is all real numbers. The domains of $\sec \theta$ and $\tan \theta$ exclude all zeros of $\cos \theta$. These are the odd multiples of $\frac{\pi}{2}$. The domain of validity is the set of real numbers except for the odd multiples of $\frac{\pi}{2}$.

B $\frac{1}{\cot \theta} = \tan \theta$

$\frac{1}{\cot \theta} = \frac{1}{\frac{1}{\tan \theta}}$ Definition of cotangent

$\qquad = \tan \theta$ Simplify.

The domain of $\cot \theta$ excludes multiples of π. Also, $\cot \theta = 0$ at the odd multiples of $\frac{\pi}{2}$. The domain of validity is the set of real numbers except *all* multiples of $\frac{\pi}{2}$.

✔ **Got It?** **2.** Verify the identity $\frac{\csc \theta}{\sec \theta} = \cot \theta$. What is the domain of validity?

2 Guided Instruction

© Each Problem is worked out and supported online.

Problem 1
Finding the Domain of Validity

Problem 2
Verifying an Identity Using Basic Identities

Problem 3
Verifying a Pythagorean Identity
Animated

Problem 4
Verifying an Identity
Animated

Problem 5
Simplifying an Expression
Animated

Support in Algebra 2 Companion
• Vocabulary
• Key Concepts
• Got It?

Problem 1

Q In 1A, for which values of θ between 0 and 4π is $\sec \theta$ undefined? $\left[\frac{\pi}{2}, \frac{3\pi}{2}, \frac{5\pi}{2}, \frac{7\pi}{2}\right]$

Q In 1B, for which values of θ is $\frac{1}{\cos \theta}$ undefined? Explain. **[It is undefined when $\cos \theta$ is 0 or undefined. The domain of $\cos \theta$ is all real numbers, so this expression is only undefined at odd multiples of $\frac{\pi}{2}$ where $\cos \theta = 0$.]**

Got It?

Q When is $\csc \theta = 0$? When is $\csc \theta$ undefined? Explain. **[$\csc \theta$ is never equal to 0. It is undefined at 0, $\pm\pi$, $\pm 2\pi$, . . . or all integral multiples of π.]**

Problem 2

Point out to students that they are not "proving" an identity; they are only verifying that one side of the equation is equal to the other side.

Q Why do the domains of $\sec \theta$ and $\tan \theta$ exclude values when $\cos \theta = 0$? **[Both $\sec \theta$ and $\tan \theta$ are equivalent to expressions with $\cos \theta$ in the denominator. The denominator must not be 0, so these values must be excluded from the domain.]**

Got It?   VISUAL LEARNERS

Suggest students make a chart to remember when trigonometric functions equal 0 or are undefined in the interval from 0 to 2π. For example,

	0	Undefined
sine	$0, \pi$	never
cosine	$\frac{\pi}{2}, \frac{3\pi}{2}$	never
tangent	$0, \pi$	$\frac{\pi}{2}, \frac{3\pi}{2}$

Answers

Solve It!

Answers may vary. Sample: $y = \frac{\cos^2 \theta}{\cos \theta}$: since the graph is the same as that of cosine, except for having holes at all the zeros, and since rational functions have holes at those values of x that are zeros common to both the numerator and denominator, this is a reasonable guess. $y = \frac{\sin \theta \cos \theta}{\sin \theta}$: again, there are holes in the graph, this time at multiples of π. Since $\frac{\sin \theta \cos \theta}{\sin \theta} = \frac{\sin \theta}{\sin \theta} \cdot \cos \theta$, and $\frac{\sin \theta}{\sin \theta} = 1$ except at multiples of π, where $\frac{\sin \theta}{\sin \theta}$ is undefined, the function $y = \frac{\sin \theta \cos \theta}{\sin \theta}$ is a reasonable guess.

Got It?

1. all real numbers except multiples of π

2. $\frac{\csc \theta}{\sec \theta} = \frac{\left(\frac{1}{\sin \theta}\right)}{\left(\frac{1}{\cos \theta}\right)} = \frac{\cos \theta}{\sin \theta} = \cot \theta$; all real numbers except multiples of $\frac{\pi}{2}$

Problem 3

Remind students that it is often helpful to rewrite everything in terms of sine and cosine. Have them rewrite the problem using common denominators to help determine how the identity can be verified.

> **Q** What are tan θ and sec θ in terms of sine and cosine? **[tan $\theta = \frac{\sin \theta}{\cos \theta}$ and sec $\theta = \frac{1}{\cos \theta}$]**
>
> **Q** How can the identity be rewritten using only sine and cosine? **[$1 + \frac{\sin^2 \theta}{\cos^2 \theta} = \frac{1}{\cos^2 \theta}$.]**

Got It?

> **Q** How can the identity in 3a be rewritten using only sine and cosine? **[$1 + \frac{\cos^2 \theta}{\sin^2 \theta} = \frac{1}{\sin^2 \theta}$]**

Take Note

Show students how to get from the first Pythagorean identity to the second by dividing $\cos^2 \theta + \sin^2 \theta = 1$ by $\cos^2 \theta$:

$$\frac{\cos^2 \theta}{\cos^2 \theta} + \frac{\sin^2 \theta}{\cos^2 \theta} = \frac{1}{\cos^2 \theta}$$
$$1 + \tan^2 \theta = \sec^2 \theta$$

Have students find the third Pythagorean identity by dividing the same equation by $\sin^2 \theta$.

EXTENSION

Terms can be moved from one side to another to put identities in a form that is useful. For example,

$$\cos^2 \theta = 1 - \sin^2 \theta$$
$$\sin^2 \theta = 1 - \cos^2 \theta$$

EXTENSION

> **Q** How can you represent 1 using only tangent and secant? Explain. **[Sample: Subtract tan$^2 \theta$ from both sides of $1 + \tan^2 \theta = \sec^2 \theta$ to get $1 = \sec^2 \theta - \tan^2 \theta$.]**

You can use the unit circle and the Pythagorean Theorem to verify another identity. The circle with its center at the origin with a radius of 1 is called the unit circle, and has an equation $x^2 + y^2 = 1$.

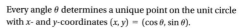

Every angle θ determines a unique point on the unit circle with x- and y-coordinates $(x, y) = (\cos \theta, \sin \theta)$.

Therefore, for every angle θ,

$$(\cos \theta)^2 + (\sin \theta)^2 = 1 \quad \text{or} \quad \cos^2 \theta + \sin^2 \theta = 1.$$

> This form allows you to write the identity without using parentheses.

This is a Pythagorean identity. You will verify two others in Problem 3.

You can use the basic and Pythagorean identities to verify other identities. To prove identities, transform the expression on one side of the equation to the expression on the other side. It often helps to write everything in terms of sines and cosines.

 Problem 3 Verifying a Pythagorean Identity

Verify the Pythagorean identity $1 + \tan^2 \theta = \sec^2 \theta$.

$$1 + \tan^2 \theta = 1 + \left(\frac{\sin \theta}{\cos \theta}\right)^2 \quad \text{Tangent Identity}$$

$$= 1 + \frac{\sin^2 \theta}{\cos^2 \theta} \quad \text{Simplify.}$$

$$= \frac{\cos^2 \theta}{\cos^2 \theta} + \frac{\sin^2 \theta}{\cos^2 \theta} \quad \text{Find a common denominator.}$$

$$= \frac{\cos^2 \theta + \sin^2 \theta}{\cos^2 \theta} \quad \text{Add.}$$

$$= \frac{1}{\cos^2 \theta} \quad \text{Pythagorean identity}$$

$$= \sec^2 \theta \quad \text{Reciprocal identity}$$

You have transformed the expression on the left side of the equation to become the expression on the right side. The equation is an identity.

Plan

With which side should you work?
It usually is easier to begin with the more complicated-looking side.

Got It? 3. a. Verify the third Pythagorean identity, $1 + \cot^2 \theta = \csc^2 \theta$.
 b. Reasoning Explain why the domain of validity is not the same for all three Pythagorean identities.

You have now seen all three Pythagorean identities.

> **take note**
>
> **Key Concept Pythagorean Identities**
>
> $$\cos^2 \theta + \sin^2 \theta = 1 \qquad 1 + \tan^2 \theta = \sec^2 \theta \qquad 1 + \cot^2 \theta = \csc^2 \theta$$

Additional Problems

1. What is the domain of validity of each trigonometric identity?

 a. $\tan \theta = \frac{1}{\cot \theta}$

 b. $\cot \theta = \frac{1}{\tan \theta}$

 ANSWERS
 a. all real numbers except multiples of $\frac{\pi}{2}$
 b. all real numbers except multiples of $\frac{\pi}{2}$

2. Verify the identity. What is the domain of validity?

 a. $(\sin \theta)(\cot \theta) = \cos \theta$

 b. $(\sec \theta)(\cot \theta) = \csc \theta$

 ANSWERS
 a. $(\sin \theta)(\cot \theta)$

 $= (\sin \theta)\left(\frac{\cos \theta}{\sin \theta}\right)$

 $= \cancel{\sin \theta} \cdot \frac{\cos \theta}{\cancel{\sin \theta}}$

 $= \cos \theta$

all real numbers except multiples of π

 b. $(\sec \theta)(\cot \theta)$

 $= \left(\frac{1}{\cos \theta}\right)\left(\frac{\cos \theta}{\sin \theta}\right)$

 $= \left(\frac{1}{\cancel{\cos \theta}}\right)\left(\frac{\cancel{\cos \theta}}{\sin \theta}\right)$

 $= \frac{1}{\sin \theta}$

 $= \csc \theta$

all real numbers except the multiples of $\frac{\pi}{2}$

3. Verify the identity
 $\frac{1 - \cos^2 \theta}{\sin \theta} = \sin \theta$.

 ANSWER

 $\frac{1 - \cos^2 \theta}{\sin \theta} = \frac{\sin^2 \theta}{\sin \theta}$

 $= \sin \theta$

4. Verify the identity
 $(\sin^2 \theta)(\sec \theta) + \cos \theta = \sec \theta$.

 ANSWER

 $(\sin^2 \theta)(\sec \theta) + \cos \theta$

 $= (\sin^2 \theta)\left(\frac{1}{\cos \theta}\right) + \cos \theta$

 $= \frac{\sin^2 \theta}{\cos \theta} + \cos \theta$

 $= \frac{\sin^2 \theta}{\cos \theta} + \frac{\cos^2 \theta}{\cos \theta}$

 $= \frac{\sin^2 \theta + \cos^2 \theta}{\cos \theta}$

 $= \frac{1}{\cos \theta}$

 $= \sec \theta$

5. What is a simplified trigonometric expression for
 $\frac{1 + \cot^2 \theta}{\cot^2 \theta}$?

 ANSWER $\sec^2 \theta$

Answers

Got It? (continued)

3. a. $1 + \cot^2 \theta$

 $= 1 + \left(\frac{\cos \theta}{\sin \theta}\right)^2$

 $= 1 + \frac{\cos^2 \theta}{\sin^2 \theta}$

 $= 1 + \frac{1 - \sin^2 \theta}{\sin^2 \theta}$

 $= 1 + \frac{1}{\sin^2 \theta} - \frac{\sin^2 \theta}{\sin^2 \theta}$

 $= 1 + \csc^2 \theta - 1$

 $= \csc^2 \theta$

 b. No; the domains of $\sin \theta$ and $\cos \theta$ are all real numbers, but the domains of $\tan \theta$, $\cot \theta$, $\sec \theta$, and $\csc \theta$ have restrictions.

There are many trigonometric identities. Most do not have specific names.

ⓒ Problem 4 Verifying an Identity

Plan

How do you begin when both sides look complicated?
It often is easier to collapse a difference (or sum) into a product than to expand a product into a difference.

Verify the identity $\tan^2\theta - \sin^2\theta = \tan^2\theta\sin^2\theta$.

$$\tan^2\theta - \sin^2\theta = \frac{\sin^2\theta}{\cos^2\theta} - \sin^2\theta \qquad \text{Tangent identity}$$

$$= \frac{\sin^2\theta}{\cos^2\theta} - \frac{\sin^2\theta\cos^2\theta}{\cos^2\theta} \qquad \text{Use a common denominator.}$$

$$= \frac{\sin^2\theta - \sin^2\theta\cos^2\theta}{\cos^2\theta} \qquad \text{Simplify.}$$

$$= \frac{\sin^2\theta(1 - \cos^2\theta)}{\cos^2\theta} \qquad \text{Factor.}$$

$$= \frac{\sin^2\theta(\sin^2\theta)}{\cos^2\theta} \qquad \text{Pythagorean identity}$$

$$= \frac{\sin^2\theta}{\cos^2\theta}\sin^2\theta \qquad \text{Rewrite the fraction.}$$

$$= \tan^2\theta\sin^2\theta \qquad \text{Tangent Identity}$$

✓ **Got It? 4.** Verify the identity $\sec^2\theta - \sec^2\theta\cos^2\theta = \tan^2\theta$.

You can use trigonometric identities to simplify trigonometric expressions.

ⓒ Problem 5 Simplifying an Expression

What is a simplified trigonometric expression for $\csc\theta\tan\theta$?

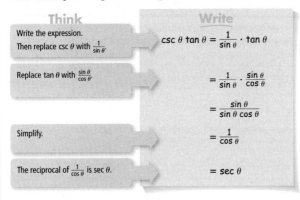

Think

Write the expression. Then replace $\csc\theta$ with $\frac{1}{\sin\theta}$.

Replace $\tan\theta$ with $\frac{\sin\theta}{\cos\theta}$.

Simplify.

The reciprocal of $\frac{1}{\cos\theta}$ is $\sec\theta$.

Write

$$\csc\theta\tan\theta = \frac{1}{\sin\theta}\cdot\tan\theta$$

$$= \frac{1}{\sin\theta}\cdot\frac{\sin\theta}{\cos\theta}$$

$$= \frac{\sin\theta}{\sin\theta\cos\theta}$$

$$= \frac{1}{\cos\theta}$$

$$= \sec\theta$$

✓ **Got It? 5.** What is a simplified trigonometric expression for $\sec\theta\cot\theta$?

Problem 4

It is not uncommon to get stuck when trying to verify an identity. Tell students they may make changes to both sides of the equation to help them determine a plan. However, the verification must show the transformation of one side only.

Q What might be the first step if you transform the right side? Explain. **[Writing $\tan^2\theta\sin^2\theta$ in terms of sine and cosine yields $\left(\frac{\sin^2\theta}{\cos^2\theta}\right)(\sin^2\theta)$.]**

Q Which Pythagorean identity was used to transform the left side? Explain. **[$\cos^2\theta + \sin^2\theta = 1$ since $\sin^2\theta = 1 - \cos^2\theta$.]**

Got It?

Q How can $\sec^2\theta\cos^2\theta$ be written in terms of sine and cosine? **[$\frac{1}{\cos^2\theta}(\cos^2\theta)$]**

Problem 5

Q How is simplifying an expression different from verifying an identity? **[When verifying an identity, you must transform an expression into a specified equivalent form. When simplifying an expression, you must transform it into a simpler (but unspecified) equivalent form.]**

Q Why is $\csc\theta$ replaced with $\frac{1}{\sin\theta}$? **[Since $\tan\theta$ includes $\sin\theta$ in the numerator, the expression can be simplified.]**

Got It?   ERROR PREVENTION

Simplifying an expression means each subsequent expression is equivalent to the previous one. Have students use their graphing calculator and graph each expression as a function. Each expression should result in the same graph.

---

4. $\sec^2\theta - \sec^2\theta\cos^2\theta$

$= \left(\frac{1}{\cos\theta}\right)^2 - \left(\frac{1}{\cos\theta}\right)^2\cos^2\theta$

$= \frac{1}{\cos^2\theta} - \frac{1}{\cos^2\theta}\cdot\cos^2\theta$

$= \frac{1}{\cos^2\theta} - \frac{\cos^2\theta}{\cos^2\theta}$

$= \frac{1 - \cos^2\theta}{\cos^2\theta}$

$= \frac{\sin^2\theta}{\cos^2\theta}$

$= \tan^2\theta$

5. $\csc\theta$

Lesson Check

1. $\tan\theta\csc\theta$

$= \frac{\sin\theta}{\cos\theta}\cdot\frac{1}{\sin\theta}$

$= \frac{1}{\cos\theta}$

$= \sec\theta$

2. $\csc^2\theta - \cot^2\theta$

$= \left(\frac{1}{\sin\theta}\right)^2 - \left(\frac{\cos\theta}{\sin\theta}\right)^2$

$= \frac{1}{\sin^2\theta} - \frac{\cos^2\theta}{\sin^2\theta}$

$= \frac{1 - \cos^2\theta}{\sin^2\theta}$

$= \frac{\sin^2\theta}{\sin^2\theta} = 1$

3. $\sin\theta\tan\theta$

$= \sin\theta\cdot\frac{\sin\theta}{\cos\theta}$

$= \frac{\sin^2\theta}{\cos\theta}$

$= \frac{1 - \cos^2\theta}{\cos\theta}$

$= \frac{1}{\cos\theta} - \frac{\cos^2\theta}{\cos\theta}$

$= \sec\theta - \cos\theta$

4. $\tan\theta\cot\theta - \sin^2\theta$

$= \tan\theta\frac{1}{\tan\theta} - \sin^2\theta$

$= \frac{\tan\theta}{\tan\theta} - \sin^2\theta$

$= 1 - \sin^2\theta = \cos^2\theta$

5. Answers may vary. Sample: Letting a and b be the legs, and

c the hypotenuse of a right triangle, the Pythagorean Theorem states that $a^2 + b^2 = c^2$. Dividing both sides by c^2, then $\frac{a^2}{c^2} + \frac{b^2}{c^2} = \left(\frac{a}{c}\right)^2 + \left(\frac{b}{c}\right)^2 = 1$. Denoting the angle between a and c as θ, then $\sin\theta = \frac{b}{c}$ and $\cos\theta = \frac{a}{c}$. By substitution, $\cos^2\theta + \sin^2\theta = 1$.

6. wrong calculation: $2 - \cos^2\theta = 2 - (1 - \sin^2\theta) = 2 - 1 + \sin^2\theta = 1 + \sin^2\theta$

Practice and Problem-Solving Exercises

7. $\cos\theta\cot\theta$

$= \cos\theta\left(\frac{\cos\theta}{\sin\theta}\right)$

$= \frac{1 - \sin^2\theta}{\sin\theta}$

$= \frac{1}{\sin\theta} - \sin\theta$; all real numbers except multiples of π

8. $\sin\theta\cot\theta$

$= \sin\theta\left(\frac{\cos\theta}{\sin\theta}\right) = \cos\theta$; all real numbers except multiples of π

3 Lesson Check

Do you know HOW? ERROR INTERVENTION

- For Exercises 1–3, encourage students to substitute values for θ after each transformation of an expression. This will help them determine whether their transformation is equivalent to the previous expression.
- If students have difficulty solving Exercise 2, have them review Problem 3. Suggest they start with the more complicated side and rewrite it in terms of sine and cosine. Next, they may choose to use a common denominator to simplify.

Do you UNDERSTAND?

- If students have trouble finding the error in Exercise 6, tell them to rewrite the expression $2 - \cos^2 \theta$ as $1 + 1 - \cos^2 \theta$.

Close

> **Q** Why must you find the domain of $\sin \theta$ when finding the domain of validity for $\sin \theta = \frac{1}{\csc \theta}$?
> **[When finding the domain of validity, you must see where all expressions are defined, not just an expression with a function in the denominator.]**
>
> **Q** How can you simplify $\sin \theta \csc \theta$? Explain.
> **[Rewriting $\csc \theta$ using the reciprocal identity, you have $(\sin \theta)\left(\frac{1}{\sin \theta}\right)$, which is equal to 1, if $\sin \theta \neq 0$.]**

 Lesson Check

Do you know HOW?

Verify each identity.

1. $\tan \theta \csc \theta = \sec \theta$

2. $\csc^2 \theta - \cot^2 \theta = 1$

3. $\sin \theta \tan \theta = \sec \theta - \cos \theta$

4. Simplify $\tan \theta \cot \theta - \sin^2 \theta$.

Do you UNDERSTAND? MATHEMATICAL PRACTICES

5. **Vocabulary** How does the identity $\cos^2 \theta + \sin^2 \theta = 1$ relate to the Pythagorean Theorem?

6. **Error Analysis** A student simplified the expression $2 - \cos^2 \theta$ to $1 - \sin^2 \theta$. What error did the student make? What is the correct simplified expression?

 Practice and Problem-Solving Exercises MATHEMATICAL PRACTICES

A Practice   Verify each identity. Give the domain of validity for each identity.   ◀ See Problems 1–4.

7. $\cos \theta \cot \theta = \frac{1}{\sin \theta} - \sin \theta$ 8. $\sin \theta \cot \theta = \cos \theta$ 9. $\cos \theta \tan \theta = \sin \theta$

10. $\sin \theta \sec \theta = \tan \theta$ 11. $\cos \theta \sec \theta = 1$ 12. $\tan \theta \cot \theta = 1$

13. $\sin \theta \csc \theta = 1$ 14. $\cot \theta = \csc \theta \cos \theta$ 15. $\csc \theta - \sin \theta = \cot \theta \cos \theta$

Simplify each trigonometric expression.   ◀ See Problem 5.

16. $\tan \theta \cot \theta$ 17. $1 - \cos^2 \theta$ 18. $\sec^2 \theta - 1$

19. $1 - \csc^2 \theta$ 20. $\sec^2 \theta \cot^2 \theta$ 21. $\cos \theta \tan \theta$

22. $\sin \theta \cot \theta$ 23. $\sin \theta \csc \theta$ 24. $\sec \theta \cos \theta \sin \theta$

25. $\sin \theta \sec \theta \cot \theta$ 26. $\sec^2 \theta - \tan^2 \theta$ 27. $\frac{\sin \theta}{\cos \theta \tan \theta}$

B Apply   28. **Think About a Plan** Simplify the expression $\frac{\tan \theta}{\sec \theta - \cos \theta}$.
   - Can you write everything in terms of $\sin \theta$, $\cos \theta$, or both?
   - Are there any trigonometric identities that can help you simplify the expression?

Simplify each trigonometric expression.

29. $\cos \theta + \sin \theta \tan \theta$ 30. $\csc \theta \cos \theta \tan \theta$

31. $\tan \theta(\cot \theta + \tan \theta)$ 32. $\sin^2 \theta + \cos^2 \theta + \tan^2 \theta$

33. $\sin \theta(1 + \cot^2 \theta)$ 34. $\sin^2 \theta \csc \theta \sec \theta$

35. $\sec \theta \cos \theta - \cos^2 \theta$ 36. $\csc \theta - \cos \theta \cot \theta$

37. $\csc^2 \theta(1 - \cos^2 \theta)$ 38. $\frac{\csc \theta}{\sin \theta + \cos \theta \cot \theta}$

39. $\frac{\cos \theta \csc \theta}{\cot \theta}$ 40. $\frac{\sin^2 \theta \csc \theta \sec \theta}{\tan \theta}$

---

3 Lesson Check

For a digital lesson check, use the Got It questions.

Support in Algebra 2 Companion
- Lesson Check

4 Practice

Assign homework to individual students or to an entire class.

Answers

1–8. See page 907.

9. $\cos \theta \tan \theta$

$= \cos \theta\left(\frac{\sin \theta}{\cos \theta}\right) = \sin \theta$; all real numbers except odd multiples of $\frac{\pi}{2}$

10. $\sin \theta \sec \theta$

$= \sin \theta\left(\frac{1}{\cos \theta}\right) = \frac{\sin \theta}{\cos \theta} = \tan \theta$; all real numbers except odd multiples of $\frac{\pi}{2}$

11. $\cos \theta \sec \theta$

$= \cos \theta\left(\frac{1}{\cos \theta}\right) = 1$; all real numbers except odd multiples of $\frac{\pi}{2}$

12. $\tan \theta \cot \theta$

$= \left(\frac{\sin \theta}{\cos \theta}\right)\left(\frac{\cos \theta}{\sin \theta}\right) = 1$; all real numbers except multiples of $\frac{\pi}{2}$

13. $\sin \theta \csc \theta$

$= \sin \theta\left(\frac{1}{\sin \theta}\right) = \frac{\sin \theta}{\sin \theta} = 1$; all real numbers except multiples of π

14. $\cot \theta = \frac{\cos \theta}{\sin \theta}$

$= \left(\frac{1}{\sin \theta}\right)\cos \theta = \csc \theta \cos \theta$; all real numbers except multiples of π

15. $\csc \theta - \sin \theta$

$= \frac{1}{\sin \theta} - \sin \theta$

$= \frac{1 - \sin^2 \theta}{\sin \theta} = \frac{\cos^2 \theta}{\sin \theta}$

$= \cot \theta \cos \theta$; all real numbers except odd multiples of $\frac{\pi}{2}$

16. 1   **17.** $\sin^2 \theta$ **18.** $\tan^2 \theta$

19. $-\cot^2 \theta$ **20.** $\csc^2 \theta$ **21.** $\sin \theta$

22. $\cos \theta$ **23.** 1   **24.** $\sin \theta$

25. 1   **26.** 1   **27.** 1

28. $\csc \theta$ **29.** $\sec \theta$ **30.** 1

31. $\sec^2 \theta$ **32.** $\sec^2 \theta$ **33.** $\csc \theta$

34. $\tan \theta$ **35.** $\sin^2 \theta$ **36.** $\sin \theta$

37. 1   **38.** 1   **39.** 1

40. 1

Express the first trigonometric function in terms of the second.

41. $\sin\theta, \cos\theta$

42. $\tan\theta, \cos\theta$

43. $\cot\theta, \sin\theta$

44. $\csc\theta, \cot\theta$

45. $\cot\theta, \csc\theta$

46. $\sec\theta, \tan\theta$

Verify each identity.

47. $\sin^2\theta\tan^2\theta = \tan^2\theta - \sin^2\theta$
48. $\sec\theta - \sin\theta\tan\theta = \cos\theta$
49. $\sin\theta\cos\theta(\tan\theta + \cot\theta) = 1$

50. $\dfrac{1 - \sin\theta}{\cos\theta} = \dfrac{\cos\theta}{1 + \sin\theta}$
51. $\dfrac{\sec\theta}{\cot\theta + \tan\theta} = \sin\theta$
52. $(\cot\theta + 1)^2 = \csc^2\theta + 2\cot\theta$

53. Express $\cos\theta\csc\theta\cot\theta$ in terms of $\sin\theta$.

54. Express $\dfrac{\cos\theta}{\sec\theta + \tan\theta}$ in terms of $\sin\theta$.

Use the identity $\sin^2\theta + \cos^2\theta = 1$ and the basic identities to answer the following questions. Show all your work.

55. Given that $\sin\theta = 0.5$ and θ is in the first quadrant, what are $\cos\theta$ and $\tan\theta$?

56. Given that $\sin\theta = 0.5$ and θ is in the second quadrant, what are $\cos\theta$ and $\tan\theta$?

57. Given that $\cos\theta = -0.6$ and θ is in the third quadrant, what are $\sin\theta$ and $\tan\theta$?

58. Given that $\sin\theta = 0.48$ and θ is in the second quadrant, what are $\cos\theta$ and $\tan\theta$?

59. Given that $\tan\theta = 1.2$ and θ is in the first quadrant, what are $\sin\theta$ and $\cos\theta$?

60. Given that $\tan\theta = 3.6$ and θ is in the third quadrant, what are $\sin\theta$ and $\cos\theta$?

61. Given that $\sin\theta = 0.2$ and $\tan\theta < 0$, what is $\cos\theta$?

 Challenge

62. The unit circle is a useful tool for verifying identities. Use the diagram at the right to verify the identity $\sin(\theta + \pi) = -\sin\theta$.
  a. Explain why the y-coordinate of point P is $\sin(\theta + \pi)$.
  b. Prove that the two triangles shown are congruent.
  c. Use part (b) to show that the two blue segments are congruent.
  d. Use part (c) to show that the y-coordinate of P is $-\sin\theta$.
  e. Use parts (a) and (d) to conclude that $\sin(\theta + \pi) = -\sin\theta$.

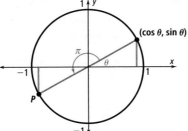

Use the diagram in Exercise 62 to verify each identity.

63. $\cos(\theta + \pi) = -\cos\theta$

64. $\tan(\theta + \pi) = \tan\theta$

Simplify each trigonometric expression.

65. $\dfrac{\cot^2\theta - \csc^2\theta}{\tan^2\theta - \sec^2\theta}$

66. $(1 - \sin\theta)(1 + \sin\theta)\csc^2\theta + 1$

---

4 Practice

ASSIGNMENT GUIDE
Basic: 7–28 all, 38–60 even
Average: 7–27 odd, 28–61
Advanced: 7–27 odd, 28–67
Standardized Test Prep: 68–73
Mixed Review: 74–84

Ⓒ **Mathematical Practices** are supported by exercises with red headings. Here are the Practices supported in this lesson:

MP 1: Make Sense of Problems Ex. 28
MP 2: Reason Abstractly Ex. 5
MP 3: Critique the Reasoning of Others Ex. 6

Applications exercises have blue headings. Exercise 67 supports MP 4: Model.

STEM exercises focus on science or engineering applications.

EXERCISE 38: Use the Think About a Plan worksheet in the **Practice and Problem Solving Workbook** (also available in the Teaching Resources in print and online) to further support students' development in becoming independent learners.

HOMEWORK QUICK CHECK
To check students' understanding of key skills and concepts, go over Exercises 7, 17, 28, 38, and 55.

---

41. $\pm\sqrt{1 - \cos^2\theta}$ **42.** $\pm\dfrac{\sqrt{1 - \cos^2\theta}}{\cos\theta}$

43. $\pm\dfrac{\sqrt{1 - \sin^2\theta}}{\sin\theta}$ **44.** $\pm\sqrt{1 + \cot^2\theta}$

45. $\pm\sqrt{\csc^2\theta - 1}$ **46.** $\pm\sqrt{1 + \tan^2\theta}$

47. $\sin^2\theta\tan^2\theta = \sin^2\theta\left(\dfrac{\sin^2\theta}{\cos^2\theta}\right)$

$= (1 - \cos^2\theta)\left(\dfrac{\sin^2\theta}{\cos^2\theta}\right)$

$= \dfrac{\sin^2\theta - \sin^2\theta\cos^2\theta}{\cos^2\theta}$

$= \dfrac{\sin^2\theta}{\cos^2\theta} - \dfrac{\sin^2\theta\cos^2\theta}{\cos^2\theta}$

$= \tan^2\theta - \sin^2\theta$

48. $\sec\theta - \sin\theta\tan\theta$

$= \dfrac{1}{\cos\theta} - \sin\theta\left(\dfrac{\sin\theta}{\cos\theta}\right)$

$= \dfrac{1}{\cos\theta} - \dfrac{\sin^2\theta}{\cos\theta} = \dfrac{1 - \sin^2\theta}{\cos\theta}$

$= \dfrac{\cos^2\theta}{\cos\theta} = \cos\theta$

49. $\sin\theta\cos\theta(\tan\theta + \cot\theta)$

$= \sin\theta\cos\theta\left(\dfrac{\sin\theta}{\cos\theta} + \dfrac{\cos\theta}{\sin\theta}\right)$

$= \dfrac{\sin^2\theta\cos\theta}{\cos\theta} + \dfrac{\cos^2\theta\sin\theta}{\sin\theta}$

$= \sin^2\theta + \cos^2\theta = 1$

50. $\dfrac{1 - \sin\theta}{\cos\theta} = \dfrac{1 - \sin\theta}{\cos\theta} \cdot \dfrac{\cos\theta}{\cos\theta}$

$= \dfrac{(1 - \sin\theta)\cos\theta}{\cos^2\theta}$

$= \dfrac{(1 - \sin\theta)\cos\theta}{1 - \sin^2\theta}$

$= \dfrac{(1 - \sin\theta)\cos\theta}{(1 - \sin\theta)(1 + \sin\theta)}$

$= \dfrac{\cos\theta}{1 + \sin\theta}$

51. $\dfrac{\sec\theta}{\cot\theta + \tan\theta}$

$= \dfrac{\dfrac{1}{\cos\theta}}{\dfrac{\cos\theta}{\sin\theta} + \dfrac{\sin\theta}{\cos\theta}} \cdot \dfrac{\sin\theta\cos\theta}{\sin\theta\cos\theta}$

$= \dfrac{\sin\theta}{\cos^2\theta + \sin^2\theta} = \dfrac{\sin\theta}{1} = \sin\theta$

52. $(\cot\theta + 1)^2 = \cot^2\theta + 2\cot\theta + 1$

$= \cot^2\theta + 1 + 2\cot\theta = \csc^2\theta + 2\cot\theta$

53. $\dfrac{1 - \sin^2\theta}{\sin^2\theta}$ **54.** $1 - \sin\theta$

55. $\sin^2\theta + \cos^2\theta = 1$

$(0.5)^2 + \cos^2\theta = 1$

$0.25 + \cos^2\theta = 1$

$\cos^2\theta = 1 - 0.25$

$\cos^2\theta = 0.75$

$\cos\theta = \pm\sqrt{0.75}$

Since θ is in the first quadrant, $\cos\theta$ is positive; $\cos\theta = 0.866025404$.

$\tan\theta = \dfrac{\sin\theta}{\cos\theta}$

$= \dfrac{0.5}{0.866025404}$

$= 0.577350269$

56–61. See next page.
62–66. See back of book.

Answers

Practice and Problem-Solving Exercises (continued)

56. $\sin^2 \theta + \cos^2 \theta = 1$

$(0.5)^2 + \cos^2 \theta = 1$

$0.25 + \cos^2 \theta = 1$

$\cos^2 \theta = 1 - 0.25$

$\cos^2 \theta = 0.75$

$\cos^2 \theta = \pm\sqrt{0.75}$

Since θ is in the second quadrant, $\cos \theta$ is positive; $\cos \theta = -0.866025404$.

$\tan \theta = \dfrac{\sin \theta}{\cos \theta}$

$= \dfrac{0.5}{-0.866025404}$

$= -0.577350269$

57. $\sin^2 \theta + \cos^2 \theta = 1$

$\sin^2 \theta + (-0.6)^2 = 1$

$\sin^2 \theta + 0.36 = 1$

$\sin^2 \theta = 1 - 0.36$

$\sin^2 \theta = 0.64$

$\sin \theta = \pm\sqrt{0.64}$

Since θ is in the third quadrant, $\sin \theta$ is negative; $\sin \theta = -0.8$.

$\tan \theta = \dfrac{\sin \theta}{\cos \theta}$

$= \dfrac{-0.8}{-0.6}$

$= 1.333333333$

58. $\sin^2 \theta + \cos^2 \theta = 1$

$\sin^2 \theta + (0.48)^2 = 1$

$\sin^2 \theta + 0.2304 = 1$

$\sin^2 \theta = 1 - 0.2304$

$\sin^2 \theta = 0.7696$

$\sin \theta = \pm\sqrt{0.7696}$

Since θ is in the second quadrant, $\cos \theta$ is negative; $\cos \theta = -0.877268488$.

$\tan \theta = \dfrac{\sin \theta}{\cos \theta}$

$= \dfrac{0.48}{-0.877268488}$

$= -0.5471529031$.

59. $\tan \theta = \dfrac{\sin \theta}{\cos \theta}$, $\sin^2 \theta + \cos^2 \theta = 1$, which can be rewritten as $\sin^2 \theta = 1 - \cos^2 \theta$

$1.2 = \dfrac{\sin \theta}{\cos \theta}$

$1.2^2 = \dfrac{\sin^2 \theta}{\cos^2 \theta}$

$1.44(\cos^2 \theta) = \sin^2 \theta$

$1.44(\cos^2 \theta) = 1 - \cos^2 \theta$

$1.44(\cos^2 \theta) + \cos^2 \theta = 1$

$2.44(\cos^2 \theta) = 1$

$\cos^2 \theta = \dfrac{1}{2.44}$

$\cos^2 \theta = 0.409836066$

$\cos \theta = \pm\sqrt{0.409836066}$

910 Chapter 14

Standardized Test Prep

SAT/ACT

68. Which expression is equivalent to $2 \cot \theta$?

Ⓐ $\dfrac{1}{2 \tan \theta}$　　Ⓑ $\dfrac{2}{\cot \theta}$　　Ⓒ $\dfrac{2 \cos \theta}{\sin \theta}$　　Ⓓ $\dfrac{\sin \theta}{\frac{1}{2}\cos \theta}$

69. Which equation is NOT an identity?

Ⓕ $\cos^2 \theta = 1 - \sin^2 \theta$　　Ⓗ $\sin^2 \theta = \cos^2 \theta - 1$

Ⓖ $\cot^2 \theta = \csc^2 \theta - 1$　　Ⓘ $\tan^2 \theta = \sec^2 \theta - 1$

70. Which expressions are equivalent?

I. $(\sin \theta)(\csc \theta - \sin \theta)$　　II. $\sin^2 \theta - 1$　　III. $\cos^2 \theta$

Ⓐ I and II only　　Ⓑ II and III only　　Ⓒ I and III only　　Ⓓ I, II, and III

71. How can you express $\csc^2 \theta - 2 \cot^2 \theta$ in terms of $\sin \theta$ and $\cos \theta$?

Ⓕ $\dfrac{1 - 2\cos^2 \theta}{\sin^2 \theta}$　　Ⓖ $\dfrac{1 - 2\sin^2 \theta}{\sin^2 \theta}$　　Ⓗ $\sin^2 \theta - 2\cos^2 \theta$　　Ⓘ $\dfrac{1}{\sin^2 \theta} - \dfrac{2}{\tan^2 \theta}$

72. Which expression is equivalent to $\dfrac{\tan \theta}{\cos \theta - \sec \theta}$?

Ⓐ $\csc \theta$　　Ⓑ $\sec \theta$　　Ⓒ $-\csc \theta$　　Ⓓ $\tan^2 \theta$

Short Response

73. Show that $(\sec \theta + 1)(\sec \theta - 1) = \tan^2 \theta$ is an identity.

Mixed Review

Graph each function in the interval from 0 to 2π.　　◀ See Lesson 13-8.

74. $y = \csc(-\theta)$　　**75.** $y = -\sec 0.5\theta$　　**76.** $y = -\sec(0.5\theta + 2)$　　**77.** $y = \pi \sec \theta$

Find the measure of an angle between 0° and 360° that is coterminal with the given angle.　　◀ See Lesson 13-2.

78. 395°　　**79.** 405°　　**80.** −225°　　**81.** −149°

Get Ready!　To prepare for Lesson 14-2, do Exercises 82–84.

For each function f, find f^{-1}.　　◀ See Lesson 6-7.

82. $f(x) = x + 1$　　**83.** $f(x) = 2x - 3$　　**84.** $f(x) = x^2 + 4$

Since θ is in the first quadrant, $\cos \theta$ is positive; $\cos \theta = 0.640184400$.

$\tan \theta = \dfrac{\sin \theta}{\cos \theta}$

$1.2 = \dfrac{\sin \theta}{0.640184400}$

$\sin \theta = 0.76822128$

60. $\tan \theta = \dfrac{\sin \theta}{\cos \theta}$, $\sin^2 \theta + \cos^2 \theta = 1$, which can be rewritten as $\sin^2 \theta = 1 - \cos^2 \theta$

$3.6 = \dfrac{\sin \theta}{\cos \theta}$

$3.6^2 = \dfrac{\sin^2 \theta}{\cos^2 \theta}$

$12.96(\cos^2 \theta) = \sin^2 \theta$

$12.96(\cos^2 \theta) = 1 - \cos^2 \theta$

$12.96(\cos^2 \theta) + \cos^2 \theta = 1$

$13.96(\cos^2 \theta) = 1$

$\cos^2 \theta = \dfrac{1}{13.96}$

$\cos^2 \theta = 0.071633238$

$\cos \theta = \pm\sqrt{0.071633238}$

Since θ is in the third quadrant, $\cos \theta$ is negative; $\cos \theta = -0.267643863$.

$\tan \theta = \dfrac{\sin \theta}{\cos \theta}$

$3.6 = \dfrac{\sin \theta}{-0.267643863}$

$\sin \theta = 0.963517810$

61. $\sin^2 \theta + \cos^2 \theta = 1$

$(0.2)^2 + \cos^2 \theta = 1$

$0.04 + \cos^2 \theta = 1$

$\cos^2 \theta = 1 - 0.04$

$\cos^2 \theta = 0.96$

$\cos \theta = \pm\sqrt{0.96}$

Since $\sin \theta$ is positive and $\tan \theta$ is negative, θ is in the fourth quadrant, so $\cos \theta$ is positive; $\cos \theta = 0.97979590$.

67–84. See back of book.

Lesson Resources

Additional Instructional Support

Algebra 2 Companion

Students can use the **Algebra 2 Companion** worktext (4 pages) as you teach the lesson. Use the Companion to support

- New Vocabulary
- Key Concepts
- Got It for each Problem
- Lesson Check

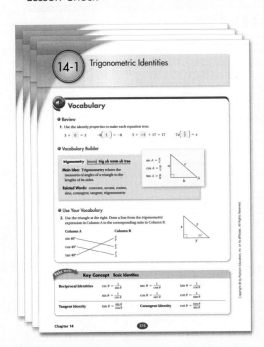

ELL Support

Focus on Communication Have students make a list of reasons used when verifying identities. Suggest that students begin with the reasons shown in each Problem. For example, the list might include Pythagorean Identity, Reciprocal Identity, tangent and cotangent identities, simplifying, common denominator, adding, subtracting, etc. Allow students to work in pairs to verify an identity. As one student writes each step, the other student can point to the reason and state it. For example,

Verify $(\cot \theta)(\tan \theta) = 1$

First student writes:

$(\cot \theta)(\tan \theta) = \dfrac{\cos \theta}{\sin \theta} \cdot \dfrac{\sin \theta}{\cos \theta}$

Second student will point and say: cotangent and tangent identities.

First student writes:

$(\cot \theta)(\tan \theta) = \dfrac{\cos \theta}{\sin \theta} \cdot \dfrac{\sin \theta}{\cos \theta} = 1$

Second student will point and say: simplifying.

5 Assess & Remediate

Lesson Quiz

1. Do you UNDERSTAND? What is the domain of validity for $\sin \theta = \dfrac{\sin^2 \theta}{\sin \theta}$?

2. Verify the identity $(1 - \cos^2 \theta)(\cot \theta) = \sin \theta \cos \theta$.

3. Verify the identity $\sin^2 \theta \cot^2 \theta = 1 - \sin^2 \theta$.

4. What is a simplified trigonometric expression for $\dfrac{1 - \cos^2 \theta}{\tan \theta}$?

ANSWERS TO LESSON QUIZ

1. the set of real numbers except for multiples of π

2. $(1 - \cos^2 \theta)(\cot \theta) = (\sin^2 \theta)\left(\dfrac{\cos \theta}{\sin \theta}\right)$
$= \sin \theta \cos \theta$

3. $\sin^2 \theta \cot^2 \theta = \sin^2 \theta \dfrac{\cos^2 \theta}{\sin^2 \theta}$
$= \cos^2 \theta$
$= 1 - \sin^2 \theta$

4. $\sin \theta \cos \theta$

PRESCRIPTION FOR REMEDIATION

Use the student work on the Lesson Quiz to prescribe a differentiated review assignment:

Points	Differentiated Remediation
0–2	Intervention
3	On-level
4	Extension

PowerAlgebra.com

5 Assess & Remediate

Assign the Lesson Quiz. Appropriate intervention, practice, or enrichment is automatically generated based on student performance.

Intervention

- **Reteaching** (2 pages) Provides reteaching and practice exercises for the key lesson concepts. Use with struggling students or absent students.

- **English Language Learner Support** Helps students develop and reinforce mathematical vocabulary and key concepts.

All-in-One Resources/Online
Reteaching

All-in-One Resources/Online
English Language Learner Support

Differentiated Remediation continued

On-Level

- **Practice** (2 pages) Provides extra practice for each lesson. For simpler practice exercises, use the Form K Practice pages found in the All-in-One Teaching Resources and online.

- **Think About a Plan** Helps students develop specific problem-solving skills and strategies by providing scaffolded guiding questions.

- **Standardized Test Prep** Focuses on all major exercises, all major question types, and helps students prepare for the high-stakes assessments.

Extension

- **Enrichment** Provides students with interesting problems and activities that extend the concepts of the lesson.

- **Activities, Games, and Puzzles** Worksheets that can be used for concepts development, enrichment, and for fun!

Practice and Problem Solving Wkbk/ All-in-One Resources/Online
Practice page 1

14-1 Practice — Form G
Trigonometric Identities

Verify each identity. Give the domain of validity for each identity. 1.–18. Verifications may vary.

1. $\sin\theta \sec\theta \cot\theta = 1$ real numbers except multiples of $\frac{\pi}{2}$
2. $\csc\theta = \cot\theta\sec\theta$ real numbers except multiples of $\frac{\pi}{2}$
3. $\frac{\sin\theta}{\csc\theta} = \sin^2\theta$ real numbers except multiples of π
4. $\cos\theta\csc\theta\tan\theta = 1$ real numbers except multiples of $\frac{\pi}{2}$
5. $\sin\theta\tan\theta + \cos\theta = \sec\theta$ real numbers except odd multiples of $\frac{\pi}{2}$
6. $\frac{\csc\theta}{\cot\theta} = \sec\theta$ real numbers except multiples of $\frac{\pi}{2}$
7. $\sec\theta = \tan\theta\csc\theta$ real numbers except multiples of $\frac{\pi}{2}$
8. $\tan\theta + \cot\theta = \sec\theta\csc\theta$ real numbers except multiples of $\frac{\pi}{2}$
9. $\tan^2\theta + 1 = \sec^2\theta$ real numbers except odd multiples of $\frac{\pi}{2}$
10. $\cos\theta\cot\theta + \sin\theta = \csc\theta$ real numbers except multiples of π
11. $\frac{\sec\theta}{\csc\theta} = \tan\theta$ real numbers except multiples of $\frac{\pi}{2}$
12. $\sec\theta\cot\theta = \csc\theta$ real numbers except multiples of $\frac{\pi}{2}$
13. $\sec^2\theta - \tan^2\theta = 1$ real numbers except odd multiples of $\frac{\pi}{2}$
14. $\sec\theta = \csc\theta\tan\theta$ real numbers except multiples of $\frac{\pi}{2}$
15. $\frac{\sin\theta + \cos\theta}{\sin\theta} = 1 + \cot\theta$ real numbers except multiples of π
16. $\cos\theta(\sec\theta - \cos\theta) = \sin^2\theta$ real numbers except odd multiples of $\frac{\pi}{2}$
17. $\cot\theta\sec\theta = \csc\theta$ real numbers except multiples of $\frac{\pi}{2}$
18. $(1 - \sin\theta)(1 + \sin\theta) = \cos^2\theta$ real numbers

Simplify each trigonometric expression.

19. $1 - \sec^2\theta$ $-\tan^2\theta$
20. $\frac{\sec\theta}{\tan\theta}$ $\csc\theta$

Practice and Problem Solving Wkbk/ All-in-One Resources/Online
Practice page 2

14-1 Practice (continued) — Form G
Trigonometric Identities

Simplify each trigonometric expression.

21. $\csc\theta\tan\theta$ $\sec\theta$
22. $\sec\theta\cos^2\theta$ $\cos\theta$
23. $\csc^2\theta - \cot^2\theta$ 1
24. $1 - \sin^2\theta$ $\cos^2\theta$
25. $\tan\theta\cot\theta$ 1
26. $\cos\theta\cot\theta + \sin\theta$ $\csc\theta$
27. $\cos\theta\tan\theta$ $\sin\theta$
28. $\frac{\sin\theta\cot\theta}{\cos\theta}$ 1
29. $\sec\theta\tan\theta\csc\theta$ $\sec^2\theta$
30. $\sec\theta\cot\theta$ $\csc\theta$
31. $\frac{\sin\theta}{\csc\theta} + \frac{\cos\theta}{\sec\theta}$ 1
32. $\frac{\tan\theta\csc\theta}{\sec\theta}$ 1
33. $\cot^2\theta - \csc^2\theta$ -1
34. $\frac{\cot\theta}{\csc\theta}$ $\cos\theta$

Express the first trigonometric function in terms of the second.

35. $\cos\theta, \sin\theta$ $\frac{1}{\sin\theta}$
36. $\cot\theta, \tan\theta$ $\frac{1}{\tan\theta}$
37. $\sec\theta, \cos\theta$ $\frac{1}{\cos\theta}$
38. $\cos\theta, \sin\theta$ $\pm\sqrt{1 - \sin^2\theta}$

39. **Writing** Which side of the equation below should you transform to verify the identity? Explain. $\frac{\cos^2\theta + \tan^2\theta - 1}{\sin^2\theta} = \tan^2\theta$ Left; it is easier to break down the left-hand side than to build up the right-hand side.

All-in-One Resources/Online
Enrichment

14-1 Enrichment
Trigonometric Identities

Reduction to a Canonical Form

When you are confronted with the problem of proving a trigonometric identity, you may ask yourself, "What substitutions should I make?" or "What basic identities should I use to prove or disprove this identity?" A good practice is to reduce both sides of the identity to a simpler, canonical form. **Canonical form** is the simplest form to which a function can be reduced.

One such form involves only terms that are expressed as powers of cosine and/or the first power of sine. Fill in the blanks below to see how each of the other four basic trigonometric functions can be expressed in this canonical form.

$\sec A = \frac{1}{\cos A}$ $\csc A = \frac{1}{\sin A}$
$\tan A = \frac{\sin A}{\cos A}$ $\cot A = \frac{\cos A}{\sin A}$

Whenever an expression contains a power of sine, it can be reduced to this canonical form by using the Pythagorean identity $\sin^2 A = 1 - \cos^2 A$.

1. Use this procedure to change $1 - 2\sin^2 A$ to canonical form. $2\cos^2 A - 1$
2. How can you express any even power of sine $(\sin^{2n} A)$ in canonical form? $(1 - \cos^2 A)^n$
3. How could you express any odd power of sine $(\sin^{2n+1} A)$ in canonical form? $(1 - \cos^2 A)^n \sin A$

Reduce each of the following trigonometric expressions to the canonical form involving powers of cosine and/or the first power of sine.

4. $\tan A + \sec A$ $\frac{\sin A + 1}{\cos A}$
5. $\cot^2 A - \sec^3 A$ $\frac{\cos^3 A + \cos^2 A - 1}{\cos^3 A - \cos^5 A}$
6. $\sec^3 A\tan^2 A$ $\frac{1 - \cos^2 A}{\cos^5 A}$
7. $\sin^2 A + \cos^3 A$ $1 - \cos^2 A + \cos^3 A$
8. $\tan A + \cot A$ $\frac{1}{\cos A\sin A}$
9. $\sin A - \cos A\cot A$ $\frac{1 - 2\cos^2 A}{\sin A}$
10. $\cot A\sin A - \sin^3 A\sec A$ $\frac{\cos^2 A - \sin A(1 - \cos^2 A)}{\cos A}$

Practice and Problem Solving Wkbk/ All-in-One Resources/Online
Think About a Plan

14-2 Think About a Plan
Solving Trigonometric Equations Using Inverses

Electricity The function $I = 40\sin 60\pi t$ models the current I in amps that an electric generator is producing after t seconds. When is the first time that the current will reach 20 amps? -20 amps?

Understanding the Problem

1. How many amps does the generator produce after t seconds? $40\sin 60\pi t$ amps

2. Write the current function using an inverse trigonometric function. $60\pi t = \sin^{-1}\left(\frac{I}{40}\right)$

3. What is the problem asking you to determine?
Answers may vary. Sample: The time when the generator first produces 20 amps and -20 amps

Planning the Solution

4. Write an equation that you can use to determine when the generator first produces 20 amps.
$60\pi t = \sin^{-1}\left(\frac{1}{2}\right)$

5. Write an equation that you can use to determine when the generator first produces -20 amps.
$60\pi t = \sin^{-1}\left(-\frac{1}{2}\right)$

Getting an Answer

6. Solve your equations to find the first time that the current will reach 20 amps and the first time that the current will reach -20 amps. $\frac{1}{360}$ s, $\frac{5}{360}$ s

---

Practice and Problem Solving Wkbk/ All-in-One Resources/Online
Standardized Test Prep

14-1 Standardized Test Prep
Trigonometric Identities

Multiple Choice

For Exercises 1–5, choose the correct letter.

1. The expression $\csc\theta\sin\theta + \cot^2\theta$ is equivalent to which of the following? C
   A. $\sin^2\theta$ B. $\cot^2\theta$ C. $\csc^2\theta$ D. $\cos^2\theta$

2. How can you express $(1 + \sin\theta)(\sec\theta - \tan\theta)$ in terms of $\cos\theta$? I
   F. $\frac{1}{\cos\theta}$ G. $\cos^2\theta$ H. $1 - \cos^2\theta$ I. $\cos\theta$

3. Which of the following expressions are equivalent? D
   I. $\frac{\cos^2\theta}{\cot^2\theta}$ II. $\sin^2\theta$ III. $1 - \cos^2\theta$
   A. I and II only C. II and III only
   B. I and III only D. I, II, and III

4. Which equation is not true? F
   F. $\tan\theta = \frac{\cos\theta}{\sin\theta}$ H. $\sin^2\theta = 1 - \cos^2\theta$
   G. $\csc\theta = \frac{1}{\sin\theta}$ I. $\csc^2\theta = \cot^2\theta + 1$

5. Which of the following is the expression $\sin\theta\cos\theta(\tan\theta + \cot\theta)$ in simplified form? B
   A. $\cos\theta$ B. 1 C. $\tan\theta$ D. $\sin^2\theta$

Short Response

6. Show that $\frac{\csc^2\theta - \cot^2\theta}{1 - \sin^2\theta} = \sec^2\theta$ is an identity.

[2] $\frac{\csc^2\theta - \cot^2\theta}{1 - \sin^2\theta} = \frac{\frac{1 - \cos^2\theta}{\sin^2\theta}}{\cos^2\theta} = \frac{\frac{\sin^2\theta}{\sin^2\theta}}{\cos^2\theta} = \frac{1}{\cos^2\theta} = \sec^2\theta$
[1] minor errors in answer
[0] incorrect answers and no work shown OR no answer given

Online Teacher Resource Center
Activities, Games, and Puzzles

14-1 Puzzle: Math Humor
Trigonometric Identities

Complete this puzzle alone or with a partner.

Question: What did the math teacher have to do so his daughter could buy a used car?

Answer: Match each trigonometric expression on the left with its simplified version on the right. Then write the correct letter to the left of each number.

Not all expressions on the right will be used, and some may be used more than once.

c 1. $1 - \cos^2\theta$ a. $\cot^2\theta$
o 2. $\sin\theta\cot\theta$ b. $\cos\theta\sin\theta$
s 3. $\sec\theta\cos\theta\sin\theta$ c. $\sin^2\theta$
i 4. $\sec^2\theta - 1$ d. 0
g 5. $\frac{\cos\theta}{\sec\theta}$ e. $\cot\theta$
n 6. $\sec\theta\cos\theta$ f. $\csc\theta\sec\theta$
  g. $\cos^2\theta$
t 7. $\frac{\cos\theta}{\cos\theta\cot\theta}$ h. $\csc\theta$
  i. $\tan^2\theta$
h 8. $\sin\theta + \cos\theta\cot\theta$ j. $\sec\theta$
e 9. $\cos\theta\sin\theta(1 + \cot^2\theta)$ k. $\sin\theta\tan\theta$
  l. $\csc^2\theta$
l 10. $\frac{\csc\theta}{\sin\theta}$ m. $\cos\theta\cot\theta$
  n. 1
o 11. $\frac{\sec\theta}{\tan^2\theta + 1}$ o. $\cos\theta$
  p. $\sec\theta\sin\theta$
a 12. $(1 - \sin^2\theta)(1 + \cot^2\theta)$ q. $\cos\theta\cot\theta$
  r. $\sec^2\theta$
n 13. $\csc^2\theta - \cot^2\theta$ s. $\sin\theta$
  t. $\tan\theta$

14-2 Solving Trigonometric Equations Using Inverses

© Content Standards
F.TF.6 Understand that restricting a trigonometric function to a domain ... allows its inverse to be constructed.
F.TF.7 Use inverse functions to solve trigonometric equations that arise in modeling contexts.

Objectives To evaluate inverse trigonometric functions
To solve trigonometric equations

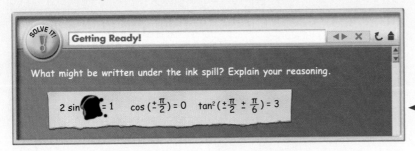

Getting Ready!

What might be written under the ink spill? Explain your reasoning.

$$2 \sin \blacksquare = 1 \qquad \cos\left(\pm\tfrac{\pi}{2}\right) = 0 \qquad \tan^2\left(\pm\tfrac{\pi}{2} \pm \tfrac{\pi}{6}\right) = 3$$

You have seen that inverse functions are useful for solving equations. To solve $x^3 = 5$, the cube root function gives $x = \sqrt[3]{5}$. To solve $x^2 = 5$, however, the square root function does not give both solutions $\sqrt{5}$ and $-\sqrt{5}$.

Because the trigonometric functions are periodic, a trigonometric equation like $\sin \theta = 0$ has infinitely many solutions. (Think of the sine graph.) Any inverse function for $\sin \theta$ must, however, give only one solution.

Essential Understanding To solve some trigonometric equations, you can use an inverse trigonometric function to find one solution. Then you can use periodicity to find all solutions.

Since a function must be single-valued, you define the inverse function for each of sine, cosine, and tangent by inverting only the representative part that has the simplest domain values.

take note

Key Concept Inverses of Three Trigonometric Functions

	Domain	Range
Function $y = \cos \theta$	$0 \le \theta \le \pi$	$-1 \le y \le 1$
Inverse Function $\theta = \cos^{-1} x$	$-1 \le x \le 1$	$0 \le \theta \le \pi$
Function $y = \sin \theta$	$-\tfrac{\pi}{2} \le \theta \le \tfrac{\pi}{2}$	$-1 \le y \le 1$
Inverse Function $\theta = \sin^{-1} x$	$-1 \le x \le 1$	$-\tfrac{\pi}{2} \le \theta \le \tfrac{\pi}{2}$
Function $y = \tan \theta$	$-\tfrac{\pi}{2} < \theta < \tfrac{\pi}{2}$	y is any real number
Inverse Function $\theta = \tan^{-1} x$	x is any real number	$-\tfrac{\pi}{2} < \theta < \tfrac{\pi}{2}$

---

1 Interactive Learning

Solve It!
PURPOSE To solve a trigonometric equation for an angle
PROCESS Students may
- divide both sides of the equation by 2 to solve for the term hidden under the ink.
- sketch a unit circle to see the quadrants in which two angles have a sine of $\tfrac{1}{2}$.

FACILITATE
Q What is the value of sin x such that 2 sin x = 1? $\left[\tfrac{1}{2}\right]$
Q What angles in Quadrants I and II have a sine of $\tfrac{1}{2}$? $\left[\tfrac{\pi}{6} \text{ and } \tfrac{5\pi}{6}\right]$
Q Do you need to use the other equations to solve for the unknown? Explain. **[No; you only need one equation to solve for one unknown.]**

ANSWER See Solve It in Answers on next page.
CONNECT THE MATH In the Solve It, students solve an equation using the inverse of the corresponding function. In this lesson, students solve trigonometric equations using inverses.

2 Guided Instruction

Take Note

Q Why does the domain of each inverse function have to be restricted? **[This is necessary for the inverse function to satisfy the definition of a function. For each element in the domain of a function, there must be exactly one element in the range.]**

14-2 Preparing to Teach

BIG idea Function
ESSENTIAL UNDERSTANDINGS
- Some trigonometric equations can be solved using an inverse trigonometric function to find one solution. Then periodicity can be used to find all solutions.
- The values of inverse trigonometric functions are measures of angles. The unit circle can be used to find the values in either radians or degrees.

Math Background
As in logarithmic equations and exponential equations, the inverse of the function can be a valuable tool in solving some trigonometric equations.

The inverses of trigonometric functions are not functions, so you define the inverse for only part of the domain, called the representative part. This allows there to be exactly one solution over the domain of the inverse. Because all trigonometric functions are periodic, you can use the periodicity to find all of the solutions to the equation.

Make sure students understand how to use the unit circle to find all possible solutions.

© Mathematical Practices
Use appropriate tools strategically.
Students will use both the unit circle and scientific calculators, when needed, in calculating the inverse trigonometric functions.

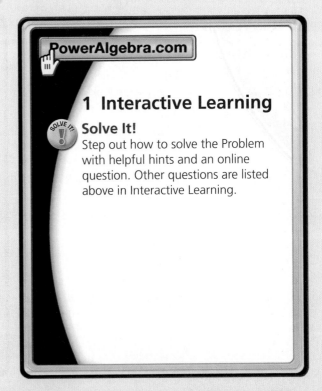

PowerAlgebra.com

1 Interactive Learning

Solve It!
Step out how to solve the Problem with helpful hints and an online question. Other questions are listed above in Interactive Learning.

Note that the range for $\sin^{-1}x$ and $\tan^{-1}x$ are the same except that the range of $\tan^{-1}x$ does not include the endpoints $\frac{-\pi}{2}$ and $\frac{\pi}{2}$.

Problem 1

The notation $\cos^{-1}\left(\frac{1}{2}\right)$ represents the measure of an angle whose cosine is $\frac{1}{2}$. A common error is to interpret this notation as $\dfrac{1}{\cos\left(\frac{1}{2}\right)}$, the multiplicative inverse of the given term.

The line $y = \frac{1}{2}$ intersects the graph of the function $y = \cos x$ in multiple points. However, in the restricted domain of the inverse of the cosine function, between 0° and 180°, there is only one angle whose cosine is $\frac{1}{2}$.

> Q Why, by inspection, is choice B incorrect? [because $\cos 30° = \frac{\sqrt{3}}{2}$]
>
> Q In what quadrants are cosine values positive? [I and IV]
>
> Q Why is $\cos 60° = \cos 300° = \cos(-60°)$? [The angles 300° and −60° lie in Quadrant IV, where their cosines are also $\frac{1}{2}$.]

Plan

How does the unit circle help you find angle measures?
The unit circle helps you recall the simplest domain values for a given trigonometric function.

The graphs on the left below show the "representative part" of the function that is inverted. The graphs on the right show the inverse functions.

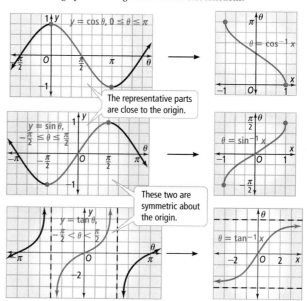

The representative parts are close to the origin.

These two are symmetric about the origin.

The values of inverse trigonometric functions are measures of angles. You can use the unit circle to find the values in either radians or degrees.

Problem 1 Using the Unit Circle

Multiple Choice What is $\cos^{-1}\left(\frac{1}{2}\right)$ in degrees?

Ⓐ −60°   Ⓑ 30°   Ⓒ 60°   Ⓓ 300°

Draw a unit circle and mark each point on the circle that has x-coordinate $\frac{1}{2}$. These points and the origin form 30°-60°-90° triangles.

The simplest domain values for cosine that allow cosine to have values from −1 to 1 are the angles in the top half of the unit circle.

Thus, even though

$$\cos 60° = \cos 300° = \cos(-60°),$$

$\cos^{-1}\left(\frac{1}{2}\right)$ must be 60°. The correct choice is C.

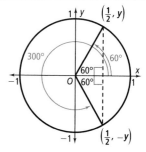

Answers

Solve It!

$\frac{\pi}{2} \pm \frac{\pi}{3}$, or $\frac{5\pi}{6}$ and $\frac{\pi}{6}$; dividing each side of the eq. by 2, we get $\sin \theta = \frac{1}{2}$, so we are looking for values of θ for which the value of sine is $\frac{1}{2}$. This happens at $\theta = \frac{\pi}{2} \pm \frac{\pi}{3}$, or $\frac{5\pi}{6}$ and $\frac{\pi}{6}$.

PowerAlgebra.com

2 Guided Instruction

Ⓒ Each Problem is worked out and supported online.

Problem 1
Using the Unit Circle
                                    Animated

Problem 2
Using a Calculator to Find the Inverse of Sine

Problem 3
Using a Calculator to Find the Inverse of Tangent

Problem 4
Solving a Trigonometric Equation

Problem 5
Solving by Factoring
                                    Animated

Problem 6
Using the Inverse of a Trigonometric Function
                                    Animated

Support in Algebra 2 Companion
• Vocabulary
• Key Concepts
• Got It?

Got It? 1. Use a unit circle. What is each inverse function value in degrees?

a. $\cos^{-1}\left(-\frac{1}{2}\right)$ b. $\sin^{-1}\left(\frac{1}{2}\right)$ c. $\tan^{-1} 1$

You can use an inverse trigonometric function and the unit circle to find all angles having a given trigonometric function value.

Problem 2 Using a Calculator to Find the Inverse of Sine

What are the radian measures of all angles whose sine is −0.9? Solve using an inverse function, a calculator, and the unit circle.

$\sin^{-1}(-0.9) \approx -1.12$ Use $\sin^{-1}$ and a calculator in radian mode.

Think

How do you find the angle in Quadrant III? From $(x_1, -0.9)$, draw a line perpendicular to the y-axis to find $(x_2, -0.9)$.

The angle must be between $-\frac{\pi}{2}$ and $\frac{\pi}{2}$, so it is in Quadrant IV. The sine function is also negative in Quadrant III, as shown in the figure at the right. So $\pi + 1.12 \approx 4.26$ is another solution.

You can write the radian measures of all the angles whose sine is −0.9 as

    n represents any integer.

$-1.12 + 2\pi n$ and $4.26 + 2\pi n$.

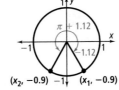

Got It? 2. What are the radian measures of all angles for each description?

a. angles whose sine is 0.44   b. angles whose sine is −0.73

Problem 3 Using a Calculator to Find the Inverse of Tangent

What are the radian measures of all angles whose tangent is −0.84? Use an inverse function, a calculator, and the unit circle.

$\tan^{-1}(-0.84) \approx -0.70$ Use $\tan^{-1}$ and a calculator in radian mode.

Think

What are the representative angles for tangent? The representative angles for tangent have values from $-\frac{\pi}{2}$ to $\frac{\pi}{2}$.

The angle must be between $-\frac{\pi}{2}$ and $\frac{\pi}{2}$, so it is in Quadrant IV. The tangent function is also negative in Quadrant II, as shown in the figure at the right. So $\pi - 0.70 \approx 2.44$ is another solution.

You can write the radian measures of all the angles whose tangent is −0.84 as

$-0.70 + 2\pi n$ and $2.44 + 2\pi n$, or simply as $-0.70 + \pi n$.

Got It? 3. What are the radian measures of all angles for each description?

a. angles whose tangent is 0.44   b. angles whose tangent is −0.73

c. **Reasoning** You can also write the radian measures for Problem 3 as $2.44 + \pi n$. Explain why.

Got It?

Q In 1a, how can you use first quadrant angles to find the value? [**Angles whose terminal sides form a 60° angle with the x-axis have a cosine value of $\pm\frac{1}{2}$. Since the range of cosine inverse is $0° \le x \le 180°$ and cosine is negative in Quadrant II, $180° - 60° = 120°$.**]

Problem 2

Q What property of the sine function gives the additional answers of $-1.12 + 2\pi n$ and $4.26 + 2\pi n$ where *n* is an integer? Explain. [**Periodicity; $2\pi n$ represents multiples of 2π, where *n* is an integer.**]

Got It?   ERROR PREVENTION

Q In 2a, in what quadrant does the angle with the least positive measure lie whose sine is 0.44? Explain. [**Quadrant I; there is also a solution in Quadrant II with a greater positive measure.**]

Problem 3

Q What is the approximate measure in radians of the angle with the least positive measure whose tangent is 0.84? Explain. [**About 0.7. The tangent ratio is positive in Quadrant I and 0.7 lies between 0 and $\frac{\pi}{2}$ radians.**]

Got It?

Q What are the approximate values of $2.44 + \pi n$ when *n* is $\{-2, -1, 0, 1\}$? [**−3.84, −0.70, 2.44, 5.58**]

Q What are the tangent values for each of the values above? [**−0.85**]

Additional Problems

1. **Multiple Choice** What is $\tan^{-1}\left(-\frac{\sqrt{3}}{3}\right)$ in degrees?

   A. −60°   B. −30°
   C. 150°   D. 210°

   ANSWER B

2. What are the radian measures of all angles whose cosine is −0.63? Solve using an inverse function, a calculator, and the unit circle.

   ANSWER $2.25 + 2\pi n$ and $4.03 + 2\pi n$, where *n* is an integer

3. What are the radian measures of all angles whose tangent is −1.42? Use an inverse function, a calculator, and the unit circle.

   ANSWER $-0.96 + \pi n$, where *n* is an integer

4. What values for $\theta\left(-\frac{\pi}{2} \le \theta \le \frac{\pi}{2}\right)$ satisfy the equation $3 \tan \theta - 2 = \tan \theta$?

   ANSWER $\frac{\pi}{4}$

5. What are the values for θ that satisfy the equation $5 \sin^2\theta - \sin \theta = 0$ for $(0 \le \theta < 2\pi)$?

   ANSWER 0, 0.2, 2.94, and π

6. In Great Britain the nautical mile can be approximated using the function $L = 6077 - 31 \cos 2\theta$, where L is the length of the nautical mile in feet and θ is the latitude in degrees. What is the approximate latitude between 0° and 90° when the nautical mile is 6101 ft?

   ANSWER 70°

Answers

Got It?

1. a. 120°
   b. 30°
   c. 45°

2. a. $0.46 + 2\pi n$ and $2.69 + 2\pi n$
   b. $-0.82 + 2\pi n$ and $3.96 + 2\pi n$

3. a. $0.41 + 2\pi n$ and $3.56 + 2\pi n$, or just $0.41 + \pi n$
   b. $-0.63 + 2\pi n$ and $2.51 + 2\pi n$, or just $-0.63 + \pi n$
   c. $\tan(\theta + \pi) = \tan \theta$

Problem 4

> **Q** Let x represent $\cos\theta$. How could you rewrite this as a linear equation? **[$4x - 1 = x$]**
>
> **Q** What is x in this new linear equation? **[$\frac{1}{3}$]**
>
> **Q** Is $\theta = -1.23$ a solution to this equation? Explain. **[No; -1.23 satisfies the equation but is not in the interval $0 \le \theta < 2\pi$.]**

Got It?
VISUAL LEARNERS

A sketch of the graphs of the sine function and the line $y = -\frac{1}{2}$ in the interval $-\frac{\pi}{2} \le \theta \le \frac{\pi}{2}$ can help students see that the solutions of this equation lie in Quadrants III and IV.

Problem 5

> **Q** If you let x represent $\cos\theta$ and let y represent $\sin\theta$, how could you use substitution to rewrite this equation? **[$2xy + y = 0$]**
>
> **Q** How can you factor the expression and solve it? Explain. **[$y(2x + 1) = 0$; then, using the Zero Product Property, $y = 0$ or $2x + 1 = 0$.]**

Got It?
ERROR PREVENTION

A common error that students make in simplifying equations of this form, whether trigonometric or algebraic, is to divide both sides of the equation by a variable term. Have students find the error in this series of steps.

> **Q** What is the equation if you add $\cos\theta$ to both sides? **[$\sin\theta\cos\theta = \cos\theta$]**
>
> **Q** What is the equation if you divide both sides of the equation by $\cos\theta$? **[$\sin\theta = 1$]**
>
> **Q** What are the solutions in the given interval? **[$\frac{\pi}{2}$ and $\frac{3\pi}{2}$]**
>
> **Q** What is the error? **[Because $\cos\theta = 0$ at $\frac{\pi}{2}$ and $\frac{3\pi}{2}$, you divided both sides of the equation by 0 while solving.]**

In contrast to trigonometric identities, most trigonometric equations are true for only certain values of the variable.

Plan

How do you begin?
You want to isolate the variable θ. First isolate $\cos\theta$. Then use inverse cosine.

 Problem 4 Solving a Trigonometric Equation

What values for θ ($0 \le \theta < 2\pi$) satisfy the equation $4\cos\theta - 1 = \cos\theta$?

$$4\cos\theta - 1 = \cos\theta$$

$$3\cos\theta = 1 \qquad \text{Add 1 and } -\cos\theta \text{ to each side.}$$

$$\cos\theta = \frac{1}{3} \qquad \text{Divide each side by 3.}$$

$$\cos^{-1}\frac{1}{3} \approx 1.23 \qquad \text{Use the inverse function to find one value of } \theta.$$

Cosine is also positive in Quadrant IV. So another value of θ is $2\pi - 1.23 \approx 5.05$. The two solutions between 0 and 2π are approximately 1.23 and 5.05.

Got It? 4. What values for θ ($0 \le \theta < 2\pi$) satisfy the equation $3\sin\theta + 1 = \sin\theta$?

Sometimes you can solve trigonometric equations by factoring.

 Problem 5 Solving by Factoring

What are the values for θ that satisfy the equation $2\cos\theta\sin\theta + \sin\theta = 0$ for $0 \le \theta < 2\pi$?

Think	Write
Write the equation.	$2\cos\theta\sin\theta + \sin\theta = 0$
Factor.	$\sin\theta\,(2\cos\theta + 1) = 0$
Use the Zero Product Property.	$\sin\theta = 0$ or $2\cos\theta + 1 = 0$
Solve for $\cos\theta$.	$\sin\theta = 0$ or $\cos\theta = -\frac{1}{2}$
Use the unit circle.	$\theta = 0, \pi, \frac{2\pi}{3}, \text{ or } \frac{4\pi}{3}$

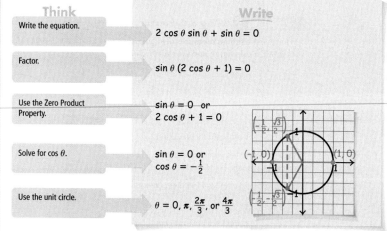

Got It? 5. What are the values for θ that satisfy the equation $\sin\theta\cos\theta - \cos\theta = 0$ for $0 \le \theta < 2\pi$?

Answers

Got It? (continued)

4. $\frac{11\pi}{6}$ and $\frac{7\pi}{6}$

5. $\frac{\pi}{2}$ and $\frac{3\pi}{2}$

You can use inverses of trigonometric functions to solve problems.

 Problem 6 Using the Inverse of a Trigonometric Function

Energy Conservation An air conditioner cools a home when the outside temperature is above 25°C. During the summer, you can model the outside temperature in degrees Celsius using the function $f(t) = 24 - 8 \cos \frac{\pi}{12} t$, where t is the number of hours past midnight. During what hours is the air conditioner cooling the home?

Plan
When does the air conditioner run?
The air conditioner runs when the temperature $f(t) > 25$.

By graphing, you can find when the graph of $y = f(t)$ is above the graph of $y = 25$, as shown at the right.

You can also solve algebraically.

The air conditioner is cooling the home between points A and B.

$24 - 8 \cos \frac{\pi}{12} t = 25$	Set $f(t) = 25$.
$-8 \cos \frac{\pi}{12} t = 1$	Subtract 24.
$\cos \frac{\pi}{12} t = -0.125$	Divide by -8.
$\frac{\pi}{12} t = \cos^{-1}(-0.125)$	Use inverse cosine.
$t = \frac{12}{\pi} \cos^{-1}(-0.125)$	Multiply by $\frac{12}{\pi}$.
$t \approx 6.5$	Evaluate.

The air conditioner comes on about 6.5 h after midnight or 6:30 A.M. By the symmetry of the graph, it goes off about 6.5 h before midnight, or 5:30 P.M.

 Got It? 6. Suppose the air conditioner is set to cool when the temperature is above 26°C. During what hours would the air conditioner run?

 Lesson Check

Do you know HOW?

Use a unit circle. What are the degree measures of all angles with the given sine value?

1. $-\frac{1}{2}$ **2.** $\frac{\sqrt{3}}{2}$

Solve each equation for θ with $0 \le \theta < 2\pi$.

3. $3 \cos \theta = -2$

4. $\sqrt{2} \cos \theta - \sqrt{2} = 0$

Do you UNDERSTAND? **MATHEMATICAL PRACTICES**

5. Writing Compare finding the inverse of $y = 3x - 4$ to finding the inverse of $y = 3 \sin \theta - 4$. Describe any similarities and differences.

6. Error Analysis A student solved the equation $\sin^2 \theta = \frac{1}{2} \sin \theta, 0 \le \theta < 2\pi$, as shown. What error did the student make?

$\sin^2 \theta = \frac{1}{2} \sin \theta$
$\sin \theta = \frac{1}{2}$
$\theta = \frac{\pi}{6}$ and $\frac{5\pi}{6}$

---

6. The air conditioner comes on about 7 hours after midnight, 7 A.M., and goes off about 7 hours before midnight, 5 P.M.

Lesson Check
1. $-30° + 360° \cdot n$ and $210° + 360° \cdot n$
2. $60° + 360° \cdot n$ and $120° + 360° \cdot n$
3. 2.30, 3.98
4. 0
5. Answers may vary. Sample: To find the inverse of $y = 3x - 4$, you interchange x and y and solve for y: $x = 3y - 4$, $y = \frac{x + 4}{3}$. Replace y with $f^{-1}(x)$ to find $f^{-1}(x) = \frac{x + 4}{3}$. To find the inverse of $y = 3 \sin \theta - 4$, you interchange θ and y and solve for $\sin y$ and then solve for y: $\theta = 3 \sin y - 4$, $\sin y = \frac{\theta + 4}{3}$ and $y = \sin^{-1}\left(\frac{\theta + 4}{3}\right)$. Replace y with $f^{-1}(\theta)$ to find $f^{-1}(\theta) = \sin^{-1}\left(\frac{\theta + 4}{3}\right)$.

The procedure for finding the inverse is the same; for $y = 3 \sin \theta - 4$ you will also use inverse sine.

6. The student divided each side of the equation by $\sin \theta$, which in the given interval can be equal to zero. There is an error in that the student failed to take into account the fact that division by zero is not possible.

Problem 6

Q Why is the graph of $f(t)$ symmetric about a vertical line between points A and B on the graph? **[f is the graph of a cosine function which is a periodic function that is always symmetric about a vertical line through one of its maximum (or minimum) points.]**

Got It?   **EXTENSION**
Have students graph $f(t)$ using a graphing calculator and determine its maximum.

Q What is the value of t when $f(t)$ is at its maximum point? **[12]**
Q Why is the maximum at $t = 12$? **[That is noon, when the sun is at its highest in the sky.]**
Q What is $f(12)$? **[32°C]**

3 Lesson Check

Do you know HOW?
• In Exercises 1–2, if students are unsure how to list an infinite number of angles, remind them to let n equal any integer.

Do you UNDERSTAND?
• For Exercise 5, suggest students find the inverses of each function first and compare the processes afterward.

Close

Q What is the advantage of defining the inverse trigonometric functions for sine, cosine, and tangent? **[It enables you to find the degree or radian measure of an angle whose trigonometric ratio is given.]**

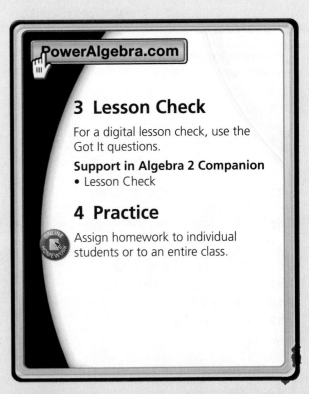

PowerAlgebra.com

3 Lesson Check
For a digital lesson check, use the Got It questions.
Support in Algebra 2 Companion
• Lesson Check

4 Practice
Assign homework to individual students or to an entire class.

4 Practice

ASSIGNMENT GUIDE

Basic: 7–34 all, 35–41 odd, 42, 43

Average: 7–33 odd, 35–61

Advanced: 7–33 odd, 35–66

Standardized Test Prep: 67–72

Mixed Review: 73–84

 Mathematical Practices are supported by exercises with red headings. Here are the Practices supported in this lesson:

MP 1: Make Sense of Problems Ex. 42
MP 2: Reason Abstractly Ex. 61a
MP 3: Compare Arguments Ex. 5
MP 3: Construct Arguments Ex. 44c
MP 3: Communicate Ex. 5, 44c
MP 3: Critique the Reasoning of Others Ex. 6

Applications exercises have blue headings. Exercises 34 and 43 support MP 4: Model.

STEM exercises focus on science or engineering applications.

EXERCISE 43: Use the Think About a Plan worksheet in the **Practice and Problem Solving Workbook** (also available in the Teaching Resources in print and online) to further support students' development in becoming independent learners.

HOMEWORK QUICK CHECK

To check students' understanding of key skills and concepts, go over Exercises 9, 19, 37, 42, and 43.

 Practice and Problem-Solving Exercises MATHEMATICAL PRACTICES

A Practice
Use a unit circle, a 30°-60°-90° triangle, and an inverse function to find the degree measure of each angle. ◀ See Problem 1.

7. angle whose sine is 1
8. angle whose tangent is $\frac{\sqrt{3}}{3}$
9. angle whose sine is $-\frac{\sqrt{3}}{2}$
10. angle whose tangent is $-\sqrt{3}$
11. angle whose cosine is 0
12. angle whose cosine is $-\frac{\sqrt{2}}{2}$

Use a calculator and inverse functions to find the radian measures of all angles having the given trigonometric values. ◀ See Problems 2 and 3.

13. angles whose tangent is 1
14. angles whose sine is 0.37
15. angles whose sine is -0.78
16. angles whose tangent is -3
17. angles whose cosine is -0.89
18. angles whose sine is -1.1

Solve each equation for θ with $0 \le \theta < 2\pi$. ◀ See Problems 4 and 5.

19. $2\sin\theta = 1$
20. $2\cos\theta - \sqrt{3} = 0$
21. $4\tan\theta = 3 + \tan\theta$
22. $2\sin\theta - \sqrt{2} = 0$
23. $3\tan\theta - 1 = \tan\theta$
24. $3\tan\theta + 5 = 0$
25. $2\sin\theta = 3$
26. $2\sin\theta = -\sqrt{3}$
27. $(\cos\theta)(\cos\theta + 1) = 0$
28. $(\sin\theta - 1)(\sin\theta + 1) = 0$
29. $2\sin^2\theta - 1 = 0$
30. $\tan\theta = \tan^2\theta$
31. $\sin^2\theta + 3\sin\theta = 0$
32. $\sin\theta = -\sin\theta\cos\theta$
33. $2\sin^2\theta - 3\sin\theta = 2$

34. **Energy Conservation** Suppose the outside temperature in Problem 6 is modeled by the function $f(t) = 27 - 6\cos\frac{\pi}{12}t$ instead. During what hours is the air conditioner cooling the house? ◀ See Problem 6.

B Apply
Each diagram shows one solution to the equation below it. Find the complete solution of each equation.

35.
$5\sin\theta = 1 + 3\sin\theta$

36.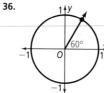
$6\cos\theta - 5 = -2$

37.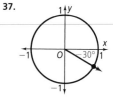
$4\sin\theta + 3 = 1$

Solve each equation for θ with $0 \le \theta < 2\pi$.

38. $\sec\theta = 2$
39. $\csc\theta = -1$
40. $\csc\theta = 3$
41. $\cot\theta = -10$

Answers

Practice and Problem-Solving Exercises

7. $90° + 360° \cdot n$

8. $30° + 360° \cdot n$ and $210° + 360° \cdot n$, or just $30° + 180° \cdot n$

9. $240° + 360° \cdot n$ and $300° + 360° \cdot n$

10. $120° + 360° \cdot n$ and $300° + 360° \cdot n$, or just $120° + 180° \cdot n$

11. $90° + 360° \cdot n$ and $270° + 360° \cdot n$, or just $90° + 180° \cdot n$

12. $135° + 360° \cdot n$ and $225° + 360° \cdot n$

13. $0.79 + \pi n$, or just $\frac{\pi}{4} + \pi n$

14. $0.38 + 2\pi n$ and $2.76 + 2\pi n$

15. $-0.89 + 2\pi n$ and $4.04 + 2\pi n$

16. $1.89 + \pi n$

17. $2.67 + 2\pi n$ and $3.62 + 2\pi n$

18. no solution

19. $\frac{\pi}{6}, \frac{5\pi}{6}$

20. $\frac{\pi}{6}, \frac{11\pi}{6}$

21. $\frac{\pi}{4}, \frac{5\pi}{4}$

22. $\frac{\pi}{4}, \frac{3\pi}{4}$

23. $0.46, 3.61$

24. $2.11, 5.25$

25. no solution

26. $\frac{4\pi}{3}, \frac{5\pi}{3}$

27. $\frac{\pi}{2}, \pi, \frac{3\pi}{2}$

28. $\frac{\pi}{2}, \frac{3\pi}{2}$

29. $\frac{\pi}{4}, \frac{3\pi}{4}, \frac{5\pi}{4}, \frac{7\pi}{4}$

30. $0, \frac{\pi}{4}, \pi, \frac{5\pi}{4}$

31. $0, \pi$

32. $0, \pi$

33. $\frac{7\pi}{6}, \frac{11\pi}{6}$

34. The air conditioner comes on about 4.7 hrs after midnight, 4:42 A.M., and goes off about 4.7 hrs before midnight, 7:18 P.M.

35. $30° + 360° \cdot n$ and $150° + 360° \cdot n$

36. $60° + 360° \cdot n$ and $300° + 360° \cdot n$

37. $210° + 360° \cdot n$ and $330° + 360° \cdot n$

38. $\frac{\pi}{3}, \frac{5\pi}{3}$

39. $\frac{3\pi}{2}$

40. $0.34, 2.80$

41. $3.04, 6.18$

42. Think About a Plan The function $h = 25 \sin\left(\frac{\pi}{20}(t - 10)\right) + 34$ models the height h of a Ferris wheel car in feet, t seconds after starting. When will the car first be 30 ft off the ground?
- What is the inverse function?
- How can the inverse function help you answer the question?

STEM 43. Electricity The function $I = 40 \sin 60\pi t$ models the current I in amps that an electric generator is producing after t seconds. When is the first time that the current will reach 20 amps? -20 amps?

44. Reasoning The graphing calculator screen shows a portion of the graphs of $y = \sin \theta$ and $y = 0.5$.
a. Write the complete solution of $\sin \theta \geq 0.5$.
b. Write the complete solution of $\sin \theta \leq 0.5$.
c. **Writing** Explain how you can solve inequalities involving trigonometric functions.

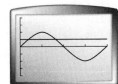

Xmin = 0
Xmax = 2π
Xscl = $\frac{\pi}{2}$
Ymin = -2
Ymax = 2
Yscl = 0.5

Find the complete solution in radians of each equation.

45. $2 \sin^2 \theta + \cos \theta - 1 = 0$ **46.** $\sin^2 \theta - 1 = \cos^2 \theta$ **47.** $2 \sin \theta + 1 = \csc \theta$

48. $3 \tan^2 \theta - 1 = \sec^2 \theta$ **49.** $\sin \theta \cos \theta = \frac{1}{2} \cos \theta$ **50.** $\tan \theta \sin \theta = 3 \sin \theta$

51. $2 \cos^2 \theta + \sin \theta = 1$ **52.** $\sin \theta \cot^2 \theta - 3 \sin \theta = 0$ **53.** $4 \sin^2 \theta + 1 = 4 \sin \theta$

Find the x-intercepts of the graph of each function.

54. $y = 2 \cos \theta + 1$ **55.** $y = 2 \sin^2 \theta - 1$ **56.** $y = \cos^2 \theta - 1$

57. $y = \tan^2 \theta - 1$ **58.** $y = 2 \sin^4 \theta - \sin^2 \theta$ **59.** $y = 2 \cos^2 \theta - 3 \cos \theta - 2$

60. Find the complete solution of $\sin^2 \theta + 2 \sin \theta + 1 = 0$. (*Hint:* How would you solve $x^2 + 2x + 1 = 0$?)

61. a. Open-Ended Write three trigonometric equations each with the complete solution $\pi + 2\pi n$.
 b. Describe how you found the equations in part (a).

Challenge Solve each trigonometric equation for θ in terms of y.

Sample $y = 2 \sin 3\theta + 4$

$\sin 3\theta = \frac{y - 4}{2}$

$3\theta = \sin^{-1}\left(\frac{y - 4}{2}\right) + 2\pi n, 2 \leq y \leq 6$

$\theta = \frac{1}{3} \sin^{-1}\left(\frac{y - 4}{2}\right) + \frac{2\pi}{3}n, 2 \leq y \leq 6$

62. $y = \cos 2\theta$ **63.** $y = 3 \sin (\theta + 2)$ **64.** $y = -4 \cos 2\pi\theta$ **65.** $y = 2 \cos \theta + 1$

64. $\theta = \frac{1}{2\pi} \cos^{-1}\left(-\frac{y}{4}\right)$

65. $\theta = \cos^{-1}\left(\frac{y - 1}{2}\right)$

---

42. ≈ 9 seconds after starting

43. 0.0028 s; 0.019 s

44. a. $\frac{\pi}{6} + 2\pi n \leq x \leq \frac{5\pi}{6} + 2\pi n$

   b. $\frac{5\pi}{6} + 2\pi n \leq x \leq \frac{13\pi}{6} + 2\pi n$

   c. Find the values of x where the graphs intersect, and then choose the appropriate interval.

45. $0 + 2\pi n, \frac{2}{3}\pi + 2\pi n, \frac{4}{3}\pi + 2\pi n$

46. $\frac{\pi}{2} + 2\pi n, \frac{3\pi}{2} + 2\pi n$

47. $\frac{\pi}{6} + 2\pi n, \frac{5\pi}{6} + 2\pi n, \frac{3\pi}{2} + 2\pi n$

48. $\frac{\pi}{4} + \frac{\pi}{2}n$

49. $\frac{\pi}{6} + 2\pi n, \frac{5\pi}{6} + 2\pi n, \frac{\pi}{2} + \pi n$

50. $\pi n, 1.25 + \pi n$

51. $\frac{\pi}{2} + 2\pi n, \frac{7\pi}{6} + 2\pi n, \frac{11\pi}{6} + 2\pi n$

52. $\frac{\pi}{6} + \pi n, \frac{5\pi}{6} + \pi n$

53. $\frac{\pi}{6} + 2\pi n, \frac{5\pi}{6} + 2\pi n$

54. $\frac{2\pi}{3} + 2\pi n, \frac{4\pi}{3} + 2\pi n$

55. $\frac{\pi}{4} + \frac{\pi n}{2}$

56. $0 + \pi n$

57. $\frac{\pi}{4} + \frac{\pi n}{2}$

58. $0 + \pi n, \frac{\pi}{4} + \frac{\pi n}{2}$

59. $\frac{2\pi}{3} + 2\pi n, \frac{4\pi}{3} + 2\pi n$

60. $\frac{3\pi}{2} + 2\pi n$

61. a. Answers may vary. Sample: $\cos \theta = -1$, $2 \cos \theta = -2$, $3 \cos \theta = -3$

   b. Start with $\cos \theta = -1$, and then multiply both sides of the eq. by any nonzero number.

62. $\theta = \frac{1}{2} \cos^{-1}(y)$

63. $\theta = \sin^{-1}\left(\frac{y}{3}\right) - 2$

Answers

Practice and Problem-Solving Exercises (continued)

66. a. 1:55 A.M., 11:05 A.M., and 2:55 P.M.

b. 12:00 midnight to 1:55 A.M., 11:05 A.M. to 2:55 P.M.

Standardized Test Prep

67. D

68. H

69. C

70. G

71. D

72. **[4]** $2 \sin^2 \theta = -\sin \theta$

$2 \sin^2 \theta + \sin \theta = 0$

$\sin \theta(2 \sin \theta + 1) = 0$

$\sin \theta = 0; \quad 2 \sin \theta + 1 = 0$

$\sin^{-1} 0 = 0, \pi \qquad \sin \theta = -\frac{1}{2}$

$\sin^{-1}\left(-\frac{1}{2}\right) = \frac{11\pi}{6}, \frac{7\pi}{6}$

[3] correct solutions, but with less efficient methods

[2] incomplete list of solutions

[1] correct answers, without work shown

Mixed Review

73. $\cot \theta$

74. $\tan^2 \theta$

75. 1

76. 1

77. $\sin \theta$

78. $\tan \theta$

79. $y = 4 \cos \frac{\pi}{4}\theta$

80. $y = 3 \cos \theta$

81. $y = \frac{\pi}{4} \cos \frac{2}{3}\theta$

82. 4

83. 21

84. $52\frac{1}{2}$

STEM **66. Tides** One day the tide at a point in Maine could be modeled by $h = 5 \cos \frac{2\pi}{13} t$, where h is the height of the tide in feet above the mean water level and t is the number of hours past midnight. At what times that day would the tide have been each of the following?

a. 3 ft above the mean water level

b. *at least* 3 ft above the mean water level

Standardized Test Prep

SAT/ACT

67. Which of the following is NOT equal to 60°?

Ⓐ $\sin^{-1} \frac{\sqrt{3}}{2}$ Ⓑ $\cos^{-1} \frac{1}{2}$ Ⓒ $\tan^{-1} \sqrt{3}$ Ⓓ $\tan^{-1} \frac{\sqrt{3}}{3}$

68. In which quadrants are the solutions to $\tan \theta + 1 = 0$?

Ⓕ Quadrants I and II   Ⓗ Quadrants II and IV

Ⓖ Quadrants II and III   Ⓘ Quadrants III and IV

69. Which of these angles have a sine of about −0.6?

I. 143.1°   II. 216.9°   III. 323.1°

Ⓐ I and II only   Ⓒ II and III only

Ⓑ I and III only   Ⓓ I, II, and III

70. What are the solutions of $2 \sin \theta - \sqrt{3} = 0$ for $0 \le \theta < 2\pi$?

Ⓕ $\frac{\pi}{6}$ and $\frac{5\pi}{6}$ Ⓖ $\frac{\pi}{3}$ and $\frac{2\pi}{3}$ Ⓗ $\frac{2\pi}{3}$ and $\frac{4\pi}{3}$ Ⓘ $\frac{4\pi}{3}$ and $\frac{5\pi}{3}$

71. Suppose $a > 0$. Under what conditions for a and b will $a \sin \theta = b$ have exactly two solutions in the interval $0 \le \theta < 2\pi$?

Ⓐ $a = b$ Ⓑ $b > a$ Ⓒ $a = -b$ Ⓓ $a > b > -a$

Extended Response

72. Solve $2 \sin^2 \theta = -\sin \theta$ for θ with $0 \le \theta < 2\pi$. Show your work.

Mixed Review

Simplify each expression.   ◀ See Lesson 14-1.

73. $\cos^2 \theta \sec \theta \csc \theta$ **74.** $\sin \theta \sec \theta \tan \theta$ **75.** $\csc^2 \theta (1 - \cos^2 \theta)$

76. $\frac{\cos \theta \csc \theta}{\cot \theta}$ **77.** $\frac{\sec \theta}{\cot \theta + \tan \theta}$ **78.** $\frac{\sin \theta + \tan \theta}{1 + \cos \theta}$

Write a cosine function for each description.   ◀ See Lesson 13-5.

79. amplitude 4, period 8   **80.** amplitude 3, period 2π **81.** amplitude $\frac{\pi}{4}$, period 3π

Get Ready! **To prepare for Lesson 14-3, do Exercises 82–84.**

Solve each proportion.   ◀ See p. 974.

82. $\frac{x}{7} = \frac{28}{49}$ **83.** $\frac{10}{14} = \frac{15}{x}$ **84.** $\frac{21}{10} = \frac{x}{25}$

See p. 974.

918 Chapter 14 Trigonometric Identities and Equations

14-2 Lesson Resources

Additional Instructional Support

Algebra 2 Companion

Students can use the **Algebra 2 Companion** worktext (4 pages) as you teach the lesson. Use the Companion to support

- New Vocabulary
- Key Concepts
- Got It for each Problem
- Lesson Check

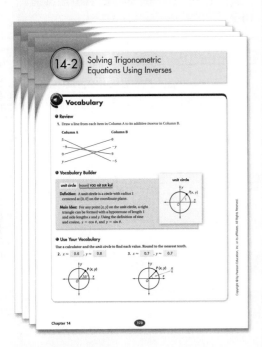

ELL Support

Connect to Prior Knowledge It may benefit some students to draw the graph of each trigonometric function and a graph of the unit circle on the same sheet of paper to see the relationship when they are evaluating inverses. For example, on a unit circle, the value for $\sin^{-1}\left(-\frac{1}{2}\right)$ is $-\frac{\pi}{6}$, which lies in Quadrant IV. On a graph of the sine function, $f\left(-\frac{\pi}{6}\right) = -\frac{1}{2}$. On the graph, the point $\left(-\frac{\pi}{6}, -\frac{1}{2}\right)$ is to the left of the y-axis and corresponds to Quadrant IV on the graph of the unit circle.

5 Assess & Remediate

Lesson Quiz

1. What is $\cos^{-1}\left(-\frac{\sqrt{2}}{2}\right)$ in degrees?
2. What are the radian measures of all angles whose sine is -0.4?
3. What are the radian measures of all angles whose tangent is -0.52?
4. What values for θ $(-\pi \le \theta \le \pi)$ satisfy the equation $5\sin\theta - 3 = \sin\theta$?
5. What are the values for θ that satisfy $\cos^2\theta = \cos\theta$ for $(0 \le \theta < 2\pi)$?
6. **Do you UNDERSTAND?** In the study of alternating electric currents, one function that models e, the instantaneous voltage, is $e = 12\sin(200\pi t)$, where t is the time in seconds. What is the least positive value of t when e is 5?

ANSWERS TO LESSON QUIZ

1. $135°$
2. $-0.41 + 2\pi n$ and $3.55 + 2\pi n$, where n is an integer
3. $-0.48 + \pi n$, where n is an integer
4. 0.85 and 2.29
5. $\frac{\pi}{2}, \frac{3\pi}{2}$ and 0
6. 0.00068

PRESCRIPTION FOR REMEDIATION

Use the student work on the Lesson Quiz to prescribe a differentiated review assignment:

Points	Differentiated Remediation
0–2	Intervention
3–4	On-level
5–6	Extension

PowerAlgebra.com

5 Assess & Remediate

Assign the Lesson Quiz. Appropriate intervention, practice, or enrichment is automatically generated based on student performance.

Differentiated Remediation

Intervention

- **Reteaching** (2 pages) Provides reteaching and practice exercises for the key lesson concepts. Use with struggling students or absent students.

- **English Language Learner Support** Helps students develop and reinforce mathematical vocabulary and key concepts.

All-in-One Resources/Online
Reteaching

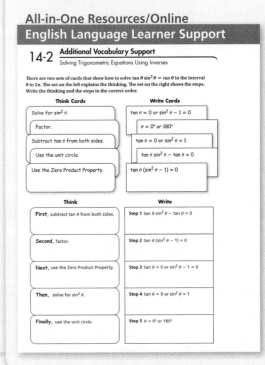

All-in-One Resources/Online
English Language Learner Support

Differentiated Remediation *continued*

On-Level

- **Practice** (2 pages) Provides extra practice for each lesson. For simpler practice exercises, use the Form K Practice pages found in the All-in-One Teaching Resources and online.

- **Think About a Plan** Helps students develop specific problem-solving skills and strategies by providing scaffolded guiding questions.

- **Standardized Test Prep** Focuses on all major exercises, all major question types, and helps students prepare for the high-stakes assessments.

Extension

- **Enrichment** Provides students with interesting problems and activities that extend the concepts of the lesson.

- **Activities, Games, and Puzzles** Worksheets that can be used for concepts development, enrichment, and for fun!

Practice and Problem Solving Wkbk/ All-in-One Resources/Online
Practice page 1

14-2 Practice — Form G
Solving Trigonometric Equations Using Inverses

Use a unit circle, a 45°-45°-90° triangle, and an inverse function to find the degree measure of each angle.

1. angle whose sine is $\frac{\sqrt{3}}{2}$ 45°
2. angle whose tangent is 1 45°
3. angle whose cosine is $-\frac{\sqrt{2}}{2}$ 135°
4. angle whose sine is 1 90°

Use a calculator and inverse functions to find the radian measures of all angles having the given trigonometric values.

5. angles whose tangent is 2.5 1.19 + πn
6. angles whose sine is 0.75 0.85 + $2\pi n$ and 2.29 + $2\pi n$
7. angles whose cosine is -0.24 1.81 + $2\pi n$ and 4.47 + $2\pi n$
8. angles whose cosine is 0.45 1.10 + $2\pi n$ and 5.18 + $2\pi n$
9. angles whose sine is -1.1 no solution
10. angles whose tangent is (-3) $-1.25 + \pi n$

Solve each equation for θ with $0 \le \theta < 2\pi$.

11. $2 \tan \theta + 2 = 0$ $\frac{3\pi}{4}, \frac{7\pi}{4}$
12. $2 \cos \theta = 1$ $\frac{\pi}{3}, \frac{5\pi}{3}$
13. $2 \cos \theta + \sqrt{3} = 0$ $\frac{5\pi}{6}, \frac{7\pi}{6}$
14. $\sqrt{3} \cot \theta - 1 = 0$ $\frac{\pi}{3}, \frac{4\pi}{3}$
15. $4 \sin \theta - 3 = 0$ 0.85, 2.29
16. $4 \sin \theta + 3 = 0$ 3.99, 5.44
17. $(2 \cos \theta + \sqrt{3})(2 \cos \theta + 1) = 0$ $\frac{5\pi}{6}, \frac{7\pi}{6}, \frac{2\pi}{3}, \frac{4\pi}{3}$
18. $\sqrt{3} \tan \theta - 2 \sin \theta \tan \theta = 0$ $0, \frac{\pi}{3}, \frac{5\pi}{3}, \pi$
19. $2 \cos^2 \theta + \cos \theta = 0$ $\frac{\pi}{2}, \frac{3\pi}{2}, \frac{2\pi}{3}, \frac{4\pi}{3}$
20. $5 \cos \theta - 3 = 0$ 0.93, 5.36
21. $\tan \theta - 2 \cos \theta \tan \theta = 0$ $0, \frac{\pi}{6}, \pi, \frac{5\pi}{6}$
22. $4 \sin \theta (\tan \theta + 1) = 0$ $0, \frac{3\pi}{4}, \pi, \frac{7\pi}{4}$
23. $(\cos \theta - 1)(2 \cos \theta - 1) = 0$ $0, \frac{\pi}{3}, \frac{5\pi}{3}$
24. $\tan^2 \theta - 1 = 0$ $\frac{\pi}{4}, \frac{3\pi}{4}, \frac{5\pi}{4}, \frac{7\pi}{4}$
25. If a model rocket is fired into the air with an initial velocity at an angle of elevation θ, then the height h in feet of the projectile at time t in seconds is given by $h = -16t^2 + vt \sin \theta$.
   a. Find the angle of elevation θ, to the nearest tenth of a degree, if a rocket launched at 1500 ft/s takes 2 s to reach a height of 750 ft. 15.7°
   b. Find the angle of elevation θ, to the nearest tenth of a degree, if a rocket launched at 1500 ft/s takes 3 s to reach a height of 750 ft. 11.5°

Practice and Problem Solving Wkbk/ All-in-One Resources/Online
Think About a Plan

14-2 Think About a Plan
Solving Trigonometric Equations Using Inverses

Electricity The function $I = 40 \sin 60 \pi t$ models the current I in amps that an electric generator is producing after t seconds. When is the first time that the current will reach 20 amps? -20 amps?

Understanding the Problem

1. How many amps does the generator produce after t seconds? $40 \sin 60\pi t$ amps

2. Write the current function using an inverse trigonometric function. $60\pi t = \sin^{-1}\left(\frac{I}{40}\right)$

3. What is the problem asking you to determine?
   Answers may vary. Sample: The time when the generator first produces 20 amps and -20 amps

Planning the Solution

4. Write an equation that you can use to determine when the generator first produces 20 amps.
   $60\pi t = \sin^{-1}\left(\frac{1}{2}\right)$

5. Write an equation that you can use to determine when the generator first produces -20 amps.
   $60\pi t = \sin^{-1}\left(-\frac{1}{2}\right)$

Getting an Answer

6. Solve your equations to find the first time that the current will reach 20 amps and the first time that the current will reach -20 amps. $\frac{1}{360}$ s, $\frac{7}{360}$ s

Practice and Problem Solving Wkbk/ All-in-One Resources/Online
Practice page 2

14-2 Practice (continued) — Form G
Solving Trigonometric Equations Using Inverses

Each diagram shows one solution to the equation below it. Find the complete solution of each equation.

26.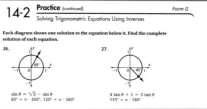
$\sin \theta = \sqrt{3} - \sin \theta$
60° + n · 360°, 120° + n · 360°

27.
$4 \tan \theta + 1 = 3 \tan \theta$
135° + n · 180°

28.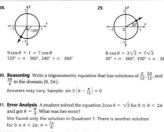
$9 \cos \theta + 1 = 7 \cos \theta$
120° + n · 360°, 240° + n · 360°

29.
$8 \cos \theta + 3\sqrt{3} = 7\sqrt{3}$
30° + n · 360°, 330° + n · 360°

30. **Reasoning** Write a trigonometric equation that has solutions of $\frac{\pi}{12}, \frac{5\pi}{12}$, and $\frac{3\pi}{4}$ in the domain [0, 2π).
Answers may vary. Sample: $\sin 3\left(\theta - \frac{\pi}{6}\right) = 0$

31. **Error Analysis** A student solved the equation $2\cos \theta = \sqrt{2}$ for $0 \le \theta < 2\pi$ and got $\theta = \frac{\pi}{4}$. What was her error?
She found only the solution in Quadrant 1. There is another solution for $0 \le \theta < 2\pi$: $\theta = \frac{7\pi}{4}$.

Find the x-intercepts of the graph of each function.

32. $y = 2 \cos^4 \theta - 1$
0.57 + πn, 2.57 + πn
33. $y = 2 \sin \theta - 1$
0.52 + 2πn, 2.62 + 2πn
34. $y = \sin^2 \theta - \cos \theta$
0.90 + 2πn, 5.38 + 2πn
35. $y = \tan^4 \theta - 2$
0.87 + πn, 2.27 + πn

Practice and Problem Solving Wkbk/ All-in-One Resources/Online
Standardized Test Prep

14-2 Standardized Test Prep
Solving Trigonometric Equations Using Inverses

Multiple Choice

For Exercises 1–5, choose the correct letter.

1. What is $\sin^{-1} \frac{\sqrt{2}}{2}$, in degrees? C
   (A) 0° (B) 30° (C) 45° (D) 90°

2. What are the radian measures of all angles whose sine is $\frac{1}{2}$? H
   (F) $\frac{\pi}{6} + 2\pi n$ and $\frac{3\pi}{2} + 2\pi n$ (H) $\frac{\pi}{6} + 2\pi n$ and $\frac{5\pi}{6} + 2\pi n$
   (G) $\frac{\pi}{6} + 2\pi n$ and $\frac{4\pi}{3} + 2\pi n$ (I) $\frac{\pi}{6} + 2\pi n$ and $\frac{7\pi}{6} + 2\pi n$

3. What values for θ satisfy the equation $3 \tan \theta + 4 = 0$ for $0 \le \theta < 2\pi$? A
   (A) 2.21 and 5.36 (C) -0.93 and -4.07
   (B) 0.93 and 4.07 (D) -2.21 and -5.36

4. What values for θ satisfy the equation $2 \cos \theta - \sqrt{3} = 0$ for $0 \le \theta < 2\pi$? G
   (F) $\frac{\pi}{6}, \frac{5\pi}{6}$ (G) $\frac{\pi}{6}, \frac{11\pi}{6}$ (H) $\frac{\pi}{3}, \frac{2\pi}{3}$ (I) $\frac{\pi}{3}, \frac{5\pi}{3}$

5. In which quadrants are the solutions to $2 \sin \theta - 1 = 0$? A
   (A) Quadrants I and II (C) Quadrants II and III
   (B) Quadrants I and III (D) Quadrants II and IV

Short Response

6. Solve $2 \cos^2 \theta + 2 \cos \theta = 0$ for $0 \le \theta < 2\pi$. Show your work.
   [2] $2 \cos \theta (\cos \theta + 1) = 0$
   $\cos \theta = 0$ or $\cos \theta + 1 = 0$
   $\theta = \frac{\pi}{2}, \pi, \frac{3\pi}{2}$
   [1] incorrect solution OR no work shown
   [0] incorrect answers and no work shown OR no answers given

All-in-One Resources/Online
Enrichment

14-2 Enrichment
Solving Trigonometric Equations Using Inverses

Polar Coordinates

So far you have graphed points on a Cartesian coordinate system where a point is represented by an ordered pair (x, y), and you have graphed points on a complex number coordinate system where a complex number $a + bi$ is represented by an ordered pair (a, b). When working with trigonometry, points are often graphed on a polar coordinate system.

1. On a polar coordinate system, points are represented by (r, θ) where r is the directed distance from the origin to the point and θ is the directed angle. For example, point P at the right has polar coordinates $(7, 65°)$. Give another polar coordinate for P using a different angle measure.
   Answers may vary. Sample: (7, 425°)

2. Another polar coordinate for P is $(-7, 245°)$ where -7 means a positive distance of 7 on the opposite ray or the ray reflected 180° about the origin. How many different polar coordinates are possible for point P?
   an infinite number of coordinates

Use a unit circle and 30°-60°-90° triangles to find the degree measure of each angle. Then express the location of the point on the unit circle using two different polar coordinates.

3. an angle whose cosine is $\frac{1}{2}$ Answers may vary. Sample: (1, 60°), (-1, 240°)

4. an angle whose sine is $\frac{\sqrt{3}}{2}$ Answers may vary. Sample: (1, 60°), (-1, 240°)

5. an angle whose tangent is $\sqrt{3}$ Answers may vary. Sample: (1, 60°), (-1, 240°)

6. an angle whose sine is $-\frac{1}{2}$ Answers may vary. Sample: (-1, 30°), (1, 210°)

Online Teacher Resource Center
Activities, Games, and Puzzles

14-2 Puzzle: Crossnumber Puzzle
Solving Trig Equations Using Inverses

Solve the following equations to complete the crossnumber puzzle below.
- All ACROSS solutions should be given in degrees and all DOWN solutions should be given in radians.
- Round your answers to the nearest hundredth if necessary.
- Use a leading zero (for example, 0.52) if necessary.
- All decimal points should be put in their own boxes.
- Be sure to give the solution over the indicated interval.
- Two examples for filling in the boxes are shown below.

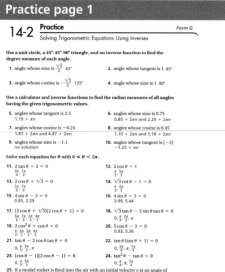

ACROSS (Degrees)

1. $2 \cos \theta = 1$; $0° \le \theta \le 180°$ 60
2. $2 \sin \theta + \sqrt{3} = 0$; $0° \le \theta \le 270°$ 240
3. $\sqrt{2}\sin \theta + \sqrt{2} = 0$; $0° \le \theta \le 270°$ 270
4. $5 + 2 \tan \theta = -3 \tan \theta$; $0° \le \theta \le 180°$ 135
5. $2 \tan \theta - 3)(\tan \theta + 3) = 0$; $0° \le \theta \le 90°$ 56.31
6. $2 \sin^2 \theta - 1 = 0$; $90° \le \theta \le 180°$ 135
7. $4 \tan^2 \theta = 0$; $0° < \theta < 180°$ 161.57
8. $5 \sin^2 \theta = 2 \sin \theta$; $90° \le \theta \le 180°$ 156.42
10. $3 \cos^2 \theta - 7 \cos \theta + 2 = 0$; $180° \le \theta < 360°$ 289.47

DOWN (Radians)

2. $4 + 3 \tan \theta = 0$; $0 \le \theta < \pi$ 2.21
9. $4 \tan^2 \theta = \tan \theta$; $0 < \theta < \pi$ 0.24
11. $5 \sin \theta = 1$; $0 \le \theta \le \pi/2$ 0.20
12. $2 \cos^2 \theta + 2 = 4$; $0 \le \theta \le \pi$ 0.84
13. $(\sin \theta)(\sin \theta + 1) = 0$; $\pi < \theta < 2\pi$ 4.71
14. $\cos^2 \theta - 1 = 0$; $2 \le \theta \le \pi$ 3.14
15. $2 \cos^2 \theta + 2 \cos \theta = 0$; $\pi/2 < \theta < \pi$ 2.30
16. $\sin^2 \theta + 2 \sin \theta + 1 = 0$; $\pi \le \theta \le \pi$ 4.71
17. $4 \sin^2 \theta - 15 \sin \theta + 9 = 0$; $\pi/2 \le \theta \le \pi$ 2.29

14-3 Right Triangles and Trigonometric Ratios

© Content Standards
G.SRT.6 Understand that by similarity, side ratios in right triangles . . . lead to definitions of trigonometric ratios for acute angles.
G.SRT.8 Use trigonometric ratios . . . to solve right triangles in applied problems.

Objective To find lengths of sides in a right triangle
To find measures of angles in a right triangle

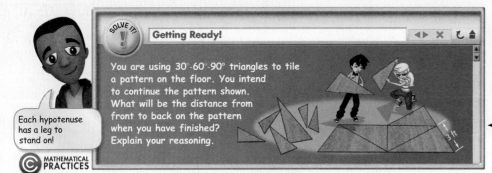

SOLVE IT

Getting Ready!

You are using 30°-60°-90° triangles to tile a pattern on the floor. You intend to continue the pattern shown. What will be the distance from front to back on the pattern when you have finished? Explain your reasoning.

Each hypotenuse has a leg to stand on!

© MATHEMATICAL PRACTICES

Lesson Vocabulary
• trigonometric ratios

There is a connection between the trigonometric functions and the right-triangle trigonometric ratios that you may have studied in geometry.

Essential Understanding If you restrict the domain of the trigonometric functions to angle measures between 0° and 90°, the function values are the trigonometric ratios associated with the acute angles of a right triangle.

Dilate the unit circle by the factor r and the terminal side of an angle θ will intersect the circle of radius r in the point $(x, y) = (r \cos \theta, r \sin \theta)$.

take note

Key Concept **Trigonometric Ratios for a Circle**

$$\sin \theta = \frac{y}{r} \qquad \csc \theta = \frac{r}{y}$$

$$\cos \theta = \frac{x}{r} \qquad \sec \theta = \frac{r}{x}$$

$$\tan \theta = \frac{y}{x} \qquad \cot \theta = \frac{x}{y}$$

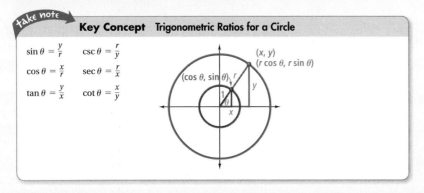

PowerAlgebra.com

Lesson 14-3 Right Triangles and Trigonometric Ratios   919

14-3 Preparing to Teach

BIG idea Function
ESSENTIAL UNDERSTANDINGS
• If the domains of the trigonometric functions are restricted to angle measures between 0° and 90°, the function values are the trigonometric ratios associated with the acute angles of a right triangle.
• In right triangle trigonometry, the value of one trigonometric ratio determines the values of the others.

Math Background
Since the measure of one angle of a right triangle is 90°, the sum of the measures of the other two angles is $180° - 90° = 90°$. Thus the domain of $0° < \theta < 90°$ includes all possible acute angles for a right triangle.

You can use the trigonometric ratios for right triangles to find unknown lengths of sides of right triangles.

Model and make sure students draw diagrams each time they solve a problem involving the trigonometric ratios for a right triangle to minimize mistakes.

© Mathematical Practices
Use appropriate tools strategically.
Students will use both the unit circle and scientific calculators, when needed, in calculating the trigonometric functions.

---

1 Interactive Learning

Solve It!
PURPOSE To use the relationships between the triangles to find the height of the final triangle
PROCESS Students may
• reason that the final pattern is an equilateral triangle and divide it into two 30°-60°-90° triangles to find the distance.
• calculate the lengths of successive rows of triangles and find the partial sum of the infinite geometric series.

FACILITATE
Q What is the measure of the base angles of the final triangle? How do you know? **[60°; the triangles are 30°-60°-90° triangles.]**
Q What kind of triangle is the pattern? Why? **[Equilateral; all the angles will be 60°.]**
Q What will each side of the pattern measure? Explain. **[12 ft; the base is formed by two hypotenuses; each measures 6 ft by the properties of a 30°-60°-90° triangle.]**
Q What is the height of the first three filled rows of triangles? **[$\frac{3}{2}\sqrt{3}$, $\frac{9}{8}\sqrt{3}$ and $\frac{27}{32}\sqrt{3}$]**
Q What is the common ratio for the sequence formed by these terms? **[$\frac{3}{4}$]**

ANSWER See Solve It in Answers on next page.
CONNECT THE MATH In the Solve It, students use the properties of special right triangles to solve for an unknown length in a triangle. In the lesson, students will develop methods for solving problems with other right triangles.

2 Guided Instruction

Take Note
The diagram shows $r > 1$. The relationships are also true for $0 < r < 1$.

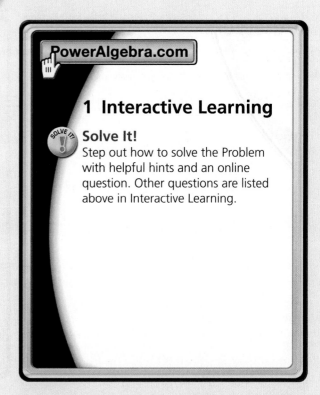

PowerAlgebra.com

1 Interactive Learning

SOLVE IT Solve It!
Step out how to solve the Problem with helpful hints and an online question. Other questions are listed above in Interactive Learning.

Lesson 14-3   **919**

Problem 1

> **Q** Would r ever be negative? Explain. **[No, r is the distance from the origin to the point, and distance is always nonnegative.]**
>
> **Q** Which trigonometric functions can you evaluate without finding the value of r? **[tan θ and cot θ]**

EXTENSION

> **Q** In which quadrants is sin θ positive? cos θ? tan θ? **[Quadrants I and II; Quadrants I and IV; Quadrants I and III]**

Got It?

> **Q** What is the value of r? **[13]**
>
> **Q** In which quadrant does the angle terminate? Which trigonometric values will be positive? **[Quadrant II; sin θ and csc θ]**

Take Note

> **Q** How are the lengths x, y, and r related? **[by the Pythagorean Theorem, $x^2 + y^2 = r^2$]**
>
> **Q** What will the measure of the angle opposite r always be? **[90°]**
>
> **Q** What can you say about the sine and cosine values of the angle complementary to θ $(90° - \theta)$? Explain. **[sin θ equals cos $(90° - \theta)$ and cos θ equals sin $(90° - \theta)$, because if you consider the angle complementary to θ, the labels adjacent and opposite are reversed, but the length of the hypotenuse is unchanged.]**

Think

How do you find r?
Use the distance formula.

 Problem 1 Trigonometric Values Beyond the Unit Circle

For a standard-position angle determined by the point $(8, -6)$, what are the values of the six trigonometric functions?

First, find the distance r of the point from the origin:

$$r = \sqrt{(8 - 0)^2 + (-6 - 0)^2} = 10.$$

Then,

$$\sin \theta = \frac{y}{r} = \frac{-6}{10} = -\frac{3}{5} \qquad \csc \theta = \frac{r}{y} = \frac{10}{-6} = -\frac{5}{3}$$

$$\cos \theta = \frac{x}{r} = \frac{8}{10} = \frac{4}{5} \qquad \sec \theta = \frac{r}{x} = \frac{10}{8} = \frac{5}{4}$$

$$\tan \theta = \frac{y}{x} = \frac{-6}{8} = -\frac{3}{4} \qquad \cot \theta = \frac{x}{y} = \frac{8}{-6} = -\frac{4}{3}$$

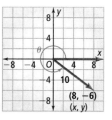

Got It? 1. For a standard-position angle determined by the point $(-5, 12)$, what are the values of the six trigonometric functions?

If you use only points in the first quadrant, the values of x, y, and r are positive. The values of the trigonometric functions are also positive and are the **trigonometric ratios** for an acute angle θ of a right triangle.

take note

Key Concept   Trigonometric Ratios for a Right Triangle

If θ is an acute angle of a right triangle, x is the length of the adjacent leg (ADJ), y is the length of the opposite leg (OPP), and r is the length of the hypotenuse (HYP), then the trigonometric ratios of θ are as follows.

$$\sin \theta = \frac{y}{r} = \frac{\text{OPP}}{\text{HYP}} \qquad \csc \theta = \frac{r}{y} = \frac{\text{HYP}}{\text{OPP}}$$

$$\cos \theta = \frac{x}{r} = \frac{\text{ADJ}}{\text{HYP}} \qquad \sec \theta = \frac{r}{x} = \frac{\text{HYP}}{\text{ADJ}}$$

$$\tan \theta = \frac{y}{x} = \frac{\text{OPP}}{\text{ADJ}} \qquad \cot \theta = \frac{x}{y} = \frac{\text{ADJ}}{\text{OPP}}$$

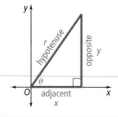

There are many applications of right-triangle trigonometry. Most involve degree measure and require the use of a calculator. Therefore, you will want to set your calculator to *degree mode*.

Answers

Solve It!

When (and if!) you finish, you will have completed an equilateral triangle with base 12 and height $6\sqrt{3}$.

Got It?

1. $\sin \theta = \frac{12}{13}$, $\cos \theta = -\frac{5}{13}$, $\tan \theta = -\frac{12}{5}$,

$\csc \theta = \frac{13}{12}$, $\sec \theta = -\frac{13}{5}$, $\cot \theta = -\frac{5}{12}$

PowerAlgebra.com

2 Guided Instruction

Each Problem is worked out and supported online.

Problem 1
Trigonometric Values Beyond the Unit Circle
Animated

Problem 2
Finding Distance

Problem 3
Finding Trigonometric Ratios
Animated

Problem 4
Using a Trigonometric Ratio to Solve a Problem
Animated

Problem 5
Finding an Angle Measure

Problem 6
Using an Inverse Trigonometric Ratio

Support in Algebra 2 Companion
• Vocabulary
• Key Concepts
• Got It?

Problem 2 Finding Distance

Plan

Which trigonometric ratio do you use?
You know an angle and an *adjacent* side. You want to find the *opposite* side. Use tangent.

The large glass pyramid at the Louvre in Paris has a square base. The angle formed by each face and the ground is 49.7°. How high is the pyramid?

The distance from the center of a side of the pyramid to a point directly below the top of the pyramid is half the length of a side, or 17.5 m.

$$\tan 49.7° = \frac{x}{17.5}$$

$$x = 17.5 \cdot \tan 49.7°$$

$$x \approx 20.6$$

The pyramid is about 20.6 m high.

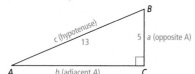

 Got It? **2.** What is each distance for the Louvre pyramid?
 a. from the center of a side of the base to the top along a lateral face
 b. from a corner of the base to the top

In right triangle trigonometry, the value of one trigonometric ratio determines the values of the others.

Problem 3 Finding Trigonometric Ratios

Plan

How do you begin?
A diagram will help you see the legs—opposite and adjacent to the angle—and the hypotenuse.

In $\triangle ABC$, $\angle C$ is a right angle and $\sin A = \frac{5}{13}$. What are $\cos A$, $\cot A$, and $\sin B$?

Step 1 Draw a diagram.

Step 2 Use the Pythagorean Theorem to find b.

$$c^2 = a^2 + b^2$$
$$13^2 = 5^2 + b^2$$
$$169 = 25 + b^2$$
$$144 = b^2$$
$$12 = b$$

Step 3 Write the ratios.

$$\cos A = \frac{\text{ADJ}}{\text{HYP}} = \frac{12}{13} \qquad \cot A = \frac{\text{ADJ}}{\text{OPP}} = \frac{12}{5} \qquad \sin B = \frac{\text{OPP}}{\text{HYP}} = \frac{12}{13}$$

 Got It? **3.** In $\triangle DEF$, $\angle D$ is a right angle and $\tan E = \frac{3}{4}$. What are $\sin E$ and $\sec F$?

Problem 2

Q Why do you use 17.5 instead of 35 in the equation? **[The right triangle is formed at the center of the square base, and the distance from the square's center to the midpoint of the baseline of any of the faces is half the length of a side of the square base.]**

Got It?

Q What part of the diagram represents the distance in 2a? **[the hypotenuse of the right triangle in the diagram]**

Q What trigonometric function could you use to find the length described by 2a? Explain. **[Sample: Sine; $\sin 49.7 = \frac{x}{r}$, and x was found in Problem 2.]**

Q How could you find the length described by 2b? **[Sample: Use the Pythagorean Theorem.]**

Problem 3

Q What does it mean for a side of a triangle to be opposite an angle? **[Sample: A side opposite an angle does not include the vertex of the angle as one of its endpoints.]**

Got It?

Q If the sides of the triangle are labeled d, e, and f, what equation will relate the side lengths? **[$e^2 + f^2 = d^2$]**

Q Which variables do you know values for in the given information? **[None; you know only the ratio of e to f.]**

Additional Problems

1. For a standard-position angle determined by the point $(-10, -24)$, what are the values of the six trigonometric functions?

ANSWER

$\sin \theta = -\frac{12}{13}$; $\cos \theta = -\frac{5}{13}$;

$\tan \theta = \frac{12}{5}$; $\csc \theta = -\frac{13}{12}$;

$\sec \theta = -\frac{13}{5}$; $\cot \theta = \frac{5}{12}$

2. Part of a circle of paper with a diameter of 10 in. is cut and taped together to form a cone and then is set upright on a table. The angle that the cone makes with the table is measured and found to be 50°. What is the height of the cone?

ANSWER 3.8 in.

3. In $\triangle TUW$, $\angle U$ is a right angle and $\cos T = \frac{24}{25}$. What are $\tan T$ and $\sin T$?

ANSWER $\tan T = \frac{7}{24}$, $\sin T = \frac{7}{25}$

4. You are on a sailboat at sea and spot a 786-ft bluff on the shore. You measure the angle from your sailboat to the top of the bluff and find that it is 16°. About how far are you from the shore at the foot of the bluff?

ANSWER about 2741.1 ft

5. In $\triangle KMN$, $\angle M$ is a right angle, $k = 3$, and $n = 5$. What is $m\angle K$?

ANSWER 31°

6. A straight stretch of highway has a grade of 6%. If you travel 3 mi along the highway, how much will your altitude have changed?

ANSWER about 0.18 mi, or 949 ft

Answers

Got It? (continued)

2. a. 27.1 m
 b. 32.2 m

3. $\sin E = \frac{3}{5}$, $\sec F = \frac{5}{3}$

Problem 4

Q How do you know that the angle inside the sketched triangle is also 3°? **[When parallel lines are cut by a transversal, alternate interior angles are congruent.]**

EXTENSION

Q What equation could you use to find the straight-line distance to the airport if you wanted to use the 87° angle the plane's path makes with the vertical? **[$\cos 87° = \frac{5000}{x}$]**

Got It?

Q What equation will you use to find the distance? **[$\sin 3° = \frac{4000}{x}$]**

EXTENSION

Q What is the distance along the ground of the plane from the airport? **[$\tan 3° = \frac{4000}{x}$, so $x = \frac{4000}{\tan 3°} = 76,324.5$ ft, or about 14.5 mi]**

Problem 5   ERROR PREVENTION

Q Why is it important to sketch and label a triangle when solving problems that use trigonometric ratios and right triangles? **[so that the legs are labeled correctly as the adjacent and opposite sides in relation to the angle being referenced]**

Got It?

Q Which trigonometric ratios relate the known sides to ∠A in 5a? 5b? **[sine; cosine]**

If you are given the measures of an acute angle and a side of a right triangle, you can find the lengths of the other two sides.

© **Problem 4** Using a Trigonometric Ratio to Solve a Problem

Aviation An airplane's angle of descent into the airport is 3°. If the airplane begins its descent at an altitude of 5000 ft, what is its straight-line distance to the airport?

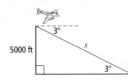

Know	Need	Plan
An airplane is 5000 ft high and starts to descend at an angle of 3° with the horizontal.	The straight-line distance from the airplane to the airport.	Draw a right triangle to show the known information. Set up a trigonometric ratio that involves the known information and what you want to find.

Let x represent the straight-line distance.

$\sin 3° = \frac{5000}{x}$ $\sin \theta = \frac{OPP}{HYP}$

$x = \frac{5000}{\sin 3°}$ Solve for x.

$\approx 95,500$ Use a calculator.

The straight-line distance is about 95,500 ft, or about 18 miles.

✔ **Got It? 4.** If the airplane in Problem 4 begins its descent at an altitude of 4000 feet, what is its straight-line distance to the airport?

Given any two sides in a right triangle, you can use inverse trigonometric functions to find the measures of the acute angles.

© **Problem 5** Finding an Angle Measure

Plan
Which trigonometric ratio do you use?
You know the side adjacent to D and the hypotenuse. Use cosine.

In △DGH, ∠H is a right angle, h = 13, and g = 5. What is m∠D?

 Side h is opposite ∠H.

 Side g is opposite ∠G.

$\cos D = \frac{5}{13}$ $\cos D = \frac{ADJ}{HYP}$

$m\angle D = \cos^{-1} \frac{5}{13}$ Solve for m∠D.

$\approx 67.38°$ Use a calculator.

To the nearest tenth of a degree, m∠D is 67.4°.

✔ **Got It? 5.** What is m∠A in each triangle? Use a trigonometric ratio.

a.

b.

Answers

Got It? (continued)

4. ≈76,430 ft ≈ 14.5 mi

5. a. 23.58°

b. 56.25°

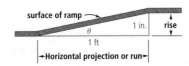

Problem 6 Using the Inverse of a Trigonometric Function STEM

Construction You must build a wheelchair ramp so the slope is not more than 1 in. of rise for every 1 ft of run. What is the maximum angle that the ramp can make with the ground, to the nearest tenth of a degree?

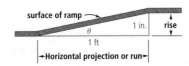

surface of ramp

1 in. | rise

θ

1 ft

←Horizontal projection or run→

Let θ = the measure of the angle the ramp makes with the ground.

You know the lengths of the leg opposite and the leg adjacent to the angle you need to find. So, use the tangent ratio.

Think

Does the answer make sense?
The angle should be small for a wheelchair ramp, so the answer makes sense.

$\tan \theta = \frac{1}{12}$ Rewrite 1 ft as 12 in.

$\theta = \tan^{-1}\frac{1}{12}$ Use the inverse tangent function.

$\theta \approx 4.76$ Use a calculator.

The maximum angle (rounded) that the ramp can make with the ground is 4.8°.

Got It? **6.** An entrance to a building is not wheelchair accessible. The entrance is 6 feet above ground level and 30 feet from the roadway.
    a. How long must the ramp be for the slope to meet the regulation of 1 inch of rise for every 1 foot of run?
    b. Reasoning How can you build a ramp to meet the regulation within the space of 30 feet?

Lesson Check

Do you know HOW?

Use the diagram for Exercises 1–3.

1. Write ratios for sin 57°, cos 57°, and tan 57°.

2. If $a = 10$, what is b?

3. Find the values of sin 33°, cos 33°, and tan 33° as fractions and as decimals. Round to the nearest tenth.

4. Find $\sin^{-1} 0.6$ to the nearest tenth of a degree.

Do you UNDERSTAND? MATHEMATICAL PRACTICES

5. Writing In a right triangle, the length of the shortest side is 8.4 m and the length of the hypotenuse is 12.9 m. Show and describe how you would find the acute angle measures.

6. Error Analysis One of the angles in a right triangle measures 0.45 radians. The side opposite the angle measures 4 cm. A student finds the length of the hypotenuse. What mistake does the student make?

$\sin 0.45 = \frac{4}{x}$

$x = 4\sin^{-1}0.45$

$x \approx 1.87$

---

6. a. 72 ft
    b. Answers may vary. Sample: Build the ramp in 3 sections, each of which is 24 ft, and with landings between sections.

Lesson Check

1. $\sin 57° = \frac{b}{c}$, $\cos 57° = \frac{a}{c}$, $\tan 57° = \frac{b}{a}$

2. 15.4

3. $\sin 33° = \frac{a}{c} = 0.5$, $\cos 33° = \frac{b}{c} = 0.8$, $\tan 33° = \frac{a}{b} = 0.6$

4. 36.9°

5. Answers may vary. Sample: Using the inverse of cosine, you can find the acute angle between the shortest side and the hypotenuse, $\theta = \cos^{-1}\left(\frac{8.4}{12.9}\right) \approx 49.4°$. Because the triangle is a right triangle, the remaining acute angle is $\approx 90° - 49.4° = 40.6°$.

6. The student confuses $\sin^{-1} \theta$ with $\frac{1}{\sin \theta}$. He or she should have divided by sin 0.45. $x = \frac{4}{\sin 0.45\pi} \approx 9.20$ cm

---

Problem 6

Q Why do you rewrite 1 ft as 12 in.? **[The units must match in the ratio, so you need to convert the foot to 12 inches; you could also convert the inch to $\frac{1}{12}$ of a foot.]**

Got It?

Q What equation will you solve to find the length of the ramp? **[$\sin 4.8° = \frac{6}{x}$]**

3 Lesson Check

Do you know HOW?
• For Exercise 1, suggest students label the sides of the triangle in relation to $\angle B$ as opposite, adjacent, and hypotenuse.
• For Exercise 2, ask which trigonometric ratio relates a and b to $\angle B$.

Do you UNDERSTAND?
• For Exercise 5, have students draw and label the right triangle that models the given information.

Close

Q How are the ratios of the lengths of pairs of sides in a right triangle related to a given acute angle in a right triangle? **[The sine of the angle is the value of the ratio of the lengths of the leg opposite the angle and the hypotenuse. The cosine of the angle is the value of the ratio of the lengths of the leg adjacent to the angle and the hypotenuse. The tangent of the angle is the value of the ratio of the lengths of the legs opposite and adjacent to the angle.]**

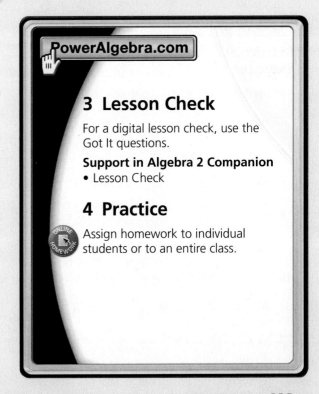

PowerAlgebra.com

3 Lesson Check
For a digital lesson check, use the Got It questions.

Support in Algebra 2 Companion
• Lesson Check

4 Practice
Assign homework to individual students or to an entire class.

4 Practice

ASSIGNMENT GUIDE

Basic: 7–25 all, 32–38 even, 45

Average: 7–25 odd, 26–46

Advanced: 7–25 odd, 26–51

Standardized Test Prep: 52–56

Mixed Review: 57–65

 Mathematical Practices are supported by exercises with red headings. Here are the Practices supported in this lesson:

MP 1: Make Sense of Problems Ex. 34
MP 2: Reason Abstractly Ex. 44b, 46
MP 3: Construct Arguments Ex. 45
MP 3: Communicate Ex. 5
MP 3: Critique the Reasoning of Others Ex. 6

Applications exercises have blue headings. Exercises 18, 25, and 35 support MP 4: Model.

EXERCISE 36: Use the Think About a Plan worksheet in the **Practice and Problem Solving Workbook** (also available in the Teaching Resources in print and online) to further support students' development in becoming independent learners.

HOMEWORK QUICK CHECK

To check students' understanding of key skills and concepts, go over Exercises 9, 13, 34, 36, and 45.

 Practice and Problem-Solving Exercises   MATHEMATICAL PRACTICES

A Practice Find the values of the six trigonometric functions for the angle in standard position determined by each point. ◀ See Problem 1.

7. $(-4, 3)$ **8.** $(5, 12)$ **9.** $(1, -5)$ **10.** $(-5, -2)$ **11.** $(-3, \sqrt{7})$

12. You want to build a bicycle ramp that is 10 ft long and makes a 30° angle with the ground. What would be the height of the ramp? ◀ See Problem 2.

13. In $\triangle ABC$, find each value as a fraction and as a decimal. Round to the nearest hundredth. ◀ See Problem 3.
  a. $\sin A$ **b.** $\sec A$ **c.** $\cot A$
  d. $\csc B$ **e.** $\sec B$ **f.** $\tan B$

14. In $\triangle GHI$, $\angle H$ is a right angle, $GH = 40$, and $\cos G = \frac{40}{41}$. Draw a diagram and find each value in fraction and in decimal form.
  a. $\sin G$ **b.** $\sin I$ **c.** $\cot G$
  d. $\csc G$ **e.** $\cos I$ **f.** $\sec H$

Find each length x. Round to the nearest tenth. ◀ See Problem 4.

15.   **16.**   **17.**

18. Indirect Measurement In 1915, the tallest flagpole in the world stood in San Francisco.
  a. When the angle of elevation of the sun was 55°, the length of the shadow cast by this flagpole was 210 ft. Find the height of the flagpole to the nearest foot.
  b. What was the length of the shadow when the angle of elevation of the sun was 34°?
  c. What do you need to assume about the flagpole and the shadow to solve these problems. Explain why.

In $\triangle ABC$, $\angle C$ is a right angle. Find the remaining sides and angles. Round your answers to the nearest tenth. ◀ See Problem 5.

19. $b = 5, c = 10$ **20.** $a = 5, b = 6$ **21.** $b = 12, c = 15$

22. $a = 8.1, b = 6.2$ **23.** $b = 4.3, c = 9.1$ **24.** $a = 17, c = 22$

STEM 25. Rocket Science An observer on the ground at point A watches a rocket ascend. The observer is 1200 ft from the launch point B. As the rocket rises, the distance d from the observer to the rocket increases. ◀ See Problem 6.
  a. Express $m\angle A$ in terms of d.
  b. Find $m\angle A$ if $d = 1500$ ft. Round your answer to the nearest degree.
  c. Find $m\angle A$ if $d = 2000$ ft. Round your answer to the nearest degree.

Answers

Practice and Problem-Solving Exercises

7. $\sin \theta = \frac{3}{5}$, $\cos \theta = -\frac{4}{5}$, $\tan \theta = -\frac{3}{4}$, $\csc \theta = \frac{5}{3}$, $\sec \theta = -\frac{5}{4}$, $\cot \theta = -\frac{4}{3}$

8. $\sin \theta = \frac{12}{13}$, $\cos \theta = \frac{5}{13}$, $\tan \theta = \frac{12}{5}$, $\csc \theta = \frac{13}{12}$, $\sec \theta = \frac{13}{5}$, $\cot \theta = \frac{5}{12}$

9. $\sin \theta = -\frac{5\sqrt{26}}{26}$, $\cos \theta = \frac{\sqrt{26}}{26}$, $\tan \theta = -5$, $\csc \theta = -\frac{\sqrt{26}}{5}$, $\sec \theta = \sqrt{26}$, $\cot \theta = -\frac{1}{5}$

10. $\sin \theta = -\frac{2\sqrt{29}}{29}$, $\cos \theta = -\frac{5\sqrt{29}}{29}$, $\tan \theta = \frac{2}{5}$, $\csc \theta = -\frac{\sqrt{29}}{2}$, $\sec \theta = -\frac{\sqrt{29}}{5}$, $\cot \theta = \frac{5}{2}$

11. $\sin \theta = \frac{\sqrt{7}}{4}$, $\cos \theta = -\frac{3}{4}$, $\tan \theta = -\frac{\sqrt{7}}{3}$, $\csc \theta = \frac{4\sqrt{7}}{7}$, $\sec \theta = -\frac{4}{3}$, $\cot \theta = -\frac{3\sqrt{7}}{7}$

12. height $= 10 \sin 30° = 5$ ft

13. a. $\frac{15}{17} \approx 0.88$
  b. $\frac{17}{8} \approx 2.13$
  c. $\frac{8}{15} \approx 0.53$
  d. $\frac{17}{8} \approx 2.13$
  e. $\frac{17}{15} \approx 1.13$
  f. $\frac{8}{15} \approx 0.53$

14.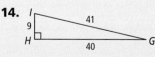
  a. $\frac{9}{41} \approx 0.22$ **b.** $\frac{40}{41} \approx 0.98$
  c. $\frac{40}{9} \approx 4.44$ **d.** $\frac{41}{9} \approx 4.56$
  e. $\frac{9}{41} \approx 0.22$ **f.** not defined

15. 41.8   **16.** 10.6

17. 25.2

18. a. 300 ft
  b. 445 ft
  c. Answers may vary. Sample: The flag pole should be straight and perpendicular to the ground, and the shadow cast on the ground should also be a straight line.

19. $a \approx 8.7$, $m\angle A = 60.0°$, $m\angle B = 30.0°$
20. $c \approx 7.8$, $m\angle A \approx 39.8°$, $m\angle B \approx 50.2°$
21. $a = 9.0$, $m\angle A \approx 36.9°$, $m\angle B \approx 53.1°$
22. $c \approx 10.2$, $m\angle A \approx 52.6°$, $m\angle B \approx 37.4°$
23. $a = 8.0$, $m\angle A \approx 61.8°$, $m\angle B \approx 28.2°$
24. $b \approx 14.0$, $m\angle A \approx 50.6°$, $m\angle B \approx 39.4°$

25. a. $m\angle A = \cos^{-1}\left(\frac{1200}{d}\right)$
  b. 37°
  c. 53°

B Apply

Sketch a right triangle with θ as the measure of one acute angle. Find the other five trigonometric ratios of θ.

26. $\sin \theta = \frac{3}{8}$ **27.** $\cos \theta = \frac{7}{20}$ **28.** $\cos \theta = \frac{1}{5}$ **29.** $\tan \theta = \frac{24}{7}$

30. $\sec \theta = \frac{16}{9}$ **31.** $\cot \theta = \frac{5}{4}$ **32.** $\sin \theta = 0.35$ **33.** $\csc \theta = 5.2$

Ⓒ 34. Think About a Plan A radio tower has supporting cables attached to it at points 100 ft above the ground. Write a model for the length d of each supporting cable as a function of the angle θ that it makes with the ground. Then find d when $\theta = 60°$ and when $\theta = 50°$.
- Which trigonometric function applies?
- How do you set up the equation?

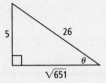

35. Indirect Measurement You are 330 ft from the base of a building. The angles of elevation to the top and bottom of a flagpole on top of the building are 55° and 53°. Find the height of the flagpole.

36. A 150-ft redwood tree casts a shadow. Express the length x of the shadow as a function of the angle of elevation of the sun θ. Then find x when $\theta = 35°$ and $\theta = 70°$.

37. Geometry An altitude inside a triangle forms 36° and 42° angles with two of the sides. The altitude is 5 m long. Find the area of the triangle.

In $\triangle ABC$, $\angle C$ is a right angle. Two measures are given. Find the remaining sides and angles. Round your answers to the nearest tenth.

38. $b = 8, c = 17$ **39.** $a = 7, b = 10$ **40.** $m\angle A = 52°, c = 10$

41. $m\angle A = 34.2°, b = 5.7$ **42.** $m\angle B = 17.2°, b = 8.3$ **43.** $m\angle B = 8.3°, c = 20$

Ⓒ 44. a. In Problem 5, use the Pythagorean Theorem to find GH.
   b. Multiple Representations Use a trigonometric ratio to find GH.

Ⓒ 45. Open-Ended If $\sin \theta = \frac{1}{2}$, describe a method you could use to find all the angles between 0° and 360° that satisfy this equation.

Ⓒ 46. Reasoning Show that $\cos A$ defined as a ratio equals $\cos \theta$ using the unit circle.

C Challenge

Use the definitions of trigonometric ratios in right $\triangle ABC$ to verify each identity.

47. $\sec A = \frac{1}{\cos A}$ **48.** $\tan A = \frac{\sin A}{\cos A}$ **49.** $\cos^2 A + \sin^2 A = 1$

50. Geometry A regular pentagon is inscribed in a circle of radius 10 cm.
   a. Find the measure of $\angle C$.
   b. Find the length of the diagonal PS. (*Hint:* First find RS.)

26.

$\cos \theta = \frac{\sqrt{55}}{8}$, $\tan \theta = \frac{3\sqrt{55}}{55}$, $\csc \theta = \frac{8}{3}$, $\sec \theta = \frac{8\sqrt{55}}{55}$, $\cot \theta = \frac{\sqrt{55}}{3}$

27.

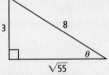

$\sin \theta = \frac{3\sqrt{39}}{20}$, $\tan \theta = \frac{3\sqrt{39}}{7}$, $\csc \theta = \frac{20\sqrt{39}}{117}$, $\sec \theta = \frac{20}{7}$, $\cot \theta = \frac{7\sqrt{39}}{117}$

28.

$\sin \theta = \frac{2\sqrt{6}}{5}$, $\tan \theta = 2\sqrt{6}$, $\csc \theta = \frac{5\sqrt{6}}{12}$, $\sec \theta = 5$, $\cot \theta = \frac{\sqrt{6}}{12}$

29.

$\sin \theta = \frac{24}{25}$, $\cos \theta = \frac{7}{25}$, $\csc \theta = \frac{25}{24}$, $\sec \theta = \frac{25}{7}$, $\cot \theta = \frac{7}{24}$

30.

$\sin \theta = \frac{5\sqrt{7}}{16}$, $\cos \theta = \frac{9}{16}$, $\tan \theta = \frac{5\sqrt{7}}{9}$, $\csc \theta = \frac{16\sqrt{7}}{35}$, $\cot \theta = \frac{9\sqrt{7}}{35}$

31.

$\sin \theta = \frac{4\sqrt{41}}{41}$, $\cos \theta = \frac{5\sqrt{41}}{41}$, $\tan \theta = \frac{4}{5}$, $\csc \theta = \frac{\sqrt{41}}{4}$, $\sec \theta = \frac{\sqrt{41}}{5}$

32.

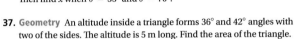

$\cos \theta = \frac{3\sqrt{39}}{20}$, $\tan \theta = \frac{7\sqrt{39}}{117}$, $\csc \theta = \frac{20}{7}$, $\sec \theta = \frac{20\sqrt{39}}{117}$, $\cot \theta = \frac{3\sqrt{39}}{7}$

33.

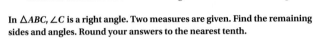

$\sin \theta = \frac{5}{26}$, $\cos \theta = \frac{\sqrt{651}}{26}$, $\tan \theta = \frac{5\sqrt{651}}{651}$, $\sec \theta = \frac{26\sqrt{651}}{651}$, $\cot \theta = \frac{\sqrt{651}}{5}$

34. $d = \frac{100}{\sin \theta}$; 115.5 ft; 130.5 ft

35. 33.4 ft

36. $x = \frac{150}{\tan \theta}$; 214.2 ft; 54.6 ft

37. 20.3 m²

38. $a = 15$, $m\angle A \approx 61.9°$, $m\angle B \approx 28.1°$

39. $c \approx 12.2$, $m\angle A \approx 35.0°$, $m\angle B \approx 55.0°$

40. $a \approx 7.9$, $b \approx 6.2$, $m\angle B = 38°$

41. $a \approx 3.9$, $c \approx 6.9$, $m\angle B = 55.8°$

42. $a \approx 26.8$, $c \approx 28.1$, $m\angle A = 72.8°$

43. $a \approx 19.8$, $b \approx 2.9$, $m\angle A = 81.7°$

44. a. 12
   b. 12

45. Using inverse sine, you can find that $\theta = 30°$. Since sine is positive in the first and second quadrants, another solution is 150°. All the solutions would be $30° + 360° \cdot n$ and $150° + 360° \cdot n$.

46.

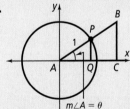

Since $\triangle APQ$ and $\triangle ABC$ are similar triangles, $\frac{AQ}{AP} = \frac{AC}{AB}$. So, $\cos \theta = AQ$, $\cos \theta = AQ = \frac{AQ}{1} = \frac{AQ}{AP} = \frac{AC}{AB} = \cos A$.

47. $\sec A = \frac{c}{b} = \frac{1}{\left(\frac{b}{c}\right)} = \frac{1}{\cos A}$

48–50. See next page.

Answers

Practice and Problem-Solving Exercises (continued)

48. $\tan A = \dfrac{a}{b} = \dfrac{\left(\frac{a}{c}\right)}{\left(\frac{b}{c}\right)} = \dfrac{\sin A}{\cos A}$

49. $\cos^2 A + \sin^2 A = \left(\dfrac{b}{c}\right)^2 + \left(\dfrac{a}{c}\right)^2$
$= \dfrac{b^2 + a^2}{c^2} = 1$

50. a. $72°$

    b. 19.0 cm

51. $y \approx 61.7$ m

Standardized Test Prep

52. A

53. G

54. C

55. I

56. **[2]** $\tan \angle A = \dfrac{135}{95}$

$m\angle A = \tan^{-1}\dfrac{135}{95}$

$m\angle A \approx 54.9°$

$\tan \angle B = \dfrac{95}{135}$

$m\angle B = \tan^{-1}\dfrac{95}{135}$

$m\angle B \approx 35.1°$

    [1] only one measure correctly calculated OR correct answers, but with less efficient method

Mixed Review

57. $180° + 360° \cdot n$

58. $45° + 180° \cdot n$ and $90° + 180° \cdot n$

59. $0° + 180° \cdot n$

60.
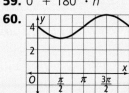

61.
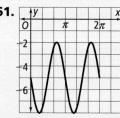

62.
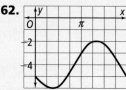

63. 6 cm^2

64. 45 in.^{2}

65. 32.76 mm^2

---

51. The tallest obelisk in Europe is the Wellington Testimonial in Dublin, Ireland. The distance between an angle of 37° from the ground and the top of the obelisk and an angle of 30° from the ground to the top of the obelisk is 25 m. Use these measurements to find the height of the obelisk. Use the diagram at the right to set up some trigonometric equations.

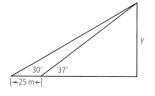

Standardized Test Prep

SAT/ACT

52. The figure at the right is a rectangle. What is the value of x?

    Ⓐ 31.0   Ⓒ 53.1

    Ⓑ 36.9   Ⓓ 59.0

53. In $\triangle XYZ$, $\angle Z$ is a right angle and $\tan X = \dfrac{8}{15}$. What is $\sin Y$?

    Ⓕ $\dfrac{8}{17}$ Ⓖ $\dfrac{15}{17}$ Ⓗ $\dfrac{17}{15}$ Ⓘ $\dfrac{15}{8}$

54. In the right triangle at the right, $\cos y° = \dfrac{5}{13}$. If $x + 2z = 7.1$ (z not pictured), what is the value of z?

    Ⓐ 67.3   Ⓒ −7.76

    Ⓑ 22.6   Ⓓ −30.1

55. The sides of a rectangle are 25 cm and 8 cm. What is the measure of the angle formed by the short side and a diagonal of the rectangle?

    Ⓕ 17.7°   Ⓖ 18.7°   Ⓗ 71.3°   Ⓘ 72.3°

Short Response

56. Find the measures of the acute angles of a right triangle, to the nearest tenth, if the legs are 135 cm and 95 cm.

Mixed Review

Find the complete solution of each equation. Express your answer in degrees.   ◀ **See Lesson 14-2.**

57. $\sec^2 \theta + \sec \theta = 0$ **58.** $\cot \theta = \cot^2 \theta$ **59.** $\sin^2 \theta + 5 \sin \theta = 0$

Graph each function on the interval from 0 to 2π.   ◀ **See Lesson 13-7.**

60. $y = \sin (x - \pi) + 4$ **61.** $y = 3 \sin 2\left(x + \dfrac{\pi}{2}\right) - 5$ **62.** $y = -2 \cos \left(x - \dfrac{\pi}{3}\right) - 4$

Get Ready!   **To prepare for Lesson 14-4, do Exercises 63–65.**

Find the area of a triangle with the given base b and height h.   ◀ **See p. 976.**

63. $b = 3$ cm, $h = 4$ cm   **64.** $b = 6$ in., $h = 15$ in.   **65.** $b = 5.2$ mm, $h = 12.6$ mm

Additional Instructional Support

Algebra 2 Companion

Students can use the **Algebra 2 Companion** worktext (4 pages) as you teach the lesson. Use the Companion to support

- New Vocabulary
- Key Concepts
- Got It for each Problem
- Lesson Check

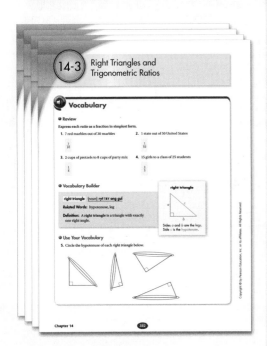

ELL Support

Connect to Prior Knowledge To help students remember the ratios associated with sine, cosine, and tangent in a right triangle, use a mnemonic device such as SOH CAH TOA or Oscar Had A Heap Of Apples. Students may come up with one of their own as well. If you allow students to come up with one on their own, check it for correctness.

Assess Understanding To aid students in working the exercises, pair students and have them work together to make a labeled sketch to go with any of the word problems that you are assigning. Ask students to explain their sketches to you as you check them to catch and correct errors in problem interpretation.

5 Assess & Remediate

Lesson Quiz

1. For a standard-position angle determined by the point $(3, -4)$, what are the values of the six trigonometric functions?
2. In $\triangle PQR$, $\angle P$ is a right angle and $\cos Q = \frac{8}{17}$. What are $\sin Q$ and $\tan Q$?
3. **Do you UNDERSTAND?** An airplane climbs at an angle of $2.7°$ from an altitude of 4500 ft to an altitude of 5600 ft. How far does the airplane travel as it climbs as measured along the horizontal?
4. In $\triangle XYZ$, $\angle Z$ is a right angle, $x = 6$ and $y = 4$. What is $m \angle Y$?
5. A box has a base with dimensions of 1 ft by 2 ft. You take a 2.4-ft baton and lay it across the bottom with one end in a bottom corner and the other end resting above the diagonally opposite corner. What angle will the baton make with the horizontal?

ANSWERS TO LESSON QUIZ

1. $\sin \theta = -\frac{4}{5}$, $\cos \theta = \frac{3}{5}$, $\tan \theta = -\frac{4}{3}$, $\csc \theta = -\frac{5}{4}$, $\sec \theta = \frac{5}{3}$, $\cot \theta = -\frac{3}{4}$

2. $\sin Q = \frac{15}{17}$; $\tan Q = \frac{15}{8}$
3. 23,325 ft or 4.4 mi
4. $33.7°$
5. $21.3°$

PRESCRIPTION FOR REMEDIATION

Use the student work on the Lesson Quiz to prescribe a differentiated review assignment:

Points	Differentiated Remediation
0–2	Intervention
3–4	On-level
5	Extension

PowerAlgebra.com

5 Assess & Remediate

Assign the Lesson Quiz. Appropriate intervention, practice, or enrichment is automatically generated based on student performance.

Intervention

- **Reteaching** (2 pages) Provides reteaching and practice exercises for the key lesson concepts. Use with struggling students or absent students.
- **English Language Learner Support** Helps students develop and reinforce mathematical vocabulary and key concepts.

All-in-One Resources/Online
Reteaching

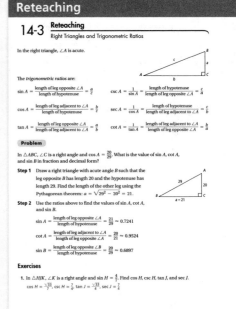

All-in-One Resources/Online
English Language Learner Support

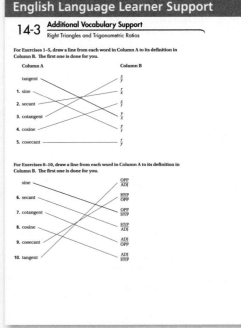

Differentiated Remediation *continued*

On-Level

- **Practice** (2 pages) Provides extra practice for each lesson. For simpler practice exercises, use the Form K Practice pages found in the All-in-One Teaching Resources and online.
- **Think About a Plan** Helps students develop specific problem-solving skills and strategies by providing scaffolded guiding questions.
- **Standardized Test Prep** Focuses on all major exercises, all major question types, and helps students prepare for the high-stakes assessments.

Extension

- **Enrichment** Provides students with interesting problems and activities that extend the concepts of the lesson.
- **Activities, Games, and Puzzles** Worksheets that can be used for concepts development, enrichment, and for fun!

Practice and Problem Solving Wkbk/ All-in-One Resources/Online

Practice page 1

14-3 **Practice** *Form G*
Right Triangles and Trigonometric Ratios

Find the values of the six trigonometric functions for the angle in standard position determined by each point.

1. $(-3, 4)$
$\sin\theta = \frac{4}{5}$, $\cos\theta = -\frac{3}{5}$, $\tan\theta = -\frac{4}{3}$,
$\csc\theta = \frac{5}{4}$, $\sec\theta = -\frac{5}{3}$, $\cot\theta = -\frac{3}{4}$
2. $(12, -5)$
$\sin\theta = -\frac{5}{13}$, $\cos\theta = \frac{12}{13}$, $\tan\theta = -\frac{5}{12}$,
$\csc\theta = -\frac{13}{5}$, $\sec\theta = \frac{13}{12}$, $\cot\theta = -\frac{12}{5}$
3. $(-2, -1)$
$\sin\theta = -\frac{\sqrt{5}}{5}$, $\cos\theta = -\frac{2\sqrt{5}}{5}$, $\tan\theta = \frac{1}{2}$,
$\csc\theta = -\sqrt{5}$, $\sec\theta = -\frac{\sqrt{5}}{2}$, $\cot\theta = 2$
4. $(\sqrt{5}, 2)$
$\sin\theta = \frac{2}{3}$, $\cos\theta = \frac{\sqrt{5}}{3}$, $\tan\theta = \frac{2\sqrt{5}}{5}$,
$\csc\theta = \frac{3}{2}$, $\sec\theta = \frac{3\sqrt{5}}{5}$, $\cot\theta = \frac{\sqrt{5}}{2}$
5. A hiker is standing on one bank of a river. A tree stands on the opposite bank, which is 750 ft away. A line from the top of the tree to the ground at the hiker's feet makes an angle of 12° with the ground. How tall is the tree?
about 159 ft
6. In $\triangle ABC$, find each value as a fraction and as a decimal. Round to the nearest hundredth.

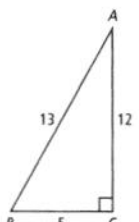

a. $\cos A$ $\frac{12}{13}$, 0.92
b. $\csc A$ $\frac{13}{5}$, 2.60
c. $\tan B$ $\frac{12}{5}$, 2.40
d. $\sec B$ $\frac{13}{5}$, 2.60
e. $\cot A$ $\frac{12}{5}$, 2.4
f. $\csc B$ $\frac{13}{12}$, 1.08

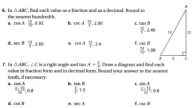

7. In $\triangle ABC$, $\angle C$ is a right angle and $\tan A = \frac{2}{3}$. Draw a diagram and find each value in fraction form and in decimal form. Round your answer to the nearest tenth, if necessary.
a. $\cos A$ $\frac{3\sqrt{13}}{13}$; 0.8
b. $\tan B$ $\frac{3}{2}$; 1.5
c. $\sin A$ $\frac{2\sqrt{13}}{13}$; 0.6
d. $\cot B$ $\frac{2}{3}$; 0.7
e. $\sec A$ $\frac{\sqrt{13}}{3}$; 1.2
f. $\csc B$ $\frac{\sqrt{13}}{3}$; 1.2

Find each length x. Round to the nearest tenth.

8. 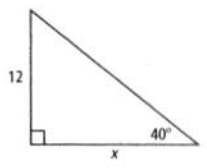

14.3

9. 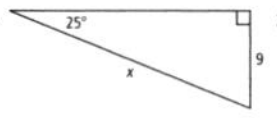

21.3

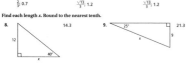

Practice and Problem Solving Wkbk/ All-in-One Resources/Online

Practice page 2

14-3 **Practice** (continued) *Form G*
Right Triangles and Trigonometric Ratios

10. A kite string makes a 62° angle with the horizontal, and 300 ft of string is let out. The string is held 6 ft off the ground. How high is the kite? about 270.9 ft

In ΔDEF, $\angle D$ is a right angle. Find the remaining sides and angles. Round answers to the nearest tenth.

11. $f = 8, e = 15$
$d = 17$; $\angle F = 28.1°$; $\angle E = 61.9°$
12. $f = 1, e = 2$
$d = 2.2$; $\angle F = 26.6°$; $\angle E = 63.4°$
13. $f = 2, e = 1$
$d = 2.2$; $\angle F = 63.4°$; $\angle E = 26.6°$
14. $f = 1, d = 500$
$e = 500$; $\angle F = 0.1°$; $\angle E = 89.9°$
15. $d = 21, e = 8$
$f = 19.4$; $\angle F = 67.6°$; $\angle E = 22.4°$
16. $e = 5, f = 1$
$d = 5.1$; $\angle F = 11.3°$; $\angle E = 78.7°$
17. You are designing several access ramps. What angle would each ramp make with the ground, to the nearest 0.1°?
a. 20 ft long, rises 16 in. 3.8°
b. 8 ft long, rises 8 in. 4.8°
c. 12 ft long, rises 6 in. 2.4°
d. 30 ft long, rises 32 in. 5.1°
e. 4 ft long, rises 6 in. 7.1°
f. 6 ft long, rises 14 in. 11.0°

Sketch a right triangle with θ as the measure of one acute angle. Find the other five trigonometric ratios of θ.

18. $\cos\theta = \frac{4}{11}$ $\sin\theta = \frac{\sqrt{105}}{11}$, $\tan\theta = \frac{\sqrt{105}}{4}$,
$\cot\theta = \frac{4\sqrt{105}}{105}$, $\csc\theta = \frac{11\sqrt{105}}{105}$, $\sec\theta = \frac{11}{4}$
19. $\sin\theta = \frac{7}{12}$ $\cos\theta = \frac{\sqrt{95}}{12}$, $\tan\theta = \frac{7\sqrt{95}}{95}$,
$\cot\theta = \frac{\sqrt{95}}{7}$, $\csc\theta = \frac{12}{7}$, $\sec\theta = \frac{12\sqrt{95}}{95}$
20. $\csc\theta = \frac{14}{6}$ $\sin\theta = \frac{3}{7}$, $\cos\theta = \frac{2\sqrt{10}}{7}$,
$\tan\theta = \frac{3\sqrt{10}}{20}$, $\cot\theta = \frac{2\sqrt{10}}{3}$, $\sec\theta = \frac{7\sqrt{10}}{20}$
21. $\cos\theta = \frac{9}{16}$ $\sin\theta = \frac{5\sqrt{7}}{16}$, $\tan\theta = \frac{5\sqrt{7}}{9}$,
$\cot\theta = \frac{9\sqrt{7}}{35}$, $\csc\theta = \frac{16\sqrt{7}}{35}$, $\sec\theta = \frac{16}{9}$
22. $\sin\theta = 0.45$ $\cos\theta \approx 0.893$, $\tan\theta \approx 0.504$,
$\cot\theta \approx 1.98$, $\csc\theta \approx 2.22$, $\sec\theta \approx 1.12$
23. $\sec\theta = 7.6$ $\sin\theta \approx 0.991$, $\cos\theta \approx 0.132$,
$\tan\theta \approx 7.53$, $\csc\theta \approx 1.01$, $\cot\theta \approx 0.133$
24. **Open-Ended** If $\cos\theta = \frac{1}{2}$, describe a method you could use to find all the angles between 0° and 360° that satisfy this equation.
Using inverse cosine, you can find that $\theta = 60°$. Because cosine is positive in the first and fourth quadrants, another solution is 300°. All the solutions would be $60° + n \cdot 360°$ and $300° + n \cdot 360°$.
25. **Reasoning** Show that if $\angle C$ is a right angle in $\triangle ABC$, then the area of $\triangle ABC$ is $\frac{bc}{2}\sin A$.
Area $= \frac{1}{2}$(base)(height) $= \frac{1}{2}ab$ and $\sin A = \frac{a}{c}$ or $a = c\sin A$. By substitution, area $= \frac{1}{2}(c\sin A)b = \frac{bc}{2}\sin A$.

All-in-One Resources/Online

Enrichment

14-3 **Enrichment**
Right Triangles and Trigonometric Ratios

Direction Cosines

Consider rectangle $ABCD$, with A at the origin and $\overline{AB}$ along the x-axis. Let P denote $\angle CAB$, and let Q denote $\angle DAC$.

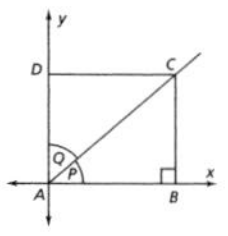

1. Write the Pythagorean Theorem applied to triangle ABC.
$AB^2 + BC^2 = AC^2$
2. Use this triangle to express AB in terms of AC and $\angle P$.
$AB = AC \cdot \cos P$
3. Express BC in terms of AC and $\angle P$.
$BC = AC \cdot \sin P$
4. Substitute these expressions for AB and BC into the equation for Exercise 1.
$AC^2\cos^2 P + AC^2\sin^2 P = AC^2$
5. Divide through by the common factor.
$\cos^2 P + \sin^2 P = 1$
6. What is the relationship between $\angle P$ and $\angle Q$?
They are complementary.
7. Express $\sin P$ in terms of $\angle Q$.
$\sin P = \cos Q$
8. Substitute this value into the equation in Exercise 5.
$\cos^2 P + \cos^2 Q = 1$
9. $\angle P$ is the angle between $\overline{AC}$ and the x-axis. Describe $\angle Q$.
Angle between $\overline{AC}$ and the y-axis.

The cosines of angles P and Q ($\cos P$, $\cos Q$) are called the direction cosines of line AC. You have shown that the sum of the squares of the direction cosines (of a line) is 1.

When you examine direction cosines in three-dimensional space, you get some interesting results. Let rectangle $A'B'C'D'$ be congruent to rectangle $ABCD$, when $A'B'C'D'$ is in a plane parallel to that of $ABCD$ as shown. (The two rectangles are the faces of a rectangular prism.)

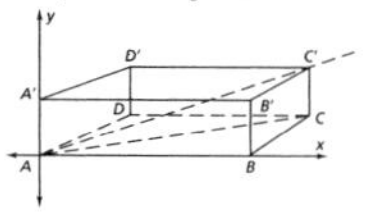

10. Write the Pythagorean Theorem as applied to triangle ACC'.
$AC^2 + (CC')^2 = (AC')^2$
11. Write the Pythagorean Theorem as applied to triangle ABC.
$AB^2 + BC^2 = AC^2$
12. What do you get when you substitute the second equation into the first?
$AB^2 + BC^2 + (CC')^2 = (AC')^2$

Practice and Problem Solving Wkbk/ All-in-One Resources/Online

Think About a Plan

14-3 **Think About a Plan**
Right Triangles and Trigonometric Ratios

A 150-ft redwood tree casts a shadow. Express the length x of the shadow as a function of the angle of elevation of the sun θ. Then find x when $\theta = 35°$ and $\theta = 70°$.

Understanding the Problem

1. How tall is the tree? 150 ft
2. How long is the shadow? x ft
3. What is the problem asking you to determine?
Answers may vary. Sample: The length of the tree's shadow at different angles of elevation of the sun.

Planning the Solution

4. How can a drawing help you solve the problem?
Answers may vary. Sample: A drawing would help me figure out which trigonometric ratio I need to use to solve the problem.
5. Make a drawing of the tree, its shadow, and the sun. Label the height of the tree, the length x of the shadow, and the angle of elevation of the sun θ.

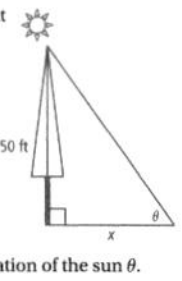

6. Use a trigonometric ratio to relate the height of the tree, x, and θ.
$\tan\theta = \frac{150}{x}$

Getting an Answer

7. Express the length x of the shadow as a function of the angle of elevation of the sun θ.
$x = \frac{150}{\tan\theta}$
8. What is x when $\theta = 35°$? What is x when $\theta = 70°$? 214.2 ft; 54.6 ft

Practice and Problem Solving Wkbk/ All-in-One Resources/Online

Standardized Test Prep

14-3 **Standardized Test Prep**
Right Triangles and Trigonometric Ratios

Multiple Choice

For Exercises 1–4, choose the correct letter.

1. Which equation could be used to find the measure of one acute angle in the right triangle at the right? B

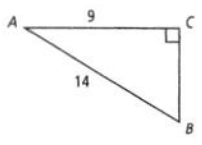

A. $\tan B = \frac{14}{9}$
B. $\cos A = \frac{9}{14}$
C. $\tan B = \frac{9}{14}$
D. $\sin A = \frac{9}{14}$

2. In $\triangle ABC$, $\angle C$ is a right angle and $\tan B = \frac{12}{35}$. What is $\sec A$? G
F. $\frac{12}{37}$ G. $\frac{37}{12}$ H. $\frac{35}{12}$ I. $\frac{12}{35}$
3. Which is the angle measure in degrees for $\tan^{-1} 0.355$? A
A. 19.5° B. 20.8° C. 34° D. 69.2°
4. A kite is on a 300-ft string. The angle of elevation from the ground to the kite is 39°. Which is the best estimate of the height of the kite above the ground? H
F. 629 ft G. 243 ft H. 189 ft I. 233 ft

Extended Response

5. What are the measures of the acute angles of a right triangle, to the nearest tenth, if the legs are 48 in. and 55 in.? Show your work.
$\tan\angle A = \frac{55}{48} \approx 1.1458$
$m\angle A \approx \tan^{-1} 1.1458$
$m\angle A \approx 48.9°$
$\tan\angle B = \frac{48}{55} \approx 0.8727$
$m\angle B \approx \tan^{-1} 0.8727$
$m\angle B \approx 41.1°$
[4] correct answer with all work shown
[3] appropriate method with minor error
[2] correct answer without work shown
[1] recognized using trigonometric ratios but did not apply them properly
[0] incorrect answers and no work shown OR no answers given

Online Teacher Resource Center

Activities, Games, and Puzzles

14-3 **Game: Gone Fishin'**
Right Triangles and Trigonometric Ratios

This game is designed for two teams of one or two students per team.

Rules

- Use a coin toss to determine who goes first.
- One team fishes the left side of the boat *from three feet above the water.*
- The other team fishes the right side of the boat *from two feet above the water.*
- When it is your turn, select a fish to catch on your side of the boat.
- To catch a fish, find the acute angle your line makes with the horizontal.
- Some line lengths are given. Fish that appear to be on integer coordinates are actually on them.
- Write the angle next to the fish to the nearest degree.
- Play alternates until all fish have been caught.
- Your teacher will reveal the correct answers when all teams have finished.
- The team that catches the most fish wins. (*Note:* A tie is possible!)

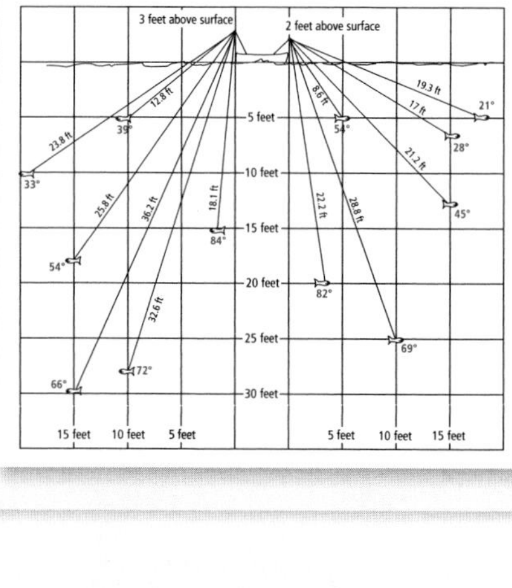

MathXL® for School
Go to PowerAlgebra.com

Do you know HOW?

Verify each identity.

1. $\sin\theta\tan\theta = \sec\theta - \cos\theta$

2. $\tan\theta = \dfrac{\sec\theta}{\csc\theta}$

3. $\dfrac{\sec\theta}{\cos\theta} = 1 + \tan^2\theta$

4. $\dfrac{\cos\theta}{\sec\theta} = 1 - \dfrac{\sin\theta}{\csc\theta}$

Simplify each trigonometric expression.

5. $\sec\theta\cot\theta$ **6.** $\sec^2\theta - 1$

7. $-1 - \cot^2\theta$ **8.** $\sin\theta\cot\theta$

9. $1 - \cos^2\theta$ **10.** $\dfrac{\sec\theta\sin\theta}{\tan\theta}$

11. $\cos\theta\tan\theta$ **12.** $\sin\theta + \cos\theta\cot\theta$

Use a unit circle and a 30°-60°-90° triangle to find the degree measures of the angles.

13. angles whose cosecant is 2

14. angles whose secant is -2

15. angles whose tangent is $\sqrt{3}$

16. angles whose cotangent is $-\sqrt{3}$

Find the value of each expression in radians to the nearest thousandth. If the expression is undefined, write *Undefined*.

17. $\cos^{-1}\left(-\dfrac{\pi}{5}\right)$ **18.** $\sin^{-1}\dfrac{\pi}{10}$

19. $\tan^{-1}4.35$ **20.** $\cos^{-1}(-2.35)$

21. $\sin^{-1}\left(-\dfrac{5\pi}{7}\right)$ **22.** $\tan^{-1}(-1.05)$

23. $\tan^{-1}\dfrac{\pi}{9}$ **24.** $\sin^{-1}(-0.45)$

Solve each equation for θ with $0 \le \theta < 2\pi$.

25. $2\cos\theta = -\sqrt{2}$

26. $\sin\theta(\cos\theta + 1) = 0$

27. $\tan^2\theta - \sqrt{3}\tan\theta = 0$

In $\triangle ABC$, $\angle C$ is a right angle. Find the remaining sides and angles. Round your answers to the nearest tenth.

28. $b = 14, c = 16$ **29.** $a = 7.9, b = 6.2$

30. $b = 29, c = 35$ **31.** $a = 6.1, c = 10.2$

32. $a = 10, c = 14$ **33.** $a = 9, b = 4$

34. $b = 7, c = 12$ **35.** $b = 11.1, c = 26.3$

Sketch a right triangle with θ as the measure of one acute angle. Find the other five trigonometric ratios of θ.

36. $\sin\theta = \dfrac{5}{7}$ **37.** $\cos\theta = \dfrac{2}{9}$

38. $\sec\theta = \dfrac{20}{11}$ **39.** $\csc\theta = \dfrac{8}{3}$

40. $\tan\theta = \dfrac{11}{4}$ **41.** $\cot\theta = 5$

Do you UNDERSTAND?

42. Writing How is solving the trigonometric equation $\tan^2\theta - 3\tan\theta + 2 = 0$ similar to solving $x^2 - 3x + 2 = 0$?

43. Open-Ended Draw a right triangle. Measure the lengths of two sides, and then find the length of the remaining side without measuring.

44. Reasoning Explain why the trigonometric equation $\sin^2\theta - \sin\theta - 6 = 0$ has no solutions.

45. Indirect Measure A man stands at the top of a building and you are standing 45 feet from the building. The angle of elevation to the top of the man's head is 54°, and the angle of elevation to the man's feet is 51°. To the nearest inch, how tall is that man?

PowerAlgebra.com   Chapter 14   Mid-Chapter Quiz   **927**

---

31. $b \approx 8.2$, $m\angle A \approx 36.7°$, $m\angle B \approx 53.3°$

32. $b \approx 9.8$, $m\angle A \approx 45.6°$, $m\angle B \approx 44.4°$

33. $c \approx 9.8$, $m\angle A \approx 66.0°$, $m\angle B \approx 24.0°$

34. $a \approx 9.7$, $m\angle A \approx 54.3°$, $m\angle B \approx 35.7°$

35. $a \approx 23.8$, $m\angle A \approx 65°$, $m\angle B \approx 25°$

36.

$\cos\theta = \dfrac{2\sqrt{6}}{7}$, $\tan\theta = \dfrac{5\sqrt{6}}{12}$, $\csc\theta = \dfrac{7}{5}$,

$\sec\theta = \dfrac{7\sqrt{6}}{12}$, $\cot\theta = \dfrac{2\sqrt{6}}{5}$

37.

$\sin\theta = \dfrac{\sqrt{77}}{9}$, $\tan\theta = \dfrac{\sqrt{77}}{2}$, $\csc\theta = \dfrac{9\sqrt{77}}{77}$,

$\sec\theta = \dfrac{9}{2}$, $\cot\theta = \dfrac{2\sqrt{77}}{77}$

38.

$\sin\theta = \dfrac{3\sqrt{31}}{20}$, $\cos\theta = \dfrac{11}{20}$, $\tan\theta = \dfrac{3\sqrt{31}}{11}$,

$\csc\theta = \dfrac{20\sqrt{31}}{93}$, $\cot\theta = \dfrac{11\sqrt{31}}{93}$

39.

$\sin\theta = \dfrac{3}{8}$, $\cos\theta = \dfrac{\sqrt{55}}{8}$, $\tan\theta = \dfrac{3\sqrt{55}}{55}$,

$\sec\theta = \dfrac{8\sqrt{55}}{55}$, $\cot\theta = \dfrac{\sqrt{55}}{3}$

40–45. See back of book

Answers

Mid-Chapter Quiz

1. $\sin\theta\tan\theta$

$= \sin\theta\dfrac{\sin\theta}{\cos\theta} = \dfrac{\sin^2\theta}{\cos\theta}$

$= \dfrac{1 - \cos^2\theta}{\cos\theta} = \dfrac{1}{\cos\theta} - \dfrac{\cos^2\theta}{\cos\theta}$

$= \sec\theta - \cos\theta$

2. $\tan\theta = \dfrac{\sin\theta}{\cos\theta} = \dfrac{\frac{1}{\csc\theta}}{\frac{1}{\sec\theta}}$

$= \dfrac{1}{\csc\theta} \cdot \dfrac{\sec\theta}{1} = \dfrac{\sec\theta}{\csc\theta}$

3. $\dfrac{\sec\theta}{\cos\theta} = \dfrac{\frac{1}{\cos\theta}}{\cos\theta} = \dfrac{1}{\cos^2\theta}$

$= \dfrac{\sin^2\theta + \cos^2\theta}{\cos^2\theta}$

$= \dfrac{\sin^2\theta}{\cos^2\theta} + \dfrac{\cos^2\theta}{\cos^2\theta}$

$= \left(\dfrac{\sin\theta}{\cos\theta}\right)^2 + 1 = \tan^2\theta + 1$

$= 1 + \tan^2\theta$

4. $\dfrac{\cos\theta}{\sec\theta} = \dfrac{\cos\theta}{\frac{1}{\cos\theta}} = \cos^2\theta = 1 - \sin^2\theta$

$= 1 - \dfrac{\sin\theta}{\csc\theta}$

5. $\csc\theta$ **6.** $\tan^2\theta$ **7.** $-\csc^2\theta$

8. $\cos\theta$ **9.** $\sin^2\theta$ **10.** 1

11. $\sin\theta$ **12.** $\csc\theta$

13. $30° + 360° \cdot n$ and $150° + 360° \cdot n$

14. $120° + 360° \cdot n$ and $240° + 360° \cdot n$

15. $60° + 360° \cdot n$ and $240° + 360° \cdot n$ or just $60° + 180° \cdot n$

16. $150° + 360° \cdot n$ and $330° + 360° \cdot n$ or just $150° + 180° \cdot n$

17. 2.250   **18.** 0.320   **19.** 1.345

20. undefined   **21.** undefined

22. -0.810 **23.** 0.336   **24.** -0.467

25. $\dfrac{3\pi}{4}, \dfrac{5\pi}{4}$ **26.** $0, \pi$

27. $0, \dfrac{\pi}{3}, \pi, \dfrac{4\pi}{3}$

28. $a \approx 7.7$, $m\angle A \approx 29.0°$, $m\angle B \approx 61.0°$

29. $c \approx 10.0$, $m\angle A \approx 51.9°$, $m\angle B \approx 38.1°$

30. $a \approx 19.6$, $m\angle A \approx 34.0°$, $m\angle B \approx 56.0°$

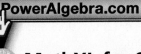

MathXL for School

Prepare students for the Mid-Chapter Quiz and Chapter Test with online practice and review.

1 Interactive Learning

Solve It!

PURPOSE To find the area of a triangle by using a trigonometric function

PROCESS Students may draw a right triangle external to the given triangle or reorient the triangle and draw the altitude to the longest side of the triangle from its opposite angle. Then use the sine relationship to find the unknown height of the triangle.

FACILITATE

Q How can you divide the triangle into right triangles? **[Draw the altitude to the longest side from the vertex of the obtuse angle.]**

Q How can you find the length of the altitude using a trigonometric relationship? **[Use sine to relate the angle measure and the lengths of the hypotenuse and altitude.]**

ANSWER See Solve It in Answers on next page.
CONNECT THE MATH In the Solve It, students use sine to find the unknown height of a triangle. In the lesson, students will use sines to find the area of triangles that are not right triangles and establish the Law of Sines.

2 Guided Instruction

Take Note

Q What parts of a triangle do you need the measurements for to use the area formula given here? **[the lengths of two sides and the measure of the angle formed by those two sides]**

Here's Why It Works

Suggest students complete the derivation for $\frac{1}{2} ac \sin B$ and $\frac{1}{2} ab \sin C$.

Content Standards
G.SRT.9 Derive the formula $A = \frac{1}{2} ab \sin (C)$ for the area of a triangle . . .
G.SRT.11 Understand and apply the Law of Sine . . .
Also G.SRT.10

Objectives To find the area of any triangle
To use the Law of Sines

What information do you need? How will you find it?

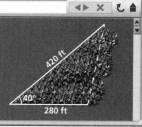

Getting Ready!

What is the area of the triangular region of wetlands? Explain your thinking. (Hint: Even though swamp and thick vegetation prevent you from making more measurements, you can still find a height of the triangle.)

420 ft
40°
280 ft

MATHEMATICAL PRACTICES

Lesson Vocabulary
• Law of Sines

Recall from geometry that if you know three parts of a triangle then you can sometimes *solve the triangle*; that is, you can determine its complete shape. This is what the congruence statements SAS, ASA, AAS, SSS were all about.

Essential Understanding If you know two angles and a side of a triangle, you can use trigonometry to solve the triangle. If you know two sides and the included angle, you can find the area of the triangle.

The area of a triangle with base b and height h is $\frac{1}{2} bh$. When you don't know h but you do know an angle measure, there may be another way to find the area.

take note   Formula   Area of a Triangle

Any $\triangle ABC$ with side lengths a, b, and c, has area

$$\frac{1}{2} bc \sin A = \frac{1}{2} ac \sin B = \frac{1}{2} ab \sin C.$$

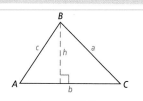

Here's Why It Works The area of the triangle above is $\frac{1}{2} bh$. The altitude h to side AC completes a right triangle. Thus, $\sin A = \frac{h}{c}$, so $h = c \sin A$. Substituting, $\frac{1}{2} bh = \frac{1}{2} bc \sin A$. You can derive $\frac{1}{2} ac \sin B$ and $\frac{1}{2} ab \sin C$ in a similar way.

BIG idea **Function**
ESSENTIAL UNDERSTANDINGS

• If two angles and a side of a triangle are known, trigonometry can be used to solve the triangle. If two sides and the included angle are known, the area of the triangle can be found.

• The *Law of Sines* relates the sines of the angles of a triangle to the side lengths.

Math Background

You can use the Law of Sines to find a missing length in *any* triangle, not just a right triangle. To use it, you need the measures of either (1) two angles and any side, or (2) two sides and an angle opposite one of them.

You can find the area of any triangle given two sides and the included angle. The formula for the area of a triangle is derived from the trigonometric ratios for a right triangle, as used in the previous lesson.

Mathematical Practices
Construct viable arguments and critique the reasoning of others. Using their knowledge of calculating the area of a triangle and of the trigonometric functions, students will construct an argument utilizing sines of the angles and side lengths of any triangle to determine the area of that triangle.

PowerAlgebra.com

1 Interactive Learning

Solve It!
Step out how to solve the Problem with helpful hints and an online question. Other questions are listed above in Interactive Learning.

Problem 1 Finding the Area of a Triangle

Gridded Response What is the area of $\triangle ABC$ to the nearest tenth of a square mile?

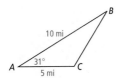

Plan

Can you use the area formula (previous page)?
You need two sides and the included angle—which is what you have here.

In $\triangle ABC$, $b = 5$, $c = 10$, and $m\angle A = 31°$.

$$\text{Area} = \tfrac{1}{2}bc\sin A = \tfrac{1}{2}(5)(10)\sin 31°$$

$$\approx 12.9$$

The area is about 12.9 mi². Write 12.9 in the grid.

 Got It? **1.** A triangle has sides of 12 in. and 15 in. The measure of the angle between them is 24°. What is the area of the triangle?

The relationship $\frac{1}{2}bc\sin A = \frac{1}{2}ac\sin B = \frac{1}{2}ab\sin C$ yields an important formula when you divide each expression by $\frac{1}{2}abc$. The formula, known as the **Law of Sines**, relates the sines of the angles of a triangle to the lengths of their opposite sides.

Theorem Law of Sines

In any triangle, the ratio of the sine of each angle to its opposite side is constant. In particular, for $\triangle ABC$, labeled as shown,

$$\frac{\sin A}{a} = \frac{\sin B}{b} = \frac{\sin C}{c}.$$

You can use the Law of Sines to find missing measures of any triangle when you know the measures of

- two angles and any side, or
- two sides and an obtuse angle opposite one of them.

In Problem 2, you know the measures of two angles and a side (AAS). In Problem 3, you know the measures of two sides and an obtuse angle opposite one of them (SSA with A obtuse).

Problem 1

Q Do you need to find the length of the third side to find the area of the triangle? Explain. **[No; you can use the formula since you have the lengths of two sides and the measure of the angle they form.]**

Q What does $c \sin A$ represent? Geometrically, where would you represent this value in the drawing? **[The height of the triangle; the altitude from B to the extension of $\overline{AC}$.]**

Got It?

Q Does it matter which of the three formulas you use to find the area? Explain. **[No; you will end up with the same numerical expression to evaluate when you substitute for the variables in the equation.]**

Take Note

Q Why does $\frac{1}{2}bc\sin A = \frac{1}{2}ac\sin B = \frac{1}{2}ab\sin C$ for a given triangle? **[Since the expressions represent the area, which is the same no matter how you calculate it, the expressions must be equal in value.]**

Q How do you get from $\frac{1}{2}bc\sin A = \frac{1}{2}ac\sin B = \frac{1}{2}ab\sin C$ to the Law of Sines? **[Multiply each expression by 2 and divide each expression by abc.]**

2 Guided Instruction

Each Problem is worked out and supported online.

Problem 1
Finding the Area of a Triangle

Problem 2
Finding a Side of a Triangle
Animated

Problem 3
Finding an Angle of a Triangle
Animated

Problem 4
Using the Law of Sines to Solve a Problem
Animated

Support in Algebra 2 Companion
- Vocabulary
- Key Concepts
- Got It?

Answers

Solve It!

$\approx$37,796 ft²; to find the height h of the triangle, use $h = 420 \sin 40°$. Substituting into the formula for area of a triangle $A = \frac{1}{2}bh = \frac{1}{2}(280)(420 \sin 40°) \approx 37,796$.

Got It?

1. 36.6 in.²

Problem 2
ERROR PREVENTION

Q If you did not draw a diagram, what mistake would it be easy to make in setting up this problem? **[You might think that the side you are asked to find is opposite the 32° angle and use 32° in place of 109°.]**

Got It?

Q Which side is opposite ∠K? **[ML]**

Q Which angle is opposite KL? **[∠M]**

Q Do you need to find the measure of the third angle of the triangle to answer this question? Explain. **[No; since you know the angle measure of the angle opposite the side you want to find, you do not need to solve for the third angle.]**

Problem 3

Q Can you solve directly for ∠S using the Law of Sines? Explain. **[No; you do not know the measure of the side opposite ∠S.]**

Q How do you know that ∠T and ∠S are acute angles? **[If either were greater than 70°, the sum of the angles of the triangle would be greater than 180°.]**

Got It?

Q In 3a, why can you use the Law of Sines to solve directly for m∠P? **[You know the length of p and another complete side and angle ratio, so you can solve for the m∠P which completes the proportion.]**

Q Where would you measure the height of the triangle in Problem 3 using TR as the base? **[using the altitude drawn from S to an extension of $\overline{TR}$]**

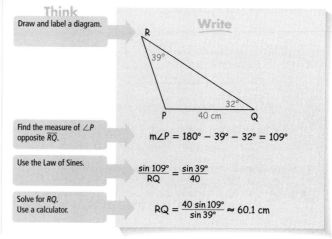

© **Problem 2** Finding a Side of a Triangle

In △PQR, m∠R = 39°, m∠Q = 32°, and PQ = 40 cm. What is RQ?

Think
Draw and label a diagram.

Write

Find the measure of ∠P opposite $\overline{RQ}$.

$m\angle P = 180° - 39° - 32° = 109°$

Use the Law of Sines.

$$\frac{\sin 109°}{RQ} = \frac{\sin 39°}{40}$$

Solve for RQ. Use a calculator.

$$RQ = \frac{40 \sin 109°}{\sin 39°} \approx 60.1 \text{ cm}$$

✓ **Got It?** 2. In △KLM, m∠K = 120°, m∠M = 50°, and ML = 35 yd. What is KL?

Plan
How do you proceed?
You have information that will give you m∠T. m∠T will give you m∠S.

© **Problem 3** Finding an Angle of a Triangle

In △RST, t = 7, r = 9, and m∠R = 110°. What is m∠S?

Step 1 Draw and label a diagram.

Step 2 Use the Law of Sines. Find m∠T.

$$\frac{\sin T}{7} = \frac{\sin 110°}{9}$$ Law of Sines.

$$\sin T = \frac{7 \sin 110°}{9}$$ Solve for sin T.

$$m\angle T = \sin^{-1}\left(\frac{7 \sin 110°}{9}\right)$$ Solve for m∠T.

$$m\angle T \approx 47°$$ Use a calculator.

Step 3 Find the measure of ∠S.

$$m\angle S \approx 180° - 110° - 47° = 23°$$

✓ **Got It?** 3. **a.** In △PQR, m∠R = 97.5°, r = 80, and p = 75. What is m∠P?
b. In Problem 3, can you use the Law of Sines to find the heights of the triangle? Explain your answer.

Additional Problems

1. What is the area of △TUV to the nearest tenth of a square centimeter?

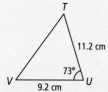

ANSWER 49.3 cm²

2. In △MNP, m∠M = 25°, m∠N = 61°, and MP = 3.8 m. What is MN?

ANSWER 4.3 m

3. In △KLM, k = 4.5 yd, m = 10.1 yd, and m∠M = 101°. What is m∠K to the nearest degree?

ANSWER 26°

4. Two wildlife spotters are 2 mi apart on an east-west line. The spotter in the eastern spot sees a bear 62° north of west, and the other spotter sees the bear 48° north of east. How far is the bear from each spotter?

ANSWER 1.6 mi from the east spotter and 1.9 mi from the west spotter

Answers

Got It? (continued)

2. 31.0 yd

3. a. 68.4°

b. yes; $\frac{\sin T}{\text{height}} = \frac{\sin 90°}{9}$; height $\approx 9 \sin 47° \approx 6.6$

In the SSA case, if the known non-included angle is acute, you have an ambiguous situation. Inverse sine is not able to distinguish whether a second angle is, say, 47° or 133°.

In the SAS and SSS congruence situations, the Law of Sines is not useful because you do not have a known angle paired with a known opposite side. You will find out how to solve these triangles in the next lesson.

Ⓒ Problem 4 Using the Law of Sines to Solve a Problem

Surveying A surveyor locates points *A* and *B* at the same elevation and measures distance and angles as pictured.

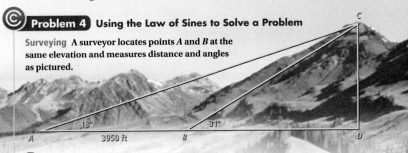

Plan
How do you write an equation to solve?
Write a proportion that includes the distance you know, *AB*, and the distance you want, *BC*.

A What is *BC*, the distance from *B* to the summit?

First find $m\angle ABC$ and $m\angle ACB$.

$$m\angle ABC = 180° - 31° = 149°$$
$$m\angle ACB = 180° - 18° - 149° = 13°$$

Now use the Law of Sines with △*ABC*.

$$\frac{\sin A}{BC} = \frac{\sin C}{AB} \qquad \text{Law of Sines}$$

$$\frac{\sin 18°}{BC} = \frac{\sin 13°}{3950} \qquad \text{Substitute.}$$

$$BC = \frac{3950 \sin 18°}{\sin 13°} \qquad \text{Solve for } BC.$$

$$BC \approx 5426 \qquad \text{Simplify.}$$

The distance from *B* to the summit is about 5426 ft.

B What is *CD*, the height of the mountain above points *A* and *B*?

In right △*BCD*, you know *BC* and $m\angle B$. Use the sine ratio.

$$\sin 31° \approx \frac{CD}{5426} \qquad \text{Definition of sine}$$

$$CD \approx 5426 \sin 31° \qquad \text{Solve for } CD.$$

$$CD \approx 2795 \qquad \text{Use a calculator.}$$

The summit is about 2795 ft higher than points *A* and *B*.

✓ **Got It?** **4.** A landscaper sights the top of a tree at a 68° angle. She then moves an additional 70 ft directly away from the tree and sights the top at a 43° angle. How tall is the tree to the nearest tenth of a foot?

4. 104.7 ft

Problem 4

Q Why is it important that points *A* and *B* be at the same elevation? **[If *A* and *B* are not at the same elevation, then $\angle ABC$ will not be a supplement of $\angle CBD$.]**

Q Why do you have to find the measure of $\angle ACB$? **[Without $m\angle ACB$, you will not have a complete ratio.]**

Q Could you have used the Law of Sines to solve for *CD* in 4B? Explain. **[Yes; you could have set up a proportion as $\dfrac{BC}{\sin 90°} = \dfrac{CD}{\sin 31°}$.]**

EXTENSION

Q If you did not know the Law of Sines, could you still solve for *CD*? How? **[Yes; set up two tangent ratios, one for the large right triangle and one for the small right triangle. Solve both equations for *CD*, and set them equal to each other. Substitute the value for *BD* into one of the original equations and solve the equation for *CD*.]**

Got It?

Q Which angle measure do you need to find in order to apply the Law of Sines to finding the height of the tree? **[You need to find the angle opposite the side that measures 70 ft.]**

3 Lesson Check

Do you know HOW?

- If students have difficulty solving Exercise 1, have them draw the triangle and label it *ABC* and then apply one of the formulas.
- If students have difficulty setting up the ratios needed to solve Exercises 2 and 3, have them draw and label the triangles that model the information in the exercises.

Do you UNDERSTAND?

- For Exercise 4, if students have difficulty applying the Law of Sines to the given conditions, ask them how many of the elements of a proportion must be known to find one unknown.
- If students have difficulty answering Exercise 5, ask them to work a few similar examples with their calculators to check if the operation is valid.

Close

> **Q** How can you find the area of a triangle if you know the lengths of two sides and the measure of the included angle? **[Multiply the side lengths and the sine of the angle and divide that by two.]**
>
> **Q** What ratios does the Law of Sines compare? **[the ratio of the sine of an angle to the length of the side opposite that angle and the similar ratio for a different angle]**

 **Lesson Check**

Do you know HOW?

1. A triangle has sides 2.4 and 9.0 and the measure of the angle between those sides is 98°. What is the area of the triangle?

2. In $\triangle PQR$, $m\angle P = 85°$, $m\angle R = 54°$, and $QR = 30$. What is PR?

3. In $\triangle HJK$, $m\angle J = 14°$, $HK = 6$, and $JK = 11$. What is $m\angle H$?

Do you UNDERSTAND? MATHEMATICAL PRACTICES

4. **Vocabulary** Suppose you are given information about a triangle according to SSS, SAS, AAS, and ASA. For which of these can you immediately use the Law of Sines to find one of the remaining measures?

5. **Error Analysis** Suppose you used the Law of Sines and wrote $a = \frac{3 \sin 22°}{\sin 45°}$. Is that the same equation as $a = 3 \sin\left(\frac{22}{45}\right)°$? Explain.

Practice and Problem-Solving Exercises
MATHEMATICAL PRACTICES

A Practice

Find the area of each triangle. Round your answer to the nearest tenth. ● See Problem 1.

6.
8 cm
51°
6 cm

7.
10 in.
15°
7 in.

8.
15 m
97°
11 m

Use the Law of Sines. Find the measure *x* to the nearest tenth. ● See Problems 2 and 3.

9.
A
x
80°   35°
B   10   C

10.
B 21°
7.3   x
C 48° A

11.
B
93°   x
48°
A   10   C

12.
D
x°
28
43°
F   27   E

13.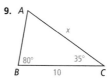
F
96°
10
D   18   x°   E

14. In $\triangle DEF$, $m\angle F = 43°$, $d = 16$ mm, and $f = 24$ mm. Find $m\angle D$.

15. In $\triangle ABC$, $m\angle A = 52°$, $c = 10$ ft, and $a = 15$ ft. Find $m\angle C$.

16. **Surveying** The distance from you to the base of a tower on top of a hill is 2760 ft. The angle of elevation of the base is 26°. The angle of elevation of the top of the tower is 32°. Draw a diagram. Find to the nearest foot the height of the tower above the top of the hill. ● See Problem 4.

 PowerAlgebra.com

3 Lesson Check

For a digital lesson check, use the Got It questions.

Support in Algebra 2 Companion
- Lesson Check

4 Practice

Assign homework to individual students or to an entire class.

Answers

Lesson Check

1. ≈ 10.7 square units
2. ≈ 19.8
3. $\approx 26.3°$ or ≈ 153.7
4. AAS, ASA
5. No; For $\frac{\sin 22°}{\sin 45°}$ you find the sine of each numerator and denominator, $\sin 22°$ and $\sin 45°$; for $\sin\left(\frac{22}{45}\right)°$ you find the sine of the quotient of $\left(\frac{22}{45}\right)°$.

Practice and Problem-Solving Exercises

6. 18.7 cm²
7. 9.1 in.²
8. 81.9 m²
9. 10.9
10. 9.2
11. 7.4
12. 41.1°
13. 33.5°
14. 27.0°
15. 31.7°
16. 340 ft

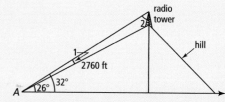

17. Think About a Plan One of the congruent sides of an isosceles triangle is 10 cm long. One of the congruent angles has a measure of 54°. Find the perimeter of the triangle. Round your answer to the nearest centimeter.
- Can drawing a diagram help you solve this problem?
- What information do you need before finding the perimeter?
- How can you find that information?

18. Forestry A forest ranger in an observation tower sights a fire 39° east of north. A ranger in a tower 10 miles due east of the first tower sights the fire at 42° west of north. How far is the fire from each tower?

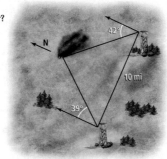

19. Geometry The sides of a triangle are 15 in., 17 in., and 16 in. The smallest angle has a measure of 54°. Find the measure of the largest angle. Round to the nearest degree.

Find the remaining sides and angles of △DEF. Round your answers to the nearest tenth.

20. $m\angle D = 54°, m\angle E = 54°,$ and $d = 20$

21. $m\angle D = 54°, e = 8$ m, and $d = 10$

22. Reasoning In △ABC, $a = 10$ and $b = 15$.
  a. Does the triangle have a greater area when $m\angle C = 1°$ or when $m\angle C = 50°$?
  b. Does the triangle have a greater area when $m\angle C = 50°$ or when $m\angle C = 179°$?
  c. For what measure of $\angle C$ does △ABC have the greatest area? Explain.

23. Open-Ended Sketch a triangle. Specify three of its measures then use the Law of Sines to find the remaining measures.

Find the area of △ABC. Round your answer to the nearest tenth.

24. $m\angle C = 68°, b = 12.9, c = 15.2$

25. $m\angle A = 52°, a = 9.71, c = 9.33$

26. $m\angle A = 23°, m\angle C = 39°, b = 14.6$

27. $m\angle B = 87°, a = 10.1, c = 9.8$

In △ABC, $m\angle A = 40°$ and $m\angle B = 30°$. Find each value to the nearest tenth.

28. Find AC for $BC = 10.5$ m.

29. Find BC for $AC = 21.8$ ft.

30. Find AC for $AB = 81.2$ yd.

31. Find BC for $AB = 5.9$ cm.

32. Measurement A vacant lot is in the shape of an isosceles triangle. It is between two streets that intersect at an 85.9° angle. Each of the sides of the lot that face these streets is 150 ft long. Find the perimeter of the lot to the nearest foot.

33. a. In the diagram at the right, $m\angle A = 30°$, $AB = 10$, and $BC = BD = 6$. Use the Law of Sines to find $m\angle D, m\angle ABD,$ and $m\angle ABC$.
  b. Reasoning Notice that two sides and a nonincluded angle of △ABC are congruent to the corresponding parts of △ABD, but the triangles are not congruent. Must △EFG be congruent to △ABD if $EF = 10$, $FG = 6$, and $\angle E \cong \angle A$? Explain.

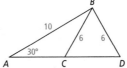

---

4 Practice

ASSIGNMENT GUIDE

Basic: 6–16 all, 17–25 odd

Average: 7–15 odd, 17–33

Advanced: 7–15 odd, 17–35

Standardized Test Prep: 36–39

Mixed Review: 40–50

Mathematical Practices are supported by exercises with red headings. Here are the Practices supported in this lesson:

MP 1: Make Sense of Problems Ex. 17
MP 2: Reason Abstractly Ex. 4, 33b
MP 2: Reason Quantitatively Ex. 22
MP 3: Construct Arguments Ex. 23
MP 3: Communicate Ex. 33b
MP 3: Critique the Reasoning of Others Ex. 5

Applications exercises have blue headings. Exercises 16, 18, and 32 support MP 4: Model.

EXERCISE 19: Use the Think About a Plan worksheet in the **Practice and Problem Solving Workbook** (also available in the Teaching Resources in print and online) to further support students' development in becoming independent learners.

HOMEWORK QUICK CHECK

To check students' understanding of key skills and concepts, go over Exercises 7, 11, 17, 19, and 23.

---

17. 32 cm

18. 7.5 mi, 7.9 mi

19. 66°

20. $m\angle F = 72°$, e = 20 in., f ≈ 23.5 in.

21. $m\angle E ≈ 40.3°$, $m\angle F ≈ 85.7°$, f ≈ 12.3 m

22. a. when $m\angle C = 50°$
  b. when $m\angle C = 50°$
  c. 90°; that is the angle measure at which sin θ is greatest.

23. Check students' work.

24. 85.0

25. 44.4

26. 29.7

27. 49.4

28. 8.2 m

29. 28.0 ft

30. 43.2 yd

31. 4.0 cm

32. 504 ft

33. a. 56.4°, 93.6°, 26.4°
  b. No; △EFG could be congruent to △ABC instead of △ABD.

Answers

Practice and Problem-Solving Exercises (continued)

34. 2.4 miles

35. No; you need at least one side in order to set up a proportion you can then solve.

Standardized Test Prep

36. A

37. I

38. C

39. [2] $A = \frac{1}{2} ab \sin C$

$\sin C = \frac{2(A)}{ab} = \frac{2(31.5)}{9(14)} = 0.5$

$m\angle C = \sin^{-1} 0.5 = 30°$

So, the measure of the included angle for the given sides is 30° or 150°.

[1] appropriate method, but with one computational error

Mixed Review

40.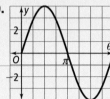

41.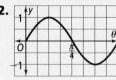

42.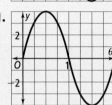

43. ⟨−1, 7⟩

44. ⟨5, 3⟩

45. ⟨−3, −1⟩

46. ⟨−6, 4⟩

47. 53.1°

48. 24.6°

49. 38.7°

50. 54.7°

Challenge

34. Sailing Buoys are located in the sea at points A, B, and C. $\angle ACB$ is a right angle. $AC = 3.0$ mi, $BC = 4.0$ mi, and $AB = 5.0$ mi. A ship is located at point D on $\overline{AB}$ so that $m\angle ACD = 30°$. How far is the ship from the buoy at point C? Round your answer to the nearest tenth of a mile.

35. Writing Suppose you know the measures of all three angles of a triangle. Can you use the Law of Sines to find the lengths of the sides? Explain.

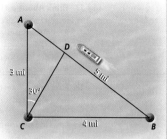

Standardized Test Prep

SAT/ACT

36. In $\triangle GDL$, $m\angle D = 57°$, $DL = 10.1$, and $GL = 9.4$. What is the best estimate for $m\angle G$?

A 64°   B 51°   C 39°   D 26°

37. For which set of given information can you compute the area of $\triangle ABC$?

F $m\angle C = 58°$, $c = 23$

G $m\angle B = 26°$, $a = 43$

H $m\angle C = 58°$, $a = 43$, $c = 23$

I $m\angle C = 26°$, $a = 43$, $b = 23$

38. Two points in front of a tall building are 250 m apart. The angles of elevation of the top of the building from the two points are 37° and 13°. What is the best estimate for the height of the building?

A 150 m   B 138 m   C 83 m   D 56 m

Short Response

39. Two sides of a scalene triangle are 9 m and 14 m. The area of the triangle is 31.5 m². Find the measure of one of the angles of the triangle to the nearest tenth of a degree. Show your work.

Mixed Review

Sketch one cycle of the graph of each sine function.   ◀ See Lesson 13-4.

40. $y = 4 \sin \theta$ **41.** $y = 4 \sin \pi\theta$ **42.** $y = \sin 4\theta$

Let $u = (-2, 3)$, $v = (1, 4)$, and $w = (4, -1)$. Find the component form of each vector.   ◀ See Lesson 12-6.

43. $u + v$ **44.** $v + w$ **45.** $u - v$ **46.** $u - w$

Get Ready!   To prepare for Lesson 14-5, do Exercises 47–50.   ◀ See Lesson 14-3.

Find each angle measure to the nearest tenth of a degree.

47. $\cos^{-1}\frac{3}{5}$ **48.** $\tan^{-1} 0.4569$ **49.** $\sin^{-1}\frac{5}{8}$ **50.** $\tan^{-1}\sqrt{2}$

Additional Instructional Support

Algebra 2 Companion

Students can use the **Algebra 2 Companion** worktext (4 pages) as you teach the lesson. Use the Companion to support

- New Vocabulary
- Key Concepts
- Got It for each Problem
- Lesson Check

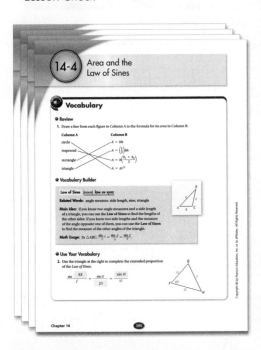

ELL Support

Assess Understanding Draw a triangle on the board and ask students to point to the pairs of angles and sides that constitute the elements of the ratios of the Law of Sines. Make sure that students can identify which sides and angles are opposite each other. Then ask students to point to three parts of the triangle that need to be known to find the area of a triangle using a sine ratio. Make sure that students can identify the sides as adjacent and the angle as included.

Pair students and ask them to draw and label triangles that model any assigned exercises that do not already have drawings. Ask students to make a list of components, such as two sides and included angle, and sides and angles that are opposite each other.

5 Assess & Remediate

Lesson Quiz

1. What is the area of the $\triangle FGH$ to the nearest hundredth of a square meter?

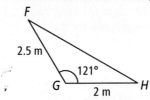

2. In $\triangle RST$, $m\angle T = 54°$, $m\angle S = 67°$, and $ST = 35$ mm. What is RS?

3. In $\triangle JKL$, $j = 2$ in., $k = 4.1$ in., and $m\angle K = 101°$. What is $m\angle L$?

4. Do you UNDERSTAND? A contractor is checking the height of the frame for a building his company is constructing. He stands at some distance from the building and measures the angle of elevation to be 73°. He then moves back 10 ft and measures the angle to be 68°. How tall is the building?

ANSWERS TO LESSON QUIZ

1. 2.14 m²

2. 33.0 mm

3. 50.4°

4. about 102 ft

PRESCRIPTION FOR REMEDIATION
Use the student work on the Lesson Quiz to prescribe a differentiated review assignment:

Points	Differentiated Remediation
0–2	Intervention
3	On-level
4	Extension

PowerAlgebra.com

5 Assess & Remediate

Assign the Lesson Quiz. Appropriate intervention, practice, or enrichment is automatically generated based on student performance.

Intervention

- **Reteaching** (2 pages) Provides reteaching and practice exercises for the key lesson concepts. Use with struggling students or absent students.

- **English Language Learner Support** Helps students develop and reinforce mathematical vocabulary and key concepts.

All-in-One Resources/Online

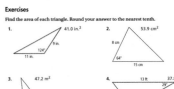

All-in-One Resources/Online

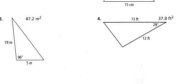

Differentiated Remediation *continued*

On-Level

- **Practice** (2 pages) Provides extra practice for each lesson. For simpler practice exercises, use the Form K Practice pages found in the All-in-One Teaching Resources and online.

- **Think About a Plan** Helps students develop specific problem-solving skills and strategies by providing scaffolded guiding questions.

- **Standardized Test Prep** Focuses on all major exercises, all major question types, and helps students prepare for the high-stakes assessments.

Extension

- **Enrichment** Provides students with interesting problems and activities that extend the concepts of the lesson.

- **Activities, Games, and Puzzles** Worksheets that can be used for concepts development, enrichment, and for fun!

Practice and Problem Solving Wkbk/All-in-One Resources/Online
Practice page 1

Practice and Problem Solving Wkbk/All-in-One Resources/Online
Practice page 2

All-in-One Resources/Online
Enrichment

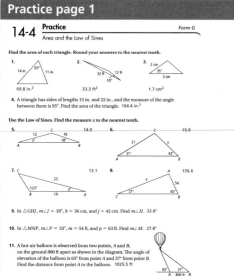

Practice and Problem Solving Wkbk/All-in-One Resources/Online
Think About a Plan

Practice and Problem Solving Wkbk/All-in-One Resources/Online
Standardized Test Prep

Online Teacher Resource Center
Activities, Games, and Puzzles

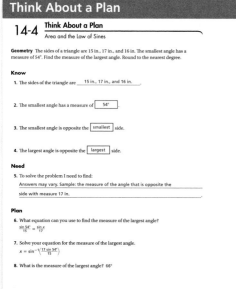

The triangles at the right have one pair of congruent angles and two pairs of congruent sides. But the triangles are not congruent. Notice that the congruent angles are not included by the congruent sides.

When you know the measures of two sides of a triangle and one of the opposite angles, there may be two triangles with those measurements. You can use the Law of Sines to find the other measures for both triangles.

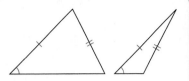

Example

In each △ABC at the right, $m\angle A = 35°$, $a = 11$, and $b = 15$. Find $m\angle B$.

$\dfrac{\sin A}{a} = \dfrac{\sin B}{b}$ Law of Sines

$\dfrac{\sin 35°}{11} = \dfrac{\sin B}{15}$ Substitute.

$\sin B = \dfrac{15 \sin 35°}{11}$ Solve for sin B.

$m\angle B = \sin^{-1}\left(\dfrac{15 \sin 35°}{11}\right) \approx 51°$ Solve for $m\angle B$. Use a calculator.

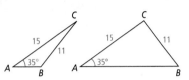

The sine function is also positive in Quadrant II. So another value of $m\angle B$ is about $180° - 51° = 129°$.

Because there are two possible angle measures for ∠B, there are two triangles that satisfy the given conditions. In one triangle the angle measures are about 35°, 51°, and 94°. In the other, the angle measures are about 35°, 129°, and 16°.

Exercises

In each △ABC, find the measures for ∠B and ∠C that satisfy the given conditions. Draw diagrams to help you decide whether two triangles are possible.

1. $m\angle A = 62°$, $a = 30$, and $b = 32$

2. $m\angle A = 16°$, $a = 12$, and $b = 37.5$

3. $m\angle A = 48°$, $a = 93$, and $b = 125$

4. $m\angle A = 112°$, $a = 16.5$, and $b = 5.4$

5. $m\angle A = 23.68$, $a = 9.8$, and $b = 17$

6. $m\angle A = 155°$, $a = 12.5$, and $b = 8.4$

7. Multiple Choice You can construct a triangle with compass and straightedge when given three parts of the triangle (except for three angles). Which of the following given sets could result in the ambiguous case?

- Ⓐ Given: three sides
- Ⓒ Given: two sides and a non-included angle
- Ⓑ Given: two sides and an included angle
- Ⓓ Given: two angles and a non-included side

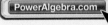 PowerAlgebra.com   Concept Byte   The Ambiguous Case   935

Guided Instruction

PURPOSE To solve for measures of angles of triangles using the Law of Sines when the ambiguous case applies

PROCESS Students will

- determine when the ambiguous case applies.
- solve for the measures of possible sets of angles that would satisfy the given conditions of $m\angle A$, a, and b in △ABC.

DISCUSS Students may remember from geometry that you can not use side-side-angle (SSA) to prove that two triangles are congruent. They may remember sketching two triangles that showed why SSA can not be used. You may want to review this and the triangle congruency theorems from geometry as you discuss the ambiguous case.

Example

Q What do you always know about the two ambiguous angles in the ambiguous case? **[One will be acute, and one will be obtuse.]**

Q What parts of the triangles vary when two non-congruent triangles fit the ambiguous SSA case? **[the other two angles and the unspecified side]**

Q Could two triangles fit the ambiguous case if they had two angles in common? Explain. **[No; the angles of a triangle must add up to 180°; if two angles are known, the third angle can only be one value.]**

Exercises

Q If one of the angles you are given is obtuse, can you have an ambiguous case? Explain. **[No; if a given angle is obtuse, the other two angles must be acute, or the angle sum for the triangle would be more than 180°.]**

© **Mathematical Practices** This Concept Byte supports students in becoming proficient at using properties, Mathematical Practice 2.

Answers

Concept Byte

1. 70.4° and 47.6°, or 109.6° and 8.4°

2. 59.5° and 104.5°, or 120.5° and 43.5°

3. 87.3° and 44.7°, or 92.7° and 39.3°

4. 17.7° and 50.3°

5. 44.2° and 112.1°, or 135.8° and 20.5°

6. 16.5° and 8.5°

7. C

1 Interactive Learning

Solve It!

PURPOSE To introduce the Law of Cosines
PROCESS Students may
- realize there is no difference between the angles and apply the given equation to *A* and *B*.
- rename the angles to show the given equation applies to any angle.

FACILITATE

Q Does it matter which angle is labeled with which letter? Explain. **[No; there is nothing which distinguishes the angles in the triangle.]**

Q How is the formula for cos *A* different from the formula for cos *C*? **[The *a*'s and *c*'s are interchanged. The *b*'s stay the same.]**

ANSWER See Solve It in Answers on next page.
CONNECT THE MATH In the Solve It, the students see the Law of Cosines. In the lesson students will apply the Law of Cosines to find measures of sides and angles of triangles given SAS or SSS.

2 Guided Instruction

Take Note

Q What is the relationship between the side lengths and the angle on the right side of each of these equations? **[The angle is formed by the sides.]**

© **Content Standards**
G.SRT.10 Prove the Laws of Sines and Cosines and use them to solve problems.
G.SRT.11 Understand and apply the Law of Cosines . . . to find unknown measurements in right and non-right triangles . . .

Objective To use the Law of Cosines in finding the measures of sides and angles of a triangle

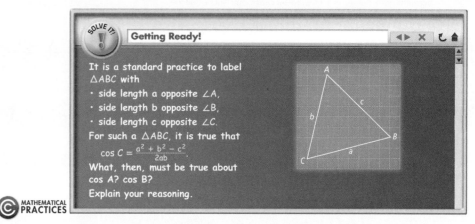

> **SOLVE IT**
>
> **Getting Ready!**
>
> It is a standard practice to label △*ABC* with
> · side length *a* opposite ∠*A*,
> · side length *b* opposite ∠*B*,
> · side length *c* opposite ∠*C*.
> For such a △*ABC*, it is true that
> $$\cos C = \frac{a^2 + b^2 - c^2}{2ab}.$$
> What, then, must be true about cos *A*? cos *B*?
> Explain your reasoning.

© **MATHEMATICAL PRACTICES**

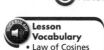
Lesson Vocabulary
· Law of Cosines

The measures of all three sides (SSS) or the measures of two sides and the included angle (SAS) determine a triangle. The Law of Sines does not enable you to solve such a triangle, but the Law of Cosines does.

Essential Understanding If you know the measures of enough parts of a triangle to completely determine the triangle, you can solve the triangle.

The **Law of Cosines** relates the length of a side of any triangle to the measure of the opposite angle.

> **Theorem   Law of Cosines**
>
> In △*ABC*, let *a*, *b*, and *c* represent the lengths of the sides opposite ∠*A*, ∠*B*, and ∠*C*, respectively.
> - $a^2 = b^2 + c^2 - 2bc \cos A$
> - $b^2 = a^2 + c^2 - 2ac \cos B$
> - $c^2 = a^2 + b^2 - 2ab \cos C$
>
>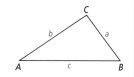

14-5 Preparing to Teach

BIG idea Equivalence

ESSENTIAL UNDERSTANDINGS
- If the measures of enough parts of a triangle to completely determine the triangle are known, the triangle can be solved.
- The *Law of Cosines* relates the length of a side of any triangle to the measure of the opposite angle and the other two side lengths.

Math Background

To "solve a triangle" is to determine the measures of all of its angles and sides. You cannot use the Law of Sines, as shown in the previous lesson, to solve triangles when you only know the measures of three sides or two sides and the included angle. To solve these triangles you need the Law of Cosines.

The Pythagorean Theorem can be thought of as a special case of the Law of Cosines. Consider the following:

$$c^2 = a^2 + b^2 - 2ab \cos C$$

Let *C* be the right angle of a right triangle. Then, *c* is the measure of the hypotenuse and *a* and *b* are the measures of the legs. Since *C* = 90°, cos *C* = 0.

Thus, the formula simplifies to $c^2 = a^2 + b^2$, the familiar Pythagorean Theorem.

© **Mathematical Practices**
Make sense of problems and persevere in solving them. Students will identify correspondences between solving for unknown angle measures and side lengths in triangles using the Law of Cosines and using the Law of Sines, and will determine when each is appropriate.

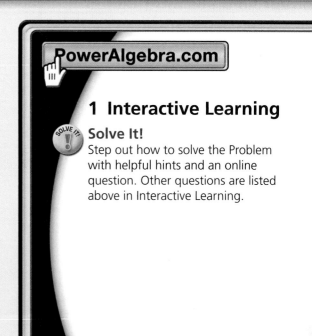

> **PowerAlgebra.com**
>
> # 1 Interactive Learning
>
> **Solve It!**
> Step out how to solve the Problem with helpful hints and an online question. Other questions are listed above in Interactive Learning.

Here's Why It Works

In this $\triangle ABC$ with altitude h, let $AD = x$.

Then $DB = c - x$.

In $\triangle ADC$,

$b^2 = x^2 + h^2$ and

$\cos A = \frac{x}{b}$ or $x = b \cos A$.

In $\triangle CBD$,

$$a^2 = (c - x)^2 + h^2 \qquad \text{Pythagorean Theorem}$$
$$= c^2 - 2cx + x^2 + h^2 \qquad \text{Square the binomial.}$$
$$= c^2 - 2cx + b^2 \qquad \text{Substitute } b^2 \text{ for } x^2 + h^2.$$
$$= c^2 - 2cb \cos A + b^2 \qquad \text{Substitute } b \cos A \text{ for } x.$$
$$= b^2 + c^2 - 2bc \cos A \qquad \text{Commutative Properties of Addition and Multiplication}$$

The last equation is the Law of Cosines.

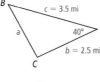

Try it yourself for obtuse $\angle B$.

Problem 1 Using the Law of Cosines to Solve a Problem

Multiple Choice The sailboat race committee wants to lay out a triangular course with a 40° angle between two sides that measure 3.5 mi and 2.5 mi. What will be the approximate length of the third side?

Ⓐ 2.0 mi

Ⓒ 5.1 mi

Ⓑ 2.3 mi

Ⓓ 9.8 mi

$c = 3.5$ mi, $b = 2.5$ mi, $40°$

This triangle is determined by SAS. Use the form of the Law of Cosines that has a^2 on one side.

$$a^2 = b^2 + c^2 - 2bc \cos A$$
$$a^2 = 2.5^2 + 3.5^2 - 2(2.5)(3.5) \cos 40° \qquad \text{Substitute.}$$
$$\approx 5.094 \qquad \text{Use a calculator.}$$
$$a \approx 2.26 \qquad \text{Use a calculator.}$$

The third side of the course will be about 2.3 mi long. The correct choice is B.

Think

Does the answer make sense?
If $3.5 - 2.5 < a$, and $a < 3.5 + 2.5$, the answer makes sense. $a \approx 2.3$, and $1 < 2.3 < 6$ is true, so the answer makes sense.

Got It? **1. a.** The lengths of two sides of a triangle are 8 and 10, and the measure of the angle between them is 40°. What is the approximate length of the third side?

b. Reasoning The measure of the included angle for the course in Problem 1 can be between 0° and 180°. Between what lengths can the length of the third side be? Explain your answer.

Here's Why It Works

Q For a triangle that is not a right triangle, what auxiliary line must be drawn to prove the Law of Cosines? Explain. **[the altitude from any vertex to the opposite side, so you can apply the Pythagorean Theorem]**

Problem 1

Q Why, when using the Law of Cosines to solve a quadratic equation for a, is there only one root? **[The two roots obtained when taking the square root of both sides of a quadratic equation are opposites. But because the length of a side is always positive, the negative root is discarded.]**

Q Would it make any difference if the vertices of $\triangle ABC$ were labeled in a different order? Explain. **[No; regardless of the labels on the triangle, the given measures represent two sides and the included angle (SAS).]**

Q Can the cosine of the included angle in $\triangle ABC$ ever be negative? Explain. **[Yes, if it is an obtuse angle; the cosine of an angle in Quadrant II is always negative.]**

Got It?

Q In 1a, what are the possible lengths of the third side? **[The third side must be greater than 2 and less than 18.]**

Q In 1b, why is the length of the third side in Problem 1 always less than 6? **[The sum of any two lengths of a triangle is always greater than the length of the third side. So, the third side in this triangle is less than (2.5 + 3.5).]**

---

2 Guided Instruction

Each Problem is worked out and supported online.

Support in Algebra 2 Companion
- Vocabulary
- Key Concepts
- Got It?

Problem 1
Using the Law of Cosines to Solve a Problem
Animated

Problem 2
Finding an Angle Measure
Animated

Problem 3
Finding an Angle Measure
Animated

Answers

Solve It!

$\cos A = \dfrac{b^2 + c^2 - a^2}{2bc}$; $\cos B = \dfrac{a^2 + c^2 - b^2}{2ac}$; since there is nothing that distinguishes one angle from another, the laws for the angles A and B should follow the same pattern as the law for angle C.

Got It?

1. a. 6.4

b. 1 mi to 6 mi;
$$a^2 = 2.5^2 + 3.5^2 - 2(2.5)(3.5) \cos A$$
$$a^2 = 18.5 - 17.5 \cos A; \text{ if } A = 0°,$$
then $\cos A = 1$ and $a = 1$; if $A = 180°$, then $\cos A = -1$ and $a = 6$.

Problem 2

Q What is the relationship between the measures of angles A and C in $\triangle ABC$? **[The angle with the greatest measure is C because it lies opposite the longest side; the angle with the least measure is A because it lies opposite the shortest side.]**

Q Since $\cos C$ is negative, how can you classify $\triangle ABC$? **[It is an obtuse triangle.]**

Q How could you write the Law of Cosines solved for C? **[$C = \cos^{-1}\left(\frac{c^2 - a^2 - b^2}{-2ab}\right)$]**

Got It?

Q If A is the angle with the greatest measure in the triangle, what equation can you write to solve for $\cos A$? **[Samples:**
$15^2 = 10^2 + 14^2 - 2(10)(14)\cos A$;
or $\cos A = \frac{15^2 - 14^2 - 10^2}{-2(14)(10)}$.]

Q What expression can you write for $m\angle A$ using inverse cosine notation?
[$A = \cos^{-1}\left(\frac{71}{280}\right) \approx \cos^{-1}(0.2536)$]

Problem 3

Q How would you describe the relationship between $m\angle B$ and $m\angle C$? **[$m\angle B < m\angle C$ because $b < c$.]**

Q What other proportions can you write to solve for $\sin B$? Explain. **[Sample: $\frac{\sin B}{\sin 45°} \approx \frac{6.2}{5.56}$. If the cross products are equal, any proportion is valid.]**

Q If you were finding the inverse sine of the same quantity, but $\angle B$ was obtuse what would $m\angle B$ be? **[128°]**

You can also use the Law of Cosines with triangles determined by the measures of all three sides (SSS).

 Problem 2 Finding an Angle Measure

What is the measure of $\angle C$ in the triangle at the right? Round your answer to the nearest tenth of a degree.

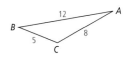

Think	Write
Choose the form of the Law of Cosines that contains $\angle C$.	$c^2 = a^2 + b^2 - 2ab \cos C$
Substitute and simplify.	$12^2 = 5^2 + 8^2 - 2(5)(8)\cos C$ $144 = 25 + 64 - 80 \cos C$
Combine like terms.	$55 = -80 \cos C$
Solve for $\cos C$.	$\cos C = -\frac{55}{80}$
Solve for $m\angle C$. Use a calculator.	$m\angle C = \cos^{-1}\left(-\frac{55}{80}\right) \approx 133.4°$

Got It? 2. The lengths of the sides of a triangle are 10, 14, and 15. What is the measure of the angle opposite the longest side?

Sometimes you need to use the Law of Cosines followed by the Law of Cosines again or by the Law of Sines.

 Problem 3 Finding an Angle Measure

In $\triangle ABC$, $b = 6.2$, $c = 7.8$, and $m\angle A = 45°$. What is $m\angle B$?

Plan

How do you start?
Drawing a diagram makes it easier to see what you know and what you are looking for.

Step 1 Draw a diagram.

Step 2 Find a. Since you cannot find $m\angle B$ directly, use the Law of Cosines to find a.

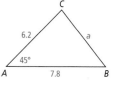

$$a^2 = b^2 + c^2 - 2bc \cos A$$
$$a^2 = 6.2^2 + 7.8^2 - 2(6.2)(7.8)\cos 45° \quad \text{Substitute.}$$
$$\approx 30.89 \quad \text{Simplify.}$$
$$a \approx 5.56 \quad \text{Solve for } a.$$

Additional Problems

1. Multiple Choice The shape of a piece of property is triangular with an 85° angle between two sides of 1.2 mi and 2.4 mi. What is the approximate length of the third side?

A 2.3 mi

B 2.6 mi

C 5.1 mi

D 6.7 mi

ANSWER B

2. What is the measure of $\angle C$? Round your answer to the nearest tenth of a degree.

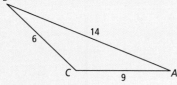

ANSWER 137.0°

3. In $\triangle ABC$, $b = 4.4$, $c = 7.6$, and $m\angle A = 51°$. What is $m\angle B$ to the nearest degree?

ANSWER 35°

Answers

Got It? (continued)

2. 75.3°

Step 3 Use the Law of Sines or the Law of Cosines to find $m\angle B$.

$$\frac{\sin B}{6.2} \approx \frac{\sin 45°}{5.56} \qquad \text{Law of Sines}$$

$$\sin B \approx \frac{6.2 \sin 45°}{5.56} \qquad \text{Solve for } \sin B.$$

$$m\angle B \approx \sin^{-1}\left(\frac{6.2 \sin 45°}{5.56}\right) \qquad \text{Solve for } m\angle B. \ (\angle B \text{ is not obtuse because } b < c.)$$

$$\approx 52° \qquad \text{Use a calculator.}$$

✓ **Got It?** **3.** In $\triangle RST$, $s = 41$, $t = 53$, and $m\angle R = 126°$. What is $m\angle T$?

Lesson Check

Do you know HOW?

1. In $\triangle ABC$, $m\angle B = 26°$, $a = 20$ in., and $c = 10$ in. Find b.

2. In $\triangle ABC$, $a = 8$ m, $b = 5$ m, and $c = 10$ m. Find $m\angle A$.

3. In $\triangle KNP$, $k = 21$ cm, $n = 12$ cm, and $m\angle P = 67°$. Find $m\angle N$.

4. In $\triangle WXY$, $w = 7.7$ ft, $x = 6.4$ ft, and $y = 8.5$ ft. Find $m\angle W$.

Do you UNDERSTAND? ⒸMATHEMATICAL PRACTICES

Ⓒ **5. Writing** Explain how you choose between the Law of Sines and the Law of Cosines when finding the measure of a missing angle or side.

Ⓒ **6. Error Analysis** A student solved for $m\angle C$, for $a = 11$ m, $b = 17$ m, and $c = 15$ m. What was the student's mistake?

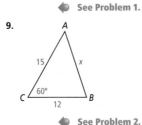

$$\cos C = \frac{15^2 - 11^2 - 17^2}{2(11)(17)}$$
$$\cos C \approx -0.495$$
$$C = \cos^{-1}(-0.495) \approx 119.7°$$

Practice and Problem-Solving Exercises ⒸMATHEMATICAL PRACTICES

Ⓐ Practice Use the Law of Cosines. Find length x to the nearest tenth. ◆ See Problem 1.

7.
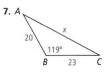

8.

9.
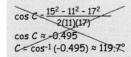

Use the Law of Cosines. Find x to the nearest tenth. ◆ See Problem 2.

10.
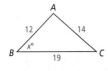

11.

12.
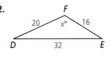

[PowerAlgebra.com] | Lesson 14-5 The Law of Cosines | **939**

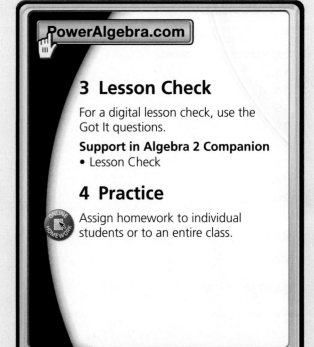

4 Practice

ASSIGNMENT GUIDE
Basic: 7–20 all, 27–29, 33–35, 50

Average: 7–19 odd, 21–50

Advanced: 7–19 odd, 21–53

Standardized Test Prep: 54–59

Mixed Review: 60–71

© **Mathematical Practices** are supported by exercises with red headings. Here are the Practices supported in this lesson:

MP 1: Make Sense of Problems Ex. 27

MP 2: Reason Abstractly Ex. 32, 50

MP 2: Reason Quantitatively Ex. 53

MP 3: Communicate Ex. 5, 33

MP 3: Critique the Reasoning of Others Ex. 6

Applications exercises have blue headings. Exercises 28, 35, and 52 support MP 4: Model.

STEM exercises focus on science or engineering applications.

EXERCISE 35: Use the Think About a Plan worksheet in the **Practice and Problem Solving Workbook** (also available in the Teaching Resources in print and online) to further support students' development in becoming independent learners.

HOMEWORK QUICK CHECK
To check students' understanding of key skills and concepts, go over Exercises 11, 17, 27, 35, and 50.

---

13. In $\triangle DEF$, $d = 15$ in., $e = 18$ in., and $f = 10$ in. Find $m\angle F$.

14. In $\triangle ABC$, $a = 20$ m, $b = 14$ m, and $c = 16$ m. Find $m\angle A$.

15. In $\triangle DEF$, $d = 12$ ft, $e = 10$ ft, and $f = 9$ ft. Find $m\angle F$.

Use the Law of Cosines and the Law of Sines. Find x to the nearest tenth. ◀ **See Problem 3.**

16.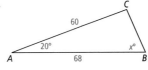

17.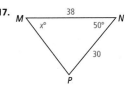

18. In $\triangle ABC$, $b = 4$ in., $c = 6$ in., and $m\angle A = 69°$. Find $m\angle C$.

19. In $\triangle RST$, $r = 17$ cm, $s = 12$ cm, and $m\angle T = 13°$. Find $m\angle S$.

20. In $\triangle DEF$, $d = 20$ ft, $e = 25$ ft, and $m\angle F = 98°$. Find $m\angle D$.

B Apply

For each triangle, write the correct form of the Law of Cosines or the Law of Sines to solve for the measure in red. Use only the information given in blue.

21.

22.

23.

24.

25.

26.

© **27. Think About a Plan** A touring boat was heading toward an island 80 nautical miles due south of where it left port. After traveling 15 nautical miles, it headed 8° east of south to avoid a fleet of commercial fishermen. After traveling 6 nautical miles, it turned to head directly toward the island. How far was the boat from the island at the time it turned?
- Can a diagram help you understand the problem?
- What are you asked to find?
- Which measurements do you need to solve the problem?

28. Sports A softball diamond is a square that is 65 ft on a side. The pitcher's mound is 46 ft from home plate. How far is the pitcher from third base?

Answers

26. $a^2 = b^2 + c^2 - 2bc \cos A$

27. ≈ 59.1 nautical miles

Practice and Problem-Solving Exercises (continued)

28. 46 ft

13. 33.7°

14. 83.3°

15. 47.2°

16. 60.5

17. 50.8

18. 71.7°

19. 27.0°

20. 35.5°

21. $b^2 = a^2 + c^2 - 2ac \cos B$

22. $c^2 = a^2 + b^2 - 2ab \cos C$

23. $\dfrac{\sin B}{b} = \dfrac{\sin C}{c}$

24. $\dfrac{\sin A}{a} = \dfrac{\sin B}{b}$

25. $\dfrac{\sin C}{c} = \dfrac{\sin A}{a}$

Find the remaining sides and angles in each triangle. Round your answers to the nearest tenth.

29.

30.

31.

 32. a. Open-Ended Sketch a triangle. Specify three of its measures so that you can use the Law of Cosines to find the remaining measures.
   b. Solve for the remaining measures of the triangle.

33. Writing Given the measures of three angles of a triangle, explain how to find the ratio of the lengths of two sides of the triangle.

34. Geometry The lengths of the sides of a triangle are 7.6 cm, 8.2 cm, and 5.2 cm. Find the measure of the largest angle.

35. Navigation A pilot is flying from city A to city B, which is 85 mi due north. After flying 20 mi, the pilot must change course and fly 10° east of north to avoid a cloudbank.
   a. If the pilot remains on this course for 20 mi, how far will the plane be from city B?
   b. How many degrees will the pilot have to turn to the left to fly directly to city B? How many degrees from due north is this course?

In △ABC, m∠A = 53° and c = 7 cm. Find each value to the nearest tenth.

36. Find $m\angle B$ for $b = 6.2$ cm.   **37.** Find a for $b = 13.7$ cm.   **38.** Find a for $b = 11$ cm.

39. Find $m\angle C$ for $b = 15.2$ cm.   **40.** Find $m\angle B$ for $b = 37$ cm.   **41.** Find a for $b = 16$ cm.

In △RST, t = 7 ft and s = 13 ft. Find each value to the nearest tenth.

42. Find $m\angle T$ for $r = 11$ ft.   **43.** Find $m\angle T$ for $r = 6.97$ ft.   **44.** Find $m\angle S$ for $r = 14$ ft.

45. Find r for $m\angle R = 35°$.   **46.** Find $m\angle S$ for $m\angle R = 87°$.   **47.** Find $m\angle R$ for $m\angle S = 70°$.

48. Geometry The lengths of the adjacent sides of a parallelogram are 54 cm and 78 cm. The larger angle measures 110°. What is the length of the longer diagonal? Round your answer to the nearest centimeter.

49. Geometry The lengths of the adjacent sides of a parallelogram are 21 cm and 14 cm. The smaller angle measures 58°. What is the length of the shorter diagonal? Round your answer to the nearest centimeter.

50. Reasoning Does the Law of Cosines apply to a right triangle? That is, does $c^2 = a^2 + b^2 - 2ab \cos C$ remain true when ∠C is a right angle? Justify your answer.

Challenge   **51. a.** Find the length of the altitude to $\overline{PQ}$ in the triangle at the right.
   b. Find the area of △PQR.

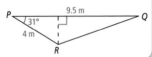

---

29. $b \approx 34.7$, $m\angle A \approx 26.7°$, $m\angle C \approx 33.3°$

30. $g \approx 53.3$, $m\angle F \approx 31.9°$, $m\angle H \approx 38.1°$

31. $m\angle A \approx 56.1°$, $m\angle B \approx 70.0°$, $m\angle C \approx 53.9°$

32. a–b. Check students' work.

33. For any two side lengths a and b, the ratio $\frac{a}{b}$ is equal to the ratio $\frac{\sin A}{\sin B}$, which can be found since A and B are given.

34. 77.2°

35. a. ≈ 45.4 mi
   b. 14.4° left; 4.4° west of north

36. 56.6°

37. 11.0 cm

38. 8.8 cm

39. 27.0°

40. 117.3°

41. 13.0 cm

42. 32.6°

43. 21.5°

44. 67.2°

45. 8.3 ft

46. 64.0°

47. 79.6°

48. 109 cm

49. 18 cm

50. Yes; since cos 90° = 0, $c^2 = a^2 + b^2 - 2ab \cos C$ reduces to $c^2 = a^2 + b^2$.

51. a. 2.1 m
   b. 9.8 m²

Answers

Practice and Problem-Solving Exercises (continued)

52. 4.8 in.

53. a. $\cos A > 0$ if $b^2 + c^2 > a^2$;
$\cos A = 0$ if $b^2 + c^2 = a^2$;
$\cos A < 0$ if $b^2 + c^2 < a^2$

b. acute $\triangle$ if $\cos A > 0$; right $\triangle$ if $\cos A = 0$;
obtuse $\triangle$ if $\cos A < 0$

Standardized Test Prep

54. 15.6

55. 85.4

56. 61.4°

57. 27.1°

58. 11.0

59. 24.1 units^2

Mixed Review

60. 17.1 in.

61. 8.9 m

62. 26.3 in.

63. 54.0°

64. 2π, $x = \pm\pi$

65. $\frac{2}{3}$, $x = \pm\frac{1}{3}$

66. $\frac{\pi}{3}$, $x = \pm\frac{\pi}{6}$

67. 1, $x = \pm\frac{1}{2}$

68. $\sin\theta$

69. $\cos\theta$

70. 1

71. $\csc^2\theta$

STEM **52. Physics** A pendulum 36 in. long swings 30° from the vertical. How high above the lowest position is the pendulum at the end of its swing? Round your answer to the nearest tenth of an inch.

53. Reasoning If you solve for cos *A* in the Law of Cosines, you get
$$\cos A = \frac{b^2 + c^2 - a^2}{2bc}.$$
a. Use this formula to explain how cos *A* can be positive, zero, or negative, depending on how $b^2 + c^2$ compares to a^2.
b. What does this tell you about $\angle A$ in each case?

Standardized Test Prep

GRIDDED RESPONSE

Use the diagram for Exercises 54–59. Angle measures are in degrees. Give each answer to the nearest tenth.

SAT/ACT

54. Let $a = 23.2$, $b = 18.5$, and $m\angle C = 42$. Find *c*.

55. Use the information in Question 54 to find $m\angle A$.

56. Suppose $a = 45.25$, $b = 39.75$, and $c = 20.65$. Find $m\angle B$.

57. Use the information in Question 56 to find $m\angle C$.

58. Suppose $b = 11.0$, $c = 11.7$, and $m\angle A = 22$. Find the length of the altitude from *A*.

59. Use the information in Question 58 to find the area of $\triangle ABC$ to the nearest tenth.

Mixed Review

60. In $\triangle RST$, $m\angle R = 37°$, $m\angle T = 59°$, and $TS = 12$ in. Find *RS*.   ◀ See Lesson 14-4.

61. In $\triangle JKL$, $m\angle L = 71°$, $j = 11$ m, and $m\angle K = 46°$. Find *k*.

62. In $\triangle MNP$, $m\angle N = 42°$, $n = 21$ in., and $m\angle M = 57°$. Find *m*.

63. In $\triangle DEF$, $m\angle F = 91°$, $d = 17$ mm, and $f = 21$ mm. Find $m\angle D$.

Identify the period and describe two asymptotes for each function.   ◀ See Lesson 13-6.

64. $y = \tan 0.5\theta$

65. $y = \tan\frac{3\pi}{2}\theta$

66. $y = \tan(-3\theta)$

67. $y = \tan\pi\theta$

Get Ready! **To prepare for Lesson 14-6, do Exercises 68–71.**

Complete the identities.   ◀ See Lesson 14-1.

68. $\csc\theta = \frac{1}{\blacksquare}$

69. $\sec\theta = \frac{1}{\blacksquare}$

70. $\cos^2\theta + \sin^2\theta = \blacksquare$

71. $1 + \cot^2\theta = \blacksquare$

Lesson Resources

Differentiated Remediation

Additional Instructional Support

Algebra 2 Companion

Students can use the **Algebra 2 Companion** worktext (4 pages) as you teach the lesson. Use the Companion to support

- New Vocabulary
- Key Concepts
- Got It for each Problem
- Lesson Check

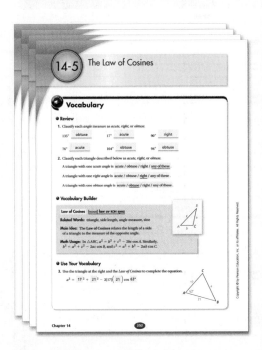

ELL Support

Connect to Prior Knowledge Students should be reminded to use their knowledge of geometry and algebra to check that solutions of triangles using the Law of Cosines are reasonable. This can include: verifying that they correctly applied the order of operations in evaluating expressions, determining that the relationship among the measures of the sides (angles) is consistent with the measures of their opposite sides (angles), confirming that if the unknown angle is obtuse, the cosine of the angle is negative, and making certain that the value of the unknown side of a triangle is the positive square root of a quadratic equation.

5 Assess & Remediate

Lesson Quiz

1. **Do you UNDERSTAND?** A map shows the location of three cities that form a triangle with a 72° angle between two sides that represent distances 2.8 mi and 4.2 mi. What is the distance represented by the length of the third side?

2. What is the measure of $\angle C$? Round your answer to the nearest tenth of a degree.

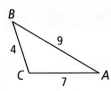

3. In $\triangle ABC$, $b = 8.4$, $c = 9.6$, and $m\angle A = 30°$. What is $m\angle B$?

ANSWERS TO LESSON QUIZ

1. 4.3 mi
2. 106.6°
3. ≈61°

PRESCRIPTION FOR REMEDIATION

Use the student work on the Lesson Quiz to prescribe a differentiated review assignment:

Points	Differentiated Remediation
0–1	Intervention
2	On-level
3	Extension

PowerAlgebra.com

5 Assess & Remediate

Assign the Lesson Quiz. Appropriate intervention, practice, or enrichment is automatically generated based on student performance.

Intervention

- **Reteaching** (2 pages) Provides reteaching and practice exercises for the key lesson concepts. Use with struggling students or absent students.

- **English Language Learner Support** Helps students develop and reinforce mathematical vocabulary and key concepts.

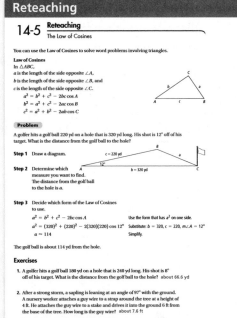

Differentiated Remediation *continued*

On-Level

- **Practice** (2 pages) Provides extra practice for each lesson. For simpler practice exercises, use the Form K Practice pages found in the All-in-One Teaching Resources and online.

- **Think About a Plan** Helps students develop specific problem-solving skills and strategies by providing scaffolded guiding questions.

- **Standardized Test Prep** Focuses on all major exercises, all major question types, and helps students prepare for the high-stakes assessments.

Extension

- **Enrichment** Provides students with interesting problems and activities that extend the concepts of the lesson.

- **Activities, Games, and Puzzles** Worksheets that can be used for concepts development, enrichment, and for fun!

Practice and Problem Solving Wkbk/All-in-One Resources/Online
Practice page 1

14-5 Practice   Form G
The Law of Cosines

Use the Law of Cosines. Find length x to the nearest tenth.

1.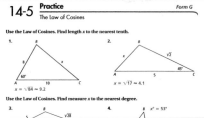
$x = \sqrt{84} \approx 9.2$

2.
$x = \sqrt{17} \approx 4.1$

Use the Law of Cosines. Find measure x to the nearest degree.

3.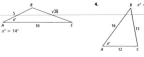
$x° = 14°$

4. $x° = 53°$

5. In $\triangle XYZ$, $x = 4$ cm, $y = 7$ cm, and $z = 10$ cm. Find $m\angle X$. 18.2°

6. In $\triangle FGH$, $f = 32$ in., $g = 79$ in., and $h = 86$ in. Find $m\angle G$. 66.7°

7. In $\triangle ABC$, $a = 3$ ft, $b = 2.9$ ft, and $c = 4.6$ ft. Find $m\angle C$. 102.4°

8. In $\triangle FGH$, $f = 34$ m, $g = 18.9$ m, and $h = 21.5$ m. Find $m\angle F$. 30.4°

9. In $\triangle ABC$, $a = 14$ yd, $b = 16$ yd, and $c = 18$ yd. Find $m\angle C$. 73.4°

Practice and Problem Solving Wkbk/All-in-One Resources/Online
Practice page 2

14-5 Practice (continued)   Form G
The Law of Cosines

For Exercises 10–13, use the Law of Cosines and the Law of Sines. Find x to the nearest tenth.

10. 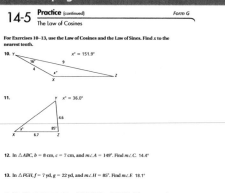 $x° = 151.9°$

11. $x° = 36.0°$

12. In $\triangle ABC$, $b = 8$ cm, $c = 7$ cm, and $m\angle A = 149°$. Find $m\angle C$. 14.4°

13. In $\triangle FGH$, $f = 7$ yd, $g = 22$ yd, and $m\angle H = 85°$. Find $m\angle F$. 18.1°

14. The sides of a triangular lot are 158 ft, 173 ft, and 191 ft. Find the measure of the angle opposite the longest side to the nearest tenth of a degree. 70.3°

15. A car travels 50 mi due west from point A. At point B, the car turns and travels at an angle of 35° north of due east. The car travels in this direction for 40 mi, to point C. How far is point C from point A? 28.7 mi

16. a. In $\triangle ABC$, $m\angle A = 84.1°$, $b = 4.8$, and $c = 7.2$. Use the Law of Cosines to find a and then use the Law of Sines to find the measure of angles B and C. Round to the nearest tenth. $a = 8.2$; $m\angle B = 35.4°$; $m\angle C = 60.5°$
  b. **Error Analysis** Your classmate says that this triangle does not exist. You say that it does. Who is correct? Explain. You; the angles of this triangle add up to 180°, which is equal to the sum of the angles of any triangle.

All-in-One Resources/Online
Enrichment

14-5 Enrichment
The Law of Cosines

Flight Paths

By using degree measurements to represent compass directions, you can describe the heading, or direction, in which a plane is traveling. In this system, 0° (360°) corresponds to due north, 90° corresponds to due east, 180° corresponds to due south, and 270° corresponds to due west.

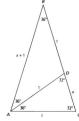

Angles are measured in a *clockwise* direction. This is different from measuring angles in standard position on a coordinate system.

With this method you can describe a flight path in terms of distances and headings. For example, suppose a plane flies 300 mi on a heading of 45°, then the plane changes course and flies 200 mi on a heading of 150°.

If you could determine the angle between the two "legs" of the trip ($\angle B$), you could then use the Law of Cosines to find how far the plane has traveled from its point of departure (b).

Because $\overline{BC}$ is parallel to $\overline{AD}$, $\angle B$ is supplementary to $\angle BAD$, which is 105°. Thus $\angle B = 180° - 105° = 75°$. Using the law of cosines, $b^2 = 300^2 + 200^2 - 2(300)(200) \cos 75°$, and $b = 314.6$ mi.

Determine the heading on which the plane would have to travel to return to point A.

1. First use the Law of Sines to find $\angle BAC$, and then add 45°.
   $m\angle BAC = 37.9°$; $m\angle BAC + 45° = 82.9°$

2. Add 180° to find the return heading.
   return heading is 262.9°

Suppose a plane flies 240 mi on a heading of 35°. Then the plane changes course and flies 160 mi on a heading of 160°.

3. Determine the heading on which the plane would have to travel to return to its point of origin. return heading is 256.5°

Practice and Problem Solving Wkbk/All-in-One Resources/Online
Think About a Plan

14-5 Think About a Plan
The Law of Cosines

Navigation A pilot is flying from city A to city B, which is 85 mi due north. After flying 20 mi, the pilot must change course and fly 10° east of north to avoid a cloud bank.

a. If the pilot remains on this course for 20 mi, how far will the plane be from city B?
b. How many degrees will the pilot have to turn to the left to fly directly to city B? How many degrees from due north is this course?

1. How can a diagram help you solve this problem?
   Answers may vary. Sample: A diagram can help me understand the angles and side lengths of the triangles in the problem .

2. Fill in the missing information in the diagram.

3. How can you find the length of the other unknown side of the triangle?
   Answers may vary. Sample: I can subtract 20 mi from 85 mi .

4. How can the Law of Cosines help you find the length x?
   Answers may vary. Sample: I can use the lengths of the other two sides and the 10° angle between them in the Law of Cosines .

5. Find x, the distance the plane is from city B.   45.4 mi

6. How can you find the number of degrees the pilot will have to turn to the left to fly directly to city B?
   Answers may vary. Sample: Use the Law of Sines with the value for x, the side with length 65 mi, and the 10° angle. There are two possible triangles, so the solution we want is the angle that is greater than 90°. The angle found will be the supplement of the angle representing the number of degrees the pilot will have to turn .

7. How many degrees will the pilot have to turn to the left to fly directly to city B?   14.4°

8. How can you find the number of degrees this course is from due north?
   Answers may vary. Sample: The other angle in the triangle represents the number of degrees the course is from due north. Subtract the sum of the two angles I know from 180°.

9. How many degrees from due north is this course?   4.4°

Practice and Problem Solving Wkbk/All-in-One Resources/Online
Standardized Test Prep

14-5 Standardized Test Prep
The Law of Cosines

Multiple Choice

For Exercises 1–5, choose the correct letter.

1. What is length x to the nearest tenth? A
   Ⓐ 10.7   Ⓒ 39.8
   Ⓑ 21.9   Ⓓ 113.9

2. What is measure x to the nearest tenth? H
   Ⓕ 7.7°   Ⓗ 59.9°
   Ⓖ 50.1°   Ⓘ 70.0°

3. What is length x to the nearest tenth? D
   Ⓐ 27.2   Ⓒ 13.4
   Ⓑ 17.3   Ⓓ 12.3

4. What is measure x to the nearest tenth? I
   Ⓔ 36.5°   Ⓗ 56.3°
   Ⓖ 49.1°   Ⓘ 74.6°

5. In $\triangle ABC$, $a = 20$, $b = 12$, and $c = 30$. What is the area of $\triangle ABC$ to the nearest tenth? B
   Ⓐ 75.5 units²   Ⓑ 80.5 units²   Ⓒ 85 units²   Ⓓ 95 units²

Short Response

6. Find the remaining side and angles in the triangle.
   [2] $r = 15.3$, $m\angle P \approx 55.7°$, $m\angle Q \approx 76.3°$
   [1] incorrect length for r OR incorrect measures for $\angle P$ and $\angle Q$
   [0] no answers given

Online Teacher Resource Center
Activities, Games, and Puzzles

14-5 Activity: Divisors of 360
The Law of Cosines

This activity can be done alone or in small groups.

Background

You have previously learned how to find the exact values of trigonometric functions for certain special angles such as 30°, 45°, 60°, 90°, 120°, and 180°. These are all divisors of 360°. In this activity, you will use the law of cosines to find values of trig functions for 36° and 72°.

Step 1: Label the following in the figure above.
$AC = 1$ and $CD = x$

Step 2: Find and label the following lengths: AD, BD, and AB.
Note: $\triangle ABC$, $\triangle ABD$, and $\triangle CAD$ are all isosceles triangles. 1; 1; $x + 1$

Step 3: Solve for x.
Note: $\triangle ABC$ and $\triangle CAD$ are similar triangles; therefore the ratios of leg-to-base in the two triangles are equal. Use this to set up an equation in the variable x. $x = \frac{-1 + \sqrt{5}}{2}$

Step 4: Apply the Law of Cosines to $\triangle CAD$ to find the exact value for $\cos 36°$. $\cos 36° = \frac{1 + \sqrt{5}}{4}$

Step 5: Apply the Law of Cosines to $\triangle CAD$ to find the exact value for $\cos 72°$. $\cos 72° = \frac{-1 + \sqrt{5}}{4}$

Step 6: Use your calculator to verify your results from Steps 4 and 5. $\cos 36° \approx 0.809$; $\cos 72° \approx 0.309$

14-6 Angle Identities

© Content Standard
F.TF.9 Prove the addition and subtraction formulas for sine, cosine, and tangent and use them to solve problems.

Objectives To verify and use angle identities
To verify and use sum and difference identities

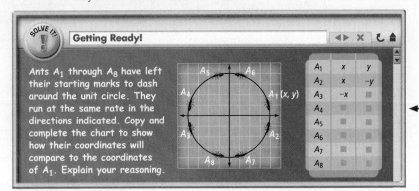

Getting Ready!

Ants A_1 through A_8 have left their starting marks to dash around the unit circle. They run at the same rate in the directions indicated. Copy and complete the chart to show how their coordinates will compare to the coordinates of A_1. Explain your reasoning.

	x	y
A_1	x	y
A_2	x	-y
A_3	-x	
A_4		
A_5		
A_6		
A_7		
A_8		

Dynamic Activity Sum and Difference Identities for Sine and Cosine

The fact that $(\pm x, \pm y)$ and $(\pm y, \pm x)$ can represent eight different points suggests that you can derive several trigonometric identities directly from the unit circle.

Essential Understanding Several trigonometric identities involve a single angle. Other trigonometric identities involve two angles. No important trigonometric identity is *additive*; for example, $\sin (A + B) \neq \sin A + \sin B$.

take note
Properties Negative Angle Identities

$$\sin (-\theta) = -\sin \theta \qquad \cos (-\theta) = \cos \theta \qquad \tan (-\theta) = -\tan \theta$$

Here's Why It Works In the figure at the right, angles θ and $-\theta$ have the same amount of rotation, but the rotations are in opposite directions.

Point Q is a reflection of P across the x-axis. The x-coordinates of P and Q (cosine) are the same and their y-coordinates (sine) are opposites. So $\cos (-\theta) = \cos \theta$ and $\sin (-\theta) = -\sin \theta$.

Similarly, S is the reflection of R across the x-axis. So $\tan (-\theta) = -\tan \theta$.

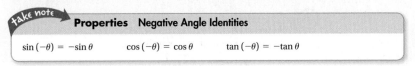

$P(\cos \theta, \sin \theta)$
$S(1, \tan (-\theta))$
$Q(\cos (-\theta), \sin (-\theta))$
$R(1, \tan \theta)$

1 Interactive Learning

Solve It!
PURPOSE To introduce the eight points on the unit circle with coordinates of $\pm x$ and $\pm y$
PROCESS Students may
- map each point as a reflection of a known point across the axes or the lines $y = x$ and $y = -x$.
- consider that each point corresponds to an angle θ, where θ is the angle measure to the x-axis.

FACILITATE

Q A segment drawn from the center to A_1 makes an angle θ with the x-axis. How does the angle between the x-axis and the segment drawn from the center to A_2 compare to θ? **[The angle is the opposite, $-\theta$.]**

Q Point A_5 is a reflection of which point across what line? How do the coordinates of the reflected point change? **[Answers may vary. Sample: A_2; $y = x$; the coordinate switch: $(x, -y)$ maps to $(-y, x)$.]**

ANSWER See Solve It in Answers on next page.
CONNECT THE MATH Students may answer the Solve It by using transformations or angles in the unit circle. The eight points demonstrate the angle identities used in this lesson.

2 Guided Instruction
Take Note

Q How can you use the sine and cosine negative-angle identities to verify that $\tan (-\theta) = -\tan \theta$?
$$\left[\tan (-\theta) = \frac{\sin(-\theta)}{\cos(-\theta)} = \frac{-\sin \theta}{\cos \theta} = -\tan \theta.\right]$$

Here's Why It Works
Have students use graphs to show that $y = \sin (-\theta)$ (the reflection of $y = \sin \theta$ in the y-axis) is equivalent to $y = -\sin \theta$ (the reflection of $y = \sin \theta$ in the x-axis).

14-6 Preparing to Teach

BIG idea Equivalence
ESSENTIAL UNDERSTANDINGS
- Several trigonometric identities involve a single angle. Other trigonometric identities involve two angles. No important trigonometric identity is *additive*; for example, $\sin (A + B) \neq \sin A + \sin B$.
- The cosine curve is the sine curve translated $\frac{\pi}{2}$ radians to the left. The cotangent curve is the tangent curve reflected over the x-axis and translated $\frac{\pi}{2}$ radians horizontally.

Math Background
Angle identities are fundamental to simplifying expressions and solving trigonometric equations.
- The negative angle identities indicate that reversing the sign of the angle reverses the sign of the sine and tangent of the

angle but does not affect the cosine of the angle.
- The cofunction angle identities allow you to simplify some trigonometric expressions by using complementary angles.
- The angle sum and difference identities give a way to simplify expressions involving trigonometric functions despite the fact that the functions are not additive.

© Mathematical Practices
Look for and express regularity in repeated reasoning. Students will use the negative angle identities and angle sum identities as a shortcut for computing the values of trigonometric functions.

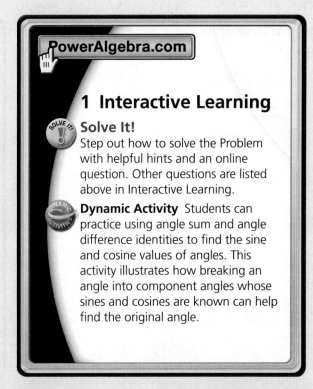

PowerAlgebra.com

1 Interactive Learning

Solve It!
Step out how to solve the Problem with helpful hints and an online question. Other questions are listed above in Interactive Learning.

Dynamic Activity Students can practice using angle sum and angle difference identities to find the sine and cosine values of angles. This activity illustrates how breaking an angle into component angles whose sines and cosines are known can help find the original angle.

Take Note

Q How would you check the sine and cosine cofunction identities using $\theta = \frac{\pi}{2}$?

$[\sin\left(\frac{\pi}{2} - \frac{\pi}{2}\right) = \sin 0 = 0 = \cos\frac{\pi}{2}$; $\cos\left(\frac{\pi}{2} - \frac{\pi}{2}\right) = \cos 0 = 1 = \sin\frac{\pi}{2}.]$

Q You know from the negative angle identities that $\cos\theta = \cos(-\theta)$. What is an equivalent way to write $\cos\left(\frac{\pi}{2} - \theta\right)$? $[\cos\left(\frac{\pi}{2} - \theta\right) = \cos\left(\theta - \frac{\pi}{2}\right)]$

Here's Why It Works

In a unit circle, have students draw an acute angle in standard position with an altitude to the x-axis. Reflect the angle across the line $y = x$ and draw an altitude again. Show how the x-coordinate (cosine) and the y-coordinate (sine) have been interchanged. Now have them do the same with an obtuse angle. Show them that subtracting an angle from $\frac{\pi}{2}$ (rotating it clockwise from the y-axis) and adding the angle to 0 (rotating it counterclockwise from the x-axis) always produces points that are reflections of each other across the line $y = x$, regardless of whether the angle is acute or obtuse or what quadrants the angles lie in.

Problem 1

Q To check this identity, you could substitute a radian angle measure for θ. Why is 0 a better angle measure than $\frac{\pi}{2}$ in this case? **[$\cos 0$ equals 1, which can be made positive or negative; $\cos\frac{\pi}{2}$ equals zero, which cannot be negative.]**

Got It?

Q To solve this problem, you used steps similar to the steps in Problem 1. Is $\cos\left(\theta - \frac{\pi}{2}\right) = -\cos\left(\frac{\pi}{2} - \theta\right)$? Explain. **[No; in the second step, the value of $\cos(-\theta)$ is $\cos\theta$, and not $-\cos\theta$.]**

The cosine curve is the sine curve translated $\frac{\pi}{2}$ radians to the left. The cotangent curve is the tangent curve reflected across the x-axis and translated $\frac{\pi}{2}$ radians horizontally.

Identities of another type relate to complementary angles. These are called *cofunction* identities.

 take note

Properties Cofunction Identities

$$\sin\left(\frac{\pi}{2} - \theta\right) = \cos\theta \qquad \cos\left(\frac{\pi}{2} - \theta\right) = \sin\theta \qquad \tan\left(\frac{\pi}{2} - \theta\right) = \cot\theta$$

Here's Why It Works In the figure at the right, θ is a counterclockwise rotation from the positive x-axis and $\frac{\pi}{2} - \theta$ is the same amount of rotation clockwise from the positive y-axis.

Point Q is a reflection of P across the line $y = x$. If (x, y) are the coordinates of P, then (y, x) are the coordinates of Q. So $\cos\left(\frac{\pi}{2} - \theta\right) = \sin\theta$ and $\sin\left(\frac{\pi}{2} - \theta\right) = \cos\theta$.

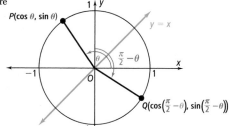

Then, by the Tangent Identity,

$$\tan\left(\frac{\pi}{2} - \theta\right) = \frac{\sin\left(\frac{\pi}{2} - \theta\right)}{\cos\left(\frac{\pi}{2} - \theta\right)}$$

$$= \frac{\cos\theta}{\sin\theta}$$

$$= \cot\theta.$$

 Problem 1 **Verifying an Angle Identity**

Verify the identity $\sin\left(\theta - \frac{\pi}{2}\right) = -\cos\theta$.

Plan

Can you use a cofunction identity?
You can use a cofunction identity if you can express the angle as $\left(\frac{\pi}{2} - \theta\right)$ instead of as $\left(\theta - \frac{\pi}{2}\right)$.

$$\sin\left(\theta - \frac{\pi}{2}\right) = \sin\left(-\left(\frac{\pi}{2} - \theta\right)\right) \qquad b - a = -(a - b)$$

$$= -\sin\left(\frac{\pi}{2} - \theta\right) \qquad \sin(-\theta) = -\sin\theta$$

$$= -\cos\theta \qquad \sin\left(\frac{\pi}{2} - \theta\right) = \cos\theta$$

✓ **Got It? 1.** Verify the identity $\cos\left(\theta - \frac{\pi}{2}\right) = \sin\theta$.

Answers

Solve It!

A_1	x	y
A_2	x	$-y$
A_3	$-x$	$-y$
A_4	$-x$	y
A_5	$-y$	x
A_6	y	x
A_7	y	$-x$
A_8	$-y$	$-x$

You can find the coordinates of all the ants by using reflections across the y-axis, the x-axis, and the lines $y = x$ and $y = -x$.

Got It?

1. $\cos\left(\theta - \frac{\pi}{2}\right) = \cos\left(-\left(\frac{\pi}{2} - \theta\right)\right)$

$$= \cos\left(\frac{\pi}{2} - \theta\right)$$

$$= \sin\theta$$

PowerAlgebra.com

2 Guided Instruction

Ⓒ Each Problem is worked out and supported online.

Problem 1
Verifying an Angle Identity

Problem 2
Deriving a Cofunction Identity

Problem 3
Solving a Trigonometric Equation
Animated

Problem 4
Using an Angle Difference Identity
Animated

Problem 5
Deriving a Sum Identity
Animated

Problem 6
Using an Angle Sum Identity

Support in Algebra 2 Companion
• Vocabulary
• Key Concepts
• Got It?

The cofunction identities were derived using the unit circle. So they apply to an angle θ of any size.

 Problem 2 Deriving a Cofunction Identity

How can you use the definitions of the trigonometric ratios for a right triangle to derive the cofunction identity for $\sin(90° - A)$?

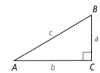

Think

What does $90° - A$ have to do with a right triangle?
If one acute angle has measure A, the other has measure $90° - A$.

In a right triangle, the acute angles are complementary. So $A + B = 90°$ and $B = 90° - A$, where A and B are the measures of acute angles.

$\sin(90° - A) = \sin B$ A and B are complementary angles.

$\qquad\qquad\quad = \dfrac{b}{c}$ Definition of sine in a right triangle

$\qquad\qquad\quad = \cos A$ Definition of cosine in a right triangle

 Got It? **2.** How can you use the definitions of the trigonometric ratios for a right triangle to derive the cofunction identity for $\sec(90° - A)$?

You can use angle identities to solve trigonometric equations.

 Problem 3 Solving a Trigonometric Equation

What are all the values that satisfy $\sin\theta = \sin\left(\frac{\pi}{2} - \theta\right)$ for $0 \le \theta < 2\pi$?

$\sin\theta = \sin\left(\dfrac{\pi}{2} - \theta\right)$

Plan

Why is it a good idea to get the angles the same?
Once the angles are identical, you can rewrite the equation in terms of one trigonometric function.

$\sin\theta = \cos\theta$ Cofunction Angle Identity

$\dfrac{\sin\theta}{\cos\theta} = 1$ Divide by $\cos\theta$.

$\tan\theta = 1$ Tangent Identity

$\theta = \tan^{-1} 1$ Solve for one value of θ.

$\theta = \dfrac{\pi}{4}$

Another solution is $\frac{\pi}{4} + \pi$, or $\frac{5\pi}{4}$.

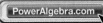 **Got It?** **3. a.** What are all values that satisfy $\sin\left(\frac{\pi}{2} - \theta\right) = \sec\theta$ for $0 \le \theta < 2\pi$?
b. Reasoning In Problem 3, if θ is not restricted to be between 0 and 2π, can you use the fact that sine is a periodic function to find all values of θ? Explain.

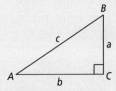

Problem 2

Explain that Problem 2 uses the same cofunction identities as described on the previous page, but written in degrees rather than radians.

Q Problem 2 shows $\sin(90° - A) = \sin B = \cos A$. What is another trigonometric expression that would return the same value? **[$\cos(90° - B)$]**

Got It?

Q What is $\sec(90° - A)$ written as a reciprocal of another function and written as a ratio of side lengths from the diagram? **[$\sec(90° - A) = \dfrac{1}{\cos(90° - A)} = \dfrac{c}{a}$.]**

Problem 3

Students should watch for division by zero. A θ value that results in zero may or may not be a correct solution, but that value must be checked in the original equation.

Q Four different angles could be drawn in the unit circle whose terminal sides form an angle of $\frac{\pi}{4}$ with the x-axis. Why does this problem have only two solutions? **[Because $\tan\theta = 1$, the $\sin\theta$ and $\cos\theta$ values must have the same sign, not just the same absolute value. This occurs in the first and third quadrants only.]**

Got It?

Q In 3a, how many solutions did you find? Why? **[Two; the equation simplifies to $\cos^2\theta = 1$ or $\cos\theta = \pm 1$.]**

Additional Problems

1. Verify the identity $\sin\left(\theta - \frac{\pi}{2}\right) = -\dfrac{1}{\sec\theta}$.

ANSWER $\sin\left(\theta - \frac{\pi}{2}\right) = \sin\left[-\left(\frac{\pi}{2} - \theta\right)\right] = -\sin\left(\frac{\pi}{2} - \theta\right) = -\cos\theta = -\dfrac{1}{\sec\theta}$

2. How can you use the definitions of the trigonometric ratios for a right triangle to derive the cofunction identity for $\cos(90° - A)$?

ANSWER $\cos(90° - A) = \cos B = \dfrac{a}{c} = \sin A$

3. What are all the values that satisfy $\sin\left(\theta - \frac{\pi}{2}\right) = \sin\theta$ for $0 \le \theta < 2\pi$?

ANSWER $\dfrac{3\pi}{4}, \dfrac{7\pi}{4}$

4. What is the exact value of $\cos 225°$?

ANSWER $-\dfrac{\sqrt{2}}{2}$

5. How can you derive an identity for $\sec(A + B)$? Use the difference identity for $\cos(A - B)$.

ANSWER
$\sec(A + B) = \sec(A - (-B))$
$= \dfrac{1}{\cos(A - (-B))} = \dfrac{1}{\cos A \cos(-B) + \sin A \sin(-B)}$
$= \dfrac{1}{\cos A \cos B + \sin A(-\sin B)}$
$= \dfrac{1}{\cos A \cos B - \sin A \sin B}$

6. What is the exact value of $\sin 195°$?

ANSWER $\dfrac{\sqrt{2} - \sqrt{6}}{4}$

Answers

Got It? (continued)

2. $\sec(90° - A) = \dfrac{1}{\cos(90° - A)} = \dfrac{1}{\sin\theta} = \csc\theta$
$\sec(90° - A) = \csc\theta$

3. a. $0, \pi$
b. yes; πn

Take Note

Q What patterns do you see in the sine and cosine angle difference identities? **[Sample: Each identity contains two terms and each term relates to both angles A and B. The sine identity is a subtraction of terms while the cosine identity is an addition of terms.]**

As students might expect, the tangent difference identity is the quotient of the sine and cosine difference identities. Have students write that quotient. Ask them to examine their quotient and the tangent difference identity.

Q What can you multiply your quotient by to end up with the tangent difference identity?

$$\frac{\frac{1}{\cos A \cos B}}{\frac{1}{\cos A \cos B}}$$

Here's Why It Works

Q In the derivation of the cosine difference identity, why are $(PO)^2$ and $(QO)^2$ each equal to 1? **[The circle is a unit circle, so the distance from the center to any point on the circle is 1.]**

To derive the sine difference identity, use the cosine difference and cofunction identities:

$$\sin \theta = \cos\left(\frac{\pi}{2} - \theta\right)$$

Substitute $A - B$ for θ.

$$\sin (A - B) = \cos\left(\frac{\pi}{2} - (A - B)\right)$$

$$= \cos\left(\left(\frac{\pi}{2} - A\right) - (-B)\right)$$

$$= \cos\left(\frac{\pi}{2} - A\right) \cos (-B)$$
$$\quad + \sin\left(\frac{\pi}{2} - A\right) \sin (-B)$$

$$= \sin A \cos B + \cos A (-\sin B)$$

$$= \sin A \cos B - \cos A \sin B$$

Trigonometric functions are not additive, that is $\cos (A + B) \neq \cos A + \cos B$. It is also true that $\cos (A - B) \neq \cos A - \cos B$.

Properties Angle Difference Identities

$$\sin (A - B) = \sin A \cos B - \cos A \sin B$$

$$\cos (A - B) = \cos A \cos B + \sin A \sin B$$

$$\tan (A - B) = \frac{\tan A - \tan B}{1 + \tan A \tan B}$$

Here's Why It Works In the figure, angles A, B, and $A - B$ are shown.

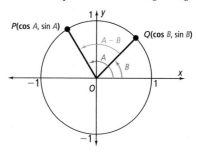

First, use the distance formula to find the square of the distance between P and Q.

$$(PQ)^2 = (x_1 - x_2)^2 + (y_1 - y_2)^2$$

$$= (\cos A - \cos B)^2 + (\sin A - \sin B)^2$$

$$= \cos^2 A - 2 \cos A \cos B + \cos^2 B + \sin^2 A - 2 \sin A \sin B + \sin^2 B$$

$$= 2 - 2 \cos A \cos B - 2 \sin A \sin B \qquad \begin{matrix}\text{Use the Pythagorean identity} \\ \sin^2 \theta + \cos^2 \theta = 1.\end{matrix}$$

Now use the Law of Cosines to find $(PQ)^2$ in $\triangle POQ$.

$$(PQ)^2 = (PO)^2 + (QO)^2 - 2(PO)(QO) \cos(A - B)$$

$$= 1^2 + 1^2 - 2(1)(1) \cos(A - B)$$

$$= 2 - 2 \cos(A - B)$$

The Transitive Property for Equality tells you that the two expressions for $(PQ)^2$ are equal.

$$2 - 2 \cos (A - B) = 2 - 2 \cos A \cos B - 2 \sin A \sin B$$

$$-2 \cos (A - B) = -2 \cos A \cos B - 2 \sin A \sin B \qquad \text{Subtract 2 from each side.}$$

$$\cos (A - B) = \cos A \cos B + \sin A \sin B \qquad \text{Divide each side by } -2.$$

You can also derive an identity for sin $(A - B)$. Then you can use the Tangent Identity to derive an identity for tan $(A - B)$.

 Problem 4 Using an Angle Difference Identity

What is the exact value of cos 15°?

$\cos (A - B) = \cos A \cos B + \sin A \sin B$ Cosine Angle Difference Identity

$\cos (60° - 45°) = \cos 60° \cos 45° + \sin 60° \sin 45°$ Substitute 60° for A and 45° for B.

$\qquad = \frac{1}{2}\left(\frac{\sqrt{2}}{2}\right) + \frac{\sqrt{3}}{2}\left(\frac{\sqrt{2}}{2}\right)$ Replace with exact values.

$\qquad = \frac{\sqrt{2}}{4} + \frac{\sqrt{6}}{4}$ Simplify.

$\qquad = \frac{\sqrt{2} + \sqrt{6}}{4}$

So $\cos 15° = \frac{\sqrt{2} + \sqrt{6}}{4}$.

Got It? 4. What is the exact value of sin 15°?

You can use difference identities to derive sum identities.

 Problem 5 Deriving a Sum Identity

How can you derive an identity for cos $(A + B)$? Use the difference identity for cos $(A - B)$.

$\cos (A + B) = \cos (A - (-B))$

$\qquad = \cos A \cos(-B) + \sin A \sin (-B)$ Cosine Angle Difference Identity

$\qquad = \cos A \cos B + \sin A (-\sin B)$ Negative Angle Identity

$\qquad = \cos A \cos B - \sin A \sin B$ Simplify.

Got It? 5. How can you derive an identity for sin $(A + B)$? Use the difference identity for sin $(A - B)$.

 **Properties Angle Sum Identities**

$\sin (A + B) = \sin A \cos B + \cos A \sin B$

$\cos (A + B) = \cos A \cos B - \sin A \sin B$

$\tan (A + B) = \frac{\tan A + \tan B}{1 - \tan A \tan B}$

Think

How do you know which measures to subtract?
You know exact values for 30°, 60°, 45°, and 90°. Use two measures with a difference of 15°.

Think

How are subtraction and addition related?
Adding a number is the same as subtracting the additive inverse of the number.

Problem 4   EXTENSION

Q What are other angle measures you could find exact values for using the difference identities? **[Sample: 75°, −15°]**

Q Which angle measures would you use to find an exact value for cos 75°? What is cos 75°? **[Sample; 120° and 45°; $\frac{\sqrt{6} - \sqrt{2}}{4}$]**

Got It?

Q What two angle measures did you use in the difference identity? **[60° and 45°]**

Q How did you expand sin $(60° − 45°)$ to find the solution? **[sin 60° cos 45° − cos 60° sin 45°]**

Problem 5

Q In the first step of the solution, why is the addition rewritten as subtraction of a negative? **[To use the angle difference identity, the argument must be written as a subtraction.]**

Got It?

Q Your solution should contain two terms. Are the terms added or subtracted? Why? **[Added, the sine angle difference formula is a subtraction of terms, but in the derivation you use the identity sin $(−\theta) = −$sin θ in the second term.]**

Take Note

Q What pattern do you see when you compare the sine angle subtraction and addition identities? **[The subtraction identity is a subtraction of terms; the addition identity is an addition of terms. Both identities have the pattern sin A cos $B \pm$ cos A sin B.]**

Answers

Got It? (continued)

4. $\frac{\sqrt{6} - \sqrt{2}}{4}$

5. $\sin(A + B)$
$= \sin(A - (-B))$
$= \sin A \cos(-B) - \cos A \sin(-B)$
$= \sin A \cos B - \cos A(-\sin B)$
$= \sin A \cos B + \cos A \sin B$

Problem 6

> **Q** How does this answer compare to the answer in Problem 4? Is this an expected result? Explain. **[The same; yes; it is expected because of the identity sin (90° + θ) = sin 90° cos θ + cos 90° sin θ = cos θ.]**

Got It?

> **Q** Before calculating, do you expect the answer to be positive or negative? Why? **[Negative; the angle is in the second quadrant, so the sine value is positive and the cosine value is negative. The tangent value is negative.]**

3 Lesson Check

Do you know HOW?
- In Exercise 1, students must use the Sine Angle Sum and Difference Identities to simplify the left side of the equation.
- For Exercises 3 and 4, several different sums or differences of angles can be used. For 3, students can try cos (−360° + 45°). For 4, students can try sin (−60° − 45°).

Do you UNDERSTAND?
- In Exercise 5, students may divide both sides of the equation by cos θ, which results in −1 = 1. Ask them what happens if they add cos θ to each side of the equation.

Close

> **Q** You have seen that sin (A + B) ≠ sin A + sin B, and that cos (A + B) ≠ cos A + cos B. Are there any functions for which f(A + B) = f(A) + f(B)? Explain. **[Yes; a direct variation has this property.]**

PowerAlgebra.com

3 Lesson Check

For a digital lesson check, use the Got It questions.

Support in Algebra 2 Companion
- Lesson Check

4 Practice

Assign homework to individual students or to an entire class.

 **Problem 6** Using an Angle Sum Identity

What is the exact value of sin 105°?

Think	Write
Write the Sine Angle Sum Identity.	$\sin (A + B) = \sin A \cos B + \cos A \sin B$
Find two angles that sum to 105° and have exact sine and cosine values. Let $A = 60°$ and $B = 45°$.	$\sin (60° + 45°) = \sin 60° \cos 45° + \cos 60° \sin 45°$
Substitute exact values and multiply.	$= \frac{\sqrt{3}}{2}\left(\frac{\sqrt{2}}{2}\right) + \frac{1}{2}\left(\frac{\sqrt{2}}{2}\right)$ $= \frac{\sqrt{6}}{4} + \frac{\sqrt{2}}{4}$
Simplify.	$= \frac{\sqrt{6} + \sqrt{2}}{4}$

 Got It? 6. What is the exact value of tan 105°?

 Lesson Check

Do you know HOW?

1. Verify the identity $\sin\left(\frac{\pi}{2} + \theta\right) + \sin\left(\frac{\pi}{2} - \theta\right) = 2 \cos \theta$.

2. Solve $\tan\left(\frac{\pi}{2} - \theta\right) = 1$ for $0 \le \theta < 2\pi$.

3. Find the exact value of $\cos(-315)°$.

4. Find the exact value of $\sin(-105)°$.

Do you UNDERSTAND? MATHEMATICAL PRACTICES

5. **Error Analysis** A question on a test asked, "Between 0 and 2π, the equation $-\cos \theta = \cos \theta$ has how many solutions?" A student divided each side by $\cos \theta$ to get $-1 = 1$ and concluded that there are no solutions. What mistake did the student make?

6. **Reasoning** Use an angle difference identity to show that $\sin\left(\frac{\pi}{2} - \theta\right) = \cos \theta$.

 Practice and Problem-Solving Exercises MATHEMATICAL PRACTICES

A Practice   Verify each identity.   ◆ See Problem 1.

7. $\csc\left(\theta - \frac{\pi}{2}\right) = -\sec \theta$ **8.** $\sec\left(\theta - \frac{\pi}{2}\right) = \csc \theta$ **9.** $\cot\left(\frac{\pi}{2} - \theta\right) = \tan \theta$

10. $\csc\left(\frac{\pi}{2} - \theta\right) = \sec \theta$ **11.** $\tan\left(\theta - \frac{\pi}{2}\right) = -\cot \theta$ **12.** $\sec\left(\frac{\pi}{2} - \theta\right) = \csc \theta$

Answers

Got It? (continued)
6. $-2 - \sqrt{3}$

Lesson Check

1. $\sin\left(\frac{\pi}{2} + \theta\right) + \sin\left(\frac{\pi}{2} - \theta\right)$
$= \sin\left(\frac{\pi}{2} - (-\theta)\right) + \sin\left(\frac{\pi}{2} - \theta\right)$
$= \cos(-\theta) + \cos \theta$
$= \cos \theta + \cos \theta = 2 \cos \theta$

2. $\frac{\pi}{4}, \frac{5\pi}{4}$ **3.** $\frac{\sqrt{2}}{2}$

4. $-\frac{\sqrt{2} + \sqrt{6}}{4}$

5. There are 2 solutions, $\frac{\pi}{2}$ and $\frac{3\pi}{2}$, between 0 and 2π because:
$-\cos \theta = \cos \theta$
$2 \cos \theta = 0$
$\cos \theta = 0; \theta = \frac{\pi}{2}, \frac{3\pi}{2}$

6. $\sin\left(\frac{\pi}{2} - \theta\right) = \sin\frac{\pi}{2}\cos\theta - \cos\frac{\pi}{2}\sin\theta$
$= (1)\cos\theta - (0)\sin\theta$
$= \cos\theta$

Practice and Problem-Solving Exercises

7. $\csc\left(\theta - \frac{\pi}{2}\right) = \dfrac{1}{\sin\left(\theta - \frac{\pi}{2}\right)}$

$= \dfrac{1}{\sin\left(-\left(\frac{\pi}{2} - \theta\right)\right)}$

$= \dfrac{1}{-\sin\left(\frac{\pi}{2} - \theta\right)}$

$= \dfrac{1}{-\cos\theta} = -\sec\theta$

8. $\sec\left(\theta - \frac{\pi}{2}\right) = \dfrac{1}{\cos\left(\theta - \frac{\pi}{2}\right)}$

$= \dfrac{1}{\cos\left(-\left(\frac{\pi}{2} - \theta\right)\right)}$

$= \dfrac{1}{\cos\left(\frac{\pi}{2} - \theta\right)}$

$= \dfrac{1}{\sin\theta} = \csc\theta$

Use the definitions of the trigonometric ratios for a right triangle to derive a cofunction identity for each expression.　　　　　◀ See Problem 2.

13. $\tan(90° - A)$　　　　**14.** $\csc(90° - A)$　　　　**15.** $\cot(90° - A)$

Solve each trigonometric equation for θ with $0 \le \theta < 2\pi$.　　　◀ See Problem 3.

16. $\cos\left(\frac{\pi}{2} - \theta\right) = \csc\theta$　　**17.** $\sin\left(\frac{\pi}{2} - \theta\right) = -\cos(-\theta)$　　**18.** $\tan\left(\frac{\pi}{2} - \theta\right) + \tan(-\theta) = 0$

19. $\tan^2\theta - \sec^2\theta = \cos(-\theta)$　**20.** $2\sin\left(\frac{\pi}{2} - \theta\right) = \sin(-\theta)$　**21.** $\tan\left(\frac{\pi}{2} - \theta\right) = \cos(-\theta)$

Ⓒ **Mental Math** Find the value of each trigonometric expression.　　◀ See Problems 4, 5, and 6.

22. $\cos 50° \cos 40° - \sin 50° \sin 40°$　　　**23.** $\sin 80° \cos 35° - \cos 80° \sin 35°$

24. $\sin 100° \cos 170° + \cos 100° \sin 170°$　　**25.** $\cos 183° \cos 93° + \sin 183° \sin 93°$

Find each exact value. Use a sum or difference identity.

26. $\cos 105°$　　**27.** $\tan 75°$　　**28.** $\tan 15°$　　**29.** $\sin 75°$　　**30.** $\cos 75°$

31. $\tan(-15°)$　　**32.** $\sin 225°$　　**33.** $\cos 240°$　　**34.** $\sin 390°$　　**35.** $\cos(-300°)$

 Apply

Ⓒ **36. Think About a Plan** At exactly $22\frac{1}{2}$ minutes after the hour, the minute hand of a clock is at point P, as shown in the diagram. Several minutes later, it has rotated θ degrees clockwise to point Q. The coordinates of point Q are $(\cos -(\theta + 45°), \sin -(\theta + 45°))$. Write the coordinates of point Q in terms of $\cos\theta$ and $\sin\theta$.
- What trigonometric identities can you use?
- How can you use the diagram to check your answer?

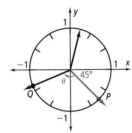

Verify each identity.

37. $\sin(A - B) = \sin A \cos B - \cos A \sin B$

38. $\tan(A - B) = \frac{\tan A - \tan B}{1 + \tan A \tan B}$

39. $\tan(A + B) = \frac{\tan A + \tan B}{1 - \tan A \tan B}$

40. $\sin\left(x + \frac{\pi}{3}\right) + \sin\left(x - \frac{\pi}{3}\right) = \sin x$

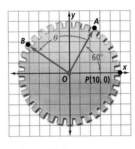

STEM **41. Gears** The diagram at the right shows a gear whose radius is 10 cm. Point A represents a 60° counterclockwise rotation of point $P(10, 0)$. Point B represents a θ-degree rotation of point A. The coordinates of B are $(10 \cos(\theta + 60°), 10 \sin(\theta + 60°))$. Write these coordinates in terms of $\cos\theta$ and $\sin\theta$.

Rewrite each expression as a trigonometric function of a single angle measure.

42. $\sin 2\theta \cos\theta + \cos 2\theta \sin\theta$　　**43.** $\sin 3\theta \cos 2\theta + \cos 3\theta \sin 2\theta$　　**44.** $\cos 3\theta \cos 4\theta - \sin 3\theta \sin 4\theta$

45. $\cos 2\theta \cos 3\theta - \sin 2\theta \sin 3\theta$　　**46.** $\frac{\tan 5\theta + \tan 6\theta}{1 - \tan 5\theta \tan 6\theta}$　　**47.** $\frac{\tan 3\theta - \tan\theta}{1 + \tan 3\theta \tan\theta}$

ASSIGNMENT GUIDE
Basic: 7–35 all, 36, 40–43, 48
Average: 7–35 odd, 36–48
Advanced: 7–35 odd, 36–55
Standardized Test Prep: 56–59
Mixed Review: 60–69

Ⓒ **Mathematical Practices** are supported by exercises with red headings. Here are the Practices supported in this lesson:

MP 1: Make Sense of Problems Ex. 36
MP 2: Reason Abstractly Ex. 6, 49a
MP 2: Reason Quantitatively Ex. 22–25
MP 3: Construct Arguments Ex. 49b
MP 3: Communicate Ex. 49b
MP 3: Critique the Reasoning of Others Ex. 5, 48

Applications exercises have blue headings. Exercise 41 supports MP 4: Model.

STEM exercises focus on science or engineering applications.

EXERCISE 41: Use the Think About a Plan worksheet in the **Practice and Problem Solving Workbook** (also available in the Teaching Resources in print and online) to further support students' development in becoming independent learners.

HOMEWORK QUICK CHECK
To check students' understanding of key skills and concepts, go over Exercises 9, 17, 36, 41, and 48.

---

9. $\cot\left(\frac{\pi}{2} - \theta\right) = \dfrac{\cos\left(\frac{\pi}{2} - \theta\right)}{\sin\left(\frac{\pi}{2} - \theta\right)}$

　　　　$= \dfrac{\sin\theta}{\cos\theta} = \tan\theta$

10. $\csc\left(\frac{\pi}{2} - \theta\right) = \dfrac{1}{\sin\left(\frac{\pi}{2} - \theta\right)}$

　　　　$= \dfrac{1}{\cos\theta} = \sec\theta$

11. $\tan\left(\theta - \frac{\pi}{2}\right) = \tan\left(-\left(\frac{\pi}{2} - \theta\right)\right)$

　　　　$= -\tan\left(\frac{\pi}{2} - \theta\right)$

　　　　$= -\cot\theta$

12. $\sec\left(\frac{\pi}{2} - \theta\right) = \dfrac{1}{\cos\left(\frac{\pi}{2} - \theta\right)}$

　　　　$= \dfrac{1}{\sin\theta} = \csc\theta$

13. $\tan(90° - A) = \cot A$

14. $\csc(90° - A) = \sec A$

15. $\cot(90° - A) = \tan A$

16. $\frac{\pi}{2}, \frac{3\pi}{2}$　　**17.** $\frac{\pi}{2}, \frac{3\pi}{2}$

18. $\frac{\pi}{4}, \frac{3\pi}{4}, \frac{5\pi}{4}, \frac{7\pi}{4}$　　**19.** π

20. 2.034, 5.176　　**21.** $\frac{\pi}{2}, \frac{3\pi}{2}$

22. 0　　**23.** $\frac{\sqrt{2}}{2}$　　**24.** −1　　**25.** 0

26. $\dfrac{\sqrt{2} - \sqrt{6}}{4}$　　**27.** $-\sqrt{3} - 2$

28. $2 - \sqrt{3}$　　**29.** $\dfrac{\sqrt{2} + \sqrt{6}}{4}$

30. $\dfrac{\sqrt{6} - \sqrt{2}}{4}$　　**31.** $-2 + \sqrt{3}$

32. $-\frac{\sqrt{2}}{2}$　**33.** $-\frac{1}{2}$　**34.** $\frac{1}{2}$　**35.** $\frac{1}{2}$

36. $Q\left(\frac{\sqrt{2}}{2}(\cos\theta - \sin\theta),\right.$

　　　　$\left.-\frac{\sqrt{2}}{2}(\sin\theta + \cos\theta)\right)$

37. $\sin(A - B) = \cos\left[\frac{\pi}{2} - (A - B)\right]$

　　　　$= \cos\left[\left(\frac{\pi}{2} - A\right) + B\right]$

　　　　$= \cos\left(\frac{\pi}{2} - A\right)\cos B - \sin\left(\frac{\pi}{2} - A\right)\sin B$

　　　　$= \sin A \cos B - \cos A \sin B$

38. $\tan(A - B) = \dfrac{\sin(A - B)}{\cos(A - B)}$

　　　　$= \dfrac{\sin A \cos B - \cos A \sin B}{\cos A \cos B + \sin A \sin B}$

　　　　$= \dfrac{\frac{\sin A \cos B - \cos A \sin B}{\cos A \cos B}}{\frac{\cos A \cos B + \sin A \sin B}{\cos A \cos B}}$

　　　　$= \dfrac{\frac{\sin A \cos B}{\cos A \cos B} - \frac{\cos A \sin B}{\cos A \cos B}}{\frac{\cos A \cos B}{\cos A \cos B} + \frac{\sin A \sin B}{\cos A \cos B}}$

　　　　$= \dfrac{\tan A - \tan B}{1 + \tan A \tan B}$

39. $\tan(A + B) = \dfrac{\sin(A + B)}{\cos(A + B)}$

　　　　$= \dfrac{\sin A \cos B + \cos A \sin B}{\cos A \cos B - \sin A \sin B}$

　　　　$= \dfrac{\frac{\sin A \cos B + \cos A \sin B}{\cos A \cos B}}{\frac{\cos A \cos B - \sin A \sin B}{\cos A \cos B}}$

　　　　$= \dfrac{\frac{\sin A \cos B}{\cos A \cos B} + \frac{\cos A \sin B}{\cos A \cos B}}{\frac{\cos A \cos B}{\cos A \cos B} - \frac{\sin A \sin B}{\cos A \cos B}}$

　　　　$= \dfrac{\tan A + \tan B}{1 - \tan A \tan B}$

40–47. See next page.

Answers

Practice and Problem-Solving Exercises (continued)

40. $\sin\left(x + \frac{\pi}{3}\right) + \sin\left(x - \frac{\pi}{3}\right)$

$= \sin x \cos \frac{\pi}{3} + \cos x \sin \frac{\pi}{3} + \sin x \cos \frac{\pi}{3}$
$\quad - \cos x \sin \frac{\pi}{3}$

$= 2 \sin x \cos \frac{\pi}{3}$

$= (2 \sin x) \cdot \frac{1}{2}$

$= \sin x$

41. $(5 \cos \theta - 5\sqrt{3} \sin \theta, \ 5 \sin \theta + 5\sqrt{3} \cos \theta)$

42. $\sin 3\theta$ **43.** $\sin 5\theta$

44. $\cos 7\theta$ **45.** $\cos 5\theta$

46. $\tan 11\theta$ **47.** $\tan 2\theta$

48. A counterexample is letting
$A = 30°$ and $B = 60°$, $\sin(30° + 60°) =$
$\sin 90° = 1 \ \sin 30° + \sin 60° = \frac{1}{2} + \frac{\sqrt{3}}{2} \neq 1$.

49. a. even: cosine, secant; odd: sine, cosecant, tangent, cotangent

    b. No; answers may vary. Sample:
$y = \sin x - \cos x$. For $x = \frac{\pi}{4}$,
$f(x) = \sin \frac{\pi}{4} - \cos \frac{\pi}{4} = 0$, and
$f(-x) = \sin\left(-\frac{\pi}{4}\right) - \cos\left(-\frac{\pi}{4}\right) = -\sqrt{2}$.
Because $f(x) \neq f(-x)$, and $-f(x) \neq f(-x)$, the function is neither even nor odd.

50. $\cos(\pi - \theta) = \cos \pi \cos \theta + \sin \pi \sin \theta$
$\qquad = (-1) \cos \theta + 0 = -\cos \theta$

51. $\sin(\pi - \theta) = \sin \pi \cos \theta - \cos \pi \sin \theta$
$\qquad = 0 - (-1) \sin \theta = \sin \theta$

52. $\sin(\pi + \theta) = \sin \pi \cos \theta + \cos \pi \sin \theta$
$\qquad = 0 + (-1) \sin \theta = -\sin \theta$

53. $\cos(\pi + \theta) = \cos \pi \cos \theta - \sin \pi \sin \theta$
$\qquad = (-1) \cos \theta - 0 = -\cos \theta$

54. $\sin\left(\frac{3\pi}{2} - \theta\right) = \sin \frac{3\pi}{2} \cos \theta - \cos \frac{3\pi}{2} \sin \theta$
$\qquad = (-1) \cos \theta - (0) \sin \theta = -\cos \theta$

55. $\cos\left(\theta + \frac{3\pi}{2}\right) = \cos \theta \cos \frac{3\pi}{2} - \sin \theta \sin \frac{3\pi}{2}$
$\qquad = \cos \theta(0) - \sin \theta(-1) = \sin \theta$

Standardized Test Prep

56. D

57. I

58. B

59. [2] $\sin(165°) = \sin(15°)$
$\qquad = \sin(45° - 30°)$
$\qquad = \sin 45° \cos 30° - \cos 45° \sin 30°$
$\qquad = \frac{\sqrt{2}}{2} \cdot \frac{\sqrt{3}}{2} - \frac{\sqrt{2}}{2} \cdot \frac{1}{2}$
$\qquad = \frac{\sqrt{6}}{4} - \frac{\sqrt{2}}{4} = \frac{\sqrt{6} - \sqrt{2}}{4}$

    [1] correct method, but with one computational error

Mixed Review

60. ≈ 16.3 ft

© 48. Error Analysis A student tries to show that
$\sin (A + B) = \sin A + \sin B$ is true by letting $A = 120°$
and $B = 240°$. Why is the student's reasoning not correct?

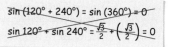

© Challenge

49. a. Reasoning A function is *even* if $f(-x) = f(x)$. A function is *odd* if $f(-x) = -f(x)$. Which trigonometric functions are even? Which are odd?

    © b. Writing Are all functions either even or odd? Explain your answer. Give a counterexample if possible.

Use the sum and difference formulas to verify each identity.

50. $\cos (\pi - \theta) = -\cos \theta$ **51.** $\sin (\pi - \theta) = \sin \theta$ **52.** $\sin (\pi + \theta) = -\sin \theta$

53. $\cos (\pi + \theta) = -\cos \theta$ **54.** $\sin\left(\frac{3\pi}{2} - \theta\right) = -\cos \theta$ **55.** $\cos\left(\theta + \frac{3\pi}{2}\right) = \sin \theta$

Standardized Test Prep

SAT/ACT

56. Which expressions are equivalent?

    I. $-\tan\left(\frac{\pi}{2} - \theta\right)$ II. $\tan\left(\theta - \frac{\pi}{2}\right)$ III. $\tan\left(-\left(\frac{\pi}{2} - \theta\right)\right)$

    Ⓐ I and II only   Ⓑ II and III only   Ⓒ I and III only   Ⓓ I, II, and III

57. Which expression is equal to cos 50°?

    Ⓕ $\sin 20° \cos 30° + \cos 20° \sin 30°$ Ⓗ $\sin 20° \cos 30° - \cos 20° \sin 30°$

    Ⓖ $\cos 20° \cos 30° + \sin 20° \sin 30°$ Ⓘ $\cos 20° \cos 30° - \sin 20° \sin 30°$

58. Which expression is NOT equivalent to cos θ?

    Ⓐ $-\sin (\theta - 90°)$ Ⓑ $-\cos (-\theta)$ Ⓒ $\sin (\theta + 90°)$ Ⓓ $-\cos (\theta + 180°)$

Short Response

59. Find an exact value for sin 165°. Show your work.

Mixed Review

Use the Law of Cosines. Find the indicated length to the nearest tenth.   ◀ **See Lesson 14-5.**

60. In $\triangle DEF$, $m\angle E = 54°$, $d = 14$ ft, and $f = 20$ ft. Find e.

61. In $\triangle RST$, $m\angle T = 32°$, $r = 10$ cm, and $s = 17$ cm. Find t.

Write each measure in radians. Express the answer in terms of π and as a decimal rounded to the nearest hundredth.   ◀ **See Lesson 13-3.**

62. $80°$ **63.** $-50°$ **64.** $-15°$ **65.** $70°$ **66.** $190°$

Get Ready!   **To prepare for Lesson 14-7, do Exercises 67– 69.**

Complete the following angle identities.   ◀ **See Lesson 14-6.**

67. $\cos (A + B) = $ ▩   **68.** $\sin (A + B) = $ ▩   **69.** $\tan (A + B) = $ ▩

---

61. ≈ 10.0 cm

62. $\frac{4\pi}{9}$ and 1.40

63. $-\frac{5\pi}{18}$ and -0.87

64. $-\frac{\pi}{12}$ and -0.26

65. $\frac{7\pi}{18}$ and 1.22

66. $\frac{19\pi}{18}$ and 3.32

67. $\cos A \cos B - \sin A \sin B$

68. $\sin A \cos B + \cos A \sin B$

69. $\dfrac{\tan A + \tan B}{1 - \tan A \tan B}$

Additional Instructional Support

Algebra 2 Companion

Students can use the **Algebra 2 Companion** worktext (4 pages) as you teach the lesson. Use the Companion to support

- New Vocabulary
- Key Concepts
- Got It for each Problem
- Lesson Check

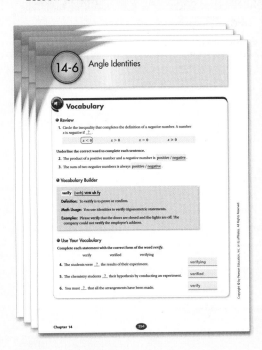

ELL Support

Assess Understanding The words *sine* and *sign* are homophones; the two words sound alike, although they have different meanings. You may want to say "plus/minus" when referring to the sign of a number.

Have students write $\sin (A - B) =$ and $\sin (A + B) =$ each followed by two long blank lines separated by a space.

- For $\sin (A - B)$ and $\sin (A + B)$ does a plus or a minus go between the blanks? The plus/minus between the blanks is the same as the plus/minus of the angles.
- Do $\sin (A - B)$ and $\sin (A + B)$ have the same pattern of sines and cosines in the blanks? What is the pattern? The pattern is $\sin A \cos B$, $\cos A \sin B$.

Repeat the procedure for the cosine angle difference and addition identities.

When students have written the sine and cosine difference and addition identities, challenge them to work with a partner to derive the tangent identities. If students have trouble getting started, explain that tangent is always sine over cosine.

5 Assess & Remediate

Lesson Quiz

1. Verify the identity $\cot \left(\theta - \frac{\pi}{2}\right) = -\tan \theta$.
2. Do you UNDERSTAND? What are all the values that satisfy $\cot^2 \theta - \csc^2 \theta = \sin (-\theta)$ for $0 \leq \theta \leq 2\pi$?
3. What is the exact value of $\tan 75°$?
4. How can you derive an identity for $\tan (A + B)$? Use the difference identity for $\tan (A - B)$.
5. What is the exact value of $\cos 285°$?

ANSWERS TO LESSON QUIZ

1. $\cot \left(\theta - \frac{\pi}{2}\right) = \cot - \left(\frac{\pi}{2} - \theta\right) = -\cot \left(\frac{\pi}{2} - \theta\right) = -\tan \theta$

2. $\frac{\pi}{2}$

3. $2 + \sqrt{3}$

4. $\tan (A + B) = \tan (A - (-B))$
$= \dfrac{\tan A - \tan(-B)}{1 + \tan A \tan(-B)} = \dfrac{\tan A + \tan B}{1 + \tan A(-\tan B)}$
$= \dfrac{\tan A + \tan B}{1 - \tan A \tan B}$

5. $\dfrac{\sqrt{6} - \sqrt{2}}{4}$

PRESCRIPTION FOR REMEDIATION

Use the student work on the Lesson Quiz to prescribe a differentiated review assignment:

Points	Differentiated Remediation
0–2	Intervention
3–4	On-level
5	Extension

PowerAlgebra.com

5 Assess & Remediate

Assign the Lesson Quiz. Appropriate intervention, practice, or enrichment is automatically generated based on student performance.

Intervention

- **Reteaching** (2 pages) Provides reteaching and practice exercises for the key lesson concepts. Use with struggling students or absent students.
- **English Language Learner Support** Helps students develop and reinforce mathematical vocabulary and key concepts.

All-in-One Resources/Online
Reteaching

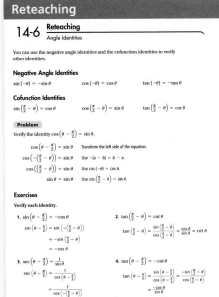

All-in-One Resources/Online
English Language Learner Support

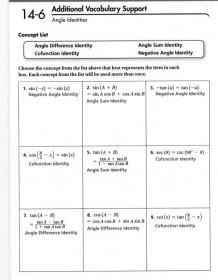

Differentiated Remediation *continued*

On-Level

- **Practice** (2 pages) Provides extra practice for each lesson. For simpler practice exercises, use the Form K Practice pages found in the All-in-One Teaching Resources and online.

- **Think About a Plan** Helps students develop specific problem-solving skills and strategies by providing scaffolded guiding questions.

- **Standardized Test Prep** Focuses on all major exercises, all major question types, and helps students prepare for the high-stakes assessments.

Extension

- **Enrichment** Provides students with interesting problems and activities that extend the concepts of the lesson.

- **Activities, Games, and Puzzles** Worksheets that can be used for concepts development, enrichment, and for fun!

Practice and Problem Solving Wkbk/ All-in-One Resources/Online
Practice page 1

14-6 Practice *Form G*
Angle Identities

Verify each identity. 1.–4. Check students' work.

1. $\cot\left(\theta - \frac{\pi}{2}\right) = -\tan\theta$
2. $\sin\left(\theta - \frac{\pi}{2}\right) = -\cos\theta$
3. $\cos\left(\theta - \frac{\pi}{2}\right) = \sin\theta$
4. $\sec\left(\theta - \frac{\pi}{2}\right) = \csc\theta$

Use the definitions of the trigonometric ratios for a right triangle to derive a cofunction identity for each expression.

5. $\cot(90° - A)\ \tan A$
6. $\cos(90° - A)\ \sin A$

Solve each trigonometric equation for θ with $0 \le \theta < 2\pi$.

7. $2\sin\left(\frac{\pi}{2} - \theta\right)\tan\theta = 1$ $\frac{\pi}{6}, \frac{3\pi}{6}$
8. $\cos\left(\frac{\pi}{2} - \theta\right)\tan\theta - \sec(-\theta) = 1$ π
9. $\sin^2\theta + \cos^2\theta = \tan\theta$ $\frac{\pi}{4}, \frac{3\pi}{4}$
10. $2\sin^2\theta = \sin(-\theta)$ $0, \pi, \frac{7\pi}{6}, \frac{11\pi}{6}$
11. $\sqrt{3}\cos\left(\frac{\pi}{2} - \theta\right) = \cos(-\theta)$ $\frac{\pi}{3}, \frac{7\pi}{3}$
12. $\cot\left(\frac{\pi}{2} - \theta\right) = \sin\theta$ $0, \pi$
13. $\csc\left(\frac{\pi}{2} - \theta\right) = \tan\theta$ No solution
14. $2\cos\left(\frac{\pi}{2} - \theta\right) = \tan(-\theta)$ $0, \frac{3\pi}{4}, \pi, \frac{4\pi}{3}$
15. $\csc^2\theta - \cot^2\theta = 2\cos\theta$ $\frac{\pi}{3}, \frac{5\pi}{3}$
16. $\sin\left(\theta - \frac{\pi}{2}\right)\cos\theta = 0$ $\frac{\pi}{2}, \frac{3\pi}{2}$

Mental Math Find the value of each trigonometric expression.

17. $\sin 10° \cos 80° + \cos 10° \sin 80°$ 1
18. $\cos 110° \cos 70° - \sin 110° \sin 70°$ −1
19. $\sin 310° \cos 130° - \cos 310° \sin 130°$ 0
20. $\cos 95° \cos 50° + \sin 95° \sin 50°$ $\frac{\sqrt{2}}{2}$

Practice and Problem Solving Wkbk/ All-in-One Resources/Online
Think About a Plan

14-6 Think About a Plan
Angle Identities

Gears The diagram at the right shows a gear whose radius is 10 cm. Point A represents a 60° counterclockwise rotation of point $P(10, 0)$. Point B represents a θ-degree rotation of point A. The coordinates of B are $(10\cos(\theta + 60°), 10\sin(\theta + 60°))$. Write these coordinates in terms of $\cos\theta$ and $\sin\theta$.

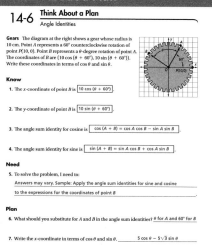

Know

1. The x-coordinate of point B is $10\cos(\theta + 60°)$.
2. The y-coordinate of point B is $10\sin(\theta + 60°)$.
3. The angle sum identity for cosine is $\cos(A + B) = \cos A \cos B - \sin A \sin B$.
4. The angle sum identity for sine is $\sin(A + B) = \sin A \cos B + \cos A \sin B$.

Need

5. To solve the problem, I need to:
   Answers may vary. Sample: Apply the angle sum identities for sine and cosine to the expressions for the coordinates of point B

Plan

6. What should you substitute for A and B in the angle sum identities? θ for A and 60° for B
7. Write the x-coordinate in terms of $\cos\theta$ and $\sin\theta$. $5\cos\theta - 5\sqrt{3}\sin\theta$
8. Write the y-coordinate in terms of $\cos\theta$ and $\sin\theta$. $5\sin\theta + 5\sqrt{3}\cos\theta$

Practice and Problem Solving Wkbk/ All-in-One Resources/Online
Practice page 2

14-6 Practice *(continued)* *Form G*
Angle Identities

Find each exact value. Use a sum or difference identity.

21. $\sin 240°$ $-\frac{\sqrt{3}}{2}$
22. $\tan(-300°)$ $\sqrt{3}$
23. $\sin(-105°)$ $\frac{-\sqrt{6} - \sqrt{2}}{4}$
24. $\cos 15°$ $\frac{\sqrt{6} + \sqrt{2}}{4}$
25. $\sin 15°$ $\frac{\sqrt{6} - \sqrt{2}}{4}$
26. $\sin 135°$ $\frac{\sqrt{2}}{2}$
27. $\cos 225°$ $-\frac{\sqrt{2}}{2}$
28. $\tan 225°$ 1
29. $\tan 240°$ $\sqrt{3}$
30. $\cos 390°$ $\frac{\sqrt{3}}{2}$
31. $\sin(-300°)$ $\frac{\sqrt{3}}{2}$
32. $\tan(-75°)$ $-2 - \sqrt{3}$

Verify each identity. 33.–34. Check students' work.

33. $\frac{1 - \cos\theta}{\sin\theta} = \frac{\sin\theta}{1 + \cos\theta}$
34. $\frac{1 + \tan\theta}{1 + \cot\theta} = \frac{\sin\theta}{\cos\theta}$

35. Which of the following is equivalent to $\sin\theta + \cot\theta\cos\theta$? B

   Ⓐ $2\sin\theta$
   Ⓑ $\frac{1}{\sin\theta}$
   Ⓒ $\cos^2\theta$
   Ⓓ $\frac{\sin\theta + \cos\theta}{\sin^2\theta}$

36. **Error Analysis** A student found the exact value of $\cos 30°$ using the fact that $30° = 90° - 60°$ and got $\frac{1}{2}$. What was his error?
   The student used the sine angle difference identity $\sin(A - B) = \sin A\cos B - \cos A\sin B$ instead of the cosine angle difference identity, $\cos(A - B) = \cos A\cos B + \sin A\sin B$.

37. **Reasoning** Explain how you can use the identity for $\cos(A - B)$ to simplify $\cos(-\theta)$. Rewrite $\cos(-\theta)$ as $\cos(0 - \theta)$. Then use the identity for $\cos(A - B)$ to simplify: $\cos(0 - \theta) = \cos 0\cos\theta + \sin 0\sin\theta = 1 \cdot \cos\theta + 0 \cdot \sin\theta = \cos\theta$.

Practice and Problem Solving Wkbk/ All-in-One Resources/Online
Standardized Test Prep

14-6 Standardized Test Prep
Angle Identities

Multiple Choice

For Exercises 1–5, choose the correct letter.

1. Which of the following expressions are equivalent? D
   I. $\sin(-\theta)$ II. $-\sin\theta$ III. $-\sin(\pi - \theta)$
   Ⓐ I and II only   Ⓑ I and III only   Ⓒ II and III only   Ⓓ I, II, and III

2. Which of the following is a solution to $\tan(\theta + \pi) + 2\sin(\theta + \pi) = 0$? F
   Ⓕ 0   Ⓖ $\frac{\pi}{2}$ Ⓗ $\frac{2\pi}{3}$ Ⓘ $\frac{7\pi}{4}$

3. Which expression is equivalent to $\tan 75°$? C
   Ⓐ $\frac{\tan 135° + \tan 60°}{1 - \tan 135° \tan 60°}$ Ⓒ $\frac{\tan 30° + \tan 45°}{1 - \tan 30° \tan 45°}$
   Ⓑ $\frac{\tan 30° - \tan 45°}{1 + \tan 30° \tan 45°}$ Ⓓ $\frac{\tan 60° - \tan 135°}{1 - \tan 60° \tan 135°}$

4. Which is the exact value of $\cos(-105°)$? F
   Ⓕ $\frac{\sqrt{2} - \sqrt{6}}{4}$ Ⓖ -1.05 Ⓗ $\frac{-\sqrt{2} + \sqrt{6}}{4}$ Ⓘ 1.05

5. Which of the following expressions are equivalent? B
   I. $\sin 2\theta\cos\theta + \cos 2\theta\sin\theta$ II. $\cos 3\theta$ III. $\sin 3\theta$
   Ⓐ I and II only   Ⓑ I and III only   Ⓒ II and III only   Ⓓ I, II, and III

Short Response

6. What is the solution to $\sin\left(\theta + \frac{\pi}{4}\right) + \sin\left(\theta - \frac{\pi}{4}\right) = 0$ for $0 \le \theta < 2\pi$? Show your work.
   [2] $0, \pi$
   [1] incorrect solution OR work not shown
   [0] incorrect answers and no work shown OR no answers given

---

All-in-One Resources/Online
Enrichment

14-6 Enrichment
Angle Identities

Sums of Sines and Cosines

Suppose you wish to graph $y = \cos x + \sin x$. One way would be to make a table of values, then draw the graph. However, you might recall that the formula for the cosine of the difference of two angles yields the sum of sines and cosines. Perhaps this formula gives you a clue to the graph of the general function $y = A\cos x + B\sin x$, where A and B are constant.

1. Expand $C\cos(x - P)$, where C is a constant and P is an angle measured in radians.
   $C\cos x\cos P + C\sin x\sin P$
2. Now suppose $C\cos(x - P) = A\cos x + B\sin x$. Express A and B in terms of $\sin P$ and/or $\cos P$.
   $A = C\cos P;\ B = C\sin P$
3. Express the ratio of B to A as a trigonometric function of P.
   $\frac{B}{A} = \frac{C\sin P}{C\cos P} = \tan P$
4. Square the equations for A and B from Exercise 2 and add them. What equation results?
   $C^2\cos^2 P + C^2\sin^2 P = A^2 + B^2$
5. Factor your equation.
   $C^2(\cos^2 P + \sin^2 P) = A^2 + B^2$
6. Solve this equation for C in terms of A and B.
   $C = \pm\sqrt{A^2 + B^2}$
7. What is the amplitude of the graph of $y = C\cos(x - P)$?
   C
8. What is its period?
   2π
9. At what value(s) does the graph reach its maximum?
   At $x = P + 2\pi n$, where n is an integer (assuming $C > 0$)
10. At what value(s) does it reach its minimum?
    At $x = P + \pi + 2\pi n$, where n is an integer (assuming $C > 0$)
11. Where does the graph cross the x-axis?
    At $x = P + \frac{\pi}{2} + n\pi$, where n is an integer
12. How are the graphs of $y = A\cos x + B\sin x$ and $y = C\cos(x - P)$ related?
    They are the same provided that $C = \pm\sqrt{A^2 + B^2}$ and $\tan P = \frac{B}{A}$, where the sign of C is determined by P.

Online Teacher Resource Center
Activities, Games, and Puzzles

14-6 Activity: Color Me Crazy
Angle Identities

This activity may be done alone or in small groups. You will need colored pencils, markers, or crayons.

Suppose the three primary colors match with specific angles: red → 30°; yellow → 45°; and blue → 60°. *Note:* A secondary color is made by mixing two primary colors.

1. a. Evaluate $\sin 75°$ using the primary angles above and a *sum* identity.
   $\frac{\sqrt{2} + \sqrt{6}}{4}$
   b. Evaluate $\cos 75°$ using the primary angles above and a *sum* identity.
   $\frac{\sqrt{6} - \sqrt{2}}{4}$
   c. Since a *sum* identity was used, what secondary color matches with 75°? orange

2. a. Evaluate $\sin 105°$ using the primary angles above and a *sum* identity.
   $\frac{\sqrt{2} + \sqrt{6}}{4}$
   b. Use your result from Part a. to evaluate $\cos 105°$.
   $\frac{-\sqrt{2} + \sqrt{6}}{2}$
   c. Since a *sum* identity was used, what secondary color matches with 105°? green

3. a. Evaluate $\sin 90°$ using two different primary angles and a *sum* identity. 1
   b. Evaluate $\cos 90°$ using your method of preference. 0
   c. Since a *sum* identity was used, what secondary color matches with 90°? purple
   d. Do your results agree with what you already know about 90°? yes

4. Color the following triangles by number. Let 1, 2, and 3 match with the colors you found in Exercises 1–3 and let 4 → red, 5 → yellow, and 6 → blue. Check students' work.

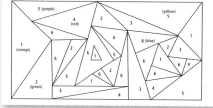

14-7 Double-Angle and Half-Angle Identities

© Content Standard
F.TF.9 Prove the addition and subtraction formulas for sine, cosine, and tangent and use them to solve problems.

Objectives To verify and use double-angle identities
To verify and use half-angle identities

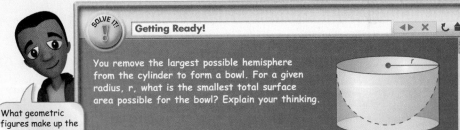

Getting Ready!

You remove the largest possible hemisphere from the cylinder to form a bowl. For a given radius, r, what is the smallest total surface area possible for the bowl? Explain your thinking.

What geometric figures make up the bowl?

If an equation contains two variables, such as radius and height, you can find a special case of the equation by replacing one of the variables with the other variable.

Essential Understanding The *double-angle identities* are special cases of the angle sum identities. Substitute $\frac{\theta}{2}$ for θ in certain double-angle identities and you get the *half-angle identities*.

take note

Properties	Double-Angle Identities
$\cos 2\theta = \cos^2 \theta - \sin^2 \theta$	$\sin 2\theta = 2 \sin \theta \cos \theta$
$\cos 2\theta = 2 \cos^2 \theta - 1$	$\tan 2\theta = \dfrac{2 \tan \theta}{1 - \tan^2 \theta}$
$\cos 2\theta = 1 - 2 \sin^2 \theta$	

Here's Why It Works

Let $\theta = A = B$.

$\cos (A + B) = \cos A \cos B - \sin A \sin B$ Cosine Angle Sum Identity
$\cos (\theta + \theta) = \cos \theta \cos \theta - \sin \theta \sin \theta$ Substitute θ for A and B.
$\cos 2\theta = \cos^2 \theta - \sin^2 \theta$ Simplify.

You can make the same substitution in the other angle sum identities.

---

1 Interactive Learning

Solve It!

PURPOSE To use surface areas of solids and introduce replacement of a variable
PROCESS Students may draw and label a diagram, using surface area formulas to find the solution, or use logical reasoning to determine the minimum height of the cylinder.

FACILITATE

Q What are the surfaces and how do you find their areas in the bowl? **[bottom: circle, πr^2; sides: lateral surface of the cylinder, $2\pi rh$; curved inside: half of a sphere, $2\pi r^2$.]**

Q When will the bowl have the least possible surface area and not have a hole in the bottom? How can you find the solution? **[When the height is equal to the radius, the bowl has the least surface area. Replace the height, h, with the radius, r.]**

ANSWER See Solve It in Answers on next page.
CONNECT THE MATH Students use surface area formulas and substitution to answer the Solve It. In the lesson, they use substitution to verify and apply the half-angle and double-angle identities.

2 Guided Instruction

Take Note

Q Why are these called the double-angle identities? **[They give a way to find exact values for the sine, cosine, and tangent of angles that can be written as twice a known angle value such as sin 120° = sin (2 · 60)°.]**

Here's Why It Works

Challenge students to derive the sin 2θ and tan 2θ identities by starting with the angle sum identities.

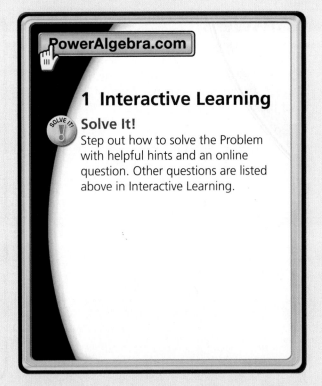

PowerAlgebra.com

1 Interactive Learning

Solve It!
Step out how to solve the Problem with helpful hints and an online question. Other questions are listed above in Interactive Learning.

14-7 Preparing to Teach

BIG idea Equivalence

ESSENTIAL UNDERSTANDINGS

- The *double-angle identities* are special cases of the angle-sum identities. The *half-angle identities* result from substituting $\frac{\theta}{2}$ for θ in certain double-angle identities.
- Double-angle and half-angle identities can be used to find exact trigonometric values for certain angle measures.

Math Background

The double-angle identities can be derived from the angle sum identities by substituting A for B in the formula. For example:

$\cos (A + B) = \cos A \cos B - \sin A \sin B$.
If $A = B$ you get $\cos (A + A) =$
$\cos A \cos A - \sin A \sin A$, and therefore
$\cos 2A = \cos^2 A - \sin^2 A$. By substituting $1 - \cos^2 A$ for $\sin^2 A$ and simplifying, you

have another identity: $\cos 2A = 2\cos^2 A - 1$. It is helpful to show students these connections.

The half-angle identity can be derived from the double-angle identity. Using known values to demonstrate can be helpful. For example, demonstrating finding $\cos 30°$ as $\cos \left(\frac{60}{2}\right)°$ can help verify the identity. A benefit of using the identities is that you can use exact known values to find values such as $\cos 15°$. Without such a formula, a calculator approximation would have to be used.

© Mathematical Practices

Look for and express regularity in repeated reasoning. With double-angle and half-angle identities, students will have a shortcut to compute by hand the values of trigonometric functions for 15 degrees, 22.5 degrees, etc.

Problem 1

> **Q** The solution uses the Pythagorean Identity $\cos^2\theta = 1 - \sin^2\theta$. What is the basic Pythagorean Identity and how does it relate to the Pythagorean Theorem? **[$\sin^2\theta + \cos^2\theta = 1$; for a point $(\cos\theta, \sin\theta)$ on the unit circle, there exists a right triangle with legs of length $\cos\theta$ and $\sin\theta$, so the Pythagorean Theorem can be applied.]**

Got It?

> **Q** What identity will you start with to solve the problem? **[$\cos 2\theta = \cos^2\theta - \sin^2\theta$]**
>
> **Q** What do you want to replace in the double-angle identity? Explain. **[$\sin^2\theta$; the final identity given in the problem does not contain $\sin^2\theta$.]**

Problem 2

> **Q** How could you check your answer? **[Samples: Draw the triangle in the unit circle and find the cosine from its shape; use an angle sum or angle difference identity.]**

Got It?

> **Q** Did you get an expected result? Explain. **[Yes; a 120° angle makes a 60° angle with the x-axis in Quadrant II, so the result should be positive and equal in value to sin 60°.]**

Problem 3

> **Q** How can you verify the Pythagorean Identity $1 + \tan^2\theta = \sec^2\theta$?
>
> **[$1 + \tan^2\theta = 1 + \dfrac{\sin^2\theta}{\cos^2\theta} = \dfrac{\cos^2\theta + \sin^2\theta}{\cos^2\theta}$**
>
> **$= \dfrac{1}{\cos^2\theta} = \sec^2\theta$]**

 Problem 1 Deriving a Double-Angle Identity

How can you derive the identity $\cos 2\theta = 1 - 2\sin^2\theta$?

Think

Now what?
You want to replace $\cos^2\theta$. A Pythagorean identity uses both $\cos^2\theta$ and $\sin^2\theta$.

Use the Pythagorean identity $\sin^2\theta + \cos^2\theta = 1$ to get $\cos^2\theta = 1 - \sin^2\theta$.

$$\cos 2\theta = \cos^2\theta - \sin^2\theta \qquad \text{Cosine Double-Angle Identity}$$
$$= (1 - \sin^2\theta) - \sin^2\theta \qquad \text{Use the Pythagorean identity.}$$
$$= 1 - 2\sin^2\theta \qquad \text{Simplify.}$$

✔ **Got It?** **1.** How can you derive the identity $\cos 2\theta = 2\cos^2\theta - 1$?

You can use the other angle sum identities to derive double-angle identities for the sine and tangent.

 Problem 2 Using a Double-Angle Identity

What is the exact value of $\cos 120°$? Use a double-angle identity.

Plan

Which of the three cosine identities should you use?
You can use any one of them.

$$\cos 120° = \cos(2 \cdot 60°) \qquad \text{Rewrite 120 as } (2 \cdot 60).$$
$$= \cos^2 60° - \sin^2 60° \qquad \text{Cosine Double-Angle Identity}$$
$$= \left(\frac{1}{2}\right)^2 - \left(\frac{\sqrt{3}}{2}\right)^2 \qquad \text{Replace with exact values.}$$
$$= -\frac{1}{2} \qquad \text{Simplify.}$$

✔ **Got It?** **2.** What is the exact value of $\sin 120°$? Use a double-angle identity.

You can use the double-angle identities to verify other identities.

 Problem 3 Verifying an Identity

Verify the identity $\cos 2\theta = \dfrac{1 - \tan^2\theta}{1 + \tan^2\theta}$.

Think

Which Pythagorean identity could you use?
You need an identity involving tangent. So use $1 + \tan^2\theta = \sec^2\theta$.

$$\frac{1 - \tan^2\theta}{1 + \tan^2\theta} = \frac{1 - \tan^2\theta}{\sec^2\theta} \qquad \text{Use a Pythagorean identity.}$$
$$= \frac{1}{\sec^2\theta} - \frac{\tan^2\theta}{\sec^2\theta} \qquad \text{Write as two fractions.}$$
$$= \frac{1}{\frac{1}{\cos^2\theta}} - \frac{\frac{\sin^2\theta}{\cos^2\theta}}{\frac{1}{\cos^2\theta}} \qquad \text{Express in terms of } \sin\theta \text{ and } \cos\theta.$$
$$= \cos^2\theta - \sin^2\theta \qquad \text{Simplify.}$$
$$= \cos 2\theta \qquad \text{Cosine Double-Angle Identity}$$

Answers

Solve It!

$5\pi r^2$; the surface area of the outside of the bowl is $\pi r^2 + 2\pi r^2$ and the surface area of the inside of the bowl is $2\pi r^2$.

Got It?

1. $\cos 2\theta = \cos^2\theta - \sin^2\theta$
$= \cos^2\theta - (1 - \cos^2\theta)$
$= \cos^2\theta - 1 + \cos^2\theta$
$= 2\cos^2\theta - 1$

2. $\dfrac{\sqrt{3}}{2}$

 PowerAlgebra.com

2 Guided Instruction

© Each Problem is worked out and supported online.

Problem 1
Deriving a Double-Angle Identity

Problem 2
Using a Double-Angle Identity

Problem 3
Verifying an Identity
Animated

Problem 4
Using Half-Angle Identities
Animated

Problem 5
Using a Half-Angle Identity
Animated

Support in Algebra 2 Companion
• Vocabulary
• Key Concepts
• Got It?

Got It? **3.** Verify the identity $2 \cos 2\theta = 4 \cos^2 \theta - 2$.

There are also half-angle identities for sine, cosine, and tangent.

> **take note**
>
> ### Properties Half-Angle Identities
>
> $$\sin \frac{A}{2} = \pm\sqrt{\frac{1 - \cos A}{2}} \qquad \cos \frac{A}{2} = \pm\sqrt{\frac{1 + \cos A}{2}} \qquad \tan \frac{A}{2} = \pm\sqrt{\frac{1 - \cos A}{1 + \cos A}}$$
>
> Choose the positive or negative sign for each radical depending on the quadrant in which $\frac{A}{2}$ lies.

You can use double-angle identities to derive half-angle identities.

Here's Why It Works

Let $\theta = \frac{A}{2}$.

$$\cos 2\theta = 2\cos^2 \theta - 1 \qquad \text{Cosine Double-Angle Identity}$$

$$\cos 2\left(\frac{A}{2}\right) = 2\cos^2 \frac{A}{2} - 1 \qquad \text{Substitute } \frac{A}{2} \text{ for } \theta.$$

$$\frac{\cos A + 1}{2} = \cos^2 \frac{A}{2} \qquad \text{Solve for } \cos^2 \frac{A}{2}.$$

$$\pm\sqrt{\frac{\cos A + 1}{2}} = \cos \frac{A}{2} \qquad \text{Take the square root of each side.}$$

Similarly, $\sin \frac{A}{2} = \pm\sqrt{\frac{1 - \cos A}{2}}$ and $\tan \frac{A}{2} = \pm\sqrt{\frac{1 - \cos A}{1 + \cos A}}$.

You can use half-angle identities to find exact trigonometric values.

© Problem 4 Using Half-Angle Identities

What is the exact value of each expression? Use the half-angle identities.

A $\sin 15°$

$$\sin 15° = \sin \left(\frac{30}{2}\right)° \qquad \text{Rewrite 15 as } \frac{30}{2}.$$

$$= \sqrt{\frac{1 - \cos 30°}{2}} \qquad \text{Use the principal square root, since } \sin 15° \text{ is positive.}$$

$$= \sqrt{\frac{1 - \frac{\sqrt{3}}{2}}{2}} \qquad \text{Substitute the exact value for } \cos 30°.$$

$$= \sqrt{\frac{2 - \sqrt{3}}{4}} \qquad \text{Simplify.}$$

$$= \frac{\sqrt{2 - \sqrt{3}}}{2}$$

> **Think**
>
> **How do you know if the result is positive or negative?**
> Sketch the angle in a unit circle and determine if its sine is positive or negative in that quadrant.

Got It?

Q Which Pythagorean Identity did you use? Explain. **[Sample: None; factoring a 2 from each term in the difference leads directly to one of the double-angle identities.]**

Take Note

Q What trigonometric function appears in all the half-angle identities? **[the cosine function]**

Q When using half-angle identities, you will choose positive or negative values based on the location of the terminal side of the half angle. In what quadrants are each of the principal trigonometric functions positive? **[Sine is positive in Quadrants I and II; cosine is positive in Quadrants I and IV; tangent is positive in Quadrants I and III.]**

Here's Why It Works

Q To derive the sine half-angle identity, which double-angle identity will you start with? Explain. **[Sample: Start with the $\cos 2\theta = 1 - 2\sin^2\theta$ double angle identity. All three half-angle identities are derived from the cosine double-angle identity.]**

Q How do you think the tangent half-angle identity is derived? **[Simplify the quotient of the sine and cosine half-angle identities.]**

Problem 4

Q In 4A, what is the angle A you use in the half-angle identity? **[30°]**

Q In Problem 4 of Lesson 14-6, you used an angle difference identity to calculate the exact value of $\sin 15°$ as $\frac{\sqrt{6} - \sqrt{2}}{4}$. Why are the answers different? **[The answers have the same value; they are written in different equivalent forms.]**

Additional Problems

1. How can you derive the identity
$$\tan 2\theta = \frac{2\tan \theta}{1 - \tan^2 \theta}?$$

ANSWER
$$\tan 2\theta = \tan (\theta + \theta) = \frac{\tan \theta + \tan \theta}{1 - \tan \theta \tan \theta}$$
$$= \frac{2\tan \theta}{1 - \tan^2 \theta}$$

2. What is the exact value of $\sin 270°$? Use a double-angle identity.

ANSWER -1

3. Verify the identity
$\sin 2\theta = 2\tan \theta - 2\tan \theta \sin^2 \theta$.

ANSWER $\sin 2\theta = 2\tan \theta - 2\tan \theta \sin^2 \theta$
$$= 2\tan \theta (1 - \sin^2 \theta)$$
$$= 2\tan \theta \cos^2 \theta = 2\frac{\sin \theta}{\cos \theta} \cos^2 \theta$$
$$= 2 \sin \theta \cos \theta = \sin 2\theta$$

4. What is the exact value of $\tan 195°$? Use half-angle identities.

ANSWER $2 - \sqrt{3}$

5. Given $\sin \theta = -\frac{5}{13}$ and $270° < \theta < 360°$, what is $\tan \frac{\theta}{2}$?

ANSWER $-\frac{1}{5}$

Answers

Got It? (continued)

3. $2 \cos 2\theta = 2(2 \cos^2 \theta - 1)$
$$= 4 \cos^2 \theta - 2$$

B cos 150°

$$\cos 150° = \cos \left(\frac{300}{2}\right)°$$ Rewrite 150 as $\frac{300}{2}$.

$$= -\sqrt{\frac{1 + \cos 300°}{2}}$$ Use the negative square root, since cos 150° is negative.

$$= -\sqrt{\frac{1 + \left(\frac{1}{2}\right)}{2}}$$ Replace with an exact value.

$$= -\sqrt{\frac{3}{4}}$$ Simplify.

$$= -\frac{\sqrt{3}}{2}$$ Simplify.

✓ **Got It? 4.** What is the exact value of each expression? Use the half-angle identities.
   a. sin 150°   **b.** tan 150°

© **Problem 5** Using a Half-Angle Identity

Given sin θ = $-\frac{24}{25}$ and 180° < θ < 270°, what is sin $\frac{\theta}{2}$?

Know	Need	Plan
sin θ, 180° < θ < 270°	sin $\frac{\theta}{2}$	Find cos θ and substitute it into the half-angle identity for sine.

$$\cos^2 \theta + \sin^2 \theta = 1$$ Pythagorean identity

$$\cos^2 \theta + \left(-\frac{24}{25}\right)^2 = 1$$ Substitute.

$$\cos^2 \theta = \frac{49}{25^2}$$ Solve for $\cos^2 \theta$.

$$\cos \theta = -\frac{7}{25}$$ Choose the negative square root since θ is in Quadrant III.

Now find sin $\frac{\theta}{2}$.

Since 180° < θ < 270°, then 90° < $\frac{\theta}{2}$ < 135° and $\frac{\theta}{2}$ is in Quadrant II.

$$\sin \frac{\theta}{2} = \pm\sqrt{\frac{1 - \cos \theta}{2}}$$ Half-angle identity

$$= \sqrt{\frac{1 - \left(-\frac{7}{25}\right)}{2}}$$ Substitute. Choose the positive square root since $\frac{\theta}{2}$ is in Quadrant II.

$$= \frac{4}{5}$$ Simplify.

© ✓ **Got It? 5.** Given sin θ = $-\frac{24}{25}$ and 180° < θ < 270°, what is the exact value of each expression?
   a. cos $\frac{\theta}{2}$ **b.** tan $\frac{\theta}{2}$
   c. Reasoning How would your answers change if 270° < θ < 360°? Explain.

Answers

Got It? (continued)

4. a. $\frac{1}{2}$

   b. $-\frac{\sqrt{3}}{3}$

5. a. $-\frac{3}{5}$

   b. $-\frac{4}{3}$

   c. If 270° < θ < 360°, 135° < $\frac{\theta}{2}$ < 180° and $\frac{\theta}{2}$ is also in Quadrant II. The answers will remain the same.

Lesson Check

1. $\frac{\sqrt{3}}{2}$

2. 1

3. a. $-\frac{5}{13}$

   b. $\sqrt{\frac{13 + 2\sqrt{13}}{26}}$

c. $-\sqrt{\frac{13 - 2\sqrt{13}}{26}}$

4. The student did not correctly determine in which quadrant $\frac{\theta}{2}$ will be. If 180° < θ < 270°, 90° < $\frac{\theta}{2}$ < 135°, then $\frac{\theta}{2}$ is in Quadrant II and the tangent will be negative.

5. sin 4A

6. sin $\frac{5A}{2}$ = $-\sqrt{\frac{1 - \cos 5A}{2}}$ if 360° < 5A < 450°, 180° < $\frac{5A}{2}$ < 225° and the sine is negative in Quadrant III.

Lesson Check

Do you know HOW?

1. Use a double-angle identity to find the exact value of sin 120°.

2. Use a half-angle identity to find the exact value of sin 90°.

3. Given $\tan\theta = \frac{3}{2}$ and $180° < \theta < 270°$, find the exact value of each expression.
   a. $\cos 2\theta$ b. $\sin\frac{\theta}{2}$ c. $\cos\frac{\theta}{2}$

Do you UNDERSTAND?
 MATHEMATICAL PRACTICES

4. **Error Analysis** A problem on a test asks for the value of $\tan\frac{\theta}{2}$ when $\tan\theta = \frac{3}{4}$ for $180° < \theta < 270°$. A student writes $\tan\frac{\theta}{2} = 3$. It is marked wrong. What is the student's mistake?

5. Express $2\sin 2A \cos 2A$ using only one trigonometric function.

6. **Writing** Explain how to express $-\sqrt{\frac{1 - \cos 5A}{2}}$ as $\sin\theta$, where θ is an expression in terms of A.

Practice and Problem-Solving Exercises
 MATHEMATICAL PRACTICES

A Practice

Use an angle sum identity to derive each double-angle identity. **See Problems 1, 2, and 3.**

7. $\sin 2\theta = 2\sin\theta\cos\theta$

8. $\tan 2\theta = \frac{2\tan\theta}{1 - \tan^2\theta}$

Use a double-angle identity to find the exact value of each expression.

9. $\sin 240°$ 10. $\cos 120°$ 11. $\tan 120°$ 12. $\sin 90°$

13. $\cos 240°$ 14. $\tan 240°$ 15. $\cos 600°$ 16. $\sin 600°$

Use a half-angle identity to find the exact value of each expression. **See Problem 4.**

17. $\cos 15°$ 18. $\tan 15°$ 19. $\sin 15°$ 20. $\sin 22.5°$

21. $\cos 22.5°$ 22. $\tan 22.5°$ 23. $\cos 90°$ 24. $\sin 7.5°$

Given $\cos\theta = -\frac{4}{5}$ and $90° < \theta < 180°$, find the exact value of each expression. **See Problem 5.**

25. $\sin\frac{\theta}{2}$ 26. $\cos\frac{\theta}{2}$ 27. $\tan\frac{\theta}{2}$ 28. $\cot\frac{\theta}{2}$

Given $\cos\theta = -\frac{15}{17}$ and $180° < \theta < 270°$, find the exact value of each expression.

29. $\sin\frac{\theta}{2}$ 30. $\cos\frac{\theta}{2}$ 31. $\tan\frac{\theta}{2}$ 32. $\sec\frac{\theta}{2}$

B Apply

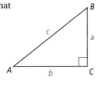 33. **Think About a Plan** Triangle ABC is a right triangle with right angle C. Show that $\cos^2\frac{B}{2} = \frac{a + c}{2c}$.
   • What identity will you use?
   • How can you find the ratio or ratios you need to substitute in the identity?
   • What will be your last step in the solution?

---

3 Lesson Check

Do you know HOW?

• In Exercises 1 and 2, students must first decide whether angle θ will be doubled or halved.

• In Exercise 3, students must first draw the correct right triangle in Quadrant III to find the value of $\cos\theta$ or $\sin\theta$.

ERROR INTERVENTION

• If students give a correct absolute value but an incorrect sign in Exercises 3b and 3c, then have them draw θ and $\frac{\theta}{2}$ in their correct quadrants.

Do you UNDERSTAND?

• If students have trouble getting started with Exercises 5 and 6, then have them replace $2A$ and $5A$, respectively, with θ. Students can then find the correct angle identities and finish by substituting for θ in the identities.

Close

Q How are the double-angle identities related to the angle sum identities? **[Sample: They are the same except that both angle A and angle B are replaced with angle A.]**

Q A negative quantity inside a radical causes an imaginary number, which cannot be plotted on a real-number number line or coordinate plane. What happens when a half-angle identity results in an imaginary number? **[The half-angle identities will never result in an imaginary number. The cosine function has a maximum value of 1, so the least value possible inside the radical is zero.]**

Practice and Problem-Solving Exercises

7. $\sin 2\theta = \sin(\theta + \theta)$
   $= \sin\theta\cos\theta + \cos\theta\sin\theta$
   $= 2\sin\theta\cos\theta$

8. $\tan 2\theta = \tan(\theta + \theta)$
   $= \frac{\tan\theta + \tan\theta}{1 - \tan\theta\tan\theta} = \frac{2\tan\theta}{1 - \tan^2\theta}$

9. $-\frac{\sqrt{3}}{2}$ 10. $-\frac{1}{2}$ 11. $-\sqrt{3}$

12. 1 13. $-\frac{1}{2}$ 14. $\sqrt{3}$

15. $-\frac{1}{2}$ 16. $-\frac{\sqrt{3}}{2}$ 17. $\frac{\sqrt{2 + \sqrt{3}}}{2}$

18. $\sqrt{7 - 4\sqrt{3}}$ or $2 - \sqrt{3}$

19. $\frac{\sqrt{2 - \sqrt{3}}}{2}$ 20. $\frac{\sqrt{2 - \sqrt{2}}}{2}$

21. $\frac{\sqrt{2 + \sqrt{2}}}{2}$

22. $\sqrt{3 - 2\sqrt{2}}$ or $\sqrt{2} - 1$

23. 0

24. $\frac{\sqrt{2 - \sqrt{2 + \sqrt{3}}}}{2}$ 25. $\frac{3\sqrt{10}}{10}$

26. $\frac{\sqrt{10}}{10}$ 27. 3

28. $\frac{1}{3}$ 29. $\frac{4\sqrt{17}}{17}$

30. $-\frac{\sqrt{17}}{17}$ 31. -4

32. $-\sqrt{17}$

33. $\cos B = 2\cos^2\frac{B}{2} - 1$
   $2\cos^2\frac{B}{2} = \cos B + 1$
   $\cos^2\frac{B}{2} = \frac{\cos B + 1}{2}$
   Since $\cos B = \frac{a}{c}$,
   $\cos^2\frac{B}{2} = \frac{\frac{a}{c} + 1}{2} = \frac{a + c}{2c}$.

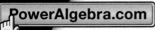

3 Lesson Check

For a digital lesson check, use the Got It questions.

Support in Algebra 2 Companion
• Lesson Check

4 Practice

 Assign homework to individual students or to an entire class.

4 Practice

ASSIGNMENT GUIDE

Basic: 7–32 all, 33–35, 40, 48–54 even

Average: 7–31 odd, 33–58

Advanced: 7–31 odd, 33–65

Standardized Test Prep: 66–70

Mixed Review: 71–78

ⓒ Mathematical Practices are supported by exercises with red headings. Here are the Practices supported in this lesson:

MP 1: Make Sense of Problems Ex. 33

MP 2: Reason Abstractly Ex. 6

MP 2: Reason Quantitatively Ex. 57

MP 3: Construct Arguments Ex. 40

MP 3: Communicate Ex. 6, 58

MP 3: Critique the Reasoning of Others Ex. 4

Applications exercises have blue headings.

EXERCISE 34: Use the Think About a Plan worksheet in the **Practice and Problem Solving Workbook** (also available in the Teaching Resources in print and online) to further support students' development in becoming independent learners.

HOMEWORK QUICK CHECK

To check students' understanding of key skills and concepts, go over Exercises 11, 27, 33, 34, and 40.

$\triangle RST$ has a right angle at T. Use identities to show that each equation is true.

34. $\sin 2R = \frac{2rs}{t^2}$

35. $\cos 2R = \frac{s^2 - r^2}{t^2}$

36. $\sin 2S = \sin 2R$

37. $\sin^2 \frac{S}{2} = \frac{t - r}{2t}$

38. $\tan \frac{R}{2} = \frac{r}{t + s}$

39. $\tan^2 \frac{S}{2} = \frac{t - r}{t + r}$

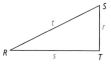

ⓒ 40. Reasoning If $\sin 2A = \sin 2B$, must $A = B$? Explain.

Given $\cos \theta = \frac{3}{5}$ and $270° < \theta < 360°$, find the exact value of each expression.

41. $\sin 2\theta$

42. $\cos 2\theta$

43. $\tan 2\theta$

44. $\csc 2\theta$

45. $\sin \frac{\theta}{2}$

46. $\cos \frac{\theta}{2}$

47. $\tan \frac{\theta}{2}$

48. $\cot \frac{\theta}{2}$

Use identities to write each equation in terms of the single angle θ. Then solve the equation for $0 \le \theta < 2\pi$.

49. $4 \sin 2\theta - 3 \cos \theta = 0$

50. $2 \sin 2\theta - 3 \sin \theta = 0$

51. $\sin 2\theta \sin \theta = \cos \theta$

52. $\cos 2\theta = -2 \cos^2 \theta$

Simplify each expression.

53. $2 \cos^2 \theta - \cos 2\theta$

54. $\sin^2 \frac{\theta}{2} - \cos^2 \frac{\theta}{2}$

55. $\frac{\cos 2\theta}{\sin \theta + \cos \theta}$

56. a. Write an identity for $\sin^2 \theta$ by using the double-angle identity $\cos 2\theta = 1 - 2\sin^2 \theta$. The resulting identity is called a *power reduction identity*.
b. Find a power reduction identity for $\cos^2 \theta$ using a double-angle identity.

ⓒ 57. Open-Ended Choose an angle measure A.
a. Find $\sin A$ and $\cos A$.
b. Use an identity to find $\sin 2A$.
c. Use an identity to find $\cos \frac{A}{2}$.

ⓒ 58. Writing Consider the graph of $y = \sqrt{\frac{1 - \cos A}{1 + \cos A}}$. Describe the period and any asymptotes if they exist.

ⓒ Challenge Use double-angle identities to write each expression, using trigonometric functions of θ instead of 4θ.

59. $\sin 4\theta$

60. $\cos 4\theta$

61. $\tan 4\theta$

Use half-angle identities to write each expression, using trigonometric functions of θ instead of $\frac{\theta}{4}$.

62. $\sin \frac{\theta}{4}$

63. $\cos \frac{\theta}{4}$

64. $\tan \frac{\theta}{4}$

65. Use the Tangent Half-Angle Identity and a Pythagorean identity to prove each identity.
a. $\tan \frac{A}{2} = \frac{\sin A}{1 + \cos A}$
b. $\tan \frac{A}{2} = \frac{1 - \cos A}{\sin A}$

Answers

Practice and Problem-Solving Exercises (continued)

34. $\sin 2R = 2 \sin R \cos R$

$= 2 \frac{r}{t} \cdot \frac{s}{t}$

$= \frac{2rs}{t^2}$

35. $\cos 2R = \cos^2 R - \sin^2 R$

$= \left(\frac{s}{t}\right)^2 - \left(\frac{r}{t}\right)^2$

$= \frac{s^2}{t^2} - \frac{r^2}{t^2}$

$= \frac{s^2 - r^2}{t^2}$

36. $\sin 2S = 2 \sin S \cos S$

$= 2 \cdot \frac{s}{t} \cdot \frac{r}{t} = \frac{2sr}{t^2}$

$= 2 \sin R \cos R = \sin 2R$

37. $\sin^2 \frac{S}{2} = \left(\sin \frac{S}{2}\right)^2$

$= \left(\pm\sqrt{\frac{1 - \cos S}{2}}\right)^2$

$= \frac{1 - \cos S}{2} = \frac{1 - \frac{r}{t}}{2}$

$= \frac{1}{2} - \frac{r}{2t} = \frac{t - r}{2t}$

38. $\tan \frac{R}{2} = \sqrt{\frac{1 - \cos R}{1 + \cos R}}$

$= \sqrt{\frac{1 - \frac{s}{t}}{1 + \frac{s}{t}}} = \sqrt{\frac{t - s}{t + s} \cdot \frac{t + s}{t + s}}$

$= \sqrt{\frac{t^2 - s^2}{(t + s)^2}} = \sqrt{\frac{r^2}{(t + s)^2}} = \frac{r}{t + s}$

39. $\tan^2 \frac{S}{2} = \left(\tan \frac{S}{2}\right)^2$

$= \left(\pm\sqrt{\frac{1 - \cos S}{1 + \cos S}}\right)^2 = \frac{1 - \cos S}{1 + \cos S}$

$= \frac{1 - \frac{r}{t}}{1 + \frac{r}{t}} = \frac{t - r}{t + r}$

40. No; since the sine function is periodic, A and B can have many different values.

41. $-\frac{24}{25}$ **42.** $-\frac{7}{25}$ **43.** $\frac{24}{7}$

44. $-\frac{25}{24}$ **45.** $\frac{\sqrt{5}}{5}$ **46.** $-\frac{2\sqrt{5}}{5}$

47. $-\frac{1}{2}$ **48.** -2

49. $\cos \theta (8 \sin \theta - 3) = 0$; $\frac{\pi}{2}, \frac{3\pi}{2}$, 0.384, 2.757

50. $\sin \theta (4 \cos \theta - 3) = 0$; 0, π, 0.723, 5.560

51. $\cos \theta (2 \sin^2 \theta - 1) = 0$; $\frac{\pi}{2}, \frac{3\pi}{2}, \frac{\pi}{4}, \frac{3\pi}{4}, \frac{5\pi}{4}, \frac{7\pi}{4}$

52. $\cos \theta = \pm\frac{1}{2}$; $\frac{\pi}{3}, \frac{2\pi}{3}, \frac{4\pi}{3}, \frac{5\pi}{3}$

53. 1 **54.** $-\cos \theta$

55. $\cos \theta - \sin \theta$

56. a. $\sin^2 \theta = \frac{1 - \cos 2\theta}{2}$

b. $\cos^2 \theta = \frac{1 + \cos 2\theta}{2}$

SAT/ACT

66. If θ is in Quadrant I and $\tan \theta = \frac{5}{12}$, what is the value of $\frac{\tan 4\theta}{5}$ to the nearest hundredth?

Ⓐ 18.10   Ⓑ 0.33   Ⓒ 0.32   Ⓓ −23.90

67. If θ is in Quadrant I and $\sin \theta = \frac{3}{5}$, what is an exact value of $\sin 2\theta$?

Ⓕ $\frac{9}{25}$ Ⓖ $\frac{24}{25}$ Ⓗ $\frac{6}{5}$ Ⓘ 73.7

68. A ladder rests against a building. The ladder is 14 ft long and forms an angle of 76.5° with the ground. Which statement is not true?

  Ⓐ The bottom of the ladder is 13.6 ft from the base of the building.

  Ⓑ The bottom of the ladder is 13.3 ft from the base of the building.

  Ⓒ The top of the ladder touches the building 13.6 ft from the ground.

  Ⓓ The ladder forms an angle of 13.5° with the building.

69. Which expressions are equivalent?

  I. $\cos \theta$ II. $\cos(-\theta)$ III. $\frac{\sin(-\theta)}{\tan(-\theta)}$

  Ⓕ I and II only   Ⓗ I and III only

  Ⓖ II and III only   Ⓘ I, II, and III

Short Response

70. Use a half-angle identity to find an exact value of sin 67.5°.

Mixed Review

Find each exact value. Use a sum or difference identity.   ◀ See Lesson 14-6.

71. cos 405°   **72.** sin (−300°)   **73.** tan (−300°)

Find the amplitude and period of each periodic function.   ◀ See Lesson 13-1.

74. 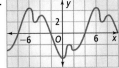   **75.**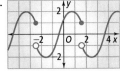

A set of data with a mean of 39 and a standard deviation of 6.2 is normally distributed. Find each value, given its distance from the mean.   ◀ See Lesson 11-10.

76. +1 standard deviation   **77.** −2 standard deviations   **78.** +3 standard deviations

57. Answers may vary. Sample:

  a. $\sin 60° = \frac{\sqrt{3}}{2}$, $\cos 60° = \frac{1}{2}$

  b. $\sin 120° = \frac{\sqrt{3}}{2}$

  c. $\cos 30° = \frac{\sqrt{3}}{2}$

58. The graph of $\sqrt{\frac{1 - \cos A}{1 + \cos A}}$ represents the positive tangent function for $\tan \frac{A}{2}$ with a period of 2π and vertical asymptotes at $-\pi$ and π ($n\pi$ for odd n). There is no amplitude because the values of the tangent are unbounded.

59. $4 \sin \theta \cos \theta (\cos^2 \theta - \sin^2 \theta)$

60. $8 \cos^4 \theta - 8 \cos^2 \theta + 1$

61. $\dfrac{4 \tan \theta (1 - \tan^2 \theta)}{\tan^4 \theta - 6 \tan^2 \theta + 1}$

62. $\pm \sqrt{\frac{1}{2} \pm \frac{1}{2}\sqrt{\frac{1}{2} + \frac{1}{2} \cos \theta}}$

63. $\pm \sqrt{\frac{1}{2} \pm \frac{1}{2}\sqrt{\frac{1}{2} + \frac{1}{2} \cos \theta}}$

64. $\sqrt{\dfrac{1 \pm \sqrt{\frac{1}{2} + \frac{1}{2} \cos \theta}}{1 \pm \sqrt{\frac{1}{2} + \frac{1}{2} \cos \theta}}}$

65. a. $\tan \frac{A}{2} = \pm \sqrt{\dfrac{1 - \cos A}{1 + \cos A}}$

$= \pm \sqrt{\dfrac{1 - \cos A}{1 + \cos A} \cdot \dfrac{1 + \cos A}{1 + \cos A}}$

$= \pm \sqrt{\dfrac{1 - \cos^2 A}{(1 + \cos A)^2}}$

$= \pm \sqrt{\dfrac{\sin^2 A}{(1 + \cos A)^2}}$

$= \dfrac{\sin A}{1 + \cos A}$

Since $\tan \frac{A}{2}$ and sin A have the same sign wherever $\tan \frac{A}{2}$ is defined, only the positive sign occurs.

  b. $\tan \frac{A}{2} = \pm \sqrt{\dfrac{1 - \cos A}{1 + \cos A}}$

$= \pm \sqrt{\dfrac{1 - \cos A}{1 + \cos A} \cdot \dfrac{1 - \cos A}{1 - \cos A}}$

$= \pm \sqrt{\dfrac{(1 - \cos A)^2}{1 - \cos^2 A}}$

$= \pm \sqrt{\dfrac{(1 - \cos A)^2}{\sin^2 A}}$

$= \dfrac{1 - \cos A}{\sin A}$

Since $\tan \frac{A}{2}$ and sin A have the same sign wherever $\tan \frac{A}{2}$ is defined, only the positive sign occurs.

Standardized Test Prep

66. D

67. G

68. A

69. I

70. **[2]** $\sin \dfrac{135°}{2} = \sqrt{\dfrac{1 - \cos 135°}{2}}$

$= \sqrt{\dfrac{1 - \left(-\frac{\sqrt{2}}{2}\right)}{2}}$

$= \sqrt{\dfrac{\frac{2 + \sqrt{2}}{2}}{2}} = \dfrac{\sqrt{2 + \sqrt{2}}}{2}$

[1] correct method, but with one computational error

Mixed Review

71. $\dfrac{\sqrt{2}}{2}$

72. $\dfrac{\sqrt{3}}{2}$

73. $\sqrt{3}$

74. about 4.1; 12

75. 2; 4

76. 45.2

77. 26.6

78. 57.6

Differentiated Remediation

Additional Instructional Support

Algebra 2 Companion

Students can use the **Algebra 2 Companion** worktext (4 pages) as you teach the lesson. Use the Companion to support

- New Vocabulary
- Key Concepts
- Got It for each Problem
- Lesson Check

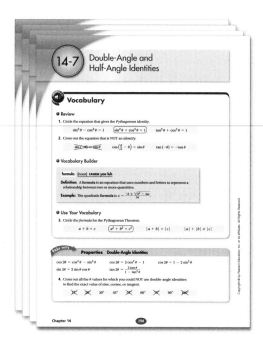

ELL Support

Use Graphic Organizers This chapter has many formulas and identities. Students will benefit from recording them on a single reference page or note card. The negative angle, cofunction, angle difference, angle sum, double-angle, and half-angle identities can be written in a table with a column for each of sine, cosine, and tangent. As time allows, ask one or more questions about each type of identity. Example questions are below:

- Negative angle identities: Why is $\tan(-\theta)$ equal to $-\tan\theta$?
- Cofunction angle identities: How do these identities relate to the trigonometric ratios in a right triangle?
- Angle difference and angle sum identities: what patterns will help you remember the identities?
- Double-angle identities: Are the double-angle identities derived from the angle difference or angle sum identities?
- Half-angle identities: The sine and cosine half-angle identities are derived from which double-angle cosine identities?

5 Assess & Remediate

Lesson Quiz

1. How can you derive the identity $\cos 2\theta = \cos^2\theta - \sin^2\theta$?

2. What is the exact value of $\tan 300°$? Use a double-angle identity.

3. Verify the identity $\tan 2\theta = \dfrac{2\tan\theta}{2 - \sec^2\theta}$.

4. What is the exact value of $\sin 135°$? Use the half-angle identities.

5. **Do you UNDERSTAND?** Given $\cot\theta = \dfrac{12}{5}$ and $180° < \theta < 270°$, what is $\cos\dfrac{\theta}{2}$?

ANSWERS TO LESSON QUIZ

1. $\cos 2\theta = \cos(\theta + \theta)$
$= \cos\theta\cos\theta - \sin\theta\sin\theta$
$= \cos^2\theta - \sin^2\theta = \cos 2\theta$

2. $-\sqrt{3}$

3. $\tan 2\theta = \dfrac{2\tan\theta}{1 - \tan^2\theta} = \dfrac{2\tan\theta}{1 - (\sec^2\theta - 1)}$
$= \dfrac{2\tan\theta}{2 - \sec^2\theta}$

4. $\dfrac{\sqrt{2}}{2}$

5. $-\dfrac{\sqrt{26}}{26}$

PRESCRIPTION FOR REMEDIATION
Use the student work on the Lesson Quiz to prescribe a differentiated review assignment:

Points	Differentiated Remediation
0–2	Intervention
3–4	On-level
5	Extension

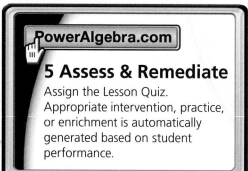

PowerAlgebra.com

5 Assess & Remediate

Assign the Lesson Quiz. Appropriate intervention, practice, or enrichment is automatically generated based on student performance.

Intervention

- **Reteaching** (2 pages) Provides reteaching and practice exercises for the key lesson concepts. Use with struggling students or absent students.

- **English Language Learner Support** Helps students develop and reinforce mathematical vocabulary and key concepts.

All-in-One Resources/Online
Reteaching

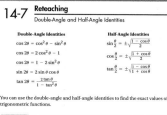

All-in-One Resources/Online
English Language Learner Support

Differentiated Remediation *continued*

On-Level

- **Practice** (2 pages) Provides extra practice for each lesson. For simpler practice exercises, use the Form K Practice pages found in the All-in-One Teaching Resources and online.

- **Think About a Plan** Helps students develop specific problem-solving skills and strategies by providing scaffolded guiding questions.

- **Standardized Test Prep** Focuses on all major exercises, all major question types, and helps students prepare for the high-stakes assessments.

Extension

- **Enrichment** Provides students with interesting problems and activities that extend the concepts of the lesson.

- **Activities, Games, and Puzzles** Worksheets that can be used for concepts development, enrichment, and for fun!

Practice and Problem Solving Wkbk/ All-in-One Resources/Online
Practice page 1

Practice and Problem Solving Wkbk/ All-in-One Resources/Online
Practice page 2

All-in-One Resources/Online
Enrichment

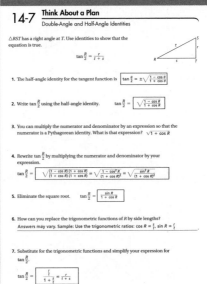

Practice and Problem Solving Wkbk/ All-in-One Resources/Online
Think About a Plan

Practice and Problem Solving Wkbk/ All-in-One Resources/Online
Standardized Test Prep

Online Teacher Resource Center
Activities, Games, and Puzzles

Performance Task

Pull It All Together
Understanding by Design principles indicate the importance of performance tasks that assess understanding.
- Make sense of problems and persevere in solving them.
- Attend to precision.

The following questions are designed to
- Help support students as they do the Performance Tasks.
- Help you gauge their progress toward becoming mathematically proficient.

Performance Task 1
Use substitution and algebra to prove a trigonometric identity.
- What will $\cos x + \cos y$ look like after you substitute expressions for x and y?
- Which trigonometric identity can you apply to the new expression?

Performance Task 2
Use graphs to compare related composite trigonometric functions in a specific domain.
- Do you notice any reflection, rotation, or translations that relate the graphs?

Performance Task 3
Use half-angle identities.
- Which trigonometric function relates the radius of the inscribed circle to the distance from the incenter to each vertex?

To solve these problems, you will pull together concepts and skills related to trigonometric functions.

BIG idea Equivalence
You can use symbols to represent an expression in an unlimited number of ways, where all representations have the same value when each variable is replaced with its assigned number.

© Performance Task 1
Prove the identity $\cos x + \cos y = 2\cos\left(\frac{x + y}{2}\right)\cos\left(\frac{x - y}{2}\right)$.

a. Show that $\frac{x + y}{2} + \frac{x - y}{2} = x$.
b. Find a similar expression using $\frac{x + y}{2}$ and $\frac{x - y}{2}$ that equals y.
c. Use parts (a) and (b) to prove the identity.

BIG idea Function
You can often represent a relationship between variables as a function, in which each value of the input variable is associated with a unique value of the output variable.

© Performance Task 2
The graphs at the right are of the representative parts of the sine and cosine functions for which their inverse functions are defined.

a. Copy the graph and draw the distance between $x = -\frac{\pi}{4}$ and $x = \cos^{-1}\left(\sin\left(-\frac{\pi}{4}\right)\right)$.
b. Use the two graphs to help you sketch the graph of the distance between x and $\cos^{-1}(\sin x)$ for $-\frac{\pi}{2} \le x \le \frac{\pi}{2}$.
c. Sketch the graph of the distance between x and $\sin^{-1}(\cos x)$ for $0 \le x \le \pi$.
d. How do the two graphs appear to be related?

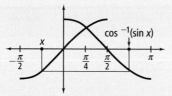

BIG idea Equivalence
The facts about a quantity may be expressed by many different equations.

© Performance Task 3
For a 30°-60°-90° triangle, how does the distance from the incenter to each vertex compare to the radius of the incircle?

Assess Performance

Pull It All Together
See p. 49 for a holistic scoring rubric to gauge a student's progress on Understanding the Problem, Planning a Solution, Getting an Answer, and Assessing Autonomy.

SOLUTION OUTLINES

Performance Task 1

a. $\frac{x + y}{2} + \frac{x - y}{2} =$
$\frac{x + y + x - y}{2} =$
$\frac{2x}{2} = x$

b. If you subtract the two expressions you end up with y. So, $y = \frac{x + y}{2} - \frac{x - y}{2}$.

c. Possible Plan: Since $x = \frac{x + y}{2} + \frac{x - y}{2}$ and $y = \frac{x + y}{2} - \frac{x - y}{2}$, you can rewrite the left side of the equation as $\cos\left(\frac{x + y}{2} + \frac{x - y}{2}\right) + \cos\left(\frac{x + y}{2} - \frac{x - y}{2}\right)$. Use the cosine angle

sum and difference identities to prove the identity.

$\cos\left(\frac{x + y}{2} + \frac{x - y}{2}\right) +$
$\cos\left(\frac{x + y}{2} - \frac{x - y}{2}\right)$
$= \cos\left(\frac{x + y}{2}\right)\cos\left(\frac{x - y}{2}\right) -$
$\sin\left(\frac{x + y}{2}\right)\sin\left(\frac{x - y}{2}\right) +$
$\cos\left(\frac{x + y}{2}\right)\cos\left(\frac{x - y}{2}\right) +$
$\sin\left(\frac{x + y}{2}\right)\sin\left(\frac{x - y}{2}\right)$
$= 2\cos\left(\frac{x + y}{2}\right)\cos\left(\frac{x - y}{2}\right)$

Performance Task 2

a–d. First, consider the distance d between x and $\cos^{-1}(\sin x)$ for $-\frac{\pi}{2} \le x \le \frac{\pi}{2}$.

For $-\frac{\pi}{2} \le x < 0$, $d = \frac{\pi}{2} + 2|x|$
$= \frac{\pi}{2} - 2x$

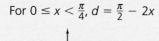

For $0 \le x < \frac{\pi}{4}$, $d = \frac{\pi}{2} - 2x$

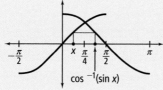

For $\frac{\pi}{4} \le x \le \frac{\pi}{2}$, $d = \frac{\pi}{2} - 2\left(\frac{\pi}{2} - x\right)$
$= 2x - \frac{\pi}{2}$.

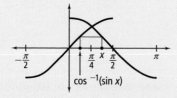

Connecting **BIG** ideas and Answering the Essential Questions

1 Equivalence	**Trigonometric Identities (Lesson 14-1)**	**Angle Identities, and Double- and Half-Angle Identities. (Lessons 14-6 and 14-7)**
To verify that an equation in θ is an identity, show that both of its sides have equal values for each possible replacement for θ.	$2 \tan \theta \cos^2 \theta = \dfrac{2 \sin \theta \cos^2 \theta}{\cos \theta}$ $= 2 \sin \theta \cos \theta$	$\sin(-\theta) = -\sin \theta$ $\sin\left(\dfrac{\pi}{2} - \theta\right) = \cos \theta$ $\sin(A + B) = \sin A \cos B - \sin B \cos A$ $\sin 2\theta = 2 \sin \theta \cos \theta$ $\sin \dfrac{A}{2} = \pm\sqrt{\dfrac{1 - \cos A}{2}}$

2 Function	**Inverse Trigonometric Functions (Lesson 14-2)**
If the domain of a trigonometric function is appropriately restricted, its inverse is a function.	$y = \sin \theta \quad 0 \le \theta \le \pi \quad \theta = \sin^{-1}x$ $y = \cos \theta \quad -\dfrac{\pi}{2} \le \theta \le \dfrac{\pi}{2} \quad \theta = \cos^{-1}x$ $y = \tan \theta \quad -\dfrac{\pi}{2} < \theta < \dfrac{\pi}{2} \quad \theta = \tan^{-1}x$

3 Equivalence	**Right Triangles and Trigonometric Ratios (Lessons 14-3)**	**Area, the Law of Sines, and the Law of Cosines (Lessons 14-4 and 14-5)**
The trigonometric function values of θ, $0° < \theta < 90°$, are the trigonometric ratios for a right triangle.	$\sin \theta = \dfrac{OPP}{HYP} = \dfrac{y}{r}$ $\cos \theta = \dfrac{ADJ}{HYP} = \dfrac{x}{r}$ $\tan \theta = \dfrac{OPP}{ADJ} = \dfrac{y}{x}$ 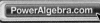	Area $\triangle ABC$: $\dfrac{1}{2}bc \sin A$ Law of Sines: $\dfrac{\sin A}{a} = \dfrac{\sin B}{b} = \dfrac{\sin C}{c}$ Law of Cosines: $a^2 = b^2 + c^2 - 2bc \cos A$

Chapter Vocabulary

- Law of Cosines (p. 936)
- Law of Sines (p. 929)
- trigonometric identity (p. 904)
- trigonometric ratios (p. 920)

Choose the correct term to complete each sentence.

1. You can find the missing measures of any triangle by using the ? if you know the measures of two angles and a side.

2. The six ratios of the lengths of the sides of a right triangle are known as the ? .

3. If you know the measures of two sides and the angle between them, you can use the ? to find missing parts of any triangle.

4. A trigonometric equation that is true for all values except those for which the expressions on either side of the equal sign are undefined is a ? .

5. The ? can be used to find missing measures of any triangle when you know two sides and the angle opposite one of them.

Thus, $d = \begin{cases} -2\left(x - \dfrac{\pi}{4}\right) & \text{if } -\dfrac{\pi}{2} \le x < \dfrac{\pi}{4} \\ 2\left(x - \dfrac{\pi}{4}\right) & \text{if } \dfrac{\pi}{4} \le x \le \dfrac{\pi}{2} \end{cases}$

or $d = \left| 2\left(x - \dfrac{\pi}{4}\right) \right|$.

Next, consider the distance d between x and $\sin^{-1}(\cos x)$ for $0 \le x \le \pi$.

For $0 \le x < \dfrac{\pi}{4}$, $d = \dfrac{\pi}{2} - 2x$.

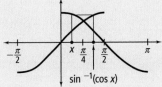

For $\dfrac{\pi}{4} \le x < \dfrac{\pi}{2}$, $d = \dfrac{\pi}{2} - 2\left(\dfrac{\pi}{2} - x\right)$ $= 2x - \dfrac{\pi}{2}$.

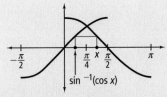

For $\dfrac{\pi}{2} \le x \le \pi$, $d = x + \left(x - \dfrac{\pi}{2}\right) = 2x - \dfrac{\pi}{2}$.

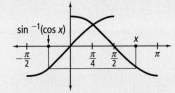

Thus, $d = \begin{cases} -2\left(x - \dfrac{\pi}{4}\right) & \text{if } 0 \le x < \dfrac{\pi}{4} \\ 2\left(x - \dfrac{\pi}{4}\right) & \text{if } \dfrac{\pi}{4} \le x \le \pi \end{cases}$

or $d = \left| 2\left(x - \dfrac{\pi}{4}\right) \right|$.

The graphs of the distance between x and $\cos^{-1}(\sin x)$ and between x and $\sin^{-1}(\cos x)$ are the graph of $d = \left| 2\left(x - \dfrac{\pi}{4}\right) \right|$ restricted to $-\dfrac{\pi}{2} \le x \le \dfrac{\pi}{2}$ and $0 \le x \le \pi$, respectively.

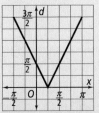

Essential Questions

BIG idea **Equivalence**

ESSENTIAL QUESTION How do you verify that an equation involving the variable x is an identity?

ANSWER If you can transform the expression on the lefthand side of the equation to make it equal the expression on the righthand side, the equation is an identity.

BIG idea **Function**

ESSENTIAL QUESTION A trigonometric function corresponds one number to many, so how can its inverse be a function?

ANSWER You restrict the domain of sine, cosine, and tangent to include only the representative part with the simplest domain values.

BIG idea **Geometry**

ESSENTIAL QUESTION How do the trigonometric *functions* relate to the trigonometric *ratios* for a right triangle?

ANSWER For the domain of angle measures between 0° and 90°, the values of the trigonometric functions are the same as the trigonometric ratios for a right triangle.

Performance Task 3. See back of book.

Summative Questions

Use the following prompts as you review this chapter with your students. The prompts are designed to help you assess your students' understanding of the BIG ideas they have studied.

- How can you use trigonometric relationships and identities to derive other identities?
- What would be your first step in the solution process of $5 \sin \theta - 2 = \sin \theta$?
- Compare and contrast the Law of Sines and the Law of Cosines. When do you use each one?

Answers

Chapter Review

1. Law of Sines
2. trig. ratios
3. Law of Cosines
4. trig. ident.
5. Law of Sines

Answers

Chapter Review (continued)

6. $\sin \theta \tan \theta = \sin \theta \dfrac{\sin \theta}{\cos \theta} = \dfrac{\sin^2 \theta}{\cos \theta}$

$= \dfrac{1 - \cos^2 \theta}{\cos \theta} = \dfrac{1}{\cos \theta} - \cos \theta$; domain of validity: all real numbers except odd multiples of $\dfrac{\pi}{2}$

7. $\cos^2 \theta \cot^2 \theta = \cos^2 \theta \dfrac{\cos^2 \theta}{\sin^2 \theta} =$

$\dfrac{\cos^2 \theta (1 - \sin^2 \theta)}{\sin^2 \theta} = \dfrac{\cos^2 \theta - \cos^2 \theta \sin^2 \theta}{\sin^2 \theta}$

$= \cot^2 \theta - \cos^2 \theta$; domain of validity: all real numbers except 0 and multiples of π

8. $\cos^2 \theta$

9. 1

10. 1

11. $-\sin^2 \theta$

12. $\cos^2 \theta$

13. 1

14. $-60°$

15. $60°$

16. $-30°$

17. $30°$

18. 0.34

19. -1.11

20. 2.27

21. 0.20

22. $\dfrac{\pi}{3}, \dfrac{5\pi}{3}$

23. $\dfrac{\pi}{6}, \dfrac{7\pi}{6}$

24. $0, \dfrac{\pi}{2}, \pi$

25. $\dfrac{\pi}{3}, \dfrac{5\pi}{3}$

14-1 Trigonometric Identities

Quick Review

A **trigonometric identity** is a trigonometric equation that is true for all values except those for which the expressions on either side of the equal sign are undefined.

Reciprocal Identities

$$\csc \theta = \frac{1}{\sin \theta} \qquad \sec \theta = \frac{1}{\cos \theta} \qquad \cot \theta = \frac{1}{\tan \theta}$$

Tangent and Cotangent Identities

$$\tan \theta = \frac{\sin \theta}{\cos \theta} \qquad \cot \theta = \frac{\cos \theta}{\sin \theta}$$

Pythagorean Identities

$$\cos^2 \theta + \sin^2 \theta = 1 \qquad 1 + \tan^2 \theta = \sec^2 \theta$$

$$1 + \cot^2 \theta = \csc^2 \theta$$

Example

Simplify the trigonometric expression $\cot \theta \sec \theta$.

$\cot \theta \sec \theta = \dfrac{\cos \theta}{\sin \theta} \cdot \sec \theta$ Cotangent Identity

$\qquad\qquad = \dfrac{\cos \theta}{\sin \theta} \cdot \dfrac{1}{\cos \theta}$ Reciprocal identity

$\qquad\qquad = \dfrac{1}{\sin \theta}$ Simplify.

$\qquad\qquad = \csc \theta$ Reciprocal identity

Exercises

Verify each identity. Give the domain of validity for each identity.

6. $\sin \theta \tan \theta = \dfrac{1}{\cos \theta} - \cos \theta$

7. $\cos^2 \theta \cot^2 \theta = \cot^2 \theta - \cos^2 \theta$

Simplify each trigonometric expression.

8. $1 - \sin^2 \theta$

9. $\dfrac{\cos \theta}{\sin \theta \cot \theta}$

10. $\csc^2 \theta - \cot^2 \theta$

11. $\cos^2 \theta - 1$

12. $\dfrac{\sin \theta \cos \theta}{\tan \theta}$

13. $\sec \theta \sin \theta \cot \theta$

14-2 Solving Trigonometric Equations Using Inverses

Quick Review

The function $\cos^{-1} x$ is the inverse of $\cos \theta$ with the restricted domain $0 \le \theta \le \pi$. The function $\sin^{-1} x$ is the inverse of $\sin \theta$ with the restricted domain $-\dfrac{\pi}{2} \le \theta \le \dfrac{\pi}{2}$, and $\tan^{-1} x$ is the inverse of $\tan \theta$ with the restricted domain $-\dfrac{\pi}{2} < \theta < \dfrac{\pi}{2}$.

Example

Solve $2 \cos \theta \sin \theta - \sqrt{3} \cos \theta = 0$ for θ with $0 \le \theta < 2\pi$.

$2 \cos \theta \sin \theta - \sqrt{3} \cos \theta = 0$

$\cos \theta (2 \sin \theta - \sqrt{3}) = 0$ Factor.

$\cos \theta = 0$ or $2 \sin \theta - \sqrt{3} = 0$ Zero-Product Property.

$\cos \theta = 0 \qquad \sin \theta = \dfrac{\sqrt{3}}{2}$ Solve for $\cos \theta$ and $\sin \theta$.

$\theta = \dfrac{\pi}{2}$ or $\dfrac{3\pi}{2} \qquad \theta = \dfrac{\pi}{3}$ or $\dfrac{2\pi}{3}$ Use the unit circle.

Exercises

Use a unit circle and 30°-60°-90° triangles to find the value in degrees of each expression.

14. $\sin^{-1}\left(-\dfrac{\sqrt{3}}{2}\right)$ **15.** $\tan^{-1} \sqrt{3}$

16. $\tan^{-1}\left(-\dfrac{\sqrt{3}}{3}\right)$ **17.** $\cos^{-1} \dfrac{\sqrt{3}}{2}$

Use a calculator and inverse functions to find the value in radians of each expression.

18. $\sin^{-1} 0.33$ **19.** $\tan^{-1}(-2)$

20. $\cos^{-1}(-0.64)$ **21.** $\cos^{-1} 0.98$

Solve each equation for $0 \le \theta < 2\pi$.

22. $2 \cos \theta = 1$ **23.** $\sqrt{3} \tan \theta = 1$

24. $\sin \theta = \sin^2 \theta$ **25.** $\sec \theta = 2$

14-3 Right Triangles and Trigonometric Ratios

Quick Review

The six different ratios of the sides of a triangle are know as the **trigonometric ratios** for a right triangle. Those ratios depend on the size of the acute angles in the right triangle.

If θ is an acute angle of a right triangle, x is the length of the adjacent leg (ADJ), y is the length of the opposite leg (OPP), and r is the length of the hypotenuse (HYP), then the trigonometric ratios of θ are as follows.

$$\sin \theta = \frac{y}{r} = \frac{OPP}{HYP} \qquad \csc \theta = \frac{r}{y} = \frac{HYP}{OPP}$$

$$\cos \theta = \frac{x}{r} = \frac{ADJ}{HYP} \qquad \sec \theta = \frac{r}{x} = \frac{HYP}{ADJ}$$

$$\tan \theta = \frac{y}{x} = \frac{OPP}{ADJ} \qquad \cot \theta = \frac{x}{y} = \frac{ADJ}{OPP}$$

Example

In $\triangle ABC$, $\angle C$ is a right angle, $a = 4$ and $c = 9$. What are $\cos A$, $\sin A$, and $\tan A$ in fraction form?

Using the Pythagorean Theorem, $b = \sqrt{65}$.

The ratios are $\cos A = \frac{b}{c} = \frac{\sqrt{65}}{9}$, $\sin A = \frac{a}{c} = \frac{4}{9}$, and $\tan A = \frac{a}{b} = \frac{4}{\sqrt{65}} = \frac{4\sqrt{65}}{65}$.

Exercises

Find the values of the six trigonometric functions for the angle in standard position determined by each point.

26. $(-3, 4)$ **27.** $(-8, -15)$

In $\triangle ABC$, $\angle B$ is a right angle, $AB = 30$, and $\sec A = \frac{5}{3}$. Find each value in fraction and in decimal form.

28. $\cos A$ **29.** $\sin A$

30. $\tan C$ **31.** $\csc C$

In $\triangle FGH$, $\angle G$ is a right angle. Find the remaining sides and angles. Round your answers to the nearest tenth.

32. $f = 3, h = 9$ **33.** $f = 12, g = 20$

34. $g = 55, h = 40$ **35.** $f = 5, h = 4$

Find each length x. Round to the nearest tenth.

36.   **37.**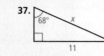

14-4 and 14-5 Law of Sines and Law of Cosines

Quick Review

You can use the Law of Sines and the Law of Cosines to find missing measures of a triangle. For $\triangle ABC$:

The **Law of Sines** states that $\frac{\sin A}{a} = \frac{\sin B}{b} = \frac{\sin C}{c}$.

The **Law of Cosines**

$$a^2 = b^2 + c^2 - 2bc \cos A \qquad b^2 = a^2 + c^2 - 2ac \cos B$$

$$c^2 = a^2 + b^2 - 2ab \cos C$$

Example

In $\triangle ABC$, $m\angle B = 60°$, $a = 12$, and $c = 8$. What is b to the nearest tenth?

$b^2 = 12^2 + 8^2 - 2(12)(8)\cos 60°$ Law of Cosines

$b^2 = 112$ Simplify.

$b \approx 10.6$ Use a calculator.

Exercises

Find the area of each triangle. Round your answers to the nearest hundredth.

38.    **39.**

40. In $\triangle LMN$, $m\angle L = 67°$, $m\angle N = 24°$, and $MN = 16$ in. Find LM to the nearest tenth.

41. In $\triangle DEF$, $d = 25$ in., $e = 28$ in., and $f = 20$ in. Find $m\angle F$ to the nearest tenth.

42. In $\triangle GHI$, $h = 8$, $i = 12$, and $m\angle G = 96°$. Find $m\angle I$ to the nearest tenth.

26. $\sin \theta = \frac{4}{5}$, $\cos \theta = -\frac{3}{5}$,
$\tan \theta = -\frac{4}{3}$, $\csc \theta = \frac{5}{4}$,
$\sec \theta = -\frac{5}{3}$, $\cot \theta = -\frac{3}{4}$

27. $\sin \theta = -\frac{15}{17}$, $\cos \theta = -\frac{8}{17}$,
$\tan \theta = \frac{15}{8}$, $\csc \theta = -\frac{17}{15}$,
$\sec \theta = -\frac{17}{8}$, $\cot \theta = \frac{8}{15}$

28. $\frac{3}{5}$, 0.6

29. $\frac{4}{5}$, 0.8

30. $\frac{3}{4}$, 0.75

31. $\frac{5}{3}$, $1.\overline{6}$

32. $g \approx 9.5$, $\angle F \approx 18.4°$, $\angle H \approx 71.6°$

33. $h = 16$, $\angle F \approx 36.9°$, $\angle H \approx 53.1°$

34. $f \approx 37.7$, $\angle F \approx 43.3°$, $\angle H \approx 46.7°$

35. $g \approx 6.4$, $\angle F \approx 51.3°$, $\angle H \approx 38.7°$

36. 13.7

37. 29.4

38. 13.14 m²

39. 92.12 ft²

40. 7.1 in.

41. 43.9°

42. 52.2°

Answers

Chapter Review (continued)

43. $\cos\left(\theta + \frac{\pi}{2}\right) = \cos\theta\cos\frac{\pi}{2} - \sin\theta\sin\frac{\pi}{2}$

$\qquad\qquad = \cos\theta \times 0 - \sin\theta \times 1 = -\sin\theta$

44. $\sin^2\left(\theta - \frac{\pi}{2}\right) = \left[\sin\left(\theta - \frac{\pi}{2}\right)\right]^2$

$\qquad\qquad = \left[\sin\theta\cos\frac{\pi}{2} - \cos\theta\sin\frac{\pi}{2}\right]^2$

$\qquad\qquad = \left[\sin\theta \times 0 - \cos\theta \times 1\right]^2$

$\qquad\qquad = (-\cos\theta)^2 = \cos^2\theta$

45. $2 - \sqrt{3}$

46. $-\dfrac{\sqrt{3}}{2}$

47. $\dfrac{\sqrt{2} - \sqrt{6}}{4}$

48. $-2 - \sqrt{3}$

49. $\dfrac{\sqrt{3}}{2}$

50. $\dfrac{\sqrt{3}}{2}$

51. $-\sqrt{3}$

52. $-\dfrac{\sqrt{3}}{2}$

14-6 Angle Identities

Quick Review

Angle identities are used to solve trigonometric equations.

Negative angle identities

$\sin(-\theta) = -\sin\theta \qquad \tan(-\theta) = -\tan\theta$

$\cos(-\theta) = \cos\theta$

Cofunction identities

$\sin\left(\frac{\pi}{2} - \theta\right) = \cos\theta \qquad \tan\left(\frac{\pi}{2} - \theta\right) = \cot\theta$

$\cos\left(\frac{\pi}{2} - \theta\right) = \sin\theta$

Angle difference identities

$\sin(A - B) = \sin A\cos B - \cos A\sin B$

$\cos(A - B) = \cos A\cos B + \sin A\sin B$

$\tan(A - B) = \dfrac{\tan A - \tan B}{1 + \tan A\tan B}$

Angle sum identities

$\sin(A + B) = \sin A\cos B + \cos A\sin B$

$\cos(A + B) = \cos A\cos B - \sin A\sin B$

$\tan(A + B) = \dfrac{\tan A + \tan B}{1 - \tan A\tan B}$

Example

What is the exact value of $\cos(165°)$?

$\cos 165° = \cos(120° + 45°)$

$\qquad = \cos 120°\cos 45° - \sin 120°\sin 45°$

$\qquad = (-\cos 60°)\cos 45° - \sin 60°\sin 45°$

$\qquad = -\dfrac{1}{2} \cdot \dfrac{\sqrt{2}}{2} - \dfrac{\sqrt{3}}{2} \cdot \dfrac{\sqrt{2}}{2}$

$\qquad = -\dfrac{\sqrt{2}}{4} - \dfrac{\sqrt{6}}{4}$

$\qquad = -\dfrac{\sqrt{2} + \sqrt{6}}{4}$

Exercises

Verify each identity.

43. $\cos\left(\theta + \frac{\pi}{2}\right) = -\sin\theta$

44. $\sin^2\left(\theta - \frac{\pi}{2}\right) = \cos^2\theta$

Find the exact value.

45. $\tan 15°$ **46.** $\sin 300°$

47. $\cos 255°$ **48.** $\tan(-75°)$

14-7 Double-Angle and Half-Angle Identities

Quick Review

You can use double-angle and half-angle identities to find exact values of trigonometric expressions. In the half-angle identities, choose the positive or negative sign for each function depending on the quadrant in which $\frac{A}{2}$ lies.

Double-angle identities

$\cos 2\theta = \cos^2\theta - \sin^2\theta \qquad \cos 2\theta = 2\cos^2\theta - 1$

$\cos 2\theta = 1 - 2\sin^2\theta \qquad\quad \sin 2\theta = 2\sin\theta\cos\theta$

$\tan 2\theta = \dfrac{2\tan\theta}{1 - \tan^2\theta}$

Half-angle identities

$\sin\dfrac{A}{2} = \pm\sqrt{\dfrac{1 - \cos A}{2}} \qquad \tan\dfrac{A}{2} = \pm\sqrt{\dfrac{1 - \cos A}{1 + \cos A}}$

$\cos\dfrac{A}{2} = \pm\sqrt{\dfrac{1 + \cos A}{2}}$

Example

What is the exact value of $\cos 75°$?

$\cos 75° = \cos\left(\dfrac{150°}{2}\right)$

$\qquad = \sqrt{\dfrac{1 + \cos 150°}{2}}$

$\qquad = \sqrt{\dfrac{1 - \frac{\sqrt{3}}{2}}{2}} = \sqrt{\dfrac{2 - \sqrt{3}}{4}} = \dfrac{\sqrt{2 - \sqrt{3}}}{2}$

Exercises

Use the double-angle identity to find the exact value of each expression.

49. $\sin 120°$ **50.** $\cos 30°$

51. $\tan 300°$ **52.** $\sin 240°$

 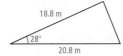
MathXL® for School
Go to PowerAlgebra.com

Do you know HOW?

Simplify each trigonometric expression.

1. $\sin\theta + \cos\theta\cot\theta$ **2.** $\sec\theta\sin\theta\cot\theta$

3. $\cot\theta\,(\tan\theta + \cot\theta)$

Verify each identity.

4. $\sec\theta\sin\theta\cot\theta = 1$

5. $\csc^2\theta - \cot^2\theta = 1$

6. $\sec\theta\cot\theta = \csc\theta$

7. $\sec^2\theta - 1 = \tan^2\theta$

Use a unit circle and 30°-60°-90° triangles to find values of θ in degrees for each expression.

8. $\sin\theta = \frac{\sqrt{3}}{2}$ **9.** $\cos\theta = \frac{\sqrt{3}}{2}$

10. $\cos\theta = -1$ **11.** $\tan\theta = \sqrt{3}$

Solve each equation for θ with $0 \le \theta < 2\pi$.

12. $4\sin\theta + 2\sqrt{3} = 0$ **13.** $2\cos\theta = 1$

14. $\sqrt{2}\sin\theta - 1 = 0$

In $\triangle ABC$, find each value as a fraction and as a decimal. Round to the nearest hundredth.

15. $\sin A$ **16.** $\sec A$ **17.** $\cot A$

18. $\csc C$ **19.** $\sec C$ **20.** $\tan C$

In $\triangle DEF$, $\angle F$ is a right angle. Find the remaining sides and angles. Round your answers to the nearest tenth.

21. $e = 6, f = 10$ **22.** $d = 10, e = 12$

23. $e = 21, f = 51$ **24.** $d = 5.5, e = 2.6$

25. Find the area of the triangle.

18.8 m
28°
20.8 m

26. In $\triangle ABC$, $m\angle A = 45°$, $m\angle C = 23°$, and $BC = 25$ in. Find AB to the nearest tenth.

27. In $\triangle MNP$, $m\angle N = 45°$, $m = 20$ cm, and $p = 41$ cm. Find n to the nearest tenth.

28. In $\triangle PQR$, $p = 51$ ft, $q = 81$ ft, and $r = 61$ ft. Find $m\angle R$ to the nearest tenth.

29. In $\triangle STU$, $m\angle S = 96°$, $t = 8$ in., and $u = 10$ in. Find $m\angle U$ to the nearest tenth.

Verify each identity.

30. $-\sin\left(\theta - \frac{\pi}{2}\right) = \cos\theta$ **31.** $\csc\left(\theta - \frac{\pi}{2}\right) = -\sec\theta$

Solve each trigonometric equation for θ with $0 \le \theta < 2\pi$.

32. $\sin\left(\theta - \frac{\pi}{2}\right) = \sec\theta$ **33.** $\cot\left(\frac{\pi}{2} - \theta\right) = \sin\theta$

Use a double-angle identity to find the exact value of each expression.

34. $\sin 60°$ **35.** $\cos 60°$ **36.** $\tan 60°$

Use a half-angle identity to find the exact value of each expression.

37. $\tan 30°$ **38.** $\sin 90°$ **39.** $\cos 180°$

Do you UNDERSTAND?

Ⓒ **40. Writing** Suppose you know the lengths of all three sides of a triangle. Can you use the Law of Sines to find the measures of the angles? Explain.

Ⓒ **41. Open-Ended** Choose an angle measure A. Find $\sin A$ and $\cos A$. Then use the identities to find $\cos 2A$ and $\sin\frac{A}{2}$.

26. 13.8 in.

27. 30.4 cm

28. 48.8°

29. 47.7°

30. $-\sin\left(\theta - \frac{\pi}{2}\right) = -\sin\left(-\left(\frac{\pi}{2} - \theta\right)\right)$
$= \sin\left(\frac{\pi}{2} - \theta\right) = \cos\theta$

31. $\csc\left(\theta - \frac{\pi}{2}\right) = \dfrac{1}{\sin\left(-\left(\frac{\pi}{2} - \theta\right)\right)}$
$= -\dfrac{1}{\sin\left(\frac{\pi}{2} - \theta\right)}$
$= -\dfrac{1}{\cos\theta} = -\sec\theta$

32. no solution

33. $0, \pi$

34. $\frac{\sqrt{3}}{2}$

35. $\frac{1}{2}$

36. $\sqrt{3}$

37. $\frac{\sqrt{3}}{3}$

38. 1

39. -1

40. No; the Law of Sines requires at least one angle in order to set up a ratio of length of side to size of angle.

41. Check students' work.

Answers

Chapter Test

1. $\csc\theta$

2. 1

3. $\csc^2\theta$

4. $\sec\theta\sin\theta\cot\theta = \dfrac{1}{\cos\theta}\cdot\dfrac{\sin\theta}{1}\cdot\dfrac{\cos\theta}{\sin\theta}$
$= \dfrac{\sin\theta\cos\theta}{\cos\theta\sin\theta} = 1$

5. $\csc^2\theta - \cot^2\theta = 1 + \cot^2\theta - \cot^2\theta$
$= 1$

6. $\sec\theta\cot\theta = \dfrac{1}{\cos\theta}\cdot\dfrac{\cos\theta}{\sin\theta} = \dfrac{1}{\sin\theta}$
$= \csc\theta$

7. $\sec^2\theta - 1 = 1 + \tan^2\theta - 1$
$= \tan^2\theta$

8. $60° + 360°\cdot n,\ 120° + 360°\cdot n$

9. $30° + 360°\cdot n,\ 330° + 360°\cdot n$

10. $180° + 360°\cdot n$

11. $60° + 180°\cdot n$

12. $\frac{4\pi}{3}, \frac{5\pi}{3}$

13. $\frac{\pi}{3}, \frac{5\pi}{3}$

14. $\frac{\pi}{4}, \frac{3\pi}{4}$

15. $\frac{4}{6.4}$, 0.63

16. $\frac{6.4}{5}$, 1.28

17. $\frac{5}{4}$, 1.25

18. $\frac{6.4}{5}$, 1.28

19. $\frac{6.4}{4}$, 1.60

20. $\frac{5}{4}$, 1.25

21. $d = 8, m\angle E \approx 36.9°, m\angle D \approx 53.1°$

22. $f \approx 15.6, m\angle E \approx 50.2°, m\angle D \approx 39.8°$

23. $d \approx 46.5, m\angle E \approx 24.3°, m\angle D \approx 65.7°$

24. $f \approx 6.1, m\angle E \approx 25.3°, m\angle D \approx 64.7°$

25. 91.8 m²

Item Number	Lesson	Content Standard
1	4-3	F.IF.4
2	1-4	A.CED.4
3	6-6	F.BF.1.b
4	6-7	F.BF.4.a
5	6-3	A.SSE.2
6	4-8	N.CN.2
7	8-4	A.SSE.2
8	8-5	A.APR.7
9	4-5	A.APR.3
10	4-1	F.IF.4
11	5-2	A.APR.3
12	8-2	F.BF.3
13	5-5	N.CN.7
14	7-2	F.IF.7.e
15	CB 2-4	F.IF.7.b
16	8-2	F.BF.3
17	7-2	F.BF.4.a
18	6-7	F.BF.4.a
19	8-6	A.REI.12
20	6-5	A.REI.2
21	4-2	F.IF.4
22	8-3	F.IF.7.d
23	2-7	F.IF.7.b
24	4-1	F.BF.3
25	7-2	F.BF.3
26	6-7	F.BF.4.a
27	6-4	N.RN.2
28	1-6	A.CED.1
29	3-2	A.CED.2
30	4-8	N.CN.7
31	CB 2-4	F.IF.7.b
32	6-4	N.RN.2
33	4-2	F.IF.4
34	5-1	F.IF.7.c
35	7-6	F.LE.4
36	7-2	F.BF.3
37	8-6	A.REI.2
38	7-2	A.CED.2
39	7-5	F.LE.4
40	4-1	A.CED.2
41	7-2	F.IF.8
42	5-9	F.BF.3
43	4-5	A.CED.1
44	3-2	A.CED.2
45	6-6	F.BF.1.b
46	1-4	A.CED.1
47	4-2	F.IF.9
48	3-2	A.REI.6
49	7-5	F.LE.4

Complete the following items. For multiple choice items, write the letter of the correct response on your paper. For all other items, show or explain your work.

1. The graph of a quadratic function $f(x)$ is shown below.

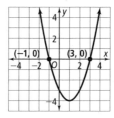

Use the graph to solve $f(x) < 0$.

- (A) $-1 < x < 3$
- (B) $-1 \le x \le 3$
- (C) $x < -1$ or $x > 3$
- (D) $x \le -1$ or $x > 3$

2. Newton's Law of Universal Gravitation is $F = \dfrac{Gm_1m_2}{r^2}$. Solve this equation for r.

- (F) $r = \sqrt{\dfrac{F}{Gm_1m_2}}$
- (G) $r = \sqrt{\dfrac{Gm_1m_2}{F}}$
- (H) $r = \dfrac{F}{2Gm_1m_2}$
- (I) $r = \dfrac{Gm_1m_2}{2F}$

3. Let $f(x) = x^3 - 4x^2 + 9x$ and let $g(x) = 6x^3 + x^2 - 5x - 12$. What is $f(x) - g(x)$?

- (A) $-5x^3 - 5x^2 + 14x + 12$
- (B) $-5x^3 - 3x^2 + 4x - 12$
- (C) $7x^3 - 3x^2 + 4x - 12$
- (D) $-5x^4 - 5x^3 + 14x^2 + 12x$

4. Let $f^{-1}(x) = 2x + 3$. What is the solution of $f(x) = f^{-1}(x)$?

- (F) $x = -1$ or $x = -2$
- (G) $x = -3$
- (H) $(x, y) = (-1, -2)$
- (I) $(x, y) = (-3, -3)$

5. Which is a simpler form of $\dfrac{\sqrt{5}}{3 - \sqrt{2}}$?

- (A) $\dfrac{\sqrt{10}}{3\sqrt{2} - 2}$
- (B) $\dfrac{5}{3\sqrt{5} - 10}$
- (C) $\dfrac{3\sqrt{5} - 10}{7}$
- (D) $\dfrac{3\sqrt{5} + \sqrt{10}}{7}$

6. What is the product of $(2 + 5i)$ and $(4 + 3i)$?

- (F) $8 + 15i$
- (G) $8 + 26i$
- (H) $-7 + 15i$
- (I) $-7 + 26i$

7. Multiply $\dfrac{x^3}{x^2 - 4} \cdot \dfrac{5x + 10}{10x}$.

- (A) $\dfrac{5x}{4}$
- (B) $\dfrac{x^2}{2(x - 2)}$
- (C) $\dfrac{x^2(x + 2)}{2(x^2 - 4)}$
- (D) $\dfrac{5x^3}{10x(x - 2)}$

8. Which is a simpler form of the complex fraction $\dfrac{\frac{1}{b} + c}{b + \frac{1}{c}}$?

- (F) 1
- (G) $\dfrac{c}{b}$
- (H) $\left(\dfrac{1}{b} + c\right)^2$
- (I) $(1 + c)(b + 1)$

9. What is the sum of the x-intercepts of the graph of the quadratic function $y = x^2 - 4x - 12$?

- (A) 6
- (B) 4
- (C) -1
- (D) -4

50	7-1	A.CED.2
51	3-3	A.REI.12
52	6-1	A.SSE.2
53	2-7	F.IF.7.b
54	3-3	A.CED.3
55	8-3	F.IF.7.d
56	8-6	A.APR.6
57	10-4	G.GPE.3
58	11-8	S.IC.3
59	11-10	S.ID.4
60	13-2	F.TF.2
61	10-4	G.GPE.3
62	12-3	N.VM.10
63	7-4	F.LE.4
64	11-4	S.CP.6
65	10-6	G.GPE.2

66	13-3	F.TF.1
67	11-10	S.ID.4
68	9-3	A.SSE.4
69	7-4	F.LE.4
70	12-3	N.VM.10
71	14-1	F.TF.8
72	7-5	F.LE.4
73	13-4	F.TF.5
74	10-3	G.GPE.1
75	13-6	F.TF.1
76	12-2	N.VM.8
77	12-6	N.VM.4
78	7-6	F.LE.4
79	9-5	A.SSE.4
80	10-6	G.GPE.2
81	12-4	N.VM.10
82	13-7	F.IF.7.e

10. What is the equation of a parabola with the following characteristics?

Axis of symmetry: $x = -3$

Range: all real numbers less than or equal to 4

  F $y = -(x - 4)^2 - 3$ **H** $y = -(x + 3)^2 + 4$

  G $y = (x - 4)^2 - 3$ **I** $y = (x + 3)^2 + 4$

11. The graph of a degree 4 polynomial function with integer zeros is shown below.

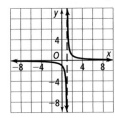

What is the equation of the polynomial function?

  A $y = x^4 - 6x^3 + 11x^2 - 6x$

  B $y = x^4 - 2x^3 - 5x^2 + 6x$

  C $y = x^4 - 2x^3 + x^2 + 3x$

  D $y = x^4 + 2x^3 - 5x^2 - 6x$

12. Which function is best represented by the graph below?

  F $y = \dfrac{1}{x - 1}$ **H** $y = \dfrac{x}{x - 1}$

  G $y = \dfrac{1}{x + 1}$ **I** $y = \dfrac{x}{x + 1}$

13. How many distinct real roots does the equation $x^4 + 3x^3 - 4x = 0$ have?

  A 1   **B** 2   **C** 3   **D** 4

14. Which function best represents the graph?

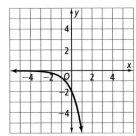

  F $f(x) = 2 \cdot 3^{-x}$

  G $f(x) = -2 \cdot 3^x$

  H $f(x) = 2 \cdot 3^x$

  I $f(x) = -2 \cdot 3^{-x}$

15. Consider the piecewise defined function graphed below.

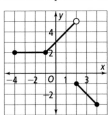

What is the equation for the piecewise defined function?

  A $f(x) = \begin{cases} 2, & \text{if } -4 \leq x < -1 \\ x + 3, & \text{if } -1 \leq x < 2 \\ -x + 1, & \text{if } 2 \leq x \leq 4 \end{cases}$

  B $f(x) = \begin{cases} 2, & \text{if } -4 \leq x \leq -1 \\ x + 3, & \text{if } -1 < x \leq 2 \\ -x + 1, & \text{if } 2 < x \leq 4 \end{cases}$

  C $f(x) = \begin{cases} 2x, & \text{if } -4 \leq x < -1 \\ x + 3, & \text{if } -1 \leq x < 2 \\ -x + 1, & \text{if } 2 \leq x \leq 4 \end{cases}$

  D $f(x) = \begin{cases} 2x, & \text{if } -4 \leq x < -1 \\ x + 3, & \text{if } -1 \leq x < 2 \\ -x - 1, & \text{if } 2 \leq x \leq 4 \end{cases}$

Answers

End-of-Course Assessment

  1. A
  2. G
  3. A
  4. G
  5. D
  6. I
  7. B
  8. G
  9. B
  10. H
  11. B
  12. F
  13. C
  14. G
  15. A

Answers

16. I

17. A

18. F

19. D

20. G

21. B

22. G

23. [2]

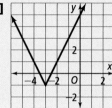

   [1] one minor error

24. [2]

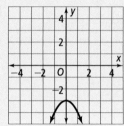

   [1] one minor error

25. [2] First, reflect the graph of $f(x) = 2(4)^x$
across the x-axis. Then shift the reflection
3 units up.

   [1] one minor error

26. [4] **a.** $y = \dfrac{4}{x - 1}$

$$yx - y = 4$$

$$x = \dfrac{4 + y}{y}$$

$$f^{-1}(x) = \dfrac{4}{x} + 1$$

b. $f\left(\dfrac{4}{x} + 1\right) = \dfrac{4}{\frac{4}{x} + 1 - 1} = \dfrac{4}{\frac{4}{x}} =$

$$= 4 \cdot \dfrac{x}{4} = x$$

$$f(f^{-1}(x)) = x.$$

$$f^{-1}\left(\dfrac{4}{x - 1}\right) = \dfrac{4}{\frac{4}{x - 1}} + 1$$

$$= 4 \cdot \dfrac{x - 1}{4} + 1$$

$$= x - 1 + 1 = x$$

$$f^{-1}(f(x)) = x.$$

c. The domain of f is equal to the range of
f^{-1} and the range of f is equal to the
domain of f^{-1}.

   [3] one minor computational error

   [2] correct answers; missing work or
explanation

   [1] only 1 portion of the item answered
correctly

---

16. The graph of a rational function is shown below.

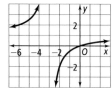

Which function best represents the graph?

   Ⓕ $f(x) = \dfrac{3}{x - 1}$

   Ⓖ $f(x) = \dfrac{1}{x + 3}$

   Ⓗ $f(x) = \dfrac{3x}{x - 1}$

   Ⓘ $f(x) = \dfrac{x}{x + 3}$

17. Consider the polynomial function
$f(x) = -2x^4 + 8x^3 + 4x^2 - 3$. What is the end
behavior of the graph?

   Ⓐ down and down

   Ⓑ down and up

   Ⓒ up and up

   Ⓓ up and down

18. If $f(x) = (x + 2)^2 - 1$, what is the largest possible
domain of f so that its inverse is also a function?

   Ⓕ $x \geq -2$ Ⓗ $x \geq 0$

   Ⓖ $x \geq -1$ Ⓘ $x \geq 2$

19. Solve $\dfrac{3}{2x + 10} + \dfrac{5}{4} = \dfrac{7}{x + 5}$ for x.

   Ⓐ $-\dfrac{50}{11}$ Ⓒ $-\dfrac{9}{5}$

   Ⓑ $-\dfrac{34}{10}$ Ⓓ $-\dfrac{3}{5}$

20. Solve $\sqrt{x - 2} - 7 = -4$ for x.

   Ⓕ 5   Ⓗ 18

   Ⓖ 11   Ⓘ 25

---

21. What is the x-coordinate of the vertex of the graph of
$f(x) = 2x^2 + 4x - 6$?

   Ⓐ -6 Ⓑ -1 Ⓒ 1   Ⓓ 4

22. The horizontal asymptote of the graph of $y = \dfrac{4x - 4}{2x - 6}$ is
$y = t$ for a real number t. What is the value of t?

   Ⓕ 1   Ⓖ 2   Ⓗ 3   Ⓘ 4

23. Graph $f(x) = |2x + 6| - 1$.

24. The graph of $y = x^2$ is shown below.

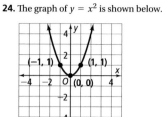

Use transformations to graph $y = -x^2 - 3$.

25. Consider the graph of the function $f(x) = 2(4)^x$. Explain
how the graph of the function $g(x) = -2(4)^x + 3$
can be obtained from the graph of $f(x)$.

26. Let $f(x) = \dfrac{4}{x - 1}$.

   a. Determine $f^{-1}(x)$. Show or explain your work.

   b. Find $f(f^{-1}(x))$ and $f^{-1}(f(x))$. Show your work.

   c. How are the domain and range of f and f^{-1}
related?

27. Consider the expression $\left(\dfrac{r^{3m}}{r^{-m}t^{4n}}\right)^{\frac{1}{n}} \cdot \left(\dfrac{r^{\frac{1}{n}}}{t^{\frac{2}{m}}}\right)^{-m}$.

   a. Simplify the expression so that r and t are only
written once. Show your work.

   b. Using your answer from part (a), evaluate the
expression when $m = 1$, $n = 2$, and $t = -3i$.
Show your work.

   c. For what values of r will the expression you found
in part (b) be a real number? Explain your answer.

---

27. [4] **a.** $\left(\dfrac{r^{4m}}{t^{4n}}\right)^{\frac{1}{2}} \cdot \left(\dfrac{t^{\frac{2}{m}}}{r^{\frac{1}{n}}}\right)^m$

$$= \dfrac{r^{\frac{4m}{n}}}{t^4} \cdot \dfrac{t^2}{r^{\frac{m}{n}}} = \dfrac{r^{\frac{3m}{n}}}{t^2}$$

b. $\dfrac{r^{\frac{3 \cdot 1}{2}}}{(-3i)^2} = \dfrac{r^{\frac{3}{2}}}{9i^2} = \dfrac{r^{\frac{3}{2}}}{9}$

c. $r \geq 0$ because the exponent
of $\dfrac{3}{2}$ means the same thing
as taking a square root of r
and then cubing the result.
A square root of a negative
number results in an imaginary
number.

   [3] one minor computational error

   [2] correct answers; missing work or
explanation

   [1] only 1 portion of the item
answered correctly

28. A company needs to ship bags of golf balls that contain 690 golf balls, plus or minus 6 golf balls. If x represents the actual number of golf balls, which inequality can represent this situation?

(A) $|x + 6| \geq 690$ (C) $|x + 690| \geq 6$

(B) $|x - 6| \leq 690$ (D) $|x - 690| \leq 6$

29. A boat took 4 h to make a trip downstream with a current of 6 km/h. The return trip against the same current took 10 h. How far did the boat travel?

(F) 48 km   (G) 84 km   (H) 160 km   (I) 196 km

30. What are all the complex solutions of $x^2 - 4x = -5$?

(A) $x = -1, x = 5$

(B) $x = 1, x = 3$

(C) $x = 2 + i, x = 2 - i$

(D) $x = 2 + 3i, x = 2 - 3i$

31. The function below can be used to find the total amount $C(x)$ an electric company charges a customer who uses x kilowatt-hours (kWh) in a month.

$$C(x) = \begin{cases} 0.07275x + 6.00, & \text{if } 0 \leq x \leq 400 \\ 0.05535x + 35.10, & \text{if } x > 400 \end{cases}$$

If a customer uses 546 kWh in a month, what is the total amount charged?

(F) $45.72   (G) $65.32   (H) $78.28   (I) $111.04

32. Simplify $\dfrac{r^{\frac{1}{2}}}{r^{-\frac{1}{4}}}$.

(A) $-r^{\frac{1}{4}}$ (B) $-r^2$ (C) $r^{\frac{1}{8}}$ (D) $r^{\frac{3}{4}}$

33. The graph of a quadratic function, $y = ax^2 + bx + c$ passes through the points shown. What is the axis of symmetry of the parabola?

(F) $x = -2$

(G) $x = -1$

(H) $x = 1$

(I) $x = 2$

34. What is the end behavior of the graph of the polynomial function $f(x) = -2x^5 + x^4 + 3x^3 - x + 1$?

(A) down and up

(B) up and up

(C) up and down

(D) down and down

35. The principal amount invested in an account with 1.5% interest compounded continuously is $500. The equation $A(x) = 500e^{0.015x}$ can be used to find the balance in the account after x years. To the nearest year, in how many years will the account have a balance of $820?

(F) 2 years   (H) 72 years

(G) 33 years   (I) 109 years

36. The graph of the exponential equation $y = 2^x$ is reflected across the y-axis and moved down 1 unit. What is the equation of the resulting graph?

(A) $y = 2^{-x-1}$ (C) $y = 2^{-x} - 1$

(B) $y = -2^{x-1}$ (D) $y = -2^x - 1$

37. The function $C(x) = \dfrac{10}{2x^2 + 1}$ can be used to find the concentration $C(x)$ in mg/L of a certain drug in the bloodstream of a patient x hours after the injection is given. In approximately how many hours after the injection will the concentration of the drug be 1.3 mg/L?

(F) 0.5 h   (H) 1.8 h

(G) 0.7 h   (I) 2.3 h

38. The half-life of radium-226 is about 1,600 years. After 4,000 years what percentage of a sample of radium-226 remains?

(A) 2.5%   (C) 40.0%

(B) 17.7%   (D) 75.8%

39. Solve $8.2(3^{2x-4}) - 11 = 557.1$. Round your answer to the nearest tenth.

(F) 1.8   (G) 2.9   (H) 3.5   (I) 3.9

28. D
29. H
30. C
31. G
32. D
33. H
34. C
35. G
36. C
37. H
38. B
39. I

Answers

End-of-Course Assessment (continued)

40. A
41. F
42. A
43. G
44. C
45. G
46. A
47. F
48. A
49. H

---

40. An exponential function is represented in the table below.

x	f(x)
-2	12
-1	6
0	3
1	1.5

Which equation best represents the function?

(A) $f(x) = 3(2^{-x})$ (C) $f(x) = 2^{-x} + 3$

(B) $f(x) = 3(2^x)$ (D) $f(x) = 2^x + 3$

41. What is the range of the graph of $f(x) = -ab^x$ if $a > 0$ and $b > 1$?

(F) $f(x) \leq 0$ (H) $f(x) \geq a$

(G) $f(x) \leq a$ (I) All real numbers

42. The characteristics of function $f(x) = ax^n$ are shown below.

Domain: All real numbers

Range: $x \leq 0$

Symmetric with respect to the y-axis

What must be true about the values of a and n?

(A) $a < 0$ and n is even   (C) $a > 0$ and n is even

(B) $a < 0$ and n is odd   (D) $a > 0$ and n is odd

43. A train leaves a city traveling due north. A car leaves the city at the same time traveling due west. The car is traveling 15 mi/h faster than the train. After 2 h they are approximately 150 mi apart. What is the speed of the train?

(F) 30 mi/h   (H) 60 mi/h

(G) 45 mi/h   (I) 75 mi/h

44. A high school sold 800 tickets for a soccer game. Three types of tickets were sold, adult, student and child. There were four times as many adult tickets sold as child tickets. And there were 62 more student tickets sold than adult tickets. How many adult tickets were sold?

(A) 82   (B) 123   (C) 328   (D) 384

45. Let $f(x) = 3x + 5$ and let $g(x) = x^2 + 2x$. What is $f(-3) \cdot g(-3)$?

(F) -32   (H) 9

(G) -12   (I) 60

46. The volume of a square pyramid with a height equal to four less than the length of a side of the base is given by $V(x) = \frac{1}{3}(x^3 + 8x^2 + 16x)$ where x is the height in cm. If the length of a side of the base is 9 cm, what is the volume of the pyramid?

(A) 135 cm^3 (C) 507 cm^3

(B) 405 cm^3 (D) 1,521 cm^3

47. A quadratic function is represented in the table below.

x	f(x)
1	-13
2	-3
3	3
4	5
5	3

Which equation best represents the function?

(F) $f(x) = -2(x - 4)^2 + 5$

(G) $f(x) = -2(x - 3)^2 + 3$

(H) $f(x) = 2(x - 4)^2 + 5$

(I) $f(x) = 2(x - 3)^2 + 3$

48. Find the x-value of the solution to the following system of equations.

$$\begin{cases} 3x + y = -3 \\ x + y = 1 \end{cases}$$

(A) -2   (C) $\frac{3}{5}$

(B) -1   (D) 3

49. Solve $4(3^x) = 26$ for x.

(F) 0.3   (H) 1.7

(G) 1.3   (I) 2.2

50. The amount of cesium-137 remaining after x years in an initial sample of 200 milligrams can be found using the equation $C(x) = 200e^{-0.02295x}$. In approximately how many years will the sample contain 120 milligrams of cesium-137?

  Ⓐ 13   Ⓑ 22   Ⓒ 26   Ⓓ 39

51. Graph the solution set of the following system of inequalities.

$$\begin{cases} x - 3y \le 6 \\ 2x + y > 5 \end{cases}$$

52. Simplify the expression. Show your work.

$$\sqrt{16x^2y^{12}}$$

53. What is the vertex of the graph of $f(x) = a|bx - 1| + c$? Explain your answer.

54. A company produces two types of doghouses, regular and deluxe. A regular doghouse requires 7 hours to build and 3 hours to paint. A deluxe doghouse requires 11 hours to build and 4 hours to paint. The company employs 5 builders and 2 painters. Each employee can work a maximum of 40 hours.

  a. Write a system of inequalities that can be used to find the number of each type of doghouse built in a week. Define the variables you use in your system.

  b. Graph the solution set of your system of inequalities from part (a). Label each line in your graph.

  c. A regular doghouse sells for $100. A deluxe doghouse sells for $200. How many of each can be built, painted, and sold in one week to maximize sales?

55. Consider the function $f(x) = \frac{1}{x}$.

  a. Graph $f(x)$.

  b. Explain how the graph of $g(x) = \frac{4}{x + 2}$ compares to the graph of $f(x)$.

  c. What is the horizontal asymptote (if any) of the graph of $g(x)$?

  d. What is the vertical asymptote of the graph of $g(x)$? Explain how this relates to the domain of $g(x)$.

56. Consider the recursive model shown below.

$$\begin{cases} a_1 = 5 \\ a_{n+1} = a_n - 7 \end{cases}$$

What is an explicit formula for this sequence?

  Ⓕ $a_n = -7 + 5n$

  Ⓖ $a_n = 5 - 7n$

  Ⓗ $a_n = -7 + 5(n - 1)$

  Ⓘ $a_n = 5 - 7(n - 1)$

57. An arch in the shape of the upper half of an ellipse supports a bridge that spans a distance of 80 ft. The maximum height of the arch is 30 ft. To the nearest tenth of a foot, what is the height of the arch 28 ft from the center?

  Ⓐ 14.4 ft   Ⓒ 28.1 ft

  Ⓑ 21.4 ft   Ⓓ 29.7 ft

58. A scientist wants to study the affects of a new medication on acne. Which type of study would give the most reliable results?

  Ⓕ Controlled experiment

  Ⓖ Observational study

  Ⓗ Survey

  Ⓘ Random sample

59. Suppose scores on an entry exam are normally distributed. The exam has a mean score of 140 and a standard deviation of 20. What is the probability that a person who took the test scored between 120 and 160?

  Ⓐ 14%   Ⓒ 68%

  Ⓑ 40%   Ⓓ 95%

60. What is $\cos \theta$ when $\sin \theta = \frac{3}{5}$ and θ is in Quadrant II?

  Ⓕ $-\frac{4}{5}$ Ⓗ $\frac{2}{5}$

  Ⓖ $-\frac{2}{5}$ Ⓘ $\frac{4}{5}$

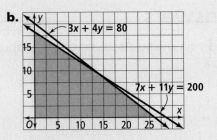

b.

c. 0 regular doghouses, 18 deluxe doghouses

[3] one minor computational error

[2] correct answers; missing work or explanation

[1] only 1 portion of the item answered correctly

55. [4] a.

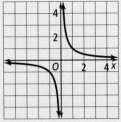

b. The factor of 4 multiplies the y-values of $f(x)$ by 4 and stretches the graph vertically. Adding 2 shifts the graph 2 units to the left.

c. $y = 0$

d. $x = -2$; The vertical asymptote occurs at the x-value omitted from the domain.

[3] one minor computational error

[2] correct answers; missing work or explanation

[1] only 1 portion of the item answered correctly

56. I

57. B

58. F

59. C

60. F

50. B

51. [2]

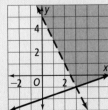

[1] one minor error

52. [2] $\sqrt{16x^2y^{12}} = \sqrt{4^2x^2(y^6)^2}$
$$= 4y^6|x|$$

[1] one minor computational error

53. [2] $\left(\frac{1}{b}, c\right)$; The x-value of the vertex makes the expression inside the absolute value zero. The solution to $bx - 1 = 0$ is $\frac{1}{b}$. The y-value of the vertex is $f\left(\frac{1}{b}\right) = c$.

[1] missing explanation

54. [4] a. $x =$ number of regular doghouses

$y =$ number of deluxe doghouses

$$\begin{cases} 7x + 11y \le 200 \\ 3x + 4y \le 80 \end{cases}$$

Answers

61. B

62. I

63. A

64. H

65. C

66. F

67. D

68. H

69. C

70. G

71. B

72. I

---

61. An equation of an ellipse is $9(x + 9)^2 + 4(y + 4)^2 = 36$. What is the y-coordinate of the center of the ellipse?

Ⓐ −9　　Ⓑ −4　　Ⓒ 4　　Ⓓ 9

62. What is the determinant of the matrix?

$$\begin{bmatrix} 1 & 3 & -1 \\ 1 & 2 & 1 \\ -2 & -5 & -4 \end{bmatrix}$$

Ⓕ −8　　Ⓗ 0

Ⓖ −4　　Ⓘ 4

63. Write the expression as a single logarithm.
$4\log_3 x + \log_3 y - 2\log_3 z$

Ⓐ $\log_3 \dfrac{x^4 y}{z^2}$

Ⓒ $\log_3 (4x + y - 2z)$

Ⓑ $\dfrac{\log_3 x^4 y}{\log_3 z^2}$

Ⓓ $\log_3 (x^4 + y - z^2)$

64. A computer manufacturing company sampled two different parts and tested for defects. The results are shown in the table below.

	Part A	Part B
Defective	14	33
Not defective	266	312

What is the probability that if a Part B is randomly chosen, it is defective?

Ⓕ 5.28%　　Ⓗ 9.57%

Ⓖ 5.71%　　Ⓘ 10.58%

65. The graph of the hyperbola
$\dfrac{(x - 2)^2}{25} - \dfrac{(y - 3)^2}{9} = 1$
is shown at the right.

How does the graph of
$\dfrac{(x - 2)^2}{9} - \dfrac{(y - 3)^2}{25} = 1$
differ from this graph?

Ⓐ The asymptotes are less steep.

Ⓑ The foci become $(-1, 3)$ and $(5, 3)$.

Ⓒ The vertices become $(-1, 3)$ and $(5, 3)$.

Ⓓ The transverse axis becomes vertical.

66. What is 64° in radians? Round your answer to the nearest hundredth.

Ⓕ 1.12　　Ⓗ 10.19

Ⓖ 5.63　　Ⓘ 402.12

67. A set of data has a normal distribution with a mean of 72 and a standard deviation of 6. What percent of data is greater than 84?

Ⓐ 84%　　Ⓒ 13.5%

Ⓑ 50%　　Ⓓ 2.35%

68. An employee's initial salary is $30,000. The person receives a 5% raise at the end of each year. What is the formula for the term s_n which represents the salary at the beginning of the nth year?

Ⓕ $s_n = 30{,}000 + 1.05n$

Ⓖ $s_n = 30{,}000 + 5(n - 1)$

Ⓗ $s_n = 30{,}000(1.05)^{n-1}$

Ⓘ $s_n = 30{,}000(1.05)^n$

69. Use the Change of Base Formula to approximate the value of $\log_2 3.2$ to the nearest tenth.

Ⓐ 0.2　　Ⓒ 1.7

Ⓑ 0.8　　Ⓓ 9.2

70. If $B = \begin{bmatrix} -2 & 1 \\ 4 & -1 \end{bmatrix}$, what is B^{-1}?

Ⓕ $\begin{bmatrix} -0.5 & 1 \\ 0.25 & -1 \end{bmatrix}$

Ⓗ $\begin{bmatrix} 2 & -1 \\ -4 & 1 \end{bmatrix}$

Ⓖ $\begin{bmatrix} 0.5 & 0.5 \\ 2 & 1 \end{bmatrix}$

Ⓘ $\begin{bmatrix} 4 & -1 \\ -2 & 1 \end{bmatrix}$

71. Which expression is equivalent to $(\sin \theta)(\sec \theta)$?

Ⓐ $\cos \theta$　　Ⓒ $\sin \theta$

Ⓑ $\tan \theta$　　Ⓓ $\csc \theta$

72. The magnitude M of an earthquake can be found using the equation $M(x) = \log\left(\frac{x}{0.001}\right)$ where x represents the seismograph reading of the earthquake in mm. An earthquake has a magnitude of 6.2. What is the seismograph reading of the earthquake in mm?

Ⓕ 0.0062　　Ⓗ 1.014

Ⓖ 0.0008　　Ⓘ 1584.9

73. Which function has a period of 4π and an amplitude of 6?

Ⓐ $y = -6\sin 8\theta$

Ⓑ $y = 6\sin 2\theta$

Ⓒ $y = 3\sin 6\theta$

Ⓓ $y = -6\sin\frac{1}{2}\theta$

74. Which equation represents a circle with center $(-4, -6)$ and radius 6?

Ⓕ $(x - 4)^2 + (y - 6)^2 = 36$

Ⓖ $(x + 4)^2 + (y + 6)^2 = 36$

Ⓗ $(x + 4)^2 + (y + 6)^2 = 6$

Ⓘ $(x - 4)^2 + (y - 6)^2 = 6$

75. What is the exact value of $\tan 240°$?

Ⓐ $\frac{\sqrt{2}}{2}$ Ⓒ 1

Ⓑ $\frac{\sqrt{3}}{3}$ Ⓓ $\sqrt{3}$

76. Multiply $\begin{bmatrix} 4 & -1 \\ 0 & 5 \end{bmatrix} \cdot \begin{bmatrix} 1 & 3 \\ -6 & 1 \end{bmatrix}$.

Ⓕ $\begin{bmatrix} 4 & 14 \\ -24 & 11 \end{bmatrix}$ Ⓗ $\begin{bmatrix} 10 & -30 \\ 11 & 5 \end{bmatrix}$

Ⓖ $\begin{bmatrix} 4 & -3 \\ 0 & 5 \end{bmatrix}$ Ⓘ $\begin{bmatrix} 10 & 11 \\ -30 & 5 \end{bmatrix}$

77. Consider the vectors **u** and **v** below.

a. Show the addition of the two vectors graphically. Label your answer **w**.

b. Using your answer from part (a), find $-0.5\mathbf{w}$.

78. Solve for x. Show or explain your work.

$2\ln 4x + 5 = 8$

79. A pendulum initially swings through an arc that is 20 inches long. On each swing, the length of the arc is 0.85 of the previous swing.

a. Write a recursive model of geometric decay to represent the sequence of lengths of the arc of each swing. Let $p_1 = 20$.

b. Rewrite your model from part (a) using an explicit formula.

c. What is the approximate total distance the pendulum has swung after 11 swings? Show your work.

d. What is the total distance, approximately, that the pendulum has swung when it stops? Show your work.

80. The equation of an ellipse is $4x^2 + 9y^2 + 8x - 54y + 49 = 0$.

a. Write the equation in standard form. Show your work.

b. What are the foci and vertices of the ellipse? Show your work or explain your answer.

c. Graph the ellipse. Label the center of the ellipse on your graph.

81. Consider the following system of equations.

$$\begin{cases} x + 2z = -1 \\ y - 2z = 2 \\ 2x + y + z = 1 \end{cases}$$

a. Represent the system of equations using the matrix equation $AX = B$.

b. Find the determinant of the matrix A.

c. Solve the equation from part (a). If it cannot be solved, use your result from part (b) to explain why.

82. Consider the function $f(x) = 2\cos(4x)$.

a. What are the period and amplitude of the graph of $f(x)$?

b. Graph $f(x)$ over two periods.

c. Solve $f(x) = 0.5$ algebraically. Show your work and give your answer in radians.

b. $a = 3, b = 2$

$c = \sqrt{9 - 4}$

Foci: $(-1 \pm \sqrt{5}, 3)$

Vertices: $(-1 \pm 3, 3)$

c.

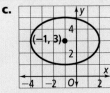

[3] one minor computational error

[2] correct answers; missing work or explanation

[1] only 1 portion of the item answered correctly

81. [4] a. $\begin{bmatrix} 1 & 0 & 2 \\ 0 & 1 & -2 \\ 2 & 1 & 1 \end{bmatrix} \cdot \begin{bmatrix} x \\ y \\ z \end{bmatrix} = \begin{bmatrix} -1 \\ 2 \\ 1 \end{bmatrix}$

b. -1

c. $x = 1, y = 0, z = -1$

[3] one minor computational error

[2] correct answers; missing work or explanation

[1] only 1 portion of the item answered correctly

82. [4] a. period: $\frac{\pi}{2}$

amplitude: 2

b.

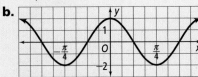

c. $0.5 = 2\cos(4x)$

$0.25 = \cos(4x)$

$2n\pi \pm \cos^{-1}(0.25) = 4x$

$2n\pi \pm 1.318 \approx 4x$

$n\frac{\pi}{2} \pm 0.33 \approx x$

0.33 radians

[3] one minor computational error

[2] correct answers; missing work or explanation

[1] only 1 portion of the item answered correctly

73. D

74. G

75. D

76. I

77. [2] a.

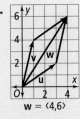

$w = \langle 4, 6 \rangle$

b. $\langle -2, -3 \rangle$

[1] one minor computational error

78. [2] $2\ln 4x = 3$

$\ln 4x = \frac{3}{2}$

$4x = e^{\frac{3}{2}}$

$x = \frac{e^{\frac{3}{2}}}{4}$

[1] correct answer; missing work or explanation

79. [4] a. $p_1 = 20; p_n = 0.85p_{n-1}, n > 1$

b. $p_n = 20(0.85)^{n-1}$

c. $1\,s_{11} = 20 \cdot \frac{1 - (0.85)^{11}}{1 - 0.85}$

$\approx 20 \cdot \frac{0.83266}{0.15}$

≈ 111 in.

d. 113 in.

[3] one minor computational error

[2] correct answers; missing work or explanation

[1] only 1 portion of the item answered correctly

80. [4] a. $4x^2 + 8x + 9y^2 - 54y = -49$

$4(x^2 + 2x + 1) + 9(y^2 - 6y + 9)$

$= -49 + 4 + 81$

$4(x + 1)^2 + 9(y - 3)^2 = 36$

$\frac{(x + 1)^2}{9} + \frac{(y - 3)^2}{4} = 1$

Skills Handbook Contents

Skills **Handbook**

Percents and Percent Applications

Percent means "per hundred." Find fraction, decimal, and percent equivalents by replacing one symbol for *hundredths* with another.

Example 1

Write each number as a percent.

a. $0.082 = 8.2\%$

Move the decimal point two places to the right and write a percent sign.

b. $\frac{3}{5} = \frac{60}{100} = 60\%$

Write the fraction as hundredths. Then replace the hundredths with a percent sign.

c. $1\frac{1}{6} = \frac{7}{6} = 1.166\overline{6} = 116.\overline{6}\%$

First, use $7 \div 6$ to write $1\frac{1}{6}$ as a decimal.

Example 2

Write each percent as a decimal.

a. $50\% = 0.50 = 0.5$

Move the decimal point two places to the left and drop the percent sign.

b. $\frac{1}{2}\% = 0.5\% = 00.5\% = 0.005$

Example 3

Use an equation to solve each percent problem.

a. What is 30% of 12?

$n = 0.3 \times 12$

$n = 3.6$

b. 18 is 0.3% of what?

$18 = 0.003 \times n$

$\frac{18}{0.003} = \frac{0.003n}{0.003}$

$6000 = n$

c. What percent of 60 is 9?

$n \times 60 = 9$

$60n = 9$

$n = \frac{9}{60} = 0.15 = 15\%$

Exercises

Write each decimal as a percent and each percent as a decimal.

1. 0.46   **2.** 1.506   **3.** 0.007   **4.** 8%   **5.** 103.5%   **6.** 3.3%

Write each fraction or mixed number as a percent.

7. $\frac{1}{4}$ **8.** $\frac{3}{8}$ **9.** $\frac{2}{3}$ **10.** $\frac{4}{9}$ **11.** $1\frac{3}{20}$ **12.** $\frac{1}{200}$

Use an equation to solve each percent problem. Round your answer to the nearest tenth, if necessary.

13. What is 25% of 50?   **14.** What percent of 58 is 37?   **15.** 120% of what is 90?

16. 8 is what percent of 40?   **17.** 15 is 75% of what?   **18.** 80% of 58 is what?

Answers

Percents and Percent Applications

1. 46%   **2.** 1150.6%

3. 0.7%   **4.** 0.08

5. 1.035   **6.** 0.033

7. 25%   **8.** 37.5%

9. 66.$\overline{6}$%   **10.** 44.$\overline{4}$%

11. 115%   **12.** 0.5%

13. 12.5   **14.** 63.8%

15. 75   **16.** 20%

17. 20%   **18.** 46.4

Operations With Fractions

To add or subtract fractions, use a common denominator. The common denominator is the least common multiple of the denominators.

Example 1

Simplify $\frac{2}{3} + \frac{3}{5}$.

$\frac{2}{3} + \frac{3}{5} = \frac{2}{3} \cdot \frac{5}{5} + \frac{3}{5} \cdot \frac{3}{3}$ For 3 and 5, the least common multiple is 15.

$\qquad = \frac{10}{15} + \frac{9}{15}$ Write $\frac{2}{3}$ and $\frac{3}{5}$ as equivalent fractions with denominators of 15.

$\qquad = \frac{19}{15}$ or $1\frac{4}{15}$ Add the numerators.

Example 2

Simplify $5\frac{1}{4} - 3\frac{2}{3}$.

$5\frac{1}{4} - 3\frac{2}{3} = 5\frac{3}{12} - 3\frac{8}{12}$ Write equivalent fractions.

$\qquad = 4\frac{15}{12} - 3\frac{8}{12}$ Write $5\frac{3}{12}$ as $4\frac{15}{12}$ so you can subtract the fractions.

$\qquad = 1\frac{7}{12}$ Subtract the fractions. Then subtract the whole numbers.

To multiply fractions, multiply the numerators and multiply the denominators. You can simplify by using a greatest common factor.

Example 3

Simplify $\frac{3}{4} \cdot \frac{8}{11}$

Method 1 $\frac{3}{4} \cdot \frac{8}{11} = \frac{24}{44} = \frac{24 \div 4}{44 \div 4} = \frac{6}{11}$ **Method 2** $\frac{3}{\cancel{4}} \cdot \frac{\cancel{8}^{2}}{11} = \frac{6}{11}$

Divide 24 and 44 by 4, their greatest common factor.   Divide 4 and 8 by 4, their greatest common factor.

To divide fractions, use a reciprocal to change the problem to multiplication.

Example 4

Simplify $3\frac{1}{5} \div 1\frac{1}{2}$

$3\frac{1}{5} \div 1\frac{1}{2} = \frac{16}{5} \div \frac{3}{2}$ Write mixed numbers as improper fractions.

$\qquad = \frac{16}{5} \cdot \frac{2}{3}$ Multiply by the reciprocal of the divisor.

$\qquad = \frac{32}{15}$ or $2\frac{2}{15}$ Simplify.

Exercises

Perform the indicated operation.

1. $\frac{3}{5} + \frac{4}{5}$ 2. $\frac{1}{2} + \frac{2}{3}$ 3. $4\frac{1}{2} + 2\frac{1}{3}$ 4. $5\frac{3}{4} + 4\frac{2}{5}$ 5. $\frac{2}{3} - \frac{3}{7}$

6. $5\frac{1}{2} - 3\frac{2}{5}$ 7. $7\frac{3}{4} - 4\frac{4}{5}$ 8. $3\frac{4}{5} \cdot 10$ 9. $2\frac{1}{2} \cdot 3\frac{1}{5}$ 10. $6\frac{3}{4} \cdot 5\frac{2}{3}$

11. $\frac{1}{2} \div \frac{1}{3}$ 12. $\frac{6}{5} \div \frac{3}{5}$ 13. $8\frac{1}{2} \div 4\frac{1}{4}$ 14. $\frac{8}{9} - \frac{2}{3}$ 15. $5\frac{1}{4} \cdot 8$

Operations With Fractions

1. $1\frac{2}{5}$ 2. $1\frac{1}{6}$

3. $6\frac{5}{6}$ 4. $10\frac{3}{20}$

5. $\frac{5}{21}$ 6. $2\frac{1}{10}$

7. $2\frac{19}{20}$ 8. 38

9. 8   10. $38\frac{1}{4}$

11. $1\frac{1}{2}$ 12. 2

13. 2   14. $\frac{2}{9}$

15. 42

Ratios and Proportions

A *ratio* is a comparison of two quantities by division. You can write *equal ratios* by multiplying or dividing each quantity by the same nonzero number.

Ways to Write a Ratio
$a : b$ a to b $\frac{a}{b}$ $(b \neq 0)$

Example 1

Write $3\frac{1}{3} : \frac{1}{2}$ as a ratio in simplest form.

$$3\frac{1}{3} : \frac{1}{2} \rightarrow \frac{3\frac{1}{3}}{\frac{1}{2}} = \frac{20}{3} \text{ or } 20 : 3$$

$\times 6$ (top) $\times 6$ (bottom)

In simplest form, both terms should be integers.
Multiply by the common denominator, 6.

A rate is a ratio that compares different types of quantities. In simplest form for a rate, the second quantity is one unit.

Example 2

Write 247 mi in 5.2 h as a rate in simplest form.

$$\frac{247 \text{ mi}}{5.2 \text{ h}} = \frac{47.5 \text{ mi}}{1 \text{ h}} \text{ or } 47.5 \text{ mi/h}$$

$\div 5.2$ Divide by 5.2 to make the second quantity one unit.

A proportion is a statement that two ratios are equal. You can find a missing term in a proportion by using the cross products.

Cross Products of a Proportion
$\frac{a}{b} = \frac{c}{d} \rightarrow ad = bc$

Example 3

The Copy Center charges \$2.52 for 63 copies. At that rate, how much will the Copy Center charge for 140 copies?

$$\begin{array}{l} \text{cost} \rightarrow \\ \text{copies} \rightarrow \end{array} \quad \frac{2.52}{63} = \frac{c}{140} \qquad \text{Set up a proportion.}$$

$$2.52 \cdot 140 = 63c \qquad \text{Use cross products.}$$

$$c = \frac{2.52 \cdot 140}{63} \qquad \text{Solve for } c.$$

$$= 5.6 \text{ or } \$5.60$$

Exercises

Write each ratio or rate in simplest form.

1. 15 to 20 **2.** $85 : 34$ **3.** 38 g in 4 oz **4.** 375 mi in 4.3 h **5.** $\frac{84}{30}$

Solve each proportion. Round your answer to the nearest tenth, if necessary.

6. $\frac{a}{5} = \frac{12}{15}$ **7.** $\frac{21}{12} = \frac{14}{x}$ **8.** $8 : 15 = n : 25$ **9.** $2.4 : c = 4 : 3$ **10.** $\frac{17}{8} = \frac{n}{20}$

11. $\frac{13}{n} = \frac{20}{3}$ **12.** $5 : 7 = y : 5$ **13.** $\frac{0.4}{3.5} = \frac{5.2}{x}$ **14.** $\frac{4}{x} = \frac{7}{6}$ **15.** $4 : n = n : 9$

16. A canary's heart beats 130 times in 12 s. Use a proportion to find about how many times its heart beats in 50 s.

Answers

Ratios and Proportions

1. 3 to 4   **2.** $5 : 2$

3. 19 g in 2 oz

4. approximately 87.2 mi in 1 h

5. $\frac{14}{5}$ **6.** 4

7. 8   **8.** $13.\overline{3}$

9. 1.8   **10.** 42.5

11. 1.95   **12.** 3.6

13. 45.5   **14.** 3.4

15. ± 6 **16.** about 542 times

Simplifying Expressions With Integers

To add two numbers with the same sign, *add* their absolute values. The sum has the same sign as the numbers. To add two numbers with different signs, find the *difference* between their absolute values. The sum has the same sign as the number with the greater absolute value.

Example 1

Add.

a. $-8 + (-5) = -13$ **b.** $-8 + 5 = -3$ **c.** $8 + (-5) = 3$

To subtract a number, add its opposite.

Example 2

Subtract.

a. $4 - 7 = 4 + (-7)$ **b.** $-4 - (-7) = -4 + 7$ **c.** $-4 - 7 = -4 + (-7)$
$\quad\quad = -3$ $= 3$ $= -11$

The product or quotient of two numbers with the same sign is positive. The product or quotient of two numbers with different signs is negative.

Example 3

Multiply or divide.

a. $(-3)(-5) = 15$ **b.** $-35 \div 7 = -5$ **c.** $24 \div (-6) = -4$

Example 4

Simplify $2^2 - 3(4 - 6) - 12$.

$$2^2 - 3(4 - 6) - 12 = 2^2 - 3(-2) - 12$$
$$= 4 - 3(-2) - 12$$
$$= 4 - (-6) - 12$$
$$= 4 + 6 - 12 = -2$$

Order of Operations

1. Perform any operation(s) inside grouping symbols.
2. Simplify any terms with exponents.
3. Multiply and divide in order from left to right.
4. Add and subtract in order from left to right.

Exercises

Simplify each expression.

1. $-4 + 5$ **2.** $12 - 12$ **3.** $-15 + (-23)$ **4.** $4 - 17$ **5.** $-5 - 12$

6. $3 - (-5)$ **7.** $-8 - (-12)$ **8.** $-19 + 5$ **9.** $(-7)(-4)$ **10.** $-120 \div 30$

11. $(-3)(4)$ **12.** $75 \div (-3)$ **13.** $(-6)(15)$ **14.** $(18)(-4)$ **15.** $-84 \div (-7)$

16. $-2(1 + 5) + (-3)(2)$ **17.** $-4(-2 - 5) + 3(1 - 4)$ **18.** $20 - (3)(12) + 4^2$

19. $\frac{-15}{-5} - \frac{36}{-12} + \frac{-12}{-4}$ **20.** $5^2 - 6(5 - 9)$ **21.** $(-3 + 2^3)(4 + \frac{-42}{7})$

Simplifying Expressions With Integers

1. 1   **2.** 0

3. -38 **4.** -13

5. -17 **6.** 8

7. 4   **8.** -14

9. 28   **10.** -4

11. -12 **12.** -25

13. -90 **14.** -72

15. 12   **16.** -18

17. 19   **18.** 0

19. 9   **20.** 49

21. -10

Area and Volume

The *area* of a plane figure is the number of square units contained in the figure.
The *volume* of a space figure is the number of cubic units contained in the figure.
Formulas for area and volume are listed on page 693.

Example 1

Find the area of each figure.

a.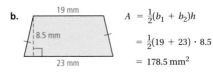

$$A = \pi r^2$$
$$\approx \frac{22}{7} \cdot \left(\frac{21}{10}\right)^2$$
$$= \frac{693}{50} = 13\frac{43}{50} \text{ in.}^2$$

b.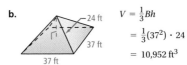

$$A = \frac{1}{2}(b_1 + b_2)h$$
$$= \frac{1}{2}(19 + 23) \cdot 8.5$$
$$= 178.5 \text{ mm}^2$$

Example 2

Find the volume of each figure.

a.

$$V = \frac{4}{3}\pi r^3$$
$$\approx \frac{4}{3} \cdot 3.14 \cdot 2.7^3$$
$$= 82.40616 \approx 82.4 m^3$$

b.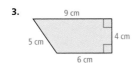

$$V = \frac{1}{3}Bh$$
$$= \frac{1}{3}(37^2) \cdot 24$$
$$= 10,952 \text{ ft}^3$$

Exercises

Find the exact area of each figure.

1. 4 m, 7 m

2. $3\frac{3}{4}$ ft, $3\frac{3}{4}$ ft

3. 9 cm, 5 cm, 4 cm, 6 cm

4. 10 in.

Find the exact volume of each figure.

5. $4\frac{1}{2}$ ft, $4\frac{1}{2}$ ft, $4\frac{1}{2}$ ft

6. 8 m

7. 12 in., 5 in.

8. 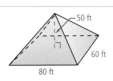 50 ft, 60 ft, 80 ft

9. Find the area of a triangle with a base of 17 in. and a height of 13 in.

10. Find the volume of a rectangular box 64 cm long, 48 cm wide, and 58 cm high.

11. Find the surface area of the cube in Exercise 5.

Answers

Area and Volume

1. 14 m^2
2. $14\frac{1}{16}$ ft^2
3. 30 cm^2
4. 25π in.^{2}
5. $91\frac{1}{8}$ ft^3
6. $\frac{2048}{3}\pi$ m^3
7. 100π in.^{3}
8. 80,000 ft^3
9. 110.5 in.^{2}
10. 178,176 cm^3
11. $121\frac{1}{2}$ ft^2

The Coordinate Plane, Slope, and Midpoint

The *coordinate plane* is formed when two perpendicular number lines intersect at a point called the origin, forming four quadrants.

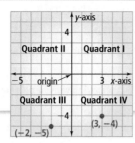

Example 1

In which quadrant would you find each point?

a. $(3, -4)$ Move 3 units right and 4 units down. The point is in Quadrant IV.

b. $(-2, -5)$ Move 2 units left and 5 units down. The point is in Quadrant III.

To find the slope of a line on the coordinate plane, choose two points on the line and use the slope formula.

Example 2

Find the slope of each line.

a.
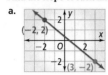
$$m = \frac{y_2 - y_1}{x_2 - x_1}$$
$$= \frac{2 - (-2)}{-2 - 3}$$
$$= \frac{4}{-5} \text{ or } -\frac{4}{5}$$

b.

$$m = \frac{y_2 - y_1}{x_2 - x_1}$$
$$= \frac{2 - 0}{-1 - (-1)} = \frac{2}{0}$$

Since you cannot divide by zero, this line has an undefined slope.

If (x_m, y_m) is the midpoint of the segment joining (x_1, y_1) and (x_2, y_2), then $x_m = \frac{x_1 + x_2}{2}$ and $y_m = \frac{y_1 + y_2}{2}$.

Example 3

Find the coordinates of the midpoint of the segment with endpoints $(-2, 5)$ and $(6, -3)$.

$\frac{-2 + 6}{2} = 2$ and $\frac{5 + (-3)}{2} = 1$ so the midpoint is $(2, 1)$.

Exercises

In which quadrant would you find each point? Graph each point on a coordinate plane.

1. $(3, 2)$ **2.** $(-4, 3)$ **3.** $(2, -3)$ **4.** $(4, -2)$ **5.** $(-4, -5)$ **6.** $(-1, -3)$

Find the slope of each line.

7.

8.

9.

10. the line containing $(-3, 4)$ and $(2, -6)$

11. the line containing $(25, 40)$ and $(100, 55)$

Find the midpoint of the segment with the given endpoints.

12. $(-4, 4), (2, -5)$ **13.** $(3, 3), (7, -6)$ **14.** $(-1, -8), (0, -3)$ **15.** $(3, 4), (2, -6)$

The Coordinate Plane, Slope, and Midpoint

1. I

2. II

3. IV

4. IV

5. III

6. III

7. $\frac{4}{5}$

8. -1

9. 0

10. -2

11. $\frac{1}{5}$

12. $\left(-1, -\frac{1}{2}\right)$

13. $\left(5, -\frac{3}{2}\right)$

14. $\left(-\frac{1}{2}, -\frac{11}{2}\right)$

15. $\left(\frac{5}{2}, -1\right)$

Operations With Exponents

An exponent indicates how many times a number is used as a factor.

	$2^n = \blacksquare$	$10^n = \blacksquare$
	$2^2 = 4$	$10^2 = 100$
	$2^1 = 2$	$10^1 = 10$
	$2^0 = 1$	$10^0 = 1$
	$2^{-1} = \frac{1}{2}$	$10^{-1} = \frac{1}{10}$
	$2^{-2} = \frac{1}{4}$	$10^{-2} = \frac{1}{100}$

Example 1

Write using exponents.

a. $3 \cdot 3 \cdot 3 \cdot 3 \cdot 3 = 3^5$ **b.** $a \cdot a \cdot b \cdot b \cdot b \cdot b = a^2b^4$

The patterns shown at the right indicate that $a^0 = 1$ and that $a^{-n} = \frac{1}{a^n}$.

Example 2

Write each expression so that all exponents are positive.

a. $a^{-2}b^3 = \frac{1}{a^2} \cdot b^3 = \frac{b^3}{a^2}$ **b.** $x^3y^0z^{-1} = x^3 \cdot 1 \cdot \frac{1}{z} = \frac{x^3}{z}$

You can simplify expressions that contain powers with the same base.

Example 3

Simplify each expression.

a. $b^5 \cdot b^3 = b^{5+3}$ Add exponents to multiply
$= b^8$ powers with the same base.

b. $\frac{x^5}{x^7} = x^{5-7}$ Subtract exponents to divide
$= x^{-2} = \frac{1}{x^2}$ powers with the same base.

You can simplify expressions that contain parentheses and exponents.

Example 4

Simplify each expression.

a. $\left(\frac{ab}{n}\right)^3 = \frac{a^3b^3}{n^3}$ Raise each factor in the parentheses to the third power.

b. $(c^2)^4 = c^{2 \cdot 4} = c^8$ Multiply exponents to raise a power to a power.

Exercises

Write each expression using exponents.

1. $x \cdot x \cdot x$ **2.** $x \cdot x \cdot x \cdot y \cdot y$ **3.** $a \cdot a \cdot a \cdot a \cdot b$ **4.** $\frac{a \cdot a \cdot a \cdot a}{b \cdot b}$

Write each expression so that all exponents are positive.

5. c^{-4} **6.** $m^{-2}n^0$ **7.** $x^5y^{-7}z^{-3}$ **8.** $ab^{-1}c^2$

Simplify each expression. Use positive exponents.

9. d^2d^6 **10.** $\frac{a^5}{a^2}$ **11.** $\frac{c^7}{c}$ **12.** $\frac{n^3}{n^6}$ **13.** $\frac{a^5b^3}{ab^8}$ **14.** $(3x)^2$

15. $\left(\frac{a}{b}\right)^4$ **16.** $\left(\frac{xz}{y}\right)^6$ **17.** $(c^3)^4$ **18.** $\left(\frac{x^2}{y^5}\right)^3$ **19.** $(u^4v^2)^3$ **20.** $(p^5)^{-2}$

21. $\frac{(2a^4)(3a^2)}{6a^3}$ **22.** $(x^{-2})^3$ **23.** $(mg^3)^{-1}$ **24.** $g^{-3}g^{-1}$ **25.** $\frac{(3a^3)^2}{18a}$ **26.** $\frac{c^3d^7}{c^{-3}d^{-1}}$

Answers

Operations With Exponents

1. x^3 **2.** x^3y^2

3. a^4b **4.** $\frac{a^4}{b^2}$

5. $\frac{1}{c^4}$ **6.** $\frac{1}{m^2}$

7. $\frac{x^5}{y^7z^3}$ **8.** $\frac{ac^2}{b}$

9. d^8 **10.** a^3

11. c^6 **12.** $\frac{1}{n^3}$

13. $\frac{a^4}{b^5}$ **14.** $9x^2$

15. $\frac{a^4}{b^4}$ **16.** $\frac{x^6z^6}{y^6}$

17. c^{12} **18.** $\frac{x^6}{y^{15}}$

19. $u^{12}v^6$ **20.** $\frac{1}{p^{10}}$

21. a^3 **22.** $\frac{1}{x^6}$

23. $\frac{1}{mg^3}$ **24.** $\frac{1}{g^4}$

25. $\frac{a^5}{2}$ **26.** c^6d^8

Factoring and Operations With Polynomials

Example 1

Perform each operation.

a. $(3y^2 - 4y + 5) + (y^2 + 9y)$

$= (3y^2 + y^2) + (-4y + 9y) + 5$ To add, group like terms.

$= 4y^2 + 5y + 5$

b. $(n + 4)(n - 3)$

$= n(n) + n(-3) + 4(n) + 4(-3)$ Distribute n and 4.

$= n^2 - 3n + 4n - 12$ Combine like terms.

$= n^2 + n - 12$

To factor a polynomial, first find the greatest common factor (GCF) of the terms. Then use the distributive property to factor out the GCF.

Example 2

Factor $6x^3 - 12x^2 + 18x$.

$6x^3 = 6 \cdot x \cdot x \cdot x;\ -12x^2 = 6 \cdot (-2) \cdot x \cdot x;\ 18x = 6 \cdot 3 \cdot x$ List the factors of each term. The GCF is 6x.

$6x^3 - 12x^2 + 18x = 6x(x^2) + 6x(-2x) + 6x(3)$ Use the distributive property to factor out 6x.

$\qquad\qquad\qquad = 6x(x^2 - 2x + 3)$

When a polynomial is the product of two binomials, you can work backward to find the factors.

$x^2 + bx + c = (x + \blacksquare)(x + \blacksquare)$

— The *sum* of these numbers must equal b.
— The *product* of these numbers must equal c.

Example 3

Factor $x^2 - 13x + 36$.

Choose numbers that are factors of 36. Look for a pair with the sum -13.

The numbers -4 and -9 have a product of 36 and a sum of -13. The factors are $(x - 4)$ and $(x - 9)$. So, $x^2 - 13x + 36 = (x - 4)(x - 9)$.

Factors	Sum
$-6 \cdot (-6)$	-12
$-4 \cdot (-9)$	-13

Exercises

Perform the indicated operations.

1. $(x^2 + 3x - 1) + (7x - 4)$

2. $(5y^2 + 7y) - (3y^2 + 9y - 8)$

3. $4x^2(3x^2 - 5x + 9)$

4. $-5d(13d^2 + 7d + 8)$

5. $(x - 5)(x + 3)$

6. $(n - 7)(n - 2)$

Factor each polynomial.

7. $a^2 - 8a + 12$

8. $n^2 - 2n - 8$

9. $x^2 + 5x + 4$

10. $3m^2 - 9$

11. $y^2 + 5y - 24$

12. $s^3 + 6s^2 + 11s$

13. $2x^3 + 4x^2 - 8x$

14. $y^2 - 10y + 25$

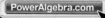
Factoring and Operations With Polynomials

1. $x^2 + 10x - 5$

2. $2y^2 - 2y + 8$

3. $12x^4 - 20x^3 + 36x^2$

4. $-65d^3 - 35d^2 - 40d$

5. $x^2 - 2x - 15$

6. $n^2 - 9n + 14$

7. $(a - 6)(a - 2)$

8. $(n - 4)(n + 2)$

9. $(x + 4)(x + 1)$

10. $3(m^2 - 3)$

11. $(y + 8)(y - 3)$

12. $s(s^2 + 6s + 11)$

13. $2x(x^2 + 2x - 4)$

14. $(y - 5)^2$

Scientific Notation and Significant Digits

In *scientific notation*, a number has the form $a \times 10^n$, where n is an integer and $1 \le a < 10$.

Example 1

Write 5.59×10^6 in standard form.

$5.59 \times 10^6 = 5\,590\,000 = 5,590,000$ A positive exponent indicates a value greater than 1.
Move the decimal point six places to the right.

Example 2

Write 0.0000318 in scientific notation.

$0.0000318 = 3.18 \times 10^{-5}$ Move the decimal point to create a number between 1 and 10.
Since the original number is less than 1, use a negative exponent.

When a measurement is in scientific notation, all the digits of the number between 1 and 10 are *significant digits*. When you multiply or divide measurements, your answer should have as many significant digits as the least number of significant digits in any of the numbers involved.

Example 3

Multiply $(6.71 \times 10^8 \text{ mi/h})$ and $(3.8 \times 10^4 \text{ h})$.

$(6.71 \times 10^8 \text{ mi/h})(3.8 \times 10^4 \text{ h}) = (6.71 \cdot 3.8)(10^8 \cdot 10^4)$ Rearrange factors.
$= 25.498 \times 10^{12}$ Add exponents when multiplying powers of 10.
$= 2.5498 \times 10^{13}$ Write in scientific notation.
$\approx 2.5 \times 10^{13} \text{mi}$ Round to two significant digits.

three significant digits

two significant digits

Exercises

Change each number to scientific notation or to standard form.

1. 1,340,000   **2.** 6.88×10^{-2} **3.** 0.000775   **4.** 0.0072   **5.** 1.113×10^5

6. 8.0×10^{-4} **7.** 1895   **8.** 2.3×10^3 **9.** 123,400   **10.** 7.985×10^4

Write each product or quotient in scientific notation. Round to the appropriate number of significant digits.

11. $(1.6 \times 10^2)(4.0 \times 10^3)$ **12.** $(2.5 \times 10^{-3})(1.2 \times 10^4)$ **13.** $(4.237 \times 10^4)(2.01 \times 10^{-2})$

14. $\dfrac{7.0 \times 10^5}{2.89 \times 10^3}$ **15.** $\dfrac{1.4 \times 10^4}{8.0 \times 10^2}$ **16.** $\dfrac{6.48 \times 10^6}{3.2 \times 10^5}$

17. $(1.78 \times 10^{-7})(5.03 \times 10^{-5})$ **18.** $(7.2 \times 10^{11})(5 \times 10^6)$ **19.** $(8.90 \times 10^8) \div (2.36 \times 10^{-2})$

20. $(3.95 \times 10^4) \div (6.8 \times 10^8)$ **21.** $(4.9 \times 10^{-8}) \div (2.7 \times 10^{-2})$ **22.** $(3.972 \times 10^{-5})(4.7 \times 10^{-4})$

Answers

Scientific Notation and Significant Digits

1. 1.34×10^6 **2.** 0.0688
3. 7.75×10^{-4} **4.** 7.2×10^{-3}
5. 111,300   **6.** 0.0008
7. 1.895×10^3 **8.** 2300
9. 1.234×10^5 **10.** 79,850
11. 6.4×10^5 **12.** 30
13. 8.52×10^2 **14.** 2.4×10^2
15. 17.5   **16.** 20
17. 8.95×10^{-12} **18.** 3.6×10^{18}
19. 3.77×10^{10} **20.** 5.8×10^{-5}
21. 1.8×10^{-6} **22.** 1.9×10^{-8}

The Pythagorean Theorem and the Distance Formula

In a right triangle, the sum of the squares of the lengths of the legs is equal to the square of the length of the hypotenuse. Use this relationship, known as the Pythagorean Theorem, to find the length of a side of a right triangle.

The Pythagorean Theorem

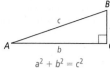

$$a^2 + b^2 = c^2$$

Example 1

Find m in the triangle below, to the nearest tenth.

$$m^2 + n^2 = k^2$$
$$m^2 + 7.8^2 = 9.6^2$$
$$m^2 = 9.6^2 - 7.8^2 = 31.32$$
$$m = \sqrt{31.32} \approx 5.6$$

To find the distance between two points on the coordinate plane, use the distance formula.

The distance d between any two points (x_1, y_1) and (x_2, y_2) is

$$d = \sqrt{(x_2 - x_1)^2 + (y_2 - y_1)^2}$$

Example 2

Find the distance between $(-3, 2)$ and $(6, -4)$.

$$d = \sqrt{(6 - (-3))^2 + (-4 - 2)^2}$$
$$= \sqrt{9^2 + (-6)^2}$$
$$= \sqrt{81 + 36}$$
$$= \sqrt{117}$$
$$\approx 10.8$$

Thus, d is about 10.8 units.

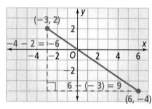

Exercises

In each problem, a and b are the lengths of the legs of a right triangle and c is the length of the hypotenuse. Find each missing length. Round your answer to the nearest tenth.

1. c if $a = 6$ and $b = 8$ **2.** a if $b = 12$ and $c = 13$ **3.** b if $a = 8$ and $c = 17$

4. c if $a = 10$ and $b = 3$ **5.** a if $b = 100$ and $c = 114$ **6.** b if $a = 12.0$ and $c = 30.1$

Find the distance between each pair of points, to the nearest tenth.

7. $(0, 0), (4, -3)$ **8.** $(-5, -5), (1, 3)$ **9.** $(-1, 0), (4, 12)$ **10.** $(-4, 2), (4, -2)$

11. $(0, 15), (17, 0)$ **12.** $(-8, 8), (8, 8)$ **13.** $(-1, 1), (1, -1)$ **14.** $(-2, 9), (0, 0)$

15. $(-5, 3), (4, 3)$ **16.** $(2, 1), (3, 4)$ **17.** $(3, -2), (3, 5)$ **18.** $(5, 4), (-3, 1)$

The Pythagorean Theorem and the Distance Formula

1. 10   **2.** 5
3. 15   **4.** 10.4
5. 54.7   **6.** 27.6
7. 5   **8.** 10
9. 13   **10.** 8.9
11. 22.7   **12.** 16
13. 2.8   **14.** 9.2
15. 9   **16.** 3.2
17. 7   **18.** 8.5

Bar and Circle Graphs

Sometimes you can draw different graphs to represent the same data, depending on the information you want to share. A *bar graph* is useful for comparing amounts; a *circle graph* is useful for comparing percents.

Example

Display the 2007 data on immigration to the United States in a bar graph and a circle graph.

To make a circle graph, first find the *percent* of the data in each category. Then express each percent as a decimal and multiply by 360° to find the size of each *central angle*.

$$\text{Africa} \rightarrow \frac{89.3}{\text{Total} \rightarrow 1003.7} \approx 0.09 \text{ or } 9\%$$

$$0.09 \times 360° \approx 32°$$

Draw a circle and use a protractor to draw each central angle.

Immigration to the United States, 2007

Place of Origin	Immigrants (1000's)
Africa	89.2
Asia	359.4
Europe	120.8
North America	331.7
South America	102.6

Source: Department of Homeland Security

To make a bar graph, place the categories along the bottom axis. Decide on a scale for the side axis. An appropriate scale would be 0–300, marked in intervals of 50. For each data item, draw a bar whose height is equal to the data value.

Immigration to the United States, 2007

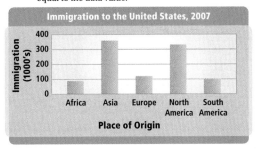

Exercises

Display the data from each table in a bar graph and a circle graph.

1. NASA Space Shuttle Expenses, 2000

Operation	Millions of Dollars
Orbiter, integration	698.8
Propulsion	1,053.1
Mission, launch operations	738.8
Flight operations	244.6
Ground operations	510.3

Source: U.S. National Aeronautics and Space Administration

2. Cable TV Revenue, 2006

	Millions of Dollars
Airtime	4,566
Basic service	42,918
Pay-per-view, premium services	13,322
Installation	729
Other	27,188

Source: U.S. Census Bureau

982

Answers

Bar and Circle Graphs

1.

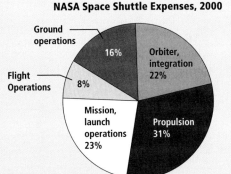

Descriptive Statistics and Histograms

For numerical data, you can find the *mean,* the *median,* and the *mode.*

Mean	The sum of the data values in a data set divided by the number of data values
Median	The middle value of a data set that has been arranged in increasing or decreasing order. If the data set has an even number of values, the median is the mean of the middle two values.
Mode	The most frequently occurring value in a data set

Example 1

Find the mean, median, and mode for the following data set.   5   7   6   3   1   7   9   5   10   7

Mean	$\dfrac{5 + 7 + 6 + 3 + 1 + 7 + 9 + 5 + 10 + 7}{10} = 6$
Median	5, 7, 6, 3, 1, 7, 9, 5, 10, 7 Rearrange the numbers from least to greatest.
	1, 3, 5, 5, 6, 7, 7, 7, 9, 10 The median is the mean of the two middle numbers, 6 and 7.
	The median is $\dfrac{6 + 7}{2} = 6.5$.
Mode	The most frequently occurring data value is 7.

The frequency of a data value is the number of times it occurs in a data set.
A *histogram* is a bar graph that shows the frequency of each data value.

Example 2

Use the survey results to make a histogram for the cost of a movie ticket at various theaters.

Survey of Movie Ticket Prices

| $7 | $8 | $7 | $9 | $8 | $9 | $8 | $10 | $8 |

Exercises

Find the mean, the median, and the mode of each data set.

1. −3 4 5 5 −2 7 1 8 9

2. 0 0 1 1 2 3 3 5 3 8 7

3. 2.4 2.4 2.3 2.3 2.4 12.0

4. 1 1 1 1 2 2 2 3 3 4

5. 1.2 1.3 1.4 1.5 1.6 1.7 1.8

6. −4 −3 −2 −1 0 1 2 3 4

Make a histogram for each data set.

7. 7 4 8 6 6 8 7 7 5 7

8. 73 75 76 75 74 75 76 74 76 75

2.

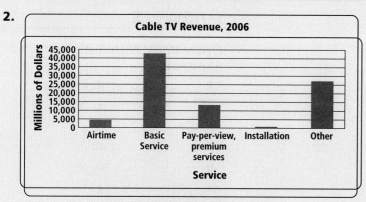

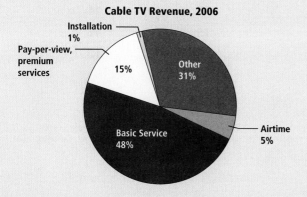

Descriptive Statistics and Histograms

1. $3.\overline{7}$; 5; 5   **2.** 3; 3; 3

3. $3.9\overline{6}$; 2.4; 2.4   **4.** 2; 2; 1

5. 1.5; 1.5; no mode

6. 0; 0; no mode

7.

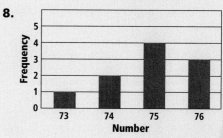

8.

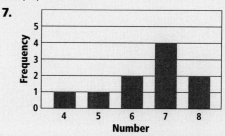

Skills Handbook   T985

Operations With Rational Expressions

A *rational expression* is an expression that can be written in the form $\frac{\text{polynominal}}{\text{polynominal}}$, where the denominator is not zero. A rational expression is in simplest form if the numerator and denominator have no common factors except 1.

Example 1

Write the expression $\frac{4x + 8}{x + 2}$ in simplest form.

$\frac{4x + 8}{x + 2} = \frac{4(x + 2)}{x + 2}$ Factor the numerator.

$= 4$ Divide out the common factor $x + 2$.

To add or subtract two rational expressions, use a common denominator.

Example 2

Simplify $\frac{x}{2y} + \frac{x}{3y}$.

$\frac{x}{2y} + \frac{x}{3y} = \frac{x}{2y} \cdot \frac{3}{3} + \frac{x}{3y} \cdot \frac{2}{2}$ The common denominator of $3y$ and $2y$ is $6y$.

$= \frac{3x}{6y} + \frac{2x}{6y}$

$= \frac{5x}{6y}$ Add the numerators.

To multiply rational expressions, first find and divide out any common factors in the numerators and the denominators. Then multiply the remaining numerators and denominators. To divide rational expressions, first use a reciprocal to change the problem to multiplication.

Example 3

Simplify $\frac{40x^2}{21} \div \frac{5x}{14}$.

$\frac{40x^2}{21} \div \frac{5x}{14} = \frac{40x^2}{21} \cdot \frac{14}{5x}$ Change dividing by $\frac{5x}{14}$ to multiplying by the reciprocal, $\frac{14}{5x}$.

$= \frac{8 \,\cancel{40x^2}^{\,1}}{3 \,\cancel{21}} \times \frac{\cancel{14}^{\,2}}{\cancel{5x}\,_1}$ Divide out the common factors 5, x, and 7.

$= \frac{16x}{3}$ Multiply the numerators ($8x \cdot 2$). Multiply the denominators ($3 \cdot 1$).

Exercises

Write each expression in simplest form.

1. $\frac{4a^2 b}{12ab^3}$ 2. $\frac{5n + 15}{n + 3}$ 3. $\frac{x - 7}{2x - 14}$ 4. $\frac{28c^2(d - 3)}{35c(d - 3)}$

Perform the indicated operation.

5. $\frac{3x}{2} + \frac{5x}{2}$ 6. $\frac{3x}{8} + \frac{5x}{8}$ 7. $\frac{5}{h} - \frac{3}{h}$ 8. $\frac{6}{11p} - \frac{9}{11p}$ 9. $\frac{3x}{5} - \frac{x}{2}$

10. $\frac{13}{2x} - \frac{13}{3x}$ 11. $\frac{7x}{5} + \frac{5x}{7}$ 12. $\frac{5a}{b} + \frac{3a}{5b}$ 13. $\frac{7x}{8} \cdot \frac{32x}{35}$ 14. $\frac{3x^2}{2} \cdot \frac{6}{x}$

15. $\frac{8x^2}{5} \cdot \frac{10}{x^3}$ 16. $\frac{7x}{8} \cdot \frac{64}{14x}$ 17. $\frac{16}{3x} \div \frac{5}{3x}$ 18. $\frac{4x}{5} \div \frac{16}{15x}$ 19. $\frac{x^3}{8} \div \frac{x^2}{16}$

Answers

Operations With Rational Expressions

1. $\frac{a}{3b^2}$ 2. 5

3. $\frac{1}{2}$ 4. $\frac{4c}{5}$

5. $4x$ 6. x

7. $\frac{2}{h}$ 8. $\frac{-3}{11p}$

9. $\frac{x}{10}$ 10. $\frac{13}{6x}$

11. $\frac{74x}{35}$ 12. $\frac{28a}{5b}$

13. $\frac{4x^2}{5}$ 14. $9x$

15. $\frac{16}{x}$ 16. 4

17. $\frac{16}{5}$ 18. $\frac{3x^2}{4}$

19. $2x$

Reference

Table 1 **Measures**

Length	**United States Customary**	**Metric**
Length	12 inches (in.) = 1 foot (ft) 36 in. = 1 yard (yd) 3 ft = 1 yard 5280 ft = 1 mile (mi) 1760 yd = 1 mile	10 millimeters (mm) = 1 centimeter (cm) 100 cm = 1 meter (m) 1000 mm = 1 meter 1000 m = 1 kilometer (km)
Area	144 square inches (in.²) = 1 square foot (ft²) 9 ft² = 1 square yard (yd²) 43,560 ft² = 1 acre (a) 4840 yd² = 1 acre	100 square millimeters (mm²) = 1 square centimeter (cm²) 10,000 cm² = 1 square meter (m²) 10,000 m² = 1 hectare (ha)
Volume	1728 cubic inches (in.³) = 1 cubic foot (ft³) 27 ft³ = 1 cubic yard (yd³)	1000 cubic millimeters (mm³) = 1 cubic centimeter (cm³) 1,000,000 cm³ = 1 cubic meter (m³)
Liquid Capacity	8 fluid ounces (fl oz) = 1 cup (c) 2 c = 1 pint (pt) 2 pt = 1 quart (qt) 4 qt = 1 gallon (gal)	1000 milliliters (mL) = 1 liter (L) 1000 L = 1 kiloliter (kL)
Weight or Mass	16 ounces (oz) = 1 pound (lb) 2000 pounds = 1 ton (t)	1000 milligrams (mg) = 1 gram (g) 1000 g = 1 kilogram (kg) 1000 kg = 1 metric ton
Temperature	32°F = freezing point of water 98.6°F = normal human body temperature 212°F = boiling point of water	0°C = freezing point of water 37°C = normal human body temperature 100°C = boiling point of water

	Customary Units and Metric Units	
Length	1 in. ≈ 2.54 cm 1 ft ≈ 0.305 m 1 mi ≈ 1.61 km	1 cm ≈ 0.39 in. 1 m ≈ 3.28 ft 1 km ≈ 0.62 mi
Area	1 acre ≈ 0.40 ha	1 ha ≈ 2.47 acres
Capacity	1 qt ≈ 0.95 L	1 L ≈ 1.06 qt
Weight and Mass	1 oz ≈ 28.4 g 1 lb ≈ 0.45 kg	1 g ≈ 0.035 oz 1 kg ≈ 2.205 lb

	Time		
60 seconds (s) = 1 minute (min) 60 minutes = 1 hour (h) 24 hours = 1 day (d) 7 days = 1 week (wk)	4 weeks (approx.) = 1 month (mo) 365 days = 1 year (yr) 52 weeks (approx.) = 1 year	12 months = 1 year 10 years = 1 decade 100 years = 1 century	

Table 2 **Reading Math Symbols**

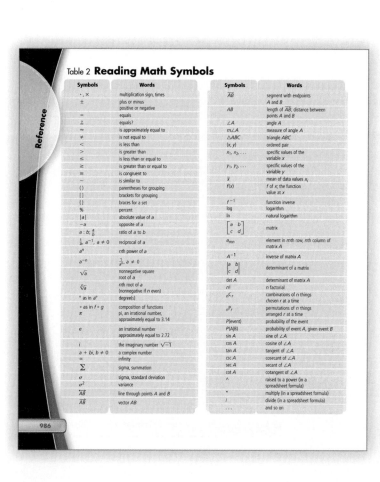

Symbols	Words
$\cdot$, $\times$	multiplication sign, times
$\pm$	plus or minus positive or negative
$=$	equals
$\stackrel{?}{=}$	equals?
$\approx$	is approximately equal to
$\neq$	is not equal to
$<$	is less than
$>$	is greater than
$\leq$	is less than or equal to
$\geq$	is greater than or equal to
$\cong$	is congruent to
$\sim$	is similar to
( )	parentheses for grouping
[ ]	brackets for grouping
{ }	braces for a set
%	percent
$|a|$	absolute value of a
$-a$	opposite of a
$a:b$; $\frac{a}{b}$	ratio of a to b
$\frac{1}{a}$, a^{-1}, $a \neq 0$	reciprocal of a
a^p	nth power of a
a^{-n}	$\frac{1}{a^n}$, $a \neq 0$
$\sqrt{a}$	nonnegative square root of a
$\sqrt[n]{a}$	nth root of a (nonnegative if n even)
" as in a°	degree(s)
$\circ$ as in $f \circ g$	composition of functions
π	pi, an irrational number, approximately equal to 3.14
e	an irrational number approximately equal to 2.72
i	the imaginary number $\sqrt{-1}$
$a + bi$, $b \neq 0$	a complex number
∞	infinity
Σ	sigma, summation
σ	sigma, standard deviation
σ^2	variance
$\overleftrightarrow{AB}$	line through points A and B
$\overrightarrow{AB}$	vector AB

Symbols	Words
$\overline{AB}$	segment with endpoints A and B
AB	length of $\overline{AB}$; distance between points A and B
$\angle A$	angle A
$m\angle A$	measure of angle A
$\triangle ABC$	triangle ABC
(x, y)	ordered pair
$x_1, x_2, \ldots$	specific values of the variable x
$y_1, y_2, \ldots$	specific values of the variable y
$\bar{x}$	mean of data values x_i
$f(x)$	f of x; the function value at x
f^{-1}	function inverse
log	logarithm
ln	natural logarithm
$\begin{bmatrix} a & b \\ c & d \end{bmatrix}$	matrix
a_{mn}	element in mth row, nth column of matrix A
A^{-1}	inverse of matrix A
$\begin{vmatrix} a & b \\ c & d \end{vmatrix}$	determinant of a matrix
det A	determinant of matrix A
$n!$	n factorial
$_nC_r$	combinations of n things chosen r at a time
$_nP_r$	permutations of n things arranged r at a time
P(event)	probability of the event
$P(A|B)$	probability of event A, given event B
sin A	sine of $\angle A$
cos A	cosine of $\angle A$
tan A	tangent of $\angle A$
csc A	cosecant of $\angle A$
sec A	secant of $\angle A$
cot A	cotangent of $\angle A$
$\wedge$	raised to a power (in a spreadsheet formula)
*	multiply (in a spreadsheet formula)
/	divide (in a spreadsheet formula)
$\ldots$	and so on

Properties and **Formulas**

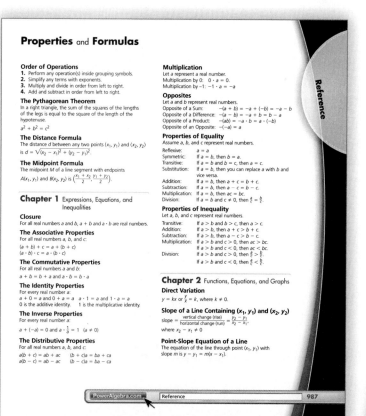

Order of Operations
1. Perform any operation(s) inside grouping symbols.
2. Simplify any terms with exponents.
3. Multiply and divide in order from left to right.
4. Add and subtract in order from left to right.

The Pythagorean Theorem
In a right triangle, the sum of the squares of the lengths of the legs is equal to the square of the length of the hypotenuse.
$$a^2 + b^2 = c^2$$

The Distance Formula
The distance d between any two points (x_1, y_1) and (x_2, y_2) is $d = \sqrt{(x_2 - x_1)^2 + (y_2 - y_1)^2}$.

The Midpoint Formula
The midpoint M of a line segment with endpoints $A(x_1, y_1)$ and $B(x_2, y_2)$ is $\left(\frac{x_1 + x_2}{2}, \frac{y_1 + y_2}{2}\right)$.

Chapter 1 Expressions, Equations, and Inequalities

Closure
For all real numbers a and b, $a + b$ and $a \cdot b$ are real numbers.

The Associative Properties
For all real numbers a, b, and c:
$(a + b) + c = a + (b + c)$
$(a \cdot b) \cdot c = a \cdot (b \cdot c)$

The Commutative Properties
For all real numbers a and b:
$a + b = b + a$ and $a \cdot b = b \cdot a$

The Identity Properties
For every real number a:
$a + 0 = a$ and $0 + a = a$ $a \cdot 1 = a$ and $1 \cdot a = a$
0 is the additive identity.   1 is the multiplicative identity.

The Inverse Properties
For every real number a:
$a + (-a) = 0$ and $a \cdot \frac{1}{a} = 1$ $(a \neq 0)$

The Distributive Properties
For all real numbers a, b, and c:
$a(b + c) = ab + ac$ $(b + c)a = ba + ca$
$a(b - c) = ab - ac$ $(b - c)a = ba - ca$

Multiplication
Let a represent a real number.
Multiplication by 0: $0 \cdot a = 0$.
Multiplication by -1: $-1 \cdot a = -a$

Opposites
Let a and b represent real numbers.
Opposite of a Sum: $-(a + b) = -a + (-b) = -a - b$
Opposite of a Difference: $-(a - b) = -a + b = b - a$
Opposite of a Product: $-(ab) = -a \cdot b = a \cdot (-b)$
Opposite of an Opposite: $-(-a) = a$

Properties of Equality
Assume a, b, and c represent real numbers.
Reflexive:	$a = a$
Symmetric:	If $a = b$, then $b = a$.
Transitive:	If $a = b$ and $b = c$, then $a = c$.
Substitution:	If $a = b$, then you can replace a with b and vice versa.
Addition:	If $a = b$, then $a + c = b + c$.
Subtraction:	If $a = b$, then $a - c = b - c$.
Multiplication:	If $a = b$, then $ac = bc$.
Division:	If $a = b$ and $c \neq 0$, then $\frac{a}{c} = \frac{b}{c}$.

Properties of Inequality
Let a, b, and c represent real numbers.
Transitive:	If $a > b$ and $b > c$, then $a > c$.
Addition:	If $a > b$, then $a + c > b + c$.
Subtraction:	If $a > b$, then $a - c > b - c$.
Multiplication:	If $a > b$ and $c > 0$, then $ac > bc$. If $a > b$ and $c < 0$, then $ac < bc$.
Division:	If $a > b$ and $c > 0$, then $\frac{a}{c} > \frac{b}{c}$. If $a > b$ and $c < 0$, then $\frac{a}{c} < \frac{b}{c}$.

Chapter 2 Functions, Equations, and Graphs

Direct Variation
$y = kx$ or $\frac{y}{x} = k$, where $k \neq 0$.

Slope of a Line Containing (x_1, y_1) and (x_2, y_2)
$$\text{slope} = \frac{\text{vertical change (rise)}}{\text{horizontal change (run)}} = \frac{y_2 - y_1}{x_2 - x_1}$$
where $x_2 - x_1 \neq 0$

Point-Slope Equation of a Line
The equation of the line through point (x_1, y_1) with slope m is $y - y_1 = m(x - x_1)$.

Reference

Function Families

Assume a, k, and h are positive numbers.

Parent	$y = f(x)$
Reflection across x-axis	$y = -f(x)$
Vertical stretch $(a > 1)$ Vertical shrink $(0 < a < 1)$	$y = af(x)$
Translation	
horizontal to left by h	$y = f(x + h)$
horizontal to right by h	$y = f(x - h)$
vertical up by k	$y = f(x) + k$
vertical down by k	$y = f(x) - k$

Chapter 4 Quadratic Functions and Equations

Quadratic Functions

Parent	$y = x^2$
Reflection across x-axis	$y = -x^2$
Stretch $(a > 1)$ Shrink $(0 < a < 1)$	$y = ax^2$
Translation horizontal by h vertical by k	$y = (x - h)^2 + k$
Vertex Form	$y = a(x - h)^2 + k$
Standard Form	$y = f(x) = ax^2 + bx + c$

The graph is a parabola that opens up if $a > 0$ and down if $a < 0$.
The vertex is (h, k) (Vertex Form) and $\left(-\frac{b}{2a}, f\left(-\frac{b}{2a}\right)\right)$ (Standard Form).
The axis of symmetry is $x = h$ (Vertex Form) and $x = -\frac{b}{2a}$ (Standard Form).

Factoring Perfect-Square Trinomials

$a^2 + 2ab + b^2 = (a + b)^2$
$a^2 - 2ab + b^2 = (a - b)^2$

Factoring a Difference of Two Squares

$a^2 - b^2 = (a + b)(a - b)$

Multiplication Property of Square Roots

For any numbers $a \geq 0$ and $b \geq 0$, $\sqrt{ab} = \sqrt{a} \cdot \sqrt{b}$.

Division Property of Square Roots

For any numbers $a \geq 0$ and $b > 0$, $\sqrt{\frac{a}{b}} = \frac{\sqrt{a}}{\sqrt{b}}$.

Zero-Product Property

If $ab = 0$, then $a = 0$ or $b = 0$.

The Quadratic Formula

If $ax^2 + bx + c = 0$, then $x = \frac{-b \pm \sqrt{b^2 - 4ac}}{2a}$

Discriminant

The discriminant of a quadratic equation in the form $ax^2 + bx + c = 0$ is $b^2 - 4ac$.

$b^2 - 4ac > 0 \Rightarrow$ two real solutions
$b^2 - 4ac = 0 \Rightarrow$ one real solution
$b^2 - 4ac < 0 \Rightarrow$ two complex solutions

Square Root of a Negative Real Number

For any positive number a,
$\sqrt{-a} = \sqrt{-1 \cdot a} = \sqrt{-1} \cdot \sqrt{a} = i\sqrt{a}$.
Example: $\sqrt{-5} = i\sqrt{5}$
Note that
$(\sqrt{-5})^2 = (i\sqrt{5})^2 = i^2(\sqrt{5})^2 = -1 \cdot 5 = -5$ (not 5).

Chapter 5 Polynomials and Polynomial Functions

End Behavior of a Polynomial Function

The end behavior of a polynomial function of degree n with leading term ax^n:

a	n	end behavior
positive	even	up and up
positive	odd	down and up
negative	even	down and down
negative	odd	up and down

Factor Theorem

The expression $x - a$ is a linear factor of a polynomial if and only if the value a is a zero of the related polynomial function.

Remainder Theorem

If you divide a polynomial $P(x)$ of degree $n \geq 1$ by $x - a$, then the remainder is $P(a)$.

Factoring a Sum or Difference of Cubes

$a^3 + b^3 = (a + b)(a^2 - ab + b^2)$
$a^3 - b^3 = (a - b)(a^2 + ab + b^2)$

Rational Root Theorem

Let $P(x) = a_nx^n + a_{n-1}x^{n-1} + \cdots + a_1x + a_0$ be a polynomial with integer coefficients.
Integer roots of $P(x) = 0$ must be factors of a_0.
Rational roots have reduced form $\frac{p}{q}$ where p is an integer factor of a_0 and q is an integer factor of a_n.

Conjugate Root Theorems

Suppose $P(x)$ is a polynomial with *rational* coefficients.
If $a + \sqrt{b}$ is an irrational root with a and b rational, then $a - \sqrt{b}$ is also a root.

Suppose $P(x)$ is a polynomial with *real* coefficients.
If $a + bi$ is a complex root with a and b real, then $a - bi$ is also a root.

Fundamental Theorem of Algebra

If $P(x)$ is a polynomial of degree $n \geq 1$, then $P(x) = 0$ has exactly n roots, including multiple and complex roots.

Binomial Theorem

For every positive integer n, $(a + b)^n =$
$P_0a^n + P_1a^{n-1}b + P_2a^{n-2}b^2 + \cdots + P_{n-1}ab^{n-1} + P_nb^n$
where $P_0, P_1, \ldots, P_n$ are the numbers in the nth row of Pascal's Triangle.

Chapter 6 Radical Functions and Rational Exponents

Properties of Exponents

For any nonzero number a and any integers m and n,

$a^0 = 1$	$(ab)^n = a^nb^n$
$\frac{a^m}{a^n} = a^{m-n}$	$a^m \cdot a^n = a^{m+n}$
$a^{-n} = \frac{1}{a^n}$	$(a^m)^n = a^{mn}$
	$\left(\frac{a}{b}\right)^n = \frac{a^n}{b^n}$

*n*th Roots of *n*th Powers

For any real number a,

$$\sqrt[n]{a^n} = \begin{cases} a \text{ if } n \text{ is odd} \\ |a| \text{ if } n \text{ is even} \end{cases}$$

Combining Radical Expressions: Products

If $\sqrt[n]{a}$ and $\sqrt[n]{b}$ are real numbers, then $\sqrt[n]{a} \cdot \sqrt[n]{b} = \sqrt[n]{ab}$.

Combining Radical Expressions: Quotients

If $\sqrt[n]{a}$ and $\sqrt[n]{b}$ are real numbers and $b \neq 0$, then $\frac{\sqrt[n]{a}}{\sqrt[n]{b}} = \sqrt[n]{\frac{a}{b}}$.

Properties of Rational Exponents

If the nth root of a is a real number and m is an integer, then $a^{\frac{1}{n}} = \sqrt[n]{a}$ and $a^{\frac{m}{n}} = \sqrt[n]{a^m} = \left(\sqrt[n]{a}\right)^m$. If m is negative, $a \neq 0$.

Composition of Inverse Functions

If f and f^{-1} are inverse functions, then $(f^{-1} \circ f)(x) = x$ and $(f \circ f^{-1})(x) = x$ for x in the domains of f and f^{-1}, respectively.

Radical Functions

	Square Root	nth Root
Parent	$y = \sqrt{x}$	$y = \sqrt[n]{x}$
Reflection across x-axis	$y = -\sqrt{x}$	$y = -\sqrt[n]{x}$
Stretch $(a > 1)$ Shrink $(0 < a < 1)$	$y = a\sqrt{x}$	$y = a\sqrt[n]{x}$
Translation horizontal by h vertical by k	$y = \sqrt{x - h} + k$	$y = \sqrt[n]{x - h} + k$

Chapter 7 Exponential and Logarithmic Functions

Exponential Functions

Parent, $b > 0, b \neq 1$	$y = b^x$
Reflection across x-axis	$y = -b^x$
Stretch $(a > 1)$ Shrink $(0 < a < 1)$	$y = ab^x$
Translation horizontal by h vertical by k	$y = b^{x-h} + k$

Continuously Compounded Interest

$A(t) = P \cdot e^{rt}$, where $A(t)$ represents the total, P represents the principal, r represents the interest rate, and t represents time in years.

Logarithmic Functions

	Base b	Base e
Parents, $b > 0, b \neq 1$	$y = \log_b x$	$y = \ln x$
Reflection across x-axis	$y = -\log_b x$	$y = -\ln x$
Stretch $(a > 1)$ Shrink $(0 < a < 1)$	$y = a \log_b x$	$y = a \ln x$
Translation horizontal by h vertical by k	$y = \log_b (x - h) + k$	$y = \ln (x - h) + k$

Properties of Logarithms

For any positive numbers m, n, and b where $b \neq 1$

Product Property:	$\log_b mn = \log_b m + \log_b n$
Quotient Property:	$\log_b \frac{m}{n} = \log_b m - \log_b n$
Power Property:	$\log_b m^n = n \log_b m$

Change of Base Formula

For any positive numbers, m, b, and c, with $b \neq 1$ and $c \neq 1$, $\log_b m = \frac{\log_c m}{\log_c b}$.

Chapter 8 Rational Functions

Inverse Variation

$xy = k$, $y = \frac{k}{x}$, or $x = \frac{k}{y}$, where $k \neq 0$.

Combined Variation

z varies jointly with x and y: $z = kxy$
z varies jointly with x and y and inversely with w: $z = \frac{kxy}{w}$
z varies directly with x and inversely with the product wy: $z = \frac{kx}{wy}$

Reciprocal Functions

Parent	$y = \frac{1}{x}, x \neq 0$
Reflection across x-axis	$y = -\frac{1}{x}, x \neq 0$
Stretch $(a > 1)$ Shrink $(0 < a < 1)$	$y = \frac{a}{x}, x \neq 0$
Translation horizontal by h vertical by k	$y = \frac{a}{x-h} + k, x \neq h$
Asymptotes	$y = k$ (horiz.), $x = h$ (vert.)

Chapter 9 Sequences and Series

Arithmetic Mean of Two Numbers

$\frac{x + y}{2}$

Arithmetic Sequence

A recursive definition for an arithmetic sequence with a starting value a and a common difference d has two parts:
$a_1 = a$: initial condition
$a_{n+1} = a_n + d$, for $n \geq 1$: recursive formula
An explicit definition for this sequence is the formula:
$a_n = a + (n - 1)d$ for $n \geq 1$.

Geometric Sequence

A recursive definition for a geometric sequence with a starting value a and a common ratio r has two parts:
$a_1 = a$: initial condition
$a_{n+1} = a_n \cdot r$, for $n \geq 1$: recursive formula
An explicit definition for this sequence is the formula:
$a_n = ar^{n-1}$, for $n \geq 1$.

Sum of a Finite Arithmetic Series

The sum S_n of a finite arithmetic series
$a_1 + a_2 + a_3 + \cdots + a_n$ is $S_n = \frac{n}{2}(a_1 + a_n)$
where a_1 is the first term, a_n is the nth term, and n is the number of terms.

Sum of a Finite Geometric Series

The sum S_n of a finite geometric series
$a_1 + a_1r + a_1r^2 + \cdots + a_1r^{n-1}$ is $S_n = \frac{a_1(1 - r^n)}{1 - r}$
where a_1 is the first term, r is the common ratio, and n is the number of terms.

Sum of an Infinite Geometric Series

An infinite geometric series with $|r| < 1$ converges to the sum S given by the following formula:
$S = \frac{a_1}{1 - r}$.

Chapter 10 Quadratic Relations and Conic Sections

Parabolas

Vertical	Vertex (0, 0)	Vertex (h, k)
Equation	$y = \frac{1}{4c}x^2$	$y = \frac{1}{4c}(x - h)^2 + k$
Focus	$(0, c)$	$(h, c + k)$
Directrix	$y = -c$	$y = -c + k$
Horizontal	**Vertex (0, 0)**	**Vertex (h, k)**
Equation	$x = \frac{1}{4c}y^2$	$x = \frac{1}{4c}(y - k)^2 + h$
Focus	$(c, 0)$	$(c + h, k)$
Directrix	$x = -c$	$x = -c + h$

Circles, radius = *r*

	Center (0, 0)	Center (h, k)
Equation	$x^2 + y^2 = r^2$	$(x - h)^2 + (y - k)^2 = r^2$

Ellipses

Horizontal, $a > b$	Center (0, 0)	Center (h, k)
Equation	$\frac{x^2}{a^2} + \frac{y^2}{b^2} = 1$	$\frac{(x - h)^2}{a^2} + \frac{(y - k)^2}{b^2} = 1$
Vertices	$(\pm a, 0)$	$(\pm a + h, k)$
Co-Vertices	$(0, \pm b)$	$(h, \pm b + k)$
Foci, $c^2 = a^2 - b^2$	$(\pm c, 0)$	$(\pm c + h, k)$
Major axis	$y = 0$	$y = k$
Minor axis	$x = 0$	$x = h$

Vertical, $a > b$	Center (0, 0)	Center (h, k)
Equation	$\frac{x^2}{b^2} + \frac{y^2}{a^2} = 1$	$\frac{(x - h)^2}{b^2} + \frac{(y - k)^2}{a^2} = 1$
Vertices	$(0, \pm a)$	$(h, \pm a + k)$
Co-Vertices	$(\pm b, 0)$	$(\pm b + h, k)$
Foci, $c^2 = a^2 - b^2$	$(0, \pm c)$	$(h, \pm c + k)$
Major axis	$x = 0$	$x = h$
Minor axis	$y = 0$	$y = k$

Hyperbolas

Horizontal, $a > b$	Center (0, 0)	Center (h, k)
Equation	$\frac{x^2}{a^2} - \frac{y^2}{b^2} = 1$	$\frac{(x - h)^2}{a^2} - \frac{(y - k)^2}{b^2} = 1$
Vertices	$(\pm a, 0)$	$(\pm a + h, k)$
Foci, $c^2 = a^2 + b^2$	$(\pm c, 0)$	$(\pm c + h, k)$
Transverse axis	$y = 0$	$y = k$
Asymptotes	$y = \pm\frac{b}{a}x$	$y = \pm\frac{b}{a}(x - h) + k$

Vertical, $a > b$	Center (0, 0)	Center (h, k)
Equation	$\frac{y^2}{a^2} - \frac{x^2}{b^2} = 1$	$\frac{(y - k)^2}{a^2} - \frac{(x - h)^2}{b^2} = 1$
Vertices	$(0, \pm a)$	$(h, \pm a + k)$
Foci, $c^2 = a^2 + b^2$	$(0, \pm c)$	$(h, \pm c + k)$
Transverse axis	$x = 0$	$x = h$
Asymptotes	$y = \pm\frac{a}{b}x$	$y = \pm\frac{a}{b}(x - h) + k$

Chapter 11 Probability and Statistics

Fundamental Counting Principle

If event M can occur in m ways and is followed by event N that can occur in n ways, then event M followed by event N can occur in $m \cdot n$ ways.

Number of Permutations

The number of permutations of n items of a set arranged r items at a time is
${}_nP_r = \frac{n!}{(n - r)!}$ for $0 \leq r \leq n$.

Number of Combinations

The number of combinations of n items of a set chosen r items at a time is
${}_nC_r = \frac{n!}{r!(n - r)!}$ for $0 \leq r \leq n$.

Probability of *A* and *B*

If A and B are independent events, then
$P(A \text{ and } B) = P(A) \cdot P(B)$.

Probability of *A* or *B*

$P(A \text{ or } B) = P(A) + P(B) - P(A \text{ and } B)$
If A and B are mutually exclusive events, then
$P(A \text{ or } B) = P(A) + P(B)$.

Conditional Probability

For any two events A and B with $P(A) \neq 0$, the probability of event B, given event A, is:
$P(B|A) = \frac{P(A \text{ and } B)}{P(A)}$

Mean, Variance, and Standard Deviation

Mean: $\bar{x} = \frac{x_1 + x_2 + x_3 + \cdots + x_n}{n}$
Variance: $\sigma^2 = \frac{\Sigma(x - \bar{x})^2}{n}$
Standard deviation: $\sigma = \sqrt{\frac{\Sigma(x - \bar{x})^2}{n}}$

Binomial Probability

For repeated independent trials, each with a probability of success p and a probability of failure q (with $p + q = 1$), the probability of x successes in n trials is $P(x) = {}_nC_xp^xq^{n-x}$.

Binomial Theorem Using Combinations

For every positive integer n, use the combinations formula ${}_nC_r$ to expand $(a + b)^n$:
$(a + b)^n = {}_nC_0a^n + {}_nC_1a^{n-1}b + {}_nC_2a^{n-2}b^2 + \cdots + {}_nC_{n-1}ab^{n-1} + {}_nC_nb^n$

Chapter 12 Matrices

Properties of Matrix Addition

If A, B, and C are $m \times n$ matrices, then

Closure Property:	$A + B$ is an $m \times n$ matrix
Commutative Property:	$A + B = B + A$
Associative Property:	$(A + B) + C = A + (B + C)$
Identity Property:	There is a unique $m \times n$ matrix O such that $O + A = A + O = A$
Inverse Property:	For each A, there is a unique opposite, $-A$, such that $A + (-A) = O$

Properties of Scalar Multiplication

If A and B are $m \times n$ matrices, c and d are scalars, and O is the $m \times n$ zero matrix, then

Closure Property:	cA is an $m \times n$ matrix
Associative Property:	$(cd)A = c(dA)$
Distributive Property:	$c(A + B) = cA + cB$ $(c + d)A = cA + dA$
Identity Property:	$1 \cdot A = A$
Property of Zero:	$0 \cdot A = O$ and $cO = O$

Properties of Matrix Multiplication

If A, B, and C are $n \times n$ matrices and O is the $n \times n$ zero matrix, then

Closure Property:	AB is an $n \times n$ matrix
Associative Property:	$(AB)C = A(BC)$
Distributive Property:	$A(B + C) = AB + AC$ $(B + C)A = BA + CA$
Property of Zero:	$OA = AO = O$

Determinants of 2 × 2 and 3 × 3 Matrices

The determinant of a 2×2 matrix $\begin{bmatrix} a & b \\ c & d \end{bmatrix}$ is $ad - bc$.

The determinant of a 3×3 matrix $\begin{bmatrix} a_1 & b_1 & c_1 \\ a_2 & b_2 & c_2 \\ a_3 & b_3 & c_3 \end{bmatrix}$ is
$a_1b_2c_3 + b_1c_2a_3 + c_1a_2b_3 - (a_3b_2c_1 + b_3c_2a_1 + c_3a_2b_1)$

Inverse of a 2 × 2 Matrix

If $A = \begin{bmatrix} a & b \\ c & d \end{bmatrix}$ and $\det A \neq 0$,
then the inverse of A is
$A^{-1} = \frac{1}{\det A}\begin{bmatrix} d & -b \\ -c & a \end{bmatrix} = \frac{1}{ad - bc}\begin{bmatrix} d & -b \\ -c & a \end{bmatrix}$.

Chapter 13 Periodic Functions and Trigonometry

Convert Between Radians and Degrees

Use the proportion $\frac{d°}{180°} = \frac{r \text{ radians}}{\pi \text{ radians}}$ to convert between radians and degrees.

To convert degrees to radians, multiply by $\frac{\pi \text{ radians}}{180°}$.

To convert radians to degrees, multiply by $\frac{180°}{\pi \text{ radians}}$.

Length of an Intercepted Arc

For a circle of radius r and a central angle of measure θ (in radians), the length s of the intercepted arc is $s = r\theta$.

Sine and Cosine Functions

	Sine	Cosine
Parents	$y = \sin x$	$y = \cos x$
Reflection across x-axis	$y = -\sin x$	$y = -\cos x$
Amplitude $\lvert a \rvert$	$y = a \sin x$	$y = a \cos x$
Period $\frac{2\pi}{b}, b > 0$	$y = \sin bx$	$y = \cos bx$
Translation horizontal by h vertical by k	$y = \sin (x - h) + k$	$y = \cos (x - h) + k$

Tangent Function

Parent	$y = \tan x$
Reflection across x-axis	$y = -\tan x$
Period $\frac{\pi}{b}$	$y = \tan bx$
Translation horizontal by h vertical by k	$y = \tan (x - h) + k$
Asymptotes ($\tan bx$)	$x = n\frac{\pi}{2b}$, n odd

Chapter 14 Trigonometric Identities and Equations

Basic Identities

Reciprocal Identities:

$\csc \theta = \frac{1}{\sin \theta}$ $\sec \theta = \frac{1}{\cos \theta}$ $\tan \theta = \frac{1}{\cot \theta}$

$\sin \theta = \frac{1}{\csc \theta}$ $\cos \theta = \frac{1}{\sec \theta}$ $\cot \theta = \frac{1}{\tan \theta}$

Tangent Identity: Cotangent Identity:

$\tan \theta = \frac{\sin \theta}{\cos \theta}$ $\cot \theta = \frac{\cos \theta}{\sin \theta}$

Pythagorean Identities

$\cos^2 \theta + \sin^2 \theta = 1$ $1 + \tan^2 \theta = \sec^2 \theta$ $\cot^2 \theta + 1 = \csc^2 \theta$

Area of a Triangle

In $\triangle ABC$ with a, b, and c the lengths of the sides opposite $\angle A$, $\angle B$, and $\angle C$, respectively,

Area $\triangle ABC = \frac{1}{2}bc \sin A = \frac{1}{2}ac \sin B = \frac{1}{2}ab \sin C$.

Law of Sines

In $\triangle ABC$ with a, b, and c the lengths of the sides opposite $\angle A$, $\angle B$, and $\angle C$, respectively,

$\frac{\sin A}{a} = \frac{\sin B}{b} = \frac{\sin C}{c}$.

Law of Cosines

In $\triangle ABC$ with a, b, and c the lengths of the sides opposite $\angle A$, $\angle B$, and $\angle C$, respectively,

$a^2 = b^2 + c^2 - 2bc \cdot \cos A$
$b^2 = a^2 + c^2 - 2ac \cdot \cos B$
$c^2 = a^2 + b^2 - 2ab \cdot \cos C$

Negative Angle Identities

$\sin (-\theta) = -\sin \theta$ $\cos (-\theta) = \cos \theta$ $\tan (-\theta) = -\tan \theta$

Cofunction Angle Identities

$\sin \left(\frac{\pi}{2} - \theta \right) = \cos \theta$ $\cos \left(\frac{\pi}{2} - \theta \right) = \sin \theta$ $\tan \left(\frac{\pi}{2} - \theta \right) = \cot \theta$

Angle Difference Identities

$\sin (A - B) = \sin A \cos B - \cos A \sin B$
$\cos (A - B) = \cos A \cos B + \sin A \sin B$
$\tan (A - B) = \frac{\tan A - \tan B}{1 + \tan A \tan B}$

Angle Sum Identities

$\sin (A + B) = \sin A \cos B + \cos A \sin B$
$\cos (A + B) = \cos A \cos B - \sin A \sin B$
$\tan (A + B) = \frac{\tan A + \tan B}{1 - \tan A \tan B}$

Double-Angle Identities

$\cos 2\theta = \cos^2 \theta - \sin^2 \theta$ $\sin 2\theta = 2 \sin \theta \cos \theta$
$\cos 2\theta = 2 \cos^2 \theta - 1$ $\tan 2\theta = \frac{2 \tan \theta}{1 - \tan^2 \theta}$
$\cos 2\theta = 1 - 2 \sin^2 \theta$

Half-Angle Identities

$\sin \frac{A}{2} = \pm \sqrt{\frac{1 - \cos A}{2}}$

$\cos \frac{A}{2} = \pm \sqrt{\frac{1 + \cos A}{2}}$

$\tan \frac{A}{2} = \pm \sqrt{\frac{1 - \cos A}{1 + \cos A}}$

Formulas of Geometry

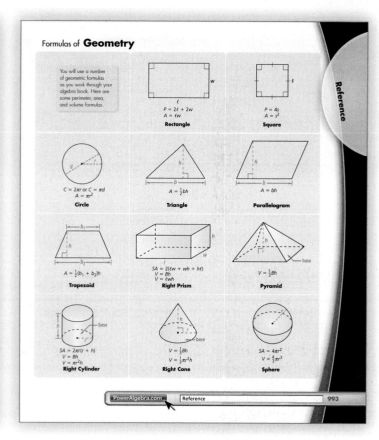

You will use a number of geometric formulas as you work through your algebra book. Here are some perimeter, area, and volume formulas.

Rectangle
$P = 2\ell + 2w$
$A = \ell w$

Square
$P = 4s$
$A = s^2$

Circle
$C = 2\pi r$ or $C = \pi d$
$A = \pi r^2$

Triangle
$A = \frac{1}{2}bh$

Parallelogram
$A = bh$

Trapezoid
$A = \frac{1}{2}(b_1 + b_2)h$

Right Prism
$SA = 2(\ell w + wh + h\ell)$
$V = Bh$
$V = \ell wh$

Pyramid
$V = \frac{1}{3}Bh$

Right Cylinder
$SA = 2\pi r(r + h)$
$V = Bh$
$V = \pi r^2 h$

Right Cone
$V = \frac{1}{3}Bh$
$V = \frac{1}{3}\pi r^2 h$

Sphere
$SA = 4\pi r^2$
$V = \frac{4}{3}\pi r^3$

English/Spanish Illustrated **Glossary**

English — A

Absolute value (p. 41) The absolute value of a real number, x, written $|x|$, is its distance from zero on the number line.

Example $|3| = 3$
$|-4| = 4$

Valor absoluto de un número real (p. 41) El valor absoluto de un número real, x, escrito como $|x|$, es su distancia desde cero en la recta numérica.

Absolute value function (p. 107) A function of the form $f(x) = |mx + b| + c$, where $m \neq 0$, is an absolute value function.

Example $f(x) = |3x - 2| + 3$
$f(x) = |2x|$

Función de valor absoluto (p. 107) Una función de la forma $f(x) = |mx + b| + c$, donde $m \neq 0$, es una función de valor absoluto.

Absolute value of a complex number (p. 249) The absolute value of a complex number is its distance from the origin on the complex number plane. In general, $|a + bi| = \sqrt{a^2 + b^2}$.

Example $|3 - 4i| = \sqrt{3^2 + (-4)^2} = 5$

Valor absoluto de un número complejo (p. 249) El valor absoluto de un número complejo es la distancia a la que está del origen en el plano de números complejo. Generalmente, $|a + bi| = \sqrt{a^2 + b^2}$.

Additive identity (p. 14) The additive identity is 0. The sum of 0 and any number is that number. The sum of opposites is 0.

Identidad aditiva (p. 14) La identidad aditiva es 0. La suma de 0 y cualquier número es ese mismo número. La suma de opuestos es 0.

Additive inverse (p. 14) The opposite or additive inverse of any number a is $-a$. The sum of opposites is 0, the additive identity.

Example $3 + (-3) = 0$
$5.2 + (-5.2) = 0$

Inverso aditivo (p. 14) El opuesto o inverso aditivo de un número a es $-a$. La suma de opuestos es 0, la identidad aditiva.

Algebraic expression (p. 5) An algebraic expression is a mathematical phrase that contains one or more variables.

Example $2x + 3$
$z - y$

Expresión algebraica (p. 5) Una expresión algebraica es una frase matemática que contiene una o más variables.

Amplitude (p. 830) The amplitude of a periodic function is half the difference between the maximum and minimum values of the function.

Example The maximum and minimum values of $y = 4 \sin x$ are 4 and -4, respectively.
amplitude $= \frac{4 - (-4)}{2} = 4$

Amplitud (p. 830) La amplitud de una función periódica es la mitad de la diferencia entre los valores máximo y mínimo de la función.

English / Spanish

Arithmetic mean (p. 574) The arithmetic mean, or average, of two numbers is their sum divided by two.

Example The arithmetic mean of 12 and 15 is $\frac{12 + 15}{2} = 13.5$.

Media aritmética (p. 574) La media aritmética, o promedio, de dos números es su suma dividida por dos.

Arithmetic sequence (p. 572) An arithmetic sequence is a sequence with a constant difference between consecutive terms.

Example The arithmetic sequence 1, 5, 9, 13, . . . has a common difference of 4.

Secuencia aritmética (p. 572) Una secuencia aritmética es una secuencia de números en la que la diferencia entre dos números consecutivos es constante.

Arithmetic series (p. 587) An arithmetic series is a series whose terms form an arithmetic sequence.

Example $1 + 5 + 9 + 13 + 17 + 21$ is an arithmetic series with six terms.

Serie aritmética (p. 587) Una serie aritmética es una serie cuyos términos forman una progresión aritmética.

Asymptote (p. 435) An asymptote is a line that a graph approaches as x or y increases in absolute value.

Example The function $y = \frac{x + 2}{x - 2}$ has $x = 2$ as a vertical asymptote and $y = 1$ as a horizontal asymptote.

Asíntota (p. 435) Una asíntota es una recta a la cual se acerca una gráfica a medida que x o y aumentan de valor absoluto.

Axis of symmetry (pp. 107, 194) The axis of symmetry is the line that divides a figure into two parts that are mirror images.

Example

axis of symmetry
$x = -1$
$y = x^2 + 2x - 1$

Eje de simetría (pp. 107, 194) El eje de simetría es la recta que divide una figura en dos partes que son imágenes una de la otra.

B

Bias (p. 726) A bias is a systematic error introduced by the sampling method.

Sesgo (p. 726) El sesgo es un error sistemático introducido por medio del método de muestreo.

Bimodal (p. 712) A bimodal data set has two modes.

Example {1, 2, 3, 3, 4, 5, 6, 6}
mode = 3 and 6

Bimodal (p. 712) Un conjunto bimodal de datos tiene dos modas.

English / Spanish

Binomial experiment (p. 731) A binomial experiment is one in which the situation involves repeated trials. Each trial has two possible outcomes (success or failure), and the probability of success is constant throughout the trials.

Experimento binomial (p. 731) Un experimento binomial es un experimento que requiere varios ensayos. Cada ensayo tiene dos resultados posibles (éxito o fracaso), y la probabilidad de éxito es constante durante todos los ensayos.

Binomial probability (p. 732) In a binomial experiment with probability of success p and probability of failure q, the probability of x successes in n trials is given by $_nC_x p^x q^{n-x}$.

Example Suppose you roll a standard number cube and that you call rolling a 1 a success. Then $p = \frac{1}{6}$ and $q = \frac{5}{6}$. The probability of rolling nine 1's in twenty rolls is $_{20}C_9 \left(\frac{1}{6}\right)^9 \left(\frac{5}{6}\right)^{11} \approx 0.0022$.

Probabilidad binomial (p. 732) En un experimento binomial con una probabilidad de éxito p y una probabilidad de fracaso q, la probabilidad de x éxitos en n ensayos se expresa con $_nC_x p^x q^{n-x}$.

Binomial Theorem (pp. 327, 733) For every positive integer n, $(a + b)^n = P_0 a^n + P_1 a^{n-1}b + P_2 a^{n-2}b^2 + \cdots + P_{n-1}ab^{n-1} + P_n b^n$ where $P_0, P_1, \ldots, P_n$ are the numbers in the row of Pascal's Triangle that has n as its second number.

Example $(x + 1)^3 = {}_3C_0(x)^3 + {}_3C_1(x)^2(1)^1 + {}_3C_2(x)^1(1)^2 + {}_3C_3(1)^3 = x^3 + 3x^2 + 3x + 1$

Teorema binomial (pp. 327, 733) Para cada número entero positivo n, $(a + b)^n = P_0 a^n + P_1 a^{n-1}b + P_2 a^{n-2}b^2 + \cdots + P_{n-1}ab^{n-1} + P_n b^n$, donde $P_0, P_1, \ldots, P_n$ son los números de la fila del Triángulo de Pascal cuyo segundo número es n.

Boundary (p. 114) A boundary of the graph of a linear inequality is a line in the coordinate plane. It separates the solutions of the inequality from the nonsolutions. Points of the line itself may or may not be solutions.

Límite (p. 114) Un límite de la gráfica de una desigualdad lineal es una línea en el plano de coordenadas. Ésta separa las soluciones de la desigualdad de las no soluciones. Las soluciones pueden ser o no puntos de la línea.

Box-and-whisker plot (p. 714) A box-and-whisker plot is a method of displaying data that uses quartiles to form the center box and the maximum and minimum values to form the whiskers.

Example

Gráfica de cajas (p. 714) Una gráfica de cajas es un método para mostrar datos que utiliza cuartiles para formar una casilla central y los valores máximos y mínimos para formar los conectores.

Branch (p. 508) Each piece of a discontinuous graph is called a branch.

Example

Rama (p. 508) Cada segmento de una gráfica discontinua se llama rama.

English — C / Spanish

Center of a circle (p. 630) The center of a circle is the point that is the same distance from every point on the circle.

Centro de un círculo (p. 630) El centro de un círculo es el punto que está situado a la misma distancia de cada punto del círculo.

Center of an ellipse (p. 639) The center of an ellipse is the midpoint of the major axis.

Centro de una elipse (p. 639) El centro de una elipse es el punto medio entre los dos ejes mayores.

Center of rotation (p. 804) A center of rotation is the fixed point of a rotation.

Example

center of rotation

Centro de rotación (p. 804) Un centro de rotación es el punto fijo de una rotación.

Central angle (p. 844) A central angle of a circle is an angle whose vertex is at the center of a circle.

Example

intercepted arc
central angle

Ángulo central (p. 844) El ángulo central de un círculo es un ángulo cuyo vértice está situado en el centro del círculo.

Change of Base Formula (p. 464) $\log_b M = \frac{\log_c M}{\log_c b}$, where M, b, and c are positive numbers, and $b \neq 1$ and $c \neq 1$.

Example $\log_3 8 = \frac{\log 8}{\log 3} \approx 1.8928$

Fórmula de cambio de base (p. 464) $\log_b M = \frac{\log_c M}{\log_c b}$, donde M, b y c son números positivos y $b \neq 1$ y $c \neq 1$.

Circle (p. 630) A circle is the set of all points in a plane at a distance r from a given point. The standard form of the equation of a circle with center (h, k) and radius r is $(x - h)^2 + (y - k)^2 = r^2$.

Example

Círculo (p. 630) Un círculo es el conjunto de todos los puntos situados en un plano a una distancia r de un punto dado. La forma normal de la ecuación cuyo centro es (h, k) y cuyo radio es r es $(x - h)^2 + (y - k)^2 = r^2$.

Coefficient (p. 20) The numerical factor in a term.

Example The coefficient of $-3k$ is -3.

Coeficiente (p. 20) El factor numérico de un término.

Coefficient matrix (p. 793) When representing a system of equations with a matrix equation, the matrix containing the coefficients of the system is the coefficient matrix.

Matriz de coeficientes (p. 793) Al representar un sistema de ecuaciones con una ecuación de matriz, la matriz que contiene los coeficientes del sistema es la matriz de coeficientes.

Example $\begin{cases} x + 2y = 5 \\ 3x + 5y = 14 \end{cases}$

coefficient matrix $\begin{bmatrix} 1 & 2 \\ 3 & 5 \end{bmatrix}$

Combination (p. 676) Any unordered selection of r objects from a set of n objects is a combination. The number of combinations of n objects taken r at a time is
$_nC_r = \dfrac{n!}{r!(n-r)!}$ for $0 \le r \le n$.

Combinación (p. 676) Cualquier selección no ordenada de r objetos tomados de un conjunto de n objetos es una combinación. El número de combinaciones de n objetos, cuando se toman r objetos cada vez, es
$_nC_r = \dfrac{n!}{r!(n-r)!}$ para $0 \le r \le n$.

Example The number of combinations of seven items taken four at a time is
$_7C_4 = \dfrac{7!}{4!(7-4)!} = 35$.
There are 35 ways to choose four items from seven items without regard to order.

Combined variation (p. 501) A combined variation is a relation in which one variable varies with respect to each of two or more variables.

Variación combinada (p. 501) Una variación combinada es una relación en la que una variable varía con respecto a cada una de dos o más variables.

Example $y = kx^2\sqrt{z}$
$z = \dfrac{kx}{y}$

Common difference (p. 572) A common difference is the difference between consecutive terms of an arithmetic sequence.

Diferencia común (p. 572) La diferencia común es la diferencia entre los términos consecutivos de una progresión aritmética.

Example The arithmetic sequence 1, 5, 9, 13, . . . has a common difference of 4.

Common logarithm (p. 453) A common logarithm is a logarithm that uses base 10. You can write the common logarithm $\log_{10} y$ as $\log y$.

Logaritmo común (p. 453) El logaritmo común es un logaritmo de base 10. El logaritmo común $\log_{10} y$ se expresa como $\log y$.

Example $\log 1 = 0$
$\log 10 = 1$
$\log 50 = 1.698970004 \ldots$

Common ratio (p. 580) A common ratio is the ratio of consecutive terms of a geometric sequence.

Razón común (p. 580) Una razón común es la razón de términos consecutivos en una secuencia geométrica.

Example The geometric sequence 2.5, 5, 10, 20, . . . has a common ratio of 2.

Completing the square (p. 235) Completing the square is the process of finding a constant c to add to $x^2 + bx$ so that $x^2 + bx + c$ is the square of a binomial.

Completar el cuadrado (p. 235) Completar un cuadrado es el proceso mediante el cual se halla una constante c que se le pueda sumar a $x^2 + bx$, de manera que $x^2 + bx + c$ sea el cuadrado de un binomio.

Example $x^2 - 12x + \blacksquare$
$x^2 - 12x + \left(\dfrac{-12}{2}\right)^2$
$x^2 - 12x + 36$

Complex conjugates (p. 251) Number pairs of the form $a + bi$ and $a - bi$ are complex conjugates.

Conjugados complejos (p. 251) Los pares de números de la forma $a + bi$ y $a - bi$ son conjugados complejos.

Example The complex numbers $2 - 3i$ and $2 + 3i$ are complex conjugates.

Complex fraction (p. 536) A complex fraction is a rational expression that has a fraction in its numerator or denominator, or in both its numerator and denominator.

Fracción compleja (p. 536) Una fracción compleja es una expresión racional en la que el numerador, el denominador o ambos son una fracción.

Example $\dfrac{\frac{2}{3}}{\frac{2}{5}}$

Complex number (p. 249) Complex numbers are the real numbers and the imaginary numbers.

Número complejo (p. 249) Los números complejos son los números reales y los números imaginarios.

Example $6 + i$
$7, 2i$

Complex number plane (p. 249) The complex number plane is identical to the coordinate plane except each ordered pair (a, b) represents the complex number $a + bi$. The horizontal axis is the Real axis. The vertical axis is the Imaginary axis.

Plano de números complejos (p. 249) El plano de los números complejos es idéntico al plano de coordenadas, a excepción de que cada par ordenado (a, b) representa el número complejo $a + bi$. El eje horizontal es el eje real. El eje vertical es el eje imaginario.

Example

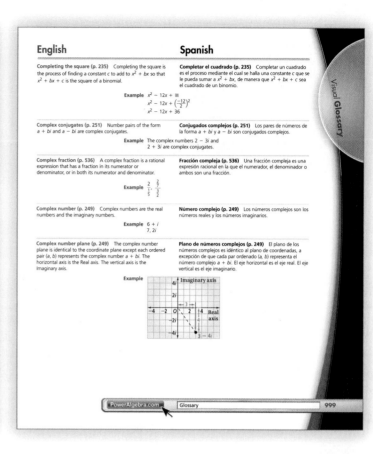

Composite function (p. 399) A composite function is a combination of two functions such that the output from the first function becomes the input for the second function.

Función compuesta (p. 399) Una función compuesta es la combinación de dos funciones de modo que la cantidad de salida de la primera función es la cantidad de entrada de la segunda función.

Example $f(x) = 2x + 1,\ g(x) = x^2 - 1$
$(g \circ f)(5) = g(f(5)) = g(2(5) + 1)$
$= g(11)$
$= 11^2 - 1 = 120$

Compound inequality (p. 36) You can join two inequalities with the word *and* or the word *or* to form a compound inequality.

Desigualdad compuesta (p. 36) Puedes unir dos desigualdades por medio de la palabra *y* o la palabra *o* para formar una desigualdad compuesta.

Example $-1 < x$ and $x \le 3$
$x < -1$ or $x \ge 3$

Conditional probability (p. 696) A conditional probability contains a condition that may limit the sample space for an event. The notation $P(B|A)$ is read "the probability of event B, given event A." For any two events A and B in the sample space, $P(B|A) = \dfrac{P(A \text{ and } B)}{P(A)}$.

Probabilidad condicional (p. 696) Una probabilidad condicional contiene una condición que puede limitar el espacio muestral de un suceso. La notación $P(B|A)$ se lee "la probabilidad del suceso B, dado el suceso A". Para dos sucesos cualesquiera A y B en el espacio muestral, $P(B|A) = \dfrac{P(A \text{ y } B)}{P(A)}$

Example $= \dfrac{P(\text{departs and arrives on time})}{P(\text{departs on time})}$
$= \dfrac{0.75}{0.83}$
≈ 0.9

Confidence interval (p. 746) Based on the mean of a sample or a sample proportion, the confidence interval indicates the interval in which the population mean or population proportion is likely to lie for a given confidence level.

Intervalo de confianza (p. 746) El intervalo de confianza se basa en la media de una muestra o en la proporción de una muestra, e indica el intervalo en el que probablemente se encuentra dicha media o proporción de la población para un nivel de confianza dado.

Example For an elementary history book, a sample of 30 trials indicates that the mean number of words in a sentence is 12.7. The margin of error at a 95% confidence level is 1.5 words per sentence. The mean number of words μ in all of the sentences in the book at a 95% confidence level is $12.7 - 1.5 \le \mu \le 12.7 + 1.5$.

Conic section (p. 614) A conic section is a curve formed by the intersection of a plane and a double cone.

Sección cónica (p. 614) Una sección cónica es una curva que se forma por la intersección de un plano con un cono doble.

Example

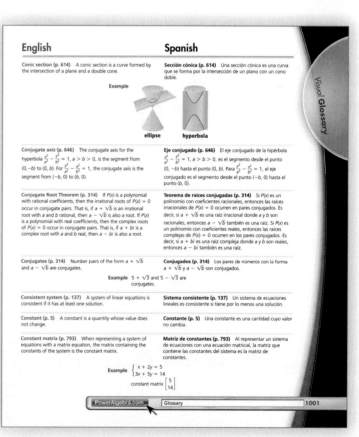

ellipse   hyperbola

Conjugate axis (p. 646) The conjugate axis for the hyperbola $\dfrac{x^2}{a^2} - \dfrac{y^2}{b^2} = 1,\ a > b > 0$, is the segment from $(0, -b)$ to $(0, b)$. For $\dfrac{y^2}{a^2} - \dfrac{x^2}{b^2} = 1$, the conjugate axis is the segment from $(-b, 0)$ to $(b, 0)$.

Eje conjugado (p. 646) El eje conjugado de la hipérbola $\dfrac{x^2}{a^2} - \dfrac{y^2}{b^2} = 1,\ a > b > 0$, es el segmento desde el punto $(0, -b)$ hasta el punto $(0, b)$. Para $\dfrac{y^2}{a^2} - \dfrac{x^2}{b^2} = 1$, el eje conjugado es el segmento desde el punto $(-b, 0)$ hasta el punto $(b, 0)$.

Conjugate Root Theorem (p. 314) If $P(x)$ is a polynomial with rational coefficients, then the irrational roots of $P(x) = 0$ occur in conjugate pairs. That is, if $a + \sqrt{b}$ is an irrational root with a and b rational, then $a - \sqrt{b}$ is also a root. If $P(x)$ is a polynomial with real coefficients, then the complex roots of $P(x) = 0$ occur in conjugate pairs. That is, if $a + bi$ is a complex root with a and b real, then $a - bi$ is also a root.

Teorema de raíces conjugadas (p. 314) Si $P(x)$ es un polinomio con coeficientes racionales, entonces las raíces irracionales de $P(x) = 0$ ocurren en pares conjugados. Es decir, si $a + \sqrt{b}$ es una raíz irracional donde a y b son racionales, entonces $a - \sqrt{b}$ también es una raíz. Si $P(x)$ es un polinomio con coeficientes reales, entonces las raíces complejas de $P(x) = 0$ ocurren en los pares conjugados. Es decir, si $a + bi$ es una raíz compleja donde a y b son reales, entonces $a - bi$ también es una raíz.

Conjugates (p. 314) Number pairs of the form $a + \sqrt{b}$ and $a - \sqrt{b}$ are conjugates.

Conjugados (p. 314) Los pares de números con la forma $a + \sqrt{b}$ y $a - \sqrt{b}$ son conjugados.

Example $5 + \sqrt{3}$ and $5 - \sqrt{3}$ are conjugates.

Consistent system (p. 137) A system of linear equations is consistent if it has at least one solution.

Sistema consistente (p. 137) Un sistema de ecuaciones lineales es consistente si tiene por lo menos una solución.

Constant (p. 5) A constant is a quantity whose value does not change.

Constante (p. 5) Una constante es una cantidad cuyo valor no cambia.

Constant matrix (p. 793) When representing a system of equations with a matrix equation, the matrix containing the constants of the system is the constant matrix.

Matriz de constantes (p. 793) Al representar un sistema de ecuaciones con una ecuación matricial, la matriz que contiene las constantes del sistema es la matriz de constantes.

Example $\begin{cases} x + 2y = 5 \\ 3x + 5y = 14 \end{cases}$

constant matrix $\begin{bmatrix} 5 \\ 14 \end{bmatrix}$

English

Constant of proportionality (p. 341) If $y = ax^b$ describes y as a power function of x, then y varies directly with, or is proportional to, the bth power of x. The constant a is the constant of proportionality.

Constant of variation (p. 68) The constant of variation is the ratio of the two variables in a direct variation and the product of the two variables in an inverse variation.

Example In $y = 3.5x$, the constant of variation k is 3.5. In $xy = 5$, the constant of variation k is 5.

Constant term (p. 20) A constant term is a term with no variables.

Constraint (p. 157) Constraints are restrictions on the variables of the objective function in a linear programming problem. See **Linear programming.**

Continuous graph (p. 516) A graph is continuous if it has no jumps, breaks, or holes.

Continuous probability distribution (p. 739) A continuous probability distribution has as its events any of the infinitely many values in an interval of real numbers.

Continuously compounded interest (p. 446) When interest is compounded continuously on principal P, the value A of an account is $A = Pe^{rt}$.

Example Suppose that $P = \$1200$, $r = 0.05$, and $t = 3$. Then
$$A = 1200e^{0.05 \cdot 3}$$
$$= 1200(2.718\ldots)^{0.15}$$
$$\approx 1394.20$$

Controlled experiment (p. 726) In a controlled experiment, you divide the sample into two groups. You impose a treatment on one group but not the other "control" group. Then you compare the effect on the treated group to the control group.

Convenience sample (p. 725) In a convenience sample you select any members of the population who are conveniently and readily available.

Spanish

Constante de proporcionalidad (p. 341) Si $y = ax^b$ describe a y como una potencia de la función de x, entonces y varía directamente con, o es proporcional a la b^{ma} potencia de x. La constante a es la constante de proporcionalidad.

Constante de variación (p. 68) La constante de variación es la razón de dos variables en una variación directa y el producto de las dos variables en una variación inversa.

Término constante (p. 20) Un término constante es un término que no tiene variables.

Restricción (p. 157) Las restricciones son limitaciones a las variables de una función objetiva en un problema de programación lineal. Ver **Linear programming.**

Gráfica continua (p. 516) Una gráfica es continua si no tiene saltos, interrupciones o huecos.

Distribución de probabilidad continua (p. 739) Una distribución de probabilidad continua tiene como sucesos a cualquiera del número infinito de valores en un intervalo de números reales.

Interés compuesto continuo (p. 446) En un sistema donde el interés es compuesto continuamente sobre el capital P, el valor de A de una cuenta es $A = Pe^{rt}$.

Experimento controlado (p. 726) En un experimento controlado, se divide la muestra en dos grupos. Uno de los grupos se manipula y el otro grupo "controlado" se mantiene en su estado original. Luego se comparan el estado del grupo manipulado y el estado del grupo controlado.

Muestra de conveniencia (p. 725) En una muestra de conveniencia se selecciona a cualquier miembro de la población que está convenientemente disponible.

English

Converge (p. 598) An infinite series $a_1 + a_2 + \cdots + a_n + \cdots$ converges if the sum $a_1 + a_2 + \cdots + a_n$ get closer and closer to a real number as n increases.

Example $1 + \frac{1}{2} + \frac{1}{4} + \frac{1}{8} + \cdots$ converges.

Coordinate space (p. 164) Coordinate space is a three-dimensional space where each point is described uniquely using an ordered triple of numbers.

Example

$A (2, -1, 3)$

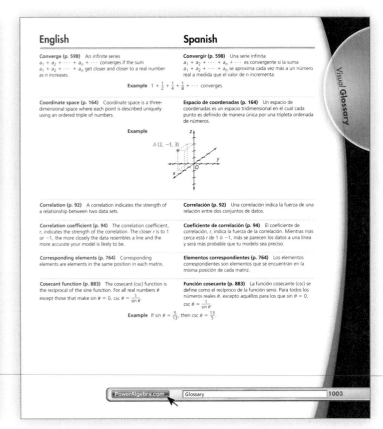

Correlation (p. 92) A correlation indicates the strength of a relationship between two data sets.

Correlation coefficient (p. 94) The correlation coefficient, r, indicates the strength of the correlation. The closer r is to 1 or -1, the more closely the data resembles a line and the more accurate your model is likely to be.

Corresponding elements (p. 764) Corresponding elements are elements in the same position in each matrix.

Cosecant function (p. 883) The cosecant (csc) function is the reciprocal of the sine function. For all real numbers θ except those that make $\sin \theta = 0$, $\csc \theta = \frac{1}{\sin \theta}$.

Example If $\sin \theta = \frac{5}{13}$, then $\csc \theta = \frac{13}{5}$.

Spanish

Convergir (p. 598) Una serie infinita $a_1 + a_2 + \cdots + a_n + \cdots$ es convergente si la suma $a_1 + a_2 + \cdots + a_n$ se aproxima cada vez más a un número real a medida que el valor de n incrementa.

Espacio de coordenadas (p. 164) Un espacio de coordenadas es un espacio tridimensional en el cual cada punto se define de manera única por una tripleta ordenada de números.

Correlación (p. 92) Una correlación indica la fuerza de una relación entre dos conjuntos de datos.

Coeficiente de correlación (p. 94) El coeficiente de correlación, r, indica la fuerza de la correlación. Mientras más cerca está r de 1 ó -1, más se parecen los datos a una línea y será más probable que tu modelo sea preciso.

Elementos correspondientes (p. 764) Los elementos correspondientes son elementos que se encuentran en la misma posición de cada matriz.

Función cosecante (p. 883) La función cosecante (csc) se define como el recíproco de la función seno. Para todos los números reales θ, excepto aquéllos para los que $\sin \theta = 0$, $\csc \theta = \frac{1}{\sin \theta}$.

English

Cosine function, Cosine of θ (pp. 838, 861) The cosine function, $y = \cos \theta$, matches the measure θ of an angle in standard position with the x-coordinate of a point on the unit circle. This point is where the terminal side of the angle intersects the unit circle. The x-coordinate is the cosine of θ.

Example

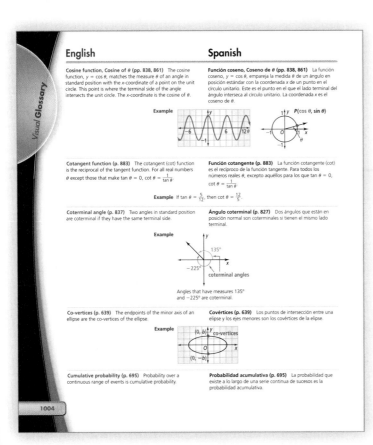

$P(\cos \theta, \sin \theta)$

Cotangent function (p. 883) The cotangent (cot) function is the reciprocal of the tangent function. For all real numbers θ except those that make $\tan \theta = 0$, $\cot \theta = \frac{1}{\tan \theta}$.

Example If $\tan \theta = \frac{5}{12}$, then $\cot \theta = \frac{12}{5}$.

Coterminal angle (p. 837) Two angles in standard position are coterminal if they have the same terminal side.

Example

135°

−225°

coterminal angles

Angles that have measures 135° and −225° are coterminal.

Co-vertices (p. 639) The endpoints of the minor axis of an ellipse are the co-vertices of the ellipse.

Example

$(0, b)$ co-vertices

$(0, -b)$

Cumulative probability (p. 695) Probability over a continuous range of events is cumulative probability.

Spanish

Función coseno, Coseno de θ (pp. 838, 861) La función coseno, $y = \cos \theta$, empareja la medida θ de un ángulo en posición estándar con la coordenada x de un punto en el círculo unitario. Este es el punto en el que el lado terminal del ángulo interseca al círculo unitario. La coordenada x es el coseno de θ.

Función cotangente (p. 883) La función cotangente (cot) es el recíproco de la función tangente. Para todos los números reales θ, excepto aquéllos para los que $\tan \theta = 0$, $\cot \theta = \frac{1}{\tan \theta}$.

Ángulo coterminal (p. 827) Dos ángulos que están en posición normal son coterminales si tienen el mismo lado terminal.

Covértices (p. 639) Los puntos de intersección entre una elipse y los ejes menores son los covértices de la elipse.

Probabilidad acumulativa (p. 695) La probabilidad que existe a lo largo de una serie continua de sucesos es la probabilidad acumulativa.

English

Cycle (p. 828) A cycle of a periodic function is an interval of x-values over which the function provides one complete pattern of y-values.

Example

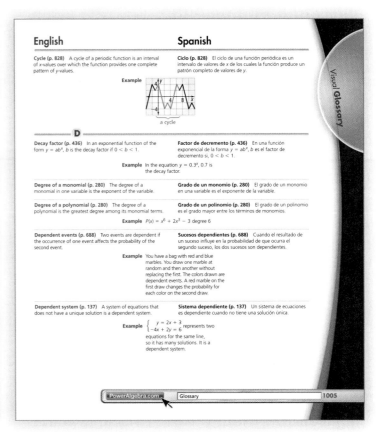

a cycle

— D —

Decay factor (p. 436) In an exponential function of the form $y = ab^x$, b is the decay factor if $0 < b < 1$.

Example In the equation $y = 0.3^x$, 0.7 is the decay factor.

Degree of a monomial (p. 280) The degree of a monomial in one variable is the exponent of the variable.

Degree of a polynomial (p. 280) The degree of a polynomial is the greatest degree among its monomial terms.

Example $P(x) = x^6 + 2x^3 - 3$ degree 6

Dependent events (p. 688) Two events are dependent if the occurrence of one event affects the probability of the second event.

Example You have a bag with red and blue marbles. You draw one marble at random and then another without replacing the first. The colors drawn are dependent events. A red marble on the first draw changes the probability for each color on the second draw.

Dependent system (p. 137) A system of equations that does not have a unique solution is a dependent system.

Example $\begin{cases} y = 2x + 3 \\ -4x + 2y = 6 \end{cases}$ represents two equations for the same line, so it has many solutions. It is a dependent system.

Spanish

Ciclo (p. 828) El ciclo de una función periódica es un intervalo de valores de x de los cuales la función produce un patrón completo de valores de y.

Factor de decremento (p. 436) En una función exponencial de la forma $y = ab^x$, b es el factor de decremento si, $0 < b < 1$.

Grado de un monomio (p. 280) El grado de un monomio en una variable es el exponente de la variable.

Grado de un polinomio (p. 280) El grado de un polinomio es el grado mayor entre los términos de monomios.

Sucesos dependientes (p. 688) Cuando el resultado de un suceso influye en la probabilidad de que ocurra el segundo suceso, los dos sucesos son dependientes.

Sistema dependiente (p. 137) Un sistema de ecuaciones es dependiente cuando no tiene una solución única.

English / Spanish

Dependent variable (p. 63) If a function is defined by an equation using the variables x and y, where y represents output values, then y is the dependent variable.

Variable dependiente (p. 63) Si una función es definida por una ecuación que usa las variables x e y, donde y representa valores de salida, entonces y es la variable dependiente.

Example $y = 2x + 1$
y is the dependent variable.

Descartes' Rule of Signs (p. 315) Let $P(x)$ be a polynomial with real coefficients written in standard form.
– The number of positive real roots of $P(x) = 0$ is either equal to the number of sign changes between consecutive coefficients of $P(x)$ or is less than that by an even number;
– The number of negative real roots of $P(x) = 0$ is either equal to the number of sign changes between consecutive coefficients of $P(-x)$ or is less than that by an even number. (Count multiple roots according to their multiplicity.)

Regla de los signos de Descartes (p. 315) Sea $P(x)$ un polinomio con coeficientes reales escritos en forma normal.
– El número de raíces positivas reales de $P(x) = 0$ es igual al número de cambios de signos entre coeficientes consecutivos de $P(x)$ o es menor que eso en un número par;
– El número de raíces negativas reales de $P(x) = 0$ es igual al número de cambios de signos entre coeficientes consecutivos de $P(-x)$ o es menor que eso en un número par. (Cuenta las raíces múltiples según su multiplicidad).

Determinant (p. 784) The determinant of a square matrix is a real number that can be computed from its elements according to a specific formula.

Determinante (p. 784) El determinante de una matriz cuadrada es un número real que se puede calcular a partir de sus elementos por medio de una fórmula específica.

Example The determinant of $\begin{bmatrix} 3 & -2 \\ 5 & 6 \end{bmatrix}$ is
$3(6) - 5(-2) = 28.$

Difference of cubes (p. 297) A difference of cubes is an expression of the form $a^3 - b^3$. It can be factored as $(a - b)(a^2 + ab + b^2)$.

Diferencia de dos cubos (p. 297) La diferencia de dos cubos es una expresión de la forma $a^3 - b^3$. Se puede factorizar como $(a - b)(a^2 + ab + b^2)$.

Example $x^3 - 27 = (x - 3)(x^2 + 3x + 9)$

Difference of two squares (p. 220) A difference of two squares is an expression of the form $a^2 - b^2$. It can be factored as $(a + b)(a - b)$.

Diferencia de dos cuadrados (p. 220) La diferencia de dos cuadrados es una expresión de la forma $a^2 - b^2$. Se puede factorizar como $(a + b)(a - b)$.

Example $25a^2 - 4 = (5a + 2)(5a - 2)$
$m^6 - 1 = (m^3 + 1)(m^3 - 1)$

Dilation (p. 802) A dilation is a transformation that can change the size of a figure. When the center of the dilation is the origin, you can use scalar multiplication to find the coordinates of the vertices of an image.

Dilatación (p. 802) Una dilatación es una transformación que puede cambiar el tamaño de una figura. Cuando el centro de dilatación está en el origen, se hallan las coordenadas de los vértices de la imagen por medio de la multiplicación de escalar.

Example

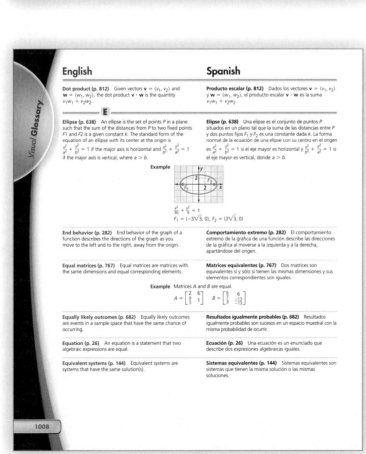

English / Spanish

Direct variation (p. 68) A linear function defined by an equation of the form $y = kx$, where $k \neq 0$, represents direct variation.

Variación directa (p. 68) Una función lineal definida por una ecuación de la forma $y = kx$, donde $k \neq 0$, representa una variación directa.

Example $y = 3.5x,\ y = 7x,\ y = -\frac{1}{2}x$

Directrix (p. 622) The directrix of a parabola is the fixed line used to define a parabola. Each point of the parabola is the same distance from the focus and the directrix.

Directriz (p. 622) La directriz de una parábola es la recta fija con que se define una parábola. Cada punto de la parábola está a la misma distancia del foco y de la directriz.

Example

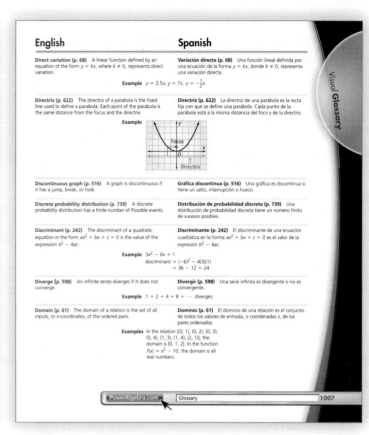

Discontinuous graph (p. 516) A graph is discontinuous if it has a jump, break, or hole.

Gráfica discontinua (p. 516) Una gráfica es discontinua si tiene un salto, interrupción o hueco.

Discrete probability distribution (p. 739) A discrete probability distribution has a finite number of Possible events.

Distribución de probabilidad discreta (p. 739) Una distribución de probabilidad discreta tiene un número finito de sucesos posibles.

Discriminant (p. 242) The discriminant of a quadratic equation in the form $ax^2 + bx + c = 0$ is the value of the expression $b^2 - 4ac$.

Discriminante (p. 242) El discriminante de una ecuación cuadrática en la forma $ax^2 + bx + c = 0$ es el valor de la expresión $b^2 - 4ac$.

Example $3x^2 - 6x + 1$
discriminant $= (-6)^2 - 4(3)(1)$
$= 36 - 12 = 24$

Diverge (p. 598) An infinite series diverges if it does not converge.

Divergir (p. 598) Una serie infinita es divergente si no es convergente.

Example $1 + 2 + 4 + 8 + \cdots$ diverges.

Domain (p. 61) The domain of a relation is the set of all inputs, or x-coordinates, of the ordered pairs.

Dominio (p. 61) El dominio de una relación es el conjunto de todos los valores de entrada, o coordenadas x, de los pares ordenados.

Examples In the relation $\{(0, 1), (0, 2), (0, 3), (0, 4), (1, 3), (1, 4), (2, 1)\}$, the domain is $\{0, 1, 2\}$. In the function $f(x) = x^2 - 10$, the domain is all real numbers.

English / Spanish

Dot product (p. 812) Given vectors $\mathbf{v} = \langle v_1, v_2 \rangle$ and $\mathbf{w} = \langle w_1, w_2 \rangle$, the dot product $\mathbf{v} \cdot \mathbf{w}$ is the quantity $v_1 w_1 + v_2 w_2$.

Producto escalar (p. 812) Dados los vectores $\mathbf{v} = \langle v_1, v_2 \rangle$ y $\mathbf{w} = \langle w_1, w_2 \rangle$, el producto escalar $\mathbf{v} \cdot \mathbf{w}$ es la suma $v_1 w_1 + v_2 w_2$.

E

Ellipse (p. 638) An ellipse is the set of points P in a plane such that the sum of the distances from P to two fixed points $F1$ and $F2$ is a given constant k. The standard form of the equation of an ellipse with its center at the origin is $\frac{x^2}{a^2} + \frac{y^2}{b^2} = 1$ if the major axis is horizontal and $\frac{x^2}{b^2} + \frac{y^2}{a^2} = 1$ if the major axis is vertical, where $a > b$.

Elipse (p. 638) Una elipse es el conjunto de puntos P situados en un plano tal que la suma de las distancias entre P y dos puntos fijos F_1 y F_2 es una constante dada k. La forma normal de la ecuación de una elipse con su centro en el origen es $\frac{x^2}{a^2} + \frac{y^2}{b^2} = 1$ si el eje mayor es horizontal y $\frac{x^2}{b^2} + \frac{y^2}{a^2} = 1$ si el eje mayor es vertical, donde $a > b$.

Example

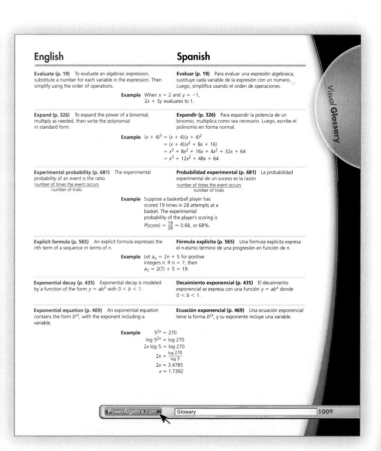

$\frac{x^2}{36} + \frac{y^2}{9} = 1$
$F_1 = (-3\sqrt{3}, 0),\ F_2 = (3\sqrt{3}, 0)$

End behavior (p. 282) End behavior of the graph of a function describes the directions of the graph as you move to the left and to the right, away from the origin.

Comportamiento extremo (p. 282) El comportamiento extremo de la gráfica de una función describe las direcciones de la gráfica al moverse a la izquierda y a la derecha, apartándose del origen.

Equal matrices (p. 767) Equal matrices are matrices with the same dimensions and equal corresponding elements.

Matrices equivalentes (p. 767) Dos matrices son equivalentes si y sólo si tienen las mismas dimensiones y sus elementos correspondientes son iguales.

Example Matrices A and B are equal.
$A = \begin{bmatrix} 2 & 6 \\ \frac{5}{3} & 1 \end{bmatrix}$ $B = \begin{bmatrix} \frac{9}{4} & 6 \\ 3 & \frac{-13}{13} \end{bmatrix}$

Equally likely outcomes (p. 682) Equally likely outcomes are events in a sample space that have the same chance of occurring.

Resultados igualmente probables (p. 682) Resultados igualmente probables son sucesos en un espacio muestral con la misma probabilidad de ocurrir.

Equation (p. 26) An equation is a statement that two algebraic expressions are equal.

Ecuación (p. 26) Una ecuación es un enunciado que describe dos expresiones algebraicas iguales.

Equivalent systems (p. 144) Equivalent systems are systems that have the same solution(s).

Sistemas equivalentes (p. 144) Sistemas equivalentes son sistemas que tienen la misma solución o las mismas soluciones.

English / Spanish

Evaluate (p. 19) To evaluate an algebraic expression, substitute a number for each variable in the expression. Then simplify using the order of operations.

Evaluar (p. 19) Para evaluar una expresión algebraica, sustituye cada variable de la expresión con un número. Luego, simplifica usando el orden de operaciones.

Example When $x = 2$ and $y = -1$, $2x + 3y$ evaluates to 1.

Expand (p. 326) To expand the power of a binomial, multiply as needed, then write the polynomial in standard form.

Expandir (p. 326) Para expandir la potencia de un binomio, multiplica como sea necesario. Luego, escribe el polinomio en forma normal.

Example $(x + 4)^3 = (x + 4)(x + 4)^2$
$= (x + 4)(x^2 + 8x + 16)$
$= x^3 + 8x^2 + 16x + 4x^2 + 32x + 64$
$= x^3 + 12x^2 + 48x + 64$

Experimental probability (p. 681) The experimental probability of an event is the ratio $\frac{\text{number of times the event occurs}}{\text{number of trials}}$

Probabilidad experimental (p. 681) La probabilidad experimental de un suceso es la razón $\frac{\text{number of times the event occurs}}{\text{number of trials}}$

Example Suppose a basketball player has scored 19 times in 28 attempts at a basket. The experimental probability of the player's scoring is $P(\text{score}) = \frac{19}{28} \approx 0.68$, or 68%.

Explicit formula (p. 565) An explicit formula expresses the nth term of a sequence in terms of n.

Fórmula explícita (p. 565) Una fórmula explícita expresa el n-ésimo término de una progresión en función de n.

Example Let $a_n = 2n + 5$ for positive integers n. If $n = 7$, then $a_7 = 2(7) + 5 = 19$.

Exponential decay (p. 435) Exponential decay is modeled by a function of the form $y = ab^x$ with $0 < b < 1$.

Decaimiento exponencial (p. 435) El decaimiento exponencial se expresa con una función $y = ab^x$ donde $0 < b < 1$.

Exponential equation (p. 469) An exponential equation contains the form b^{cx}, with the exponent including a variable.

Ecuación exponencial (p. 469) Una ecuación exponencial tiene la forma b^{cx}, y su exponente incluye una variable.

Example $5^{2x} = 270$
$\log 5^{2x} = \log 270$
$2x \log 5 = \log 270$
$2x = \frac{\log 270}{\log 5}$
$2x = 3.4785$
$x \approx 1.7392$

Panel 1 (top left)

English

Exponential function (p. 434) The general form of an exponential function is $y = ab^x$, where x is a real number, $a \neq 0$, $b > 0$, and $b \neq 1$. When $b > 1$, the function models exponential growth with growth factor b. When $0 < b < 1$, the function models exponential decay with decay factor b.

Spanish

Función exponencial (p. 434) La forma general de una función exponencial es $y = ab^x$, donde x es un número real, $a \neq 0$, $b > 0$ y $b \neq 1$. Cuando $b > 1$, la función representa un incremento exponencial con factor de incremento b. Cuando $0 < b < 1$, la función representa el decremento exponencial con factor de decremento b.

Example

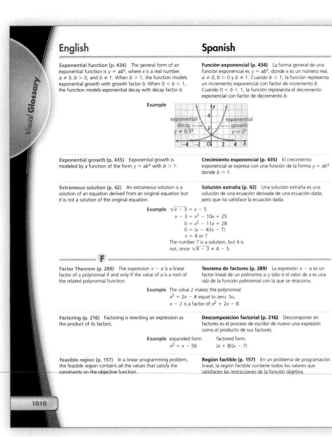

Exponential growth (p. 435) Exponential growth is modeled by a function of the form $y = ab^x$ with $b > 1$.

Crecimiento exponencial (p. 435) El crecimiento exponencial se expresa con una función de la forma $y = ab^x$ donde $b > 1$.

Extraneous solution (p. 42) An extraneous solution is a solution of an equation derived from an original equation but it is not a solution of the original equation.

Solución extraña (p. 42) Una solución extraña es una solución de una ecuación derivada de una ecuación dada, pero que no satisface la ecuación dada.

Example
$$\sqrt{x-3} = x - 5$$
$$x - 3 = x^2 - 10x + 25$$
$$0 = x^2 - 11x + 28$$
$$0 = (x-4)(x-7)$$
$$x = 4 \text{ or } 7$$
The number 7 is a solution, but 4 is not, since $\sqrt{4-3} \neq 4 - 5$.

— F —

Factor Theorem (p. 289) The expression $x - a$ is a linear factor of a polynomial if and only if the value of a is a root of the related polynomial function.

Teorema de factores (p. 289) La expresión $x - a$ es un factor lineal de un polinomio si y sólo si el valor de a es una raíz de la función polinomial con la que se relaciona.

Example The value 2 makes the polynomial $x^2 + 2x - 8$ equal to zero. So, $x - 2$ is a factor of $x^2 + 2x - 8$.

Factoring (p. 216) Factoring is rewriting an expression as the product of its factors.

Descomposición factorial (p. 216) Descomponer en factores es el proceso de escribir de nuevo una expresión como el producto de sus factores.

Example expanded form   factored form
$$x^2 + x - 56 \qquad (x+8)(x-7)$$

Feasible region (p. 157) In a linear programming problem, the feasible region contains all the values that satisfy the constraints on the objective function.

Región factible (p. 157) En un problema de programación lineal, la región factible contiene todos los valores que satisfacen las restricciones de la función objetiva.

Panel 2 (top right)

English

Finite Series (p. 587) A finite series is a series with a finite number of terms.

Spanish

Serie finita (p. 587) Una serie finita es una serie con un número finito de términos.

Focal length (p. 622) The focal length of a parabola is the distance between the vertex and the focus.

Distancia focal (p. 622) La distancia focal de una parábola es la distancia entre el vértice y el foco.

Focus (plural: foci) of a hyperbola (p. 645) A hyperbola is the set of all points P in a plane such that the difference of the distances from P to two fixed points is constant. Each of the fixed points is a focus of the hyperbola.

Foco de una hipérbola (p. 645) Una hipérbola es el conjunto de puntos P en un plano tal que la diferencia de las distancias desde P hasta dos puntos fijos es constante. Cada uno de los puntos fijos es el foco de la hipérbola.

Focus (plural: foci) of a parabola (p. 622) A parabola is the set of all points in a plane that are the same distance from a fixed line and a fixed point not on the line. The fixed point is the focus of the parabola.

Foco de una parábola (p. 622) Una parábola es el conjunto de todos los puntos en un plano con la misma distancia desde una línea fija y un punto fijo que no permanece en la línea. El punto fijo es el foco de la parábola.

Focus (plural: foci) of an ellipse (p. 638) An ellipse is the set of all points P in a plane such that the sum of the distances from P to two fixed points is constant. Each of the fixed points is a focus of the ellipse.

Foco de una elipse (p. 638) Una elipse es el conjunto de todos los puntos P en un plano en el cual la suma de las distancias desde P hasta dos puntos fijos es constante. Cada uno de estos puntos fijos es un foco de la elipsis.

Frequency table (p. 694) A frequency table is a list of the outcomes in a sample space and the number of times each outcome occurs.

Tabla de frecuencias (p. 694) Una tabla de frecuencias es una lista de los resultados de un espacio muestral y el número de veces que cada resultado ocurre.

Function (p. 62) A function is a relation in which each element of the domain corresponds with exactly one element in the range.

Función (p. 62) Una función es una relación en la que cada elemento del dominio corresponde exactamente con un elemento del rango.

Example The relation $y = 3x^3 - 2x + 3$ is a function. $f(x) = 3x^3 - 2x + 3$ is the same relation written in function notation.

Function notation (p. 63) If f is the name of a function, the function notation $f(x)$ shows the function name f and also represents the range value $f(x)$ for the domain value x. You read the function notation $f(x)$ as "f of x" or "a function of x." Note that $f(x)$ does not mean "f times x."

Notación de una función (p. 63) Si f es el nombre de una función, la notación de la función $f(x)$ indica el nombre de la función y también representa el valor del rango $f(x)$ para el valor del dominio x. La función de la notación $f(x)$ se lee "f de x" o "una función de x." Observa que $f(x)$ no significa "f por x."

Example When the value of x is 3, $f(3)$, read "f of 3," represents the value of the function at 3.

Function rule (p. 63) A function rule represents an output value in terms of an input value.

Regla de función (p. 63) Una regla de función representa un valor de salida en función a un valor de entrada.

Fundamental Counting Principle (p. 674) The Fundamental Counting Principle is a tool that you can use to quickly count the number of ways certain things can happen.

Principio básico de conteo (p. 674) El principio básico de conteo es una herramienta que se puede utilizar para hacer un conteo rápido del número de formas en que pueden ocurrir ciertas cosas.

Panel 3 (bottom left)

English

Fundamental Theorem of Algebra (p. 320) If $P(x)$ is a polynomial of degree $n \geq 1$ with complex coefficients, then $P(x) = 0$ has at least one complex root.

Spanish

Teorema fundamental de álgebra (p. 320) Si $P(x)$ es un polinomio de grado $n \geq 1$ con coeficientes complejos, entonces $P(x) = 0$ tiene por lo menos una raíz compleja.

Example $P(x) = 3x^3 - 2x + 3$ is of degree 3, so $P(x) = 0$ has at least one complex root.

— G —

Geometric mean (p. 583) The geometric mean of any two positive numbers is the positive square root of the product of the two numbers.

Media geométrica (p. 583) La media geométrica de dos números positivos es la raíz cuadrada positiva del producto de los dos números.

Example The geometric mean of 12 and 18 is $\sqrt{12 \cdot 18} \approx 14.6969$.

Geometric sequence (p. 580) A geometric sequence is a sequence with a constant ratio between consecutive terms.

Secuencia geométrica (p. 580) Una secuencia geométrica es una secuencia con una razón constante entre términos consecutivos.

Example The geometric sequence 2.5, 5, 10, 20, 40 . . ., has a common ratio of 2.

Geometric series (p. 595) A geometric series is the sum of the terms in a geometric sequence.

Serie geométrica (p. 595) Una serie geométrica es la suma de términos en una progresión geométrica.

Example One geometric series with five terms is $2.5 + 5 + 10 + 20 + 40$.

Greatest common factor (p. 218) The greatest common factor (GCF) of an expression is the common factor of each term of the expression that has the greatest coefficient and the greatest exponent.

Máximo factor común (p. 218) El máximo factor común de una expresión es el factor común de cada término de la expresión que tiene el mayor coeficiente y el mayor exponente.

Example The GCF of $4x^2 + 20x - 12$ is 4.

Greatest integer function (p. 90) The greatest integer function corresponds each input x to the greatest integer less than or equal to x.

Función del entero mayor (p. 90) La función del entero mayor relaciona cada entrada x con el entero mayor que es menor o igual a x.

Growth factor (p. 436) In an exponential function of the form $y = ab^x$, b is the growth factor if $b > 1$.

Factor de incremento (p. 436) En una función exponencial de la forma $y = ab^x$, b es el factor de incremento si $b > 1$.

Example In the exponential function $y = 2^x$, 2 is the growth factor.

— H —

Half-plane (p. 114) A half-plane is the set of points in a coordinate plane that are on one side of the boundary of the graph of a linear inequality.

Semiplano (p. 114) Un semiplano es el conjunto de puntos de un plano de coordenadas que están a un lado del límite de la gráfica de desigualdad lineal.

Panel 4 (bottom right)

English

Hyperbola (p. 645) A hyperbola is a set of points P in a plane such that the difference between the distances from P to the foci F_1 and F_2 is a given constant k: $|PF_1 - PF_2| = k$. The standard form of an equation of a hyperbola centered at $(0, 0)$ is $\frac{x^2}{a^2} - \frac{y^2}{b^2} = 1$ if the transverse axis is horizontal and $\frac{y^2}{a^2} - \frac{x^2}{b^2} = 1$ if the transverse axis is vertical.

Spanish

Hipérbola (p. 645) Una hipérbola es un conjunto de puntos P en un plano tal que la diferencia entre las distancias de P a los focos F_1 y F_2 es una constante k dada. $|PF_1 - PF_2| = k$. La forma normal de la ecuación de una hipérbola centrada en $(0, 0)$ es $\frac{x^2}{a^2} - \frac{y^2}{b^2} = 1$, si el eje transversal es horizontal, y $\frac{y^2}{a^2} - \frac{x^2}{b^2} = 1$, si el eje transversal es vertical.

Example

$$\frac{x^2}{5^2} - \frac{y^2}{3^2} = 1$$

i (p. 248) The imaginary number i is the principal square root of -1.

i (p. 248) El número imaginario i es la raíz cuadrada principal de -1.

Example $i = \sqrt{-1}$ and $i^2 = -1$.

Identity (p. 28) An equation that is true for every value of the variable is an identity.

Identidad (p. 28) Una ecuación que es verdadera para cada valor de la variable es una identidad.

Image (p. 801) An image is a figure obtained by a transformation of a preimage.

Imagen (p. 801) Una imagen es la figura que resulta después de que la preimagen sufre una transformación.

Example

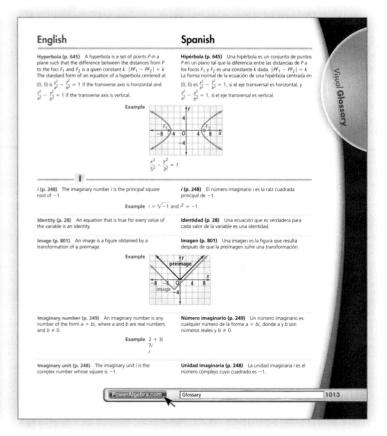

Imaginary number (p. 249) An imaginary number is any number of the form $a + bi$, where a and b are real numbers and $b \neq 0$.

Número imaginario (p. 249) Un número imaginario es cualquier número de la forma $a + bi$, donde a y b son números reales y $b \neq 0$.

Example $2 + 3i$
$7i$
i

Imaginary unit (p. 248) The imaginary unit i is the complex number whose square is -1.

Unidad imaginaria (p. 248) La unidad imaginaria i es el número complejo cuyo cuadrado es -1.

English | Spanish

Inconsistent system (p. 137) A system of equations that has no solution is an inconsistent system.

Sistema incompatible (p. 137) Un sistema incompatible es un sistema de ecuaciones para el cual no hay solución.

Example $\begin{cases} y = 2x + 3 \\ -2x + y = 1 \end{cases}$ is a system of parallel lines, so it has no solution. It is an inconsistent system.

Independent events (p. 688) When the outcome of one event does not affect the probability of a second event, the two events are independent.

Sucesos independientes (p. 688) Cuando el resultado de un suceso no altera la probabilidad de otro, los dos sucesos son independientes.

Example The results of two rolls of a number cube are independent. Getting a 5 on the first roll does not change the probability of getting a 5 on the second roll.

Independent system (p. 137) A system of linear equations that has a unique solution is an independent system.

Sistema independiente (p. 137) Un sistema de ecuaciones lineales que tenga una sola solución es un sistema independiente.

Example $\begin{cases} x + 2y = -7 \\ 2x - 3y = 0 \end{cases}$ has the unique solution $(-3, -2)$. It is an independent system.

Independent variable (p. 63) If a function is defined by an equation using the variables x and y, where x represents input values, then x is the independent variable.

Variable independiente (p. 63) Si una función es definida por una ecuación con las variables x e y, donde x representa los valores de entrada, entonces x es la variable independiente.

Example $y = 2x + 1$
x is the independent variable.

Index (p. 362) With a radical sign, the index indicates the degree of the root.

Índice (p. 362) Con un signo de radical, el índice indica el grado de la raíz.

Example index 2   index 3   index 4
$\sqrt{16}$ $\sqrt[3]{16}$ $\sqrt[4]{16}$

Infinite series (p. 587) An infinite series is a series with infinitely many terms.

Serie infinita (p. 587) Una serie infinita es una serie con un número infinito de términos.

Initial point (p. 809) The initial point of a vector is the endpoint (not the tip) of a vector arrow.

Punto de inicio (p. 809) El punto de inicio de un vector es el extremo (no la punta) de una flecha vectorial.

English | Spanish

Initial side (p. 836) When an angle is in standard position, the initial side of the angle is given to be on the positive x-axis. The other ray is the terminal side of the angle.

Lado inicial (p. 836) Cuando un ángulo está en posición normal, el lado inicial del ángulo se ubica en el eje positivo de las x. El otro rayo, o semirrecta, forma el lado terminal del ángulo.

Example

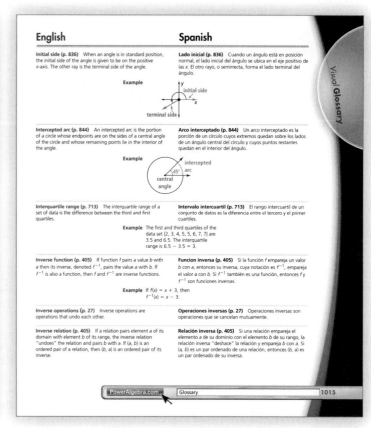

Intercepted arc (p. 844) An intercepted arc is the portion of a circle whose endpoints are on the sides of a central angle of the circle and whose remaining points lie in the interior of the angle.

Arco interceptado (p. 844) Un arco interceptado es la porción de un círculo cuyos extremos quedan sobre los lados de un ángulo central del círculo y cuyos puntos restantes quedan en el interior del ángulo.

Example

Interquartile range (p. 713) The interquartile range of a set of data is the difference between the third and first quartiles.

Intervalo intercuartil (p. 713) El rango intercuartil de un conjunto de datos es la diferencia entre el tercero y el primer cuartiles.

Example The first and third quartiles of the data set {2, 3, 4, 5, 5, 6, 7, 7} are 3.5 and 6.5. The interquartile range is $6.5 - 3.5 = 3$.

Inverse function (p. 405) If function f pairs a value b with a then its inverse, denoted f^{-1}, pairs the value a with b. If f^{-1} is also a function, then f and f^{-1} are inverse functions.

Funcion inversa (p. 405) Si la función f empareja un valor b con a, entonces su inversa, cuya notación es f^{-1}, empareja el valor a con b. Si f^{-1} también es una función, entonces f y f^{-1} son funciones inversas.

Example If $f(x) = x + 3$, then $f^{-1}(x) = x - 3$.

Inverse operations (p. 27) Inverse operations are operations that undo each other.

Operaciones inversas (p. 27) Operaciones inversas son operaciones que se cancelan mutuamente.

Inverse relation (p. 405) If a relation pairs element a of its domain with element b of its range, the inverse relation "undoes" the relation and pairs b with a. If (a, b) is an ordered pair of a relation, then (b, a) is an ordered pair of its inverse.

Relación inversa (p. 405) Si una relación empareja el elemento a de su dominio con el elemento b de su rango, la relación inversa "deshace" la relación y empareja b con a. Si (a, b) es un par ordenado de una relación, entonces (b, a) es un par ordenado de su inversa.

English | Spanish

Inverse variation (p. 498) An inverse variation is a relation represented by an equation of the form $xy = k$, $y = \frac{k}{x}$, or $x = \frac{k}{y}$, where $k \neq 0$.

Variación inversa (p. 498) Una variación inversa es una relación representada por la ecuación $xy = k$, $y = \frac{k}{x}$, ó $x = \frac{k}{y}$, donde $k \neq 0$.

Example

$xy = 5$, or $y = \frac{5}{x}$

J

Joint variation (p. 501) A joint variation is a relation in which one variable varies directly with respect to each of two or more variables.

Variación conjunta (p. 501) Una variación conjunta es una relación en la cual el valor de una variable varía directamente con respecto a cada una de dos o más variables.

Example $z = 8xy$
$T = kPV$

L

Law of Cosines (p. 936) In $\triangle ABC$, let a, b, and c represent the lengths of the sides opposite $\angle A$, $\angle B$, and $\angle C$, respectively. Then
$a^2 = b^2 + c^2 - 2bc \cos A$,
$b^2 = a^2 + c^2 - 2ac \cos B$, and
$c^2 = a^2 + b^2 - 2ab \cos C$

Ley de cosenos (p. 936) En $\triangle ABC$, sean a, b y c las longitudes de los lados opuestos a $\angle A$, $\angle B$ y $\angle C$, respectivamente. Entonces
$a^2 = b^2 + c^2 - 2bc \cos A$,
$b^2 = a^2 + c^2 - 2ac \cos B$ y
$c^2 = a^2 + b^2 - 2ab \cos C$

Example

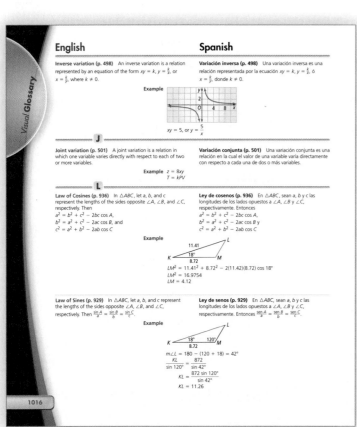

$LM^2 = 11.41^2 + 8.72^2 - 2(11.42)(8.72) \cos 18°$
$LM^2 = 16.9754$
$LM = 4.12$

Law of Sines (p. 929) In $\triangle ABC$, let a, b, and c represent the lengths of the sides opposite $\angle A$, $\angle B$, and $\angle C$, respectively. Then $\frac{\sin A}{a} = \frac{\sin B}{b} = \frac{\sin C}{c}$.

Ley de senos (p. 929) En $\triangle ABC$, sean a, b y c las longitudes de los lados opuestos a $\angle A$, $\angle B$ y $\angle C$, respectivamente. Entonces $\frac{\sin A}{a} = \frac{\sin B}{b} = \frac{\sin C}{c}$.

Example

$m\angle L = 180 - (120 + 18) = 42°$
$\frac{KL}{\sin 120°} = \frac{872}{\sin 42°}$
$KL = \frac{872 \sin 120°}{\sin 42°}$
$KL = 11.26$

English | Spanish

Like radicals (p. 374) Like radicals are radical expressions that have the same index and the same radicand.

Radicales semejantes (p. 374) Los radicales semejantes son expresiones radicales que tienen el mismo índice y el mismo radicando.

Example $4\sqrt[3]{7}$ and $\sqrt[3]{7}$ are like radicals.

Like terms (p. 21) Like terms have the same variables raised to the same powers.

Términos semejantes (p. 21) Los términos semejantes tienen las mismas variables elevadas a las mismas potencias.

Limits (p. 589) Limits in summation notation are the least and greatest integer values of the index n.

Límites (p. 589) Los límites en notación de sumatoria son el menor y el mayor valor del índice n en números enteros.

Example limits $\sum_{n=1}^{3}(3n + 5)$

Line of best fit (p. 94) The trend line that gives the most accurate model of related data is the line of best fit.

Recta de mayor aproximación (p. 94) La línea de tendencia que representa con mayor precisión los datos relacionado es la recta de mayor aproximación.

Linear equation (p. 75) A linear equation in two variables is an equation that can be written in the form $ax + by = c$. See also **Standard form of a linear equation.**

Ecuación lineal (p. 75) Una ecuación lineal de dos variables es una ecuación que se puede escribir de la forma $ax + by = c$. Ver también **Standard form of a linear equation.**

Example $y = 2x + 1$ can be written as $-2x + y = 1$.

Linear function (p. 75) A function whose graph is a line is a linear function. You can represent a linear function with a linear equation.

Función lineal (p. 75) Una función cuya gráfica es una recta es una función lineal. La función lineal se representa con una ecuación lineal.

Example

Linear inequality (p. 114) A linear inequality is an inequality in two variables whose graph is a region of the coordinate plane that is bounded by a line.

Desigualdad lineal (p. 114) Una desigualdad lineal es una desigualdad de dos variables cuya gráfica es una región del plano de coordenadas delimitado por una recta.

Example

$y > x + 1$

Linear programming (p. 157) Linear programming is a method for finding a minimum or maximum value of some quantity, given a set of constraints.

Programación lineal (p. 157) Programación lineal es un método para hallar el valor mínimo y máximo de una cantidad que se expresa como un conjunto de limitaciones.

Example Restrictions $x \geq 0$, $y \geq 0$, $x + y \leq 7$, and $y \leq -2x + 8$
Objective function: $B = 2x + 4y$
Evaluate $B = 2x + 4y$ at each vertex.
The minimum value of B occurs when $x = 0$ and $y = 0$. The maximum value of B occurs when $x = 0$ and $y = 7$.

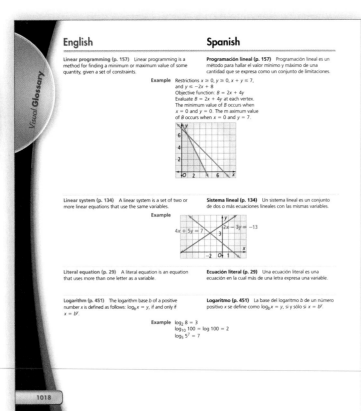

Linear system (p. 134) A linear system is a set of two or more linear equations that use the same variables.

Sistema lineal (p. 134) Un sistema lineal es un conjunto de dos o más ecuaciones lineales con las mismas variables.

Example

Literal equation (p. 29) A literal equation is an equation that uses more than one letter as a variable.

Ecuación literal (p. 29) Una ecuación literal es una ecuación en la cual más de una letra expresa una variable.

Logarithm (p. 451) The logarithm base b of a positive number x is defined as follows: $\log_b x = y$, if and only if $x = b^y$.

Logaritmo (p. 451) La base del logaritmo b de un número positivo x se define como $\log_b x = y$, si y sólo si $x = b^y$.

Example $\log_2 8 = 3$
$\log_{10} 100 = \log 100 = 2$
$\log_5 5^7 = 7$

Logarithmic equation (p. 471) A logarithmic equation is an equation that includes a logarithm involving a variable.

Ecuación logarítmica (p. 471) Una ecuación logarítmica es una ecuación que incluye un logaritmo con una variable.

Example $\log_3 x = 4$

Logarithmic function (p. 454) A logarithmic function is the inverse of an exponential function.

Función logarítmica (p. 454) Una función logarítmica es la inversa de una función exponencial.

Example

Logarithmic scale (p. 453) A logarithmic scale is a scale that uses the logarithm of a quantity instead of the quantity itself.

Escala logarítmica (p. 453) Una escala logarítmica es una escala que usa el logaritmo de una cantidad vez de la cantidad misma.

— M —

Magnitude (p. 809) The magnitude of a vector **v** is the length of the arrow.

Magnitud (p. 809) La magnitud de un vector **v** es la longitud de la flecha.

Major axis (p. 639) The major axis of an ellipse is the segment that contains the foci of the ellipse and has endpoints on the ellipse.

Eje mayor (p. 639) En una elipsis, el eje mayor es el segmento que contiene los focos de la elipsis y tiene puntos extremos sobre la elipsis.

Example

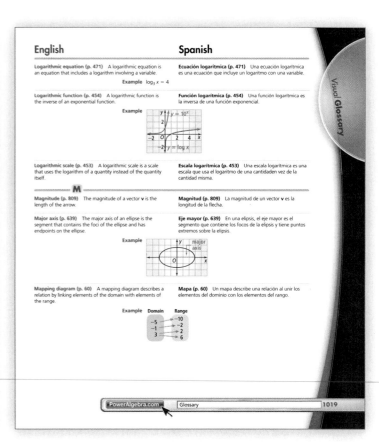

Mapping diagram (p. 60) A mapping diagram describes a relation by linking elements of the domain with elements of the range.

Mapa (p. 60) Un mapa describe una relación al unir los elementos del dominio con los elementos del rango.

Example Domain   Range
−5 → −10
−1 → −2
3 → 2, 6

Margin of error (p. 746) The distance from the sample mean or sample proportion that is used to create a confidence interval for the population mean or the population proportion. For a 95% confidence level, $ME = 1.96 \cdot \frac{s}{\sqrt{n}}$, where ME is the margin of error, s is the standard deviation of the sample data, and n is the number of values in the sample.

Margen de error (p. 746) La distancia desde la media de una muestra o desde la proporción de una muestra que se usa para crear el intervalo de confianza para la media o proporción de una población. Para un nivel de confianza de 95%, $ME = 1.96 \cdot \frac{s}{\sqrt{n}}$, siendo ME el margen de error, s la desviación estándar de los datos de la muestra, y n el número de valores en la muestra.

Example The standard deviation of a sample is 5.0 and the number of trials is 30. The margin of error at a 95% confidence level is $ME = 1.96 \cdot \frac{5.0}{\sqrt{30}} \approx 1.79$.

Matrix (p. 174) A matrix is a rectangular array of numbers written within brackets.

Matriz (p. 174) Una matriz es un conjunto de números encerrados en corchetes y dispuestos en forma de rectángulo.

Example $A = \begin{bmatrix} 1 & -2 & 0 & 10 \\ 9 & 7 & -3 & 8 \\ 2 & -10 & 1 & -6 \end{bmatrix}$

The number 2 is the element in the third row and first column. A is a 3×4 matrix.

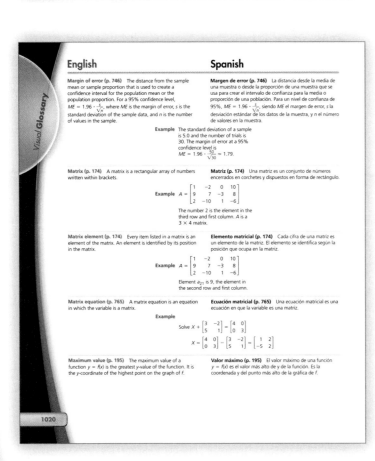

Matrix element (p. 174) Every item listed in a matrix is an element of the matrix. An element is identified by its position in the matrix.

Elemento matricial (p. 174) Cada cifra de una matriz es un elemento de la matriz. El elemento se identifica según la posición que ocupa en la matriz.

Example $A = \begin{bmatrix} 1 & -2 & 0 & 10 \\ 9 & 7 & -3 & 8 \\ 2 & -10 & 1 & -6 \end{bmatrix}$

Element a_{21} is 9, the element in the second row and first column.

Matrix equation (p. 765) A matrix equation is an equation in which the variable is a matrix.

Ecuación matricial (p. 765) Una ecuación matricial es una ecuación en que la variable es una matriz.

Example Solve $X + \begin{bmatrix} 3 & -2 \\ 5 & 1 \end{bmatrix} = \begin{bmatrix} 4 & 0 \\ 0 & 3 \end{bmatrix}$

$X = \begin{bmatrix} 4 & 0 \\ 0 & 3 \end{bmatrix} - \begin{bmatrix} 3 & -2 \\ 5 & 1 \end{bmatrix} = \begin{bmatrix} 1 & 2 \\ -5 & 2 \end{bmatrix}$

Maximum value (p. 195) The maximum value of a function $y = f(x)$ is the greatest y-value of the function. It is the y-coordinate of the highest point on the graph of f.

Valor máximo (p. 195) El valor máximo de una función $y = f(x)$ es el valor más alto de y de la función. Es la coordenada y del punto más alto de la gráfica de f.

Mean (p. 711) The sum of the data values divided by the number of data values is the mean. See also **Arithmetic mean.**

Media (p. 711) La suma de los valores de datos dividida por el número de valores de datos sumados es la media. Ver también **Arithmetic mean.**

Example {1, 2, 3, 3, 6, 6}
mean $= \frac{1 + 2 + 3 + 3 + 6 + 6}{6}$
$= \frac{21}{6} = 3.5$

Measures of central tendency (p. 711) The mean, the median, and the mode are each central values that help describe a set of data. They are called measures of central tendency.

Medidas de tendencia central (p. 711) La media, la mediana y la moda son los valores centrales que facilitan la descripción de un conjunto de datos. A estos valores se les llama medidas de tendencia central.

Example {1, 2, 3, 3, 4, 5, 6, 6}
mean = 3.75
median = 3.5
modes = 3 and 6

Measure of variation (p. 719) Measures of variation, such as the range, the interquartile range, and the standard deviation, describe how the data in a data set are spread out.

Medida de dispersión (p. 719) Las medidas de dispersión, tal como el rango, el intervalo intercuartil y la desviación típica, describen cómo se dispersan los datos en un conjunto de datos.

Median (p. 711) The median is the middle value in a data set. If the data set contains an even number of values, the median is the mean of the two middle values.

Mediana (p. 711) La mediana es el valor situado en el medio en un conjunto de datos. Si el conjunto de datos contiene un número par de valores, la mediana es la media de los dos valores del medio.

Example {1, 2, 3, 3, 4, 5, 6, 6}
median $= \frac{3 + 4}{2} = \frac{7}{2} = 3.5$

Midline (p. 830) The horizontal line through the average of the maximum and minimum values.

Línea media (p. 830) Recta horizontal que pasa a través de la media de los valores máximos y mínimos.

Example

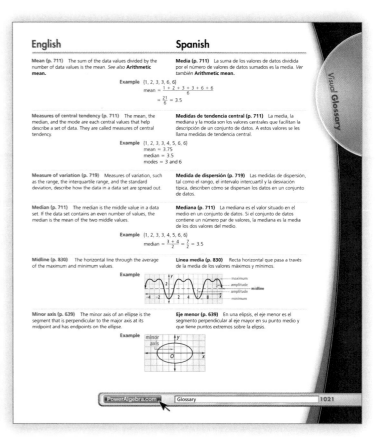

Minor axis (p. 639) The minor axis of an ellipse is the segment that is perpendicular to the major axis at its midpoint and has endpoints on the ellipse.

Eje menor (p. 639) En una elipsis, el eje menor es el segmento perpendicular al eje mayor en su punto medio y que tiene puntos extremos sobre la elipsis.

Example

English | Spanish

Minimum value (p. 195) The minimum value of a function $y = f(x)$ is the least y-value of the function. It is the y-coordinate of the lowest point on the graph of f.

Valor mínimo (p. 195) El valor mínimo de una función $y = f(x)$ es el valor más bajo de y de la función. Es la coordenada y del punto más bajo de la gráfica de f.

Mode (p. 711) The mode is the most frequently occurring value (or values) in a set of data.

Moda (p. 711) La moda es el valor o valores que ocurren con mayor frecuencia en un conjunto de datos.

Example $\{1, 2, 3, 4, 5, 6, 6\}$
The modes are 3 and 6.

Monomial (p. 280) A monomial is either a real number, a variable, or a product of real numbers and variables with whole number exponents.

Monomio (p. 280) Un monomio es un número real, una variable o un producto de números reales y variables cuyos exponentes son números enteros.

Example $1, x, 2z, 4ab^2$

Multiple zero (p. 291) If a linear factor is repeated in the complete factored form of a polynomial, the zero related to that factor is a multiple zero.

Cero múltiplo (p. 291) Si un factor lineal se repite en la forma factorizada completa de un polinomio, el cero relacionado con ese factor es un cero múltiplo.

Example The zeros of the function
$P(x) = 2x(x - 3)^2(x + 1)$ are 0, 3,
and -1. Since $(x - 3)$ occurs twice
as a factor, 3 is a multiple zero.

Multiplicative identity (p. 14) The multiplicative identity is 1. The product of 1 and any number is that number. The product of reciprocals is 1.

Identidad multiplicativa (p. 14) La identidad multiplicativa es 1. El producto de 1 y cualquier otro número es ese número. El producto del recíproco es 1.

Multiplicative identity matrix (p. 782) For an $n \times n$ square matrix, the multiplicative identity matrix is an $n \times n$ square matrix I, or $I_{n \times n}$, with 1's along the main diagonal and 0's elsewhere.

Matriz de identidad multiplicativa (p. 782) Para una matriz cuadrada $n \times n$, la matriz de identidad multiplicativa es la matriz cuadrada I de $n \times n$, o $I_{n \times n}$, con unos por la diagonal principal y ceros en los demás lugares.

Example $I_{2 \times 2} = \begin{bmatrix} 1 & 0 \\ 0 & 1 \end{bmatrix}$, $I_{3 \times 3} = \begin{bmatrix} 1 & 0 & 0 \\ 0 & 1 & 0 \\ 0 & 0 & 1 \end{bmatrix}$

Multiplicative inverse (p. 14) The reciprocal or multiplicative inverse of any nonzero number a is $\frac{1}{a}$. The product of reciprocals is 1, the multiplicative identity.

Inverso multiplicativo (p. 14) El recíproco o inverso multiplicativo de cualquier número a, que no sea cero, es $\frac{1}{a}$. El producto de recíprocos es 1, la identidad multiplicativa.

Example $5 \times \frac{1}{5} = 1$

Multiplicative inverse of a matrix (p. 782) If A and X are $n \times n$ matrices, and $AX = XA = I$, then X is the multiplicative inverse of A, written A^{-1}.

Inverso multiplicativo de una matriz (p. 782) Si A y X son matrices $n \times n$, y $AX = XA = I$, entonces X es el inverso multiplicativo de A, expresado como A^{-1}.

Example $A = \begin{bmatrix} 2 & 1 \\ 4 & 0 \end{bmatrix}$, $X = \begin{bmatrix} 0 & \frac{1}{4} \\ 1 & \frac{1}{2} \end{bmatrix}$

$AX = \begin{bmatrix} 1 & 0 \\ 0 & 1 \end{bmatrix} = I$, so $X = A^{-1}$

English | Spanish

Multiplicity (p. 291) The multiplicity of a zero of a polynomial function is the number of times the related linear factor is repeated in the factored form of the polynomial.

Multiplicidad (p. 291) La multiplicidad de un cero de una función polinomial es el número de veces que el factor lineal relacionado se repite en la forma factorizada del polinomio.

Example The zeros of the function
$P(x) = 2x(x - 3)^2(x + 1)$ are 0, 3,
and -1. Since $(x - 3)$ occurs twice as
a factor, the zero 3 has multiplicity 2.

Mutually exclusive events (p. 689) When two events cannot happen at the same time, the events are mutually exclusive. If A and B are mutually exclusive events, then $P(A \text{ or } B) = P(A) + P(B)$.

Sucesos mutuamente excluyentes (p. 689) Cuando dos sucesos no pueden ocurrir al mismo tiempo, son mutuamente excluyentes. Si A y B son sucesos mutuamente excluyentes, entonces $P(A \text{ or } B) = P(A) + P(B)$.

Example Rolling an even number E and
rolling a multiple of five M on a
standard number cube are
mutually exclusive events.
$P(E \text{ or } M) = P(E) + P(M)$
$= \frac{3}{6} + \frac{1}{6}$
$= \frac{4}{6}$, or $\frac{2}{3}$

N

n factorial ($n!$) (p. 675) For any positive integer n, n factorial is $n(n - 1) \cdot \cdots \cdot 3 \cdot 2 \cdot 1$. Zero factorial ($0!$) = 1.

n factorial ($n!$) (p. 675) Para cualquier entero n, n factorial es $n(n - 1) \cdot \cdots \cdot 3 \cdot 2 \cdot 1$. El cero factorial ($0!$) = 1.

Example $4! = 4 \cdot 3 \cdot 2 \cdot 1 = 24$

nth root (p. 361) For any real numbers a and b, and any positive integer n, if $a^n = b$, then a is an nth root of b.

raíz n-ésima (p. 361) Para todos los números reales a y b, y todo número entero positivo n, si $a^n = b$, entonces a es la n-ésima raíz de b.

Example $\sqrt[5]{32} = 2$ because $2^5 = 32$.
$\sqrt[4]{81} = 3$ because $3^4 = 81$.

Natural base exponential function (p. 446) A natural base exponential function is an exponential function with base e.

Función exponencial con base natural (p. 446) Una función exponencial con base natural es una función exponencial con base e.

English | Spanish

Natural logarithmic function (p. 478) A natural logarithmic function is a logarithmic function with base e. The natural logarithmic function, $y = \ln x$, is $y = \log_e x$. It is the inverse of $y = e^x$.

Función logarítmica natural (p. 478) Una función logarítmica natural es una función logarítmica con base e. La función logarítmica natural, $y = \ln x$, es $y = \log_e x$. Ésta es la función inversa de $y = e^x$.

Example

$\ln e^3 = 3$
$\ln 10 \approx 2.3026$
$\ln 36 \approx 3.5835$

Non-removable discontinuity (p. 516) A non-removable discontinuity is a point of discontinuity that is not removable. It represents a break in the graph of f where you cannot redefine f to make the graph continuous.

Discontinuidad irremovible (p. 516) Una discontinuidad irremovible es un punto de discontinuidad que no se puede remover. Representa una interrupción en la gráfica f donde no se puede redefinir f para volverla una gráfica continua.

Normal distribution (p. 739) A normal distribution shows data that vary randomly from the mean in the pattern of a bell-shaped curve.

Distribución normal (p. 739) Una distribución normal muestra, con una curva en forma de campana, datos que varían aleatoriamente respecto a la media.

Example

Distribution of Test Scores

13.5%   13.5%
2.5%   34%   34%   2.5%
53.5 60.0 66.5 73.0 79.5

In a class of 200 students, the scores
on a test were normally distributed.
The mean score was 66.5 and the
standard deviation was 6.5. The
number of students who scored greater
than 73 percent was about 13.5% + 2.5% of
those who took the test.
16% of 200 = 32
About 32 students scored 73 or higher
on the test.

Normal vectors (p. 812) Normal vectors are perpendicular vectors. Their dot product is 0.

Vectores normales (p. 812) Los vectores normales son vectores perpendiculares. El producto escalar es 0.

Numerical expression (p. 5) A numerical expression is a mathematical phrase that contains numbers and operation symbols.

Expresión numérica (p. 5) Una expresión numérica es una expresión matemática compuesta de números y símbolos de operación.

English | Spanish

O

Objective function (p. 157) In a linear programming model, the objective function is a model of the quantity that you want to make as large or as small as possible. See **Linear programming.**

Función objetiva (p. 157) En un modelo de programación lineal, la función objetiva es un modelo de la cantidad que se quiere aumentar o disminuir cuanto sea posible. Ver **Linear programming.**

Observational study (p. 726) In an observational study, you measure or observe members of a sample in such a way that they are not affected by the study.

Estudio de observación (p. 726) En un estudio de observación, se miden u observan a los miembros de una muestra de tal manera que no les afecte el estudio.

One-to-one function (p. 408) A one-to-one function is a function for which each y-value in the range corresponds to exactly one x-value in the domain. A one-to-one function f has an inverse f^{-1} that is also a function.

Función uno a uno (p. 408) Una función uno a uno es una función donde cada valor y que se encuentra en el rango corresponde exactamente a un valor x en el dominio. Una función uno a uno f tiene un inverso f^{-1} que también es una función.

Opposite (p. 14) The opposite or additive inverse of any number a is $-a$. The sum of opposites is zero, the additive identity.

Opuesto (p. 14) El opuesto o inverso aditivo de cualquier número a es $-a$. La suma de opuestos es cero, la identidad aditiva.

Example $3 + (-3) = 0$
$5.2 + (-5.2) = 0$

Ordered triples (p. 164) Ordered triples of the form (x, y, z) represent the location of a point in coordinate space.

Tripletas ordenadas (p. 164) Las tripletas ordenadas de la forma (x, y, z) representan la ubicación de un punto en el espacio de coordenadas.

Example $(2, 4, 5)$
$(0, 1, 2)$
$(0, 0, 0)$

Outlier (p. 712) An outlier is a value substantially different from the rest of the data in a set.

Valor extremo (p. 712) Un valor extremo es un valor considerablemente diferente al resto de los datos en un conjunto.

Example The outlier in the data set
$\{56, 64, 73, 59, 98, 65, 59\}$ is 98.

P

Parabola (p. 194) A parabola is the graph of a quadratic function. It is the set of all points P in a plane that are the same distance from a fixed point F, the focus, as they are from a line d, the directrix.

Parábola (p. 194) La parábola es la gráfica de una función cuadrática. Es el conjunto de todos los puntos P situados en un plano a la misma distancia de un punto fijo F, o foco, y de la recta d, o directriz.

Example

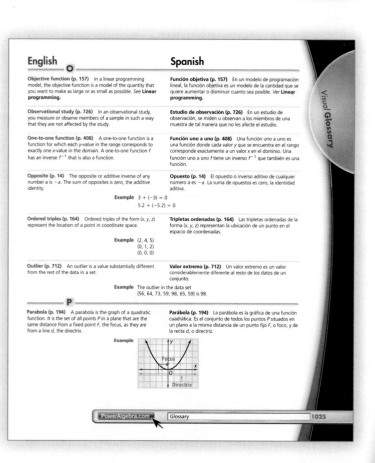

Page 1026

English | Spanish

Parallel lines (p. 85) Parallel lines are coplanar lines that do not intersect. In the coordinate plane, parallel lines have the same slope.

Rectas paralelas (p. 85) Rectas paralelas son líneas coplanares que no se intersecan. En un plano de coordenadas, las rectas paralelas tienen la misma pendiente.

Parent function (p. 99) A parent function is the simplest form of a set of functions that form a family.

Función elemental (p. 99) Una función madre es la mínima expresión de un conjunto de funciones que forma una familia.

Example $y = x$ is the parent function for the functions of the form $y = x + k$.

Pascal's Triangle (p. 327) Pascal's Triangle is a triangular array of numbers in which the first and last number is 1. Each of the other numbers in the row is the sum of the two numbers above it.

Triángulo de Pascal (p. 327) El Triángulo de Pascal es una distribución triangular de números en la cual el primer número y el último número son 1. Cada uno de los otros números en la fila es la suma de los dos números de encima.

Example **Pascal's Triangle**
```
        1
      1   1
    1   2   1
  1   3   3   1
1   4   6   4   1
1   5  10  10   5   1
```

Percentiles (p. 714) A percentile is a number from 0 to 100 that you can associate with a value x from a data set. It shows the percent of the data that are less than or equal to x.

Percentiles (p. 714) Un percentil es un número de 0 a 100 que se puede asociar con un valor x de un conjunto de datos. Éste muestra el porcentaje de los datos que son menores o iguales a x.

Perfect square trinomial (p. 219) A perfect square trinomial is a trinomial that is the square of a binomial.

Trinomio cuadrado perfecto (p. 219) Un trinomio cuadrado perfecto es un trinomio que es el cuadrado de un binomio.

Example perfect square trinominal / binominal square
$$16x^2 - 24x + 9 = (4x - 3)^2$$

Period (p. 828) The period of a periodic function is the horizontal length of one cycle.

Periodo (p. 828) El período de una función periódica es el intervalo horizontal de un ciclo.

Example

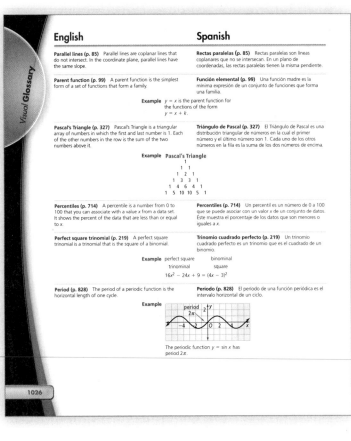

The periodic function $y = \sin x$ has period 2π.

1026

Page 1027

English | Spanish

Periodic function (p. 828) A periodic function repeats a pattern of y-values at regular intervals.

Función periódica (p. 828) Una función periódica repite un patrón de valores y a intervalos regulares.

Example

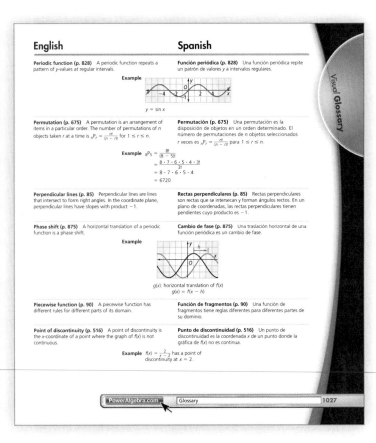

$y = \sin x$

Permutation (p. 675) A permutation is an arrangement of items in a particular order. The number of permutations of n objects taken r at a time is ${}_nP_r = \frac{n!}{(n-r)!}$ for $1 \le r \le n$.

Permutación (p. 675) Una permutación es la disposición de objetos en un orden determinado. El número de permutaciones de n objetos seleccionados r veces es ${}_nP_r = \frac{n!}{(n-r)!}$ para $1 \le r \le n$.

Example ${}_8P_5 = \frac{8!}{(8-5)!}$
$$= \frac{8 \cdot 7 \cdot 6 \cdot 5 \cdot 4 \cdot 3!}{3!}$$
$$= 8 \cdot 7 \cdot 6 \cdot 5 \cdot 4$$
$$= 6720$$

Perpendicular lines (p. 85) Perpendicular lines are lines that intersect to form right angles. In the coordinate plane, perpendicular lines have slopes with product -1.

Rectas perpendiculares (p. 85) Rectas perpendiculares son rectas que se intersecan y forman ángulos rectos. En un plano de coordenadas, las rectas perpendiculares tienen pendientes cuyo producto es -1.

Phase shift (p. 875) A horizontal translation of a periodic function is a phase shift.

Cambio de fase (p. 875) Una traslación horizontal de una función periódica es un cambio de fase.

Example

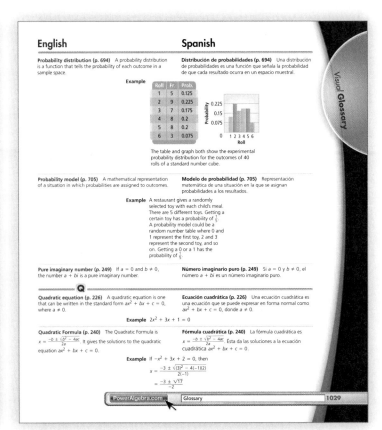

$g(x)$: horizontal translation of $f(x)$
$g(x) = f(x - h)$

Piecewise function (p. 90) A piecewise function has different rules for different parts of its domain.

Función de fragmentos (p. 90) Una función de fragmentos tiene reglas diferentes para diferentes partes de su dominio.

Point of discontinuity (p. 516) A point of discontinuity is the x-coordinate of a point where the graph of $f(x)$ is not continuous.

Punto de discontinuidad (p. 516) Un punto de discontinuidad es la coordenada x de un punto donde la gráfica de $f(x)$ no es continua.

Example $f(x) = \frac{2}{x-2}$ has a point of discontinuity at $x = 2$.

Page 1028

English | Spanish

Point-slope form (p. 81) The point-slope form of an equation of a line is $y - y_1 = m(x - x_1)$, where m is the slope of the line and (x_1, y_1) is a point on the line.

Forma punto-pendiente (p. 81) La forma punto-pendiente de una ecuación lineal es $y - y_1 = m(x - x_1)$, donde m es la pendiente de la recta y (x_1, y_1) es un punto de la recta.

Example $y - 3 = 2(x - 1)$
$y + 4 = 5(x - 2)$
$y - 2 = 3(x + 2)$

Polynomial (p. 280) A polynomial is a monomial or the sum of monomials.

Polinomio (p. 280) Un polinomio es un monomio o la suma de dos o más monomios.

Example $3x^3 + 4x^2 - 2x + 5$
$8x$
$x^2 + 4x + 2$

Polynomial function (p. 280) A polynomial in the variable x defines a polynomial function of x.

Función polinomial (p. 280) Un polinomio en la variable x define una función polinomial de x.

Example $P(x) = a_nx^n + a_{n-1}x^{n-1} + \cdots + a_1x + a_0$ is a polynomial function, where n is a nonnegative integer and the coefficients $a_n, \ldots, a_0$ are real numbers.

Population (p. 725) A population is the members of a set.

Población (p. 725) Una población está compuesta por los miembros de un conjunto.

Power function (p. 341) A power function is a function of the form $y = a \cdot x^b$, where a and b are nonzero real numbers.

Función de potencia (p. 341) Una función de potencia es una función de la forma $y = a \cdot x^b$, donde a y b son números reales diferentes de cero.

Preimage (p. 801) The preimage is the original figure before a transformation.

Preimagen (p. 801) La preimagen es la figura original antes de sufrir una transformación.

Example

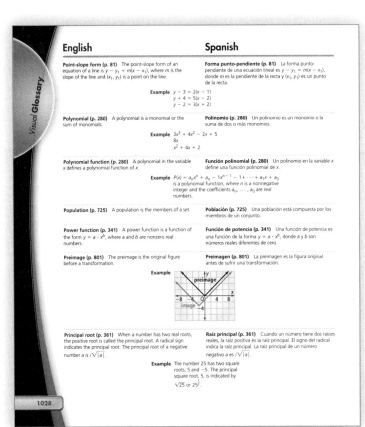

Principal root (p. 361) When a number has two real roots, the positive root is called the principal root. A radical sign indicates the principal root. The principal root of a negative number a is $i\sqrt{|a|}$.

Raíz principal (p. 361) Cuando un número tiene dos raíces reales, la raíz positiva es la raíz principal. El signo del radical indica la raíz principal. La raíz principal de un número negativo a es $i\sqrt{|a|}$.

Example The number 25 has two square roots, 5 and -5. The principal square root, 5, is indicated by $\sqrt{25}$ or $25^{\frac{1}{2}}$.

1028

Page 1029

English | Spanish

Probability distribution (p. 694) A probability distribution is a function that tells the probability of each outcome in a sample space.

Distribución de probabilidades (p. 694) Una distribución de probabilidades es una función que señala la probabilidad de que cada resultado ocurra en un espacio muestral.

Example

Roll	Fr.	Prob.
1	5	0.125
2	9	0.225
3	7	0.175
4	8	0.2
5	8	0.2
6	3	0.075

(bar graph: Probability vs Roll, 1 2 3 4 5 6)

The table and graph both show the experimental probability distribution for the outcomes of 40 rolls of a standard number cube.

Probability model (p. 705) A mathematical representation of a situation in which probabilities are assigned to outcomes.

Modelo de probabilidad (p. 705) Representación matemática de una situación en la que se asignan probabilidades a los resultados.

Example A restaurant gives a randomly selected toy with each child's meal. There are 5 different toys. Getting a certain toy has a probability of $\frac{1}{5}$. A probability model could be a random number table where 0 and 1 represent the first toy, 2 and 3 represent the second toy, and so on. Getting a 0 or a 1 has the probability of $\frac{1}{5}$.

Pure imaginary number (p. 249) If $a = 0$ and $b \ne 0$, the number $a + bi$ is a pure imaginary number.

Número imaginario puro (p. 249) Si $a = 0$ y $b \ne 0$, el número $a + bi$ es un número imaginario puro.

— Q —

Quadratic equation (p. 226) A quadratic equation is one that can be written in the standard form $ax^2 + bx + c = 0$, where $a \ne 0$.

Ecuación cuadrática (p. 226) Una ecuación cuadrática es una ecuación que se puede expresar en forma normal como $ax^2 + bx + c = 0$, donde $a \ne 0$.

Example $2x^2 + 3x + 1 = 0$

Quadratic Formula (p. 240) The Quadratic Formula is $x = \frac{-b \pm \sqrt{b^2 - 4ac}}{2a}$. It gives the solutions to the quadratic equation $ax^2 + bx + c = 0$.

Fórmula cuadrática (p. 240) La fórmula cuadrática es $x = \frac{-b \pm \sqrt{b^2 - 4ac}}{2a}$. Ésta da las soluciones a la ecuación cuadrática $ax^2 + bx + c = 0$.

Example If $-x^2 + 3x + 2 = 0$, then
$$x = \frac{-3 \pm \sqrt{(3)^2 - 4(-1)(2)}}{2(-1)}$$
$$= \frac{-3 \pm \sqrt{17}}{-2}$$

Visual Glossary

English / Spanish

Quadratic function (p. 194) A quadratic function is a function that you can write in the form $f(x) = ax^2 + bx + c$ with $a \neq 0$.

Función cuadrática (p. 194) Una función cuadrática es una función que puedes escribir como $f(x) = ax^2 + bx + c$ con $a \neq 0$.

Example

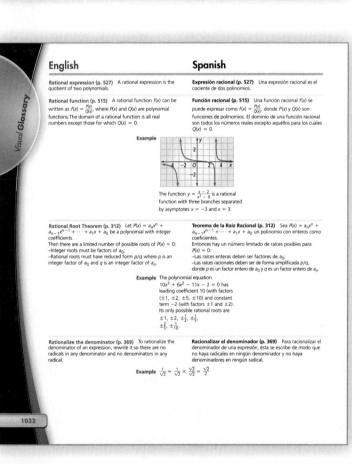

$$y = x^2 + 2x - 2$$

Quantity (p. 5) A mathematical quantity is anything that can be measured or counted.

Cantidad (p. 5) Una cantidad matemática es cualquier cosa que se puede medir o contar.

Quartile (p. 713) Quartiles are values that separate a finite data set into four equal parts. The second quartile (Q_2) is the median of the data. The first and third quartiles (Q_1 and Q_3) are the medians of the lower half and upper half of the data, respectively.

Cuartil (p. 713) Los cuartiles son valores que separan un conjunto finito de datos en cuatro partes iguales. El segundo cuartil (Q_2) es la mediana de los datos. Los cuartiles primero y tercero (Q_1 y Q_3) son las medianas de la mitad superior e inferior de los datos, respectivamente.

Example $\{2, 3, 4, 5, 5, 6, 7, 7\}$
$$Q_1 = 3.5$$
$$Q_2 \text{ (median)} = 5$$
$$Q_3 = 6.5$$

R

Radian (p. 844) $\frac{d^{\circ}}{180^{\circ}} = \frac{r \text{ radians}}{\pi \text{ radians}}$

Radián (p. 844) $\frac{d^{\circ}}{180^{\circ}} = \frac{r \text{ radianes}}{\pi \text{ radianes}}$

Example $60^{\circ} \rightarrow \frac{60}{180} = \frac{x}{\pi}$
$$x = \frac{60\pi}{180}$$
$$= \frac{\pi}{3}$$
Thus, $60^{\circ} = \frac{\pi}{3}$ radians.

Radical equation (p. 390) A radical equation is an equation that has a variable in a radicand or has a variable with a rational exponent.

Ecuación radical (p. 390) La ecuación radical es una ecuación que contiene una variable en el radicando o una variable con un exponente racional.

Example $(\sqrt{x})^3 + 1 = 65$
$$x^{\frac{3}{2}} + 1 = 65$$

Radical function (p. 415) A radical function is a function that can be written in the form $f(x) = a\sqrt[n]{x - h} + k$, where $a \neq 0$. For even values of n, the domain of a radical function is the real numbers $x \geq h$. See also **Square root function.**

Función radical (p. 415) Una función radical es una función que puede expresarse como $f(x) = a\sqrt[n]{x - h} + k$, donde $a \neq 0$. Para n par, el dominio de la función radical son los números reales tales que $x \geq h$. Ver también **Square root function.**

Example $f(x) = \sqrt{x - 2}$

English / Spanish

Radicand (p. 362) The number under a radical sign is the radicand.

Radicando (p. 362) La expresión que aparece debajo del signo radical es el radicando.

Example The radicand in $3\sqrt[4]{7}$ is 7.

Radius (p. 630) The radius r of a circle is the distance between the center of the circle and any point on the circumference.

Radio (p. 630) El radio r de un círculo es la distancia entre el centro del círculo y cualquier punto de la circunferencia.

Example

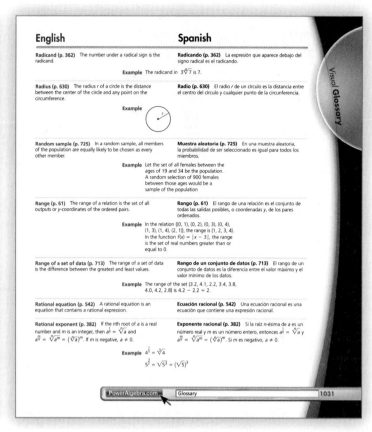

Random sample (p. 725) In a random sample, all members of the population are equally likely to be chosen as every other member.

Muestra aleatoria (p. 725) En una muestra aleatoria, la probabilidad de ser seleccionado es igual para todos los miembros.

Example Let the set of all females between the ages of 19 and 34 be the population. A random selection of 900 females between those ages would be a sample of the population

Range (p. 61) The range of a relation is the set of all outputs or y-coordinates of the ordered pairs.

Rango (p. 61) El rango de una relación es el conjunto de todas las salidas posibles, o coordenadas y, de los pares ordenados.

Example In the relation $\{(0, 1), (0, 2), (0, 3), (0, 4), (1, 3), (1, 4), (2, 1)\}$, the range is $\{1, 2, 3, 4\}$. In the function $f(x) = |x - 3|$, the range is the set of real numbers greater than or equal to 0.

Range of a set of data (p. 713) The range of a set of data is the difference between the greatest and least values.

Rango de un conjunto de datos (p. 713) El rango de un conjunto de datos es la diferencia entre el valor máximo y el valor mínimo de los datos.

Example The range of the set $\{3.2, 4.1, 2.2, 3.4, 3.8, 4.0, 4.2, 2.8\}$ is $4.2 - 2.2 = 2$.

Rational equation (p. 542) A rational equation is an equation that contains a rational expression.

Ecuación racional (p. 542) Una ecuación racional es una ecuación que contiene una expresión racional.

Rational exponent (p. 382) If the nth root of a is a real number and m is an integer, then $a^{\frac{1}{n}} = \sqrt[n]{a}$ and $a^{\frac{m}{n}} = \sqrt[n]{a^m} = (\sqrt[n]{a})^m$. If m is negative, $a \neq 0$.

Exponente racional (p. 382) Si la raíz n-ésima de a es un número real y m es un número entero, entonces $a^{\frac{1}{n}} = \sqrt[n]{a}$ y $a^{\frac{m}{n}} = \sqrt[n]{a^m} = (\sqrt[n]{a})^m$. Si m es negativo, $a \neq 0$.

Example $4^{\frac{1}{3}} = \sqrt[3]{4}$
$$5^{\frac{3}{2}} = \sqrt{5^3} = (\sqrt{5})^3$$

English / Spanish

Rational expression (p. 527) A rational expression is the quotient of two polynomials.

Expresión racional (p. 527) Una expresión racional es el cociente de dos polinomios.

Rational function (p. 515) A rational function $f(x)$ can be written as $f(x) = \frac{P(x)}{Q(x)}$, where $P(x)$ and $Q(x)$ are polynomial functions. The domain of a rational function is all real numbers except those for which $Q(x) = 0$.

Función racional (p. 515) Una función racional $f(x)$ se puede expresar como $f(x) = \frac{P(x)}{Q(x)}$, donde $P(x)$ y $Q(x)$ son funciones de polinomios. El dominio de una función racional son todos los números reales excepto aquéllos para los cuales $Q(x) = 0$.

Example

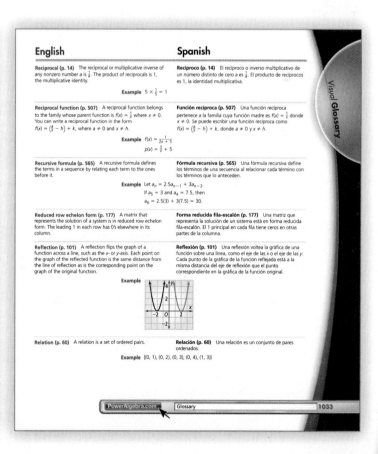

The function $y = \frac{x - 2}{x^2 - 9}$ is a rational function with three branches separated by asymptotes $x = -3$ and $x = 3$.

Rational Root Theorem (p. 312) Let $P(x) = a_n x^n + a_{n-1}x^{n-1} + \cdots + a_1 x + a_0$ be a polynomial with integer coefficients. Then there are a limited number of possible roots of $P(x) = 0$:
–Integer roots must be factors of a_0.
–Rational roots must have reduced form p/q where p is an integer factor of a_0 and q is an integer factor of a_n.

Teorema de la Raíz Racional (p. 312) Sea $P(x) = a_n x^n + a_{n-1}x^{n-1} + \cdots + a_1 x + a_0$ un polinomio con enteros como coeficientes. Entonces hay un número limitado de raíces posibles para $P(x) = 0$:
–Las raíces enteras deben ser factores de a_0.
–Las raíces racionales deben ser de forma simplificada p/q, donde p es un factor entero de a_0 y q es un factor entero de a_n.

Example The polynomial equation $10x^3 + 6x^2 - 11x - 2 = 0$ has leading coefficient 10 (with factors $\pm 1, \pm 2, \pm 5, \pm 10$) and constant term -2 (with factors ± 1 and ± 2). Its only possible rational roots are $\pm 1, \pm 2, \pm\frac{1}{2}, \pm\frac{1}{5}, \pm\frac{2}{5}, \pm\frac{1}{10}$.

Rationalize the denominator (p. 369) To rationalize the denominator of an expression, rewrite it so there are no radicals in any denominator and no denominators in any radical.

Racionalizar el denominador (p. 369) Para racionalizar el denominador de una expresión, ésta se escribe de modo que no haya radicales en ningún denominador y no haya denominadores en ningún radical.

Example $\frac{1}{\sqrt{2}} = \frac{1}{\sqrt{2}} \times \frac{\sqrt{2}}{\sqrt{2}} = \frac{\sqrt{2}}{2}$

English / Spanish

Reciprocal (p. 14) The reciprocal or multiplicative inverse of any nonzero number a is $\frac{1}{a}$. The product of reciprocals is 1, the multiplicative identity.

Recíproco (p. 14) El recíproco o inverso multiplicativo de un número distinto de cero a es $\frac{1}{a}$. El producto de recíprocos es 1, la identidad multiplicativa.

Example $5 \times \frac{1}{5} = 1$

Reciprocal function (p. 507) A reciprocal function belongs to the family whose parent function is $f(x) = \frac{1}{x}$ where $x \neq 0$. You can write a reciprocal function in the form $f(x) = \left(\frac{a}{x} - h\right) + k$, where $a \neq 0$ and $x \neq h$.

Función recíproca (p. 507) Una función recíproca pertenece a la familia cuya función madre es $f(x) = \frac{1}{x}$ donde $x \neq 0$. Se puede escribir una función recíproca como $f(x) = \left(\frac{a}{x} - h\right) + k$, donde $a \neq 0$ y $x \neq h$.

Example $f(x) = \frac{1}{2x + 5}$
$$p(v) = \frac{3}{v} + 5$$

Recursive formula (p. 565) A recursive formula defines the terms in a sequence by relating each term to the ones before it.

Fórmula recursiva (p. 565) Una fórmula recursiva define los términos de una secuencia al relacionar cada término con los términos que lo anteceden.

Example Let $a_n = 2.5a_{n-1} + 3a_{n-2}$. If $a_3 = 3$ and $a_4 = 7.5$, then $a_6 = 2.5(3) + 3(7.5) = 30$.

Reduced row echelon form (p. 177) A matrix that represents the solution of a system is in reduced row echelon form. The leading 1 in each row has 0's elsewhere in its column.

Forma reducida fila-escalón (p. 177) Una matriz que representa la solución de un sistema está en forma reducida fila-escalón. El 1 principal en cada fila tiene ceros en otras partes de la columna.

Reflection (p. 101) A reflection flips the graph of a function across a line, such as the x- or y-axis. Each point on the graph of the reflected function is the same distance from the line of reflection as is the corresponding point on the graph of the original function.

Reflexión (p. 101) Una reflexión voltea la gráfica de una función sobre una línea, como el eje de las x o el eje de las y. Cada punto de la gráfica de la función reflejada está a la misma distancia del eje de reflexión que el punto correspondiente en la gráfica de la función original.

Example

Relation (p. 60) A relation is a set of ordered pairs.

Relación (p. 60) Una relación es un conjunto de pares ordenados.

Example $\{(0, 1), (0, 2), (0, 3), (0, 4), (1, 3)\}$

English — Spanish

Relative maximum (minimum) (p. 291) A relative maximum (minimum) is the value of the function at an up-to-down (down-to-up) turning point.

Máximo (mínimo) relativo (p. 291) El máximo (mínimo) relativo es el valor de la función en un punto de giro de arriba hacia abajo (de abajo hacia arriba).

Example

Remainder Theorem (p. 307) If you divide a polynomial $P(x)$ of degree $n > 1$ by $x - a$, then the remainder is $P(a)$.

Teorema del residuo (p. 307) Si divides un polinomio $P(x)$ con un grado $n > 1$ por $x - a$, el residuo es $P(a)$.

Example If $P(x) = x^3 - 4x^2 + x + 6$ is divided by $x - 3$, then the remainder is $P(3) = 3^3 - 4(3)^2 + 3 + 6 = 0$ (which means that $x - 3$ is a factor of $P(x)$).

Removable discontinuity (p. 516) A removable discontinuity is a point of discontinuity, a, of function f that you can remove by redefining f at $x = a$. Doing so fills in a hole in the graph of f with the point $(a, f(a))$.

Discontinuidad removible (p. 516) Una discontinuidad removible es un punto de discontinuidad a en una función f que se puede remover al redefinir f en $x = a$. Al hacer esto, se llena un hueco en la gráfica f con el punto $(a, f(a))$.

Root (p. 232) A root of a function is the input value for which the value of the function is zero. A root of an equation is a value that makes the equation true. *See also* **Zero of a function.**

Raíz (p. 232) La raíz de una función es el valor de entrada para el cual el valor de la función es cero. La raíz de una ecuación es un valor que hace verdadera la ecuación. *Ver también* **Zero of a function.**

Example -2 and 3 are roots of the function $f(x) = (x + 2)(x - 3)$ and the equation $(x + 2)(x - 3) = 0$.

Rotation (p. 804) A rotation is a transformation that turns a figure about a fixed point called the center of rotation.

Rotación (p. 804) Rotación es una transformación que hace girar una figura alrededor de un punto fijo llamado centro de rotación.

Example

Row operation (p. 176) A row operation on an augmented matrix is any of the following: switch two rows, multiply a row by a constant, add one row to another.

Operación de fila (p. 176) Una operación de fila en una matriz ampliada es cualquiera de las siguientes opciones: el intercambio de dos filas, la multiplicación de una fila por una constante o la suma de dos filas.

English — S — Spanish

Sample (p. 725) A sample from a population is some of the population.

Muestra (p. 725) Una muestra de una población es una parte de la población.

Example Let the set of all males between the ages of 19 and 34 be the population. A random selection of 900 males between those ages would be a sample of the population.

Sample proportion (p. 747) The ratio $\hat{p}$ compares x to n where x is the number of times an event occurs and n is the sample size. $\hat{p} = \frac{x}{n}$.

Proporción de una muestra (p. 747) La razón $\hat{p}$ compara x a n, siendo x el número de veces que sucede un evento y n el tamaño de la muestra. $\hat{p} = \frac{x}{n}$.

Example In a taste test, 120 persons sampled two types of cola; 40 people preferred cola A. The sample proportion is $\frac{40}{120}$, or $\frac{1}{3}$.

Sample space (p. 682) The set of all possible outcomes of an experiment is called the sample space.

Espacio muestral (p. 682) El espacio muestral es el conjunto de todos los resultados posibles de un suceso.

Example When you roll a number cube, the sample space is $\{1, 2, 3, 4, 5, 6\}$.

Scalar (p. 772) A scalar is a real number factor in a special product, such as the 3 in the vector product 3v.

Escalar (p. 772) Un escalar es un factor que es un número real en un producto especial, como el 3 en el producto vectorial 3v.

Scalar multiplication (p. 772) Scalar multiplication is an operation that multiplies a matrix A by a scalar c. To find the resulting matrix cA, multiply each element of A by c.

Multiplicación escalar (p. 772) La multiplicación escalar es la que multiplica una matriz A por un número escalar c. Para hallar la matriz cA resultante, multiplica cada elemento de A por c.

Example

$$2.5\begin{bmatrix} 1 & 0 \\ -2 & 3 \end{bmatrix} = \begin{bmatrix} 2.5(1) & 2.5(0) \\ 2.5(-2) & 2.5(3) \end{bmatrix}$$
$$= \begin{bmatrix} 2.5 & 0 \\ -5 & 7.5 \end{bmatrix}$$

Scatter plot (p. 92) A scatter plot is a graph that relates two different sets of data by plotting the data as ordered pairs. You can use a scatter plot to determine a relationship between the data sets.

Diagrama de puntos (p. 92) Un diagrama de puntos es una gráfica que relaciona dos conjuntos de datos presentando los datos como pares ordenados. El diagrama de puntos sirve para definir la relación entre conjuntos de datos.

Example

Dollars Spent Per Capita on Entertainment

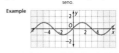

TV, Radio, and Sound Equipment
Source: U.S. Bureau of Labor Statistics

English — Spanish

Secant function (p. 883) The secant (sec) function is the reciprocal of the cosine function. For all real numbers θ except those that make $\cos \theta = 0$, $\sec \theta = \frac{1}{\cos \theta}$.

Función secante (p. 883) La función secante (sec) es el recíproco de la función coseno. Para todos los números reales θ, excepto aquéllos para los que $\cos \theta = 0$, $\sec \theta = \frac{1}{\cos \theta}$.

Example If $\cos \theta = \frac{5}{13}$, then $\sec \theta = \frac{13}{5}$.

Self-selected sample (p. 725) In a self-selected sample you select only members of the population who volunteered for the sample.

Muestra de voluntarios (p. 725) En una muestra de voluntarios se seleccionan sólo a los miembros de la población que se ofrecen voluntariamente para ser parte de la muestra.

Sequence (p. 564) A sequence is an ordered list of numbers.

Progresión (p. 564) Una progresión es una sucesión de números.

Example 1, 4, 7, 10, . . .

Series (p. 587) A series is the sum of the terms of a sequence.

Serie (p. 587) Una serie es la suma de los términos de una secuencia.

Example The series $3 + 6 + 9 + 12 + 15$ corresponds to the sequence 3, 6, 9, 12, 15. The sum of the series is 45.

Simplest form of a radical expression (p. 368) A radical expression with index n is in simplest form if there are no radicals in any denominator, no denominators in any radical, and any radicand has no nth power factors.

Mínima expresión de una expresión radical (p. 368) Una expresión radical con índice n está en su mínima expresión si no tiene radicales en ningún denominador ni denominadores en ningún radical y los radicandos no tienen factores de potencia.

Simplest form of a rational expression (p. 527) A rational expression is in simplest form if its numerator and denominator are polynomials that have no common divisor other than 1.

Forma simplificada de una expresión racional (p. 527) Una expresión racional se encuentra en su mínima expresión si su numerador y su denominador son polinomios que no tienen otro divisor aparte de 1.

Example $\dfrac{x^2 - 7x + 12}{x^2 - 9} = \dfrac{(x - 4)(x - 3)}{(x + 3)(x - 3)} = \dfrac{x - 4}{x + 3}$, where $x \neq -3$

Simulation (p. 682) A simulation is a model that imitates one or more events.

Simulación (p. 682) Una simulación es un modelo que imita uno o más sucesos.

Example Suppose a weather forecaster predicts a 50% chance of rain for the next three days. You can use three coins landing heads up to simulate three days in a row of rain.

English — Spanish

Sine curve (p. 852) A sine curve is the graph of a sine function.

Sinusoide (p. 852) Sinusoide es la gráfica de la función seno.

Example

Sine function, Sine of θ (pp. 838, 851) The sine function, $y = \sin \theta$, matches the measure θ of an angle in standard position with the y-coordinate of a point on the unit circle. This point is where the terminal side of the angle intersects the unit circle. The y-coordinate is the sine of θ.

Función seno, Seno de θ (pp. 838, 851) La función seno, $y = \sin \theta$, empareja la medida θ de un ángulo en posición estándar con la coordenada y de un punto en el círculo unitario. Este es el punto en el que el lado terminal del ángulo interseca al círculo unitario. La coordenada y es el seno de θ.

Example

$P(\cos \theta, \sin \theta)$

Singular matrix (p. 785) A singular matrix is a square matrix with no inverse. Its determinant is 0.

Matriz singular (p. 785) Una matriz singular es una matriz al cuadrado que no tiene inverso. El determinante de la matriz es 0.

Slope (p. 74) The slope of a non-vertical line is the ratio of the vertical change to the horizontal change between points. You can calculate slope by finding the ratio of the difference in the y-coordinates to the difference in the x-coordinates for any two points on the line. The slope of a vertical line is undefined.

Pendiente (p. 74) La pendiente de una línea no vertical es la razón del cambio vertical al cambio horizontal entre puntos. Puedes calcular la pendiente al hallar la razón de la diferencia de la coordenada y a la diferencia de la coordenada x para dos puntos cualesquiera de la línea. La pendiente de una línea vertical es indefinida.

Example The slope of the line through points $(-1, -1)$ and $(1, -2)$ is $\dfrac{-2 - (-1)}{1 - (-1)} = \dfrac{-1}{2} = -\dfrac{1}{2}$.

Slope-intercept form (p. 76) The slope-intercept form of an equation of a line is $y = mx + b$, where m is the slope and b is the y-intercept.

Forma pendiente-intercepto (p. 76) La forma pendiente-intercepto de una ecuación lineal es $y = mx + b$, donde m es la pendiente y b es el intercepto en y.

Example $y = 8x + 2$
$y = -x + 1$
$y = -\frac{1}{2}x - 14$

Solution of a system (p. 134) A solution of a system is a set of values for the variables that makes all the equations true.

Solución de un sistema (p. 134) Una solución de un sistema es un conjunto de valores para las variables que hace que todas las ecuaciones sean verdaderas.

English / Spanish

Solution of an equation (p. 27) A solution of an equation is a number that makes the equation true.

Solución de una ecuación (p. 27) Una solución de una ecuación es cualquier número que haga verdadera la ecuación.

Example The solution of $2x - 7 = -12$ is $x = -2.5$.

Square matrix (p. 782) A square matrix is a matrix with the same number of columns as rows.

Matriz cuadrada (p. 782) Una matriz cuadrada es la que tiene la misma cantidad de columnas y filas.

Example Matrix A is a square matrix.
$$A = \begin{bmatrix} 1 & 2 & 0 \\ -1 & 0 & -2 \\ 1 & 2 & 3 \end{bmatrix}$$

Square root equation (p. 390) A square root equation is a radical equation in which the radical has index 2.

Ecuación de raíz cuadrada (p. 390) Una ecuación de raíz cuadrada es una ecuación radical en la cual el radical tiene índice 2.

Example $\sqrt{x} = 4$

Square root function (p. 415) A square root function that can be written in the form $f(x) = a\sqrt{x - h} + k$, where $a \neq 0$. The domain of a square root function is all real numbers $x \geq h$.

Función de raíz cuadrada (p. 415) Una función de raíz cuadrada es una función que puede ser expresada como $f(x) = a\sqrt{x - h} + k$, donde $a \neq 0$. El dominio de una función de raíz cuadrada son todos los números reales tales que $x \geq h$.

Example $f(x) = 2\sqrt{x - 3} + 4$

Standard deviation (p. 719) Standard deviation is a measure of how much the values in a data set vary, or deviate, from the mean, $\bar{x}$. To find the standard deviation, follow five steps:
- Find the mean of the data set.
- Find the difference between each data value and the mean.
- Square each difference.
- Find the mean of the squares.
- Take the square root of the mean of the squares. This is the standard deviation.

Desviación típica (p. 719) La desviación típica denota cuánto los valores de un conjunto de datos varían, o se desvían, de la media, $\bar{x}$. Para hallar la desviación típica, se siguen cinco pasos:
- Se halla la media del conjunto de datos.
- Se calcula la diferencia entre cada valor de datos y la media.
- Se eleva al cuadrado cada diferencia.
- Se halla la media de los cuadrados.
- Se calcula la raíz cuadrada de la media de los cuadrados. Ésa es la desviación típica.

Example {0, 2, 3, 4, 6, 7, 8, 9, 10, 11}
$\bar{x} = 6$
standard deviation $= \sqrt{12} \approx 3.46$

Standard form of a circle (p. 630) See **Circle**.

Forma normal de un círculo (p. 630) Ver **Circle**.

Example $(x - 3)^2 + (y - 4)^2 = 4$

English / Spanish

Standard form of a linear equation (p. 82) The standard form of a linear equation is $Ax + By = C$, where A, B, and C are real numbers, and A and B are not both zero.

Forma normal de una ecuación lineal (p. 82) La forma normal de una ecuación lineal es $Ax + By = C$, donde A, B y C son números reales, y A y B no son cero ambos.

Example In standard form, the equation
$y = \frac{4}{3}x - 1$ is
$4x + (-3)y = 3$.

Standard form of a polynomial function (p. 281) The standard form of a polynomial function arranges the terms by degree in descending numerical order. A polynomial function, $P(x)$, in standard form is $P(x) = a_n x^n + a_{n-1} x^{n-1} + \cdots + a_1 x + a_0$, where n is a nonnegative integer and $a_n, \ldots, a_0$ are real numbers.

Forma normal de una función polinomial (p. 281) La forma normal de una función polinomial organiza los términos por grado en orden numérico descendente. Una función polinomial, $P(x)$, en forma normal es $P(x) = a_n x^n + a_{n-1} x^{n-1} + \cdots + a_1 x + a_0$, donde n es un número entero no negativo y $a_n, \ldots, a_0$ son números reales.

Example $2x^3 - 5x^2 - 2x + 5$

Standard form of a quadratic function (p. 202) The standard form of a quadratic function is $f(x) = ax^2 + bx + c$ with $a \neq 0$.

Forma normal de una función cuadrática (p. 202) La forma normal de una función cuadrática es $f(x) = ax^2 + bx + c$ con $a \neq 0$.

Example $f(x) = 2x^2 + 5x + 2$

Standard position (p. 836) An angle in the coordinate plane is in **standard position** when the vertex is at the origin and one ray is on the positive x-axis.

Posición estándar (p. 836) Un ángulo en el plano de coordenadas se encuentra en **posición estándar** si el vértice se encuentra en el origen y una semirrecta se encuentra en el eje x positivo.

Example

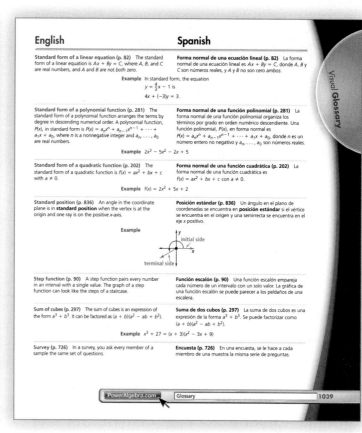

Step function (p. 90) A step function pairs every number in an interval with a single value. The graph of a step function can look like the steps of a staircase.

Función escalón (p. 90) Una función escalón empareja cada número de un intervalo con un solo valor. La gráfica de una función escalón se puede parecer a los peldaños de una escalera.

Sum of cubes (p. 297) The sum of cubes is an expression of the form $a^3 + b^3$. It can be factored as $(a + b)(a^2 - ab + b^2)$.

Suma de dos cubos (p. 297) La suma de dos cubos es una expresión de la forma $a^3 + b^3$. Se puede factorizar como $(a + b)(a^2 - ab + b^2)$.

Example $x^3 + 27 = (x + 3)(x^2 - 3x + 9)$

Survey (p. 726) In a survey, you ask every member of a sample the same set of questions.

Encuesta (p. 726) En una encuesta, se le hace a cada miembro de una muestra la misma serie de preguntas.

English / Spanish

Synthetic division (p. 306) Synthetic division is a process for dividing a polynomial by a linear expression $x - a$. You list the standard-form coefficients (including zeros) of the polynomial, omitting all variables and exponents. You use a for the "divisor" and add instead of subtract throughout the process.

División sintética (p. 306) La división sintética es un proceso para dividir un polinomio por una expresión lineal $x - a$. En este proceso, escribes los coeficientes de forma normal (incluyendo los ceros) del polinomio, omitiendo todas las variables y todos los exponentes. Usas a como "divisor" y sumas, en vez de restar, a lo largo del proceso.

Example
$$-3 \,|\, \begin{array}{rrrrr} 2 & 5 & 0 & -2 & -8 \\ & -6 & 3 & -9 & 33 \\ \hline 2 & -1 & 3 & -11 & 25 \end{array}$$

Divide $2x^4 + 5x^3 - 2x - 8$ by $x + 3$. $2x^4 + 5x^3 - 2x - 8$ divided by $x + 3$ gives $2x^3 - x^2 + 3x - 11$ as quotient and 25 as remainder.

System of equations (p. 134) A system of equations is a set of two or more equations using the same variables.

Sistema de ecuaciones (p. 134) Un sistema de ecuaciones es un conjunto de dos o más ecuaciones que contienen las mismas variables.

Example $\begin{cases} 2x - 3y = -13 \\ 4x + 5y = 7 \end{cases}$

Systematic sample (p. 725) In a systematic sample you order the population in some way, and then select from it at regular intervals.

Muestra sistemática (p. 725) En una muestra sistemática se ordena la población de cierta manera y luego se selecciona una muestra de esa población a intervalos regulares.

T

Tangent function, Tangent of θ (pp. 868, 869) The tangent function, $y = \tan \theta$, matches the measure θ, of an angle in standard position with the y/x ratio of the (x, y) coordinates of a point on the unit circle. This point is where the terminal side of the angle intersects the unit circle. y/x is the tangent of θ.

Función tangente, Tangente de θ (pp. 868, 869) La función tangente, $y = \tan \theta$, empareja la medida θ, de un ángulo en posición estándar con la razón y/x de las coordenadas (x, y) de un punto en el círculo unitario. Este es el punto en el cual el lado terminal del ángulo interseca al círculo unitario. y/x es la tangente de θ.

Example

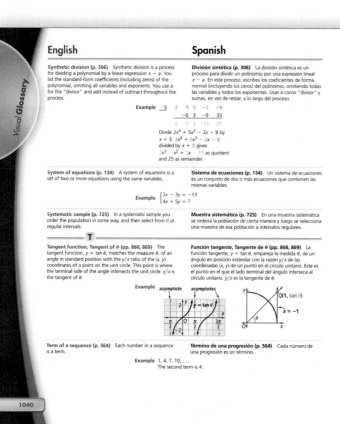

Term of a sequence (p. 564) Each number in a sequence is a term.

Término de una progresión (p. 564) Cada número de una progresión es un término.

Example 1, 4, 7, 10, ...
The second term is 4.

English / Spanish

Term of an expression (p. 20) A term is a number, a variable, or the product of a number and one or more variables.

Término de una expresión (p. 20) Un término es un número, una variable o el producto de un número y una o más variables.

Example The expression $4x^2 - 3y + 7.3$ has 3 terms.

Terminal point (p. 809) The terminal point of a vector is the tip (not the endpoint) of a vector arrow.

Punto terminal (p. 809) El punto terminal de un vector es la punta (no el extremo) de una flecha vectorial.

Terminal side (p. 836) See **Initial side**.

Lado terminal (p. 836) Ver **Initial side**.

Test point (p. 115) A test point is a point that you pick on one side of the boundary of the graph of a linear inequality. If the test point makes the inequality true, then all points on that side of the boundary are solutions of the inequality. If the test point makes the inequality false, then all points on the other side are solutions.

Punto de prueba (p. 115) Un punto de prueba es un punto que escoges a un lado del límite de la gráfica de una desigualdad lineal. Si el punto de prueba hace que la desigualdad sea verdadera, entonces todos los puntos en ese límite son soluciones de la desigualdad. Si el punto de prueba hace que la desigualdad sea falsa, entonces todos los puntos del otro lado del límite son soluciones.

Theoretical probability (p. 683) If a sample space has n equally likely outcomes, and an event A occurs in m of these outcomes, then the theoretical probability of event A is $P(A) = \frac{m}{n}$.

Probabilidad teórica (p. 683) Si un espacio muestral tiene n resultados con la misma probabilidad de ocurrir, y ocurre un suceso A en m de estos resultados, entonces la probabilidad teórica del suceso A es $P(A) = \frac{m}{n}$.

Example Use the set {1, 4, 9, 16, 25, 36, 49, 64, 81, 100}. The probability that a number selected at random is greater than 50 is $P(A) = \frac{3}{10} = 0.3$.

Transformation (p. 99) A transformation of a function $y = af(x - h) + k$ is a change made to at least one of the values a, h, and k. The four types of transformations are dilations, reflections, rotations, and translations.

Transformación (p. 99) Una transformación de una función $y = af(x - h) + k$ es un cambio que se le hace a por lo menos uno de los valores a, h y k. Hay cuatro tipos de transformaciones: dilataciones, reflexiones, rotaciones y traslaciones.

Example $g(x) = 2(x - 3)$ is a transformation of $f(x) = x^2$.

Translation (p. 99) A translation shifts the graph of the parent function horizontally, vertically, or both without changing its shape or orientation.

Traslación (p. 99) Una traslación desplaza la gráfica de la función madre horizontalmente, verticalmente o en ambas direcciones, sin cambiar su forma u orientación.

Example

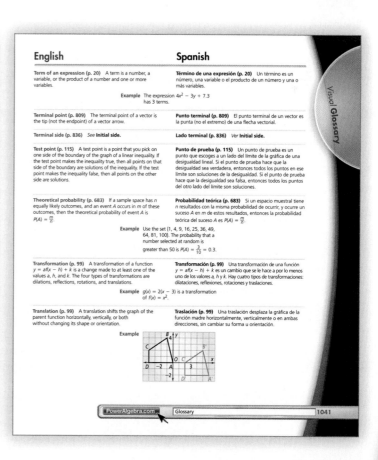

Transverse axis (p. 646) The transverse axis of a hyperbola is the segment that is on the line containing the foci and has endpoints on the hyperbola.

Eje transversal (p. 646) El eje transversal de una hipérbola es el segmento que se encuentra sobre la línea que contiene los focos y tiene sus puntos extremos sobre la hipérbola.

Example

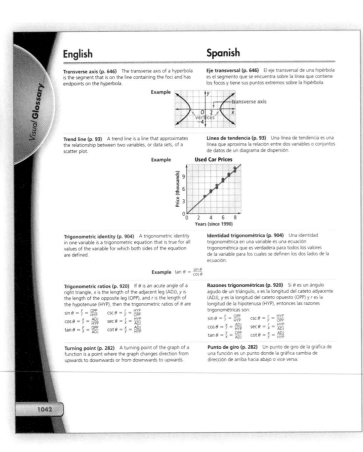

Trend line (p. 93) A trend line is a line that approximates the relationship between two variables, or data sets, of a scatter plot.

Línea de tendencia (p. 93) Una línea de tendencia es una línea que aproxima la relación entre dos variables o conjuntos de datos de un diagrama de dispersión.

Example

Used Car Prices

Trigonometric identity (p. 904) A trigonometric identity in one variable is a trigonometric equation that is true for all values of the variable for which both sides of the equation are defined.

Identidad trigonométrica (p. 904) Una identidad trigonométrica en una variable es una ecuación trigonométrica que es verdadera para todos los valores de la variable para los cuales se definen los dos lados de la ecuación.

Example $\tan \theta = \frac{\sin \theta}{\cos \theta}$

Trigonometric ratios (p. 920) If θ is an acute angle of a right triangle, x is the length of the adjacent leg (ADJ), y is the length of the opposite leg (OPP), and r is the length of the hypotenuse (HYP), then the trigonometric ratios of θ are
$\sin \theta = \frac{y}{r} = \frac{OPP}{HYP}$ $\csc \theta = \frac{r}{y} = \frac{HYP}{OPP}$
$\cos \theta = \frac{x}{r} = \frac{ADJ}{HYP}$ $\sec \theta = \frac{r}{x} = \frac{HYP}{ADJ}$
$\tan \theta = \frac{y}{x} = \frac{OPP}{ADJ}$ $\cot \theta = \frac{x}{y} = \frac{ADJ}{OPP}$

Razones trigonométricas (p. 920) Si θ es un ángulo agudo de un triángulo, x es la longitud del cateto adyacente (ADJ), y es la longitud del cateto opuesto (OPP) y r es la longitud de la hipotenusa (HYP), entonces las razones trigonométricas son:
$\sin \theta = \frac{y}{r} = \frac{OPP}{HYP}$ $\csc \theta = \frac{r}{y} = \frac{HYP}{OPP}$
$\cos \theta = \frac{x}{r} = \frac{ADJ}{HYP}$ $\sec \theta = \frac{r}{x} = \frac{HYP}{ADJ}$
$\tan \theta = \frac{y}{x} = \frac{OPP}{ADJ}$ $\cot \theta = \frac{x}{y} = \frac{ADJ}{OPP}$

Turning point (p. 282) A turning point of the graph of a function is a point where the graph changes direction from upwards to downwards or from downwards to upwards.

Punto de giro (p. 282) Un punto de giro de la gráfica de una función es un punto donde la gráfica cambia de dirección de arriba hacia abajo o vice versa.

Uniform Distribution (p. 694) A uniform distribution is a probability distribution that is equal for each event in the sample space.

Distribución uniforme (p. 694) Una distribución uniforme es una distribución de probabilidad que es igual para cada suceso en el espacio muestral.

Unit circle (p. 838) The unit circle has a radius of 1 unit and its center is at the origin of the coordinate plane.

Círculo unitario (p. 838) El círculo unitario tiene un radio de 1 unidad y el centro está situado en el origen del plano de coordenadas.

Example

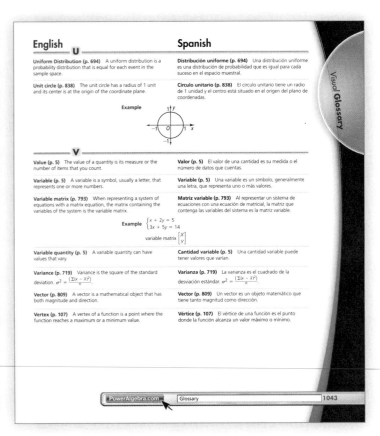

V

Value (p. 5) The value of a quantity is its measure or the number of items that you count.

Valor (p. 5) El valor de una cantidad es su medida o el número de datos que cuentas.

Variable (p. 5) A variable is a symbol, usually a letter, that represents one or more numbers.

Variable (p. 5) Una variable es un símbolo, generalmente una letra, que representa uno o más valores.

Variable matrix (p. 793) When representing a system of equations with a matrix equation, the matrix containing the variables of the system is the variable matrix.

Matriz variable (p. 793) Al representar un sistema de ecuaciones con una ecuación de matricial, la matriz que contenga las variables del sistema es la matriz variable.

Example $\begin{cases} x + 2y = 5 \\ 3x + 5y = 14 \end{cases}$

variable matrix $\begin{bmatrix} x \\ y \end{bmatrix}$

Variable quantity (p. 5) A variable quantity can have values that vary.

Cantidad variable (p. 5) Una cantidad variable puede tener valores que varían.

Variance (p. 719) Variance is the square of the standard deviation. $\sigma^2 = \frac{\sum(x - \bar{x})^2}{n}$.

Varianza (p. 719) La varianza es el cuadrado de la desviación estándar. $\sigma^2 = \frac{\sum(x - \bar{x})^2}{n}$.

Vector (p. 809) A vector is a mathematical object that has both magnitude and direction.

Vector (p. 809) Un vector es un objeto matemático que tiene tanto magnitud como dirección.

Vertex (p. 107) A vertex of a function is a point where the function reaches a maximum or a minimum value.

Vértice (p. 107) El vértice de una función es el punto donde la función alcanza un valor máximo o mínimo.

Vertex form of a quadratic function (p. 194) The vertex form of a quadratic function is $f(x) = a(x - h)^2 + k$, where $a \neq 0$ and (h, k) is the coordinate of the vertex of the function.

Forma del vértice de una función cuadrática (p. 194) La forma vértice de una función cuadrática es $f(x) = a(x - h)^2 + k$, donde $a \neq 0$ y (h, k) es la coordenada del vértice de la función.

Example $f(x) = x^2 + 2x - 1 = (x + 1)^2 - 2$
The vertex is $(-1, -2)$.

Vertex of a parabola (p. 194) The vertex of a parabola is the point where the function for the parabola reaches a maximum or a minimum value. The parabola intersects its axis of symmetry at the vertex.

Vértice de una parábola (p. 194) El vértice de una parábola es el punto donde la función de la parábola alcanza un valor máximo o mínimo. La parábola y su eje de simetría se intersecan en el vértice.

Example

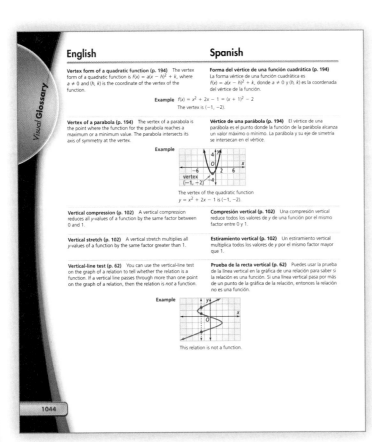

vertex $(-1, -2)$

The vertex of the quadratic function $y = x^2 + 2x - 1$ is $(-1, -2)$.

Vertical compression (p. 102) A vertical compression reduces all y-values of a function by the same factor between 0 and 1.

Compresión vertical (p. 102) Una compresión vertical reduce todos los valores de y de una función por el mismo factor entre 0 y 1.

Vertical stretch (p. 102) A vertical stretch multiplies all y-values of a function by the same factor greater than 1.

Estiramiento vertical (p. 102) Un estiramiento vertical multiplica todos los valores de y por el mismo factor mayor que 1.

Vertical-line test (p. 62) You can use the vertical-line test on the graph of a relation to tell whether the relation is a function. If a vertical line passes through more than one point on the graph of a relation, then the relation is not a function.

Prueba de la recta vertical (p. 62) Puedes usar la prueba de la línea vertical en la gráfica de una relación para saber si la relación es una función. Si una línea vertical pasa por más de un punto de la gráfica de la relación, entonces la relación no es una función.

Example

This relation is not a function.

Vertices of a hyperbola (p. 646) The endpoints of the transverse axis of a hyperbola are the vertices of the hyperbola.

Vértices de una hipérbola (p. 646) Los dos puntos de intersección de la hipérbola y su eje mayor son los vértices de la hipérbola.

Example

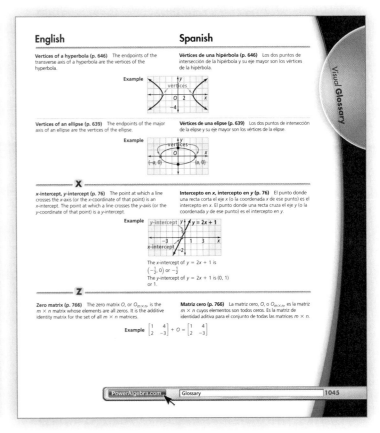

Vertices of an ellipse (p. 639) The endpoints of the major axis of an ellipse are the vertices of the ellipse.

Vértices de una elipse (p. 639) Los dos puntos de intersección de la elipse y su eje mayor son los vértices de la elipse.

Example

X

x-intercept, y-intercept (p. 76) The point at which a line crosses the x-axis (or the x-coordinate of that point) is an x-intercept. The point at which a line crosses the y-axis (or the y-coordinate of that point) is a y-intercept.

Intercepto en x, intercepto en y (p. 76) El punto donde una recta corta el eje x (o la coordenada x de ese punto) es el intercepto en x. El punto donde una recta cruza el eje y (o la coordenada y de ese punto) es el intercepto en y.

Example $y = 2x + 1$

The x-intercept of $y = 2x + 1$ is $\left(-\frac{1}{2}, 0\right)$ or $-\frac{1}{2}$.
The y-intercept of $y = 2x + 1$ is $(0, 1)$ or 1.

Z

Zero matrix (p. 766) The zero matrix O, or $O_{m \times n}$, is the $m \times n$ matrix whose elements are all zeros. It is the additive identity matrix for the set of all $m \times n$ matrices.

Matriz cero (p. 766) La matriz cero, O, o $O_{m \times n}$, es la matriz $m \times n$ cuyos elementos son todos ceros. Es la matriz de identidad aditiva para el conjunto de todas las matrices $m \times n$.

Example $\begin{bmatrix} 1 & 4 \\ 2 & -3 \end{bmatrix} + O = \begin{bmatrix} 1 & 4 \\ 2 & -3 \end{bmatrix}$

English

Spanish

Zero of a function (p. 226) A zero of a function $f(x)$ is any value of x for which $f(x) = 0$.

Cero de una función (p. 226) Un cero de una función $f(x)$ es cualquier valor de x para el cual $f(x) = 0$.

Example

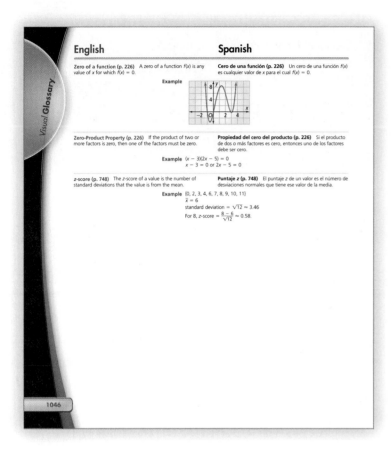

Zero-Product Property (p. 226) If the product of two or more factors is zero, then one of the factors must be zero.

Propiedad del cero del producto (p. 226) Si el producto de dos o más factores es cero, entonces uno de los factores debe ser cero.

Example $(x - 3)(2x - 5) = 0$
$x - 3 = 0$ or $2x - 5 = 0$

z-score (p. 748) The z-score of a value is the number of standard deviations that the value is from the mean.

Puntaje z (p. 748) El puntaje z de un valor es el número de desviaciones normales que tiene ese valor de la media.

Example $\{0, 2, 3, 4, 6, 7, 8, 9, 10, 11\}$
$\bar{x} = 6$
standard deviation $= \sqrt{12} \approx 3.46$
For 8, z-score $= \frac{8 - 6}{\sqrt{12}} \approx 0.58$.

Selected **Answers**

Chapter 1

Get Ready! pp. 1 1. 0 **2.** −2 **3.** −2.09 **4.** 8.05
5. −$\frac{3}{4}$ **6.** $\frac{11}{12}$ **7.** 10$\frac{7}{10}$ **8.** 3$\frac{1}{3}$ **9.** −42 **10.** 72 **11.** 9
12. −9.8 **13.** −3$\frac{1}{3}$ **14.** −5$\frac{1}{2}$ **15.** −4$\frac{2}{3}$ **16.** −$\frac{3}{4}$
17. −21 **18.** 7.35 **19.** −$\frac{1}{6}$ **20.** −$\frac{3}{2}$ **21.** −20 **22.** 8
23. 0.97 **24.** −5 **25.** 55 **26.** 3 **27.** because the
placement of the parentheses changes the order of
operations **28.** 3 **29.** 3 terms **30.** Calculate the answer
numerically. **31.** $\frac{-3}{n-3}$

Lesson 1-1 pp. 4–10

Got It? 1. The pattern shows a center
square and a yellow square added to
each side with the number of squares
per side increasing by one.

2. 52 tiles **3. a.** $12 **b.** $20 **c.** The
number of platys must be a whole number whereas the
length of fish can be a fraction or a decimal.
Lesson Check 1. add 35 **2.** rotate 90° clockwise
3.

Input	Process Column	Output
1	2(1)	2
2	2(2)	4
3	2(3)	6
4	2(4)	8
⋮	⋮	⋮
n	2(n)	2n

4.

Input	Process Column	Output
1	3(1)	3
2	3(2)	6
3	3(3)	9
4	3(4)	12
⋮	⋮	⋮
n	3(n)	3n

5. Answers may vary. Sample: Look for the same type of
change between consecutive figures.
6. Answers may vary. Sample: Tables of values and
pictorial representations are both convenient ways to
organize data and discover patterns. Tables give more

detail. Pictorial representations are visual. **7.** No; the
output is $\frac{1}{3}$ the input for all values except the first (Input:
3; Output: 2).
Exercises 9. Base of 3 squares with the number
of squares increasing vertically by one on each of
the outer squares of the base.

11. One square, then 2^2 or 4 squares, then
3^2 or 9 squares, then 4^2 or 16 squares. In
general, the number of squares is $n \times n$
or n^2.

13. 2n

Input	Process Column	Output
1	2(1)	2
2	2(2)	4
3	2(3)	6
4	2(4)	8
⋮	⋮	⋮
n	2(n)	2n

15. 4n − 1

Input	Process Column	Output
1	4(1) − 1	3
2	4(2) − 1	7
3	4(3) − 1	11
4	4(4) − 1	15
⋮	⋮	⋮
n	4(n) − 1	4n − 1

17. 7; 8; n + 2
19. Output = Input + 1

Input	Process Column	Output
1	(1) + 1	2
2	(2) + 1	3
4	(4) + 1	5
5	(5) + 1	6
⋮	⋮	⋮
n	(n) + 1	n + 1

---

21. Output = Input − 1

Input	Process Column	Output
1	(1) − 1	0
2	(2) − 1	1
3	(3) − 1	2
4	(4) − 1	3
5	(5) − 1	4
⋮	⋮	⋮
n	(n) − 1	n − 1

23. 40 **25.** add 6 or 6n; 30, 36, 42 **27.** add 3, then add
4, then add 5, and so on; 21, 28, 36 **29.** multiply by 3;
243, 729, 2187 **31.** The black square and dot each move
clockwise one block
33. 9216 in.^{3} **35.** n + 10, where n is the number of
months **37.** 21; 4n + 1 **39.** −13; 7 − 4n; or −4n + 7
41. Answers may vary. Sample: Jesse will not grow at the
same rate between the ages of 15 and 20 as he has
during the 4 years prior to age 15. **43.** D **45. a.** Each
number is a result of the division of the previous number
by 2. **b.** 36 ÷ 2 = 18, 18 ÷ 2 = 9, 9 ÷ 2 = 4.5, so 4.5
is the first noninteger number. **46.** 1.9 **47.** −3.8 **48.** 27
49. 0 **50.** −0.4 **51.** 7 **52.** 50% **53.** 25% **54.** 33.33%
55. 140% **56.** 172% **57.** 123%

Lesson 1-2 pp. 11–17

Got It? 1. rational numbers
2.

3. a. $\sqrt{26}$ < 6.25 or 6.25 > $\sqrt{26}$ **b.** a < c; a will be
to the left of c on the number line.
4. a. Distr. Prop.
b. a + [3 + (−a)]
   = a + [(−a) + 3]   Comm.
   = [a + (−a)] + 3   Assoc.
   = 0 + 3   Inverse
   = 3   Identity
Lesson Check 1. Answers may vary. Sample: the
number of times a cricket chirps **2.** Answers may vary.
Sample: the change in number of people on a bus after
a stop **3.** Answers may vary. Sample: the outdoor
temperature in tenths of a degree. Inv. Prop. of Add.
5. Assoc. Prop. of Mult. **6.** multiplicative inverse **7.** Both
properties result in the original term; 0 is the additive
identity, whereas 1 is the multiplicative identity. **8.** The
equation illustrates the Comm. Prop. of Add. **9.** Answers
may vary. Sample: $\sqrt{2}$ is not a rational number because it
cannot be written as a quotient of integers.
Exercises 11. y, natural numbers; p, rational numbers
13.

15.

17.

19.

21.

23. > **25.** < **27.** > **29.** > **31.** > **33.** <
35. Distr. Prop. **37.** Assoc. Prop. of Mult. **39.** Ident.
Prop. of Add. **41–48.** Answers may vary. Samples are
given. **41.** −5 **43.** −1$\frac{1}{4}$ **45.** 1$\frac{3}{4}$ **47.** 4 **49.** $\sqrt{50}$ in. ×
$\sqrt{50}$ in. × $\sqrt{50}$ in. **51.** natural numbers **53.** irrational
numbers **55.** irrational numbers **57.** 8, 1, $\frac{1}{3}$, −$\sqrt{2}$, −3
59. 5.73, $\frac{1}{4}$, −0.06, −3$\sqrt{3}$, −17 **61.** Answers may vary.
Sample: 7 **63.** Answers may vary. Sample: $\sqrt{2}$ and
$\sqrt{2}$ **65.** Answers may vary. **67.** Answers may vary.
69. 5(x + 2y − 7) **71.** No; $\frac{1}{0}$ is undefined. **73.** H
75. add 4; 20, 24, 28 **76.** add 1; 12, 13, 14 **77.** add 1;
0, 1, 2 **78.** 2$\frac{1}{4}$ **79.** 11$\frac{2}{3}$ **80.** 1$\frac{1}{2}$ **81.** 5 **82.** 38 **83.** 15

Lesson 1-3 pp. 18–24

Got It? 1. H **2.** 150 − 2d, with d = the number of
days **3. a.** 18 **b.** Yes; the numerator will become
2x² − y², not 2x² − 2y². **4.** Let x = the number of
two-point shots, y = the number of three-point shots,
z = the number of one-point free throws,
2x + 3y + 1z; 42 points **5. a.** −3j² − 7k + 5j
b. 12a − 53b
Lesson Check 1. $\frac{2+b}{3}$ **2.** 4k + m **3.** 12 **4.** 13
5. −5 **6.** −5 **7.** The student did not distribute the −1.
3p²q + 2p − (5q + p − 2p²q) = 3p²q + 2p −
5q − p + 2p²q = 5p²q + p − 5q **8.** A constant is a
term with no variables, whereas a coefficient is the
numerical factor in a term. **9.** Answers may vary. Sample:
Both algebraic expressions and numerical expressions
represent a quantity using numbers, operations and
grouping symbols. An algebraic expression includes
variables when representing a quantity. Examples:
numerical expression: 3 + 6(5 − 2); algebraic expression:
2z + 3z(6 + 5z).
Exercises 11. 8(x + 3) **13.** 130 − 10w, with w =
number of weeks **15.** 250 − 60w, with w = number of
weeks **17.** −16 **19.** −12 **21.** 4 ft **23.** 1600 ft
25. $1331 **27.** $1610.51 **29.** Let x = the number of
3-run home runs and y = the number of 2-run hits;
3x + 2y; 14 **31.** 2s + 5 **33.** 6a + 3b **35.** −0.5x
37. 4g − 2 **39.** 3 **41.** 37 **43.** 10 **45.** $\frac{584}{m}$
47. $\frac{5x}{2}$ **49.** y **51.** −2x² + 2y² **53.** 8.5x − 15 **55.** No;
John did not use the opposite of a sum correctly;
−(x + y) + 3(x − 4y); −x − y + 3x − 12y;
2x − 13y **57.** Distr. Prop. **59.** Opposite of a Difference

---

61. Answers may vary. Sample:
2(b − a) + 5(b − a)
   = (2 + 5)(b − a)   Distr. Prop.
   = 7(b − a)   Add.
   = 7b − 7a   Distr. Prop.
63. A **65.** C **67.** −1.5, −$\sqrt{2}$, −1.4, −0.5
68. −$\frac{5}{6}$, −$\frac{3}{8}$, $\frac{3}{2}$, 1 **69.** −20, 0.2, $\frac{1}{2}$, $\sqrt{2}$
70. −3, −0.5, −$\frac{1}{3}$, $\frac{3}{4}$ **71.** 7x − 4 **72.** −p − $\frac{2q}{3}$
73. 2b − 28 **74.** 2k − 2m

Lesson 1-4 pp. 26–32

Got It? 1. $\frac{3}{2}$ **2.** −1 **3.** 40 m × 120 m **4. a.** never
b. always **5. a.** C = K − 273 **b.** always
Lesson Check 1. 23.2 **2.** −90 **3.** 12
4. k = $\frac{1}{2}$(r − 15) **5.** k = $\frac{1}{3}$(z + 6)
6. k = −($\frac{1}{6}$)(h + 14) **7.** To find a solution of an
equation means to find the value of the variable that
makes the equation true. **8.** Four buses are not enough.
The number of buses must be a whole number, so round
the number of buses to 5. **9.** The 2nd line is incorrect;
subtract 10 from both sides: 12x = −12x = −1
Exercises 11. −81 **13.** 14 **15.** 8 **17.** −5
19. −$\frac{1}{9}$ **21.** $\frac{3}{2}$ **23.** −6 **25.** 0 **27.** 300 mi/h; 600 mi/h
29. sometimes **31.** sometimes **33.** h = $\frac{2A}{b}$ **35.** w = $\frac{V}{\ell h}$
37. x = $\frac{c}{a+b}$, a ≠ −b **39.** x = 2(m + n) + 2 **41.** 1.5
43. $\frac{23}{4}$, or 7$\frac{3}{4}$ **45.** 34° and 56° **47.** b₂ = $\frac{2A}{h}$ − b₁
49. v = $\frac{h+5r^2}{2}$ **51.** r₂ = $\frac{Rr_1}{r_1-R}$ **53.** 40°, 140°
55. x = $\frac{3b+2c−5}{b−c}$, $\frac{b}{c}$ ≠ 1 **57.** x = $\frac{4a−3bc}{aq−5bp}$, 5bp ≠ aq
59. x = $\frac{10c}{3}$, a ≠ 0 **61.** Let c = number of swim days;
3c = 82 + c; 41 days **63.** No; n = $\frac{1}{r−5}$ **not** $\frac{1}{5−r}$
65. 264 ft **67.** 3200 **69.** 7 ft **70.** −7 **71.** −$\frac{16}{3}$
72. −20 **73.** −$\frac{11}{2}$ **74.** −x + 5 **75.** 16x
76. 3(12 − x) **77.** true **78.** false **79.** true

Lesson 1-5 pp. 33–40

Got It? 1. $\frac{4}{3}$ ≤ 15
2. x ≤ −8

3. more than 32 songs **4.** always
5. a. x ≥ 2 and x < 6

b. sometimes; The compound inequality is true when
x = 5 and not true when x = 7.

6. a. w < −3 or w > $\frac{8}{7}$

b. x < −1 or x > 3

Lesson Check 1. R ≥ J **2.** w ≥ 40 and w < 74
3. x ≤ −2

4. 1 < x < $\frac{6}{5}$

5. x ≤ 0 or x > 3

6. Answers may vary. Sample: 5 < 6, but −5 > −6.
7. The transitive, addition and subtraction properties of
inequality are similar to the properties of equality. The
multiplication and division properties differ. Multiplying or
dividing each side of an inequality by a negative number
reverses the direction of the inequality symbol.
8. Answers may vary. Sample: 3x + 5 < 3(x + 5)
9. No; Answers may vary. Sample: 2x < x + 1 and
x + 1 > 3
Exercises 11. 8x ≥ 25 **13.** $\frac{x}{12}$ ≤ 6
15. k > −9

17. t ≤ 11

19. y ≤ −6

21. m < 10

23. w > 6

25. The longest side is less than 21 cm. **27.** at most 40
students **29.** always **31.** never **33.** always
35. sometimes
37. −4 ≤ x ≤ 2

39. −5 < x ≤ 6

41. all real numbers
43. x ≤ −3 or x ≥ 9

45. $z \geq 6$

47. $x \geq -48$

49. no solution **51.** 98 **53.** $2 < AB < 6$ **55.** The classmate reversed the direction of the $\geq$ symbol to $\leq$ incorrectly. The correct answer is $y \leq -20$. **57.** Distr. Prop.; arithmetic; Subtr. Prop. of Inequality; Mult. Prop. of Inequality

59. $-1 < x < 8$

61. $x < -2$ or $x > 2$

63. Answers may vary. Sample: $-3x + 1 > 4$
65. Answers may vary. Sample: $2x + 4 \leq 0$ or $-3x - 3 \leq 0$
67. D **69.** D **71.** $7a + 5$ **72.** $-2x + 14y$
73. $\frac{b}{12} + 1$ **74.** $1.61 - 0.1k$ **75.** 4
76. no solution **77.** $\frac{9}{10}$ **78.** -20

Lesson 1-6 pp. 41–48
Got It?
1. $\frac{2}{3}, -2$

2. $-7, -11$

3. -1 **4.** $-\frac{4}{3} \leq x \leq 4$

5. a. $x < -5$ or $x > 1$

b. The graph will have two closed circles with an arrow extending to the left of one and to the right of the other. **6.** $|h - 52.5| \leq 0.5$
Lesson Check 1. $-4, 4$ **2.** $-12, 4$ **3.** $-\frac{6}{5}$
4. $-11 < x < 9$

5. $x \leq -1$ or $x \geq 4$

6. A solution of an eq. is extraneous if it is a solution to a derived eq., but is not a solution to the original eq.
7. when the number is positive or 0 **8.** Answers may vary. Sample: $d < -5$ and $5d > 25$ **9.** Answers may vary. Sample: An absolute value equation or inequality

represents two equations or inequalities; each equation or inequality is solved in the same manner as a linear equation or inequality.
Exercises 11. $-8, 8$ **13.** $-\frac{5}{2}, 3$ **15.** no solution
17. $-7, 17$ **19.** $-\frac{3}{2}, \frac{3}{2}$ **21.** $\frac{3}{2}, \frac{3}{2}$ **23.** $-1, \frac{3}{2}$
25. $0 < y < 18$

27. $-2 < x < 6$

29. $-3\frac{1}{2} \leq w \leq \frac{1}{2}$

31. $x < -12$ or $x > 6$

33. $y \leq -9$ or $y \geq 15$

35. $x \leq -3$ or $x \geq 4$

37. $|h - 1.4| \leq 0.1$ **39.** $|C - 27.5| \leq 0.25$
41. $|m - 1250| \leq 50$ **43.** no solution **45.** $-\frac{14}{3}, \frac{16}{3}$
47. no solution **49.** $\frac{11}{6}$ **51.** $-\frac{71}{36}$ **53.** $|c - 28.75| \leq 0.25$; 0.25; 28.50 $\leq c \leq 29.00$ **55.** $|x| < 4$
57. $-6 \leq x \leq 8\frac{1}{2}$

59. all real numbers

61. all real numbers

63. $x \leq -8.4$ or $x \geq 9.6$

65. $-5 < x < 11$

67. The graph of $|x| < a$ is the set of all points on the number line that lie between a and $-a$. The graph of $|x| > a$ has two parts; the left part consists of the points to the left of $-a$, and the right part consists of the points to the right of a. **69.** $|t - 350| \leq 5$ **71.** $|t - 15| \leq 30$ **73.** $|x - 9.55| \leq 0.02$; $9.53 \leq x \leq 9.57$
75. never; absolute value is nonnegative **77.** sometimes; $|5| = 5$ but $|-5| \neq -5$ **79.** sometimes; $|-4 + 2| \neq -4 + 2$ **81.** The "3" in the second set of equations should be "-3."
$$-4x + 1 < -3$$
$$-4x < -4$$
$$x > 1 \, not \, x > -\frac{1}{2}$$

83. $\frac{ab + d}{c}, \frac{-ab + d}{c}, c \neq 0, ab \geq 0$
85. $(-6 \leq x \leq -5)$ or $(5 \leq x \leq 6)$

87. $x \geq \frac{5}{2}$

89. Use *and* if the absolute value is less than a value and use *or* if the absolute value is greater than a value.
91. 0 **93.** 0.04
94. $y < 6$

95. $s < \frac{2}{15}$

96. $a > 4$

97. Each figure has 4 more squares than the previous figure.

98. Each figure has *n* more circles than the previous figure.

99. 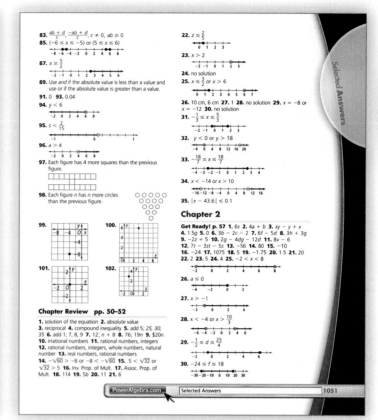 **100.**

101. **102.**

Chapter Review pp. 50–52
1. solution of the equation **2.** absolute value
3. reciprocal **4.** compound inequality **5.** add 5; 25, 30, 35 **6.** add 1; 7, 8, 9 **7.** 12; $n + 8$ **8.** 76; 19n **9.** $20n$
10. irrational numbers **11.** rational numbers, integers
12. rational numbers, integers, whole numbers, natural number **13.** real numbers, rational numbers
14. $-\sqrt{60} > -8$ or $-8 < -\sqrt{60}$ **15.** $5 < \sqrt{32}$ or $\sqrt{32} > 5$ **16.** Inv. Prop. of Mult. **17.** Assoc. Prop. of Mult. **18.** 114 **19.** 5b **20.** 11 **21.** 6

22. $z \leq \frac{2}{5}$

23. $x > 2$

24. no solution
25. $x \leq \frac{3}{2}$ or $x > 6$

26. 10 cm, 6 cm **27.** 1 **28.** no solution **29.** $x = -8$ or $x = -12$ **30.** no solution
31. $-\frac{1}{3} \leq x \leq \frac{5}{3}$

32. $y < 0$ or $y > 18$

33. $-\frac{18}{7} \leq x \leq \frac{18}{7}$

34. $x < -14$ or $x > 10$

35. $|x - 43.6| \leq 0.1$

Chapter 2
Get Ready! p. 57 1. $6s$ **2.** $4a + b$ **3.** $xy - y + x$
4. $1.5g$ **5.** 0 **6.** $3b - 2c - 2$ **7.** $6f - 5d$ **8.** $3h + 3g$
9. $-2z + 5$ **10.** $2g - 4dg - 12d$ **11.** $8v - 6$
12. $7t - 3st - 5s$ **13.** -56 **14.** 80 **15.** -10
16. -24 **17.** 1075 **18.** 5 **19.** -1.75 **20.** 1.5 **21.** 20
22. 2 **23.** 5 **24.** 4 **25.** $-2 < x < 8$
26. $a \leq 0$

27. $x > -1$

28. $x < -4$ or $x > \frac{10}{3}$

29. $-\frac{1}{2} \leq d \leq \frac{25}{4}$

30. $-24 \leq f \leq 18$

---

31. Answers may vary. Sample: the Civil War, the Great Depression, the Louisiana Purchase **32.** Answers may vary. Sample: From 1 to 2 years of age; a person has usually stopped growing by age 30, but a baby is still growing at age 1. **33.** Answers may vary. Sample: The image is a reflection, left to right, of what other people see; the size is the same. **34.** Answers may vary. Sample: An inequality determines the limit of a value, or a boundary, for the solution on the number line.

Lesson 2-1 pp. 60–67
Got It?
1. Let Jan = 1, Feb = 2, Mar = 3, and Apr = 4.

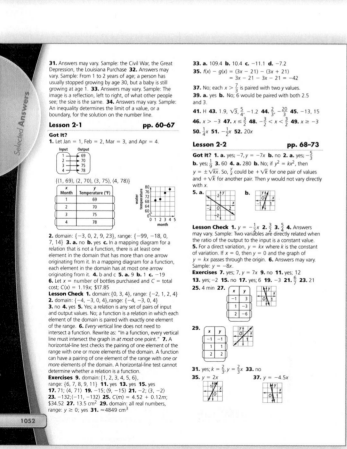

$\{(1, 69), (2, 70), (3, 75), (4, 78)\}$

Month	Temperature (°F)
1	69
2	70
3	75
4	78

2. domain: $\{-3, 0, 2, 9, 23\}$, range: $\{-99, -18, 0, 7, 14\}$ **3. a.** no **b.** yes **c.** In a mapping diagram for a relation that is not a function, there is at least one element in the domain that has more than one arrow originating from it. In a mapping diagram for a function, each element in the domain has at most one arrow originating from it. **4.** b and c **5. a.** 9 **b.** 1 **c.** -19 **6.** Let x = number of bottles purchased and C = total cost; $C(x) = 1.19x$; $17.85
Lesson Check 1. domain: $\{0, 3, 4\}$, range: $\{-2, 1, 2, 4\}$ **2.** domain: $\{-4, -3, 0, 4\}$, range: $\{-4, -3, 0, 4\}$
3. no **4.** yes **5.** Yes; a relation is any set of pairs of input and output values. No; a function is a relation in which each element of the domain is paired with exactly one element of the range. **6.** *Every* vertical line does not need to intersect a function. Rewrite as: "In a function, every vertical line must intersect the graph in *at most* one point." **7.** A horizontal test checks the pairing of one element of the range with one or more elements of the domain. A function can have a pairing of one element of the range with *one or more* elements of the domain. A horizontal-line test cannot determine whether a relation is a function.
Exercises 9. domain: $\{1, 2, 3, 4, 5, 6\}$, range: $\{6, 7, 8, 9, 11\}$ **11.** yes **13.** yes **15.** yes
17. 71; (4, 71) **19.** -15; (9, -15) **21.** -2; (3, -2)
23. -132; $(-11, -132)$ **25.** $C(m) = 4.52 + 0.12m$; $34.52 **27.** 13.5 cm² **29.** domain: all real numbers, range: $y \geq 0$; yes **31.** ≈ 4849 cm³

33. a. 109.4 **b.** 10.4 **c.** -11.1 **d.** -7.2
35. $f(x) - g(x) = (3x - 21) - (3x + 21)$
$= 3x - 21 - 3x - 21 = -42$
37. No; each $x > \frac{7}{2}$ is paired with two values.
39. a. yes **b.** No; 6 would be paired with both 2.5 and 3.
41. H **43.** 1.9, $\sqrt{3}, \frac{5}{4}, -1.2$ **44.** $\frac{2}{3}, -\frac{20}{3}$ **45.** $-13, 15$
46. $x > -3$ **47.** $x \leq \frac{3}{2}$ **48.** $-\frac{3}{2} < x < \frac{3}{2}$ **49.** $x \geq -3$
50. $\frac{1}{4}x$ **51.** $-\frac{1}{2}x$ **52.** $20x$

Lesson 2-2 pp. 68–73
Got It? 1. a. yes; $-7, y = -7x$ **b.** no **2. a.** yes; $-\frac{5}{3}$
b. yes; $\frac{1}{3}$ **3.** 60 **4. a.** 280 **b.** No; if $y^2 = kx^2$, then $y = \pm \sqrt{k}x$. So, $\frac{y}{x}$ could be $\sqrt{k}$ for one pair of values and $+\sqrt{k}$ for another pair. Then y would not vary directly with x.
5. a. **b.**

Lesson Check 1. $y = -\frac{1}{3}x$ **2.** $\frac{2}{3}$ **3.** $\frac{5}{4}$ **4.** Answers may vary. Sample: Two variables are directly related when the ratio of the output to the input is a constant value. **5.** For a direct variation, $y = kx$ where k is the constant of variation. If $x = 0$, then $y = 0$ and the graph of $y = kx$ passes through the origin. **6.** Answers may vary. Sample: $y = -8x$.
Exercises 7. yes; 7, $y = 7x$ **9.** no **11.** yes; 12
13. yes; -2 **15.** no **17.** yes; 6 **19.** -3 **21.** $\frac{6}{7}$ **23.** 21
25. 4 min **27.**

29.

31. yes; $k = \frac{2}{3}, y = \frac{2}{3}x$ **33.** no
35. $y = 2x$ **37.** $y = -4.5x$

39. $y = \frac{3}{5}x$ **41.** $y = \frac{2}{3}x$

43. 0.625 **45.** 0.225 **47.** First, it does not say that y varies directly with x. Second, every direct variation includes the point $(0, 0)$, so x cannot be determined because k could be any value.
49. Answers may vary. Sample: $y = 3.2x$

51. Answers may vary. Sample: If y varies directly with x^2, and $y = 2$ when $x = 4$, then $y = \frac{9}{4}$ when $x = 9$.
53. $c = 0, a \neq 0, b \neq 0$
55. y is divided by 7; $y = kx$, so if x is divided by 7, $y = k(\frac{x}{7})$ or $\frac{1}{7}$ the original value of y.
57. 1091 **59.** 0 **61.** -5
62. **63.**
domain: $\{4, 7\}$; range: $\{-1, 0\}$

domain: $\{-2, 0, 1, 3\}$; range: $\{-3, 1\}$
64. **65.**
domain: $\{1, 2, 4, 5\}$; range: $\{-2, -1, 1, 2\}$
domain: $\{1, 2, 3, 4\}$; range: $\{7, 8, 9, 10\}$
66. $8n$; 40, 48, 56 **67.** $7 - 2n$; $-3, -5, -7$
68. $12(13 - n)$; 96, 84, 72 **69.** $15(n + 1)$; 90, 105,120 **70.** $\frac{17}{7}$; 7; $\frac{23}{7}, \frac{29}{7}$ **71.** $-3.2; -2; -1.4; 0.4$
72. -5; 1; 4; 13 **73.** -9; -8; -7.5; -6

Lesson 2-3 pp. 74–80
Got It? 1. a. -1 **b.** 1 **c.** undefined **d.** $\frac{1-4}{8-5} = \frac{-3}{3} = -1 = \frac{-3}{3} = \frac{4-1}{5-8}$ **2. a.** $y = 6x + 5$
b. $y = -\frac{1}{2}x - 3$ **c.** No; any two points on a line can be used to calculate the slope.

3. a. $y = -\frac{3}{4}x + 9$; $-\frac{3}{4}$; (0, 9)
b. $y = -\frac{7}{5}x - 7$; $-\frac{7}{5}$; (0, -7)
4. $y = \frac{4}{3}x - 2$

Lesson Check 1. $y = \frac{1}{3}x + 1$ **2.** $y = \frac{4}{3}x + \frac{1}{3}$ **3.** -1
4. 1 **5.** The y-intercept of a line is the point at which the line crosses the y-axis. The x-intercept is the point at which the line crosses the x-axis. **6.** Since division by zero is undefined, the slope of a vertical line that passes through (a, b) and (a, c), $\frac{c - b}{a - a}$, is undefined. **7.** She subtracted the x-coordinates in the wrong order. The x- and y-coordinates of each point must be subtracted consistently.
Exercises 9. -2 **11.** $\frac{4}{11}$ **13.** 1 **15.** 0 **17.** $y = 3x + 2$
19. $y = \frac{5}{6}x + 12$ **21.** $y = -5x - 7$ **23.** $y = \frac{3}{2}x + \frac{7}{2}$; $\left(0, \frac{7}{2}\right)$ **25.** $y = -\frac{3}{5}x + \frac{4}{5}$; $-\frac{4}{5}$; $\left(0, \frac{6}{8}\right)$ **27.** $y = 7$; 0; (0, 7)
29. **31.**
33. **35.**
37. **39.**
41. **43.**

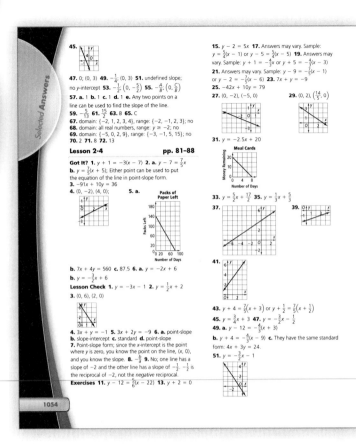

45.

47. 0; (0, 3) **49.** $-\frac{1}{4}$; (0, 3) **51.** undefined slope; no y-intercept **53.** $-\frac{1}{2}$; $\left(0, -\frac{5}{2}\right)$ **55.** $-\frac{A}{B}$; $\left(0, \frac{C}{B}\right)$
57. a. 1 **b.** 1 **c.** 1 **d.** 1 **e.** Any two points on a line can be used to find the slope of the line.
59. $-\frac{5}{13}$ **61.** $\frac{13}{2}$ **63.** B **65.** C
67. domain: $\{-2, 1, 2, 3, 4\}$, range: $\{-2, -1, 2, 3\}$; no
68. domain: all real numbers, range: $y \ge -2$; no
69. domain: $\{-5, 0, 2, 9\}$, range: $\{-3, -1, 5, 15\}$; no
70. 2 **71.** 8 **72.** 13

Lesson 2-4 pp. 81–88

Got It? 1. $y + 1 = -3(x - 7)$ **2. a.** $y - 7 = \frac{7}{5}x$
b. $y = \frac{7}{5}(x + 5)$; Either point can be used to put the equation of the line in point-slope form.
3. $-91x + 10y = 36$
4. (0, −2), (4, 0); **5. a.**

b. $7x + 4y = 560$ **c.** 87.5 **6. a.** $y = -2x + 6$
b. $y = -\frac{3}{4}x + 6$
Lesson Check 1. $y = -3x - 1$ **2.** $y = \frac{1}{2}x + 2$
3. (0, 6), (2, 0)

4. $3x + y = -1$ **5.** $3x + 2y = -9$ **6. a.** point-slope
b. slope-intercept **c.** standard **d.** point-slope
7. Point-slope form; since the x-intercept is the point where y is zero, you know the point on the line, $(x, 0)$, and you know the slope. **8.** $-\frac{9}{2}$ **9.** No; one line has a slope of -2 and the other line has a slope of $-\frac{1}{2}$. $-\frac{1}{2}$ is the reciprocal of -2, not the negative reciprocal.
Exercises 11. $y - 12 = \frac{2}{6}(x - 22)$ **13.** $y + 2 = 0$

15. $y - 2 = 5x$ **17.** Answers may vary. Sample:
$y = \frac{5}{4}(x - 1)$ or $y - 5 = \frac{5}{4}(x - 5)$ **19.** Answers may vary. Sample: $y + 1 = -\frac{4}{4}x$ or $y + 5 = -\frac{4}{4}(x - 3)$
21. Answers may vary. Sample: $y - 9 = -\frac{7}{5}(x - 1)$
or $y - 2 = -\frac{7}{5}(x - 6)$ **23.** $7x + y = -9$
25. $-42x + 10y = 79$
27. (0, −2), (−5, 0) **29.** (0, 2), $\left(\frac{14}{5}, 0\right)$

31. $y = -2.5x + 20$

33. $y = \frac{5}{2}x + \frac{17}{2}$ **35.** $y = \frac{1}{3}x + \frac{5}{3}$
37.

39.

41.

43. $y + 4 = \frac{7}{5}(x + 3)$ or $y + \frac{1}{2} = \frac{7}{5}\left(x + \frac{1}{2}\right)$
45. $y = \frac{3}{4}x + 3$ **47.** $y = -\frac{3}{2}x - \frac{1}{2}$
49. a. $y - 12 = -\frac{4}{3}(x + 3)$
b. $y + 4 = -\frac{4}{3}(x - 9)$ **c.** They have the same standard form: $4x + 3y = 24$.
51. $y = -\frac{3}{2}x - 1$

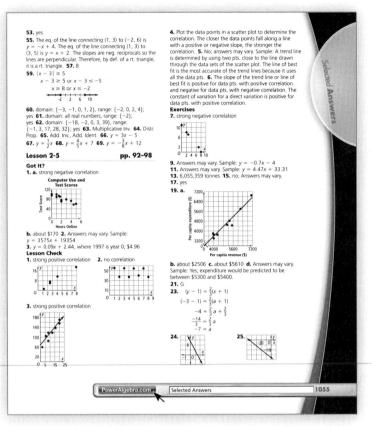

53. yes
55. The eq. of the line connecting (1, 3) to (−2, 6) is $y = -x + 4$. The eq. of the line connecting (1, 3) to (3, 5) is $y = x + 2$. The slopes are neg. reciprocals so the lines are perpendicular. Therefore, by def. of a rt. triangle, it is a rt. triangle. **57.** B
59. $|x - 3| \ge 5$
$x - 3 \ge 5$ or $x - 3 \le -5$
$x \ge 8$ or $x \le -2$

60. domain: $\{-3, -1, 0, 1, 2\}$, range: $\{-2, 0, 2, 4\}$; yes **61.** domain: all real numbers, range: $\{-2\}$; yes **62.** domain: $\{-18, -2, 0, 3, 39\}$, range: $\{-1, 3, 17, 28, 32\}$; yes **63.** Multiplicative Inv. **64.** Distr. Prop. **65.** Add. Inv., Add. Ident. **66.** $y = 3x - 5$
67. $y = \frac{1}{2}x$ **68.** $y = \frac{5}{8}x + 4$ **69.** $y = -\frac{3}{8}x + 12$

Lesson 2-5 pp. 92–98

Got It?
1. a. strong negative correlation

b. about $170 **2.** Answers may vary. Sample:
$y = 3575x + 19354$
3. $y = 0.09x + 2.44$, where 1997 is year 0; $4.96
Lesson Check
1. strong positive correlation **2.** no correlation

3. strong positive correlation

4. Plot the data points in a scatter plot to determine the correlation. The closer the data points fall along a line with a positive or negative slope, the stronger the correlation. **5.** No; answers may vary. Sample: A trend line is determined by using two pts. close to the line drawn through the data sets of the scatter plot. The line of best fit is the most accurate of the trend lines because it uses all the data pts. **6.** The slope of the trend line or line of best fit is positive for data pts. with positive correlation and negative for data pts. with negative correlation. The constant of variation for a direct variation is positive for data pts. with positive correlation.
Exercises
7. strong negative correlation

9. Answers may vary. Sample: $y = -0.7x - 4$
11. Answers may vary. Sample: $y = 4.47x + 33.31$
13. 6,055,359 tonnes **15.** no; Answers may vary.
17. yes
19. a.

b. about $2506 **c.** about $5610 **d.** Answers may vary. Sample: Yes; expenditure would be predicted to be between $5300 and $5400.
21. G
23. $(y - 1) = \frac{2}{3}(x + 5)$
$(-3 - 1) = \frac{2}{3}(a + 1)$
$-4 = \frac{2}{3}a + \frac{2}{3}$
$-\frac{14}{3} = \frac{2}{3}a$
$-7 = a$
24. **25.**

26.

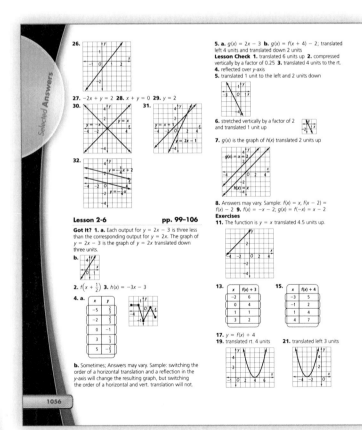

27. $-2x + y = 2$ **28.** $x + y = 0$ **29.** $y = 2$
30. **31.**
32.

Lesson 2-6 pp. 99–106

Got It? 1. a. Each output for $y = 2x - 3$ is three less than the corresponding output for $y = 2x$. The graph of $y = 2x - 3$ is the graph of $y = 2x$ translated down three units.
b.

2. $f\left(x + \frac{1}{2}\right)$ **3.** $h(x) = -3x - 3$
4. a.

x	y
−5	$\frac{3}{2}$
−1	$\frac{1}{2}$
0	−1
3	$\frac{1}{2}$
5	$\frac{3}{2}$

b. Sometimes; Answers may vary. Sample: switching the order of a horizontal translation and a reflection in the y-axis will change the resulting graph, but switching the order of a horizontal and vert. translation will not.

5. a. $g(x) = 2x - 3$ **b.** $g(x) = f(x + 4) - 2$; translated left 4 units and translated down 2 units
Lesson Check 1. translated 6 units up **2.** compressed vertically by a factor of 0.25 **3.** translated 4 units to the rt.
4. reflected over y-axis
5. translated 1 unit to the left and 2 units down

6. stretched vertically by a factor of 2 and translated 1 unit up
7. $g(x)$ is the graph of $h(x)$ translated 2 units up

8. Answers may vary. Sample: $f(x) = x$, $f(x - 2) = f(x) - 2$. **9.** $f(x) = -x$; $g(x) = f(-x) = x - 2$
Exercises
11. The function is $y = x$ translated 4.5 units up.

13.

x	$f(x) + 3$
−2	6
0	4
1	1
3	2

15.

x	$f(x) + 4$
−3	5
0	1
1	4
4	7

17. $y = f(x) + 4$
19. translated rt. 4 units **21.** translated left 3 units

23. $g(x) = -x - 1$ **25.** $g(x) = -2x + 4$
27. $y = 2x$ **29.** $y = \frac{1}{4}x$ **31.** $g(x) = -0.5x$
33. vertically compressed by a factor of $\frac{1}{4}$ and translated down 2 units
35. translate to the right 10 s
37. $f(x) = -\frac{1}{3}x - 1$; $g(x) = \frac{1}{3}x + 1$; $g(x) = -f(x)$
41. translated 6 units down **43.** translated 4 units up

45. The first two steps are incorrect; the transformations should be: shift 1 unit left, vertically stretch by a factor of 2, and shift 3 units down.
47. **49.**

51. D **53.** A
55. $y = -15.82x + 914.59$
56. −2, 8 **57.** −12, 11 **58.** −3, $\frac{21}{5}$

Lesson 2-7 pp. 107–113

Got It?
1. a.

vertex at (0, 2); translated up 2 units from the parent function
b. No; transformations of this form move the vertex up or down along the axis of symmetry, so the axis stays the same.
2.

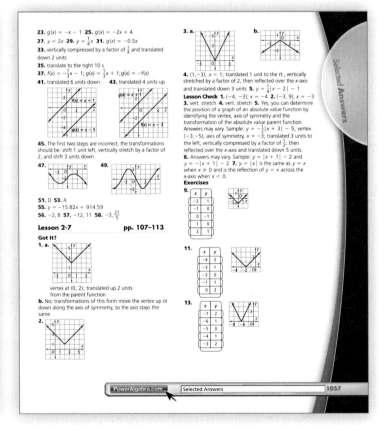

3. a. **b.**

4. (1, −3); $x = 1$; translated 1 unit to the rt., vertically stretched by a factor of 2, then reflected over the x-axis and translated down 3 units **5.** $y = \frac{1}{4}|x - 2| - 1$
Lesson Check 1. (−4, −3); $x = -4$ **2.** (−3, 9); $x = -3$
3. vert. stretch **4.** vert. stretch **5.** Yes; you can determine the position of a graph of an absolute value function by identifying the vertex, axis of symmetry and the transformation of the absolute value parent function. Answers may vary. Sample: $y = -\frac{1}{2}|x + 3| - 5$; vertex (−3, −5); axis of symmetry, $x = -3$; translated 3 units to the left, vertically compressed by a factor of $\frac{1}{2}$, then reflected over the x-axis and translated down 5 units.
6. Answers may vary. Sample: $y = |x + 1| - 2$ and $y = -|x + 1| - 2$ **7.** $y = |x|$ is the same as $y = x$ when $x \ge 0$ and is the reflection of $y = x$ across the x-axis when $x < 0$.
Exercises
9.

x	y
−2	1
−1	0
0	1
1	2
2	1

11.

x	y
−4	2
−3	1
−2	0
−1	1
0	2

13.

x	y
−7	2
−6	1
−5	0
−4	1
−3	2

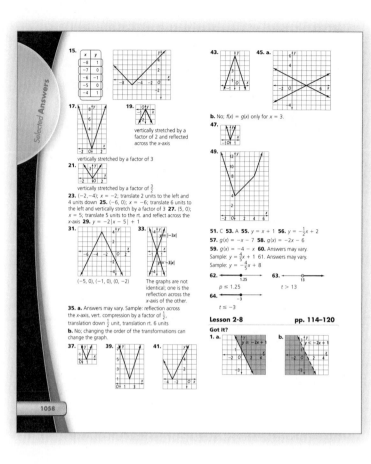

Page 1058:

15.

x	y
−8	1
−7	0
−6	−1
−5	0
−4	1

17. vertically stretched by a factor of 2 and reflected across the x-axis

19.

21. vertically stretched by a factor of 3

vertically stretched by a factor of $\frac{2}{3}$

23. $(-2, -4)$; $x = -2$; translate 2 units to the left and 4 units down **25.** $(-6, 0)$; $x = -6$; translate 6 units to the left and vertically stretch by a factor of 3 **27.** $(5, 0)$; $x = 5$; translate 5 units to the rt. and reflect across the x-axis. $y = -2|x - 5| + 1$ **29.** $y = -2|x - 5| + 1$

31.

33. $y = |-3x|$

$(-5, 0), (-1, 0), (0, -2)$ $\quad y = |-3x|$

The graphs are not identical; one is the reflection across the x-axis of the other.

35. a. Answers may vary. Sample: reflection across the x-axis, vert. compression by a factor of $\frac{1}{2}$, translation down $\frac{1}{2}$ unit, translation rt. 6 units **b.** No; changing the order of the transformations can change the graph.

37. **39.** **41.**

43. **45. a.**

b. No; $f(x) = g(x)$ only for $x = 3$.

47.

49.

51. C **53.** A **55.** $y = x + 1$ **56.** $y = -\frac{1}{2}x + 2$ **57.** $g(x) = -x - 7$ **58.** $g(x) = -2x - 6$ **59.** $g(x) = -4 - x$ **60.** Answers may vary. Sample: $y = \frac{5}{6}x + 1$ **61.** Answers may vary. Sample: $y = -\frac{4}{5}x + 8$

62. $p \le 1.25$

63. $t > 13$

64. $t \le -3$

Lesson 2-8   pp. 114–120

Got It?
1. a. $y \ge -2x + 1$ **b.** $y < -2x + 1$

1058

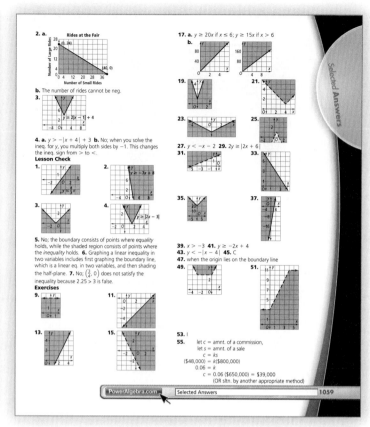

Page 1059:

2. a.

Rides at the Fair
(graph: Number of Large Rides vs Number of Small Rides)
$(0, 24)$ ... $(40, 0)$

b. The number of rides cannot be neg.

3. $y \ge 2|x - 1| + 4$

4. a. $y > -|x + 4| + 3$ **b.** No; when you solve the ineq. for y, you multiply both sides by −1. This changes the ineq. sign from > to <.

Lesson Check
1. **2.**
3. **4.** $y \ge |2x - 3|$

5. No; the boundary consists of points where *equality* holds, while the shaded region consists of points where the *inequality* holds. **6.** Graphing a linear inequality in two variables includes first graphing the boundary line, which is a linear eq. in two variables, and then shading the half-plane. **7.** No; $\left(\frac{3}{4}, 0\right)$ does not satisfy the inequality because 2.25 > 3 is false.

Exercises
9. **11.**
13. **15.**

17. a. $y \ge 20x$ if $x \le 6$; $y \ge 15x$ if $x > 6$
b.

19. **21.**
23. **25.**

27. $y < -x - 2$ **29.** $2y \ge |2x + 6|$
31. **33.**
35. **37.**

39. $x > -3$ **41.** $y \ge -2x + 4$
43. $y < -|x - 4|$ **45.** C
47. when the origin lies on the boundary line
49. **51.**

53. I
55. let c = amnt. of a commission,
let s = amnt. of a sale
$c = ks$
$(\$48,000) = k(\$800,000)$
$0.06 = k$
$c = 0.06 (\$650,000) = \$39,000$
(OR sltn. by another appropriate method)

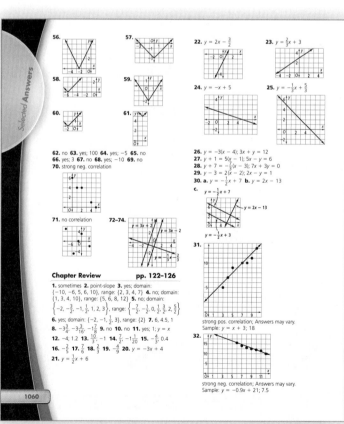

Page 1060:

56. **57.**
58. **59.**
60. **61.**

62. no **63.** yes; 100 **64.** yes; −5 **65.** no
66. yes; 3 **67.** no **68.** yes; −10 **69.** no
70. strong neg. correlation

71. no correlation **72–74.** $y = 3x + 2$, $y = -3x + 2$

Chapter Review   pp. 122–126

1. sometimes **2.** point-slope **3.** yes; domain: $\{-10, -6, 5, 6, 10\}$, range: $\{2, 3, 4, 7\}$ **4.** no; domain: $\{1, 3, 4, 10\}$, range: $\{5, 6, 8, 12\}$ **5.** no; domain: $\left\{-2, -\frac{3}{2}, -1, \frac{1}{2}, 1, 2, 3\right\}$, range: $\left\{-\frac{7}{2}, -\frac{1}{2}, 0, \frac{1}{2}, \frac{3}{2}, 2, \frac{5}{2}\right\}$
6. yes; domain: $\{-2, -1, \frac{1}{2}, 3\}$, range: $\{2\}$ **7.** 6, 4.5, 1
8. $-3\frac{3}{4}, -3\frac{3}{16}, -1\frac{7}{8}$ **9.** no **10.** no **11.** yes; 1; $y = x$
12. −4; 1.2 **13.** $\frac{10}{3}$, −1 **14.** $\frac{7}{2}$, $-1\frac{1}{2}$ **15.** $-\frac{4}{3}$; 0.4
16. $-\frac{2}{5}$ **17.** $\frac{1}{6}$ **18.** $\frac{2}{9}$ **19.** $-\frac{4}{9}$ **20.** $y = -3x + 4$
21. $y = \frac{1}{2}x + 6$

22. $y = 2x - \frac{3}{2}$ **23.** $y = \frac{2}{3}x + 3$
24. $y = -x + 5$ **25.** $y = -\frac{1}{3}x + \frac{5}{3}$
26. $y = -3(x - 4); 3x + y = 12$
27. $y + 1 = 5(x - 1); 5x - y = 6$
28. $y + 7 = -\frac{7}{3}(x - 3); 7x + 3y = 0$
29. $y - 3 = 2(x - 2); 2x - y = 1$
30. a. $y = -\frac{1}{2}x + 7$ **b.** $y = 2x - 13$
c. $y = -\frac{1}{2}x + 7$ ... $y = 2x - 13$

31. strong pos. correlation; Answers may vary. Sample: $y = x + 3$; 18

32. strong neg. correlation; Answers may vary. Sample: $y = -0.9x + 21$; 7.5

1060

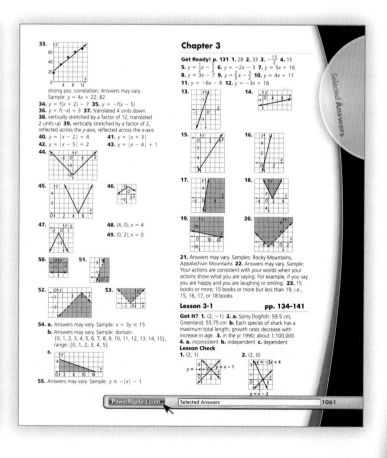

Page 1061:

33. strong pos. correlation; Answers may vary. Sample: $y = 4x + 22$; 82
34. a. $y = f(x + 2) - 7$ **35.** $y = -f(x - 5)$
36. $y = f(-x) + 3$ **37.** translated 4 units down
38. vertically stretched by a factor of 12, translated 2 units up **39.** vertically stretched by a factor of 2, reflected across the y-axis, reflected across the x-axis
40. $y = |x - 2| + 4$ **41.** $y = |x + 3|$
42. $y = |x - 5| + 2$ **43.** $y = |x - 4| + 1$
44.

45. **46.**
47. **48.** $(4, 0); x = 4$
49. $(0, 2); x = 0$
50. **51.**
52. **53.**

54. a. Answers may vary. Sample: $x + 3y \le 15$
b. Answers may vary. Sample: domain: $\{0, 1, 2, 3, 4, 5, 6, 7, 8, 9, 10, 11, 12, 13, 14, 15\}$, range: $\{0, 1, 2, 3, 4, 5\}$
c.

55. Answers may vary. Sample: $y \le -|x| - 1$

Chapter 3

Get Ready! p. 131 1. 28 **2.** 33 **3.** $-\frac{15}{2}$ **4.** 15
5. $y = \frac{1}{3}x - \frac{7}{2}$ **6.** $y = -2x - 3$ **7.** $y = 5x + 16$
8. $y = \frac{5}{3}x - 7$ **9.** $y = \frac{2}{3}x - \frac{3}{2}$ **10.** $y = 4x + 11$
11. $y = -6x - 8$ **12.** $y = -3x + 18$
13. **14.**
15. **16.**
17. **18.**
19. **20.**

21. Answers may vary. Samples: Rocky Mountains, Appalachian Mountains **22.** Answers may vary. Sample: Your actions are consistent with your words when your actions show what you are saying. For example, if you say you are happy and you are laughing or smiling. **23.** 15 books or more; 15 books or more but less than 19, i.e., 15, 16, 17, or 18 books

Lesson 3-1   pp. 134–141

Got It? 1. $(2, -1)$ **2. a.** Spiny Dogfish: 59.5 cm; Greenland: 55.75 cm **b.** Each species of shark has a maximum total length; growth rates decrease with increase in age. **3.** in the yr 1990; about 1,100,000 **4. a.** inconsistent **b.** independent **c.** dependent
Lesson Check
1. $(2, 1)$ **2.** $(2, 0)$
$y = \frac{1}{4}x - 1$ $y = -2x + 4$
   $y = x - 2$

3. 2 pens; 4 pencils **4.** No; an independent system has a unique solution whereas an inconsistent system has no solution.
5. Answers may vary. Sample: $\begin{cases} y = 2x + 1 \\ y = 2x - 3 \end{cases}$
6. Independent; if the slope of one equation is the negative reciprocal of the slope of the other equation, the lines are perpendicular and intersect at a unique point.
Exercises 7–11. How solutions are determined may vary (graphing or using a table).
7. (3, 1)

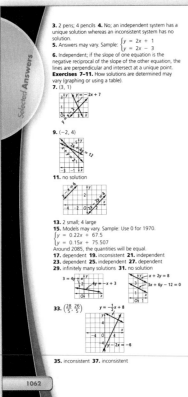

9. (−2, 4)

11. no solution

13. 2 small; 4 large
15. Models may vary. Sample: Use 0 for 1970.
$\begin{cases} y = 0.22x + 67.5 \\ y = 0.15x + 75.507 \end{cases}$
Around 2085, the quantities will be equal.
17. dependent **19.** inconsistent **21.** independent
23. dependent **25.** independent **27.** dependent
29. infinitely many solutions **31.** no solution

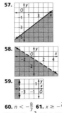

33. $\left(\frac{28}{5}, \frac{26}{5}\right)$

35. inconsistent **37.** inconsistent

39.

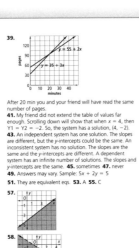

After 20 min you and your friend will have read the same number of pages.
41. My friend did not extend the table of values far enough. Scrolling down will show that when $x = 4$, then Y1 = Y2 = −2. So, the system has a solution, (4, −2).
43. An independent system has one solution. The slopes are different, but the y-intercepts could be the same. An inconsistent system has no solution. The slopes are the same and the y-intercepts are different. A dependent system has an infinite number of solutions. The slopes and y-intercepts are the same. **45.** sometimes **47.** never
49. Answers may vary. Sample: $5x + 2y = 5$
51. They are equivalent eqs. **53.** A **55.** C
57.
58.
59.
60. $n < -\frac{8}{3}$ **61.** $x \geq -\frac{20}{2}$ or −14.5 **62.** $x > \frac{5}{8}$
63. 2 **64.** $-\frac{3}{2}$ **65.** 2 **66.** 10 **67. a.** −3 **b.** −3 **c.** −10

Lesson 3-2 pp. 142–148

Got It? 1. (−2.5, 2.5) **2.** $.95 per download; $5.50 one-time registration fee **3.** (4, 0) **4. a.** (−2, 3) **b.** Yes; the solution (−5, 2) is a solution to both eqs. in the system, so substituting $y = 2$ into either equation will result in $x = -5$. **5. a.** no solution; The eq. is always false. **b.** infinite number of solutions; The eq. is always true.
Lesson Check 1. (1, 2) **2.** (−6, −6) **3.** (2, 1)
4. (5, −3) **5.** $\left(-\frac{1}{5}, \frac{19}{5}\right)$ **6.** (2, 1)

---

7. Answers may vary. Sample:
$\begin{cases} 4x - 3y = -2 \\ 3x - 2y = -1 \end{cases}$
$\begin{cases} -8x + 6y = 4 \\ 9x - 6y = -3 \end{cases}$
8. In the substitution method of solving a system of equations, you first solve one equation for one of the variables. Then substitute this variable in the other equation and solve for the other variable. In the elimination method, you create an equivalent system of equations that contain a pair of additive inverses so that you can eliminate one variable and solve for the remaining variable.
9. Let r = number of regular cups of coffee and c = number of large cups of coffee. First, $r + c = 5$: because a total of 5 cups of coffee were purchased. Second, $r + 1.5c = 6$: because each regular cup of coffee is $1, each large cup is $1.50, and the total spent is $6. Then, solve the system of equations using elimination by subtracting the first equation from the second to eliminate r and solve for c: $c = 2$; 2 large cups
Exercises 11. (−2, 4) **13.** (0.75, 2.5) **15.** (8, −1)
17. (−2, −5) seven $1-bills; eight $5-bills
21. 3 vans and 2 sedans **23.** (2, 4) **25.** (2, −2)
27. (4, 1) **29.** (1, 1) **31.** infinite number of solutions; $\{(x, y)|-2x + 3y = 13\}$ **33.** (3, 2) **35.** (5, 4)
37. $\left(\frac{20}{17}, \frac{19}{17}\right)$ **39.** (4, 1) **41.** no solution
43. 10 deliveries **45.** (4, −3) **47.** (3, 4)
49. (300, 150) **51.** (0.5, 0.25)
53. Error in 5th line: $-4(-7 - x) = 28 + 4x$ not $-28 - 4x$; Lines 5–9 should be: $3x + 28 + 4x = 14$; $7x = -14$; $x = -2$; $y = -7 - (-2)$; $y = -5$
55. Answers may vary. Sample:
$\begin{cases} -3x + 4y = 12 \\ 5x - 3y = 13 \end{cases}$ (8, 9)
57. In determining whether to use substitution or elimination to solve an equation, look at the equations to determine if one is solved or can be easily solved for a particular variable. If that is the case, substitution can easily be used. Otherwise, elimination might be easier.
59. Substitution; the second equation is solved for y; (−7, −26) **61.** Elimination; substitution would be difficult since no coefficient is 1 in the original system. Dividing the first equation by 3 and dividing the second equation by 5 results in an equivalent system where y would be eliminated from the system if the equations were subtracted; (−1, −3)
63. yes; −40 degrees **65.** 0 **67.** 2 **69.** 6 **71.** 4
72. no solution

73. infinite number of solutions, $\{(x, y)|-9x - 3y = 1\}$

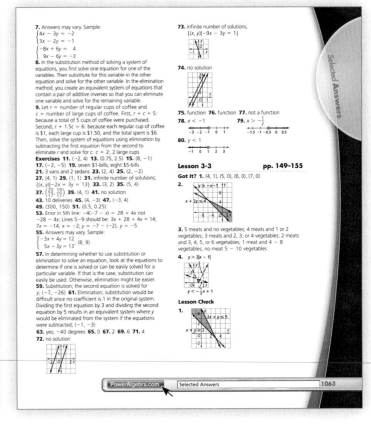

74. no solution

75. function **76.** function **77.** not a function
78. $x < -1$ **79.** $x > -\frac{1}{2}$
80. $y < 1$

Lesson 3-3 pp. 149–155

Got It? 1. (4, 1), (5, 0), (6, 0), (7, 0)
2.

3. 5 meats and no vegetables; 4 meats and 1 or 2 vegetables; 3 meats and 2, 3, or 4 vegetables; 2 meats and 3, 4, 5, or 6 vegetables; 1 meat and 4 − 8 vegetables; no meat 5 − 10 vegetables
4. $y > 2|x - 1|$

Lesson Check
1.

2.

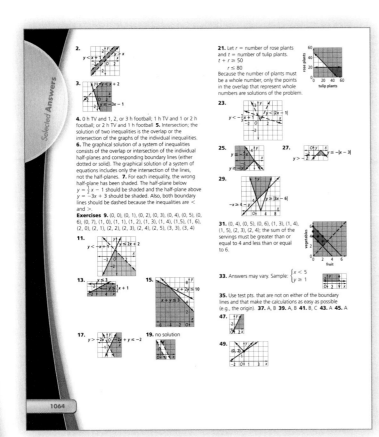

3.

4. 0 h TV and 1, 2, or 3 h football; 1 h TV and 1 or 2 h football; or 2 h TV and 1 h football **5.** Intersection; the solution of two inequalities is the overlap or the intersection of the graphs of the individual inequalities.
6. The graphical solution of a system of inequalities consists of the overlap or intersection of the individual half-planes and corresponding boundary lines (either dotted or solid). The graphical solution of a system of equations includes only the intersection of the lines, not the half-planes. **7.** For each inequality, the wrong half-plane has been shaded. The half-plane below $y = \frac{1}{3}x - 1$ should be shaded and the half-plane above $y = -3x + 3$ should be shaded. Also, both boundary lines should be dashed because the inequalities are $<$ and $>$.
Exercises 9. (0, 0), (0, 1), (0, 2), (0, 3), (0, 4), (0, 5), (0, 6), (0, 7), (1, 0), (1, 1), (1, 2), (1, 3), (1, 4), (1, 5), (1, 6), (2, 0), (2, 1), (2, 2), (2, 3), (2, 4), (2, 5), (3, 3), (3, 4)
11.
13. **15.**
17. **19.** no solution

21. Let r = number of rose plants and t = number of tulip plants.
$t + r \geq 50$
$r \leq 80$
Because the number of plants must be a whole number, only the points in the overlap that represent whole numbers are solutions of the problem.
23.
25. **27.** $\leq -|x - 3|$
29. $\geq |x - 6|$
31. (0, 4), (0, 5), (0, 6), (1, 3), (1, 4), (1, 5), (2, 3), (2, 4); the sum of the servings must be greater than or equal to 4 and less than or equal to 6.
33. Answers may vary. Sample: $\begin{cases} x < 5 \\ y \geq 1 \end{cases}$
35. Use test pts. that are not on either of the boundary lines and that make the calculations as easy as possible (e.g., the origin). **37.** A, B **39.** A, B **41.** B, C **43.** A **45.** A
47.
49.

51.

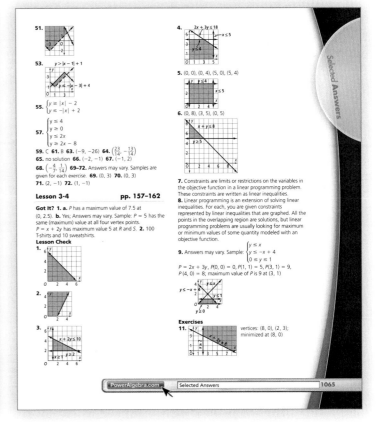

53. $y > |x - 1| + 1$
55. $\begin{cases} y \geq |x| - 2 \\ y \leq -|x| + 2 \end{cases}$
57. $\begin{cases} y \leq 4 \\ y \geq 0 \\ y \leq 2x \\ y \geq 2x - 8 \end{cases}$
59. C **61.** B **63.** (−9, −26) **64.** $\left(\frac{23}{14}, -\frac{13}{14}\right)$
65. no solution **66.** (−2, −1) **67.** (−1, 2)
68. $\left(-\frac{4}{7}, \frac{1}{14}\right)$ **69–72.** Answers may vary. Samples are given for each exercise. **69.** (0, 3) **70.** (0, 3)
71. (1, −1) **72.** (1, −1)

Lesson 3-4 pp. 157–162

Got It? 1. a. P has a maximum value of 7.5 at (0, 2.5). **b.** Yes; Answers may vary. Sample: $P = 5$ has the same (maximum) value at all four vertex points. $P = x + 2y$ has maximum value 5 at R and S. **2.** 100 T-shirts and 10 sweatshirts.
Lesson Check
1.
2.
3.

4.
5. (0, 0), (0, 4), (5, 0), (5, 4)
6. (0, 8), (3, 5), (0, 5)
7. Constraints are limits or restrictions on the variables in the objective function in a linear programming problem. These constraints are written as linear inequalities.
8. Linear programming is an extension of solving linear inequalities. For each, you are given constraints represented by linear inequalities that are graphed. All the points in the overlapping region are solutions, but linear programming problems are usually looking for maximum or minimum values of some quantity modeled with an objective function.
9. Answers may vary. Sample: $\begin{cases} y \leq x \\ y \leq -x + 4 \\ 0 \leq y \leq 1 \end{cases}$
$P = 2x + 3y$, $P(0, 0) = 0$, $P(1, 1) = 5$, $P(3, 1) = 9$, $P(4, 0) = 8$; maximum value of P is 9 at (3, 1)
Exercises
11. vertices: (8, 0), (2, 3); minimized at (8, 0)

13. Let s = number of Spruce trees and m = number of Maple trees.
a.
$$\begin{cases} 30s + 40m \le 2100 \\ 600s + 900m \le 45,000 \\ s \ge 0, m \ge 0 \end{cases}$$
b. $P = 650s + 300m$

c.
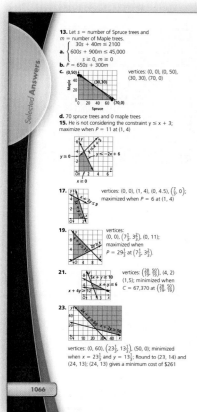
vertices: (0, 0), (0, 50), (30, 30), (70, 0)

d. 70 spruce trees and 0 maple trees
15. He is not considering the constraint $y \le x + 3$; maximize when $P = 11$ at (1, 4).

17. vertices: (0, 0), (1, 4), (0, 4.5), $\left(\frac{7}{3}, 0\right)$; maximized when $P = 6$ at (1, 4)

19. vertices: (0, 0), $\left(7\frac{1}{3}, 3\frac{2}{3}\right)$, (0, 11); maximized when $P = 29\frac{1}{3}$ at $\left(7\frac{1}{3}, 3\frac{2}{3}\right)$.

21. vertices: $\left(\frac{28}{19}, \frac{50}{19}\right)$, (4, 2) (1,5); minimized when $C = 67,370$ at $\left(\frac{28}{19}, \frac{50}{19}\right)$

23. vertices: (0, 60), $\left(23\frac{1}{3}, 13\frac{1}{3}\right)$, (50, 0); minimized when $x = 23\frac{1}{3}$ and $y = 13\frac{1}{3}$; Round to (23, 14) and (24, 13); (24, 13) gives a minimum cost of $261

25. C
27.
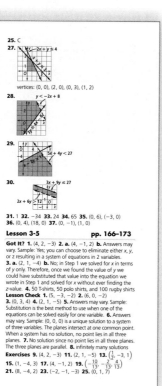
vertices: (0, 0), (2, 0), (0, 3), (1, 2)

28.

29.

30.

31. 1 **32.** −34 **33.** 24 **34.** 65 **35.** (0, 6), (−3, 0)
36. (0, 4), (18, 0) **37.** (0, −1), (1, 0)

Lesson 3-5   pp. 166–173

Got It? 1. (4, 2, −3) **2. a.** (4, −1, 2) **b.** Answers may vary. Sample: Yes; you can choose to eliminate either x, y, or z resulting in a system of equations in 2 variables. **3. a.** (2, 1, −4) **b.** No; in Step 1 we solved for x in terms of y only. Therefore, once we found the value of y we could have substituted that value into the equation we wrote in Step 1 and solved for x without ever finding the z-value. **4.** 50 T-shirts, 50 polo shirts, and 100 rugby shirts
Lesson Check 1. (5, −3, −2) **2.** (6, 0, −2)
3. (0, 3, 4) **4.** (2, 1, −5) **5.** Answers may vary. Sample: Substitution is the best method to use when one of the equations can be solved easily for one variable. **6.** Answers may vary. Sample: (0, 0, 0) is a unique solution to a system of three variables. The planes intersect at one common point. When a system has no solution, no point lies in all three planes. The three planes are parallel. **7.** No solution since no point lies in all three planes. **8.** infinitely many solutions
Exercises 9. (4, 2, −3) **11.** (2, 1, −5) **13.** $\left(\frac{1}{2}, -3, 1\right)$
15. (1, −4, 3) **17.** (4, −1, 2) **19.** $\left(-\frac{10}{13}, -\frac{2}{13}, \frac{4}{13}\right)$
21. (8, −4, 2) **23.** (−2, −1, −3) **25.** (0, 1, 7)

27. (5, −2, 0) **29.** (1, 3, 2) **31.** $m\angle P = 32°$; $m\angle Q = 96°$; $m\angle R = 52°$ **33.** (8, 1, 3)
35. $\left(\frac{1}{2}, 2, -3\right)$ **37.** no solution **39.** (2, 4, 6)
41. (0, 2, −3)
43. Answers may vary. Sample: Solution is (1, 2, 3).
$$\begin{cases} x + y + z = 6 \\ x + y + z = 2 \\ 2x - y + 2z = 6 \\ 3x + 3y + z = 12 \end{cases}$$
45. Let E, F, and V represent the number of edges, faces, and vertices, respectively. From the first statement, $E = \frac{5}{2}F$. From the second statement, $V = \frac{5}{6}F$. From the third statement, $V + F = E + 2$. Solving this system of 3 equations yields $E = 30$, $F = 12$, and $V = 20$.
47. $\frac{3}{2}$
49. 144 mezzanine seats
50. $P = 12$ is maximized at (0, 4).
51. $x \ge -\frac{7}{2}$
52. $x \le -18$;
53. $x < -1$;
54. $\left(7, \frac{5}{4}\right)$ **55.** dependent system; infinite number of solutions, $\left\{(x, y) \mid y = -\frac{1}{2}x - \frac{3}{4}\right\}$
56. inconsistent system; no solution

Lesson 3-6   pp. 174–181

Got It? 1. 17
2. a. $\begin{bmatrix} -4 & -2 & 7 \\ 3 & 1 & -5 \end{bmatrix}$ **b.** $\begin{bmatrix} 4 & -1 & 2 & 1 \\ 0 & 1 & 5 & 20 \\ 2 & 1 & 0 & 7 \end{bmatrix}$
3. $\begin{cases} 2x = 6 \\ 5x - 2y = 1 \end{cases}$
4. a. (1, 2) **b.** elimination; you use the same steps to solve **5.** $\left(1, \frac{1}{2}, 3\right)$
Lesson Check 1. 2×1 **2.** 2×4
3. $\begin{bmatrix} 3 & 5 & 0 \\ 1 & 1 & 2 \end{bmatrix}$ **4.** $\begin{bmatrix} 1 & 3 & -1 & 2 \\ 1 & 0 & 2 & 8 \\ 0 & 2 & -1 & 1 \end{bmatrix}$
5. 16 **6.** a_{21} is 0, the element in row 2, column 1. a_{12} is −9, the element in row 1 and column 2. **7.** Answers may vary. Sample: The entry fee to a school play is $2 for adults. Jamie paid a total of $8 for 4 student entry fees and 2 adult entry fees. What is the student entry fee?
Exercises 9. 1 **11.** 8
13. $\begin{bmatrix} 3 & 2 & 16 \\ 0 & 1 & 5 \end{bmatrix}$ **15.** $\begin{bmatrix} 1 & -1 & 150 \\ 2 & 0 & 1 & 425 \\ 0 & 1 & 3 & 0 \end{bmatrix}$

17. $\begin{bmatrix} 1 & -1 & 1 & 0 \\ 1 & -2 & 1 & 5 \\ 2 & -1 & 2 & 8 \end{bmatrix}$ **19.** $\begin{cases} 5x + y = -3 \\ -2x + 2y = 4 \end{cases}$
21. $\begin{cases} 2x + y + z = 1 \\ x + y + z = 2 \\ x - y + z = -2 \end{cases}$ **23.** $\begin{cases} 5x + 2y + z = 5 \\ 4x + y + 2z = 8 \\ x + 3y - 6z = 2 \end{cases}$
25. (−1, 0) **27.** (4, 6) **29.** (2, 3)
31. $10,000 at 4% and $15,000 at 6%; Let x = amount invested at 4% and y = amount invested at 6%.
$\begin{cases} x + y = 25,000 \\ 0.04x + 0.06y = 1300 \end{cases}$
$\begin{bmatrix} 1 & 1 & 25000 \\ 0.04 & 0.06 & 1300 \end{bmatrix} = \begin{bmatrix} 1 & 0 & 10000 \\ 0 & 1 & 15000 \end{bmatrix}$
33. (3, 1, 1) **35.** (35, −22, −16) **37.** (1, 1, 1, 1)
39. (2, 3) **41.** 1 qt. of red paint: $7.75; 1 qt. of yellow paint: $5.75 **43.** Answers may vary. Sample: 0; 0
45. (8, 2) **47.** $\left(\frac{1}{8}, -\frac{1}{17}\right)$ **49.** G
51. $x \ge -\frac{3}{2}$;
52. $x \ge -35$;
53. $x \ge 4$;
54. $\frac{15}{2}, -\frac{9}{2}$ **55.** −10, −10 **56.** 10, −6 **57.** $y = 2x$
58. $y = \frac{1}{3}x$

Chapter Review   pp. 183–186

1. independent system **2.** Linear programming; constraints
3. 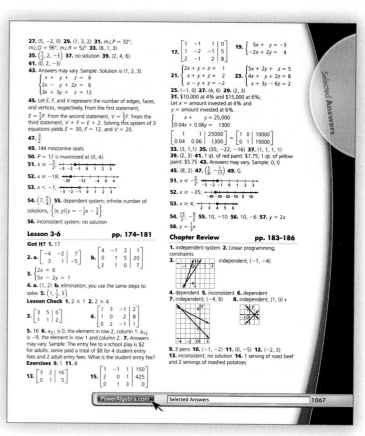 independent; (−1, −4)
4. dependent **5.** inconsistent **6.** dependent **7.** independent; (−4, 6) **8.** independent; (1, 0) v
9. 3 pens **10.** (−1, −2) **11.** (0, −5) **12.** (−2, 3) **13.** inconsistent; no solution **14.** 1 serving of roast beef and 2 servings of mashed potatoes

---

15.
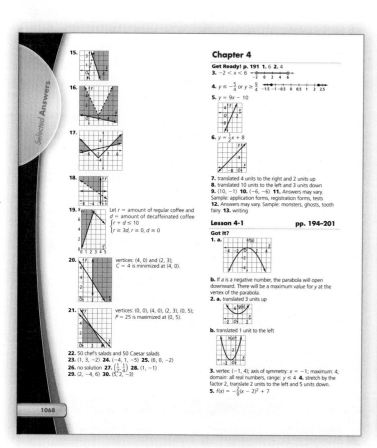

16.

17.

18.

19. Let r = amount of regular coffee and d = amount of decaffeinated coffee $\begin{cases} r + d \le 10 \\ r \ge 3d, r \ge 0, d \ge 0 \end{cases}$

20. vertices: (4, 0) and (2, 3); $C = 4$ is minimized at (4, 0).

21. vertices: (0, 0), (4, 0), (2, 3), (0, 5); $P = 25$ is maximized at (0, 5).

22. 50 chef's salads and 50 Caesar salads
23. (1, 3, −2) **24.** (−4, 1, −5) **25.** (6, 0, −2)
26. no solution **27.** $\left(\frac{1}{3}, 1\right)$ **28.** (1, −1)
29. (2, −4, 6) **30.** $\left(5, 2, -3\right)$

Chapter 4

Get Ready! p. 191 **1.** 6 **2.** 4
3. $-2 < x < 6$
4. $y \le -\frac{5}{4}$ or $y \ge \frac{9}{4}$
5. $y = 9x - 10$
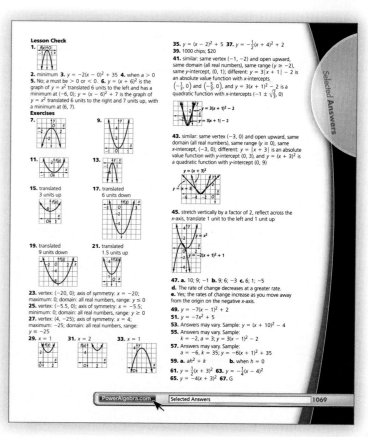
6. $y = \frac{1}{3}x + 8$

7. translated 4 units to the right and 2 units up
8. translated 10 units to the left and 3 units down
9. (10, −1) **10.** (−6, −6) **11.** Answers may vary. Sample: application forms, registration forms, tests
12. Answers may vary. Sample: monsters, ghosts, tooth fairy **13.** writing

Lesson 4-1   pp. 194–201

Got It?
1. a.
b. If a is a negative number, the parabola will open downward. There will be a maximum value for y at the vertex of the parabola.
2. a. translated 3 units up
b. translated 1 unit to the left
3. vertex: (−1, 4); axis of symmetry: $x = -1$; maximum: 4; domain: all real numbers; range: $y \le 4$ **4.** stretch by the factor 2, translate 2 units to the left and 5 units down.
5. $f(x) = -\frac{2}{9}(x - 2)^2 + 7$

Lesson Check
1.
2. minimum **3.** $y = -2(x - 0)^2 + 35$ **4.** when $a > 0$
5. No; a must be > 0 or < 0. **6.** $y = (x + 6)^2$ is the graph of $y = x^2$ translated 6 units to the left and has a minimum at (−6, 0); $y = (x - 6)^2 + 7$ is the graph of $y = x^2$ translated 6 units to the right and 7 units up, with a minimum at (6, 7).
Exercises
7. **9.**
11. **13.**
15. translated 3 units up **17.** translated 6 units down
19. translated 9 units down **21.** translated 1.5 units up
23. vertex: (−20, 0); axis of symmetry: $x = -20$; maximum: 0; domain: all real numbers, range: $y \le 0$
25. vertex: (−5.5, 0); axis of symmetry: $x = -5.5$; minimum: 0; domain: all real numbers, range: $y \ge 0$
27. vertex: (4, −25); axis of symmetry: $x = 4$; maximum: −25; domain: all real numbers, range: $y \le -25$
29. $x = 1$ **31.** $x = 2$ **33.** $x = 1$

35. $y = (x - 2)^2 + 5$ **37.** $y = -\frac{1}{2}(x + 4)^2 + 2$
39. 1000 chips; $20
41. similar: same vertex (−1, −2) and open upward, same domain (all real numbers), same range ($y \ge -2$), same y-intercept, (0, 1); different: $y = 3|x + 1| - 2$ is an absolute value function with x-intercepts $\left(-\frac{1}{3}, 0\right)$ and $\left(-\frac{5}{3}, 0\right)$, and $y = 3(x + 1)^2 - 2$ is a quadratic function with x-intercepts $(-1 \pm \sqrt{\frac{2}{3}}, 0)$
43. similar: same vertex (−3, 0) and open upward, same domain (all real numbers), same range ($y \ge 0$), same x-intercept, (−3, 0); different: $y = |x + 3|$ is an absolute value function with y-intercept (0, 3), and $y = (x + 3)^2$ is a quadratic function with y-intercept (0, 9)
45. stretch vertically by a factor of 2, reflect across the x-axis, translate 1 unit to the left and 1 unit up
47. a. 10; 9; −1 **b.** 9; 6; −3 **c.** 6; 1; −5
d. The rate of change decreases at a greater rate.
e. Yes; the rates of change increase as you move away from the origin on the negative x-axis.
49. $y = -7(x - 1)^2 + 2$
51. $y = -7x^2 + 5$
53. Answers may vary. Sample: $y = (x + 10)^2 - 4$
55. Answers may vary. Sample: $k = -2, a = 3; y = 3(x - 1)^2 - 2$
57. Answers may vary. Sample: $a = -6, k = 35; y = -6(x + 1)^2 + 35$
59. a. $ah^2 + k$ **b.** when $h = 0$
61. $y = \frac{1}{2}(x + 3)^2$ **63.** $y = -\frac{1}{4}(x - 4)^2$
65. $y = -4(x + 3)^2$ **67.** G

69. $2x + 2y = 225$
$2y = 225 - 2x$
$y = \frac{225}{2} - x$
$A = xy = x\left(\frac{225}{2} - x\right)$
$A = -x^2 + 112.5x$
Graph the function. There is a max. at about (56.25, 3164.06), so the max. area is about 3164.06 ft^2 and the length of each side is 56.25 ft.
70. (3, 2) **71.** (−10, 6) **72.** (1, 0, 3) **73.** (0, 0) **74.** (−1, 0) **75.** (5, 0)

Lesson 4-2 pp. 202–208

Got It? 1. vertex: $\left(-\frac{2}{3}, 7\frac{1}{3}\right)$; axis of symmetry: $x = -\frac{2}{3}$; maximum: $7\frac{1}{3}$; range: $y \le 7\frac{1}{3}$
2. 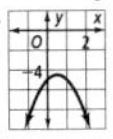
3. $y = -(x - 2)^2 - 1$ **4. a.** 4 ft **b.** because the y-intercept is (0, 0)
Lesson Check 1. vertex: (0, −4); axis of symmetry: $x = 0$; minimum: −4
2. 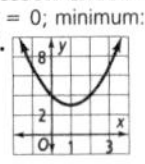 **3.** 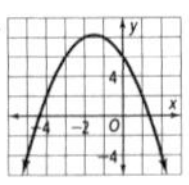
4. $y = (x - 1)^2 + 8$ **5.** $y = -\left(x - \frac{3}{2}\right)^2 + \frac{5}{4}$
6. Error in calculation of x. The correct calculation is:
$x = \frac{-(-4)}{2(2)} = 1$
$y = 2(1) - 4(1) - 3$
$= 2 - 4 - 3$
$= -5$
Vertex: (1, −5) 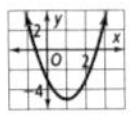
7. The vertex of a function written in vertex form can easily be determined. It is (h, k) where $f(x) = a(x - h)^2 + k$. The vertex of a function in standard form is $\left(\frac{-b}{2a}, f\left(\frac{-b}{2a}\right)\right)$ where $f(x) = ax^2 + bx + c$.
Exercises 9. vertex: (1, 2); axis of symmetry: $x = 1$; maximum: 2; range: $y \le 2$ **11.** vertex: (1, 6); axis of symmetry: $x = 1$; maximum: 6; range: $y \le 6$
13. vertex: $\left(-\frac{3}{4}, 5\frac{1}{8}\right)$; axis of symmetry: $x = -\frac{3}{4}$; maximum: $5\frac{1}{8}$; range: $y \le 5\frac{1}{8}$ **15.** vertex: $\left(-\frac{1}{2}, \frac{1}{4}\right)$; axis of symmetry: $x = -\frac{1}{2}$; maximum: $\frac{1}{4}$; range: $y \le \frac{1}{4}$
17. 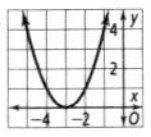 **19.** 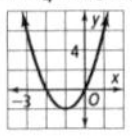
21. 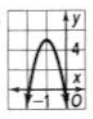 **23.** 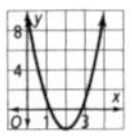
25. 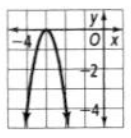
27. $y = (x + 1)^2 + 4$ **29.** $y = 2\left(x - \frac{5}{4}\right)^2 + \frac{71}{8}$
31. $y = \frac{9}{4}\left(x + \frac{2}{3}\right)^2 - 2$
33. 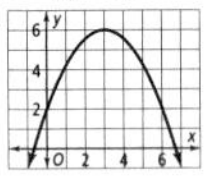 **35.** 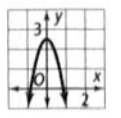
37. 4 cm × 9 cm × 9 cm **39.** $b = -6; c = 5$
41. $a = 1; c = -2$ **43. a.** The projectile represented by the equation goes higher by 28 feet. **b.** equation: $t = 0.27$ s and $t = 3.73$ s; table: $t = 0.38$ s and $t = 2.62$ s
45. (0, 3) **47.** (0, −54) **49.** $a = -6, b = 24$
51. $a = 3, b = -12$
53. 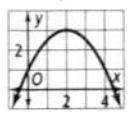
55. 0 **57.** $\frac{1}{4}$ **58.** −2.5
59. Explanations may vary. Sample: Elimination because the x's have opposite signs; (7, −1).
60. Explanations may vary. Sample: Substitution because the first equation is already solved for y; (27, 15).
61. Explanations may vary. Sample: Elimination because you can multiply the second equation by −3 to eliminate n; (3, 2).
62. vertex: (−2, −1); axis of symmetry: $x = -2$; minimum at (−2, −1); domain: all real numbers, range: $y \ge -1$

63. vertex: (1, 3); axis of symmetry: $x = 1$; maximum at (1, 3); domain: all real numbers, range: $y \le 3$
64. vertex: (3, −2); axis of symmetry: $x = 3$; minimum at (3, −2); domain: all real numbers, range: $y \ge -2$
65. vertex: (−3, 5); axis of symmetry: $x = -3$; maximum at (−3, 5); domain: all real numbers, range: $y \le 5$
66. vertex: (−4, 0); axis of symmetry: $x = -4$; minimum at (−4, 0); domain: all real numbers, range: $y \ge 0$
67. vertex: (4, 6); axis of symmetry: $x = 4$; maximum at (4, 6); domain: all real numbers, range: $y \le 6$

Lesson 4-3 pp. 209–214

Got It? 1. $y = -3x^2 + x$ **2a.** Rocket 2 **b.** Rocket 1: D: $0 \le t \le 9.4$, R: $0 \le h \le 352.6$; Rocket 2: D: $0 \le t \le 12$, R: $0 \le h \le 580$ **c.** The domains tell you how many seconds the rockets were in the air. The domains are different because the rockets were in the air for different amounts of time.
3. $y = -0.329x^2 + 9.798x + 15.571$; 88.5°F at 2:53 P.M. (although the meteorologist's prediction is 89° at 3 P.M.)
Lesson Check 1. $y = -2x^2 + 3x - 1$
2. $y = 2x^2 + 6x + 7.5$ **3.** $y = -2x^2 + 10x - 13.5$
4. Answers may vary. Sample: A rough plot of the data will indicate whether the data are collinear (linear regression) or non-collinear where the data follows a curve (quadratic regression). **5.** A parabola that opens up always attains greater values than one that opens down. **6.** y is not a function of x since for one value of x, "3," there are 2 values of y, "4" and "0."
Exercises 7. $y = -x^2 + 3x - 4$ **9.** $y = 2x^2 - x + 3$ **11.** $y = x^2 - 6x + 3$ **13.** $y = x^2 + 2x$
15. $y = -x^2 + x - 2$ **17. a.** $y = -16x^2 + 33x + 46$, where x is the number of seconds after release and y is the height in ft **b.** 28.5 ft **c.** about 63 ft **19.** yes; $y = -2x^2 + 3x + 5$ **21.** yes; $y = 0.625x^2 - 1.75x + 1$
23. $y = 0.005x^2 - 1.95x + 120$; 66 mm
25. a. $y = -0.004x^2 + 0.859x + 27.53$ **b.** Answers may vary. Sample: domain: integers from −10 to 17; range: whole numbers from 18 to 42 **c.** the year 2003 **d.** The year 2022; the year is outside the domain of the data pts. **27. a.** (3, 5) **b.** 3; substitute x- and y-values in the general form of a quadratic, then solve the resulting linear system for the coefficients. **29.** A **31.** D
33. 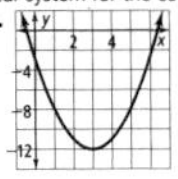 **34.** 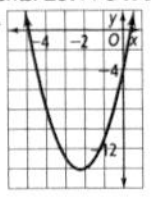 **35.** 
36. (2, 5) **37.** (5, 8) **38.** (−1, −1) **39.** $\frac{4}{5}$ **40.** $-\frac{7}{2}$
41. $x^2 + 5x - 1$ **42.** $6x^2 - 10x - 3$ **43.** $4x^2 - x - 10$

Lesson 4-4 pp. 216–223

Got It? 1. a. $(x + 10)(x + 4)$ **b.** $(x - 5)(x - 6)$ **c.** $-(x + 2)(x - 16)$ **2. a.** $7(n^2 - 3)$ **b.** $9(x + 2)(x - 1)$ **c.** $4(x^2 + 2x + 3)$ **3. a.** $(x + 1)(4x + 3)$ **b.** $(x - 2)(2x - 3)$ **c.** No; $2x^2 + 2x + 2 = 2(x^2 + x + 1)$, there are no real factors of a and c whose product is 1 and whose sum is 1. **4.** $(8x - 1)^2$
5. $(4x - 9)(4x + 9)$
Lesson Check 1. $(x + 4)(x + 2)$ **2.** $(x - 12)(x - 1)$ **3.** $(x - 9)(x + 9)$ **4.** $(5y - 6)(5y + 6)$ **5.** $(y - 3)^2$ **6.** $(2x - 1)^2$ **7.** 5x **8.** $4a^2$ **9.** 6 **10.** 7h **11.** No; the middle term is not twice the product of the square root of the end terms. **12.** For $a \ne 1$, look for two factors whose sum is b and whose product is ac. For $a = 1$, look for two factors whose sum is b and whose product is c.
13. $a^2 - 2ab + b^2 - 25$ Group the first 3 terms.
$= (a^2 - 2ab + b^2) - 25$
$= (a - b)^2 - 5^2$
$= (a - b - 5)(a - b + 5)$
Exercises 15. $(x + 2)(x + 3)$ **17.** $(x + 2)(x + 8)$ **19.** $(x + 2)(x + 20)$ **21.** $-(x - 1)(x - 12)$ **23.** $(x - 4)(x - 6)$ **25.** $(x - 4)(x - 9)$ **27.** $-(x - 4)(x + 5)$ **29.** $(c - 7)(c + 9)$ **31.** $-(t - 11)(t + 4)$ **33.** 5b; $5b(5b - 4)$ **35.** 5; $5(t + 1)(t - 2)$ **37.** 9; $9(3p^2 - p + 2)$ **39.** $(x - 8)(2x - 3)$ **41.** $(m - 3)(2m - 5)$ **43.** $(x - 12)(2x - 3)$ **45.** $(y + 4)(5y - 8)$ **47.** $(x + 1)^2$ **49.** $(k - 9)^2$
51. cannot be factored; 8 is not a perfect square and there are no positive factors of 32 that have a sum of 16.
53. $(x - 2)(x + 2)$ **55.** cannot be factored; This is a sum of squares, not a difference of squares.
57. $(5x - 1)$ cm by $(5x - 1)$ cm **59.** $2(3z + 2)(3z - 2)$ **61.** $16(2t + 1)(2t - 1)$ **63.** $3(y + 5)(y + 3)$ **65.** $3(x + 1)(x - 9)$ **67.** $2(x - 5)(2x - 1)$
69. $-\left(\frac{1}{4}s - 1\right)\left(\frac{1}{4}s + 1\right)$
71. The third line should be $x(2x - 5) - (2x - 5)$, and the final line should be $(x - 1)(2x - 5)$. **73.** y; $y(y - 1)$ **75.** 10; $10(x - 3)(x + 3)$ **77.** 2; $2(x^2 - 37x + 6)$ **79.** D **81.** Answers may vary. **83.** $(0.5t + 0.4)(0.5t - 0.4)$ **85.** $(x + 12)(x - 3)$ **87.** $(2x + 9)(3x + 14)$
89. Factor the GCF, $4x^2$, from the terms to get $4x^2(x^2 + 6x + 8)$. Look for numbers whose product is 8 and whose sum is 6. The numbers 4 and 2 work. The complete factorization is $4x^2(x + 4)(x + 2)$.
91. $(2x - 5y)(2x + 5y)(4x^2 + 25y^2)$
93. $(x - 8)(x + 3)$ **95.** B **97. a.** By entering the given lists into a graphing calculator and then calculating the quadratic regression, you get $h = -16t^2 + 22t + 3$ as the quadratic model for the ball's height as a function of time.

b. $h = -16t^2 + 22t + 3$
$h = -[8t(2t - 3) + 1(2t - 3)]$
$h = -(2t - 3)(8t + 1)$
98. $y = -0.149x^2 + 5.171x + 16.971$ **99.** penny: 2.5g, nickel: 5g, dime: 2.3g
100. 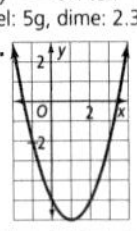 **101.** 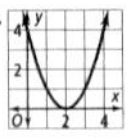
102. 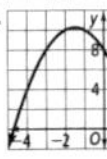
Algebra Review p. 225 1. $3\sqrt{2}$ **3.** $-4\sqrt{2}$ **5.** $\frac{-\sqrt{91}}{13}$ **7.** $-10\sqrt{2}$ **9.** 108 **11.** $|xy|$ **13.** $-\frac{|x|\sqrt{35}}{5}$ **15.** $\frac{5\sqrt{14}}{7}$

Lesson 4-5 pp. 226–231

Got It? 1. 3, 4 **2.** 3, $\frac{1}{4}$ **3.** −6, 4 **4. a.** $53\frac{1}{3}$ m; $21\frac{1}{3}$ m; answers may vary. Sample: domain: $0 \le x \le 60$, range: $0 \le y \le 30$ **b.** No; domains and ranges are constrained by real-world limits.
Lesson Check 1. 3, −3 **2.** −4, −9 **3.** $-\frac{2}{3}$, 1 **4.** 4.372, −1.372 **5.** 2.608, −2.108 **6.** −1; since $y = 0$ when $x = 5$, substitute these values into the equation to find b. **7.** when the coefficients are integers and a recognizable pattern of factoring is evident **8.** One solution: when the table's range consists of zero and all positive numbers or zero and all negative numbers. No solution: when the table does not include zero and the y-values are either all positive or all negative numbers
Exercises 9. −4, −2 **11.** −1, $\frac{3}{2}$ **13.** −2, −1 **15.** 0, 4 **17.** 0, 4 **19.** 3, 8 **21.** −0.78, 1.28 **23.** 4, −10 **25.** 0.8, −1 **27.** −1.67, −1.5 **29.** −0.94, 2.34 **31.** −1, 0.25 **33.** −1.46, 5.46 **35.** −1.16, 2.16 **37.** 3 in. **39.** about 3.6 ft **41.** Answers may vary. Samples are given: **a.** $x^2 - 8x + 15 = 0$ **b.** $x^2 + x - 6 = 0$ **c.** $x^2 + 7x + 6 = 0$ **43.** $-\frac{3}{2}, -\frac{2}{3}$ **45.** −4, $\frac{5}{2}$ **47.** −1, 4 **49.** −4, 0 **51.** 4.37, −1.37
53. −1, $\frac{10}{3}$ **55.** (0, −2), (2, 2) **57.** Solve $(x - 4)(x - 6) = 0$ to find that the zeros of $y = x^2 - 10x + 24$ are 4 and 6. Average 4 and 6 to get 5. This is the x-coordinate of the vertex. Substitute 5 for x in $x^2 - 10x + 24$ to find that −1 is the y-coordinate of the vertex. The vertex is (5, −1).
59. a. 2.45m **b.** ≈1.3s **61.** H
63. reflection across the x-axis, followed by a vertical translation 2 units up, and stretched by a factor of 3
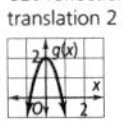
64. $(4x - 1)(4x + 1)$ **65.** $(5x - 1)(x - 5)$ **66.** $(2x - 1)(x + 7)$ **67.** (2, 0, −2) **68.** (−2, 1, 5) **69.** (7, 1, −1) **70.** vertex: (−9, 4); axis of symmetry: $x = -9$; translation 9 units to the left and 4 units up **71.** vertex: $\left(\frac{7}{2}, 0\right)$; axis of symmetry: $x = \frac{7}{2}$; stretch by a factor of 2, translation $3\frac{1}{2}$ units to the right **72.** vertex: (0, −1); axis of symmetry: $x = 0$; vert. compression by a factor of $\frac{3}{4}$, translation 1 unit down **73.** $x^2 + 8x + 13$ **74.** $4x^2 - 4x + 1$ **75.** $x^2 - 6x + 9$

Lesson 4-6 pp. 233–239

Got It? 1. a. $\sqrt{5}, -\sqrt{5}$ **b.** $\sqrt{2}, -\sqrt{2}$ **2.** 42 in. × 67.2 in. **3.** 2, 12 **4. a.** 9 **b.** No; $\left(\frac{b}{2}\right)^2 = \frac{b^2}{4}$, which is a function of b. **5.** $\frac{1}{2} \pm \frac{\sqrt{13}}{2}$
6. $y = \left(x + \frac{3}{2}\right)^2 - \frac{33}{4}$; vertex: $\left(-\frac{3}{2}, -\frac{33}{4}\right)$; y-intercept: (0, −6)
Lesson Check 1. 6, −6 **2.** 3, −3 **3.** 1 **4.** 25 **5.** 4 **6.** 36 **7.** 2500 **8.** 256 **9.** First, you rewrite the eq. to get all terms with x on one side. Then, you find $\left(\frac{b}{2}\right)^2$ and add it to both sides of the eq. Then, you factor the resulting trinomial.
10. $x^2 + 12x + 5 = 3$
$x^2 + 12x = -2$ Rewrite to get all terms with x on one side of the eq.
$\left(\frac{12}{2}\right)^2 = 6^2 = 36$ Find $\left(\frac{b}{2}\right)^2 = 36$.
$x^2 + 12x + 36 = -2 + 36$ Add 36 to each side.
$(x + 6)^2 = 34$ Factor the trinomial.
11. Your friend should also have subtracted 49; $(x^2 - 14x + 49) + 36 - 49 = (x - 7)^2 - 13$
Exercises 13. 2, −2 **15.** $\frac{5}{3}, -\frac{5}{3}$ **17.** $2\sqrt{2}, -2\sqrt{2}$ **19.** −4, −2 **21.** −1, 3 **23.** −4, 3 **25.** $-\frac{4}{5}, \frac{2}{5}$ **27.** $-\frac{10}{3}, \frac{2}{3}$ **29.** $\frac{1}{4}$ **31.** 100 **33.** 4 **35.** $6 \pm \sqrt{29}$ **37.** $1 \pm \sqrt{6}$ **39.** $5 \pm \sqrt{13}$ **41.** $3 \pm \sqrt{11}$ **43.** $-\frac{5}{4} \pm \frac{1}{4}\sqrt{37}$ **45.** $-\frac{3}{5} \pm \frac{\sqrt{21}}{5}$
47. $y = 2(x - 2)^2 - 7$ **49.** $y = (x + 2)^2 - 11$ **51.** $y = -(x - 2)^2 + 3$ **53.** 10, −10 **55.** 22, −22 **57.** 18, −18 **59.** 1, −1 **61.** 84, −84
63. $\frac{-5 \pm \sqrt{37}}{2}$ **65.** $\frac{1 \pm \sqrt{21}}{2}$ **67.** $\frac{2 \pm \sqrt{10}}{3}$

69. $\frac{-3 \pm \sqrt{41}}{8}$ **71.** $\frac{1}{3}, -\frac{2}{3}$ **73.** $-3 \pm \sqrt{7}$
75. a. $-.01(x - 59)^2 + 36.81$; 36.81 ft **b.** 7.65 ft **c.** about 120 ft **77.** $\frac{-a \pm a\sqrt{13}}{6}$
79. $-\frac{3}{2a}, -\frac{1}{2a}, a \ne 0$ **81.** $-\frac{2}{3a}, \frac{5}{2a}, a \ne 0$
83. $y = -4\left(x + \frac{5}{8}\right)^2 + \frac{73}{16}; \left(-\frac{5}{8}, \frac{73}{16}\right)$
85. $y = -\frac{1}{5}(x - 2)^2 + 3$; (2, 3) **87.** G
89. $x^2 - 9 = -8x$
$x^2 + 8x = 9$ Move the variables to the left side and the constant to the right by using the Add. Prop. of Eq.
$\left(\frac{8}{2}\right)^2 = 4^2 = 16$ Find $\left(\frac{b}{2}\right)^2 = 16$.
$x^2 + 8x + 16 = 9 + 16$ Add 16 to each side.
$(x + 4)^2 = 25$ Factor left side. Simplify right side.
$x + 4 = \pm 5$ Take the square root of each side.
$x = -4 \pm 5$ Add −4 to each side.
$x = -9, 1$ Simplify.
90. $\frac{1}{2}$, 1 **91.** −4, 1 **92.** 8, $-\frac{2}{3}$
93. yes; $y = \frac{1}{2}x^2 + \frac{7}{2}x + 9$ **94.** yes; $y = -\frac{1}{2}x^2 + x + 2$ **95.** yes; $y = 3x^2 - 5x + 2$
96. (2, 0) **97.** (3, 1) **98.** (3, 1) **99.** 24 **100.** 84

Lesson 4-7 pp. 240–247

Got It? 1. a. −2 **b.** $-2 \pm \sqrt{7}$ **2. a.** \$10.74 **b.** Yes; a neg. profit means more money was spent than earned. **3. a.** no real solutions **b.** two real solutions **4.** Yes; $b^2 - 4ac = (85)^2 - 4(-16)\left(-109\frac{11}{12}\right) = 190\frac{1}{3}$. The discriminant is pos. So the eq. has two real solutions.
Lesson Check 1. $\frac{5 \pm \sqrt{53}}{2}$ **2.** $\frac{-3 \pm \sqrt{61}}{2}$ **3.** 3, $-\frac{1}{2}$ **4.** no real solutions **5.** −32; no real solutions **6.** 273; two real solutions **7.** 0; one real solution **8.** $k = \pm 6$ for one real solution; $k > 6$ or $k < -6$ for two real solutions **9.** Answers may vary. Sample: The discriminants of eqs. with one real solution are all zero and thus equal, but the solutions may or may not be equal. An example is $x^2 - 8x + 16$ and $x^2 - 4x + 4$. Each has a discriminant of zero, but the solutions are 4 and 2. **10.** Yes; the eqs. can share common factors such as for $x^2 + 2x - 8$ where the discriminant is 36 and the solutions are 2 and −4, and $x^2 - 4x + 4$ where the discriminant is zero and the solution is 2.
Exercises 11. 1, 3 **13.** $-\frac{7}{2}$, 1 **15.** −5 **17.** $\frac{3 \pm \sqrt{5}}{2}$ **19.** $\frac{2 \pm \sqrt{10}}{3}$ **21.** 1, 4 **23.** \$16.34 **25.** −4; no real solutions **27.** 0; one **29.** 169; two **31.** 1; two
33. 0; one **35.** −23; no real solutions **37.** no
39. 2.29 in. × 15.71 in. **41.** $-\frac{1}{6}$, 1 **43.** −2.49, 0.89 **45.** −0.19, 2.69 **47.** 1, 10 **49.** $-\frac{3}{2}, \frac{1}{2}$ **51.** −1.70, 4.70 **53.** −8.47, 0.47 **55.** 1.47, −7.47 **57.** about 1.89 s **59.** one **61.** two **63.** two **65.** two **67. a.** k such that $|k| < 12$ **b.** 12 or −12 **c.** k such that $|k| > 12$
69. a. $x^2 = 100\pi$ **b.** 17.72 cm
71. Answers may vary. Sample: $x^2 + 5x + 3 = 0$
73. 0, $\pm\sqrt{5}$ **75.** −5, 1 **77.** The absolute value of $\frac{\sqrt{b^2 - 4ac}}{2a}$ is the distance from the axis of symmetry to the x-intercepts, if the discriminant is nonnegative.
79. 3 **81.** 15 **82.** −2, 10 **83.** $\frac{2 \pm \sqrt{2}}{2}$ **84.** $\frac{3 \pm \sqrt{41}}{2}$ **85.** $9z^2 + 3z$ **86.** $4x + k$ **87.** $2y - 8x$ **88.** $2\sqrt{17}$ **89.** 5 **90.** 13

Lesson 4-8 pp. 248–255

Got It? 1. a. $2i\sqrt{3}$ **b.** 5i **c.** $i\sqrt{7}$ **d.** $8i \ne -8$
2. a. 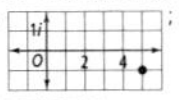 ; $\sqrt{26}$
b. 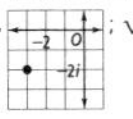 ; $\sqrt{13}$ **c.**  ; $\sqrt{17}$
3. a. $4 - i$ **b.** $-2 + 7i$ **c.** 12i **d.** 18i **4. a.** −21 **b.** $23 - 2i$ **c.** 41 **5. a.** $\frac{7}{25} - \frac{26}{25}i$ **b.** $-\frac{1}{6} - \frac{2}{3}i$ **c.** $\frac{15}{113} - \frac{112}{113}i$ **6. a.** $5(x + 2i)(x - 2i)$ **b.** $(x + 9i)(x - 9i)$ **7. a.** $\frac{1 \pm i\sqrt{23}}{6}$ **b.** $2 \pm i$
Lesson Check 1. $5i\sqrt{3}$ **2.** 5 **3.** $(x + 4i)(x - 4i)$ **4.** $7 - 3i$ **5.** $13 - 6i$ **6.** The add. inv. of a complex number, $a + bi$, is the opposite of the complex number, or $-a - bi$. The complex conjugate of a complex number, $a + bi$, is the real part plus the opposite of the imaginary part of the complex number, or $a - bi$. **7.** error in the sign of the last term of the first line, which carries through to the end of the calculation; the line should be: "...
$= 16 + 28i - 28i - 49i^2$
$= 16 + 49$
$= 65.$"
Exercises 9. $i\sqrt{7}$ **11.** 9i
13. ; 2 **15.** 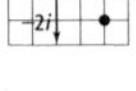 ; $2\sqrt{2}$

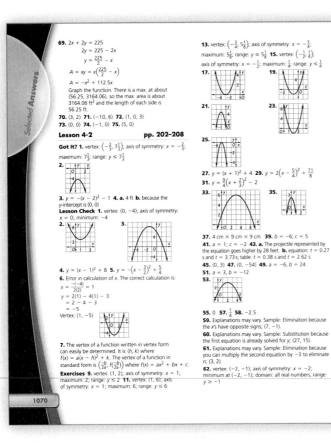

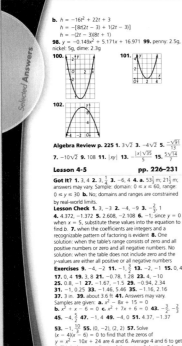

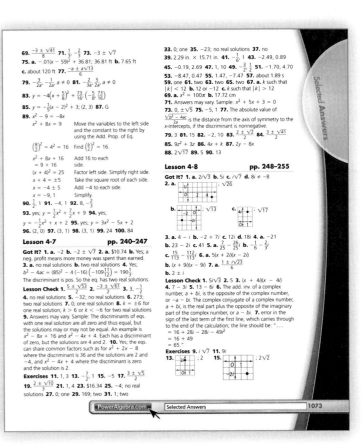

17. 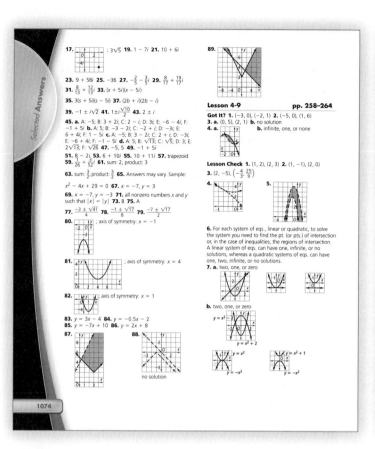; $3\sqrt{5}$ **19.** $1 - 7i$ **21.** $10 + 6i$

23. $9 + 58i$ **25.** -36 **27.** $-\frac{2}{5} - \frac{3}{5}i$ **29.** $\frac{8}{17} + \frac{19}{17}i$
31. $\frac{8}{13} + \frac{15}{13}i$ **33.** $(x + 5i)(x - 5i)$
35. $3(s + 5i)(s - 5i)$ **37.** $(2b + i)(2b - i)$
39. $-1 \pm i\sqrt{2}$ **41.** $1 \pm \frac{\sqrt{10}}{2}$ **43.** $2 \pm i$
45. a. A: -5; B: $3 + 2i$; C: $2 - i$; D: $3i$; E: $-6 - 4i$; F: $-1 + 5i$ **b.** A: 5; B: $-3 - 2i$; C: $-2 + i$; D: $-3i$; E: $6 + 4i$; F: $1 - 5i$ **c.** A: -5; B: $3 - 2i$; C: $2 + i$; D: $-3i$; E: $-6 + 4i$; F: $-1 - 5i$ **d.** A: 5; B: $\sqrt{13}$; C: $\sqrt{5}$; D: 3; E: $2\sqrt{13}$; F: $\sqrt{26}$ **47.** $-5, 5$ **49.** $-1 + 5i$
51. $8 - 2i$ **53.** $6 + 10i$ **55.** $10 + 11i$ **57.** trapezoid
59. $\frac{5}{26} + \frac{5}{26}i$ **61.** sum: 2, product: 3
63. sum: $\frac{3}{2}$, product: $\frac{3}{2}$ **65.** Answers may vary. Sample:
$x^2 - 4x + 29 = 0$ **67.** $x = -7, y = 3$
69. $x = -7, y = -3$ **71.** all nonzero numbers x and y such that $|x| = |y|$ **73.** B **75.** A
77. $\frac{-3 \pm \sqrt{41}}{4}$ **78.** $\frac{-1 \pm \sqrt{17}}{8}$ **79.** $\frac{-7 \pm \sqrt{17}}{2}$
80. 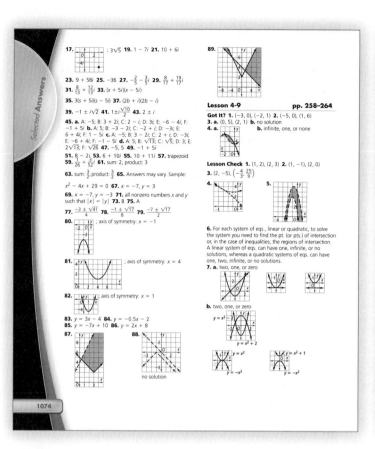; axis of symmetry: $x = -1$
81. ; axis of symmetry: $x = 4$
82. ; axis of symmetry: $x = 1$
83. $y = 3x - 4$ **84.** $y = -0.5x - 2$
85. $y = -7x + 10$ **86.** $y = 2x + 8$
87. **88.** no solution **89.**

Lesson 4-9 pp. 258–264
Got It? 1. $(-3, 0), (-2, 1)$ **2.** $(-5, 0), (1, 6)$
3. a. $(0, 5), (2, 1)$ **b.** no solution
4. a. **b.** infinite, one, or none
Lesson Check 1. $(1, 2), (2, 3)$ **2.** $(1, -1), (2, 0)$
3. $(2, -5), \left(-\frac{4}{3}, \frac{25}{9}\right)$
4. **5.**
6. For each system of eqs., linear or quadratic, to solve the system you need to find the pt. (or pts.) of intersection or, in the case of inequalities, the regions of intersection. A linear system of eqs. can have one, infinite, or no solutions, whereas a quadratic systems of eqs. can have one, two, infinite, or no solutions.
7. a. two, one, or zero
b. two, one, or zero
$y = x^2$

c. four, three, two, one, or zero
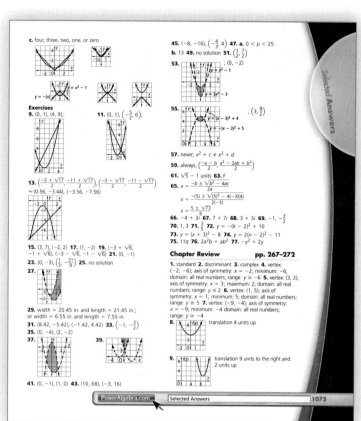
$y = -|x|$ $y = x^2 - 1$
Exercises
9. $(0, 1), (4, 9)$; **11.** $(0, 1), \left(-\frac{5}{2}, 6\right)$;
13. $\left(\frac{-3 + \sqrt{17}}{2}, \frac{-11 + \sqrt{17}}{2}\right), \left(\frac{-3 - \sqrt{17}}{2}, \frac{-11 - \sqrt{17}}{2}\right)$ $\approx (0.56, -3.44), (-3.56, -7.56)$
15. $(3, 7), (-2, 2)$ **17.** $(1, -2)$ **19.** $(-3 + \sqrt{6}, -1 + \sqrt{6}), (-3 - \sqrt{6}, -1 - \sqrt{6})$ **21.** $(0, -1)$
23. $(0, -3), \left(\frac{1}{3}, -\frac{31}{9}\right)$ **25.** no solution
27.
29. width = 20.45 in. and length = 21.45 in.; or width = 6.55 in. and length = 7.55 in.
31. $(8.42, -5.42), (-1.42, 4.42)$ **33.** $\left(-1, -\frac{3}{2}\right)$
35. $(0, -4), (2, -2)$
37. **39.**
41. $(0, -1), (1, 0)$ **43.** $(10, 68), (-3, 16)$

45. $(-8, -16), \left(-\frac{4}{3}, 4\right)$ **47. a.** $0 < p < 25$
b. 13 **49.** no solution **51.** $\left(\frac{1}{2}, \frac{7}{2}\right)$
53. ; $(0, -2)$
55. ; $\left(3, \frac{9}{2}\right)$
57. never; $x^2 + c \ne x^2 + d$
59. always; $\left(\frac{-a - b}{2}, \frac{a^2 - 2ab + b^2}{2}\right)$
61. $\sqrt{5} - 1$ units **63.** F
65. $x = \frac{-b \pm \sqrt{b^2 - 4ac}}{2a}$
$x = \frac{-(5) \pm \sqrt{(5)^2 - 4(-3)(4)}}{2(-3)}$
$x = \frac{5 \pm \sqrt{73}}{6}$
66. $-4 + 3i$ **67.** $7 + 7i$ **68.** $3 + 3i$ **69.** $-1, -\frac{3}{2}$
70. $1, 3$ **71.** $\frac{2}{3}$ **72.** $y = -(k - 2)^2 + 10$
73. $y = (x + 3)^2 - 8$ **74.** $y = 2(n - 2)^2 - 11$
75. $11q$ **76.** $2a^2b + ab^2$ **77.** $-y^2 + 2y$

Chapter Review pp. 267–272
1. standard **2.** discriminant **3.** complex **4.** vertex: $(-2, -6)$; axis of symmetry: $x = -2$; minimum: -6; domain: all real numbers; range: $y \ge -6$ **5.** vertex: $(3, 2)$; axis of symmetry: $x = 3$; maximum: 2; domain: all real numbers; range: $y \le 2$ **6.** vertex: $(1, 5)$; axis of symmetry: $x = 1$; minimum: 5; domain: all real numbers; range: $y \ge 5$ **7.** vertex: $(-9, -4)$; axis of symmetry: $x = -9$; minimum: -4 domain: all real numbers; range: $y \ge -4$
8. translation 4 units up
9. translation 9 units to the right and 2 units up

10. 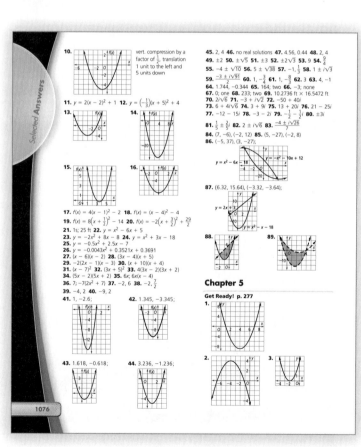 vert. compression by a factor of $\frac{1}{2}$, translation 1 unit to the left and 5 units down
11. $y = 2(x - 2)^2 + 1$ **12.** $y = \left(-\frac{1}{3}\right)(x + 5)^2 + 4$
13. **14.**
15. **16.**
17. $f(x) = 4(x - 1)^2 - 2$ **18.** $f(x) = (x - 4)^2 - 4$
19. $f(x) = 8\left(x + \frac{1}{2}\right)^2 - 14$ **20.** $f(x) = -2\left(x + \frac{3}{2}\right)^2 + \frac{29}{2}$
21. 1s; 25 ft **22.** $y = 2x^2 - 6x + 5$
23. $y = -2x^2 + 8x - 24$ **24.** $y = x^2 + 3x - 18$
25. $y = -0.5x^2 + 2.5x - 7$
26. $y = -0.0043x^2 + 0.3521x + 0.3691$
27. $(x - 6)(x - 2)$ **28.** $(3x - 4)(x + 5)$
29. $-2(2x - 1)(x - 3)$ **30.** $(x + 10)(x + 4)$
31. $(x - 7)^2$ **32.** $(3x + 5)^2$ **33.** $4(3x - 2)(3x + 2)$
34. $(5x - 2)(5x + 2)$ **35.** $6x(x - 4)$
36. 7; $-7(2x^2 + 7)$ **37.** $-2, 6$ **38.** $-2, \frac{7}{2}$
39. $-4, 2$ **40.** $-9, 2$
41. $1, -2.6$; **42.** $1.345, -3.345$;
43. $1.618, -0.618$; **44.** $3.236, -1.236$;

45. 2, 4 **46.** no real solutions **47.** 4.56, 0.44 **48.** 2, 4
49. ± 50 **50.** $\pm\sqrt{5}$ **51.** ± 3 **52.** $\pm 2\sqrt{3}$ **53.** 9 **54.** $\frac{4}{3}$
55. $-4 \pm \sqrt{10}$ **56.** $5 \pm \sqrt{38}$ **57.** $-1, \frac{1}{3}$ **58.** $-1, \frac{1}{3}$
59. $\frac{-3 \pm i\sqrt{91}}{2}$ **60.** $1, -\frac{3}{4}$ **61.** $1, -\frac{8}{3}$ **62.** 3 **63.** 4, -1
64. 1.744, -0.344 **65.** 164; two **66.** -3; none
67. 0; one **68.** 233; two **69.** 10.2736 ft × 16.5472 ft
70. $2i\sqrt{6}$ **71.** $-3 + i\sqrt{2}$ **72.** $-50 + 40i$
73. $6 + 4i\sqrt{6}$ **74.** $3 + 9i$ **75.** $13 + 20i$ **76.** $21 - 25i$
77. $-12 - 15i$ **78.** $-3 - 2i$ **79.** $-\frac{1}{2} - \frac{1}{2}i$ **80.** $\pm 3i$
81. $\frac{1}{2} \pm \frac{5}{2}i$ **82.** $2 \pm i\sqrt{6}$ **83.** $\frac{-4 \pm i\sqrt{26}}{7}$
84. $(7, -6), (-2, 12)$ **85.** $(5, -27), (-2, 8)$
86. $(-5, 37), (3, -27)$;
$y = x^2 - 6x$ $-10x + 12$
87. $(6.32, 15.64), (-3.32, -3.64)$;
$y = 2x^2$ $y = x^2 - x - 18$
88. **89.**

Chapter 5

Get Ready! p. 277
1.
2. **3.**

4. $y = x^2 + 3x - 4$ **5.** $y = x^2 - 2x + 1$
6. $y = -x^2 - x + 12$ **7.** 0.25, -1 **8.** $-6.39, 4.39$
9. $-6.38, 0.38$ **10.** $-4, 5$ **11.** $-9, 3$ **12.** 1, 2
13. 24; two solutions **14.** 0; one real solution
15. 0; one real solution **16.** south **17.** The highest pt. in Maine may be lower than the highest pt. in the United States. The relative maximum of a graph for a given region is the maximum for that region only, whereas the maximum of the graph may be greater than or equal to the relative maximum for the region.
18. $4x^2 + 4x + 1$

Lesson 5-1 pp. 280–287
Got It? 1. a. $5x^4 + 3x^3 - x$; quartic trinomial
b. $-4x^5 + 2x^2 + 13$; quintic trinomial **2.** up and down
3. a. end behavior: up and down; two turning points, $(0.33, -2.15)$ and $(1, -2)$; decreases from $-\infty$ to $\frac{1}{3}$, increases from $\frac{1}{3}$ to 1, and decreases from 1 to ∞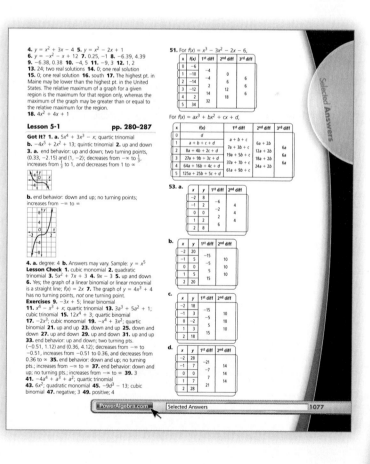
b. end behavior: down and up; no turning points; increases from $-\infty$ to ∞
4. a. degree: 4 **b.** Answers may vary. Sample: $y = x^5$
Lesson Check 1. cubic monomial **2.** quadratic trinomial **3.** $5x^2 + 7x + 3$ **4.** $9x - 3$ **5.** up and down
6. Yes; the graph of a linear binomial or linear monomial is a straight line; $f(x) = 2x$ **7.** The graph of $y = 4x^3 + 4$ has no turning points, not one turning point.
Exercises 9. $-3x + 5$; linear binomial
11. $x^4 - x^3 + x$; quartic trinomial **13.** $3a^3 + 5a^2 + 1$; cubic trinomial **15.** $12x^4 + 3$; quartic binomial
17. $-2x^3$; cubic monomial **19.** $-x^4 + 3x^2$; quartic binomial **21.** up and up **23.** down and up **25.** down and down **27.** up and down **29.** up and down **31.** up and up
33. end behavior: up and down; two turning pts. $(-0.51, 1.12)$ and $(0.36, 4.12)$; decreases from $-\infty$ to -0.51, increases from -0.51 to 0.36, and decreases from 0.36 to ∞ **35.** end behavior: down and up; no turning pts.; increases from $-\infty$ to ∞ **37.** end behavior: down and up; no turning pts.; increases from $-\infty$ to ∞ **39.** 3
41. $-4a^3 + a^3 + a^2$; quartic trinomial
43. $6x^2$; quadratic monomial **45.** $-9d^3 - 13$; cubic binomial **47.** negative; 3 **49.** positive; 4

51. For $f(x) = x^3 - 3x^2 - 2x - 6$,

x	f(x)	1st diff	2nd diff	3rd diff
0	−6			
1	−10	−4		
2	−14	−4	0	
3	−12	2	6	6
4	2	14	12	6
5	34	32	18	6

For $f(x) = ax^3 + bx^2 + cx + d$,

x	f(x)	1st diff	2nd diff	3rd diff
0	d			
1	$a + b + c + d$	$a + b + c$		
2	$8a + 4b + 2c + d$	$7a + 3b + c$	$6a + 2b$	
3	$27a + 9b + 3c + d$	$19a + 5b + c$	$12a + 2b$	$6a$
4	$64a + 16b + 4c + d$	$37a + 7b + c$	$18a + 2b$	$6a$
5	$125a + 25b + 5c + d$	$61a + 9b + c$	$24a + 2b$	$6a$

53. a.

x	y	1st diff	2nd diff
−2	8		
−1	2	−6	4
0	0	−2	4
1	2	2	4
2	8	6	

b.

x	y	1st diff	2nd diff
−2	20		
−1	5	−15	10
0	0	−5	10
1	5	5	10
2	20	15	

c.

x	y	1st diff	2nd diff
−2	18		
−1	3	−15	10
0	−2	−5	10
1	3	5	10
2	18	15	

d.

x	y	1st diff	2nd diff
−2	28		
−1	7	−21	14
0	0	−7	14
1	7	7	14
2	28	21	

Selected Answers

e.

x	y	1st diff	2nd diff
−2	29		
		−21	
−1	8		14
		−7	
0	1		14
		7	
1	8		14
		21	
2	29		

f.

x	y	1st diff	2nd diff
−2	23		
		−18	
−1	5		14
		−4	
0	1		14
		10	
1	11		14
		24	
2	35		

Second differences of quadratic functions are constant. **55.** missing values: y: 0, −6, −4; first differences: −6, 2 **57.** −35; Let $y = 2x^3 + bx^2 + cx + 7$. Evaluate $f(1) = 7$ and $f(2) = 9$ to find a system of equations for b and c. $b = -5$ and $c = 3$, so $f(-2) = -35$. **59.** F **61.** $x^2(3x^2 - 2x) - 3x^4 = 3x^4 - 2x^3 - 3x^4 = -2x^3$; The degree is 3 and there is 1 term, so this is a cubic monomial. **62.** (3.7, −4.4), (−2.7, 8.4) **63.** (−20, 360) **64.** (−3, 0), (−1, −8) **65.** $35x - 5y = -2$ **66.** $6x + 2y = -5$ **67.** $2x + 7y = 28$ **68.** $12x - 10y = 5$ **69.** $(x + 4)(x + 3)$ **70.** $(x + 10)(x - 2)$ **71.** $(x - 12)(x - 2)$

Lesson 5-2 pp. 288–295

Got It? 1. $x(x - 4)(x + 3)$ **2.** 0, 3, −5;

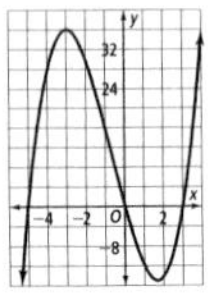

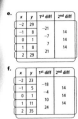

3. a. $f(x) = x^2 - 9$ **b.** $P(x) = x^3 - 3x^2 - 9x + 27$

c.

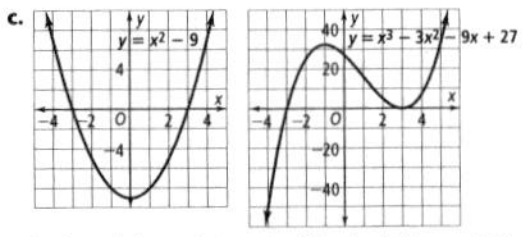

Both graphs have x-intercepts of 3 and −3. The quadratic has up and up end behavior and one turning pt., and the cubic has down and up end behavior and two turning pts. **4.** 0 is a zero of multiplicity 1, the graph looks close to linear at $x = 0$; 2 is a zero of multiplicity 2, the graph looks close to quadratic at $x = 2$. **5.** relative maximum: (−0.86, 3.13); relative minimum: (0.64, −2) **6.** 2.28 in.^{3}
Lesson Check 1. 0, 6 **2.** −4, 5 **3.** −12, 7, 9 **4.** $f(x) = x^3 - x$ **5.** $h(x) = x^4 + 4x^3 - 26x^2 - 60x + 225$ **6.** Error in writing the factors: a function that has zeros at 3 and −1 has factors of $x - 3$ and $x + 1$ *not* $x + 3$ and $x - 1$, so $f(x) = x^2 - 2x - 3$ *not* $x^2 + 2x - 3$.
Exercises 7. $x(x + 5)(x + 2)$ **9.** $x(x - 7)(x + 3)$ **11.** $x(x + 4)^2$
13. 1, −2;

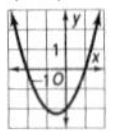

15. 0, −5, 8;

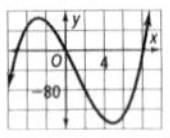

17. −1, 1, 2;

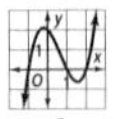

19. $y = x^3 - 18x^2 + 107x - 210$ **21.** $y = x^3 + 9x^2 + 15x - 25$ **23.** $y = x^3 + 2x^2 - x - 2$ **25.** $y = x^4 - 5x^3 + 6x^2$ **27.** −3 (multiplicity 3) **29.** −1, 0, $\frac{1}{2}$ **31.** 4 (multiplicity 2) **33.** $-\frac{3}{2}$, 1 (multiplicity 2) **35.** relative maximum: (−3.19, 24.19); relative minimum: (0.52, −1.38) **37.** relative maximum: (2.15, 12.32); relative minimum: (−0.15, −12.32) **39. a.** $\ell = 16 - 2x$; $w = 12 - 2x$; $h = x$ **b.** $V = x(16 - 2x)(12 - 2x)$
c.

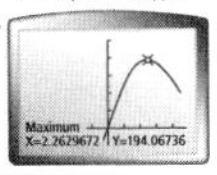

194 in.^{3}, 2.26 in.

41. $y = -2x(x + 5)(x - 4)$ **43.** 1 ft increase in each dimension **45.** $V = 12x^3 - 27x$ **47.** relative maximum: (2.53, 10.51); relative minimum: (5.14, −7.14); $\frac{3}{2}$, 4, 6 **49.** no relative maximum; relative minimum: (−1, −1); −2, 0 **51.** Answers may vary. Sample: The linear factors can be determined by examining the x-intercepts of the graph. **53.** −1, 4, $\frac{3}{2}$ **55.** $y = x^4 - 1$ **57.** B **59.** B **61.** $-3x^5 + 3x^2 - 1$; quintic trinomial **62.** $-7x^4 - x^3$; quartic binomial **63.** $x^3 - 2$; cubic binomial **64.** $(x + 4)(x + 1)$ **65.** $(x - 5)(x + 3)$ **66.** $(x - 6)^2$ **67.** −3, 2 **68.** $\frac{1}{2}$, 3 **69.** $\pm\frac{5}{2}$

Lesson 5-3 pp. 296–302

Got It? 1. a. ±1, ±2i **b.** 0, 2, 3 **2. a.** ±2, ±2i **b.** 0, −4, 2 **c.** 2, $-1 \pm i\sqrt{3}$ **3. a.** −1.84 **b.** The second method seems to be a more reliable way to find the solutions because you do not risk missing a pt. of intersection. **4.** 7, 8, 9
Lesson Check 1. $(x - 6)(x + 3)$ **2.** $(x - 3)(x^2 + 3x + 9)$ **3.** $(x^2 + 4)(x + 3)$ **4.** $(x - 2)(x + 2)(x^2 + 2)$ **5.** −4, $\frac{1}{2}$ **6.** −2, 0, 1 **7. a.** difference of squares **b.** sum of cubes **c.** difference of cubes **d.** difference of squares **8.** Graphing; imaginary numbers don't exist on the x-axis. **9.** Method 1: Graph $y = x^6 - x^2$. Find the zeros for the real solutions.

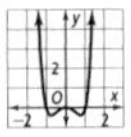

Method 2: Factor and solve x for $x^6 - x^2 = 0$.
$x^2(x^4 - 1) = x^2(x^2 - 1)(x^2 + 1) =$
$x^2(x - 1)(x + 1)(x^2 + 1) = 0$
$x = 0, \pm 1$

Exercises 11. 10, $-5 \pm 5i\sqrt{3}$ **13.** $\frac{1}{4}$, $\frac{-1 \pm i\sqrt{3}}{8}$ **15.** $\frac{1}{3}$, $-\frac{5}{2}$ **17.** 4, $-2 \pm 2i\sqrt{3}$ **19.** $-\frac{1}{2}$, $\frac{1 \pm i\sqrt{3}}{4}$ **21.** ±2 **23.** $\pm\sqrt{2}$, ±3i **25.** −2, 1, 5 **27.** 0, 1 **29.** 0, −1, −2 **31.** 0, −0.5, 1.5 **33.** 1, 7 **35.** −2, 5 **37.** 16 yrs old; $x^2(x + 2) = 3x + 4560$;

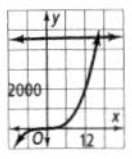

39. 0, $5 \pm 2\sqrt{3}$ **41.** 0, $\frac{5 \pm 5\sqrt{2}}{2}$ **43.** $\frac{4}{3}$, $\frac{-2 \pm 2i\sqrt{3}}{3}$ **45.** $1.9(1 \pm i)$, $-1.9(1 \pm i)$ **47.** 0, ±1, ±2 **49.** −1, ±i **51.** 2 ft × 3 ft × 6 ft **53.** 5 m

55. ±3, ±1; $y = (x - 1)(x + 1)(x - 3)(x + 3)$;

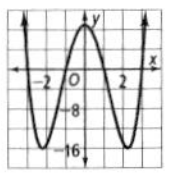

57. Answers may vary.
59. Answers may vary. Sample:
$f(x) = 4x(x + 12)\left(x - \frac{1}{4}\right)\left(x - \frac{1}{6}\right)$
$p(x) = x(x + 12)(4x - 1)(6x - 1)$
61. C **63.** B **65.** $3(x - 4)(x - 2)$ **66.** $2x(x + 3)^2(x - 3)$ **67.** $x^2(x - 5)(x + 1)$ **68.** −2, 6 **69.** ±6 **70.** $-\frac{1}{2}$, 3 **71.** 12 **72.** $-\frac{1}{5}$

Lesson 5-4 pp. 303–310

Got It? 1. $3x - 8$, R 0 **2. a.** yes; $P(x) = (x + 5)(x^4 - 1)$ **b.** $(x + 2)(3x + 1)$ **3.** $x^2 + 7x - 8$, R 0 **4.** width: $(x + 1)$ in.; height: $(x + 2)$ in.; length: $(x + 3)$ in. **5.** 0
Lesson Check 1. $2x + 3$, R 5 **2.** $x^2 + 2x + 5$ **3.** $x^2 + x - 2$ **4.** $4x^2 + x - 6$, R 6 **5.** $9x^2 + 12x + 40$, R 120 **6.** $x - a$ is a factor of $P(x)$. **7.** The polynomials need to be written in standard form since the leading coefficient of both polynomials determines the leading term of the quotient. **8.** Answers may vary. Check student's work.
Exercises 9. $x - 8$ **11.** $x^2 + 4x + 3$, R 5 **13.** $3x^2 + 3x + 2$ **15.** $x - 10$, R 40 **17.** no **19.** yes **21.** $x^2 + 4x + 3$ **23.** $x^2 - 11x + 37$, R −128 **25.** $x + 1$, R 4 **27.** $x^2 - 3x + 9$ **29.** $y = (x + 1)(x + 3)(x - 2)$ **31.** width = x; length = $x + 3$; height = $x - 2$ **33.** 0 **35.** 12 **37.** 10 **39.** 0 **41.** The constant term of the dividend is missing and the divisor is −1 *not* 1: $x^3 - x^2 - 2x = (x + 1)(x^2 - 2x) = x(x + 1)(x - 2)$ **43.** $x + 2$ **45.** $x^3 - 3x^2 + 12x - 35$, R 109 **47.** $x + 4$ **49.** no **51.** yes **53.** yes **55.** no **57.** $x^3 - x^2 + 1$ **59.** $x^3 + 7x + 5$ **61.** $x^3 - 2x^2 - x + 6$ **63. a.** $x + 1$ **b.** $x^2 + x + 1$ **c.** $x^3 + x^2 + x + 1$ **d.** $(x - 1)(x^4 + x^3 + x^2 + x + 1)$ **65.** $x + 2i$ **67.** D **69.** A **71.** 0, −1 **72.** 0, 1 **73.** −5, 0, 5 **74.** $\frac{-3 \pm \sqrt{17}}{2}$ **75.** $-1 \pm \sqrt{3}$ **76.** 1, $-\frac{5}{7}$ **77.** $\frac{5 \pm \sqrt{5}}{2}$ **78.** $3 \pm \sqrt{2}$ **79.** $\frac{-7 \pm \sqrt{5}}{2}$

80.

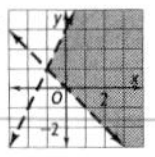

81.

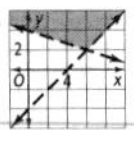

82.

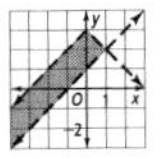

83. 24 **84.** 5 **85.** $23 - 11i$

Lesson 5-5 pp. 312–317

Got It? 1. $\frac{2}{3}$ **2.** 2, −1, $-\frac{3}{2}$ **3.** $3 + 2i$ **4.** $P(x) = x^4 - 14x^3 + 69x^2 - 194x + 208$ **5. a.** There are three or one positive real roots and one negative real root. The graph confirms one negative and one positive real root. **b.** Real roots can be confirmed graphically because they are x-intercepts. Complex roots cannot be confirmed graphically because they have an imaginary component.
Lesson Check 1. ±1, ±2 **2.** ±1, ±2, ±3, ±6, $\pm\frac{1}{2}$, $\pm\frac{3}{2}$ **3.** ±1, ±2, ±3, ±4, ±6, ±12, $\pm\frac{1}{3}$, $\pm\frac{2}{3}$, $\pm\frac{4}{3}$ **4.** $P(x) = x^2 - 14x + 45$ **5.** $P(x) = x^3 + 4x^2 + 4x + 16$ **6.** Answers may vary. Samples: $1 + 2i$, $1 - 2i$; $1 + \sqrt{2}$, $1 - \sqrt{2}$ **7. a.** never; 5 does not divide 8 evenly **b.** always; −2 divides 8 evenly **8.** Complex number roots come in pairs; if −4i is a root, so is 4i.
Exercises 9. ±1; no rational roots **11.** ±1, ±2, ±2, ±4, $\pm\frac{1}{2}$; no rational roots **13.** ±1, ±2, ±3, ±4, ±6, ±12, $\pm\frac{1}{4}$, $\pm\frac{1}{2}$, $\pm\frac{3}{4}$, $\pm\frac{3}{2}$; no rational roots **15.** ±1, ±2, ±5, ±10, $\pm\frac{1}{7}$, $\pm\frac{2}{7}$, $\pm\frac{5}{7}$, $\pm\frac{10}{7}$; no rational roots **17.** ±1, ±2, ±5, ±10, $\pm\frac{1}{2}$, $\pm\frac{5}{2}$, $\pm\frac{1}{5}$, $\pm\frac{2}{5}$, $\pm\frac{1}{10}$; no rational roots **19.** $14 + \sqrt{2}$, 6i **21.** $\sqrt{3}$, $5 + \sqrt{11}$ **23.** $P(x) = x^2 + 24x + 135$ **25.** $P(x) = x^2 - 18x + 90$ **27.** $P(x) = x^4 - 10x^3 + 294x^2 - 1690x + 21{,}125$ **29.** $P(x) = x^4 - 58x^3 + 1290x^2 - 13{,}066x + 51{,}545$ **31.** two or no positive real roots; one negative real root **33.** no rational roots **35.** no rational roots **37.** no rational roots **39.** $P(x) = x^4 + 3x^3 + 207x^2 + 675x - 4050$ **41.** $P(x) = x^4 + 6x^3 + 27x^2 - 366x - 518$ **43.** Error in second line, sign of second term; the line should be: $P(-1) = -x^3 + x^2 - x + 1$. Since there are three sign changes in $P(-x)$, there are three or one negative real roots. **45.** height: 5 ft; bases: 10 ft, 14 ft **47.** Answers may vary. Samples: **a.** $x - 1 - \sqrt{2} = 0$ **b.** $x^2 - 2(1 + \sqrt{2})x + (1 + \sqrt{2})^2 = 0$ **c.** −1 **49.** Answers may vary. Sample: You cannot use the Conjugate Root Theorem for irrational roots unless the equation has rational coefficients. **51.** −4 **53.** $\frac{1}{6}$ **55.** $x^2 + 6x + 6$, R 3 **56.** $8x^2 - 36x + 216$, R −1289 **57.** $7x - 3$, R 2

58. ±3i **59.** ±9i **60.** ±12i **61.** $-5x^4 + 6x^2 + 9x + 11$; quartic polynomial of four terms **62.** $-4x^5 + 7x^3 + 13x + 2$; quintic polynomial of four terms

Lesson 5-6 pp. 319–324

Got It? 1. 0, 1, −5, 2 **2. a.** −1, 2, $\frac{1 \pm i\sqrt{23}}{4}$ **b. i.** A 5th degree polynomial function has four, two, or no turning pts. Three turning pts. are visible, so there must be a fourth one. This will turn the graph back across the x-axis. **ii.** The Fundamental Thm. of Algebra states there will be five roots, and the Conjugate Root Thm. requires pairs of irrational or complex roots. Only two zeros appear in the graph, so there are three zeros remaining. Of the remaining roots, either there are three real roots, or one real and two complex roots. Either way, there is at least one real root that does not appear in the graph.
Lesson Check 1. four roots **2.** fourteen roots **3.** 5, ±4i **4.** 0, 2, ±i **5.** By the Fundamental Thm. of Algebra, polynomial equation of degree n has exactly n roots. **6.** Answers may vary. Sample: $y = x^4 + 8x^2 + 16$ **7.** Use synthetic division to test for and factor out linear factors until a quadratic factor is obtained. Then use the Quadratic Formula if the quadratic factor cannot be factored further.
Exercises 9. −1, ±2i **11.** −1, 2, 4 **13.** 2, $\pm\sqrt{3}$ **15.** 0, ±3, ±i **17.** 3, ±i **19.** 2, $\pm\sqrt{3}$ **21.** ±2, ±i **23.** −6, ±i **25.** ±4, $\frac{-1 \pm i\sqrt{3}}{2}$ **27.** five complex roots; one, three, or five real roots; possible rational roots: ±1, ±2, ±3, ±6, ±9, ±18 **29.** six complex roots; zero, two, four, or six real roots; possible rational roots: $\pm\frac{1}{4}$, $\pm\frac{1}{2}$, $\pm\frac{3}{4}$, ±1, $\pm\frac{3}{2}$, ±2, ±3, ±4, ±6, ±8, ±12, ±24 **31.** −2, $\pm\sqrt{5}$ **33.** −2, $\frac{4}{3}$, 3 **35.** 3, $-1 \pm i\sqrt{2}$ **37.** $-\frac{1}{2}$, −1, ±3 **39.** 3 bridges **41.** sometimes **43.** always **45.** Answers may vary. Sample: $y = x^4 + 3x^2 + 2$ **47.** Given any polynomial eq. of odd degree $n \geq 1$, the eq. has exactly n roots. Since imaginary roots occur in pairs, a polynomial of odd degree n will have an even number of imaginary roots and thus an odd number of real roots. So, any odd degree polynomial eq. with real coefficients has at least one real root. **49.** 5th degree; rational zero:
$-\frac{5}{6}(x - \sqrt{2})(x + \sqrt{2})(x - \sqrt{3})(x + \sqrt{3})(x + \frac{5}{6})$
$= x^5 + \frac{5}{6}x^4 - 5x^3 - \frac{25}{6}x^2 + 6x + 5.$
51. G **53.** Substitute (2, −2) into both inequalities to see if the pt. satisfies both inequalities. If it does, then (2, −2) is a solution of the system. If one or both inequalities are not satisfied by the pt.(2, −2), then (2, −2) is not a solution of the system.

54. $x^4 + 6x^3 + 14x^2 + 24x + 40 = 0$ **55.** $3 \pm 2\sqrt{2}$ **56.** $\frac{-5 \pm i\sqrt{47}}{4}$ **57.** $\frac{3 \pm i\sqrt{23}}{4}$ **58.** $f(x) = -x^2 + 2x + 3$ **59.** $f(x) = 2x^2 + 24x + 75$ **60.** $x^3 + 3x^2 + 3x + 1$ **61.** $x^3 - 9x^2 + 27x - 27$ **62.** $x^4 - 8x^3 + 24x^2 - 32x + 16$ **63.** $x^2 - 2x + 1$ **64.** $x^3 + 15x^2 + 75x + 125$ **65.** $-x^3 + 12x^2 + 48x + 64$

Lesson 5-7 pp. 326–330

Got It? 1. $a^8 + 8a^7b + 28a^6b^2 + 56a^5b^3 + 70a^4b^4 + 56a^3b^5 + 28a^2b^6 + 8ab^7 + b^8$ **2. a.** $16x^4 - 96x^3 + 216x^2 - 216x + 81$ **b.** If you express 11 as (10 + 1) and calculate the powers using Pascal's triangle, it will be the coefficients.
Lesson Check 1. $x^3 + 3x^2a + 3xa^2 + a^3$ **2.** $x^5 - 10x^4 + 40x^3 - 80x^2 + 80x - 32$ **3.** $4x^2 + 16x + 16$ **4.** $27a^3 - 54a^2 + 36a - 8$ **5. a.** yes **b.** yes **c.** no **6.** The coefficients for the expansion of $(a + b)^n$ are equal to the numbers in the nth row of Pascal's Triangle, respectively. **7.** 13; $n + 1$
Exercises 9. $a^4 + 8a^3 + 24a^2 + 32a + 16$ **11.** $x^3 - 15x^2 + 75x - 125$ **13.** $x^{10} + 20x^9 + 180x^8 + 960x^7 + 3360x^6 + 8064x^5 + 13{,}440x^4 + 15{,}360x^3 + 11{,}520x^2 + 5120x + 1024$ **15.** $b^9 + 27b^8 + 324b^7 + 2268b^6 + 10{,}206b^5 + 30{,}618b^4 + 61{,}236b^3 + 78{,}732b^2 + 59{,}049b + 19{,}683$ **17.** $a^4 + 12a^3b + 54a^2b^2 + 108ab^3 + 81b^4$ **19.** $65{,}536 - 131{,}072x + 114{,}688x^2 - 57{,}344x^3 + 17{,}920x^4 - 3584x^5 + 448x^6 - 32x^7 + x^8$ **21.** $27a^3 - 189a^2 + 441a - 343$ **23.** $81y^4 - 1188y^3 + 6534y^2 - 15{,}972y + 14{,}641$ **25. a.** 6 **b.** 489,888 **27.** $135x^4$ **29.** $625b^8$ **31.** The challenge of the Binomial Theorem occurs when there is a coefficient with the x. However, it is much more efficient to use the Binomial Theorem than FOIL when expanding a binomial that is raised to a high power. **33.** $x^{20} + 40x^{18} + 720x^{16} + 7680x^{14} + 53{,}760x^{12} + 258{,}048x^{10} + 860{,}160x^8 + 1{,}966{,}080x^6 + 2{,}949{,}120x^4 + 2{,}621{,}440x^2 + 1{,}048{,}576$ **35.** $a^5 - 5a^4b^2 + 10a^3b^4 - 10a^2b^6 + 5ab^8 - b^{10}$ **37.** $256x^4 - 1792x^3y + 4704x^2y^2 - 5488xy^3 + 2401y^4$ **39.** $4096x^{18} + 12{,}288x^{15}y^2 + 15{,}360x^{12}y^4 + 10{,}240x^9y^6 + 3840x^6y^8 + 768x^3y^{10} + 64y^{12}$ **41.** $125a^3 + 150a^2b + 60ab^2 + 8b^3$ **43.** $-32y^{10} + 80y^8x - 80y^6x^2 + 40y^4x^3 - 10y^2x^4 + x^5$ **45.** Answers may vary. Sample: Since one of the terms is negative ($-y$) and it is alternately raised to odd and even powers; the term is negative when raised to an odd power and positive when raised to an even power.

47. $-29{,}113 + 17{,}684i$ **49.** $(x^{14} - 21x^{10} + 35x^6 - 7x^2) + i(-7x^{12} + 35x^8 - 21x^4 + 1)$ **51.** $\frac{1}{64}$
53. $(-1 + i\sqrt{3})^3 = -1 + 3i\sqrt{3} + 9 - 3i\sqrt{3} = 8$
55. G **57.** Let c_a = the first company's cost per month and let c_b = the second company's cost per month: $c_a = 2.25t + 7.95$ and $c_b = 2.75t$

$$c_a = c_b$$
$$2.25t + 7.95 = 2.75t$$
$$7.95 = 0.5t$$
$$15.9 = t$$

The cost will be equal after 15.9 hours of use.
58. −3, −1, $\frac{-3 \pm i\sqrt{11}}{2}$ **59.** 1, ±i, ±3i **60.** −4, $\frac{-3 \pm i\sqrt{7}}{4}$ **61.** −1, 1, 2, 7 **62.** $-18 + 43i$ **63.** 600i **64.** −2 **65.** $\frac{7}{5} + \frac{31}{5}i$ **66.** $2x^3 + 5x^2 - x + 9$; cubic polynomial of 4 terms **67.** $-7x^2 + 4x + 1$; quadratic trinomial **68.** $12x^4 - 3x^3 - 9x^2 + x - 8$; quartic polynomial of 5 terms

Lesson 5-8 pp. 331–338

Got It? 1. $y = 1.667x^3 + 1.3 \times 10^{-12}x^2 - 4.667x + 5$ **2.** 22.52 billion lbs **3.** Answers may vary. Sample: The cubic model would fit the data better than the linear model because of the $(n + 1)$ Pt. Principle. Both models have down and up end behavior and increasing growth. The cubic shows slowing growth followed by rapidly increasing growth.
4. a. $y = 0.269867411x - 3.919692952$

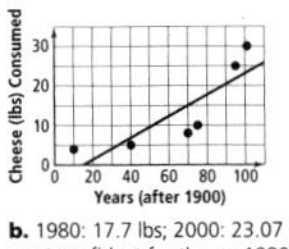

b. 1980: 17.7 lbs; 2000: 23.07 lbs; 2012: 26.31 lbs; most confident for the yrs 1980 and 2000, since they are within the domain of the data set; least confident for the yr 2012, since it is outside the domain of the data set
Lesson Check 1. linear **2.** quadratic **3.** cubic **4.** quartic **5.** interpolation since the data point is within the domain of the data set **6.** yes, since the four pts. pass the vertical-line test, a cubic function will fit the pts.; $y = -x^3 - 3x^2 - 3x$ **7.** cubic model; the closer R^2 is to 1, the better the fit

Exercises 9. $y = \frac{1}{2}x - 3$ **11.** $y = -0.929x^2 + 7.786x + 4$ **13.** $y = x^2 - 6x + 1$ **15.** $y = 2x^3 - x^2 - 4x + 6$ **17.** (where $x =$ yrs after 1900) quadratic: $y = -1.25 \times 10^{-4}x^2 - 0.003x + 2.804$, cubic: $y = -8.33 \times 10^{-6}x^3 + 0.002x^2 - 0.190x + 8.142$; cubic; cubic **19.** linear: $y = -0.057x + 19.93$, quadratic: $y = -0.025x^2 + 0.14x + 19.595$; quadratic; quadratic **21.** 1950: 2.60%; 1988: 1.23%; 2010: 0.35% **23.** January: 19.714 millions of barrels/day; March: 19.8 millions of barrels/day; October: 18.535 millions of barrels/day **25.** cubic: $y = 10.25x^3 + 5x^2 - 2.25x - 8.2$; quartic: $y = 2.042x^4 + 10.25x^3 - 4.042x^2 - 2.25x - 4$; quartic, ($R^2 = 1$) **27.** $y = -0.275x^4 + 0.85x^3 - 4.025x^2 - 8.15x + 7$ **29.** $y = 0.0611511911x^3 - 0.9276466231x^2 + 6.184642324x + 1.750778723$; $R^2 = 0.9994739763$; good fit **31.** $y = 0.111x^4 - 45.618x^3 + 6997.73x^2 - 476,931.355x + 12,185,696.59$ **33.** A quadratic model would be more appropriate, given the real world context. According to the cubic model, there would be a negative number of students enrolled in the course in the year 2024. **35. a.** -0.48; -0.75
b.

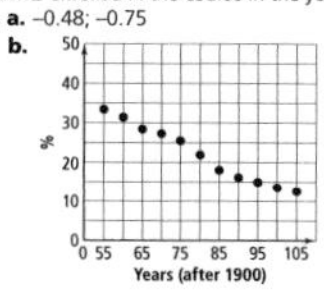

A linear model seems to be most appropriate.
c. Answers may vary. Sample: $y = -0.4464x + 57.77$ **d.** 4.2% **e.** No; although R^2 is close to 1, the model is not realistic since it predicts that the percentage will eventually become 0, and then negative.

37. $y = \frac{1}{8}(x^2 - 4)^2$

39. 1 **41.** $-\frac{7}{6}$
43. $32x^5 + 240x^4 + 720x^3 + 1080x^2 + 810x + 243$ **44.** $1331x^3 - 363x^2 + 33x - 1$ **45.** $4096 - 6144x + 3456x^2 - 864x^3 + 81x^4$ **46.** $64x + 432x + 972x^2 + 729x^3$ **47.** $|x - 8| < 1$ **48.** $|x - \frac{3}{8}| \leq \frac{1}{8}$ **49.** $|y - 2.8| < 1.1$ **50.** $|t - 750| < 250$ **51.** $s = \sqrt{A}$ **52.** $\ell = \frac{P}{2} - w$ **53.** $r = \frac{C}{2\pi}$ **54.** $b = \frac{A}{h}$

55.
56.
57.
58.

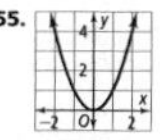

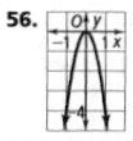

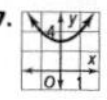

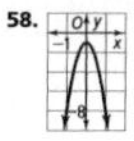

Lesson 5-9   pp. 339–345

Got It? 1. $y = 2(x + 3)^3 - 4$ **2.** $1 - \sqrt[3]{2}$
3. a. Answers may vary. Sample: $y = x^4 - 6x^3 + x^2 - 6x$ **b.** Yes; $-f(x)$ is the function reflected across the x-axis, so the zeros will stay the same. **4.** 972 kW
Lesson Check 1. -2 **2.** 3 **3.** $\frac{1}{3}$ **4.** No; a power function is of the form $y = ax^b$, where y varies directly with the bth power of x. **5.** $y = x^3$ has end behavior of down and up with no turning pt. Thus, at most, there is one real root. **6.** Both $y = x^3$ and $y = 4x^3$ pass through the origin, have the same end behavior of down and up, and no turning pts. $y = 4x^3$ is $y = x^3$ stretched vertically by a factor of 4.
Exercises 7. $y = -3(x - 1)^3$
9. $y = -(x + 5)^3 - 1$ **11.** $y = -3\left(x + \frac{1}{2}\right)^3 + \frac{3}{4}$
13. $\frac{8}{3}$ **15.** $-\frac{2}{15}$ **17.** $1 - \frac{1}{2}\sqrt[3]{20}$ **For Exercises 19–24, answers may vary. Samples: 19.** $x^4 - x^3 - x^2 - x$ **21.** $x^4 - 2x^3 - 2x^2 - 2x - 3$ **23.** $x^4 + 5x^3 + 5x^2 + 5x + 4$ **25.** $38.4 \approx 38$ slices **27.** 90 lb·ft²/s² **29.** Yes; using parent function $y = x^2$, stretch vertically by a factor of 2, then translate 5 units up and 3 units to the right. **31.** Yes; using parent function $y = x^2$, translate 9 units down and 4 units to the right. **33.** reflection across the x-axis, vert. stretch by a factor of 2, translation 1 unit up and 1 unit to the right **35.** vert. stretch by a factor of 3, translation 2 units down and 1 unit to the right **37.** reflection across the x-axis, translation 2 units up and 4 units to the right **39.** 40 lb·ft²/s² **41.** Some quartic polynomials have four x-intercepts and cannot be written in that form; $y = x^4 - 20x^2 + 64$; $y = x^4 - 5x^2 + 4$.
43. 150 watts **45.** B
47. $y = (x - 2)^2 - 1$
$\quad = x^2 - 4x + 4 - 1$
$\quad = x^2 - 4x + 3$
48. $y = -2x^3 + 3x^2 - x - 2$ **49.** $y = 3x^3 - 5x - 3$
50. $y = -\frac{4}{5}x + \frac{16}{5}$ **51.** $y = -3x + 5$ **52.** yes **53.** no

54. $x^2(x^8 + 1)$ **55.** $(x - y)(x + y)(x^2 + y^2)$
56. $13x^3y^5(13x^3y^6 - 1)$

Chapter Review   pp. 347–352

1. D **2.** B **3.** C **4.** A **5.** $y = -x^4 + 12$; quartic binomial; down and down **6.** $y = x^2 - x + 7$; quadratic trinomial; up and up **7.** $y = -x^4 + 2x^3 + 3x^2 - 6x + 12$; quartic polynomial of five terms; down and down **8.** $y = x^3 + 2x^2 - 4x + 8$; cubic polynomial of four terms; down and up **9.** $y = x^4 - 3x^3 + 3x^2 + 10$; quartic polynomial of four terms; up and up **10.** 3 **11.** If n is even there are an odd number of turning points; if n is odd there are an even number of turning points. **12.** $f(x) = x^3 - 6x^2 - 11x - 6$ **13.** $f(x) = x^3 - x^2 - 2x$ **14.** $f(x) = x^3 - 6x^2 + 11x - 6$ **15.** $f(x) = x^3 - 3x^2 - 6x + 8$ **16.** $0, -2$ (multiplicity 3) **17.** 2 (multiplicity 2), -2 (multiplicity 2) **18.** $0, -\frac{1}{2}, 1$ **19.** $5, -2$ (multiplicity 2) **20.** relative maximum: $(0.8672, -1.9351)$; relative minimums: $(0, -3)$, $(2.8828, -12.1704)$; zeros: $x = -0.5992$, $x = 3.7115$ **21.** relative maximum: $(-0.8441, 9.3023)$; relative minimum: $(0.7108, -0.0964)$; zeros: $x = -1.6180$, $x = 0.6180$, $x = 0.8$ **22.** relative minimum: $(1, -4)$; zeros: $x = -0.2491$, $x = 1.6633$ **23.** relative maximum: $(-0.4142, -3.3432)$; relative minimum: $(2.4142, -14.6569)$; zero: $x = 4$ **24.** 3, 8
25. $-\frac{1}{3}$ **26.** 0, $\frac{-1 \pm \sqrt{5}}{2}$ **27.** $\frac{2 \pm i\sqrt{2}}{3}$
28. no real roots;
29. 2, 3949;
30. 4.87 in. × 2.87 in. × 2.87 in. **31.** $x^2 + 6x + 9$ **32.** $2x^2 + x - 3$, R 1 **33.** yes **34.** no **35.** $x^2 - x^2 - 2x - 1$ **36.** $2x^2 - 6x + 2$, R -20 **37.** $5x^2 + 18x + 36$, R 12 **38.** -14 **39.** 2 **40.** $\pm 1, \pm 2, \pm 3, \pm 6$
41. $\pm 1, \pm 2, \pm \frac{1}{3}, \pm \frac{2}{3}$ **42.** $\pm 1, \pm 2, \pm 3, \pm 4, \pm 6, \pm 12, \pm \frac{1}{4}, \pm \frac{1}{2}, \pm \frac{3}{4}, \pm \frac{3}{2}$ **43.** $\pm 1, \pm 7, \pm \frac{1}{3}, \pm \frac{7}{3}$ **44.** -3 **45.** -5 **46.** $1, -4, -\frac{1}{2}$ **47.** $1, -\frac{2}{3}$ **48.** $1 + i$
49. $5 - \sqrt{3}, \sqrt{2}$ **50.** $3i, -7i$ **51.** $-2, -\sqrt{11}, -4 + 6i$ **52.** $y = x^3 - 17x + 70$ **53.** $y = x^3 + 3x^2 + 25x + 75$ **54.** $y = x^2 - 12x + 37$ **55.** $y = x^4 - 4x^3 - 10x^2 + 68x - 80$ **56.** one positive real zero; two or no negative real zeros **57.** two or no positive real zeros; one negative real zero **58.** four, two, or no positive real zeros; no negative real zeros **59.** two or no positive real zeros; two or no negative real zeros **60.** 3 **61.** 4 **62.** 5 **63.** 6

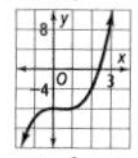

64. $1, -3 \pm \sqrt{7}$ **65.** $2, \pm\sqrt{5}$ **66.** $\frac{1 \pm \sqrt{15}}{2}$
67. $-3, 6, \frac{1 \pm \sqrt{5}}{2}$ **68.** $\frac{4}{9}$ **69.** 1, 8, 28, 56, 70, 56, 28, 8, 1
70. 16 **71.** 105 **72.** $x^3 + 27x^2 + 243x + 729$
73. $b^4 + 8b^3 + 24b^2 + 32b + 16$
74. $27a^3 + 27a^2 + 9a + 1$ **75.** $x^3 - 15x^2 + 75x - 125$ **76.** $x^3 - 6x^2y + 12xy^2 - 8y^3$
77. $243a^5 + 1620a^4b + 4320a^3b^2 + 5760a^2b^3 + 3840ab^4 + 1024b^5$ **78.** $x^6 + 6x^5 + 15x^4 + 20x^3 + 15x^2 + 6x + 1$ **79.** $64x^6 - 192x^5 + 240x^4 - 160x^3 + 60x^2 - 12x + 1$ **80.** 108 **81.** $6a^2c^2$
82. $y = 3.5x^2 - 4.5x + 5$
83. $y = 2.082999x - 2.475234$; $y = 0.086232x^2 + 0.008929x + 5.963724$; $y = -0.002554x^3 + 0.178307x^2 - 0.913645x + 8.205128$; cubic is best fit since $R^2 = 1$.
84. $y = -5.8667x^3 + 120.5333x^2 - 629.2667x + 1421$; $1097.2 \approx 1097$ **85.** $y = -(x - 2)^3 + 1$
86. $y = 6(x + 3)^3$ **87.** Answers may vary. Sample: $y = 6x^3 - 10x^2 + 25x^2 - 10x + 24$ **88.** $y = 0.3x^5 + 3$

Chapter 6

Get Ready! p. 357 1. domain: $\{1, 2, 3, 4\}$, range: $\{2, 3, 4, 5\}$ **2.** domain: $\{1, 2, 3, 4\}$, range: $\{2\}$ **3.** domain: all real numbers, range: $y \geq -8$ **4.** domain: all real numbers, range: $y \geq 3$
5.

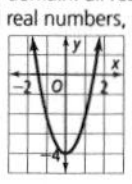

6.

7.

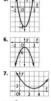

8. $3y^2 - 14y + 9$ **9.** $49a^2 - 100$
10. $x^3 + 4x^2 - 15x - 18$ **11.** $-2, 7$ **12.** $\frac{5}{3}$
13. $-4, \frac{2}{3}$ **14.** $\frac{1}{2}$ **15.** $\pm\frac{7}{2}$ **16.** $\pm\sqrt{7}$ **17.** Yes; it is a better deal to first take 50% off the shirt and then use the $10 coupon. **18.** A "one-to-one function" is a function where there is exact correspondence of every element of the domain with exactly one element of the range. **19.** the non-negative root

---

Lesson 6-1   pp. 361–367

Got It? 1. a. 0; -1; 2 **b.** ± 0.1; no real square root; $\pm\frac{6}{11}$ **c.** Any negative number multiplied by itself an even number of times will always be positive. Therefore, there can be no real nth roots (where n is even) for a negative number **b. 2. a.** -3 **b.** no real root **c.** 7 **d.** no real root
3. a. $9x^2$ **b.** a^4b^5 **c.** $|x^3|^4$ **d.** 100
Lesson Check 1. ± 5 **2.** ± 2 **3.** ± 0.4 **3.** no real root
4. $3|b|$ **5.** $a^4|b^3|$ **6.** $-5a$ **7.** 16 has two real fourth roots, ± 2. **8.** The real roots of a number are the positive and negative (but not imaginary) roots of the number; the principal root of a number is the nonnegative root of the number. **9.** n is odd.

Exercises 11. ± 0.07 **13.** $\pm\frac{8}{13}$ **15.** 0.5 **17.** 0.07
19. none **21.** $\pm\frac{10}{3}$ **23.** 0.5 **25.** -3 **27.** $3y^2$ **29.** y^2
31. ± 10 **33.** ± 0.5 **35.** about 0.8 in. **37. a.** about 79.01 ft **b.** about 44.44 ft **39.** $\frac{1}{3}$ **41.** $\frac{1}{4}$ **43.** Answers may vary. Sample: $\sqrt[3]{-8x^6}$, $-\sqrt[4]{16x^8}$, $\sqrt[5]{-32x^{10}}$ **45.** always; x^2 is always nonnegative **47.** some; they are equal for $x = -1, 0, 1$ **49.** even; $|m|$; odd; m
51. even; $|m^3|$; odd; m^3 **53.** 48
55. a diagonal of a square with side 5 **57.** G
59. System: $-35 = (-3)^3a + (-3)^2b + (-3)c + d$, $1 = (0)^3a + (0)^2b + (0)c + d$, $3 = (2)^3a + (2)^2b + (2)c + d$, $7 = (4)^3a + (4)^2b + (4)c + d$ (OR equivalent system); solution: $a = 0.35$, $b = -1.85$, $c = 3.3$, $d = 1$, cubic polynomial: $y = 0.35x^3 - 1.85x^2 + 3.3x + 1$.
60. $y = (x + 2)^3 + 3$ **61.** $y = -2$ **62.** $1, \frac{3}{4}$
63. $\frac{5 \pm i\sqrt{11}}{6}$ **64.** $\frac{11}{65}$ **65.** $2x^3y^3$ **66.** $\frac{4}{x^3}$ **67.** $\frac{4}{x^2}$

Lesson 6-2   pp. 367–373

Got It? 1. a. No; the indexes are different. **b.** Yes; $\sqrt[3]{10}$
2. $4x^2\sqrt[3]{2x}$ **3.** $15x^3y^3\sqrt[3]{y}$ **4. a.** $5|x|$ **b.** yes;
$\frac{3x^2\sqrt{2x}}{x\sqrt{2x}} = 3x$ **5. a.** $\frac{\sqrt[3]{175xy}}{5y}$ **b.** D; there is no y in the expression.
Lesson Check 1. $\sqrt[3]{10}$ **2.** $-3\sqrt[3]{4}$ **3.** Not possible, the indexes are different. **4.** not possible; $\sqrt{-4}$ is not a real number. **5.** $3\sqrt[3]{6x}$ **6.** $x^2\sqrt[3]{3x}$ **7.** $x\sqrt[4]{4x}$ **8.** $x \leq 0$; for $x \leq 0$, $-4x^3 \geq 0$ and $\sqrt{-4x^3}$ is real. **9.** error in line 1: $\frac{\sqrt[3]{4\cdot5}}{4} \neq \frac{7-4\sqrt[3]{5}}{4}$
Exercises 11. 4 **13.** not possible **15.** 5 **17.** 6
19. $2x\sqrt{5x}$ **21.** $5x^2\sqrt{2x}$ **23.** $3y^3\sqrt[3]{2y}$ **25.** $-2xy\sqrt{6}$
27. $-2xy\sqrt[3]{xy^2}$ **29.** $8y^3\sqrt{5y}$ **31.** $40x|y|\sqrt{3}$
33. $-2xy\sqrt[3]{30x}$ **35.** $4xy^2\sqrt{3y}$ **37.** 10 **39.** $2x^3y^2\sqrt{2}$
41. $\frac{2\sqrt{x^2y}}{x}$ **43.** $\frac{\sqrt{2x}}{2}$ **45.** $\frac{x}{2}$ **47.** $\frac{\sqrt[4]{250}}{5}$ **49.** $\frac{\sqrt{15y}}{5y}$

51. $\frac{\sqrt[3]{150ab^2c}}{5a}$ **53.** 6 cm² **55.** about 212 mi/h
57. $\sqrt[3]{10}$ **59.** $3x^5y^5\sqrt{2y}$ **61.** $10 + 7\sqrt{2}$ **63.** $\frac{|x|\sqrt{10y}}{2y}$
65. $\frac{\sqrt{3x^2}}{xy}$ **67.** $\frac{\sqrt{2xy}}{xy}$ **69.** 4 g/cm³ **71.** Check students' work. **73.** always **75.** sometimes **77.** $2\sqrt{5}$
79. $a = -2c$, $b = -6d$ **81.** H **83.** F **85.** $11|a^{45}|$ **86.** $9c^{24}d^{32}$ **87.** $4a^{27}$ **88.** $2y^2 - 4y + 16$, R -128 **90.** $6a^2 - 5a + 4$ **91.** 25 **92.** 25 **93.** $\frac{121}{4}$
94. $\frac{1}{16}$ **95.** $\frac{5}{3} + \frac{1}{3}i$ **96.** $\frac{13}{13} - \frac{5}{13}i$ **97.** $-\frac{16}{17} - \frac{4}{17}i$
98. $-\frac{7}{74} - \frac{5}{74}i$

Lesson 6-3   pp. 374–380

Got It? 1. a. The indexes are different. You cannot combine the expressions. **b.** $7x\sqrt{y}$ **c.** $2\sqrt[3]{3x^2}$
2. a. about 84.9 in. **b.** The length of the diagonal of a square of side 6 can be found using the Pythagorean Thm. to be $\sqrt{6^2 + 6^2} = 6\sqrt{2}$. Using this information you can calculate the perimeter of the window and simplify the expression at the end. **3.** $6\sqrt[3]{2}$
4. $46 + 16\sqrt{5}$ **5. a.** 24 **b.** 1 **6. a.** $-\sqrt{21} - \sqrt{35}$
b. $\frac{1}{3}(12x + 4x\sqrt{6})$ **c.** after rationalizing; When the numerator is multiplied by the conjugate of the denominator it is more convenient if $\sqrt{6}$ is not yet simplified.
Lesson Check 1. $12\sqrt{6}$ **2.** cannot combine **3.** $3\sqrt{3x}$
4. $7\sqrt{3}$ **5.** 13 **6.** $75 + 34\sqrt{5}$ **7.** $-16 - 3\sqrt{2}$
8. a. not like radicals **b.** like radicals; $9\sqrt{3}$ **c.** not like radicals **9.** They are alike in that you can also use the FOIL method and Distr. Prop. to multiply binomial radical expressions; they are different in that you cannot multiply like radicands together if they do not have the same index.
Exercises 11. $4\sqrt[3]{3}$ **13.** $-2\sqrt{x}$ **15.** $5\sqrt[3]{x^2}$
17. $33\sqrt{2}$ **19.** $7\sqrt{2}$ **21.** $9\sqrt[3]{3}$ **23.** $-6\sqrt[3]{2}$ **25.** $8 + 4\sqrt{5}$
27. $63 - 38\sqrt{2}$ **29.** $49 + 12\sqrt{13}$ **31.** 14 **33.** -40
35. $-2 + 2\sqrt{3}$ **37.** $13 + 7\sqrt{3}$ **39.** 140.3 in.²
41. $5\sqrt{3} - 4\sqrt{2}$ **43.** $-2\sqrt{y}$
45. $-11 + \sqrt{21}$ **47.** $84 + 24\sqrt{6}$ **49.** 2 **51.** $4x\sqrt{3}$
53. No; to simplify first, you must estimate three square roots and then add the estimates. If they are first simplified, then they can be combined as $13\sqrt{2}$. Then only one square root need be estimated. **55.** Answers may vary. Sample: $(\sqrt{7} + 2)(\sqrt{7} - 2)$, $(2\sqrt{2} + \sqrt{5})(2\sqrt{2} - \sqrt{5})$
57. $2\sqrt{3} - \sqrt{2}$ **59.** $11|x| - 3|x|\sqrt{11}$
61. $\frac{3\sqrt{5} + 2\sqrt{3}}{2}$ **63.** $\frac{x + 5\sqrt{x}y}{x - y}$ **65.** $-\frac{1}{2}$
67. $a = 0$ and $b \geq 0$, or $b = 0$ and $a \geq 0$ **69.** 13
71. $\frac{15}{7}$ **73.** 9 **74.** $3\sqrt[3]{2}$ **75.** $\frac{2\sqrt{x^2}}{x}$ **76.** 4 **77.** 6 **78.** 2x

79. $7x^2\sqrt{2}$ **80.** $x\sqrt{15}$ **81.** $15x^2$ **82.** $2, -1 \pm i\sqrt{3}$
83. $-10, 5 \pm 5\sqrt{3}$
84. $\frac{1}{5}, \frac{-1 \pm i\sqrt{3}}{10}$ **85.** $\sqrt{2}$ (multiplicity 2), $-\sqrt{7}$ (multiplicity 2) **86.** $\frac{\sqrt{5}}{5}$ (multiplicity 2), $-\frac{2\sqrt{5}}{5}$ (multiplicity 2) **87.** $\pm\frac{1}{3}, \pm\frac{1}{4}$ **88.** x^6 **89.** p^5q^5
90. 2^9 or 512 **91.** 3^3 or 27

Lesson 6-4   pp. 381–388

Got It? 1. a. 8 **b.** 11 **c.** 6 **2. a.** $\sqrt[3]{\frac{w^2}{y^5}}$ **b.** $\sqrt[4]{y^3}$ **c.** $x^{\frac{7}{3}}y^{\frac{3}{4}}$
c. If m is negative, a is in the denominator and $\frac{1}{a}$ is undefined when $a = 0$. **3. a.** The length of a Venusian year is about 0.61 Earth years. **b.** The length of a Jovian year is about 12.76 Earth years. **4. a.** $\sqrt[3]{27}$ **b.** $\sqrt[3]{x^5}$
c. $\sqrt[3]{16,807}$ **5. a.** $\frac{1}{8}$ **b.** $c\frac{1}{2187}$ **6. a.** $\frac{1}{2x^5}$
b. $27x^9\sqrt[4]{x^3}y^3$
Lesson Check 1. 5 **2.** 5 **3.** $\frac{1}{125}$ **4.** $\frac{1}{5}$ **5.** $\sqrt[9]{11^3}$
6. $\frac{\sqrt{7}}{2}$ **7.** $(1 + \sqrt{2})$ or any nonzero number times $(1 + \sqrt{2})$ **8.** error in third line, second term; $5(5^{\frac{1}{2}}) = 5^{\frac{3}{2}}$. The third and fourth lines should be: $\frac{20 - 5^{\frac{1}{2}}}{20}$
9. $(-64)^{\frac{1}{3}} = \sqrt[3]{-64} = -4$ and $-64^{\frac{1}{3}} = -\sqrt[3]{64} = -4$; $(-64)^{\frac{1}{2}} = \sqrt{-64}$, is not a real number, but $-64^{\frac{1}{2}} = -\sqrt{64} = -8$ is a real number.
Exercises 11. 3 **13.** 10 **15.** $7\sqrt{3}$ **17.** 3 **19.** $\sqrt[5]{x}$
21. $\sqrt[3]{x^2}$ or $(\sqrt[3]{x})^2$ **23.** $\frac{1}{\sqrt[4]{x^3}}$ or $\frac{1}{(\sqrt[4]{x})^3}$ **25.** $\sqrt{x^3}$ or $(\sqrt{x})^3$
27. $(-10)^{\frac{2}{3}}$ **29.** $(7x)^{\frac{2}{5}}$ **31.** $a^{\frac{1}{2}}$ **33.** $c^{\frac{2}{3}}$ **35.** ≈ 72.8 m
37. ≈ 7.9 m **39.** $\sqrt[12]{6^7}$ **41.** $\sqrt[15]{5^2}$ **43.** $\frac{\sqrt[4]{45}}{6}$ **45.** $\frac{\sqrt[12]{7776}}{6}$
47. 4 **49.** 4 **51.** $\frac{1}{16}$ **53.** 64 **55.** $\frac{1}{57}$ **57.** $\frac{x^{\frac{1}{2}}}{3x}$ **59.** $-\frac{1}{3}$
61. $\frac{y^4}{x}$ **63.** $\frac{1}{2}$ **65.** x^3y^6 **67.** about 78%; 61%; 37%
69. -7 **71.** 64 **73.** 2,097,152 **75.** $-\frac{81}{7}$ **77.** 125
79. $x^{\frac{1}{2}}$ **81.** $x^{\frac{3}{4}}$ **83.** $x^{\frac{1}{3}}y^{\frac{3}{4}}$ **85.** $\frac{4x^2}{3y}$ **87.** $\frac{x^2}{y^3}$
89. a. $(\sqrt{x})^4 = \sqrt{x} \cdot \sqrt{x} \cdot \sqrt{x} \cdot \sqrt{x} = x \cdot x = x^2$, so $\sqrt[4]{x} = \sqrt{x}$. **b.** $\sqrt[8]{x} = (x^2)^{\frac{1}{8}} = x^{\frac{1}{4}}$ so $\sqrt[8]{x} = \sqrt[4]{x}$.
91. 49 **93.** x^{24} **95.** $3\sqrt{2}$ **97.** 33.13 mi/h
99. 12 **101.** 3 **102.** $4\sqrt[3]{3}$ **103.** $21\sqrt{2}$
104. $1 + 3\sqrt{5}$ **105.** -7 **106.** $-8\sqrt{3}$ **107.** $9\sqrt[3]{2}$
108. $4x(x^2 - 2x + 4)$ **109.** $\frac{1}{2}$ **110.** $(x - 9)^2$ **111.** $(4a - 3b)(4a + 3b)$
112. $(5x - 4y)^2$ **113.** $(3x + 8)^2$ **114.** $-3, 2$

115. $7, -2$ **116.** $-\frac{3}{2}, 1$ **117.** $-\frac{1}{3}, 2$
118. $-\frac{5}{2}, \frac{1}{2}$ **119.** $-\frac{2}{3}, \frac{3}{2}$

Lesson 6-5   pp. 390–397

Got It? 1. 6 **2.** 5, -11 **3.** 37,500,000 m³
4. a. 10 **b.** when you raise each side of an equation to a power **5.** 9
Lesson Check 1. 12 **2.** 27 **3.** $\frac{4}{15}$ **4.** 4 **5.** 1 **6.** 512
7. 3; The solution of 3 yields a negative value for $x - 6$, but the right side of the equation $\sqrt{3(3)}$ cannot be negative. **8.** Solving square root equations is different from solving absolute value equations in that you use a different technique to isolate the variable. In square root equations, you square each side. In absolute value equations, you write two new equations and solve both. Solving square root equations is similar to solving absolute value equations in that both can introduce extraneous solutions.
Exercises 9. 16 **11.** 22 **13.** 15 **15.** 4 **17.** $\frac{2}{5}$
19. $-29, 25$ **21.** 78 **23.** 0 **25.** about 4 in. **27.** 1
29. 3 **31.** $-3, -4$ **33.** 1, 35 **37.** 39 **41.** $-2 - 41$, 1
43. 5 **45.** $10\sqrt{3}$ cm or about 13.16 cm **47.** 5 **49.** 8
51. 5 **53.** 1 **55.** 9, -7 **57.** 9 **59.** $x = a$ solution, but $x = 1$ is an extraneous solution. **61.** Answers may vary. Sample: $\sqrt{x - 3} = 1$ **63.** $\sqrt{x} + 5$ **63.** C **65.** 0, 2
67. 0 **69.** $\sqrt{6}$ **71.** $\sqrt{10}$ **73.** B **75.** D
77. 3 **78.** 2 **79.** 625 **80.** 512 **81.** $\frac{1}{1000}$
82. 16 **83.** 125 **84.** $6\sqrt{2}$ **85.** 3, 4 **86.** 3, 5
87. $-5, -4$ **88.** $-2, -\frac{5}{3}$ **89.** $-\frac{1}{3}, -\frac{4}{9}$ **90.** $-2, -\frac{3}{4}$
91. domain: $\{0, 2, 4\}$, range: $\{-5, -3, -1\}$; yes **92.** domain: $\{-1, 0, 1\}$, range: $\{2, 0, 1\}$; yes **93.** domain: $\{-2, 0, 1\}$, range: $\{-2, 0, 1\}$; yes **94.** domain: $\{3, 4, 5\}$, range: $\{-1\}$; yes **95.** domain: $\{0, 1, 2\}$, range: $\{0, 1, 2\}$; no **96.** domain: $\{0\}$, range: $\{-2, 0, 2\}$; no

Lesson 6-6   pp. 398–404

Got It? 1. $(f + g)(x) = 2x^2 + x + 5$, domain: all real numbers; $(f - g)(x) = 2x^2 - x + 11$, domain: all real numbers. **2.** $(f \cdot g)(x) = 9x^3 - 30x^2 - 23x - 4$, domain: all real numbers; $(\frac{f}{g})(x) = x - 4$, domain: all real numbers except $x = -\frac{1}{3}$ **3. 4.** Let $D(x) =$ cost after applying the 15% store discount, $E(x) =$ cost after applying the 20% employee discount, and $x =$ cost of items. Then $D(x) = 0.85x$ and $E(x) = 0.80x$.
a. $(E \circ D)(x) = 0.68x$ **b.** $(D \circ E)(x) = 0.68x$
c. The total discounts are the same.
Lesson Check 1. $3x^3 - 2x^2 + 3x - 2$
2. $-x^2 + 3x - 3$ **3.** $x^2 + x + 4$ **4.** $x^2 + 3x - 1$

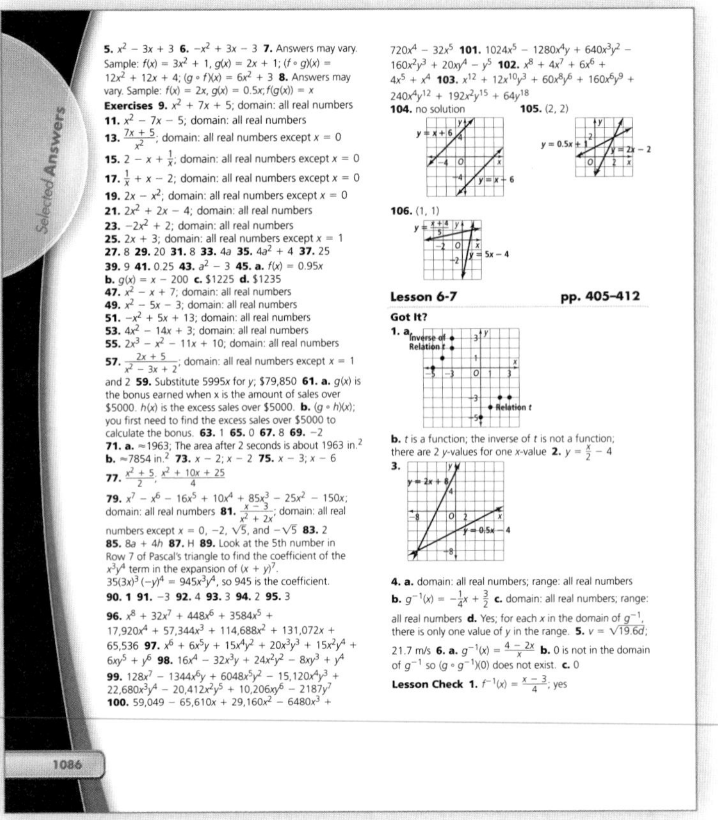

5. $x^2 - 3x + 3$ **6.** $-x^2 + 3x - 3$ **7.** Answers may vary. Sample: $f(x) = 3x^2 + 1$, $g(x) = 2x + 1$; $(f \circ g)(x) = 12x^2 + 12x + 4$; $(g \circ f)(x) = 6x^2 + 3$ **8.** Answers may vary. Sample: $f(x) = 2x$, $g(x) = 0.5x$; $f(g(x)) = x$
Exercises 9. $x^2 + 7x + 5$; domain: all real numbers
11. $x^2 - 7x - 5$; domain: all real numbers
13. $\frac{7x+5}{x^2}$; domain: all real numbers except $x = 0$
15. $2 - x + \frac{1}{x}$; domain: all real numbers except $x = 0$
17. $\frac{1}{x} + x - 2$; domain: all real numbers except $x = 0$
19. $2x - x^2$; domain: all real numbers except $x = 0$
21. $2x^2 + 2x - 4$; domain: all real numbers
23. $-2x^2 + 2$; domain: all real numbers
25. $2x + 3$; domain: all real numbers except $x = 1$
27. 8 **29.** 20 **31.** 8 **33.** $4a$ **35.** $4a^2 + 4$ **37.** 25
39. 9 **41.** 0.25 **43.** $a^2 - 3$ **45. a.** $f(x) = 0.95x$
b. $g(x) = x - 200$ **c.** \$1225 **d.** \$1235
47. $x^2 - x + 7$; domain: all real numbers
49. $x^2 - 5x - 3$; domain: all real numbers
51. $-x^2 + 5x + 13$; domain: all real numbers
53. $4x^2 - 14x + 3$; domain: all real numbers
55. $2x^3 - x^2 - 11x + 10$; domain: all real numbers
57. $\frac{2x+5}{x^2-3x+2}$; domain: all real numbers except $x = 1$ and 2 **59.** Substitute $5995x$ for y; \$79,850 **61. a.** $g(x)$ is the bonus earned when x is the amount of sales over \$5000. $h(x)$ is the excess sales over \$5000. **b.** $(g \circ h)(x)$; you first need to find the excess sales over \$5000 to calculate the bonus. **63.** 1 **65.** 0 **67.** 8 **69.** −2
71. a. ≈1963; The area after 2 seconds is about 1963 in.^{2} **b.** ≈7854 in.^{2} **73.** $x - 2$; $x - 2$ **75.** $x - 3$; $x - 6$
77. $\frac{x^2+5}{2}$; $\frac{x^2+10x+25}{4}$
79. $x^7 - x^6 - 16x^5 + 10x^4 + 85x^3 - 25x^2 - 150x$; domain: all real numbers **81.** $\frac{x-3}{x^2+2x}$; domain: all real numbers except $x = 0, -2, \sqrt{5}$, and $-\sqrt{5}$ **83.** 2
85. $8a + 4h$ **87.** H **89.** Look at the 5th number in Row 7 of Pascal's triangle to find the coefficient of the x^3y^4 term in the expansion of $(x + y)^7$.
$35(3x)^3(-y)^4 = 945x^3y^4$, so 945 is the coefficient.
90. 1 **91.** −3 **92.** 4 **93.** 3 **94.** 2 **95.** 3
96. $x^8 + 32x^7 + 448x^6 + 3584x^5 + 17{,}920x^4 + 57{,}344x^3 + 114{,}688x^2 + 131{,}072x + 65{,}536$ **97.** $x^6 + 6x^5y + 15x^4y^2 + 20x^3y^3 + 15x^2y^4 + 6xy^5 + y^6$ **98.** $16x^4 - 32x^3y + 24x^2y^2 - 8xy^3 + y^4$
99. $128x^7 - 1344x^6y + 6048x^5y^2 - 15{,}120x^4y^3 + 22{,}680x^3y^4 - 20{,}412x^2y^5 + 10{,}206xy^6 - 2187y^7$
100. $59{,}049 - 65{,}610x + 29{,}160x^2 - 6480x^3 + 720x^4 - 32x^5$ **101.** $1024x^5 - 1280x^4y + 640x^3y^2 - 160x^2y^3 + 20xy^4 - y^5$ **102.** $x^8 + 4x^7 + 6x^6 + 4x^5 + x^4$ **103.** $x^{12} + 12x^{10}y^3 + 60x^8y^6 + 160x^6y^9 + 240x^4y^{12} + 192x^2y^{15} + 64y^{18}$
104. no solution **105.** (2, 2)
106. (1, 1)

Lesson 6-7 **pp. 405–412**

Got It?
1. a.
b. t is a function; the inverse of t is not a function; there are 2 y-values for one x-value **2.** $y = \frac{x}{2} - 4$
3.
4. a. domain: all real numbers; range: all real numbers
b. $g^{-1}(x) = -\frac{1}{4}x + \frac{3}{2}$ **c.** domain: all real numbers; range: all real numbers **d.** Yes; for each x in the domain of g^{-1}, there is only one value of y in the range. **5.** $v = \sqrt{19.6d}$; 21.7 m/s **6. a.** $g^{-1}(x) = \frac{4-2x}{x}$ **b.** 0 is not in the domain of g^{-1} so $(g \circ g^{-1})(0)$ does not exist. **c.** 0
Lesson Check 1. $f^{-1}(x) = \frac{x-3}{4}$; yes

1086

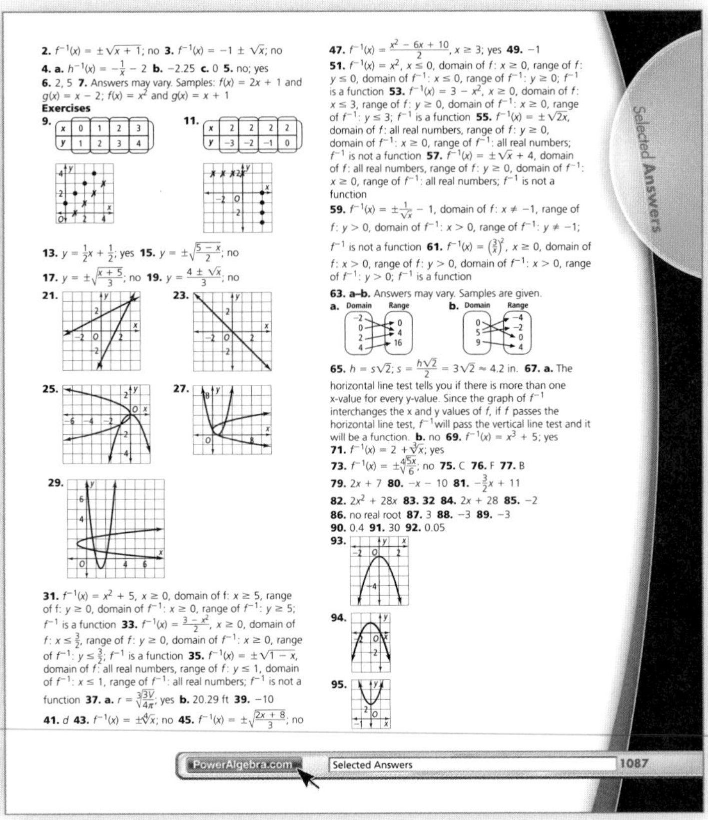

2. $f^{-1}(x) = \pm\sqrt{x+1}$; no **3.** $f^{-1}(x) = -1 \pm \sqrt{x}$; no
4. a. $h^{-1}(x) = -\frac{1}{x} - 2$ **b.** −2.25 **c.** 0 **5.** no; yes
6. 2, 5 **7.** Answers may vary. Samples: $f(x) = 2x + 1$ and $g(x) = x - 2$; $f(x) = x^2$ and $g(x) = x + 1$
Exercises
9.

x	0	1	2	3
y	1	2	3	4

11.

x	2	2	2	2
y	−3	−2	−1	0

13. $y = \frac{1}{2}x + \frac{1}{2}$; yes **15.** $y = \pm\sqrt{\frac{5-x}{2}}$; no
17. $y = \pm\sqrt{\frac{x+5}{3}}$; no **19.** $y = \frac{4 \pm \sqrt{x}}{3}$; no
21. **23.** **25.** **27.** **29.**
31. $f^{-1}(x) = x^2 + 5$, $x \ge 0$, domain of f: $x \ge 5$, range of f: $y \ge 0$, domain of f^{-1}: $x \ge 0$, range of f^{-1}: $y \ge 5$; f^{-1} is a function **33.** $f^{-1}(x) = \frac{3-x^2}{2}$, $x \ge 0$, domain of f: $x \le \frac{3}{2}$, range of f: $y \ge 0$, domain of f^{-1}: $x \ge 0$, range of f^{-1}: $y \le \frac{3}{2}$; f^{-1} is a function **35.** $f^{-1}(x) = \pm\sqrt{1-x}$, domain of f: all real numbers, range of f: $y \le 1$, domain of f^{-1}: $x \le 1$, range of f^{-1}: all real numbers; f^{-1} is not a function **37. a.** $r = \sqrt[3]{\frac{3V}{4\pi}}$; yes **b.** 20.29 ft **39.** −10
41. d **43.** $f^{-1}(x) = \pm\sqrt[4]{x}$; no **45.** $f^{-1}(x) = \pm\sqrt{\frac{2x+8}{3}}$; no
47. $f^{-1}(x) = \frac{x^2-6x+10}{2}$, $x \ge 3$; yes **49.** −1
51. $f^{-1}(x) = x^2$, $x \le 0$, domain of f: $x \ge 0$, range of f: $y \le 0$, domain of f^{-1}: $x \le 0$, range of f^{-1}: $y \ge 0$; f^{-1} is a function **53.** $f^{-1}(x) = 3 - x^2$, $x \ge 0$, domain of f: $x \le 3$, range of f: $y \ge 0$, domain of f^{-1}: $x \ge 0$, range of f^{-1}: $y \le 3$; f^{-1} is a function **55.** $f^{-1}(x) = \pm\sqrt{2x}$, domain of f: all real numbers, range of f: $y \ge 0$, domain of f^{-1}: $x \ge 0$, range of f^{-1}: all real numbers; f^{-1} is not a function **57.** $f^{-1}(x) = \pm\sqrt{x} + 4$, domain of f: all real numbers, range of f: $y \ge 0$, domain of f^{-1}: $x \ge 0$, range of f^{-1}: all real numbers; f^{-1} is not a function
59. $f^{-1}(x) = \pm\frac{1}{\sqrt{x}} - 1$, domain of f: $x \ne -1$, range of f: $y > 0$, domain of f^{-1}: $x > 0$, range of f^{-1}: $y \ne -1$; f^{-1} is not a function **61.** $f^{-1}(x) = \left(\frac{3}{x}\right)^2$, $x \ge 0$, domain of f: $x > 0$, range of f: $y > 0$, domain of f^{-1}: $x > 0$, range of f^{-1}: $y > 0$; f^{-1} is a function
63. a–b. Answers may vary. Samples are given.
a. Domain Range **b.** Domain Range
65. $h = s\sqrt{2}$; $s = \frac{h\sqrt{2}}{2} = 3\sqrt{2} \approx 4.2$ in. **67. a.** The horizontal line test tells you if there is more than one x-value for every y-value. Since the graph of f^{-1} interchanges the x and y values of f, if f passes the horizontal line test, f^{-1} will pass the vertical line test and it will be a function. **b.** no **69.** $f^{-1}(x) = x^3 + 5$; yes
71. $f^{-1}(x) = 2 + \sqrt[3]{x}$; yes
73. $f^{-1}(x) = \pm\sqrt[4]{\frac{5x}{6}}$; no **75.** C **76.** F **77.** B
79. $2x + 7$ **80.** $-x - 10$ **81.** $-\frac{3}{2}x + 11$
82. $2x^2 + 28x$ **83.** 32 **84.** $2x + 28$ **85.** −2
86. no real root **87.** 3 **88.** −3 **89.** −3
90. 0.4 **91.** 30 **92.** 0.05
93. **94.** **95.**

PowerAlgebra.com Selected Answers 1087

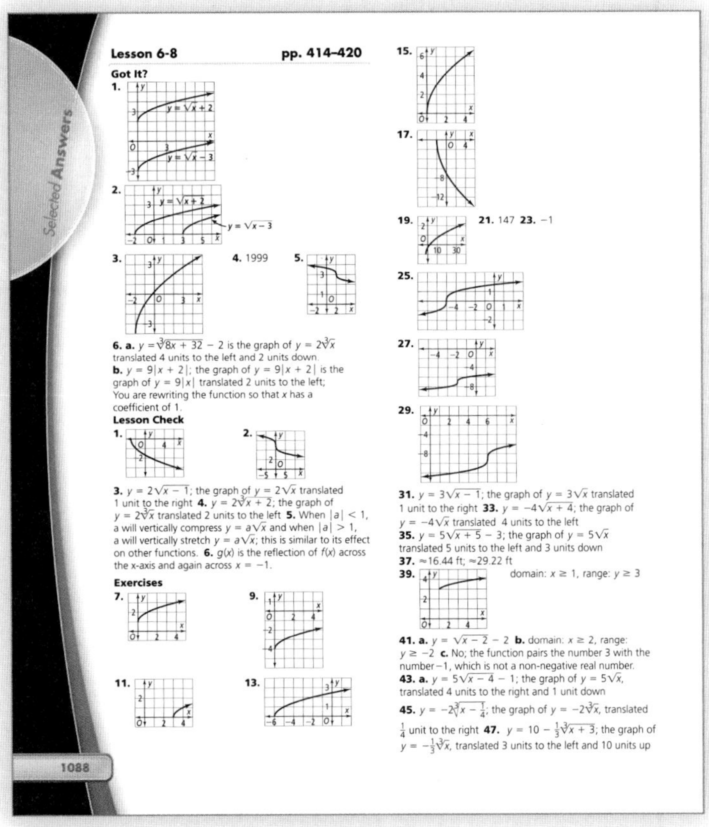

Lesson 6-8 **pp. 414–420**

Got It?
1. **2.** **3.** **4.** 1999 **5.**
6. a. $y = \sqrt[3]{8x+32} - 2$ is the graph of $y = 2\sqrt[3]{x}$ translated 4 units to the left and 2 units down.
b. $y = 9|x + 2|$; the graph of $y = 9|x + 2|$ is the graph of $y = 9|x|$ translated 2 units to the left; You are rewriting the function so that x has a coefficient of 1.
Lesson Check
1. **2.**
3. $y = 2\sqrt{x-1}$; the graph of $y = 2\sqrt{x}$ translated 1 unit to the right **4.** $y = 2\sqrt[3]{x+2}$; the graph of $y = 2\sqrt[3]{x}$ translated 2 units to the left **5.** When $|a| < 1$, a will vertically compress $y = a\sqrt{x}$ and when $|a| > 1$, a will vertically stretch $y = a\sqrt{x}$; this is similar to its effect on other functions. **6.** $g(x)$ is the reflection of $f(x)$ across the x-axis and again across $x = -1$.
Exercises
7. **9.** **11.** **13.** **15.** **17.** **19.** **21.** 147 **23.** −1
25. **27.** **29.**
31. $y = 3\sqrt{x-1}$; the graph of $y = 3\sqrt{x}$ translated 1 unit to the right **33.** $y = -4\sqrt{x+4}$; the graph of $y = -4\sqrt{x}$ translated 4 units to the left
35. $y = 5\sqrt{x+5} - 3$; the graph of $y = 5\sqrt{x}$ translated 5 units to the left and 3 units down
37. ≈16.44 ft; ≈29.22 ft
39. domain: $x \ge 1$, range: $y \ge 3$
41. a. $y = \sqrt{x-2} - 2$ **b.** domain: $x \ge 2$, range: $y \ge -2$ **c.** No; the function pairs the number 3 with the number −1, which is not a non-negative real number.
43. a. $y = 5\sqrt{x-4} - 1$; the graph of $y = 5\sqrt{x}$, translated 4 units to the right and 1 unit down
45. $y = -2\sqrt[3]{x - \frac{1}{4}}$; the graph of $y = -2\sqrt[3]{x}$, translated $\frac{1}{4}$ unit to the right **47.** $y = 10 - \frac{1}{3}\sqrt[3]{x+3}$; the graph of $y = -\frac{1}{3}\sqrt[3]{x}$, translated 3 units to the left and 10 units up

1088

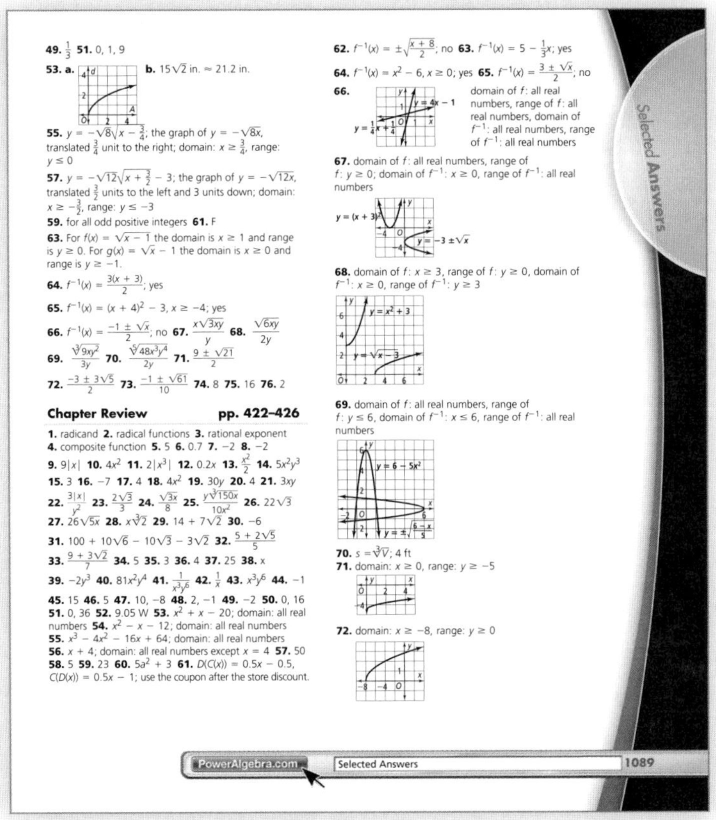

49. $\frac{1}{3}$ **51.** 0, 1, 9
53. a. **b.** $15\sqrt{2}$ in. ≈ 21.2 in.
55. $y = -\sqrt{8}\sqrt{x - \frac{3}{4}}$; the graph of $y = -\sqrt{8x}$, translated $\frac{3}{4}$ unit to the right; domain: $x \ge \frac{3}{4}$, range: $y \le 0$
57. $y = -\sqrt{12}\sqrt{x + \frac{3}{2}} - 3$; the graph of $y = -\sqrt{12x}$, translated $\frac{3}{2}$ units to the left and 3 units down; domain: $x \ge -\frac{3}{2}$, range: $y \le -3$
59. for all odd positive integers **61.** F
63. For $f(x) = \sqrt{x-1}$ the domain is $x \ge 1$ and range is $y \ge 0$. For $g(x) = \sqrt{x} - 1$ the domain is $x \ge 0$ and range is $y \ge -1$.
64. $f^{-1}(x) = \frac{3(x+3)}{2}$; yes
65. $f^{-1}(x) = (x + 4)^2 - 3$, $x \ge -4$; yes
66. $f^{-1}(x) = \frac{-1 \pm \sqrt{x}}{2}$; no **67.** $\frac{x\sqrt{3xy}}{y}$ **68.** $\frac{\sqrt{6xy}}{2y}$
69. $\frac{\sqrt[3]{9xy^2}}{3y}$ **70.** $\frac{\sqrt[5]{48x^3y^4}}{2y}$ **71.** $\frac{9 \pm \sqrt{21}}{2}$
72. $\frac{-3 \pm 3\sqrt{5}}{2}$ **73.** $\frac{-1 \pm \sqrt{61}}{10}$ **74.** 8 **75.** 16 **76.** 2

Chapter Review **pp. 422–426**

1. radicand **2.** radical functions **3.** rational exponent **4.** composite function **5.** 5 **6.** 0.7 **7.** −2 **8.** −2
9. $9|x|$ **10.** $4x^2$ **11.** $2|x^3|$ **12.** $0.2x$ **13.** $\frac{x^2}{2}$ **14.** $5x^2y^3$
15. 3 **16.** −7 **17.** 4 **18.** $4x^2$ **19.** $30y$ **20.** 4 **21.** $3xy$
22. $\frac{3|x|}{y^2}$ **23.** $\frac{2\sqrt{3}}{3}$ **24.** $\frac{\sqrt{3x}}{8}$ **25.** $\frac{y\sqrt[3]{150x}}{10x^2}$ **26.** $22\sqrt{3}$
27. $26\sqrt{5x}$ **28.** $x\sqrt[3]{2}$ **29.** $14 + 7\sqrt{2}$ **30.** −6
31. $100 + 10\sqrt{6} - 10\sqrt{3} - 3\sqrt{2}$ **32.** $\frac{5+2\sqrt{5}}{5}$
33. $\frac{9+3\sqrt{2}}{7}$ **34.** 5 **35.** 3 **36.** 4 **37.** 25 **38.** x
39. $-2y^3$ **40.** $81x^2y^4$ **41.** $\frac{1}{x^3y^6}$ **42.** $\frac{1}{x}$ **43.** x^3y^6 **44.** −1
45. 15 **46.** 5 **47.** 10, −8 **48.** 2, −1 **49.** −2 **50.** 0, 16
51. 0, 36 **52.** 9.05 W **53.** $x^2 + x - 20$; domain: all real numbers **54.** $x^2 - x - 12$; domain: all real numbers
55. $x^3 - 4x^2 - 16x + 64$; domain: all real numbers
56. $x + 4$; domain: all real numbers except $x = 4$ **57.** 50
58. 5 **59.** 23 **60.** $5a^2 + 3$ **61.** $D(C(x)) = 0.5x - 0.5$, $C(D(x)) = 0.5x - 1$; use the coupon after the store discount.
62. $f^{-1}(x) = \pm\sqrt{\frac{x+8}{2}}$; no **63.** $f^{-1}(x) = 5 - \frac{1}{3}x$; yes
64. $f^{-1}(x) = x^2 - 6$, $x \ge 0$; yes **65.** $f^{-1}(x) = \frac{3 \pm \sqrt{x}}{2}$; no
66. domain of f: all real numbers, range of f: all real numbers, domain of f^{-1}: all real numbers, range of f^{-1}: all real numbers
67. domain of f: all real numbers, range of f: $y \ge 0$; domain of f^{-1}: $x \ge 0$, range of f^{-1}: all real numbers
68. domain of f: $x \ge 3$, range of f: $y \ge 0$, domain of f^{-1}: $x \ge 0$, range of f^{-1}: $y \ge 3$
69. domain of f: all real numbers, range of f: $y \le 6$, domain of f^{-1}: $x \le 6$, range of f^{-1}: all real numbers
70. $s = \sqrt[3]{V}$; 4 ft
71. domain: $x \ge 0$, range: $y \ge -5$
72. domain: $x \ge -8$, range: $y \ge 0$

PowerAlgebra.com Selected Answers 1089

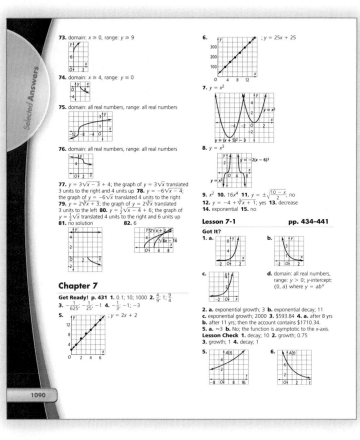

73. domain: $x \geq 0$, range: $y \geq 9$

74. domain: $x \geq 4$, range: $y \leq 0$

75. domain: all real numbers, range: all real numbers

76. domain: all real numbers, range: all real numbers

77. $y = 3\sqrt{x-3} + 4$; the graph of $y = 3\sqrt{x}$ translated 3 units to the right and 4 units up 78. $y = -6\sqrt{x-4}$; the graph of $y = -6\sqrt{x}$ translated 4 units to the right 79. $y = 2\sqrt[3]{x} + 3$; the graph of $y = 2\sqrt[3]{x}$ translated 3 units to the left 80. $y = \frac{1}{2}\sqrt{x-4} + 6$; the graph of $y = \frac{1}{2}\sqrt{x}$ translated 4 units to the right and 6 units up 81. no solution 82. 6

Chapter 7

Get Ready! p. 431 1. 0.1; 10; 1000 2. $\frac{4}{9}$; 1; $\frac{9}{4}$
3. $-\frac{1}{625}$; $-\frac{1}{25}$; -1 4. $-\frac{1}{3}$; -1; -3
5. ; $y = 2x + 2$

6. ; $y = 25x + 25$
7. $y = x^2$
8. $y = x^3$
9. x^2 10. $16x^4$ 11. $y = \pm\sqrt{\frac{10-x}{2}}$; no
12. $y = -4 + \sqrt[3]{x + 1}$; yes 13. decrease
14. exponential 15. no

Lesson 7-1 pp. 434–441

Got It?
1. a. b. c. d. domain: all real numbers, range: $y > 0$; y-intercept: $(0, a)$ where $y = ab^x$
2. a. exponential growth; 3 b. exponential decay; 1 c. exponential growth; 2000 3. $593.84 4. a. after 8 yrs b. after 11 yrs; then the account contains $1710.34.
5. a. ≈3 b. No; the function is asymptotic to the x-axis.
Lesson Check 1. decay; 10 2. growth; 0.75 3. growth; 1 4. decay; 1
5. 6.

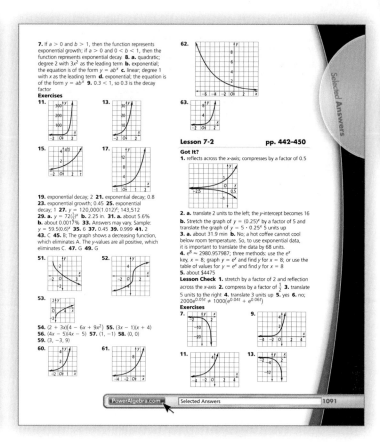

7. If $a > 0$ and $b > 1$, then the function represents exponential growth; if $a > 0$ and $0 < b < 1$, then the function represents exponential decay. 8. a. quadratic; degree 2 with $3x^2$ as the leading term b. exponential; the equation is of the form $y = ab^x$ c. linear; degree 1 with x as the leading term d. exponential; the equation is of the form $y = ab^x$ 9. $0.3 < 1$, so 0.3 is the decay factor
Exercises
11. 13.
15. 17.
19. exponential decay; 2 21. exponential decay; 0.8
23. exponential growth; 0.45 25. exponential decay; 1 27. $y = 120{,}000(1.012)^t$; 143,512
29. a. $y = 72(\frac{1}{2})^x$ b. 2.25 in. 31. a. about 5.6% b. about 0.0017% 33. Answers may vary. Sample: $y = 59.5(0.6)^x$ 35. 6 37. 0.45 39. 0.999 41. 2
43. C 45. B; The graph shows a decreasing function, which eliminates A. The y-values are all positive, which eliminates C. 47. G 49. G
51. 52.
53.
54. $(2 + 3x)(4 - 6x + 9x^2)$ 55. $(3x - 1)(x + 4)$
56. $(4x - 5)(4x - 5)$ 57. $(1, -1)$ 58. $(0, 0)$
59. $(3, -3, 9)$
60. 61.

62.
63.

Lesson 7-2 pp. 442–450

Got It?
1. reflects across the x-axis; compresses by a factor of 0.5
2. a. translate 2 units to the left; the y-intercept becomes 16 b. Stretch the graph of $y = (0.25)^x$ by a factor of 5 and translate the graph of $y = 5 \cdot 0.25^x$ 5 units up
3. a. about 31.9 min b. No; a hot coffee cannot cool below room temperature. So, to use exponential data, it is important to translate the data by 68 units.
4. $e^8 \approx 2980.957987$; three methods: use the e^x key, $x = 8$; graph $y = e^x$ and find y for $x = 8$; or use the table of values for $y = e^x$ and find y for $x = 8$
5. about $4475
Lesson Check 1. stretch by a factor of 2 and reflection across the x-axis 2. compress by a factor of $\frac{1}{3}$ 3. translate 5 units to the right 4. translate 3 units up 5. yes 6. no; $2000e^{0.05t} \neq 1000(e^{0.04t} + e^{0.06t})$
Exercises
7. 9.
11. 13.

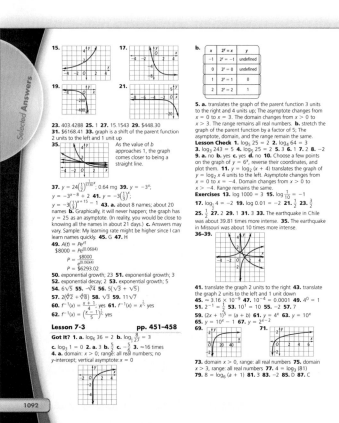

15. 17.
19. 21.
23. 403.4288 25. 1 27. 15.1543 29. $448.30
31. $6168.41 33. graph is a shift of the parent function 2 units to the left and 1 unit up
35. As the value of b approaches 1, the graph comes closer to being a straight line.
37. $y = 24(\frac{1}{2})^{(1/10)x}$; 0.64 mg 39. $y = -3^x$; $y = -3^{x-8} + 2$ 41. $y = -3(\frac{1}{3})^x$; $y = -3(\frac{1}{3})^{x+15} - 1$ 43. a. about 8 names; about 20 names b. Graphically, it will never happen; the graph has $y = 25$ as an asymptote. (In reality, you would be close to knowing all the names in about 21 days.) c. Answers may vary. Sample: My learning rate might be higher since I can learn names quickly. 45. G 47. H
49. $A(t) = Pe^{rt}$
$8000 = Pe^{(0.06)(4)}$
$P = \frac{8000}{e^{0.06(4)}}$
$P \approx \$6293.02$
50. exponential growth; 23 51. exponential growth; 3
52. exponential decay; 2 53. exponential growth; 5
54. $6\sqrt{5}$ 55. $-\sqrt[3]{4}$ 56. $5(\sqrt{3} + \sqrt{5})$
57. $2(\sqrt[3]{2} + \sqrt[4]{8})$ 58. $\sqrt{3}$ 59. $11\sqrt{7}$
60. $f^{-1}(x) = \frac{x + 1}{4}$; yes 61. $f^{-1}(x) = x^{\frac{1}{5}}$; yes
62. $f^{-1}(x) = (x - 1)^{\frac{1}{3}}$; yes

Lesson 7-3 pp. 451–458

Got It? 1. a. $\log_6 36 = 2$ b. $\log_3 \frac{8}{27} = 3$
c. $\log_3 1 = 0$ 2. a. 3 b. $\frac{5}{2}$ c. $-\frac{5}{3}$ 3. ≈16 times
4. a. domain: $x > 0$; range: all real numbers; no y-intercept; vertical asymptote: $x = 0$

b.

x	$2^y = x$	y
-1	$2^y = -1$	undefined
0	$2^y = 0$	undefined
1	$2^y = 1$	0

5. a. translates the graph of the parent function 3 units to the right and 4 units up; The asymptote changes from $x = 0$ to $x = 3$. The domain changes from $x > 0$ to $x > 3$. The range remains all real numbers. b. stretch the graph of the parent function by a factor of 5; The asymptote, domain, and the range remain the same.
Lesson Check 1. $\log_5 25 = 2$ 2. $\log_4 64 = 3$ 3. $\log_3 243 = 5$ 4. $\log_5 25 = 2$ 5. 3 6. 1 7. 2 8. -2
9. a. no b. yes c. yes d. no 10. Choose a few points on the graph of $y = 6^x$, reverse their coordinates, and plot them. 11. $y = \log_2 (x + 4)$ translates the graph of $y = \log_2 x$ 4 units to the left. Asymptote changes from $x = 0$ to $x = -4$. Domain changes from $x > 0$ to $x > -4$. Range remains the same.
Exercises 13. $\log 1000 = 3$ 15. $\log \frac{1}{10} = -1$
25. $\frac{1}{2}$ 27. 2 29. 1 31. 3 33. The earthquake in Chile was about 39.81 times more intense. 35. The earthquake in Missouri was about 10 times more intense.
36–39.
41. translate the graph 2 units to the right 43. translate the graph 2 units to the left and 1 unit down
45. $\approx 3.16 \times 10^{-9}$ 47. $10^{-4} = 0.0001$ 49. $4^0 = 1$
51. $2^{-1} = \frac{1}{2}$ 53. $10^1 = 10$ 55. -2 57. 7
59. $(2x + 1)^5 = (a + b)$ 61. $y = 4^x$ 63. $y = 10^x$
65. $y = 10^{x-1}$ 67. $y = 2^{x-2}$
69. 71.
73. domain $x > 0$, range: all real numbers 75. domain $x > 3$, range: all real numbers 77. $4 = \log_3 (81)$
79. $8 = \log_2 (a + 1)$ 81. 3 83. -2 85. D 87. C

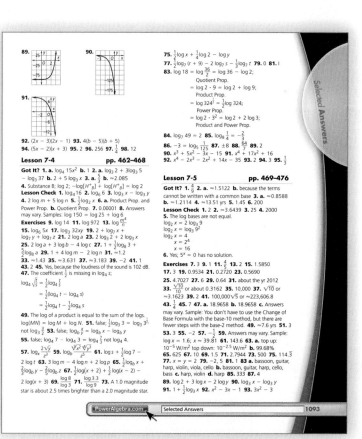

89. 90.
91.
92. $(2x - 3)(2x - 1)$ 93. $4(b - 5)(b + 5)$
94. $(5x - 2)(x + 3)$ 95. 2 96. 256 97. $\frac{4}{9}$ 98. 12

Lesson 7-4 pp. 462–468

Got It? 1. a. $\log_4 15x^2$ b. 1 2. a. $\log_3 2 + 3\log_3 5 - \log_3 37$ b. $2 + 5 \log_3 x$ 3. a. $\frac{3}{2}$ b. 2.085
4. Substance B; log 2; $-\log[H^+_B] + \log[H^+_A] = \log 2$
Lesson Check 1. $\log_4 16$ 2. $\log_4 6$ 3. $\log_3 9 x^2$
4. $2 \log m + 5 \log n$ 5. $\frac{1}{2} \log_2 y$ 6. a. Product Prop. and Power Prop. b. Quotient Prop. 7. 0.0001 8. Answers may vary. Samples: $\log 150 = \log 25 + \log 6$
Exercises 9. $\log 14$ 11. $\log 972$ 13. $\log \frac{m^4}{n}$
15. $\log_6 5x$ 17. $\log_3 32xy$ 19. $2 + \log_7 x + \log_7 y + \log_7 z$ 21. $2 \log a$ 23. $2 \log_3 3 + 2 \log_3 x$
25. $2 \log a + 3 \log b - 4 \log C$ 27. $1 + \frac{1}{2} \log_3 3 + \frac{2}{3} \log_3 a$ 29. $1 + 4 \log m - 2 \log n$ 31. ≈1.2
33. ≈1.43 35. ≈3.631 37. ≈3.183 39. -2 41. 1
43. 2 45. Yes, because the loudness of the sound is 102 dB.
47. The coefficient $\frac{1}{2}$ is missing in $\log_4 s$:
$\log_4 \sqrt{\frac{t}{s}}$
$= \frac{1}{2}\log_4 t - \log_4 s$
$= \frac{1}{2}\log_4 t - \frac{1}{2}\log_4 s$
49. The log of a product is equal to the sum of the logs. $\log(MN) = \log M + \log N$ 51. false; $\frac{1}{3} \log_3 3 = \log_3 3^{\frac{1}{3}}$, not $\log_3 \frac{3}{3}$ 53. false; $\log_5 \frac{5}{y} = \log_5 5 - \log_5 y$
55. false; $\log_4 \frac{1}{y} = \log_4 1 - \log_4 y$
57. $\log_2 \frac{2\sqrt{y}}{z^3}$ 59. $\log_3 \frac{\sqrt{x^2}\sqrt[3]{y^2}}{z^5}$ 61. $\log s + \frac{1}{2} \log 7 - 2 \log t$ 63. $3 \log m - 4 \log n + 2 \log p$ 65. $\frac{1}{3}\log_6 x + \frac{2}{3}\log_6 y - \frac{2}{3}\log_6 z$ 67. $\frac{1}{2} \log(x + 2) + \frac{1}{2}\log(x - 2) - 2 \log(x + 3)$ 69. $\frac{\log 8}{\log 3}$ 71. $\frac{\log 3.3}{\log 3}$ 73. A 1.0 magnitude star is about 2.5 times brighter than a 2.0 magnitude star.

75. $\frac{1}{2}\log x + \frac{1}{4}\log 2 - \log y$
77. $\frac{1}{2}\log_7 (r + 9) - 2 \log_7 s - \frac{1}{3}\log_7 t$ 79. 0 81. 1
83. $\log 18 = \log \frac{36}{2} = \log 36 - \log 2$;
Quotient Prop.
$= \log 2 \cdot 9 = \log 2 + \log 9$;
Product Prop.
$= \log 324^{\frac{1}{2}} = \frac{1}{2}\log 324$;
Power Prop.
$= \log 2 \cdot 3^2 = \log 2 + 2 \log 3$;
Product and Power Prop.
84. $\log_7 49 = 2$ 85. $\log_8 \frac{1}{4} = -\frac{2}{3}$
86. $-3 = \log_5 \frac{1}{125}$ 87. ±8 88. $\frac{64}{27}$ 89. 2
90. $x^3 + 5x^2 - 3x - 15$ 91. $x^4 + 17x^2 + 16$
92. $x^4 - 2x^3 - 2x^2 + 14x - 35$ 93. 2 94. 3 95. $\frac{1}{3}$

Lesson 7-5 pp. 469–476

Got It? 1. $\frac{4}{9}$ 2. a. ≈1.5122 b. because the terms cannot be written with a common base 3. a. ≈0.8588 b. ≈1.2114 4. ≈13.51 yrs 5. 1.45 6. 200
Lesson Check 1. 2 2. ≈3.6439 3. 25 4. 2000
5. The log bases are not equal.
$\log_2 x = 2 \log_2 9$
$\log_2 x = \log_3 9^2$
$\log_2 x = 4$
$x = 2^4$
$x = 16$
6. Yes; $5^x = 0$ has no solution.
Exercises 7. 3 9. 1 11. $\frac{4}{3}$ 13. 2 15. 1.5850
17. 3 19. 0.9534 21. 0.2720 23. 0.5690
25. 4.7027 27. 6 29. 0.64 31. about the yr 2012
33. $\frac{\sqrt{10}}{10}$ or about 0.3162 35. 10,000 37. $\sqrt{10}$ or ≈3.1623 39. 4 41. $100{,}000\sqrt{5}$ or ≈223,606.8
43. $\frac{1}{4}$ 45. 7 47. a. 18.9658 b. 18.9658 c. Answers may vary. Sample: You don't have to use the Change of Base Formula with the base-10 method, but there are fewer steps with the base-10 method. 49. 3
53. 3 55. -2 57. $-\frac{1}{2}$ 59. Answers may vary. Sample: $\log x = 1.6$; $x = 39.81$ 61. 143.6 63. a. top up: 10^{-5} W/m² top down: $10^{-2.5}$ W/m² b. 99.68% 65. 625 67. 10 69. 1.5 71. 2.7944 73. 500 75. 114.3 77. $x = y = 2$ 79. -2, 5 81. 1 83. a. bassoon, guitar, harp, violin, viola, cello b. bassoon, guitar, harp, cello, bass c. harp, violin d. harp 85. 333 87. 4
89. $\log 2 + 3 \log x - 2 \log y$ 90. $\log_3 x - \log_3 y$ 91. $1 + \frac{1}{2}\log_3 x$ 92. $x^2 - 3x - 1$ 93. $3x^2 - 3$

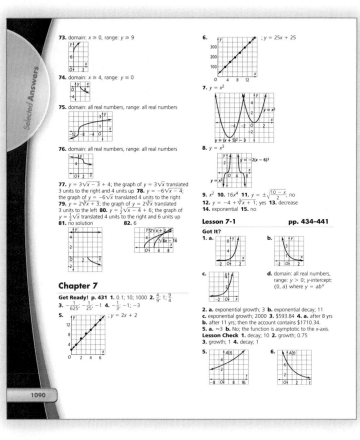

94. $9x^2 - 1$ **95.** $1, \pm i$ **96.** $\pm 2, \pm 2i$
97. $\pm\sqrt{3}, \pm\sqrt{2}$ **98.** $\log_2 3$ **99.** $\log 3x^4$ **100.** $\log_7 \frac{32}{y^2}$

Lesson 7-6 pp. 478–483

Got It? 1. a. $\ln 175$ **b.** $\ln \frac{x}{4}$ **c.** $\ln 5x^3y^2$ **2. a.** e^2, or about 7.39 **b.** $\frac{-5 \pm e^2}{2}$, or about 0.8 or −4.13 **c.** $\frac{e^2}{6}$, or about 1.23 **3. a.** $\ln 2 + 2$, or about 4.48 **b.** $-\ln 10$, or about −2.3 **c.** $\frac{\ln 10}{3}$, or about 0.77 **4. a.** No; the maximum velocity of 5.4 km/s is less than the 7.7 km/s needed for a stable orbit. **b.** Yes; if, R could be changed so that $V > 7.7$.
Lesson Check 1. $\ln 81$ **2.** $\ln 1.8$ **3.** $\ln 12$ **4.** $-\ln 4$ **5.** ≈10.9 **6.** ≈14.4 **7.** ≈7.39 **8.** ≈−0.718
9. error in 3rd line: $4x = 5$
should be: $4x = e^5$
$x = \frac{e^5}{4}; x \approx 37.1$
10. No; ln 5 has base e and $\log_2 10$ has base 2.
Exercises 11. $\ln 125$ **13.** $\ln 4$ **15.** $\ln \frac{\sqrt[3]{xy}}{z^4}$ **17.** $\ln 40{,}960$
19. $\ln 1$ **21.** 0.135 **23.** ±11.588 **25.** ±2.241
27. 1488.979 **29.** ≈2.890 **31.** ≈1.242 **33.** ≈2.401
35. 0 **37.** ≈2.2 **39.** at least 25 s **41.** ≈11,552 yrs
43. $\frac{1}{4}$ **45.** 83 **47.** 2 **49.** 10 **51.** $\frac{1}{2}$ **53.** ≈301 days
55. never **57.** 10.8 **59.** ≈19.8 h **61.** 78.342
63. Because the function is simplified in the beginning and the sq. root of the exponential function is not calculated.
65. a. ≈43 min
b. $t = -\frac{1}{0.041} \ln\left(\frac{T - 72}{164}\right)$

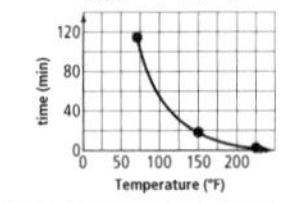

Temperature (°F)	225	200	175	150	125	100	75
Minutes Later	1.7	6.0	11.3	18.1	27.6	43.1	97.6

67. 4 **69.** 0.2975 **71.** 3 **72.** 4 **73.** 2.846
74. 0.272 **75.** $3333.\overline{3}$ **76.** 1.002 **77.** 9.0×10^{-5}
78. $y = \frac{x - 7}{5}$; yes **79.** $y = \sqrt[3]{\frac{x - 10}{2}}$; yes
80. $y = \pm\sqrt{5 - x}$; no **81.** $y = \frac{x - 2}{3}$; yes **82.** 10
83. 15 **84.** $\frac{6}{5}$

Chapter Review pp. 487–490

1. exponential decay; exponential growth **2.** asymptote **3.** logarithm; natural logarithm function **4.** continuously compounded interest **5.** natural logarithmic function **6.** exponential growth; (0, 1) **7.** exponential growth; (0, 2) **8.** exponential growth; (0, 0.2) **9.** exponential decay; (0, 3) **10.** exponential growth; $\left(0, \frac{25}{7}\right)$ **11.** exponential growth; (0, 0.0015) **12.** exponential decay; (0, 2.25) **13.** exponential decay; (0, 0.5) **14.** $y = 12{,}500(0.91)^x$; \$7800 **15.** $y = 50(1.03)^x$; \$58 **16.** The parent graph $y = 2^x$ is stretched by a factor of 5, translated 1 unit to the left, and 3 units up. **17.** The parent graph $y = \left(\frac{1}{3}\right)^x$ is reflected across the x-axis, stretched by a factor of 2, and translated 2 units to the right. **18.** \$1100.76 **19.** \$291.91 **20.** 0.0498
21. 0.3679 **22.** 148.4132 **23.** 0.6065 **24.** $2 = \log_6 36$
25. $-3 = \log_2 0.125$ **26.** $3 = \log_3 27$
27. $-3 = \log 0.001$ **28.** 6 **29.** −2 **30.** −5 **31.** 0
32.
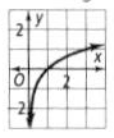
33.
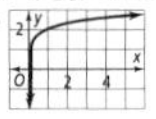
34.
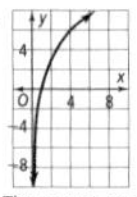
35.
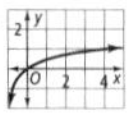
36. The parent graph $y = \log_4 x$ is stretched by a factor of 3 and translated 1 unit to the left.
37. The parent graph $y = \ln x$ is reflected across the x-axis and translated 2 units up. **38.** log 24; Product Prop.
39. $\log_2 \frac{5}{3}$; Quotient Prop. **40.** $\log_3 7x^4$; Power and Product Prop. **41.** $\log \frac{x}{y}$; Quotient Prop. **42.** $\log \frac{5}{x^2}$; Power and Quotient Prop. **43.** $\log_4 x^5$; Power and Product Prop. **44.** $2 \log_4 x + 3 \log_4 y$; Product and Power Prop. **45.** $\log 4 + 4 \log s + \log t$; Product and Power Prop. **46.** $\log_3 2 - \log_3 x$; Quotient Prop.
47. $2 \log(x + 3)$; Power Prop.
48. $3 \log_2 2 + 3 \log_2 (y - 2)$; Power and Product Prop. **49.** $2 \log z - \log 5$; Power and Quotient Prop.
50. ≈2.8 **51.** ≈2.1 **52.** 0.75 **53.** 3.2619
54. 4.6542 **55.** 1.3652 **56.** 3.3333 **57.** 8 **58.** 50
59. 7.6256×10^{12} **60.** 0.9307 **61.** 0.6599
62. 0.6658 **63.** 3.0589 **64.** ≈18.2 h **65.** ≈0.83
66. ≈2.26 **67.** ≈4.31 **68.** ≈0.54 **69.** ≈3.77
70. ≈6.03 **71.** ≈3.4%

Chapter 8

Get Ready! p. 495 1. $\frac{4}{3}$; −4 **2.** $-\frac{2}{3}$; 2 **3.** $-\frac{10}{3}$; 10
4. $-\frac{16}{7}$; $\frac{48}{7}$ **5.** $(x + 3)(x - 2)$ **6.** $(4x + 5)(x + 3)$
7. $(3x - 5)(3x + 5)$ **8.** $(x - 6)^2$ **9.** $(3x + 4)(x + 2)$
10. $(x - 3)(x - 2)$ **11.** 1, −8 **12.** −6, −8 **13.** 4, 2
14. 0, $-\frac{2}{3}$ **15.** 8, $\frac{1}{2}$ **16.** 15, −2 **17.** Answers may vary. Sample: Inverse is used when one quantity increases as the other quantity decreases.
18. Answers may vary. Sample:

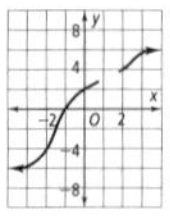

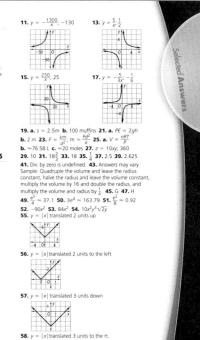

Lesson 8-1 pp. 498–505

Got It? 1. a. direct; $y = 40x$ **b.** inverse; $y = \frac{8}{x}$ **c.** neither **2. a.** $y = -\frac{56}{x}$
b.
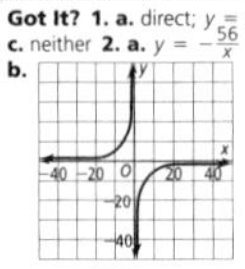
c. −28
3. a. $t = \frac{225}{n}$ **b.** 9 students **4.** 23 bags
5. a. 4018 joules **b.** 12 m; No, you need not calculate PE to find the height. Substitute the mass and height of the first diver, and the mass of the second diver in $PE = mgh$ and set the two expressions equal. Solve the equation for h to calculate the height of the second diver.
Lesson Check 1. inverse; $y = \frac{6}{x}$ **2.** direct; $y = 5x$
3. In direct variation, two positive quantities either increase together or decrease together. In an inverse variation, as one quantity increases, the other quantity decreases and vice versa. **4.** p varies directly with q, r, and t and inversely with s. **5.** d varies directly with the cube root of r and inversely with the square of t.
Exercises 7. neither **9.** inverse; $y = \frac{0.3}{x}$

11. $y = -\frac{1300}{x}$; −130
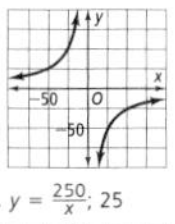
13. $y = \frac{5}{x}$; $\frac{1}{2}$
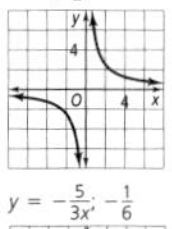
15. $y = \frac{250}{x}$; 25
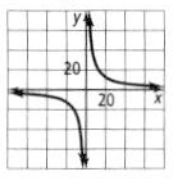
17. $y = -\frac{5}{3x}$; $-\frac{1}{6}$
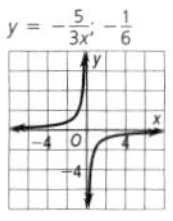
19. a. $s = 2.5m$ **b.** 100 muffins **21. a.** $PE = 2gh$
b. 2 m **23.** $F = \frac{km}{d^2}$; $m = \frac{Fd^2}{k}$ **25. a.** $V = \frac{nRT}{P}$
b. ≈76.58 L **c.** ≈20 moles **27.** $z = 10xy$; 360
29. 10 **31.** $18\frac{2}{3}$ **33.** 18 **35.** $\frac{1}{4}$ **37.** 2.5 **39.** 2.625
41. Div. by zero is undefined. **43.** Answers may vary. Sample: Quadruple the volume and leave the radius constant, halve the radius and leave the volume constant, multiply the volume by 16 and double the radius, and multiply the volume and radius by $\frac{1}{4}$. **45.** G **47.** H
49. $\frac{e^5}{4} \approx 37.1$ **50.** $3e^4 \approx 163.79$ **51.** $\frac{e^2}{8} \approx 0.92$
52. $-90x^2$ **53.** $84x^2$ **54.** $10x^2y^3\sqrt{2y}$
55. $y = |x|$ translated 2 units up
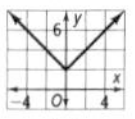
56. $y = |x|$ translated 2 units to the left
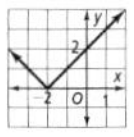
57. $y = |x|$ translated 3 units down
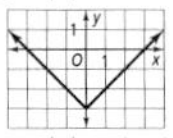
58. $y = |x|$ translated 3 units to the rt.
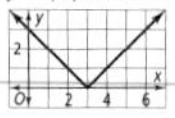

59. $y = |x|$ translated 4 units to the left and 5 units down
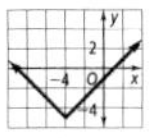
60. $y = |x|$ translated 10 units to the rt. and 7 units up
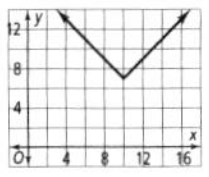

Lesson 8-2 pp. 507–514

Got It?
1. a.
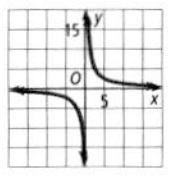
no x- or y-intercept; horizontal asymptote: $y = 0$; vertical asymptote: $x = 0$; domain: all real numbers except $x = 0$, range: all real numbers except $y = 0$
b. Yes; because all the functions have similar graphs.
2. a. $y = \frac{1}{2x}$ is a shrink of the graph of $y = \frac{1}{x}$ by a factor of $\frac{1}{2}$. **b.** $y = \frac{2}{x}$ is a stretch of the graph of $y = \frac{1}{x}$ by a factor of 2. **c.** $y = -\frac{1}{2x}$ is a reflection across the x-axis and a shrink of the graph of $y = \frac{1}{x}$ by a factor of $\frac{1}{2}$.
3.
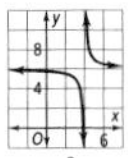
domain: all real numbers except $x = 4$, range: all real numbers except $y = 6$
4. $y = \frac{2}{x - 1} - 4$ **5. a.** $C = \frac{1200}{n}$; domain: whole numbers from 1 to 312; 160 students **b.** $C = \frac{1200}{n - 30}$; Domain: whole numbers from 1 to 282; 190 students
Lesson Check
1.
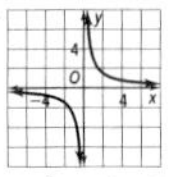
2. $y = \frac{1}{x}$ translated 5 units up **3.** $y = \frac{1}{x}$ reflected across the x-axis and stretched by a factor of 4 **4.** horizontal asymptote: $y = -7$, vertical asymptote: $x = -2$
5. shrink of the graph of $y = \frac{1}{x}$ by a factor of $\frac{1}{2}$

6. Answers may vary. Sample: $y = -\frac{2}{x}$ **7.** For $y = \frac{a}{x}$: stretch if $|a| > 1$ and shrink if $0 < |a| < 1$
Exercises
9.
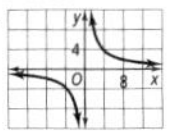
no x- or y-intercept; horizontal asymptote: $y = 0$, vertical asymptote: $x = 0$; domain: all real numbers except $x = 0$, range: all real numbers except $y = 0$
11.
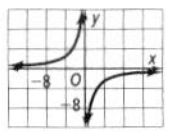
no x- or y-intercept; horizontal asymptote: $y = 0$, vertical asymptote: $x = 0$; domain: all real numbers except $x = 0$, range: all real numbers except $y = 0$
13.
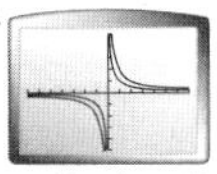
stretch by a factor of 2
15.
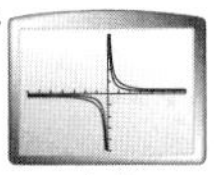
compression by a factor of 0.5
17.
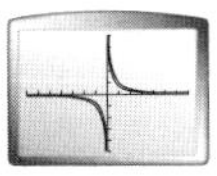
compression by a factor of 0.75
19.
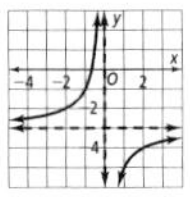
domain: all real numbers except $x = 0$, range: all real numbers except $y = -3$
21.
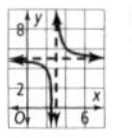
domain: all real numbers except $x = 3$, range: all real numbers except $y = 4$
23.
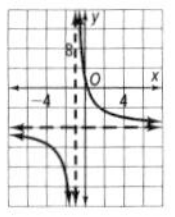
domain: all real numbers except $x = -1$, range: all real numbers except $y = -8$

25.
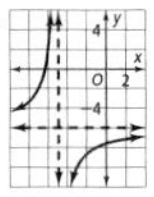
domain: all real numbers except $x = -5$, range: all real numbers except $y = -6$
27. $y = \frac{2}{x + 2} + 3$ **29.** 7.67 ft
33.
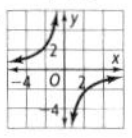
35.
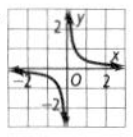
37. Answers may vary. Sample: The graph of the translation looks similar to the graph of $y = \frac{1}{x}$, so knowing the asymptotes helps to position the translation; check students' work.
39.
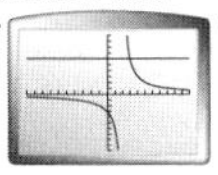
; (3, 6)
41.
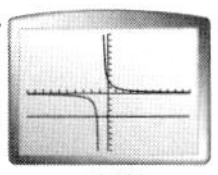
; (−1.75, −4)
43. a. $m = \frac{10{,}000}{g}$
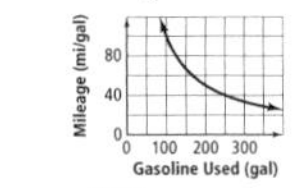

b. $m = \frac{10{,}000}{g - 50}$ **c.** 25 mi/gal; 28.57 mi/gal
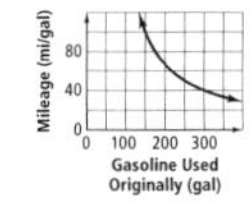

45. The branches of $y = \frac{1}{x^2}$ are in Quadrants I and II. The branches of $y = \frac{1}{x}$ are in Quadrants I and III. The graphs intersect at (1, 1). The graph of $y = \frac{1}{x^2}$ is closer to the x-axis for $x > 1$, and the graph of $y = \frac{1}{x}$ is closer to the y-axis for $0 < x < 1$. **47.** $y = \frac{16}{x}$, $y = -\frac{16}{x}$
49. A **51.** A
53. $81 = 27b^{-1}$
$81 = \frac{27}{b}$
$b = \frac{27}{81}$
$b = \frac{1}{3}$
54. $y = \frac{24}{x}$; $-\frac{24}{5}$ **55.** $y = \frac{50}{x}$; −10 **56.** $y = \frac{48}{x}$; $-\frac{48}{5}$
57. exponential growth; 3 **58.** exponential growth; 0.1
59. exponential decay; 5 **60.** exponential decay; 3
61. $79 - 20\sqrt{3}$ **62.** 6 **63.** −2 **64.** $(x - 4)(x - 2)$
65. $(x + 9)(x - 3)$ **66.** $(2x - 7)(x + 4)$
67. $(2x - 3)(x - 8)$

Lesson 8-3 pp. 515–523

Got It? 1. a. domain: all real numbers except $x = 4$ and $x = -4$; points of discontinuity: non-removable at $x = 4$ and $x = -4$; no x-intercept, y-intercept: $\left(0, -\frac{1}{16}\right)$
b. domain: all real numbers; no points of discontinuity; x-intercepts: (1, 0) and (−1, 0), y-intercept: $\left(0, -\frac{1}{3}\right)$
c. domain: all real numbers except $x = -2$ and $x = -1$; points of discontinuity: non-removable at $x = -2$, removable at $x = -1$; no x-intercept, y-intercept: $\left(0, \frac{1}{2}\right)$ **2. a.** $x = 1$ and $x = -3$ **b.** $x = -3$ **c.** no vertical asymptotes **3. a.** $y = -2$ **b.** $y = 0$ **c.** no horizontal asymptote
4.
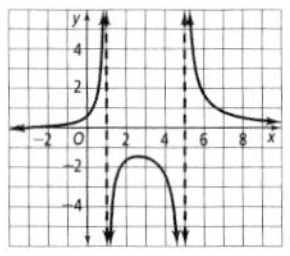
5. a. 4 gal **b.** No, because the graph changes when $y_1 = 0.8$ and intersects the graph of $y_2 = \frac{2 + (0.1)x}{2 + x}$ at $x \approx 0.6$. So, to have 80% orange juice, about 0.6 gal should be added.
Lesson Check 1. $x = -5$ and $x = -4$ **2.** $x = 9$ and $x = -2$ **3.** $x = -1$ **4.** $x = \frac{1}{3}$ and $x = 2$ **5.** $x = -5$

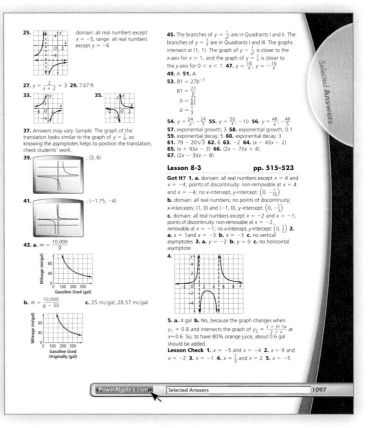

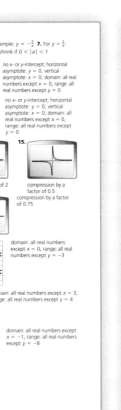

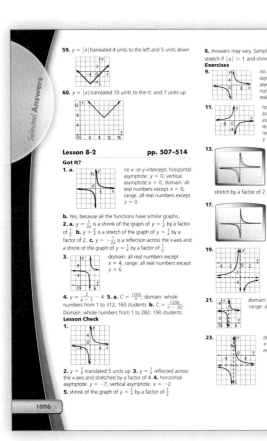

Selected Answers

6. $x = -2$ and $x = -3$ 7. $x = 1$
8. $x = 1$ and $x = -3$

9. 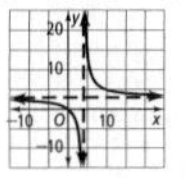
10. 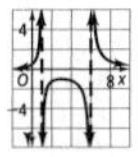

11. the function is undefined at $x = 1$ and $x = -3$
12. degree 2; function is discontinuous at 2 values of x
Exercises 13. domain: all real numbers except $x = 0$ and $x = 2$; points of discontinuity: non-removable at $x = 0$ and $x = 2$; no x- or y-intercept **15.** domain: all real numbers except $x = \pm 1$; pts. of discontinuity: non-removable at $x = -1$, removable at $x = 1$; no x-intercept; y-intercept: (0, 3) **17.** vertical asymptote at $x = -2$
19. vertical asymptotes at $x = -\frac{3}{2}$ and $x = 1$
21. hole at $x = -2$ **23.** $y = 0$ **25.** $y = 1$ **27.** $y = 0$

29. 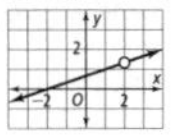
31. 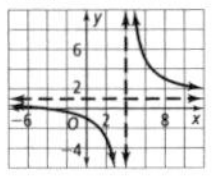
33. 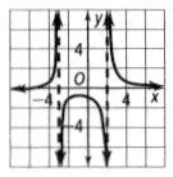

35. 900 ml **37.** vertical asymptote at $x = -2$
39. 6 free throws
41. correct answer: vertical asymptotes: $x = -5$ and $x = -1$, horizontal asymptote: $y = 1$

43. 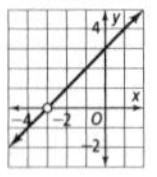
45. 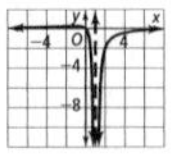

47. Answers may vary. Sample: There is no value of x for which the denominator equals 0.
49. Answers may vary. Samples: **a.** $y = \frac{x^2 - 7x + 12}{x^2 + 2x - 3}$ **b.** $y = \frac{x + 4}{x^2 - 3x}$ **c.** $y = \frac{3(x + 1)^2}{x^2 - 4}$ **51.** 8 **53.** $\frac{2}{3}$

55. 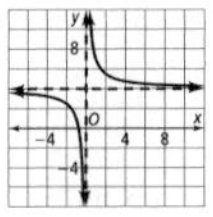
domain: all real numbers except $x = 0$, range: all real numbers except $y = 4$

56. 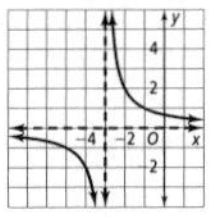
domain: all real numbers except $x = -3$, range: all real numbers except $y = 0$

57. 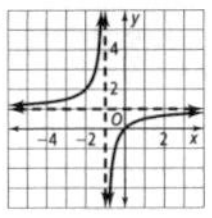
domain: all real numbers except $x = -1$, range: all real numbers except $y = 1$

58. 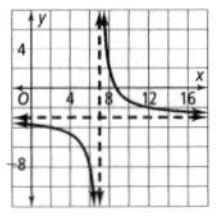
domain: all real numbers except $x = 7$, range: all real numbers except $y = -3$

59. 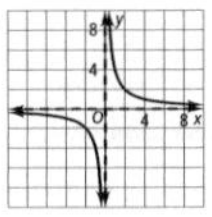
domain: all real numbers except $x = 0$, range: all real numbers except $y = 0$

60. 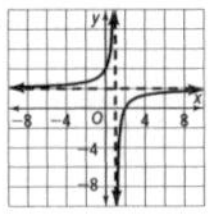
domain: all real numbers except $x = 1$, range: all real numbers except $y = 2$

61. $y = \frac{x + 3}{2}$; yes **62.** $y = 6 - x$; yes **63.** $y = \pm\sqrt{\frac{x}{2}}$; no **64.** $y = \pm\sqrt{5x}$; no **65.** $y = \frac{1}{x} - 2$; yes
66. $y = (x - 1)^2 + 2$; yes
67. $a < 10\frac{2}{3}$

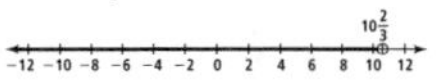

68. $x \geq 36$

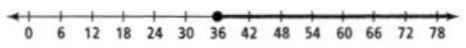

69. $x \geq 17\frac{4}{5}$

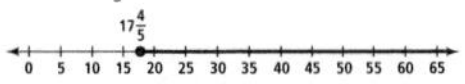

70. $y > 4$

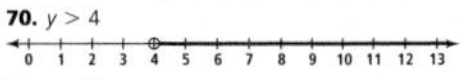

71. $x < 3$

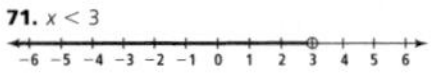

72. $b < 5$

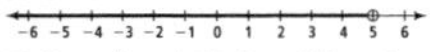

73. $(2x - 1)(x - 1)$ **74.** $(2x - 3)(2x + 3)$
75. $(5x + 1)(x + 1)$ **76.** $10(x - 1)(x + 1)$

Lesson 8-4 pp. 527–533

Got It? 1. a. $-\frac{4x}{y}$; $x \neq 0, y \neq 0$ **b.** $\frac{x + 4}{x - 3}$; $x \neq 2$ or 3 **c.** $-\frac{4}{x + 3}$; $x \neq \pm 3$ **2.** $\frac{2(x + 1)}{(x + 4)^2}$; $x \neq \pm 4$ **3. a.** $\frac{2x}{x - 1}$; $x \neq 1, -1, -4, 0,$ or 3 **b.** 6 restrictions; 2 in each of the original denominators, and 2 in the denominator of the reciprocal of the second rational expression. **4.** a square
Lesson Check 1. $\frac{z - 3}{2(z + 3)}$; $z \neq -3$ **2.** $\frac{3}{x}$; $x \neq 0$ or 1 **3.** $\frac{3(x + 5)}{x + 3}$; $x \neq -3, -6,$ or 2
4. $-\frac{x + 6}{x + 2}$; $x \neq -6, -2, 2, 3,$ or 5 **5.** Yes; the numerator and denominator are polynomials with no common factor. **6.** No; $x = 2$ will make the denominator of $\frac{x}{x - 2}$ 0, so $x = 2$ is not a solution. There is no solution to the eq.
7. Length $= \frac{2(a + 8)}{a + 5}$, $-10 < a < -5, a \neq -8$
Exercises 9. $\frac{1}{2x - 1}$; $x \neq 0$ or $\frac{1}{2}$ **11.** $7 - z$; $z \neq -7$
13. $-\frac{x + 4}{x - 5}$; $x \neq 5$ or 3 **15.** $\frac{xy^5}{4}$; $x \neq 0, y \neq 0$
17. $-\frac{4(x + 6)}{3(3x + 8)}$; $x \neq 3$ or $-\frac{8}{3}$ **19.** 1; $x \neq -2, -1, 2,$ or 3

21. $\frac{y}{2x^2}$; $x \neq 0, y \neq 0$ **23.** 1; $y \neq -2$ or 4 **25.** $\frac{4(y - 3)}{y(y + 5)}$; $y \neq 2, -5,$ or 0 **27.** $\frac{x - 8}{x - 10}$; $x \neq -3$ or 10
29. $\frac{y(y + 3)}{12(y + 4)}$; $x \neq 0, y \neq -4$ or 3
31. $R_{cylinder} = \frac{V_{cylinder}}{SA_{cylinder}} = \frac{rh}{2(r + h)}$; $R_{cube} = \frac{V_{cube}}{SA_{cube}} = \frac{s}{6}$; if $r = h = s$, then $R_{cylinder} = \frac{r}{4}$ and $R_{cube} = \frac{r}{6}$. $R_{cylinder} > R_{cube}$. The cylindrical shaped box is more efficient. If $s = h = 2r$ (diameter), then $R_{cylindrical} = R_{cube}$. The boxes are equally efficient.
33. $\frac{18x}{(x + 9)(x + 3)}$; $x \neq -9, -3,$ or 3 **35.** $\frac{x + 1}{x - 1}$; $x \neq -\frac{1}{2}, \frac{1}{2}, 1,$ or -2 **37.** They are equally efficient.
39. never **41.** never **43.** 2; $x \neq -3$ or 1
45. a. $2x^n + 1$ **b.** 2 is a factor of $2x^n$, so $2x^n$ is even and $2x^n + 1$ is odd. **47.** $\frac{-3a^2b^2}{4}$; $a \neq 0, a \neq b, b \neq 0$
49. $\frac{(x + 1)(x + 5)}{(x - 3)(x + 4)}$; $x \neq 3, -3, -4, 1,$ or -5 **51.** H
53.
$$-x \log 3 = \log \frac{1}{243}$$
$$-x = \frac{\log \frac{1}{243}}{\log 3}$$
$$-x = -5$$
$$x = 5$$
54. hole at $x = 3$ **55.** vertical asymptotes at $x = -\frac{2}{3}$ and $x = -1$ **56.** hole at $x = 4$, vertical asymptote at $x = -3$ **57.** 3 **58.** -5 **59.** $\frac{3}{2}$ **60.** $\frac{3}{4}$ **61.** 49 **62.** 168
63. 2 **64.** $\frac{17}{38}$ **65.** $\frac{19}{75}$ **66.** $\frac{11}{72}$ **67.** $\frac{137}{180}$

Lesson 8-5 pp. 534–541

Got It? 1. a. $2(x + 2)(x - 3)$
b. $(x - 1)(x - 2)^2(x + 4)$ **2. a.** $\frac{x + 2}{x}$, $x \neq 1$ or 0
b. $\frac{2(x - 1)}{x^2 - 4}$; $x \neq \pm 2$ **c.** Yes, however the denominator could have to be factored more and there would be additional, incorrect limitations on x. **3. a.** $\frac{x - 2}{x - 1}$, $x \neq 1$ or 2 **b.** $\frac{x^2 - x - 4}{x^2 + 6x + 5}$; $x \neq -5$ or -1 **4. a.** $\frac{x^2y}{x + y}$
b. $\frac{(x - 1)^2}{2x}$; $x \neq 0, -2,$ or ± 1 **5.** Option 1 still gives the better combined mpg since Option 3 gives 18.46 mpg.
Lesson Check 1. $\frac{2a - 10}{3a - 5}$; $a \neq \frac{5}{3}$ **2.** $\frac{6x - 11}{x^2 - 4}$; $x \neq \pm 2$
3. $\frac{-11m}{3m + 6}$; $m \neq -2$ **4.** $\frac{-4(2b - 5)}{(b - 4)(b + 4)(b - 2)}$; $b \neq 2$ or ± 4

Selected Answers

5. error in finding a common denominator:
$$\frac{1 + \frac{1}{x}}{\frac{3}{x}} = \frac{\frac{x + 1}{x}}{\frac{3}{x}} = \frac{x + 1}{x} \cdot \frac{x}{3} = \frac{x + 1}{3}$$
6. Answers may vary. Sample: $\frac{x^2 - 1}{x^2 - 6x + 5}$, $\frac{x^2 + 6x + 5}{x^2 - 25}$
Exercises 7. $9(x + 2)(2x - 1)$ **9.** $5(y + 4)(y - 4)$
11. $\frac{1}{x}$; $x \neq 0$ **13.** $\frac{-3}{x}$; $x \neq 0$ **15.** $\frac{xy + 8y + 4}{2xy^2}$; $x \neq 0, y \neq 0$ **17.** $\frac{y - 6}{2(y + 2)}$; $y \neq -2$
19. $\frac{-x + 6}{(x - 3)(x + 3)}$; $x \neq \pm 3$ **21.** $\frac{-2x(x + 3)}{(x - 2)(x - 1)(x + 1)}$; $x \neq \pm 1$ or 2 **23.** $\frac{15}{28}$ **25.** $\frac{b}{9}$ **27.** $\frac{3x}{2 + xy}$ **29.** $\frac{3}{x - 6}$
31. $\frac{3x - 8}{4x^2}$; $x \neq 0$ **33.** $\frac{7x - 17}{(x - 3)(x + 3)}$; $x \neq \pm 3$
35. $\frac{x(3x^2 + x - 1)}{x^2 - 2}$; $x \neq \pm\sqrt{2}$ **37.** 3.84 in. **39.** Yes; when you add, subtract, multiply, or divide rational expressions you get another rational expression. The restriction is that you must divide by a nonzero rational expression. **41.** $\frac{3x + 2y}{7x - 5y}$ **43.** x **45. a.** $\frac{2}{3}$ **b.** $\frac{3}{5}$ **c.** $\frac{2}{3}$ **d.** $\frac{1}{3}$
47. a. ≈1.18 ohms **b.** 6 ohms, 6 ohms, 3 ohms
49. G **51.** F **53.** $\frac{12x}{x + 3}$; $x \neq 2$ or ± 3
54. $\frac{3(x + 2)}{4(x - 3)}$; $x \neq \pm 2$ or 3 **55.** $\frac{3(x + 1)}{2(x + 3)}$; $x \neq \pm 1$ or -3
56. $\log_3 yt^4$ **57.** $\log p^7q^2$ **58.** $\log_5 \frac{x}{\sqrt[5]{y}}$ **59.** 30
60. 82 **61.** $\frac{15}{4}$ **62.** 101 **63.** $-\frac{4}{5}$ **64.** 21 **65.** 18

Lesson 8-6 pp. 542–548

Got It? 1. a. 1 **b.** 0 **2. a.** ≈4.47 m/h **b.** The direction of wind affects the speed (rate) of the bike. Since the speed is inversely related to time, change in speed will lead to change in time. Since there is no wind, the speed of the bike will remain same to and from the store, hence the time to and from the store will remain the same. **3.** $0.\overline{27}$
Lesson Check 1. 5 **2.** -1 **3.** -2 **4.** 310 mi/h
5. LCD was not found. The correct answer is
$$\frac{35 + 9x}{7x} = \frac{28(7)}{7x}, x \neq 0$$
$$9x = 161$$
$$x = \frac{161}{9} = 17.\overline{8}$$
6. Answers may vary. Sample: $\frac{2}{x - 3} + \frac{1}{x + 3} = \frac{5x}{x^2 - 9}$

7. Answers may vary. Sample: (1) Substitute the solution into the original equation. (2) Check to see if the solution is in the domain of the graph of the original equation.
Exercises 9. 10 **11.** 2 **13.** -1, 12 **15.** ≈-1.45, ≈1.65 **17.** $-3, -2$ **19.** 1 **21.** 0.6 **23.** 1.5 **25.** 1.75 **27.** ± 2
29. ≈1.69, ≈-0.44 **31.** $E = mc^2$ **33.** $c = \pm\sqrt{a^2 - b^2}$
35. $B = \pm\sqrt{\frac{2Vm}{r^2q}}$ **37.** $1\frac{5}{7}$ h **39.** 4 test scores **41. a.** \$2250 **b.** $\frac{15{,}000}{24 + x}(3.60)$ **c.** $2250 - \frac{15{,}000}{24 + x}(3.60)$ **d.** ≈32.7 mpg
43. 3 **45.** no solution **47.** no solution **49.** no solution
51. $1, -\frac{2}{3}$ **53.** Answers may vary. **55.** Answers may vary. **57.** D **59.** B **61.** $\frac{-y - 13}{4(y + 1)}$ **62.** $\frac{5xy - 12}{2y(y + 2)}$
63. $\frac{x^2 + 3}{2(x - 1)(x + 3)}$ **64.** $x = -3$ **65.** $x = -1$
66. $x = -0.875$ **67.** $y = \frac{5 - x}{2}$; yes **68.** $y = \pm\sqrt{x - 1}$; no **69.** $y = \sqrt[3]{x + 4}$; yes **70.** add 2; 9, 11, 13
71. subtract 2; $-10, -12, -14$ **72.** multiply by 5; 625, 3125, 15625 **73.** subtract 5; 30, 25, 20
74. multiply by 2; 128, 256, 512 **75.** subtract 4; $-19, -23, -27$

Chapter Review pp. 553–556

1. simplest form **2.** combined variation **3.** complex fraction **4.** point of discontinuity **5.** branch **6.** 12
7. $y = \frac{72}{x}$ **8.** $y = 6x$ **9.** $z = \frac{7}{4}xy$; 56 **10.** $z = \frac{4x}{y}$; 2

11. 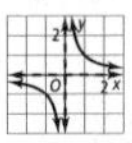
no x- or y-intercept; vert. asymptote: $x = 0$, horizontal asymptote: $y = 0$

12. 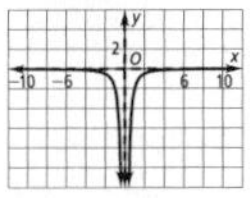
no x- or y-intercept; vert. asymptote: $x = 0$, horizontal asymptote: $y = 0$

13. 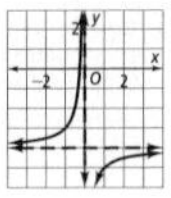
x-intercept: $(-0.25, 0)$, no y-intercept; vert. asymptote: $x = 0$, horizontal asymptote: $y = -4$

14. 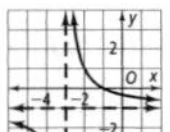
x-intercept: $(-1, 0)$, y-intercept: $(0, -\frac{1}{3})$; vert. asymptote: $x = -3$, horizontal asymptote: $y = -1$

15. $y = \frac{4}{x} + 3$ **16.** $y = \frac{4}{x - 2} + 2$ **17.** $y = \frac{4}{x + 3} - 4$
18. $y = \frac{4}{x - 4} - 3$
19. pts. of discontinuity: $x = -2, 1$;

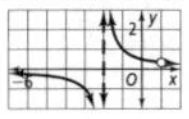

vert. asymptote: $x = -2$, horizontal asymptote: $y = 0$; hole at $x = 1$
20. $1, -1$

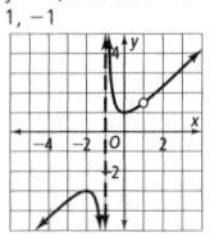

vert. asymptote: $x = -1$; hole at $x = 1$

21. no pts. of discontinuity

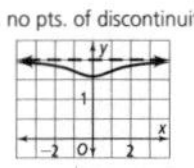

horizontal asymptote: $y = 2$

22. 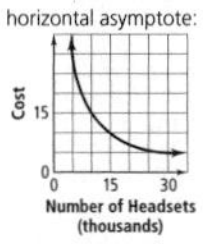

≈31,056 headsets

23. $\frac{x + 5}{x + 4}$; $x \neq -4$ or -5 **24.** $\frac{(x - 1)(x + 1)}{x + 3}$; $x \neq -4, -3,$ or 6 **25.** $\frac{(2x - 1)(x + 1)}{x + 4}$; $x \neq -4, -1,$ or 0
26. $\frac{r}{3}$, where r is the radius **27.** $\frac{3(3x - 4)}{(x - 2)(x + 2)}$; $x \neq \pm 2$
28. $\frac{-x^2 + 3x + 2}{x(x + 1)(x - 1)(x + 3)}$; $x \neq \pm 1, 0,$ or -3

29. $\frac{2(x - 1)}{3x - 1}$ **30.** $\frac{1}{4(x + y)}$ **31.** -1 **32.** no solution
33. $-12, 9$ **34.** you: 10 mi/h friend: 8 mi/h

Chapter 9

Get Ready! p. 561 1. 9, 11, 13, 15 **2.** 1, 6, 11, 16 **3.** 0.9, 1.1, 1.3, 1.5 **4.** $-2, -7, -12, -17$
5. $3\frac{1}{3}, 7\frac{1}{3}, 11\frac{1}{3}, 15\frac{1}{3}$ **6.** $-12, -15, -18, -21$ **7.** subtract 5; $-11, -16, -21$ **8.** mult. by 2; 16, 32, 64 **9.** alternate subtract 9 and add 1; $-7, -6, -15$ **10.** add 3; 19, 22, 25
11. $\frac{4}{3}$ **12.** $\frac{3}{4}$ **13.** $\frac{5}{3}$ **14.** $\frac{5}{18}$ **15.** Answers may vary. Sample: $f(x) = 2x - 1$; 1, 3, 5, 7, 9 **16.** Answers may vary. Sample: $g(x) = 1 - 2x$; $-1, -3, -5, -7, -9$; yes; common difference: -2 **17.** Answers may vary. Sample: $h(x) = 5(2)^x$; 10, 20, 40, 80, 160; yes; common ratio: 2

Lesson 9-1 pp. 564–571

Got It? 1. 147 **2. a.** $a_1 = 1$ and $a_n = na_{n-1}$ **b.** $a_1 = 1$ and $a_n = a_{n-1} + n^2$ **3. a.** $a_n = n^2 - 1$; 399 **b.** To find the nth term using an explicit formula, you simply substitute for n in the formula. To find the nth term using a recursive definition may require many iterations. **4.** 18 months
Lesson Check 1. 2, 7, 12, 17, 22 **2.** $-1, 0, 3, 8, 15$ **3.** $a_1 = 3$ and $a_n = 2a_{n-1}$ **4.** $a_n = 2 + 3n$ **5.** A recursive formula defines the terms in a sequence by relating each term after the first term to the one before it and requires that the previous term be known to find a given term. An example of a recursive formula for the sequence 8, 4, 2, 1, . . . is $a_1 = 8$ and $a_n = \frac{1}{2}a_{n-1}$. An explicit formula describes the nth term of a sequence using the variable n and only requires the number of the term to be known. An example of an explicit formula for the sequence 1, 3, 5, 7, . . . is $a_n = 2n - 1$.
6. The "+1" in $a_n = 3n + 1$ is incorrect for the sequence 1, 4, 7, 10, ... The correct explicit formula is $a_n = -2 + 3n$.
Exercises 7. 5, 8, 11, 14, 17, 20 **9.** $\frac{1}{2}, 1, \frac{3}{2}, 2, \frac{5}{2}, 3$
11. 2, 10, 24, 44, 70, 102 **13.** $-\frac{1}{2}, 3, \frac{25}{2}, 31, \frac{123}{2}, 107$
15. $a_1 = 80$ and $a_n = a_{n-1} - 3$ **17.** $a_1 = 0$ and $a_n = a_{n-1} + (n + 1)$ **19.** $a_1 = 100$ and $a_n = \frac{1}{10}a_{n-1}$
21. $a_1 = 4$ and $a_n = -2a_{n-1}$ **23.** $a_1 = 1$ and $a_n = a_{n-1} + n^2$ **25.** $a_n = 3n + 1$; 31 **27.** $a_n = \frac{n - 6}{2}$; 2
29. $a_n = n^2 + 1$; 101 **31.** $a_n = 3^{n-1}$; 19,683
33. 5 **35.** $\frac{5}{16}$ **37.** $\frac{9}{1024}$ **39.** -47 **41.** $-\frac{9}{8}$ **43.** recursive; 3, 9, 21, 45, 93 **45.** explicit; $-24, -21, -16, -9, 0$
47. explicit; $-6, -18, -38, -66, -102$ **49.** 25, 36, 49, 64

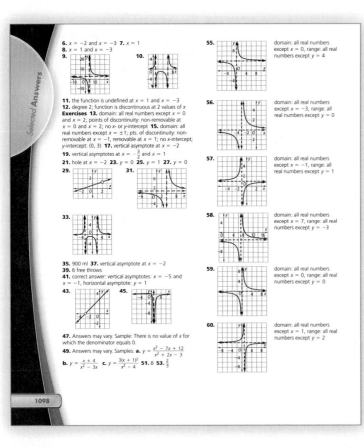

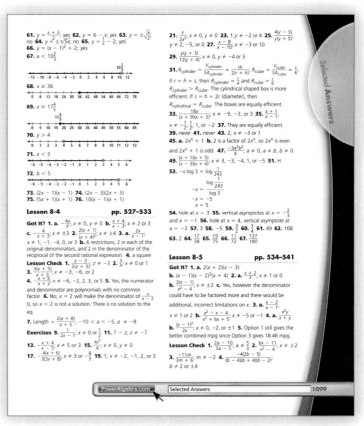

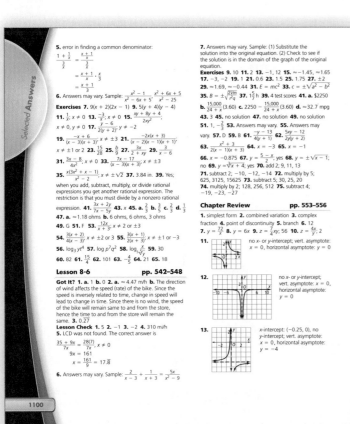

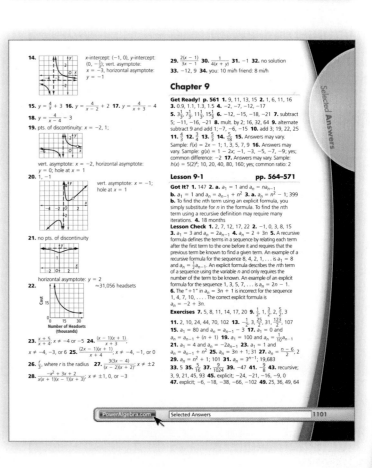

51. $\frac{16}{5}, \frac{25}{6}, \frac{36}{7}, \frac{49}{8}$ **53.** \$140 **55.** 20, 23; $a_n = 3n + 2$, explicit OR $a_n = a_{n-1} + 3$; $a_1 = 5$, recursive
57. 216, 343; $a_n = n^3$, explicit
59. 144, 169; $a_n = (n + 6)^2$, explicit OR $a_n = a_{n-1} + 2n + 11$, $a_1 = 49$, recursive **61.** $-1, -\frac{1}{2}$; $a_n = \frac{-32}{2^n}$, explicit OR $a_n = \frac{a_{n-1}}{2}$, $a_1 = -16$, recursive
63. $-11, -19$; $a_n = 29 - 8n$, explicit OR $a_n = a_{n-1} - 8$, $a_1 = 21$, recursive **65. a.** 25 boxes **b.** 110 boxes **c.** 9 levels **67.** $a_n = 10 \cdot 2^{n-1}$
69. $a_n = 1 + 4(n - 1)$ **71.** 34.9 **73.** 2.19 **75.** 36.5
76. 2 **77.** 4 **78.** -5 **79.** -1 **80.** 1 **81.** 2
82. subtract 2; $-2, -4, -6$
83. add 17; 185, 202, 219 **84.** add $\frac{3}{7}$; $\frac{17}{7}, \frac{20}{7}, \frac{23}{7}$

Lesson 9-2 pp. 572–577

Got It? 1. a. not arithmetic **b.** arithmetic **2. a.** 93 **b.** 95, 110 **3. a.** 115 **b.** yes, use the formula for arithmetic mean and solve for a_7, $a_7 = 2a_6 - a_5$ **4.** 65 seats
Lesson Check 1. 56 **2.** 87 **3.** 13 **4.** 39 **5.** In an arithmetic sequence, the diff. between any two consecutive terms is always the same number. **6.** Answers may vary. Sample: 2, 4, 8, 16, 32, . . .
Exercises 7. yes; 10 **9.** yes; 3 **11.** yes; 4 **13.** 127 **15.** 240 **17.** 12.5 **19.** -7 **21.** 13 **23.** 7.5 **25.** \$135 **27.** 18 **29.** 36 **31.** 2 **33.** The student multiplied the third term by 2 instead of adding 2. The correct answer is 6. **35.** 120 **37.** 1.1 **39.** 0
41. $a_n = 2 + 2(n - 1)$; $a_n = a_{n-1} + 2$, $a_1 = 2$
43. $a_n = -5 + 1(n - 1)$; $a_n = a_{n-1} + 1$, $a_1 = -5$
45. $a_n = -5 + 1.5(n - 1)$; $a_n = a_{n-1} + 1.5$, $a_1 = -5$
47. $a_n = 1 + \frac{1}{3}(n - 1)$; $a_n = a_{n-1} + \frac{1}{3}$, $a_1 = 1$
49. $a_n = 27 - 12(n - 1)$; $a_n = a_{n-1} - 12$, $a_1 = 27$
51. Answers may vary. Sample: An advantage of a recursive formula is that only the preceding term must be known to find the next term; a disadvantage is that many calculations may be required to find a term. An advantage of an explicit formula is that it is easy to find any term. Use the recursive formula when the previous term and common diff. are known. Use the explicit formula when the term number and common diff. are known. **53.** $-4, -10, -16$
55. $-8, -17, -26$ **57.** 17, 17, 17 **59.** $-12.5, -8, -3.5$
61. \$5055 **63.** 21st term **65.** 54 **67.** $a_1 = -1, d = 3$
69. $a_1 = 52, d = -10$ **71.** $a_1 = -100.5, d = 22$
73. $9k + 32$ **75.** D
77.

$$\frac{3}{(x-1)(x+1)} + \frac{4x(x-1)}{(x-1)(x+1)} = \frac{1.5(x+1)}{(x-1)(x+1)}, x \neq \pm 1$$
$$3 + 4x^2 - 4x = 1.5x + 1.5$$
$$4x^2 - 5.5x + 1.5 = 0$$
$$x^2 - \frac{11}{8}x + \frac{3}{8} = 0$$
$$(x - 1)\left(x - \frac{3}{8}\right) = 0$$
$$x = \frac{3}{8}$$

(Reject $x = 1$ because 1 is not in the domain.)
78. recursive; $-2, -7, -12, -17, -22$
79. explicit; 6, 18, 36, 60, 90 **80.** explicit; 0, 3, 8, 15, 24
81. recursive; $-121, -108, -95, -82, -69$
82. $y - 3 = \frac{8}{3}x$ or $y - 11 = \frac{8}{3}(x - 3)$
83. $y - 6 = 4(x - 4)$ or $y - 30 = 4(x - 10)$
84. $y - 10 = 8(x - 1)$ or $y - 42 = 8(x - 5)$
85. $r = \frac{\sqrt[3]{6\pi^2 V}}{2\pi}$ **86.** 32 **87.** 625 **88.** -81

Lesson 9-3 pp. 580–586

Got It? 1. a. yes; $a_1 = 2, r = 2$ **b.** no **c.** yes; $a_1 = 2^3$, $r = 2^4$ **2.** 6 or -6 **3. a.** explicit; it is easier to use because only one calculation is needed. **b.** about 16.8 cm, about 4 cm **4.** ± 60
Lesson Check 1. no **2.** yes; 2 **3.** 729 **4.** 0.0064
5. The third term would be the geometric mean of 5 and 80 which is 20. Since a is pos. and r^2 is always pos., the third term, ar^2, cannot be neg.
6. For both the arithmetic mean and the geometric mean, the middle term of any three consecutive terms can be determined using the first and last of the three terms. The arithmetic mean is the sum of the first and last terms divided by 2, whereas the geometric mean is the square root (or its opposite) of the product of the first and the last terms.
Exercises 7. yes; 2 **9.** yes; -2 **11.** yes; 0.4
13. yes; $-\frac{1}{3}$ **15.** yes; 1.5 **17.** yes; 6 **19.** 6561
21. 0.078125 **23.** $\frac{-3}{2048}$ **25.** about 656.1 g; about 182.5 g; about 96.2 g
27. ± 1530 **29.** ± 1.5 **31.** ± 6 **33.** $a_n = 100(-20)^{n-1}$; (100, -2000, 40,000, $-800{,}000$, 16,000,000
35. $a_n = 1024(0.5)^{n-1}$; 1024, 512, 256, 128, 64
37. $a_n = 10(-1)^{n-1}$; 10, -10, 10, -10, 10 **39.** arithmetic; 125, 150 **41.** geometric; -80, 160 **43.** neither; 25, 36
45. 7.5, 22.5, 67.5 or -7.5, 22.5, -67.5
47. $-6.64, -11.02, -18.30$ or $6.64, -11.02, 18.30$
49. about 74.3 mi **51.** 768 **53.** 3×4^{19} or 824,633,720,832 **55.** 4 **57.** 10 **59.** Both the common diff. and the common ratio are used to find the next term in a sequence, but a common diff. is added and a common ratio is multiplied. **61.** 7 **63.** B **65.** C **67.** $x \neq -1, -5$; there's a hole in the graph at $x = -1$. There's a vert. asymptote at $x = -5$.
68. $a_n = -3 + 3(n - 1)$; $a_n = a_{n-1} + 3$, $a_1 = -3$
69. $a_n = 17 - 9(n - 1)$; $a_n = a_{n-1} - 9$, $a_1 = 17$
70. $a_n = -2 - 11(n - 1)$; $a_n = a_{n-1} - 11$, $a_1 = -2$

71. $7\sqrt{14}$ **72.** $\frac{3\sqrt{3x}}{7x}$ **73.** $\frac{x}{y}$ **74.** $5\sqrt[3]{6}$ **75.** vert. asymptote: $x = -3$ **76.** vert. asymptote: $x = -1$
77. vert. asymptotes: $x = 0, 1$ **78.** vert. asymptote: $x = 3$; hole at $x = -3$ **79.** $a_n = a_{n-1} + n$, $a_1 = 1$
80. $a_n = a_{n-1} + (2n - 1)$, $a_1 = 1$
81. $a_n = a_{n-1} + n^2$, $a_1 = 1$

Lesson 9-4 pp. 587–593

Got It? 1. a. 1030 **b.** Yes; no; the sum of any number of even numbers is always even. The sum of an odd number of odd numbers is odd, but the sum of an even number of odd numbers is even. **2.** 59 sales; 1725 sales
3. a. $\sum_{n=1}^{40}(-12 + 7n)$ **b.** $\sum_{n=1}^{50}(510 - 10n)$ **4. a.** 2140 **b.** 100 **c.** 1 **5.** 41,650
Lesson Check 1. 91 **2.** 780 **3.** $\sum_{n=1}^{7} 3n$
4. $\sum_{n=1}^{12}(-3 + 4n)$ **5.** An arithmetic sequence is a list of numbers for which successive numbers have a common difference. **6.** The lower limit should not be 3, it should be one and the expression $5n - 2$ should be in parentheses. The correct summation notation is $\sum_{n=0}^{8}(3 + 5n)$. **7.** Yes; $44 = 2(a_1 + a_4)$, so any combination of a_1 and a_4 with a sum of 22 is a possible series.
Exercises 9. 92 **11.** 176 **13.** -165 **15.** $\sum_{n=1}^{5} 4n$
17. $\sum_{n=1}^{12}(2 + 3n)$ **19.** $\sum_{n=1}^{10}(-3n)$ **21.** 25 **23.** 20
25. -2 **27.** 2400 **29.** 682 **31.** -8556 **33.** 432 seats
35. sequence; finite **37.** series; infinite **39.** series; finite
41. -48 **43.** 35 **45.** -146 **47. a.** $a_n = n + 1$
b. $\sum_{n=1}^{9}(n + 1)$ **c.** 18 cans **d.** No; no; 13 rows have 104 cans, 14 rows have 119 cans, 15 rows have 135 cans, and 16 rows have 152 cans. The number of rows would not be an integer for 110 cans or 140 cans. **49.** -765
51. 300 **53.** 34 **55.** $10x + 45y$ **57.** C **59.** B
61. $\left(\frac{b}{2}\right)^2 = \left(\frac{10}{2}\right)^2 = 25$

$$x^2 + 10x + 25 = -35 + 25$$
$$(x + 5)^2 = -10$$
$$x + 5 = \pm i\sqrt{10}$$
$$x = -5 \pm i\sqrt{10}$$

62. $a_n = 2^{n-1}$; 1, 2, 4 **63.** $a_n = -1(-1)^{n-1}$; $-1, 1, -1$
64. $a_n = 3\left(\frac{3}{2}\right)^{n-1}$; 3, $\frac{9}{2}$, $\frac{27}{4}$ **65.** $\frac{x+3}{x-4}$; $x \neq 4, x \neq -1$
66. $\frac{c-2}{c-5}$; $c \neq 5, c \neq 6$ **67.** $\frac{z^2 + 12z + 20}{z - 1}$; $z \neq 1$, $z \neq 0$ **68.** $-\frac{1}{3}$ **69.** $\frac{3}{4}$ **70.** $-\frac{1}{2}$

Lesson 9-5 pp. 595–601

Got It? 1. a. 315 **b.** -1705 **2.** about \$2138.43
3. a. diverges **b.** converges; $\frac{1}{4}$ **c.** converges; 2 **d.** Yes; if $|r| < 1$, the series converges. If $|r| \geq 1$, the series diverges.
Lesson Check 1. $\frac{31}{80}$ **2.** $\frac{55}{9}$ **3.** converges **4.** diverges
5. Since $r = 1.1 > 1$, the series diverges and does not have a sum. **6.** An infinite geometric series has a sum only when the series converges, which is when $|r| < 1$.
7. The sum of a finite arithmetic series is $S_n = \frac{n}{2}(a_1 + a_n)$. The sum of finite geometric series is $S_n = \frac{a_1(1 - r^n)}{1 - r}$.
The formulas are similar in that each sum requires the first term and the number of terms in the series. The formulas are different in that the sum of a finite arithmetic series needs the last term, while the sum of a finite geometric series needs the common ratio.
Exercises 9. 1456 **11.** -5115 **13.** $\frac{15}{32}$ **15.** $\frac{121}{81}$
17. converges; $\frac{4}{3}$ **19.** converges; 8 **21.** diverges; no sum
23. diverges; no sum **25.** diverges; no sum **27.** 1 **29.** $\frac{9}{2}$
31. $\frac{9}{5}$ **33.** arithmetic; 420 **35.** geometric; about 96.47
37. geometric; about 121.5
39. a.

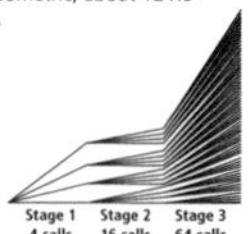

Stage 1
4 calls
Stage 2
16 calls
Stage 3
64 calls

b. $4 + 16 + 64 + 256 + 1024 + 4096$
c. 5460 employees **41.** $\frac{5}{4}$ **43.** $\frac{3}{4}$ **45.** $0.8\overline{3}$ **47. a.** $\frac{7}{8}$
b. 10 **49. a.** Answers may vary. Sample: The student used $r - 1$ instead of $1 - r$ in the formula for the sum of an infinite geometric series. **b.** $\frac{1}{2}$
51. a. $rS_n = r(a_1 + a_1r + \cdots + a_1r^{n-1}) = a_1r + a_1r^2 + \cdots + a_1r^n$
b. $S_n - rS_n = a_1 + a_1r + a_1r^2 + \cdots + a_1r^{n-1} - a_1r - a_1r^2 - \cdots - a_1r^{n-1} - a_1r^n = a_1 - a_1r^n$
c. $S_n - rS_n = a_1 - a_1r^n$

$$S_n(1 - r) = a_1 - a_1r^n$$
$$S_n = \frac{a_1 - a_1r^n}{1 - r} = \frac{a_1(1 - r^n)}{1 - r}$$

53. $a_1 = \frac{9}{10}, r = \frac{1}{10}; S = \frac{\frac{9}{10}}{1 - \frac{1}{10}} = 1$ **55.** $\frac{2}{3}$ **57.** 1.11
59. 140 **60.** -825 **61.** $\frac{7c - 4}{2c^2}$ **62.** $\frac{10(2y + 3)}{(y + 3)(y - 3)}$

63. $\frac{x^2 + 6x + 4}{(x + 6)(x - 6)}$ **64.** 0 **65.** 2 **66.** 1
67.
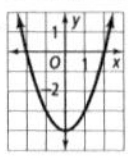
68.
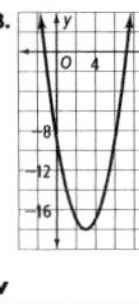
69.
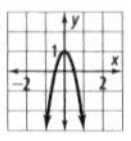

Chapter Review pp. 603–606

1. limits **2.** sequence **3.** converges **4.** common ratio
5. explicit formula **6.** 1, -1, -3, -5, -7
7. 1, 0, -3, -8, -15 **8.** 2, 3, 5, 9, 17 **9.** 20, 10, 5, 2.5, 1.25 **10.** $a_n = a_{n-1} + 17$, $a_1 = 5$ **11.** $a_n = a_{n-1} + 9$, $a_1 = -2$ **12.** $a_n = 3n - 2$ **13.** $a_n = 6.5 - 2.5n$ **14.** no
15. yes; $d = 15$, $a_{32} = 468$ **16.** yes; $d = 3$, $a_{32} = 100$
17. no **18.** 5 **19.** 101.5 **20.** 5 **21.** -4.9
22. $-10.5, -8, -5.5$ **23.** 1.4, 0.8, 0.2
24. $a_n = -2 + 9(n - 1)$ **25.** $a_n = 62 - 3(n - 1)$
26. yes; $r = \frac{1}{2}$; $\frac{1}{16}, \frac{1}{32}$ **27.** no **28.** yes; $r = 1.2$; 6.2208, 7.46496 **29.** ± 6 **30.** ± 0.04
31. $\pm 10, -5, \pm 2.5$ **32.** $a_n = 2^{n-1}$
33. $a_n = 25\left(\frac{1}{5}\right)^{n-1}$ **34.** 2560 **35.** 1536
36. $\sum_{n=1}^{5}(13 - 3n)$; 20 **37.** $\sum_{n=1}^{7}(45 + 5n)$; 455
38. $\sum_{n=1}^{11}(4.6 + 1.4n)$; 143 **39.** $\sum_{n=1}^{8}(23 - 2n)$; 112
40. 3; -8, 26; 27 **41.** 9; 4, 8; 54 **42.** 31 **43.** $53\frac{1}{8}$
44. $14\frac{7}{18}$ **45.** converges; $S = 187.5$ **46.** diverges
47. diverges **48.** converges; $S = 2$

Chapter 10

Get Ready! p. 611

1.
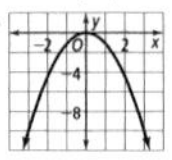
2.
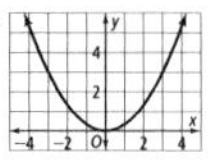
3.
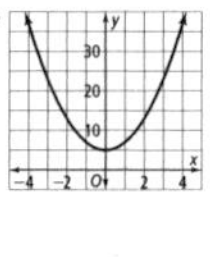
4.
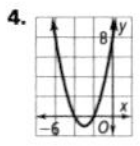

5. quadratic; $-x^2$, $6x$, 1 **6.** linear; none, $-12x$, -18
7. linear; none, x, $-\frac{13}{2}$ **8.** quadratic; $-8x^2$, $28x$, none
9. quadratic; $-2x^2$, $-3x$, 6 **10.** linear; none, $-x$, -10
11. 16 **12.** $\frac{25}{4}$ **13.** 49
14. $y = (x + 3)^2 - 2$
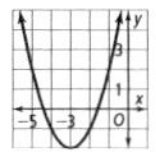
15. $y = 2(x - 1)^2 + 8$
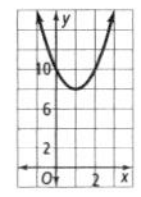
16. $y = -3\left(x - \frac{1}{6}\right)^2 + \frac{1}{12}$
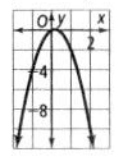
17.
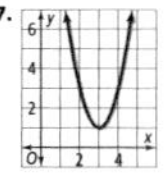
18.
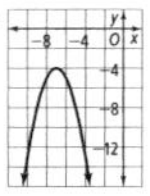
19.
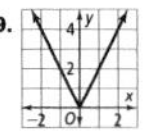
20.
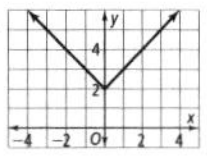

21. The radius of a circle is the distance from the center of the circle to any pt. on the circle. The radius extends in every direction from the center and ends on the circle. All radii of the same circle are equal. **22.** The vertex of a parabola is the lowest or highest pt. of a parabola; it is the pt. where the parabola changes direction.

Lesson 10-1 pp. 614–621

Got It?
1. a.
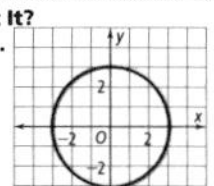
circle: center (0,0); radius 3; lines of sym.: every line through the origin; domain: $-3 \leq x \leq 3$, range: $-3 \leq y \leq 3$

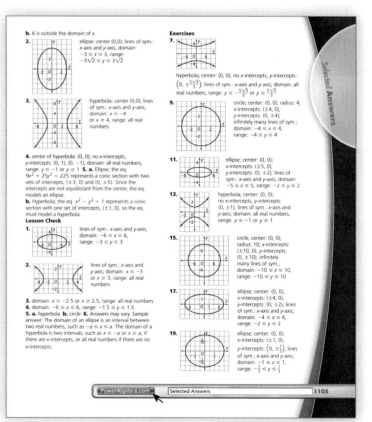

b. 6 is outside the domain of x.
2.
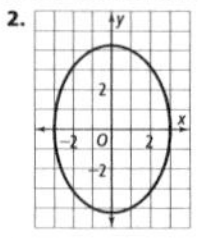
ellipse: center (0,0); lines of sym.: x-axis and y-axis; domain: $-3 \leq x \leq 3$, range: $-3\sqrt{2} \leq y \leq 3\sqrt{2}$
3.
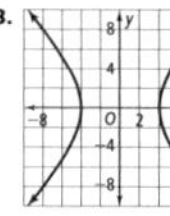
hyperbola: center (0,0); lines of sym.: x-axis and y-axis; domain: $x \leq -4$ or $x \geq 4$, range: all real numbers

4. center of hyperbola: (0, 0); no x-intercepts, y-intercepts: (0, 1), (0, -1); domain: all real numbers, range: $y \leq -1$ or $y \geq 1$ **5. a.** Ellipse; the eq. $9x^2 + 25y^2 = 225$ represents a conic section with two sets of intercepts, (± 3, 0) and (0, ± 5). Since the intercepts are not equidistant from the center, the eq. models an ellipse.
b. Hyperbola; the eq. $x^2 - y^2 = 1$ represents a conic section with one set of intercepts, (± 1, 0), so the eq. must model a hyperbola.
Lesson Check
1.
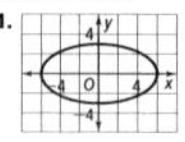
lines of sym.: x-axis and y-axis; domain: $-6 \leq x \leq 6$, range: $-3 \leq y \leq 3$
2.
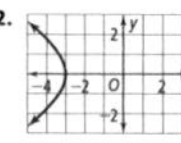
lines of sym.: x-axis and y-axis; domain: $x \leq -3$ or $x \geq 3$, range: all real numbers

3. domain: $x \leq -2.5$ or $x \geq 2.5$, range: all real numbers
4. domain: $-6 \leq x \leq 6$, range: $-1.5 \leq y \leq 1.5$
5. a. hyperbola **b.** circle **6.** Answers may vary. Sample answer: The domain of an ellipse is an interval between two real numbers, such as $-a \leq x \leq a$. The domain of a hyperbola is two intervals, such as $x \leq -a$ or $x \geq a$, if there are x-intercepts, or all real numbers if there are no x-intercepts.

Exercises
7.
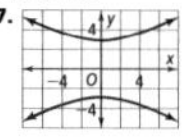
hyperbola; center: (0, 0); no x-intercepts, y-intercepts: $\left(0, \pm\frac{5\sqrt{3}}{3}\right)$; lines of sym.: x-axis and y-axis; domain: all real numbers, range: $y \leq -\frac{5\sqrt{3}}{3}$ or $y \geq \frac{5\sqrt{3}}{3}$
9.
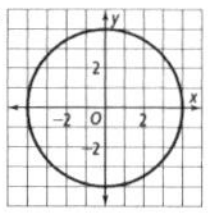
circle; center: (0, 0); radius: 4; x-intercepts: (± 4, 0), y-intercepts: (0, ± 4); infinitely many lines of sym.; domain: $-4 \leq x \leq 4$, range: $-4 \leq y \leq 4$
11.
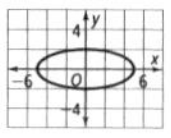
ellipse; center: (0, 0); x-intercepts: (± 5, 0), y-intercepts: (0, ± 2); lines of sym.: x-axis and y-axis; domain: $-5 \leq x \leq 5$, range: $-2 \leq y \leq 2$
13.
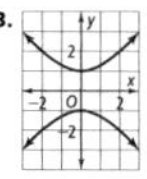
hyperbola; center: (0, 0); no x-intercepts, y-intercepts: (0, ± 1); lines of sym.: x-axis and y-axis; domain: all real numbers, range: $y \leq -1$ or $y \geq 1$
15.
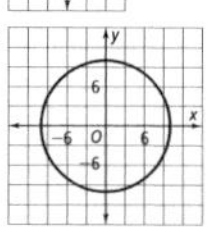
circle; center: (0, 0); radius: 10; x-intercepts: (± 10, 0), y-intercepts: (0, ± 10); infinitely many lines of sym.; domain: $-10 \leq x \leq 10$, range: $-10 \leq y \leq 10$
17.
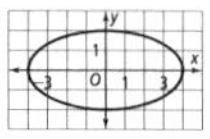
ellipse; center: (0, 0); x-intercepts: (± 4, 0), y-intercepts: (0, ± 2); lines of sym.: x-axis and y-axis; domain: $-4 \leq x \leq 4$, range: $-2 \leq y \leq 2$
19.
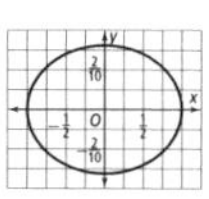
ellipse; center: (0, 0); x-intercepts: (± 1, 0), y-intercepts: $\left(0, \pm\frac{1}{3}\right)$; lines of sym.: x-axis and y-axis; domain: $-1 \leq x \leq 1$, range: $-\frac{1}{3} \leq y \leq \frac{1}{3}$

21. 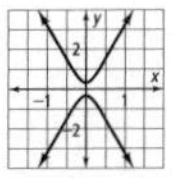
hyperbola; center: (0, 0); no x-intercepts, y-intercepts: $\left(0, \pm\frac{1}{2}\right)$; lines of sym.: x-axis and y-axis; domain: all real numbers, range: $y \le -\frac{1}{2}$ or $y \ge \frac{1}{2}$

23. hyperbola; center: (0, 0); no x-intercepts, y-intercepts: $(0, \pm 2)$; domain: all real numbers, range: $y \le -2$ or $y \ge 2$ **25.** hyperbola; center: (0, 0); x-intercepts: $(\pm 3, 0)$, no y-intercepts; domain: $x \le -3$ or $x \ge 3$, range: all real numbers **27.** hyperbola; center: (0, 0); no x-intercepts, y-intercepts: $(0, \pm 3)$; domain: all real numbers, range: $y \le -3$ or $y \ge 3$ **29.** 22
31. 24 **33.** 27

35. 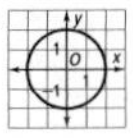
circle; center: (0, 0); radius: 2; x-intercepts: $(\pm 2, 0)$, y-intercepts: $(0, \pm 2)$; infinitely many lines of sym.; domain: $-2 \le x \le 2$, range: $-2 \le y \le 2$

37. 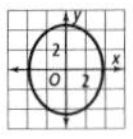
ellipse; center: (0, 0); x-intercepts: $\left(\pm\frac{8\sqrt{5}}{5}, 0\right)$, y-intercepts: $(0, \pm 2\sqrt{5})$; lines of sym.: x-axis and y-axis; domain: $-\frac{8\sqrt{5}}{5} \le x \le \frac{8\sqrt{5}}{5}$, range: $-2\sqrt{5} \le y \le 2\sqrt{5}$

39. a. All lines in the plane that pass through the center of a circle are axes of sym. of the circle. **b.** The axes of sym. of an ellipse intersect at the center of the ellipse. The same is true for a hyperbola. This can be confirmed using, for example, $4x^2 + 9y^2 = 36$ and $4x^2 - 9y^2 = 36$.

41. 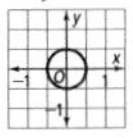
$x^2 + y^2 = \frac{1}{4}$

43. 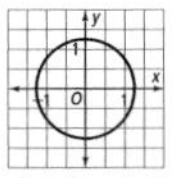
$x^2 + y^2 = 1.5625$

45. Sample: $(\sqrt{2}, 1)$ **47.** Sample: (2, 0) **49.** $(0, -\sqrt{7})$
51. Answers may vary.

53. a. **b.** 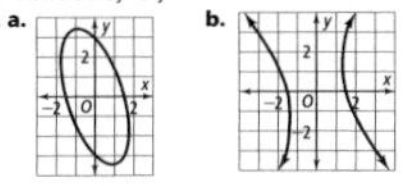

55. I **57.** H **59.** diverges **60.** diverges **61.** converges
62. $x^3 - 3x^2y + 3xy^2 - y^3$

63. $p^6 + 6p^5q + 15p^4q^2 + 20p^3q^3 + 15p^2q^4 + 6pq^5 + q^6$ **64.** $x^4 - 8x^3 + 24x^2 - 32x + 16$
65. $243 - 405x + 270x^2 - 90x^3 + 15x^4 - x^5$

66.

x	−2	−1	0	1	2
y	2	1	0	1	2

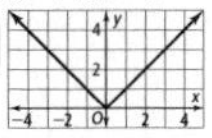

67.

x	−2	−1	0	1	2
y	5	4	3	4	5

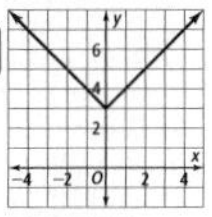

68.

x	0	1	2	3	4
y	2	1	0	1	2

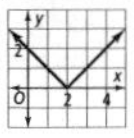

69.

x	−3	−2	−1	0	1
y	−2	−3	−4	−3	−2

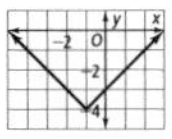

Lesson 10-2 pp. 622–629

Got It? 1. a. $y = -\frac{1}{6}x^2$ **b.** vertex: (0, 0); focus: (0, 1); directrix: $y = -1$ **c.** As the distance between the vertex and focus increases, the width of the parabola increases. **2. a.** $x = \frac{1}{10}y^2$ **b.** vertex: (0, 0); focus: $\left(-\frac{1}{16}, 0\right)$; directrix: $x = \frac{1}{16}$ **3.** 1 cm **4.** vertex: (−4, 2); focus: $\left(-4, 2\frac{1}{4}\right)$; directrix: $y = 1\frac{3}{4}$ **5.** $y = \frac{1}{8}(x - 1)^2 + 4$
Lesson Check 1. $y = \frac{1}{2}x^2$ **2.** $x = \frac{1}{4}(y - 2)^2 + 3$
3. vertex: (0, 0); focus: (4, 0); directrix: $x = -4$
4. vertex: (−3, −4); focus: (−3, −3.75); directrix: $y = -4.25$ **5.** 6 units **6.** With the focus one unit away from the vertex of a parabola at the origin, $c = \pm 1$. Given this information, the student cannot tell whether the parabola opens in the vert. direction, with one of the eqs. $y = \frac{1}{4}x^2$ or $y = -\frac{1}{4}x^2$, or whether the parabola opens in the horizontal direction, with one of the eqs. of $x = \frac{1}{4}y^2$ or $x = -\frac{1}{4}y^2$.
Exercises 7. $x = \frac{1}{24}y^2$ **9.** $y = \frac{1}{28}x^2$ **11.** $x = \frac{1}{8}y^2$

13. vertex: (0, 0); focus: $\left(0, \frac{1}{16}\right)$; directrix: $y = -\frac{1}{16}$
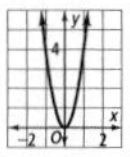

15. vertex: (0, 0); focus: $\left(\frac{1}{4}, 0\right)$; directrix: $x = -\frac{1}{4}$
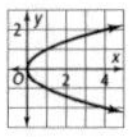

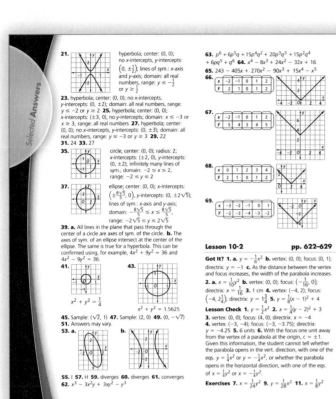

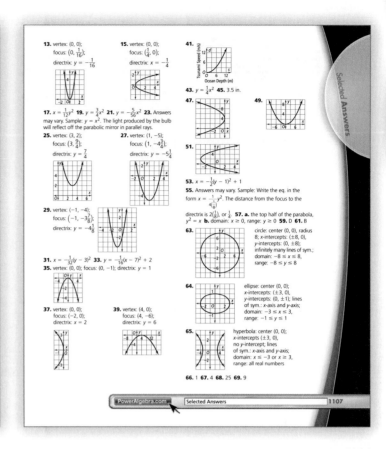

17. $x = \frac{1}{12}y^2$ **19.** $y = \frac{3}{4}x^2$ **21.** $y = -\frac{5}{56}x^2$ **23.** Answers may vary. Sample: $y = x^2$. The light produced by the bulb will reflect off the parabolic mirror in parallel rays.

25. vertex: (3, 2); focus: $\left(3, \frac{9}{4}\right)$; directrix: $y = \frac{7}{4}$
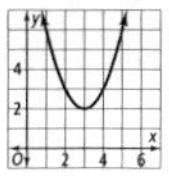

27. vertex: (1, −5); focus: $\left(1, -4\frac{3}{4}\right)$; directrix: $y = -5\frac{1}{4}$
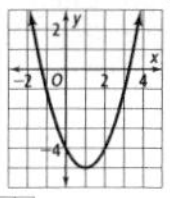

29. vertex: (−1, −4); focus: $\left(-1, -3\frac{7}{8}\right)$; directrix: $y = -4\frac{1}{8}$
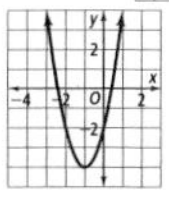

31. $x = -\frac{1}{32}(y - 3)^2$ **33.** $y = -\frac{1}{16}(x - 7)^2 + 2$
35. vertex: (0, 0); focus: (0, −1); directrix: $y = 1$
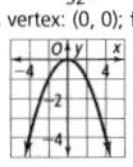

37. vertex: (0, 0); focus: (−2, 0); directrix: $x = 2$
39. vertex: (4, 0); focus: (4, −6); directrix: $y = 6$
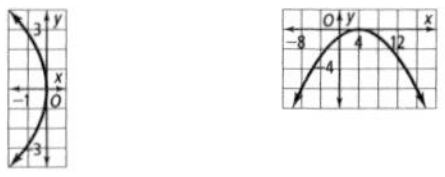

41. 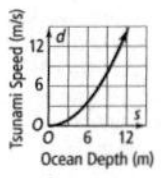

43. $y = \frac{1}{4}x^2$ **45.** 3.5 in.

47. 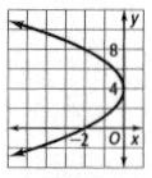

49. 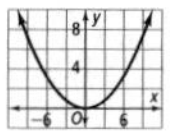

51. 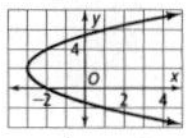

53. $x = -\frac{1}{2}(y - 1)^2 + 1$
55. Answers may vary. Sample: Write the eq. in the form $x = \frac{1}{4\left(\frac{1}{8}\right)}y^2$. The distance from the focus to the directrix is $2\left(\frac{1}{8}\right)$, or $\frac{1}{4}$. **57. a.** the top half of the parabola, $y^2 = x$ **b.** domain: $x \ge 0$, range: $y \ge 0$ **59.** D **61.** B

63. 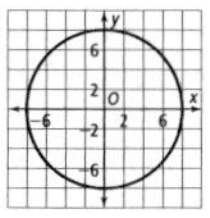
circle: center (0, 0), radius 8; x-intercepts: $(\pm 8, 0)$, y-intercepts: $(0, \pm 8)$; infinitely many lines of sym.; domain: $-8 \le x \le 8$, range: $-8 \le y \le 8$

64. 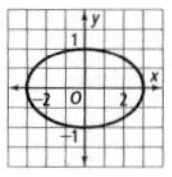
ellipse: center (0, 0); x-intercepts: $(\pm 3, 0)$, y-intercepts: $(0, \pm 1)$; lines of sym.: x-axis and y-axis; domain: $-3 \le x \le 3$, range: $-1 \le y \le 1$

65. 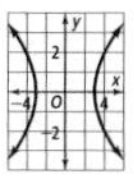
hyperbola: center (0, 0); x-intercepts $(\pm 3, 0)$, no y-intercept; lines of sym.: x-axis and y-axis; domain: $x \le -3$ or $x \ge 3$, range: all real numbers

66. 1 **67.** 4 **68.** 25 **69.** 9

Lesson 10-3 pp. 630–636

Got It? 1. $(x - 5)^2 + (y + 2)^2 = 64$ **2. a.** $(x + 5)^2 + (y + 3)^2 = 1$ **b.** $(x - 2)^2 + (y - 3)^2 = 9$
3. a. $(x - 7)^2 + (y + 10)^2 = 144$ **b.** Yes; the values h and k determine the position of the circle and r determines the size. **4. a.** center (−8, −3), radius 11 **b.** center (3, −7), radius $\sqrt{66}$

5. 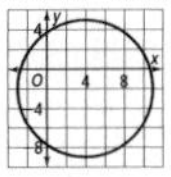

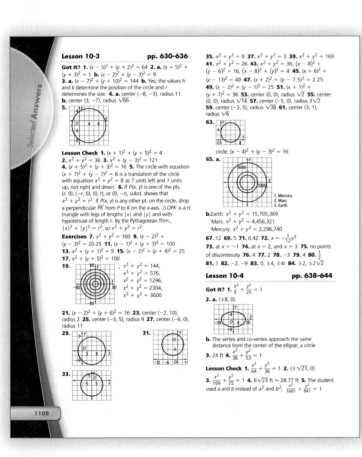

Lesson Check 1. $(x + 1)^2 + (y + 5)^2 = 4$
2. $x^2 + y^2 = 36$ **3.** $x^2 + (y - 3)^2 = 121$
4. $(x + 5)^2 + (y + 3)^2 = 16$ **5.** The circle with equation $(x + 7)^2 + (y - 7)^2 = 8$ is a translation of the circle with equation $x^2 + y^2 = 8$ as 7 units left and 7 units up, not right and down. **6.** If $P(x, y)$ is one of the pts. $(r, 0)$, $(-r, 0)$, $(0, r)$, or $(0, -r)$, subst. shows that $x^2 + y^2 = r^2$. If $P(x, y)$ is any other pt. on the circle, drop a perpendicular $\overline{PK}$ from P to K on the x-axis. $\triangle OPK$ is a rt. triangle with legs of lengths $|x|$ and $|y|$ and with hypotenuse of length r. By the Pythagorean Thm., $|x|^2 + |y|^2 = r^2$, so $x^2 + y^2 = r^2$.
Exercises 7. $x^2 + y^2 = 100$ **9.** $(x - 2)^2 + (y - 3)^2 = 20.25$ **11.** $(x - 1)^2 + (y + 3)^2 = 100$
13. $x^2 + (y + 1)^2 = 9$ **15.** $(x - 2)^2 + (y + 4)^2 = 25$
17. $x^2 + (y + 5)^2 = 100$

19. 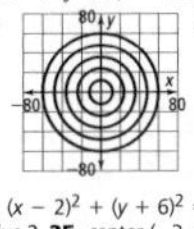
; $x^2 + y^2 = 144$, $x^2 + y^2 = 576$, $x^2 + y^2 = 1296$, $x^2 + y^2 = 2304$, $x^2 + y^2 = 3600$

21. $(x - 2)^2 + (y + 6)^2 = 16$ **23.** center (−2, 10), radius 2 **25.** center (−3, 5), radius 9 **27.** center (−6, 0), radius 11

29. 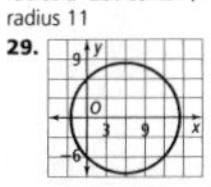

31. 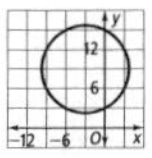

33. 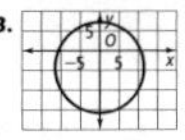

35. $x^2 + y^2 = 9$ **37.** $x^2 + y^2 = 3$ **39.** $x^2 + y^2 = 169$
41. $x^2 + y^2 = 26$ **43.** $x^2 + y^2 = 36$, $(x - 8)^2 + (y - 6)^2 = 16$, $(x - 8)^2 + (y)^2 = 4$ **45.** $(x + 6)^2 + (y - 13)^2 = 49$ **47.** $(x + 2)^2 + (y - 7.5)^2 = 2.25$
49. $(x - 2)^2 + (y - 1)^2 = 25$ **51.** $(x + 1)^2 + (y + 7)^2 = 36$ **53.** center (0, 0), radius $\sqrt{2}$ **55.** center (0, 0), radius $\sqrt{14}$ **57.** center (−5, 0), radius $3\sqrt{2}$
59. center (−3, 5), radius $\sqrt{38}$ **61.** center (3, 1), radius $\sqrt{6}$

63. 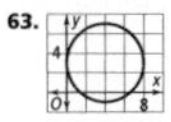
circle; $(x - 4)^2 + (y - 3)^2 = 16$

65. a. 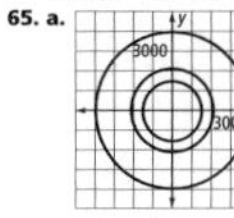

b. Earth: $x^2 + y^2 = 15{,}705{,}369$
Mars: $x^2 + y^2 = 4{,}456{,}321$
Mercury: $x^2 + y^2 = 2{,}296{,}740$

67. 12 **69.** 5 **71.** 0.42 **72.** $x = -\frac{1}{12}y^2$
73. at $x = -1$ **74.** at $x = 2$, and $x = 3$ **75.** no points of discontinuity **76.** 4 **77.** 2 **78.** −3 **79.** 4 **80.** $\frac{1}{2}$
81. 1 **82.** −2, −9 **83.** 0, ±4, ±4i **84.** ±2, $\pm 2\sqrt{2}$

Lesson 10-4 pp. 638–644

Got It? 1. $\frac{x^2}{4} + \frac{y^2}{25} = 1$
2. a. (±8, 0).
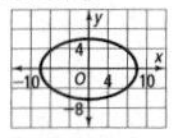

b. The vertex and co-vertex approach the same distance from the center of the ellipse; a circle
3. 24 ft **4.** $\frac{x^2}{36} + \frac{y^2}{53} = 1$
Lesson Check 1. $\frac{x^2}{64} + \frac{y^2}{36} = 1$ **2.** $(\pm\sqrt{21}, 0)$
3. $\frac{x^2}{169} + \frac{y^2}{25} = 1$ **4.** $6\sqrt{23}$ ft ≈ 28.77 ft **5.** The student used a and b instead of a^2 and b^2; $\frac{x^2}{1681} + \frac{y^2}{841} = 1$

6. The eq. of an ellipse with center at the origin is $\frac{x^2}{a^2} + \frac{y^2}{b^2} = 1$. For a circle, the major axis and the minor axis are of equal length such that $a = b = r$. Thus, by subst., $\frac{x^2}{r^2} + \frac{y^2}{r^2} = 1$ or $x^2 + y^2 = r^2$.
Exercises 7. $\frac{x^2}{16} + \frac{y^2}{9} = 1$ **9.** $\frac{x^2}{9} + y^2 = 1$
11. $\frac{x^2}{16} + \frac{y^2}{49} = 1$ **13.** $\frac{x^2}{81} + \frac{y^2}{4} = 1$

15. $(0, \pm\sqrt{5})$ **17.** $(\pm 4\sqrt{2}, 0)$
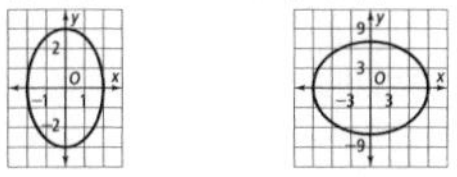

19. (0, ±6) **21.** $(\pm 2\sqrt{3}, 0)$
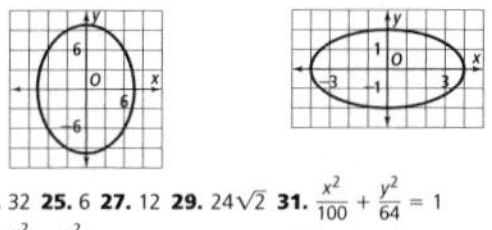

23. 32 **25.** 6 **27.** 12 **29.** $24\sqrt{2}$ **31.** $\frac{x^2}{100} + \frac{y^2}{64} = 1$
33. $\frac{x^2}{89} + \frac{y^2}{64} = 1$ **35. a.** about 22.25 ft **b.** Due to the reflective prop. of an ellipse, you can aim your putt at any part of the border. The ball will reflect off the border and go directly into the hole. **37.** $(0, \pm 2\sqrt{3})$ **39.** $(0, \pm\sqrt{21})$
41. (0, ±1) **43. a.** 0.9 **b.** 0.1 **c.** The shape is close to a circle. **d.** The shape is close to a line segment.
45. $\frac{x^2}{16} + y^2 = 1$ **49.** $\frac{x^2}{25} + \frac{y^2}{4} = 1$
51. $\frac{x^2}{702.25} + \frac{y^2}{210.25} = 1$ **53.** $\frac{x^2}{256} + \frac{y^2}{324} = 1$
55. $\frac{x^2}{16} + \frac{y^2}{12} = 1$ **57.** $\frac{x^2}{36} + \frac{y^2}{27} = 1$ **59.** $\frac{x^2}{20} + \frac{y^2}{18} = 1$
61. a. 3×10^6 min **b.** about 0.016
c. $\frac{x^2}{8.649 \times 10^{15}} + \frac{y^2}{8.64675 \times 10^{15}} = 1$ **63.** B **65.** A
67. $(x - 1)^2 + (y + 5)^2 = 9$ **68.** $(x + 2)^2 + (y - 4)^2 = 81$ **69.** $\frac{1}{2x - 3x^4}$; $x \ne 0$, $x \ne \sqrt[3]{\frac{2}{3}}$ **70.** $\frac{x - 6}{x - 1}$; $x \ne 1$, $x \ne -6$ **71.** $\frac{x - 5}{x^2 - 2x + 4}$; $x \ne -2$ **72.** log 15
73. $\log_3 6$ **74.** log 2 **75.** $y = 2x + 4$ **76.** $y = \frac{1}{3}x$

Lesson 10-5 pp. 645–652

Got It? 1. a. $\frac{y^2}{16} - \frac{x^2}{9} = 1$
b. 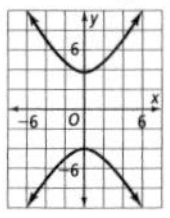
c. when $a = b$

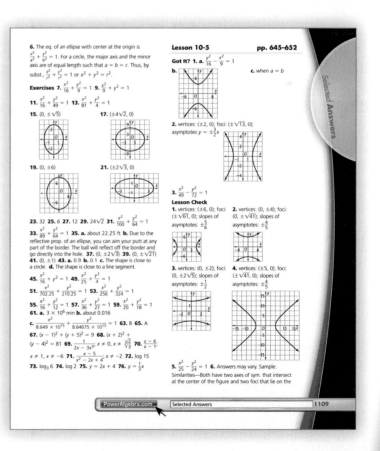

2. vertices: (±2, 0); foci: $(\pm\sqrt{13}, 0)$; asymptotes: $y = \pm\frac{3}{2}x$
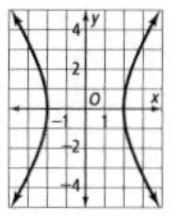

3. $\frac{x^2}{49} - \frac{y^2}{72} = 1$
Lesson Check
1. vertices: (±6, 0); foci: $(\pm\sqrt{61}, 0)$; slopes of asymptotes: $\pm\frac{5}{6}$
2. vertices: (0, ±4); foci: $(0, \pm\sqrt{41})$; slopes of asymptotes: $\pm\frac{4}{5}$
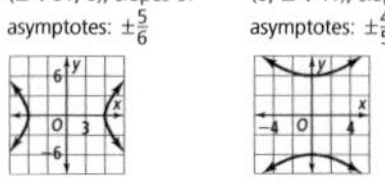

3. vertices: (0, ±2); foci: $(0, \pm 2\sqrt{5})$; slopes of asymptotes: $\pm\frac{1}{2}$
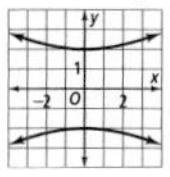

4. vertices: (±5, 0); foci: $(\pm\sqrt{41}, 0)$; slopes of asymptotes: $\pm\frac{4}{5}$
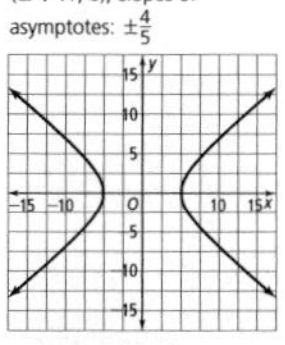

5. $\frac{x^2}{25} - \frac{y^2}{24} = 1$ **6.** Answers may vary. Sample: Similarities—Both have two axes of sym. that intersect at the center of the figure and two foci that lie on the

Page 1110

same line as the two "principal" vertices. Differences— An ellipse consists of pts. whose distances from the foci have a constant sum, whereas a hyperbola consists of pts. whose distances from the foci have a constant diff. **7.** Answers may vary. Sample: A hyperbola is vert. or horizontal depending on whether it has a positive coefficient not because the larger denominator is under the y^2 term.

Exercises 9. $\frac{x^2}{144} - \frac{y^2}{25} = 1$ **11.** $\frac{x^2}{49} - \frac{y^2}{121} = 1$
13. $\frac{x^2}{4} - \frac{y^2}{5} = 1$
15. vertices: $(0, \pm 7)$; foci: $(0, \pm\sqrt{113})$; asymptotes: $y = \pm\frac{7}{8}x$ **17.** vertices: $(\pm 8, 0)$; foci: $(\pm 10, 0)$; asymptotes: $y = \pm\frac{3}{4}x$
19. vertices: $(0, \pm 3)$; foci: $(0, \pm 3\sqrt{10})$; asymptotes: $y = \pm\frac{1}{3}x$ **21.** vertices: $(\pm 2\sqrt{2}, 0)$; foci: $(\pm 2\sqrt{11}, 0)$; asymptotes: $y = \pm\frac{3\sqrt{2}}{2}x$
23. $x^2 - \frac{y^2}{6} = 1$ **25.** $\frac{x^2}{9} - \frac{y^2}{16} = 1$
27. $y^2 - \frac{x^2}{3} = 1$ **29.** $\frac{x^2}{20.25} - \frac{y^2}{4} = 1$
31. $\frac{x^2}{32} - \frac{y^2}{64} = 1$
33. $y = \pm\sqrt{x^2 - 1}$; $(\pm 1, 0)$ **35.**
37.

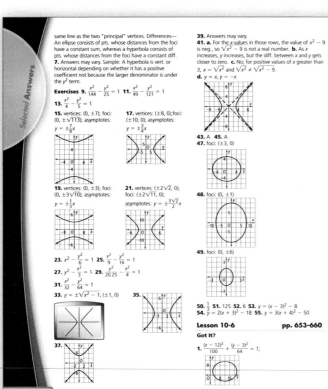

39. Answers may vary.
41. a. For the x-values in those rows, the value of $x^2 - 9$ is neg., so $\sqrt{x^2 - 9}$ is not a real number. **b.** As x increases, y increases, but the diff. between x and y gets closer to zero. **c.** No; for positive values of x greater than 3, $x = \sqrt{x^2}$ and $\sqrt{x^2} \neq \sqrt{x^2 - 9}$. **d.** $y = x, y = -x$
43. A **45.** A
47. foci: $(\pm 3, 0)$
48. foci: $(0, \pm 1)$
49. foci: $(0, \pm 6)$
50. $\frac{1}{3}$ **51.** 125 **52.** 6 **53.** $y = (x - 3)^2 - 8$
54. $y = 2(x + 3)^2 - 18$ **55.** $y = 3(x + 4)^2 - 50$

Lesson 10-6 pp. 653–660
Got It?
1. $\frac{(x - 12)^2}{100} + \frac{(y - 3)^2}{64} = 1$;

Page 1111

2. center $(2, -2)$; vertices: $(-4, -2), (8, -2)$; foci: $(-8, -2), (12, -2)$; asymptotes: $y + 2 = \pm\frac{4}{3}(x - 2)$

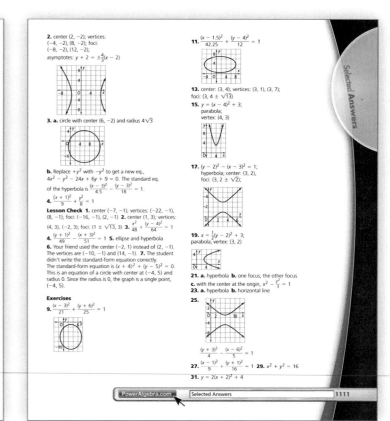

3. a. circle with center $(6, -2)$ and radius $4\sqrt{3}$

b. Replace $+y^2$ with $-y^2$ to get a new eq., $4x^2 - y^2 - 24x + 6y + 9 = 0$. The standard eq. of the hyperbola is $\frac{(x-3)^2}{4.5} - \frac{(y-3)^2}{18} = 1$.
4. $\frac{(x+1)^2}{9} + \frac{y^2}{8} = 1$
Lesson Check 1. center $(-7, -1)$; vertices: $(-22, -1), (8, -1)$; foci: $(-16, -1), (2, -1)$ **2.** center $(1, 3)$; vertices: $(4, 3), (-2, 3)$; foci: $(1 \pm \sqrt{13}, 3)$ **3.** $\frac{x^2}{48} + \frac{(y-4)^2}{64} = 1$
4. $\frac{(y-4)^2}{49} - \frac{(x+3)^2}{51} = 1$ **5.** ellipse and hyperbola
6. Your friend used the center $(-2, 1)$ instead of $(2, -1)$. The vertices are $(-10, -1)$ and $(14, -1)$. **7.** The student didn't write the standard-form equation correctly. The standard-form equation is $(x + 4)^2 + (y - 5)^2 = 0$. This is an equation of a circle with center at $(-4, 5)$ and radius 0. Since the radius is 0, the graph is a single point, $(-4, 5)$.

Exercises
9. $\frac{(x-3)^2}{21} + \frac{(y+6)^2}{25} = 1$

11. $\frac{(x-1.5)^2}{42.25} + \frac{(y-4)^2}{12} = 1$

13. center: $(3, 4)$; vertices: $(3, 1), (3, 7)$; foci: $(3, 4 \pm \sqrt{13})$
15. $y = (x - 4)^2 + 3$; parabola; vertex: $(4, 3)$
17. $(y - 2)^2 - (x - 3)^2 = 1$; hyperbola; center: $(3, 2)$, foci: $(3, 2 \pm \sqrt{2})$
19. $x = \frac{1}{3}(y - 2)^2 + 3$; parabola; vertex: $(3, 2)$
21. a. hyperbola **b.** one focus; the other focus **c.** with the center at the origin, $x^2 - \frac{y^2}{3} = 1$
23. a. hyperbola **b.** horizontal line
25.
$\frac{(y+3)^2}{4} - \frac{(x-6)^2}{5} = 1$
27. $\frac{(x-1)^2}{16} + \frac{(y+1)^2}{16} = 1$ **29.** $x^2 + y^2 = 16$
31. $y = 2(x + 2)^2 + 4$

Page 1112

33. **35.**

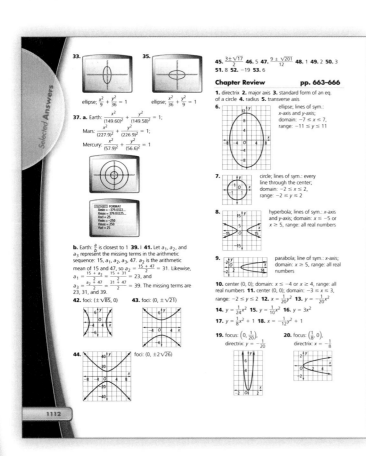

ellipse; $\frac{x^2}{9} + \frac{y^2}{36} = 1$ ellipse; $\frac{x^2}{36} + \frac{y^2}{9} = 1$
37. a. Earth: $\frac{x^2}{(149.60)^2} + \frac{y^2}{(149.58)^2} = 1$; Mars: $\frac{x^2}{(227.9)^2} + \frac{y^2}{(226.9)^2} = 1$; Mercury: $\frac{x^2}{(57.9)^2} + \frac{y^2}{(56.6)^2} = 1$

b. Earth: $\frac{9}{?}$ is closest to 1 **39.** I **41.** Let $a_1, a_2,$ and a_3 represent the missing terms in the arithmetic sequence: 15, a_1, a_2, a_3, 47. a_2 is the arithmetic mean of 15 and 47, so $a_2 = \frac{15 + 47}{2} = 31$. Likewise, $a_1 = \frac{15 + a_2}{2} = \frac{15 + 31}{2} = 23$, and $a_3 = \frac{a_2 + 47}{2} = \frac{31 + 47}{2} = 39$. The missing terms are 23, 31, and 39.
42. foci: $(\pm\sqrt{85}, 0)$ **43.** foci: $(0, \pm\sqrt{21})$
44. foci: $(0, \pm 2\sqrt{26})$

45. $\frac{3 \pm \sqrt{17}}{2}$ **46.** 5 **47.** $\frac{9 + \sqrt{201}}{12}$ **48.** 1 **49.** 1 **50.** 3
51. 8 **52.** -19 **53.** 6

Chapter Review pp. 663–666
1. directrix **2.** major axis **3.** standard form of an eq. of a circle **4.** radius **5.** transverse axis
6. ellipse; lines of sym.: x-axis and y-axis; domain: $-7 \leq x \leq 7$, range: $-11 \leq y \leq 11$
7. circle; lines of sym.: every line through the center; domain: $-2 \leq x \leq 2$, range: $-2 \leq y \leq 2$
8. hyperbola; lines of sym.: x-axis and y-axis; domain: $x \leq -5$ or $x \geq 5$, range: all real numbers
9. parabola; line of sym.: x-axis; domain: $x \geq 5$, range: all real numbers
10. center (0, 0); domain: $x \leq -4$ or $x \geq 4$, range: all real numbers **11.** center (0, 0); domain: $-3 \leq x \leq 3$, range: $-2 \leq y \leq 2$ **12.** $x = -\frac{1}{20}y^2$ **13.** $y = 3x^2$
14. $y = \frac{1}{24}x^2$ **15.** $y = \frac{1}{10}x^2$ **16.** $y = 3x^2$
17. $y = \frac{1}{8}x^2 + 1$ **18.** $x = -\frac{1}{12}y^2 + 1$
19. focus: $\left(0, \frac{1}{20}\right)$; directrix: $y = -\frac{1}{20}$ **20.** focus: $\left(\frac{1}{8}, 0\right)$; directrix: $x = -\frac{1}{8}$

Page 1113

21. focus: $(-2, 0)$; directrix: $x = 2$
22. $x^2 + y^2 = 16$ **23.** $(x - 8)^2 + (y - 1)^2 = 25$
24. $(x + 3)^2 + (y - 2)^2 = 100$
25. $(x - 5)^2 + (y + 3)^2 = 64$
26. center (1, 0), radius 8

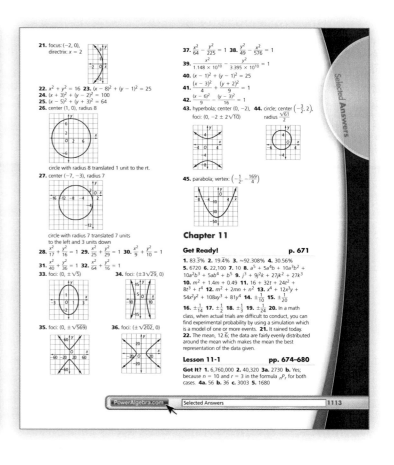

circle with radius 8 translated 1 unit to the rt.
27. center $(-7, -3)$, radius 7

circle with radius 7 translated 7 units to the left and 3 units down
28. $\frac{x^2}{17} + \frac{y^2}{16} = 1$ **29.** $\frac{x^2}{25} + \frac{y^2}{29} = 1$ **30.** $\frac{x^2}{9} + \frac{y^2}{10} = 1$
31. $\frac{x^2}{40} + \frac{y^2}{36} = 1$ **32.** $\frac{x^2}{64} + \frac{y^2}{16} = 1$
33. foci: $(0, \pm\sqrt{5})$ **34.** foci: $(\pm 3\sqrt{29}, 0)$
35. foci: $(0, \pm\sqrt{569})$ **36.** foci: $(\pm\sqrt{202}, 0)$

37. $\frac{x^2}{64} - \frac{y^2}{225} = 1$ **38.** $\frac{y^2}{49} - \frac{x^2}{576} = 1$
39. $\frac{x^2}{1.148 \times 10^{10}} - \frac{y^2}{3.395 \times 10^{10}} = 1$
40. $(x - 1)^2 + (y - 1)^2 = 25$
41. $\frac{(x-1)^2}{4} + \frac{(y+2)^2}{9} = 1$
42. $\frac{(x-6)^2}{4} - \frac{(y-3)^2}{16} = 1$
43. hyperbola; center $(0, -2)$, foci: $(0, -2 \pm 2\sqrt{10})$ **44.** circle; center $\left(-\frac{3}{2}, 2\right)$, radius $\frac{\sqrt{61}}{2}$
45. parabola; vertex: $\left(-\frac{1}{2}, -\frac{169}{4}\right)$

Chapter 11

Get Ready! p. 671
1. 83.3% **2.** 19.4% **3.** ~92.308% **4.** 30.56%
5. 6720 **6.** 22,100 **7.** 10 **8.** $a^5 + 5a^4b + 10a^3b^2 + 10a^2b^3 + 5ab^4 + b^5$ **9.** $j^3 + 9j^2k + 27jk^2 + 27k^3$
10. $m^2 + 1.4m + 0.49$ **11.** $16 + 32t + 24t^2 + 8t^3 + t^4$ **12.** $m^2 + 2mn + n^2$ **13.** $x^4 + 12x^3y + 54x^2y^2 + 108xy^3 + 81y^4$ **14.** $\pm\frac{1}{6}$ **15.** $\pm\frac{1}{20}$
16. $\pm\frac{1}{14}$ **17.** $\pm\frac{1}{3}$ **18.** $\pm\frac{1}{3}$ **19.** $\pm\frac{1}{24}$ **20.** In a math class, when actual trials are difficult to conduct, you can find experimental probability by using a simulation which is a model of one or more events. **21.** It rained today. **22.** The mean, 12.6; the data are fairly evenly distributed around the mean which makes the mean the best representation of the data given.

Lesson 11-1 pp. 674–680
Got It? 1. 6,760,000 **2.** 40,320 **3a.** 2730 **b.** Yes; because $n = 10$ and $r = 3$ in the formula $_nP_r$ for both cases. **4a.** 56 **b.** 36 **c.** 3003 **5.** 1680

Lesson Check **1.** 120 **2.** 3024 **3.** 10 **4.** 21 **5.** 4,151,347,200 **6.** A permutation is an arrangement of items in a particular order; order is important. An arrangement in which order does not matter is a combination. **7.** ${}_nP_r = \frac{n!}{(n-r)!}$; substituting $n = r$, we get ${}_nP_n = \frac{n!}{(n-n)!} = \frac{n!}{0!}$; but ${}_nP_n = n! = \frac{n!}{1}$; substituting values again, we get $\frac{n!}{1} = \frac{n!}{(n-n)!}$, and so $0! = 1$.
Exercises **9.** 20 **11.** 12 **13.** 3,628,800 **15.** 720 **17.** 120 **19.** 3003 **21.** 8 **23.** 336 **25.** 6 **27.** 60,480 **29.** 10,897,286,400 **31.** 56 **33.** 4 **35.** 15 **37.** $\frac{5}{18}$ **39.** combination; 4368 **41.** combination; 70 **43.** True because of the Assoc. Prop. of Mult. **45.** False; answers may vary. Sample: $(3 \cdot 2)! = 6! = 720$ and $3! \cdot 2! = 6 \cdot 2 = 12$ **47.** False; answers may vary. Sample: $(3!)^2 = 6^2 = 36$ and $3^{(2!)} = 3^2 = 9$ **49.** C **51.** Two ways, because order matters. **53a.** 2 **b.** 6 **c.** $(n-1)!$ **55. a.** 35 **b.** 6 **c.** ${}_7C_3 = \frac{7!}{3!4!}$, so ${}_7C_3 \cdot 3! = \frac{7!}{4!}$, which is the permutation formula for ${}_7P_3$. **57.** H **59.** G **61.** center: (2, 1); vertices: (2, 6), (2, −4); co-vertices: (5, 1), (−1, 1); foci: (2, 5), (2, −3) **62.** $(x-1)^2 + (y-1)^2 = 36$ is a circle (not an ellipse) with center (1, 1) and radius 6. **63.** $4(x-1)^2$ **64.** $-(x+3)^2$ **65.** $3(x-5)(x+5)$ **66.** 30,240 **67.** $\frac{4}{5}$ **68.** 210

Lesson 11-2 pp. 681–687

Got It? **1.** 0.40 or 40% **2.** 0.20 or 20% **3a.** $\frac{1}{2}$ **b.** The likelihood of getting an even or odd is the same, i.e. $\frac{1}{2}$. **4.** $\frac{48}{2{,}598{,}960}$ or 0.0000184689 or ≈0.00185% **5.** 0.05 or 5%
Lesson Check **1.** 0.75 or 75% **2.** 0.80 or 80% **3.** $\frac{1}{6}$ **4.** $\frac{1}{3}$ **5.** Experimental probabilities are calculated on the basis of data from an experiment, actual or simulated. Given equally likely outcomes, the basis for calculating theoretical probability is being able to determine the no. of ways that an event can occur within these outcomes. Comparisons of measures such as length and area are the basis of geometric probability. **6.** Answers may vary. Samples: Flip a coin; generate random numbers on a calculator; roll a die with odd numbers as true and even numbers as false. **7.** Because you are averaging over more samples, you are getting a more accurate average.
Exercises **9.** the number 1: $\frac{21}{134} \approx 15.7\%$; the number 2: $\frac{11}{67} \approx 16.4\%$; the number 3: $\frac{45}{268} \approx 16.8\%$; the number 4: $\frac{11}{67} \approx 16.4\%$; the number 5: $\frac{47}{268} \approx 17.5\%$; the number 6: $\frac{23}{134} \approx 17.2\%$ **11.** Answers may vary. Sample: Toss 5 coins. Keep a tally of the times three or more heads are tossed. (A head represents a correct answer.) Do this 100 times. The total number of tally marks, as a percent, gives the experimental probability. The simulated probability should be about 50%. **13.** $\frac{3}{10}$, or 30% **15.** $\frac{4}{5}$, or 80% **17.** $\frac{48}{125}$, or 38.4% **19.** $\frac{103}{125}$, or 82.4% **21.** $\frac{77}{125}$, or 61.6% **23.** $\frac{{}_{30}C_3 \cdot {}_{120}C_6}{{}_{150}C_9} \approx 0.17879 \approx 17.9\%$ **25.** $\frac{5}{8}$, or 62.5% **27.** $\frac{3}{4}$, or 75% **29.** $\frac{116}{147} \approx 78.9\%$ **31.** $\frac{43}{147} \approx 29.3\%$ **33.** 1 chance in 2,869,685 or ≈0.00003485% **35.** if there are any restrictions on the last digit of a ZIP code **37.** B **39.** B
41.
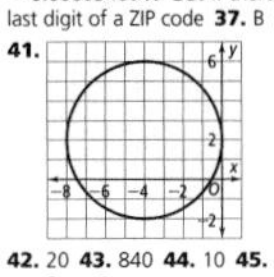

42. 20 **43.** 840 **44.** 10 **45.** 45 **46.** $\frac{25b - 7a^3}{5a^2b^2}$ **47.** $\frac{3q + 7p}{pq}$ **48.** 0 **49.** $\frac{7}{36} = 19.\overline{4}\%$ **50.** $\frac{25}{36} = 69.\overline{4}\%$ **51.** $\frac{1}{2}$, or 50%

Lesson 11-3 pp. 688–693

Got It? **1.** Independent; the number of coins is the same after the coin is replaced. **2.** 0.20, or 20% **3a.** Not mutually exclusive; 2 is a prime number and an even number. **b.** Mutually exclusive; there is no even number less than 2 in the roll of a number cube. **4a.** 0.61, or 61% **b.** Yes; the percentage of students tells which language is chosen by more students. **5a.** $\frac{5}{9}$ **b.** $\frac{5}{9}$
Lesson Check **1.** $\frac{1}{15}$, or $6.\overline{6}\%$ **2.** $\frac{27}{80}$, or 33.75% **3.** 1, or 100% **4.** $\frac{7}{8}$, or 87.5% **5.** $\frac{5}{8}$, or 62.5% **6.** Events A and B are independent if the outcomes of A do not affect the outcomes of B. The events are mutually exclusive if A and B cannot occur at the same time. For independent events, $P(A \text{ and } B) = P(A) \cdot P(B)$. For mutually exclusive events, $P(A \text{ and } B) = 0$. For any events, $P(A \text{ or } B) = P(A) + P(B) - P(A \text{ and } B)$. **7.** Since these are not mutually exclusive events, $P(A \text{ and } B) \neq 0$. The student should have multiplied to get the correct answer, which is 0.21 or 21%.
Exercises **9.** independent **11.** dependent **13.** $\frac{1}{6}$ **15.** 0.54 **17.** $\frac{9}{25}$ **19.** mutually exclusive; if the numbers are equal, then the sum is even **21.** $\frac{3}{4}$ **23.** 39% **25.** $\frac{1}{2}$

27. $\frac{5}{6}$ **29.** $\frac{2}{3}$ **31.** $\frac{2}{5}$ **33.** 14.5% **35.** 87.4% **37.** $\frac{4}{15}$ **39.** $\frac{8}{15}$ **41.** not mutually exclusive **43.** $\frac{4}{9}$ **45.** $\frac{8}{11}$ **47.** 8 **49.** 5 **51.** $\frac{1}{6}$ **52.** $\frac{1}{2}$ **53.** $\frac{1}{2}$ **54.** $\frac{3}{7}$ **55.** $-\frac{3}{2}$, 2 **56.** $\frac{1}{6}$ **57.** $\frac{1}{2}e^3 \approx 10.04$ **58.** $\frac{1}{2}e^6 \approx 201.71$ **59.** $\pm e^2 \approx \pm 7.39$ **60.** $\frac{1}{16}$ **61.** $\frac{1}{16}$ **62.** $\frac{3}{16}$

Lesson 11-4 pp. 696–702

Got It? **1a.** ≈0.57355 or ≈57.355% **b.** Female; there are more females enrolled. **2a.** ≈0.026448 or ≈2.64% **b.** ≈0.040302 or ≈4.03% **3.** 0.2 **4.** 9%
Lesson Check **1.** $\frac{1}{2}$ **2.** $\frac{1}{13}$, or 7.7% **3.** 0% **4.** 50% **5.** The sum of the probability of an event happening and the probability of an event not happening is 1. Each branch represents either the event happening or the event not happening. **7.** Answers may vary. Sample: Tree diagrams apply to cases in which more than one event occurs in a sequence. The Fundamental Counting Principle applies to situations in which there are multiple outcomes of a single event. With a tree diagram, but not with the Fundamental Counting Principle, you can determine probabilities of dependent events, or conditional probabilities.
Exercises **9.** 0.6 **11.** ≈0.085 **13.** ≈0.682 **15.** ≈0.709 **17.** ≈23%
19.
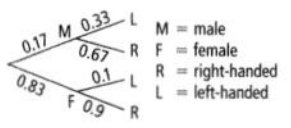

$P(L|F) = 10\%$, $P(M \text{ and } R) \approx 11.4\%$
21. 75% **23.** P(S and W) **25.** $\frac{2}{3}$, or 66.67% **27.** 0.08, or 8% **29.** 0.84 **31.** 0.16
33.
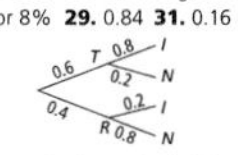

T = representative that completed training seminars
R = representative that didn't complete a training seminar
I = representative with increased sales
N = representative without increased sales

$P(I|N) = 0.2$

35. H **37.** (1, 1), (1, 2), (1, 3), (2, 1), (2, 2), (2, 3), (3, 1), (3, 2), (3, 3); yes **38.** $\frac{1}{3} = 33.\overline{3}\%$ **39.** $\frac{17}{76} \approx 0.22368 \approx 22.37\%$ **40.** $x = \frac{1}{4}(y-2)^2 + 5$ **41.** $y = \frac{1}{12}(x+2)^2 + 3$ **42.** 2 **43.** 0.830 **44.** 1.404 **45.** 3.465 **46.** $\frac{1}{7}$ **47.** $\frac{3}{7}$ **48.** $\frac{2}{7}$ 49. $\frac{1}{7}$

Lesson 11-5 pp. 703–709

Got It? **1.** Answers may vary. Sample answer: No, it is not likely that both siblings have an equal chance of winning the race. **2. a.** 1, 6, 8, 9, 3 **b.** Yes, each student has an equal chance of being selected for either team. **3.** Answers may vary. Sample answer: Roll the cube until you get a 6. Keep track of the results. Repeat several times and take the average number of rolls needed. **4.** Answers may vary. Sample answer: No, almost as many volunteers who received the placebo reported improvement as received the drug. Fewer than half of those who received the drug reported improvement.
Lesson Check **1.** about 0.89 **2.** about 0.86 **3.** Answers may vary. Sample answer: Flipping a coin to decide who has to wash the dishes is a fair decision. Arm wrestling to see who has to wash the dishes might be unfair if one brother is stronger than the other. **4.** Answers may vary. Sample answer: He only conducted 1 trial of the simulation, which is not enough to arrive at an accurate prediction. He should conduct the simulation at least 25 times and find the average number of boxes needed. **5.** Answers may vary. Sample answer: A simulation is an imitation or way of acting something out. In a mathematical simulation, a probability model is used to act out a situation that would be difficult or impractical to actually perform.
Exercises **7.** Answers may vary. Sample answer: This will not result in a fair decision because the first person chooses the second person and might favor someone over someone else. **9.** 01, 05, 16, 03, 08 **11. a.** about 0.82 **b.** about 0.35 **c.** Sample answer: Yes, a high percentage of students who took the class passed the board exams on their first attempt so the class appears to be beneficial. **13.** 28 trials; about 1.14 correct answers per trial **15.** Answers may vary. Sample answer: Yes, the defensive driving course appears to be very effective and should be offered again. None of the drivers who took the course were involved in a major accident in the previous year. **17.** Answers may vary. Sample answer: Use a graphing calculator to generate random integers from 1 to 5. Let the integers 1, 2, 3, and 4 represent a made field goal, and let 5 represent a missed field goal. Generate random integers in groups of 3 to simulate the attempts in the next game. Perform the simulation at least 20 or 25 times and find the average number of field goals made. **19.** A **21.** C **23.** 0.35 **24.** 0.52 **25.** 0.7 **26.** 18

Lesson 11-6 pp. 711–718

Got It? **1.** mean: 5.25, median: 5, mode: 5 **2a.** Yes; it is unlikely that the water temperature of a lake would change by 25 degrees. **b.** No; 98 would represent the busiest night of the week and it may relate to a weekly event. **3.** Dauphin Island: mean: $69.08\overline{3}$, mode: 84, range: 33, $Q_1 = 58$, median: 71, $Q_3 = 81$, interquartile range: 23; Grand Isle: mean: $73.41\overline{6}$, modes: 61, 70, 77, 83, 85, range: 24, $Q_1 = 64.5$, median: 73.5, $Q_3 = 83$, interquartile range: 18.5; The range and the interquartile range show the temperatures varying less at Grand Isle than at Dauphin Island. Also, the temperatures at Grand Isle are generally higher. **4a.** Use STAT PLOT, select a box-and-whisker plot. Enter data for the three remaining Gulf Coast sites. Enter the window values. Draw the box-and-whisker plots. Use TRACE on the plot to find quartiles Q_1, Q_2 and Q_3.
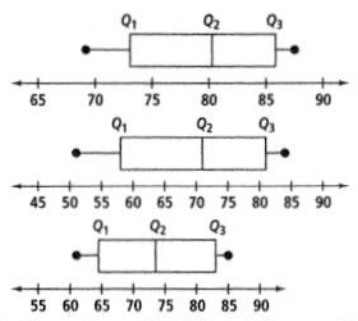

b. Yes, a box-and-whisker plot uses minimum and maximum values, the median, and the first and third quartiles to display the variability in a data set. **5a.** 79 **b.** 98
Lesson Check **1.** outlier: 54; outlier included: mean: 22.8, median: 19.5, mode: 18; outlier not included: mean: $19.\overline{3}$, median: 19, mode: 18 **2.** outlier: 40; outlier included: mean: $92.\overline{6}$, median: 98, mode: 90; outlier not included: mean: 99.25, median: 99, mode: 90 **3.** the mean because the sum of the data values is affected and the mean depends on the sum **4.** 40%: 49 and below; 80%: 58 and below **5.** the mean; when data are somewhat sym, the best representation is the mean **6.** The error is in how to calculate the median. The median is the middle value or the 11th value which is 90.
Exercises **7.** mean: $112.\overline{3}$, median: 95, mode: none **9.** 9.8 **11.** Jacksonville: mean: $67.99\overline{16}$, mode: none, range: 29.2, $Q_1 = 58.15$, median: 68.4, $Q_3 = 78.6$, interquartile range: 20.45; Austin: mean: $68.58\overline{3}$, mode: none, range: 36, $Q_1 = 56.85$, median: 70.5, $Q_3 = 80.75$, interquartile range: 23.9; the range and the interquartile range show the temperatures varying less at Jacksonville than at Austin.
13.
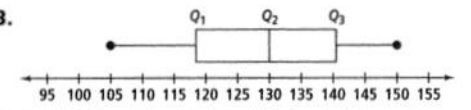

15. 5; 17 **17.** outlier: 381; outlier included: mean: ≈161.214, median: 158, mode: none; outlier not included: mean: ≈144.308, median: 142, mode: none
19.
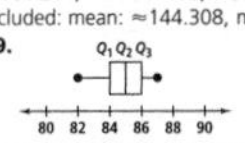

21. 30th **23.** 89 is at the 100th percentile, since 100% of the values are less than or equal to 89. **25.** The median; a few outliers can heavily influence the mean without drastically affecting the median. **27.** 83.9 **29.** Answers may vary. Sample: The range for women's shot put is greater than that for men's. The men are more consistent, as indicated by the shorter box and whiskers. Overall the men tend to throw farther. **31.** G
33. $P(H|I) = 0.40$, $P(H \text{ and } I) = 0.20$

$$P(H|I) = \frac{P(H \text{ and } I)}{P(I)}$$
$$0.40 = \frac{0.20}{P(I)}$$
$$P(I) = 0.50$$

34. 0.20 **35.** 0.56 **36.** yes; −9 **37.** yes; 17 **38.** no **39.** yes; 0 **40.** ±16 **41.** ±0.09 **42.** $\pm\frac{11}{4}$ **43.** $\pm\frac{19}{5}$

Lesson 11-7 pp. 719–724

Got It? **1.** $\bar{x} = 69.8\overline{3}$, $\sigma^2 = 115.1389$, $\sigma = 10.7303$ **2.** $\bar{x} = 7.2\overline{6}$, $\sigma = 3.316$ **3a.** within 3 standard deviations of the mean **b.** FEMA can expect that the no. of hurricanes for a 15-year period will fall within 3 standard deviations of the mean.
Lesson Check **1.** $\bar{x} = 10$, $\sigma^2 = 19.8$, $\sigma = 4.45$ **2.** within 2 standard deviations of the mean **3.** Measures of central tendency are specific data pts. which give a summary of the middle of the data set, whereas the measures of variation give a summary of the variation of the data set within the range of distribution. **4.** Standard deviation measures how widely spread the data values are. If the data pts. are close to the mean, the standard deviation is small; if the data pts. are far from the mean, the standard deviation is large. The data pts. of Set B are closer to the mean of 70 than the data pts. of Sets A and C; likewise, the data pts. of Set A are closer to 70 than the data pts. of Set C. **5.** The effect of an outlier on the standard deviation is to increase the standard deviation.
Exercises **7.** $\bar{x} \approx 15.1$, $\sigma^2 \approx 12.4$, $\sigma \approx 3.5$ **9.** $\bar{x} = 43.8$, $\sigma^2 = 75.76$, $\sigma \approx 8.7$ **11.** $\bar{x} \approx 12320.00$, $\sigma \approx 273.71$ **13.** 3 standard deviations **15.** $\bar{x} = 53.8$, $\sigma \approx 3.4$; 1σ: 7; 2σ: 9; 3σ: 10 **17.** Overall farm income increased slightly, but there was less variability among the states in 2002. The income in 2001 clustered more tightly around the mean. (2001: $\sigma_x \approx 2679$, 2002: $\sigma_x \approx 2758$) **21.** Your first friend; one standard deviation encompasses all values within one standard deviation above and below the mean. The graph shows that all values are within 3 standard deviations of the mean. **23. a.** no change to σ **b.** σ increases by a factor of 10 **25.** 13 **27.** $\frac{5}{6}$
28.
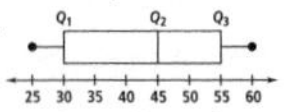

29.
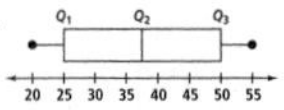

30. center (2, −1); radius 6 **31.** center (1, 1); radius 2 **32.** $\frac{1}{2}$ **33.** $-\frac{1}{3}$ **34.** $\frac{1}{6}$ **35.** $-\frac{1}{11}$ **36.** $-\frac{1}{9}$ **37.** $\frac{1}{7}$

Lesson 11-8 pp. 725–730

Got It? **1a.** convenience sample; yes; since the location is at the food court in the mall, the sample may over-represent food court or fast food supporters. **b.** Answers may vary. Sample: population data for the US census **2.** Controlled study; If other factors of the volunteers are random, like age, gender, and overall health, are known, the results can be used to make a general conclusion. **3.** Answers may vary. Sample: Use a systematic sample. Go to every fifth house in your neighborhood. State the first and last names of the governor and ask a household member to identify the named person. A possible unbiased survey question is, "Who is this person?".
Lesson Check **1a.** convenience sample **b.** Yes; since the location is near the exit of a history museum, the sample may over represent people who enjoy learning history and the results will have a bias. **2.** Yes; the question is leading and loaded. It suggests the person wants a particular answer. **3.** All members of the set are the population. A sample is a subset of the population. Answers may vary. Sample: population: students in a high school; sample: students who like to snowboard **4.** It is important to have as little error as poss. in a sample, thus giving an unbiased sample. An unbiased sample is more representative of an entire population. **5.** A large sample size would give a better estimate. The size of the sample is important to the reliability of the sample.
Exercises **7.** systematic sampling; no bias **9.** Survey; the statistics can be used to make a general conclusion about the population because the sample is randomly generated, and the survey question does not introduce a bias into the study. **11.** Controlled experiment; the statistics from this study can be used to make a general conclusion about the effectiveness of the plant food for this particular plant type as compared with giving no plant food at all. **13.** Answers may vary. Sample: Convenience sampling; interview students at a local high school. **15.** Answers may vary. Sample: Self-selected sampling; a newspaper article invites females over the age of 21 to call the paper and express their opinions. **17.** self-selected sampling; biased because only those who spend time online will respond. **19. a.** all students at the school **b.** every tenth student who enters the school building the day of the survey **c.** Answers may vary. Sample: A little over half of students favor the new dress code. **21.** Answers will vary. Sample: No, because you would have to assume that all registered voters will actually vote on Election Day. **23. a.** convenience sample **b.** observational study **c.** Answers may vary. Sample: The statistics do not necessarily represent the school population because a random sample was not used to conduct the study. **25.** Yes, the question is leading the respondent to a particular desired answer, and it gives statistics that may elicit a strong reaction. Also, it requires the respondent to answer a question about whether a person *should* wear a safety belt, which may not necessarily influence whether they support the law. **27.** G **29.** $\bar{x} \approx 2.83$, $\sigma \approx 2.54$ **30.** $\bar{x} \approx 5.62$, $\sigma \approx 3.67$ **31.** $y = \frac{1}{2}(x-5)$; yes **32.** $y = \pm\sqrt{x}$; no **33.** $y = \pm\sqrt{\frac{9x}{5}}$; no **34.** $y = \frac{x^2}{9}$, $x \geq 0$; yes **35.** 6 **36.** 1 **37.** 10 **38.** 792

Lesson 11-9 pp. 731–738

Got It?
1. $P(0) = 0.07776$; $P(1) = 0.2592$; $P(2) = 0.3456$; $P(3) = 0.2304$; $P(5) = 0.01024$
2. $81x^4 + 108x^3y + 54x^2y^2 + 12xy^3 + y^4$
3. ≈0.1035, or about 10.4%
Lesson Check **1.** ≈0.3110, or ≈31.10% **2.** ≈0.1641, or ≈16.41% **3.** $20c^3d^3$ **4.** $-10x^4y$ **5.** 0.2646, or 26.46% **6.** Answers may vary. Sample: A binomial experiment has three important features: **a.** The situation involves repeated trials; flipping a coin 10 times has 10 trials. **b.** Each trial has two possible outcomes; in this case, heads or tails. **c.** The probability of success is constant throughout the trials; the trials of flipping a coin, are independent. **7.** The student wrote "5" instead of "4". It should be: ${}_nC_{(5-1)}a^{n-4}b^4 = {}_7C_4 j^3(-k)^4 = 35j^3k^4$
Exercises **9.** ≈0.1361, or ≈13.61%

11. ≈ 0.0015, or $\approx 0.15\%$
13. $a^4 + 4a^3b + 6a^2b^2 + 4ab^3 + b^4$
15. $243x^5 + 810x^4y + 1080x^3y^2 + 720x^2y^3 + 240xy^4 + 32y^5$ **17.** $896g^6h$ **19.** e^6
21. $P(0) \approx 0.1176$, $P(1) \approx 0.3025$, $P(2) \approx 0.3241$, $P(3) \approx 0.1852$, $P(4) \approx 0.0595$, $P(5) \approx 0.0102$, $P(6) \approx 0.0007$
23. $P(0) \approx 0.000001$, $P(1) \approx 0.000054$, $P(2) \approx 0.0012$, $P(3) \approx 0.0146$, $P(4) \approx 0.0984$, $P(5) \approx 0.3543$, $P(6) \approx 0.5314$
25. 0.99328 **27.** ≈ 0.2824 **29.** ≈ 0.1109
31. ≈ 0.2461 **33.** ≈ 0.6230 **35a.** 0.0914 **b.** The probability that three boxes would be underweight is 0.0001. You can conclude that there might be a malfunction in the machinery or that the company's claim may be false. **37.** The probability of a group of 30 students having 4 or fewer left-handed students is about 77.05%. This means that more than three quarters of the classes will have enough left-handed desks; 4 is an adequate no.
39a. $P(0) = 0.001$, $P(1) = 0.027$, $P(2) = 0.243$, $P(3) = 0.729$

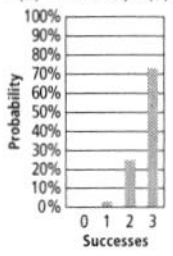

b. $P(0) = 0.166375$, $P(1) = 0.408375$, $P(2) = 0.334125$, $P(3) = 0.091125$

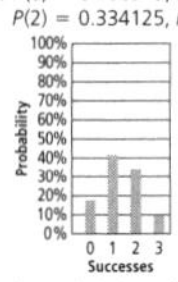

c. The probabilities of each graph sum to 1; $P(0) + P(1) + P(2) + P(3) = 1$. The probabilities of part (a) increase with increasing success numbers; the maximum probability occurring at $P(3)$. The probabilities of part (b) peak with a maximum at $P(1)$ and then decrease with increasing success numbers. **41.** Answers may vary.
43. a. The graph is sym. about the line $x = 3.5$.

b.

x	y
0	0.0078
1	0.0547
2	0.1641
3	0.2734
4	0.2734
5	0.1641
6	0.0547
7	0.0078

c. No; the bulge in the graph has shifted rt. **45.** G **47.** H **49.** loaded and leading question by the use of the word "beautiful" and the phrase "Do you agree" **50.** does not provide enough information about the amendments to make a decision **51.** vertices: $(0, \pm 7)$; foci: $(0, \pm\sqrt{74})$; asymptotes: $y = \pm\frac{7}{5}x$ **52.** vertices: $(0, \pm 3)$; foci: $(0, \pm\sqrt{13})$; asymptotes: $y = \pm\frac{3}{2}x$ **53.** vertices: $(0, \pm 3)$; foci: $(0, \pm 5)$; asymptotes: $y = \pm\frac{3}{4}x$ **54.** $\frac{2}{3}$ **55.** $\frac{1}{2}$ **56.** $\frac{2}{3}$ **57.** $\bar{x} = 24.4$, $\sigma \approx 5.04$ **58.** $\bar{x} = 81.8$, $\sigma \approx 4.77$ **59.** $\bar{x} = 8.6$, $\sigma \approx 0.47$ **60.** $\bar{x} \approx 24.74$, $\sigma \approx 2.046$

Lesson 11-10 pp. 739–745

Got It? 1a. 71% **b.** 88%
2.

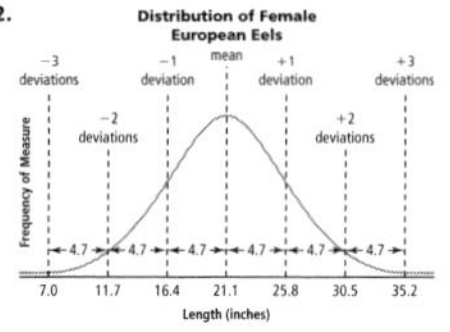

3a. 2.5% **b.** 210 students **c.** The students that received a B had scores between 165 and 180.
Lesson Check 1. 94%
2.

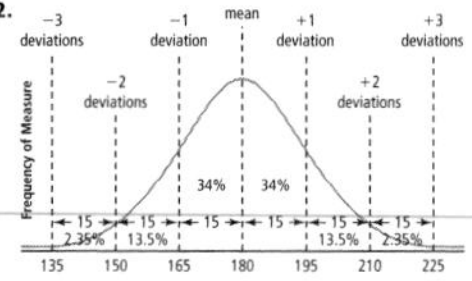

3. 47.5% **4.** Normal distribution means that most of the examples in a data set are close to the mean; the distribution of the data is within 1, 2, or 3 standard deviations of the mean. **5.** The mean and median are equivalent in a normal distribution. **6.** mean increases by 10: the bell curve is translated 10 units to the rt.; standard deviation increases by 10: the bell curve is stretched out by a factor of 10; the bell curve will be less steep due to the larger standard deviation.
Exercises 7. $\approx 43\%$ **9.** ≈ 43 men
11.

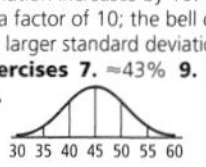

13.

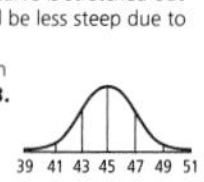

15. 68% **17.** 50% **19a.** Set 2
b. and c.

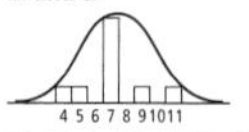

21. 59 min **23.** 47.5% **25.** 81.5% **27.** 84%
29a.

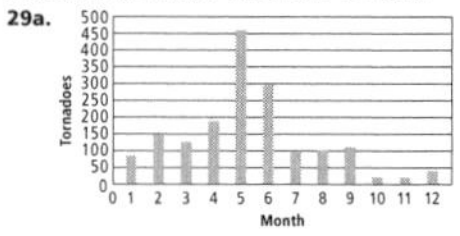

b. No; the curve is skewed to the left. **c.** No, mean and standard deviation are appropriate only for measuring normally distributed data. **31.** Yes; Elena scored within the top 10% of her group. Her score is 2.75 standard deviations above the mean, which places her in the top 1%. Jake did not score in the top 10%. His score is 1.16 standard deviations above the mean, or at the 88th percentile. **33.** A binomial distribution has a finite no. of probabilities, which sum to 1 and are a subset of a larger normal distribution. For example, using $n = 6$, $p = 0.5$, the binomial distribution probabilities are $P(0) \approx 0.0156$, $P(1) \approx 0.0938$, $P(2) \approx 0.2344$, $P(3) \approx 0.3125$, $P(4) \approx 0.2344$, $P(5) \approx 0.0938$, $P(6) \approx 0.0156$.

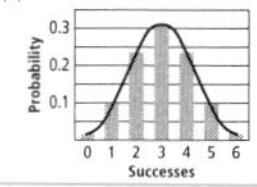

35. I **37.** For Distribution A with 50 data values, 25 values are at or below 40, which is the mean. For Distribution B with 30 data values, 15 values are at or below the mean 40. So Distribution A has more values at or below 40. **38.** 0.02867 **39.** 0.1612 **40.** 0.03676
41.

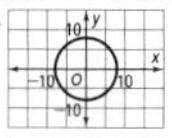

circle; center: $(0, 0)$, radius: 8; lines of sym.: all lines through the center; domain: $-8 \le x \le 8$, range: $-8 \le y \le 8$

42.

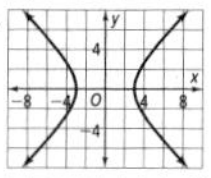

hyperbola; center: $(0, 0)$, foci: $(\pm 3\sqrt{2}, 0)$; lines of sym.: $x = 0$, $y = 0$; domain: $x \le -3$ or $x \ge 3$; range: all real numbers

43.

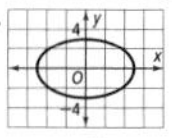

ellipse; center: $(0, 0)$, foci: $(\pm 4, 0)$; lines of sym.: $x = 0$, $y = 0$; domain: $-5 \le x \le 5$, range: $-3 \le y \le 3$

44. $y = x - 3$;

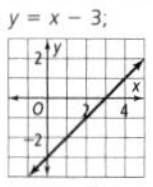

45. $y = x$;

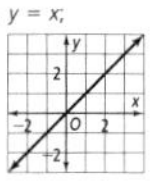

46. $y = x - \frac{5}{4}$;

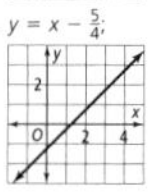

Chapter Review pp. 751–756

1. sample **2.** outlier **3.** probability distribution **4.** range of a set of data **5.** 6 **6.** 362,880 **7.** 12 **8.** 30 **9.** 21 **10.** 10 **11.** 30 **12.** 744 **13.** 220; 84; 20; 1 **14.** 3.315312×10^9 **15.** 216 **16.** $\frac{47}{70}$ **17.** 0 **18.** $\frac{2}{5}$ **19.** Not necessarily; you may pick a 5 zero times, one time, or more than once. Each time you pick, the prob. that it will be a 5 is $\frac{1}{20}$. **20.** dependent **21.** independent **22.** 0.21 **23.** 0.79 **24.** 0.3 **25.** 0.7 **26.** $\frac{1}{4}$ **27.** $\frac{1}{5}$ **28.** $\frac{1}{8}$ **29.** This will not necessarily result in a fair decision, because the principal may aim at a particular name, which means that not all students have an equally likely chance of being chosen. **30.** Yes, this will result in a fair decision, because the probabilities of each goalie being chosen are the same. **31.** Answers may vary. **32.** 9 **33.** mean: 6,

median: 6, mode: 9 **34.** mean: $10.\overline{6}$, median: 7, modes: 3 and 7 **35.** mean: 15, median: 15, mode: 18 **36.** mean: 9.5, median: 9.5, mode: none **37.** range: 35; $Q_1 = 30$; $Q_3 = 55$ **38.** range: 35; $Q_1 = 25$; $Q_3 = 50$ **39.** range: 65; $Q_1 = 42$; $Q_3 = 87$ **40.** heights of 3 people **41.** ages of thirty college students **42.** gas mileage of 18 automobiles of various types
43. $\bar{x} \approx 6.64$, $\sigma \approx 5.12$ **44.** $\bar{x} \approx 17.14$, $\sigma \approx 3.52$ **45.** $\bar{x} = 7.5$, $\sigma \approx 2.67$ **46.** not a random sample; they will all begin with the letter "a" **47.** not a random sample; the lawyers will choose jurors that are likely to support their side **48.** random sample; all students have an equal chance to be chosen **49.** not a random sample; the five with the largest (or smallest) circulation size will be picked **50.** People at the bus station may be less likely to own a car and therefore less likely to be in favor of a new garage. **51.** $\frac{1}{2}$ **52.** $\frac{1}{3}$
53. ≈ 0.14 **54.** ≈ 0.0710 **55.** ≈ 0.2066 **56.** ≈ 0.1766 **57.** $21a^5b^2$ **58.** $56a^3b^5$ **59.** continuous **60.** discrete **61.** discrete **62.** continuous **63.** 16%; 2.5%

Chapter 12

Get Ready! p. 761

1. 6 **2.** $\frac{1}{3}$ **3.** $-\frac{3}{8}$ **4.** $\frac{7}{72}$ **5.** -9 **6.** 11 **7.** 3 **8.** $\left(\frac{1}{2}, -4\right)$ **9.** $\left(-\frac{2}{3}, -\frac{2}{3}\right)$ **10.** $\left(\frac{3}{4}, \frac{11}{4}\right)$ **11.** $(7, 9, -6)$ **12.** $(0, 0, 8)$ **13.** $(7, 5, 0)$

Lesson 12-1 pp. 764–770

Got It?
1a. $\begin{bmatrix} -15 & 25 \\ -1 & 1 \\ -2 & 15 \end{bmatrix}$ **b.** $\begin{bmatrix} -9 & 23 \\ -5 & 9 \\ 0 & 5 \end{bmatrix}$
c. Yes; it does not matter in which order you add matrices.
2. $A = \begin{bmatrix} 3 & 6 & -1 \\ 1 & 3 & 7 \\ 1 & 1 & 3 \end{bmatrix}$ **3a.** $\begin{bmatrix} 0 & 0 \\ 0 & 0 \end{bmatrix}$ **b.** $\begin{bmatrix} -1 & 10 & -5 \\ 0 & 2 & -3 \end{bmatrix}$
4a. $x = 6$, $y = -6$ **b.** $x = 4$, $y = -3$, $z = 2$
Lesson Check
1. $\begin{bmatrix} 1 & 1 \\ -2 & 8 \end{bmatrix}$ **2.** $\begin{bmatrix} 1 & -9 & 8 \\ -3 & -1 & 8 \end{bmatrix}$ **3.** $\begin{bmatrix} -3 & 4 \\ -5 & 11 \end{bmatrix}$ **4.** $\begin{bmatrix} 6 & 10 \\ 13 & -4 \end{bmatrix}$
5. Yes; the elements in each of the corresponding positions are equal.
6. The elements were not subtracted. The correct answer is $\begin{bmatrix} 6 \\ 5 \end{bmatrix} - \begin{bmatrix} 3 \\ 7 \end{bmatrix} = \begin{bmatrix} 3 \\ -2 \end{bmatrix}$

Exercises
7. $\begin{bmatrix} 6 & 5 & 4 \\ 2 & -1 & 7 \end{bmatrix}$ **9.** $\begin{bmatrix} 3.9 & -2.3 \\ -0.6 & 9.1 \end{bmatrix}$ **11.** $\begin{bmatrix} 4 & -8 \\ -1 & -1 \\ 11 & 1 \end{bmatrix}$
13. $\begin{bmatrix} 6 & 2 \\ -1 & 3 \end{bmatrix}$ **15.** $\begin{bmatrix} 2 & -3 & 4 \\ 5 & 6 & -7 \end{bmatrix}$
17. $x = -2$, $y = 3$, $z = 1$ **19.** $\begin{bmatrix} 0 & 5 \\ 8 & -6 \\ 0 & 5 \end{bmatrix}$ **21.** $\begin{bmatrix} 6 & 3 \\ -3 & 3 \end{bmatrix}$
23. $\begin{bmatrix} -4 & 1 \\ -3 & -1 \end{bmatrix}$ **25a.** $\begin{bmatrix} 952 \\ 720 \\ 1108 \\ 1172 \\ 1044 \end{bmatrix}$; $\begin{bmatrix} 760 \\ 832 \\ 1252 \\ 1144 \\ 1064 \end{bmatrix}$
b. Allen: 4996; Iagorashvili: 5052
27. Matrix B would have the same dimensions as A. Its elements would be the opposites of the corresponding elements in A.
29. $c = \frac{5}{2}$, $d = \frac{2}{5}$, $f = 7$, $g = 5$, $h = -1$
31. Consider any two 2×2 matrices, $A = \begin{bmatrix} a & b \\ c & d \end{bmatrix}$ and $B = \begin{bmatrix} w & x \\ y & z \end{bmatrix}$. By the definition of matrix addition and the Comm. Prop. of Add.

$$A + B = \begin{bmatrix} a & b \\ c & d \end{bmatrix} + \begin{bmatrix} w & x \\ y & z \end{bmatrix} = \begin{bmatrix} a + w & b + x \\ c + y & d + z \end{bmatrix}$$
$$= \begin{bmatrix} w + a & x + b \\ y + c & z + d \end{bmatrix} = \begin{bmatrix} w & x \\ y & z \end{bmatrix} + \begin{bmatrix} a & b \\ c & d \end{bmatrix}$$
$$= B + A$$

33. B **35.** B **37.** 68% **38.** 97.5% **39.** 47.5% **40.** 2, -6 **41.** $\frac{2}{3}$, 2 **42.** $-\frac{1}{2}$, -6 **43.** 5, 0 **44.** $\begin{bmatrix} 9 & 15 \\ 6 & 24 \end{bmatrix}$ **45.** $\begin{bmatrix} -20 \\ 35 \end{bmatrix}$

Lesson 12-2 pp. 772–779

Got It?
1. $\begin{bmatrix} 8 & 24 & -19 \\ -3 & 9 & 10 \end{bmatrix}$ **2.** $\begin{bmatrix} 5 & -1 \\ \frac{7}{3} & 0 \end{bmatrix}$ **3a.** $\begin{bmatrix} -6 & 0 \\ -9 & 11 \end{bmatrix}$
b. $\begin{bmatrix} -3 & 7 \\ 6 & 8 \end{bmatrix}$ **c.** No; explanations may vary. Sample: For the matrices in parts (a) and (b), $AB = \begin{bmatrix} -6 & 0 \\ -9 & 11 \end{bmatrix}$ and $BA = \begin{bmatrix} -3 & 7 \\ 6 & 8 \end{bmatrix}$, so $AB \ne BA$. **4.** player from 1994: 100 pts., player from 2006: 81 pts. **5a.** no **b.** yes **c.** yes **d.** no **e.** yes

Lesson Check
1. $\begin{bmatrix} 6 & -2 \\ 4 & 0 \end{bmatrix}$ **2.** $\begin{bmatrix} -3 & 11 \\ -10 & 6 \end{bmatrix}$ **3.** $\begin{bmatrix} 5 & 7 \\ 2 & 6 \end{bmatrix}$ **4.** $\begin{bmatrix} 9 & -1 \\ -2 & 2 \end{bmatrix}$
5. Scalar; repeated matrix addition is repeated addition of each element of the matrix, which is the same as scalar multiplication of the matrix. **6.** The product of two matrices A and B exists only if the number of columns of A is equal to the number of rows of B. Since A is a 2×4 matrix with 4 columns and B is a 3×6 matrix with 3 rows and $4 \ne 3$, the product AB does not exist. Likewise, since $6 \ne 2$, the product BA does not exist.
Exercises
7. $\begin{bmatrix} 9 & 12 \\ 18 & -6 \\ 3 & 0 \end{bmatrix}$ **9.** $\begin{bmatrix} -3 & -6 \\ 9 & -3 \end{bmatrix}$ **11.** $\begin{bmatrix} 9 & 2 \\ 2 & 6 \\ 3 & -10 \end{bmatrix}$
13. $\begin{bmatrix} 19 & 11 \\ -12 & 10 \end{bmatrix}$ **15.** $\begin{bmatrix} 8 & -2.5 \\ -1.5 & -1 \end{bmatrix}$ **17.** $\begin{bmatrix} -4 & 8 \\ -22 & 2 \end{bmatrix}$
19. $\begin{bmatrix} 5 & -12 \\ 9 & -6 \end{bmatrix}$ **21.** $\begin{bmatrix} -8 & 0 \\ 0 & -8 \end{bmatrix}$ **23.** $[34 \quad 0]$
25. $\begin{bmatrix} -15 & 0 \\ 25 & 0 \end{bmatrix}$ **27.** $\begin{bmatrix} -2 \\ 5 \end{bmatrix}$ **29.** yes **31.** yes **33.** yes
35a. River's Edge: 99 pts.; West River: 97 pts. **b.** West River
37. $\begin{bmatrix} 9 & -6 \\ 15 & -3 \\ -6 & -12 \end{bmatrix}$ **39.** $\begin{bmatrix} 17 & -24 \\ -33 & -7 \\ 69 & -18 \end{bmatrix}$ **41.** $\begin{bmatrix} 34 & -1 \\ 6 & -13 \\ -7 & 16 \end{bmatrix}$
43. $\begin{bmatrix} -90 & 0 \\ -78 & 42 \\ -30 & -30 \end{bmatrix}$ **45.** yes **47.** yes **49.** B **51.** C
53. Since the center is at the origin, the vertices are $\left(\pm\frac{50}{2}, 0\right)$ and the co-vertices are $\left(0, \pm\frac{40}{2}\right)$. Using $\frac{x^2}{a^2} + \frac{y^2}{b^2} = 1$, $a = \pm 25$ and $b = \pm 20$, so $\frac{x^2}{625} + \frac{y^2}{400} = 1$.
54. $\begin{bmatrix} -33 & -12 \\ -6 & 27 \end{bmatrix}$ **55.** $\begin{bmatrix} 9 & -6 & 12 \\ 2 & 20 & 12 \end{bmatrix}$
56a. 12 **b.** 12 **c.** 0 **57a.** -12 **b.** -12 **c.** 0

Lesson 12-3 pp. 782–790

Got It? 1a. yes **b.** yes **c.** No; no matrix that is multiplied by the zero matrix will give an identity matrix. **2a.** 3 **b.** 0 **c.** -48 **3a.** 12 units^2 **b.** 28 units^2
4a. yes; $\begin{bmatrix} 1 & -1 \\ -\frac{3}{2} & 2 \end{bmatrix}$ **b.** no **c.** yes; $\begin{bmatrix} 3 & -4 \\ -5 & 7 \end{bmatrix}$
5a. 88, 68, 84, 60, 12, 32, 52, 72, 28, 30, 14, 18, 2, 8, 14, 20 **b.** Multiply the coded information by the inverse of the coding matrix: $\begin{bmatrix} 4 & 1 & 7 & 3 & 1 & 2 & 3 & 4 \\ 9 & 8 & 7 & 6 & 1 & 3 & 5 & 7 \end{bmatrix}$
Lesson Check 1. 16 **2.** 7 **3.** does not exist
4. yes; $\begin{bmatrix} 3 & -2 \\ -7 & 5 \end{bmatrix}$

5. The student did not subtract correctly.
$$\det\begin{bmatrix} 2 & 5 \\ -3 & 1 \end{bmatrix} = (2)(1) - (-3)(5) = 2 - (-15) = 2 + 15 = 17$$
6. A 2×3 matrix does not have a multiplicative inverse because it is not a square matrix. The number of rows must equal the number of columns for a multiplicative inverse to be possible.
Exercises 7. yes **9.** yes **11.** no **13.** 0 **15.** $-\frac{11}{40}$ **17.** 11 **19.** -6 **21.** -5 **23.** 106 **25.** 6 **27.** 466,250 mi^2
29. yes; $\begin{bmatrix} -1 & 3 \\ 1 & -2 \end{bmatrix}$ **31.** yes; $\begin{bmatrix} 0 & \frac{1}{2} \\ \frac{1}{3} & -\frac{1}{6} \end{bmatrix}$
33. yes; $\begin{bmatrix} -\frac{1}{8} & -\frac{1}{2} \\ \frac{3}{16} & \frac{1}{4} \end{bmatrix}$ **35.** yes; $\begin{bmatrix} 0 & \frac{1}{3} \\ -\frac{1}{2} & \frac{1}{6} \end{bmatrix}$
37. 2, 10, 10, 6, 9, 55, 15, 15, 9, 20 **39.** -120 **41.** 9 **43.** -3 **45.** 1 **47.** Answers may vary. Sample: Form a new matrix by switching the element in row 1, column 1 with the element in row 2, column 2. Then replace the other two elements with their opposites. Finally, divide each element by the determinant of the original matrix. **49.** 38 units^2
51. yes; $\begin{bmatrix} -5 & 7 \\ 3 & -4 \end{bmatrix}$ **53.** yes; $\begin{bmatrix} 0.5 & 0 \\ 0 & 0.5 \end{bmatrix}$
55. yes; $\begin{bmatrix} 0.4 & 0.4 & 0.2 \\ -0.6 & -0.6 & 0.2 \\ -0.2 & 0.8 & 0.4 \end{bmatrix}$
57. no inverse because the determinant equals zero
59. 6 **61.** $MN = \begin{bmatrix} ae + bg & af + bh \\ ce + dg & cf + dh \end{bmatrix}$

$$\det MN = (ae + bg)(cf + dh) - (af + bh)(ce + dg)$$
$$= acef + adeh + bcfg + bdgh - acef - adfg - bceh - bdgh$$
$$= adeh + bcfg - adfg - bceh$$

Also, $\det M \cdot \det N = (ad - bc)(eh - fg) = adeh - adfg - bceh + bcfg$.
So, $\det M \cdot \det N = \det MN$
63. $\frac{1}{2}$ **65.** 15 **67.** $\begin{bmatrix} 2 & 5 \\ 1 & 1 \end{bmatrix}$ **68.** $\begin{bmatrix} -10 & 19 \\ -20 & 7 \end{bmatrix}$ **69.** 720
70. 362,880 **71.** $1.08972864 \times 10^{10}$ **72.** 110,880 **73.** no solution **74.** $(6, 0, -3)$ **75.** $(3, -3, 9)$ **76.** $(-2, -1, -3)$

Lesson 12-4 pp. 792–800

Got It?
1a. $\begin{bmatrix} -8 \\ 9 \end{bmatrix}$ **b.** $\begin{bmatrix} -14 & -20 \\ 19 & 28 \end{bmatrix}$
c. Since matrix A has no inverse, the eq. has no solution.
2a. $\begin{bmatrix} 3 & -7 \\ 5 & 1 \end{bmatrix}\begin{bmatrix} x \\ y \end{bmatrix} = \begin{bmatrix} 8 \\ -2 \end{bmatrix}$

b. $\begin{bmatrix} 1 & 3 & 5 \\ -2 & 1 & -4 \\ 7 & -2 & 0 \end{bmatrix}\begin{bmatrix} x \\ y \\ z \end{bmatrix} = \begin{bmatrix} 12 \\ -2 \\ 7 \end{bmatrix}$

c. $\begin{bmatrix} 2 & -8 \\ -1 & 1 \end{bmatrix}\begin{bmatrix} x \\ y \end{bmatrix} = \begin{bmatrix} -3 \\ -4 \end{bmatrix}$

3a. (5, −21) **b.** no solution **4.** run: 32 min; jog: 8 min

Lesson Check

1. $\begin{bmatrix} -6 & 3 \\ 4 & -2 \end{bmatrix}\begin{bmatrix} x \\ y \end{bmatrix} = \begin{bmatrix} 8 \\ 10 \end{bmatrix}$ **2.** $\begin{bmatrix} 2 & 3 & 0 \\ 1 & -2 & 1 \\ 0 & 6 & -4 \end{bmatrix}\begin{bmatrix} x \\ y \\ z \end{bmatrix} = \begin{bmatrix} 12 \\ 9 \\ 8 \end{bmatrix}$

3. (5, 3) **4.** (−6, −6) **5.** The student did not separate the coefficient matrix and the variable matrix. The matrix eq. should be written as $\begin{bmatrix} 2 & 3 \\ -4 & 5 \end{bmatrix}\begin{bmatrix} x \\ y \end{bmatrix} = \begin{bmatrix} 5 \\ 1 \end{bmatrix}$.

6. Use matrix multiplication to combine the coefficient matrix and the variable matrix into a product matrix. Then set the first element in the product matrix equal to the first element in the constant matrix and set the second element in the product matrix equal to the second element in the constant matrix. The result will be a system of equations.;

$-2p + 3q = 2$
$4p + q = -5$

Exercises

7. $\begin{bmatrix} -15 & -17 \\ 26 & 29 \end{bmatrix}$ **9.** $\begin{bmatrix} \frac{29}{31} \\ -\frac{66}{217} \\ \frac{34}{217} \end{bmatrix}$ **11.** $\begin{bmatrix} 1 & 1 \\ 1 & -2 \end{bmatrix}\begin{bmatrix} x \\ y \end{bmatrix} = \begin{bmatrix} 5 \\ -4 \end{bmatrix}$; coefficient matrix: $\begin{bmatrix} 1 & 1 \\ 1 & -2 \end{bmatrix}$, variable matrix: $\begin{bmatrix} x \\ y \end{bmatrix}$, constant matrix: $\begin{bmatrix} 5 \\ -4 \end{bmatrix}$ **13.** $\begin{bmatrix} 3 & 5 \\ 1 & 1 \end{bmatrix}\begin{bmatrix} a \\ b \end{bmatrix} = \begin{bmatrix} 0 \\ 2 \end{bmatrix}$; coefficient matrix: $\begin{bmatrix} 3 & 5 \\ 1 & 1 \end{bmatrix}$, variable matrix: $\begin{bmatrix} a \\ b \end{bmatrix}$, constant matrix: $\begin{bmatrix} 0 \\ 2 \end{bmatrix}$

15. $\begin{bmatrix} 1 & -1 & 1 \\ 2 & 0 & 1 \\ 0 & 1 & 3 \end{bmatrix}\begin{bmatrix} r \\ s \\ t \end{bmatrix} = \begin{bmatrix} 150 \\ 425 \\ 0 \end{bmatrix}$; coefficient matrix: $\begin{bmatrix} 1 & -1 & 1 \\ 2 & 0 & 1 \\ 0 & 1 & 3 \end{bmatrix}$, variable matrix: $\begin{bmatrix} r \\ s \\ t \end{bmatrix}$, constant matrix: $\begin{bmatrix} 150 \\ 425 \\ 0 \end{bmatrix}$

17. (2, 1) **19.** $\left(\frac{1}{2}, 20\right)$ **21.** (3, 2) **23.** (2, −1, 3) **25.** (1, 2, −2) **27.** 2.5 lb of almonds, 3.5 lb of peanuts, and 3 lb of raisins **29.** (−2, −1) **31.** (−1, 0) **33.** (5, 0, 1) **35.** (1, 0, 3) **37.** (1, 1, 1, 1) **39.** (6, 2) **41.** (16, −22)

43. (5.4, 7.4) **45.** (6, 1) **47.** (2, −1, 4) **49.** length = 280 ft, width = 140 ft **51.** $\begin{bmatrix} -3 & 2 \\ -5 & 8 \end{bmatrix}$ **53.** $\begin{bmatrix} 10 \\ 3 \\ -2 \end{bmatrix}$ **55.** 14

57. Answers may vary. Sample: $y + z = 0$; $y + z = 1$

59. B **61.** A **63.** −44 **64.** 4913 **65.** −218

66. $34.\overline{4}$; 30.9; 5.56 **67.** 4.17; 1.32; 1.15 **68.** $19.\overline{6}$ m; $22.\overline{2}$ m; 4.7 m **69.** 57.4 mi; 345.44 mi²; 18.6 mi

70. 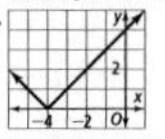

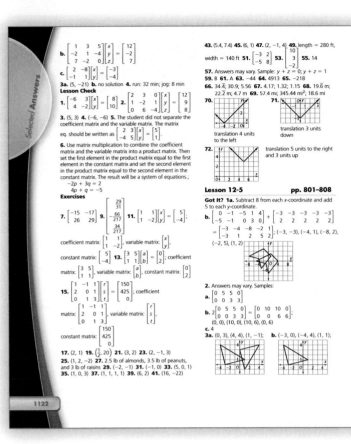

translation 4 units to the left

71. 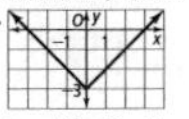

translation 3 units down

72. 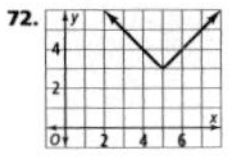

translation 5 units to the right and 3 units up

Lesson 12-5 pp. 801–808

Got It? 1a. Subtract 8 from each x-coordinate and add 5 to each y-coordinate.

b. $\begin{bmatrix} 0 & -1 & -5 & 1 & 4 \\ -5 & -1 & 0 & 3 & 0 \end{bmatrix} + \begin{bmatrix} -3 & -3 & -3 & -3 & -3 \\ 2 & 2 & 2 & 2 & 2 \end{bmatrix} = \begin{bmatrix} -3 & -4 & -8 & -2 & 1 \\ -3 & 1 & 2 & 5 & 2 \end{bmatrix}$; (−3, −3), (−4, 1), (−8, 2), (−2, 5), (1, 2)

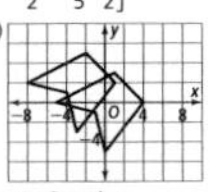

2. Answers may vary. Samples:

a. $\begin{bmatrix} 0 & 5 & 5 & 0 \\ 0 & 0 & 3 & 3 \end{bmatrix}$

b. $2\begin{bmatrix} 0 & 5 & 5 & 0 \\ 0 & 0 & 3 & 3 \end{bmatrix} = \begin{bmatrix} 0 & 10 & 10 & 0 \\ 0 & 0 & 6 & 6 \end{bmatrix}$; (0, 0), (10, 0), (10, 6), (0, 6)

c. 4

3a. (0, 3), (4, 4), (1, −1);

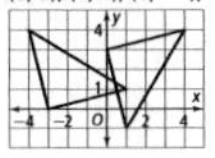

b. (−3, 0), (−4, 4), (1, 1);

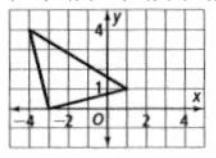

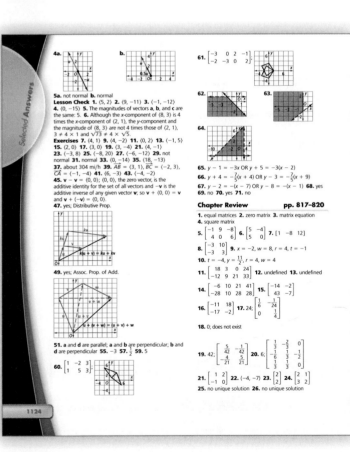

4a. (1, −1), (3, −1), (6, −4), (1, −3);

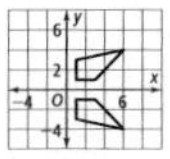

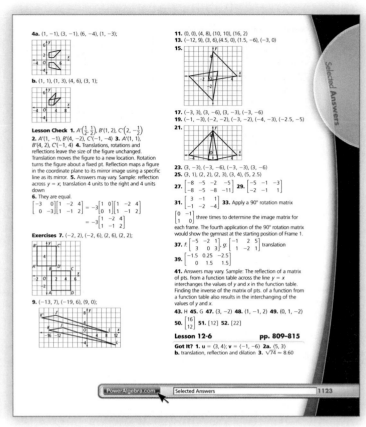

b. (1, 1), (1, 3), (4, 6), (3, 1);

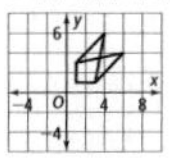

Lesson Check 1. $A'\left(\frac{1}{2}, \frac{1}{2}\right)$, $B'(1, 2)$, $C'\left(2, -\frac{1}{2}\right)$ **2.** $A'(1, -1)$, $B'(4, -2)$, $C'(-1, -4)$ **3.** $A'(1, 1)$, $B'(4, 2)$, $C'(-1, 4)$ **4.** Translations, rotations and reflections leave the size of the figure unchanged. Translation moves the figure to a new location. Rotation turns the figure about a fixed pt. Reflection maps a figure in the coordinate plane to its mirror image using a specific line as its mirror. **5.** Answers may vary. Sample: reflection across $y = x$; translation 4 units to the right and 4 units down

6. They are equal.

$\begin{bmatrix} -3 & 0 \\ 0 & -3 \end{bmatrix}\begin{bmatrix} 1 & -2 & 4 \\ 1 & -1 & 2 \end{bmatrix} = -3\begin{bmatrix} 1 & 0 \\ 0 & 1 \end{bmatrix}\begin{bmatrix} 1 & -2 & 4 \\ 1 & -1 & 2 \end{bmatrix} = -3\begin{bmatrix} 1 & -2 & 4 \\ 1 & -1 & 2 \end{bmatrix}$

Exercises 7. (−2, 2), (−2, 6), (2, 6), (2, 2);

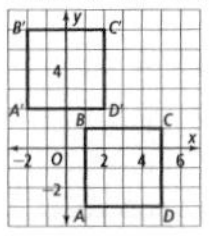

9. (−13, 7), (−19, 6), (9, 0);

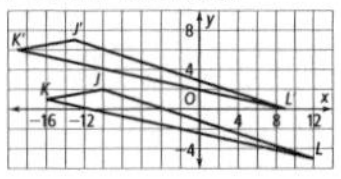

11. (0, 0), (4, 8), (10, 10), (16, 2)

13. (−12, 9), (3, 6), (4.5, 0), (1.5, −6), (−3, 0)

15. 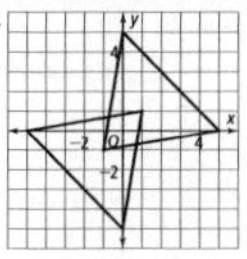

17. (−3, 3), (3, −6), (3, −3), (−3, −6)

19. (−1, −3), (−2, −2), (−3, −2), (−4, −3), (−2.5, −5)

21. 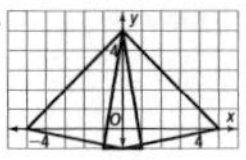

23. (3, −3), (−3, −6), (−3, −3), (3, −6)

25. (3, 1), (2, 2), (2, 3), (3, 4), (5, 2.5)

27. $\begin{bmatrix} -8 & -5 & -2 & -5 \\ -8 & -5 & -8 & -11 \end{bmatrix}$ **29.** $\begin{bmatrix} -5 & -1 & -3 \\ -2 & -1 & 1 \end{bmatrix}$

31. $\begin{bmatrix} 3 & -1 & 1 \\ -1 & -2 & -4 \end{bmatrix}$ **33.** Apply a 90° rotation matrix $\begin{bmatrix} 0 & -1 \\ 1 & 0 \end{bmatrix}$ three times to determine the image matrix for each frame. The fourth application of the 90° rotation matrix would show the gymnast at the starting position of Frame 1.

37. f: $\begin{bmatrix} -5 & -2 & 1 \\ 3 & 0 & 3 \end{bmatrix}$, g: $\begin{bmatrix} -1 & 2 & 5 \\ 1 & -2 & 1 \end{bmatrix}$ translation

39. $\begin{bmatrix} -1.5 & 0.25 & -2.5 \\ 0 & 1.5 & 1.5 \end{bmatrix}$

41. Answers may vary. Sample: The reflection of a matrix of pts. from a function table across the line $y = x$ interchanges the values of y and x in the function table. Finding the inverse of the matrix of pts. of a function from a function table also results in the interchanging of the values of y and x.

43. H **45.** G **47.** (3, −2) **48.** (1, −1, 2) **49.** (0, 1, −2)

50. $\begin{bmatrix} 16 \\ 12 \end{bmatrix}$ **51.** [12] **52.** [22]

Lesson 12-6 pp. 809–815

Got It? 1. **u** = ⟨3, 4⟩; **v** = ⟨−1, −6⟩ **2a.** ⟨5, 3⟩ **b.** translation, reflection and dilation **3.** $\sqrt{74} \approx 8.60$

4a. 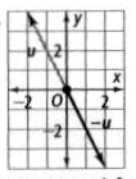

b. 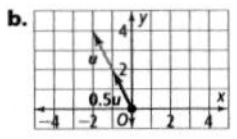

5a. not normal **b.** normal

Lesson Check 1. ⟨5, 2⟩ **2.** ⟨9, −11⟩ **3.** ⟨−1, −12⟩ **4.** ⟨0, −15⟩ **5.** The magnitudes of vectors **a**, **b**, and **c** are the same: 5. **6.** Although the x-component of ⟨8, 3⟩ is 4 times the x-component of ⟨2, 1⟩, the y-component and the magnitude of ⟨8, 3⟩ are not 4 times those of ⟨2, 1⟩, $3 \neq 4 \times 1$ and $\sqrt{73} \neq 4 \times \sqrt{5}$.

Exercises 7. ⟨4, 1⟩ **9.** ⟨4, −2⟩ **11.** ⟨0, 2⟩ **13.** ⟨−1, 5⟩ **15.** ⟨2, 0⟩ **17.** ⟨3, 0⟩ **19.** ⟨3, −4⟩ **21.** ⟨4, −1⟩ **23.** ⟨−3, 8⟩ **25.** ⟨−8, 20⟩ **27.** ⟨−6, −12⟩ **29.** not normal **31.** normal **33.** ⟨0, −14⟩ **35.** ⟨18, −13⟩ **37.** about 304 mi/h **39.** $\overrightarrow{AB} = \langle 3, 1\rangle$, $\overrightarrow{BC} = \langle -2, 3\rangle$, $\overrightarrow{CA} = \langle -1, -4\rangle$ **41.** ⟨6, −3⟩ **43.** ⟨−4, −2⟩

45. **v** − **v** = ⟨0, 0⟩; ⟨0, 0⟩, the zero vector, is the additive identity for the set of all vectors and −**v** is the additive inverse of any given vector **v**; so **v** + ⟨0, 0⟩ = **v** and **v** + (−**v**) = ⟨0, 0⟩.

47. yes; Distributive Prop.

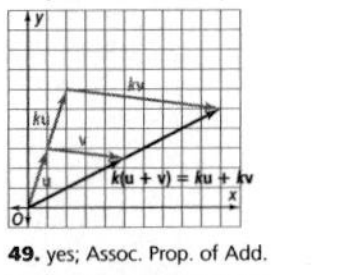

49. yes; Assoc. Prop. of Add.

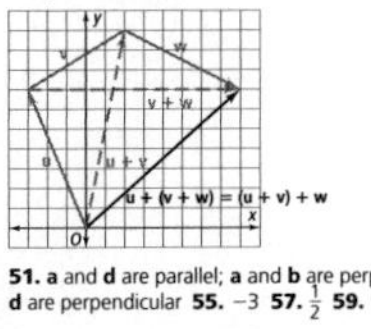

51. **a** and **d** are parallel; **a** and **b** are perpendicular; **b** and **d** are perpendicular **55.** −3 **57.** $\frac{1}{2}$ **59.** 5

60. $\begin{bmatrix} 1 & -2 & 3 \\ 1 & 5 & 3 \end{bmatrix}$; 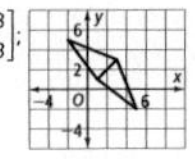

61. $\begin{bmatrix} -3 & 0 & 2 & -1 \\ -2 & -3 & 0 & 2 \end{bmatrix}$; 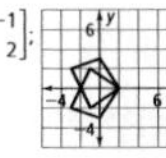

62. 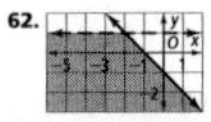

63. 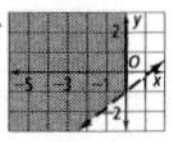

64. 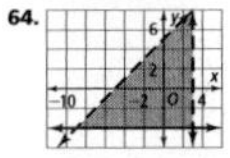

65. $y - 1 = -3x$ OR $y + 5 = -3(x - 2)$

66. $y + 4 = -\frac{7}{5}(x + 4)$ OR $y - 3 = -\frac{7}{5}(x + 9)$

67. $y - 2 = -(x - 7)$ OR $y - 8 = -(x - 1)$ **68.** yes **69.** no **70.** yes **71.** no

Chapter Review pp. 817–820

1. equal matrices **2.** zero matrix **3.** matrix equation **4.** square matrix

5. $\begin{bmatrix} -1 & 9 & -8 \\ 4 & 0 & 6 \end{bmatrix}$ **6.** $\begin{bmatrix} 5 & -4 \\ 5 & 0 \end{bmatrix}$ **7.** [1 −8 12]

8. $\begin{bmatrix} -3 & 10 \\ -3 & 3 \end{bmatrix}$ **9.** $x = -2, w = 8, r = 4, t = -1$

10. $t = -4, y = \frac{11}{2}, r = 4, w = 4$

11. $\begin{bmatrix} 18 & 3 & 0 & 24 \\ -12 & 9 & 21 & 33 \end{bmatrix}$ **12.** undefined **13.** undefined

14. $\begin{bmatrix} -6 & 10 & 21 & 41 \\ -28 & 10 & 28 & 28 \end{bmatrix}$ **15.** $\begin{bmatrix} -14 & -2 \\ 43 & -7 \end{bmatrix}$

16. $\begin{bmatrix} -11 & 18 \\ -17 & -2 \end{bmatrix}$ **17.** 24; $\begin{bmatrix} \frac{1}{6} & -\frac{1}{24} \\ 0 & \frac{1}{4} \end{bmatrix}$

18. 0; does not exist

19. 42; $\begin{bmatrix} \frac{5}{42} & -\frac{1}{42} \\ -\frac{4}{21} & \frac{5}{21} \end{bmatrix}$ **20.** 6; $\begin{bmatrix} \frac{1}{3} & -\frac{2}{3} & 0 \\ -\frac{1}{6} & \frac{1}{3} & -\frac{1}{2} \\ \frac{1}{3} & \frac{1}{3} & 0 \end{bmatrix}$

21. $\begin{bmatrix} 1 & 2 \\ -1 & 0 \end{bmatrix}$ **22.** (−4, −7) **23.** $\begin{bmatrix} 2 \\ 2 \end{bmatrix}$ **24.** $\begin{bmatrix} 2 & 1 \\ 3 & 2 \end{bmatrix}$

25. no unique solution **26.** no unique solution

27. $\begin{bmatrix} 0 & -5 & -2 \\ 5 & 4 & 9 \end{bmatrix}$ **28.** $\begin{bmatrix} -3 & 2 & -1 \\ 1 & 0 & 5 \end{bmatrix}$ **29.** $\begin{bmatrix} 1 & 0 & 5 \\ 3 & -2 & 1 \end{bmatrix}$

30. $\begin{bmatrix} 1.5 & -1 & 0.5 \\ 0.5 & 0 & 2.5 \end{bmatrix}$ **31.** $\begin{bmatrix} 6 & -4 & 2 \\ 2 & 0 & 10 \end{bmatrix}$ **32.** $\begin{bmatrix} 1 & 0 & 5 \\ -3 & 2 & -1 \end{bmatrix}$

33. ⟨−1, 8⟩; about 8.1 **34.** ⟨7, −5⟩; about 8.6 **35.** ⟨−9, 12⟩; 15 **36.** ⟨−2, 14⟩; about 14.1 **37.** ⟨−8, 14⟩; about 16.1 **38.** ⟨−4, 21⟩; about 21.4 **39.** 0; normal **40.** 0; normal

Chapter 13

Get Ready! p. 825

1. vert. asymptote: $x = 3$ **2.** vert. asymptotes: $x = -\frac{1}{2}$ and $x = 4$ **3.** $\frac{2b}{a}$ **4.** $\frac{55}{18}$ **5.** $\frac{3}{2(c + d)}$ **6.** $\frac{c}{16}$ **7.** $\frac{c + 4}{9}$ **8.** $\frac{16}{x}$ **9.** $\frac{15}{7}$ **10.** 6 **11.** 4, 1; $a_n = 19 - 3n$, explicit or $a_1 = 16$, $a_n = a_{n-1} - 3$, recursive

12. −216, −343; $a_n = -n^3$, explicit

13. $(x - 1)^2 + (y + 4)^2 = 16$;

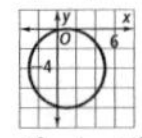

14. $\frac{(x - 2)^2}{9} + \frac{(y - 5)^2}{4} = 1$;

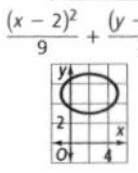

15. $y = \frac{1}{32}x^2 - 3$;

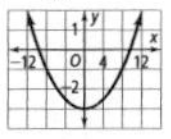

16. $\frac{(y - 1)^2}{9} - \frac{(x - 6)^2}{16} = 1$;

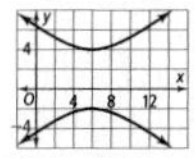

17. Answers may vary. Sample: Similar data tends to recur after a certain period has lapsed. In this case, 12 months.

Lesson 13-1 pp. 828–834

Got It? 1a. from $x = -3$ to $x = 1$ or from $x = 0$ to $x = 4$; 4 **b.** from $x = -4$ to $x = -1$ or from $x = 0$ to $x = 3$; 3 **2a.** no **b.** yes; 4 **c.** 15 cycles; $\frac{1}{3}$ s; $\frac{1}{440}$ s **3a.** 1.5; $y = -0.5$ **b.** 1.5; $y = 0.5$

4. period: 0.006; amplitude: 0.25; $y = -0.75$

Lesson Check 1. periodic; 5 **2.** no **3.** Answers may vary. Sample: hands of a clock, phases of the moon

4. The amplitude is not 2, but $\frac{2}{2} = 1$. **5.** $f(6) = f(11) = 2$; for any x, $f(x + 5)$ will always equal $f(x)$ because the period is 5. **6.** −4

Exercises 7. $x = -2$ to $x = 3$, $x = 2$ to $x = 7$; 5 **9.** $x = 0$ to $x = 4$, $x = 2$ to $x = 6$; 4 **11.** periodic; 12 **13.** not periodic **15.** periodic; 7 **17.** 3; $y = -1$

19. 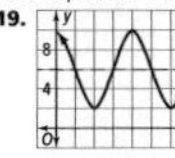

1 unit on the x-axis is 0.005 s.

21. a. y **b.** x **23.** repeating of a pattern at regular intervals **25. a.** 1 s **b.** 1.5 mV

27. 3, −3, 4;

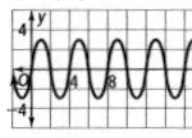

29. 4, −4, 8;

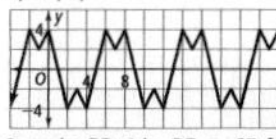

31. 2 weeks **33.** 1 hr **35. a.** 67 **b.** 70 **c.** 70 **d.** 67 **37.** C **39.** B **41.** 64 s; The first two functions are at the beginning of their cycles together every 6 · 7 = 42 seconds: 42, 84, 126, . . . The third function is at the beginning of its cycle every 8 seconds, starting at (42 + 20) seconds: 62, 70, 78, 86, 94, 102, 110, 118, 126, . . . The three functions are all at the beginning of their cycles at 126 seconds, which is 64 seconds after the third function achieves its first maximum. **42.** about 302 mph

43. 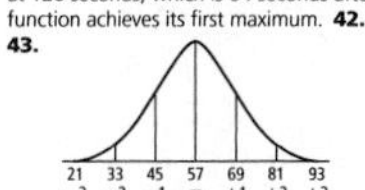
21 −3 std dev
33 −2 std dev
45 −1 std dev
57 m
69 +1 std dev
81 +2 std dev
93 +3 std dev

44. $x^2 + y^2 = 1$ **45.** $x^2 + y^2 = 13$ **46.** $x^2 + y^2 = 25$ **47.** $x^2 + y^2 = 2$ **48.** $x^2 + y^2 = 1$ **49.** $x^2 + y^2 = 1$

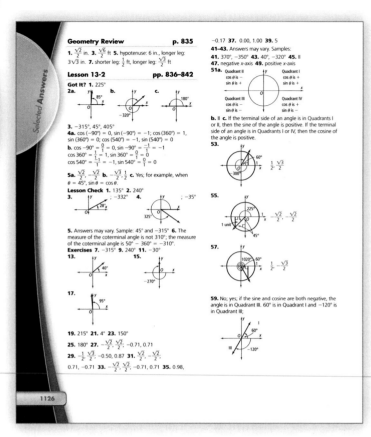

Geometry Review   p. 835

1. $\frac{\sqrt{2}}{2}$ in. **3.** $\frac{\sqrt{6}}{2}$ ft **5.** hypotenuse: 6 in., longer leg: $3\sqrt{3}$ in. **7.** shorter leg: $\frac{1}{2}$ ft, longer leg: $\frac{\sqrt{3}}{2}$ ft

Lesson 13-2   pp. 836–842

Got It? 1. 225°
2a. [graph] **b.** [graph] **c.** [graph]
3. −315°, 45°, 405°
4a. cos (−90°) = 0, sin (−90°) = −1; cos (360°) = 1, sin (360°) = 0; cos (540°) = −1, sin (540°) = 0
b. cos −90° = $\frac{0}{1}$ = 0, sin −90° = $\frac{-1}{1}$ = −1
cos 360° = $\frac{1}{1}$ = 1, sin 360° = $\frac{0}{1}$ = 0
cos 540° = $\frac{-1}{1}$ = −1, sin 540° = $\frac{0}{1}$ = 0
5a. $\frac{\sqrt{2}}{2}$, $-\frac{\sqrt{2}}{2}$ **b.** $-\frac{\sqrt{3}}{2}$, $\frac{1}{2}$ **c.** Yes; for example, when $\theta = 45°$, sin θ = cos θ.
Lesson Check 1. 135° **2.** 240°
3. [graph]; −332° **4.** [graph]; −35°
5. Answers may vary. Sample: 45° and −315° **6.** The measure of the coterminal angle is not 310°; the measure of the coterminal angle is 50° − 360° = −310°.
Exercises 7. −315° **9.** 240° **11.** −30°
13. [graph] **15.** [graph]
17. [graph]
19. 215° **21.** 4" **23.** 150°
25. 180° **27.** $-\frac{\sqrt{2}}{2}$, $\frac{\sqrt{2}}{2}$, −0.71, 0.71
29. $-\frac{1}{2}$, $\frac{\sqrt{3}}{2}$, −0.50, 0.87 **31.** $\frac{\sqrt{3}}{2}$, $-\frac{\sqrt{2}}{2}$, 0.71, −0.71 **33.** $-\frac{\sqrt{2}}{2}$, $\frac{\sqrt{2}}{2}$, −0.71, 0.71 **35.** 0.98,

−0.17 **37.** 0.00, 1.00 **39.** 5
41–43. Answers may vary. Samples:
41. 370°, −350° **43.** 40°, −320° **45.** II
47. negative x-axis **49.** positive x-axis
51a.

Quadrant II	Quadrant I
cos θ is −	cos θ is +
sin θ is +	sin θ is +
Quadrant III	Quadrant IV
cos θ is −	cos θ is +
sin θ is −	sin θ is −

b. II **c.** If the terminal side of an angle is in Quadrants I or II, then the sine of the angle is positive. If the terminal side of an angle is in Quadrants I or IV, then the cosine of the angle is positive.
53. [graph] 60° $\frac{1}{2}$, $\frac{\sqrt{3}}{2}$
55. [graph] 225° $-\frac{\sqrt{2}}{2}$, $-\frac{\sqrt{2}}{2}$
57. [graph] 1020°, 60° $\frac{1}{2}$, $-\frac{\sqrt{3}}{2}$
59. No; yes; if the sine and cosine are both negative, the angle is in Quadrant III. 60° is in Quadrant I and −120° is in Quadrant III; [graph]

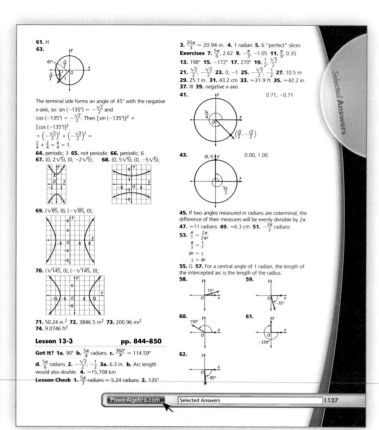

61. H
63. [graph]
The terminal side forms an angle of 45° with the negative x-axis, so: sin (−135°) = $-\frac{\sqrt{2}}{2}$ and cos (−135°) = $-\frac{\sqrt{2}}{2}$. Then $[\sin(-135°)]^2 + [\cos(-135°)]^2$ = $\left(-\frac{\sqrt{2}}{2}\right)^2 + \left(-\frac{\sqrt{2}}{2}\right)^2$ = $\frac{2}{4} + \frac{2}{4} = \frac{4}{4} = 1$.
64. periodic; 3 **65.** not periodic **66.** periodic; 6
67. $(0, 2\sqrt{5})$, $(0, -2\sqrt{5})$; [graph] **68.** $(0, 5\sqrt{5})$, $(0, -5\sqrt{5})$; [graph]
69. $(\sqrt{85}, 0)$, $(-\sqrt{85}, 0)$; [graph]
70. $(\sqrt{145}, 0)$, $(-\sqrt{145}, 0)$; [graph]
71. 50.24 in.² **72.** 3846.5 m² **73.** 200.96 mi²
74. 9.0746 ft²

Lesson 13-3   pp. 844–850

Got It? 1a. 90° **b.** $\frac{5\pi}{4}$ radians **c.** $\frac{360°}{\pi} \approx 114.59°$
d. $\frac{5\pi}{6}$ radians **2.** $-\frac{\sqrt{3}}{2}$, $-\frac{1}{2}$ **3a.** 6.3 in. **b.** Arc length would also double. **4.** ≈15,708 km
Lesson Check 1. $\frac{5\pi}{3}$ radians ≈ 5.24 radians **2.** 135°

3. $\frac{20\pi}{3} \approx 20.94$ in. **4.** 1 radian **5.** 6 "perfect" slices
Exercises 7. $\frac{5\pi}{6}$, 2.62 **9.** $-\frac{\pi}{3}$, −1.05 **11.** $\frac{\pi}{9}$, 0.35
13. 198° **15.** −172° **17.** 270° **19.** $\frac{1}{2}$, $\frac{\sqrt{3}}{2}$
21. $\frac{\sqrt{2}}{2}$, $-\frac{\sqrt{2}}{2}$ **23.** 0, −1 **25.** $-\frac{\sqrt{3}}{2}$, $-\frac{1}{2}$ **27.** 10.5 m
29. 25.1 in. **31.** 43.2 cm **33.** ≈31.9 ft **35.** ≈42.2 in.
37. III **39.** negative x-axis
41. [graph] 0.71, −0.71
43. [graph] (0, 1) 0.00, 1.00
45. If two angles measured in radians are coterminal, the difference of their measures will be evenly divisible by 2π.
47. ≈11 radians **49.** ≈6.3 in. **51.** $-\frac{3\pi}{2}$ radians
53. $\frac{\theta}{s} = \frac{2\pi}{2\pi r}$; $\frac{\theta}{s} = \frac{1}{r}$; $\theta r = s$; $s = \theta r$
55. G **57.** For a central angle of 1 radian, the length of the intercepted arc is the length of the radius.
58. [graph] 15° **59.** [graph] −75°
60. [graph] 150° **61.** [graph] −270°
62. [graph] −85°

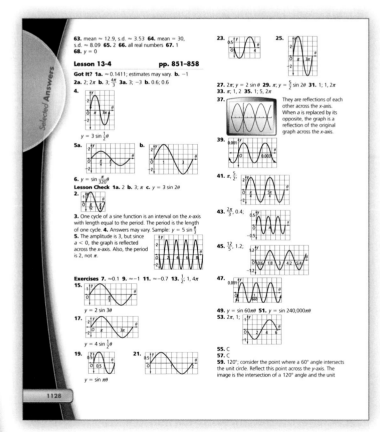

63. mean ≈ 12.9, s.d. ≈ 3.53 **64.** mean = 30, s.d. ≈ 8.09 **65.** 2 **66.** all real numbers **67.** 1 **68.** y = 0

Lesson 13-4   pp. 851–858

Got It? 1a. ≈0.1411; estimates may vary. **b.** −1
2a. 2; 2π **b.** 3; $\frac{4\pi}{3}$ **3a.** 3; **b.** 0.6; 0.6
4. [graph] $y = 3 \sin \frac{1}{2}\theta$
5a. [graph] **b.** [graph]
6. [graph] $y = \sin \frac{\pi}{320}\theta$
Lesson Check 1a. 2 **b.** 3; π **c.** y = 3 sin 2θ
2. [graph]
3. One cycle of a sine function is an interval on the x-axis with length equal to the period. The period is the length of one cycle. **4.** Answers may vary. Sample: $y = 5 \sin \frac{\theta}{5}$
5. The amplitude is 3, but since a < 0, the graph is reflected across the x-axis. Also, the period is 2, not π.
Exercises 7. ≈0.1 **9.** ≈−1 **11.** ≈−0.7 **13.** $\frac{1}{2}$, 4π
15. [graph] $y = 2 \sin 3\theta$
17. [graph] $y = 4 \sin \frac{1}{2}\theta$
19. [graph] $y = \sin \pi\theta$
21. [graph]

23. [graph] **25.** [graph]
27. 2π; y = 2 sin θ **29.** π; $y = \frac{5}{2} \sin 2\theta$ **31.** 1; 2π
33. π; 1, 2 **35.** 1; 5, 2π
37. [graph] They are reflections of each other across the x-axis. When a is replaced by its opposite, the graph is a reflection of the original graph across the x-axis.
39. [graph]
41. π, $\frac{5}{2}$ [graph]
43. $\frac{2\pi}{3}$, 0.4; [graph]
45. $\frac{12}{5}$, 1.2; [graph]
47. [graph]
49. y = sin 60πθ **51.** y = sin 240,000πθ
53. 2π, 1; [graph]
55. C
57. C
59. 120°; consider the point where a 60° angle intersects the unit circle. Reflect this point across the y-axis. The image is the intersection of a 120° angle and the unit

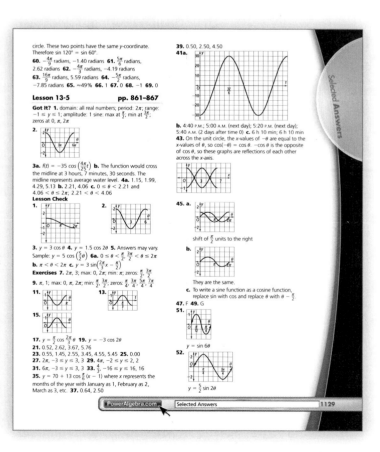

circle. These two points have the same y-coordinate. Therefore sin 120° = sin 60°.
60. $-\frac{4\pi}{9}$ radians, −1.40 radians **61.** $\frac{5\pi}{9}$ radians, 2.62 radians **62.** $-\frac{4\pi}{3}$ radians, −4.19 radians
63. $\frac{16\pi}{9}$ radians, 5.59 radians **64.** $-\frac{5\pi}{3}$ radians, −7.85 radians **65.** ≈49% **66.** 1 **67.** 0 **68.** −1 **69.** 0

Lesson 13-5   pp. 861–867

Got It? 1. domain: all real numbers; period: 2π; range: −1 ≤ y ≤ 1; amplitude: 1 sine: max at $\frac{\pi}{2}$; min at $\frac{3\pi}{2}$; zeros at 0, π, 2π
2. [graph]
3a. $f(t) = -35 \cos\left(\frac{4\pi}{25}t\right)$ **b.** The function would cross the midline at 3 hours, 7 minutes, 30 seconds. The midline represents average water level. **4a.** 1.15, 1.99, 4.29, 5.13 **b.** 2.21, 4.06 **c.** 0 ≤ θ < 2.21 and 4.06 < θ ≤ 2π; 2.21 < θ < 4.06
Lesson Check
1. [graph] **2.** [graph]
3. y = 3 cos θ **4.** y = 1.5 cos 2θ **5.** Answers may vary. Sample: $y = 5 \cos\left(\frac{1}{3}\theta\right)$ **6a.** $0 \le \theta < \frac{\pi}{3}$, $\frac{3\pi}{2} < \theta \le 2\pi$ **b.** π < θ < 2π **c.** $y = 3 \sin\left(\frac{2\pi}{3}x - \frac{\pi}{3}\right)$
Exercises 7. 2π, 3; max: 0, 2π; min: π; zeros: $\frac{\pi}{2}$, $\frac{3\pi}{2}$
9. π, 1; max: 0, π; min: $\frac{\pi}{2}$; zeros: $\frac{\pi}{4}$, $\frac{3\pi}{4}$, $\frac{5\pi}{4}$, $\frac{7\pi}{4}$
11. [graph] **13.** [graph]
15. [graph]
17. $y = \frac{\pi}{2} \cos \frac{2\pi}{3}\theta$ **19.** y = −3 cos 2θ
21. 0.52, 2.62, 3.67, 5.76
23. 0.55, 1.45, 2.55, 3.45, 4.55, 5.45 **25.** 0.00
27. 2π, −3 ≤ y ≤ 3, 3 **29.** 4π, −2 ≤ y ≤ 2, 2
31. 6π, −3 ≤ y ≤ 3, 3 **33.** $\frac{3}{4}$, −16 ≤ y ≤ 16, 16
35. $y = 70 + 13 \cos \frac{\pi}{6}(x - 1)$ where x represents the months of the year with January as 1, February as 2, March as 3, etc. **37.** 0.64, 2.50

39. 0.50, 2.50, 4.50
41a. [graph]
b. 4:40 P.M.; 5:00 A.M. (next day); 5:20 P.M. (next day); 5:40 A.M. (2 days after time 0) **c.** 6 h 10 min; 6 h 10 min
43. On the unit circle, the x-values of −θ are equal to the x-values of θ, so cos(−θ) = cos θ. −cos θ is the opposite of cos θ, so these graphs are reflections of each other across the x-axis. [graph]
45. a. [graph] shift of $\frac{\pi}{2}$ units to the right
b. [graph] They are the same.
c. To write a sine function as a cosine function, replace sin with cos and replace θ with $\theta - \frac{\pi}{2}$.
47. F **49.** G
51. [graph] y = sin 6θ
52. [graph] $y = \frac{5}{2} \sin 2\theta$

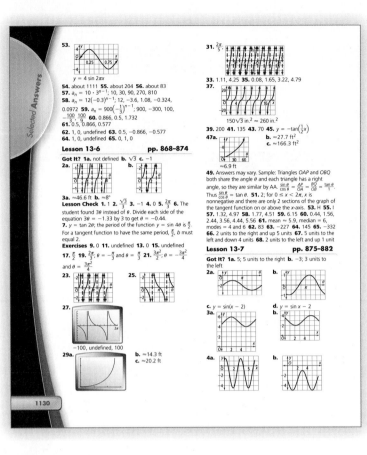

53. $y = 4 \sin 2\pi x$
54. about 1111 **55.** about 204 **56.** about 83
57. $a_n = 10 \cdot 3^{n-1}$; 10, 30, 90, 270, 810
58. $a_n = 12(-0.3)^{n-1}$; 12, -3.6, 1.08, -0.324, 0.0972 **59.** $a_n = 900\left(-\frac{1}{3}\right)^{n-1}$; 900, -300, 100, $-\frac{100}{3}$, $\frac{100}{9}$ **60.** 0.866, 0.5, 1.732
61. 0.5, 0.866, 0.577
62. 1, 0, undefined **63.** 0.5, -0.866, -0.577
64. 1, 0, undefined **65.** 0, 1, 0

Lesson 13-6 pp. 868–874
Got It? 1a. not defined **b.** $\sqrt{3}$ **c.** -1
2a. **b.**
3a. ≈46.6 ft **b.** ≈8°
Lesson Check 1. 1 **2.** $\frac{\sqrt{3}}{3}$ **3.** -1 **4.** 0 **5.** $\frac{2\pi}{3}$ **6.** The student found 3θ instead of θ. Divide each side of the equation $3\theta = -1.33$ by 3 to get $\theta = -0.44$.
7. $y = \tan 2\theta$; the period of the function $y = \sin 4\theta$ is $\frac{\pi}{2}$. For a tangent function to have the same period, $\frac{\pi}{2}$, b must equal 2.
Exercises 9. 0 **11.** undefined **13.** 0 **15.** undefined
17. $\frac{\pi}{2}$ **19.** $\frac{2\pi}{3}$; $\theta = -\frac{\pi}{3}$ and $\theta = \frac{\pi}{3}$ **21.** $\frac{3\pi}{2}$; $\theta = -\frac{3\pi}{4}$ and $\theta = \frac{3\pi}{4}$
23. **25.**
27. -100, undefined, 100
29a. **b.** ≈14.3 ft **c.** ≈20.2 ft

31. $\frac{2\pi}{5}$.
33. 1.11, 4.25 **35.** 0.08, 1.65, 3.22, 4.79
37. $150\sqrt{3}$ in.^{2} ≈ 260 in.^{2}
39. 200 **41.** 135 **43.** 70 **45.** $y = -\tan\left(\frac{1}{2}x\right)$
47a. **b.** ≈27.7 ft^2 **c.** ≈166.3 ft^2 ≈6.9 ft
49. Answers may vary. Sample: Triangles OAP and OBQ both share the angle θ and each triangle has a right angle, so they are similar by AA. $\frac{\sin\theta}{\cos\theta} = \frac{AP}{OA} = \frac{BQ}{OB} = \frac{\tan\theta}{1}$. Thus $\frac{\sin\theta}{\cos\theta} = \tan\theta$. **51.** 2; for $0 \le x < 2\pi$, x is nonnegative and there are only 2 sections of the graph of the tangent function on or above the x-axis. **53.** I **55.** I
57. 1.32, 4.97 **58.** 1.77, 4.51 **59.** 6.15 **60.** 0.44, 1.56, 2.44, 3.56, 4.44, 5.56 **61.** mean = 5.9, median = 6, modes = 4 and 6 **62.** 83 **63.** -227 **64.** 145 **65.** -332
66. 2 units to the right and up 5 units **67.** 5 units to the left and down 4 units **68.** 2 units to the left and up 1 unit

Lesson 13-7 pp. 875–882
Got It? 1a. 5; 5 units to the right **b.** -3; 3 units to the left
2a. **b.**
c. $y = \sin(x - 2)$ **d.** $y = \sin x - 2$
3a. **b.**
4a. **b.**

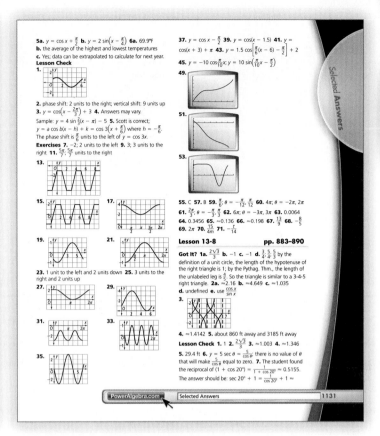

5a. $y = \cos x + \frac{\pi}{2}$ **b.** $y = 2\sin\left(x - \frac{\pi}{2}\right)$ **6a.** 69.9°F
b. the average of the highest and lowest temperatures
c. Yes; data can be extrapolated to calculate for next year.
Lesson Check
1.
2. phase shift: 2 units to the right; vertical shift: 9 units up
3. $y = \cos\left(x - \frac{2\pi}{3}\right) + 3$ **4.** Answers may vary.
Sample: $y = 4\sin\frac{\pi}{3}(x - \pi)$ **5.** Scott is correct; $y = a\cos b(x - h) + k = \cos 3\left(x + \frac{\pi}{6}\right)$ where $h = -\frac{\pi}{6}$. The phase shift is $\frac{\pi}{6}$ units to the left of $y = \cos 3x$.
Exercises 7. -2; 2 units to the left **9.** 3; 3 units to the right **11.** $\frac{5\pi}{7}, \frac{5\pi}{7}$; units to the right
13.
15. **17.**
19. **21.**
23. 1 unit to the left and 2 units down **25.** 3 units to the right and 2 units up
27. **29.**
31. **33.**
35.

37. $y = \cos x - \frac{\pi}{2}$ **39.** $y = \cos(x - 1.5)$ **41.** $y = \cos(x + 3) + \pi$ **43.** $y = 1.5\cos\left[\frac{\pi}{6}(x - 6) - \frac{\pi}{2}\right] + 2$
45. $y = -10\cos\frac{\pi}{10}x$; $y = 10\sin\left(\frac{\pi}{10}x - \frac{\pi}{2}\right)$
49.
51.
53.
55. C **57.** 8 **59.** $\frac{\pi}{6}$; $\theta = -\frac{\pi}{12}, \frac{5\pi}{12}$ **60.** 4π; $\theta = -2\pi, 2\pi$
61. $\frac{2\pi}{3}$; $\theta = -\frac{\pi}{3}, \frac{2\pi}{3}$ **62.** 6π; $\theta = -3\pi, 3\pi$ **63.** 0.0064
64. 0.3456 **65.** ≈0.136 **66.** ≈0.198 **67.** $\frac{13}{9}$ **68.** $-\frac{8}{5}$
69. 2π **70.** $\frac{15}{4m}$ **71.** $-\frac{t}{14}$

Lesson 13-8 pp. 883–890
Got It? 1a. $\frac{2\sqrt{3}}{3}$ **b.** -1 **c.** -1 **d.** $\frac{3}{4}, \frac{5}{4}, \frac{5}{3}$ by the definition of a unit circle, the length of the hypotenuse of the right triangle is 1; by the Pythag. Thm., the length of the unlabeled leg is $\frac{4}{5}$. So the triangle is similar to a 3-4-5 right triangle. **2a.** ≈2.16 **b.** ≈4.649 **c.** ≈1.035
d. undefined **e.** use $\frac{\cos x}{\sin x}$
3.
4. ≈1.4142 **5.** about 860 ft away and 3185 ft away
Lesson Check 1. 1 **2.** $\frac{2\sqrt{3}}{3}$ **3.** ≈1.003 **4.** ≈1.346
5. 29.4 ft **6.** $y = 5\sec\theta = \frac{5}{\cos\theta}$; there is no value of θ that will make $\frac{5}{\cos\theta}$ equal to zero. **7.** The student found the reciprocal of $(1 + \cos 20°) = \frac{1}{1 + \cos 20°} \approx 0.5155$. The answer should be: $\sec 20° + 1 = \frac{1}{\cos 20°} + 1 \approx$

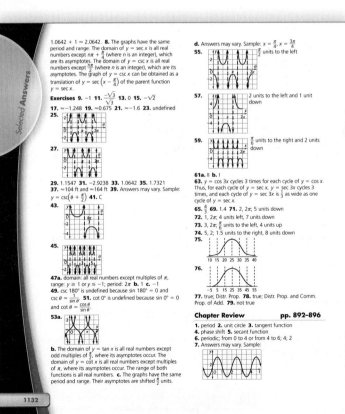

$1.0642 + 1 \approx 2.0642$. **8.** The graphs have the same period and range. The domain of $y = \sec x$ is all real numbers except $n\pi + \frac{\pi}{4}$ (where n is an integer), which are its asymptotes. The domain of $y = \csc x$ is all real numbers except $\frac{n\pi}{2}$ (where n is an integer), which are its asymptotes. The graph of $y = \csc x$ can be obtained as a translation of $y = \sec\left(x - \frac{\pi}{2}\right)$ of the parent function $y = \sec x$.
Exercises 9. -1 **11.** $\frac{-\sqrt{3}}{\sqrt{3}}$ **13.** 0 **15.** $-\sqrt{2}$
17. ≈-1.248 **19.** ≈0.675 **21.** ≈-1.6 **23.** undefined
25.
27.
29. 1.1547 **31.** -2.9238 **33.** 1.0642 **35.** 1.7321
37. ≈104 ft and ≈164 ft **39.** Answers may vary. Sample: $y = \csc\left(\theta + \frac{\pi}{2}\right)$ **41.** C
43.
45.
47a. domain: all real numbers except multiples of π, range: $y \ge 1$ or $y \le -1$; period: 2π **b.** 1 **c.** -1
49. csc 180° is undefined because sin 180° = 0 and $\csc\theta = \frac{1}{\sin\theta}$. **51.** cot 0° is undefined because sin 0° = 0 and $\cot\theta = \frac{\cos\theta}{\sin\theta}$.
53a.
b. The domain of $y = \tan x$ is all real numbers except odd multiples of $\frac{\pi}{2}$, where its asymptotes occur. The domain of $y = \cot x$ is all real numbers except multiples of π, where its asymptotes occur. The range of both functions is all real numbers. **c.** The graphs have the same period and range. Their asymptotes are shifted $\frac{\pi}{2}$ units.

d. Answers may vary. Sample: $x = \frac{\pi}{4}$, $x = \frac{3\pi}{4}$
55. $\frac{\pi}{2}$ units to the left
57. 2 units to the left and 1 unit down
59. $\frac{\pi}{6}$ units to the right and 2 units down
61a. II **b.** I
63. $y = \cos 3x$ cycles 3 times for each cycle of $y = \cos x$. Thus, for each cycle of $y = \sec x$, $y = \sec 3x$ cycles 3 times, and each cycle of $y = \sec 3x$ is $\frac{1}{3}$ as wide as one cycle of $y = \sec x$.
65. $\frac{5}{3}$ **69.** 1.4 **71.** 2, 2π; 5 units down
72. 1, 2π; 4 units left, 7 units down
73. 3, 2π; $\frac{\pi}{2}$ units to the left, 4 units up
74. 5, 2; 1.5 units to the right, 8 units down
75.
76.
77. true; Distr. Prop. **78.** true; Distr. Prop. and Comm. Prop. of Add. **79.** not true

Chapter Review pp. 892–896
1. period **2.** unit circle **3.** tangent function
4. phase shift **5.** secant function
6. periodic; from 0 to 4 or from 4 to 6; 4; 2
7. Answers may vary. Sample:

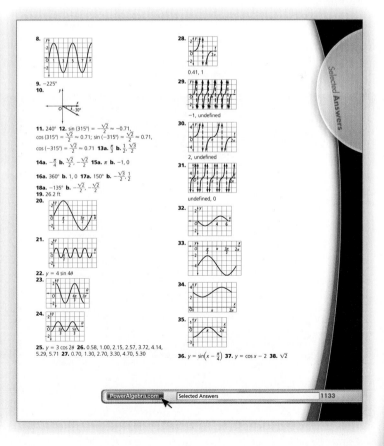

8.
9. -225°
10.
11. 240° **12.** $\sin(315°) = -\frac{\sqrt{2}}{2} \approx -0.71$, $\cos(315°) = \frac{\sqrt{2}}{2} \approx 0.71$; $\sin(-315°) = \frac{\sqrt{2}}{2} \approx 0.71$, $\cos(-315°) = \frac{\sqrt{2}}{2} \approx 0.71$ **13a.** $\frac{\sqrt{3}}{3}$ **b.** $\frac{1}{2}, \frac{\sqrt{3}}{2}$
14a. $-\frac{\pi}{6}$ **b.** $\frac{\sqrt{2}}{2}, -\frac{\sqrt{2}}{2}$ **15a.** π **b.** -1, 0
16a. 360° **b.** 1, 0 **17a.** 150° **b.** $-\frac{\sqrt{3}}{2}, \frac{1}{2}$
18a. -135° **b.** $-\frac{\sqrt{2}}{2}, -\frac{\sqrt{2}}{2}$
19. 26.2 ft
20.
21.
22. $y = 4\sin 4\theta$
23.
24.
25. $y = 3\cos 2\theta$ **26.** 0.58, 1.00, 2.15, 2.57, 3.72, 4.14, 5.29, 5.71 **27.** 0.70, 1.30, 2.70, 3.30, 4.70, 5.30

28. 0.41, 1
29. -1, undefined
30. 2, undefined
31. undefined, 0
32.
33.
34.
35.
36. $y = \sin\left(x - \frac{\pi}{4}\right)$ **37.** $y = \cos x - 2$ **38.** $\sqrt{2}$

39. $-\frac{\sqrt{3}}{3}$ **40.** 2 **41.** $\sqrt{3}$

42.

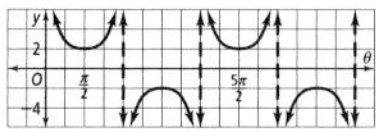

43.

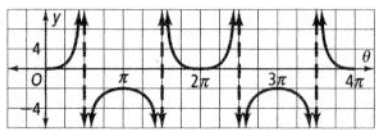

44.

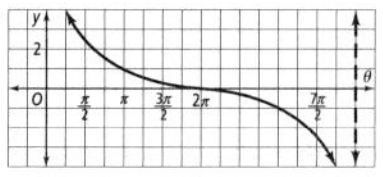

45.

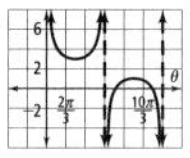

Chapter 14

Get Ready! p. 901

1. $x = \pm\frac{5}{2}$ **2.** $x = \pm\sqrt{23}$ **3.** $x = \pm 4\sqrt{\frac{5}{3}}$ **4.** $x = \pm\sqrt{\frac{11}{2}}$ **5.** $x = \pm\sqrt{30}$ **6.** $x = \pm 2$ **7.** $f^{-1}(x) = \frac{x-2}{5}$; domain of f and range of f^{-1}: all real numbers, range of f and domain of f^{-1}: all real numbers; yes **8.** $f^{-1}(x) = x^2 - 3$; domain of f and range of f^{-1}: all real numbers ≥ -3, domain of f^{-1}: all real numbers; range of f: all real numbers ≥ 0; yes **9.** $f^{-1}(x) = \frac{x^2+4}{3}$; domain of f and range of f^{-1}: all real numbers $\geq \frac{4}{3}$, domain of f^{-1}: all real numbers; range of f: all real numbers ≥ 0; yes **10.** $f^{-1}(x) = \frac{5}{x}$; domain of f and range of f^{-1}: all real numbers except 0, domain of f^{-1} and range of f: all real numbers except 0; yes **11.** $f^{-1}(x) = \frac{10}{x} + 1$; domain of f and range of f^{-1}: all real numbers except 1, domain of f^{-1} and range of f: all real numbers except 0; yes **12.** $f^{-1}(x) = \frac{10}{x+1}$; domain of f and range of f^{-1}: all real numbers except 0, domain of f^{-1} and range of f: all real numbers except -1; yes **13.** $x = -\frac{3}{2}$ **14.** $x = 0.002$ **15.** $x = 1.0646$ **16.** $x = 18257.4$ **17.** $x = 0.00003$ **18.** $x = 5$ **19.** 0.67; 0.74; 1.11 **20.** -0.26; -0.97; 3.73 **21.** 0.96; 0.28; 0.29 **22.** -0.87; 0.50; -0.58

23. Answers may vary. Sample: The eq. is true for all values of θ for which $\tan^2\theta$ and $\sec^2\theta$ are defined.
24. Answers may vary. Sample: the lengths of the sides of rt. triangles

Lesson 14-1 pp. 904–910

Got It? 1. all real numbers except multiples of π

2. $\frac{\csc\theta}{\sec\theta} = \frac{\left(\frac{1}{\sin\theta}\right)}{\left(\frac{1}{\cos\theta}\right)} = \frac{\cos\theta}{\sin\theta} = \cot\theta$; all real numbers except multiples of $\frac{\pi}{2}$

3a. $1 + \cot^2\theta = 1 + \left(\frac{\cos\theta}{\sin\theta}\right)^2$
$= 1 + \frac{\cos^2\theta}{\sin^2\theta}$
$= 1 + \frac{1-\sin^2\theta}{\sin^2\theta}$
$= 1 + \frac{1}{\sin^2\theta} - \frac{\sin^2\theta}{\sin^2\theta}$
$= 1 + \csc^2\theta - 1$
$= \csc^2\theta$

b. No; the domains of $\sin\theta$ and $\cos\theta$ are all real numbers, but the domains of $\tan\theta$, $\cot\theta$, $\sec\theta$, and $\csc\theta$ have restrictions.

4. $\sec^2\theta - \sec^2\theta\cos^2\theta$
$= \left(\frac{1}{\cos\theta}\right)^2 - \left(\frac{1}{\cos\theta}\right)^2\cos^2\theta$
$= \frac{1}{\cos^2\theta} - \frac{1}{\cos^2\theta}\cdot\cos^2\theta$
$= \frac{1}{\cos^2\theta} - \frac{\cos^2\theta}{\cos^2\theta}$
$= \frac{1-\cos^2\theta}{\cos^2\theta}$
$= \frac{\sin^2\theta}{\cos^2\theta}$
$= \tan^2\theta$

5. $\csc\theta$

Lesson Check

1. $\tan\theta\csc\theta$
$= \frac{\sin\theta}{\cos\theta}\cdot\frac{1}{\sin\theta}$
$= \frac{1}{\cos\theta}$
$= \sec\theta$

2. $\csc^2\theta - \cot^2\theta$
$= \left(\frac{1}{\sin\theta}\right)^2 - \left(\frac{\cos\theta}{\sin\theta}\right)^2$
$= \frac{1}{\sin^2\theta} - \frac{\cos^2\theta}{\sin^2\theta}$
$= \frac{1-\cos^2\theta}{\sin^2\theta}$
$= \frac{\sin^2\theta}{\sin^2\theta}$
$= 1$

3. $\sin\theta\tan\theta$
$= \sin\theta\cdot\frac{\sin\theta}{\cos\theta}$
$= \frac{\sin^2\theta}{\cos\theta}$
$= \frac{1-\cos^2\theta}{\cos\theta}$
$= \frac{1}{\cos\theta} - \frac{\cos^2\theta}{\cos\theta}$
$= \sec\theta - \cos\theta$

4. $\tan\theta\cot\theta - \sin^2\theta$
$= \tan\theta\frac{1}{\tan\theta} - \sin^2\theta$
$= \frac{\tan\theta}{\tan\theta} - \sin^2\theta$
$= 1 - \sin^2\theta$
$= \cos^2\theta$

5. Answers may vary. Sample: Letting a and b be the legs, and c the hypotenuse of a right triangle, the Pythagorean Theorem states that $a^2 + b^2 = c^2$. Dividing both sides by c^2, then $\frac{a^2}{c^2} + \frac{b^2}{c^2} = \left(\frac{a}{c}\right)^2 + \left(\frac{b}{c}\right)^2 = 1$. Calling the angle between a and c θ, then $\sin\theta = \frac{b}{c}$ and $\cos\theta = \frac{a}{c}$. By substitution, $\cos^2\theta + \sin^2\theta = 1$. **6.** wrong calculation: $2 - \cos^2\theta = 2 - (1 - \sin^2\theta) = 2 - 1 + \sin^2\theta = 1 + \sin^2\theta$

Exercises

7. $\cos\theta\cot\theta$
$= \cos\theta\left(\frac{\cos\theta}{\sin\theta}\right)$
$= \frac{1-\sin^2\theta}{\sin\theta}$
$= \frac{1}{\sin\theta} - \sin\theta$; all real numbers except multiples of π

9. $\cos\theta\tan\theta$
$= \cos\theta\left(\frac{\sin\theta}{\cos\theta}\right) = \sin\theta$; all real numbers except odd multiples of $\frac{\pi}{2}$

11. $\cos\theta\sec\theta$
$= \cos\theta\left(\frac{1}{\cos\theta}\right) = 1$; all real numbers except odd multiples of $\frac{\pi}{2}$

13. $\sin\theta\csc\theta$
$= \sin\theta\left(\frac{1}{\sin\theta}\right) = \frac{\sin\theta}{\sin\theta} = 1$; all real numbers except multiples of π

15. $\csc\theta - \sin\theta$
$= \frac{1}{\sin\theta} - \sin\theta$
$= \frac{1-\sin^2\theta}{\sin\theta}$
$= \frac{\cos^2\theta}{\sin\theta}$
$= \cot\theta\cos\theta$; all real numbers except odd multiples of $\frac{\pi}{2}$

17. $\sin^2\theta$ **19.** $-\cot^2\theta$ **21.** $\sin\theta$ **23.** 1 **25.** 1 **27.** 1 **29.** $\sec\theta$ **31.** $\sec^2\theta$ **33.** $\csc\theta$ **35.** $\sin^2\theta$ **37.** 1 **39.** 1 **41.** $\pm\sqrt{1-\cos^2\theta}$ **43.** $\pm\frac{\sqrt{1-\sin^2\theta}}{\sin\theta}$ **45.** $\pm\sqrt{\csc^2\theta - 1}$

47. $\sin^2\theta\tan^2\theta = \sin^2\theta\left(\frac{\sin^2\theta}{\cos^2\theta}\right)$
$= (1-\cos^2\theta)\left(\frac{\sin^2\theta}{\cos^2\theta}\right)$
$= \frac{\sin^2\theta - \sin^2\theta\cos^2\theta}{\cos^2\theta}$
$= \frac{\sin^2\theta}{\cos^2\theta} - \frac{\sin^2\theta\cos^2\theta}{\cos^2\theta}$
$= \tan^2\theta - \sin^2\theta$

49. $\sin\theta\cos\theta(\tan\theta + \cot\theta)$
$= \sin\theta\cos\theta\left(\frac{\sin\theta}{\cos\theta} + \frac{\cos\theta}{\sin\theta}\right)$
$= \frac{\sin^2\theta\cos\theta}{\cos\theta} + \frac{\cos^2\theta\sin\theta}{\sin\theta}$
$= \sin^2\theta + \cos^2\theta = 1$

51. $\frac{\sec\theta}{\cot\theta + \tan\theta}$
$= \frac{\frac{1}{\cos\theta}}{\frac{\cos\theta}{\sin\theta} + \frac{\sin\theta}{\cos\theta}}\cdot\frac{\sin\theta\cos\theta}{\sin\theta\cos\theta}$
$= \frac{\sin\theta}{\cos^2\theta + \sin^2\theta} = \frac{\sin\theta}{1} = \sin\theta$

53. $\frac{1-\sin^2\theta}{\sin^2\theta}$

55. $\sin^2\theta + \cos^2\theta = 1$
$(0.5)^2 + \cos^2\theta = 1$
$0.25 + \cos^2\theta = 1$
$\cos^2\theta = 1 - 0.25$
$\cos^2\theta = 0.75$
$\cos\theta = \pm\sqrt{0.75}$
Since θ is in the first quadrant, $\cos\theta$ is positive;
$\cos\theta = 0.866025404$
$\tan\theta = \frac{\sin\theta}{\cos\theta}$
$= \frac{0.5}{0.866025404}$
$= 0.577350269$

57. $\sin^2\theta + \cos^2\theta = 1$
$\sin^2\theta + (-0.6)^2 = 1$
$\sin^2\theta + 0.36 = 1$
$\sin^2\theta = 1 - 0.36$
$\sin^2\theta = 0.64$
$\sin\theta = \pm\sqrt{0.64}$
Since θ is in the third quadrant, $\sin\theta$ is negative; $\sin\theta = -0.8$

$\tan\theta = \frac{\sin\theta}{\cos\theta}$
$= \frac{-0.8}{-0.6}$
$= 1.333333333$

59. $\tan\theta = \frac{\sin\theta}{\cos\theta}$, $\sin^2\theta + \cos^2\theta = 1$, which can be rewritten as $\sin^2\theta = 1 - \cos^2\theta$
$1.2 = \frac{\sin\theta}{\cos\theta}$
$1.2^2 = \frac{\sin^2\theta}{\cos^2\theta}$
$1.44(\cos^2\theta) = \sin^2\theta$
$1.44(\cos^2\theta) = 1 - \cos^2\theta$
$1.44(\cos^2\theta) + \cos^2\theta = 1$
$2.44(\cos^2\theta) = 1$
$\cos^2\theta = \frac{1}{2.44}$
$\cos^2\theta = 0.409836066$
$\cos\theta = \pm\sqrt{0.409836066}$
Since θ is in the first quadrant, $\cos\theta$ is positive;
$\cos\theta = 0.640184400$
$\tan\theta = \frac{\sin\theta}{\cos\theta}$
$1.2 = \frac{\sin\theta}{0.640184400}$
$\sin\theta = 0.76822128$

61. $\sin^2\theta + \cos^2\theta = 1$
$(0.2)^2 + \cos^2\theta = 1$
$0.04 + \cos^2\theta = 1$
$\cos^2\theta = 1 - 0.04$
$\cos^2\theta = 0.96$
$\cos\theta = \pm\sqrt{0.96}$
Since $\sin\theta$ is positive and $\tan\theta$ is negative, θ is in the fourth quadrant, so $\cos\theta$ is positive;
$\cos\theta = 0.97979590$

63. $\cos(\theta + \pi) = |\cos\theta|$, but is also in Quadrant III and is negative, so $\cos(\theta + \pi) = -\cos\theta$ **65.** 1 **67.** If $n_2 > n_1$, then $\theta_1 > \theta_2$; if $n_2 < n_1$, then $\theta_1 < \theta_2$; if $n_2 = n_1$, then $\theta_2 = \theta_1$. **69.** H **71.** F **73.** By the Difference of Squares Property and the second Pythagorean Identity: $(\sec\theta + 1)(\sec\theta - 1) = \sec^2\theta - 1$
$= \tan^2\theta$

74.

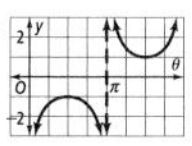

75.

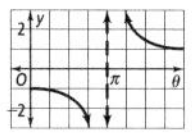

76.

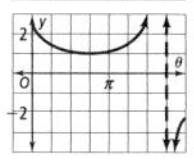

77.

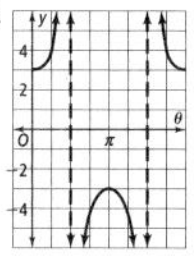

78. 35° **79.** 45° **80.** 135° **81.** 211° **82.** $f^{-1}(x) = x - 1$ **83.** $f^{-1}(x) = \frac{x+3}{2}$ **84.** $f^{-1}(x) = \pm\sqrt{x-4}$

Lesson 14-2 pp. 911–918

Got It? 1a. 120° **b.** 30° **c.** 45° **2a.** $0.46 + 2\pi n$ and $2.69 + 2\pi n$ **b.** $-0.82 + 2\pi n$ and $3.96 + 2\pi n$ **3a.** $0.41 + 2\pi n$ and $3.56 + 2\pi n$, or just $0.41 + \pi n$ **b.** $-0.63 + 2\pi n$ and $2.51 + 2\pi n$, or just $-0.63 + \pi n$ **c.** $\tan(\theta + \pi) = \tan\theta$ **4.** $\frac{11\pi}{6}$ and $\frac{7\pi}{6}$ **5.** $\frac{\pi}{2}$ and $\frac{3\pi}{2}$ **6.** The air conditioner comes on about 7 hours after midnight, 7 A.M., and goes off about 7 hours before midnight, 5 P.M.

Lesson Check 1. $-30° + 360°\cdot n$ and $210° + 360°\cdot n$ **2.** $60° + 360°\cdot n$ and $120° + 360°\cdot n$ **3.** 2.30, 3.98 **4.** 0 **5.** Answers may vary. Sample: To find the inverse of $y = 3x - 4$, you interchange x and y and solve for y: $x = 3y - 4$, $y = \frac{x+4}{3}$. Replace y with $f^{-1}(x)$ to find $f^{-1}(x) = \frac{x+4}{3}$. To find the inverse of $y = 3\sin\theta - 4$, you interchange θ and y and solve for $\sin y$ and then solve for y: $\theta = 3\sin y - 4$, $\sin y = \frac{\theta+4}{3}$ and $y = \sin^{-1}\left(\frac{\theta+4}{3}\right)$. Replace y with $f^{-1}(\theta)$ to find $f^{-1}(\theta) = \sin^{-1}\left(\frac{\theta+4}{3}\right)$. The procedure for finding the inverse is the same; for $y = 3\sin\theta - 4$ you will also use the inverse sine function. **6.** The student divided both sides of the equation by $\sin\theta$, which in the given interval can be equal to zero. There is an error in that the student failed to take into account the fact that division by zero is not possible.

Exercises 7. $90° + n\cdot 360°$ **9.** $240° + n\cdot 360°$ and $300° + n\cdot 360°$ **11.** $90° + n\cdot 360°$ and $270° + n\cdot 360°$, or just $90° + n\cdot 180°$ **13.** $0.79 + \pi n$, or just $\frac{\pi}{4} + \pi n$ **15.** $-0.89 + 2\pi n$ and $4.04 + 2\pi n$ **17.** $2.67 + 2\pi n$ and $3.62 + 2\pi n$ **19.** $\frac{\pi}{6}, \frac{5\pi}{6}$ **21.** $\frac{\pi}{4}, \frac{5\pi}{4}$ **23.** 0.46, 3.61 **25.** no solution **27.** $\frac{\pi}{2}, \pi, \frac{3\pi}{2}$ **29.** $\frac{\pi}{4}, \frac{3\pi}{4}, \frac{5\pi}{4}, \frac{7\pi}{4}$ **31.** $0, \pi$ **33.** $\frac{7\pi}{6}, \frac{11\pi}{6}$ **35.** $30° + n\cdot 360°$ and $150° + n\cdot 360°$ **37.** $210° + n\cdot 360°$ and $330° + n\cdot 360°$ **39.** $\frac{3\pi}{2}$ **41.** 3.04, 6.18 **43.** 0.0028 s; 0.019 s **45.** $0 + 2\pi n, \frac{2}{3}\pi + 2\pi n, \frac{4}{3}\pi + 2\pi n$ **47.** $\frac{\pi}{6} + 2\pi n, \frac{5\pi}{6} + 2\pi n, \frac{3\pi}{2} + 2\pi n$ **49.** $\frac{\pi}{6} + 2\pi n, \frac{5\pi}{6} + 2\pi n, \frac{\pi}{2} + \pi n$ **51.** $\frac{\pi}{2} + 2\pi n, \frac{7\pi}{6} + 2\pi n, \frac{11\pi}{6} + 2\pi n$ **53.** $\frac{\pi}{6} + 2\pi n, \frac{5\pi}{6} + 2\pi n$ **55.** $\frac{\pi}{4} + \frac{\pi n}{2}$ **57.** $\frac{\pi}{4} + \frac{\pi n}{2}$ **59.** $\frac{2\pi}{3} + 2\pi n, \frac{4\pi}{3} + 2\pi n$ **61a.** Answers may vary. Sample: $\cos\theta = -1$, $2\cos\theta = -2$, $3\cos\theta = -3$ **b.** Start with $\cos\theta = -1$, and then multiply both sides of the eq. by any nonzero number. **63.** $\theta = \sin^{-1}\left(\frac{y}{3}\right) - 2$ **65.** $\theta = \cos^{-1}\left(\frac{y-1}{2}\right)$ **67.** D **69.** C **71.** D **73.** $\cot\theta$ **74.** $\tan^2\theta$ **75.** 1 **76.** 1 **77.** $\sin\theta$ **78.** $\tan\theta$ **79.** $y = 4\cos\frac{\pi}{4}\theta$ **80.** $y = 3\cos\theta$ **81.** $y = \frac{\pi}{4}\cos\frac{2}{3}\theta$ **82.** 4 **83.** 21 **84.** $52\frac{1}{2}$

Lesson 14-3 pp. 919–926

Got It? 1. $\sin\theta = \frac{12}{13}$, $\cos\theta = -\frac{5}{13}$, $\tan\theta = -\frac{12}{5}$, $\csc\theta = \frac{13}{12}$, $\sec\theta = -\frac{13}{5}$, $\cot\theta = -\frac{5}{12}$ **2a.** 27.1 m **b.** 32.3 m **3.** $\sin E = \frac{3}{5}$, $\sec F = \frac{5}{3}$ **4.** ≈76,430 ft ≈ 14.5 mi **5a.** 23.58° **b.** 56.25° **6a.** 72 ft **b.** Answers may vary. Sample: Build the ramp in 3 sections, each of which is 24 ft, and with landings between sections.

Lesson Check 1. $\sin 57° = \frac{b}{c}$, $\cos 57° = \frac{a}{c}$, $\tan 57° = \frac{b}{a}$ **2.** 15.4 **3.** $\sin 33° = \frac{a}{c} = 0.5$, $\cos 33° = \frac{b}{c} = 0.8$, $\tan 33° = \frac{a}{b} = 0.6$ **4.** 36.9° **5.** Answers may vary. Sample: Using the inverse of cosine, you can find the acute angle between the shortest side and the hypotenuse, $\theta = \cos^{-1}\left(\frac{8.4}{12.9}\right) \approx 49.4°$. Because the triangle is a right triangle, the remaining acute angle is $\approx 90° - 49.4° = 40.6°$. **6.** The student confuses $\sin^{-1}\theta$ with $\frac{1}{\sin\theta}$. He or she should have divided by sin 0.45. $x = \frac{4}{\sin 0.45} \approx 9.20$ cm

Exercises

7. $\sin\theta = \frac{3}{5}$, $\cos\theta = -\frac{4}{5}$, $\tan\theta = -\frac{3}{4}$, $\csc\theta = \frac{5}{3}$, $\sec\theta = -\frac{5}{4}$, $\cot\theta = -\frac{4}{3}$
9. $\sin\theta = -\frac{5\sqrt{26}}{26}$, $\cos\theta = \frac{\sqrt{26}}{26}$, $\tan\theta = -5$, $\csc\theta = -\frac{\sqrt{26}}{5}$, $\sec\theta = \sqrt{26}$, $\cot\theta = -\frac{1}{5}$
11. $\sin\theta = \frac{\sqrt{7}}{4}$, $\cos\theta = -\frac{3}{4}$, $\tan\theta = -\frac{\sqrt{7}}{3}$, $\csc\theta = \frac{4\sqrt{7}}{7}$, $\sec\theta = -\frac{4}{3}$, $\cot\theta = -\frac{3\sqrt{7}}{7}$
13a. $\frac{15}{17} \approx 0.88$ **b.** $\frac{17}{8} \approx 2.13$ **c.** $\frac{8}{15} \approx 0.53$ **d.** $\frac{17}{8} \approx 2.13$ **e.** $\frac{17}{15} \approx 1.13$ **f.** $\frac{8}{15} \approx 0.53$ **15.** 41.8 **17.** 25.2 **19.** $a \approx 8.7$, $m\angle A = 60.0°$, $m\angle B = 30.0°$ **21.** $a = 9.0$, $m\angle A \approx 36.9°$, $m\angle B \approx 53.1°$ **23.** $a \approx 8.0$, $m\angle A \approx 61.8°$, $m\angle B \approx 28.2°$ **25a.** $m\angle A = \cos^{-1}\left(\frac{1200}{d}\right)$ **b.** 37° **c.** 53°

27.

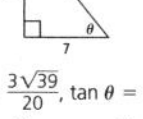

$\sin\theta = \frac{3\sqrt{39}}{20}$, $\tan\theta = \frac{3\sqrt{39}}{7}$, $\csc\theta = \frac{20\sqrt{39}}{117}$, $\sec\theta = \frac{20}{7}$, $\cot\theta = \frac{7\sqrt{39}}{117}$

29.

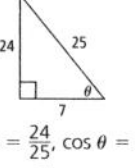

$\sin\theta = \frac{24}{25}$, $\cos\theta = \frac{7}{25}$, $\csc\theta = \frac{25}{24}$, $\sec\theta = \frac{25}{7}$, $\cot\theta = \frac{7}{24}$

31.

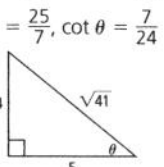

$\sin\theta = \frac{4\sqrt{41}}{41}$, $\cos\theta = \frac{5\sqrt{41}}{41}$, $\tan\theta = \frac{4}{5}$, $\csc\theta = \frac{\sqrt{41}}{4}$, $\sec\theta = \frac{\sqrt{41}}{5}$

33.

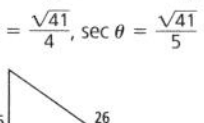

$\sin\theta = \frac{5}{26}$, $\cos\theta = \frac{\sqrt{651}}{26}$, $\tan\theta = \frac{5\sqrt{651}}{651}$, $\sec\theta = \frac{26\sqrt{651}}{651}$, $\cot\theta = \frac{\sqrt{651}}{5}$

35. 33.4 ft **37.** 20.3 m^2 **39.** $c \approx 12.2$, $m\angle A \approx 35.0°$, $m\angle B \approx 55.0°$ **41.** $a \approx 3.9$, $c \approx 6.9$, $m\angle B = 55.8°$
43. $a \approx 19.8$, $b \approx 2.9$, $m\angle A = 81.7°$ **45.** Using inverse sine, you can find that $\theta = 30°$. Since sine is positive in the first and second quadrants, another solution is 150°. All the solutions would be $30° + n \cdot 360°$ and $150° + n \cdot 360°$.

47. $\sec A = \frac{c}{b} = \frac{1}{\left(\frac{b}{c}\right)} = \frac{1}{\cos A}$

49. $\cos^2 A + \sin^2 A = \left(\frac{b}{c}\right)^2 + \left(\frac{a}{c}\right)^2 = \frac{b^2 + a^2}{c^2} = 1$

51. $y \approx 61.7$ m **53.** G **54.** C **55.** I

57. $180° + n \cdot 360°$ **58.** $45° + n \cdot 180°$ and $90° + n \cdot 180°$ **59.** $0° + n \cdot 180°$

60.

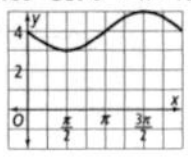

61.

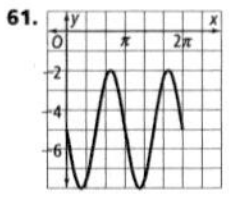

62.

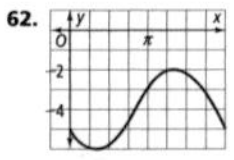

63. 6 cm^2 **64.** 45 in.^{2} **65.** 32.76 mm^2

Lesson 14-4 pp. 928–934

Got It? 1. 36.6 in.^{2} **2.** 31.0 yd **3a.** 68.4° **b.** yes; $\frac{\sin T}{\text{height}} = \frac{\sin 90°}{9}$; height $\approx 9 \sin 47° \approx 6.6$
4. 104.7 ft

Lesson Check 1. $\approx$10.7 square units **2.** $\approx$19.8 **3.** $\approx$26.3° or $\approx$153.7° **4.** AAS, ASA **5.** No; For $\frac{\sin 22°}{\sin 45°}$ you find the sine of each numerator and denominator, sin 22° and sin 45°; for $\sin\left(\frac{22°}{45°}\right)$ you find the sine of the quotient of $\left(\frac{22°}{45°}\right)$.
Exercises 7. 9.1 in.^{2} **9.** 10.9 **11.** 7.4 **13.** 33.5° **15.** 31.7° **17.** 32 cm **19.** 66° **21.** $m\angle E \approx 40.3°$, $m\angle F \approx 85.7°$, $f \approx 12.3$ m **25.** 44.4 **27.** 49.4

29. 28.0 ft **31.** 4.0 cm **33a.** 56.4°, 93.6°, 26.4° **b.** No; $\triangle EFG$ could be congruent to $\triangle ABC$ instead of $\triangle ABD$.
35. No; you need at least one side in order to set up a proportion you can then solve.
37. I
39. $A = \frac{1}{2}ab \sin C$

$\sin C = \frac{2(A)}{ab} = \frac{2(31.5)}{9(14)} = 0.5$

$m\angle C = \sin^{-1} 0.5 = 30°$

So, the measure of the included angle for the given sides is 30° or 150°.

40.

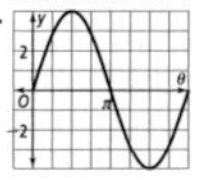

41.

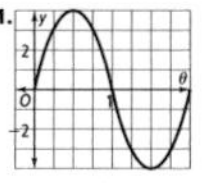

42.

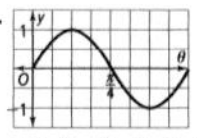

43. $\langle -1, 7\rangle$ **44.** $\langle 5, 3\rangle$ **45.** $\langle -3, -1\rangle$ **46.** $\langle -6, 4\rangle$
47. 53.1° **48.** 24.6° **49.** 38.7° **50.** 54.7°

Lesson 14-5 pp. 936–942

Got It? 1a. 6.4
b. 1 mi to 6 mi;
$a^2 = 2.5^2 + 3.5^2 - 2(2.5)(3.5)\cos A$
$a^2 = 18.5 - 17.5 \cos A$;
if $A = 0°$, then $\cos A = 1$ and $a = 1$; if $A = 180°$, then $\cos A = -1$ and $a = 6$. **2.** 75.3° **3.** 30.7°
Lesson Check 1. $\approx$11.85 in. **2.** $\approx$52.4° **3.** $\approx$34.1°
4. $\approx$60.3° **5.** Use the Law of Sines when you have two sides and a non-included angle or two angles and a side; use the Law of Cosines when you have two sides and an included angle or three sides. **6.** The denominator should be negative. The answer should be:

$\cos C = \frac{15^2 - 11^2 - 17^2}{-2(11)(17)} \approx 0.495$

$C = \cos^{-1}(0.495) \approx 60.3°$

Exercises 7. 37.1 **9.** 13.7 **11.** 27.0 **13.** 33.7° **15.** 47.2° **17.** 50.8 **19.** 27.0° **21.** $b^2 = a^2 + c^2 - 2ac \cos B$

23. $\frac{\sin B}{b} = \frac{\sin C}{c}$ **25.** $\frac{\sin C}{c} = \frac{\sin A}{a}$ **27.** $\approx$59.1 nautical miles **29.** $b \approx 34.7$, $m\angle A \approx 26.7°$, $m\angle C \approx 33.3°$
31. $m\angle A \approx 56.1°$, $m\angle B \approx 70.0°$, $m\angle C \approx 53.9°$
33. For any two side lengths a and b, the ratio $\frac{a}{b}$ is equal to the ratio $\frac{\sin A}{\sin B}$, which can be found since A and B are given.
35a. $\approx$45.4 mi **b.** 14.4° left; 4.4° west of north
37. 11.0 cm **39.** 27.0° **41.** 13.0 cm **43.** 21.5°
45. 8.3 ft **47.** 79.6° **49.** 18 cm
51. a. 2.1 m
b. 9.8 m^2
53. a. $\cos A > 0$ if $b^2 + c^2 > a^2$;
$\cos A = 0$ if $b^2 + c^2 = a^2$;
$\cos A < 0$ if $b^2 + c^2 < a^2$
b. acute $\triangle$ if $\cos A > 0$; right $\triangle$ if $\cos A = 0$; obtuse $\triangle$ if $\cos A < 0$
55. 85.4 **57.** 27.1° **59.** 24.1 units^2 **60.** 17.1 in. **61.** 8.9 m **62.** 26.3 in. **63.** 54.0° **64.** 2π, $x = \pm\pi$
65. $\frac{2}{3}$, $x = \pm\frac{1}{3}$ **66.** $\frac{\pi}{3}$, $x = \pm\frac{\pi}{6}$ **67.** 1, $x = \pm\frac{1}{2}$
68. $\sin\theta$ **69.** $\cos\theta$ **70.** 1 **71.** $\csc^2\theta$

Lesson 14-6 pp. 943–950

Got It?
1. $\cos\left(\theta - \frac{\pi}{2}\right) = \cos\left(-\left(\frac{\pi}{2} - \theta\right)\right) = \cos\left(\frac{\pi}{2} - \theta\right) = \sin\theta$
2. $\sec(90° - A) = \frac{1}{\cos(90° - A)} = \frac{1}{\sin\theta} = \csc\theta$
$\sec(90° - A) = \csc\theta$
3a. $0, \pi$ **b.** yes; πn
4. $\frac{\sqrt{6} - \sqrt{2}}{4}$
5. $\sin(A + B) = \sin(A - (-B))$
$= \sin A \cos(-B) - \cos A \sin(-B)$
$= \sin A \cos B - \cos A(-\sin B)$
$= \sin A \cos B + \cos A \sin B$
6. $-2 - \sqrt{3}$
Lesson Check
1. $\sin\left(\frac{\pi}{2} + \theta\right) + \sin\left(\frac{\pi}{2} - \theta\right)$
$= \sin\left(\frac{\pi}{2} - (-\theta)\right) + \sin\left(\frac{\pi}{2} - \theta\right)$
$= \cos(-\theta) + \cos\theta$
$= \cos\theta + \cos\theta$
$= 2\cos\theta$
2. $\frac{\pi}{4}, \frac{5\pi}{4}$ **3.** $\frac{\sqrt{2}}{2}$ **4.** $-\frac{\sqrt{2} + \sqrt{6}}{4}$
5. There are 2 solutions, $\frac{\pi}{2}$ and $\frac{3\pi}{2}$, between 0 and 2π because: $-\cos\theta = \cos\theta$
$2\cos\theta = 0$
$\cos\theta = 0;\ \theta = \frac{\pi}{2}, \frac{3\pi}{2}$

6. $\sin\left(\frac{\pi}{2} - \theta\right) = \sin\frac{\pi}{2}\cos\theta - \cos\frac{\pi}{2}\sin\theta$
$= (1)\cos\theta - (0)\sin\theta$
$= \cos\theta$
Exercises
7. $\csc\left(\theta - \frac{\pi}{2}\right) = \frac{1}{\sin\left(\theta - \frac{\pi}{2}\right)} = \frac{1}{\sin\left(-\left(\frac{\pi}{2} - \theta\right)\right)} = \frac{1}{-\sin\left(\frac{\pi}{2} - \theta\right)} = \frac{1}{-\cos\theta} = -\sec\theta$
9. $\cot\left(\frac{\pi}{2} - \theta\right) = \frac{\cos\left(\frac{\pi}{2} - \theta\right)}{\sin\left(\frac{\pi}{2} - \theta\right)} = \frac{\sin\theta}{\cos\theta} = \tan\theta$
11. $\tan\left(\theta - \frac{\pi}{2}\right) = \tan\left(-\left(\frac{\pi}{2} - \theta\right)\right) = -\tan\left(\frac{\pi}{2} - \theta\right) = -\cot\theta$
13. $\tan(90° - A) = \cot A$ **15.** $\cot(90° - A) = \tan A$
17. $\frac{\pi}{2}, \frac{3\pi}{2}$ **19.** π **21.** $\frac{\pi}{2}, \frac{3\pi}{2}$ **23.** $\frac{\sqrt{2}}{2}$ **25.** 0
27. $-\sqrt{3} - 2$ **29.** $\frac{\sqrt{2} + \sqrt{6}}{4}$
31. $-2 + \sqrt{3}$ **33.** $-\frac{1}{2}$ **35.** $\frac{1}{2}$
37. $\sin(A - B) = \cos\left[\frac{\pi}{2} - (A - B)\right]$
$= \cos\left[\left(\frac{\pi}{2} - A\right) + B\right]$
$= \cos\left(\frac{\pi}{2} - A\right)\cos B - \sin\left(\frac{\pi}{2} - A\right)\sin B$
$= \sin A \cos B - \cos A \sin B$
39. $\tan(A + B) = \frac{\sin(A + B)}{\cos(A + B)} = \frac{\sin A \cos B + \cos A \sin B}{\cos A \cos B - \sin A \sin B} = \frac{\frac{\sin A \cos B + \cos A \sin B}{\cos A \cos B}}{\frac{\cos A \cos B - \sin A \sin B}{\cos A \cos B}} = \frac{\frac{\sin A \cos B}{\cos A \cos B} + \frac{\cos A \sin B}{\cos A \cos B}}{\frac{\cos A \cos B}{\cos A \cos B} - \frac{\sin A \sin B}{\cos A \cos B}} = \frac{\tan A + \tan B}{1 - \tan A \tan B}$
41. $(5\cos\theta - 5\sqrt{3}\sin\theta, 5\sin\theta + 5\sqrt{3}\cos\theta)$
43. $\sin 5\theta$ **45.** $\cos 5\theta$ **47.** $\tan 2\theta$

49. a. even: cosine, secant; odd: sine, cosecant, tangent, cotangent
b. No; answers may vary. Sample:
$y = \sin x - \cos x$. For $x = \frac{\pi}{4}$, $f(x) = \sin\frac{\pi}{4} - \cos\frac{\pi}{4} = 0$, and $f(-x) = \sin\left(-\frac{\pi}{4}\right) - \cos\left(-\frac{\pi}{4}\right) = -\sqrt{2}$. Because $f(x) \neq f(-x)$, and $-f(x) \neq f(-x)$, the function is neither even nor odd.
51. $\sin(\pi - \theta) = \sin\pi\cos\theta - \cos\pi\sin\theta$
$= 0 - (-1)\sin\theta = \sin\theta$
53. $\cos(\pi + \theta) = \cos\pi\cos\theta - \sin\pi\sin\theta$
$= (-1)\cos\theta - 0 = -\cos\theta$
55. $\cos\left(\theta + \frac{3\pi}{2}\right) = \cos\theta\cos\frac{3\pi}{2} - \sin\theta\sin\frac{3\pi}{2}$
$= \cos\theta(0) - \sin\theta(-1) = \sin\theta$
57. I
59. $\sin(165°) = \sin(15°)$
$= \sin(45° - 30°)$
$= \sin 45° \cos 30° - \cos 45° \sin 30°$
$= \frac{\sqrt{2}}{2} \cdot \frac{\sqrt{3}}{2} - \frac{\sqrt{2}}{2} \cdot \frac{1}{2}$
$= \frac{\sqrt{6}}{4} - \frac{\sqrt{2}}{4} = \frac{\sqrt{6} - \sqrt{2}}{4}$
60. $\approx$16.34 ft **61.** $\approx$10.0 cm **62.** $\frac{4\pi}{9}$ and 1.40
63. $-\frac{5\pi}{18}$ and -0.87 **64.** $-\frac{\pi}{12}$ and -0.26
65. $\frac{7\pi}{18}$ and 1.22 **66.** $\frac{19\pi}{18}$ and 3.32
67. $\cos A \cos B - \sin A \sin B$
68. $\sin A \cos B + \cos A \sin B$ **69.** $\frac{\tan A + \tan B}{1 - \tan A \tan B}$

Lesson 14-7 pp. 951–957

Got It?
1. $\cos 2\theta = \cos^2\theta - \sin^2\theta$
$= \cos^2\theta - (1 - \cos^2\theta)$
$= \cos^2\theta - 1 + \cos^2\theta$
$= 2\cos^2\theta - 1$
2. $\frac{\sqrt{3}}{2}$ **3.** $2\cos 2\theta = 2(2\cos^2\theta - 1) = 4\cos^2\theta - 2$
4a. $\frac{1}{2}$ **b.** $-\frac{\sqrt{3}}{3}$
5a. $-\frac{3}{5}$ **b.** $-\frac{4}{3}$ **c.** If $270° < \theta < 360°$, $135° < \frac{\theta}{2} < 180°$ and $\frac{\theta}{2}$ is also in Quadrant II. The answers will remain the same.
Lesson Check 1. $\frac{\sqrt{3}}{2}$ **2.** 1 **3a.** $-\frac{5}{13}$ **b.** $\sqrt{\frac{13 + 2\sqrt{13}}{26}}$
c. $-\sqrt{\frac{13 - 2\sqrt{13}}{26}}$
4. The student did not correctly determine in which quadrant $\frac{\theta}{2}$ will be. If $180° < \theta < 270°, 90° < \frac{\theta}{2} < 135°$, then $\frac{\theta}{2}$ is in Quadrant II and the tangent will be negative. **5.** $\sin 4A$

6. $\sin\frac{5A}{2} = -\sqrt{\frac{1 - \cos 5A}{2}}$ if $360° < 5A < 450°$, $180° < \frac{5A}{2} < 225°$ and the sine is negative in Quadrant III.
Exercises
7. $\sin 2\theta = \sin(\theta + \theta)$
$= \sin\theta\cos\theta + \cos\theta\sin\theta$
$= 2\sin\theta\cos\theta$
9. $-\frac{\sqrt{3}}{2}$ **11.** $-\sqrt{3}$ **13.** $-\frac{1}{2}$ **15.** $-\frac{1}{2}$ **17.** $\frac{\sqrt{2 + \sqrt{3}}}{2}$
19. $\frac{\sqrt{2 - \sqrt{3}}}{2}$ **21.** $\frac{\sqrt{2 + \sqrt{2}}}{2}$ **23.** 0 **25.** $\frac{3\sqrt{10}}{10}$ **27.** 3
29. $\frac{4\sqrt{17}}{17}$ **31.** -4
33. $\cos B = 2\cos^2\frac{B}{2} - 1$
$2\cos^2\frac{B}{2} = \cos B + 1$
$\cos^2\frac{B}{2} = \frac{\cos B + 1}{2}$
Since $\cos B = \frac{a}{c}$,
$\cos^2\frac{B}{2} = \frac{\frac{a}{c} + 1}{2} = \frac{a + c}{2c}$.
35. $\cos 2R = \cos^2 R - \sin^2 R$
$= \left(\frac{s}{t}\right)^2 - \left(\frac{r}{t}\right)^2$
$= \frac{s^2}{t^2} - \frac{r^2}{t^2}$
$= \frac{s^2 - r^2}{t^2}$
37. $\sin^2\frac{S}{2} = \left(\sin\frac{S}{2}\right)^2$
$= \left(\pm\sqrt{\frac{1 - \cos S}{2}}\right)^2$
$= \frac{1 - \cos S}{2} = \frac{1 - \frac{r}{t}}{2}$
$= \frac{1}{2} - \frac{r}{2t} = \frac{t - r}{2t}$
39. $\tan^2\frac{S}{2} = \left(\tan\frac{S}{2}\right)^2$
$= \left(\pm\sqrt{\frac{1 - \cos S}{1 + \cos S}}\right)^2 = \frac{1 - \cos S}{1 + \cos S} = \frac{1 - \frac{r}{t}}{1 + \frac{r}{t}}$
$= \frac{t - r}{t + r}$
41. $-\frac{24}{25}$ **43.** $\frac{24}{7}$ **45.** $\frac{\sqrt{5}}{5}$ **47.** $-\frac{1}{2}$
49. $\cos\theta(8\sin\theta - 3) = 0$; $\frac{\pi}{2}, \frac{3\pi}{2}$, 0.384, 2.757
51. $\cos\theta(2\sin^2\theta - 1) = 0$; $\frac{\pi}{2}, \frac{3\pi}{2}, \frac{\pi}{4}, \frac{3\pi}{4}, \frac{5\pi}{4}, \frac{7\pi}{4}$
53. 1 **55.** $\cos\theta - \sin\theta$ **57.** Answers may vary. Sample:
a. $\sin 60° = \frac{\sqrt{3}}{2}$, $\cos 60° = \frac{1}{2}$ **b.** $\sin 120° = \frac{\sqrt{3}}{2}$
c. $\cos 30° = \frac{\sqrt{3}}{2}$

59. $4\sin\theta\cos\theta(\cos^2\theta - \sin^2\theta)$
61. $\frac{4\tan\theta(1 - \tan^2\theta)}{\tan^4\theta - 6\tan^2\theta + 1}$
63. $\pm\sqrt{\frac{1}{2} \pm \frac{1}{2}\sqrt{\frac{1}{2} + \frac{1}{2}\cos\theta}}$
65. a. $\tan\frac{A}{2} = \pm\sqrt{\frac{1 - \cos A}{1 + \cos A}}$
$= \pm\sqrt{\frac{1 - \cos A}{1 + \cos A}} \cdot \sqrt{\frac{1 + \cos A}{1 + \cos A}}$
$= \pm\sqrt{\frac{1 - \cos^2 A}{(1 + \cos A)^2}}$
$= \pm\sqrt{\frac{\sin^2 A}{(1 + \cos A)^2}}$
$= \frac{\sin A}{1 + \cos A}$
Since $\tan\frac{A}{2}$ and $\sin A$ have the same sign wherever $\tan\frac{A}{2}$ is defined, only the positive sign occurs.
67. G **69.** I **71.** $\frac{\sqrt{2}}{2}$ **72.** $\frac{\sqrt{3}}{2}$ **73.** $\sqrt{3}$ **74.** about 4.1; 12 **75.** 2; 4 **76.** 45.2 **77.** 26.6 **78.** 57.6

Chapter Review pp. 959–962

1. Law of Sines **2.** trig. ratios **3.** Law of Cosines **4.** trig. ident. **5.** Law of Sines **6.** $\sin\theta\tan\theta = \sin\theta\frac{\sin\theta}{\cos\theta} = \frac{\sin^2\theta}{\cos\theta} = \frac{1 - \cos^2\theta}{\cos\theta} = \frac{1}{\cos\theta} - \cos\theta$; domain of validity: all real numbers except odd multiples of $\frac{\pi}{2}$
7. $\cos^2\theta\cot^2\theta = \cos^2\theta\frac{\cos^2\theta}{\sin^2\theta} = \frac{\cos^2\theta(1 - \sin^2\theta)}{\sin^2\theta} = \frac{\cos^2\theta - \cos^2\theta\sin^2\theta}{\sin^2\theta} = \cot^2\theta - \cos^2\theta$; domain of validity: all real numbers except 0 and multiples of π
8. $\cos^2\theta$ **9.** 1 **10.** 1 **11.** $-\sin^2\theta$ **12.** $\cos^2\theta$ **13.** 1
14. $-60°$ **15.** 60° **16.** $-30°$ **17.** 30° **18.** 0.34
19. -1.11 **20.** 2.27 **21.** 0.20 **22.** $\frac{\pi}{3}, \frac{5\pi}{3}$ **23.** $\frac{\pi}{6}, \frac{7\pi}{6}$
24. $0, \frac{\pi}{2}, \pi$ **25.** $\frac{\pi}{3}, \frac{5\pi}{3}$ **26.** $\sin\theta = \frac{4}{5}$, $\cos\theta = -\frac{3}{5}$, $\tan\theta = -\frac{4}{3}$, $\csc\theta = \frac{5}{4}$, $\sec\theta = -\frac{5}{3}$, $\cot\theta = -\frac{3}{4}$
27. $\sin\theta = -\frac{15}{17}$, $\cos\theta = -\frac{8}{17}$, $\tan\theta = \frac{15}{8}$, $\csc\theta = -\frac{17}{15}$, $\sec\theta = -\frac{17}{8}$, $\cot\theta = \frac{8}{15}$ **28.** $\frac{3}{5}$, 0.6 **29.** $\frac{4}{5}$, 0.8
30. $\frac{3}{4}$, 0.75 **31.** $\frac{5}{3}$, $1.\overline{6}$ **32.** $g \approx 9.5$, $\angle F \approx 18.4$, $\angle H \approx 71.6$ **33.** $h = 16$, $\angle F \approx 36.9$, $\angle H \approx 53.1$
34. $f \approx 37.7$, $\angle F \approx 43.3$, $\angle H \approx 46.7$
35. $g \approx 6.4$, $\angle F \approx 51.3$, $\angle H \approx 38.7$ **36.** 13.7
37. 29.4 **38.** 13.14 m^2 **39.** 92.12 ft^2 **40.** 7.1 in.

41. 43.9° **42.** 52.2°
43. $\cos\left(\theta + \frac{\pi}{2}\right) = \cos\theta\cos\frac{\pi}{2} - \sin\theta\sin\frac{\pi}{2}$
$= \cos\theta \times 0 - \sin\theta \times 1 = -\sin\theta$
44. $\sin^2\left(\theta - \frac{\pi}{2}\right) = \left[\sin\left(\theta - \frac{\pi}{2}\right)\right]^2$
$= \left[\sin\theta\cos\frac{\pi}{2} - \cos\theta\sin\frac{\pi}{2}\right]^2$
$= [\sin\theta \times 0 - \cos\theta \times 1]^2$
$= (-\cos\theta)^2 = \cos^2\theta$
45. $2 - \sqrt{3}$ **46.** $-\frac{\sqrt{3}}{2}$ **47.** $\frac{\sqrt{2} - \sqrt{6}}{4}$ **48.** $-2 - \sqrt{3}$
49. $\frac{\sqrt{3}}{2}$ **50.** $\frac{\sqrt{3}}{2}$ **51.** $-\sqrt{3}$ **52.** $-\frac{\sqrt{3}}{2}$

Skills Handbook

p. 972 1. 46% **3.** 0.7% **5.** 1.035 **7.** 25% **9.** $66.\overline{6}$% **11.** 115% **13.** 12.5 **15.** 75 **17.** 20%
p. 973 1. $1\frac{2}{5}$ **3.** $6\frac{5}{6}$ **5.** $\frac{5}{21}$ **7.** $2\frac{19}{20}$ **9.** 8 **11.** $1\frac{1}{2}$ **13.** 2 **15.** 42
p. 974 1. 3 to 4 **3.** 19 g in 2 oz **5.** $\frac{14}{5}$ **7.** 8 **9.** 1.8 **11.** 1.95 **13.** 45.5 **15.** ± 6
p. 975 1. 1 **3.** -38 **5.** -17 **7.** 4 **9.** 28 **11.** -12 **13.** -90 **15.** 12 **17.** 19 **19.** 9 **21.** -10
p. 976 1. 14 m^2 **3.** 30 cm^2 **5.** $91\frac{1}{8}$ ft^3 **7.** 100π in.^{3} **9.** 110.5 in.^{2} **11.** $121\frac{1}{2}$ ft^2
p. 977 1. I **3.** IV **5.** III **7.** $\frac{4}{5}$ **9.** 0 **11.** $\frac{1}{5}$ **13.** $(5, -\frac{3}{2})$ **15.** $(\frac{5}{2}, -1)$
p. 978 1. x^3 **3.** a^4b **5.** $\frac{1}{c^4}$ **7.** $\frac{x^5}{y^7z^3}$ **9.** d^8 **11.** c^6 **13.** $\frac{a^4}{b^5}$ **15.** $\frac{a^4}{b^4}$ **17.** c^{12} **19.** $u^{12}v^6$ **21.** a^3 **23.** $\frac{1}{mg^3}$ **25.** $\frac{a^5}{2}$
p. 979 1. $x^2 + 10x - 5$ **3.** $12x^4 - 20x^3 + 36x^2$ **5.** $x^2 - 2x - 15$ **7.** $(a - 6)(a - 2)$ **9.** $(x + 4)(x + 1)$ **11.** $(y + 8)(y - 3)$ **13.** $2x(x^2 + 2x - 4)$
p. 980 1. 1.34×10^6 **3.** 7.75×10^{-4} **5.** 111,300 **7.** 1.895×10^3 **9.** 1.234×10^5 **11.** 6.4×10^5 **13.** 8.52×10^2 **15.** 17.5 **17.** 8.95×10^{-12} **19.** 3.77×10^{10} **21.** 1.8×10^{-6}
p. 981 1. 10 **3.** 15 **5.** 54.7 **7.** 5 **9.** 13 **11.** 22.7 **13.** 2.8 **15.** 9 **17.** 7

p. 982 1.

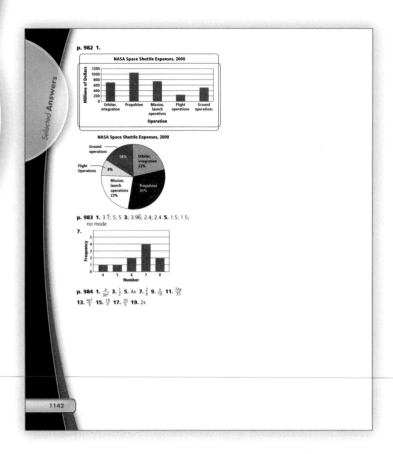

p. 983 1. $3.\overline{7}$; 5; 5 **3.** $3.9\overline{6}$; 2.4; 2.4 **5.** 1.5; 1.5; no mode

7.

p. 984 1. $\frac{a}{3b^2}$ **3.** $\frac{1}{2}$ **5.** $4x$ **7.** $\frac{2}{h}$ **9.** $\frac{x}{10}$ **11.** $\frac{74x}{35}$
13. $\frac{4x^2}{5}$ **15.** $\frac{16}{x}$ **17.** $\frac{16}{5}$ **19.** $2x$

1142

Additional Answers

Chapter 2

Lesson 2-7

page 112 Practice and Problem Solving Exercises

45. a.
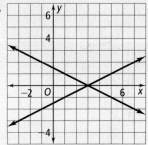

b. No; $f(x) = g(x)$ only for $x = 3$.

46. a. Check students' work.

b. Check students' work.

c. The graphs of y_1 and y_2 are the same for zero and positive values of k, and are mirror images for negative values of k.

47.

48.

49.
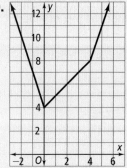

50. B

page 113 Standardized Test Prep

51. C

52. G

53. A

54. [2] No; both $(1, -1)$ and $(1, 1)$ are pts. on the graph of $|y| = x$. Since there is more than one y-value (-1 and 1) for a given x-value (1), $|y| = x$ is not a function. (OR equivalent explanation)

[1] incomplete explanation

---

page 113 Mixed Review

55. $y = x + 1$

56. $y = -\frac{1}{2}x + 2$

57. $g(x) = -x - 7$

58. $g(x) = -2x - 6$

59. $g(x) = -4 - x$

60. Answers may vary. Sample:
$y = \frac{4}{5}x + 1$

61. Answers may vary. Sample:
$y = -\frac{4}{5}x + 8$

62.
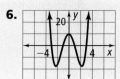
$p \le 1.25$

63.

$t > 13$

64.

Chapter 5

Lesson 5-6

page 325 Concept Byte

5.
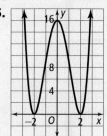

6.

Chapter 7

Mid-Chapter Quiz

page 461 Mid-Chapter Quiz

24. domain: $x > 1$, range: all real numbers
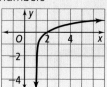

25. domain: all real numbers, range: all real numbers

26. $y = 2144.23(0.95)^x$; about 6 minutes

27. The y-intercept is when $x = 0$ i.e. $(0, a)$.

28. If $a > 0$ and $b > 1$, the function represents exponential growth; if $a > 0$ and $0 < b < 1$, the function represents exponential decay.

29. The graphs are a reflection of each other over the line $y = x$. The domain of one is the range of the other, and vice-versa. They both share a common y-intercept, $(0, 0)$.

30. The annually compounded interest formula is $A = P(1 + r)^t$. The continuously compounded interest formula is $A = Pe^{rt}$.

Chapter 8

Lesson 8-2

page 506 Concept Byte

5.
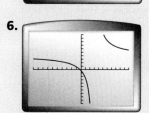

6.

7.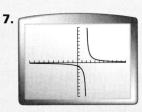

8.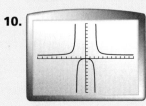

9.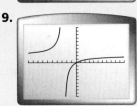

10.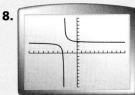

11.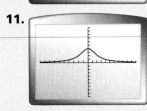

page 512   Practice and Problem Solving Exercises

10.

no *x*- or *y*-intercept; horizontal asymptote: $y = 0$, vertical asymptote: $x = 0$; domain: all real numbers except $x = 0$, range: all real numbers except $y = 0$

11.

no *x*- or *y*-intercept; horizontal asymptote: $y = 0$, vertical asymptote: $x = 0$; domain: all real numbers except $x = 0$, range: all real numbers except $y = 0$

12.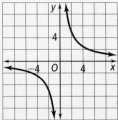

no *x*- or *y*-intercept; horizontal asymptote: $y = 0$, vertical asymptote: $x = 0$; domain: all real numbers except $x = 0$, range: all real numbers except $y = 0$

13.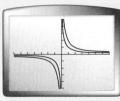

stretch by a factor of 2

14.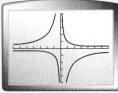

reflection across the *x*-axis and a stretch by a factor of 4

15.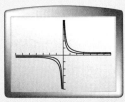

compression by a factor of 0.5

16.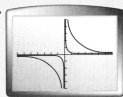

stretch by a factor of 12

17.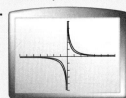

compression by a factor of 0.75

18.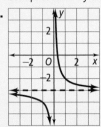

domain: all real numbers except $x = 0$, range: all real numbers except $y = -3$

19.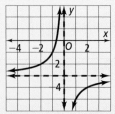

domain: all real numbers except $x = 0$, range: all real numbers except $y = -3$

20.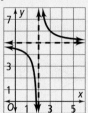

domain: all real numbers except $x = 2$, range: all real numbers except $y = 5$

21.

domain: all real numbers except $x = 3$, range: all real numbers except $y = 4$

22.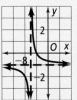

domain: all real numbers except $x = -6$, range: all real numbers except $y = -1$

23.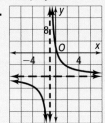

domain: all real numbers except $x = -1$, range: all real numbers except $y = -8$

24.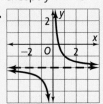

domain: all real numbers except $x = 0$, range: all real numbers except $y = -2$

25.

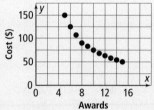

domain: all real numbers except $x = -5$, range: all real numbers except $y = -6$

26. $y = \dfrac{2}{x} + 4$

27. $y = \dfrac{2}{x + 2} + 3$

28. $y = \dfrac{2}{x - 4} - 8$

29. 7.67 ft

30.

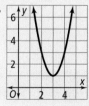

$c = \dfrac{750}{a}$; domain: whole numbers from 5 to 15, range: $50 \le c \le 750$

Chapter 10

Get Ready

page 611 Get Ready!

15. $y = 2(x - 1)^2 + 8$

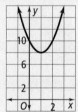

16. $y = -3\left(x - \dfrac{1}{6}\right)^2 + \dfrac{1}{12}$

17.

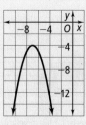

18.

19.

20.

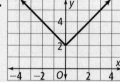

21. The radius of a circle is the distance from the center of the circle to any pt. on the circle. The radius extends in every direction from the center and ends on the circle. All radii of the same circle are equal.

22. The vertex of a parabola is the lowest or highest pt. of a parabola; it is the pt. where the parabola changes direction.

Lesson 10-1

page 619 Practice and Problem Solving Exercises

38. parabola: Hold the lamp so that the edge of the shade furthest from the wall is parallel to the plane of the wall.

circle: Hold the lamp so that the circular top rim of the shade is parallel to the wall.

hyperbola: Let the lamp sit in a normal, upright position, but close enough to the wall for the bottom rim of the shade to almost touch the wall.

ellipse: Hold the lamp at an angle so that the light from the top of the shade gives a closed, curved oblong area of light on the wall.

39. a. All lines in the plane that pass through the center of a circle are axes of sym. of the circle.

b. The axes of sym. of an ellipse intersect at the center of the ellipse. The same is true for a hyperbola. This can be confirmed using, for example, $4x^2 + 9y^2 = 36$ and $4x^2 - 9y^2 = 36$.

40.

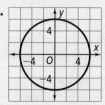

$x^2 + y^2 = 36$

41.

$x^2 + y^2 = \dfrac{1}{4}$

42.

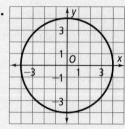

$x^2 + y^2 = 16$

43.

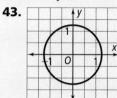

$x^2 + y^2 = 1.5625$

44–49. Answers may vary. Samples are given.

44. $(2, 4)$

45. $(\sqrt{2}, 1)$

46. $(-2, 2\sqrt{2})$

47. $(2, 0)$

48. $(3, \sqrt{51})$

49. $(0, -\sqrt{7})$

50. one branch of a hyperbola

51. Check students' work.

52. a.

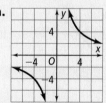

b. hyperbola

c. no intercepts; lines of symmetry: $y = x$ and $y = -x$

d. yes; $f(x) = \dfrac{16}{x}$

53. a.

b.

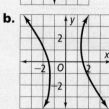

54. D

55. I

56. D

57. H

58. [2]

$a_n = (n + 1)^2$; $a_9 = (9 + 1)^2 = 100$

[1] correct explicit formula, incorrect ninth term

page 620   Mixed Review

59. diverges

60. diverges

61. converges

62. $x^3 - 3x^2y + 3xy^2 - y^3$

63. $p^6 + 6p^5q + 15p^4q^2 + 20p^3q^3 + 15p^2q^4 + 6pq^5 + q^6$

64. $x^4 - 8x^3 + 24x^2 - 32x + 16$

65. $243 - 405x + 270x^2 - 90x^3 + 15x^4 - x^5$

66.

x	−2	−1	0	1	2
y	2	1	0	1	2

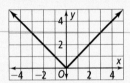

67.

x	−2	−1	0	1	2
y	5	4	3	4	5

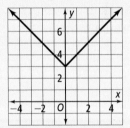

68.

x	0	1	2	3	4
y	2	1	0	1	2

69.

x	−3	−2	−1	0	1
y	−2	−3	−4	−3	−2

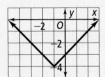

p. 621   Concept Byte

7. a.

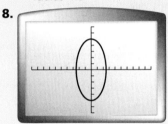

b. x-intercepts: (±4.5, 0), y-intercepts: (0, ±4.5)

c. Check students' work.

d. circle with center at the origin and radius 4.5

8.

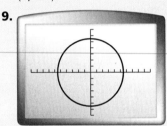

x-intercepts: (±2.5, 0), y-intercepts: (0, ±5)

9.

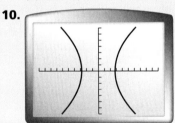

x-intercepts: (± $\sqrt{30}$, 0), y-intercepts: (0, ± $\sqrt{30}$)

10.

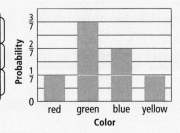

x-intercepts: (±2 $\sqrt{2}$, 0), no y-intercepts

11. Answers may vary. Sample: Graph on the same screen: $y = 3 - x$ where $x \geq 0$ and $y = 3 + x$ where $x \geq 0$.

12. Parabolas with a vert. axis of sym.; other conic sections have the x-axis as a line of sym., so they fail the vert. line test.

Chapter 11

pp. 694–695   Concept Byte

9.

Event: Color	Red	Green	Blue	Yellow
Frequency	1	3	2	1
Probability	$\frac{1}{7}$	$\frac{3}{7}$	$\frac{2}{7}$	$\frac{1}{7}$

Chapter 14

Lesson 14-1

page 910 Practice and Problem Solving Exercises

62. a. In the unit circle, the coordinates of any point are $(\cos \phi, \sin \phi)$ For P, $\phi = \theta + \pi$. Thus, the y-coordinate of point P is $\sin(\theta + \pi)$.

  b. The triangles are right triangles by definition. The hypotenuse of each triangle is the radius of the unit circle, 1, and so they are congruent to each other. The acute angles with vertices at the origin are vertical angles and are congruent by the Vertical Angle Theorem. So, the two right triangles are congruent by HA; their hypotenuses and acute angles are congruent.

  c. The legs opposite the vertical angles are congruent because they are corresponding parts of congruent triangles.

  d. In Quadrant I, the y-coordinate is $y = \sin \theta$. In Quadrant III, the x- and y-coordinates are negative. Also, since the blue segments are congruent, the absolute values of the y-coordinates in Quadrants I and III are equal. So, the y-coordinate of P is $-\sin \theta$.

  e. Since the y-coordinate of P is $\sin(\theta + \pi)$, which was shown in (a), and is also $-\sin \theta$, which was shown in (d), by transitivity: $\sin(\theta + \pi) = -\sin \theta$.

63. $\cos(\theta + \pi) = |\cos \theta|$, but is also in Quadrant III and is negative, so $\cos(\theta + \pi) = -\cos \theta$

64. $\tan(\theta + \pi) = \dfrac{\sin(\theta + \pi)}{\cos(\theta + \pi)} = \dfrac{-\sin \theta}{-\cos \theta} = \tan \theta$

65. 1

66. $\csc^2 \theta$

67. If $n_2 > n_1$, then $\theta_1 > \theta_2$; if $n_2 < n_1$, then $\theta_1 < \theta_2$; if $n_2 = n_1$, then $\theta_2 = \theta_1$.

page 910 Standardized Test Prep
68. C
69. H
70. C
71. F
72. C

73. [2] By the Difference of Squares Property and the second Pythagorean Identity:
$(\sec \theta + 1)(\sec \theta - 1) = \sec^2 \theta - 1 = \tan^2 \theta$

  [1] correctly worked out, but in more steps than used here

page 910 Mixed Review
74.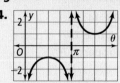

75.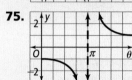

76.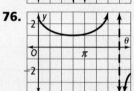

77.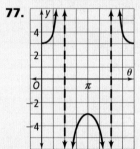

78. 35°   **79.** 45°
80. 135°   **81.** 211°
82. $f^{-1}(x) = x - 1$
83. $f^{-1}(x) = \dfrac{x + 3}{2}$
84. $f^{-1}(x) = \pm\sqrt{x - 4}$

p. 927 Mid-Chapter Quiz
40.

$\sin \theta = \dfrac{11\sqrt{137}}{137}$, $\cos \theta = \dfrac{4\sqrt{137}}{137}$,
$\csc \theta = \dfrac{\sqrt{137}}{11}$,
$\sec \theta = \dfrac{\sqrt{137}}{4}$, $\cot \theta = \dfrac{4}{11}$

41.

$\sin \theta = \dfrac{\sqrt{26}}{26}$, $\cos \theta = \dfrac{5\sqrt{26}}{26}$,
$\tan \theta = \dfrac{1}{5}$,
$\csc \theta = \sqrt{26}$, $\sec \theta = \dfrac{\sqrt{26}}{5}$

42. Answers may vary. Sample: In the eq. $x^2 - 3x + 2 = 0$, you isolate the variable x to get the solution. In the eq. $\tan^2 \theta - 3 \tan \theta + 2 = 0$, you first isolate the tangent function, but then you must continue to find the inverse tangent to solve for θ:
$x^2 - 3x + 2 = 0$
$\tan^2 \theta - 3 \tan \theta + 2 = 0$
$(x - 2)(x - 1) = 0$
$(\tan \theta - 2)(\tan \theta - 1) = 0$
$x - 2 = 0; x - 1 = 0$
$\tan \theta = 2; \tan \theta = 1$
$x = 2; x = 1$
$\theta \approx 63° + 180° \cdot n$;
$\theta = 45° + 180° \cdot n$

43. Answers may vary. Sample: Use the Pythagorean Theorem, $c^2 = a^2 + b^2$. Check students' work.

44. $\sin^2 \theta - \sin \theta - 6 = 0$
$(\sin \theta - 3)(\sin \theta + 2) = 0$
$\sin \theta = 3; \sin \theta = -2$
There is no solution because the zeros of the eq. are 3 and -2, but the range of sine is between 1 and -1.

45. 76 in.

p. 958 Pull It All Together
3. $d_1 = r\sqrt{2}$; $d_2 = 2r$; $d_3 = r(\csc 15)$

Index

H

I

Index

Index

defined, 99
dilations, 801, 802, 803, 820
of ellipses, 653–654
equations of, 631
of exponential functions, 444
geometric, 801–808, 820
graphing, 108, 125, 126, 196, 510, 861, 876–878
horizontal, 100–101, 102, 108, 125, 415
of hyperbola, 655
image, 820
of logarithmic functions, 455
of parabola, 197
phase shifts, 876
of quadratic functions, 195, 196
of reciprocal functions, 509, 510
rotation, 801, 804, 810, 820, 836
sine and cosine graphs, 861
sine function, 875–882, 896, 944
square root function, 415
tangent function, 944
types of, 108
using matrix addition, 802
vertical, 100, 102, 108, 109, 125, 415, 639
writing, 877, 879

transverse axis, 645, 646

tree diagrams, 699, 732

trend line, 93–94, 125

triangles
angles of, 928–932, 935, 936–939
area of, 784, 928, 929
congruent, 935
finding height of, 921
finding sides of, 928–932, 935, 936–939
Law of Cosines, 936–942
Law of Sines, 928–934
right, 919–926
special right, 835

trigonometric
expressions, 904, 907
ratios, 919–926, 961

trigonometric equations
modeling with, 879
solving by factoring, 914
solving using angle identities, 935
solving using inverses, 911–919, 960
trigonometric identities vs., 914

trigonometric functions
graphing, 860, 886
inverse, 911–918
non-additive, 947
reciprocal, 883–890, 896

trigonometric identities, 904–910
additive, 943
angles of, 943
cotangent, 904
defined, 904, 960
domain of validity, 904
reciprocal, 904
tangent, 904
trigonometric equations vs., 914
verifying, 907

trinomial
defined, 281
perfect square, 219, 220, 234–235, 271, 297
quadratic, 196–197, 198, 218–219, 297

turning point, 282, 348

Twain, Mark, 228

U

Understanding by Design 2, 4, 11, 18, 26, 33, 41, 49, 50, 58, 60, 68, 74, 81, 92, 99, 107, 114, 121, 122, 132, 134, 142, 149, 157, 166, 174, 182, 183, 192, 194, 202, 209, 216, 226, 234, 241, 249, 259, 266, 267, 278, 280, 288, 296, 303, 312, 319, 326, 331, 339, 346, 347, 358, 361, 367, 374, 381, 390, 398, 405, 414, 421, 422, 432, 434, 442, 451, 462, 469, 478, 486, 487, 495, 498, 507, 515, 527, 534, 542, 552, 553, 562, 564, 572, 580, 587, 595, 602, 603, 612, 614, 622, 630, 638, 645, 653, 662, 663, 672, 674, 681, 688, 696, 711, 719, 725, 739, 750, 751, 762, 764, 772, 782, 801, 809, 816, 817, 826, 828, 836, 844, 868, 875, 883, 892, 902, 904, 919, 928, 936, 951, 958, 959

uniform distribution, 694

unit circle
angles in, 836–842, 894
cosine of angle, 861
defined, 838
inverse trigonometric functions, 912–913
sine of angle, 851
tangent of angle, 868
to verify identity, 906

V

variable(s)
as Big Idea, 49, 50, 346, 602, 603
clarifying, 12
classifying, 12
dependent, 63
independent, 63

variable
matrix, 793, 819
quantity, 5

variance, 719, 720, 754

variation
combined, 500, 501, 502
constant of, 68, 123, 554
direct, 68–73, 123, 498–499
inverse, 498–505, 554
joint, 501, 554
measure of, 719, 754

VARS feature, 413, 460

vectors, 809–815
adding, 811
defined, 809
direction of, 809, 820
dot product, 812
initial point, 809, 820
magnitude of, 809, 820
normal, 812
operations with, 811
representing, 810
rotating, 810
scalar multiplication of, 811
size and direction, 809
subtracting, 811
terminal point, 809, 820
in two dimensions, 809
writing in matrix form, 810

vertex(ices)
of absolute value functions, 107, 126
defined, 107

of ellipse, 639, 665
of feasible region, 158, 185
of hyperbola, 645, 646
matrix representation of, 801
of parabolas, 194, 196

vertex form of quadratic functions, 194, 195, 196–197, 198, 203, 204, 236, 268

Vertex Principle of Linear Programming, 158, 185

vertical
asymptotes, 518, 554
ellipse, 639
line, 75, 107, 414
translation, 102, 108, 109, 125, 195, 415

Vertical-line test, 62–63, 414

Visual Learners 4, 20, 33, 43, 61, 82, 91, 108, 150, 158, 215, 217, 219, 235, 243, 250, 258, 264B, 291, 304, 340, 375, 416, 444, 446, 459, 471, 524, 616, 617, 661, 674, 675, 684, 689, 690, 721, 780, 813, 830, 839, 862, 877, 905, 914

vocabulary
Chapter Vocabulary, 50, 122, 183, 267, 347, 422, 487, 553, 751, 817, 893
exercises, 15, 22, 30, 45, 64, 71, 78, 86, 138, 145, 152, 160, 171, 179, 198, 221, 229, 235, 237, 285, 293, 300, 315, 322, 328, 335, 342, 370, 378, 394, 409, 439, 456, 461, 465, 512, 530, 557, 568, 591, 617, 627, 658, 678, 685, 691, 707, 710, 715, 722, 728, 735, 743, 768, 777, 813, 848, 855, 871, 880, 908, 932
Lesson Vocabulary, 4, 11, 18, 26, 33, 41, 60, 68, 74, 81, 91, 99, 107, 114, 125, 134, 142, 157, 166, 174, 194, 202, 209, 216, 226, 234, 241, 249, 259, 280, 288, 296, 303, 312, 319, 326, 331, 339, 361, 367, 374, 390, 398, 405, 414, 434, 442, 451, 462, 469, 478, 498, 515, 527, 534, 542, 564, 572, 580, 587, 595, 614, 622, 630, 638, 645, 674, 681, 688, 696, 711, 719, 725, 739, 764, 772, 782, 792, 801, 809, 829, 836, 844, 851, 861, 868, 875, 883, 904, 919, 928, 936
Looking Ahead Vocabulary, 57, 131, 191, 277, 431, 495, 561, 611, 671, 761, 825, 901
Vocabulary Audio Online, 2, 58, 132, 192, 278, 358, 432, 495, 562, 612, 672, 762, 826, 902
Vocabulary Builder, 54, 128, 188, 274, 758, 822, 899, 959

W

Whispering Gallery, 641

whole numbers, 12

words modeling algebraic expressions, 18–19

work backwards, 362

writing
equations, 74–80, 83, 124, 232, 452
exercises, 16, 17, 24, 25, 31, 32, 39, 47, 48, 53, 72, 89, 96, 97, 105, 112, 120, 127, 140, 145, 147, 154, 171, 179, 180, 187, 207, 213, 222, 224, 245, 273, 294, 302, 310, 311, 317, 329, 336, 345, 353, 372, 379, 411, 413, 418, 427, 460, 461, 466, 474, 477, 482, 484, 491, 503, 505, 512, 513, 522, 540, 547, 557, 576, 585,

598, 600, 607, 621, 629, 636, 644, 661, 667, 679, 680, 685, 686, 701, 709, 717, 723, 728, 736, 744, 752, 757, 769, 778, 781, 789, 790, 791, 806, 807, 814, 821, 831, 833, 841, 849, 859, 860, 865, 871, 874, 889, 898, 915, 917, 923, 927, 934, 939, 941, 950, 956, 963

expressions, 20, 385

functions, 110, 451–458

inequalities, 33, 34, 117

technical writing, 525

Think/Write problems, 6, 35, 101, 108, 144, 168, 176, 198, 220, 234, 243, 252, 259, 300, 328, 364, 368, 376, 384, 417, 437, 465, 519, 529, 538, 543, 566, 582, 588, 648, 654, 677, 682, 698, 786, 795, 830, 870, 879, 884, 907, 914, 930, 938, 948

translations, 877

X

x-axis, 101, 102, 164, 195, 197, 226, 256, 435

x-coefficient, 175

x-coordinate, 61, 62, 74, 123, 124, 203, 416

x-intercept, 76, 243, 289, 291, 319, 348

Xmax feature, 413

Xmin feature, 413

xy-coordinate plane, 164

Y

y-axis, 101, 102, 164

y-coefficient, 175

y-coordinate, 61, 62, 74, 123, 124, 203

y-intercept, 76

YLIST feature, 477

Z

z-axis, 164

zero(s)
additive identity, 13
multiplication by, 21
multiplicative inverse and, 13
multiplicative property of, 773, 776
multiplicity of, 291

of polynomial functions, 288, 289, 348

properties of, 13, 226, 270, 289, 773

of quadratic equation, 226, 270

of quadratic function, 226

of quartic functions, 341

as a real number, 13

of transformed cubic function, 339–340

ZERO option, 163, 227, 299

Zero-Product Property, 226, 270, 288, 289, 349

zoology, 440, 740, 741

ZOOM feature, 460

z-score, 748

Acknowledgments

Staff Credits

The people who made up the High School Mathematics team—representing composition services, core design digital and multimedia production services, digital product development, editorial, editorial services, manufacturing, marketing, and production management—are listed below.

Dan Anderson, Scott Andrews, Christopher Anton, Carolyn Artin, Michael Avidon, Margaret Banker, Charlie Bink, Niki Birbilis, Suzanne Biron, Beth Blumberg, Kyla Brown, Rebekah Brown, Judith Buice, Sylvia Bullock, Stacie Cartwright, Carolyn Chappo, Christia Clarke, Mary Ellen Cole, Tom Columbus, Andrew Coppola, AnnMarie Coyne, Bob Craton, Nicholas Cronin, Patrick Culleton, Damaris Curran, Steven Cushing, Sheila DeFazio, Cathie Dillender, Emily Dumas, Patty Fagan, Frederick Fellows, Jorgensen Fernandez, Mandy Figueroa, Suzanne Finn, Sara Freund, Matt Frueh, Jon Fuhrer, Andy Gaus, Mark Geyer, Mircea Goia, Andrew Gorlin, Shelby Gragg, Ellen Granter, Jay Grasso, Lisa Gustafson, Toni Haluga, Greg Ham, Marc Hamilton, Chris Handorf, Angie Hanks, Scott Harris, Cynthia Harvey, Phil Hazur, Thane Heninger, Aun Holland, Amanda House, Chuck Jann, Linda Johnson, Blair Jones, Marian Jones, Tim Jones, Gillian Kahn, Matthew Keefer, Brian Keegan, Jonathan Kier, Jennifer King, Tamara King, Elizabeth Krieble, Meytal Kotik, Brian Kubota, Roshni Kutty, Mary Landry, Christopher Langley, Christine Lee, Sara Levendusky, Lisa Lin, Wendy Marberry, Dominique Mariano, Clay Martin, Rich McMahon, Eve Melnechuk, Cynthia Metallides, Hope Morley, Christine Nevola, Michael O'Donnell, Michael Oster, Ameer Padshah, Stephen Patrias, Jeffrey Paulhus, Jonathan Penyack, Valerie Perkins, Brian Reardon, Wendy Rock, Marcy Rose, Carol Roy, Irene Rubin, Hugh Rutledge, Vicky Shen, Jewel Simmons, Ted Smykal, Emily Soltanoff, William Speiser, Jayne Stevenson, Richard Sullivan, Dan Tanguay, Dennis Tarwood, Susan Tauer, Tiffany Taylor-Sullivan, Catherine Terwilliger, Mark Tricca, Maria Torti, Leonid Tunik, Ilana Van Veen, Lauren Van Wart, John Vaughan, Laura Vivenzio, Samuel Voigt, Kathy Warfel, Don Weide, Laura Wheel, Eric Whitfield, Sequoia Wild, Joseph Will, Kristin Winters, Allison Wyss, Dina Zolotusky

Additional Credits: Michele Cardin, Robert Carlson, Kate Dalton-Hoffman, Dana Guterman, Narae Maybeth, Carolyn McGuire, Manjula Nair, Rachel Terino, Steve Thomas

Illustration

Stephen Durke: 574; **Phil Guzy:** 596, 597; **Rob Schuster:** 4, 5, 11, 18, 26, 33, 39, 41, 48, 60, 68, 74, 81, 84, 99, 107, 114, 116, 134, 142, 143, 149, 157, 165, 166, 168, 171, 174, 194, 202, 207, 216, 226, 233, 240, 258, 280, 288, 294, 296, 303, 308, 312, 326, 331, 367, 374, 375, 381, 390, 395, 398, 405, 414, 429, 434, 449, 451, 469, 498, 515, 522, 527, 534, 542, 547, 564, 566, 567, 570, 571, 572, 580, 587, 595, 609, 614, 617, 619, 630, 638, 641, 653, 865; **Ted Smykel:** 209; **Pearson Education:** 596, 597; **Judi Pinkham:** 230; **Pronk&Associates:** 12, 362, 399, 462, 589; **XNR Productions:** 788

Technical Illustration

GGS Book Services

Photography

All photographs not listed are the property of Pearson Education

Back Cover: Klein J.-L & Hube/Biosphoto

Page 3, ©Franck Seguin/Corbis; **28,** ©BL Images Ltd/Alamy; **39,** ©Richard Wahlstrom/JupiterImages; **45,** ©UPI Photo/Roger Williams/Newscom; **59,** ©Joe McBride/Getty Images; **61,** ©JUPITERIMAGES/Brand X/Alamy; **61,** ©JUPITERIMAGES/Brand X/Alamy; **61,** ©JUPITERIMAGES/Brand X/Alamy; **61,** ©JUPITERIMAGES/Brand X/Alamy; 61, ©Roberto Mettifogo/Getty Images; **84,** ©www.indepthexposure.com; **84,** ©Zen Shui/SuperStock; **133,** ©Hisham Ibrahim/Getty Images; **135,** ©Doug Perrine/Peter Arnold Inc.; **135,** ©PAUL NICKLEN/National Geographic Stock; **159,** ©Andy Crawford/Dorling Kindersley; **159,** ©Thomas Northcut/Photodisc/Getty Images; **159,** ©Steve Gorton/Dorling Kindersley; **164,** ©Image Source/Getty Images; **193,** ©Atlantide Phototravel/Corbis; **198,** ©Stuart Westmorland/Getty Images; **205,** Jeff Greenberg/PhotoEdit Inc.; **210,** ©Thomas Barwick/Getty Images; **228,** ©Andy Harmer/Photo Researchers, Inc.; **228,** ©Harvey Lloyd/Getty Images; **234,** ©Rolf Hicker Photography/Alamy; **279,** ©Claudius/zefa/Corbis; **306,** ©James Baigrie/Botanica/Jupiterimages; **333,** ©D. Hurst/Alamy; **333,** ©Peter Cade/Getty Images; **333,** ©D. Hurst/Alamy; **333,** ©FOOD DRINK AND DIET/MARK SYKES/Alamy; **333,** ©Andre Gallant/Getty Images; **342,** ©Ed Darack/Getty Images; **359,** ©Jake Norton/Getty Images; **375,** ©Panoramic Images/Getty Images; **383,** ©Detlev van Ravenswaay/Photo Researchers, Inc.; **392,** ©Bob Llewellyn/Jupiterimages; **408,** ©Bob Krist/CORBIS; **433,** ©Peter Mason/Getty Images; **438,** ©Jose B. Ruiz/npl/Minden Pictures; **453,** ©Earth Imaging/Getty Images; **467,** ©Jerry Lodriguss/Photo Researchers, Inc.; **476,** ©Dave King/Dorling Kindersley; **480,** ©NASA; **497,** ©Stephen Dalton/Minden Pictures; **502,** ©Corbis Super RF/Alamy; **502,** ©Chase Jarvis/Photolibrary; **513,** ©NASA-HQ-GRIN; **544,** ©NASA - JPL; **563,** ©Yu Xiangquan/Xinhua Press/Corbis; **578,** ©John Glover/Alamy; **578,** ©Bob Gibbons/Alamy; **578,** ©Courtesy of Unwins/Dorling Kindersley; **578,** ©Peter Anderson/Dorling Kindersley; **582,** ©Thomas J. Peterson/Alamy; **613,** ©Iain Masterton/Alamy; **618,** ©B.A.E. Inc./Alamy; **625,** ©Roger Ressmeyer/CORBIS; **632,** ©George Steinmetz/Corbis; **641,** ©Museum of Science and Industry; **673,** Photolibrary.com; **675,** Ron Chapple Stock/Corbis; **684,** Koji Aoki/Getty Images; **763,** Jim Sanborn; **775,** Jason Lugo/iStockphoto; **803,** Wolfgang Spunbarg/PhotoEdit; **827,** Ron Watts/Getty Images; **847 t,** Steve Gorton/Dorling Kindersley; **847 b,** European Space/Photo Researchers Inc.; **889,** Demetrio Carrasco/Dorling Kindersley; **903,** AFP Photo/Fabrice/Newscom; **921,** age footstock/Superstock; **931,** mediacolor's/Alamy Images